SAFETY SYMBOLS	HAZARD	PRECAUTION	REMEDY
Disposal	Special disposal required	Dispose of wastes as directed by your teacher.	Ask your teacher how to dispose of laboratory materials.
Biological	Organisms that can harm humans	Avoid breathing in or skin contact with organisms. Wear dust mask or gloves. Wash hands thoroughly.	Notify your teacher if you suspect contact.
Extreme Temperature	Objects that can burn skin by being too cold or too hot	Use proper protection when handling.	Go to your teacher for first aid.
Sharp Object	Use of tools or glassware that can easily puncture or slice skin	Practice common sense behavior and follow guidelines for use of the tool.	Go to your teacher for first aid.
Fumes	Potential danger from smelling fumes	Must have good ventilation and never smell fumes directly.	Leave foul area and notify your teacher immediately.
Electrical	Possible danger from electrical shock or burn	Double-check setup with instructor. Check condition of wires and apparatus.	Do not attempt to fix electrical problems. Notify your teacher immediately.
Irritant	Substances that can irritate your skin or mucous membranes	Wear dust mask or gloves. Practice extra care when handling these materials.	Go to your teacher for first aid.
Chemical	Substances (acids and bases) that can react with and destroy tissue and other materials	Wear goggles and an apron.	Immediately flush with water and notify your teacher.
Toxic	Poisonous substance	Follow your teacher's instructions. Always wash hands thoroughly after use.	Go to your teacher for first aid.
Fire	Flammable and combustible materials may burn if exposed to an open flame or spark	Avoid flames and heat sources. Be aware of locations of fire safety equipment.	Notify your teacher immediately. Use fire safety equipment if necessary.

Eye Safety
This symbol appears when a danger to eyes exists.

Clothing Protection
This symbol appears when substances could stain or burn clothing.

Animal Safety
This symbol appears whenever live animals are studied and the safety of the animals and students must be ensured.

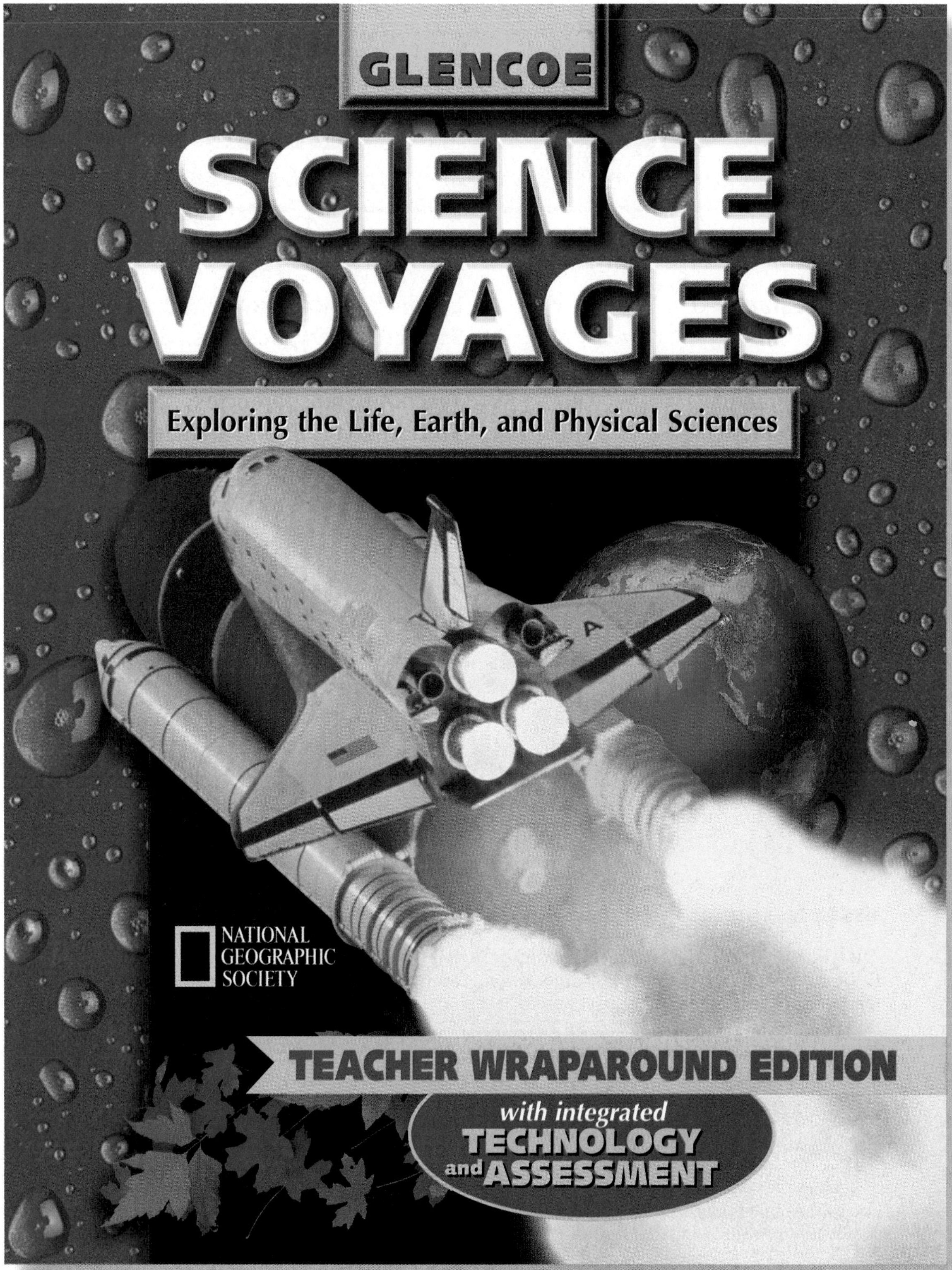

GLENCOE

SCIENCE VOYAGES

Exploring the Life, Earth, and Physical Sciences

NATIONAL GEOGRAPHIC SOCIETY

TEACHER WRAPAROUND EDITION

with integrated TECHNOLOGY and ASSESSMENT

New York, New York Columbus, Ohio Woodland Hills, California Peoria, Illinois

SCIENCE VOYAGES

Exploring the Life, Earth, and Physical Sciences

Student Edition
Teacher Wraparound Edition
Assessment
- Chapter Review
- Standardized Test Practice
- Performance Assessment
- Assessment—Chapter and Unit Tests
- ExamView Test Bank Software
- Performance Assessment in the Science Classroom
- Alternate Assessment in the Science Classroom

Study Guide for Content Mastery, SE and TE
Chapter Overview Study Guide, SE and TE
Reinforcement
Enrichment
Critical Thinking/Problem Solving
Multicultural Connections
Activity Worksheets
Laboratory Manual, SE and TE
Science Inquiry Activities, SE and TE
Home Involvement
Teaching Transparencies
Section Focus Transparencies
Science Integration Transparencies
Spanish Resources
Lesson Plans
Lab and Safety Skills in the Science Classroom
Cooperative Learning in the Science Classroom
Exploring Environmental Issues
MindJogger Videoquizzes and Teacher Guide
English/Spanish Audiocassettes
Interactive Lesson Planner CD-ROM
Interactive CD-ROM
Internet Site
Using the Internet in the Science Classroom

"Test-Taking Tip" and Test Practice features in this book were written by the Princeton Review, the nation's leader in test preparation. Through its association with McGraw-Hill, the Princeton Review offers the best way to help students excel on standardized assessments.

Glencoe/McGraw-Hill

A Division of The ***McGraw-Hill*** *Companies*

Send all inquiries to:

Glencoe/McGraw-Hill
8787 Orion Place
Columbus, OH 43240

ISBN 0-02-828668-5

Printed in the United States of America.

4 5 6 7 8 9 071/043 05 04 03 02 01

TEACHER GUIDE

TABLE of CONTENTS

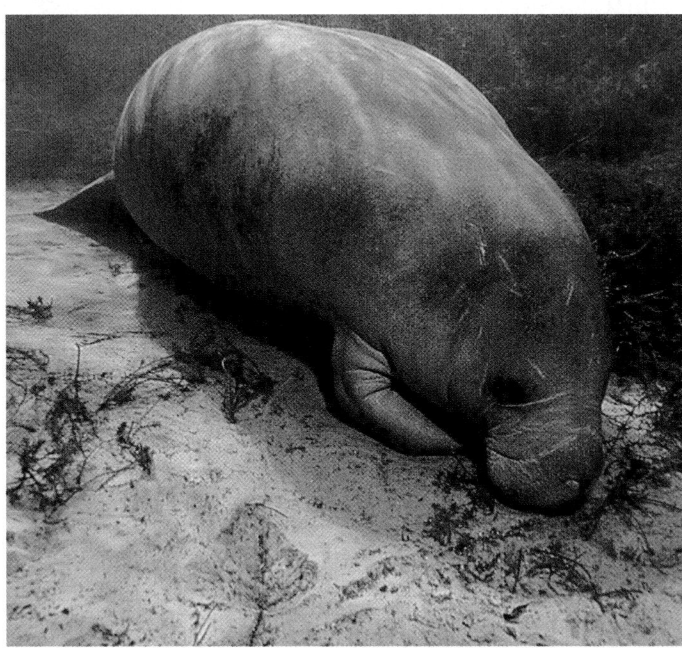

Authors

Alton Biggs is a Texas science teacher in Allen ISD. He has taught grades 7–12 for 25 years. He received his B.S. and M.S. degrees from Texas A&M University at Commerce. He is past president of the National Association of Biology Teachers and Texas Association of Biology Teachers, and an Honorary Member of both organizations.

John Burns teaches science at Ramona Junior High School, Chino, California. He received his B.S. in biology from California State University, Bakersfield, and M.A.T. Science from California State University, Fullerton. In 1992, he was a recipient of the Science and Mathematics Fellowship from the Council for Basic Education.

Lucille H. Daniel, Ed.D is a Rutherford County North Carolina science teacher with more than 38 years of experience. She has received the Presidential Award of Excellence in Mathematics and Science Teaching, the North Carolina Science Teachers Association Distinguished Service Award, and the Governor's Business Award for Excellence in Science Education.

Cathy Ezrailson is a Physics Teaching Resource Agent and field adjunct for the State of Texas. She is an active science writer, holding a B.S. from Ashland College and an M.S. from the University of Houston. She has been the Teacher of the Year in her region, and has received the Texas Presidential Award and the Tandy Scholars Award.

Dr. Ralph M. Feather, Jr. teaches Earth science, geology, and astronomy in Derry, Pennsylvania. He received his Ph.D. from the University of Pittsburgh in science education. Dr. Feather received the Presidential Award for Excellence in Science Teaching in 1991.

Patricia M. Horton is a mentor teacher and middle school science and math chairperson in the Etiwanda School District, California. She earned her master's degree at California State University San Bernadino in middle school grades education. She received the 1993 Commitment to Excellence in Education Award.

Thomas K. McCarthy teaches physics and is the department chair at Saint Edward's School in Florida. He earned his bachelor's degree in physics from Loyola University in Chicago and his Ph.D. from the University of Texas at Dallas. He received the Presidential Scholar Distinguished Teacher Award in 1998.

Ed Ortleb is a science consultant and researcher in St. Louis, Missouri. He has advanced degrees from Washington University, and is a life member of NSTA. He served as NSTA president in 1978–79 and has received numerous awards for service to science education.

Susan L. Snyder teaches at Jones Middle School in Ohio. She received her B.S. from Miami University, Ohio, and M.S. in entomology from the University of Hawaii. She was the Ohio Teacher of the Year and a finalist for the National Teacher of the Year in 1987.

Eric Werwa is a professor of physics at Otterbein College in Westerville, Ohio. Dr. Werwa received his B.S. in materials science and engineering from the University of Pennsylvania, and holds a Ph.D. in electronic materials from the Massachusetts Institute of Technology.

The National Geographic Society and Glencoe have joined forces to bring exciting new features and technologies to ***Science Voyages.*** By incorporating National Geographic's world-renowned photographs, illustrations, and content features, ***Science Voyages*** will engage students as never before.

THREE-BOOK CONTENT GUIDE

Level Red			Level Green			Level Blue		
Unit	1	**The Nature of Science**	Unit	1	**The Nature of Matter**	Unit	1	**Chemical Interactions**
Chapter	1	The Nature of Science	Chapter	1	The Nature of Science	Chapter	1	The Nature of Science
Chapter	2	Measurement	Chapter	2	Waves	Chapter	2	Inside the Atom
Chapter	3	Matter	Chapter	3	Light, Mirrors, and Lenses	Chapter	3	The Periodic Table
Chapter	4	Properties and Changes	Chapter	4	States of Matter	Chapter	4	Chemical Bonds
Unit	2	**Interactions in the Physical World**	Chapter	5	Solutions	Chapter	5	Chemical Reactions
Chapter	5	Energy	Unit	2	**Electricity and Magnetism**	Unit	2	**Forces and Motion**
Chapter	6	Motion and Forces	Chapter	6	Electricity	Chapter	6	Motion
Chapter	7	Work and Simple Machines	Chapter	7	Magnetism	Chapter	7	Force and Newton's Laws
Unit	3	**Earth Materials and Resources**	Unit	3	**Earth's Changing Surface**	Unit	3	**Earth's Interior**
Chapter	8	Views of Earth	Chapter	8	Weathering and Soil	Chapter	8	Earthquakes
Chapter	9	Minerals	Chapter	9	Erosional Forces	Chapter	9	Volcanoes
Chapter	10	Rocks	Chapter	10	Water Erosion and Deposition	Chapter	10	Plate Tectonics
Chapter	11	Resources	Unit	4	**Oceans**	Unit	4	**Change Through Time**
Unit	4	**Earth's Air and Water**	Chapter	11	Ocean Motion	Chapter	11	Clues to Earth's Past
Chapter	12	Atmosphere	Chapter	12	Oceanography	Chapter	12	Change Through Time
Chapter	13	Weather	Unit	5	**You and the Environment**	Chapter	13	Geologic Time
Chapter	14	Climate	Chapter	13	Our Impact on Land	Unit	5	**Foundations of Life**
Unit	5	**Classifying Life**	Chapter	14	Our Impact on Air and Water	Chapter	14	Carbon Chemistry
Chapter	15	The Structure of Organisms	Unit	6	**Interactions in the Living World**	Chapter	15	Plant Processes
Chapter	16	Classifying Living Things	Chapter	15	Cell Processes	Chapter	16	Plant Reproduciton
Chapter	17	Bacteria	Chapter	16	Cell Reproduction	Unit	6	**Ecology**
Chapter	18	Protists and Fungi	Chapter	17	Heredity	Chapter	17	Life and the Environment
Unit	6	**Plants and Animals**	Unit	7	**The Human Body**	Chapter	18	Ecosystems
Chapter	19	Plants	Chapter	18	Bones, Muscles, and Skin	Chapter	19	Resources and the Environment
Chapter	20	Invertebrate Animals	Chapter	19	Nutrients and Digestion	Unit	7	**Astronomy**
Chapter	21	Vertebrate Animals	Chapter	20	The Circulatory System	Chapter	20	Exploring Space
Chapter	22	Animal Behavior	Chapter	21	Respiration and Excretion	Chapter	21	The Sun-Earth-Moon System
			Chapter	22	Nervous and Endocrine Systems	Chapter	22	The Solar System
			Chapter	23	Reproduction and Growth	Chapter	23	Stars and Galaxies
			Chapter	24	Immunity			

Physical Science | Life Science | Earth Science

STUDENT EDITION

TABLE of CONTENTS

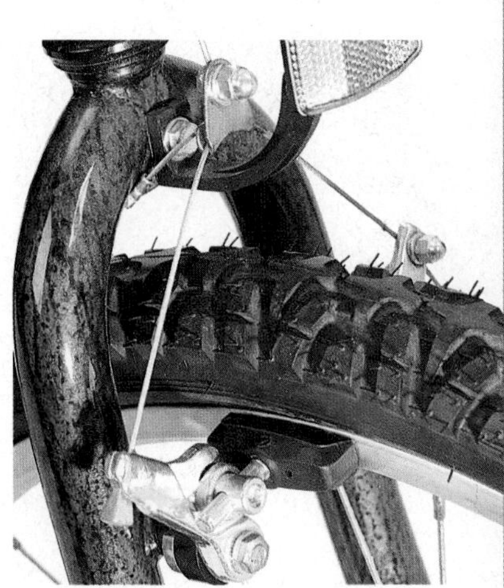

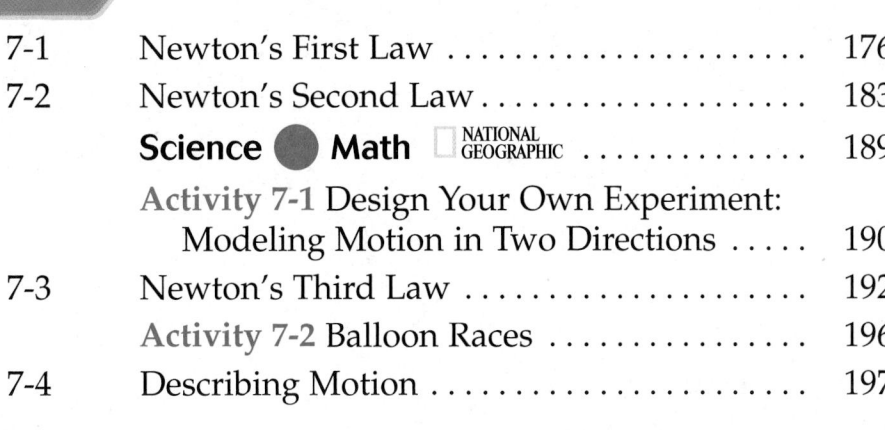

UNIT 3 Earth's Interior 206

UNIT 4 Change Through Time 300

Table of Contents

UNIT 5 Foundations of Life 394

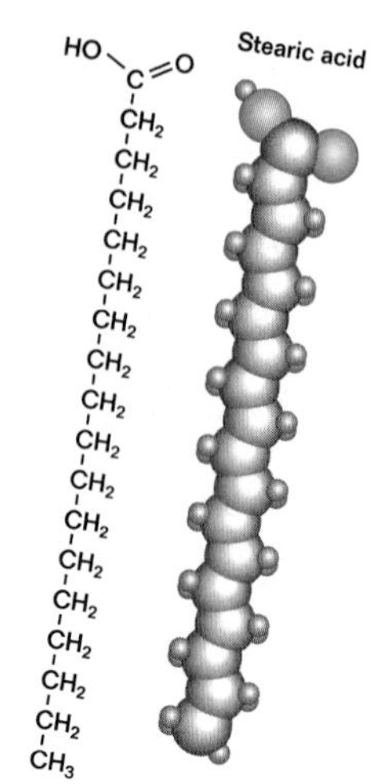

Chapter 14 Carbon Chemistry 396

Chapter 15 Plant Processes 424

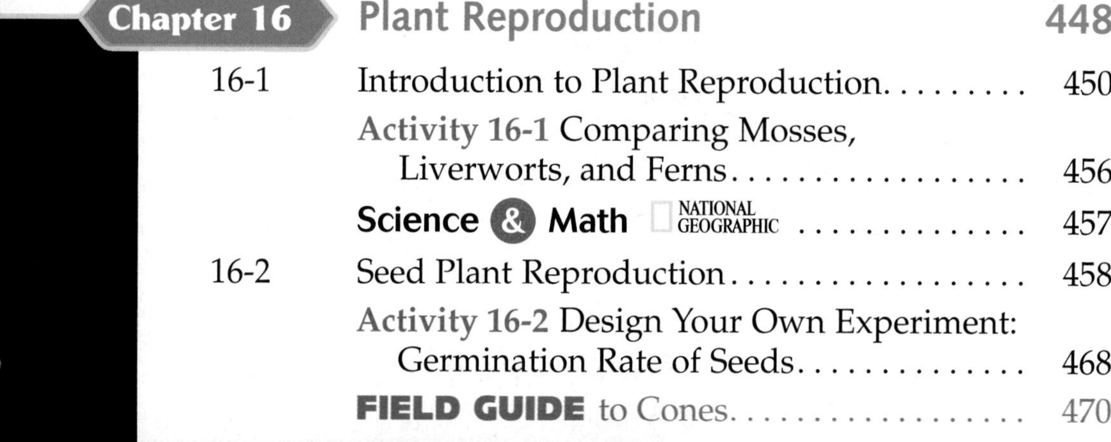

Chapter 16 Plant Reproduction 448

UNIT 6 Ecology 478

UNIT 7 Astronomy 570

Appendices 696

Science Connections

History of Science

Science & Society

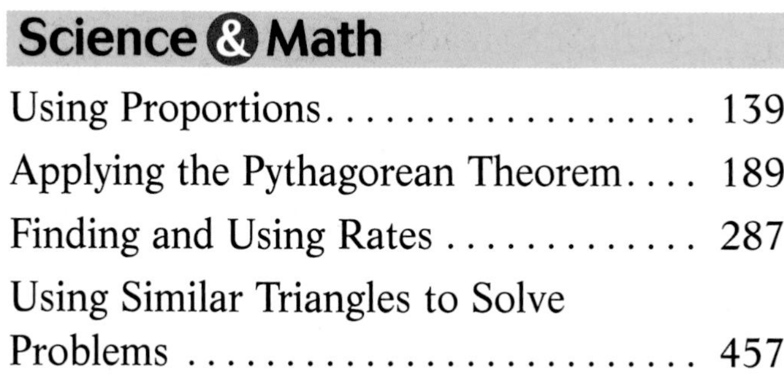

Science & Math

Reading & Writing in Science

How it Works

Activities

Activities

Try at Home MiniLab

Explore Activities

Problem Solving

Skill Builders

Skill Activities

Benchmarks for Science Literacy

Benchmarks in Science Education

Students need to be aware of the science around them. They need to be science literate. Several programs have been proposed that have the goal of achieving science literacy for every student. Project 2061 is an example of one of these programs. Project 2061, developed by the American Association for Advancement of Science, proposes that the success of students can be measured by comparing their achievement at various benchmarks during their time in school. As stated in Project 2061's ***Benchmarks for Science Literacy,*** "benchmarks are statements of what all students should know or be able to do in science, mathematics, and technology by the end of grades 2, 5, 8, and 12." Benchmarks for students leaving the eighth grade describe what all middle school students should know before entering the ninth grade.

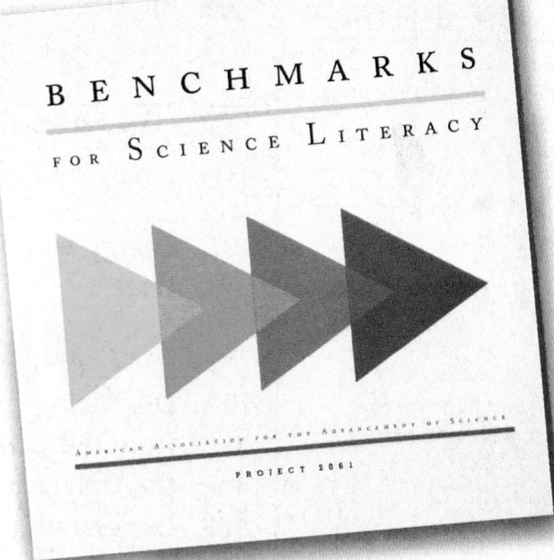

Benchmarks for Science Literacy proposes several ways to promote reform in science education. These guiding principles can be used by teachers as they develop new directions for their methods of science instruction.

Science Literacy

People who are science literate are defined in ***Benchmarks for Science Literacy*** as those who are "equipped with knowledge and skills they need to make sense of how the world works, to think critically and independently, and to lead interesting, responsible, and productive lives in a culture increasingly shaped by science and technology."

How does it work?

The benchmarks proposed by Project 2061 are not considered levels of achievement for an average student or an advanced student, but for all students. The number of technical terms learned by students is kept at a minimum.

What are the benefits?

Students and teachers can benefit from the reform proposals in ***Benchmarks for Science Literacy.*** Teachers have the opportunity to work with students as they explore for themselves. They also can work independently with students of varied abilities. Through activities, students develop skills in problem solving and critical thinking. This gives them the tools they need to make sense of how the world works. It provides them with science literacy.

Benchmarks and Science Voyages

In ***Science Voyages,*** subject core material is presented in a way that reduces the number of new science terms students must learn with each chapter. Concepts are presented in ways that help students understand the how and why of science, not just learn a number of facts that they commit to short-term memory. Students are shown how science concepts learned in class pertain to their daily experiences.

They experience activities of various designs that involve students in learning and applying scientific methods to practice thinking skills and construct scientific concepts. The table on page 24T shows how ***Science Voyages*** covers many of the topics in depth.

SCIENCE VOYAGES

Benchmark Correlation

The following table illustrates how the *Science Voyages* series addresses many of the Benchmarks for Science Literacy.

Benchmark	Level	Chapter(s)
4 The Physical Setting		
4A. The Universe	Blue	21, 22, 23
4B. The Earth	Red	11, 12, 13, 14
	Green	13, 14
	Blue	21
4C. Processes that Shape the Earth	Red	8, 10, 11
	Green	8, 9, 10, 13
	Blue	8, 9, 10, 11, 13
4D. Structure of Matter	Red	3, 4
	Green	4, 5
	Blue	2, 3, 4, 5, 14
4E. Energy Transformation	Red	4, 5, 6, 7, 12, 13
	Green	2, 9, 11, 18
	Blue	6, 7, 23
4F. Motion	Red	5
	Green	3, 22
	Blue	6, 7, 8
4G. Forces of Nature	Red	5, 6, 7
	Green	7, 9, 10, 11
	Blue	7, 10
5 The Living Environment		
5A. Diversity of Life	Red	11, 15–21
	Blue	15–18
5B. Heredity	Green	23
	Blue	17
5C. Cells	Red	15
	Green	15
	Blue	15
5D. Interdependence of Life	Red	17, 18, 19, 22
	Green	15
	Blue	17, 18
5E. Flow of Matter and Energy	Red	19
	Green	15
	Blue	17
5F. Evolution of Life	Green	17
	Blue	11, 12, 13
6 The Human Organism		
6A. Human Identity	Green	15, 19, 22, 23, 24
	Blue	11, 12
6B. Human Development	Green	23
6C. Basic Functions	Red	15
	Green	15, 21, 22, 23, 24
6D. Learning	Red	22
6E. Physical Health	Red	11
	Green	19, 24
	Blue	17
6F. Mental Health	Red	15
8 The Designed World		
8C. Energy Sources and Use	Red	11
	Blue	19
10 Historical Perspectives		
10A. Displacing the Earth from the Center of the Universe	Blue	20
10F. Understanding Fire	Red	3
	Blue	2, 5
10G. Splitting the Atom	Red	11
10I. Discovering Germs	Red	17
	Green	24
12 Habits of Mind		
12A. Values and Attitudes	Red	1, 6, 10, 11, 12, 14, 16–18, 21,
	Green	1, 5, 6, 9, 10, 11, 13, 14, 16, 19, 23, 24
	Blue	1–6, 12–14, 19, 20, 22, 23
12B. Computation and Estimation	Red	1–21
	Green	1–24
	Blue	1–23
12D. Communication Skills	Red	2 and all skill activities
	Green	All skill activities
	Blue	All skill activities

SCIENCE VOYAGES

NATIONAL SCIENCE EDUCATION STANDARDS

The *National Science Education Standards,* published by the National Research Council and representing the contribution of thousands of educators and scientists, offers a comprehensive vision of a scientifically literate society. The standards not only describe what students should know but also offers guidelines for science teaching and assessment. If you are using or plan to use the standards to guide changes in your science curriculum, you can be assured that ***Science Voyages*** aligns with the National Science Education Standards.

Science Voyages reflects how Glencoe's commitment to science education is changing the materials used in science classrooms today. ***Science Voyages*** is a program that provides numerous opportunities for students, teachers, and school districts to meet the National Science Education Standards.

Content Standards

The table on pages 26–28T shows the close alignment between ***Science Voyages*** and the grade-appropriate content standards. ***Science Voyages*** allows students to discover concepts within each of the content standards, giving them opportunities to make connections between the science disciplines. Our hands-on activities and inquiry-based lessons reinforce the science processes emphasized in the standards.

Teaching Standards

Alignment with the National Science Education Standards requires much more than alignment with the outcomes in the content standards. The way in which concepts are presented is critical to effective learning. The teaching standards within the National Science Education Standards recommend an inquiry-based program facilitated and guided by teachers. ***Science Voyages*** provides such opportunities through activities and discussions that allow students to discover critical concepts by inquiry and apply the knowledge they've constructed to their own lives. Throughout the program, students are building critical skills that will be available to them for lifelong learning. The ***Teacher Wraparound Edition*** helps you make the most of every instructional moment. It offers an abundance of effective strategies and suggestions for guiding students as they explore science.

Assessment Standards

The assessment standards are supported by many of the components that make up the ***Science Voyages*** program. ***The Teacher Wraparound Edition*** and ***Teacher Classroom Resources*** provide multiple chances to assess students' understanding of important concepts, as well as their ability to perform a wide range of skills. Ideas for portfolios, performance activities, written reports, and other assessment activities accompany every lesson. Rubrics and Performance Task Assessment Lists can be found in Glencoe's Professional Series booklet ***Performance Assessment in the Science Classroom.***

Program Coordination

The scope of the content standards requires students to meet the outcomes over the course of their education. The correlation on the following pages demonstrates the close alignment of this course of ***Science Voyages*** with the content standards.

Correlation to

NATIONAL SCIENCE EDUCATION STANDARDS

Correlation of Science Voyages, Level Blue, to the National Science Standards

Content Standard	Page Numbers
(UCP) Unifying Concepts and Process	
1. Systems, order, and organization	36, 113, 210–222, 225–230, 242–260, 312, 319, 321–327, 371, 458–463, 483–495, 528–531
2. Evidence, models, and explanation	12, 14–21, 25, 26, 28, 104, 124, 131, 159, 160, 164, 190, 191, 212, 213, 216–219, 224, 255–260, 272–286, 304–311, 334, 351, 353–357, 413, 417, 419, 496–502, 649, 686, 689
3. Change, constancy, and measurement	13–16, 19–21, 25, 28, 125–127, 129, 133, 150, 151, 153–156, 161, 162, 166, 167, 184, 186, 188, 201, 225–230, 268–271, 277–286, 304–311, 334–351, 353–357, 510–513, 516–526, 575, 665, 666, 674, 681, 682
4. Evolution and equilibrium	161, 177, 210–214, 304–311, 334–351, 353–357, 369, 370, 387, 510, 512, 513
5. Form and function	25, 27, 28, 250–261, 464, 577–580, 586, 635
(A) Science as Inquiry	
1. Abilities necessary to do scientific inquiry	8, 10–21, 25, 26, 53, 56, 57, 112, 124, 125, 128, 232, 233, 246, 247, 252, 253, 256, 260, 270, 276, 277, 279, 282, 288, 289, 312–319, 321–327, 342, 343, 375, 378, 385, 435, 442, 443, 456, 460, 464–466, 468, 469, 487, 492–495, 499, 500, 514, 515, 517, 519, 520, 530, 540, 541, 547, 586, 610, 686, 687
2. Understandings about scientific inquiry	7, 9–13, 22, 23, 25, 27, 28, 43–46, 98, 109, 130, 131, 157, 268–277, 288, 289, 312–319, 321–327, 342, 343, 353, 379, 388, 389, 468, 469, 487, 494, 495, 514, 515, 519, 540, 541, 585–587, 594, 595, 611, 617, 620–622, 635, 637–640, 642, 644, 646–648, 654, 668, 671, 676

Correlation to

NATIONAL SCIENCE EDUCATION STANDARDS

Content Standard	Page Numbers
(B) Physical Science	
1. Properties and changes of properties in matter	28, 47–53, 106–111, 115, 122–138, 399–417
2. Motions and forces	8, 20, 25, 210–222, 225–230, 240–260, 277–286
3. Transfer of energy	20, 210–222, 225–230, 240–245, 426–434, 496–499, 516, 517
(C) Life Science	
1. Structure and function in living systems	7, 135, 194, 398, 407, 411, 414–418, 426–434, 458–466, 677
2. Reproduction and heredity	8, 450–455, 458–466
3. Regulation and behavior	70, 77, 78, 615
4. Populations and ecosystems	385, 482–499, 510–513, 520–526, 528–531, 542–546
5. Diversity and adaptations of organisms	304–311, 334–351, 353–357, 367–370, 376, 382–384, 458–466, 510–513, 542–547
(D) Earth and Space Science	
1. Structure of the earth system	26, 78, 110, 159, 181, 210–214, 219–222, 240–245, 268–286, 370, 377, 381, 386, 387, 483, 484, 516–525, 528–531, 577, 584–586, 602, 604, 669
2. Earth's history	268–286, 304–319, 321–327, 334–351, 353–357, 364–389, 400, 618, 652, 654
3. Earth in the solar system	25, 154, 158, 176, 177, 182, 183, 194, 575, 582, 583, 585–587, 590–592, 602, 603, 605–608, 610, 612–616, 618–620, 623, 630–633, 635, 638, 641, 644, 648–650, 652, 653, 663–667, 669, 670, 679, 681, 682, 685

Correlation to

NATIONAL SCIENCE EDUCATION STANDARDS

Content Standard	Page Numbers
(E) Science and Technology	
1. Abilities of technological design	8–10, 19, 23–25, 27, 53, 115, 225–230, 261, 527, 581
2. Understandings about science and technology	7–10, 17, 22–27, 37–39, 41, 42, 44, 51–53, 73–76, 78, 79, 81, 82, 84–86, 88, 115, 151, 159, 200, 225–230, 261, 401, 402, 404, 527, 575–579, 581, 583, 585, 586, 590–595, 617, 620–622, 634, 636–640, 642, 643, 645–647
(F) Science in Personal and Social Perspectives	
1. Personal health	9, 26–28, 229, 261, 408, 411, 418, 610, 615, 671
2. Populations, resources, and environments	383, 385, 489, 590
3. Natural hazards	22, 24, 225–230, 240–245, 248–254, 544–546
4. Risks and benefits	23, 24, 83, 261, 418
5. Science and technology in society	8, 55, 89, 115, 225–230, 261, 409, 527, 581, 655
(G) History and Nature of Science	
1. Science as a human endeavor	6–8, 11, 12, 19, 22–25, 27, 178, 180, 183, 198, 320, 335–338, 352, 527, 577, 578, 586, 587, 590–593, 595, 614, 630, 631, 651, 654, 672–674, 679, 682
2. Nature of science	11–19, 21, 23, 25, 39, 41, 42, 178, 179, 335–338, 634
3. History of science	8, 27, 36–40, 44, 64, 65, 71, 79, 85, 87, 112, 158, 159, 165, 166, 178, 179, 183, 192, 320, 335–338, 352, 381, 398, 579, 582, 584, 586, 587, 593, 602, 614, 616, 618, 630–632, 634, 643, 646, 650, 668, 674, 677

PLANNING YOUR COURSE

Traditional Scheduling

Science Voyages provides flexibility in the selection of topics and content, which allows teachers to adapt the text to the needs of individual students and classes. In this regard, the teacher is in the best position to decide which topics to present, the pace at which to cover the content, and which material to emphasize.

Science Voyages may be used in a full-year, two-semester course that is comprised of 180 periods of approximately 45 minutes each.

Block Scheduling

To build flexibility into the curriculum, many schools are introducing a block-scheduling approach. Block scheduling often involves covering the same information in fewer days with longer class periods than with traditional scheduling. This approach allows curriculum supervisors and teachers to tailor the curriculum to meet students' needs while achieving local and/or state curriculum goals.

When following a block schedule, consider either combining lessons or eliminating certain topics and spending more time on the topics you do cover. *Science Voyages* also provides a wide variety of support materials that will help teachers and students, whether following a block schedule or full-year schedule.

Lesson Plans

The *Science Voyages* Lesson Plans include complete lesson planning guides for every numbered section. Program components are listed along with page numbers or other identifiers for easy reference. The Lesson Plans include schedules, objectives, and references to the ***Teacher Classroom Resources*** and strategies in the ***Teacher Wraparound Edition.***

Interactive Lesson Planner

The *Science Voyages* Interactive Lesson Planner integrates the ***Teacher Classroom Resources*** with an electronic lesson planner to make the teacher's job easier. The easy-to-use CD-ROM allows a teacher to plan daily, weekly, monthly, or year-long lessons in a versatile calendar format. Teachers can select a built-in plan, customize the built-in plan, or create a new plan. Lesson plans can be saved and printed.

An extensive list of resources, including all print components of the ***Teacher Classroom Resources,*** is accessible through a convenient pop-up menu. All pages can be printed easily—student pages and answer keys—from either the resource list or directly from the lesson plan.

Ron Chapple/FPG

SCIENCE VOYAGES

Planning Guide

Unit	Chapter/Section	Single-Class (180 days)	Block (90 days)
1	The Nature of Matter	45.5	24
	1 The Nature of Science	**7**	**4**
	1-1 Scientific Problem Solving	3	2
	1-2 Using Science to Explore	2	1
	Reading and Writing in Science	1	0.5
	Chapter Review	1	0.5
	2 Inside the Atom	**10.5**	**5.5**
	2-1 The Story of the Atom	4.5	2.5
	Science and Society	1	0.5
	2-2 The Nucleus	4	2
	Chapter Review	1	0.5
	3 The Periodic Table	**11**	**6**
	3-1 Introduction to the Periodic Table	1.5	1
	3-2 Representative Elements	4	2
	3-3 Transition Elements	3.5	2
	Science and Society	1	0.5
	Chapter Review	1	0.5
	4 Chemical Bonds	**8**	**4**
	4-1 Why do atoms combine?	2.5	1.5
	4-2 Ionic and Covalent Bonds	3.5	1.5
	How It Works	1	0.5
	Chapter Review	1	0.5
	5 Chemical Reactions	**9**	**4.5**
	5-1 Describing a Chemical Reaction	4	2
	5-2 Rates of Chemical Reactions	3	1.5
	Science and Math	1	0.5
	Chapter Review	1	0.5
2	Forces and Motion	20	10
	6 Motion	**11**	**5.5**
	6-1 What is motion?	4	2
	6-2 What is momentum?	4	2
	6-3 What is energy?	1	0.5
	Science and Society	1	0.5
	Chapter Review	1	0.5
	7 Force and Newton's Laws	**9**	**4.5**
	7-1 Newton's First Law	1	0.5
	7-2 Newton's Second Law	3	1.5
	Science and Math	1	0.5
	7-3 Newton's Third Law	2	1
	7-4 Describing Motion	1	0.5
	Chapter Review	1	0.5
3	Earth's Interior	27.5	13.5
	8 Earthquakes	**10.5**	**5**
	8-1 Forces Inside Earth	1	0.5
	8-2 Earthquake Information	4	2
	8-3 Destruction by Earthquakes	3.5	1.5
	Reading and Writing in Science	1	0.5
	Chapter Review	1	0.5
	9 Volcanoes	**8**	**4**
	9-1 What causes volcanoes?	2	1
	9-2 Types of Volcanoes	1	0.5
	9-3 Igneous Rock Features	3	1.5
	Science and Society	1	0.5
	Chapter Review	1	0.5
	10 Plate Tectonics	**9**	**4.5**
	10-1 Continental Drift	1	0.5
	10-2 Seafloor Spreading	2	1
	10-3 Plate Tectonics	4	2
	Science and Math	1	0.5
	Chapter Review	1	0.5
4	Change Through Time	28	14
	11 Clues to Earth's Past	**7**	**3.5**
	11-1 Fossils	1	0.5
	11-2 Relative Ages of Rocks	2	1
	History of Science	1	0.5
	11-3 Absolute Ages of Rocks	2	1
	Chapter Review	1	0.5
	12 Change Through Time	**11**	**5.5**
	12-1 Mechanisms of Evolution	4	2
	12-2 Evidence for Evolution	3	1.5
	History of Science	1	0.5
	12-3 Primate Evolution	2	1
	Chapter Review	1	0.5

* The suggested number of days are the recommended maximum number of days needed to thoroughly cover a chapter. Individual planning will vary.

Unit	Chapter/Section	Single-Class (180 days)	Block (90days)
	13 Geologic Time	**10**	**5**
	13-1 Life and Geologic Time	2	1
	13-2 Early Earth History	3	1.5
	Science and Society	1	0.5
	13-3 Middle and Recent Earth History	3	1.5
	Chapter Review	1	0.5
5	Foundations of Life	29	14.5
	14 Carbon Chemistry	**10.5**	**5.5**
	14-1 Simple Organic Compounds	1.5	1
	14-2 Other Organic Compounds	3	1.5
	Science and Society	1	0.5
	14-3 Biological Compounds	4	2
	Chapter Review	1	0.5
	15 Plant Processes	**8**	**4**
	15-1 Photosynthesis and Respiration	4	2
	15-2 Plant Responses	2	1
	How It Works	1	0.5
	Chapter Review	1	0.5
	16 Plant Reproduction	**10.5**	**5**
	16-1 Introduction to Plant Reproduction	3	1.5
	Science and Math	1	0.5
	16-2 Seed Plant Production	5.5	2.5
	Chapter Review	1	0.5
6	Ecology	30	15
	17 Life and the Environment	**10**	**5**
	17-1 The Living and Nonliving Environment	2	1
	17-2 Interactions Among Living Organisms	4	2
	17-3 Matter and Energy	2	1
	Reading and Writing in Science	1	0.5
	Chapter Review	1	0.5
	18 Ecosystems	**9**	**4.5**
	18-1 How Ecosystems Change	2	1
	18-2 Land Environments	4	2
	Science and Society	1	0.5
	18-3 Water Environments	1	0.5
	Chapter Review	1	0.5

Unit	Chapter/Section	Single-Class (180 days)	Block (90days)
	19 Resources and the Environment	**11**	**5.5**
	19-1 Natural Resources	1	0.5
	19-2 Conservation and Wildlife Protection	4	2
	Reading and Writing in Science	1	0.5
	19-3 Maintaining a Healthy Environment	4	2
	Chapter Review	1	0.5
7	Astronomy	37	17.5
	20 Exploring Space	**8.5**	**4**
	20-1 Radiation from Space	3.5	1.5
	How It Works	1	0.5
	20-2 Early Space Missions	2	1
	20-3 Recent and Future Space Missions	1	0.5
	Chapter Review	1	0.5
	21 The Sun-Earth-Moon System	**8**	**4**
	21-1 Planet Earth	3	1.5
	Reading and Writing in Science	1	0.5
	21-2 Earth's Moon	1	0.5
	21-3 Exploration on the Moon	2	1
	Chapter Review	1	0.5
	22 The Solar System	**9.5**	**4.5**
	22-1 The Solar System	2.5	1
	22-2 The Inner Planets	1	0.5
	22-3 The Outer Planets	3	1.5
	22-4 Other Objects in the Solar System	1	0.5
	Science and Society	1	0.5
	Chapter Review	1	0.5
	23 Stars and Galaxies	**11**	**5**
	23-1 Stars	1	0.5
	23-2 The Sun	3.5	1.5
	23-3 Evolution of Stars	1	0.5
	Reading and Writing in Science	1	0.5
	23-4 Galaxies and the Universe	3.5	1.5
	Chapter Review	1	0.5

STUDENT EDITION

Helping you reach all students

This table will help you choose from many options available in the student edition of *Science Voyages.* Choose features that will assist you the most when you teach the chapter.

Feature Name	Where and How Many?	Suggestions For Use
Activities	• In every chapter • At the point where concept is taught	• Assign to groups in a lab setting. • Use to strengthen lab skills and understanding of science process.
Design Your Own Experiment	• At the point where concept is taught	• Assign to groups in a lab setting. • Open-ended activities help students learn science process. • Helps reinforce understanding of scientific methods
MiniLab	• In every chapter • At the point where concept is taught	• Do as a demonstration. • Assign to pairs or groups in lab setting. • Conduct these simple activities as short demonstrations. • Requires common inexpensive materials.
Try at Home MiniLab	• At the point where concept is taught	• Simple activities can be done at home or school • Assign as homework or class work.
On The Internet	• At the point where concept is taught	• Integrate the Internet into your class easily with these Internet activities. • Assign as homework or as a group project.
Explore Activity	• Begins each chapter • Focuses students' attention; stimulates curiosity for the chapter topic	• Do as a demonstration. • Assign as homework or class work. • Capture student's interest at the beginning of each chapter with these lesson launchers that use common, inexpensive materials.
Problem Solving	• One per chapter • At the point where concept is taught	• Assign as homework • Assign as a sponge activity after reading or other work. • Strengthens critical-thinking skills with Problem-Solving practice after reading or other work.
interNET CONNECTION	• In every chapter • At the point where concept is taught	• Assign as homework. • Assign as group project. • Focus student's Internet time with predetermined links for each chapter related to chapter content • Assign as homework or during class to easily integrate the Internet into your classroom.

Feature Name	Where and How Many?	Suggestions For Use
Skill Builder	• Found at the end of every Section Assessment in each chapter	• Assign as homework or class work. • Go over in a group discussion. • Students feel comfortable with skills when practiced as an integral part of each lesson. Skill practice is easy when used often.
Science and Technology Skill Handbooks	• Aids student with specific science-related and technology skills	• Use to teach students how to organize information. • Use to teach students scientific processes. • Students always have skill assistance nearby with the skill handbook. • All skills are referenced to the handbook.
Skill Activity	• Found on pages 688–709 • One for each chapter	• Use as a demonstration. • Assign as homework or class work. • Further reinforce process skills with this bank of full-page activities.
Career CONNECTION	• Found on the Reviewing Main Ideas Pages	• Use to encourage students to pursue careers in science. • Use to show students that people of all ages, ethnicities, and educational training work in science.
NATIONAL GEOGRAPHIC How it Works Reading & Writing in Science Science & Math History of Science Science & Society	• One per chapter • Found after the related section	• Use to show relationships between science and art, history, reading, and writing . • Use to illustrate how scientific concepts make things work.
FIELD GUIDE	• Periodically found at the end of the chapter	• Use to teach students how to use a key. • Assign as a group project or homework.
Reading Check	• At the beginning and end of every chapter • In every section	• Strategies for advancing reading skills • Focuses on important vocabulary and concepts
Reviewing Main Ideas	• One per chapter • Found at the end of the chapter	• Use as a review. • Use to preview the chapter content.

HANDS-ON ACTIVITIES

Explore Activity

This photograph was taken by astronauts aboard the space shuttle *Endeavour.* It shows an area of the Pacific Ocean near the Hawaiian Islands. Other photographs of Earth in space are taken by cameras attached to satellites in orbit around our planet. These pictures show detailed features of Earth's surface, such as mountains and rivers. Scientists use these photos to make maps. In the activity below, you'll use a map or globe to explore Earth's surface.

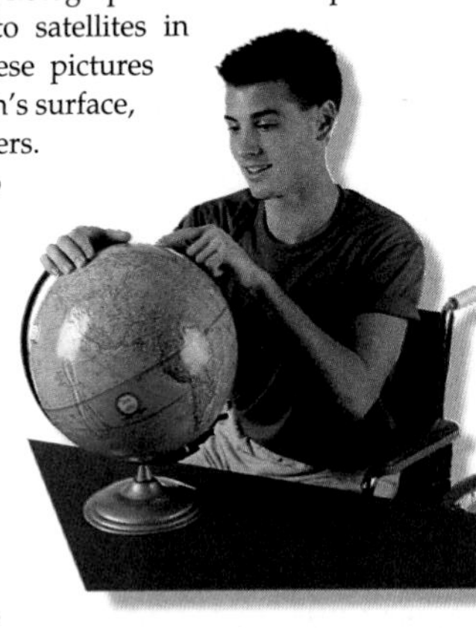

Describe Landforms

1. Find the Andes Mountains on a globe or map.
2. Locate the Amazon, the Ganges, and the Mississippi Rivers.
3. Locate the Indian Ocean, the Sea of Japan, and the Baltic Sea.
4. Now, find the continents of Australia, South America, and North America.
5. Locate your own country.

Science Journal

Choose one country on the globe or map and describe its major physical features in your Science Journal.

Explore Activity

Explore activities help you capture students' attention at the beginning of a chapter. These easy-to-manage activities ...

- set the stage for learning chapter content.
- require minimal equipment.
- promote inquiry learning.
- allow students to experience the natural world before they learn the content terms, symbols, or definitions.

MiniLab

MiniLabs occur within the chapter and help reinforce the concept that is being taught. These short labs ...

- allow students to experience the concept being taught.
- require few materials.
- occur two times in each chapter.
- contain numbered procedures.
- some can be done at home.

Try at Home MiniLab

Profiling the United States

Procedure

1. Place the bottom edge of a piece of paper across the middle of **Figure 6-2,** extending from the West Coast to the east coast.
2. Mark where different landforms are located along this edge.
3. Use a map of the United States and the descriptions of the landforms in Section 6-1 to help you draw a profile, or side view, of the United States. Use steep, jagged lines to represent mountains. Low, flat lines can represent plains.

Analysis

1. Describe how your profile changed shape as you moved from west to east.
2. Describe how the shape of your profile would be different if you moved from north to south.

Activity

One-page activities allow students to utilize scientific methods to obtain results.
Each one-page activity ...

- occurs at the end of the section where the concept is taught.
- requires a full period to set up.
- contains numbered procedures and data tables if necessary.
- asks students to conclude, analyze, and apply.

Using Scientific Methods

Activity 6•2

Making a Topographic Map

Materials

- Plastic model landform
- Water tinted with food coloring
- Transparency
- Clear, plastic storage box with lid
- Beaker
- Metric ruler
- Tape
- Transparency marker

Have you ever wondered how topographic maps are made? Today, radar and remote-sensing devices aboard satellites collect data, and computers and graphic systems make the maps. In the past, surveyors and aerial photographers collected data. Then, maps were hand drawn by cartographers, or map-makers. In this activity, you can try your hand at cartography.

What You'll Investigate

How is a topographic map made?

Goals

- **Make** a topographic map.
- **Compare and contrast** contour intervals.

Procedure

1. Using the ruler and the transparency marker, make marks up the side of the storage box 2 cm apart.
2. **Secure** the transparency to the outside of the box lid with tape.
3. Place the plastic model in the box. The bottom of the box will be zero elevation.
4. Using the beaker, **pour** water into the box to a height of 2 cm. Place the lid on the box.
5. Use the transparency marker to **trace** the top of the water line on the transparency.
6. Using the scale 2 cm = 10 m, **mark** the elevation on the line.
7. Remove the lid and **add** water until a depth of 4 cm is reached.
8. **Map** this level on the storage box lid and **record** the elevation.
9. Repeat the process of **adding** water and **tracing** until you have the hill **mapped.**
10. **Transfer** the tracing of the hill onto a sheet of white paper.

Conclude and Apply

1. What is the contour interval of this topographic map?
2. How does the distance between contour lines on the map show the steepness of the slope on the landform model?
3. **Determine** the total elevation of the hill.
4. How was elevation represented on your map?
5. How are elevations shown on topographic maps?
6. Must all topographic maps have a 0-m elevation contour line? **Explain.**
7. **Compare** the contour interval of an area of high relief with one of low relief on a topographic map.

HANDS-ON ACTIVITIES

Design Your Own Experiment

Activity 1 • 1

Using Scientific Methods

Model an Archaeological Dig

Possible Materials
- Small stones and pebbles
- Craft sticks
- Bits of black tissue paper
- Toothpicks
- Sand
- Small plastic, interlocking building blocks
- Small paintbrushes
- Plastic shovels
- Large plastic dish-washing tub or clear storage box
- Ruler, pencil, and paper

Have you ever put together a model airplane? If so, your model was a small version of a large object. Scientists often use models to study objects that are too large or too small to observe directly. In this activity, your group will construct a model of a prehistoric site. You'll cover the site with sand and give it to another group to unearth. As amateur archaeologists, each of you will attempt to reconstruct the site based on what you find.

Recognize the Problem

What can be learned from an archaeological excavation?

Form a Hypothesis

Think about some of the things you use every day. Based on your basic needs, make a hypothesis as to what you might find at a prehistoric site once inhabited by humans.

Goals
- **Make a model** of a prehistoric site.
- **Design an experiment** to show how the prehistoric site might be excavated.
- **Make a map** of the site you construct.

Safety Precautions

12 Chapter 1 The Nature of Science

Test Your Hypothesis

Plan
1. Based on the basic needs generated by your group, **make a model** of an ancient site where people once lived. You might want to include a hearth used for cooking, a trash pit, some sort of shelter, a protective wall, a burial site, a water source, and some tools.
2. **Decide** which of the possible materials listed would be best for each item you include in your site. Remember that others will be trying to determine what is contained at your site.
3. How will you cover your site so that other groups can **excavate** the artifacts?
4. Using the ruler, **determine** a way to make a map of your site.

Do
1. Make sure your teacher approves your plan before you proceed. Make any suggested changes in your plan before you start.
2. **Make the model** in the plastic dish-washing tub or storage box.
3. **Make a map** of your site.
4. **Exchange** your model with another group. Carefully **excavate** the site your group is given using the brushes and shovels.
5. **Make a map** that shows where you found each item in the model you are excavating.
6. While doing the experiment, **record** your observations in your Science Journal.

Analyze Your Data

1. Were any of the items in the site similar to the items you use or see around your community every day? Were any of the items unfamiliar? **Explain.**
2. Why did you make maps of your site and the site you excavated?
3. Did any of the excavating tools damage or disturb the site?
4. **Write** a report explaining what you found and what it might have been used for.

Draw Conclusions

1. How did your map of the site you excavated **compare** with those produced by the group that made the site?
2. Radar surveys that penetrate the ground are often conducted over possible archaeological sites. Why?

1-1 How Science Works 13

Design Your Own Activity

Design Your Own activities allow students to construct their own activity. A topic and plan are provided, but students have the freedom of design. These activities ...
- occur in about half of the chapters.
- require a full period to perform.
- promote inquiry learning.
- ask students to conclude and apply.

Skill Activity

Skill activities give students extra practice with the skill used in science. There is one skill activity for each chapter and they …

- occur at the back of the book after the Skill Handbook.
- require few materials.
- can usually be done by a single student.
- usually require less than one period.
- can be done as homework.

Chapter 6 **Skill Activity** Use After Section 6-3

Making Models

Background

Architects, builders, and designers often use detailed drawings as they plan their work. These are known as floorplans and represent a type of scale drawing. A scale drawing is a 2-dimensional model where an object's size and location are kept in the same proportions as in the actual object. For example, suppose a floorplan has a scale of 1 cm = 1 m. A room shown on this plan measures 10 cm × 15 cm. The actual room is 10 m × 15 m. A 1 m × 2 m desk in that room would be drawn as a rectangle 1 cm × 2 cm. The procedure below will help you make a scale drawing of your classroom.

Procedure

1. Measure the length and width of your classroom and decide on a scale to use that will allow your plan to cover most of your piece of paper. For example, if your paper is 25 cm × 36 cm and your room is 12 m × 15 m you could use a scale of 1 cm = 0.5 m. This would create a drawing of the classroom that measures 24 cm × 30 cm, which would fit on the paper.
2. Convert the dimensions of the room to your floorplan scale. Use a pencil and ruler to neatly draw the outline of the room on your paper.
3. Measure the width of the doorway and where it is located. Convert these measurements to your floorplan scale and draw the doorway on your plan.
4. Measure your teacher's desk and how far it is located from the walls. Use these measurements to accurately draw the desk in its proper position on your floorplan.
5. Repeat the procedure for any windows and other furniture in the classroom.
6. Title your classroom map and be sure to include your scale in the map key.

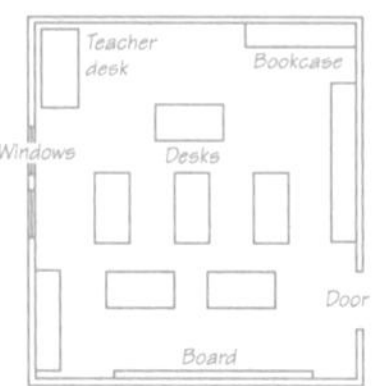

Classroom floor plan (scale: 1 cm = 2 m)

Practicing the SKILL

Imagine that your teacher has received two new computer work-stations. Each station has a desk that measures 1 m × 2 m. Use your scale drawing to determine where these work-stations might fit in the classroom. You may need to "move" some furniture on your map. Draw the workstations on your classroom floorplan.

For more skill practice, do the Chapter 6 Interactive Exploration on the **Science Voyages Level Red CD-ROM.**

6-3 Skill Activity 677

Internet Activity

Two-page Internet activities encourage students to use the Internet to explore concepts further. These activities …

- occur at the point where the concept is being taught.
- can be used as homework or research projects.

Activity 8•2 Using Scientific Methods

Making a Paper Airplane

Materials

- Paper
- Measuring tape (50 m)
- Metric ruler
- Stopwatch
- Balance
- Tape
- Stapler
- Paper clips
- Scissors

When the Wright brothers set out to make the first powered airplane, they spent time researching flight and studying designs that had failed, as well as gliders that had been successful. They recognized the forces involved in flight, such as gravity, lift, thrust, and drag (a form of friction). If the lift is greater than gravity, then the plane will stay in the air. If the thrust is greater than the drag, then the plane will move forward. Even today, these same forces must be considered when a new airplane is designed.

Recognize the Problem

How can a paper airplane that flies the longest time or the farthest distance be designed?

Form a Hypothesis

The design of the wing plays an important role in maximizing lift while reducing drag. An airfoil is the part of the wing responsible for controlling lift. The size, shape, angle, and cover material of the airfoil determine the lift and the drag that the wing will experience at a certain wind speed. **Form a hypothesis** about how your group can design a paper airplane that will either fly the longest period of time or go the farthest distance.

Goals

- **Research** paper airplane strategies.
- **Design** a paper airplane whose airfoil maximizes lift and minimizes drag.
- **Analyze** and **communicate** experimental results.

Safety Precautions

Data Sources

Visit the Glencoe Science Web Site at www.glencoe.com/sec/science/ca to find more information, hints, and data from other students.

Test Your Hypothesis

Plan

1. You may use a single sheet of any type of paper. You also may cut, fold, tape, glue, or staple the paper to form your airplane.
2. **Design** one or more types of paper airplanes. What type of paper will you use? What will be the shape of the wing?
3. **Sketch** your design. **Organize** the data you expect to collect in a table similar to the one below.
4. The testing area should be flat and open. Where will you test your designs?

Do

1. Be sure your teacher approves your plan before you begin.
2. **Build** your design. Record its mass in your data table.
3. **Experiment** with different ways of flying your airplane. Record your observations in your data table.
4. **Modify** your design as you think necessary. Remember to change only one variable at a time.
5. Tell your teacher when you have finished the airplane that you think will fly as long and as far as possible.
6. Hold a class contest to determine three categories: greatest time in the air, greatest distance flown from starting point, and the greatest overall flight.

Draw Conclusions

1. **Compare and contrast** the designs your class came up with. What features did the winning planes have?
2. How did the planes that flew long distances differ from the planes that flew for a long time?
3. Which design minimized drag? Maximized lift?
4. Post your design at the Glencoe Science Web Site. How do your designs compare with the designs other classes have posted?

Flight Data

Trial	Mass (g)	Design change	Flight distance (m)	Flight time (s)
		Student data will vary with different designs.		

Reading in the Content Area

Science Voyages is designed to increase science literacy. The techniques developed are active, constructive, and engaging and help improve reading comprehension and deepen students' understanding of ideas and concepts.

Several important strategies are recommended before reading and studying the chapter. For example, previewing the chapters' visuals, questions, vocabulary, and captions will set a purpose for reading the material for all students. Reading the introductory Explore Activity aloud or as a group helps engage students from the beginning of study.

While reading the chapter, periodic Reading Check questions will assist in comprehension of the material. In addition, a variety of learning strategies and engaging activities are found throughout each chapter, giving additional exposure to the material. These ideas include graphic organizers, creative responses, and journal writing.

In the Student Edition

Reading Check

Before you begin this chapter, write its headings and subheadings in an outline form to see how the chapter is organized.

Reading Checks occur at the beginning, throughout, and at the end of each chapter. Reading checks at the chapter opener make students think about the chapter content before it is discussed.

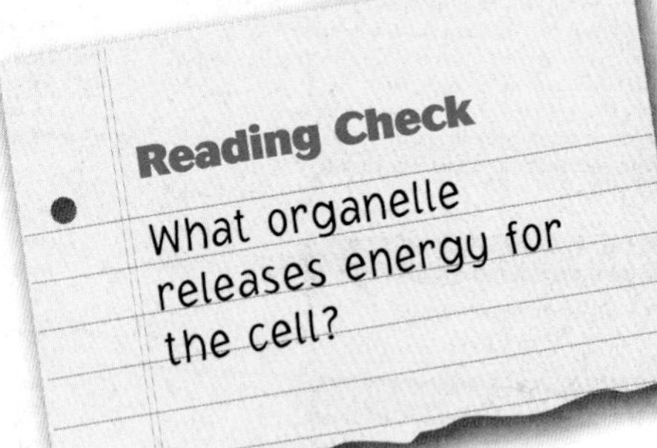

Reading Check
What organelle releases energy for the cell?

In-text Reading Checks ask students questions about the content they just read. This reinforces the chapter text and vocabulary.

Reading Check

Variables, controls, and *trials* are used in scientific experiments. Compare the meaning of each word in this context with its meaning in a nonscientific context.

The Reviewing Main Ideas Reading Check has the students use their knowledge of the chapter content to perform a reading activity.

In the
Teacher Wraparound Edition

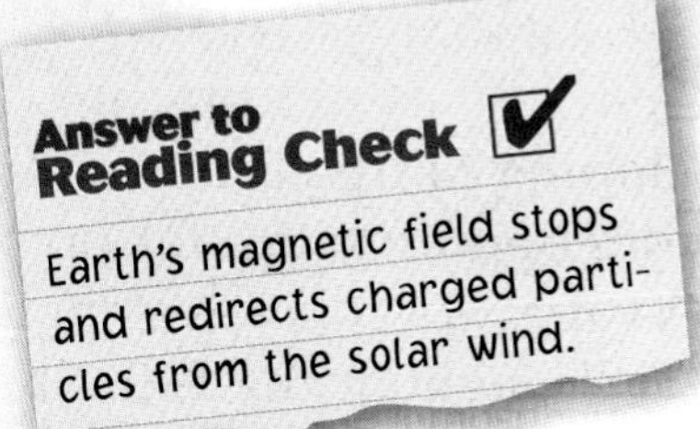

Answers to Reading Check questions are provided in the margin of the Teacher Wraparound Edition.

Guided Reading Strategy

Think-Pair Share This strategy encourages students to think first before discussing their ideas or thoughts about a topic. Students are asked to respond to a question by writing a response. After thinking for a few minutes, partners share responses to the question. Finally, the teacher asks the student to share responses with the class. Have students become involved in a Think-Pair Share about a topic in this section.

Guided Reading Strategies

Strategies that cover a variety of learning styles

- **Bubble Map**
  This strategy helps students start ideas flowing about a given topic.
- **Double Entry Journal**
  In this strategy, the student takes notes and adds his or her own reflections while reading the student text.
- **Prediction Journal**
  This strategy allows students to examine events and speculate about their possible long-term effects.
- **Think-Pair Share**
  This strategy encourages students to think first before discussing their ideas or thoughts about a topic.
- **Write-Draw-Discuss**
  This strategy encourages students to actively participate in reading and lectures, assimilating content creatively.
- **Buddy Interview**
  Students interview each other to help them understand and clarify the reading.
- **Reciprocal Teaching**
  This strategy is designed to help construct meaning and apply reading skills.
- **Pair of Pairs**
  This strategy encourages students as partners to respond to a question.
- **News Summary**
  This strategy helps students explain and make connections to their study of science by being news reporters.

***Guided Reading Strategies** provided by Gary Kroesch, University of California at San Diego. Mr. Kroesch also teaches social studies at Mount Carmel High School in San Diego, California.*

Concept maps

Helping students understand concepts through visuals

In science, concept maps make abstract information concrete and useful, improve retention of information, and show students that thought has shape.

Concept maps are visual representations or graphic organizers of relationships among particular concepts. Concept maps can be generated by individual students, small groups, or an entire class. *Science Voyages* develops and reinforces four types of concept maps—the **network tree, events chain, cycle concept map,** and **spider concept map**—that are most applicable to studying science. Students can learn how to construct each of these types of concept maps by referring to the **Skill Handbook.** To further develop concept mapping skills, each chapter of the *Study Guide for Content Mastery* in the *Teacher Classroom Resources* has a concept map.

Building Concept Mapping Skills

The **Developing Skills** section of the **Chapter Review** provides opportunities for practicing concept mapping. A variety of concept mapping approaches is also used throughout the text. Students may be directed to make a specific type of concept map and may be provided the terms to use. At other times, students may be given only general guidelines. For example, concept terms to be used may be provided and students may be required to select the appropriate model to apply, or vice versa. Finally, students may be asked to provide both the terms and type of concept map to explain relationships among concepts. Look for the conceptual strength of student responses, not absolute accuracy. You'll notice that most network tree maps provide connecting words that explain the relationships between concepts. We recommend that you require all students to supply these words, but many students may be challenged by this aspect.

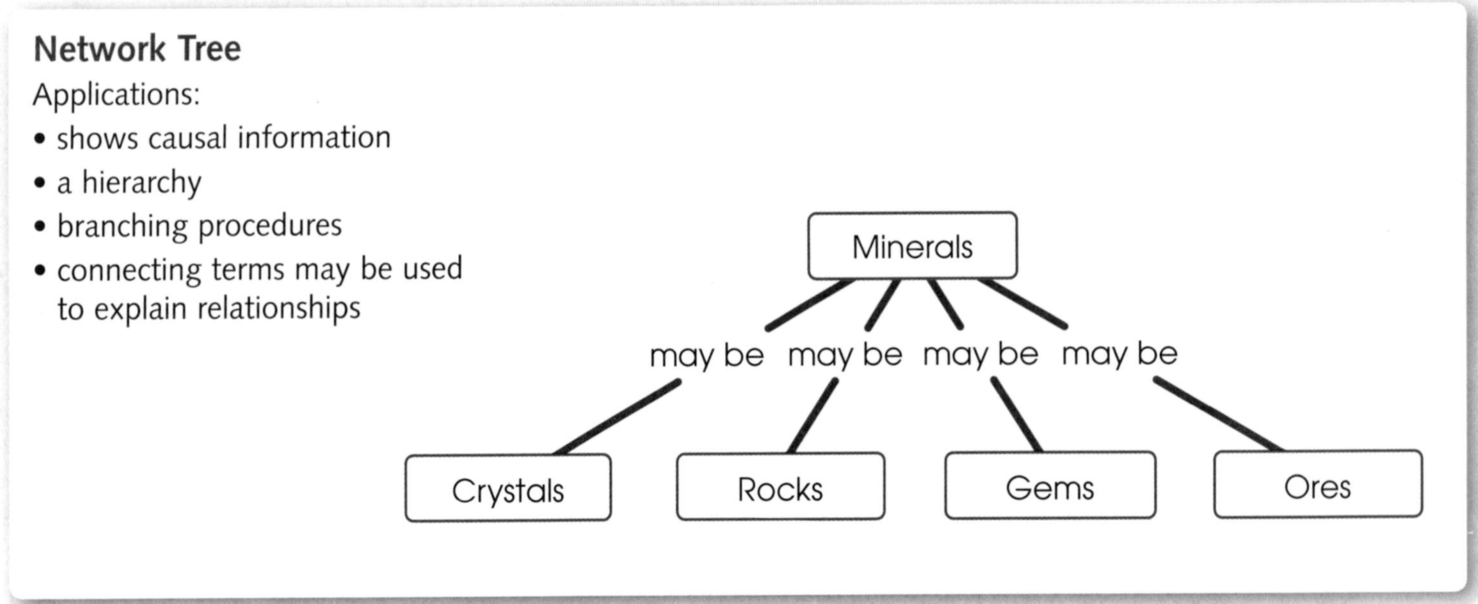

Study Guide for Content Mastery

The *Study Guide for Content Mastery* book of the *Teacher Classroom Resources,* too, provides a developmental approach for students to practice concept mapping.

As a teaching strategy, generating concept maps can be used to preview a chapter's content by visually relating the concepts to be learned and allowing the students to read with purpose. Using concept maps for previewing is especially useful when there are many new key science terms for students to learn. As an assessment and review strategy, constructing concept maps reinforces main ideas and clarifies their relationships. Construction of concept maps using cooperative learning strategies as described in this Teacher Guide will allow students to practice both interpersonal and process skills.

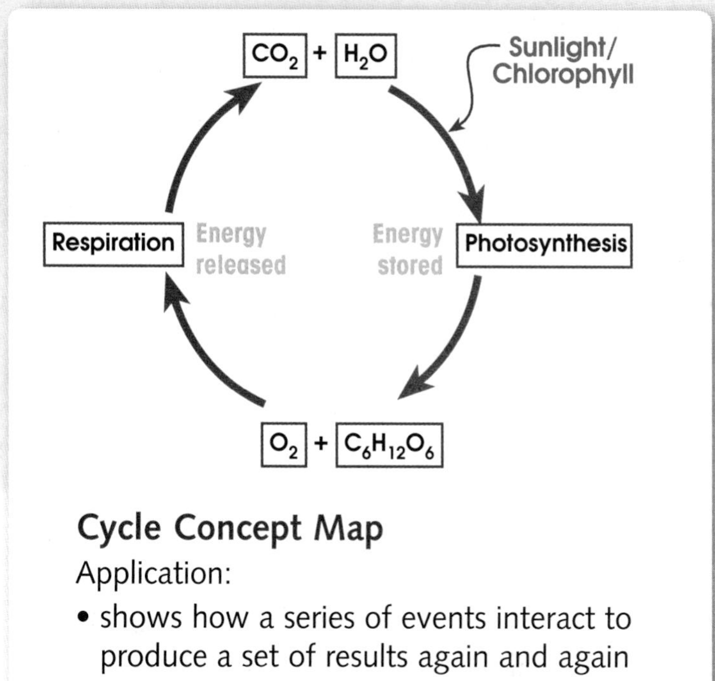

Cycle Concept Map

Application:

- shows how a series of events interact to produce a set of results again and again

Events Chain

Applications:

- describes the stages of a process
- the steps in a linear procedure
- a sequence of events

Initiating Event

Determine the problem.
↓
Make a hypothesis.
↓
Test your hypothesis.
↓
Analyze the results.
↓
Draw conclusions.

Spider Concept Map

Applications:

- nonhierarchical, except within a category
- unparallel categories
- brainstorming

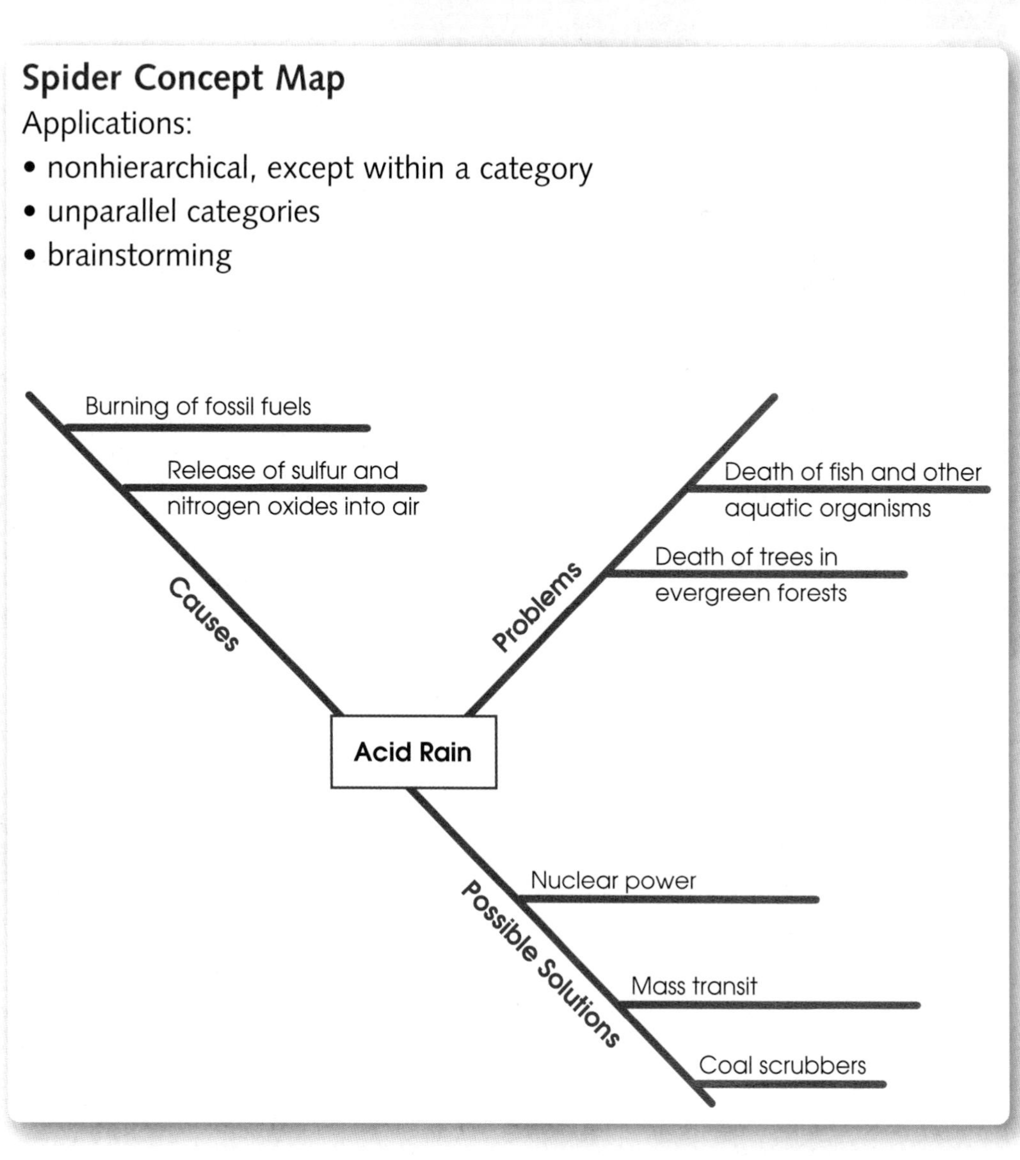

Assessment

Science Voyages offers the Glencoe Assessment Advantage, a system of assessment options designed to give you the flexibility and tools to conduct standardized test preparation, content, and performance assessment.

Standardized Test Preparation

Glencoe is dedicated to helping you prepare students for success. Therefore, Glencoe provides a number of features designed to help you prepare students for state-mandated tests.

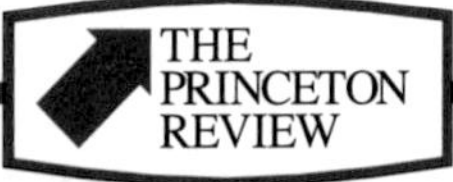

The Princeton Review is a nationally renowned company that specializes in preparing students for standardized assessments. For 15 years, they have been helping students prepare for the state and national tests that students are required to take. Glencoe has partnered with *The Princeton Review* in order to ensure that all of our materials meet the same tough standards that state and national testing agencies use themselves. This partnership has resulted in Student Edition **Test-Taking Tips** and **Test Practice** questions at the end of each **Chapter Assessment.**

Glencoe in association with *The Princeton Review* provides test practice booklets. The booklets contain questions that will assist you in preparing your students for success on standardized tests.

Content Assessment

Glencoe *Science Voyages* Student Edition contains numerous strategies and formative checkpoints for evaluating student progress toward mastery of science concepts.

Throughout the chapters, **Section Assessment** questions and application tasks are presented. A two-page **Reviewing Main Ideas** at the end of each chapter allows you to evaluate student responses and determine if reteaching is needed. The two-page **Chapter Assessment** is a useful tool for evaluating students' knowledge of scientific terminology, their understanding of scientific principles, and their ability to apply these principles.

MindJogger Videoquizzes offer interactive videos that provide a fun way for your students to review chapter concepts. You can extend the use of the videoquizzes by implementing them in a testing situation. The game-show format allows students to work as teams to answer questions and gain points. Questions are at three difficulty levels: basic, intermediate, and advanced.

The Interactive CD-ROM provides an interactive approach to quiz taking. The quizzes can be used as a whole-class presentation or as a review for individual students. The CD-ROM also is available on the ***Science Voyages*** Web Site.

Assessment—Chapter Tests present recognition and recall of vocabulary and facts in addition to interpretation of information. Students are asked to demonstrate their ability to determine relationships among facts, generalizations, definitions, and skills.

ExamView Test Bank Software for Macintosh and Windows makes creating, editing, and printing tests quick and easy. You can add your own questions and graphics to the tests.

Glencoe *Science Voyages* has been designed to provide you with a variety of assessment tools, both formal and informal, to help you develop a clearer picture of your students' progress.

Performance Assessment

Performance Assessment refers to the strategies used to assess students' level of science literacy. Performance assessment is based on judging the quality of a student's response to a performance task. A performance task is constructed to require the use of important concepts with supporting information, work habits important to science, and one or more of the elements of scientific literacy.

Performance Task Assessment Lists

Performance task assessment lists break the assessment criteria into several well-defined categories. Possible points for each category are assigned by the teacher. Both the teacher and the student assess the work and assign the number of points earned.

Science Voyages provides task assessment lists in Glencoe's ***Performance Assessment in the Science Classroom.*** These lists were developed for the summative and skill-performance tasks in the ***Performance Assessment*** book that accompanies the *Science Voyages* program.

Assessing Student Work with Rubrics

A rubric is a set of descriptions of the quality of a process and a product. The set of descriptions includes a continuum of quality from excellent to poor. Rubrics for various types of assessment products are in the Glencoe Professional Development Series booklet ***Performance Assessment in the Science Classroom.***

Portfolios

The **Portfolio** should help the student see the big picture of how he or she is performing in gaining knowledge and skills and how effective his or her work habits are. The process of assembling the portfolio should be both integrative (of process and content) and reflective. The performance portfolio is not a complete collection of all worksheets and other assignments but rather a collection that reflects the student's growth in concept attainment and skill development.

Group Assessment

Research has shown that a cooperative learning environment improves student-learning outcomes for students of all ability levels. An example, along with information about evaluating cooperative work, is provided in the booklet ***Alternate Assessment in the Science Classroom.***

The Science Journal

A Science Journal is intended to help the student organize his or her thinking. It is not a lecture or laboratory notebook. It is a place for students to make their thinking explicit in drawings and writing. It is the place to explore what makes science fun and what makes it hard.

Geoff Butler

Flex Your Brain

A key element in the coverage of problem-solving and critical-thinking skills in *Science Voyages* is a critical-thinking matrix called **Flex Your Brain.**

Flex Your Brain provides students with an opportunity to explore a topic in an organized, self-checking way, and then identify how they arrived at their responses during each step of their investigation. The activity incorporates many of the skills of critical thinking. It helps students to consider their own thinking and learn about thinking from their peers.

Where is Flex Your Brain found?

Chapter 1, The Nature of Science, is an introduction to critical thinking and problem solving. **Flex Your Brain** accompanies the text section in the introductory chapter. A worksheet for **Flex Your Brain** appears on page 5 of the *Activity Worksheets* book and as a transparency (Teaching Transparency 1) in the *Teacher Classroom Resources.* The *Activity Worksheets* version provides spaces for students to write in their responses.

In the *Teacher Wraparound Edition,* suggested topics are given in each chapter for the use of **Flex Your Brain.** You can photocopy the worksheet master from the *Teacher Classroom Resources.*

Using Flex Your Brain

Flex Your Brain can be used as a whole-class activity or in cooperative groups, but is primarily designed to be used by individual students within the class. There are three basic steps.

1. Teachers assign a class topic to be investigated using **Flex Your Brain.**
2. Students use **Flex Your Brain** to guide them in their individual explorations of a topic.
3. After students have completed their explorations, teachers guide them in a discussion of their experiences with **Flex Your Brain,** bridging content and thinking processes.

Flex Your Brain

1 Topic: ______

2 What do I already know? 1. ___ 2. ___ 3. ___ 4. ___ 5. ___

3 Q: Ask a question ______

4 A: Guess an answer ______

5 How sure am I? (circle one)
Not sure 1 2 3 4 5 Very sure

6 How can I find out? 1. ___ 2. ___ 3. ___ 4. ___ 5. ___

7 EXPLORE

8 Do I think differently? yes no

9 What do I know now? 1. ___ 2. ___ 3. ___ 4. ___ 5. ___

10 SHARE 1. ___ 2. ___ 3. ___

Flex Your Brain can be used at many different points in the lesson plan.

Introduction: Ideal for introducing a topic, **Flex Your Brain** elicits students' prior knowledge and identifies misconceptions, enabling the teacher to formulate plans specific to student needs.

Development: **Flex Your Brain** leads students to find out more about a topic on their own, and develops their research skills while increasing their knowledge.

Review and Extension: **Flex Your Brain** allows teachers to check student understanding while allowing students to explore aspects of the topic that go beyond the material presented in class.

TEACHER WRAPAROUND EDITION

Helping you prepare for the lesson

This table will help you locate features of the Teacher Wraparound Edition that will help you develop your lesson plans. Choose those features that will assist you the most when you teach in the *Science Voyages* program.

Feature Name	Where and How Many?	Suggestions For Use
Chapter Organizers	• One per chapter, only in Teacher Wraparound Edition • Spans A, B, C, and D pages preceding each chapter	• Determine objectives. • Determine in which sections labs and other features occur. • Determine which materials are available from the TCR box for each section. • View list of transparencies to use for each section. • View list of materials for labs. **For C and D pages** • Note L1, L2, L3 coding to assist in planning for different levels of students.
Assessment Planner	• One per chapter • Found at the bottom of the Teacher Wraparound Edition on the first page of each chapter	• Use as a source of ideas for alternative assessments.
Multiple Learning Styles	• One per chapter • Found at the bottom of the Teacher Wraparound Edition opposite the first page of each chapter	• Use to develop teaching strategies for various learning styles or multiple intelligences.
Flex Your Brain	• One per chapter • Found in the margin of the Teacher Wraparound Edition	• Use to check for understanding. • Let students use as a self-assessment.
Key to Teaching Strategies	• On B pages of Chapter Organizers in the Teacher Wraparound Edition	• Use to select materials appropriate for different levels of learners.
Four-Step Teaching Cycle	• Steps are: **1 Motivate**, **2 Teach**, **3 Assess**, and **4 Close** • Repeated for each section in every chapter	• Great help for a first-year teacher • Great help for experienced teacher in the first year in a new program

How to use your

Teacher Wraparound Edition

Interleaf Pages E and F help you prepare for the lesson by giving you more information about each section. The information goes beyond the student text and can assist you with questions the students might ask.

The Teacher's Corner lists the products available from the National Geographic Society that can help teach the lesson.

Chapter 1 The Nature of Science

Helping You Prepare

What Science Is (Section 1-1)

Deep-sea refers to more than 150 m below the water's surface. Most submarines can dive only to a depth of about 400 m.

A submersible is a special underwater craft that can descend to about 6100 m when unpiloted and 6500 m when piloted. They are usually equipped with cameras, floodlights, baskets, and mechanical arms for collecting samples.

An unpiloted submersible is referred to as an ROV, or remotely operated vehicle. Scientists are developing autonomous underwater vehicles (AUV), which need no cable.

Form a Hypothesis (Section 1-1)

A hypothesis that holds up under many experiments by different scientists may become a theory. Scientific theories and laws are often confused, but they are not the same.

A law is a statement of what happens, such as Newton's third law of motion, which states that for every action force, there is an equal and opposite reaction force.

Theories explain why or how something happens. The theories of plate tectonics and continental drift explain how these phenomena take place on and within Earth. Keep in mind that no theory is completely proven. A theory is subject to correction as new facts or observations emerge.

GLENCOE TECHNOLOGY

Glencoe Science Voyages Interactive CD-ROM

Chapter Summaries

Use the Chapter Summary to introduce, teach, or review chapter material.

Controlled Experiments (Section 1-1)

Ideally, the experimental and the control group each should have several samples. This minimizes individual differences that cannot be controlled. This is particularly important when the independent variable is not changed but applied equally to all samples. An example is testing the effects of a new drug at a particular dosage for subjects in the experimental group.

Plan (Section 1-1)

A clinical trial is an experiment in which the subject is a human. Controlling variables is often difficult, particularly psychological variables. For example, volunteers who know they are receiving a new drug may allow this to influence how they feel.

NATIONAL GEOGRAPHIC — Teacher's Corner

Products Available from National Geographic Society

To order the following products for use with this chapter, call National Geographic Society at 1-800-368-2728:

Book

Everyday Science Explained

Video

Scientific Method

Index to National Geographic Magazine

The following articles may be used for research relating to this chapter:

"Making Sense of the Millennium," by Joel L. Swerdlow, January 1998.

These sample pages are not complete sections.

A single-blind clinical trial is an experiment in which the subject does not know what treatment has been given. In a double-blind clinical trial, neither the subjects nor the investigators know which treatment has been given.

Using Technology (Section 1-2)

Robots range from having simple arms to being increasingly sophisticated "thinking" machines. Many robots have video-camera-based vision systems. Some robots even have smelling and tasting devices.

Some robots are programmed with a set of instructions and perform the same boring task repetitively. Some robots are much more sophisticated.

Sojourner, the first Mars rover, is a lightweight robotic machine on wheels. Sojourner is described as "thinking" because it is equipped with sophisticated laser eyes and can react to unplanned events on the surface of another planet.

Sojourner's intelligence is based on a mathematical model that emulates animal behavior. The ability for animals to avoid or flee from danger is a low-level reflex.

Sojourner was equipped with a spectrometer used to analyze the chemical composition of Martian rock and a camera that relayed images of the landscape back to Earth. Sojourner was carried to Mars via the space probe *Pathfinder,* which landed on Mars in July, 1997. This mission has been said to set the standard for twenty-first century space exploration. The Marie Curie rover is planned to be sent to Mars in 2001.

SCIENCE UPDATE

For current events or science in the news, access the Glencoe Science Web Site at **www.glencoe.com/sec/science**

Space probes are designed to land on a surface or to orbit around a planet or moon. They can determine composition, temperature, and pressure of atmospheres; pick up radio emissions; probe magnetic fields around planets; and collect and analyze soil samples.

The largest, most complex, and most expensive interplanetary probe launched is *Cassini. Cassini's* four-year mission is to provide information about Saturn, its rings, and moons.

Most space shuttles are equipped with a remote manipulator system or RMS. The RMS resembles a human arm with a shoulder and elbow joint. It measures over 15 meters when extended. Because of its design and construction, it would collapse under its own weight if used on Earth. The end of the RMS does not have fingers. It looks like a canister and can grab only large, sturdy objects. Engineers still do not know how to construct robotic fingers that are skillful and light, yet strong.

Interleaf Page F is a continuation of the content background found on the previous page.

Teacher to Teacher

"Before teaching a new topic, get students involved and help them recall prior knowledge. Using one set of index cards, write key vocabulary words and concepts. On a second set of cards, write the definition or information that the students will learn. Students work in pairs to try to match the cards."

Rebecca S. Buckingham
Rebecca S. Buckingham, Teacher
Lisbon Central School
Lisbon, NY

Teacher to Teacher consists of a teaching tip that directly relates to teaching chapter content or activities.

These sample pages are not complete sections.

How to use your

Teacher Wraparound Edition

Using Science to Explore

SECTION 1·2

Prepare

Refer to **Using Technology** on p. 4F.

Preplanning

Refer to the **Chapter Organizer** on pp. 4A–B.

Easy-to-use **teaching cycle of Motivate, Teach, Assess,** and **Close** organizes all of the teacher material for each lesson into four easy steps.

1 Motivate

Bellringer

Before presenting the lesson, display **Section Focus Transparency 2** on the overhead projector. Use the accompanying **Focus Activity** worksheet. L2 ELL

Bellringer Activities suggest the use of **Section Focus Transparencies** to get your students' attention and help focus them on the day's lesson.

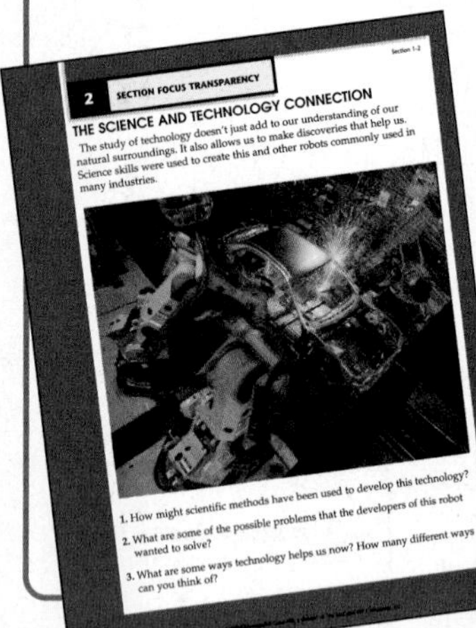

Section 1-2

2 SECTION FOCUS TRANSPARENCY

THE SCIENCE AND TECHNOLOGY CONNECTION

The study of technology doesn't just add to our understanding of our natural surroundings. It also allows us to make discoveries that help us. Science skills were used to create this and other robots commonly used in many industries.

1. How might scientific methods have been used to develop this technology?
2. What are some of the possible problems that the developers of this robot wanted to solve?
3. What are some ways technology helps us now? How many different ways can you think of?

Tying to Previous Knowledge

Ask students to recall ways that scientists have explored outer space without going there. This section will describe how scientists explore environments that are dangerous to humans.

Tying to Previous Knowledge ties the current lesson to a previous lesson or experience.

What You'll Learn

- How remotely operated vehicles help humans to explore
- How scientists use science skills in different ways

Vocabulary
technology
sequence
inference

Why It's Important

- Using science skills and technology helps you gather information about places that you cannot observe directly.

Using Technology

A week had passed since Mr. Hayes's assignment. The students were eager to share what they had found out.

Mr. Hayes opened the discussion. "Before we begin, who can tell us the difference between science and technology?"

Gabriella raised her hand. "Science is the process of trying to understand the world around you. **Technology** is the application of what has been learned through science."

"Excellent," Mr. Hayes said. "Why don't you go first, Gabriella?"

Gabriella stood. "The ocean is a frontier just waiting to be explored like the American West used to be. There's a difference, though. There are few places people may go underwater. It's too deep and the pressure is too great. That's what is known as a hostile environment—an environment in which the conditions are hazardous to people. People need technology to help them."

She continued, "Remotely operated vehicles, or ROVs, can withstand the pressure at several thousand feet. They have cameras and other instruments that gather data about things such as salinity (salt content) and currents. They have manipulators, or arms, that take samples."

Figure 1-14 This manned submersible, MIR I, is used to study and explore to a depth of 6000 m.

Resource Manager shows you exactly when to use Reproducible Masters, Color Transparencies, Multimedia, and other resources to support each lesson.

Resource Manager

The following **Teacher Classroom Resources** can be used with Section 1-2:

Reproducible Masters
Activity Worksheets, pp. 3–4, 6 L2
Critical Thinking/Problem Solving, p. 1 L2
Enrichment, p. 2 L3
Home Involvement, p. 28 L2
Multicultural Connections, pp. 1–2 L2
Reinforcement, p. 2 L2
Study Guide, pp. 3–4 L1 ELL

Transparencies
Teaching Transparency 2 L2
Science Integration Transparency 1 L2

22 CHAPTER 1 THE NATURE OF SCIENCE

These sample pages are not complete sections.
The entire section can be found in this book in the corresponding chapter.

"Volcanoes are another frontier on Earth," Jared volunteered. "I read about a spiderlike, walking robot that was designed to explore the inside of an active volcano."

Hiromi spoke next. "Space is another hostile environment," she said. "I read about a robot that NASA developed that's able to travel over rough terrain. They tested it in a desert that resembled the surface of the moon. Once on the moon, scientists would operate it from Earth. But, one thing that makes this robot different is that it has its own navigation system. Suppose it were going toward a cliff. It would take 2.5 seconds for the scientists to signal the robot on the moon, and by that time, the robot might have fallen off. But, this robot can determine what is safe and what is dangerous. It might even ignore the operator's commands if it detects a hazard."

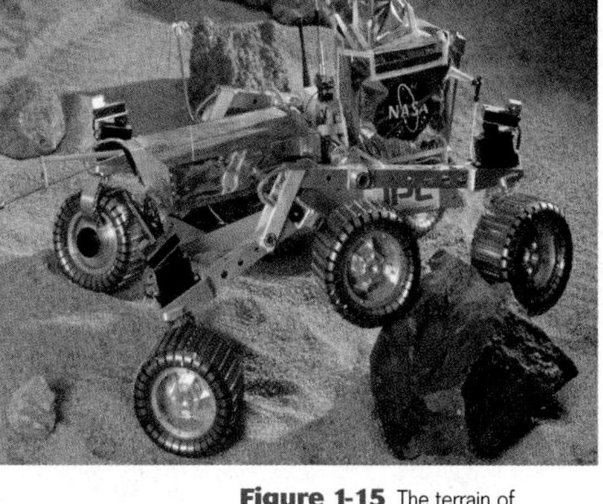

Figure 1-15 The terrain of Mars was photographed and explored by this rover.

"That's the kind of technology I read about," said Kashanna. "Scientists are making robots to explore hostile environments that don't need someone giving them commands all the time. One robot is called STAR—that's the Spiral Track Autonomous Robot. It travels on two giant screws—that's the 'spiral' part—so it can turn around in tight spaces and climb steep terrain that other robots can't. It has an onboard computer system that allows it to make decisions—that's the 'autonomous' part."

Figure 1-16 Technology, such as STAR, is developed to solve specific problems and explore unique environments.

2 Teach

Using Science Words

Robot comes from the Czech word *robota*, meaning "work" or "slavery." Karel Čapek invented the word for a play he wrote about a man who creates robots to work in his factory.

Content Background

The relative movements of the giant screws determine how STAR moves. The robot goes forward when the screws rotate in opposite directions. The robot goes sideways when they rotate in the same direction. The robot turns in place when one screw rotates while the other holds still.

Content Background provides additional information about a concept. This information is not in the student edition text.

Enrichment

Have students research for whom JASON was named and write a brief report about its namesake. How many other underwater vessels and spacecrafts can they find that were named after mythological characters? L2

GLENCOE TECHNOLOGY

Videodisc

The Infinite Voyage: Miracles by Design

Chapter 9 *"Smart Materials" and Their Construction* 3:00

Refer to the Teacher Guide for bar codes and teaching strategies.

Content Background

JASON is a submersible that is linked by cables and video cameras to scientists at the surface. JASON can collect seafloor samples and delicate objects such as those from shipwrecks. It can dive as deep as 6100 m. A person who dives with scuba gear can safely dive only about 40 m.

These sample pages are not complete sections.
The entire section can be found in this book in the corresponding chapter.

How to use your
Teacher Wraparound Edition

Glencoe Technology and other multimedia references at point of use make it easy to integrate technology into every lesson.

Multiple Learning Styles Provide opportunities for all students. Look for learning styles logos throughout each Teacher Wraparound chapter.

3 Assess

Check for Understanding
Using Science Words

Have students compare and contrast the ways in which scientists who design technology and scientists who explore use science skills. L2

Reteach

Have students list the hostile environments that are explored with robots or ROVs. Ask them to describe characteristics of the robots or ROVs that make it possible for them to function in hostile environments. L2

Extension

For students who have mastered this section, use the **Reinforcement** and **Enrichment** masters.

GLENCOE TECHNOLOGY

 **Videodisc**

The Infinite Voyage: To the Edge of the Earth

Chapter 3 *Exploring Volcanoes: To the Center of the Earth* 10:00

Refer to the Teacher Guide for bar codes and teaching strategies.

Glencoe Science Interactive Videodisc—Earth

Side 2, Lesson 8 *Space Exploration*

33975

36541

Refer to Videodisc Teacher Guide for additional bar codes.

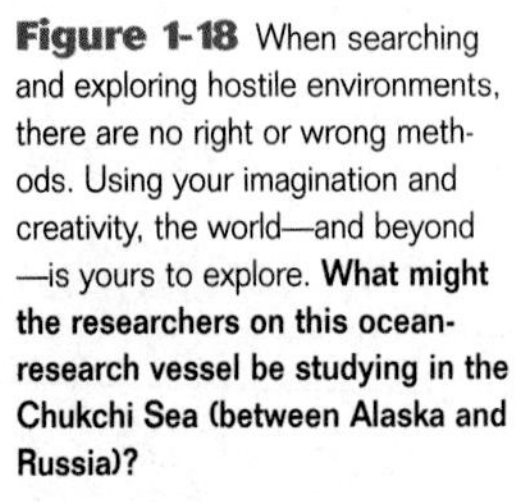

Figure 1-18 When searching and exploring hostile environments, there are no right or wrong methods. Using your imagination and creativity, the world—and beyond—is yours to explore. **What might the researchers on this ocean-research vessel be studying in the Chukchi Sea (between Alaska and Russia)?**

Using Science Skills to Explore

From their assignment, the class decided that the scientists who explore hostile environments using technology do not necessarily follow step-by-step scientific methods. For example, scientists who explore the ocean, as in **Figure 1-18,** might not have a formal hypothesis. The question might be "What's down there?" But, the scientists still use a variety of science skills while following their particular method.

These skills might include observing (looking at the pictures transmitted), inferring (explaining what the pictures are), measuring (determining how much cable to use to lower the ROV in the water), interpreting (using meteorological data to forecast the weather at sea), and communicating (sharing information to position the ROV correctly).

Safe Science

Mr. Hayes emphasized that safety is an important reason for using technology to explore hostile environments. Having equipment become damaged is far less critical than risking a

Science Journal

Technology and Skills Have students think of a hostile environment they would like to explore that is not mentioned in the text. They should list the science skills they would use and the technology they would need. L2

Caption Answer

Figure 1-18 *Answers may vary. The researchers might be studying how the animals live in this cold climate. Or, they might be gathering information about the organisms that live in this part of the ocean. They might even be collecting meteorological data.*

26 CHAPTER 1 THE NATURE OF SCIENCE

These sample pages are not complete sections.

person's life. The class discussed safety rules to follow when conducting science activities or experiments. They designed a poster called SAFE TIPS.

Start a lab activity only with your teacher's permission.
Ask your teacher if you do not understand a procedure.
Follow all safety symbols. Wear goggles during labs.
Engage in responsible behavior.

Tell your teacher immediately of accidents or injuries.
Identify the location of emergency equipment.
Put away chemicals and supplies properly.
Slant test tubes away from you and others when heating.

The students also created the slogan NO TIDE. TIDE stands for **T**asting chemicals, **I**nhaling chemicals, **D**rinking, or **E**ating. This helps them to remember that they should never eat or drink anything in a laboratory. It also reminds them to be cautious around fumes or vapors that could be harmful.

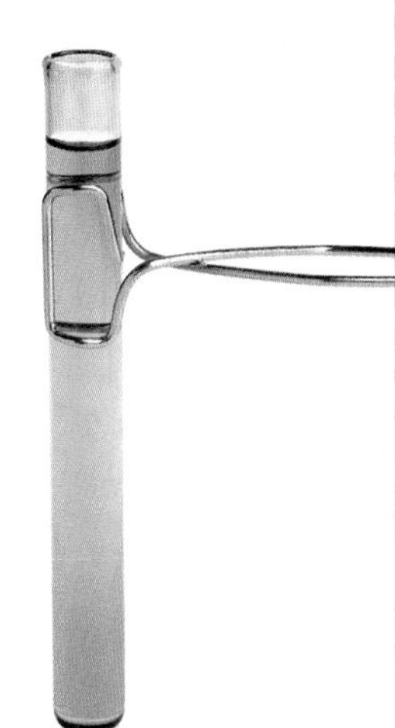

Figure 1-19 Lab equipment, like the test tube shown, must be handled properly.

Section Assessment

1. What are some ways technology is used to explore hostile environments?
2. What are some science skills scientists use to form a hypothesis about the design of an ROV or robot?
3. **Think Critically:** You have read about ways that scientists are like explorers. How are modern scientists different from explorers of the past?
4. **Skill Builder** **Interpreting Data** Suppose you have three plants that are supposed to bloom but are not blooming. You give one plant only water, another plant water and one type of plant fertilizer, and the third plant water and a different type of plant fertilizer. None of the plants bloom. How would you interpret your observations? If you need help, refer to Interpreting Data in the **Skill Handbook** on page 566.

Using Computers

Word Processing Think of a problem faced by your community such as water pollution. Using a word processor, write a report describing how you would design a robot or an ROV to help solve the problem. If you need help, refer to page 574.

4. **Skill Builder** Answers may include that neither fertilizer helped the plants to bloom. Maybe too much or too little fertilizer was used. Or, maybe the plants need nutrients from another kind of fertilizer to bloom. More experiments need to be performed.

Assessment

Portfolio Have students design a poster that illustrates the importance of following a safety rule when performing science activities. Students may choose one or more rules. Use **Performance Assessment in the Science Classroom,** p. 73.

4 Close

Proficiency Prep

Use this quiz to check students' recall of section content.

1. **What is the application of knowledge learned through science?** *technology*
2. **What are the two reasons that data are organized into tables and graphs?** *to help you analyze the results and draw conclusions*
3. **What should you do before starting any lab activity?** *get permission from your teacher*

Section Assessment

1. ROVs and robots are sent to sites of nuclear accidents, deep into the ocean, into volcanoes, into outer space, and into mines.
2. Answers could include using numbers, comparing, contrasting, sequencing, graphing, and communicating.
3. Think Critically Past explorers did not have the technology that scientists have today. Also, scientists today have access to a lot more information because of research done in the past.

Using Computers

Answers will vary according to the community problem the student chooses to solve.

Proficiency Prep questions develop and reinforce the chapter content.

The **Section Assessment** includes answers to review questions in the Student Edition assessment.

Answers are provided at point of use for student edition **Reading Check questions, Using Math, Internet Connections,** and **Using Computers.**

These sample pages are not complete sections.

How to use your

Teacher Wraparound Edition

Reviewing Main Ideas gives you activity ideas to use before, during, and after the lesson is taught.

Chapter 1 Reviewing Main Ideas

Reviewing Main Ideas can be used to preview, review, reteach, and condense chapter content.

Preview

Linguistic Have students try to answer the questions in their Science Journals. Use student answers as a source for discussion throughout the chapter.

Review

Interpersonal Have students answer the questions on separate pieces of paper and compare their answers with those of other students in the class.

Reteach

Visual-Spatial Have students look at the illustrations on these pages. Ask them to describe details that support the main ideas of the chapter found in the statement for each illustration.

OUT OF TIME?

Auditory-Musical If time does not permit teaching the entire chapter, use the information on these pages along with the chapter Audiocassettes to present the material in a condensed format.

Chapter 1 Reviewing Main Ideas

For a **preview** of this chapter, study this Reviewing Main Ideas before you read the chapter. After you have studied this chapter, you can use the Reviewing Main Ideas to **review** the chapter.

The Glencoe MindJogger, Audiocassettes, and CD-ROM provide additional opportunities for review.

Section

1-1 SCIENTIFIC PROBLEM SOLVING

Scientific methods are steps taken to try to solve a problem. One step is to recognize a problem. A second step is to form a **hypothesis**—a prediction about a problem that can be tested. In another step, scientists test hypotheses by conducting controlled experiments or observational studies. In a controlled experiment, scientists change the **independent variable** and measure its effect on the **dependent variable.** Scientists who conduct observational studies do not change or control variables. They observe the relationships among variables. Another scientific method is to analyze data. Scientists organize data into tables or **graphs.** Often, the final step in a scientific method is to draw conclusions. A conclusion may or may not support the hypothesis. This does not necessarily mean the hypothesis is wrong. Sometimes, experiments are not designed correctly or unknown variables produce effects on the dependent variable. Scientists often must do many experiments and look at problems in different ways to find answers. ***Why should only one variable at a time be changed in a controlled experiment?***

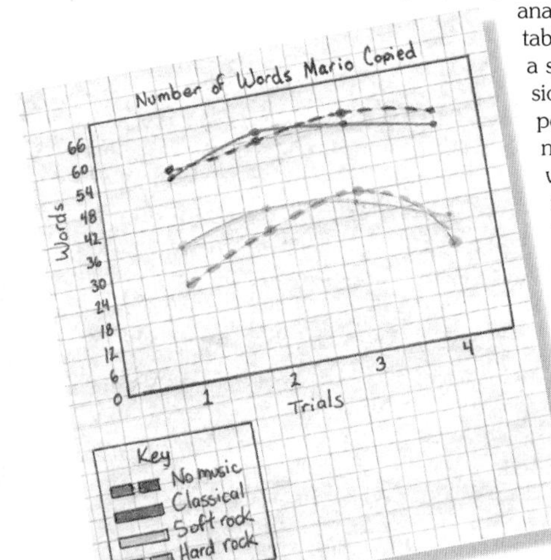

Cultural Diversity gives a current or historical background on a custom or belief associated with a science concept.

Cultural Diversity

Shamanic Medicine Principles of science are used to solve problems throughout the world. In the rain forests of Latin America, much of the healing is done by shamans, who are local people who use native plants for medicines. Today, researchers are working with shamans and investigating the medicinal value of the plants. Perhaps the cure to some diseases can be found in these plants.

These sample pages are not complete sections.
The entire section can be found in this book in the corresponding chapter.

Reading Check ✓
Variables, controls, and *trials* are used in scientific experiments. Compare the meaning of each word in this context with its meaning in a nonscientific context.

Section 1-2
USING SCIENCE TO EXPLORE

A hostile environment is an environment in which the conditions are hazardous to people. Many places on Earth and in outer space cannot be explored directly by humans. Scientists have constructed robots and remotely operated vehicles, or ROVs, to go to sites of nuclear accidents, deep in the ocean, into volcanoes, into outer space, and into mines. People have increased their knowledge of hostile environments by analyzing data gathered through **technology.** Scientists who design technology to explore hostile environments use various approaches when forming a **scientific method** that will help them solve a particular problem. They design and conduct experiments to test models. Scientists who use technology to explore hostile environments use science skills. In both cases, scientists use science skills to solve a problem or to answer a question. ***Does a scientist always have to follow certain steps in a scientific method? Why or why not?***

Career CONNECTION

John Swallow, Forest Technician

John Swallow works in South Dakota's Black Hills National Forest. He is an Oglala Sioux and a forest technician. John determines which trees in the forest can be safely cut down and which trees must be saved. Much of the cutting of trees is done for thinning—to reduce competition between trees for light and nutrients—thus promoting quicker growth. John also works to conserve sensitive or endangered plants in logging areas. ***How can science help our understanding of the impact of logging on a forest?***

CHAPTER 1 REVIEWING MAIN IDEAS 31

Answers to Questions

Answers are provided for the questions asked in **Reviewing Main Ideas.**

Section 1-1

Scientific Problem Solving The scientist will know that any effect on the dependent variable was caused by the independent variable.

Section 1-2

Using Science to Explore No, because following any scientific method step-by-step is not necessary to solve every problem or answer all questions.

GLENCOE TECHNOLOGY

CD-ROM

Glencoe Science Voyages Interactive CD-ROM

Chapter Summaries and Quizzes

Have students read the Chapter Summary then take the Chapter Quiz to determine whether they have mastered the chapter content.

Career CONNECTION

By using science skills, we can learn what methods are best to protect plants and trees in logging areas.

✓ Assessment

Assessment boxes tell you where to find additional assessment activities.

Portfolio Encourage students to place in their portfolios one or two items of what they consider to be their best work. Examples include:
- Across the Curriculum, pp. 14, 25
- Using Math, p. 19
- Assessment, p. 27 P

Performance Additional performance assessments may be found in **Performance Assessment** and **Science Integration Activities.** Performance Task Assessment Lists and rubrics for evaluating these activities can be found in Glencoe's **Performance Assessment in the Science Classroom.**

CHAPTER 1 REVIEWING MAIN IDEAS 31

These sample pages are not complete sections.
The entire section can be found in this book in the corresponding chapter.

Chapter Assessment gives the answers to student edition questions.

Internet Connection tells you where to look on the Glencoe Science Voyages Web Site for reinforcement activities.

Chapter 1 Assessment

Using Vocabulary

1. k
2. e
3. i
4. b
5. c

interNET CONNECTION To reinforce chapter vocabulary, use the **Study Guide for Content Mastery** booklet. Also available are activities for **Glencoe Science Voyages** on the Glencoe Science Web Site. **www.glencoe.com/sec/science/ca**

Checking Concepts

6. A	11. B
7. C	12. A
8. D	13. B
9. C	14. A
10. D	15. B

Thinking Critically

16. Answers will vary. Answers might include that they would forget a step or that they would find it difficult to get ready on time.
17. The scientist wants to make sure it is the drug that is causing the effect.
18. Answers will vary. An example is observing the number and types of birds in their yards.
19. Following safety rules reduces the risk that someone could get injured.
20. Information helps scientist make better, educated guesses. They can base the hypothesis on what is already known.

32 CHAPTER 1 THE NATURE OF SCIENCE

Chapter 1 Assessment

Using Vocabulary

a. constant
b. control
c. dependent variable
d. graph
e. hypothesis
f. independent variable
g. inference
h. law
i. science
j. scientific method
k. sequence
l. technology
m. theory

Each of the following sentences is false. Make the sentence true by replacing the italicized word with a word from the list above.

1. *Controls* are approaches taken to try to solve a problem.
2. An *inference* is a prediction about a problem that can be tested.
3. *Technology* is the process of trying to understand the world around you.
4. A *constant* is a standard to compare with.
5. The *independent variable* is the factor being measured in a controlled experiment.

Checking Concepts

Choose the word or phrase that best answers the question.

6. How is a hypothesis tested?
   A) experiment
   B) infer
   C) graph
   D) conclude
7. What will a scientist never do in an observational study?
   A) use technology
   B) record data
   C) control variables
   D) observe variables
8. What does a scientist use to reduce the effect of errors?
   A) observations
   B) constants
   C) hypotheses
   D) multiple trials
9. You decide to find out which of three cat foods your cat likes the best. What is the cat food that you try each time called?
   A) control
   B) dependent variable
   C) independent variable
   D) trial
10. How does a blind experiment differ from other experiments?
    A) Data are collected and interpreted.
    B) A hypothesis is formed after observations are made.
    C) Variables are changed to test the hypothesis.
    D) Some or all of the information is withheld from the subject.
11. What does it mean if an experiment does **NOT** support the hypothesis?
    A) The scientist has failed.
    B) The scientist has learned more.
    C) The scientist is not creative.
    D) The scientist did something wrong.
12. Why are ROVs and robots so useful?
    A) They gather information from hostile environments.
    B) They must follow commands from a person.
    C) They allow people to see hostile environments directly.
    D) They make all decisions on their own.
13. How do scientists who build ROVs use scientific methods?
    A) They test the effects of gravity.
    B) They work according to a sequence.
    C) They keep their data secret.
    D) They use every approach in the model.
14. What is a graph **NOT** used for?
    A) conducting an experiment
    B) interpreting data
    C) communicating information
    D) drawing conclusions
15. What is an explanation backed by experimental results?
    A) a control
    B) a theory
    C) a law
    D) a hypothesis

32 CHAPTER 1 THE NATURE OF SCIENCE

These sample pages are not complete sections.

Thinking Critically

16. You use the skill of sequencing when you get ready for school. What might happen if you changed the order of your actions?
17. A scientist wants to try a new drug that might relieve symptoms for a particular illness. Why is it important to use a control?
18. Give an example of an observational study you can do at home.
19. Why is it important to follow safety rules in the lab?
20. Why do scientists often do research before forming a hypothesis?

Developing Skills

If you need help, refer to the **Skill Handbook.**

21. **Concept Mapping:** Complete the events chain that shows the order in which science skills might be used in observational studies. Use these phrases: *analyze data, ask a question, draw conclusions, observe,* and *record data.*

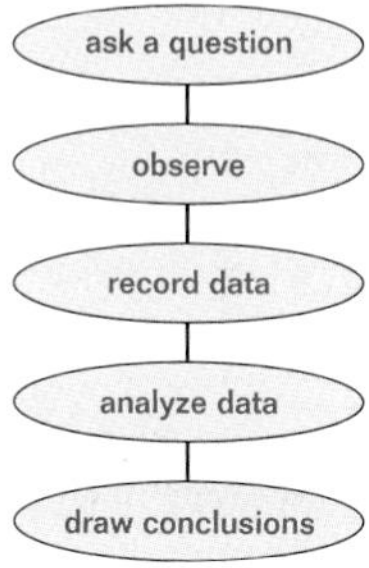

Test-Taking Tip

Beat the Clock and Then Go Back As you take a test, pace yourself to finish a few minutes early so you can go back and check over your work. You'll usually find a mistake or two. Don't worry. It's better to make corrections than to hand in a test with wrong answers.

Test Practice

Use these questions to test your Science Proficiency.

1. Michaela set up an experiment to find out if running would help her basketball game. Her basketball game did not improve. What can Michaela conclude from her results?
   A) Her hypothesis was wrong.
   B) Her results did not support the hypothesis.
   C) Running does not help a person do well in sports.
   D) A person who plays basketball should not run.
2. Alex eagerly arrived to science class early to begin his experiment. He set up the materials, popped a piece of gum into his mouth, and got right to work by himself, even though he wasn't quite sure of the procedure. What is the safety precaution that he ignored **FIRST?**
   A) He didn't put on goggles.
   B) He didn't ask questions about the correct procedure.
   C) He didn't get the teacher's permission to start the lab activity.
   D) He was eating during a lab activity.

THE PRINCETON REVIEW **Test Practice**

The Test-Taking Tip was written by The Princeton Review, the nation's leader in test preparation.

1. B
2. C

Developing Skills

21. See student page.

Bonus Question

Identify a problem or question that would best be answered by an observational study. *Answers will vary but may include the following: What are the mating behaviors of a particular animal? or What toys do infants prefer to play with?* **Identify a problem or question that would best be answered by a controlled experiment.** *Answers will vary but may include the following: How much medicine will supress a cough for four hours? or Which house paint holds up the best?*

Test Practice is designed to introduce standardized test format to the student.

Assessment Resources

The **Test Practice Workbook** provides students with practice in the format, concepts, and critical-thinking skills tested in standardized exams.

Reproducible Masters

Chapter Review, pp. 1–2 L2
Performance Assessment, p. 13 L2
Assessment, pp. 1–4 L2

Glencoe Technology

Chapter Review Software
Computer Test Bank
MindJogger Videoquiz

These sample pages are not complete sections.

Making Hypotheses
Students are given many opportunities to practice proposing hypotheses. Possible hypotheses are given. Make certain their hypotheses are always testable.

Activity 1-2

Possible Hypotheses
Students might hypothesize that the type of surface material has no effect on how high the ball bounces. They might hypothesize that balls bounce higher on softer materials than on harder ones.

Activity 1-2 — Using Scientific Methods

Comparing Densities

Density is a physical property of a substance. It relates to how much material is contained within an object. In general, an object will float if its density is less than the density of the liquid. The more dense the liquid, the greater the mass it can support. How do the densities of various liquids compare?

Materials
- Graduated cylinder (100 mL)
- Balance and masses
- Water
- Cooking oil
- Table salt
- Paper cups
- Plastic spoons or stirrers
- Plastic beverage containers (to dispose of oil)

What You'll Investigate
How do the densities of liquids compare?

Goals
- **Infer** why objects float in some liquids but not in others.
- **Measure** liquids to determine their density.
- **Graph** the densities of the liquids.

Safety Precautions
 Never taste anything during a lab activity. Wipe up any spills on the floor immediately.

Procedure
1. **Copy** the data table below for recording your measurements.
2. **Measure** the mass of a paper cup and record.
3. **Measure** 100 mL of water and pour it into the cup. Record the mass.
4. **Make** salt water by dissolving 3.5 g of table salt into 100 mL of tap water. Using a fresh paper cup each time, repeat steps 2 and 3 for the salt water and oil.
5. **Subtract** the mass of the cup to find the mass of the liquid. **Calculate** the density of each liquid using the formula, *density = mass/volume.* The unit used to express density is g/cm^3. One cubic centimeter occupies the same volume as one milliliter.
6. **Graph** your data using a bar graph. How does a graph help you analyze your results?

Conclude and Apply
1. Would a ship be able to carry more cargo in freshwater or salt water? Why?
2. Why might it be harder for aquatic birds to swim in an oil spill than in water?

Sample Data

Liquid's Measurement Data

Liquid	Mass of paper cup (g)	Mass of liquid in cup (g)	Mass of liquid only (g)	Volume of liquid (mL)	Density (g/mL)
Tap water	7	106	99	100	0.99
Salt water	6	110	104	100	1.04
Oil	6	98	92	100	0.92

Assessment

Possible Procedures
Attach a strip of white paper on a wall and drop the ball close to the wall. Mark the highest spot the ball reached. Use different colored markers for each type of surface material. Or, label the spot with the type of material. Use a stationary object, such as a desktop, to align the ball at the same height each time. Have the same

28 CHAPTER 1 THE NATURE OF SCIENCE

These sample pages are not complete sections.
The entire section can be found in this book in the corresponding chapter.

TEACHER CLASSROOM RESOURCES

Technology helps you adapt your teaching methods to the needs of your students. Glencoe classroom technology products provide many pathways to help you match students' different learning styles. To make your lesson planning easier, all of the technology products listed below are correlated to the student text.

Assessment

- Chapter Review
- Standardized Test Practice
- Performance Assessment
- Assessment—Chapter and Unit Tests
- Performance Assessment in the Science Classroom
- Alternate Assessment in the Science Classroom

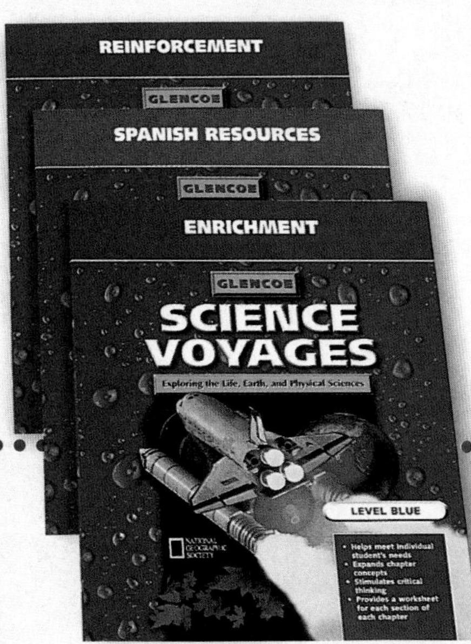

Meeting Individual Needs

- Study Guide for Content Mastery SE and TE
- Chapter Overview Study Guide, SE and TE
- Reinforcement
- Enrichment
- Spanish Resources

TEACHER CLASSROOM RESOURCES

Teacher Support and Planning
- Interactive Lesson Planner CD-ROM
- Lesson Plans

Transparencies
- Section Focus Transparencies
- Teaching/Integration Transparencies

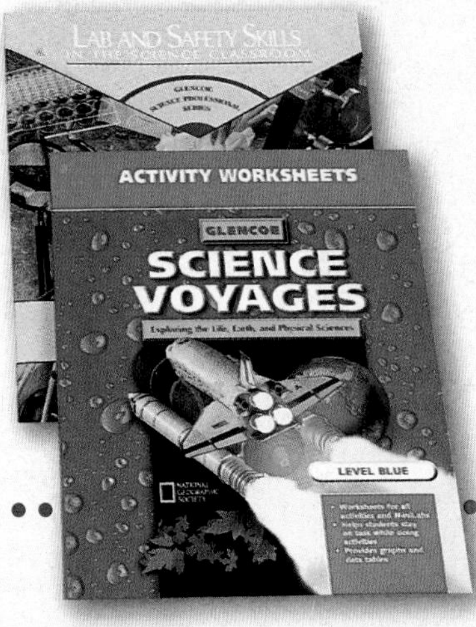

Hands-On Activities
- Lab and Safety Skills in the Science Classroom
- Laboratory Manual, SE and TE
- Activity Worksheets
- Science Inquiry Activities, SE and TE

Extending Content
- Multicultural Connections
- Home Involvement
- Critical Thinking/Problem Solving
- Using the Internet in the Science Classroom
- Exploring Environmental Issues
- Cooperative Learning in the Science Classroom

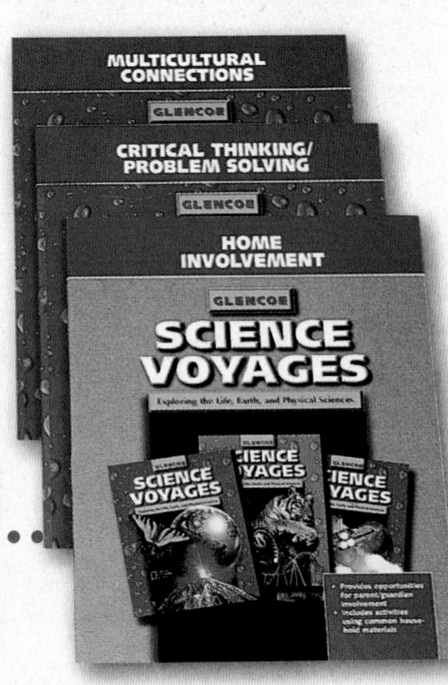

Meeting Individual Needs

Each student brings his or her own unique set of abilities, perceptions, and needs into the classroom. It is important that the teacher try to make the classroom environment as receptive to these differences as possible and to ensure a good learning environment exists for all students.

In an effort to provide all students with a positive science experience, this text offers a variety of ways for students to interact with materials so that they can utilize their preferred methods of learning the concepts.

Ability Levels

The activities are broken down into three levels to accommodate students of all ability levels. ***Science Voyages Teacher Wraparound Edition*** designates the activities as follows:

L1 Activities are basic activities designed to be within the ability range of lower-ability students. These activities reinforce the concepts presented.

L2 Activities are application activities designed for all students. These activities give students an opportunity for practical application of the concepts presented.

L3 Activities are challenging activities designed for the students who are able to go beyond the basic concepts presented. These activities allow students to expand their perspectives on the basic concepts.

English-Language Learners

In providing for the student with limited English proficiency, the focus needs to be on overcoming a language barrier. It is important not to confuse ability in speaking/reading English with academic ability or "intelligence." Look for this symbol ELL in the teacher margin for specific strategies for students with limited English proficiency.

Learning Styles

We at Glencoe believe it is our responsibility to provide you with a program that allows you to apply diverse instructional strategies to a population of students with diverse learning styles. A student with a kinesthetic style learns from touch, movement, and manipulating objects. Visual-spatial learners respond to images and illustrations. Using numbers and reasoning are characteristics of the logical-mathematical learner. A student with an interpersonal style has confidence in social settings, while a student with an intrapersonal style may prefer to learn on his or her own. Linguistic learning involves the use and understanding of words. Finally, auditory-musical learning involves listening to the spoken word and to tones and rhythms.

Any student may display any or all of these styles. The ***Student Edition*** and ***Teacher Wraparound Edition*** provide a number of strategies for encouraging students with diverse learning styles. These include **Using Math, Activities, MiniLabs,** and **Science Journal** features.

The chart on pages 60T–61T gives tips you may find useful in structuring the learning environment in your classroom to meet students' special needs.

Gail Meese

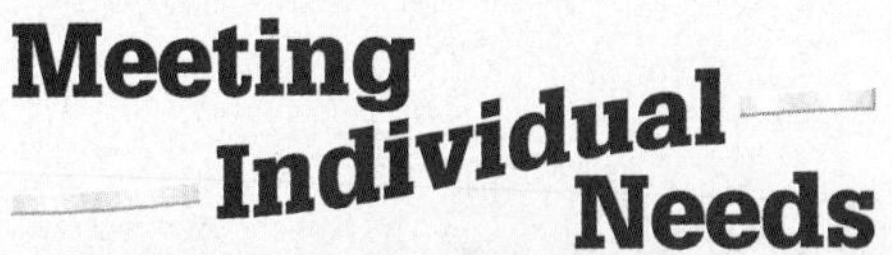

Meeting Individual Needs

Tips for Instruction	With careful planning, the needs of all students can be met in the science classroom
Learning Disabled	1. Provide support and structure; clearly specify rules, assignments, and duties. 2. Practice skills frequently. Use games and drills to help maintain student interest. 3. Allow students to record answers on tape and allow extra time to complete tests and assignments. 4. Provide outlines or tape lecture material. 5. Pair students with peer helpers, and provide class time for pair interaction.
Behaviorally Disordered	1. Provide a clearly structured environment with regard to scheduling, rules, room arrangement, and safety. 2. Clearly outline objectives and how you will help students obtain objectives. 3. Reinforce appropriate behavior and model it for students. 4. Do not expect immediate success. Instead, work for long-term improvement. 5. Balance individual needs with group requirements.
Physically Challenged	1. Openly discuss with the student any uncertainties you have about when to offer aid. 2. Ask parents or therapists and students what special devices or procedures are needed, and whether any special safety precautions need to be taken. 3. Allow physically disabled students to do everything their peers do, including participating in field trips, special events, and projects. 4. Help nondisabled students and adults understand physically disabled students.
Visually Impaired	1. Help the student become independent. Modify assignments as needed. 2. Teach classmates how to serve as guides. 3. Limit unnecessary noise in the classroom. 4. Provide tactile models whenever possible. 5. Describe people and events as they occur in the classroom. 6. Provide taped lectures and reading assignments. 7. Team the student with a sighted peer for laboratory work.
Hearing Impaired	1. Seat students where they can see your lip movements easily, and avoid visual distractions. 2. Avoid standing with your back to the window or light source. 3. Use an overhead projector to maintain eye contact while writing. 4. Seat students where they can see speakers. 5. Write all assignments on the board, or hand out written instructions. 6. If the student has a manual interpreter, allow both student and interpreter to select the most favorable seating arrangements.
English-Language Learners	1. Remember, students' ability to speak English does not reflect their academic abilities. 2. Try to incorporate the student's cultural experience into your instruction. The help of a bilingual aide may be effective. 3. Include information about different cultures in your curriculum to help build students' self-images. Avoid cultural stereotypes. 4. Encourage students to share their cultures in the classroom.
Gifted	1. Make arrangements for students to take selected subjects early and to work on independent projects. 2. Let students express themselves in art forms such as drawing, creative writing, or acting. 3. Make public services available through a catalog of resources, such as agencies providing free and inexpensive materials, community services and programs, and people in the community with specific expertise. 4. Ask "what if" questions to develop high-level thinking skills. Establish an environment safe for risk taking. 5. Emphasize concepts, theories, ideas, relationships, and generalizations.

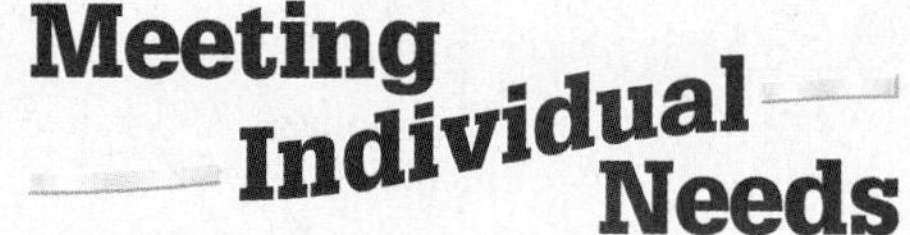

Multiple Learning Styles

People learn in many different ways. There are several different learning styles that help us approach and solve problems. Everyone possesses varying degrees of each of these learning styles, but the ways in which they combine and blend are as varied as the personalities of the individuals. Glencoe's **Science Voyages** provides you with ways to accommodate students with these diverse learning styles.

Learning Style	Characteristics of Students	Activities in Student Edition
Linguistic	read regularly, write clearly, and easily understand the written word	**Science Journal** activities ask students to tell, write, and explain science concepts. Students express what they have learned in their Science Journals.
Logical–Mathematical	use numbers, logic, and critical thinking skills	Each clearly written **Explore Activity** presents an important concept and **Think Critically** questions, **Skill Builders,** and **Problem Solving** exercises encourage students to practice their logical thinking skills by using various strategies.
Visual–Spatial	think in terms of pictures and images	**Activities** and **Assessment** questions often ask students to draw or show science concepts through modeling, concept maps, charts, graphs, and illustrations.
Auditory–Musical	remember spoken words and can produce rhythms and melodies	Multimedia software, such as the **Interactive CD-ROM, MindJogger Videoquizzes,** and **Interactive Videodiscs,** can easily be incorporated into lessons.
Kinesthetic	learn from touch, movement, and manipulating objects	**Activities** and **Minilabs** provide for physical involvement in learning.
Interpersonal	understand and work well with other people	**Activities, Science Integrations, Internet Connections,** and **Minilabs** allow students to collaborate with others.
Intrapersonal	have a realistic understanding of their strengths and weaknesses	**Science Journals** and **Try at Home Minilabs** help students personalize science.
Naturalist	can distinguish among, classify, and use features of the environment	**National Geographic** features show students how science relates to the world around them.

As a science teacher, you may want to assign activities to students that accommodate their strongest learning styles, but frequently ask them to use their weakest learning styles. Additional activities are provided in the Teacher Wraparound Edition.

The resources available in **Science Voyages** guarantee that your classroom will be a multisensory environment, providing multiple paths for student learning.

Meeting Classroom

Interactive Lesson Planner CD-ROM
With Teacher Classroom Resources

- An electronic Lesson-Plan format
- Lesson Planners are designed to save you time
- Makes planning quick and easy

Reach visual learners with
Color Transparencies

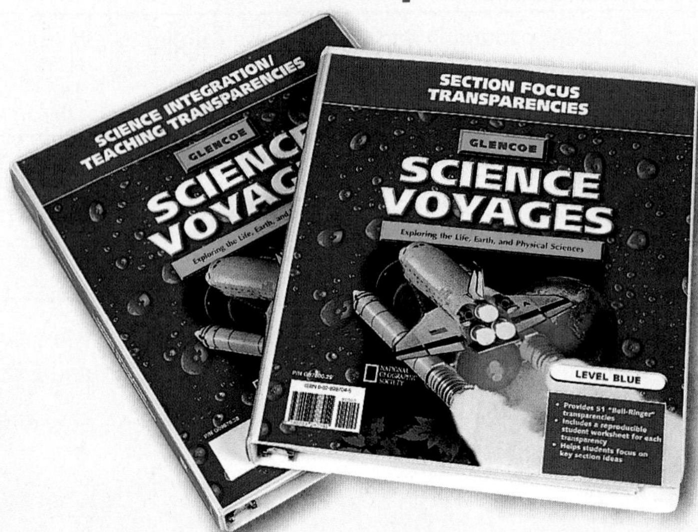

- Teaching/Science Integration Transparencies
- Section Focus Transparencies
- Use a separate transparency as an introduction to each section
- Use as a review.
- Use to stimulate a classroom discussion.

Help students with reading and comprehension with English and Spanish
Audiocassettes

- Available in English or Spanish
- Audiocassettes can be used as a supplement with the text for students who have difficulty reading.
- Students can use individually during class.
- Students can check out tapes and use them at home to reinforce what they have read.
- Use to review chapter before a test..

Technology Needs

Videodiscs

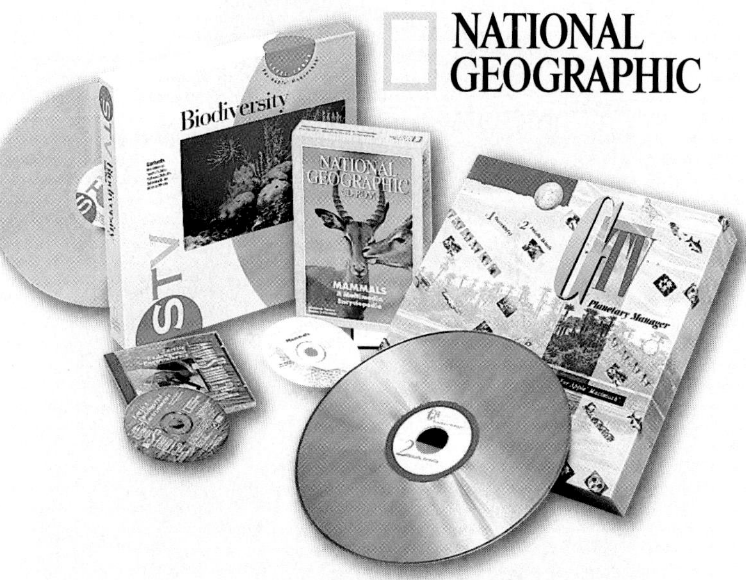

- Videodiscs are designed to be used interactively in the classroom.
- Bar codes in this Teacher Wraparound Edition allow you to step through a program and pause to discuss and answer on-screen questions.

Have fun preparing students for Assessment with MindJogger VideoQuizzes

- Chapter quizzes in video-game format
- Play with teams of four, as suggested on the tape.
- Run copies of questions on paper and have students answer for homework.
- Play as a pre-test or use as a review game.
- Each row forms a team. Every student records his or her answer on a card, then holds it up. Teacher pauses the tape while the row captain tallies points and writes updated scores on the board.

Infinite Voyages

Meeting Classroom

Interactive Videodiscs

- Videodiscs are designed to be used interactively in the classroom.
- Bar codes in this book allow you to step through the programs and pause to discuss and answer on-screen questions.
- Use as a review.

Make customized tests easily and quickly with

ExamView Test Bank Software

- Versions created for Macintosh and Windows.
- Makes creating, editing, and printing tests quick and easy
- You can also use it to edit questions or add your own favorite questions and graphics.
- On CD-ROM and floppy disc

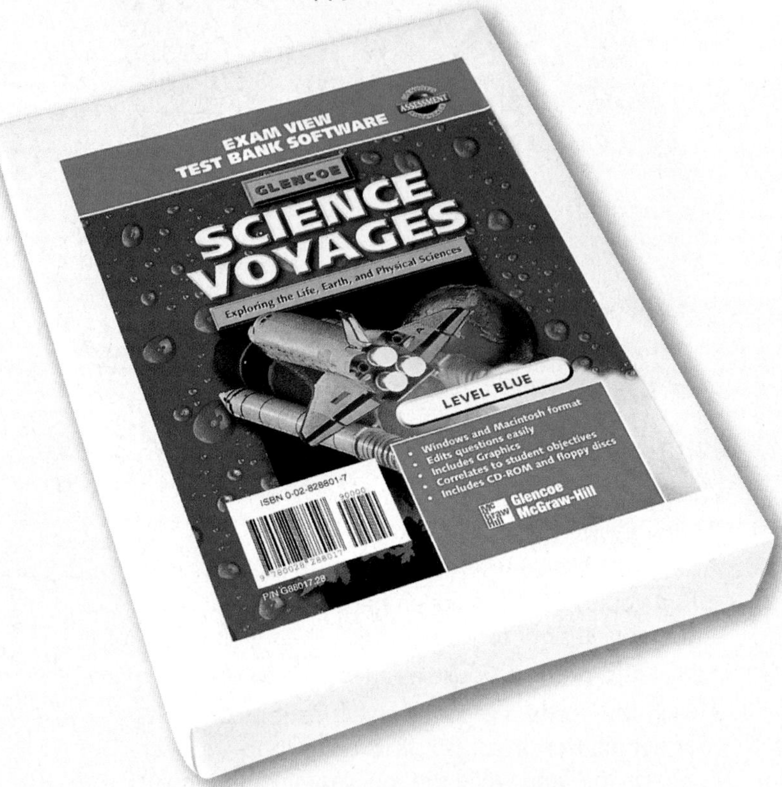

Technology Needs

Interactive CD-ROM

Explorations and Quizzes

- Glencoe has an interactive CD-ROM for each of the textbooks in the ***Science Voyages*** series.
- Can be used as a library resource
- Use as a whole-class presentation.
- Use as a review for individual students.

Internet

- The Glencoe Science Web Site can be found at **http://www.glencoe.com/sec/science.**
- Use to extend textbook content.
- Use as a classroom resource.
- Use as an exploration tool for classroom projects.

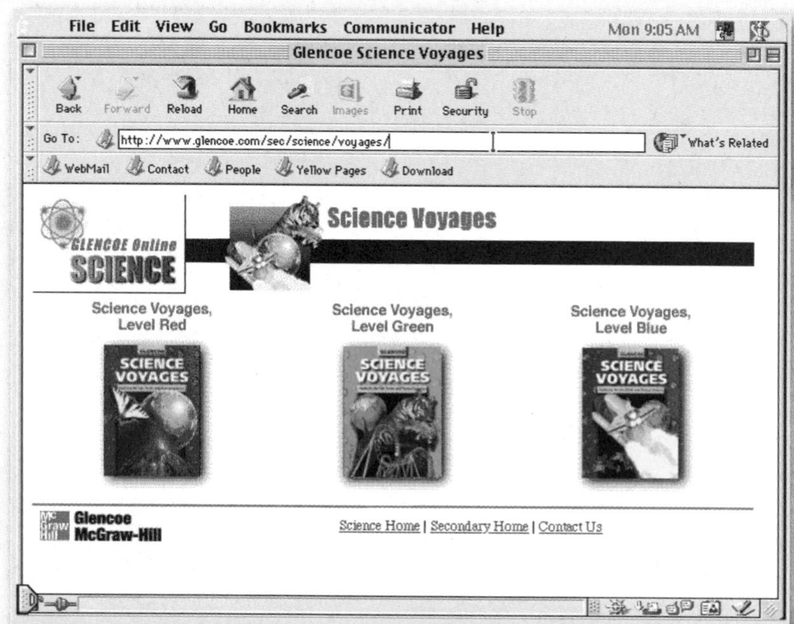

using the interNET

Getting Started

If you're already familiar with the Internet, skip to the next page. To read more about the **Science Voyages** Web Site, keep reading.

The Internet is an enormous reference library and a communication tool. You can use it to retrieve information quickly from computers around the globe. Like any good reference, it has an index so you can locate the right piece of information. An Internet index entry is called a Universal Resource Locator, or URL. Here's an example. It is the URL for Glencoe science products. **http://www.glencoe.com/sec/science**

The first part of the URL tells the computer how to display the information. The second part, after the double slash, names the organization and the computer where the information is stored. The part after the first single slash tells the computer which directory to search and which file to retrieve. File locations change frequently. If you can't find what you're looking for, use the first part of the address only and follow links to what you need.

The World Wide Web

The World Wide Web (WWW), a subset of the Internet, began in 1992. Unlike regular text files, Web files can have links to other text files, images, and sound files. By clicking on a link, you can see or hear the linked information.

How do I get access?

To use the Internet, you need a computer, a modem, a telephone line, and a connection to the Internet. If your school doesn't have a connection, contact your local public library or a university; they often give free access to students and educators.

Glencoe Online Science

The **Science Voyages** Web Site at **www.glencoe.com/sec/science** provides students and teachers with a wide range of materials. On the **Science Voyages** Web Site are links to other Web Sites on the Internet that provide more information on the topics students are studying. Internet projects give students an opportunity to research and share data with other students from around the country and even around the world. Professional development materials give teachers additional resources for teaching science.

Additional Information

You can obtain additional information about using the Internet from Glencoe's *Using the Internet in the Science Classroom,* a booklet that contains hints on how to safely use the Internet, as well as more detailed instructions on how to use it in the science classroom.

CAUTION: Contents may shift!

The sites referenced on any portion of Glencoe's Web Site are not under Glencoe's control. Therefore, Glencoe can make no representation concerning the content of these sites. To protect students, extreme care has been taken to provide only reputable links by using educational and government sites whenever possible. Internet searches have been conducted that, at this time and to Glencoe's knowledge, lead students to sites that contain no content intended for mature audiences.

Science Voyages Web Site Features

Web Links—Links to other previewed web sites that provide information on science topics

Interactive Tutor—Online worksheets and interactive games for study, practice, and review, along with answers

Skill Handbook—A handbook describing how to use basic science skills

Internet Activities—Internet-based projects, including additional information for teachers to help students carry out the projects

Teacher Corner—Professional Development

Activity Materials

Science Voyages has a variety of hands-on activities, short to long, directed and open ended. Many use common, inexpensive materials, making it easier for you to do activities in your classroom. They also are easy to manage with clearly numbered steps and illustrations that help students meet activity objectives. Our full-sized labs were bench-tested by Science Kit to ensure that they use the most common, inexpensive, and appropriate materials.

All MiniLabs have been teacher tested and all laboratory activities have been thoroughly reviewed for safety.

Science Voyages full-sized labs have been Bench-tested by Science Kit to ensure quality and safety.

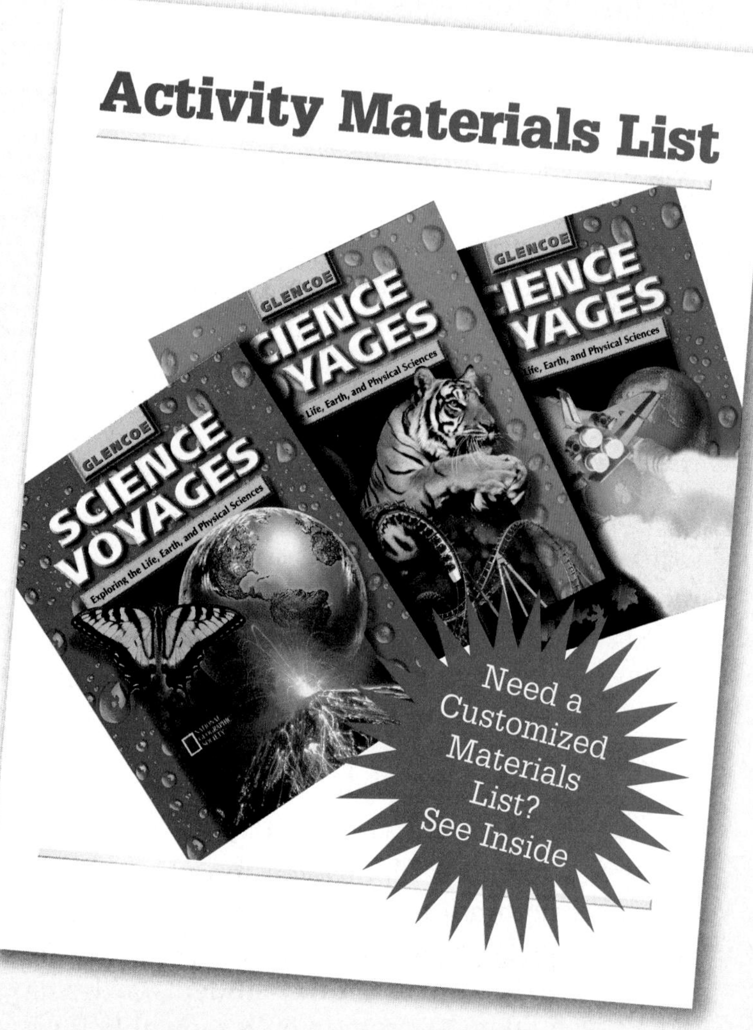

Get the materials you need quickly and easily!

Glencoe and Science Kit, Inc., have teamed up to make materials selection for ***Science Voyages*** easier with an activity-materials folder. This folder contains two convenient ways to order materials and equipment for the program: the **Activity Plan Checklist** and the **Activity Materials List** master.

Call Science Kit at 1-800-828-7777 to get your folder.

Materials Support Provided by

Science Kit® & Boreal® Laboratories
Your Classroom Resource
777 East Park Drive
Tonawanda, NY 14151-5003
Phone: 800-828-7777; Fax: 800-828-3299
www.sciencekit.com

Non-Consumables

It is assumed that goggles, laboratory aprons, tap water, textbooks, paper, calculator, pencil, and pen are available for all activities.

Item	Explore Activity Page	MiniLab Page	Activities Section
Balance	5		17-1
Balls, baseball, table tennis, etc.			1-1
Basketball or volleyball		603	
Beakers		187	3-1, 5-2, 16-2, 17-1
Beverage containers, plastic			1-2
Binoculars			18-2
Blocks		218	
Box, sealed			2-1
Brass Fasteners (100)			11-2
Bucket, small	5		
Clipboard			23-1
Coins			4-1
Compass		683	
Containers	541		
Containers, small		560	
Dissecting needle			16-1
Drawing compass		644	
Droppers	541	256	16-1, 18-1
Evaporating dishes		124	3-1
Flashlights	573		20-1
Floor Materials—carpet, tile, etc.			1-1
Forceps			15-1, 16-1
Glass		25	
Glass container, clear, colorless		282	
Glass jar, 1L, clean with lid			18-1
Glass, large			20-1
Gooseneck lamp with 75 watt bulb			21-1
Graduated cylinder		13	1-1, 14-1, 16-2
Graduated cylinder 10mL		124	
Graduated cylinder 25mL			5-1, 5-2
Graduated cylinder 50mL	121		

Activity Materials

Non-Consumables

Item	Explore Activity Page	MiniLab Page	Activities Section
Gravel or other debris from pond bottom		520	19-1
Hand lens		459, 492	16-1, 17-1, 18-2, 19-1, 20-1
Hot plate		282	3-1, 5-2
Jar with lid			17-1
Lamp with 100 watt light bulb			19-2
Lamp without shade	601		21-2
LP record		592	
Magnet	97		
Magnetic board			4-1
Magnetic strips—rubber			4-1
Magnifying glass			12-1
Marbles	175	592	6-2
Marker			14-2
Metal objects—washers, nuts, bolts, etc.	35		
Meterstick	175, 481	152, 322, 614, 683	1-1, 6-1, 6-2, 7-1, 7-2, 22-2, 23-2
Microscope			15-1, 16-1, 18-1
Microscope slide and coverslip			15-1, 16-1
Microscope slide coverslips (3)			18-1
Microscope slides (3)			18-1
Mirror, concave			20-1
Mirror, convex			20-1
Mirror, plane			20-1
Objects to use as fossils		270	
Pans, flat	629		
Paper clips	97		11-2
Paper punch	333		
Pennies			2-2, 3-1, 11-2
Petri Dish			15-2
Plant trays or plastic cups			16-2
Planting containers, small			17-2
Plastic cup, clear		500	
Plastic spoon, small			5-2

Non-Consumables

Item	Explore Activity Page	MiniLab Page	Activities Section
Polystyrene ball on pencil			21-2
Potting soil			16-2, 19-1, 19-2
Prepared slide—Nitrogen fixing bacteria		492	
Protractors		253	21-1
Quarter	5		
Reference—Botany texts, research materials		465	
Reference—Field Guides			18-2
Reference—Globe	601		8-1, 21-2
Reference—Globe or World Map	509	385	
Reference—Periodic Table		102	
Reference—Pond Life Guide			18-1
Reference—Protein-containing foods table		411	
Reference—World Map		519	9-1
Refrigerator or oven			17-2
Ruler with groove	147		
Ruler, metric	629, 661	385, 603, 644	8-1, 10-1, 12-1, 22-1, 23-2
Sand		253	
Sand and topsoil	541		
Scissors	267, 333, 363	109, 592	4-2, 14-2, 19-1, 22-2, 23-1
Shoebox with lid			11-2
Skateboard, 1 per group		180	
Small Objects—marbles, weights, nuts, etc.	629		
Soda Can, empty	5		
Soil			17-2
Spoons, plastic			1-2
Spray bottles	541		
Spring scale marked in Newtons (2)			7-1
Spring scale, 1 per group		180, 187	
Stopwatch			5-1, 6-1, 7-1, 7-2
Sunny window or light source			17-2
Tape Measure			18-2
Teaspoon	121	124	

Activity Materials

Non-Consumables

Item	Explore Activity Page	MiniLab Page	Activities Section
Telescope, small refracting			23-1
Test tube and stopper			14-1
Test tube rack			5-1, 5-2, 14-1
Test tubes		429, 432	5-1, 5-2
Thermal Mitts		282	
Thermometer, Celsius			21-1
Thermometers			5-1, 16-2, 18-2, 19-2
Thumbtacks			22-1
Thumbtacks, 2 colors			4-2
Tongs			3-1
Tripod, small			23-1
Trowel or spoon			17-2
Turntable		592	
Watch			21-1
Watch or clock			19-2
Weight		166	
Weights made of different materials		187	
Zinc, 30 mesh			3-1

Consumables

Item	Explore Activity Page	MiniLab Page	Activities Section
Adding machine tape		322	
Aluminum foil			17-2
Bags, resealable	425		
Balloon, 1 per group	661		
Balloons, different sizes and shapes			7-2
Beans, red and white, 10 each			12-2
Candle			20-1
Cardboard 25 × 30cm			22-1

Non-Consumables

Item	Explore Activity Page	MiniLab Page	Activities Section
Cardboard tube from paper towel roll		586	20-1
Cardboard, 8 x 12cm			23-1
Cardboard, corrugated			4-2
Cardboard, white, 50cm x 60cm			20-1
Cellophane sheets, clear, green, blue, red	573		
Cement mix, gray, dry	629		
Chalk		614	8-1
Classified ads, newspaper	333		
Clothespin, 1 per group	661		
Cones with seeds		459	
Deck of playing cards			13-1
Felt-tip marker, 1 per group	661		
Food—baking soda	121, 239	124	
Food—bread			14-2
Food—candy coated peanuts			4-1
Food—cheese			14-2
Food—chocolate chip cookie		543	
Food—cooked bacon			14-2
Food—cooked egg white			14-2
Food—cooking oil			1-2, 14-2
Food—cooking oil (colored)		256	
Food—cracker			14-2
Food—egg			7-1
Food—flour, white	629		
Food—grapes	397		4-1
Food—gumdrops	397		
Food—lettuce in a dish of water			15-1
Food—lima beans, 1 per student	449		
Food—packages		124	
Food—potato chip			14-2
Food—raisins	397		
Food—raw liver			5-1
Food—raw potato			5-1

Activity Materials

Consumables

Item	Explore Activity Page	MiniLab Page	Activities Section
Food—raw potato slice			14-2
Food—salt			16-2
Food—salt solution			15-1
Food—sugar solution 10 drops		432	
Food—table salt			1-2
Food—vinegar	121, 239	124	
Food—yeast suspension 20 drops		432	
Food coloring		25, 282	
Food coloring—red	239		
Freezer bag, self sealing		520	
Glue		43	
Graph paper		51, 218	2-2, 8-2, 11-2, 12-1, 18-2
Ice cube		25	
Index cards, 8 per group	363		
Labels			17-2, 19-1
Large sheet of paper		683	
Leaves, flowers, and seeds of one plant			12-1
Leaves, shells, or bones	303		
Markers		500	1-1, 4-1
Milk carton, small, 1 per student	303		
Modeling clay	35, 239, 397		
Modeling clay, 3 different colors	209		
Modeling clay, various colors		270	
Newspaper			17-1
Notebook			18-2
Paper bag			12-2
Paper cups		13, 345	1-2
Paper cups, small, containing freshly dug soil			17-1
Paper grocery bag			14-2
Paper plates		253, 543	
Paper towels	535	13, 459	15-2
Paper, ½ inch squares			4-1

Consumables

Item	Explore Activity Page	MiniLab Page	Activities Section
Paper, 21.5 x 28cm			22-1
Paper, 3 colors		109	
Paper, 8 colors			4-2
Paper, colored, precut shapes	63		
Paper, construction		592	
Paper, construction, black			21-1
Paper, construction, black and white	333		
Paper, drawing, 5 sheets			23-1
Paper, poster			1-1
Paper, thin white	267		
Paper, tracing (2–4 pieces)			9-1
Paper, unlined		43	
Paper, white	573		
Pencils, colored		43	11-2
Pens or markers	363		
Petroleum jelly	303		
Plaster of Paris	303	253, 345	
Plastic bag, sealable	121		
Plastic cup, transparent (2)		256	
Plastic lid			7-1
Plastic teaspoon			19-1
Plastic wrap		500	19-1, 19-2
Pointed toothpicks	397		
Pond vegetation, dried			18-1
Pond water, boiled, cooled			18-1
Round toothpicks		402	
Rubber bands		228	19-2
Seashell or other object		345	
Softdrink bottles, 2L			19-1, 19-2
Straws (2)		429	
Straws, drinking			7-2
String		166, 385, 603, 614	7-2, 8-1, 15-2
String, 1 per group	661		

Activity Materials

Consumables

Item	Explore Activity Page	MiniLab Page	Activities Section
String, 25cm			22-1
String, several meters			22-2
Tape			7-2, 15-2, 21-1
Tape, masking		152, 166, 592	7-1, 19-2, 20-1, 23-2
Tape, transparent			19-1
Toothpick	35	543	
Twist tie	121		
Waste materials, biodegradable and nonbiodegradable			19-1
Wooden splint			5-2

Chemical Supplies

Item	Explore Activity Page	MiniLab Page	Activities Section
$AgNo_3$ (Silver Nitrate)		80	
Bromothymol blue 10mL		432	
Ethanol, 3 drops			14-1
Hydrogen peroxide solution, 3%			5-1
Iodine solution in dropper bottle			14-2
Manganese Dioxide MnO_2			5-2
NaCl (Chloride)		80	
Nitric Acid, dilute			3-1
Phenol red 25mL		429	
Potassium permanganate solution 1mL			14-1
Sodium hydroxide solution 1mL			14-1
Sodium hydroxide, dilute			3-1
Test paper, pH		560	14-1

Live Organisms

Item	Explore Activity Page	MiniLab Page	Activities Section
Bean seeds			15-2, 17-2
Corn seeds			15-2
Elodea, pieces		429	
Legume plant (clover, alfalfa)		492	
Moss clumps			
Mosses, liverworts, and fern with gametophytes and sporophytes			16-1
Non-legume plant (geranium, coleus)		492	
Pond plants		520	
Seedling plants in pots	425		
Seeds			16-2
Small animals		520	

Lab Safety

Be Prepared

Safety is important in every classroom. However, the need for safety is even greater when science is taught. The activities in *Science Voyages* are designed to minimize dangers in the laboratory. Even so, there are no guarantees against accidents. Careful planning and preparation, as well as being aware of hazards, can keep accidents to a minimum. Many books and pamphlets are available on laboratory safety. In addition, the *Science Voyages* program provides safety guidelines in several forms. The ***Lab and Safety Skills*** booklet contains detailed guidelines, in addition to masters you can use to test students' lab and safety skills. The ***Student Edition*** and ***Teacher Wraparound Edition*** provide safety precautions and symbols designed to alert students to possible dangers. Know the rules of safety and what common violations occur. Know the **Safety Symbols** used in this book. Know where emergency equipment is stored and how to use it. Practice good laboratory housekeeping and management to ensure the safety of your students.

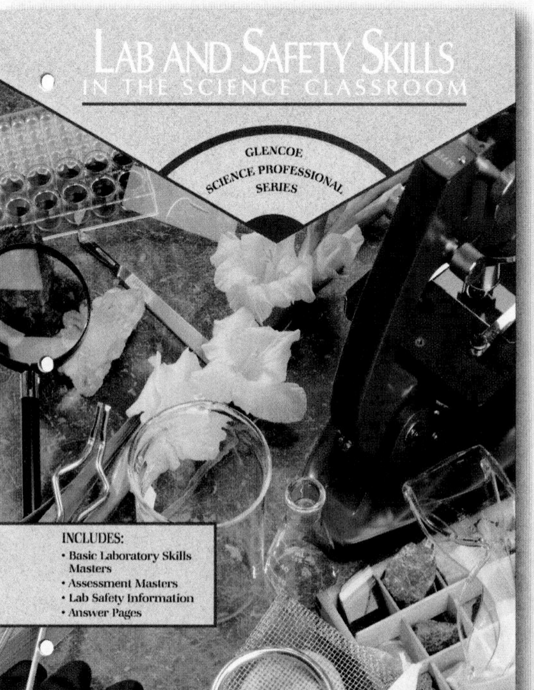

Using Chemicals in the Lab

It is most important to use safe laboratory techniques when handling all chemicals. Many substances may appear harmless but are, in fact, toxic, corrosive, or very reactive. Always check with the manufacturer. Chemicals should never be ingested. Be sure to use proper techniques to smell solutions or other agents. Always wear safety goggles, gloves, and an apron. The following general cautions should be used.

1. Poisonous/corrosive liquid and/or vapor. Use in the fume hood. Examples: ***acetic acid, hydrochloric acid, ammonia hydroxide, nitric acid.***
2. Poisonous and corrosive to eyes, lungs, and skin. Examples: ***acids, limewater, iron(III) chloride, bases, silver nitrate, iodine, potassium permanganate.***
3. Poisonous if swallowed, inhaled, or absorbed through the skin. Examples: ***glacial acetic acid, copper compounds, barium chloride, lead compounds, chromium compounds, lithium compounds, cobalt(II) chloride, silver compounds, and concentrated acids.***
4. Always add acids to water, never the reverse.
5. When sulfuric acid or sodium hydroxide is added to water, a large amount of thermal energy is released. Sodium metal reacts violently with water. Use extra care when handling any of these substances.

Preparation of Solutions

Unless otherwise specified, solutions are prepared by adding the solid to a small amount of distilled water and then diluting with water to the volume listed. For example, to make a 0.1*M* solution of aluminum sulfate, dissolve 34.2 g of $Al_2(SO_4)_3$ in a small amount of distilled water and dilute to a liter with water. If you use a hydrate that is different from the one specified in a particular preparation, you will need to adjust the amount of the hydrate to obtain the required concentration. Premixed solutions can be purchased from scientific supply houses in order to reduce the amount of chemicals that are on hand.

A major consideration for any school offering a science program is safety. Although posting safety guidelines and procedures has been held by recent court rulings an insufficient safety instruction, it should be done anyway. Post fire drill regulations and a chart of emergency procedures in a prominent place in the laboratory. Remind students of proper safety procedures at the beginning of each laboratory session.

Before each session, check all setups for proper assembly and make sure each student is wearing proper safety attire. Students must wear safety goggles and aprons when using any chemical, heat source, or hammer (to split rocks). Be sure that students with long hair secure it and avoid wearing loose-fitting clothing in the presence of an open flame. Wearing contact lenses, even with safety glasses, should not be permitted. Splashing chemicals could infuse under the lenses causing eye damage.

Familiarize yourself with each activity before the class session. Instruct students to follow directions carefully and not to take shortcuts or switch steps. (Such shortcuts may lead to an unsafe situation.) Allow for sufficient clean up time at the end of each laboratory session. At this time, inspect all materials and equipment. Always be present during the laboratory session. Do not allow students to work unsupervised. Familiarize yourself and your students with emergency and first aid procedures. The Red Cross frequently offers classes in first aid. Contact them to find out when they offer these classes. Demonstrate the parts and proper use of laboratory equipment before class. A sample laboratory contract is included below. You may wish to have each student fill out a contract for safety at the beginning of each semester.

STUDENT SAFETY CONTRACT

Date: ________________

I will:

- follow all instructions given by the teacher.
- protect eyes, face, hands, and body while conducting class activities.
- carry out good housekeeping practices.
- know the location of first aid and fire fighting equipment.
- conduct myself in a responsible manner at all times in a laboratory situation.

I,______________________________________, have read and agree to abide by the safety regulations as set forth above and also any additional printed instructions provided by the teacher and/or district. I further agree to follow all other written and verbal instructions given in class.

Signature ____________________________

Materials

Chemical Storage and Disposal

General Guidelines

Be sure to store all chemicals properly. The following are guidelines commonly used. Your school, city, county, or state may have additional requirements for handling chemicals. It is the responsibility of each teacher to become informed as to what rules or guidelines are in effect in his or her area.

1. Separate chemicals by reaction type. Strong acids should be stored together. Likewise, strong bases should be stored together and should be separated from acids. Oxidants should be stored away from easily oxidized materials, and so on.
2. Be sure all chemicals are stored in labeled containers indicating contents, concentration, source, date purchased (or prepared), any precautions for handling and storage, and expiration date.
3. Dispose of any outdated or waste chemicals properly according to accepted disposal procedures.
4. Do not store chemicals above eye level.
5. Wood shelving is preferable to metal. All shelving should be firmly attached to the wall and should have antiroll edges.
6. Store only those chemicals that you plan to use.
7. Hazardous chemicals require special storage containers and conditions. Be sure to know what those chemicals are and the accepted practices for your area. Some substances must even be stored outside the building.
8. When working with chemicals or preparing solutions, observe the same general safety precautions that you would expect from students. These include wearing an apron and goggles. Wear gloves and use the fume hood when necessary. Students will want to do as you do whether they admit it or not.
9. If you are a new teacher in a particular laboratory, it is your responsibility to survey the chemicals stored there and to be sure they are stored properly or disposed of. Consult the rules and laws in your area concerning what chemicals can be kept in your classroom. For disposal, consult up-to-date disposal information from the state and federal governments.

Disposal of Chemicals

Local, state, and federal laws regulate the proper disposal of chemicals. These laws should be consulted before chemical disposal is attempted. Although most substances encountered in biology can be flushed down the drain with plenty of water, it is not safe to assume that this is always true. It is recommended that teachers who use chemicals consult the following books from the National Research Council:

Prudent Practices for Handling Hazardous Chemicals in Laboratories. Washington, DC: National Academy Press, 1981.

Prudent Practices for Disposal of Chemicals from Laboratories. Washington, DC: National Academy Press, 1983.

Safety in Academic Chemistry Laboratories. Washington, DC: American Chemical Society, 1995.

Current laws in your area do, of course, supersede the information in these books.

Disclaimer

Glencoe/McGraw-Hill makes no claims to the completeness of this discussion of laboratory safety and chemical storage. The material presented is not all-inclusive, nor does it address all of the hazards associated with handling, storage, and disposal of chemicals, or with laboratory management.

Supplier Addresses

Scientific Suppliers

Carolina Biological Supply Co.
2700 York Road
Burlington, NC 27215
800-334-5551

Fisher Scientific Co.
1600 W. Glenlake
Itaska, IL 60143

Flinn Scientific Co.
P.O. Box 219
770 N. Raddant Road
Batavia, IL 60510
800-452-1261

Frey Scientific
100 Paragon Parkway
Mansfield, OH 44903
800-235-3739

Sargent-Welch Scientific Co.
P.O. Box 5229
911 Commerce Ct.
Buffalo Grove, IL 60089
800-727-4368

Science Kit & Boreal Laboratories
777 East Park Drive
Tonawanda, NY 14151-5003
800-828-7777

Ward's Natural Science Establishment, Inc.
P.O. Box 92912
Rochester, NY 14692
800-962-2660

Software Distributors

(AIT) Agency for Instructional Technology
Box A
Bloomington, IN 47402-0120
800-457-4509

Cambridge Development Laboratory, Inc.
86 West Street
Waltham, MA 02154

COMpress
P.O. Box 102
Wentworth, NH 03282

Earthware Computer Services
P.O. Box 30039
Eugene, OR 97403

Educational Activities, Inc.
1937 Grand Avenue
Baldwin, NY 11510
800-645-3739

Educational Materials and Equipment Company (EME)
P.O. Box 2805
Danbury, CT 06813-2805

GEMSTAR MEDIA, INC.
P.O. Box 50228
Staten Island, NY 10305

IBM Educational Systems
Department PC
4111 Northside Parkway
Atlanta, GA 30327
800-426-4968

McGraw-Hill Webster Division
1221 Avenue of the Americas
New York, NY 10020

Microphys
12 Bridal Way
Sparta, NJ 07871
800-832-6591

Queue, Inc.
338 Commerce Drive
Fairfield, CT 06432

School Division of The Learning Co.
6160 Summit Drive
Minneapolis, MN 55430

Texas Instruments, Data Systems Group
P.O. Box 1444
Houston, TX 77251

Ventura Educational Systems
910 Ramona, Suite E
Grover Beach, CA 93433

Audiovisual Distributors

Aims Multimedia
9710 Desoto Avenue
Chatsworth, CA 91311-4409
800-367-2467

BFA Educational Media
2349 Chaffee Dr.
St. Louis, MO 63146
800-221-1274

CRM Films
2215 Faraday Avenue
Carlsbad, CA 92008

Diversified Educational Enterprise
725 Main Street
Lafayette, IN 47901

Encyclopaedia Britannica Educational Corp. (EBEC)
310 S. Michigan Avenue
Chicago, IL 60604

Focus Media, Inc.
485 S. Broadway, Suite 12
Hicksville, NY 11801

Hawkill Associates, Inc.
125 E. Gilman Street
Madison, WI 53703
800-422-4295

Journal Films, Inc.
930 Pitner Avenue
Evanston, IL 60202

Lumivision
877 Federal Blvd.
Denver, CO 80204

National Earth Science Teachers Association
NESTA/MESTA Publications
C/O Lisa Bouda
2000 Florida Avenue, NW
Washington, DC 20009

National Geographic Society Education Services
17th and "M" Streets, NW
Washington, DC 20036-4688
800-368-2728

Phoenix Learning Group
2349 Chaffee Drive
St. Louis, MO 63146

Science Software Systems
11890 W. Pico Blvd.
Los Angeles, CA 90064

Society for Visual Education & Churchill Media
6677 N. Northwest Highway
Chicago, IL 60631-1304

Time-Life Videos
Time and Life Building
1271 Avenue of the Americas
New York, NY 10020

Universal Education & Visual Arts (UEVA)
100 Universal City Plaza
Universal City, CA 91608

Video Discovery
Suite 600
1700 Westlake Avenue, N
Seattle, WA 98109
800-548-3472

UNIT 1

Chemical Interactions

In this unit, students are introduced to the important role of science in solving problems. The unit describes the arrangement of particles within the atom and how characteristics of elements determine their arrangement in the periodic table. The properties of chemical bonding and how chemical changes occur are explained. The unit concludes with a discussion of how chemical reactions are represented by chemical equations.

Unit Overview

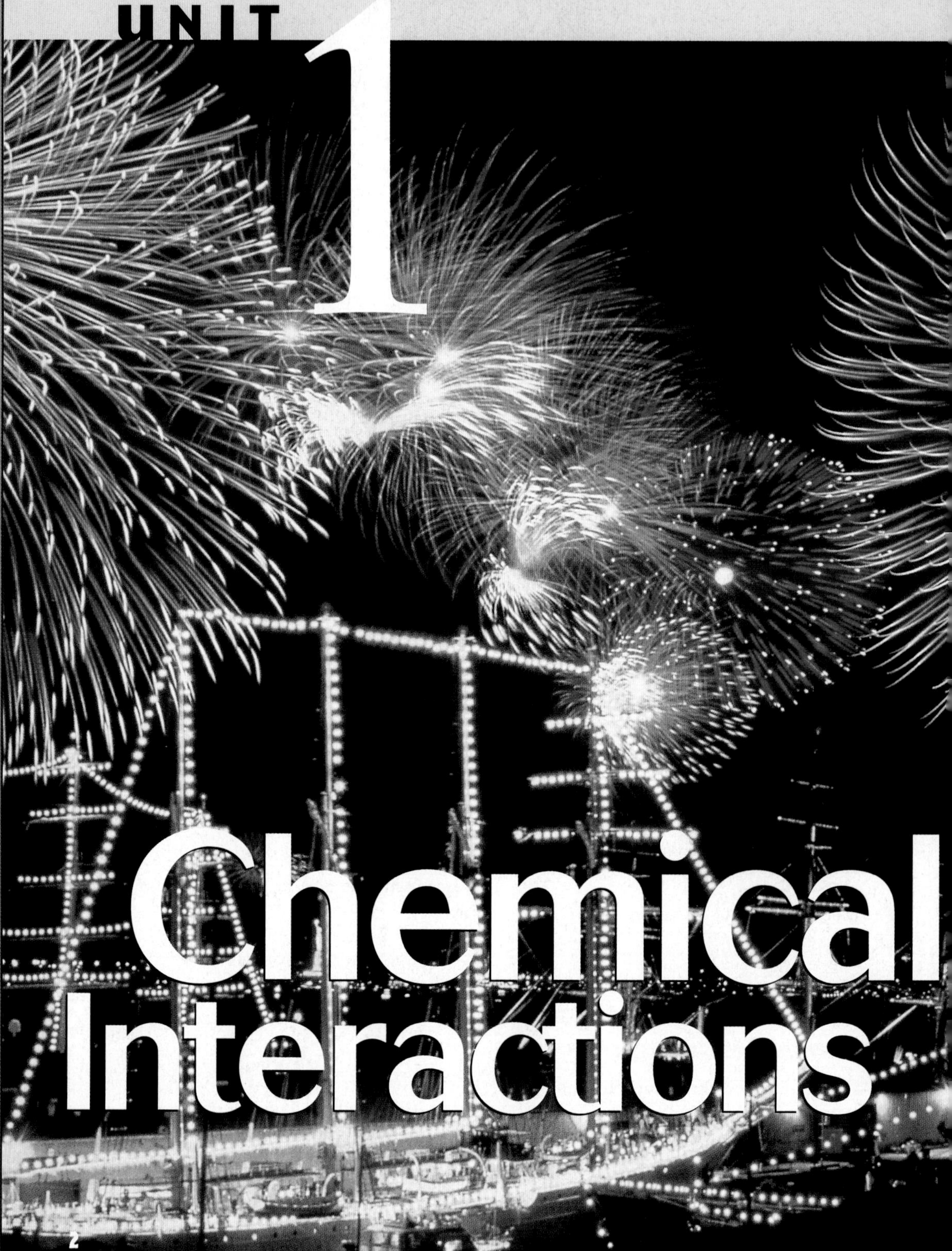

Science at Home

It's Elemental Have students select an element from the periodic table and use reference books to find and write five facts about the element. Have them try to identify items in their homes that may contain the element.

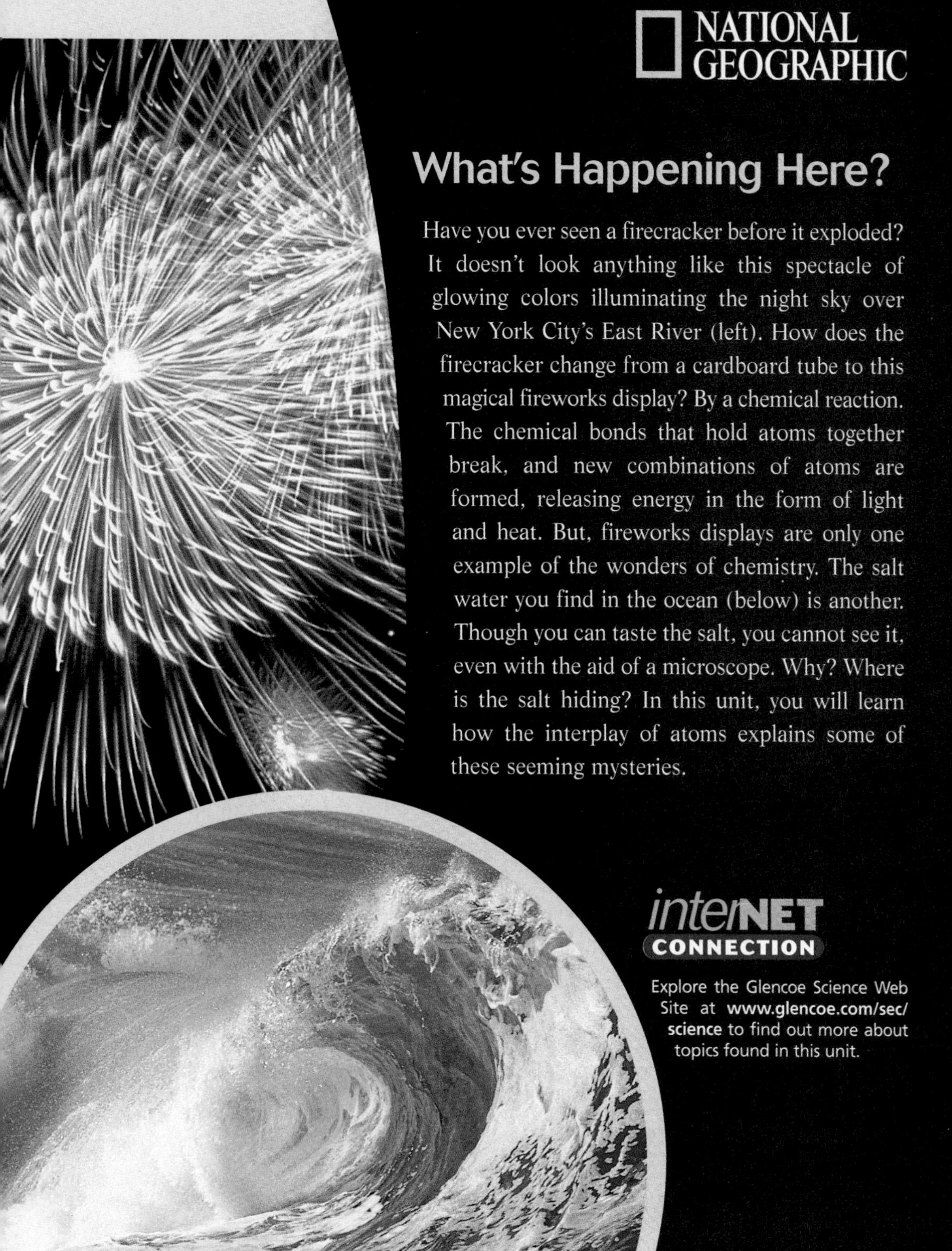

What's Happening Here?

Have you ever seen a firecracker before it exploded? It doesn't look anything like this spectacle of glowing colors illuminating the night sky over New York City's East River (left). How does the firecracker change from a cardboard tube to this magical fireworks display? By a chemical reaction. The chemical bonds that hold atoms together break, and new combinations of atoms are formed, releasing energy in the form of light and heat. But, fireworks displays are only one example of the wonders of chemistry. The salt water you find in the ocean (below) is another. Though you can taste the salt, you cannot see it, even with the aid of a microscope. Why? Where is the salt hiding? In this unit, you will learn how the interplay of atoms explains some of these seeming mysteries.

interNET CONNECTION

Explore the Glencoe Science Web Site at **www.glencoe.com/sec/science** to find out more about topics found in this unit.

3

interNET CONNECTION

Internet Addresses

Explore the Glencoe Science Web Site at **www.glencoe.com/sec/science** to find out more about topics found in this unit.

Introducing the Unit

What's happening here?

Have students read the text and examine the pictures. Ask students to name other items that might have the same chemicals as fireworks. *flares, matches, explosives* Point out that they will learn how chemicals react to produce fireworks. They will also learn how the atoms in the salt and the atoms in the water are held together with different types of bonds.

Content Background

The flames from fireworks occur when magnesium reacts with oxygen to form magnesium oxide—the result of an ionic bond. When magnesium burns, it gives the two electrons in its outer energy level to oxygen. Oxygen then has eight electrons in its outer energy level. Other chemicals give fireworks their colors: strontium, scarlet; barium, yellowish-green; borax, green; and lithium, purple.

Previewing the Chapters

- Have students find models of atoms.
- Have students recall the difference between physical and chemical changes. Have them identify photographs that indicate chemical changes have taken place.

Tying to Previous Knowledge

- Have students study the periodic table, name familiar elements, and describe what they already know about them.
- Have students recall that an equation is a statement in which one quantity is equivalent to another. Tell them they will learn how equations represent chemical reactions.

Chapter 1 The Nature of Science

Section	Objectives	Activities/Features
Chapter Opener		**Explore Activity:** Observe Water Displacement, p. 5
1-1 **Scientific Problem Solving** 3 Sessions 2 Blocks	1. **Define** *science.* 2. **Discuss** how to use scientific methods in problem solving.	**Life Science Integration,** p. 7 **Using Math,** p. 8 **MiniLab:** Measuring Accurately, p. 13 **Problem Solving:** Flex Your Brain, p. 16 **Skill Builder:** Sequencing, p. 19 **Using Math,** p. 19 **Activity 1-1:** Follow the Bouncing Ball, pp. 20–21
1-2 **Using Science to Explore** 2 Sessions 1 Block	3. **Describe** how remotely operated vehicles help humans to explore. 4. **Discuss** how scientists use science skills in different ways.	**MiniLab:** Inferring Density, p. 25 **Skill Builder:** Interpreting Data, p. 27 **Using Computers,** p.27 **Activity 1-2:** Comparing Densities, p. 28 **Reading and Writing in Science:** The Circle of Life, p. 29

The number of recommended single-period sessions The number of recommended blocks
One session and one-half block are allowed for chapter review and assessment.

Activity Materials

Explore	Activities	MiniLabs
p. 5 small bucket, 2-L bottle, balance, aluminum can, quarter, water	pp. 20–21 many types of balls, meterstick, poster paper, markers, floor materials p. 28 100-mL graduated cylinder, balance and masses, water, cooking oil, table salt, paper cups, plastic spoons, plastic beverage containers	p. 13 water, graduated cylinder p. 25 warm water, glass bowl, ice cube, food coloring

Need Materials? Contact Science Kit at 1-800-828-7777 or at www.sciencekit.com on the Internet.
For alternate materials, see the activity on the listed page.

Chapter Organizer

Standards		Reproducible Resources	Technology
National	State/Local	Test Practice Workbooks are available for use with each chapter.	English and Spanish audiocassettes are available for use with each section.
National Content Standards: UCP2, UCP3, A1, A2, B2, B3, C1, C2, E1, E2, F1, F5, G1, G2, G3		**Activity Worksheets,** pp. 1–2, 5 **Enrichment,** p. 1 **Laboratory Manual,** pp. 1–4 **Laboratory Manual,** pp. 5–8 **Reinforcement,** p. 1 **Study Guide,** pp. 1–3	**Section Focus Transparency 1** **Teaching Transparency 1** **Glencoe Science Voyages Interactive Videodisc—Physical** **National Geographic Society: STV** **Internet Connection,** p. 11 **The Infinite Voyage Series** **Glencoe Science Voyages Interactive CD-ROM**
National Content Standards: UCP2, UCP3, UCP5, A1, A2, B1, B2, D1, D3, E1, E2, F1, F3, F4, G1, G2, G3		**Activity Worksheets,** pp. 3–4, 6 **Critical Thinking/Problem Solving,** p. 1 **Enrichment,** p. 2 **Home Involvement,** p. 28 **Multicultural Connections,** pp. 1–2 **Reinforcement,** p. 2 **Study Guide,** pp. 3–4	**Section Focus Transparency 2** **Teaching Transparency 2** **Science Integration Transparency 1** **Glencoe Science Voyages Interactive Videodisc—Earth** **Internet Connection,** p. 25 **The Infinite Voyage Series**

Key to Teaching Strategies

The following designations will help you decide which activities are appropriate for your students.

L1 Level 1 activities should be appropriate for students with learning difficulties.

L2 Level 2 activities should be within the ability range of all students.

L3 Level 3 activities are designed for above-average students.

ELL ELL activities should be within the ability range of English Language Learners.

COOP LEARN Cooperative Learning activities are designed for small group work.

P These strategies represent student products that can be placed into a best-work portfolio.

Multiple Learning Styles logos, as described on page 61T, are used throughout to indicate strategies that address different learning styles.

Assessment Resources

Chapter Review, pp. 1–2
Assessment, pp. 1–4
Performance Assessment in the Science Classroom (PASC)
MindJogger Videoquiz
Alternate Assessment in the Science Classroom
Performance Assessment, p. 15
Chapter Review Software
Computer Test Bank

Chapter 1

The Nature of Science

This is a representation of key blackline masters available in the Teacher Classroom Resources. See Resource Manager boxes within the chapter for additional information.

Transparencies

Section Focus Transparencies

1 SECTION FOCUS TRANSPARENCY

Section 1-1

SCIENTIST OR EXPLORER?

This scientist looks like he's ready for a walk in space, but he's really studying something on Earth—an active volcano. Active volcanoes are extremely dangerous. That's why the scientist is wearing a safety suit.

1. What are some other hostile environments that scientists explore?
2. How does using technology help scientists to gather new information?
3. If you could study one thing, what would it be and how might you go about it?

L2

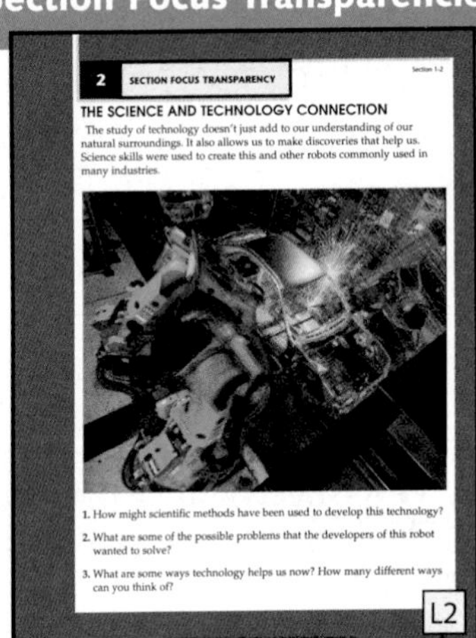
2 SECTION FOCUS TRANSPARENCY

Section 1-2

THE SCIENCE AND TECHNOLOGY CONNECTION

The study of technology doesn't just add to our understanding of our natural surroundings. It also allows us to make discoveries that help us. Science skills were used to create this and other robots commonly used in many industries.

1. How might scientific methods have been used to develop this technology?
2. What are some of the possible problems that the developers of this robot wanted to solve?
3. What are some ways technology helps us now? How many different ways can you think of?

L2

Science Integration Transparencies

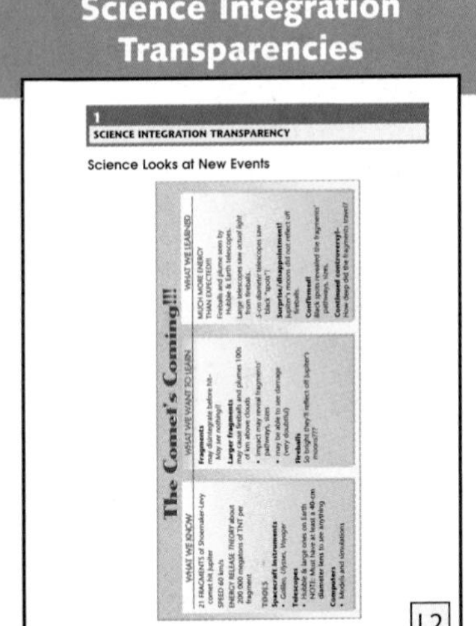
1 SCIENCE INTEGRATION TRANSPARENCY

Science Looks at New Events

The Comet's Coming!!!

WHAT WE KNOW | WHAT WE WANT TO LEARN | WHAT WE LEARNED

L2

Teaching Transparencies

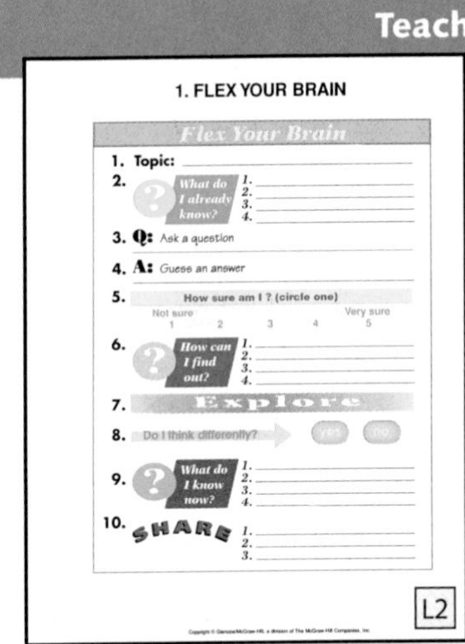
1. FLEX YOUR BRAIN

Flex Your Brain

1. Topic:
2. What do I already know? 1. 2. 3. 4.
3. Q: Ask a question
4. A: Guess an answer
5. How sure am I ? (circle one) Not sure 1 2 3 4 5 Very sure
6. How can I find out? 1. 2. 3. 4.
7. Explore
8. Do I think differently? yes no
9. What do I know now? 1. 2. 3. 4.
10. SHARE 1. 2. 3.

L2

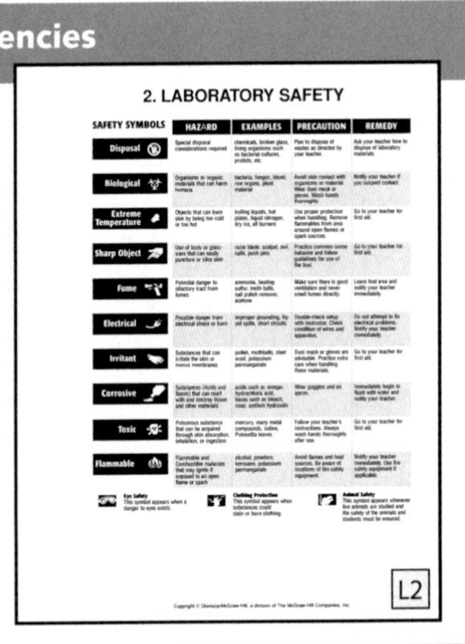
2. LABORATORY SAFETY

SAFETY SYMBOLS	HAZARD	EXAMPLES	PRECAUTION	REMEDY
Disposal				
Biological				
Extreme Temperature				
Sharp Object				
Fume				
Electrical				
Irritant				
Corrosive				
Toxic				
Flammable				

Eye Safety · Clothing Protection · Animal Safety

L2

Meeting Different Ability Levels

Study Guide for Content Mastery

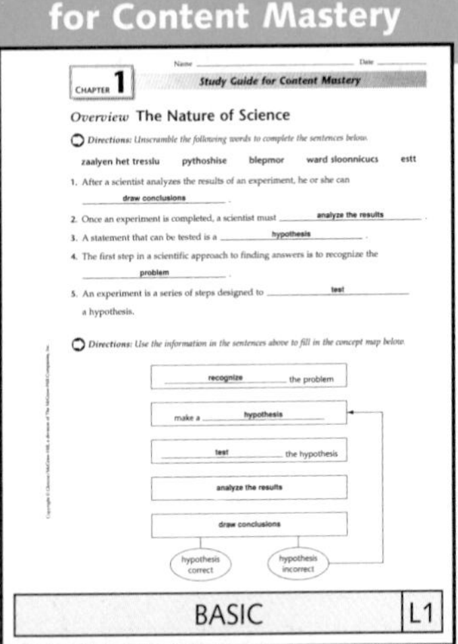
CHAPTER 1 Name Date

Study Guide for Content Mastery

Overview The Nature of Science

Directions: Unscramble the following words to complete the sentences below.

zaalyen het tresslu pythoshise blepmor ward sloonnicucs estt

1. After a scientist analyzes the results of an experiment, he or she can draw conclusions.
2. Once an experiment is completed, a scientist must analyze the results.
3. A statement that can be tested is a hypothesis.
4. The first step in a scientific approach to finding answers is to recognize the problem.
5. An experiment is a series of steps designed to test a hypothesis.

Directions: Use the information in the sentences above to fill in the concept map below.

recognize the problem
make a hypothesis
test the hypothesis
analyze the results
draw conclusions
hypothesis correct
hypothesis incorrect

BASIC L1

Reinforcement

NAME DATE CLASS

Chapter 1 REINFORCEMENT • Scientific Problem Solving

Use with Section 1

Use the numbers 1–7 to put these problem-solving approaches in a logical order.

_____ a. test your hypothesis
_____ b. make a plan
_____ c. draw conclusions
_____ d. record observations and results
_____ e. recognize the problem
_____ f. analyze your data
_____ g. form a hypothesis

A student wanted to know how his weight on Mars would compare with his weight on Earth. Pretend that traveling to Mars is possible. Answer the following questions.

8. What is one hypothesis the student might form?
9. The student decides to perform a controlled experiment to test his hypothesis.
   a. What is the independent variable?
   b. What is the dependent variable?
   c. What is the control?
   d. What factors should be kept constant?
10. The student finds that his weight on Mars is about 1/3 of his weight on Earth. He concludes that all things weigh 1/3 as much on Mars as on Earth. Do you think his conclusion is correct? Why or why not?

AT LEVEL L2

Enrichment Worksheets

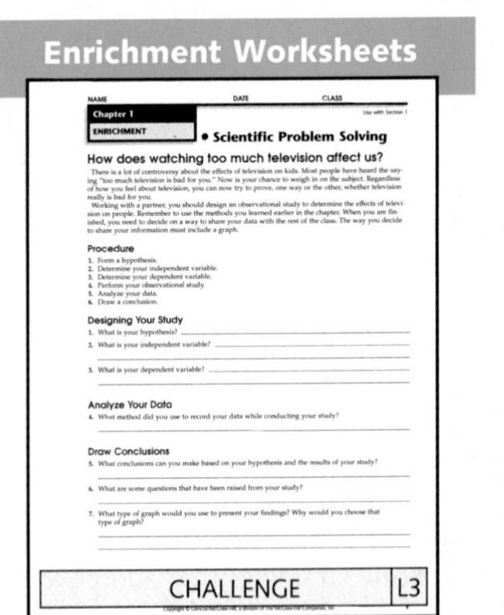
NAME DATE CLASS

Chapter 1 ENRICHMENT • Scientific Problem Solving

Use with Section 1

How does watching too much television affect us?

There is a lot of controversy about the effects of television on kids. Most people have heard the saying "too much television is bad for you." Now is your chance to weigh in on the subject. Regardless of how you feel about television, you can now try to prove, one way or the other, whether television really is bad for you.

Working with a partner, you should design an observational study to determine the effects of television on people. Remember to use the methods you learned earlier in the chapter. When you are finished, you need to decide on a way to share your data with the rest of the class. The way you decide to share your information must include a graph.

Procedure
1. Form a hypothesis.
2. Determine your independent variable.
3. Determine your dependent variable.
4. Perform your observational study.
5. Analyze your data.
6. Draw a conclusion.

Designing Your Study
1. What is your hypothesis?
2. What is your independent variable?
3. What is your dependent variable?

Analyze Your Data
4. What method did you use to record your data while conducting your study?

Draw Conclusions
5. What conclusions can you make based on your hypothesis and the results of your study?
6. What are some questions that have been raised from your study?
7. What type of graph would you use to present your findings? Why would you choose that type of graph?

CHALLENGE L3

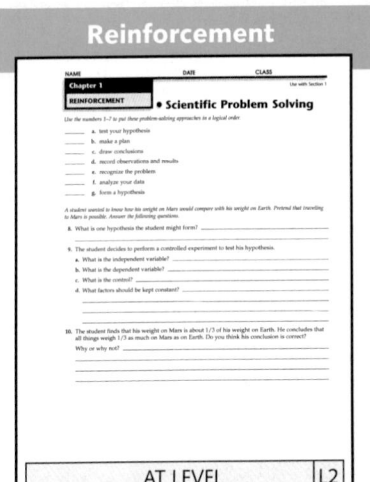

Hands-on Activities

Activity Worksheets

Chapter 1
ACTIVITY 1-1
• Follow the Bouncing Ball
Design Your Own Experiment
Lab Preview
Recognize the Problem
Form a Hypothesis
Goals
Safety Precautions
Possible Materials
Test Your Hypothesis
L2

Lab Manual

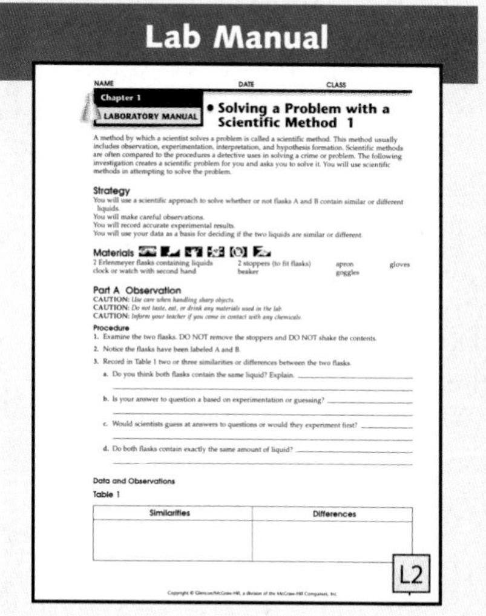
Chapter 1
LABORATORY MANUAL
• Solving a Problem with a Scientific Method 1
Strategy
Materials
Part A Observation
Procedure
Data and Observations
Table 1
L2

Accessibility

Spanish Resources

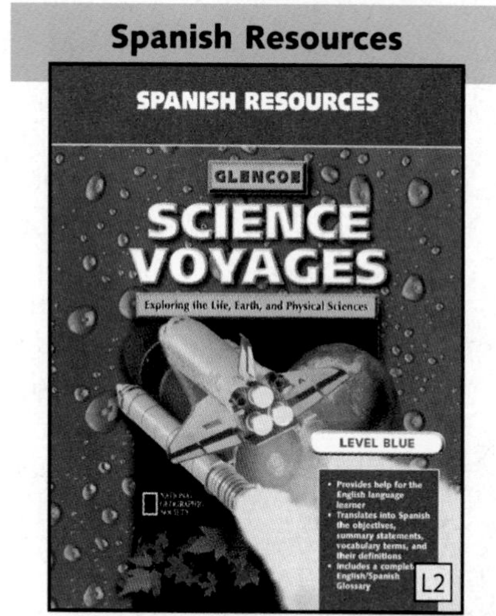

Assessment

Performance Assessment

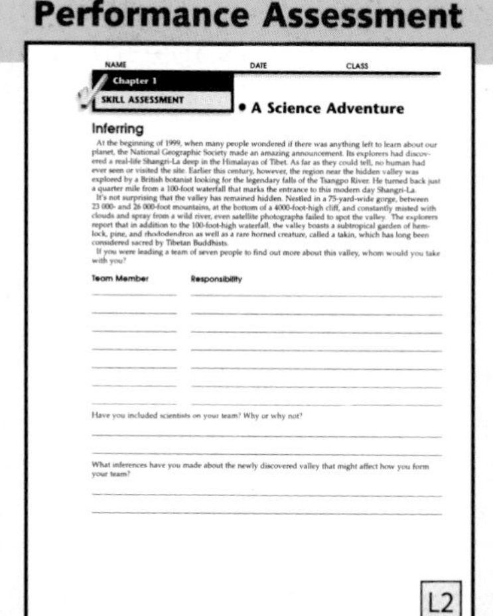
Chapter 1
SKILL ASSESSMENT
• A Science Adventure
Inferring
Team Member
Responsibility
L2

Chapter Review

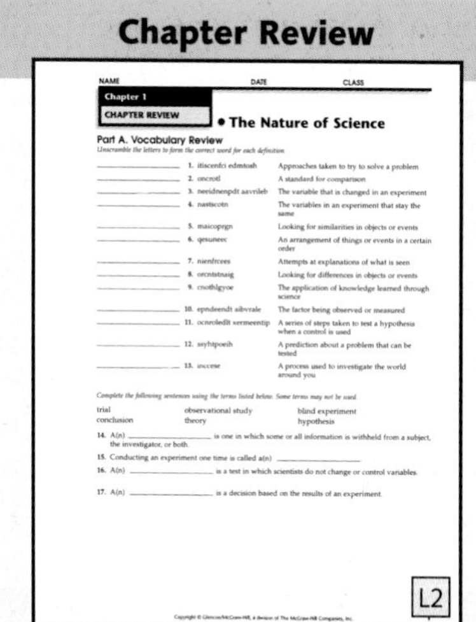
Chapter 1
CHAPTER REVIEW
• The Nature of Science
Part A. Vocabulary Review
L2

Assessment

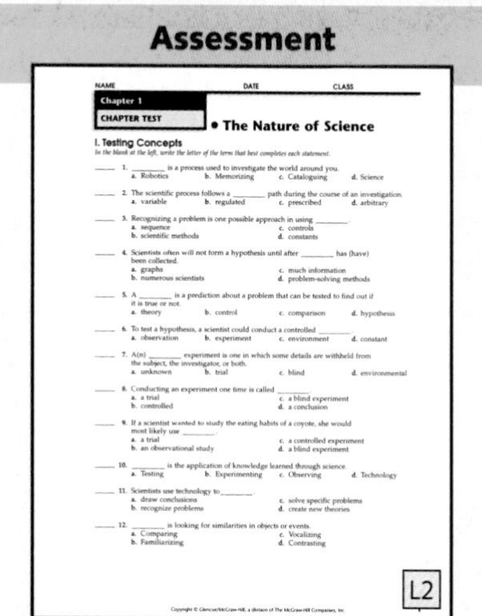
Chapter 1
CHAPTER TEST
• The Nature of Science
I. Testing Concepts
L2

Test Practice Workbook

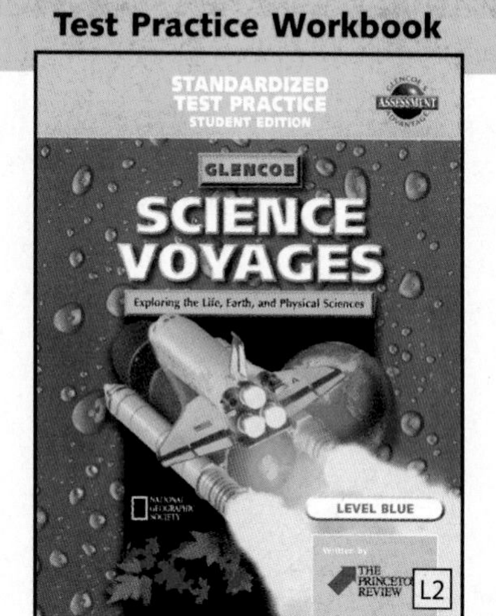

Extending Content

Critical Thinking/ Problem Solving

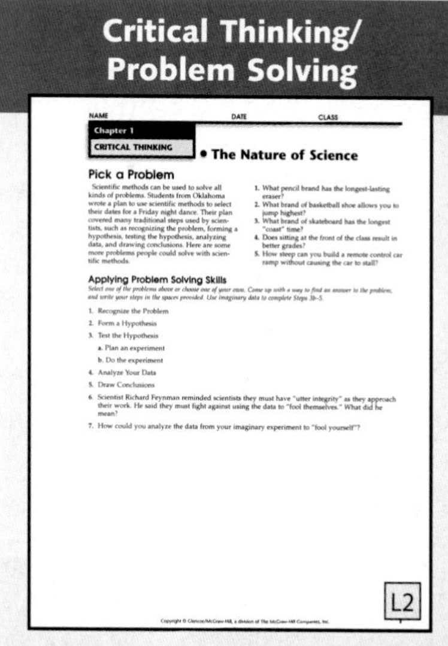
Chapter 1
CRITICAL THINKING
• The Nature of Science
Pick a Problem
Applying Problem Solving Skills
L2

Multicultural Connections

Chapter 1
MULTICULTURAL CONNECTIONS
• Stephen Hawking: Theories About the Universe

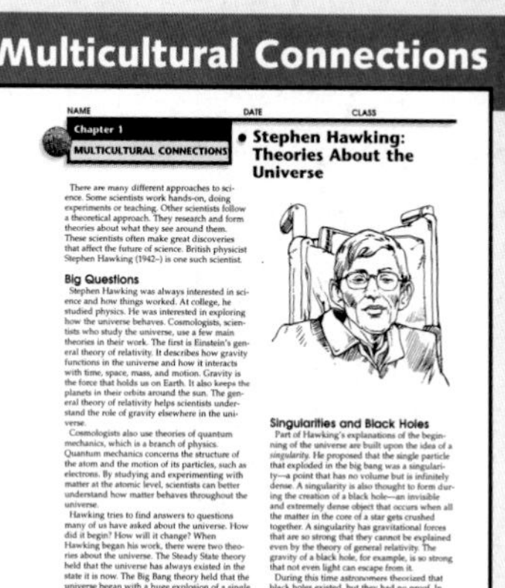
Big Questions
Singularities and Black Holes
L2

The Nature of Science

Helping You Prepare

What Science Is (Section 1-1)

Deep-sea refers to more than 150 m below the water's surface. Most submarines can dive only to a depth of about 400 m.

A submersible is a special underwater craft that can descend to depths of 6500 m. They are usually equipped with cameras, floodlights, baskets, and mechanical arms for collecting samples.

An unpiloted submersible is referred to as an ROV, or remotely operated vehicle. Scientists are developing autonomous underwater vehicles (AUV), which need no cable.

Form a Hypothesis (Section 1-1)

A hypothesis that holds up under many experiments by different scientists may become a theory. Scientific theories and laws are often confused, but they are not the same.

A law is a statement of what happens, such as Newton's third law of motion, which states that for every action force, there is an equal and opposite reaction force.

Theories explain why or how something happens. The theories of plate tectonics and continental drift explain how these phenomena take place on and within Earth. Keep in mind that no theory is completely proven. A theory is subject to correction as new facts or observations emerge.

GLENCOE TECHNOLOGY

CD-ROM

Glencoe Science Voyages Interactive CD-ROM

Chapter Summaries

Use the Chapter Summary to introduce, teach, or review chapter material.

Controlled Experiments (Section 1-1)

Ideally, the experimental and the control group each should have several samples. This minimizes individual differences that cannot be controlled. This is particularly important when the independent variable is not changed but applied equally to all samples. An example is testing the effects of a new drug at a particular dosage for subjects in the experimental group.

Plan (Section 1-1)

A clinical trial is an experiment in which the subject is a human. Controlling variables is often difficult, particularly psychological variables. For example, volunteers who know they are receiving a new drug may allow this to influence how they feel.

NATIONAL GEOGRAPHIC — **Teacher's Corner**

Products Available from National Geographic Society

To order the following products for use with this chapter, call National Geographic Society at 1-800-368-2728:

Book

Everyday Science Explained

Video

Scientific Method

Index to National Geographic Magazine

The following articles may be used for research relating to this chapter:

"Making Sense of the Millennium," by Joel L. Swerdlow, January 1998.

A single-blind clinical trial is an experiment in which the subject does not know what treatment has been given. In a double-blind clinical trial, neither the subjects nor the investigators know which treatment has been given.

Using Technology (Section 1-2)

Robots range from having simple arms to being increasingly sophisticated "thinking" machines. Many robots have video-camera-based vision systems. Some robots even have smelling and tasting devices.

Some robots are programmed with a set of instructions and perform the same boring task repetitively. Some robots are much more sophisticated.

Sojourner, the first Mars rover, is a lightweight robotic machine on wheels. Sojourner is described as "thinking" because it is equipped with sophisticated laser eyes and can react to unplanned events on the surface of another planet.

Sojourner's intelligence is based on a mathematical model that emulates animal behavior. The ability for animals to avoid or flee from danger is a low-level reflex.

Sojourner was equipped with a spectrometer used to analyze the chemical composition of Martian rock and a camera that relayed images of the landscape back to Earth. Sojourner was carried to Mars via the space probe *Pathfinder,* which landed on Mars in July, 1997. This mission has been said to set the standard for twenty-first century space exploration. The Marie Curie rover is planned to be sent to Mars in 2001.

Space probes are designed to land on a surface or to orbit around a planet or moon. They can determine composition, temperature, and pressure of atmospheres; pick up radio emissions; probe magnetic fields around planets; and collect and analyze soil samples.

The largest, most complex, and most expensive interplanetary probe launched is *Cassini. Cassini's* four-year mission is to provide information about Saturn, its rings, and moons.

Most space shuttles are equipped with a remote manipulator system or RMS. The RMS resembles a human arm with a shoulder and elbow joint. It measures over 15 meters when extended. Because of its design and construction, it would collapse under its own weight if used on Earth. The end of the RMS does not have fingers. It looks like a canister and can grab only large, sturdy objects. Engineers still do not know how to construct robotic fingers that are skillful and light, yet strong.

SCIENCE UPDATE

For current events or science in the news, access the Glencoe Science Web Site at **www.glencoe.com/sec/science**

Teacher to Teacher

"Before teaching a new topic, get students involved and help them recall prior knowledge. Using one set of index cards, write key vocabulary words and concepts. On a second set of cards, write the definition or information that the students will learn. Students work in pairs to try to match the cards."

Rebecca S. Buckingham

Rebecca S. Buckingham, Teacher
Lisbon Central School
Lisbon, NY

CHAPTER 1 The Nature of Science

CHAPTER OVERVIEW

Section 1-1 This section explains some logical steps in scientific problem solving.

Section 1-2 This section describes how scientists develop and use technology to explore environments too dangerous for humans.

Chapter Vocabulary

science
scientific method
hypothesis
theory
law
control
independent variable
dependent variable
constant
graph
technology
sequence
inference

Theme Connection

Stability and Change Scientific methods enable us to develop technology to explore and understand stability and change in the natural world.

00:00 OUT OF TIME?

If time does not permit teaching the entire chapter, use Reviewing Main Ideas on pages 30–31.

CHAPTER 1 The Nature of Science

Chapter Preview

Section 1-1
Scientific Problem Solving

Section 1-2
Using Science to Explore

Skills Preview

Skill Builders
- Sequence
- Interpret Data

Activities
- Design an Experiment
- Use Scientific Methods

MiniLabs
- Measure
- Infer

Reading Check

Before you begin this chapter, write its headings and subheadings in an outline form to see how the chapter is organized.

4

Multiple Learning Styles

Look for the following logos for strategies that emphasize different learning modalities.

Linguistic Science Journal, pp. 9, 12; Across the Curriculum, pp. 10, 25; Multiple Learning Styles, p. 24; Preview, p. 30

Logical-Mathematical Quick Demo, p. 7; MiniLab, pp. 13, 25; Across the Curriculum, pp. 11, 14; Activity, pp. 20–21, 28; Science Journal, p. 26

Visual-Spatial Explore Activity, p. 5; Making a Model, p. 24; Assessment, p. 27; Reteach, p. 30

Auditory-Musical Across the Curriculum, p. 11; Out of Time, p. 30

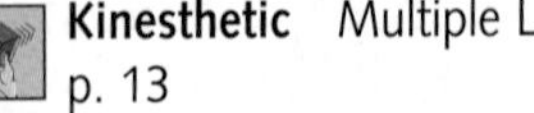

Kinesthetic Multiple Learning Styles, p. 13

Interpersonal Assessment, p. 19; Review, p. 30

Explore Activity

How can a ship that weighs several thousand tons float on water while a coin would sink right next to the ship? Why will the ship sink if the hull of a ship is damaged and water pours in? Around the world, there are many ships at the bottom of the ocean. How can they be floating one minute and sinking the next?

Observe Water Displacement

1. Fill a small bucket with two liters of water.
2. Use a balance to find the mass of an empty soda-pop can and a quarter.
3. Record the mass of each object.
4. Predict which object will float. Place the can on its side in the water. Observe what happens.
5. Place the quarter in the water. Observe what happens.

Science Journal

In your Science Journal, record whether your prediction was correct. Compare and contrast the empty can and the quarter to try to explain what you observed.

Explore Activity

Purpose

Visual-Spatial Use the Explore Activity to help students understand how heavier objects can float while lighter ones sink. L2 ELL COOP LEARN

Preparation

If a sink is not available, bring in plastic milk or beverage containers filled with water.

Materials

small bucket or dishpan, 2 L water, balance, empty soda can, quarter, paper towels

Teaching Strategies

Make sure students make their predictions before placing the objects in water.

Science Journal Students will state their prediction about which object they think will float. Students will state various reasons to explain their observations.

Assessment

Process Have students describe ways they could make the quarter float. If they need help, tell them to assume they can change the shape of the quarter or attach it to other materials. Use **Performance Assessment in the Science Classroom,** p. 21.

Assessment Planner

Portfolio

Refer to p. 31 for suggested items that students might select for their portfolios.

Performance Assessment

See p. 31 for additional Performance Assessment options.
Skill Builder, p. 27
MiniLab, pp. 13, 25
Activity 1-1, pp. 20–21; 1-2, p. 28

Content Assessment

Section Assessment, pp. 19, 27
Chapter Assessment, pp. 32–33
Proficiency Prep, pp. 19, 27

SECTION 1-1

Prepare

Refer to **What Science Is, Form a Hypothesis, Controlled Experiments,** and **Plan** on pp. 4E–F.

Preplanning

Refer to the **Chapter Organizer** on pp. 4A–B.

1 Motivate

Bellringer

Before presenting the lesson, display **Section Focus Transparency 1** on the overhead projector. Use the accompanying **Focus Activity** worksheet. L2 ELL

Section 1-1

1 SECTION FOCUS TRANSPARENCY

SCIENTIST OR EXPLORER?

This scientist looks like he's ready for a walk in space, but he's really studying something on Earth—an active volcano. Active volcanoes are extremely dangerous. That's why the scientist is wearing a safety suit.

1. What are some other hostile environments that scientists explore?
2. How does using technology help scientists to gather new information?
3. If you could study one thing, what would it be and how might you go about it?

Tying to Previous Knowledge

Have students identify several science skills and describe how they used them to find out something.

Scientific Problem Solving

What You'll Learn

- What science is
- How to use a scientific method in problem solving

Vocabulary
science
scientific method
hypothesis
theory
law
control
independent variable
dependent variable
constant
graph

Why It's Important

- You can use scientific methods to search for new knowledge and to solve everyday problems.

What Science Is

It was Current Events Day in Mr. Hayes's science class. Every other Wednesday, each student presented an article from a newspaper or magazine on a topic that related to science. Mr. Hayes wanted his students to be aware of the latest scientific advances. He also wanted them to understand that science wasn't a subject that disappeared when they closed their science books. "Science affects you every day," he often reminded them.

Several students presented their articles. Then, Deon stood to present. "This article describes how scientists found a shipwreck that was sunk in more than 2400 meters of water. They were able to find hundreds of articles used by the passengers, such as dishes and clothing. They even—"

Brianna waved her hand impatiently. "Excuse me," she interrupted, "but this is science class, not social studies or a movie review. Check your schedule, Dee!"

Several students laughed.

Mr. Hayes spoke. "Why do you think this article doesn't apply to science, Brianna?"

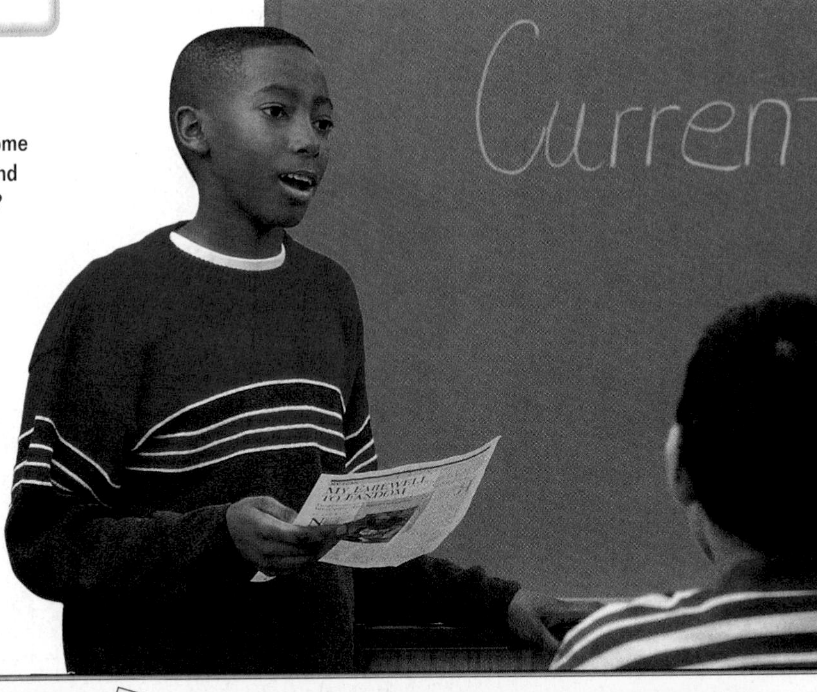

Figure 1-1 What are some ways science affects you and your classmates every day?

Resource Manager

The following **Teacher Classroom Resources** can be used with Section 1-1:

 **Reproducible Masters**

Activity Worksheets, pp. 1–2, 5 L2
Enrichment, p. 1 L3
Laboratory Manual, pp. 1–4 L2
Laboratory Manual, pp. 5–8 L2
Reinforcement, p. 1 L2
Study Guide, pp. 1–3 L1 ELL

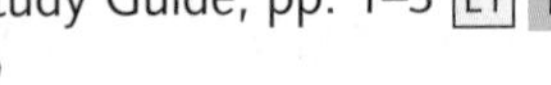

Transparencies

Teaching Transparency 1 L2

Brianna replied, "Because people who look at shipwrecks aren't scientists, they're explorers. They're just looking for something, not inventing something or testing some theory. They're not using scientific methods. They should be discussed in history class."

Mr. Hayes looked at Deon. "Deon, can you respond to what Brianna said? How is your article related to science?"

Deon looked embarrassed. "Well, I'm not sure either. This article says scientists looked for the shipwreck. And, the article was interesting, so I cut it out of the newspaper."

"Why don't you finish your report, Deon," said Mr. Hayes. "Then, we'll continue to debate whether or not it relates to science."

Deon described more of the objects from the ship that were found. He told the class that sonar was used to help find the wreck. Sonar stands for **SO**und **NA**vigation **R**anging. Sound waves are sent through the water and bounce back when they hit something, such as the ocean floor or part of a ship. Scientists can calculate how deep that spot is by the amount of time it takes the sound waves to reach the object and bounce back. A remotely operated vehicle, or ROV, was used to help recover the sunken objects. ROVs are unpiloted, and a person operates them at a distance. They can go places that are too deep or too dangerous for people to go.

LIFE SCIENCE INTEGRATION

Robot Researcher

Dolphins, bats, and barn owls were all models for a new robot named "Rodolph." These animals depend heavily on sound to help them navigate or find prey. The robot emits sound and "listens" for the echoes to detect objects underwater. Rodolph is so sensitive that it can even tell heads from tails on a dime. Infer how this robot can be used underwater to help scientists explore.

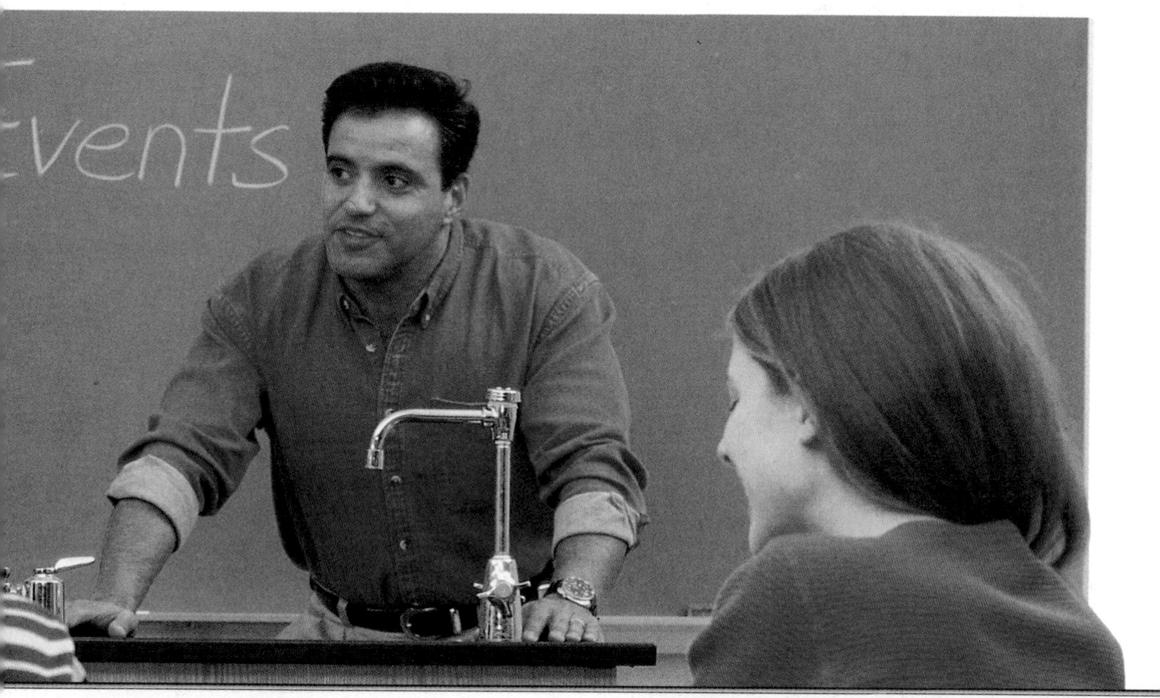

Caption Answer

Figure 1-1 *Answers will vary but may include ideas about medical research, computers, synthetic fabrics and dyes, communications, plastics, transportation, weather forecasting, and food production.*

Across the Curriculum

Health Sonography is using sound to "see" inside the human body. It works on the same principle as echolocation. Ultrasound waves penetrate the body, bounce off internal structures, and are transmitted to a computer. The computer constructs a visual image of the inside of the body. Physicians can "see" normal and diseased tissues, fetuses in utero, and even blood as it moves through the body.

2 Teach

LIFE SCIENCE INTEGRATION

Bats and dolphins use echolocation to navigate and to find food. They emit short bursts of ultrasound, which is sound that is too high-pitched for humans to hear. Bats emit squeaks or clicks through their mouths and listen to the pattern of echoes. Dolphins emit clicks and whistles from an organ on the top of the head and feel the returning sound waves as vibrations in their inner ear.

Answer *Rodolph could be used to help scientists detect and locate buried shipwrecks and other hidden objects more quickly. It could also help a submersible vehicle navigate through dark waters so the vehicle avoids hitting anything that can't be seen easily.*

Quick Demo

Logical-Mathematical Ask a student to measure the time in seconds that it takes for you to throw a ball across the room to another student and have the student throw it back to you. Explain that the ball represents sound waves, which travel at a constant speed of 334 m/s in air. Multiply this speed by the time it takes for sound waves to bounce and return, or echo. Then divide by two to find an object's distance. Use the student's time to perform the calculation. L2 ELL COOP LEARN

Using Math

1522 m/s × 20 s = 30 440 m (down and back)

30 440 ÷ 2 = 15 220 m

The answer is 15 220 m.

Correcting Misconceptions

Students might think that people look for shipwrecks primarily to find gold. But, many excavations are done to increase scientific and historical knowledge. We have learned how shipbuilding developed, which trade routes were used in ancient times, and how people on the ships lived.

Using Science Words

The word science comes from the Latin word *scientia*, or knowledge. Science is sometimes erroneously used to describe a collection of scientific facts. Facts by themselves are not science. Science is an activity—a way of knowing and doing. Science involves not only what happens but also how and why it happens.

GLENCOE TECHNOLOGY

Videodisc

Glencoe Science Voyages Interactive Videodisc—Physical

Side 2, Lesson 7 *Waves and Sound*

28088

Refer to Videodisc Teacher Guide for additional bar codes.

Figure 1-2 The submarine Atlantis helps scientists explore the water off the big island of Hawaii.

Using Math

The speed of a sound wave traveling in ocean water at 20°C is 1522 meters per second. Suppose that a sound wave takes 20 seconds to reach the bottom and return. How deep is the water at that location?

When Deon had finished, Mr. Hayes looked around at the class. "Let's get back to the point Brianna raised. **Science** is a process used to investigate the world around you, providing you with some possible answers. Does anyone see a connection between looking for shipwrecks and science?"

Scientists as Explorers

Enrique raised his hand. "I think the article does relate to science. People use science to find the answers to questions. The people who explored that shipwreck had questions. They were curious. Scientists are curious about the unknown. There are all sorts of scientists, you know. Explorers are scientists because they are curious about the unknown. I guess, in a way, all scientists are explorers. Hey! When I'm curious about something and I try to search for the answer, maybe that makes me an explorer, too."

Mr. Hayes replied, "I think you're on the right track, Enrique. Scientific exploration and discovery has never been limited to one race, sex, culture, or time period. As in the past, people all over the world make discoveries. These people are not only professional scientists. Often, discoveries are made by people pursuing a hobby. In fact, some important discoveries might be made by one of your classmates. Now, let's go back to your other point, Enrique. Are you saying that scientists and explorers only have curiosity in common? What did the explorers mentioned in the article do?"

Content Background

Before the shipwreck of the *Titanic* was discovered, it was a mystery why the ship had sunk so quickly. The iceberg with which the ship collided had indeed gashed a hole in its side. But, laboratory tests showed that steel plates along the side of the ship were fractured. Water poured in all along the plates, not just in the hole made by the iceberg.

Enrique thought a moment. "Well, I guess they would have had to use some kind of organized method. They had to pay attention to things like the position of the stars to know where they were headed and cloud formations to predict the weather."

Mr. Hayes asked, "Would the people who found the shipwreck in Deon's article have used some organized or scientific methods?"

Enrique looked confused. "I suppose. But Brianna's right. They didn't do any experiments. They just looked for things."

Sunghee raised her hand. "I think I see how Deon's article relates to science. It's because of the technology they used. I mean, the little robot and stuff. Technology is using science, right? But I have to agree with Brianna and Enrique. Doesn't a scientist always have to do an experiment?"

Mr. Hayes asked, "Well class, does anyone have an answer for Sunghee?"

The class was silent.

Mr. Hayes had an idea he thought might help the class answer his question. He walked to the chalkboard, paused, and began writing. "I have an assignment for you, due next Wednesday. I'd like you to find information that you think shows how scientists are like explorers and how technology helps them. You may look in magazines and books, or use the Internet. Then, list the skills you think the scientists used.

Figure 1-3 This scientist uses technology, such as scientific equipment and instruments, to help her explore.

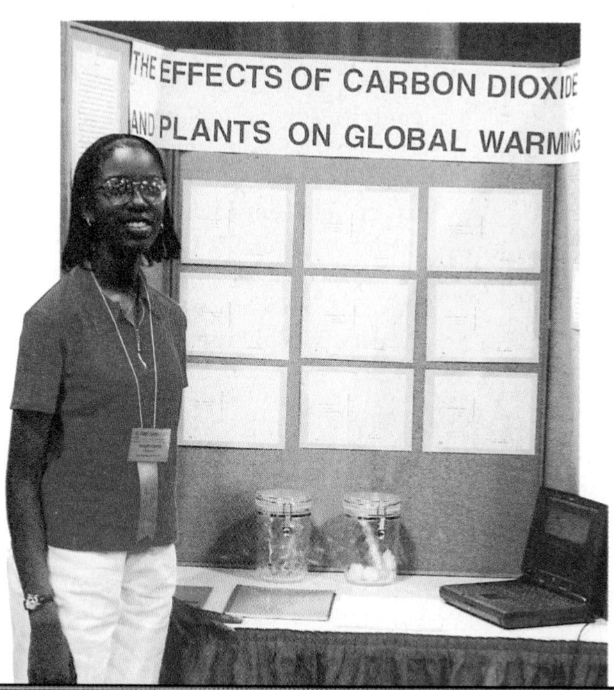

Figure 1-4 Students can be scientists, too. **In what ways have you been a scientific explorer?**

Correcting Misconceptions

Point out that technology is not a recent development. Since prehistoric times, people have invented tools, machines, and techniques to make their lives easier. The people who developed early technologies were not familiar with scientific principles. But they created technologies nonetheless.

Content Background

Submarines are equipped with special tanks that make the ship heavier or lighter to descend or rise, respectively. Submarines dive when the tanks are filled with water. To resurface, compressed air blows water out of the tanks.

Teacher FYI

The richest deep-sea treasure may be on the *SS Central America.* It sank off the coast of North Carolina in 1857. The ship is believed to have carried 21 tons of gold.

Caption Answer

Figure 1-4 *Answers will vary depending upon the students' experiences.*

Science Journal

Explorations Have students write about a time when they explored something. Have them describe the technology they used. L2

Integrating the Sciences

Life Science Scientists have discovered organisms living as deep as 805 m below the ocean floor. The organisms live on sulfur, ammonia, and other chemicals. Some scientists believe that similar life-forms could be living deep within Mars or Europa, a satellite of Jupiter.

Activity

- Have students begin an outline and fill it in as they read about scientific methods. L2
- Have students write the name of a topic that interests them. Assign them the task of finding and writing the names of two books, two magazines or journals, and two Internet Web Sites that contain information about the topic. L3

Using an Analogy

Ask several students to share some study methods they use. Write these on the chalkboard. Explain that students in the class may use all or some of these methods. Students may vary the methods according to whether, for example, they are studying for a test or preparing for an oral report. In the same way, people might use all or some scientific methods, according to the most appropriate way to solve a problem or answer a question.

GLENCOE TECHNOLOGY

Videodisc

The Infinite Voyage: To the Edge of the Earth

Chapter 3 *Exploring the Galápagos Islands* 8:00

Refer to the Teacher Guide for bar codes and teaching strategies.

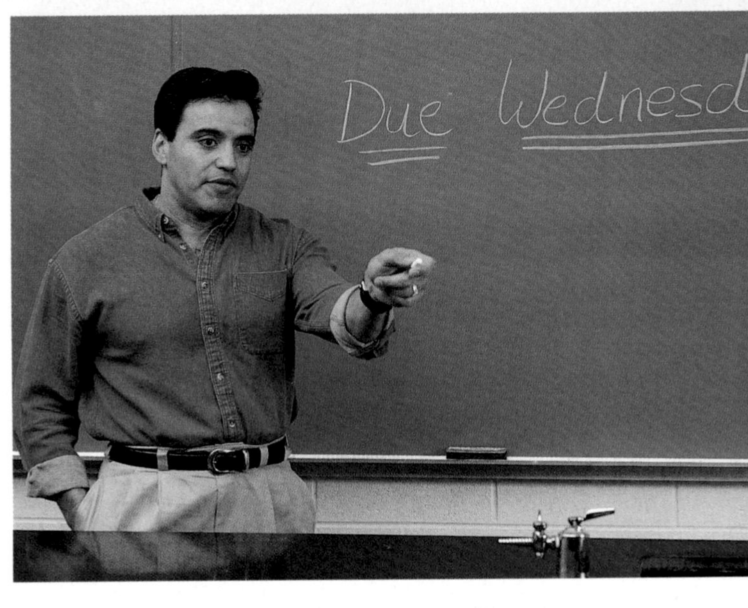

Figure 1-5 What are some things scientists do while searching for new information and solving problems?

Also list the steps they took in searching for new knowledge. Finally, compare the two and come up with your answer to the question, 'Does a scientist always need to use an organized approach to solving problems?'"

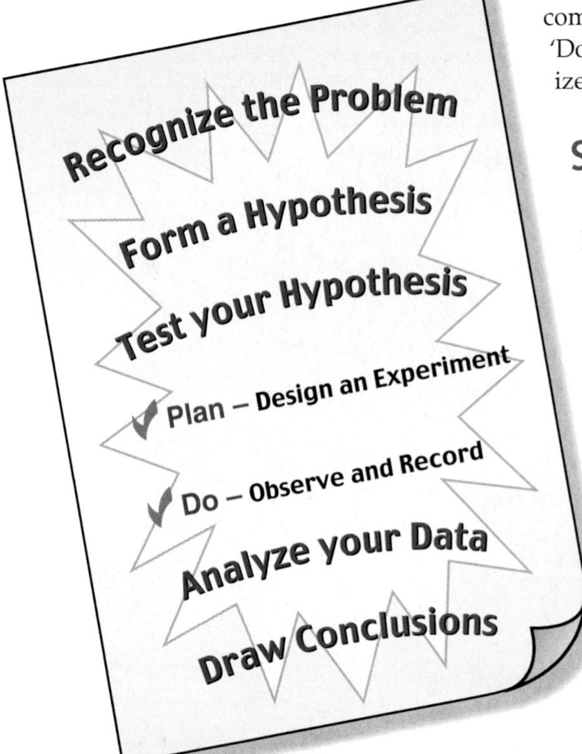

Recognize the Problem
Form a Hypothesis
Test your Hypothesis
Plan – Design an Experiment
Do – Observe and Record
Analyze your Data
Draw Conclusions

Figure 1-6 This poster shows one possible way to solve problems.

Scientific Methods

Scientists use a variety of ways to solve problems. A **scientific method** is an approach taken to try to solve a problem. The steps, as listed in **Figure 1-6,** form a model to solve problems. But, these steps serve only as a guide. Sometimes, several of the steps are used while others are not needed when solving a particular problem. Or, the steps might be performed in a different order. Let's take a look at a possible method that a person might use.

Across the Curriculum

History Before the sixteenth century, science was not a recognized discipline. Processes of nature often were explained as philosophical ideas. An explanation was accepted if it was logical. Science as a separate discipline began to emerge when people used experiments to test their explanations. Have students present a skit about a scientific discovery that refuted earlier teachings. L2

Caption Answers

Figure 1-5 *Answers can include that scientists research results from prior experiments, design and perform experiments, record data, make observations, make calculations, and use technology.*

Figure 1-7 *Answers will vary depending upon the student.*

Recognize the Problem

The problem-solving process generally begins when you recognize a problem or ask a question. Once you know what you want to study, you then choose the methods that will help you find the answers. Kashanna, shown in **Figure 1-7,** liked to listen to hard rock music as she studied. She and her parents argued about it.

"Kashanna, you can't possibly concentrate with that type of music," her mother would say.

"My grades are okay," Kashanna would argue.

"But I think your grades would be higher if you listened to quiet music, like classical," her mother would reply. "I know that soothing music helps me to think more clearly," she explained.

Kashanna decided to use a scientific method to see whether her mother was right. She asked her friend Hiromi to help.

"You're off to a great start. You've definitely got a problem you want to solve," Hiromi laughed.

Preparing to solve a problem or ask a question often involves making observations and doing research. For example, scientists who develop ways to improve crop yields find out the growth needs of the plant. They learn what has worked and not worked. Many times, scientists identify a real problem only after collecting lots of information from their observations.

interNET CONNECTION

Visit the Glencoe Science Web Site at **www.glencoe.com/sec/science** for more information about the effects of music on concentration. In your Science Journal, compare and contrast the results from different studies.

Figure 1-7 Under what conditions do you study the best?

Content Background

In 1993, scientists published the results of an experiment in which college students listened to music composed by Mozart. Immediately afterwards, the students took a spatial IQ test in which they mentally manipulated folded cut paper. Their scores were improved, but the effect of the music was brief. More recent experiments show that rats move more rapidly through a maze after being exposed to Mozart's music. The researchers think the reason may be that certain types of music directly stimulate and reorganize cells in the thinking center in mammals' brains.

interNET CONNECTION

Internet Addresses

____

____

____

____

For Internet tips, see Glencoe's **Using the Internet in the Science Classroom.**

Discussion

Why do many scientists do research before forming a hypothesis? *They will know what has already been done with the topic. Research helps them understand the topic, propose a hypothesis, and design an experiment.*

Across the Curriculum

Health and Math Music is used to treat a number of conditions. Patients who have surgery recover faster if they listen to music before, during, or after surgery. Patients who listen to their favorite music report less anxiety and discomfort while undergoing medical exams. In one study, premature infants gained weight faster when they listened to soft music. Music affects respiratory rate, heart rate, and blood pressure. Have students bring in a variety of musical tapes or CDs. Conduct a classroom experiment in which students measure their heart rate while listening to different kinds of music. Have them graph the results.

L2  

Activity

Ask each student to think of a hypothesis. Have them write the if part on a slip of paper and the then part on another slip of paper. Collect the slips in two separate containers and mix them up. Have each student draw a slip from each container and read the hypothesis aloud. The results may be humorous and will reinforce the structure of a hypothesis. L2 COOP LEARN

Using an Analogy

Compare the variables in a sports game to those in an experiment. The independent variable is the actions of the players. The dependent variable is the number of times a team scores. The constants are following the rules.

Teacher FYI

Aristotle's teachings were not based on experimentation. He taught that pain, pleasure, and emotions came from the heart. The heart warmed blood and the brain cooled it. People really believed that kind people had a warm heart. You were coolheaded if your brain was working well.

Answer to Reading Check

The independent variable is the factor that is manipulated or changed. The dependent variable is the factor that is observed or measured. It is affected when the independent variable is changed.

Form a Hypothesis

Often, the next step in solving a problem is to form a hypothesis. A **hypothesis** (hi PAHTH uh sus) is a prediction about a problem that can be tested. A hypothesis may be based upon a variety of things. It can come about from observations, from personal experiences, or from new information gathered during other experiments. Hypotheses are often written as if-and-then statements. For example, a scientist observes that plants, such as those in **Figure 1-8,** that are fertilized grow taller than plants that are not. A scientist may form the following hypothesis: If plants are fertilized more, then they will grow taller. This hypothesis can be tested by an experiment. Scientists are able to form theories from well-tested hypotheses.

A **theory** is an explanation backed by results obtained from repeated tests or experiments. Not all results lead to the formation of a theory. Actually, there are only a few theories and even fewer laws.

A scientific **law** is a well-tested description of how something in nature works. Generally, laws predict or describe a given situation but don't explain why. An example of a law is Newton's first law of motion. According to this law, an object continues in motion, or stays at rest, until it's acted upon by an outside force. Some other laws include the law of conservation of mass, the law of conservation of energy, and the laws of reflection.

Figure 1-8 One scientist might hypothesize that one plant grew taller than the other because it was fertilized more. **What other hypothesis could you make about the plants?**

Kashanna wrote in her Science Journal, "My hypothesis is that if I perform a task while listening to different types of music, then my ability to concentrate will not be affected."

Once a hypothesis is formed, a scientist will find ways to test it. Kashanna must now decide how to test the effects of listening to different types of music on her concentration. Two ways to test a hypothesis are by conducting controlled experiments and by making observational studies.

Caption Answer

Figure 1-8 *Answers may vary but can include that if a plant is given more water, more sunlight, or a different type of fertilizer, it will grow taller than the other plant.*

Science Journal

Drug Testing Have students write why a scientist who is trying a new drug on people should use a control. L2 

Test Your Hypothesis

In order to form conclusions that make sense from your results, you often need a **control**—a standard with which to compare the results. In Kashanna's experiment, she wants to compare the effects of different kinds of music on concentration. The standard that the results will be compared to is her level of concentration when no music is playing. Kashanna's control is to have no music playing during an activity that requires concentration.

Controlled Experiments

A controlled experiment is made up of a series of steps that test a hypothesis in which a control is used. The basic idea of a controlled experiment is to change only one factor, or variable. The variable that is changed is the **independent variable.** The **dependent variable** is the factor being observed or measured. Scientists observe or measure the effect on the dependent variable when they change the independent variable. Kashanna determined that the independent variable is the type of music listened to while performing a task. She chose to test the effects of hard rock, soft rock, classical music, and no music. The dependent variable is how well Kashanna performs the task, which is related to her concentration while the music is playing.

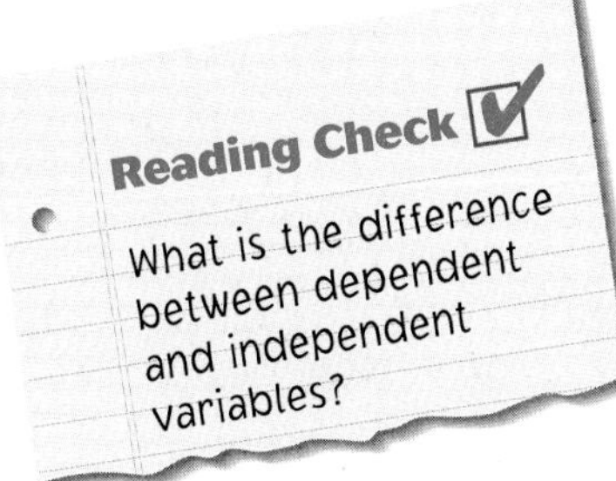

Reading Check
What is the difference between dependent and independent variables?

Plan the Experiment

"How will you know the effect each type of music has on your ability to concentrate?" Hiromi asked. "You need to be able to measure the effect. I don't think you'll convince your parents if you say you felt you concentrated the same with any kind of music."

Kashanna and Hiromi decided to have Kashanna copy various passages out of their science textbook as she listened to each kind of music. Hiromi tried to select passages from the book that wouldn't be any more or less difficult to copy than any of the other passages. Kashanna couldn't copy the same page over and over or she might memorize it, which would affect the results. The number of words written down during a given time period would be the dependent variable.

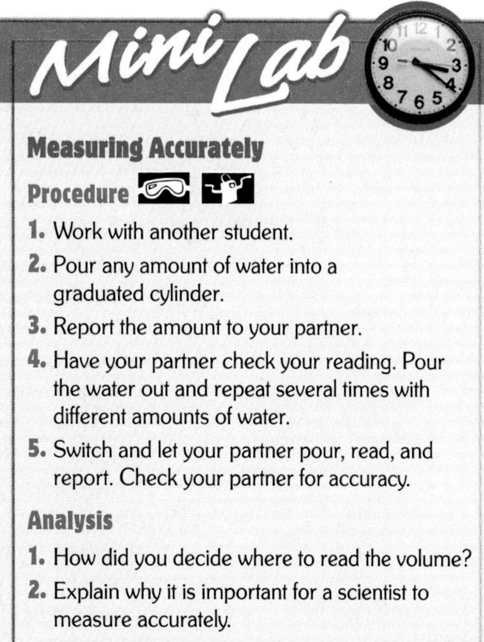

MiniLab

Measuring Accurately

Procedure

1. Work with another student.
2. Pour any amount of water into a graduated cylinder.
3. Report the amount to your partner.
4. Have your partner check your reading. Pour the water out and repeat several times with different amounts of water.
5. Switch and let your partner pour, read, and report. Check your partner for accuracy.

Analysis

1. How did you decide where to read the volume?
2. Explain why it is important for a scientist to measure accurately.

MiniLab

Purpose

Logical-Mathematical Students will practice measuring volume using a graduated cylinder. L2 ELL COOP LEARN

Materials

graduated cylinder, water, paper cups, paper towels

Teaching Strategies

Draw a graduated cylinder on the chalkboard and the curve of a liquid. Point to the bottom of the curve to show how to read the measurement. Explain that they should make the reading at eye level.

Troubleshooting Make sure students are reading at eye level.

Analysis

1. Student answers will vary. Possible answers might include viewing the readings from the same position each time.
2. Student answers will vary. Possible answers might include that measuring accurately is important to determine the effect of the independent variable on the dependent variable. Also, experiments might not work if the correct amounts of materials are not used.

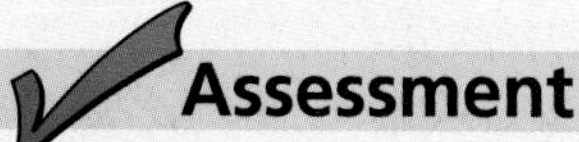

Assessment

Process Have students measure length in the same way with their partners. They should recognize that they need to view the readings from the same position each time. Use **Performance Assessment in the Science Classroom,** p. 29.

Multiple Learning Styles

Kinesthetic Crumple a piece of paper and give it to a student. Have the student stand close to the trash can and throw it in. Do the same with another student but have the student stand on the other side of the room. Ask the class if the competition was fair. Have them describe how to make it fair. Point out that in this demonstration, the students were the independent variables. Each change in the independent variable should have an equal chance to affect the dependent variable. Have students explain why an experiment with uncontrolled variables is not fair. L2 COOP LEARN

Caption Answer

Figure 1-9 *CDs of the three different kinds of music, science textbook, a table and chair, and paper for Mario*

 **Videodisc**

STV: Solar System

Unit 1: *The Big Picture, Landing on the Moon* 1:41

08780–11815

Refer to the Teacher Guide for additional bar codes and teaching strategies.

Discussion

Why is it important to collect data accurately? *Recording data incorrectly can cause you to draw conclusions that are not true. You might think your hypothesis is supported or not when the opposite is true.*

GLENCOE TECHNOLOGY

 **CD-ROM**

Glencoe Science Voyages Interactive CD-ROM

Explorations

Have students do the interactive exploration *How is a controlled experiment performed?*

Figure 1-9 What else does Kashanna need to do her experiment?

As they wrote their plan, Kashanna and Hiromi tried to think of other variables that might affect the dependent variable. They knew that these variables should be kept the same while changing only the independent variable. That way, any effect on the dependent variable would be caused only by the independent variable. A variable in an experiment that stays the same is a **constant.** Constants that Kashanna and Hiromi identified were the similar passages in the book to be copied, the amount of time given to copy each passage, the volume of the music, the lighting in the room, and interruptions from people entering the room. They also were careful to select three pieces of music that could each be played uninterrupted for five minutes.

Kashanna thought of something else. "What if I speed up, without even realizing it, when I listen to hard rock to try to prove that hard rock is not harmful to my concentration? I would be influencing the results."

To avoid this problem, they asked their friend Mario to participate in the experiment. They did not tell Mario the hypothesis. An experiment in which some or all information is withheld from a subject (Mario) or the investigator (Kashanna) is called a blind experiment.

Kashanna gathered the materials, shown in **Figure 1-9,** she would need before Mario arrived. An important part of planning an experiment is determining the materials needed. You

Across the Curriculum

Math Have students survey members of their class on their favorite music and construct a graph to show the results. Have them survey other classes, construct graphs, and develop hypotheses regarding any differences between classes. L2 COOP LEARN P

Content Background

Bias in an experiment is an error that is caused by favoring one outcome over another. Scientists must not let their results be influenced by what they want or expect to happen. Bias also can occur when the experimental group and the control group are not similar.

do not want to be in the middle of conducting an experiment and find you do not have everything you need to complete the experiment.

Do the Experiment

When Mario arrived, Kashanna told him only that he would be listening to music and trying to copy as much of the passage as he could until she told him to stop. She took away his watch and any clocks in the room. She did not want Mario to try to "beat the clock." Mario did not know why Kashanna was doing this experiment. That way, he would not try to make the results come out a particular way. This is why the experiment was a blind experiment.

Look at **Figure 1-10.** Kashanna kept the lighting in the room and the volume of the music the same throughout the experiment. She put headphones on Mario to minimize other noises. When Kashanna said "Go!", Mario copied the science textbook page for five minutes. He copied down a different passage from the textbook each time he listened to each of three types of music and also when no music was played.

Part of doing an experiment is observing and recording data. Observations can include measurements and descriptions that can be written in your Science Journal. Each time five minutes was over, Kashanna observed the number of words Mario wrote. She counted and recorded them in her Science Journal. When the experiment was over, she analyzed the data. Mario had copied the fewest words while listening to hard rock.

"These aren't the results I was looking for!" Kashanna exclaimed.

Figure 1-10 There are many variables to consider before doing an experiment. **What variables might be out of Kashanna's control?**

Teacher FYI

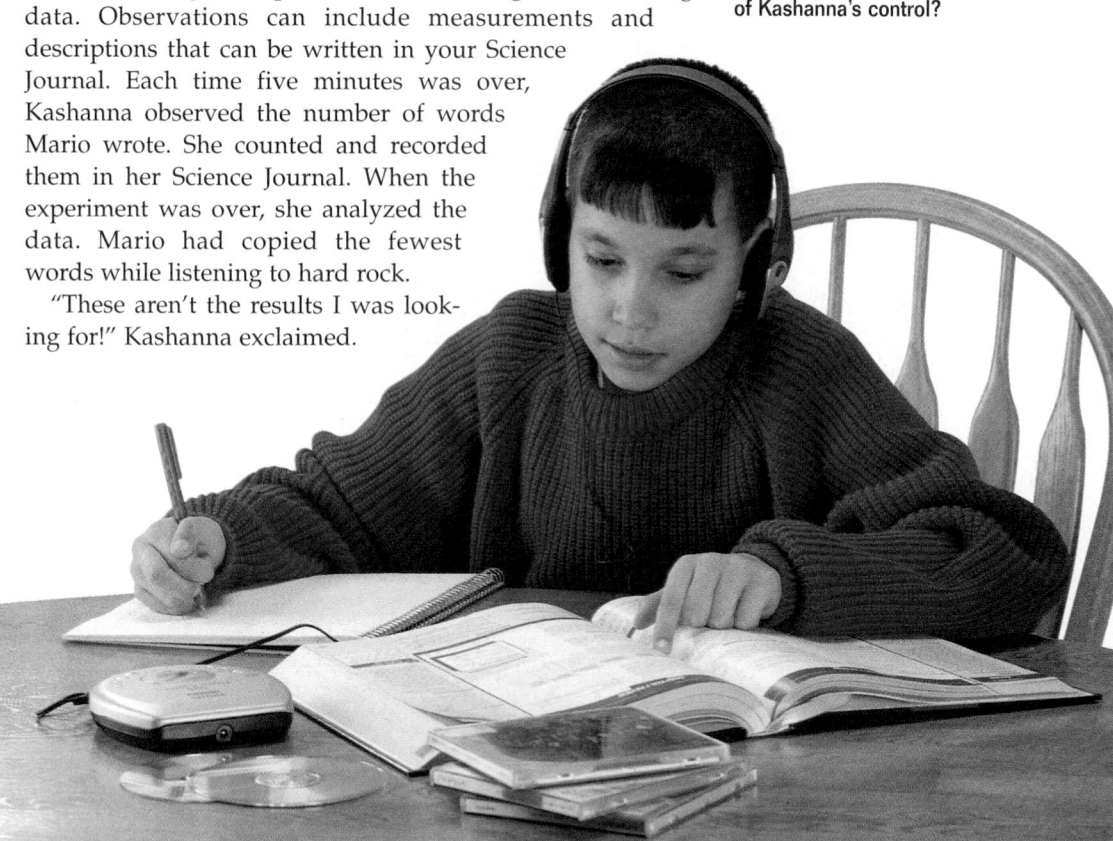

Tell students that they should be precise when communicating about procedures and observations. For example, they should write, "Pour 1 L of water" instead of "Pour some water." They should say, "He copied 50 words in five minutes" instead of "He copied a lot of words in a short time."

Discussion

Challenge students to ask a question about human behavior, form a hypothesis, and design an experiment to test the hypothesis. Examples are: What is the best time of day to do homework? and Do computers help a person get better grades? L2

Enrichment

Have students research several superstitions such as that crops should be planted under a full moon. Have them try to find out (1) why the superstitions started, (2) whether the superstitions have any truth to them, (3) how they would they test the superstitions. Students should not test them without teacher approval. L3

Caption Answer

Figure 1-10 *Answers can include how Mario feels that day, how interested Mario is in each passage he copies, how hard he tries to do his best in each trial, and Mario's taste in music.*

Integrating the Sciences

Life Science Plants generate electric fields that relate to how they grow. Certain cells in the root show growth responses to applied electric fields. These cells exhibit an ability to grow under adverse conditions. Scientists want to understand this ability so that they can engineer other plants that can grow under marginal conditions. However, these cells also respond to gravity. Scientists on the ground can control every type of variable except gravity. So, these experiments and many others are done in space. Scientists can establish how gravity affects physical, chemical, and biological processes.

Problem Solving

Remind students that sonar stands for SOund NAvigation Ranging. Sound waves that are sent and reflected are analyzed. Sonar is used in medicine, in industry, and in underwater navigation.

Think Critically

Students can use the Internet, computerized card catalog, or look for television specials and videos.

Discussion

Explain that another reason to perform multiple trials is the difficulty in measuring accurately. Repeated measurements often are not the same, even in the most careful work. Ask students to recall what they did in the MiniLab when the curve of water in the graduated cylinder fell between markings. They may say they estimated. Point out that other errors in measuring can occur. Ask them what happened if they looked at the curve from different positions. They probably will say the readings were different. Errors in measuring can be reduced, but not eliminated. Averaging several results can reduce the influence of these errors.

Flex Your Brain

Use the Flex Your Brain activity to have students explore SONAR.

Hiromi suggested that Kashanna repeat the experiment a few more times. Conducting an experiment once is called a trial. Repeating an experiment several times is making multiple trials. A subject in an experiment will perform slightly differently each time. The scientist takes an average of the results. A multiple trial helps strengthen the support or lack of support for the hypothesis. In Kashanna's experiment, each time a different trial was done, the order of the types of music was changed to help reduce the effect that the tiring of Mario's brain or hand muscles would have on the results.

Kashanna set up a data table to record the results of each trial. Data tables help you organize your observations and test results. **Table 1-1** shows Kashanna's data table.

Table 1-1

Number of Words Copied					
Type of Music	Trial 1	Trial 2	Trial 3	Trial 4	Average
No music	56	60	64	60	
Classical	54	62	60	56	
Soft rock	36	42	38	32	
Hard rock	26	36	42	24	

Problem Solving

Flex Your Brain

Solving problems requires a plan. This plan may be a simple thing that you do in your head, or it may be something more complicated that you actually write down. To the right is a process called *Flex Your Brain,* which is one way to help you organize a plan for solving a problem. Skills that you might find helpful in solving problems can be found in the **Skill Handbook** at the back of your textbook.

Sonar uses sound waves to determine ocean depths and to find unseen objects. Use the *Flex Your Brain* chart to help you explore the other possible uses of sound waves.

Think Critically: How can you use technology to help you find the answer to the problem? Why does *Flex Your Brain* ask you to share what you've learned?

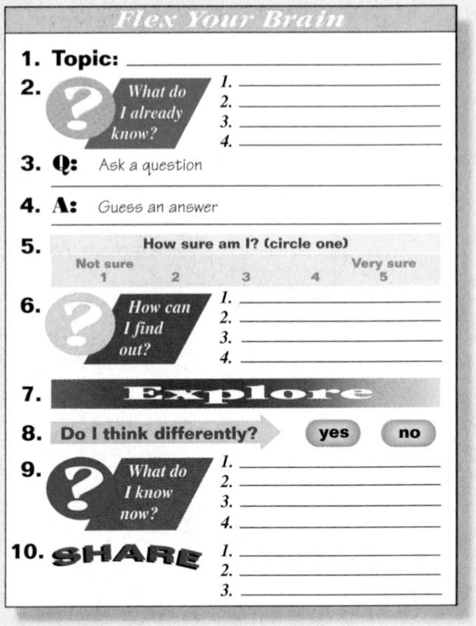

Flex Your Brain

1. Topic: ______
2. What do I already know? 1. ____ 2. ____ 3. ____ 4. ____
3. Q: Ask a question
4. A: Guess an answer
5. How sure am I? (circle one) Not sure 1 2 3 4 5 Very sure
6. How can I find out? 1. ____ 2. ____ 3. ____ 4. ____
7. Explore
8. Do I think differently? yes no
9. What do I know now? 1. ____ 2. ____ 3. ____ 4. ____
10. SHARE 1. ____ 2. ____ 3. ____

Inclusion Strategies

Learning Disabled Help students stay on track when performing a science activity. Tell them to write the details of the procedure and keep them nearby when working. They should design tables and logs before beginning an experiment. Emphasize recording every result in writing at the time it is observed. Caution them not to jump ahead to analyze the data while they are observing and recording. This will reduce their concentration and possibly bias the results.

Observational Study

Using scientific methods does not always involve doing a controlled experiment. In an observational study, a scientist does not change or control the variables that are already present in a situation or an environment. The scientist observes and records his or her observations, as in **Figure 1-11.** Suppose scientists wanted to learn more about a particular planet. They might observe the planet with powerful telescopes. They might send a probe, a device to gather information. Suppose scientists wanted to learn more about a particular animal. They might want to know how the animal lives in its natural environment. The scientists would observe the animal without changing its living conditions. Or, suppose scientists wanted to find out more about what causes heart disease. They might observe the rate of heart disease in a group of people and note differences between people who develop heart disease and those who do not.

In each of these three cases, a controlled experiment would not help the scientists obtain the information they seek. This is not to say that observational studies never have variables. Suppose a scientist observes the rate of cancer in people who have a low-fat diet compared to those who have a high-fat diet. The scientist classifies people as belonging in one of the two groups. The independent variable is the amount of fat a person eats. The dependent variable is the rate of cancer.

Figure 1-11 Each of these three scientists must decide, or at times guess, which types of experiments will provide the best information.

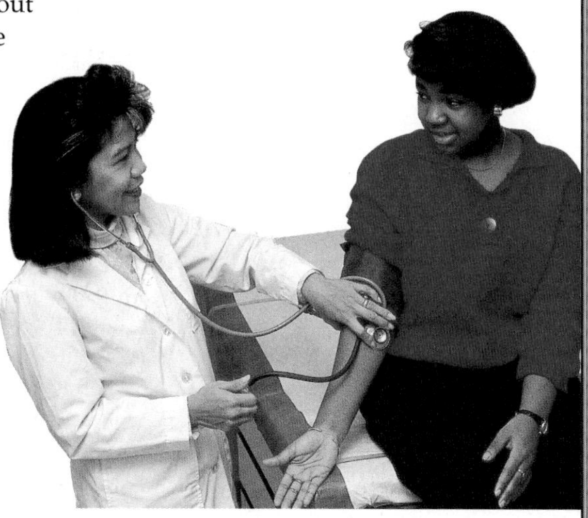

Enrichment

It is difficult for scientists to study some diseases that have many causes. Have students research the factors that can increase the risk of heart disease. Have them design a study to observe the causes. L3

Content Background

The Framingham Heart Study is the longest-running medical project in history. It began in 1948 in Framingham, Massachusetts. For more than 30 years, medical researchers have observed thousands of residents for development of heart disease. They have obtained information about personal habits such as exercise and type of diet. When the study started, physicians were unclear about the role of such factors as cholesterol, blood pressure, and blood sugar. Today, largely due to this observational study in one small town, many people worldwide practice habits to reduce their risk of heart disease.

Guided Reading Strategy

Bubble Map Using a bubble map helps students start ideas flowing about a given topic. Words are clustered to describe a topic or idea that is studied. Students can use the bubble map for prewriting, to generate ideas before writing in their Science Journals, or to review for a test. Have students design a Bubble Map for a concept in this section.

Sample map:

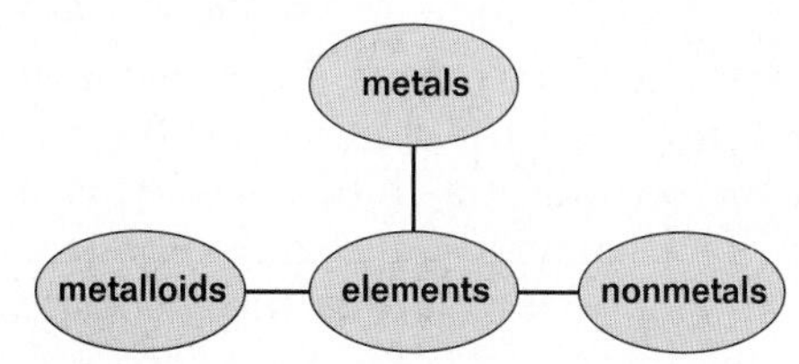

Answer to Text Question

Do the results support her hypothesis? *No, Kashanna wanted to prove that the type of music that was played did not affect concentration. The results suggest that concentration was affected differently by each type of music.*

Teacher FYI

Explain to students that drawing a smooth curve through a set of points plotted on a graph is not like a game of connect the dots. Show students examples of plotted data and guide their practice in drawing lines that best fit the data.

3 Assess

Check for Understanding

Discussion

Ask students to explain the relationship between the independent variable and the dependent variable. *The experimenter changes the independent variable to see what effect it has on the dependent variable.*

Reteach

Ask students to read the hypothesis in this section concerning the plants. Have them identify the independent variable, dependent variable, control, and constants in an experiment to test this hypothesis. L2

Extension

For students who have mastered this section, use the **Reinforcement** and **Enrichment** masters.

Analyze Your Data

Once a set of data has been collected and organized, it can be analyzed to see if it supports the hypothesis. Data can be analyzed in a number of ways, including performing calculations and making different types of graphs. A **graph** is a diagram that shows the relationship of one variable to another. A graph makes interpretation and analysis of data easier. Look at Kashanna's graph in **Figure 1-12.** Do the results support her hypothesis?

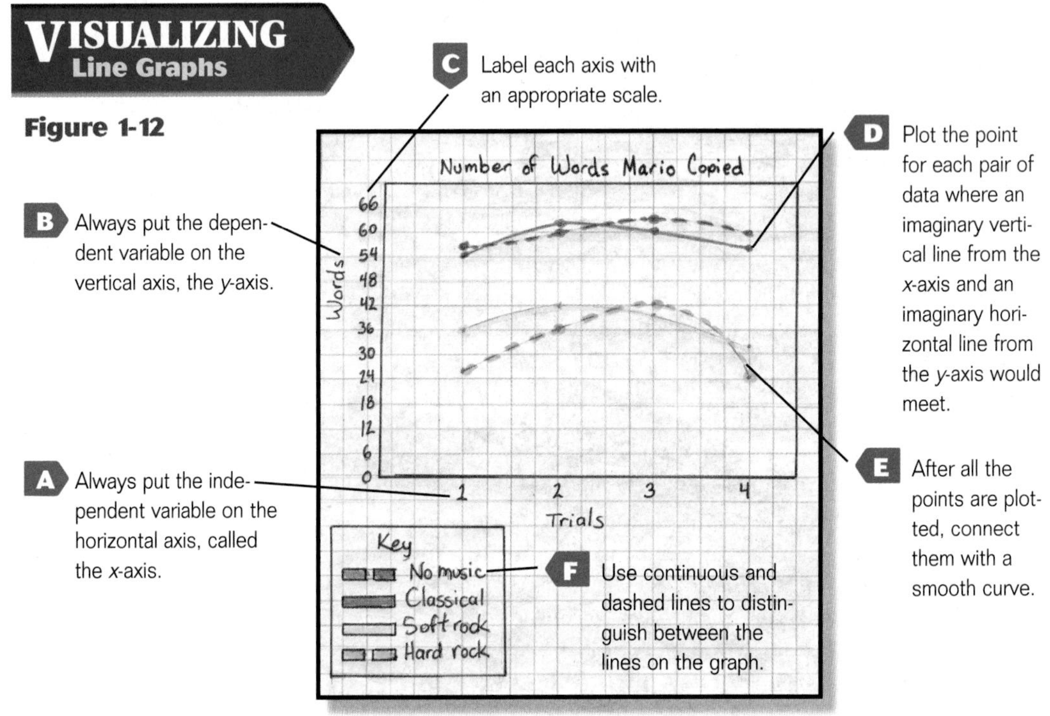

VISUALIZING
Line Graphs
Figure 1-12
C Label each axis with an appropriate scale.
D Plot the point for each pair of data where an imaginary vertical line from the x-axis and an imaginary horizontal line from the y-axis would meet.
B Always put the dependent variable on the vertical axis, the y-axis.
A Always put the independent variable on the horizontal axis, called the x-axis.
E After all the points are plotted, connect them with a smooth curve.
F Use continuous and dashed lines to distinguish between the lines on the graph.
Number of Words Mario Copied
Words
66
60
54
48
42
36
30
24
18
12
6
0
1
2
3
4
Trials
Key
No music
Classical
Soft rock
Hard rock

Draw Conclusions

A conclusion is a statement based on the results of the experiment. It might or might not support the hypothesis. Kashanna's hypothesis was not supported. She concluded that the type of music did have an effect on the ability to concentrate. Keep in mind that a hypothesis is not necessarily wrong just because the results do not support it. An experiment might not be designed correctly. A scientist might make errors in observing, measuring, or recording data. An unidentified variable might affect the dependent variable.

VISUAL Learning

Figure 1-12 Students should recognize a pattern in which the number of words in the first and fourth trials is less than the number in the second and third trials. This holds true for each type of music. One explanation is that Mario was careful the first time, became more relaxed the second and third times, and became tired the fourth time. If Kashanna had looked only at trial three, she might have concluded that hard rock was less distracting than soft rock. Conducting multiple trials provided a more accurate picture of the effects of different music types on concentration.

18 CHAPTER 1 THE NATURE OF SCIENCE

As Kashanna and Hiromi reviewed their results, they identified problems in the design. They concluded that more than one variable could have affected Mario's performance. What if some passages contained a greater number of long or difficult words? Or, what if he became bored during the experiment? What if these results could be applied only to Mario? Was his experience typical of everyone's experience? Kashanna and Hiromi decided to conduct more experiments with other classmates.

Scientists who conduct observational studies also draw conclusions from analyzing data. A scientist who observes a higher rate of skin cancer in people who sunbathe often might conclude that frequent sun exposure is a factor in causing skin cancer.

Scientists, like the astronaut in **Figure 1-13,** often must do many experiments and look at problems in different ways to find answers. Scientists have not failed if they do not get answers the first time, or the second, or even the hundredth. They learn a little more each time. Often, results from scientific experiments and observations raise more questions. An important part of doing science is persistence.

Figure 1-13 This astronaut is using a specially designed chair and helmet to test the effects of space flight on humans.

Section Assessment

1. What are five possible approaches one might take in solving a problem?
2. What is a constant?
3. Why is conducting multiple trials a good idea?
4. **Think Critically:** What else could Kashanna have used as the independent variable in her experiment?
5. **Skill Builder**
   Sequencing Complex tasks are often accomplished by following a series of steps in order. Do the **Chapter 1 Skill Activity** on page 742 to plan a mission to Mars by arranging the steps in the proper sequence.

Using Math

Use the data in **Table 1-1** to find the average number of words copied for each trial. Make a bar graph to show the results of your calculations. Under which conditions would Mario study best?

Assessment

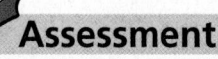

Oral Have students work in pairs and take turns. One student asks a "why " question. The other student constructs a hypothesis from the question. Use **Performance Assessment in the Science Classroom,** p. 21.

4 Close

Proficiency Prep

Use this quiz to check students' recall of section content.

1. **What are two ways to test a hypothesis?** *controlled experiment and observational study*
2. **What are two types of observations?** *measurements and descriptions*

Section Assessment

1. Steps in the scientific method discussed are: 1) recognize a problem, 2) form a hypothesis, 3) test the hypothesis, 4) analyze the data, and 5) draw conclusions.
2. Constants are the variables in an experiment that stay the same.
3. A scientist might make an error during an experiment. Or, a subject might perform differently each time. Then, the results may be averaged. Multiple trials helps strengthen the support or lack of support for the hypothesis.
4. **Think Critically** Possible answers include using math problems at the same level of difficulty.

Using Math

The averages are: no music, 60; classical, 58; soft rock, 37; hard rock, 32. The bar graph should have the number of words copied along the *y*-axis and the type of music along the *x*-axis. These results indicate that Mario would study best if no music plays. He may study almost as well with classical music playing. P

Activity 1·1 Design Your Own Experiment

Recognize the Problem

Purpose

Logical-Mathematical Students will gain skill in designing a controlled experiment. L2 ELL COOP LEARN

Process Skills

designing an experiment, forming a hypothesis, communicating, observing and inferring, comparing and contrasting, separating and controlling variables, making and using a graph, measuring

Time

45 minutes

Form a Hypothesis

Possible Hypotheses

Students might hypothesize that the type of surface material has no effect on how high the ball bounces; that balls bounce higher on softer materials than on harder ones; or that balls will bounce higher on harder materials.

Test Your Hypothesis

Possible Procedures

Attach a strip of white paper on a wall and drop the ball close to the wall. Mark the highest spot the ball reached. Use different colored markers for each type of surface material. Or, label the spot with the type of material. Use a stationary object, such as a desktop, to align the ball at the same height each time. Have the same person drop the ball, observe the high point of the bounce, and measure the paper to minimize errors.

Design Your Own Experiment

Activity 1·1

Follow the Bouncing Ball

Science might be the last thing you are thinking about as you watch a commercial on TV. But, many manufacturers rely on scientists to design and test their products. Suppose you are the owner of a sports store. You want to advertise how high a particular ball bounces. Conduct an experiment to find the surface material on which your ball bounces the highest.

Possible Materials

- Balls, such as a baseball, table-tennis ball, golf ball, tennis ball, racquetball, and high-bounce rubber ball
- Meterstick
- Poster paper
- Markers
- Floor materials, such as carpet, foam, hard tile, and wood

Recognize the Problem

How does the surface of a material affect how high a ball bounces?

Form a Hypothesis

Before a ball is dropped, it has potential energy. Potential energy is energy that is stored. As the ball falls, the potential energy is converted into kinetic energy, which is energy of motion. Some energy is transferred as a ball deforms when it hits the surface. Use this knowledge of potential and kinetic energy to **make a hypothesis** about how the kind of surface material helps determine the bounce of a ball.

Goals

- **Design an experiment** to find out how high a ball bounces on different surface materials.
- **Separate and control** variables.
- **Measure and record** observations.

Safety Precautions

Do not throw the balls in the classroom.

Inclusion Strategies

Behaviorally Disordered Make sure the student has a specific task in the group that requires his or her continual attention. Check that the student understands what to do.

Test Your Hypothesis

Plan

1. **Decide** how your group will test your hypothesis.
2. **List** the steps that you need to take to test your hypothesis. **Include** in your plan (a) the materials you will use, (b) the dependent variable and how you will **determine** the effect of the independent variable, (c) how you will keep the constants the same, d) the independent variable and how you will **adjust** it, and (e) how many trials you will conduct.
3. **Prepare** a data table in your Science Journal so that it is ready to use as your group collects data. Will the data be summarized in graphs? **Decide** which type of graph to use.

Do

1. Make sure your teacher approves your plan and your data table before you proceed.
2. **Perform** the experiment as planned.
3. **Record** your observations and **complete** the data table in your Science Journal.

Analyze Your Data

1. **Construct** a graph to compare results.
2. **List** the materials in the order that provided the highest bounce to those that provided the lowest bounce. Which surface material provided the highest bounce?
3. **Identify** any other variables that could affect the height of the bounce.

Draw Conclusions

1. **Infer** which surface materials absorb the most energy from the ball.
2. **Explain** why the surface material and the material of the ball are important in how sports, such as tennis and basketball, are played.
3. **Apply** what you learned. Write an advertisement that tells customers how to get the most bounce from the ball.

Teaching Strategies

Demonstrate the meaning of deform by pressing a rubber ball with your fingers. Encourage students to feel how the ball and surface materials deform by pushing them with their fingers or hands. This will help them form a hypothesis.

Troubleshooting Students may find it difficult to observe the highest point of the bounce. Emphasize that this is a reason to conduct multiple trials.

Expected Outcome

Students will recognize the importance of controlling variables and conducting multiple trials.

Error Analysis

Have students compare their results and their hypotheses and explain why any differences occurred.

Analyze Your Data

1. Students should make a bar graph to compare to different surface materials when balls are dropped from the same height. They may also make a line graph comparing the height of the bounce with the height of the dropped ball for the same surface material.
2. Answers may vary according to the type of ball used.
3. Students might identify that the height at which the ball is dropped affects the height of the bounce.

Draw Conclusions

1. The lower the bounce, the more energy the surface material absorbed from the ball.
2. Sports such as tennis and basketball require that the ball bounces, so the surface material used should not absorb much energy. The ball should recover its shape quickly after bouncing.
3. Answers will vary.

Assessment

Content To further assess students' understanding of identifying and controlling variables, have them design an experiment that shows which type of ball bounces the highest on which type of surface material. Use **Performance Assessment in the Science Classroom,** p. 23.

Have students describe how the height of the bounce could be measured using existing technology or technology they imagine. *Answers will vary. Students might suggest using a sensor that could transmit data to an instrument that would record and display the height.*

SECTION 1·2

Prepare

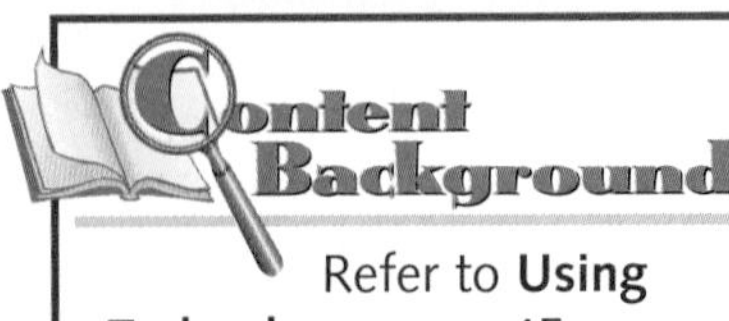

Refer to **Using Technology** on p. 4F.

Preplanning

Refer to the **Chapter Organizer** on pp. 4A–B.

1 Motivate

Bellringer

Before presenting the lesson, display **Section Focus Transparency 2** on the overhead projector. Use the accompanying **Focus Activity** worksheet. L2 ELL

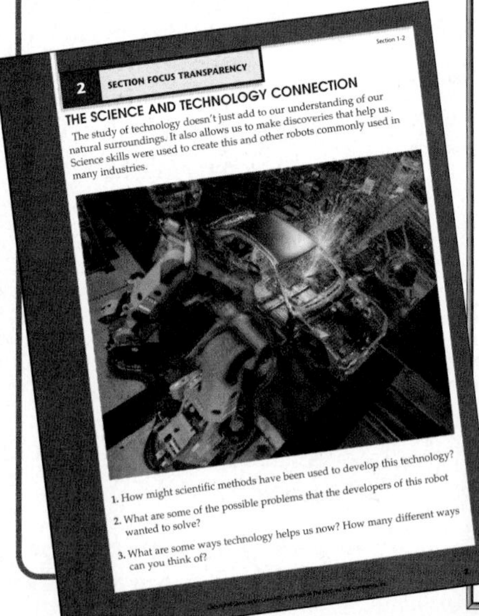

Section 1-2

2 SECTION FOCUS TRANSPARENCY

THE SCIENCE AND TECHNOLOGY CONNECTION

The study of technology doesn't just add to our understanding of our natural surroundings. It also allows us to make discoveries that help us. Science skills were used to create this and other robots commonly used in many industries.

1. How might scientific methods have been used to develop this technology?
2. What are some of the possible problems that the developers of this robot wanted to solve?
3. What are some ways technology helps us now? How many different ways can you think of?

Tying to Previous Knowledge

Ask students to recall ways that scientists have explored outer space without going there. This section will describe how scientists explore environments that are dangerous to humans.

Using Science to Explore

What You'll Learn

- How remotely operated vehicles help humans to explore
- How scientists use science skills in different ways

Vocabulary
technology
sequence
inference

Why It's Important

- Using science skills and technology helps you gather information about places that you cannot observe directly.

Using Technology

A week had passed since Mr. Hayes's assignment. The students were eager to share what they had found out.

Mr. Hayes opened the discussion. "Before we begin, who can tell us the difference between science and technology?"

Gabriella raised her hand. "Science is the process of trying to understand the world around you. **Technology** is the application of what has been learned through science."

"Excellent," Mr. Hayes said. "Why don't you go first, Gabriella?"

Gabriella stood. "The ocean is a frontier just waiting to be explored like the American West used to be. There's a difference, though. There are few places people may go underwater. It's too deep and the pressure is too great. That's what is known as a hostile environment—an environment in which the conditions are hazardous to people. People need technology to help them."

She continued, "Remotely operated vehicles, or ROVs, can withstand the pressure at several thousand feet. They have cameras and other instruments that gather data about things such as salinity (salt content) and currents. They have manipulators, or arms, that take samples."

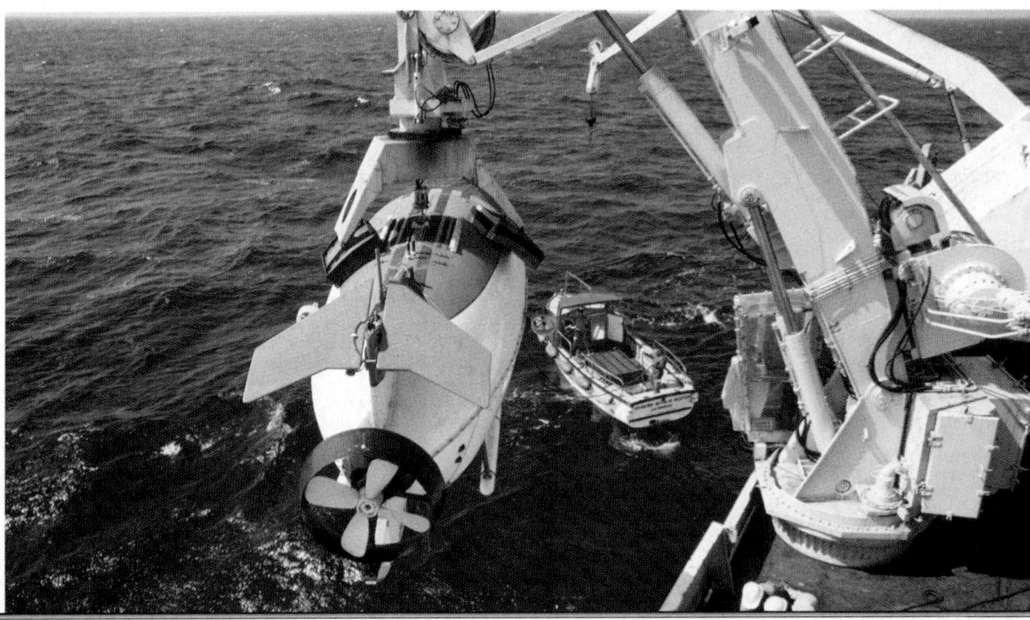

Figure 1-14 This manned submersible, MIR I, is used to study and explore to a depth of 6000 m.

Resource Manager

The following **Teacher Classroom Resources** can be used with Section 1-2:

Reproducible Masters

Activity Worksheets, pp. 3–4, 6 L2
Critical Thinking/Problem Solving, p. 1 L2
Enrichment, p. 2 L3
Home Involvement, p. 28 L2
Multicultural Connections, pp. 1–2 L2
Reinforcement, p. 2 L2
Study Guide, pp. 3–4 L1 ELL

Transparencies

Teaching Transparency 2 L2
Science Integration Transparency 1 L2

"Volcanoes are another frontier on Earth," Jared volunteered. "I read about a spiderlike, walking robot that was designed to explore the inside of an active volcano."

Hiromi spoke next. "Space is another hostile environment," he said. "I read about a robot that NASA developed that's able to travel over rough terrain. They tested it in a desert that resembled the surface of the moon. Once on the moon, scientists would operate it from Earth. But, one thing that makes this robot different is that it has its own navigation system. Suppose it were going toward a cliff. It would take 2.5 seconds for the scientists to signal the robot on the moon, and by that time, the robot might have fallen off. But, this robot can determine what is safe and what is dangerous. It might even ignore the operator's commands if it detects a hazard."

Figure 1-15 The terrain of Mars was photographed and explored by this rover.

"That's the kind of technology I read about," said Kashanna. "Scientists are making robots to explore hostile environments that don't need someone giving them commands all the time. One robot is called STAR—that's the Spiral Track Autonomous Robot. It travels on two giant screws—that's the 'spiral' part—so it can turn around in tight spaces and climb steep terrain that other robots can't. It has an onboard computer system that allows it to make decisions—that's the 'autonomous' part."

Figure 1-16 Technology, such as STAR, is developed to solve specific problems and explore unique environments.

Content Background

JASON is a submersible that is linked by cables and video cameras to scientists at the surface. JASON can collect seafloor samples and delicate objects such as those from shipwrecks. It can dive as deep as 6100 m. A person who dives with scuba gear can safely dive only about 40 m.

2 Teach

Using Science Words

Robot comes from the Czech word *robota,* meaning "work" or "slavery." Karel Čapek invented the word for a play he wrote about a man who creates robots to work in his factory.

The relative movements of the giant screws determine how STAR moves. The robot goes forward when the screws rotate in opposite directions. The robot goes sideways when they rotate in the same direction. The robot turns in place when one screw rotates while the other holds still.

Enrichment

Have students research for whom JASON was named and write a brief report about its namesake. How many other underwater vessels and spacecrafts can they find that were named after mythological characters? L2

GLENCOE TECHNOLOGY

Videodisc

The Infinite Voyage: Miracles by Design

Chapter 6 *"Smart Materials" and Their Construction* 3:00

Refer to the Teacher Guide for bar codes and teaching strategies.

Answer to Reading Check

Comparing is looking for similarities in objects or events. Contrasting is looking for differences.

Correcting Misconceptions

Students should be cautious when making a conclusion from an observation. Review the difference between an observation and an inference. An observation is careful watching. An inference is an explanation of why something happened. Set up a scenario to help illustrate some possible pitfalls of drawing conclusions from observations.

Making a Model

Visual-Spatial Have students design a robot from materials such as craft sticks and pipe cleaners. Have them first write a plan that describes what the robot will do and contains a blueprint of the design. L1 ELL COOP LEARN

PHYSICS INTEGRATION

Satellites and other spacecrafts tend to move in a straight line, like any other moving objects. But gravity pulls them back toward the ground. The result is that, at a certain velocity, the spacecraft travels in a circle. Occupants in an orbiting spacecraft seem to be weightless because they are falling at the same rate as the spacecraft.

Several students described other uses for technology in hostile environments such as mining and cleaning up nuclear or chemical spills.

Mr. Hayes pointed out that ROVs and robots help people "see" places they cannot visit directly. "Keep in mind," he said, "that people are seeing the data that are sent back, not the environments themselves. Even the camera images aren't the same as directly seeing something."

Using Science to Develop Technology

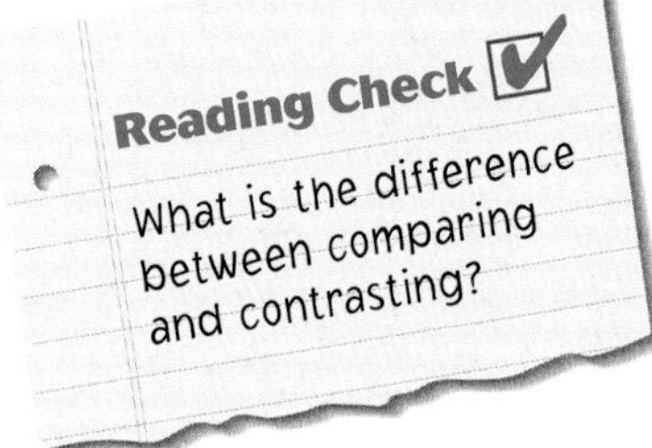

The class then discussed the science skills they thought would have been used to explore hostile environments. As they talked, Mr. Hayes wrote the science skills on the board. They agreed that the scientists who built the technology used various skills as they followed some scientific method. The scientists recognized a problem for which they wanted to design an ROV or robot. They compared and contrasted different designs and recorded their findings in their Science Journals, as shown in **Figure 1-17.** Comparing is looking for similarities in objects or events. Contrasting is looking for differences in objects or events. They also used math skills to design a model. For example, they might have calculated the energy needed for the machine to function or have drawn a scale model.

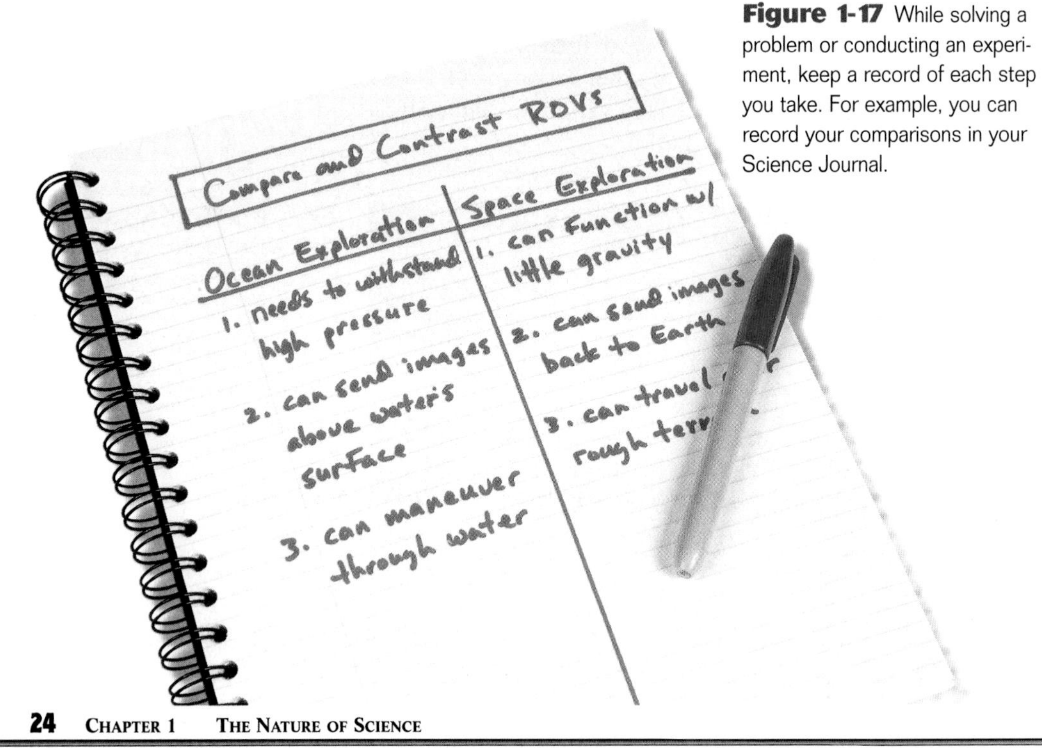

Figure 1-17 While solving a problem or conducting an experiment, keep a record of each step you take. For example, you can record your comparisons in your Science Journal.

Multiple Learning Styles

Linguistic Have students list the science skills used in designing and testing robots as identified in the text. Ask students to think of additional science skills. Then have them arrange the science skills within an outline of the five possible steps in the scientific method. They should recognize that the skills can be used in different steps.

After forming a hypothesis that their design would work, the scientists tested the hypothesis. They planned and conducted a controlled experiment. They used sequencing to test the model. A **sequence** is an arrangement of things or events in a certain order. For example, they might test the ROV's ability to grasp and hold an object, then test how much mass the robot's arm can support before dropping an object. They identified and controlled variables. Only one independent variable was changed at a time so that the scientists could pinpoint the cause of any malfunctions. They carefully observed the model's performance to record accurate data.

As they worked, the scientists constantly made inferences. An **inference** is an attempt at an explanation based on observations. This helped them know how to modify the design. As they worked, they made careful measurements. They might have measured the speed of the model or the size of objects it could lift.

Gravity acts on every particle in an object. The center of mass of an object is the point where an object will balance without tipping over. The position of the center of gravity affects an object's stability. When designing a robot, scientists must make sure the robot remains stable as it moves forward, stops, turns, and moves up or down an incline. If a robot is too heavy near the top, it may tip over easily.

Stability can be increased by lowering the center of gravity and by widening the base. Think of football players. They are harder to knock down if their knees are bent, which lowers their center of gravity, and when their feet are spread apart, which widens their base.

Finally, the scientists organized their data into tables and graphs so they could analyze the results and draw conclusions. Scientists use any number of graphs (line, bar, and circle) to help them interpret data. Communicating was an important skill throughout the process. The scientists worked as a team so they needed to share what they were doing and seeing.

interNET CONNECTION

Visit the Glencoe Science Web Site at **www.glencoe.com/sec/science** for information about ROVs that have been developed recently. In your Science Journal, compare and contrast the designs and functions of several ROVs.

Inferring Density

Procedure

1. Fill a large, transparent glass or glass jar with warm water. Gently add a drop of food coloring in the center of the water's surface.
2. Carefully float an ice cube on top of the food coloring. Observe for one minute. What happens to the food coloring?
3. Add two drops of food coloring directly on the ice cube to help you see what is happening.

Analysis

1. Record your observations in your Science Journal.
2. Describe where areas of water having different temperatures are located in a lake.

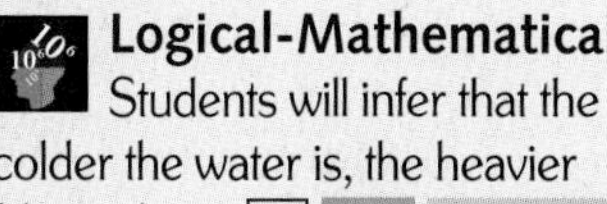

For additional help doing this activity at home, see the corresponding pages in the **Home Involvement** booklet.

Purpose

Logical-Mathematical Students will infer that the colder the water is, the heavier (denser) it is. L2 ELL COOP LEARN

Materials

a glass or glass jar, warm water, food coloring, ice cube

Teaching Strategies

- The container should be deep so that the food coloring can be observed as it moves to the bottom.
- Tell students to make their observations from the side of the container.

Analysis

1. Students will observe that the food coloring disperses rather uniformly in the warm water but tends to be carried downward when an ice cube is added. This happens because the ice cube cools part of the water, which becomes denser and sinks.
2. The cooler, denser water sinks below the surface of a lake. The colder the water is, the deeper it sinks. Warmer, less-dense water is located at and near the lake's surface.

Assessment

Performance Have students relate their observations to how the ocean waters behave at the North and South poles. *Cold air near the North and South poles cools the water, causing it to become denser than water in nonpolar areas. The cool, dense water sinks, forming a vertical current.* Use **Performance Assessment in the Science Classroom,** p. 17.

interNET CONNECTION

Internet Addresses

For Internet tips, see Glencoe's **Using the Internet in the Science Classroom.**

Across the Curriculum

Literature Have students locate a fictional book on robots and write a report. They should include an analysis of whether they think robots function or can be made to function as portrayed in the book. L2 P

3 Assess

Check for Understanding

Using Science Words

Have students compare and contrast the ways in which scientists who design technology and scientists who explore use science skills. L2

Reteach

Have students list the hostile environments that are explored with robots or ROVs. Ask them to describe characteristics of the robots or ROVs that make it possible for them to function in hostile environments. L2

Extension

 For students who have mastered this section, use the **Reinforcement** and **Enrichment** masters.

GLENCOE TECHNOLOGY

Videodisc

The Infinite Voyage: To the Edge of the Earth

Chapter 2 *Exploring Volcanoes: To the Center of the Earth* 10:00

Refer to the Teacher Guide for bar codes and teaching strategies.

Glencoe Science Voyages Interactive Videodisc—Earth

Side 2, Lesson 8 *Space Exploration*

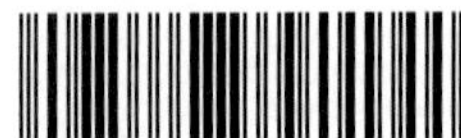

33975

36541

Refer to Videodisc Teacher Guide for additional bar codes.

Figure 1-18 When searching and exploring hostile environments, there are no right or wrong methods. Using your imagination and creativity, the world—and beyond—is yours to explore. **What might the researchers on this ocean-research vessel be studying in the Chukchi Sea (between Alaska and Russia)?**

Using Science Skills to Explore

From their assignment, the class decided that the scientists who explore hostile environments using technology do not necessarily follow step-by-step scientific methods. For example, scientists who explore the ocean, as in **Figure 1-18,** might not have a formal hypothesis. The question might be "What's down there?" But, the scientists still use a variety of science skills while following their particular method.

These skills might include observing (looking at the pictures transmitted), inferring (explaining what the pictures are), measuring (determining how much cable to use to lower the ROV in the water), interpreting (using meteorological data to forecast the weather at sea), and communicating (sharing information to position the ROV correctly).

Safe Science

Mr. Hayes emphasized that safety is an important reason for using technology to explore hostile environments. Having equipment become damaged is far less critical than risking a

Technology and Skills Have students think of a hostile environment they would like to explore that is not mentioned in the text. They should list the science skills they would use and the technology they would need. L2

Caption Answer

Figure 1-18 *Answers may vary. The researchers might be studying how the animals live in this cold climate. Or, they might be gathering information about the organisms that live in this part of the ocean. They might even be collecting meteorological data.*

person's life. The class discussed safety rules to follow when conducting science activities or experiments. They designed a poster called SAFE TIPS.

Start a lab activity only with your teacher's permission.
Ask your teacher if you do not understand a procedure.
Follow all safety symbols. Wear goggles during labs.
Engage in responsible behavior.

Tell your teacher immediately of accidents or injuries.
Identify the location of emergency equipment.
Put away chemicals and supplies properly.
Slant test tubes away from you and others when heating.

The students also created the slogan NO TIDE. TIDE stands for **T**asting chemicals, **I**nhaling chemicals, **D**rinking, or **E**ating. This helps them to remember that they should never eat or drink anything in a laboratory. It also reminds them to be cautious around fumes or vapors that could be harmful.

Figure 1-19 Lab equipment, like the test tube shown, must be handled properly.

Section Assessment

1. What are some ways technology is used to explore hostile environments?
2. What are some science skills scientists use to form a hypothesis about the design of an ROV or robot?
3. **Think Critically:** You have read about ways that scientists are like explorers. How are modern scientists different from explorers of the past?
4. **Skill Builder**
   Interpreting Data Suppose you have three plants that are supposed to bloom but are not blooming. You give one plant only water, another plant water and one type of plant fertilizer, and the third plant water and a different type of plant fertilizer. None of the plants bloom. How would you interpret your observations? If you need help, refer to Interpreting Data in the **Skill Handbook** on page 724.

Using Computers

Word Processing
Think of a problem faced by your community such as water pollution. Using a word processor, write a report describing how you would design a robot or an ROV to help solve the problem. If you need help, refer to page 732.

4. **Skill Builder**
   Answers may include that neither fertilizer helped the plants to bloom. Maybe too much or too little fertilizer was used. Or, maybe the plants need nutrients from another kind of fertilizer to bloom. More experiments need to be performed.

Assessment

Portfolio Have students design a poster that illustrates the importance of following a safety rule when performing science activities. Students may choose one or more rules. Use **Performance Assessment in the Science Classroom,** p. 73. P 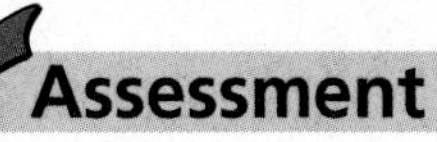

4 Close

Proficiency Prep

Use this quiz to check students' recall of section content.

1. **What is the application of knowledge learned through science?** *technology*
2. **What are the two reasons that data are organized into tables and graphs?** *to help you analyze the results and draw conclusions*
3. **What should you do before starting any lab activity?** *get permission from your teacher*

Section Assessment

1. ROVs and robots are sent to sites of nuclear accidents, deep into the ocean, into volcanoes, into outer space, and into mines.
2. Answers could include using numbers, comparing, contrasting, sequencing, graphing, and communicating.
3. **Think Critically** Past explorers did not have the technology that scientists have today. Also, scientists today have access to a lot more information because of research done in the past.

Using Computers

Answers will vary according to the community problem the student chooses to solve.

Activity 1·2

Purpose

Logical-Mathematical Students will compare densities of different liquids. L2 ELL COOP LEARN

Process Skills

communicating, making and using tables, making and using graphs, observing and inferring, measuring, using numbers, interpreting data, comparing and contrasting

Time

45 minutes

Materials

Students can use 4 g of table salt if the balance weighs only to the nearest gram.

Teaching Strategies

- Review correct use of the balance and how to read the scale.
- Designate separate graduated cylinders for each liquid and explain to students that any mixing could result in errors.

Answers to Questions

1. A ship would be able to carry more cargo in salt water because salt water is denser and will support more mass.
2. Oil is less dense than water so it will not support as much mass as water. The birds would have to expend more effort to stay afloat. The oil also would coat the feathers and make it more difficult for them to swim.

Activity 1·2 — Using Scientific Methods

Comparing Densities

Density is a physical property of a substance. It relates to how much material is contained within an object. In general, an object will float if its density is less than the density of the liquid. For example, ice floats in water because ice is less dense than water. How do the densities of various liquids compare?

Materials

- Graduated cylinder (100 mL)
- Balance and masses
- Water
- Cooking oil
- Table salt
- Paper cups
- Plastic spoons or stirrers
- Plastic beverage containers (to dispose of oil)

What You'll Investigate

How do the densities of liquids compare?

Goals

- **Infer** why objects float in some liquids but not in others.
- **Measure** liquids to determine their density.
- **Graph** the densities of the liquids.

Safety Precautions

Never taste anything during a lab activity. Wipe up any spills on the floor immediately.

Procedure

1. **Copy** the data table below for recording your measurements.
2. **Measure** the mass of a paper cup and record.
3. **Measure** 100 mL of water and pour it into the cup. Record the mass.
4. **Make** salt water by dissolving 3.5 g of table salt into 100 mL of tap water. Using a fresh paper cup each time, repeat steps 2 and 3 for the salt water and oil.
5. **Subtract** the mass of the cup to find the mass of the liquid. **Calculate** the density of each liquid using the formula, *density = mass/volume.* The unit used to express density is g/cm^3. One cubic centimeter occupies the same volume as one milliliter.
6. **Graph** your data using a bar graph. How does a graph help you analyze your results?

Conclude and Apply

1. Would a ship be able to carry more cargo in freshwater or salt water? Why?
2. Why might it be harder for aquatic birds to swim in an oil spill than in water?

Sample Data

Liquid's Measurement Data

Liquid	Mass of paper cup (g)	Mass of liquid in cup (g)	Mass of liquid only (g)	Volume of liquid (mL)	Density (g/cm^3)
Tap water	7	106	99	100	0.99
Salt water	6	110	104	100	1.04
Oil	6	98	92	100	0.92

Assessment

Performance Have students think of and perform another method for finding the relative densities of liquids. Use the **Performance Assessment in the Science Classroom,** p. 23.

28 CHAPTER 1 THE NATURE OF SCIENCE

The Circle of Life
From: *Nature's Numbers* by Ian Stewart

"We live in a universe of patterns. (See sample patterns at left.) *Every night the stars move in circles across the sky. The seasons cycle at yearly intervals. No two snowflakes are ever exactly the same, but they all have sixfold symmetry. Tigers and zebras are covered in patterns of stripes, leopards and hyenas are covered in patterns of spots. Intricate trains of waves march across the oceans; very similar trains of sand dunes march across the desert. Colored arcs of light adorn the sky in the form of rainbows, and a bright circular halo sometimes surrounds the moon on winter nights. Spherical drops of water fall from clouds."*

Throughout history, people of various cultures have tried to organize and explain the world around them. Long ago, an elder in the Sioux Nation observed the rings within tree trunks, the structure of birds' nests, the shape of raindrops, and other circular patterns around him. He believed that all of nature is like a circle.

In this Native American view of the world, all of the unique communities in nature interact as part of a whole. An elder and teacher of the Chippewa Nation taught that all living creatures are related because they have the same mother (Earth) and share her gifts. For example, plants take in carbon dioxide and release oxygen for organisms to breathe.

Many cultures that have lived close to nature share the world view that nature is based on circular patterns. In recent times, scientists have provided circular models of the solar system and the atom. Thus, we are finding that some native peoples' view of nature corresponds well with the findings of modern science.

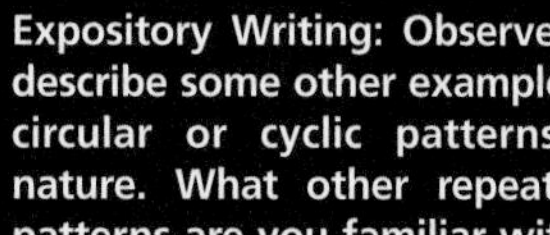

Expository Writing: Observe and describe some other examples of circular or cyclic patterns in nature. What other repeating patterns are you familiar with? What responsibility do humans have in "the circle of life"?

Think Critically

Look through your textbook for additional examples of cyclic patterns. Write down these examples and the pages on which they are located in your Science Journal.

Teaching Strategies

- **Reading** Have students read about various Native American peoples and have them compare each culture's world views about patterns and cycles.
- **Writing** Have different students research different ecosystems, such as a pond and a forest, for example. Have them create a pamphlet that lists at least six types of plants, animals, or other organisms that are found in a particular ecosystem. They should also include how the plants and animals are connected to each other. Finally, students should describe what the physical environment supplies to the plants and animals. They can create original drawings to illustrate the pamphlet.

NATIONAL GEOGRAPHIC

Reading & Writing in Science

Content Background

- The idea of circular patterns has many applications in understanding science. From the smallest objects of study to the largest, circular patterns in nature occur over and over again. In the Bohr model of the atom, electrons follow a circular path around the atomic nucleus. In the solar system, planets follow elongated circular orbits (ellipses) around the sun. Interacting forces keep electrons moving around the atomic nucleus and planets moving around the sun. When you observe galaxies or the rest of the stellar universe, you also observe circular patterns.
- Circular patterns are very important in the science of ecology. An ecosystem is an interacting network of living creatures and their surroundings. In such a network, oxygen, water, nutrients, and other elements are cycled and recycled many times. As these materials are cycled through living and nonliving parts of the ecosystem, they follow a circular path.

Science JOURNAL Have students share in class their observations of circular, cyclic, and repeating patterns. Have a class discussion of the role that humans play in the circle of life.

Source of Passage

Stewart, Ian, *Nature's Numbers: The Unreal Reality of Mathematics,* Portland, OR: Book News, 1995.

Reviewing Main Ideas can be used to preview, review, reteach, and condense chapter content.

Preview

Linguistic Have students try to answer the questions in their Science Journals. Use student answers as a source for discussion throughout the chapter.

Review

Interpersonal Have students answer the questions on separate pieces of paper and compare their answers with those of other students in the class.

Reteach

Visual-Spatial Have students look at the illustrations on these pages. Ask them to describe details that support the main ideas of the chapter found in the statement for each illustration.

OUT OF TIME?

Auditory-Musical If time does not permit teaching the entire chapter, use the information on these pages along with the chapter Audiocassettes to present the material in a condensed format.

Chapter 1 Reviewing Main Ideas

For a **preview** of this chapter, study this Reviewing Main Ideas before you read the chapter. After you have studied this chapter, you can use the Reviewing Main Ideas to **review** the chapter.

The Glencoe MindJogger, Audiocassettes, and CD-ROM provide additional opportunities for review.

Section 1-1 SCIENTIFIC PROBLEM SOLVING

A **scientific method** consists of steps taken to try to solve a problem. One step is to recognize a problem. A second step is to form a **hypothesis**—a prediction about a problem that can be tested. In another step, scientists test hypotheses by conducting controlled experiments or observational studies. In a controlled experiment, scientists change the **independent variable** and measure its effect on the **dependent variable.** Scientists who conduct observational studies do not change or control variables. They observe the relationships among variables. Another important step is to analyze data. Scientists organize data into tables or **graphs.** Often, the final step in a scientific method is to draw conclusions. A conclusion may or may not support the hypothesis. This does not necessarily mean the hypothesis is wrong. Sometimes, experiments are not designed correctly or unknown variables produce effects on the dependent variable. Scientists often must do many experiments and look at problems in different ways to find answers. ***Why should only one variable at a time be changed in a controlled experiment?***

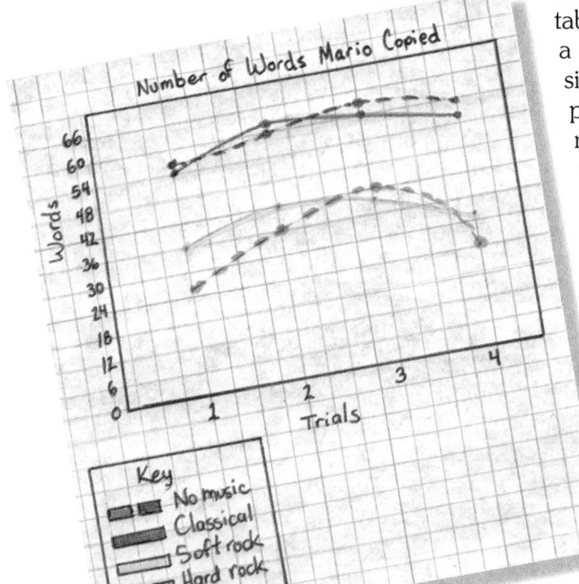

Cultural Diversity

Shamanic Medicine Principles of science are used to solve problems throughout the world. In the rain forests of Latin America, much of the healing is done by shamans, who are local people who use native plants for medicines. Today, researchers are working with shamans and investigating the medicinal value of the plants. Perhaps the cure to some diseases can be found in these plants.

Reading Check ✓

- *Variables, controls,* and *trials* are used in scientific experiments. Compare the meaning of each word in this context with its meaning in a nonscientific context.

Section 1-2

USING SCIENCE TO EXPLORE

A hostile environment is an environment in which the conditions are hazardous to people. Many places on Earth and in outer space cannot be explored directly by humans. Scientists have constructed robots and remotely operated vehicles, or ROVs, to go to sites of nuclear accidents, deep in the ocean, into volcanoes, into outer space, and into mines. People have increased their knowledge of hostile environments by analyzing data gathered through **technology.** Scientists who design technology to explore hostile environments use various approaches when forming a **scientific method** that will help them solve a particular problem. They design and conduct experiments to test models. Scientists who use technology to explore hostile environments use science skills. In both cases, scientists use science skills to solve a problem or to answer a question. ***Does a scientist always have to follow certain steps in a scientific method? Why or why not?***

Career CONNECTION

John Swallow, Forest Technician

John Swallow works in South Dakota's Black Hills National Forest. He is an Oglala Sioux and a forest technician. John determines which trees in the forest can be safely cut down and which trees must be saved. Much of the cutting of trees is done for thinning—to reduce competition between trees for light and nutrients—thus promoting quicker growth. John also works to conserve sensitive or endangered plants in logging areas. ***How can science help our understanding of the impact of logging on a forest?***

Answers to Questions

Section 1-1

Scientific Problem Solving The scientist will know that any effect on the dependent variable was caused by the independent variable.

Section 1-2

Using Science to Explore No, because following any scientific method step-by-step is not necessary to solve every problem or answer all questions.

GLENCOE TECHNOLOGY

CD-ROM

Glencoe Science Voyages Interactive CD-ROM

Chapter Summaries and Quizzes

Have students read the Chapter Summary then take the Chapter Quiz to determine whether they have mastered the chapter content.

Career CONNECTION

By using science skills, we can learn what methods are best to protect plants and trees in logging areas.

✓ Assessment

Portfolio Encourage students to place in their portfolios one or two items of what they consider to be their best work. Examples include:

- Across the Curriculum, pp. 14, 25
- Using Math, p. 19
- Assessment, p. 27 P

Performance Additional performance assessments may be found in **Performance Assessment** and **Science Integration Activities.** Performance Task Assessment Lists and rubrics for evaluating these activities can be found in Glencoe's **Performance Assessment in the Science Classroom.**

Using Vocabulary

1. k
2. e
3. i
4. b
5. c

*inter*NET CONNECTION To reinforce chapter vocabulary, use the **Study Guide for Content Mastery** booklet. Also available are activities for **Glencoe Science Voyages** on the Glencoe Science Web Site. **www.glencoe.com/sec/science**

Checking Concepts

6. A
7. C
8. D
9. C
10. D
11. B
12. A
13. B
14. A
15. B

Thinking Critically

16. Answers will vary. Answers might include that they would forget a step or that they would find it difficult to get ready on time.
17. The scientist wants to make sure it is the drug that is causing the effect.
18. Answers will vary. An example is observing the number and types of birds in their yards.
19. Following safety rules reduces the risk that someone could get injured.
20. Information helps scientist make better, educated guesses. They can base the hypothesis on what is already known.

Chapter 1 Assessment

Using Vocabulary

a. constant
b. control
c. dependent variable
d. graph
e. hypothesis
f. independent variable
g. inference
h. law
i. science
j. scientific method
k. sequence
l. technology
m. theory

Each of the following sentences is false. Make the sentence true by replacing the italicized word with a word from the list above.

1. A *control* is an approach taken to try to solve a problem.
2. An *inference* is a prediction about a problem that can be tested.
3. *Technology* is the process of trying to understand the world around you.
4. A *constant* is a standard to compare with.
5. The *independent variable* is the factor being measured in a controlled experiment.

Checking Concepts

Choose the word or phrase that best answers the question.

6. How is a hypothesis tested?
   A) experiment
   B) infer
   C) graph
   D) conclude
7. What will a scientist never do in an observational study?
   A) use technology
   B) record data
   C) control variables
   D) observe variables
8. What does a scientist use to reduce the effect of errors?
   A) observations
   B) constants
   C) hypotheses
   D) multiple trials
9. You decide to find out which of three cat foods your cat likes the best. What is the cat food that you try each time called?
   A) control
   B) dependent variable
   C) independent variable
   D) trial
10. How does a blind experiment differ from other experiments?
   A) Data are collected and interpreted.
   B) A hypothesis is formed after observations are made.
   C) Variables are changed to test the hypothesis.
   D) Some or all of the information is withheld from the subject.
11. What does it mean if an experiment does **NOT** support the hypothesis?
   A) The scientist has failed.
   B) The scientist has learned more.
   C) The scientist is not creative.
   D) The scientist did something wrong.
12. Why are ROVs and robots so useful?
   A) They gather information from hostile environments.
   B) They must follow commands from a person.
   C) They allow people to see hostile environments directly.
   D) They make all decisions on their own.
13. How do scientists who build ROVs use scientific methods?
   A) They test the effects of gravity.
   B) They work according to a sequence.
   C) They keep their data secret.
   D) They use every approach in the model.
14. What is a graph **NOT** used for?
   A) conducting an experiment
   B) interpreting data
   C) communicating information
   D) drawing conclusions
15. What is an explanation backed by experimental results?
   A) a control
   B) a theory
   C) a law
   D) a hypothesis

Thinking Critically

16. You use the skill of sequencing when you get ready for school. What might happen if you changed the order of your actions?
17. A scientist wants to test a new drug that might relieve symptoms for a particular illness. Why is it important to use a control?
18. Give an example of an observational study you can do at home.
19. Why is it important to follow safety rules in the lab?
20. Why do scientists often do research before forming a hypothesis?

Developing Skills

If you need help, refer to the **Skill Handbook.**

21. **Concept Mapping:** Complete the events chain that shows the order in which science skills might be used in observational studies. Use these phrases: *analyze data, ask a question, draw conclusions, observe,* and *record data.*

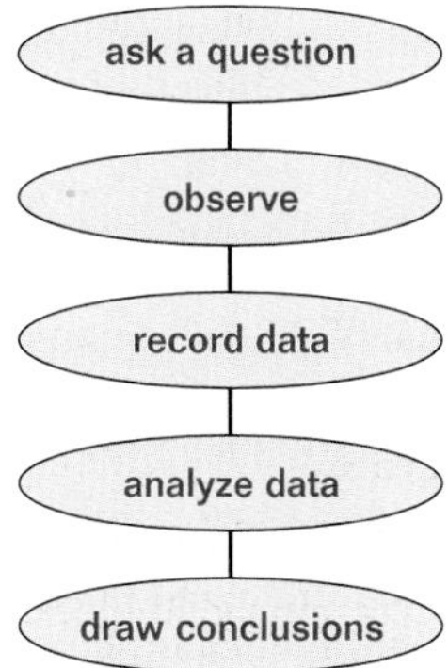

Test-Taking Tip

Beat the Clock and Then Go Back As you take a test, pace yourself to finish a few minutes early so you can go back and check over your work. You'll usually find a mistake or two. Don't worry. It's better to make corrections than to hand in a test with wrong answers.

Test Practice

Use these questions to test your Science Proficiency.

1. Michaela set up an experiment to find out if running would help her basketball game. Her basketball game did not improve. What can Michaela conclude from her results?
   A) Her hypothesis was wrong.
   B) Her results did not support the hypothesis.
   C) Running does not help a person do well in sports.
   D) A person who plays basketball should not run.
2. Alex eagerly arrived to science class early to begin his experiment. He set up the materials, popped a piece of gum into his mouth, and got right to work by himself, even though he wasn't quite sure of the procedure. What is the safety precaution that he ignored **FIRST?**
   A) He didn't put on goggles.
   B) He didn't ask questions about the correct procedure.
   C) He didn't get the teacher's permission to start the lab activity.
   D) He was eating during a lab activity.

THE PRINCETON REVIEW Test Practice

The Test-Taking Tip was written by The Princeton Review, the nation's leader in test preparation.

1. B
2. C

Developing Skills

21. See student page.

Bonus Question

Identify a problem or question that would best be answered by an observational study. *Answers will vary but may include the following: What are the mating behaviors of a particular animal? or What toys do infants prefer to play with?* **Identify a problem or question that would best be answered by a controlled experiment.** *Answers will vary but may include the following: How much medicine will supress a cough for four hours? or Which house paint holds up the best?*

Assessment Resources

The **Test Practice Workbook** provides students with practice in the format, concepts, and critical-thinking skills tested in standardized exams.

Reproducible Masters

Chapter Review, pp. 1–2 L2
Performance Assessment, p. 15 L2
Assessment, pp. 1–4 L2

Glencoe Technology

- Chapter Review Software
- Computer Test Bank
- MindJogger Videoquiz

Chapter 2 Inside the Atom

Section	Objectives	Activities/Features
Chapter Opener		**Explore Activity:** Observe Inside an Atom, p. 483
2-1 **The Story of the Atom** 4½ Sessions 2½ Blocks	1. **Describe** key experiments that led to the discovery of subatomic particles. 2. **Discuss** the development of the modern atomic model. 3. **Compare** the locations and properties of protons, electrons, and neutrons.	**MiniLab:** Modeling the Nuclear Atom, p. 491 **Skill Builder:** Concept Mapping, p. 493 **Using Math,** p. 493 **Activity 2-1:** Making a Model of the Invisible, p. 494
2-2 **The Nucleus** 4 Sessions 2 Blocks	4. **Describe** isotopes in terms of atomic number and mass number. 5. **Describe** the process of radioactive decay. 6. **Define** and use the term *half-life* in a sentence. 7. **Discuss** different uses of radioactive isotopes.	**Using Math,** pp. 496, 498 **MiniLab:** Graphing Half-Life, p. 499 **Life Science Integration,** p. 500 **Problem Solving:** Designing a Safe Container, p. 501 **Skill Builder:** Making Models, p. 502 **Using Computers,** p. 502 **Science and Society:** Preserving Food by Irradiation, p. 503 **Activity 2-2:** Half-Life, pp. 504–505

The number of recommended single-period sessions The number of recommended blocks
One session and one-half block are allowed for chapter review and assessment.

Activity Materials

Explore	Activities	MiniLabs
p. 483 clay, washers, screws, toothpick, nuts, bolts, paper towel	p. 494 sealed box, marble pp. 504–505 pennies, graph paper, pencil, graphing calculator	p. 491 compass, colored paper, glue, pencil, paper p. 499 calculator, pencil, paper

Need Materials? Contact Science Kit at 1-800-828-7777 or at www.sciencekit.com on the Internet.
For alternate materials, see the activity on the listed page.

Standards		Reproducible Resources	Technology
National	State/Local	Test Practice Workbooks are available for use with each chapter.	English and Spanish audiocassettes are available for use with each section.
National Content Standards: UCP1, UCP2, A2, B1, B2, C3, E2, G2, G3		**Activity Worksheets,** pp. 7–8, 11 **Enrichment,** p. 3 **Home Involvement,** p. 37 **Laboratory Manual,** pp. 9–10 **Reinforcement,** p. 3 **Study Guide,** pp. 5–7	**Section Focus Transparency 3** **Teaching Transparency 3** **The Infinite Voyage Series** **Glencoe Science Voyages Interactive Videodisc—Physical**
National Content Standards: A1, B1, B2, B3, E1, E2		**Activity Worksheets,** pp. 9–10, 12 **Critical Thinking/Problem Solving,** p. 2 **Enrichment,** p. 4 **Laboratory Manual,** pp. 11–12 **Multicultural Connections,** pp. 3–4 **Reinforcement,** p. 4 **Study Guide,** pp. 6–8	**Section Focus Transparency 4** **Teaching Transparency 4** **Science Integration Transparency 2** **Internet Connection,** p. 48 **Internet Connection,** p. 55 **The Infinite Voyage Series**

Key to Teaching Strategies

The following designations will help you decide which activities are appropriate for your students.

L1 Level 1 activities should be appropriate for students with learning difficulties.

L2 Level 2 activities should be within the ability range of all students.

L3 Level 3 activities are designed for above-average students.

ELL ELL activities should be within the ability range of English Language Learners.

COOP LEARN Cooperative Learning activities are designed for small group work.

P These strategies represent student products that can be placed into a best-work portfolio.

Multiple Learning Styles logos, as described on page 61T, are used throughout to indicate strategies that address different learning styles.

Assessment Resources

Chapter Review, pp. 3–4
Assessment, pp. 5–8
Performance Assessment in the Science Classroom (PASC)
MindJogger Videoquiz
Alternate Assessment in the Science Classroom
Performance Assessment, p. 16
Chapter Review Software
Computer Test Bank

Chapter 2 Inside the Atom

This is a representation of key blackline masters available in the Teacher Classroom Resources. See Resource Manager boxes within the chapter for additional information.

Transparencies

Section Focus Transparencies

3 SECTION FOCUS TRANSPARENCY Section 2-1

WHO IS IT?

Have you ever tried to guess someone's identity without looking? These girls are playing "who is it?" using their sense of touch to identify each other. They can touch each other's faces and feel each other's hair for clues.

1. List some things you know exist that you can't see. How do you know they exist?
2. What kinds of things might scientists study that they can't see?

L2

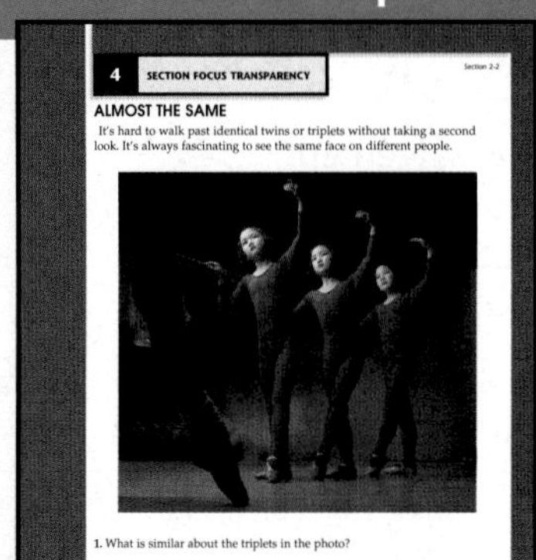

4 SECTION FOCUS TRANSPARENCY Section 2-2

ALMOST THE SAME

It's hard to walk past identical twins or triplets without taking a second look. It's always fascinating to see the same face on different people.

1. What is similar about the triplets in the photo?
2. Are there visible differences? Describe how they are different.
3. How might atoms look identical but vary in some way?

L2

Science Integration Transparencies

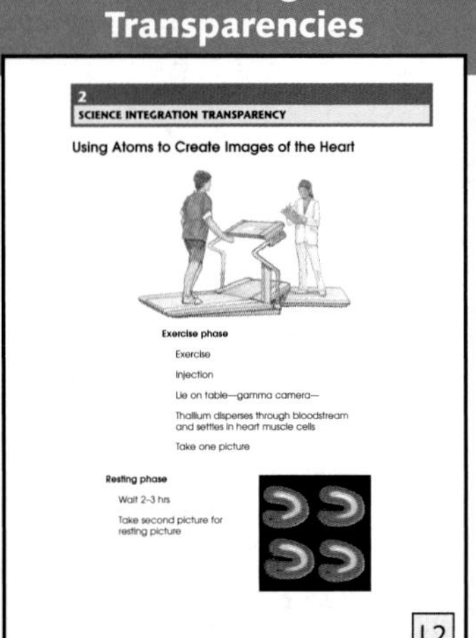

2 SCIENCE INTEGRATION TRANSPARENCY

Using Atoms to Create Images of the Heart

L2

Teaching Transparencies

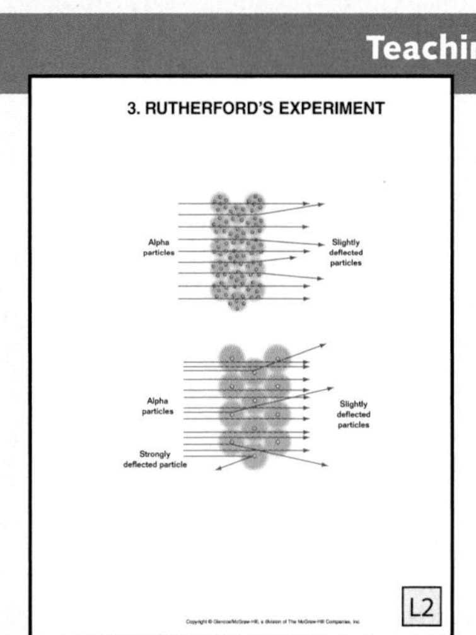

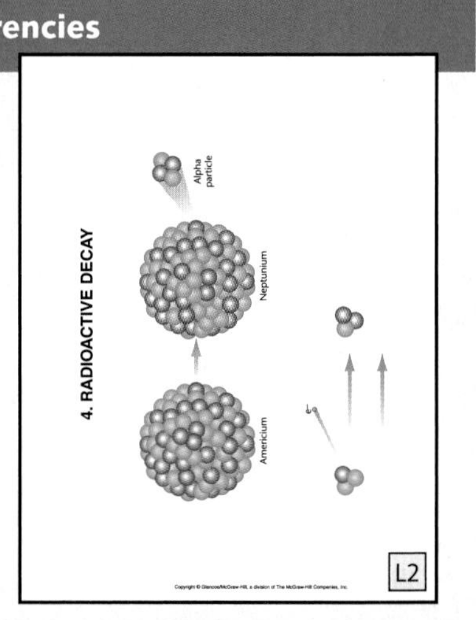

Meeting Different Ability Levels

Study Guide for Content Mastery

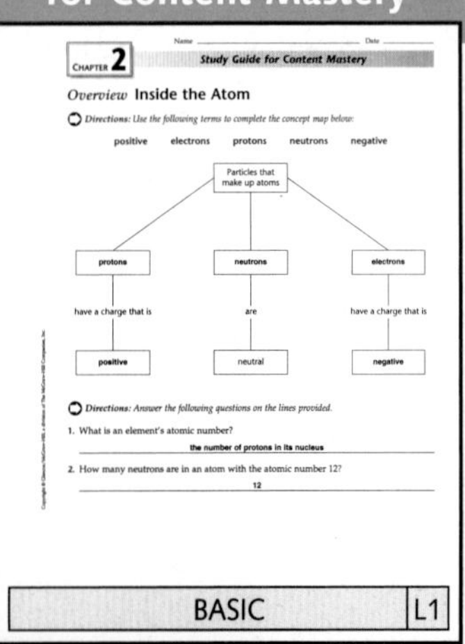

Name Date

Chapter 2 Study Guide for Content Mastery

Overview Inside the Atom

Directions: Use the following terms to complete the concept map below.

positive electrons protons neutrons negative

Particles that make up atoms

protons — have a charge that is — positive

neutrons — are — neutral

electrons — have a charge that is — negative

Directions: Answer the following questions on the lines provided.

1. What is an element's atomic number?
   the number of protons in its nucleus
2. How many neutrons are in an atom with the atomic number 12?
   12

BASIC L1

Reinforcement

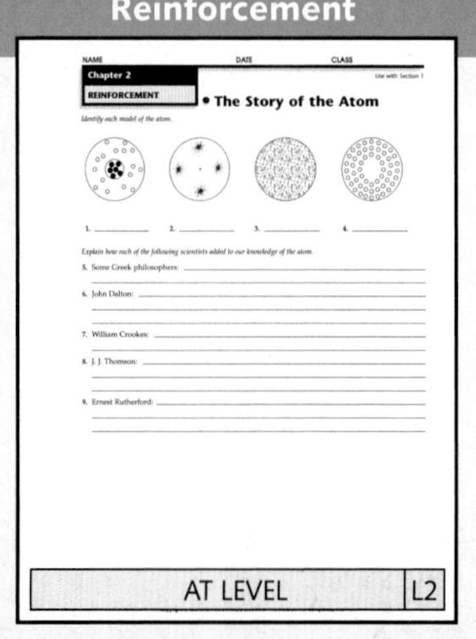

NAME DATE CLASS

Chapter 2 REINFORCEMENT Use with Section 1

• The Story of the Atom

Identify each model of the atom.

1. ______ 2. ______ 3. ______ 4. ______

Explain how each of the following scientists added to our knowledge of the atom.

5. Some Greek philosophers:
6. John Dalton:
7. William Crookes:
8. J. J. Thomson:
9. Ernest Rutherford:

AT LEVEL L2

Enrichment Worksheets

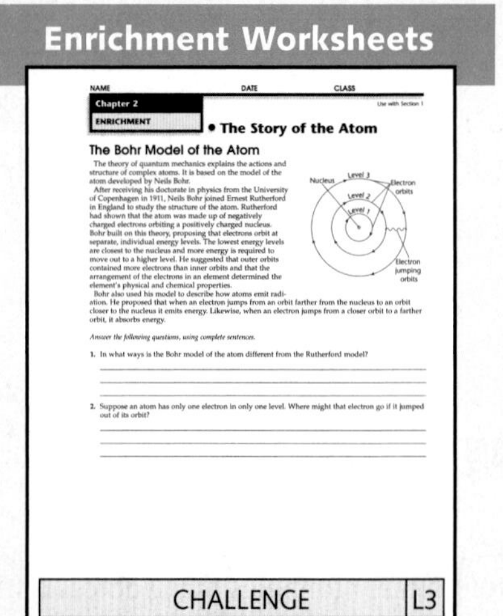

NAME DATE CLASS

Chapter 2 ENRICHMENT Use with Section 1

• The Story of the Atom

The Bohr Model of the Atom

The theory of quantum mechanics explains the actions and structure of complex atoms. It is based on the model of the atom developed by Neils Bohr.

After receiving his doctorate in physics from the University of Copenhagen in 1911, Neils Bohr joined Ernest Rutherford in England to study the structure of the atom. Rutherford had shown that the atom was made up of negatively charged electrons orbiting a positively charged nucleus. Bohr built on this theory, proposing that electrons orbit at separate, individual energy levels. The lowest energy levels are closest to the nucleus and more energy is required to move out to a higher level. He suggested that outer orbits contained more electrons than inner orbits and that the arrangement of the electrons in an element determined the element's physical and chemical properties.

Bohr also used his model to describe how atoms emit radiation. He proposed that when an electron jumps from an orbit farther from the nucleus to an orbit closer to the nucleus it emits energy. Likewise, when an electron jumps from a closer orbit to a farther orbit, it absorbs energy.

Answer the following questions, using complete sentences.

1. In what ways is the Bohr model of the atom different from the Rutherford model?
2. Suppose an atom has only one electron in only one level. Where might that electron go if it jumped out of its orbit?

CHALLENGE L3

Hands-on Activities

Activity Worksheets

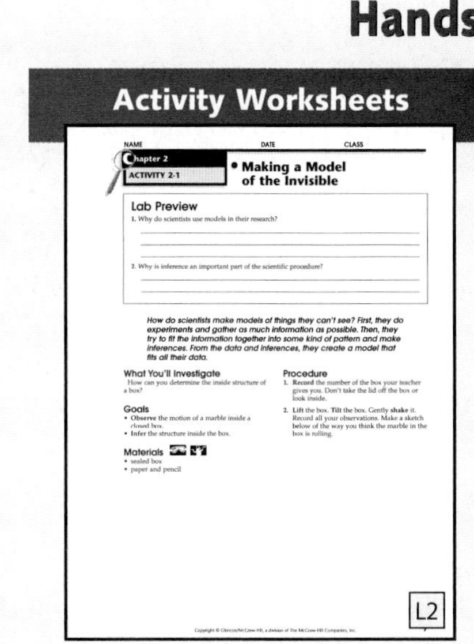
Chapter 2 ACTIVITY 2-1 • Making a Model of the Invisible

Lab Preview

1. Why do scientists use models in their research?

2. Why is inference an important part of the scientific procedure?

How do scientists make models of things they can't see? First, they do experiments and gather as much information as possible. Then, they try to fit the information together into some kind of pattern and make inferences. From the data and inferences, they create a model that fits all their data.

What You'll Investigate

Goals

Materials

Procedure

L2

Lab Manual

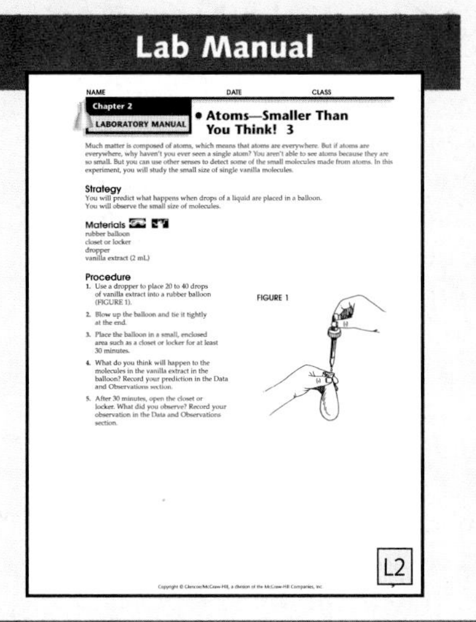
Chapter 2 LABORATORY MANUAL • Atoms—Smaller Than You Think! 3

Strategy

Materials

Procedure

FIGURE 1

L2

Accessibility

Spanish Resources

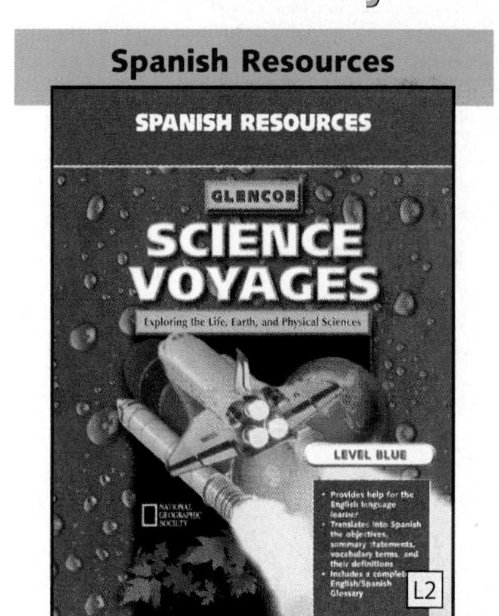
SPANISH RESOURCES

GLENCOE SCIENCE VOYAGES

Exploring the Life, Earth, and Physical Sciences

LEVEL BLUE

L2

Assessment

Performance Assessment

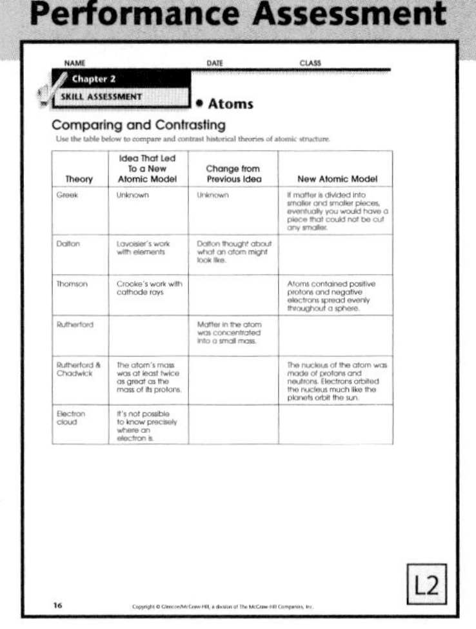
Chapter 2 SKILL ASSESSMENT • Atoms

Comparing and Contrasting

L2

Assessment

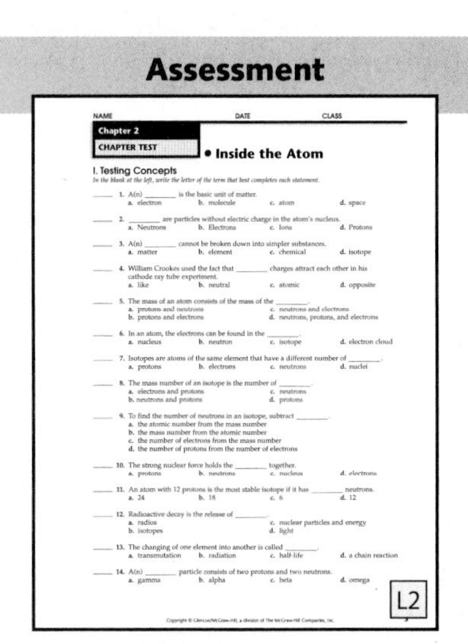
Chapter 2 CHAPTER TEST • Inside the Atom

I. Testing Concepts

L2

Chapter Review

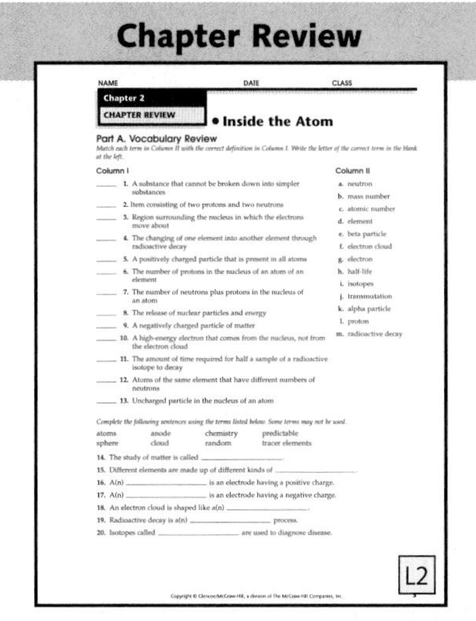
Chapter 2 CHAPTER REVIEW • Inside the Atom

Part A. Vocabulary Review

L2

Test Practice Workbook

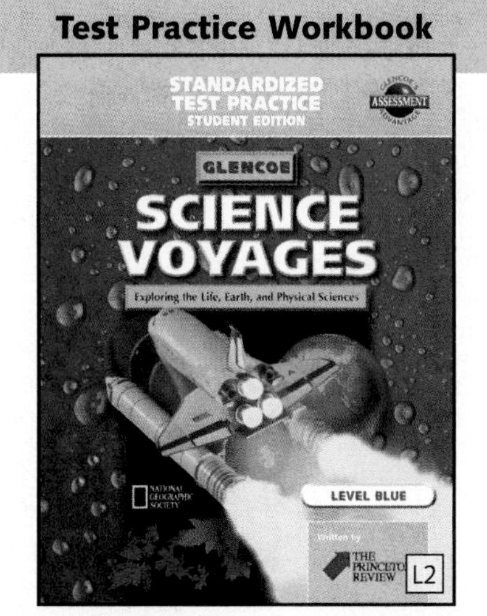
STANDARDIZED TEST PRACTICE STUDENT EDITION

GLENCOE SCIENCE VOYAGES

Exploring the Life, Earth, and Physical Sciences

LEVEL BLUE

THE PRINCETON REVIEW

L2

Extending Content

Critical Thinking/ Problem Solving

Multicultural Connections

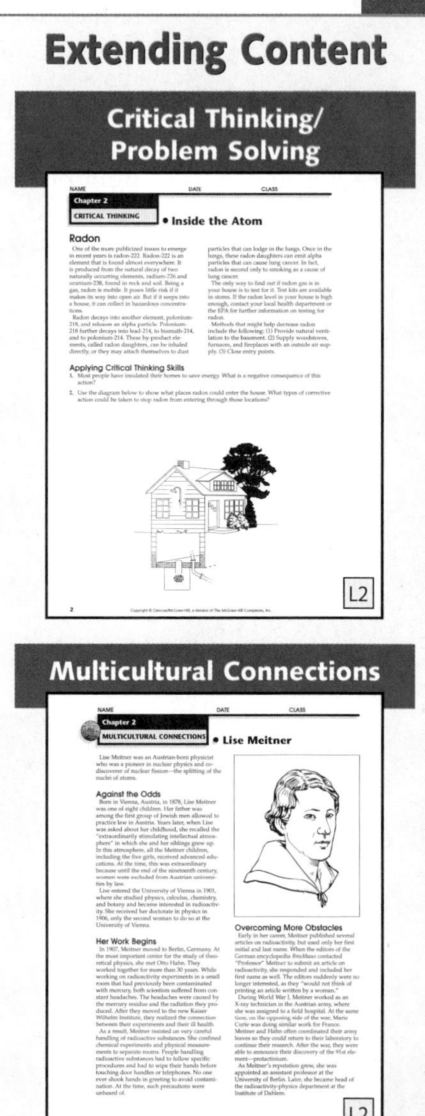
Chapter 2 CRITICAL THINKING • Inside the Atom

Radon

Applying Critical Thinking Skills

L2

Chapter 2 MULTICULTURAL CONNECTIONS • Lise Meitner

Against the Odds

Her Work Begins

Overcoming More Obstacles

L2

Inside the Atom

Helping You Prepare

Behind the Story (Section 2-1)

In his treatise, *A new System of Chemical Philosophy*, published in 1808 and 1810, John Dalton defined the atom, the basic unit of matter, as indivisible and unchangeable. Atoms combine with each other in a definite proportion and are neither created nor destroyed. Most of Dalton's theory still stands today; only the structure of the atom has been further described.

After Alessandro Volta had invented the first battery in 1800, Humphrey Davy and Michael Faraday began to take compounds apart by passing an electric current through them. Their experiments established a connection between matter and electricity. They found that the amount of a compound that decomposed was directly related to the amount of electric current that was passed through the compound. Faraday calculated mass-to-charge ratios for many known elements including the lightest, hydrogen.

In 1855, Heinrich Geissler invented the vacuum pump and ushered in experiments of another sort. Sir William Crookes used the Geissler pump to reduce the pressure of gas inside a glass tube to 0.01 of an atmosphere. The tube, fitted with electrodes at both ends and connected to a high-voltage source, was used to study the transmission of electricity through the gas. The nature of the rays that traveled from the cathode to the anode was a puzzle. The rays were deflected by a magnetic field and they were capable of causing a chemical reaction. Some scientists thought they were electromagnetic radiation of high frequency. Others wondered if they were charged particles.

J.J. Thomson settled the debate 25 years later when he undertook experiments that proved Dalton to be wrong about the indivisibility of the atom. Not only was Thomson able to definitely prove that cathode rays were negatively charged particles, he also determined their charge-to-mass ratio. All of the particles emitted from cathodes of different materials had the same charge-to-mass ratio—1.76×10^{11} coulombs per gram. This value was many times larger than the ratio Faraday had determined for the smallest element, hydrogen, in his electrolysis experiments. Thomson reasoned that either the charge of the cathode particles was much larger than that of the hydrogen ion, or the mass of the cathode particles was much smaller.

R.A. Millikan showed that the latter was true. Millikan sprayed charged oil droplets into a viewing chamber and watched the drops as he applied an upward electric force that just matched the downward force of gravity on the drops. The magnitude of the electric field, when a drop was held motionless in air, was a measure of the charge on the drop. Millikan found that all the drops had charges that were multiples of 1.6×10^{-16} coulombs. This value was taken to be the unit charge and the charge on the electron. From the charge-to-mass ratio, the mass of the electron was then found to be 9.1×10^{-28} g.

Ernest Rutherford was studying alpha radiation in the new field of radioactivity when he carried out the alpha particle scattering experiment that led to a description of the nuclear atom. Quantitative measurements of alpha particle scattering using various metal foils allowed Rutherford to calculate the total charge on the nuclei of the metals. This new information resulted in the reordering of the periodic table which, until that time, listed the elements in order of atomic mass.

GLENCOE TECHNOLOGY

CD-ROM

Glencoe Science Voyages Interactive CD-ROM

Chapter Summaries

Use the Chapter Summary to introduce, teach, or review chapter material.

NATIONAL GEOGRAPHIC Teacher's Corner

Index to NATIONAL GEOGRAPHIC Magazine

The following articles may be used for research relating to this chapter:

"Worlds Within the Atom," by John Boslough, May 1985.

"Unlocking the Climate Puzzle," by Curt Suplee, May 1998.

Radioactive Decay (Section 2-2)

Rutherford identified three kinds of nuclear radiation—alpha, beta, and gamma. In alpha and beta radiation, energy is emitted along with a particle. Gamma radiation does not involve a particle, only high-energy electromagnetic radiation similar in frequency and energy to X rays. Besides their differences in charge and mass, the three types of radiation can be further characterized by velocity and penetrating power. Alpha particles are ejected at high speed, but can be stopped by a sheet of aluminum (a sheet thicker than the foil used in Rutherford's experiment). Beta particles can have speeds approaching the speed of light and can penetrate several millimeters of aluminum. Gamma rays travel at the speed of light and penetrate at least 30 cm of lead.

Transmutation (Section 2-2)

Rutherford is credited with the first artificial transmutation. He bombarded nitrogen-14 with alpha particles and obtained oxygen-17. To effect more difficult transmutations, cyclotrons and linear accelerators have been built to boost the energy of the bombarding particles. In this way, many isotopes, including the elements beyond uranium on the periodic table, have been synthesized.

Transmutation and Nuclear Power (Section 2-2)

In 1938, scientists tried to create a new synthetic element by bombarding uranium with neutrons. However, instead of absorbing the neutron to become a heavier nucleus, the uranium nucleus split into two nuclei of intermediate size. In the process, which is now called fission, a large amount of energy was quickly released. Scientists realized that fission reactions, such as this one, could be used to make an enormously destructive bomb. The first such atom bomb brought World War II to a close.

In a nuclear power plant using uranium-235, neutrons are slowed using moderators. Control rods in the reaction chamber change the rate of the reaction. The released energy is used to convert water to steam that turns turbines and creates electricity. Unfortunately, the by-products of nuclear reactions are radioactive and must be permanently kept from contact with people and the environment.

SCIENCE UPDATE

For current events or science in the news, access the Glencoe Science Web Site at **www.glencoe.com/sec/science**

Half-Life (Section 2-2)

Half-lives vary from millionths of a second to billions of years. In general, decay processes that occur by gamma emission are the shortest. Some are too short to measure, for example, on the order of 10^{-14} s. Decay processes by alpha and beta emission tend to have longer half-lives.

Teacher to Teacher

"Multicolored modeling clay is an inexpensive and reusable material for middle school students to use to visualize science concepts. Students use their creativity to make 'atoms' that have touchable protons, neutrons, and electrons."

Petrolia Moss
Petrolia Moss, Teacher
North Heights Junior High
Texarkana, AR

CHAPTER 2
Inside the Atom

CHAPTER OVERVIEW

Section 2-1 This section describes the development of the model of the nuclear atom and defines *electron, proton,* and *neutron.*

Section 2-2 Nuclear transmutation by alpha and beta emission are discussed. The uses of radioactive isotopes for energy and medical purposes are presented.

Chapter Vocabulary

element
electron
proton
neutron
electron cloud
atomic number
isotope
mass number
radioactive decay
half-life

Theme Connection

Stability and Change In this chapter, students will learn that the nucleus of an atom can undergo changes that can be useful and dangerous. These changes have a predictable pattern.

If time does not permit teaching the entire chapter, use Reviewing Main Ideas on pp. 58–59.

CHAPTER 2 Inside the Atom

Reading Check

Before reading this chapter, list the vocabulary terms for each section. As you read, write a definition next to each term.

34

Multiple Learning Styles

Look for the following logos for strategies that emphasize different learning modalities.

Linguistic Using Science Words, pp. 38, 44, 49; Science Journal, pp. 39, 43; Multiple Learning Styles, p. 41; Activity, p. 41; Across the Curriculum, p. 48; Enrichment, p. 52; Preview, p. 58

Logical-Mathematical Activity, p. 46

Visual-Spatial Activity, pp. 38, 49, 56–57; Quick Demo, p. 39; Inclusion Strategies, p. 42; Reteach, pp. 44, 58; Assessment, p. 45; MiniLab, p. 51

Auditory-Musical Out of Time, p. 58

Kinesthetic Explore Activity, p. 35; Making a Model, pp. 37, 48; MiniLab, p. 43

Interpersonal Using an Analogy, p. 42; Reteach, p. 52; Review, p. 58

Intrapersonal Inclusion Strategies, p. 49

Explore Activity

By day, they are clear, glass tubes filled with colorless gases. Flip the switch, and they instantly light up the night with their messages. This is advertising magic! Electricity paints pictures that you can't help but notice. What's going on? What are the gases in the tubes? What are they made of, and why do they glow with color at the flick of a switch?

Observe Inside an Atom

1. Your teacher will give you a piece of clay and some pieces of metal. Count the pieces of metal.
2. Bury these pieces in the modeling clay so they can't be seen.
3. Exchange clay balls with another group.
4. With a toothpick, probe the clay to find out how many pieces of metal are in the ball and what shapes they are.

Science Journal

In your Science Journal, sketch the shapes of the metal pieces as you identify them. How does the number of pieces you found compare with the number that were actually in the clay ball? How do their shapes compare?

Explore Activity

Purpose

Kinesthetic Use this Explore Activity to help students discover how scientists find out about things they can't see. L2 COOP LEARN

Preparation

Obtain small, blunt objects; clay; toothpicks; and paper towels.

Materials

small metal objects such as washers, nuts, and bolts; modeling clay; toothpick; paper towels

Teaching Strategies

Demonstrate step 4 to show students how to use a probe to feel things that can't be seen.

Answers will vary. Encourage students to draw pictures of the objects and then compare their pictures with the actual object taken from the clay.

Assessment

Oral Have students work in groups to share their results. Ask them to compare their evidence and to discuss how they discovered what each hidden item was. Use **Performance Assessment in the Science Classroom,** p. 17.

Assessment Planner

Portfolio

Refer to p. 59 for suggested items that students might select for their portfolio.

Performance Assessment

See p. 59 for additional Performance Assessment options.
Skill Builder, p. 45
MiniLab, pp. 43, 51
Activity, 2-1, p. 46; 2-2, pp. 56–57

Content Assessment

Section Assessment, pp. 45, 54
Chapter Assessment, pp. 60–61
Proficiency Prep, pp. 45, 54

SECTION 2-1

Prepare

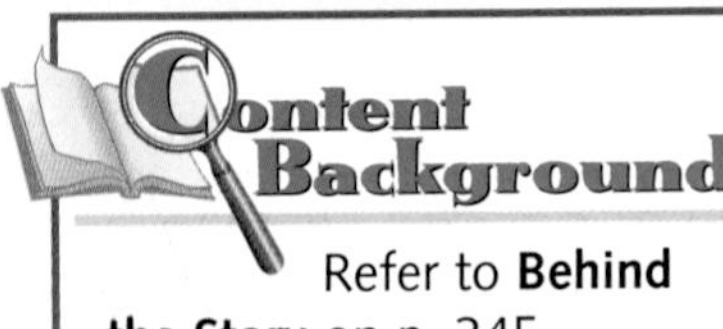

Refer to **Behind the Story** on p. 34E.

Preplanning

Refer to the **Chapter Organizer** on pp. 34A–B.

1 Motivate

Bellringer

Before presenting the lesson, display **Section Focus Transparency 3** on the overhead projector. Use the accompanying **Focus Activity** worksheet. L2 ELL

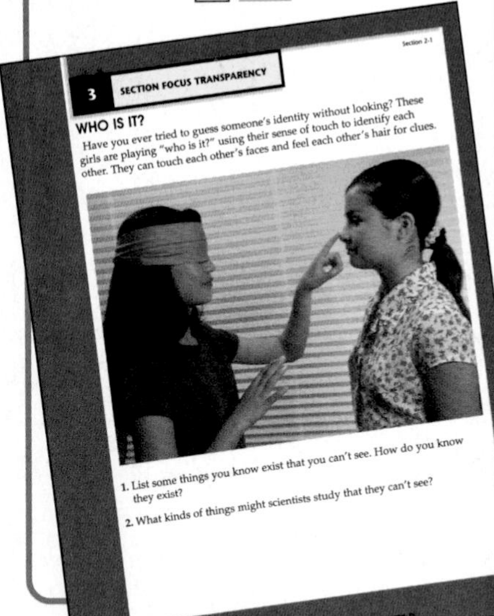

Section 2-1

3 SECTION FOCUS TRANSPARENCY

WHO IS IT?

Have you ever tried to guess someone's identity without looking? These girls are playing "who is it?" using their sense of touch to identify each other. They can touch each other's faces and feel each other's hair for clues.

1. List some things you know exist that you can't see. How do you know they exist?
2. What kinds of things might scientists study that they can't see?

2-1 The Story of the Atom

What You'll Learn

- How scientists discovered subatomic particles
- How today's model of the atom developed
- The structure of the nuclear atom

Vocabulary

element
electron
proton
neutron
electron cloud

Why It's Important

- Atoms make up everything in your world.

An Old Idea

Trying to find out what something looks like when you can't see it is not a new challenge. People began wondering about matter more than 2500 years ago. Some of the Greek philosophers thought that matter was composed of tiny particles. They reasoned that you could take a piece of matter, cut it in half, cut the half-piece in half again, and continue to cut again and again. Eventually, you wouldn't be able to cut any more. You would have only one particle left. They named these particles atoms, a term that means "cannot be divided." Think about matter as being like a string of beads. If you keep dividing the string into pieces, you eventually come to one single bead.

The Greek philosophers didn't try to prove their theories by doing experiments as scientists now do. Today, scientists like the one in **Figure 2-1** will not accept a theory that is not supported by experimental evidence. But even if the Greeks had experimented, they could not have proven the existence of atoms. People had not yet discovered much about what is now called chemistry, the study of matter. The kind of equipment needed to study matter was a long way from being invented. Even 2000 years later, atoms were a mystery.

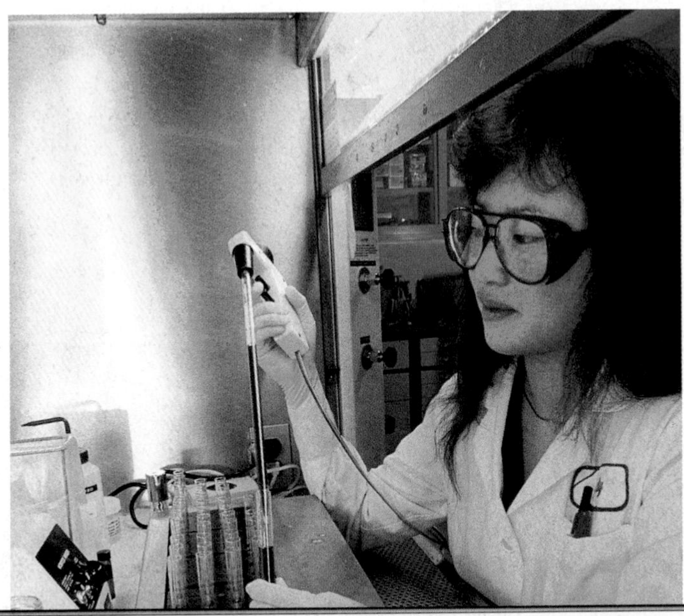

Figure 2-1 Modern scientists design and carry out experiments to either support or disprove new hypotheses.

Resource Manager

The following **Teacher Classroom Resources** can be used with Section 2-1:

Reproducible Masters

Activity Worksheets, pp. 7–8, 11 L2
Enrichment, p. 3 L3
Home Involvement, p. 37 L2
Laboratory Manual, pp. 9–10 L2
Reinforcement, p. 3 L2
Study Guide, pp. 5–7 L1 ELL

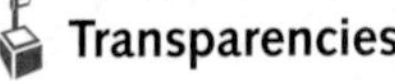

Transparencies

Teaching Transparency 3 L2

Figure 2-2 The 1700s were years of great interest in science. Scientists created laboratories like this one to test their theories by doing experiments.

Dalton's Atomic Model

For a long time after the ancient Greeks, people didn't think much about atoms. Finally, during the eighteenth century, scientists in laboratories like the one in **Figure 2-2** again began debating the existence of atoms. Chemists were learning about matter and how it changes. They were putting substances together to form new substances and taking substances apart to find out what they were made of. They found that there was a limit to how far a substance could be broken down. Certain substances couldn't be broken down into simpler substances. Scientists came to realize that all matter is made up of elements. An **element** is a substance that cannot be broken down into simpler substances. John Dalton, an English schoolteacher, combined the idea of elements with the Greek theory of the atom. He proposed that matter is made up of atoms, that atoms cannot be divided into smaller pieces, and that all the atoms of an element are exactly alike, and different elements are made of different kinds of atoms. For example, iron is an element made of iron atoms. Silver, another element, is made of silver atoms. Dalton pictured an atom as a hard sphere that was the same throughout, something like a tiny marble. His model is shown in **Figure 2-3.**

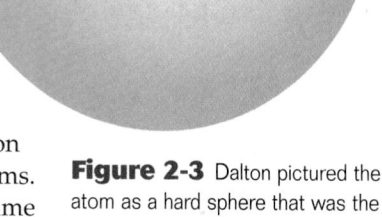

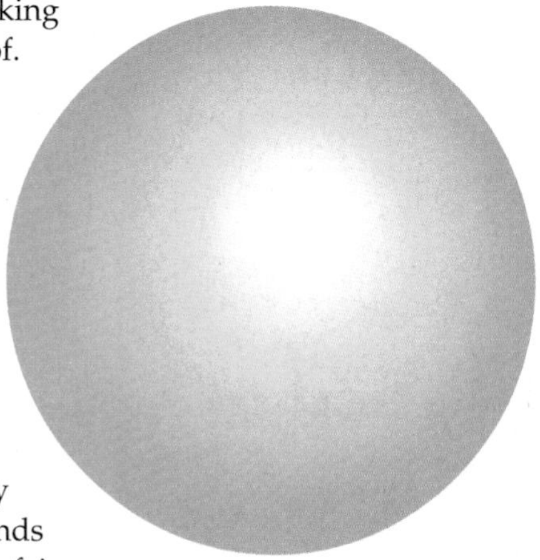

Figure 2-3 Dalton pictured the atom as a hard sphere that was the same throughout.

Where's the proof?

By the second half of the nineteenth century, scientists had equipment to test Dalton's theory of the atom. In 1870, the English scientist William Crookes did experiments with a glass tube that had almost all the air removed from it. The glass tube had two pieces of metal called electrodes sealed in the glass. The electrodes were connected to a battery by wires.

Tying to Previous Knowledge

Elicit from students that they already know a lot about matter from having observed various substances and from having used matter and measured it. Now they will find out what's inside matter that makes it behave the way it does.

2 Teach

Making a Model

Kinesthetic As students learn the story of the atom, have them construct a three-dimensional model of the atom. They can use materials such as clay, paper, aluminum foil, Velcro, toothpicks, and wire. The model should include a nucleus with removable parts (protons and neutrons) and an electron cloud.

GLENCOE TECHNOLOGY

CD-ROM

Glencoe Science Voyages Interactive CD-ROM

Explorations

Have students do the interactive exploration *How can you simulate the radioactive half-life of an element?*

Content Background

The experiments that laid the foundation for Dalton's model of the atom also provided evidence to support the law of conservation of matter. This law states that although matter changes in a chemical reaction, the same number and kind of atoms present before the chemical reaction still remain after the reaction. Another way of stating this law is that matter can neither be created nor destroyed.

Caption Answer

Figure 2-4 *a stream of particles*

Activity

Visual-Spatial As you move ahead in your discussion of the story of the atom, have students create a time line of events that led to the modern model of the atom. Include the date or time period (if given) and contributions of John Dalton, William Crookes, J.J. Thomson, and Ernest Rutherford to the discovery of the neutron. L2 COOP LEARN

The green glow in Crookes's tube was the result of the action of the energetic electrons on the glass of the tube. The electrons striking the walls of the tube caused the glass to glow. Where the glass was shielded from the electrons by the cross-shaped object, the glass did not glow. Students should be aware that the green glow is not the electrons themselves, but evidence of their presence.

Using Science Words

Linguistic Have students find out about other devices that have an anode and a cathode. Have them summarize what is similar in all the devices they list. Students may list batteries, fuel cells, CRTs, and X-ray tubes. In all, electric current passes from one electrode to the other. L3

Teacher FYI

In 1933, Wolfgang Pauli proposed that another particle called a neutrino was emitted in some nuclear reactions. The neutrino is a massless or almost massless neutral particle. Its existence was not verified until 1956.

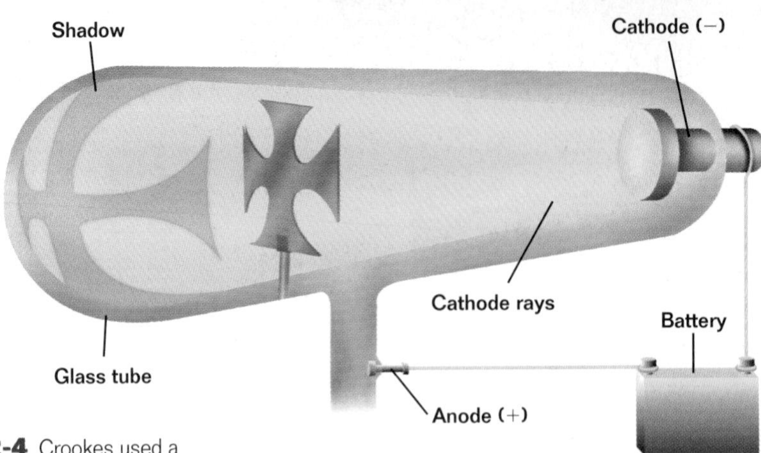

Figure 2-4 Crookes used a glass tube containing only a small amount of gas. When the glass tube was connected to a battery, something flowed from the negative electrode on the right to the positive electrode. **Was this "something" light or a stream of particles?**

An electrode is a piece of metal that can conduct electric current. One electrode, called the anode, has a positive charge. The other, called the cathode, has a negative charge. In Crookes's tube, the metal cathode was a disk at the right end of the tube. Beyond the anode was an object shaped like a cross, as you can see in **Figure 2-4.** When the battery was connected, the glass tube suddenly lit up with a greenish glow. A shadow of the cross-shaped object appeared at the left end of the tube. The shadow indicated that something was traveling in a straight line from the cathode to the anode, just like the beam of a flashlight. The object was getting in the way of the beam and casting a shadow just like the shadow you would get of your hand if you put it in the beam of a flashlight or movie projector. You can see this in **Figure 2-5.**

Was the greenish glow light? Or, was it a stream of charged particles? This question was answered by placing a magnet beside the tube. In **Figure 2-6,** you can see that the beam is bent by the magnet. Light is not bent by a magnet, so the

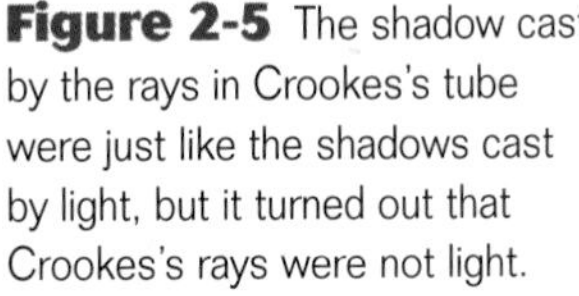

Figure 2-5 The shadow cast by the rays in Crookes's tube were just like the shadows cast by light, but it turned out that Crookes's rays were not light.

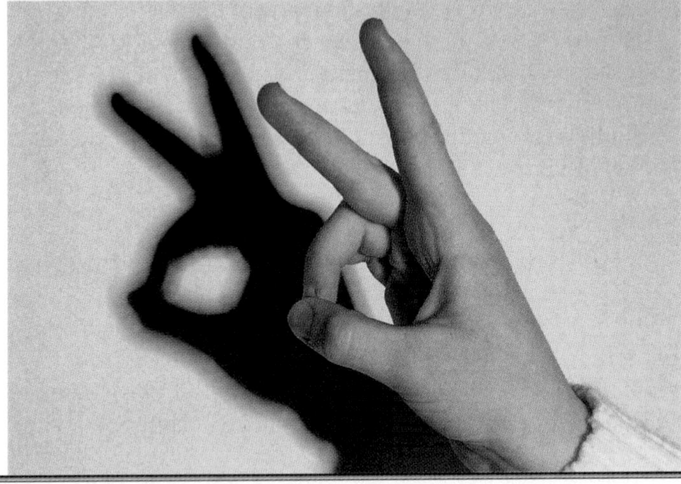

Guided Reading Strategy

Metacognition Journal In this strategy, each student analyzes his or her own thought processes. Have students divide the paper in half. On the left, have them record what they learned about a topic. On the right, have them record why they think it's important that they learned it. Have students write a Metacognition Journal about a concept in this section; for example, they could write about the nuclear atom.

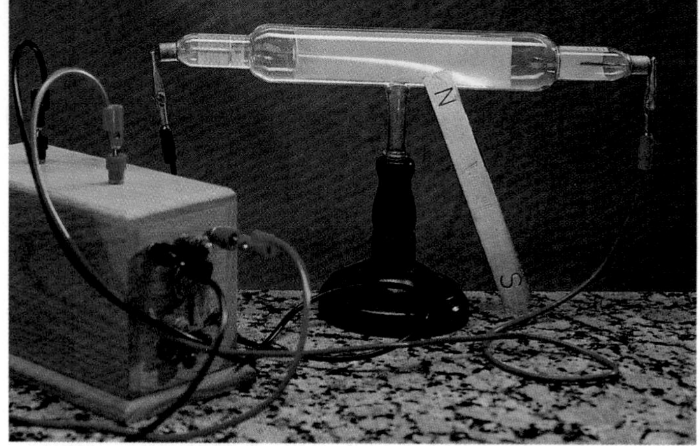

Figure 2-6 When a magnet is placed near a glass tube similar to the one Crookes used, the rays bend. **A magnet cannot bend light, so what must be the "something" that causes the green glow?**

beam is not light. Therefore, the beam must be negatively charged particles of matter that came from the metal of the cathode. How was it posssible to know that the particles were negatively charged? Opposite charges attract each other. These particles were attracted to the positively charged anode, so the particles must be negatively charged. These rays were called cathode rays because they were produced at the cathode. Crookes's tube is known as a cathode-ray tube, or CRT. It's the forerunner of all TV and computer display screens like the one in' **Figure 2-7.**

J. J. Thomson's Contribution

You can imagine how excited scientists were when they heard the results of Crookes's work. But, many scientists were not convinced that the cathode rays were streams of particles. In 1897, J. J. Thomson, an English physicist, repeated the CRT experiment using different metals for the cathode and different gases in the tube. But, the same negatively charged particles were produced regardless of the metal used for the cathode or the gas in the tube. Thomson concluded that cathode rays are negatively charged particles of matter. These particles are now called **electrons.** He also inferred that electrons are a part of every kind of atom because they are produced by every kind of cathode material. Thomson's experiments also proved that atoms are not impossible to divide because atoms are made up of even smaller particles.

Figure 2-7 Crookes's tube became known as a cathode-ray tube because the particles he observed started at the cathode and traveled to the anode. There is a cathode-ray tube or CRT in every TV and computer monitor.

Quick Demo

Visual-Spatial Place a magnet and some iron filings on the overhead projector to demonstrate the magnet's ability to exert a force on an object at a distance. The electric force that affects the stream of particles in the cathode-ray tube is not the same as the magnetic force of the magnet on iron filings, but students can see from this demo that the magnet can act on the iron filings without touching them, just as the anode can act on the cathode-ray particles without contact.

Caption Answer

Figure 2-6 *The "something" must be a stream of negatively charged particles.*

VISUAL Learning

Figure 2-6 **How did Crookes know that the beam was not light?** *The beam bent, and light does not bend in the presence of a magnet.* **How is this related to his discovery that the beam had electric charges?** *Negatively charged particles of matter do bend when they come close to a magnet.*

Figure 2-7 **How are television tubes and computer display screens related to the cathode-ray tube that Crookes used?** *TVs and computer monitors contain cathode-ray tubes, so electrons must be part of how pictures and information appear on these screens.*

Crookes's Evidence Have students write a paragraph describing how Crookes's experiment demonstrates the presence of a negative particle. L2 P

Teacher FYI

Students will find it easier to deal with this abstract material if you use physical models of atoms or chalkboard drawings as often as possible while you are discussing the parts of the atom.

VISUAL Learning

Figure 2-8 In the Thomson model of the atom, what do the raisins represent? *electrons* **Does the atom have a positive or negative charge, or is it neutral?** *The atom is neutral because the positive charges of the protons are balanced by the negative charges of the electrons.*

GLENCOE TECHNOLOGY

Videodisc

The Infinite Voyage: Unseen Worlds

Chapter 6 *Studying the Basic Building Blocks: The Atom* 2:00

Refer to the Teacher Guide for bar codes and teaching strategies.

Thomson's Atomic Model

Thomson's experiments answered some of the questions scientists had about atoms. But, they led to another scientific puzzle. If atoms contain one or more negatively charged particles, then matter, which is made of the atoms, also should be negatively charged. But, it isn't. How can this be explained? Could it be that atoms also contain one or more positively charged particles? The negatively charged electrons and the unknown positively charged particles would then neutralize each other in the atom. Thomson continued his experiments and found evidence for the existence of a particle that has the same mass and charge as a positively charged hydrogen atom. However, it took until 1920 for scientists to identify this particle as a proton. A **proton** is a positively charged particle that is present in all atoms. A proton is almost 2000 times heavier than an electron.

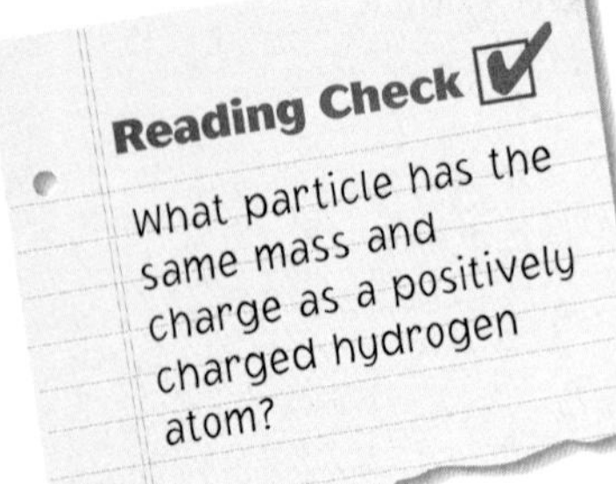

Using his new findings, Thomson revised Dalton's model of the atom. Instead of a solid ball that was the same throughout, Thomson pictured a sphere that contained all the positive charge. The negatively charged electrons were spread evenly throughout the sphere. You can compare Thomson's idea of the atom to the ball of raisin-cookie dough shown in **Figure 2-8.** The cookie dough represents the protons, which are most of the mass of the atom. The raisins represent the electrons. They are scattered throughout the dough and make the atom electrically neutral.

Figure 2-8 Well-mixed cookie dough is a model for the J.J. Thomson atom.

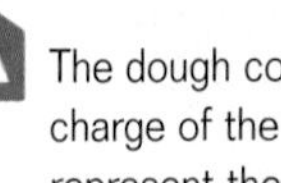

A The dough contains all the positive charge of the atom. The raisins, which represent the negatively charged electrons, are mixed evenly in the dough.

B Thomson pictured the negatively charged electrons as evenly spaced throughout the atom. The negative charges of the electrons and the positive charges of the protons balanced each other.

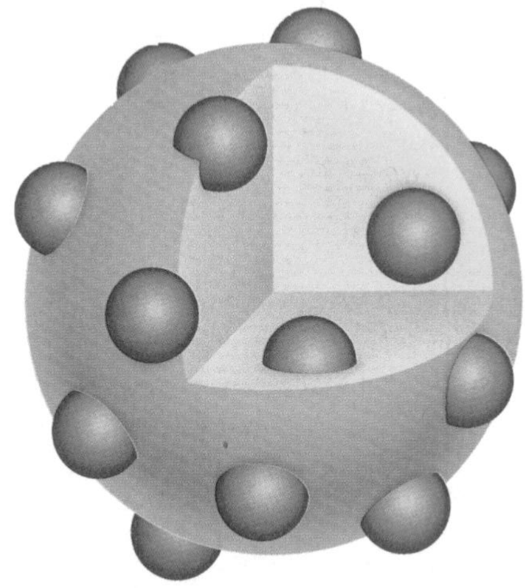

Inclusion Strategies

Gifted Students are learning that there are three different particles in an atom. However, under certain conditions, physicists have identified particles called quarks that may be the substructure of the neutron and proton. Have students use library and Internet sources to find out about these particles and make an oral report to the class. L3

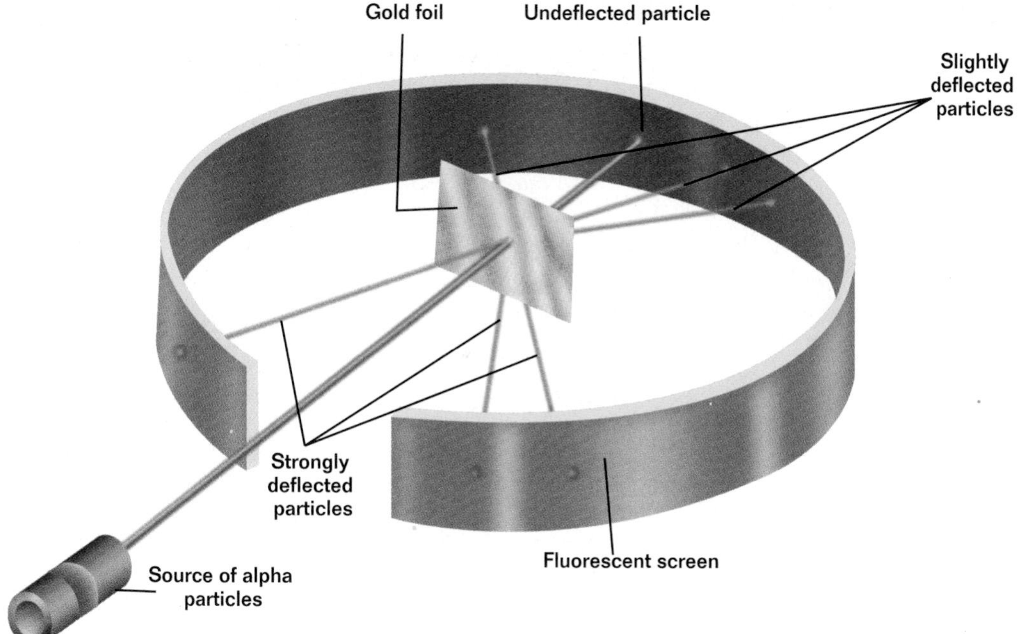

Figure 2-9 In Rutherford's experiment, alpha particles bombarded the gold foil. Most particles passed right through the foil or veered slightly from a straight-line path, but some particles bounced right back. The path of a particle is shown by a flash of light when it hits the fluorescent screen.

Rutherford's Atom

Was Thomson's model of the atom correct? In 1906, Ernest Rutherford and his coworkers began an experiment to find out. They wanted to see what would happen when they bombarded a thin film of a metal such as gold with fast-moving bits of matter called alpha particles. Alpha particles come from unstable atoms. Because they are positively charged, alpha particles are repelled by particles of matter with a positive charge.

Figure 2-9 shows how the experiment was set up. A source of alpha particles was aimed at the sheet of thin gold foil. The foil was surrounded by a fluorescent (fluh RES unt) screen that gave a flash of light when it was hit by a charged particle.

Rutherford thought he knew what the results of this experiment would be. He expected that most of the speeding alpha particles would crash right through the foil and hit the screen on the other side, just like a bullet fired through a glass pane. Rutherford reasoned that in the thin gold film, there wasn't enough matter to stop the speeding alpha particle or to change its path. There also wasn't enough charge in any one place in the cookie-dough atom to strongly repel the alpha particle. He thought that the positive charges on the protons in the gold atoms might cause a few minor deflections if an alpha particle happened to come close to a proton. However, he assumed that there would be only a few of these occasions.

Activity

Linguistic After students have read about Ernest Rutherford's work, have groups of students work together to write plays about how his experiments led him to hypothesize the nuclear atom. Reserve some time to allow students to present their plays. L2 COOP LEARN

Flex Your Brain

Use the Flex Your Brain activity to have students explore ELECTRONS.

GLENCOE TECHNOLOGY

Videodisc

Glencoe Science Voyages Interactive Videodisc—Physical

Side 1, Lesson 4 *Periodicity*

32018

38625

40584

Refer to the Videodisc Teacher Guide for additional bar codes.

Multiple Learning Styles

Linguistic Ask students to pretend that they are co-workers with Crookes at the time of his experiments with a cathode-ray tube. Have them write a letter to a fellow scientist telling her or him about the exciting results they obtained and how they were interpreting the results. P

Integrating the Sciences

Physics The stimulus for the development of nuclear energy, the energy released when a nucleus transmutes, had its foundation in the work of Ernest Rutherford. In 1919, Rutherford bombarded nitrogen gas with alpha particles and found that the nitrogen atom was converted to an oxygen atom and a hydrogen atom. This was the first artificially induced nuclear reaction.

Using an Analogy

Interpersonal Have students discuss the analogy in **Figure 2-10** and then ask them to create an analogy of their own for the astounding results that Rutherford obtained. L2 COOP LEARN

Teacher FYI

Scientists postulate the existence of quarks, which are elementary particles that come in pairs. The particles in a pair of quarks have similar masses to each other but one has a charge of $+\frac{2}{3}$ and the other, $-\frac{1}{3}$.

Discussion

Students have previously studied mass in the context of macroscopic matter. Elicit from them the idea that mass is a measure of the amount of matter that makes up an object. In the model of the nuclear atom, most of the mass is in the tiny nucleus. The electrons add a negligible amount of mass to an atom's overall mass.

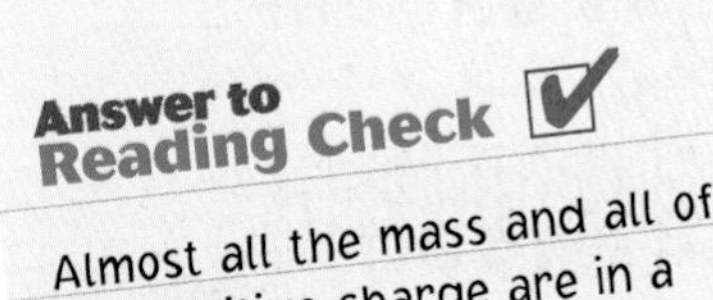

Answer to Reading Check

Almost all the mass and all of the positive charge are in a tiny nucleus at the center of the atom. The electrons occupy the empty space around the nucleus.

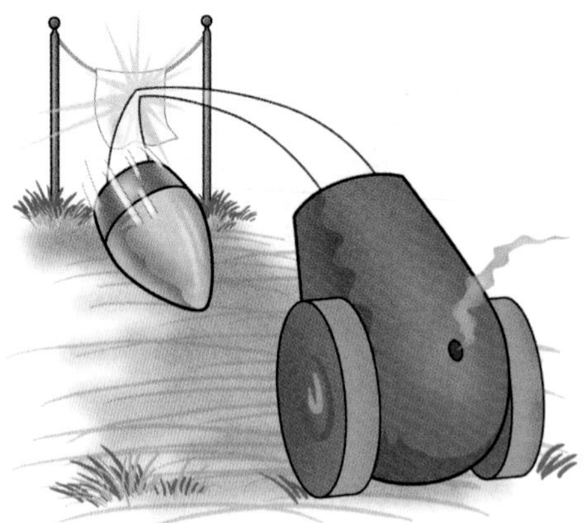

Figure 2-10 Rutherford had some explaining to do when he realized how amazing the results of his experiment were. A 15-inch shell just doesn't bounce off a piece of tissue paper!

That was a reasonable assumption to make because in the cookie-dough model, the positive charges of the protons are essentially neutralized by nearby electrons. Rutherford was so sure of what the results would be that he turned the work over to a graduate student.

Surprising Results

Imagine Rutherford's surprise when his student rushed in to tell him that some alpha particles were veering off at large angles. You can see this in **Figure 2-9.** Rutherford expressed his amazement by saying, "It was about as believable as if you had fired a 15-inch shell at a piece of tissue paper, and it came back and hit you." How could an event like the cartoon in **Figure 2-10** be explained? The positively charged alpha particles were moving with such high speed that it would take a large positive charge to cause them to bounce back. But, in the cookie-dough model of the atom, the mass and charges of the electrons and protons are all uniformly mixed.

The Nuclear Atom

Picture in your mind Rutherford and his team wrestling to make sense of this experiment. They might have drawn diagrams like those in **Figure 2-11.** Diagram A, using the cookie-dough model, shows what Rutherford expected. Now and then, an alpha particle might be slightly affected by a positive charge in the atom and turn a bit off course. However, no large changes in direction would be expected. The actual results did not fit this model, so Rutherford proposed a new one. He hypothesized that almost all the mass of the atom and all of its positive charge are crammed into an incredibly small region of space at the center of the atom called the nucleus. The rest of the atom is empty space occupied by the atom's almost-massless electrons. ✓

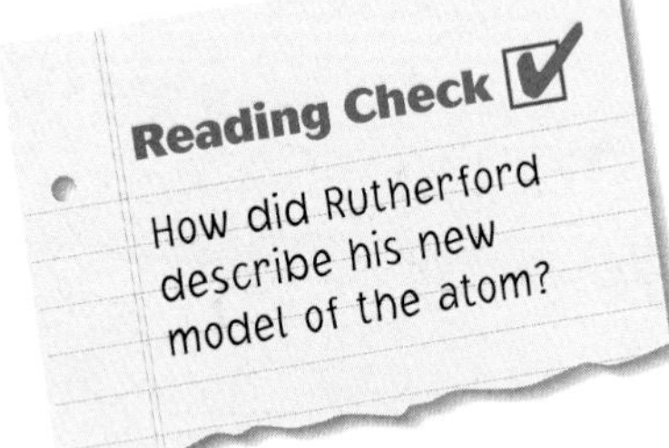

Reading Check ✓

How did Rutherford describe his new model of the atom?

Diagram B, in **Figure 2-11,** shows Rutherford's new model of the atom and how it fits the experimental data. You could

Inclusion Strategies

Learning Disabled Have students draw diagrams of the Dalton, Thomson, and Rutherford models of the atom. Make sure they show Dalton's model as a featureless sphere, and Thomson's as a homogeneous spherical mass with electrons embedded in it at regular points. Rutherford's nuclear atom should be a tiny mass at the center of a large, empty space. L2 P

VISUALIZING The Nuclear Atom

Figure 2-11 Rutherford had to relate his findings to the structure of the atom.

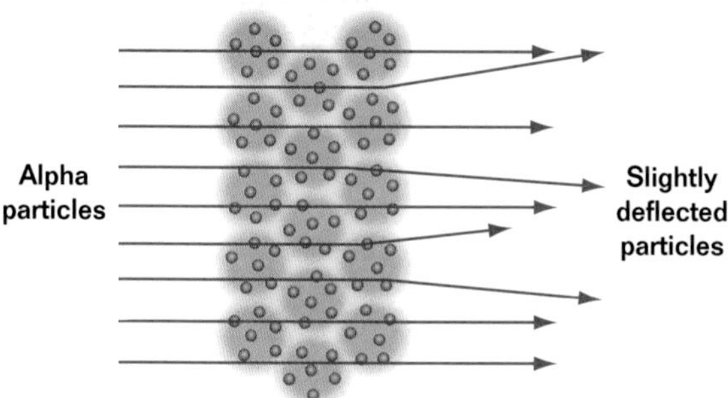

A He thought that if the atom could be described by Thomson's cookie-dough model, then only minor bends in the paths of the particles would have occurred. However, some particles bounced back off the foil.

B What could send an alpha particle bouncing off in the opposite direction? Rutherford thought it had to be a tiny nucleus that contains all the positive charge and most of the mass of the atom.

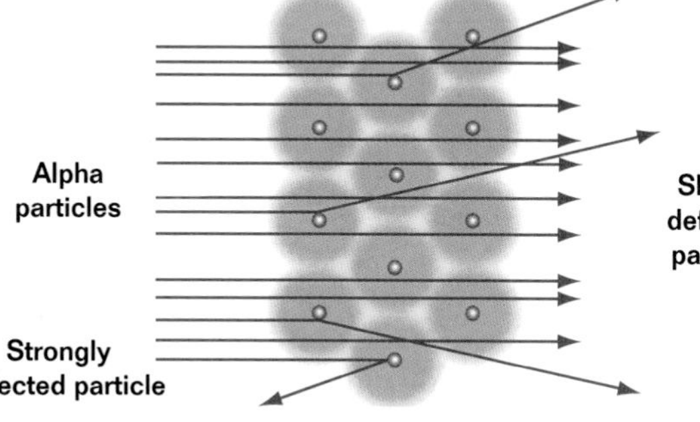

predict that if an alpha particle made a direct hit on the nucleus of a gold atom, which has 79 protons, the alpha particle would be strongly repelled and bounce back. But, most alpha particles could move through the foil with little or no interference because most of the atom is empty space.

The Neutron

Other scientists reviewed Rutherford's nuclear model of the atom with great interest and enthusiasm. However, some data didn't fit. For instance, recall that an atom's electrons have almost no mass. That means that the mass of an atom should be approximately equal to the mass of its protons. But, it isn't. The mass of most atoms is at least twice as great as the mass of its protons. Where does the extra mass come from?

Try at Home MiniLab

Modeling the Nuclear Atom

Procedure

1. On a sheet of paper, draw a circle with a diameter equal to the width of the paper.
2. Small dots of paper in two colors will represent protons and neutrons. Using a dab of glue on each paper dot, make a model of the nucleus of the oxygen atom in the center of your circle. Oxygen has eight protons and eight neutrons.

Analysis

1. What particle is missing from your model of the oxygen atom?
2. How many of the missing particles should there be, and where should they be placed?

VISUAL Learning

Figure 2-11 Help students recognize that **A** shows what the experimental results would have been if the cookie-dough model were correct. **B** shows how the model of the nuclear atom explains the large deflections of some alpha particles.

Try at Home MiniLab

For additional help doing this activity at home, see the corresponding pages in the **Home Involvement** booklet.

Purpose

 **Kinesthetic** Students will make a model of Rutherford's atom. L2

Materials

unlined paper, colored pencils or markers, glue

Teaching Strategies

Demonstrate step 2 with an element other than oxygen.

Analysis

1. the electron
2. Eight electrons; they should be placed in the circle surrounding the nucleus.

Assessment

Performance Have each student create a nucleus for a different element. Use the models to reinforce the concept of atomic number and its relationship to the number of protons and electrons. Use **Performance Assessment in the Science Classroom,** p. 51.

Rutherford's Contribution After students have read about Ernest Rutherford, have them summarize the contributions he made to an understanding of the structure of the atom. Summaries will vary but should include Rutherford's gold foil experiment and how Rutherford interpreted the results. L2 P

Caption Answer

Figure 2-12 *six*

3 Assess

Check for Understanding

Using Science Words

Linguistic Have teams of students take turns using the vocabulary words in sentences. When one team has used a word, the other team can challenge the accuracy of the sentence. Insist that the sentences be substantive. L2 COOP LEARN

Reteach

Visual-Spatial On the chalkboard, make diagrams of Dalton's, Thomson's, and Rutherford's models of the atom. Ask students what evidence there was to support Dalton's model. What experiments led to the abandonment of Dalton's model and the adoption of Thomson's? Do the same for Thomson's and Rutherford's models. Ask students if they think it's possible that another model will someday replace Rutherford's model. L1

Extension

For students who have mastered this section, use **Reinforcement** and **Enrichment** masters.

Figure 2-12 This atom of carbon has six protons and six neutrons in its nucleus. **How many electrons are in the "empty" space surrounding the nucleus?**

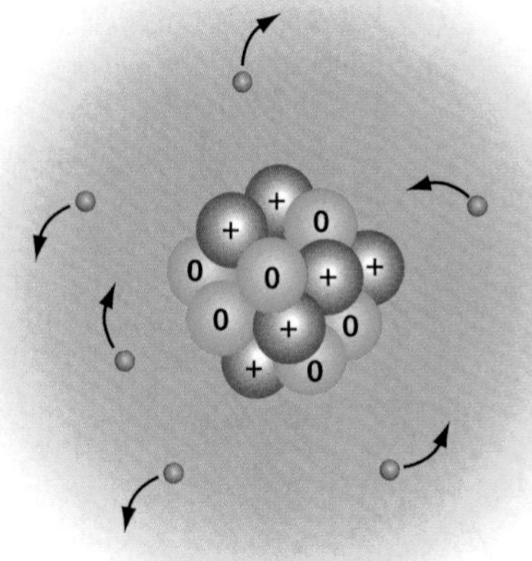

Rutherford reasoned that there must be another particle in the nucleus. The particle, which was later called the **neutron** (NEW trahn), would have the same mass as a proton and be electrically neutral. Proving the existence of neutrons was difficult, however, because a neutron has no charge, so it doesn't respond to magnets or cause fluorescent screens to light up. It took another 20 years before scientists were able to show by experiments that atoms contain neutrons.

The model of the atom was revised again to include neutrons in the nucleus. The nuclear atom, shown in **Figure 2-12,** has a tiny nucleus tightly packed with positively charged protons and neutral neutrons. Electrons occupy the space surrounding the nucleus. The number of electrons in an atom equals the number of protons in the atom.

Comparing Atom and Nucleus

When you look at drawings of atoms such as **Figure 2-12,** be aware that the nuclei are always drawn much larger than they actually are compared to the size of the atom. Picture the nucleus as being the size of a ping-pong ball. Then, the atom would have a diameter of more than 2.4 km. Another way to compare the size of a nucleus with the size of the atom is shown in **Figure 2-13.** You can see that it isn't surprising that in Rutherford's experiment, most of the alpha particles went directly through the gold foil without any interference from the gold atoms. An atom is mostly empty space.

Figure 2-13 If the nucleus of an atom were the size of one poppyseed on your bagel, the atom would have the diameter of this stadium.

Content Background

In 1932, Irene and Frederic Joliot-Curie found that when they bombarded beryllium with alpha particles, neutral radiation was emitted. At first, they thought it might be gamma radiation, but the energy of the radiation was too high to fit the experimental situation. When the radiation struck substances containing hydrogen atoms, protons were released. James Chadwick proposed that the radiation was a stream of neutrons, a particle having the same mass as the proton but no charge. The neutron had been hypothesized earlier but its existence had never been proven.

What about the electrons?

In the early 1900s, physicists were trying to figure out how the electrons are arranged in an atom. It was natural to think that the negatively charged electrons are attracted to the positive nucleus in the same way Earth's moon is attracted to Earth. Then, electrons would travel in orbits around the nucleus. But, scientists soon learned that electrons are in constant, unpredictable motion and can't be pinned down. It's impossible to know precisely where an electron is at any moment. Instead, scientists talk about where the atom's electrons probably are. Electrons are probably in a region surrounding the nucleus, which is called the **electron cloud.** The model for the electron cloud, shown in **Figure 2-14,** is shaped like a sphere with the nucleus at its center. The electrons are more likely to be close to the nucleus rather than farther away because they are attracted to the positive charges of the protons. Notice the fuzzy outline of the cloud. There is no firm boundary because the electrons could be anywhere.

Figure 2-14 The electrons are more likely to be close to the nucleus rather than farther away, but they could be anywhere.

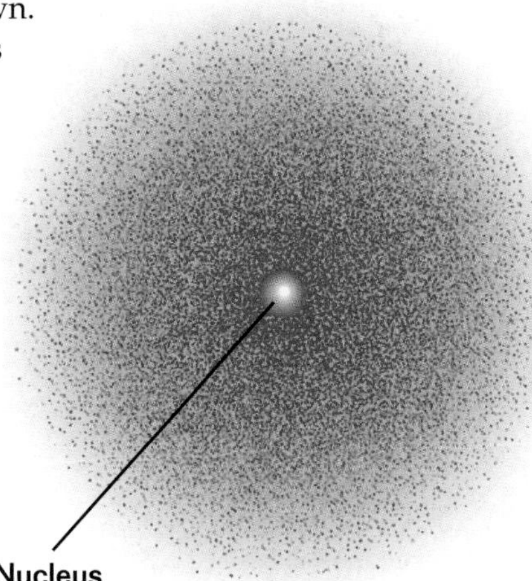

Section Assessment

1. Describe the three kinds of particles found in atoms. Where are they located in the atom and what are their charges?
2. If an atom has 49 protons, how many electrons does it have?
3. How does the nuclear atom differ from the uniform sphere model of the atom?
4. **Think Critically:** In Rutherford's experiment, why wouldn't the electrons in the atoms of the gold foil affect the paths of the alpha particles?
5. **Skill Builder**
   Concept Mapping Make a concept map using all the words in the Vocabulary list for this section. Add any other terms or words that will help create a complete diagram of the section. If you need help, refer to Concept Mapping in the **Skill Handbook** on page 714.

Using Math

The mass of an elec-tron is 9.11×10^{-28} g. The proton is 1836 times heavier. What is the mass of the pro-ton in grams and in kilograms?

4 Close

Proficiency Prep

Use this quiz to check students' recall of section content.

1. **What is located in the nucleus of an atom and has a positive electrical charge?** *a proton*
2. **The number of protons is the same in all atoms of an element, but the number of what particle can be different?** *neutrons*
3. **What particle is much lighter than a proton?** *electron*

Section Assessment

1. protons: in the nucleus, positive charge; neutrons: in the nucleus, neutral; electrons: outside the nucleus, negative charge
2. 49 electrons
3. In the nuclear atom, almost all the mass and all the positive charge are in a tiny nucleus with the electrons occupying the space around it.
4. Think Critically Electrons are too small to affect the path of an alpha particle.

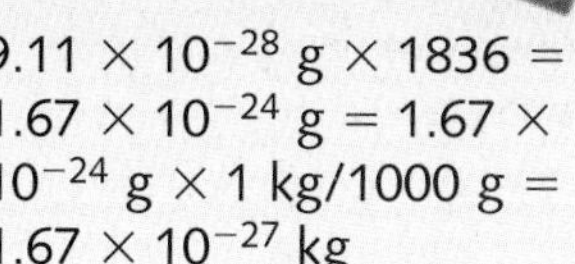

Using Math

9.11×10^{-28} g $\times$ 1836 = 1.67×10^{-24} g = 1.67×10^{-24} g $\times$ 1 kg/1000 g = 1.67×10^{-27} kg

5. **Skill Builder** Student concept maps should include that elements consist of one kind of atom; atoms consist of a nucleus made up of neutrons and protons, and an electron cloud, which is where the electrons are found. Equal numbers of electrons and protons exist.

Assessment

Portfolio Have students draw models of the Dalton, Thomson, and Rutherford atoms. Have them label all parts and write brief descriptions. Encourage them to use their creativity. Use **Performance Assessment in the Science Classroom,** p. 105.

Activity 2•1

Purpose

Logical-Mathematical Students will discover how scientists make models of systems they can't see. L2 ELL COOP LEARN

Process Skills

classifying, observing and inferring, comparing and contrasting

Time

40 minutes

Materials

sealed box with a marble inside

Teaching Strategies

Shoe boxes with taped lids can be used. If the boxes are fitted with sturdy partitions inside, they can be reused for years. Use the pattern shown in the visual, and make two or three other patterns. Number the boxes using the same number for boxes having the same pattern.

Allow students time to discuss their ideas and repeat their observations.

Answers to Questions

1. Answers will vary.
2. Answers will vary.
3. An observation is evidence that you can obtain by the use of your senses. An inference is a conclusion based upon evidence.

Activity 2•1

Using Scientific Methods

Making a Model of the Invisible

Materials

- Sealed box
- Paper and pencil

How do scientists make models of things they can't see? First, they do experiments and gather as much information as possible. Then, they try to fit the information together into some kind of pattern and make inferences. From the data and inferences, they create a model that fits all their data.

What You'll Investigate

How can you determine the inside structure of a box?

Goals

- **Observe** the motion of a marble inside a closed box.
- **Infer** the structure inside the box.

Procedure

1. **Record** the number of the box your teacher gives you. Don't take the lid off the box or look inside.
2. **Lift** the box. **Tilt** the box. Gently **shake** it. In your Science Journal, record all your observations. Make a sketch of the way you think the marble in the box is rolling.
3. Use your observations to **infer** what the inside of the box looks like.
4. **Compare** your inferences with those of students who have the same box as you do. Then, you may want to make more observations or revise your inferences.
5. When you have gathered all the information you can, **sketch** your model in your Science Journal.
6. **Open** your box and **compare** your model with the actual inside structure of the box.

Conclude and Apply

1. How did your model of the inside of the box compare with the actual inside?
2. Is there any other test you could have used to gather more information?
3. How is an observation different from an inference?

Assessment

Oral Ask students how this activity and the inferences they made are like the experiment done by Crookes. Ask what observations they made and what observations Crookes made. Use **Performance Assessment in the Science Classroom,** p. 71.

The Nucleus

What's in the nucleus?

The modern idea of the atom pictures all of the protons and neutrons packed into a tiny nucleus that is surrounded by electrons. How does the nucleus in an atom of one element differ from the nucleus of an atom of another element? The atoms of different elements contain different numbers of protons. The **atomic number** of an element is the number of protons in the nucleus of an atom of that element. The smallest of the atoms, the hydrogen atom, has one proton in its nucleus, so hydrogen's atomic number is 1. Chlorine has 17 protons, so chlorine's atomic number is 17. Uranium, the heaviest naturally occurring element, has 92 protons. Its atomic number is 92. Atoms of the same element always have the same number of protons.

Isotopes

The atomic number tells the number of protons, but what about the number of neutrons in an atom's nucleus? Atoms can have the same number of neutrons as protons, or they can have more or fewer neutrons than protons. Most atoms of carbon have six protons and six neutrons. But, some carbon atoms have seven neutrons and some have eight, as you can see in **Figure 2-15.** They are all carbon atoms because they all have six protons. These three kinds of carbon atoms are called isotopes. **Isotopes** (I suh tohps) are atoms of the same element that have different numbers of neutrons. The isotopes of carbon are called carbon-12, carbon-13, and carbon-14. The numbers 12, 13, and 14 are the mass numbers of the isotopes.

What You'll Learn
- The process of radioactive decay
- What is meant by half-life
- How radioactive isotopes are used

Vocabulary
atomic number
isotope
mass number
radioactive decay
half-life

Why It's Important
- Radioactive elements are both beneficial and dangerous.

VISUALIZING Isotopes

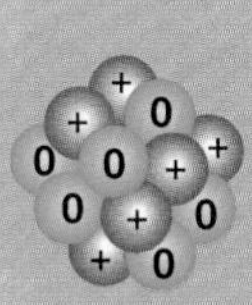

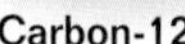

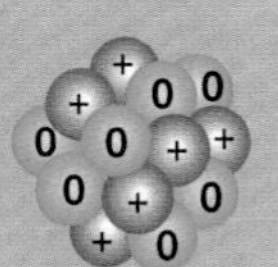

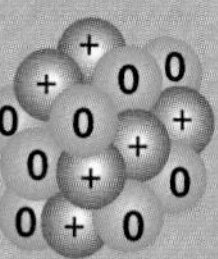

Figure 2-15 The three isotopes of carbon differ only in the number of neutrons in each nucleus.

SECTION 2-2

Prepare

Content Background

Refer to **Radioactive Decay, Transmutation, Transmutation and Nuclear Power**, and **Half-Life** on p. 34F.

Preplanning

Refer to the **Chapter Organizer** on pp. 34A–B.

1 Motivate

Bellringer

Before presenting the lesson, display **Section Focus Transparency 4** on the overhead projector. Use the accompanying **Focus Activity** worksheet. L2 ELL

4 SECTION FOCUS TRANSPARENCY

Section 2-2

ALMOST THE SAME

It's hard to walk past identical twins or triplets without taking a second look. It's always fascinating to see the same face on different people.

1. What is similar about the triplets in the photo?
2. Are there visible differences? Describe how they are different.
3. How might atoms look identical but vary in some way?

Tying to Previous Knowledge

In the previous section, students learned about the particles that make up an atom and how they are arranged in the nuclear atom. Now they will learn what kinds of reactions occur in the nucleus.

Resource Manager

The following **Teacher Classroom Resources** can be used with Section 2-2:

Reproducible Masters

Activity Worksheets, pp. 9–10, 12 L2
Critical Thinking/Problem Solving, p. 2 L2
Enrichment, p. 4 L3
Laboratory Manual, pp. 11–12 L2
Multicultural Connections, pp. 3–4 L2
Reinforcement, p. 4 L2
Study Guide, pp. 6–8 L1 ELL

Transparencies

Teaching Transparency 4 L2
Science Integration Transparency 2 L2

2 Teach

VISUAL Learning

Figure 2-15 Have students count the nuclear particles in the diagrams of the three carbon atoms. **How are the carbon atoms the same? How are they different?** *They have the same number of protons but different numbers of neutrons.*

Using Math

Thorium-234 has 234 − 90 = 144 neutrons.

Uranium-234 has 234 − 92 = 142 neutrons.

Making a Model

Kinesthetic Using **Figure 2-15** as a reference, have students make models of nitrogen-14 and nitrogen-15. Tell them that the atomic number of nitrogen is 7. Each model should include the correct number of protons, neutrons, and electrons. Ask students what the mass numbers of the two isotopes are. L1 ELL

Enrichment

Have students research isotopes and how they are used for medical purposes. L2

*inter***NET** CONNECTION

Internet Addresses

____

____

____

____

For Internet tips, see Glencoe's **Using the Internet in the Science Classroom.**

Table 2-1

Isotopes of Carbon	Carbon-12	Carbon-13	Carbon-14
Mass Number	12	13	14
Number of Protons	6	6	6
Number of Neutrons	6	7	8
Number of Electrons	6	6	6
Atomic Number	6	6	6

Using Math

The atomic number of thorium-234 is 90. The atomic number of uranium-234 is 92. How many neutrons does each isotope have?

The **mass number** of an isotope is the number of neutrons plus protons in the nucleus. **Table 2-1** shows the particles that make up each of the carbon isotopes. You can find the number of neutrons in an isotope by subtracting the atomic number (the number of protons) from the mass number. For example, carbon-14 has 14 – 6 = 8 neutrons.

Nuclear Glue

When you need to hold something together, what do you use? Rubber bands? String? Glue? What do you suppose holds the protons and neutrons together in the nucleus of an atom? Because protons are positively charged, they repel each other just as the north ends of two magnets tend to push each other apart. The uncharged neutrons neither attract nor repel the protons, but they help keep the protons apart and reduce the repelling electric force. So, what force holds the nucleus together? That force is called the strong nuclear force. The strong nuclear force can hold the protons together only if they are nearly touching, as they are in the nucleus of the atom.

*inter***NET** CONNECTION

Visit the Glencoe Science Web Site at **www.glencoe.com/sec/science** for more information about radioactive decay.

Radioactive Decay

Many atomic nuclei are stable when they have about the same number of protons and neutrons. Carbon-12 is the most stable isotope of carbon. It has six protons and six neutrons. Some nuclei are unstable because they have too many or too few neutrons. This is especially true for heavier elements such as uranium and plutonium. In these nuclei, repulsion builds up. The nucleus must release a particle to become stable. When particles are released, energy is given off. The release of nuclear particles and energy is called **radioactive decay.** When particles are ejected from a nucleus, the atomic number of the nucleus can change. One element is changed into another. The changing of one element into another through radioactive decay is called transmutation.

Across the Curriculum

Literature The Roman poet Lucretius wrote these words about atoms in his poem *De Rerum Natura (On the Nature of Things)*. "Their nature lies beyond our range of sense. Far, far beyond." Have students think about what Lucretius meant and write a paragraph about his idea of the nature of atoms. L3

48 CHAPTER 2 INSIDE THE ATOM

Figure 2-16 This life-saving smoke detector makes use of the radioactive isotope americium-241. The isotope is located inside the slotted chamber. When smoke particles enter the chamber, the alarm goes off.

Some Isotopes Release Alpha Particles

Each year, thousands of homes are saved from fires by smoke detectors like the one in **Figure 2-16.** This device makes use of americium-241, which undergoes transmutation by ejecting an alpha particle. An alpha particle consists of two protons and two neutrons. Energy is released with the alpha particle. Together, the energy and particles are called nuclear radiation. In the smoke detector, the fast-moving alpha particles cause air to conduct an electric current. As long as the electric current is flowing, the smoke detector is silent. When smoke enters the detector, the flow of electric current is interrupted and the alarm is triggered. ☑

The atomic number of americium (a muh RIH shee um) is 95, so americium has 95 protons. When americium expels an alpha particle, it loses two protons and two neutrons. It's no longer americium. It has become the element that has 93 protons, neptunium. In **Figure 2-17,** notice that the mass and atomic numbers of neptunium and the alpha particle add up to the mass and atomic number of americium. All the nuclear particles of americium still exist after the transmutation, but a good deal of energy has been released.

Figure 2-17 Americium expels an alpha particle, which is made up of two protons and two neutrons, so americium is changed into the element neptunium which has two fewer protons than americium.

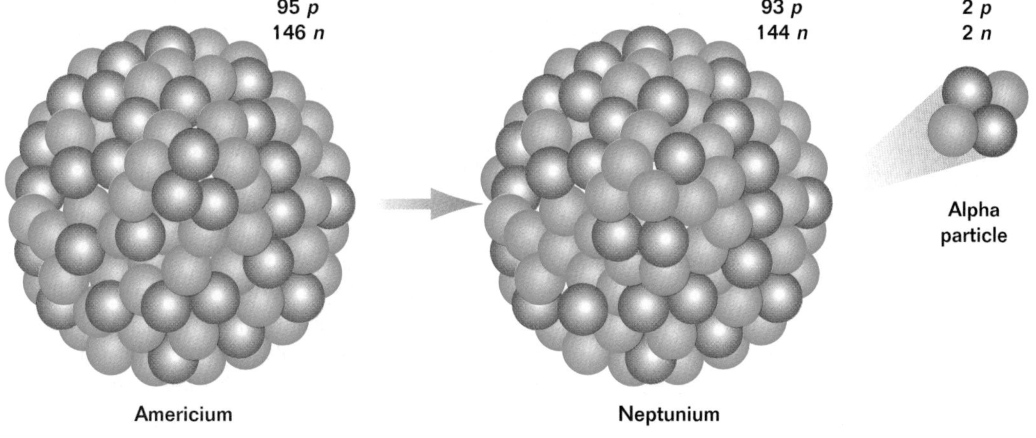

Activity

Visual-Spatial Have students make a drawing of an alpha particle. Their drawings should consist of representations of two protons and two neutrons bunched together. Ask: **Is this particle neutral?** *no* **What is the charge on the alpha particle?** *2+* L2

Using Science Words

Linguistic Have students use the phrase *radioactive decay* and the word *transmutation* in a labeled illustration of a decay process. Examples could be in the form of a comic strip. L2

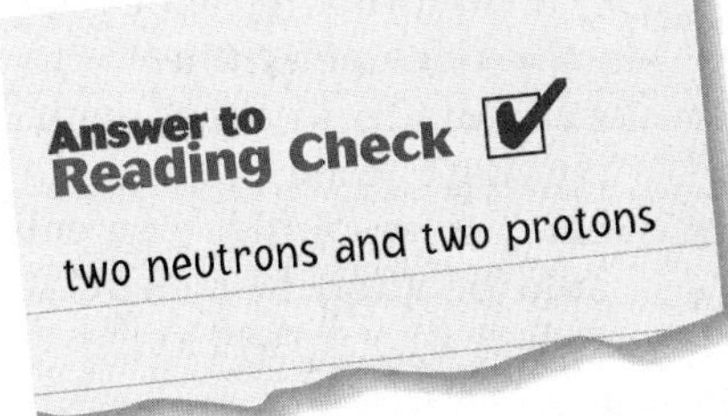

Teacher FYI

Every day, people are exposed to many forms of radiation, for example, solar radiation, cosmic radiation, radiation from smoke detectors, radon gas, and medical or dental X rays. In addition, there is radiation from radioactive elements in Earth's crust. All of these sources produce an inescapable background radiation.

VISUAL Learning

Figure 2-17 **How many protons are in the americium nucleus?** *95* **How many protons are in the neptunium nucleus?** *93* **What happened to the missing protons?** *They are part of the emitted alpha particle.*

Inclusion Strategies

Learning Disabled Ask students whether they have smoke detectors in their homes. Have them find out where the smoke detectors are located and whether they have ever gone off. Ask whether there have been any false alarms and, if so, what caused them. Have them check with an adult to find out whether the battery is checked regularly. L2

Discussion

How does the mass of a beta particle differ from the mass of an alpha particle? *Protons and neutrons have the same mass, which is 1836 times the mass of a beta particle (an electron). Therefore, the mass of an alpha particle is* $4 \times 1836 \times 9.11 \times 10^{-28}\ g = 6.7 \times 10^{-24}\ g$. Help students work out the math, if necessary.

Enrichment

Assign each student a different element from the actinide series of the periodic table. Have them find out what the resulting element would be after their element expelled an alpha particle. Use the information about the decay of americium-95 to neptunium-93 to assist them. Then have them determine what the resulting element would be after their element expelled a beta particle. L3

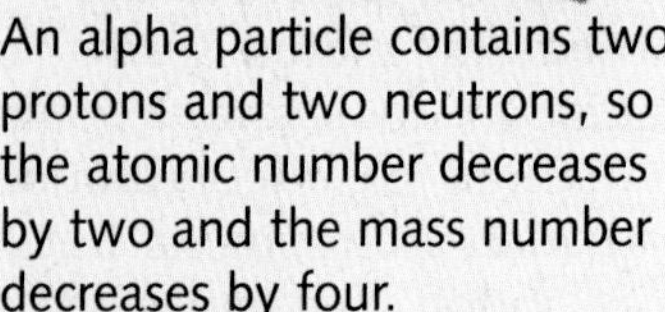

Using Math

An alpha particle contains two protons and two neutrons, so the atomic number decreases by two and the mass number decreases by four.

$84 - 2 = 82$

$218 - 4 = 214$

The new isotope is lead-214.

GLENCOE TECHNOLOGY

Videodisc

The Infinite Voyage: Unseen Worlds

Chapter 7 *The Scanning Tunneling Microscope: Observing Atomic Particles* 2:00

Chapter 11 *The Fermi Lab Accelerator: Splitting the Atom* 8:30

Refer to the Teacher Guide for bar codes and teaching strategies.

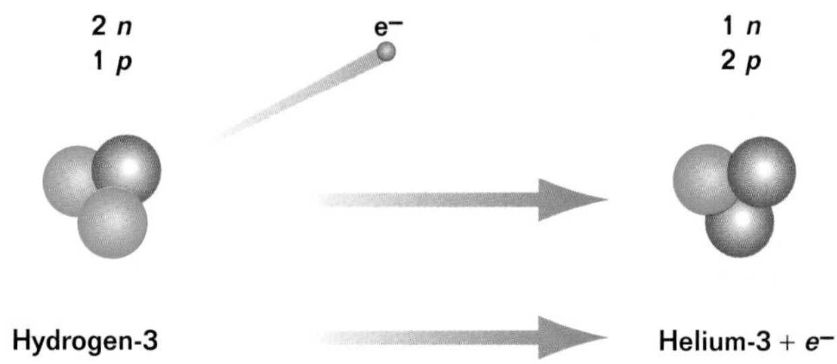

Figure 2-18 The hydrogen-3 isotope converts a neutron into a proton and an electron and tosses out the electron. **What is the element with two protons that remains?**

Using Math

The atomic number of polonium-218 is 84. Its mass number is 218. When this isotope decays by releasing an alpha particle, what is the atomic number of the resulting isotope? What is its mass number?

Some Isotopes Release Beta Particles

Some elements undergo transmutations through a different process. Their nuclei emit an electron called a beta particle. A beta particle is a high-energy electron that comes from the nucleus, not from the electron cloud. But, the nucleus only contains protons and neutrons. How can it give off or emit an electron? During this kind of transmutation, a neutron becomes unstable and splits into an electron and a proton. The electron or beta particle is released with a large amount of energy.

Because a neutron has been changed into a proton, the nucleus of the element has an additional proton. The atomic number of the element that results is greater by one. **Figure 2-18** shows the beta decay of the hydrogen-3 isotope. With two neutrons in its nucleus, hydrogen-3 is unstable. One neutron is converted to a proton by beta decay, and an isotope of helium is produced. The mass of the element stays almost the same because the mass of an electron is so small.

Half-Life

How can you tell when a nucleus in a sample will decay? You can't. Radioactive decay is random. It's like watching popcorn begin to pop. You can't predict which kernel will explode or when. But, if you're an experienced popcorn maker, you might be able to predict how long it will take for half the kernels to pop. A convenient way to measure the rate of decay of a nucleus is by half-life. The **half-life** of a radioactive isotope is the amount of time required for half of a sample of the element to decay. For example, iodine-131 has a half-life of eight days. If you start with a sample of 4 g of iodine-131, after eight days you would have only 2 g of iodine-131 remaining. After 16 days, or two half-lives, half of the 2 g would have decayed and you would have only 1 g. After yet another half-life, only 0.5 g would remain. **Figure 2-19** is a diagram of the process.

Figure 2-19 Half-life is the amount of time in which one half of a sample decays. **What happens to the mass of the remaining isotope at the end of each eight days?**

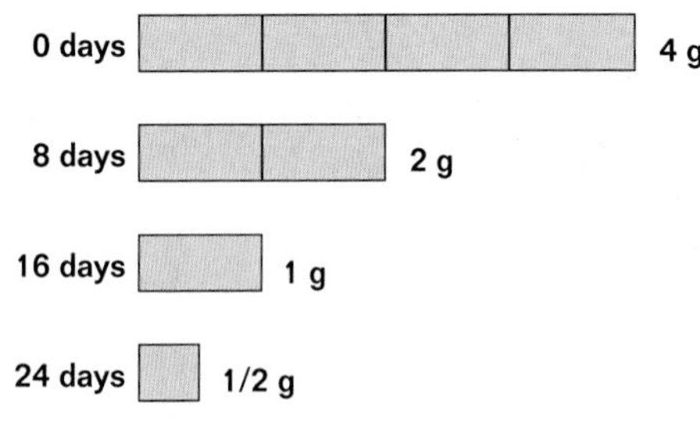

Caption Answers

Figure 2-18 *helium*

Figure 2-19 *The mass is reduced by one half.*

Content Background

For the chemist, it is usually not important that there are different isotopes of an element. Most isotopes of an element behave the same in chemical reactions. A chemical reaction involves interactions between the electrons in the electron clouds of two atoms.

The radioactive decay of unstable atoms goes on at a steady pace, unaffected by conditions such as weather, pressure, magnetic or electric fields, and even chemical reactions. Half-lives, which are different for each isotope, range in length from fractions of a second to billions of years.

Carbon Dating

Carbon-14 is used to determine the age of dead animals, plants, and humans. The half-life of carbon-14 is 5730 years. In a living organism, the amount of carbon-14 remains in constant balance with the levels of the isotope in the atmosphere or ocean. This balance occurs because living organisms both take in and release carbon. For example, animals take in carbon from food such as plants, and release carbon as carbon dioxide. While life processes go on, any carbon-14 nucleus that decays is replaced by another from the environment. When the plant or animal dies, the decaying nuclei can no longer be replaced. When archaeologists find an ancient item, such as the one in **Figure 2-20,** they can find out how much carbon-14 it has and compare it with the amount of carbon-14 there would have been in the organism when it was alive. Knowing the half-life of carbon-14, they can then calculate when the organism lived.

Graphing Half-Life

Procedure

1. Make a table with three columns. Label the first column *Number of Half-Lives.* Label the second column *Days Passed* and the third column *Mass of Thorium Remaining.*
2. Thorium-234 has a half-life of 24 days. Fill the first column with the number of half-lives: zero, one, two, and so on up to the number of half-lives that equals 144 days.
3. Fill the second column with the number of days that have passed since the start of the experiment: zero days, 24 days, 48 days, 72 days, and so on up to 144 days.
4. Assume that you have a sample of 64 kg of thorium. Calculate the mass of thorium remaining after each half-life and fill in the third column.
5. Plot the data in the first and third columns on a graph with half-life on the *x*-axis and mass of thorium on the *y*-axis.

Analysis

1. During which 24-day period does the most thorium-234 decay?
2. How much thorium-234 was left in your sample on the 144th day?
3. Compare the mass of thorium-234 after each half-life to the previous mass. How are they related?

Figure 2-20 Using carbon-14 dating techniques, archaeologists can find out when the biological materials in this artifact were living.

Mini Lab

Purpose

Visual-Spatial Students will make a graph that shows the decay of thorium-234 over a 144-day period. L2 COOP LEARN

Materials

paper, graph paper, pencil

Teaching Strategies

- Have students recall that the *x*-axis is the horizontal axis and the *y*-axis is vertical.
- 144 days is six half-lives, so there should be six or seven major divisions along the *x*-axis. The *y*-axis should have at least seven major divisions each equal to 10 kg.
- Recommend to students that they draw the line without a ruler, connecting the points in a smooth curve.

Troubleshooting Assist students in setting up the intervals for their graph so that the graph fills one piece of graph paper.

Analysis

1. the first 24-day period
2. 1 kg
3. The mass remaining is always one half of what was present after the previous half-life.

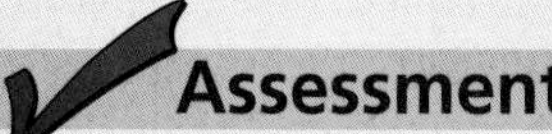

Assessment

Oral Ask students how many days beyond the 144 days it would take before the mass of thorium would be 0.25 kg. *48 days* Use **Performance Assessment in the Science Classroom,** p. 29.

Content Background

The carbon ingested in food by plants and animals contains a definite amount of carbon-14, which becomes part of the materials of the plant or animal. The carbon dioxide released in respiration contains that same percentage of carbon-14. Intake and outgo maintain a balance of the isotope between the organism and the environment. When the organism dies, carbon-14 continues to decay but without replacement. At any time, the amount of carbon-14 present in a dead organism can be compared with how much would have been there if the organism were alive.

Correcting Misconceptions

Students may think that when an atom undergoes beta decay and becomes a different element, its mass changes. However, the mass stays almost the same because the mass of an electron is negligibly small.

Enrichment

Linguistic Have students research nuclear power plants to discover how they work, the required safety regulations, and the locations of nuclear power plants in the United States. Have them make a poster or write a paper explaining their findings. L3 P

Radiation therapy is given in small doses over a long period to maximize the effect on cancer cells and to minimize the damage to healthy cells. Damaged cells have the capacity to repair themselves.

3 Assess

Check for Understanding

Discussion

Ask students to define *transmutation,* and to compare alpha emission with beta emission. L2

Reteach

Interpersonal Have groups of students write definitions for half of the vocabulary words and other groups write definitions for the other half. Have them exchange definitions and challenge each other on the accuracy of the definitions. L1 COOP LEARN

LIFE SCIENCE INTEGRATION

Radiation Therapy

When a person has cancer, cells reproduce rapidly, causing a tumor. When radiation is focused directly on the tumor, it can slow or stop the cell division while leaving healthy surrounding tissue largely unaffected. Find out more about radiation therapy and summarize your findings in your Science Journal.

Nuclear Waste Products

Waste products from nuclear power plants are a problem because nuclear fuels produce leftover isotopes that still release much radiation. This radioactive waste must be permanently isolated from people and the environment because it continues to produce harmful radiation. Special disposal sites that can contain the radiation must be found. One such site is in Carlsbad, New Mexico, where nuclear waste is buried 655 m below the surface of Earth.

New Elements by Transmutation

Scientists now create elements by smashing atomic particles into a target element. Alpha and beta particles, for example, are accelerated in particle accelerators like the one in **Figure 2-21** to speeds high enough that they can smash into a large nucleus and be absorbed on impact. The absorbed particle converts the target element into another element with a higher atomic number. These artificial transmutations have created new elements that do not exist in nature. Elements with atomic numbers 93 to 112 have been made in this way.

Tracer Elements

The process of artificial transmutation has been adapted so that radioactive isotopes of normally stable elements can be made in hospitals and clinics using specially designed equipment. These isotopes, called tracer elements, are used to diagnose disease and to study environmental conditions. The radioactive isotope is introduced into a living system and then followed as it decays by a device that detects radiation. These devices often present the results as a visual display or photograph. The isotopes chosen for medical purposes have short

Figure 2-21 Giant particle accelerators, such as HERA in Hamburg, Germany, are needed to speed up particles to the speeds necessary to cause an atomic transmutation.

Across the Curriculum

History Much of the early work on radioactivity was done by Henri Becquerel and Marie and Pierre Curie. Have students research the contributions of these scientists to the discovery and understanding of radioactivity. Becquerel found that uranium compounds give off radioactivity. Marie and Pierre Curie isolated polonium and radium. L2

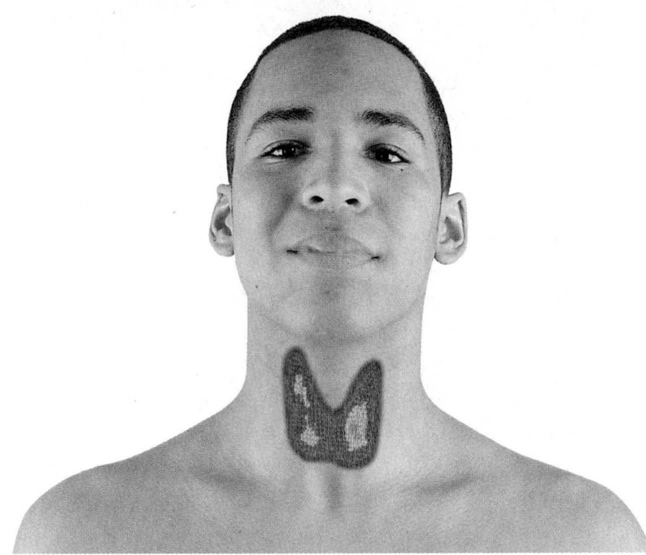

Figure 2-22 Most of the iodine in your diet goes to your thyroid. This image of a healthy thyroid was made by injecting a solution of iodine-131 into the bloodstream. The colors in the image indicate amounts of iodine-131 absorbed at various locations inside the thyroid. **How could this image be used to help diagnose thyroid disease?**

half-lives, which allow them to be used without the risk of exposing living organisms to prolonged radiation.

The isotope iodine-131 has been used to diagnose problems with the thyroid, a gland located at the base of the neck. The radioactive iodine, which is absorbed by the thyroid, creates an image of the thyroid like the one in **Figure 2-22.** Other radioactive isotopes are used to detect cancer, digestion problems, and circulation difficulties.

Problem Solving

Designing a Safe Container

You have been hired to design a container to transport radioactive waste. A whole raw egg will represent the waste. You must consider problems such as accidents, leaks, and ease of transportation. Your design will need to withstand the following tests.

Drop Test: Your teacher will drop your container of radioactive waste from the top of a ladder or a high structure (7 m – 10 m) onto a hard surface.

Side Impact Test: A 1-L plastic bottle filled with sand will be suspended from a door frame. When it is released at a 45 degree angle, it will strike your radioactive waste container.

After each test, open your container to examine the egg. Did it leak? Break apart? Stay in one piece?

Solve the Problem

1. In your Science Journal, write a hypothesis about how you can keep your waste from breaking or spilling.
2. Build your radioactive waste container.
3. Test your hypothesis using the Drop Test and Side Impact Test.
4. Was your hypothesis supported?

Think Critically

1. What could be improved in your design?
2. What other test would you propose?
3. What safety measures must be considered when transporting and storing radioactive waste? Why are these safety measures important?

Content Background

In 1938, Otto Hahn and Fritz Strassman tried bombarding uranium with neutrons in order to cause a transmutation of uranium to a heavier element. To their surprise, they obtained the much lighter element barium. Lise Meitner was able to explain these strange results. The neutron did not have enough energy to penetrate the nucleus and cause the transmutation. Instead, it caused the atom to split. Two smaller nuclei and a great deal of energy were the result. This fission reaction was the beginning of the atomic bomb and the peacetime use of nuclear reactions to create electricity.

Extension

For students who have mastered this section, use the **Reinforcement** and **Enrichment** masters.

Caption Answer

Figure 2-22 *An image of a thyroid suspected of being diseased could be compared to this image.*

Problem Solving

Nuclear waste is a controversial issue. Problems include finding appropriate storage sites and safe means of transporting waste from nuclear power plants to storage sites. Concerns for future generations include the integrity of long-term storage containers. In time, will these facilities allow radioactive contamination to enter water and soil? The most desirable current storage is in geologic formations that are stable and deep in the ground. Yucca Mountain in Nevada was the first permanent underground nuclear waste storage facility.

Solve the Problem

Students' hypotheses about materials will vary. They could include light, thick, strong, and flexible materials.

Think Critically

1. Answers will vary.
2. Answers will vary but could include crushing or piercing.
3. Answers will vary but should include the need to avoid accidents when transporting nuclear waste and that nuclear waste must be kept away from people for the foreseeable future and beyond.

*inter***NET**
CONNECTION

Internet Addresses

For Internet tips, see Glencoe's **Using the Internet in the Science Classroom.**

4 Close

Proficiency Prep

Use this quiz to check students' recall of section content.

1. **What number tells the number of protons in the nucleus?** *atomic number*
2. **What are atoms of the same element that have different numbers of neutrons?** *isotopes*
3. **What is a process in which there is a release of nuclear particles and energy?** *radioactive decay or transmutation*

Section Assessment

1. atoms of the same element that have different numbers of neutrons
2. A radioactive isotope is introduced into a living system and followed by a detector.
3. Radioactive decay is the release of nuclear particles and energy from the nucleus of an atom. Half-life is a measure of the rate of radioactive decay.
4. **Think Critically** No, the 25-g sample would eject only half as many particles as the 50-g sample. During a single half-life, one half of the sample decays, so the rate of decay is twice as great for the 50-g sample.

Figure 2-23 Using fertilizer containing a small amount of a radioactive isotope, scientists can see how the fertilizer is absorbed by the plant.

*inter***NET**
CONNECTION

Visit the Glencoe Science Web Site at **www.glencoe.com/sec/science** for more information about the use of isotopes in medicine and agriculture.

In the environment, tracers such as sulfur-35 can be placed in pesticides and followed to see what impact the pesticide has as it moves through an ecosystem. As you can see in **Figure 2-23,** fertilizers containing small amounts of radioactive isotopes are used to see how well plants absorb fertilizers.

Section Assessment

1. What are isotopes?
2. How are radioactive isotopes used to detect health problems?
3. Explain what is meant by radioactive decay. How is the rate of radioactive decay measured?
4. **Think Critically:** Suppose you had two samples of the same radioactive isotope. One sample was 25 g. The other was 50 g. Would the same number of particles be ejected from each sample in the first hour? Explain.
5. **Skill Builder**
   Making Models You have learned how scientists used marbles, cookie dough, and a cloud to model the structure of the atom. The poppy seed and the stadium in this chapter modeled the difference in size between the nucleus and atom. Do the **Chapter 2 Skill Activity** on page 743 to make paper-and-pencil models of the electrons, protons, and neutrons in the atoms of different isotopes.

Using Computers

Word Processing Use a word processing program to make a table of the three particles found in atoms. Include columns labeled *Particle, Charge,* and *Mass.* For the masses of the three particles, refer to Using Math in the Section 2-1 Section Assessment. Protons and neutrons have approximately the same mass. If you need help, refer to page 732.

Using Computers

Particle	Charge	Mass
electron	negative	9.11×10^{-28} g
proton	positive	1.67×10^{-24} g
neutron	neutral	1.67×10^{-24} g

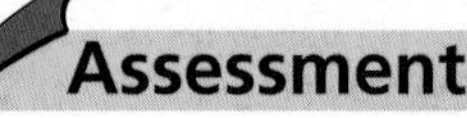

Assessment

Content Ask students to give a written answer to this question. **If an atom ejects a beta particle, does the atom's atomic number change? Explain.** *Yes, its atomic number increases by one unit because one neutron has been changed to a proton and an electron.* Use **Performance Assessment in the Science Classroom,** p. 87.

Preserving Food by Irradiation

Eating food contaminated with harmful bacteria, parasites, or fungi can be a serious health risk. According to the Centers for Disease Control and Prevention in Atlanta, Georgia, every year millions of people in the United States become ill from eating contaminated food, and some 9000 Americans die as a result of food-borne illnesses. Worldwide, many more people die of malnutrition and starvation because they don't have enough fresh, high-quality food to eat.

For centuries, people have been preserving food—and in so doing preventing the growth of harmful bacteria and other organisms—by canning, pickling, drying, smoking, freezing, and freeze-drying it. However, all of these methods change the flavor, texture, and consistency of the preserved food in some way. Food irradiation, on the other hand, is a food preservation process that is growing in popularity because it destroys potentially harmful organisms in food without changing the food's quality.

What is irradiation?

In the irradiation process, food is exposed to low-level radiation but never comes into direct contact with the radiation source. Irradiation kills bacteria, prevents cell division in other kinds of organisms, helps prevent spoilage, and slows ripening in fresh vegetables and fruits, such as the papayas at left.

Foods that are commonly irradiated are ground wheat and other cereal grain products, spices, fresh fruits and vegetables, frozen seafood, poultry, and pork.

Are irradiated foods safe?

Many people fear radiation and any nuclear-related technology. Consumers need to understand that food does not become radioactive as a result of exposure to low-level radiation and that the nutritional quality of the food does not change. Based on decades of research, the Food and Drug Administration (FDA) has approved a variety of specific applications of food irradiation. FDA regulations require that irradiated food be labeled as such.

interNET CONNECTION

Visit the Glencoe Science Web Site at www.glencoe.com/sec/science to find more information about the debate on food irradiation.

NATIONAL GEOGRAPHIC

Science & Society

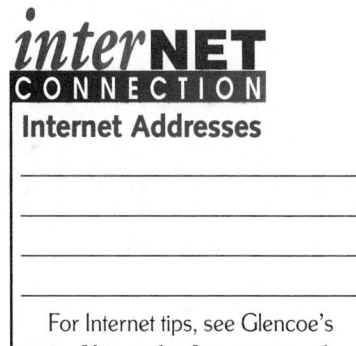

Teaching Strategies

Ask students what kinds of preserved foods they are familiar with. Make a list on the chalkboard: dried, salted, smoked, canned, frozen, and so on. Ask students whether these foods taste the same as fresh foods.

Have students research hunger in the world and the work of organizations such as Care and Oxfam.

For More Information

Food and Drug Administration
5600 Fishers Lane
Room 15B-32
Rockville, MD 20857

interNET CONNECTION

Internet Addresses

____

____

____

____

For Internet tips, see Glencoe's **Using the Internet in the Science Classroom.**

Content Background

Sterilization of foods by irradiation requires less energy than sterilization by heat, for example, in canning. Irradiated foods are not significantly different in quality from fresh foods. However, irradiation can cause chemical changes. Ionizing radiation will oxidize oxidizable materials and reduce reducible materials. Nutrients are somewhat reduced by radiation, but not to the extent that they are in processes that depend upon heat.

Because enzymes that break down foods can be resistant to radiation, a complementary process may be necessary to inactivate them.

Recognize the Problem

Purpose

Visual-Spatial Students will design a demonstration to model half-life. L2 ELL COOP LEARN

Process Skills

observing and inferring, comparing and contrasting, interpreting data, making and using tables, making models

Time

40 minutes

Form a Hypothesis

Possible Hypotheses

The tossing of pennies can be a model for half-life. If a radioactive sample has a known half-life, then you can predict how much of the sample will be left after that period of time.

Test Your Hypothesis

Possible Procedures

Count all the coins and record the number. Declare one half-life to be the tossing of all the coins. Toss each coin in turn and record the number of coins that land heads up. These will be the atoms that have not yet decayed. Repeat the procedure for as many half-lives as are needed, each time tossing only the coins that landed heads up. For each round, record the number of coins that have not decayed.

Teaching Strategies

- Establish rules for tossing the coins to avoid the hazards of flying objects.
- Students may need help establishing the *x* and *y* scales on their graphs and in plotting and drawing their curves. Be sure students understand that they should draw a smooth line through their points.

Design Your Own Experiment

Activity 2•2

Half-Life

Possible Materials

- Pennies
- Graph paper

The decay rates of most radioactive isotopes range from milliseconds to billions of years. If you know the half-life of an isotope and the size of a sample of the isotope, can you predict how much will remain after a certain amount of time? Is it possible to predict when a specific atom will decay?

Recognize the Problem

How can you use pennies to create a model that will show how half-life can predict the amount of a radioactive isotope remaining after specific periods of time?

Form a Hypothesis

Based on the definition of *half-life*, write a hypothesis that shows how half-life can be used to predict how much of a radioactive isotope will remain after a certain amount of time.

Goals

- **Model** isotopes in a radioactive sample. For each half-life, determine the amount of change in the objects that represent the isotopes in the model.
- **Design an experiment** to test the usefulness of half-life in predicting how much radioactive material still remains after a specific length of time.

Sample Data Table

Toss number	Number of heads	Toss number	Number of heads
1	60	6	2
2	28	7	1
3	13	8	1
4	5	9	0
5	3		

Test Your Hypothesis

Plan

1. With your group, **write** the hypothesis statement.
2. **Write** down the steps of the procedure you will use to test your hypothesis. Assume that each penny represents an atom in a radioactive sample. Each coin that lands heads up after flipping has decayed.
3. **List** the materials you will need.
4. In your Science Journal, **make a data table** with two columns. Label one *Half-Life* and the other *Atoms Remaining.*
5. Decide how you can use the pennies to represent the radioactive decay of an isotope.
6. **Determine** (a) what will represent one half-life in your model, and (b) how many half-lives you will investigate.
7. **Decide** (a) what variables there will be in your model, and (b) which variable will be represented on the y-axis of your graph and which will be represented on the x-axis.

Do

1. Make sure your teacher approves your plan and your data table before you proceed.
2. Carry out your plan.

Analyze Your Data

1. The relationship among the starting number of pennies, the number of pennies remaining (Y), and the number of half-lives (X) is the following:

$$Y = \frac{\text{(starting number of pennies)}}{2^X}$$

Graph this equation using a graphing calculator. Use your graph to find the number of pennies remaining after 2.5 half-lives.

2. **Compare** your results with those of other groups in your class.

Draw Conclusions

1. Is it possible to use your model to predict which individual atoms will decay during one half-life? Why or why not?
2. Can you predict the total number of atoms that will decay in one half-life? **Explain.**
3. How many half-lives are necessary for the transmutation of the entire sample?

Expected Outcome

Approximately one-half of the coins should land heads up in every toss. At the end of each toss, approximately one-half the number of coins remain undecayed.

Error Analysis

Have students compare their results with others. Did their results support their prediction that the coin toss could be a model for half-life? If not, have them determine whether they tossed the coins in any way that may have influenced how they landed.

Analyze Your Data

1. Student graphs should plot the number of tosses (half-lives) on the x-axis and the number of heads on the y-axis. The number of coins remaining after 2.5 half-lives will depend on the starting number of coins.

Draw Conclusions

1. You cannot predict which individual atoms will decay just as you cannot predict whether a coin will land heads up.
2. Yes, in each half-life, one half of the nuclei in a sample of a radioactive isotope will decay.
3. Students may suggest it is the number of half-lives needed to reduce a sample to a negligible mass or to a single atom.

GO Further

Have students research to find the half-lives of iodine-131 and sulfur-35. Have them discover how these isotopes are used in medical science and in agriculture.

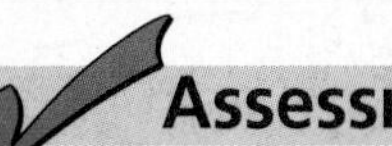

Assessment

Performance Have students total the number of coins used by the entire class and use what they have learned to make a diagram or graph that shows how many half-lives would be needed to decay the entire sample. Some students might use a model such as the one in **Figure 2-19.** Use **Performance Assessment in the Science Classroom,** p. 39.

2-2 The Nucleus 57

Reviewing Main Ideas can be used to preview, review, reteach, and condense chapter content.

Preview

Linguistic Have students try to answer the Reviewing Main Ideas questions in their Science Journals. Use student answers as a source for discussion throughout the chapter.

Review

Interpersonal Have students answer the questions on separate pieces of paper and compare their answers with those of other students in the class. COOP LEARN

Reteach

Visual-Spatial Have students look at the illustrations on these pages. Ask them to describe details that support the main ideas of the chapter found in the statement for each illustration.

00:00 OUT OF TIME?

Auditory-Musical If time does not permit teaching the entire chapter, use the information on these pages along with the chapter Audiocassettes to present the material in a condensed format.

Chapter 2 Reviewing Main Ideas

For a **preview** of this chapter, study this Reviewing Main Ideas before you read the chapter. After you have studied this chapter, you can use the Reviewing Main Ideas to **review** the chapter.

The Glencoe MindJogger, Audiocassettes, and CD-ROM provide additional opportunities for review.

Section

2-1 EARLY MODELS OF THE ATOM

The idea that matter is composed of indivisible atoms was first introduced in ancient Greece. In the eighteenth and nineteenth centuries, scientists performed experiments to determine the properties of an atom. John Dalton proposed that an atom is a sphere of matter that is the same throughout. Then, J.J. Thomson discovered that all atoms contain **electrons,** which are tiny, negatively charged particles. Thomson proposed that an atom is a sphere containing all the **protons** with their positive charges. The electrons are mixed uniformly in the sphere like raisins in a ball of cookie dough. ***How does the number of protons compare with the number of electrons?***

THE NUCLEAR ATOM

Ernest Rutherford tested Thomson's model by bombarding thin gold foil with speeding, positively charged **alpha particles.** Rutherford expected the alpha particles to pass through the foil because Dalton's model predicted there would be no large concentration of mass or charge to change the paths of the alpha particles. Because some of the alpha particles were deflected from their paths, Rutherford revised the model of the atom again. He hypothesized that almost all the mass and all the positive charge of an atom is concentrated in an extremely tiny nucleus at the center of the atom. ***Where are the electrons in this model of the atom?***

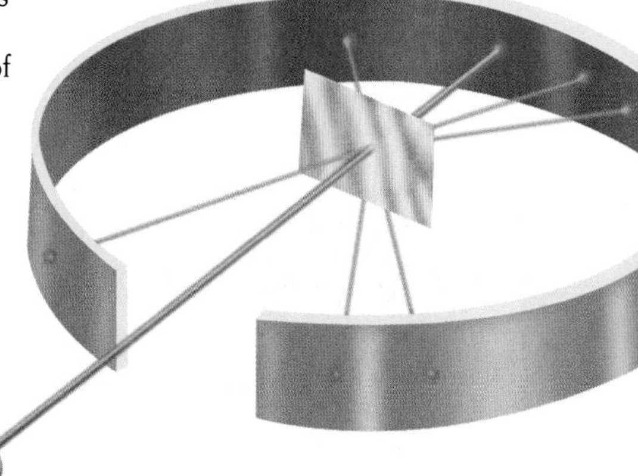

Cultural Diversity

Dr. Wu and Parity One of the foundations of physics was the law of atomic parity. Dr. Chien-Shiung Wu was able to disprove this basic law experimentally.

Dr. Wu's colleagues in the study were awarded the Nobel prize in 1957 for their theoretical contributions to the project, but Dr. Wu was overlooked. Dr. Wu, born near Shanghai, China, immigrated to the United States in 1936. At the age of 27, she served briefly as a physics instructor at Princeton—at a time when Princeton would not accept women as students. Dr. Wu was the first woman to receive the Comstock Prize from the National Academy of Sciences and the Research Corporation Award. In 1976, she received the U.S. Medal of Science. Today, Dr. Wu is a highly honored scienctist.

Reading Check

Should the early models of atom structure be labeled as fact or opinion? Explain your answer.

Section

2-2 RADIOACTIVITY

An atom's nucleus contains protons and neutrons held together by the strong nuclear force. If the numbers of neutrons and protons are not approximately equal, the nucleus can become unstable and undergo radioactive decay. Some nuclei decay by emitting an alpha particle. Other nuclei decay by ejecting a **beta particle.** Transmutation is a process in which one element is changed into another through radioactive decay. Some radioactive **isotopes** are made in this way by smashing speeding atomic particles into a target element. These isotopes may be used in medicine and for the study of the environment. ***What particles are released from the nucleus in alpha emission and in beta emission?***

HALF-LIFE

Half-life is a measure of the decay rate of a nucleus. It is the time needed for one-half of the mass of a sample of a radioactive isotope to decay. Half-lives vary from fractions of a second to billions of years. ***If an isotope has a half-life of 4 s, how many grams remain of a 100-g sample after 8 s have passed?***

Answers to Questions

Section 2-1

Early Models of the Atom The number of protons is the same as the number of electrons in a neutral atom.

The Nuclear Atom The electrons are located in a sphere outside the nucleus.

Section 2-2

Radioactivity In alpha emission, an alpha particle consisting of two protons and two neutrons is released. In beta emission, an electron is released.

Half-Life 25 g

GLENCOE TECHNOLOGY

CD-ROM

Glencoe Science Voyages Interactive CD-ROM

Chapter Summaries and Quizzes

Have students read the Chapter Summary and then take the Chapter Quiz to determine whether they have mastered chapter content.

Assessment

Portfolio Encourage students to place in their portfolios one or two items of what they consider to be their best work. Examples include:

Science Journal, pp. 39, 43
Multiple Learning Styles, p. 41
Inclusion Strategies, p. 42
Enrichment, p. 52 P

Performance Additional performance assessments may be found in **Performance Assessment** and **Science Integration Activities.** Performance Task Assessment Lists and rubrics for evaluating these activities can be found in Glencoe's **Performance Assessment in the Science Classroom.**

Chapter 2 Assessment

Using Vocabulary

1. An alpha particle has a positive charge and consists of two protons and two neutrons. A beta particle is an electron that is negatively charged.
2. An electron is a negatively charged particle. A proton is a positively charged particle about 2000 times more massive than an electron.
3. Mass number is the number of protons and neutrons in a nucleus. Atomic number is the number of protons.
4. An element is a substance made up of one kind of atom. An isotope is one of a number of different forms of the atoms of an element, each having a different number of neutrons. Isotopes of an element have the same number of protons and the same properties.
5. Radioactive decay is the release of nuclear particles and energy. Half-life is the rate of radioactive decay.

*inter***NET** CONNECTION To reinforce chapter vocabulary, use the **Study Guide for Content Mastery** booklet. Also available are activities for **Glencoe Science Voyages** on the Glencoe Science Web Site. **www.glencoe.com/sec/science**

Checking Concepts

6. B	11. C
7. C	12. D
8. D	13. B
9. A	14. B
10. D	15. D

Chapter 2 Assessment

Using Vocabulary

a. atomic number
b. electron
c. electron cloud
d. element
e. half-life
f. isotope
g. mass number
h. neutron
i. proton
j. radioactive decay

Explain the difference between terms in each of the following sets.

1. alpha particle, beta particle
2. electron, proton
3. mass number, atomic number
4. element, isotope
5. half-life, radioactive decay

Checking Concepts

Choose the word or phrase that best answers the question.

6. What is the atomic number of an element equal to?
   A) the number of energy levels in an atom
   B) the number of protons in an atom's nucleus
   C) the number of neutrons in an atom's nucleus
   D) the total number of protons and neutrons in an atom's nucleus
7. The atomic number of boron is 5, so boron-11 contains which particles?
   A) 11 electrons
   B) five neutrons
   C) five protons and six neutrons
   D) six protons and five neutrons
8. What are atoms of the same element that have different numbers of neutrons?
   A) protons
   B) electrons
   C) ions
   D) isotopes
9. In beta decay, a neutron in the nucleus of an isotope is converted to which of the following?
   A) a proton and an electron
   B) a nucleus
   C) an alpha particle
   D) a beta particle
10. What is the process by which an atom of one element changes into an atom of another element?
    A) half-life
    B) a chemical reaction
    C) a chain reaction
    D) transmutation
11. How did William Crookes know that the glow in the cathode-ray tube resulted from a stream of charged particles?
    A) It was green.
    B) It caused a shadow of the anode.
    C) It was deflected by a magnet.
    D) It occurred only when the battery was connected.
12. Why did Rutherford infer that most of the mass and all of the positive charge in an atom is in a tiny nucleus?
    A) All of the alpha particles went straight through the gold foil.
    B) None of the alpha particles went straight through the gold foil.
    C) The positive and negative charges were uniform throughout the atom.
    D) Only a concentrated charge could deflect energetic alpha particles.
13. What did J.J. Thomson's experiment show?
    A) The atom is like a uniform sphere.
    B) Cathode rays are made up of electrons.
    C) All atoms undergo radioactive decay.
    D) Isotopes undergo radioactive decay.

60 CHAPTER 2 INSIDE THE ATOM

14. A radioactive isotope has a half-life of two years. At the end of four years, how much of the original isotope remains?
A) one half C) one third
B) one fourth D) none

15. How can the model of the nuclear atom be described?
A) a nucleus that can decay
B) a ball of raisin cookie dough
C) an electron cloud
D) a nucleus in an electron cloud

Thinking Critically

16. How is it possible for atoms of an element to have different masses?

17. Matter can neither be created nor destroyed, but would it be possible for the amounts of some elements in Earth's crust to decrease? Increase?

18. Why must a neutral atom have the same number of protons and electrons?

Developing Skills

If you need help, refer to the Skill Handbook.

19. **Predicting:** If radium-226 releases an alpha particle, what is the mass number of the isotope formed?

20. **Using Graphs:** The radioactive decay of an isotope is plotted in the graph. What is the half-life of the isotope? How many grams of the isotope remain after three half-lives?

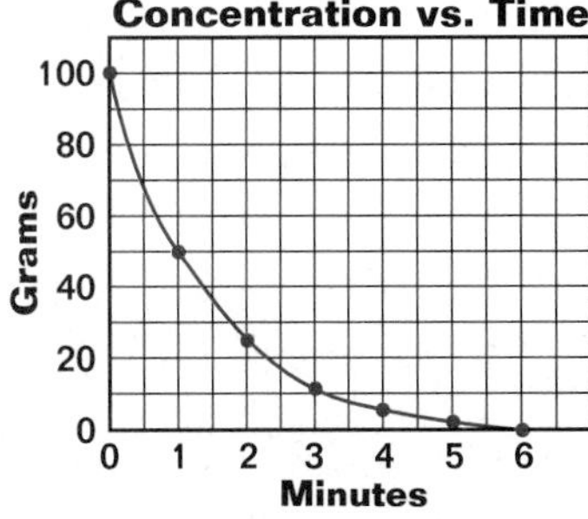

Test-Taking Tip

Use Process of Elimination On any multiple-choice test, you can use a process of elimination to exlude any answers that you know are wrong. Find the ones you know are wrong, eliminate them, and you'll have fewer choices from which to select your answer.

Test Practice

Use these questions to test your Science Proficiency.

1. What did Rutherford's alpha particle experiment show?
A) Electrons have a negative charge.
B) Most of the mass and all of the positive charge of an atom is found in a tiny nucleus.
C) A proton is a hydrogen atom without its electron.
D) Electrons circle the nucleus of an atom in orbits.

2. What is the difference between chlorine-35 and chlorine-37?
A) Chlorine-37 has two more electrons than chlorine-35.
B) Chlorine-37 has two more protons than chlorine-35.
C) Chlorine-37 has two more neutrons than chlorine-35.
D) Chlorine-37 has one more proton and one more neutron than chlorine-35.

The Test-Taking Tip was written by The Princeton Review, the nation's leader in test preparation.

1. B
2. C

Thinking Critically

16. Atoms of an element may be isotopes and have different numbers of neutrons.

17. Through transmutation, atoms of an element can change into atoms of another element. Therefore, the amount of the first element decreases as the amount of the second element increases. The amount of mass remains the same.

18. To be neutral, the positive charges of the protons must be equal to the negative charges of the electrons.

Developing Skills

19. 222
20. 1 min; 12.5 g

Bonus Question

How are radioactive isotopes used in the preservation of food and in experiments to monitor plant growth? *Radiation kills bacteria in food and increases shelf life. Radioactive isotopes can be added to soil nutrients. When they are taken up by plants, the radioactivity can be monitored by detectors as it moves through the plant system.*

Assessment Resources

The **Test Practice Workbook** provides students with practice in the format, concepts, and critical-thinking skills tested in standardized exams.

Reproducible Masters

Chapter Review, pp. 3–4 L2
Performance Assessment, p. 16 L2
Assessment, pp. 5–8 L2

Glencoe Technology

Chapter Review Software
Computer Test Bank
MindJogger Videoquiz

Chapter 3 The Periodic Table

Section	Objectives	Activities/Features
Chapter Opener		**Explore Activity:** Model a Periodic Pattern, p. 63
3-1 **Introduction to the Periodic Table** 1½ Sessions, 1 Block	1. **Describe** the historical development of the modern periodic table. 2. **Interpret** the element key of any element. 3. **Explain** the organization of a modern periodic table.	**MiniLab:** Designing the Periodic Table, p. 65 **Using Math,** p. 70 **Skill Builder:** Classifying, p. 71 **Using Math,** p. 71
3-2 **The Representative Elements** 4 Sessions, 2 Blocks	4. **Identify** properties of the representative elements. 5. **State** some uses for the representative elements.	**Life Science Integration:** A Strand of Evidence, p. 79 **Problem Solving:** Predicting Periodicity, p. 79 **MiniLab:** Inferring the Presence of Chlorine, p. 80 **Skill Builder:** Predicting, p. 82 **Using Computers,** p. 82 **Activity 3-1:** Preparing an Alloy, p. 83
3-3 **The Transition Elements** 3½ Sessions, 2 Blocks	6. **Identify** properties of the transition elements. 7. **Distinguish** lanthanides from actinides.	**Using Math,** p. 87 **Skill Builder:** Observing and Inferring, p. 88 **Science Journal,** p. 88 **Science and Society:** Dentistry and the Elements, p. 89 **Activity 3-2:** Health Risks from Heavy Metals, pp. 90–91

The number of recommended single-period sessions. The number of recommended blocks.
One session and one-half block are allowed for chapter review and assessment.

Activity Materials

Explore	Activities	MiniLabs
Page 63 pencil, paper, colored paper, scissors	Page 83 copper penny, zinc 30, mesh; hot plate, diluted nitric acid, diluted sodium hydroxide, 2 evaporating dishes, tongs, beaker of cold tap water Page 90-91 computer	Page 65 No materials needed Page 80 2 mL salt water, 2 mL distilled water, 2 mL tap water, test tubes, silver nitrate, dropper

Need Materials? Contact Science Kit at 1-800-828-7777 or at www.sciencekit.com on the Internet.
For alternate materials, see the activity on the listed page.

Standards		Reproducible Resources	Technology
National	State/Local	Test Practice Workbooks are available for use with each chapter.	English and Spanish audiocassettes are available for use with each section.
National Content Standards: B1, C3, G3		**Activity Worksheets,** p. 15 **Enrichment,** p. 5 **Laboratory Manual,** pp. 13–14 **Reinforcement,** p. 5 **Study Guide,** pp. 9–10 **Home Involvement,** p. 26	**Section Focus Transparency 5** **Teaching Transparency 5** **Glencoe Science Voyages Interactive Videodisc—Physical** **Glencoe Science Voyages Interactive Videodisc—Earth** **The Infinite Voyage Series** **Glencoe Science Voyages Interactive CD-ROM**
National Content Standards: B1, B3, C3, D1, E2, F4, G3		**Activity Worksheets,** pp. 13–14, 16 **Enrichment,** p. 6 **Reinforcement,** p. 6 **Study Guide,** p. 11	**Section Focus Transparency 6** **Teaching Transparency 6** **Glencoe Science Voyages Interactive Videodisc—Physical** **The Infinite Voyage Series** **Internet Connection,** p. 82
National Content Standards: B1, E2, G3		**Critical Thinking/Problem Solving,** p. 3 **Enrichment,** p. 7 **Laboratory Manual,** pp. 15–16 **Multicultural Connections,** pp. 5–6 **Reinforcement,** p. 7 **Study Guide,** pp. 11–12	**Section Focus Transparency 7** **Teaching Transparency 6** **Science Integration Transparency 3** **Glencoe Science Voyages Interactive Videodisc—Earth** **The Infinite Voyage Series** **Internet Connection,** p. 89

Key to Teaching Strategies

The following designations will help you decide which activities are appropriate for your students.

L1 Level 1 activities should be appropriate for students with learning difficulties.

L2 Level 2 activities should be within the ability range of all students.

L3 Level 3 activities are designed for above-average students.

ELL ELL activities should be within the ability range of English Language Learners.

COOP LEARN Cooperative Learning activities are designed for small group work.

P These strategies represent student products that can be placed into a best-work portfolio.

Multiple Learning Styles logos, as described on page 61T, are used throughout to indicate strategies that address different learning styles.

Assessment Resources

Chapter Review, pp. 5–6
Assessment, pp. 9–12
Performance Assessment in the Science Classroom (PASC)
MindJogger Videoquiz
Alternate Assessment in the Science Classroom
Performance Assessment, p. 17
Chapter Review Software
Computer Test Bank

Chapter 3 The Periodic Table

This is a representation of key blackline masters available in the Teacher Classroom Resources. See Resource Manager boxes within the chapter for additional information.

Transparencies

Section Focus Transparencies

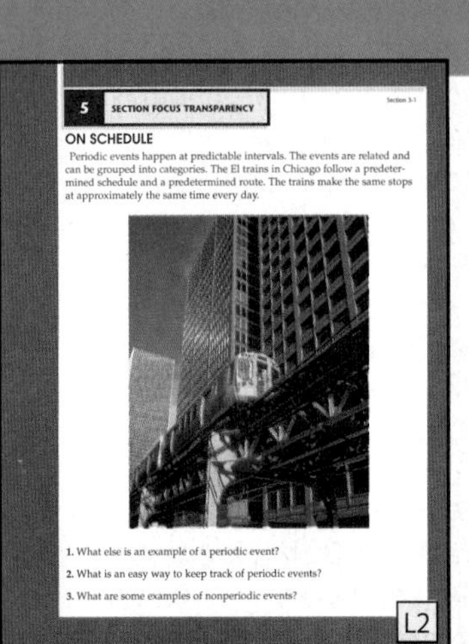

5 SECTION FOCUS TRANSPARENCY
ON SCHEDULE
Periodic events happen at predictable intervals. The events are related and can be grouped into categories. The El trains in Chicago follow a predetermined schedule and a predetermined route. The trains make the same stops at approximately the same time every day.
1. What else is an example of a periodic event?
2. What is an easy way to keep track of periodic events?
3. What are some examples of nonperiodic events?
L2

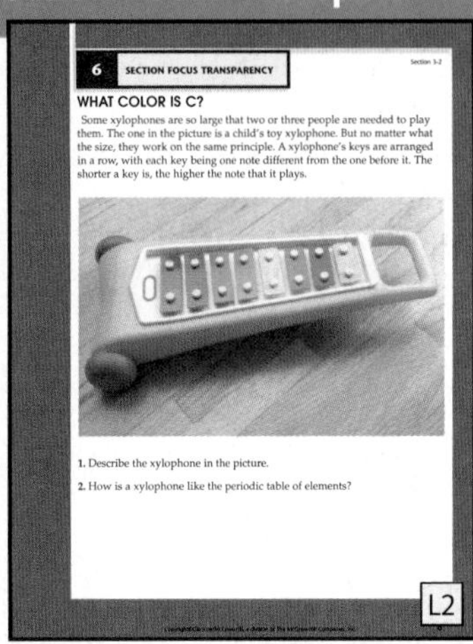

6 SECTION FOCUS TRANSPARENCY
WHAT COLOR IS C?
Some xylophones are so large that two or three people are needed to play them. The one in the picture is a child's toy xylophone. But no matter what the size, they work on the same principle. A xylophone's keys are arranged in a row, with each key being one note different from the one before it. The shorter a key is, the higher the note that it plays.
1. Describe the xylophone in the picture.
2. How is a xylophone like the periodic table of elements?
L2

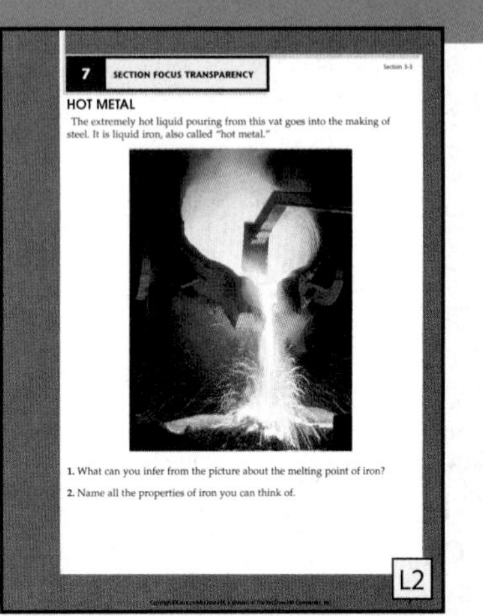

7 SECTION FOCUS TRANSPARENCY
HOT METAL
The extremely hot liquid pouring from this vat goes into the making of steel. It is liquid iron, also called "hot metal."
1. What can you infer from the picture about the melting point of iron?
2. Name all the properties of iron you can think of.
L2

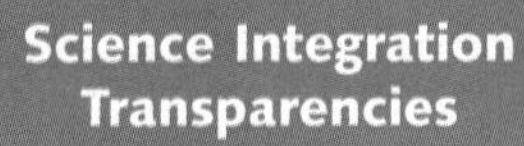

Science Integration Transparencies

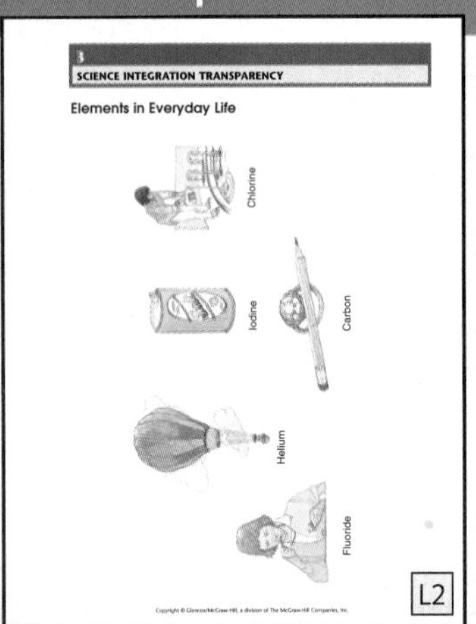

Teaching Transparencies

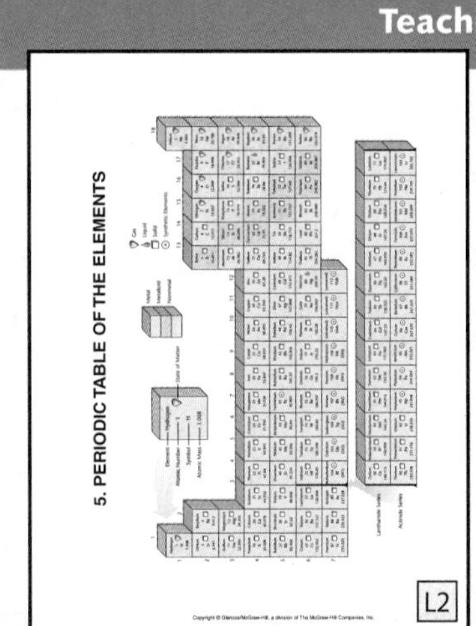

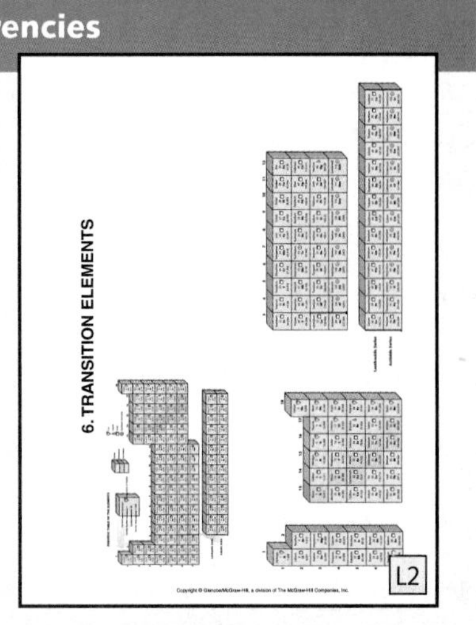

Meeting Different Ability Levels

Study Guide for Content Mastery

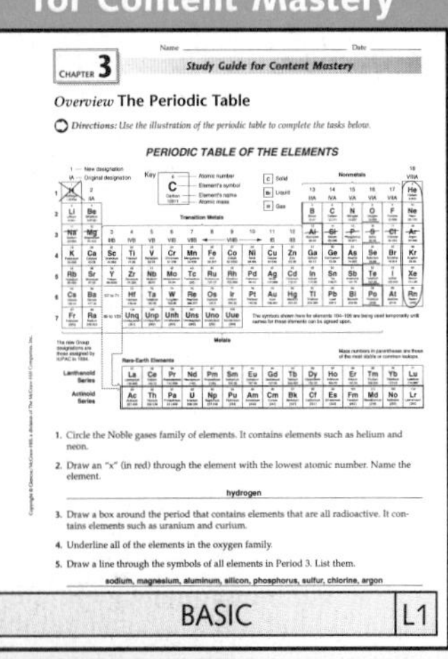

Reinforcement

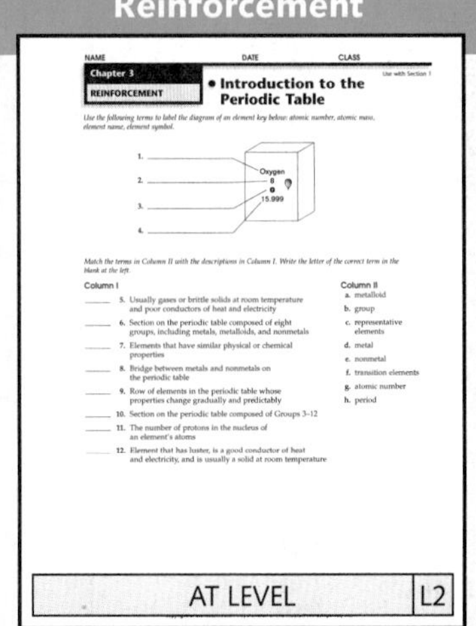

Enrichment Worksheets

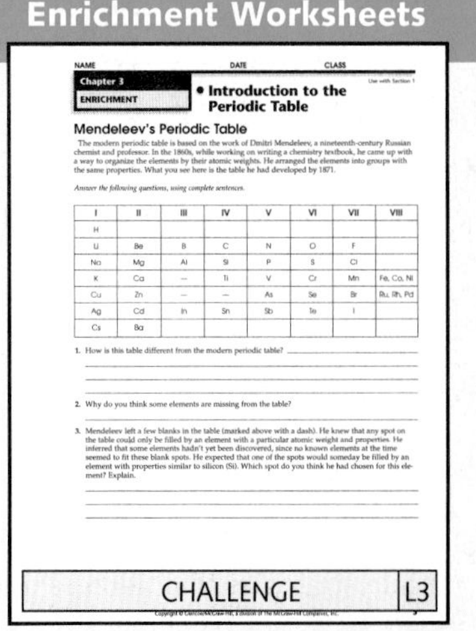

Resource Manager

Hands-on Activities

Activity Worksheets

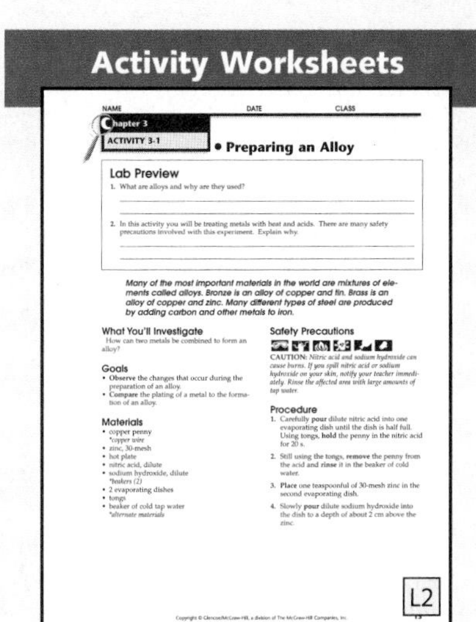
Chapter 3
ACTIVITY 3-1
• Preparing an Alloy
Lab Preview
Many of the most important materials in the world are mixtures of elements called alloys. Bronze is an alloy of copper and tin. Brass is an alloy of copper and zinc. Many different types of steel are produced by adding carbon and other metals to iron.
What You'll Investigate
Safety Precautions
Goals
Materials
Procedure
L2

Lab Manual

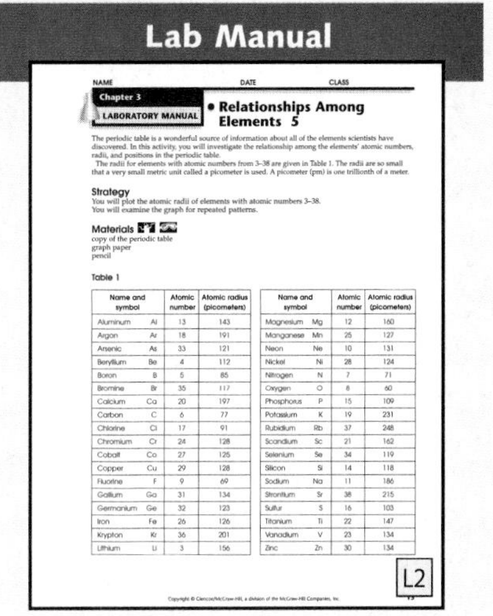
Chapter 3
LABORATORY MANUAL
• Relationships Among Elements 5
Strategy
Materials
Table 1
L2

Accessibility

Spanish Resources

SPANISH RESOURCES
GLENCOE
SCIENCE VOYAGES
Exploring the Life, Earth, and Physical Sciences
LEVEL BLUE
L2

Assessment

Performance Assessment

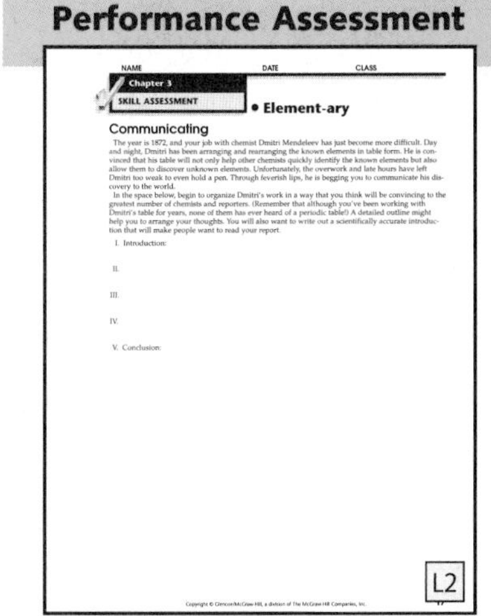
Chapter 3
SKILL ASSESSMENT
• Element-ary
Communicating
L2

Chapter Review

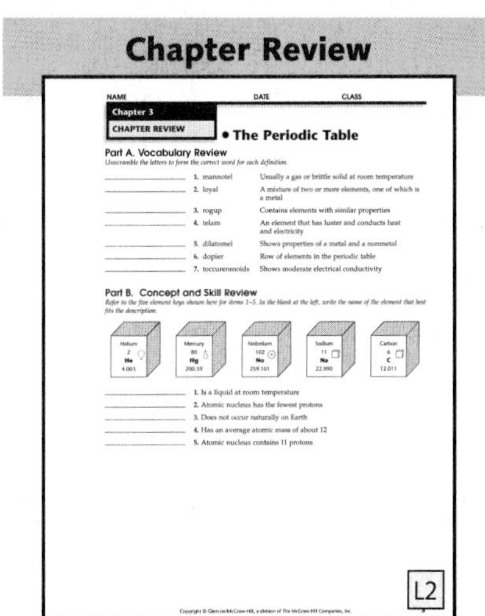
Chapter 3
CHAPTER REVIEW
• The Periodic Table
Part A. Vocabulary Review
Part B. Concept and Skill Review
L2

Assessment

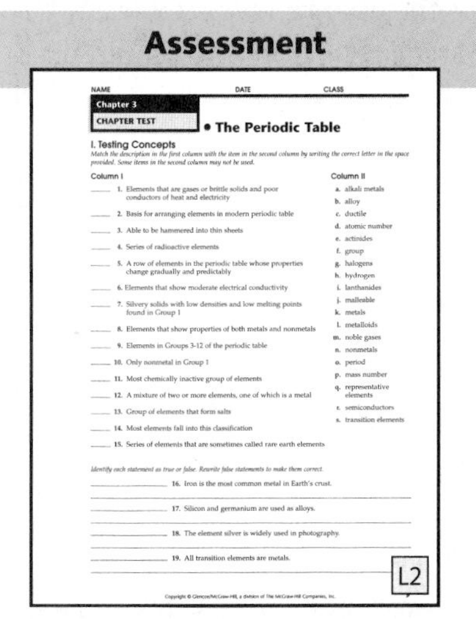
Chapter 3
CHAPTER TEST
• The Periodic Table
I. Testing Concepts
L2

Test Practice Workbook

STANDARDIZED TEST PRACTICE
STUDENT EDITION
GLENCOE
SCIENCE VOYAGES
Exploring the Life, Earth, and Physical Sciences
LEVEL BLUE
L2

Extending Content

Critical Thinking/ Problem Solving

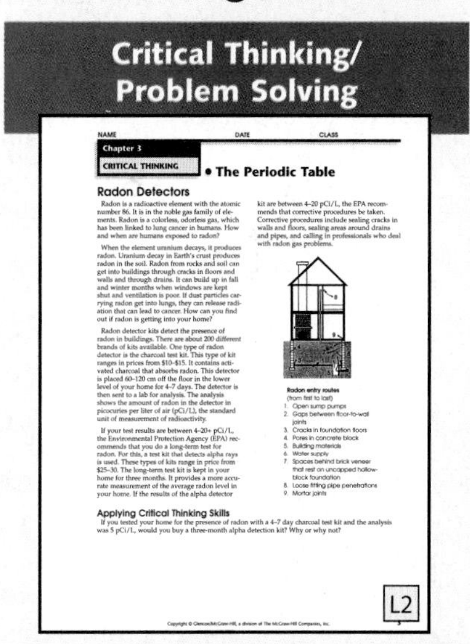
Chapter 3
CRITICAL THINKING
• The Periodic Table
Radon Detectors
Applying Critical Thinking Skills
L2

Multicultural Connections

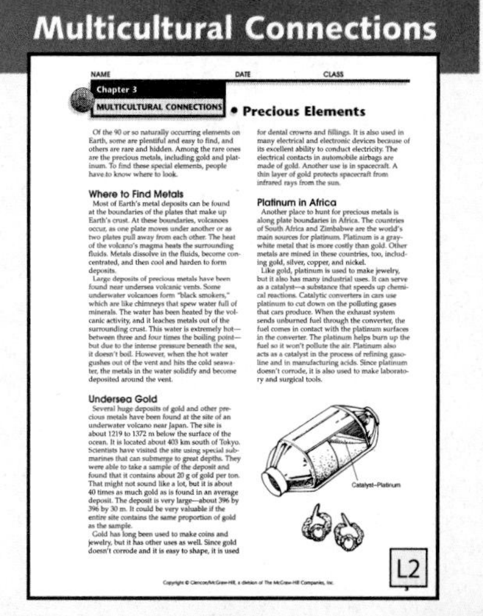
Chapter 3
MULTICULTURAL CONNECTIONS
• Precious Elements
Where to Find Metals
Platinum in Africa
Undersea Gold
L2

Helping You Prepare

Development of the Periodic Table (Section 3-1)

As the science of chemistry grew during the nineteenth century, chemists amassed a great deal of information about known elements and their chemistry. Chemists could analyze compounds, such as the oxides of the elements, and determine the ratios of combining atoms. They found different ratios depending upon the metal atom with which oxygen was combined, but some elements combined with oxygen in the same ratio. For example, magnesium and calcium form oxides with a 1:1 ratio.

Such information helped in the search for an organizing principle for the elements. In 1817, the German chemist Johann Dobereiner found that he could arrange many elements into groups that he called triads. For example, he noticed that lithium, sodium, and potassium react vigorously with water. When these elements are arranged in order of atomic mass, the mass of the middle element, sodium, is almost the same as the average of the lightest and heaviest elements. Similar regularities were uncovered for calcium, strontium, and barium, and for fluorine, chlorine, and bromine.

Dobereiner's early work laid the groundwork for other chemists in the search for an organizing principle based upon similarities in chemical properties and trends in atomic mass. In 1864, English chemist John Newlands proposed that when the known elements were arranged according to atomic mass, similarities in chemical properties occurred with every eighth element. He called this regularity the law of octaves.

The German chemist Lothar Meyer devised a periodic table for his chemistry textbook that proved to be much like Mendeleev's, but the publication of this table came after Mendeleev's, so Mendeleev is given most of the credit for the first useful periodic table. Not only did the table organize the elements in a useful way, it also allowed scientists to predict the properties of unknown elements. These predictions helped guide the search for the missing elements.

The modern periodic table didn't come into being until a Dutch physicist, Anton van den Brock, proposed that the elements should be arranged according to nuclear charge rather than atomic mass. Henry Mosely confirmed this hypothesis through studies of the X-ray spectra of a series of elements that had consecutive positions on the table. The change to ordering by atomic number resulted in the reversal of the positions of some elements. The table that emerged reflects the nuclear and electronic structure of the atom.

GLENCOE TECHNOLOGY

 **CD-ROM**

Glencoe Science Voyages Interactive CD-ROM

Chapter Summaries

Use the Chapter Summary to introduce, teach, or review chapter material.

Sections of the Periodic Table (Section 3-2)

The periodic table divides into sections of representative elements, transition elements, and inner transition elements. The sections of the table reflect the electron configurations of the elements and the sublevels occupied by the electrons. For every principal quantum number, there are sublevels designated by letters, such as *s, p, d,* and *f*. Electrons enter sublevels in the order 1*s*, 2*s*, 2*p*, 3*s*, 3*p*, 4*s*, 3*d*, 4*p*, 5*s*, 4*d*, 5*p*, 6*s*, 4*f*, 5*d*, 6*p*, 7*s*, 5*f*, and 6*d*, where 1, 2, 3, 4, 5, 6, and 7 are electron energy levels. The sublevels don't always fill in the order given above because the outer parts of the energy levels overlap.

In the sublevels, electrons are paired up in orbitals. For each *s* sublevel, there is one orbital that can hold two electrons; there are three *p* orbitals that can hold six electrons, five *d* orbitals with room for ten electrons, and seven *f* orbitals that hold 14 electrons.

Each element in the periodic table has one more electron in its outer energy level than the element that precedes it. As you move across any period of the table, Groups 1 and 2 are filling *s* orbitals with two electrons. Groups 13–18 are filling *p* orbitals with six electrons. In periods 4 through 7, the transition elements, Groups 2–12, are filling five *d* orbitals with ten electrons. The *d* orbitals are slightly lower in energy than

the *s* electrons of the same period. The inner transition elements, located below the periodic table, are filling the 4*f* and 5*f* orbitals with 14 electrons. It is the electron configuration of the atom that determines its chemical reactivity.

From Metals to Nonmetals

(Section 3-2)

The alkali metals have one electron in an outer *s* orbital. This single electron is in a higher energy level than any inner level of electrons, and the inner electrons shield it from the full attractive force of the nucleus. As a result, relatively little energy is needed to remove the electron, and thus ionize the atom. Therefore, the chemistry of the alkali metals revolves around the 1+ ion. As you move down the alkali metal group, the outermost *s* electron is farther and farther from the nucleus and ionization becomes successively easier. As a result, the reactivity of the alkali metals increases down the family.

The alkaline earth metals have two electrons in an outer *s* orbital. The energy needed to remove both of these electrons and achieve the noble gas configuration is low enough to make this group of elements almost as active as the alkali metals. Their chemistry is the chemistry of the 2+ ion. The activity of the Group 2 elements increases down the group because ionization energies decrease down the group.

As nuclear charge increases across Groups 13–18, shielding by inner electrons becomes less effective. Ionization energies increase, so the compounds of Groups 13, 14, and 15 are more covalent than ionic. Groups 16 and 17, however, have electron affinities high enough to attract and hold one or two electrons and form, for example, the O^{2-} and Cl^{-} ions. Electron affinity measures the readiness of an element to attract and hold an extra electron. The trend in reactivity for the oxygen group and the halogens is opposite that of Groups 1 and 2. Fluorine is the most active of the halogens, and activity decreases down the group.

The Metals in the Middle

(Section 3-3)

Across any period of transition elements, the elements tend to be more similar than different. That is because electrons are being added to the same large energy sublevels.

SCIENCE UPDATE

For current events or science in the news, access the Glencoe Science Web Site at **www.glencoe.com/sec/science**

Teacher to Teacher

"A game I have found helpful for reviewing I call "Who Am I?" Each student is given an element with which to become familiar. On game day, the class may ask a student five questions in order to identify his or her identity. I reward each student who correctly identifies an element."

Deborah P Huffine

Deborah Peters Huffine, Teacher
Noblesville Intermediate School
Noblesville, IN

CHAPTER 3
The Periodic Table

CHAPTER OVERVIEW

Section 3-1 The development of the periodic table is discussed. Information that can be used to interpret the table is provided.

Section 3-2 Each group of representative elements is discussed in terms of trends in activity within the group and uses for individual elements.

Section 3-3 General properties of transition elements are discussed with attention given to the properties and uses of some common metals.

Chapter Vocabulary

period
group
metal
nonmetal
metalloid
alloy
semiconductor

Theme Connection

Stability and Change The periodic table reflects the changing reactivity of the elements across each period and down each group. These changes are related to the atom's tendency to form chemical bonds and thereby increase stability.

If time does not permit teaching the entire chapter, use Reviewing Main Ideas on pp. 92–93.

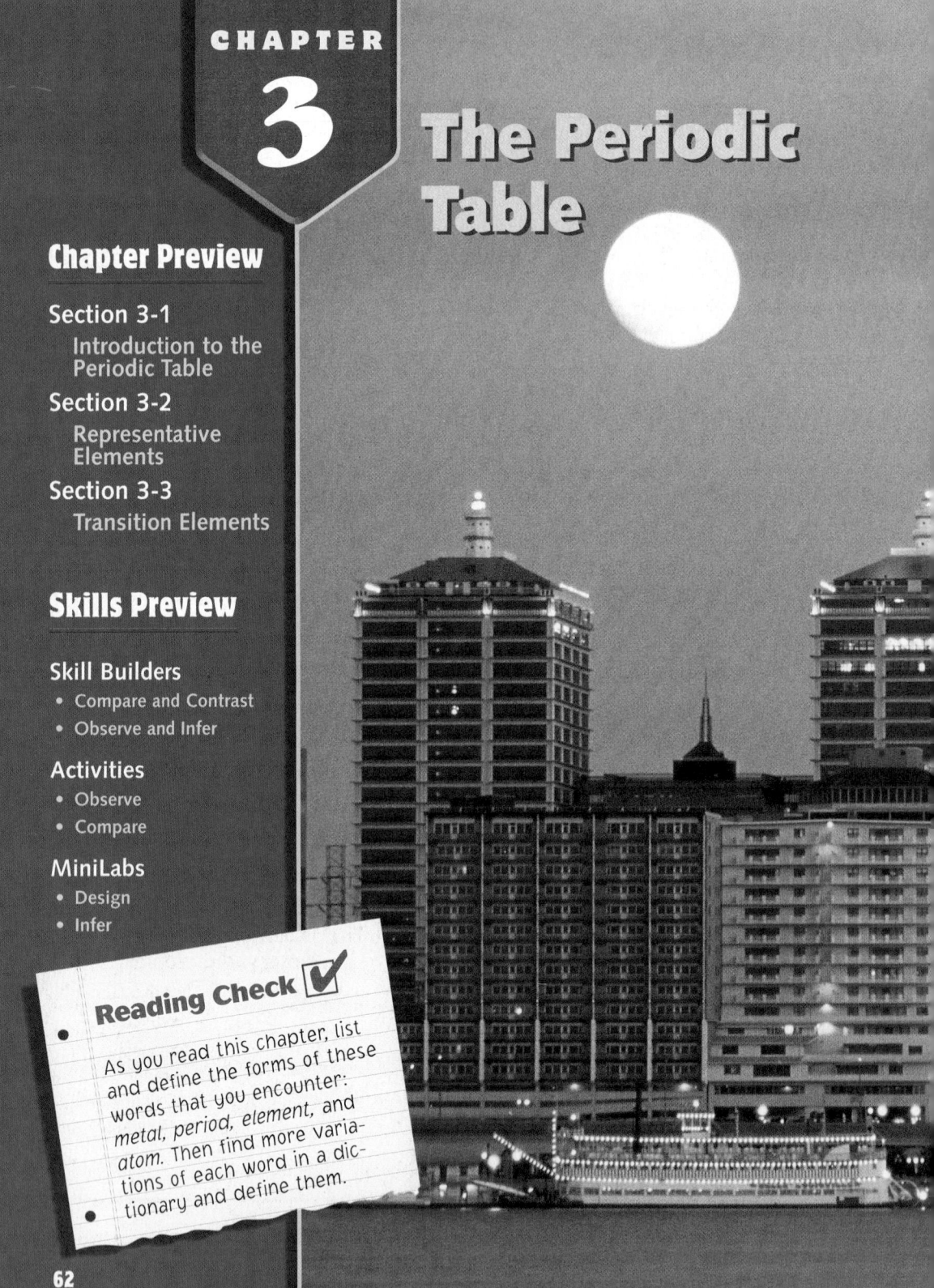

CHAPTER 3
The Periodic Table

Chapter Preview

Section 3-1
Introduction to the Periodic Table
Section 3-2
Representative Elements
Section 3-3
Transition Elements

Skills Preview

Skill Builders
- Compare and Contrast
- Observe and Infer

Activities
- Observe
- Compare

MiniLabs
- Design
- Infer

Reading Check

As you read this chapter, list and define the forms of these words that you encounter: *metal, period, element,* and *atom.* Then find more variations of each word in a dictionary and define them.

62

Multiple Learning Styles

Look for the following logos for strategies that emphasize different learning modalities.

Linguistic Activity, p. 70; Assessment, pp. 71, 82; Science Journal, pp. 74, 86; Across the Curriculum, p. 76; Inclusion Strategies, p. 80; Preview, p. 92

Logical-Mathematical Using Math, p. 70

Visual-Spatial Explore Activity, p. 63; Quick Demo, pp. 66, 69, 74; Multiple Learning Styles, p. 68; Reteach, pp. 70, 81, 92; MiniLab, p. 80; Assessment, p. 83; Activity, p. 83

Auditory-Musical Out of Time, p. 92

Kinesthetic MiniLab, p. 65; Inclusion Strategies, p. 67; Activity, p. 77

Interpersonal Activity, pp. 69, 81, 87; Multiple Learning Styles, p. 78; Visual Learning, p. 85; Review, p. 92

Intrapersonal Using an Analogy, p. 68

Explore Activity

Every 29.5 days, the full moon rises over Louisville, Kentucky, and begins to cycle through its phases from full moon to new moon and back again to full moon. This monthly cycle was one of the earliest patterns recognized and recorded by humans. Events that follow a predictable pattern are called periodic events. Modern calendars are based on a different periodic event—Earth's yearly journey around the sun. The opening of school in the fall and the celebration of your birthday are periodic events. What other periodic events can you think of?

Model a Periodic Pattern

1. On a blank sheet of paper, make a grid with four squares across and four squares down. The grid should fill the sheet of paper.
2. Your teacher will give you 16 pieces of paper with different shapes and colors. Identify properties you can use to distinguish one piece of paper from another.
3. Place a piece of paper in each square on your grid. Arrange the pieces on the grid so that each column contains pieces that are similar.
4. Within each column, arrange the pieces to show a gradual change in their appearance.

In your Science Journal, describe the patterns you created. Explain how the properties change in the rows across the grid and in the columns down the grid.

Explore Activity

Purpose

Visual-Spatial Use the Explore Activity to help students classify items according to properties. L2 ELL COOP LEARN

Preparation

For the 16 cutouts, use four colors. For example, cut red circles with diameters of 5 cm, 4 cm, 3 cm, and 2 cm. Cut orange circles having the same diameters and remove a wedge-shaped quarter of the circle. Cut yellow circles and divide them in half. Cut white circles and divide them into quarters.

Materials

sheet of paper (1), set of precut shapes with four of each shape in four different colors for each group of students

Teaching Strategies

Allow students to experiment. Some may arrange the pieces in columns of like color with the largest cutout on top; others may place the smallest cutout on top.

Answers will vary depending on student patterns. Check to see that descriptions and tables match.

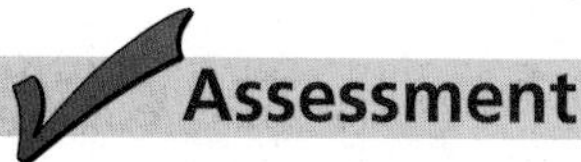

Assessment

Oral Ask students how their tables might be a model for elements if they were placed in a table. Use **Performance Assessment in the Science Classroom,** p. 49.

Assessment Planner

Portfolio
Refer to p. 93 for suggested items that students might select for their portfolios.

Performance Assessment
See p. 93 for additional Performance Assessment options.
Skill Builder, pp. 71, 82, 88
MiniLab, pp. 65, 80
Activity 3-1, p. 83; 3-2, pp. 90–91

Content Assessment
Section Assessment, pp. 71, 82, 88
Chapter Assessment, pp. 94–95
Proficiency Prep, pp. 71, 82, 88

SECTION 3-1

Prepare

Refer to **Development of the Periodic Table** on p. 62E.

Preplanning

Refer to the **Chapter Organizer** on pp. 62A–B.

1 Motivate

Bellringer

Before presenting the lesson, display **Section Focus Transparency 5** on the overhead projector. Use the accompanying **Focus Activity** worksheet. L2 ELL

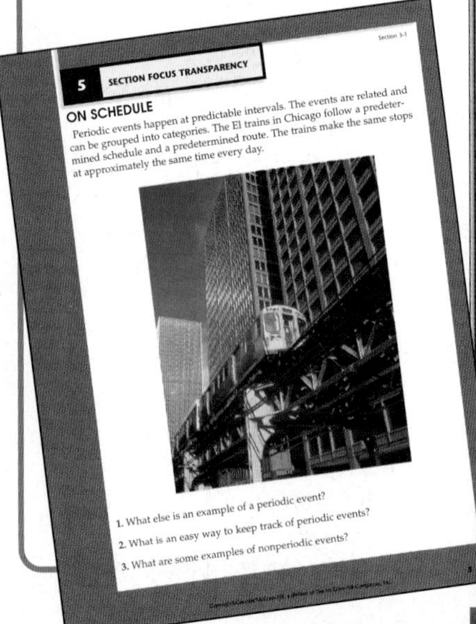

5 SECTION FOCUS TRANSPARENCY

Section 3-1

ON SCHEDULE

Periodic events happen at predictable intervals. The events are related and can be grouped into categories. The El trains in Chicago follow a predetermined schedule and a predetermined route. The trains make the same stops at approximately the same time every day.

1. What else is an example of a periodic event?
2. What is an easy way to keep track of periodic events?
3. What are some examples of nonperiodic events?

Tying to Previous Knowledge

Students know that atoms of different elements contain different numbers of protons. Now they will learn that atomic number determines the position of an element in the periodic table.

3-1 Introduction to the Periodic Table

What You'll Learn

- The history of the periodic table
- How to interpret an element key
- How the periodic table is organized

Vocabulary

period, group, metal, nonmetal, metalloid

Why It's Important

- The periodic table organizes a lot of information about the elements and makes it easier for you to learn.

Development of the Periodic Table

Early civilizations were familiar with a few of the substances scientists now call elements. They made coins and jewelry from gold and silver. Warriors at the Battle of Troy wore armor and carried shields made from bronze, a mixture of copper and tin. The Assyrians built an empire using steel weapons made by combining iron with carbon. In the nineteenth century, chemists began to search for new elements. By 1830, they had isolated and named 55 different elements. As the list of elements grew, chemists wondered how many elements were left to be discovered.

Mendeleev's Contribution

In 1860, the First International Chemical Congress met in Germany. One of the 140 delegates who attended was the Russian chemist Dmitri Mendeleev (men duh LAY uhf). When he returned to Russia, he used what he had learned at the congress to build a table of the elements. When Mendeleev arranged the elements in order of increasing atomic mass, as shown in **Figure 3-1,** he began to see a pattern. Elements with similar properties fell into groups on the table.

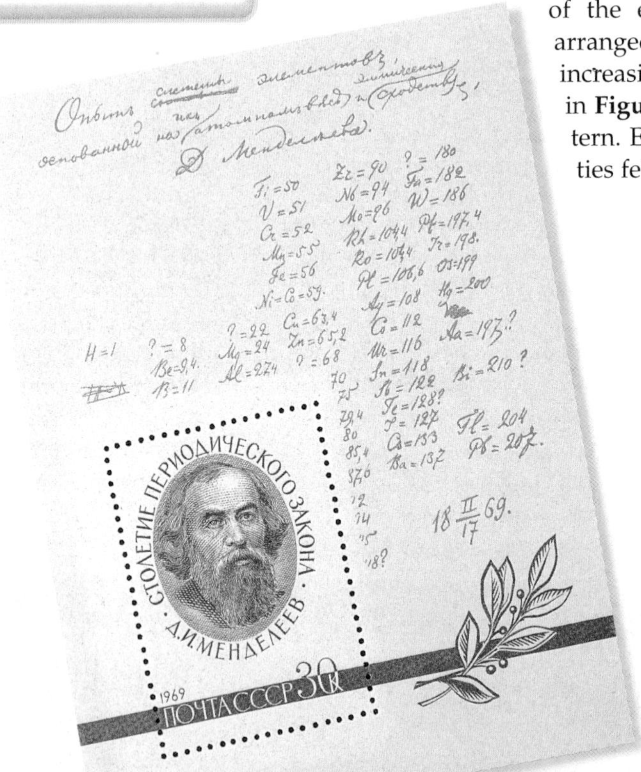

Figure 3-1 Mendeleev continued to work on this table. Notice where he put question marks. He predicted that elements would be discovered to fill these places on the table.

Resource Manager

The following **Teacher Classroom Resources** can be used with Section 3-1:

 **Reproducible Masters**

Activity Worksheets, p. 15 L2

Enrichment, p. 5 L3

Home Involvement, p. 26

Laboratory Manual, pp. 13–14 L2

Reinforcement, p. 5 L2

Study Guide, pp. 9–10 L1 ELL

 **Transparencies**

Teaching Transparency 5 L2

Mendeleev published the first version of his periodic table in the *Journal of the Russian Chemical Society* in 1869. At that time, not all the elements were known. To make his table work, Mendeleev had to leave gaps for undiscovered elements. Based on the groupings in his table, he predicted the properties for six of the unknown elements. Mendeleev's predictions spurred other chemists to look for the missing elements. Within 15 years, three of the missing elements—gallium, scandium, and germanium—were discovered. In **Table 3-1,** you can see that Mendeleev's predictions about germanium were close.

Table 3-1

Properties of Germanium		
Property	Predicted (1869)	Actual (1886)
Atomic mass	72	72.6
Melting point	very high	937°C
Density	5.5 g/cm^3	5.32 g/cm^3
Color	dark gray	gray-white

Moseley's Improvement

Although Mendeleev's table correctly organized most of the elements, a few elements seemed out of place. In the early twentieth century, the English physicist Henry Moseley realized that Mendeleev's table could be improved by arranging the elements according to atomic number rather than atomic mass. The atomic number of an element is the number of protons in the nucleus of its atoms. Each element in the table has one more proton than the previous element, so the atomic numbers of missing elements could be filled in by comparing the number of protons in each known element. With Moseley's table, it was clear how many elements were still undiscovered.

The Modern Periodic Table

In the table on the following pages, the elements are organized by increasing atomic number into rows or periods labeled 3-7. A **period** is a row of elements in the periodic table whose properties change gradually and predictably. The first period has only two elements. The second and third periods each have eight elements. Periods 4 and 5 have 18 elements. Period 6 has 32. New elements are still being added to period 7.

Try at Home MiniLab

Designing a Periodic Table

Procedure

1. Collect pens and pencils from everyone in your class.
2. Decide which properties of the pens and pencils you will use to organize them into a periodic table. Consider properties such as color, mass, or length. Then, create your table.

Analysis

1. Explain how your periodic table is similar to the periodic table of the elements.
2. If your classmates brought different pens or pencils to class tomorrow, how would you decide where to place them on the table?

2 Teach

Try at Home MiniLab

Purpose

Kinesthetic Students arrange writing utensils into a model of the periodic table. L2 ELL COOP LEARN

Materials

students' pencils and pens

Teaching Strategies

- Ask students to bring to school an extra pen or pencil.
- Have students compare and contrast the writing utensils and use the results as the rationale for setting up the table.

Analysis

1. Student tables could show that the writing utensils in a column have similar properties; for example, color, length, and shape. The properties of the utensils in a row change gradually.
2. Student answers will vary based on their tables but could include that you would place them in a column with similar utensils and in a row in which their properties were intermediate between the utensils to the right and left.

Assessment

Performance Have students make a calendar for the present month and write on it any events that they have scheduled, such as soccer practice or music lessons. Have them look for periodic events. Use **Performance Assessment in the Science Classroom,** p. 51. P

Inclusion Strategies

Visually Impaired The MiniLab can be revised to use a collection of small hardware pieces of various sizes such as screws, nuts, washers, and bolts.

Content Background

How did Mendeleev know that elements were missing from his periodic table? Mendeleev's first criterion in setting up his table was the atomic mass of the elements. But, he also was familiar with the physical properties and the chemistry of all the known elements. Mendeleev arranged the elements in his periodic table according to atomic mass. But, sometimes the atomic mass of an element placed it in a group with other elements that have different properties. He recognized that an undiscovered element probably belonged in that space. He marked the space with a question mark.

Quick Demo

Visual-Spatial Ask students why it might be helpful to classify elements. Then, use a conductivity tester to test a variety of pure elements. Touch the tester to each in turn and have students classify the elements as either conductors or non-conductors. L2

GLENCOE TECHNOLOGY

Videodisc

Glencoe Science Voyages Interactive Videodisc—Physical

Side 1, Lesson 4 *Periodicity*

32018

Refer to the Videodisc Teacher Guide for additional bar codes.

VISUALIZING The Periodic Table

PERIODIC TABLE OF THE ELEMENTS

Element — Hydrogen
Atomic Number — 1
Symbol — H
Atomic Mass — 1.008
State of Matter

	1	2	3	4	5	6	7	8	9
1	Hydrogen 1 **H** 1.008								
2	Lithium 3 **Li** 6.941	Beryllium 4 **Be** 9.012							
3	Sodium 11 **Na** 22.990	Magnesium 12 **Mg** 24.305							
4	Potassium 19 **K** 39.098	Calcium 20 **Ca** 40.078	Scandium 21 **Sc** 44.956	Titanium 22 **Ti** 47.88	Vanadium 23 **V** 50.942	Chromium 24 **Cr** 51.996	Manganese 25 **Mn** 54.938	Iron 26 **Fe** 55.847	Cobalt 27 **Co** 58.933
5	Rubidium 37 **Rb** 85.468	Strontium 38 **Sr** 87.62	Yttrium 39 **Y** 88.906	Zirconium 40 **Zr** 91.224	Niobium 41 **Nb** 92.906	Molybdenum 42 **Mo** 95.94	Technetium 43 **Tc** 97.907	Ruthenium 44 **Ru** 101.07	Rhodium 45 **Rh** 102.906
6	Cesium 55 **Cs** 132.905	Barium 56 **Ba** 137.327	Lanthanum 57 **La** 138.906	Hafnium 72 **Hf** 178.49	Tantalum 73 **Ta** 180.948	Tungsten 74 **W** 183.85	Rhenium 75 **Re** 186.207	Osmium 76 **Os** 190.2	Iridium 77 **Ir** 192.22
7	Francium 87 **Fr** 223.020	Radium 88 **Ra** 226.025	Actinium 89 **Ac** 227.028	Rutherfordium 104 **Rf** (261)	Dubnium 105 **Db** (262)	Seaborgium 106 **Sg** (263)	Bohrium 107 **Bh** (262)	Hassium 108 **Hs** (265)	Meitnerium 109 **Mt** (266)

Lanthanide Series	Cerium 58 **Ce** 140.115	Praseodymium 59 **Pr** 140.908	Neodymium 60 **Nd** 144.24	Promethium 61 **Pm** 144.913	Samarium 62 **Sm** 150.36	Europium 63 **Eu** 151.965
Actinide Series	Thorium 90 **Th** 232.038	Protactinium 91 **Pa** 231.036	Uranium 92 **U** 238.029	Neptunium 93 **Np** 237.048	Plutonium 94 **Pu** 244.064	Americium 95 **Am** 243.061

Inclusion Strategies

Gifted The German scientist Lothar Meyer published a periodic table that was almost identical to Mendeleev's table. Have students find out why Meyer was not given equal credit for the periodic table. *Mendeleev used his table to predict successfully the existence of undiscovered elements, and he spent the rest of his life promoting the validity of his table. Meyer's similarly useful table was published after Mendeleev's periodic table, so Mendeleev received the most credit.*

66 CHAPTER 3 THE PERIODIC TABLE

For an online update of this data, visit **www.glencoe.com/sec/science** and select the appropriate chapter.

Metal
Metalloid
Nonmetal

Gas
Liquid
Solid
Synthetic Elements

10	11	12	13	14	15	16	17	18
								Helium 2 **He** 4.003
			Boron 5 **B** 10.811	Carbon 6 **C** 12.011	Nitrogen 7 **N** 14.007	Oxygen 8 **O** 15.999	Fluorine 9 **F** 18.998	Neon 10 **Ne** 20.180
			Aluminum 13 **Al** 26.982	Silicon 14 **Si** 28.086	Phosphorus 15 **P** 30.974	Sulfur 16 **S** 32.066	Chlorine 17 **Cl** 35.453	Argon 18 **Ar** 39.948
Nickel 28 **Ni** 58.693	Copper 29 **Cu** 63.546	Zinc 30 **Zn** 65.39	Gallium 31 **Ga** 69.723	Germanium 32 **Ge** 72.61	Arsenic 33 **As** 74.922	Selenium 34 **Se** 78.96	Bromine 35 **Br** 79.904	Krypton 36 **Kr** 83.80
Palladium 46 **Pd** 106.42	Silver 47 **Ag** 107.868	Cadmium 48 **Cd** 112.411	Indium 49 **In** 114.82	Tin 50 **Sn** 118.710	Antimony 51 **Sb** 121.757	Tellurium 52 **Te** 127.60	Iodine 53 **I** 126.904	Xenon 54 **Xe** 131.290
Platinum 78 **Pt** 195.08	Gold 79 **Au** 196.967	Mercury 80 **Hg** 200.59	Thallium 81 **Tl** 204.383	Lead 82 **Pb** 207.2	Bismuth 83 **Bi** 208.980	Polonium 84 **Po** 208.982	Astatine 85 **At** 209.987	Radon 86 **Rn** 222.018
(unnamed) 110 **Uun**	(unnamed) 111 **Uuu**	(unnamed) 112 **Uub**						

Gadolinium 64 **Gd** 157.25	Terbium 65 **Tb** 158.925	Dysprosium 66 **Dy** 162.50	Holmium 67 **Ho** 164.930	Erbium 68 **Er** 167.26	Thulium 69 **Tm** 168.934	Ytterbium 70 **Yb** 173.04	Lutetium 71 **Lu** 174.967
Curium 96 **Cm** 247.070	Berkelium 97 **Bk** 247.070	Californium 98 **Cf** 251.080	Einsteinium 99 **Es** 252.083	Fermium 100 **Fm** 257.095	Mendelevium 101 **Md** 258.099	Nobelium 102 **No** 259.101	Lawrencium 103 **Lr** 260.105

Enrichment

If you have a copy of the short-form periodic table that was used in the early part of the twentieth century, you might show it to students. This table predates an understanding of the electron configuration of atoms. Both representative and transition elements were placed in the same group marked by Roman numerals. The representative elements were designated as A and the transition elements as B. Thus, aluminum is in Group IIIA and scandium is in Group IIIB.

VISUAL Learning

The Periodic Table To help familiarize students with the periodic table, call attention to the color coding of metals, nonmetals, and metalloids. Point out the band of green blocks that separates the metals from the nonmetals. Ask students to locate elements they already know about and classify them as metals, metalloids, or nonmetals. Ask them if they have heard about any of the synthetic elements. Have them locate the liquid elements and list all the gaseous elements that they already know.

Inclusion Strategies

Learning Disabled To help students appreciate the different properties of the elements, allow them to handle as many samples of safe-to-handle elements (metals and nonmetals) as you have available. Give them metals in the form of wire and in the form of sheets, such as aluminum foil. This will be a good prelude to later discussions of malleability and ductility.

Using Science Words

Have students explain the difference between a period and a group. L1

Using an Analogy

Intrapersonal Ask students to brainstorm similar characteristics of human family members. Include those characteristics that can be seen and those that can't be seen, such as disposition and artistic talent. Have them suggest ways in which groups of elements might also have similar properties that can be observed with the eyes and those that can't. For example, chlorine and bromine exist in different states at room temperature, but their chemical properties are similar. L2

Caption Answer

Figure 3-2 *Family members are different sizes and have similar hair color and facial features.*

GLENCOE TECHNOLOGY

Videodisc

Glencoe Science Voyages Interactive Videodisc—Earth

Side 1, Lesson 3 *Thunderstorms: Flashes and Crashes*

38418

The Infinite Voyage: The Future of the Past

Chapter 7 *Restoring the Parthenon* 9:00

Refer to the Teacher Guide for bar codes and teaching strategies.

Figure 3-2 Groups of elements can be compared to human families. The members of this family have noticeable family traits. **What traits do they share? How are they different?**

The periodic table has 18 columns of elements. Each column contains a group, or family, of elements. A **group** contains elements that have similar physical or chemical properties. The human family in **Figure 3-2** has similarities such as facial features, hair color, and build, but the similarities among a family of elements may not always be clear from appearance alone. For example, Group 17 contains a greenish-yellow gas called chlorine, a red-brown liquid called bromine, and a shiny black solid called iodine. Despite these differences, the elements in Group 17 behave in similar ways.

Sections of the Periodic Table

The periodic table can be divided into two sections. One section consists of the first two groups, Groups 1 and 2, plus the elements in Groups 13-18. These eight groups are called the representative elements. They include metals, metalloids, and nonmetals. The elements in Groups 3-12 are called transition elements. They are all metals. Some transition elements, called the inner transition elements, are placed below the main table. These elements are called the lanthanide and actinide series because one series follows the element lanthanum, element 57, and the other series follows actinium, element 89. The lanthanides and actinides are placed below the table so that the table will take up less space. **Figure 3-3** shows what the periodic table would look like with the inner transition elements included.

Figure 3-3 This table shows you how the inner transition elements fit into the periodic table.

	1	2	3													
1	H															
2	Li	Be														
3	Na	Mg														
4	K	Ca	Sc													
5	Rb	Sr	Y													
6	Cs	Ba	La	Ce	Pr	Nd	Pm	Sm	Eu	Gd	Tb	Dy	Ho	Er	Tm	Yb
7	Fr	Ra	Ac	Th	Pa	U	Np	Pu	Am	Cm	Bk	Cf	Es	Fm	Md	No

Multiple Learning Styles

Visual-Spatial Cut pictures of people of all ages, genders, and races out of the newspaper and magazines. Give groups of students six or more pictures and ask them to list similarities and differences. L2 COOP LEARN P

68 CHAPTER 3 THE PERIODIC TABLE

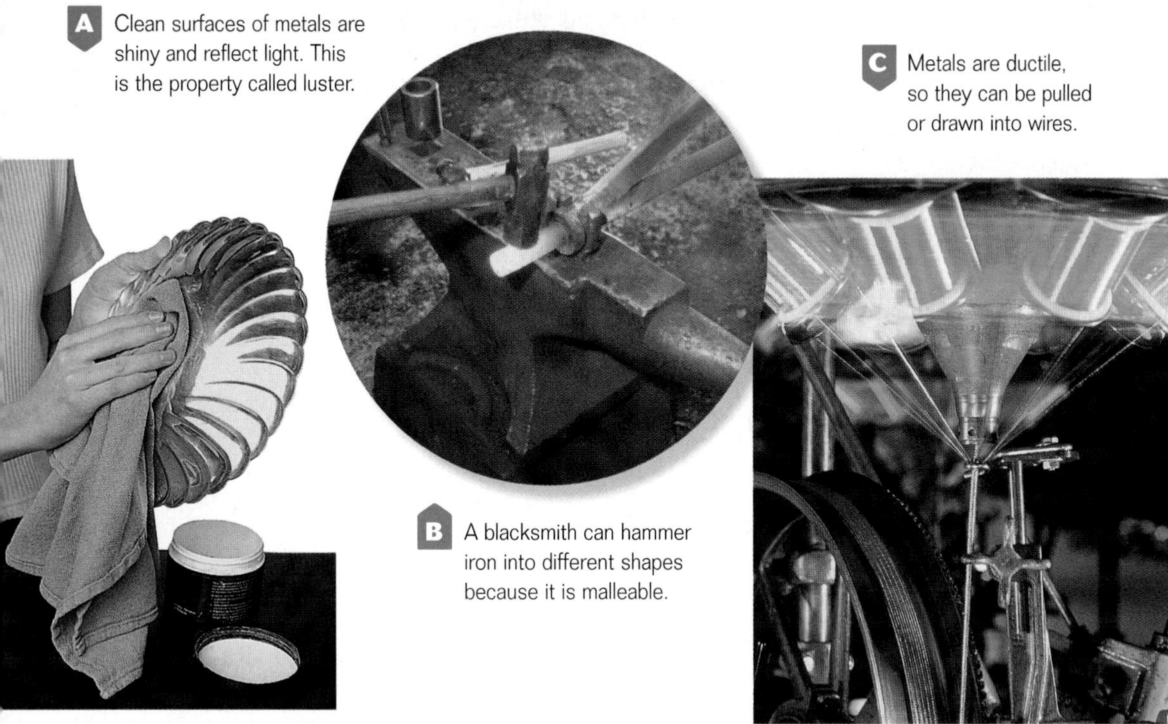

A Clean surfaces of metals are shiny and reflect light. This is the property called luster.

B A blacksmith can hammer iron into different shapes because it is malleable.

C Metals are ductile, so they can be pulled or drawn into wires.

Figure 3-4 Metals can be distinguished from nonmetals and metalloids by their physical properties—luster, malleability, and ductility.

Metals, Nonmetals, and Metalloids

Look again at the periodic table. The table is color coded to show which elements are metals, which are nonmetals, and which are metalloids. With the exception of mercury, all the metals are solids, most with high melting points. A **metal** is an element that has luster and is a good conductor of heat and electricity. Other properties of metals are illustrated in **Figure 3-4.**

	4	5	6	7	8	9	10	11	12	13	14	15	16	17	18
															He
										B	C	N	O	F	Ne
										Al	Si	P	S	Cl	Ar
	Ti	V	Cr	Mn	Fe	Co	Ni	Cu	Zn	Ga	Ge	As	Se	Br	Kr
	Zr	Nb	Mo	Tc	Ru	Rh	Pd	Ag	Cd	In	Sn	Sb	Te	I	Xe
Lu	Hf	Ta	W	Re	Os	Ir	Pt	Au	Hg	Tl	Pb	Bi	Po	At	Rn
Lr	Rf	Db	Sg	Bh	Hs	Mt	Uun	Uuu	Uub						

Content Background

Originally, lanthanum and actinium were thought to start the lanthanide and actinide series of inner transition elements. This would have meant that the last electron to enter their orbitals would have entered an *f* sublevel. Later studies showed that the last electron actually went into a *d* sublevel. Therefore, lanthanum and actinium belong in Group 3 and the two series of inner transition elements start with cerium and thorium.

Quick Demo

Visual-Spatial To help students visualize the properties of nonmetals, show students a piece of roll sulfur. Have them note that the surface is dull compared to the shiny surfaces of metals. Cover the sulfur with a cloth and use a hammer to break off some pieces. Students should see that sulfur is brittle rather than malleable and can be hammered to dust.

Activity

Interpersonal Provide pairs or groups of students with small samples of a metal and a nonmetal and have them distinguish between them. Ask them to write an explanation for their conclusion. L2 COOP LEARN

VISUAL Learning

Figure 3-4 The first mirrors ever used were made of metal. What two properties of metals made that use possible? *luster and malleability*

GLENCOE TECHNOLOGY

CD-ROM

Glencoe Science Voyages Interactive CD-ROM

Explorations

Have students do the interactive exploration *How is the structure of an atom related to its position on the periodic table?*

Using Math

One kilogram of high-quality coal can produce enough energy to extract 55 g of aluminum from its bauxite ore. Recycling aluminum requires only five percent of the energy used to extract aluminum from bauxite. How many grams of aluminum can be recycled using 1 kg of high-quality coal?

The ability to reflect light is a property of metals called luster. When a metal is polished or cut to expose a fresh surface, it reflects light. Many metals can be pressed or pounded into thin sheets or shaped into objects because they are malleable (MAL yuh bul). Metals are also ductile (DUK tul), which means that they can be drawn out into wires.

Nonmetals are usually gases or brittle solids at room temperature and poor conductors of heat and electricity. Although there are only 16 nonmetals, they include many elements that are essential for life: carbon, sulfur, nitrogen, oxygen, phosphorus, and iodine.

The elements that form a bridge between metals and nonmetals on the periodic table are called metalloids (MET ul oydz). As you might expect from the name, a **metalloid** is an element that shares some properties with metals and some with nonmetals. For example, boron has luster like a metal, but, like a nonmetal, it is a poor conductor of electricity.

The Element Keys

Each element is represented on the periodic table by a box called the element key. An enlarged key for hydrogen is shown in **Figure 3-5.** An element key contains the name of the element, its atomic number, its symbol, and its average atomic mass. Elements that do not occur naturally on Earth are marked with a bull's-eye logo. These are synthetic elements. Element keys for elements that occur naturally on Earth include a logo that tells you whether the element is a solid, a liquid, or a gas at room temperature. All the gases except hydrogen are located on the right side of the table. They are marked by a balloon logo. Most of the other elements are solids at room temperature and are marked by a cube. Locate the two elements on the periodic table that are liquids at room temperature. Their logo is a drop. ☑

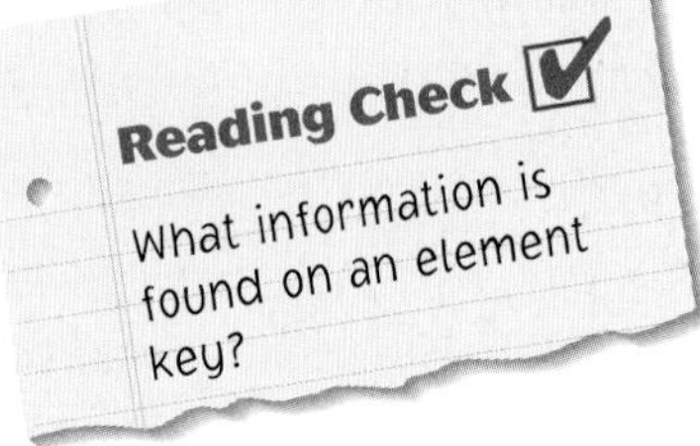

Reading Check ☑
What information is found on an element key?

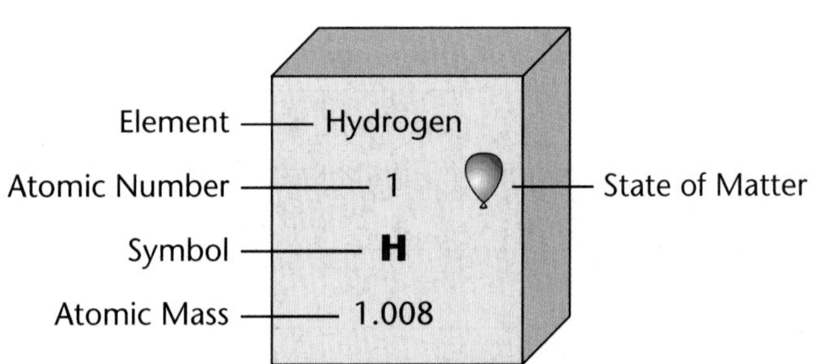

Figure 3-5 As you begin to use the periodic table, the element keys on the periodic table will provide you with useful information.

Using Math

 **Logical-Mathematical** $\frac{55\text{ g}}{5\%} \times 100\% = 11\text{ g} \times 100 = 1100\text{ g}$ of aluminum. Ask students to outline the steps they used to find the answer.

Answer to Reading Check ☑

The element key contains the name and symbol of the element, its atomic number, and average atomic mass. Some elements have a logo that indicates that the element is synthetic. The remaining elements have a logo that indicates whether the element is a solid, liquid, or gas at room temperature.

3 ASSESS

Check for Understanding Activity

Linguistic Have students make up written questions about the periodic table. Then, sort them out and use them to have a rapid-fire oral quiz. L2 COOP LEARN

Reteach

Visual-Spatial Give students a copy of a blank periodic table. Ask them to identify the areas of the table occupied by the representative elements, the transition elements, and the inner transition elements. Ask them to label the 18 groups and the seven periods. L1

Extension

For students who have mastered this section, use the **Reinforcement** and **Enrichment** masters.

Content Background

Atomic mass is measured relative to a standard, the carbon-12 atom. For example, the mass of hydrogen is 1/12 the mass of carbon. The mass shown in the element key is the average of the naturally occurring isotopes of the element.

Symbols for the Elements

The symbols for the elements are either one- or two-letter abbreviations, often based on the element name. For example, V is the symbol for vanadium, and Sc is the symbol for scandium. Sometimes, the symbols don't match the names, for example, Ag for silver and Na for sodium. In those cases, the symbol may come from Greek or Latin names for the elements. Some elements are named for scientists such as Lise Meitner (meitnerium, Mt). Some are named for geographic locations such as France (francium, Fr). The symbols Uun, Uuu, and Uub are temporary symbols for unnamed elements. **Table 3-2** shows the origin of some element names and symbols.

Table 3-2

Chemical Symbols and Their Origins

Name	Symbol	Origin
Mendelevium	Md	For Dmitri Mendeleev
Lead	Pb	The Latin name for lead is *plumbum.*
Thorium	Th	The Norse god of thunder is Thor.
Polonium	Po	For Poland, where Marie Curie was born
Hydrogen	H	From Greek words meaning "water former"
Mercury	Hg	Hydrargyrum means "liquid silver" in Greek.
Gold	Au	*Aurum* means "shining dawn" in Latin

Section Assessment

1. Use the elements in period 4 to show how the physical state of the elements changes as the atomic number increases across a period.
2. What are the two sections of the periodic table?
3. Where are the metals located in the periodic table? The nonmetals? The metalloids?
4. **Think Critically:** How would the modern periodic table be different if elements were still arranged by average atomic mass instead of atomic number? Give two specific examples.
5. **Skill Builder**
Classifying Every day, you compare, contrast, and classify objects in the world around you. Then, you classify what you have learned. Do the **Chapter 3 Skill Activity** on page 728 to classify some of the elements.

Using Math

Prepare a circle graph of the most abundant elements by weight in Earth's crust. What percent by weight of the crust is from metals? Metalloids? Nonmetals?

Data: oxygen, 46.6%; silicon, 27.7%; aluminum, 8.1%; iron, 5.0%; calcium, 3.6%; sodium, 2.8%; potassium, 2.6%; magnesium, 2.1%; other, 1.5%

4 Close

Proficiency Prep

Use this quiz to check students' recall of section content.

1. **What table arranges the elements according to repeating properties?** *the periodic table*
2. **In the modern periodic table, how are the elements arranged?** *according to atomic number*

Section Assessment

1. The elements are solid through Group 16, liquid in Group 17, and gaseous in Group 18.
2. the representative and transition elements
3. Metals are on the left side; nonmetals are on the right; metalloids follow a slanting line between metals and nonmetals.
4. **Think Critically** Some pairs of elements would exchange places: potassium and argon, and nickel and cobalt.

Using Math

Student graphs should reflect data multiplied by 360° to obtain the part of the circle used by each element (168° O, 100° Si, 29° Al, 18° Fe, 13° Ca, 10° Na, 9° K, 8° Mg, and 5° other). A total of 24.2% are metals; 27.7%, metalloids; 46.6%, nonmetals; and 1.5%, unclassified.

Assessment

Process Have students compare and contrast beryllium with fluorine and beryllium with magnesium. Have them write a conclusion about whether more similarities exist between elements in the same period or in the same group. Use **Performance Assessment in the Science Classroom,** p. 17.

P

SECTION 3-2

Prepare

Content Background

Refer to **Sections of the Periodic Table** and **From Metals to Nonmetals** on pp. 62E–F.

Preplanning

Refer to the **Chapter Organizer** on pp. 62A–B.

1 Motivate

Bellringer

Before presenting the lesson, display **Section Focus Transparency 6** on the overhead projector. Use the accompanying **Focus Activity** worksheet. L2 ELL

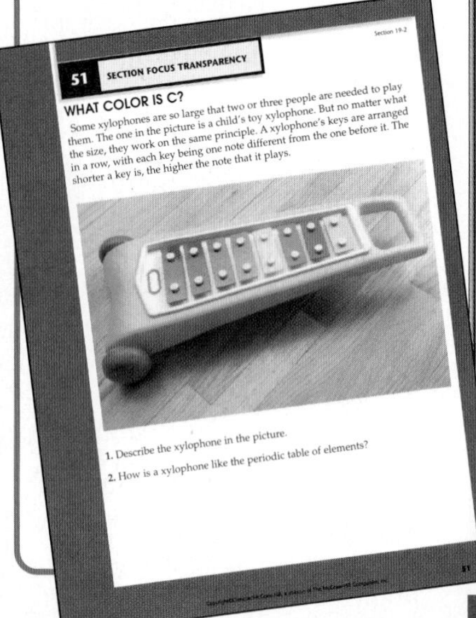

Section 19-2

51 SECTION FOCUS TRANSPARENCY

WHAT COLOR IS C?

Some xylophones are so large that two or three people are needed to play them. The one in the picture is a child's toy xylophone. But no matter what the size, they work on the same principle. A xylophone's keys are arranged in a row, with each key being one note different from the one before it. The shorter a key is, the higher the note that it plays.

1. Describe the xylophone in the picture.
2. How is a xylophone like the periodic table of elements?

51

Tying to Previous Knowledge

Students have learned the features of the periodic table and the significance of groups. Now they will investigate each representative group in turn.

3-2 Representative Elements

What You'll Learn

- Properties of the representative elements
- Uses for the representative elements

Vocabulary

alloy
semiconductor

Why It's Important

- Many representative elements play key roles in your body, your environment, and in the the things you use every day.

Groups 1 and 2

You probably have friends who like to interact with other people and do so easily and often. They're like the elements in Groups 1 and 2. These two groups of elements are always found in nature combined with other elements. They're called active metals because of their readiness to form new substances with other elements. They are all metals except hydrogen, the first element in Group 1. Although hydrogen is placed in Group 1, it shares properties with the elements in both Group 1 and Group 17.

The Alkali Metals

The Group 1 elements—lithium, sodium, potassium, rubidium, cesium, and francium—have a special family name. They are called the alkali metals. All the alkali metals are silvery solids with low densities and low melting points as shown in **Figure 3-6.** From lithium at the top of the group to francium at the bottom, the elements become more and more ready to combine with other substances to form new substances. Some other properties and uses of the alkali metals are shown in **Figure 3-7.**

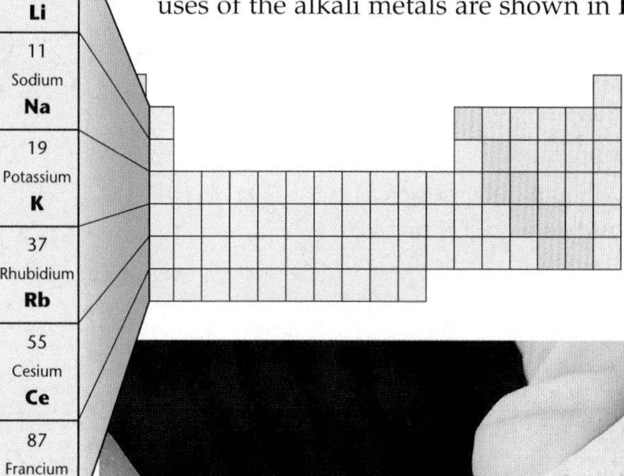

Figure 3-6 Sodium is so soft, it can be cut with a knife. Sodium chloride, or table salt, contains sodium and chlorine. Sodium chloride is one of the salts left behind when seawater evaporates.

Resource Manager

The following **Teacher Classroom Resources** can be used with Section 3-2:

 **Reproducible Masters**

Activity Worksheets, pp. 13–14, 18 L2

Enrichment, p. 6 L3

Reinforcement, p. 6 L2

Study Guide, p. 15

VISUALIZING The Alkali Metals

Figure 3-7 The activity of the alkali metals makes them useful elements.

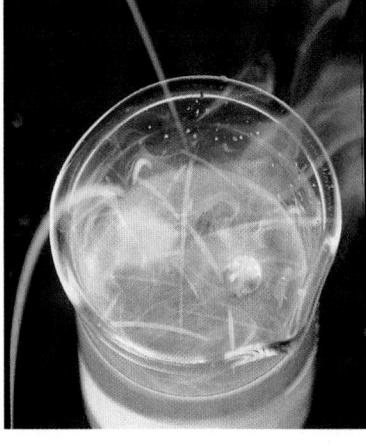

A Potassium is more active than lithium and sodium. Look at what happens when a small piece of potassium is dropped into water. Heat and hydrogen gas are generated. Enough heat is released to cause the hydrogen gas to burst into flames.

B When sodium is added to water, the same kind of reaction occurs. After the reaction, the water contains a substance known as sodium hydroxide or lye. Lye can eat away at grease in clogged drains or digest wood pulp during the manufacture of paper.

C In your body, sodium and potassium have the important job of transmitting nerve impulses. Potassium and sodium are lost from the body in sweat and urine. Most diets contain more than enough sodium. It's more difficult to make sure that you get enough potassium. Bananas and potatoes are good sources of potassium.

2 Teach

Teacher FYI

The alkali metals are stored under mineral oil or kerosene because they react so readily with both oxygen and water vapor in the air.

Correcting Misconceptions

Many people avoid salt (sodium chloride) in their diets because they think it's harmful. It's true that too much salt can cause problems, but too little also can be unhealthy. Sodium, as Na^+, helps maintain the body's electrolyte balance. Chlorine, as Cl^-, is used to produce HCl—stomach acid.

VISUAL Learning

Figure 3-7 Why is there no photo of a use of francium? *Francium is rare and difficult to work with because it is radioactive.*

GLENCOE TECHNOLOGY

Videodisc

Glencoe Science Voyages Interactive Videodisc—Physical

Side 1, Lesson 4 *Periodicity*

32888

34496

Refer to the Videodisc Teacher Guide for additional bar codes.

Content Background

Alkali metals are an important part of everyday life. Substances containing sodium are used in making detergents, paper, petroleum products, glass, and soaps. Sodium vapor lamps provide outdoor lighting recognizable by its yellowish color. Potassium chloride sometimes substitutes for sodium chloride in the diets of people who must reduce their sodium intake.

Quick Demo

Visual-Spatial Magnesium burns readily with an intense, white light. Fireworks displays make use of this property. Although looking directly at burning magnesium could be harmful to eyes, you can safely demonstrate this intense energy by darkening the room and burning a strip of magnesium inside an empty can. Students will observe the reflected light.

Teacher FYI

- Beryllium, the lightest of the alkaline earth metals, is present in emeralds.
- Magnesium explodes a brilliant white and strontium explodes red in fireworks displays.
- When calcium and magnesium compounds are dissolved in water, the water is said to be hard water. Problems arise when these substances form soap scum or solidify and clog pipes.

Flex Your Brain

Use the Flex Your Brain activity to have students explore ALLOYS.

The Alkaline Earth Metals

Next door to the alkali metals' family are their Group 2 neighbors, the alkaline earth metals—beryllium, magnesium, calcium, strontium, barium, and radium. The two families have much in common, but some differences. Each alkaline earth metal is denser and harder and has a higher melting point than the alkali metal in the same period. Alkaline earth metals are active, but not as active as the alkali metals.

Magnesium and calcium are the most common elements in Group 2. When magnesium combines with water, a substance called magnesium hydroxide is formed. Magnesium hydroxide is used as the medicine milk of magnesia to soothe an upset stomach. Chlorophyll, the green pigment found in the leaves of trees and plants, contains magnesium atoms. Magnesium is often combined with aluminum to form alloys that resist corrosion. Corrosion can occur when a metal combines with oxygen in the air. An **alloy** (AL oy) is a mixture of two or more elements, one of which is a metal. Some uses of the alkaline earth elements are shown in **Figure 3-8.**

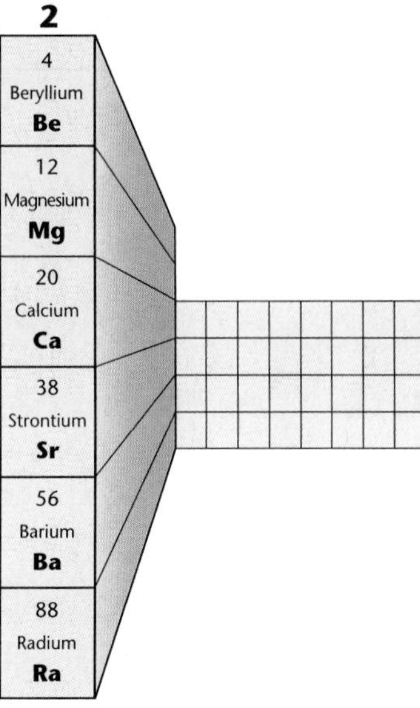

Figure 3-8 Alkaline earth metals are a big part of your life.

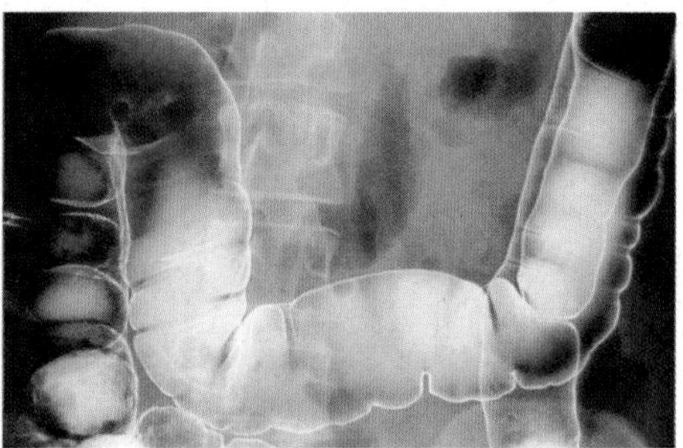

A You have probably been advised to drink milk so that you get the calcium you need for strong bones and teeth. Calcium is also important in controlling your heartbeat and preventing blood clots.

B Barium is used when X rays are taken of the intestinal tract. Ordinarily, the soft tissues of the intestinal tract don't show up on X rays, but when the tract is filled with a substance containing barium, the tissues can be seen on an X ray.

C Alloys of magnesium and aluminum are used to make frames for racing bikes and tennis rackets, and parts for automobile and aircraft engines. An alloy of magnesium and aluminum is not only strong and durable, but lightweight.

Properties of Metals Ask students to write a paragraph explaining why it's particularly important for racing bikes to be made of a metal that is both strong and lightweight. P

From Metals to Nonmetals

The next group of representative elements is Group 13, located on the other side of the transition elements. Notice that the elements in Groups 13-18 are not all solid metals like the elements of Groups 1 and 2. A single group may contain metals, nonmetals, and metalloids, and have members that are solids, liquids, and gases.

13
5 Boron **B**
13 Aluminum **Al**
31 Galium **Ga**
49 Indium **In**
81 Thallium **Tl**

Boron's Family

The elements in Group 13—boron, aluminum, gallium, indium, and thallium—are all metals except boron, which is a brittle, black metalloid. **Figure 3-9** tells you more about this family.

Figure 3-9 Here are some of the many uses and properties of the elements of Group 13.

A Cookware made with boron can be moved directly from the refrigerator into the oven without cracking.

B Aluminum is the most common metal in Earth's crust. **What property of metals makes it possible to shape aluminum into soft-drink cans, cookware, aluminum siding, and baseball bats?**

C Gallium follows aluminum in Group 13. Gallium is a solid metal, but its melting point is low enough that it will melt in your hand.

Boron has the high luster of metals, but because its bonds are not the same as those of metals, it is not malleable or ductile. Boron carbide is one of the hardest substances known and is used to make bulletproof armor. Compounds of boron are used in mild cleaning solutions such as those used for contact lenses, and in tough abrasives used for shaping metal tools and parts.

Teacher FYI

Gallium, indium, and thallium are three of the elements that are added to silicon to produce semiconductor devices. Semiconductor devices are used in radios, TVs, computers, and other electronic equipment.

Enrichment

Have students think about the properties of aluminum that make it a good metal for soft-drink cans. Aluminum can be rolled and shaped, it is light and strong, and it does not corrode. L2

Caption Answer

Figure 3-9B *malleability*

Integrating the Sciences

Earth Science In Earth's crust, calcium is found as calcium carbonate in marble and limestone rocks. Giant columns of calcium carbonate called stalagmites and stalactites build up in underground caves when the calcium carbonate that dissolves in groundwater slowly comes out of solution as the water evaporates.

VISUAL Learning

Figure 3-9C Ask students if they can tell from the figure what the approximate melting temperature of gallium is. It is approximately the same as human body temperature.

The Carbon Group

14
6 Carbon **C**
14 Silicon **Si**
32 Germanium **Ge**
50 Tin **Sn**
82 Lead **Pb**

If you look down Group 14, you can see that carbon is a nonmetal, silicon and germanium are metalloids, and tin and lead are metals. The nonmetal carbon exists in several forms. You're familiar with two of them—diamond and graphite. A diamond is an array of carbon atoms arranged in an interlocking pattern. Graphite's atoms have a different arrangement, and so graphite and diamond have different properties. Diamond is one of the hardest materials on Earth, whereas graphite is soft. It is soft graphite that rubs off on the paper as you write.

Carbon is followed by the metalloid silicon, an abundant element contained in sand. Sand is ground-up particles of minerals such as quartz, which is composed of silicon and oxygen. Glass is an important product made from sand.

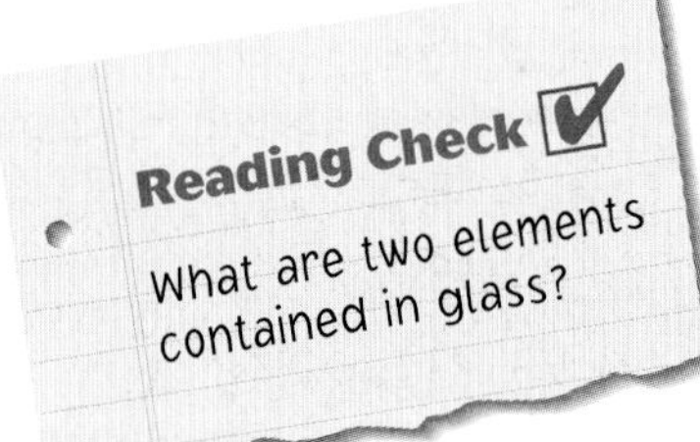

Reading Check

What are two elements contained in glass?

Both silicon and its Group 14 neighbor, germanium, are metalloids. They are used in electronics as semiconductors. A **semiconductor** is an element that doesn't conduct electricity as well as a metal but does conduct electricity better than a nonmetal. Through a process called *doping,* traces of elements such as boron or arsenic are added to silicon to increase its electrical conductivity. One use for doped silicon is shown in **Figure 3-10.**

Tin and lead are the two heaviest elements in Group 14. When you think of the element tin, the tin cans filled with canned fruit and vegetables at the grocery store may come to mind. These cans are actually made of steel coated with tin to protect them from corrosion.

As you can see in **Figure 3-11,** lead is no longer used in gasoline because it is poisonous. Today, the most important use for lead is in car batteries.

Figure 3-10 Doped silicon is used in computer chips and in solar cells, like these that convert sunlight to electricity.

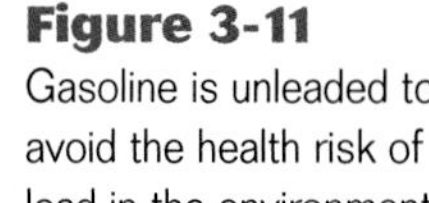

Figure 3-11 Gasoline is unleaded to avoid the health risk of lead in the environment.

Content Background

In diamond, each carbon atom bonds with four other carbon atoms in a rigid, three-dimensional array. In graphite, the carbon atoms form sheets of connecting hexagons. The sheets are not connected by carbon-to-carbon bonds, so one sheet can slide easily past another. This property makes graphite a good lubricant for the moving parts of machinery and explains the use of graphite in pencils.

Carbon combines with other elements, particularly hydrogen, nitrogen, and oxygen, to form a huge number of substances that students will learn more about when they study carbon chemistry.

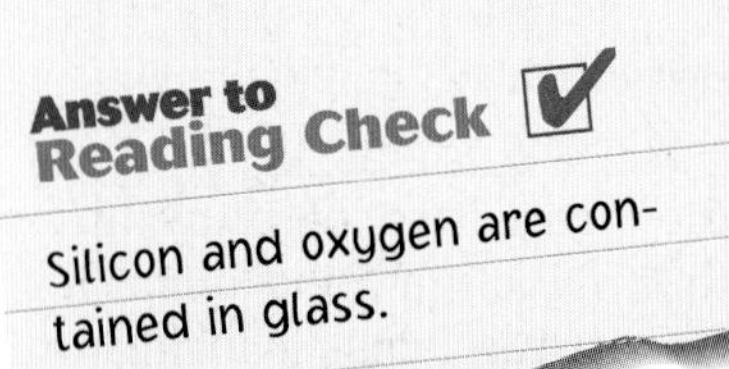

Answer to Reading Check

Silicon and oxygen are contained in glass.

Discussion

Solar, or photovoltaic, cells are made of layers of semiconductors. When radiant energy falls on the boundary between semiconductors, the energy is converted to an electric current. **What would be the disadvantage of using only solar energy?** *No power would be available on cloudy days and at night.*

Across the Curriculum

History Bronze, an alloy of tin and copper, was used as early as 3000 B.C. The importance of bronze in ancient civilizations is revealed by the fact that this period in history is called the Bronze Age. Ask students to find out about the extent of the Bronze Age and what was significant about it. Have them write a paragraph describing their findings.

P L2 

Nitrogen's Group

At the top of Group 15 are the two nonmetals nitrogen and phosphorus. Next come two metalloids, arsenic and antimony, and one metal, bismuth. Nitrogen and phosphorus are required by living beings. These elements are parts of the biological materials that store genetic information and energy in living organisms. Although almost 80 percent of the air you breathe is nitrogen, you can't get the nitrogen your body needs by breathing nitrogen gas. Bacteria in the soil must first change nitrogen gas into substances that can be absorbed through the roots of plants. Then, by eating the plants, nitrogen becomes available to your body.

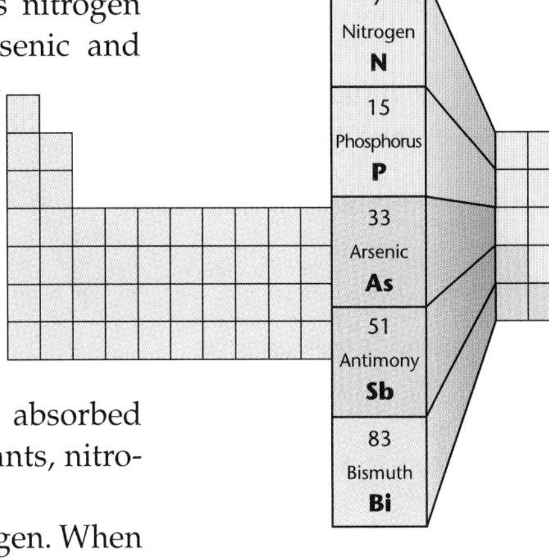

Ammonia is a gas containing nitrogen and hydrogen. When ammonia is dissolved in water, it can be used as a cleaner and disinfectant. You can smell the sharp fumes of ammonia gas when you open a bottle of ammonia cleaning solution. In **Figure 3-12A,** liquid ammonia is being applied directly to soil as a fertilizer. Ammonia also can be converted into solid fertilizers. Ammonia also is used in the making of many products, such as the nylon of the parachute in **Figure 3-12B.**

The element phosphorus comes in two forms—white and red. White phosphorus is so active it can't be exposed to oxygen in the air or it will burst into flames. The heads of matches contain the less active red phosphorus, which ignites from the heat produced by friction when the match is struck. **Figure 3-12C** shows both forms of phosphorus. Phosphorus is an essential ingredient of healthy teeth and bones. Plants also need phosphorus, so phosphorus is one of the nutrients in most fertilizers.

Figure 3-12 Nitrogen and phosphorus are necessary for your body and useful in your daily life.

A Ammonia is a nitrogen-containing substance that can be injected into the soil and used directly by plants.

B Nylon is a tough, light fiber capable of replacing silk in many applications, such as in parachutes.

C Both white and red phosphorus are active. **Why is white phosphorus submerged in a liquid in this photo?**

Quick Demo

Dampen a cloth with some household cleaning solution containing ammonia and let students smell the sharp odor as it diffuses through the air. **CAUTION:** *Do not let students smell the ammonia directly.* Tell them that smelling salts containing ammonia and a compound made from ammonia have often been used to arouse a fainting person. Ammonia is the starting material for a large number of substances that are vital to modern life.

Activity

Kinesthetic Allow students to feel a piece of nylon cloth and a piece of silk. Tell them that nylon fiber is a manufactured substitute for the fiber made by silkworms. L1

Caption Answer

Figure 3-12C *White phosphorus is so reactive that it can't be exposed to oxygen in the air.*

GLENCOE TECHNOLOGY

Videodisc

The Infinite Voyage: Crisis in the Atmosphere

Chapter 4 *Chlorofluorocarbons and Their Effect on the Ozone Layer* 4:00

Refer to the Teacher Guide for bar codes and teaching strategies.

Across the Curriculum

History In the 1930s, the age of polymers and plastics was ushered in by the polymerization of adipic acid and hexamethylene diamine to form the macromolecule nylon. Nylon is most often drawn into long fibers and in this form is exceptionally strong and tough. Have students research the development of nylon, particularly the raw materials from which it is made—petroleum and coal—and its uses, for example, clothing, carpets, and rope. Have them present their findings as a written or oral report. P

3-2 REPRESENTATIVE ELEMENTS 77

Discussion

Ask students if they have used hydrogen peroxide as an antiseptic. Show them a bottle of hydrogen peroxide. Hydrogen peroxide decomposes into water and oxygen gas when exposed to light or enzymes. Demonstrate this by dropping some raw potato into some of the solution. The bubbles are released oxygen. The same reaction occurs when hydrogen peroxide is used as bleach. L2

Teacher FYI

About 46 percent of Earth's crust is oxygen, and nearly all of it is combined with other elements. This is a good illustration of oxygen's reactivity.

GLENCOE TECHNOLOGY

Videodisc

Glencoe Science Voyages Interactive Videodisc—Physical

Side 1, Lesson 4 *Periodicity*

37023

42981

Refer to the Videodisc Teacher Guide for additional bar codes.

Figure 3-13 Other members of Group 15 have everyday uses.

A substance containing gallium and arsenic is responsible for the lighted time display on digital clocks.

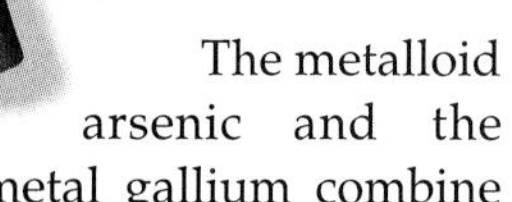

B Overhead sprinkler heads use the low melting point of bismuth as a trigger.

The metalloid arsenic and the metal gallium combine to form a substance used to create the lighted display on digital clocks, radios, and VCRs, as you can see in **Figure 3-13A.** Bismuth is used in the sprinkler heads of fire-fighting systems like the one in **Figure 3-13B.** The system turns on automatically when a fire starts because bismuth has a low enough melting point that the heat from a fire causes it to melt. The melting triggers a signal that opens the water valves.

Oxygen's Family

The first two members of Group 16, oxygen and sulfur, are essential for life. Selenium is also necessary for health, but in trace amounts. The heavier members of the group, tellurium and polonium, are both metalloids.

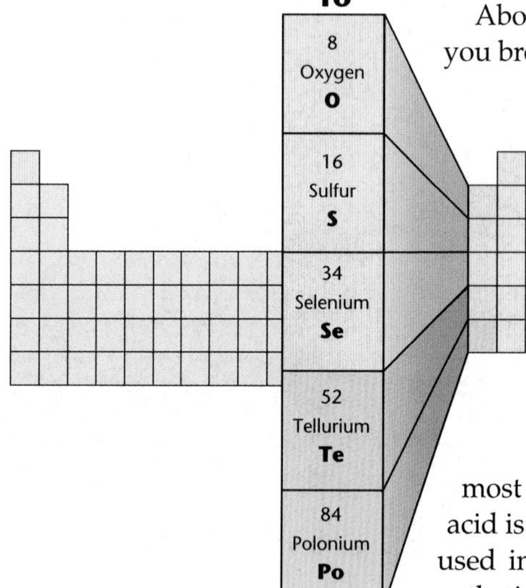

About 20 percent of Earth's atmosphere is the oxygen you breathe. Your body needs oxygen to release the energy from the foods you eat. Ozone, a less common form of oxygen, is formed in the upper atmosphere through the action of electricity during thunderstorms. The presence of ozone is important because it shields living beings from some harmful radiation from the sun. Oxygen is abundant in Earth's rocks and minerals because it readily combines with other elements.

Sulfur is a solid, yellow nonmetal, as you can see in **Figure 3-14.** Large amounts of sulfur are used to manufacture sulfuric acid, one of the most commonly used chemicals in the world. Sulfuric acid is a combination of sulfur, hydrogen, and oxygen. It is used in the manufacture of paints, fertilizers, detergents, synthetic fibers, and rubber.

Multiple Learning Styles

Interpersonal Have groups of students make posters of photos and drawings that illustrate the importance of carbon, oxygen, and nitrogen in their lives. P L2 COOP LEARN

Figure 3-14 These piles of sulfur will be used to make sulfuric acid, one of the most important chemicals for making a wide variety of products you use every day.

Selenium conducts electricity when exposed to light, so it is used in solar cells and in light meters. Its most important use is as the light-sensitive component in photocopy machines. You'll find a small amount of selenium in some multivitamin preparations because selenium is one of the trace elements your body needs. Large amounts of selenium, however, can be poisonous.

LIFE SCIENCE INTEGRATION

A Strand of Evidence
Arsenic disrupts the normal function of an organism by combining with sulfur, which is an essential element. Because arsenic builds up in hair, forensic scientists can test hair samples to confirm or disprove a case of arsenic poisoning. Tests of Napoleon's hair suggest that he was poisoned. Use reference books to find out who Napoleon was and why someone might have wanted to poison him.

Problem Solving

Predicting Periodicity

Comets are large masses of frozen water in which pieces of rock are embedded. Seen through a telescope, a comet has a glowing head and a long, bright tail. Comets orbit the sun just as Earth and the sun's other planets do. To *orbit* means "to follow a path usually shaped like an ellipse." Some comets orbit the sun every few years. Some take thousands of years to complete one trip. The time it takes for a comet to make one trip around the sun is called its period.

People have been watching comets since they first noticed them in the night sky. Early astronomers kept records of unusual events such as eclipses, meteor showers, and the appearance of comets. The famous Comet Halley is named for the eighteenth-century English astronomer Edmund Halley. While researching the records of earlier astronomers, Halley noticed descriptions of bright comets that appeared in 1531, 1607, and 1682. Halley thought these comets might all be a single comet and that the dates of the three observations were evidence of the comet's periodic motion. He correctly predicted the return of Halley's comet.

Think Critically: What year did Halley predict the comet would return? Approximately how long is the period of Halley's comet—the time it takes to orbit the sun? When was it last seen from Earth? When will it be seen again?

LIFE SCIENCE INTEGRATION

The toxicity of arsenic derives from its extraordinary affinity for sulfur. Sulfur is a part of almost all enzymes, which are catalysts that carry out cell functions. Replacement of sulfur in the enzyme by arsenic can seriously affect the healthy functioning of cells and can lead to death. Napoleon Bonaparte was emperor of France (1852–1871). He was ruthless in his exercise of power and was defeated in the Franco-German War (1870–1871).

Problem Solving

Comets are part of the solar system, but they're not seen as regularly as the planets. Planets are visible in the sky from some part of Earth every night. Comets appear to come from space because their orbits are long ellipses with the sun close to one end of the ellipse. On the chalkboard, draw representations of the orbit of a typical planet such as Earth. Earth's orbit is almost a circle. Draw a representation of a comet's orbit showing that its path takes it much farther from the sun than any of the planets.

Think Critically
1757 or 1758; 75 or 76 years; Answers within two to three years of 1986 are acceptable. 2061 or 2062

Inclusion Strategies

Gifted The Frasch Method is a unique way of removing sulfur from deposits below Earth's surface. Hot water is forced into the sulfur deposit where it melts the sulfur. Then, air is forced into the deposit to sweep out the liquid sulfur. Have students research this mining method and write a description of the process that includes a diagram.

Discussion

Ask students whether their families use household chlorine bleach to whiten clothes. Ask whether they can identify the odor of this bleach. Chlorine's characteristic odor is similar to the odors of the other halogens.

Purpose

Visual-Spatial Students will observe the presence of chlorine in drinking water. L2

ELL COOP LEARN

Materials

Standard chloride: dissolve 0.10 g of NaCl in 1 L of water. Silver nitrate: dissolve 1.7 g of $AgNO_3$ in 100 mL of distilled water (0.10*M*). **CAUTION:** *Silver nitrate will stain skin and clothing.*

Teaching Strategies

Make sure students know that salt water contains chlorine.

Safety Precautions Review warnings about contact of silver nitrate with skin.

Analysis

1. The salt water became cloudy.
2. Nothing happened.
3. Yes; the tap water became cloudy just like the salt water.

Assessment

Oral Ask students whether this experiment would have been possible if the silver nitrate solution had been made using tap water instead of distilled water. Have them explain their answers. Use **Performance Assessment in the Science Classroom,** p. 71.

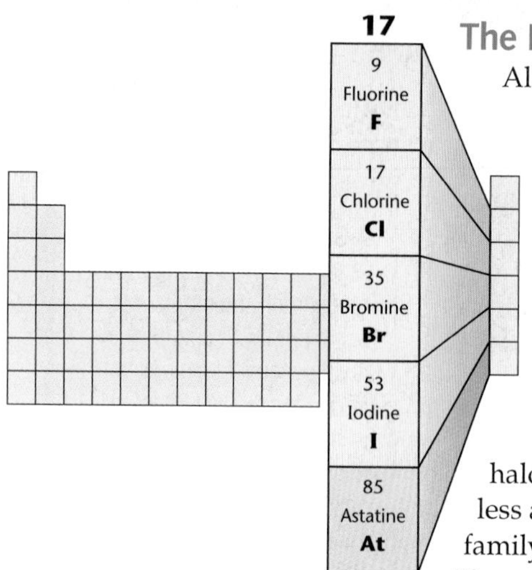

The Halogens

All the elements in Group 17 are nonmetals except for astatine, which is a radioactive metalloid. These elements—fluorine, chlorine, bromine, iodine, and astatine—are called halogens, which means "salt-former." Table salt, sodium chloride, is a substance made from sodium and chlorine. All of the halogens form similar salts with sodium and with the other alkali metals. Fluorine and chlorine are gases. Bromine is a reddish-brown liquid. Iodine is a shiny black solid.

The halogen fluorine is the most active of the halogens in combining with other elements. Chlorine is less active than fluorine, and the trend continues down the family to iodine, which is the least active of the four. **Figure 3-15** shows some of the uses of the halogens.

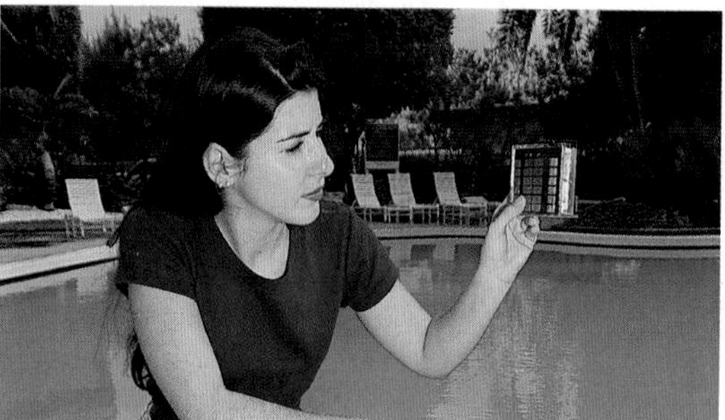

Figure 3-15 Because they are active, you'll find that the halogens are useful in many ways.

A The halogens are used to fight bacteria. For example, chlorine is at work in this swimming pool.

B When the halogens are combined with other elements, they form substances such as table salt and sodium fluoride, the toothpaste additive for fighting tooth decay.

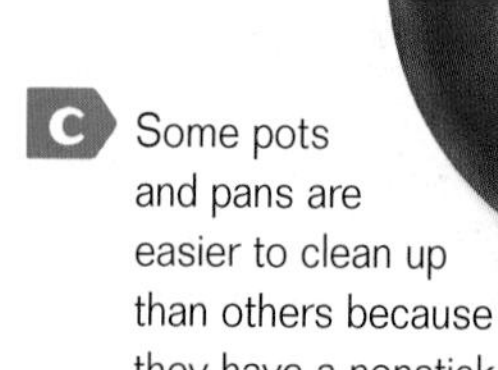

C Some pots and pans are easier to clean up than others because they have a nonstick surface made from a substance containing fluorine.

Inferring the Presence of Chlorine

Procedure

1. Place 2 mL of salt water, 2 mL of distilled water, and 2 mL of tap water into separate test tubes.
2. Carefully add 5 drops of silver nitrate solution to each test tube and stir. **CAUTION:** *Silver nitrate solution can stain skin and clothing.*

Analysis

1. What happened when you added silver nitrate to the salt water?
2. What happened in the test tube with distilled water?
3. Does your tap water contain chlorine? Explain.

Inclusion Strategies

Learning Disabled Have students write or dictate letters to toothpaste manufacturers asking for a copy of the results of studies that support the use of fluoride as a decay-fighting additive in toothpaste. Have them share their letters and the responses with the class. L2 P

The Noble Gases

Why are the Group 18 elements called the noble gases? The answer is because they rarely combine with other elements. Like the nobility, they stand apart from the crowd. All the Group 18 elements—helium, neon, argon, krypton, xenon (ZEE nawn), and radon—are colorless gases.

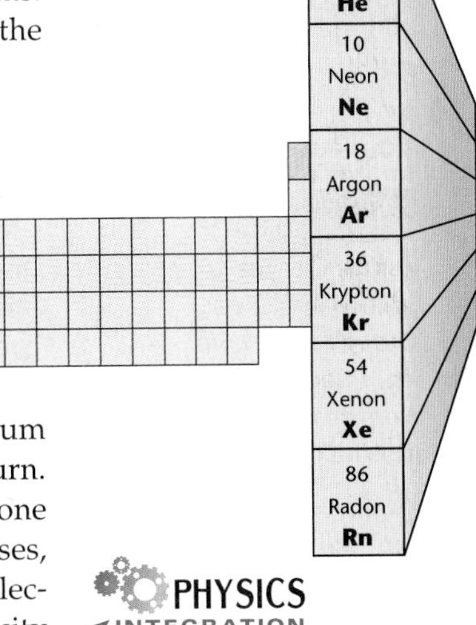

Helium is a lighter-than-air gas, so it's great for all kinds of balloons, from party balloons to blimps that carry television cameras high above sporting events. Helium balloons, such as the one in **Figure 3-16A,** lift instruments into the upper atmosphere to measure atmospheric conditions. Even though hydrogen is lighter than helium, helium is preferred for these purposes because helium will not burn.

The "neon" lights you see in advertising signs, like the one in **Figure 3-16B,** may actually contain any of the noble gases, not just neon. In the glass tubes that make up the sign, electricity is passed through the noble gas and the electricity causes the gas to glow. Each noble gas produces its own color. Helium glows pink, neon glows red-orange, and argon produces a purple color.

PHYSICS INTEGRATION

Figure 3-16 Scientists used to call the noble gases inert gases because they were never found combined with other elements.

A Instruments carried by weather balloons contain helium that gathers information about the conditions in the upper atmosphere around the world. **How might this information be helpful to you?**

B Each color in this advertising sign is caused by a different noble gas.

PHYSICS INTEGRATION

The light emitted by noble gases in advertising signs is directly related to the arrangement of electrons in the atom. Electrons, energized by electricity, move to higher energy levels. When they drop back to their stable, or ground state, they emit energy in the form of visible light of a characteristic color.

3 Assess

Check for Understanding Activity

Interpersonal Have teams of students make charts on the chalkboard with a column for each family of the representative elements. Challenge the groups to list in each column as many of the uses of the elements in that family as they know. L2 COOP LEARN

Reteach

Visual-Spatial Give students a blank periodic table and have them fill in the symbols and group numbers. Have them identify by color or shading the metals, nonmetals, and metalloids. L1

Extension

For students who have mastered this section, use the **Reinforcement** and **Enrichment** masters.

Teacher FYI

Approximately 250 000 tons of argon are obtained annually in the United States by fractional distillation of liquid air. Smaller amounts of neon, krypton, and xenon also are obtained in this way.

Caption Answer

Figure 3-16A *The local weather service might use this information in making local weather forecasts.*

***inter*NET CONNECTION**

Visit the Glencoe Science Web Site at **www.glencoe.com/sec/science** for more information about representative elements.

Argon, the most abundant of the noble gases on Earth, was first found in 1894. Krypton is used with nitrogen in ordinary lightbulbs because these gases keep the glowing filament from burning out. When a mixture of argon, krypton, and xenon is used, a bulb can have a life ten times longer than bulbs available today. Krypton lights are used to illuminate landing strips at airports, and xenon is used in strobe lights and photographic flash cubes.

At the bottom of the group is radon, a radioactive gas produced naturally as uranium in rocks and soil decays. If radon seeps into a home, the gas can be harmful because it continues to emit radiation. When people breathe the gas over a period of time, it can cause lung cancer. People in regions where granite and shale are abundant are encouraged to have their homes tested for radon.

Chemists originally thought that it was impossible for any of the noble gases to combine with other elements. However, in 1962, a new substance was formed that contained xenon, platinum, and fluorine. Since then, chemists have succeeded in making combinations of xenon and krypton with fluorine.

Section Assessment

1. What do the elements in Group 1 have in common with the elements in Group 17? How are Group 1 elements different from the elements in Group 18?
2. Explain how silicon's role as a semiconductor confirms that silicon is a metalloid.
3. List the five most important elements for life and tell what groups on the periodic table they are in.
4. **Think Critically:** Francium is a rare radioactive alkali metal at the bottom of Group 1. Its properties have not been studied carefully. Would you predict that francium would combine with water more or less readily than cesium?
5. **Skill Builder**
   Predicting Predict how readily astatine would form a salt compared to the other elements in Group 17. If you need help, refer to Predicting in the **Skill Handbook** on page 714.

Using Computers

Using a Database
Search an on-line database for recent articles on the environment. Pick one area of concern such as water quality, air quality, or global warming. Then track the impact of one representative element. If you need help, refer to page 717.

***inter*NET CONNECTION**

Internet Addresses

For Internet tips, see Glencoe's **Using the Internet in the Science Classroom.**

4 Close

Proficiency Prep

Use this quiz to check students' recall of section content.

1. **Classify each pair of elements as metals, nonmetals, or metalloids: lithium and magnesium; boron and silicon; carbon and oxygen.** *metals; metalloids; nonmetals*
2. **Table salt and sodium fluoride in toothpaste contain elements in what two families?** *alkali metals, halogen*

Section Assessment

1. They combine readily with other elements. The elements in Group 18 do not usually combine with other elements.
2. Silicon's ability to conduct is between that of true conductors (metals) and insulators (nonmetals).
3. oxygen and sulfur, Group 16; nitrogen and phosphorus, Group 15; carbon, Group 14
4. **Think Critically** more readily because the activity of alkali metals increases down the family
5. **Skill Builder**
   Astatine would combine less readily than any of the other halogens because activity decreases down the family.

Using Computers

Student results will vary.

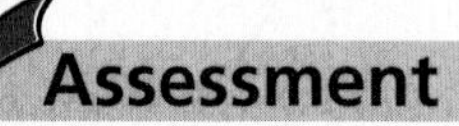

Assessment

Performance Have students choose one halogen and use library or Internet resources to find out more about its uses. Ask them to summarize their findings in a paragraph. Use **Performance Assessment in the Science Classroom,** p. 87. P

Preparing an Alloy

Many of the most important materials in the world are mixtures of elements called alloys. Bronze is an alloy of copper and tin. Brass is an alloy of copper and zinc. Many types of steel are produced by adding carbon and other metals to iron.

What You'll Investigate

How can two metals be combined to form an alloy?

Goals

- **Observe** the changes that occur during the preparation of an alloy.
- **Compare** the plating of a metal to the formation of an alloy.

Safety Precautions

CAUTION: *Nitric acid and sodium hydroxide can cause burns. If you spill nitric acid or sodium hydroxide on your skin, notify your teacher immediately. Rinse the affected area with large amounts of tap water.*

Procedure

1. Carefully **pour** dilute nitric acid into one evaporating dish until the dish is half full. Using tongs, **hold** the penny in the nitric acid for about 20 s.
2. Still using the tongs, **remove** the penny from the acid and rinse it in the beaker of cold water.
3. **Place** one teaspoonful of 30-mesh zinc in the second evaporating dish.
4. Slowly **pour** dilute sodium hydroxide into the dish to a depth of about 2 cm above the zinc.
5. Using tongs, gently **place** the penny on top of the zinc. Rinse the tongs in cold water.
6. Gently **heat** the contents of the evaporating dish on a hot plate until the penny turns a silver color.
7. Set the control on the hot plate to medium high. Using tongs, **remove** the penny from the dish and rinse it in the cold tap water.
8. Dry the penny and **place** it directly on the hot plate until the penny turns a golden color.
9. Your teacher will dispose of the contents of the two evaporating dishes.

Materials

- Copper penny
  **copper wire*
- Zinc, 30-mesh
- Hot plate
- Nitric acid, dilute
- Sodium hydroxide, dilute
- Evaporating dishes
  **beakers (2)*
- Tongs
- Beaker of cold tap water

**Alternate Materials*

Conclude and Apply

1. What caused the change in the appearance of the penny when it was placed in the nitric acid?
2. When one metal is coated with a layer of a second metal, the process is called plating. At which point in this activity did plating occur?
3. What alloy formed when the penny was heated on the hot plate?
4. **Infer** why heat is necessary for the alloy to form.

Purpose

Visual-Spatial Students will experience the making of an alloy. They will distinguish between an alloy and a plated metal. L2 ELL COOP LEARN

Process Skills

observing, comparing, inferring

Time

40 minutes

Materials

To prepare dilute nitric acid, add 15 mL of concentrated acid to 85 mL of distilled water with constant stirring. To prepare 2*M* NaOH solution, dissolve 80 g of NaOH in 1 L of distilled water. Because the solution becomes hot, make it well in advance.

Safety Precautions

Students should wear gloves, goggles, and lab aprons at all times. Remind students to carefully follow all safety precautions.

Teaching Strategies

- Demonstrate the procedure, emphasizing the use of tongs.
- To dispose of the contents of the evaporating dishes, filter any remaining zinc. Mix the two liquids together and dilute with water. Flush the liquids down the sink. If the zinc cannot be reused, wrap it in newspaper and put it into the trash.

Answers to Questions

1. The copper color became brighter. The nitric acid removed dirt and substances formed when copper combines with oxygen and other gases in the air.
2. Plating occurred when the penny was placed on top of the zinc and heated.
3. brass
4. The atoms of zinc and copper must have enough energy to move so that they can mix with one another.

Assessment

Portfolio After discussion of question 4, ask students to draw a diagram of the process of formation of an alloy. Have them use two different colors to represent atoms of copper and zinc. Their diagrams could be placed in their portfolios. Use **Performance Assessment in the Science Classroom,** p. 105. P 

SECTION 3-3

Prepare

Refer to **The Metals in the Middle** on p. 62F.

Preplanning

Refer to the **Chapter Organizer** on pp. 62A–B.

1 Motivate

Bellringer

Before presenting the lesson, display **Section Focus Transparency 7** on the overhead projector. Use the accompanying **Focus Activity** worksheet. L2 ELL

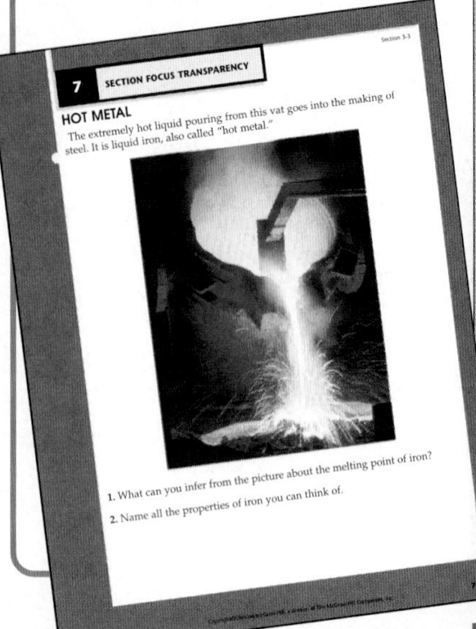

Section 3-3

7 SECTION FOCUS TRANSPARENCY

HOT METAL

The extremely hot liquid pouring from this vat goes into the making of steel. It is liquid iron, also called "hot metal."

1. What can you infer from the picture about the melting point of iron?
2. Name all the properties of iron you can think of.

Tying to Previous Knowledge

Having gained familiarity with the representative elements, students will now explore some of the properties and uses of the transition metals, including the inner transition elements.

3-3 Transition Elements

What You'll Learn

- Properties of some transition elements
- How to distinguish lanthanides from actinides

Why It's Important

- Without transition elements, your electrical appliances wouldn't work, there would be no magnets on your refrigerator, and the world would be a less colorful place.

The Metals in the Middle

What about that large block of elements sandwiched between Group 2 and Group 13? Groups 3-12 are called the transition elements. All transition elements are metals. Across any period from Group 3 through Group 12, the properties of the elements change less noticeably than they do across a period of representative elements. Most transition elements are found combined with oxygen, sulfur, or other elements in ores such as malachite shown in **Figure 3-17.** A few transition elements such as gold, silver, and copper are sometimes found as pure elements in Earth's crust.

Figure 3-17 Many substances that contain transition elements are colored.

The Iron Triad

Three elements in period 4—iron, cobalt, and nickel—have such similar properties that they are known as the iron triad. A triad is a group of three. The elements in the iron triad have magnetic properties. Industrial magnets are made from an alloy of nickel, cobalt, and aluminum. Nickel is used in batteries along with cadmium. Iron is a necessary part of hemoglobin, the substance that transports oxygen in the blood.

8	9	10
26 Iron Fe	27 Cobalt Co	28 Nickel Ni

Iron is the most important of the transition elements. Usually, iron is mixed with other metals and with carbon to create a variety of steels with different properties. Structures such as bridges and skyscrapers like the one shown in **Figure 3-18** depend upon steel for their strength. But, structures made from steel can be eaten away by rust, which results when iron and steel are

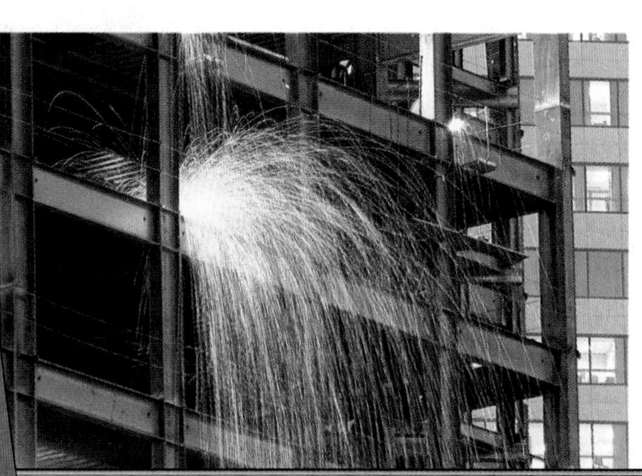

Figure 3-18 The strength of a tall building is in its skeleton, which is made from steel. **What qualities of steel are important in its use in buildings and bridges?**

Resource Manager

The following **Teacher Classroom Resources** can be used with Section 3-3:

Reproducible Masters

Critical Thinking/Problem Solving, p. 3 L2
Enrichment, p. 7 L3
Laboratory Manual, pp. 15–16 L2
Multicultural Connections, pp. 5–6 L2
Reinforcement, p. 7 L2
Study Guide, pp. 11–12 L1 ELL

Transparencies

Teaching Transparency 6 L2
Science Integration Transparency 3 L2

exposed to oxygen in the air. Iron or steel can be painted to protect the metal from rusting. Iron structures also can be coated with zinc for protection from corrosion.

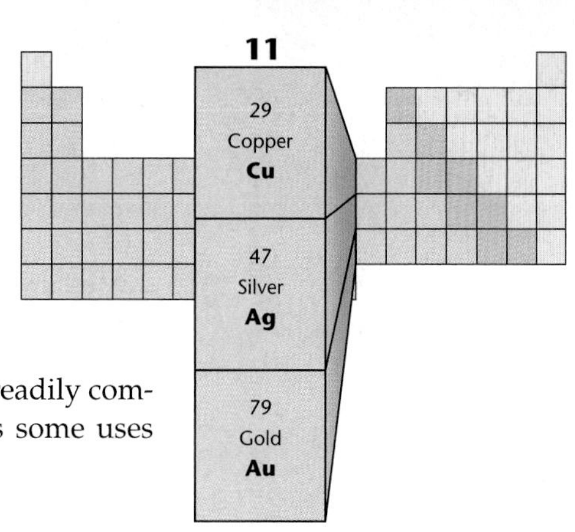

The Coinage Metals

Ancient civilizations made coins from copper, silver, and gold, so these three elements came to be called the coinage metals. They are often found uncombined in nature because they don't readily combine with other elements. **Figure 3-19** illustrates some uses for the coinage metals.

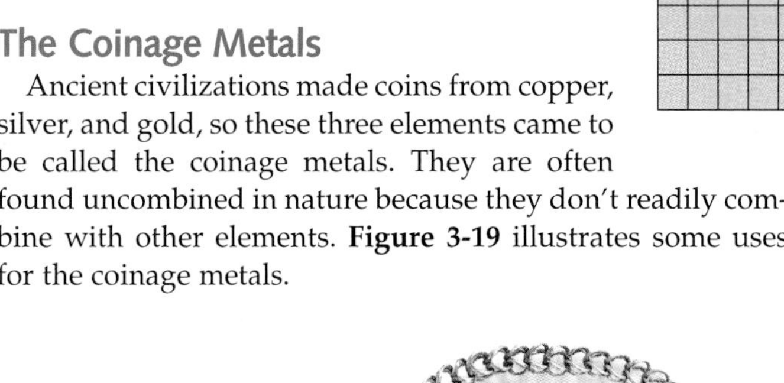

Figure 3-19 Today, copper, silver, and gold are no longer used for coins, but they have many other uses.

A From earliest times, silver and gold were used for jewelry and precious objects of art.

B Photographic film is coated with a thin layer of gelatin that contains a substance composed of silver and bromine or silver and iodine. These substances release silver when they are exposed to light. The amount of silver released depends upon the intensity of the light and the length of exposure. The silver atoms form a pattern that emerges when the film is developed.

C Copper is a good conductor of both electricity and heat. Copper wires carry electricity, and copper-bottomed pans distribute heat evenly. Copper resists corrosion so it used to be the preferred choice for plumbing pipes. Now copper is getting scarcer and more expensive. Plastic piping is being used instead.

Caption Answer

Figure 3-18 *Steel is strong, malleable, and durable.*

2 Teach

VISUAL Learning

Figure 3-22 Draw students' attention to the three diverse uses of copper, silver, and gold in the figure. Then ask them to work together to compile a list of other uses they may have observed. L2

COOP LEARN 

GLENCOE TECHNOLOGY

 **Videodisc**

Glencoe Science Voyages Interactive Videodisc—Earth

Side 1, Lesson 1 *The Rock Cycle*

13

8162

Refer to the Videodisc Teacher Guide for additional bar codes.

Guided Reading Strategy

Learning Journal This strategy encourages students to interact with the reading, allowing personal responses. The left column entries can be research notes, lecture notes, or vocabulary terms. The right column entries are the student's response to, interpretation of, questions about, or analysis of the left column entries. Have students write a Learning Journal related to the transition elements.

Discussion

Mercury is one of the toxic heavy metals. Like all liquids, mercury evaporates if it is not in an enclosed container. Ask: **Why are mercury thermometers not recommended for school laboratory work?** *If the thermometer were to break, the mercury would be hard to pick up. Some of it might remain in the classroom and contaminate the air with its vapors.* L2

Caption Answer

Figure 3-20 *The filament breaks.*

GLENCOE TECHNOLOGY

Videodisc

The Infinite Voyage: The Future of the Past

Chapter 3 *The Statue of Liberty Restoration Project* 9:00

Miracles by Design

Chapter 2 *Improving Steel: Examining Chemical Makeup* 5:00

Refer to the Teacher Guide for bar codes and teaching strategies.

Figure 3-20 You can see that the tungsten filament can be heated to a high temperature but it doesn't melt. **What happens to the filament after long use?**

Other Transition Metals

Most of the transition metals have higher melting points than the representative elements. The filaments of lightbulbs like the one in **Figure 3-20** are made of tungsten, element 74, because it has the highest melting point of any metal (3410ºC) and will not melt with the heat of the bulb.

Mercury, which has the lowest melting point of any metal (–39ºC), is used in thermometers and in barometers. Mercury is the only liquid metal at ordinary temperatures. Like many of the heavy metals, mercury is poisonous to living beings.

Chromium's name comes from the Greek word for color, *chroma,* and the element lives up to its name. Two substances containing chromium are shown in **Figure 3-21.** Many other transition elements combine to form substances with equally brilliant colors.

Ruthenium, rhodium, palladium, osmium, iridium, and platinum are sometimes called the platinum group because they have similar properties. They do not combine easily with other elements, so they can be used for electrodes and as catalysts. A catalyst is a substance that can cause changes to occur faster but is not changed itself. The catalytic converters in automobiles, like the one in **Figure 3-22,** help change pollutants into harmless substances before they are exhausted from the tailpipe into the air.

Figure 3-21 These two substances containing chromium are typical of many substances containing transition elements. They are used to make brightly colored paints.

Figure 3-22 The presence of catalytic converters in all recently manufactured cars has improved the quality of the air you breathe.

Platinum Platinum is a neighbor of gold in period 6, so it's not surprising that platinum is considered a precious metal. Have students find out more about the properties and uses of platinum and summarize them in a written paragraph. P L2

Inner Transition Elements

Do any of the elements in the two rows located below the table seem familiar to you? Except for uranium, which you may have heard about, they are not the metals that you find in most of the things you use every day. But, some inner transition elements have important uses, particularly when combined with other metals.

There are two series of inner transition elements. The first series, from cerium to lutetium, is called the lanthanides. The lanthanides also are called the rare earths because at one time they were thought to be scarce. The word *earth* is an old-fashioned word that refers to a substance formed when a metal combines with oxygen. The lanthanides are usually found combined with oxygen in Earth's crust. The second series of elements, from thorium to lawrencium, are called the actinides.

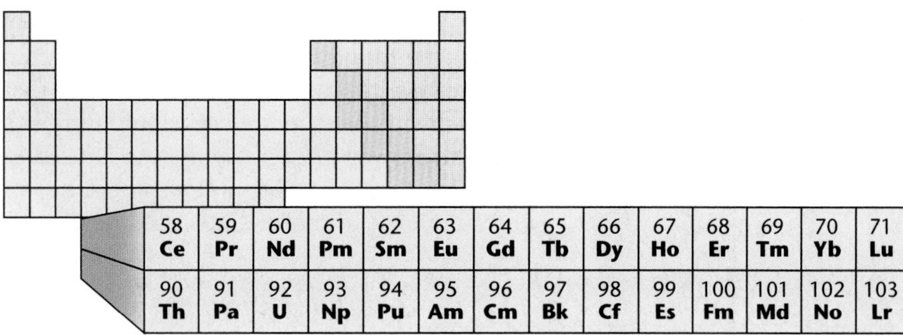

58 Ce
59 Pr
60 Nd
61 Pm
62 Sm
63 Eu
64 Gd
65 Tb
66 Dy
67 Ho
68 Er
69 Tm
70 Yb
71 Lu
90 Th
91 Pa
92 U
93 Np
94 Pu
95 Am
96 Cm
97 Bk
98 Cf
99 Es
100 Fm
101 Md
102 No
103 Lr

The Lanthanides

The lanthanides are soft metals that can be cut with a knife. The elements are so similar that they are hard to separate when they occur in the same ore, which they often do. The element dysprosium gets its name from the Greek word meaning "hard to get at." Three of the lanthanides are named for a town in Sweden, Ytterby, where their ores are mined—erbium (Er), ytterbium (Yb), and terbium (Tb).

Despite the name *rare earth*, the lanthanides are not as rare as originally thought. Earth's crust contains three times as much cerium as lead. Cerium makes up 50 percent of an alloy called misch metal. The other ingredients are lanthanum, neodymium, and iron. Flints in lighters, like the one in **Figure 3-23**, are made from misch metal.

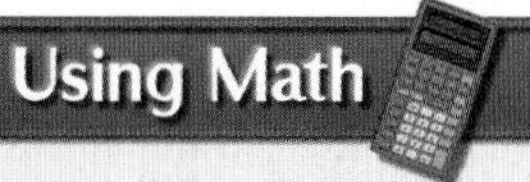

Gold jewelry that is 100 percent pure gold is called 24-carat gold. How much gold is in 18-carat gold? In 12-carat gold?

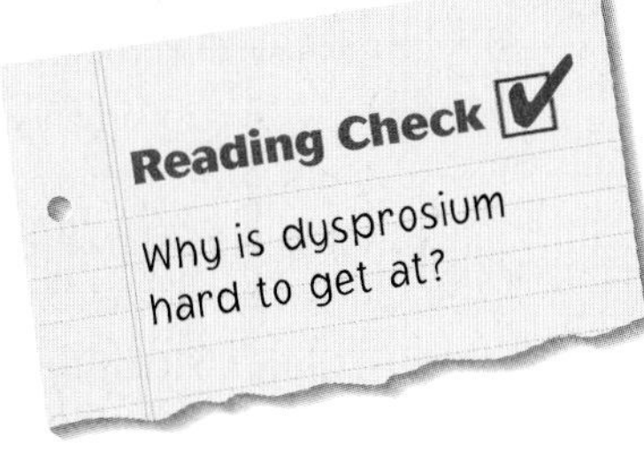

Reading Check
Why is dysprosium hard to get at?

Figure 3-23 The flint in this lighter is made of an alloy called misch metal, whose principal ingredient is the lanthanide cerium.

Using Math

$\frac{18 \text{ carat}}{24 \text{ carat}} \times 100\% = 75\%;$

$\frac{12 \text{ carat}}{24 \text{ carat}} \times 100\% = 50\%$

Challenge students to give a carat rating to a mixture of gold and silver that is 80 percent gold. *0.80 × 24 carats = 19.2 carats*

Answer to Reading Check

Dysprosium occurs in ores with other similar lanthanides and is hard to separate from them.

3 Assess

Check for Understanding Activity

Interpersonal Have students divide into teams and make up questions about the transition elements shown in the figures in this chapter. Then allow each team to challenge another team to answer their questions. L2 COOP LEARN

Reteach

Give students a blank periodic table and have them enter information as you call it out. For example, show the positions of the coinage metals, Group 11. L1

Extension

For students who have mastered this section, use the **Reinforcement** and **Enrichment** masters.

interNET CONNECTION

Internet Addresses

____

____

____

____

For Internet tips, see Glencoe's **Using the Internet in the Science Classroom.**

4 Close

Proficiency Prep

Use this quiz to check students' recall of section content.

1. **What are iron, cobalt, and nickel called?** *the iron triad*
2. **What is the coinage metal that is used in photography?** *silver*

Section Assessment

1. The lanthanides exist in nature; the actinides are mostly synthetic elements. Yes, because they are in the same group.
2. They are magnetic.
3. Steel rusts. Painting can prevent rusting.
4. Think Critically Cadmium is likely to be toxic because it is a neighbor of mercury in the same group. Iridium is likely to be a catalyst because it is close to platinum.

Science Journal

Gold and silver are valuable because they are rare and beautiful. Metals such as iron and aluminum are valuable because they have so many uses. P

interNET CONNECTION

Visit the Glencoe Science Web Site at **www.glencoe.com/sec/science** for more information about transition elements.

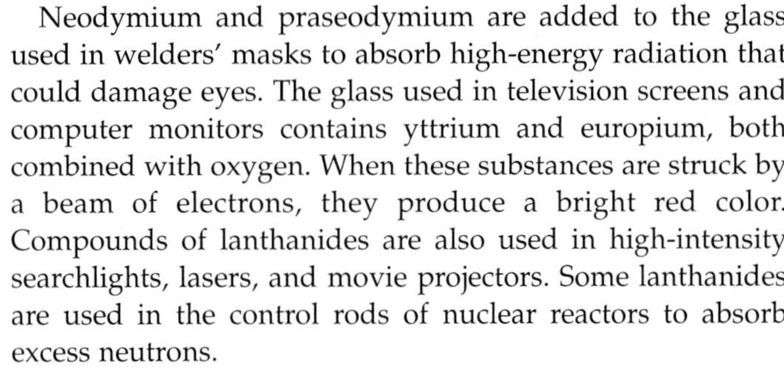

Neodymium and praseodymium are added to the glass used in welders' masks to absorb high-energy radiation that could damage eyes. The glass used in television screens and computer monitors contains yttrium and europium, both combined with oxygen. When these substances are struck by a beam of electrons, they produce a bright red color. Compounds of lanthanides are also used in high-intensity searchlights, lasers, and movie projectors. Some lanthanides are used in the control rods of nuclear reactors to absorb excess neutrons.

The Actinides

All the actinides are radioactive. The nuclei of atoms of radioactive elements are unstable and decay to form other elements. Thorium, protactinium, and uranium are the only actinides that are now found naturally on Earth. All the others are synthetic elements. They may have existed on Earth at one time, but because most decay within a few days, none can be found today. Uranium is still found in Earth's crust because its half-life is long—4.5 billion years. The synthetic elements have many uses. Plutonium is used as a fuel in nuclear power plants. Americium is used in some home smoke detectors. Some actinide isotopes have medical uses. For example, californium-232 is used to kill cancer cells.

Section Assessment

1. What is the major difference between the lanthanides and actinides? Would you expect neodymium and uranium to have similar properties? Explain.
2. How do the elements in the iron triad differ from other transition metals?
3. What is one drawback to using steel for structures such as skyscrapers, and how can that drawback be overcome?
4. **Think Critically:** Of the elements iridium and cadmium, predict which is likely to be toxic and which could act as a catalyst. Explain.
5. **Skill Builder**
   Observing and Inferring How does the appearance of a burned-out lightbulb compare to a new bulb? What could explain the difference? If you need help, refer to Observing and Inferring in the **Skill Handbook** on page 704.

Science Journal

In your Science Journal, discuss the term *valuable* as it relates to elements. How do relative abundance, number of uses, and durability contribute to value?

5. **Skill Builder**
The bulb darkens from deposits of tungsten from the constant heating of the metal.

Assessment

Oral Ask students to draw an analogy between the deposits of tungsten on the bulb and the droplets of water that form on a cool window in a room where a teakettle is boiling. Use **Performance Assessment in the Science Classroom,** p. 71.

Dentistry and the Elements

Dental Materials

Before dentistry became a science, a person's decayed tooth would eventually fall out or have to be pulled. Since the 1930s, dentists, like the one at left, have successfully used elements found in the periodic table to repair and replace decayed teeth. The elements mercury and silver traditionally have been used to fill cavities. Mercury is a poisonous liquid metal, but mixing it with silver, copper, and zinc forms a hard substance that has been considered safe to put in people's mouths. Today, other materials also are used for fillings.

A combination of gold, silver, and copper is used to make gold coverings, called crowns, for damaged or weakened teeth. If a tooth is broken off at the root and needs single-tooth replacement, the element titanium is used as a post to support a replacement tooth made from plastic.

The framework for dentures—replacements for teeth that have fallen out—is made from the elements chromium and cobalt. When mixed together, these metals are flexible, strong, and rust resistant.

Elements and the Orthodontist

Orthodontists, dentists who are specialists in the positioning of teeth, use braces (see below) or retainers to reposition crowded or misplaced teeth. Braces are often made of stainless steel, a combination of iron, nickel, and carbon. The stainless steel is mixed with chromium to keep the braces from rusting.

With all these materials available for fixing teeth, dentists still emphasize prevention: regular brushing, flossing, and checkups.

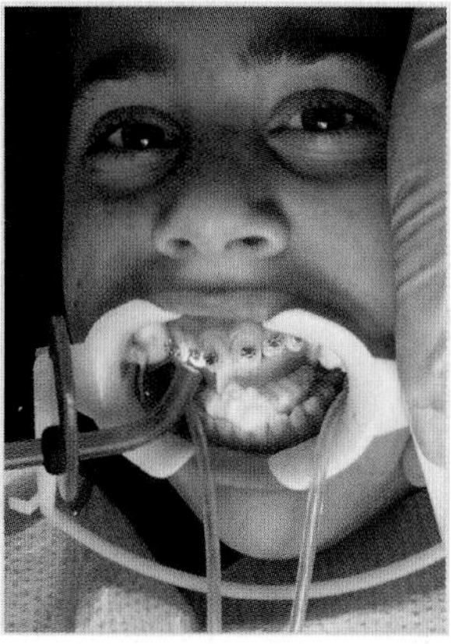

Science JOURNAL

In your Science Journal, write a paragraph summarizing some of the advantages of modern materials in dentistry. Base your summary on library or online research.

Science & Society

Content Background

Many dentists are using nonmetallic materials for fillings. These materials called composites are plastics containing a large percentage of carbon. They have the advantage of avoiding any possibility of toxicity from mercury and also being less noticeable because they match the color of teeth. Amalgam fillings have a limited lifetime. They are constantly in a wet environment, which enhances corrosion and leads to pitting, cracking, and finally breaking. Gold, silver, and copper—the elements used for crowns—are unreactive and less prone to corrosion. Gold crowns are used mostly in the back of the mouth because they are noticeable, but in some cultures, gold teeth are considered a sign of wealth.

Teaching Strategies

- Have students who are undergoing an orthodontic procedure ask their orthodontists about the materials they are using. Have them share what they learn.
- Have other students contact local dentists to find out what materials they are using and present their findings as a short oral or written report.
- Students can list and locate on the periodic table all the elements mentioned. Have them label them as representative or transition elements.
- Students can use the Internet or library sources to find out if there is controvery concerning the use of mercury in fillings. Have them debate the pros and cons of the issue.
- Invite a local dentist to visit the class and answer students' questions.

For More Information

American Dental Association
211 E. Chicago Avenue
Chicago, IL 60611

interNET CONNECTION

Internet Addresses

For Internet tips, see Glencoe's **Using the Internet in the Science Classroom.**

Activity 3·2 **On the Internet**

Recognize the Problem

Students will research possible harmful chemicals that are used in their local area. They will search for, gather, and analyze information from the Internet and other sources. After they have compiled and synthesized their information, they will post their report on the Internet.

Form a Hypothesis

Internet Students will gather data from the Internet that can be accessed through the Glencoe Homepage at **www.glencoe.com/sec/science**.

Students can post their findings and get information from other schools around the country.

Non-Internet Sources If you do not have access to the Internet, your school and local libraries are good places to start. Newspapers and local television news broadcasts often provide information connecting health issues to chemicals in the environment.

Time Required

one to two weeks

Activity 3·2

Health Risks from Heavy Metals

Whether it's lip balm that blocks UV rays from the sun or cream cheese with lower fat, society benefits from using chemicals in many products. But, chemicals, such as heavy metals, can be dangerous if they are used incorrectly or leak into the environment where they are not meant to be.

Recognize the Problem

Do heavy metals and other chemicals pose a threat to the health of humans? One way to reduce any threat is to know as much as possible about the chemical, its source, and its environmental impact.

Form a Hypothesis

Could health problems be caused by exposure to heavy metals, such as lead, or a radioactive chemical element, such as radon? Is the incidence of these problems higher in one area than another? Form a hypothesis as to the potential health risk of a chemical in your area.

Goals

- **Organize and synthesize** information on a chemical or heavy metal thought to cause health problems in your area.
- **Communicate** your findings with others in your class.

Data Sources

Go to the Glencoe Science Web Site at **www.glencoe.com/sec/science** to obtain information, hints, and data from other students.

Health Risk Data Table

Location	Chemical or Heavy Metal	How People Come in Contact with Chemical	Potential Health Problem	Who is affected
Chicago, Illinois	lead	in paint, eaten	causes brain damage	mainly small children

Preparation

Internet Access the Glencoe Homepage at **www.glencoe.com/sec/science** to run through the steps that the students will follow.

Non-Internet Sources Scan the local newspaper for articles connecting health with chemical use.

interNET CONNECTION

Internet Addresses

____

____

____

____

For Internet tips, see Glencoe's **Using the Internet in the Science Classroom.**

Test Your Hypothesis

Plan

1. **Read** general information concerning heavy metals and other potentially hazardous chemicals.
2. Use the sites listed on the Glencoe Science Web Site to **research** possible health problems in your area caused by exposure to chemicals or heavy metals.
3. Check the Glencoe Science Web Site to see what others have learned.

Do

1. Make sure your teacher approves your plan before you proceed.
2. **Search** for resources that can help you find out about health risks in your area.
3. **Organize** your information in a data table like the one shown.
4. **Write** a report in your Science Journal about the results of your research.
5. **Post your data** in the table provided on the Glencoe Science Web Site.

Analyze Your Data

1. Did all your sources agree on the health risk of the chemical or heavy metal?
2. Analyze all your sources for possible bias. Are some sources more reliable than others?
3. How did the health risk differ for adults and children?

Draw Conclusions

1. Were the same substances found to be health risks in other parts of the country? From the data on the Glencoe Science Web Site try to predict what chemicals or heavy metals are health risks in different parts of the country.
2. From your report, what information do you think is the most important for the public to be aware of?
3. What could be done to decrease the risk of the health problems you identified?

Test Your Hypothesis

Teaching Strategies

- Motivate students' investigations by brainstorming ways that chemicals benefit society. Then, present a few examples of severe health or environmental problems that have resulted from lack of information about chemicals, such as dioxin, DDT, or CFCs.
- Present examples of some initial research questions, such as: Are there heavy metals in fertilizer? How harmful is antimony to humans? Where in the human body does mercury accumulate?
- **Troubleshoot** Go over some of the unfamiliar words the students may encounter such as carcinogenic, soluble, and toxic.

Have students explore the effects of biomagnification, which is the building up of concentrations of heavy metals and other chemicals in the tissues of organisms along the food chain. Students can diagram their findings on a poster indicating food chains that lead to chemical biomagnification.

Assessment

Portfolio Have students design and produce an informational pamphlet. The pamphlet should be geared to the general population. The intent of the pamphlet might be to provide facts and figures explaining the potential health risks that certain chemicals pose for the local environment and/or population. P COOP LEARN

References

W. Salomons, U. Forstner, P. Mader. *Heavy Metals: Problems and Solutions.* Springer Verlag, 1995.

Marc Kusinitz. *Poisons and Toxins (Encyclopedia of Health, Medical Disorders and Their Treatment).* Chelsea House Pub, 1992.

Reviewing Main Ideas can be used to preview, review, reteach, and condense chapter content.

Preview

Linguistic Have students try to answer the questions in their Science Journals. Use student answers as a source for discussion throughout the chapter.

Review

Interpersonal Have students answer the questions on separate pieces of paper and compare their answers with those of other students in the class. COOP LEARN

Reteach

Visual-Spatial Have students look at the illustrations on these pages. Ask them to describe details that support the main ideas of the chapter found in the statement for each illustration.

00:00 OUT OF TIME?

Auditory-Musical If time does not permit teaching the entire chapter, use the information on these pages along with the chapter Audiocassettes to present the material in a condensed format.

Chapter 3 Reviewing Main Ideas

For a **preview** of this chapter, study this Reviewing Main Ideas before you read the chapter. After you have studied this chapter, you can use the Reviewing Main Ideas to **review** the chapter.

The Glencoe MindJogger, Audiocassettes, and CD-ROM provide additional opportunities for review.

Section

3-1 PERIODICITY

When organized according to atomic number in a table, elements with similar properties occupy the same column, called a **group** or family. The properties of the elements change gradually across a horizontal row called a **period. Metals** are usually shiny, malleable, and ductile. They are good conductors of heat and electricity. Many **nonmetals** are gases. Solid nonmetals are often brittle and poor conductors of heat and electricity. **Metalloids** have properties between those of metals and nonmetals. The periodic table can be divided into representative elements and transition elements. ***What do families on the periodic table have in common with human families?***

Section

3-2 ALKALI AND ALKALINE EARTH METALS

Atoms of elements in Groups 1 and 2 readily combine with atoms of other elements. The ease with which the atoms of the elements combine with other atoms increases down the two groups. Each element in Group 2 combines less readily than its neighbor in Group 1. Each alkaline earth metal is denser and has a higher melting point than the alkali metal in its period. Sodium, potassium, magnesium, and calcium have important biological roles. ***What element is magnesium mixed with to form strong, lightweight alloys?***

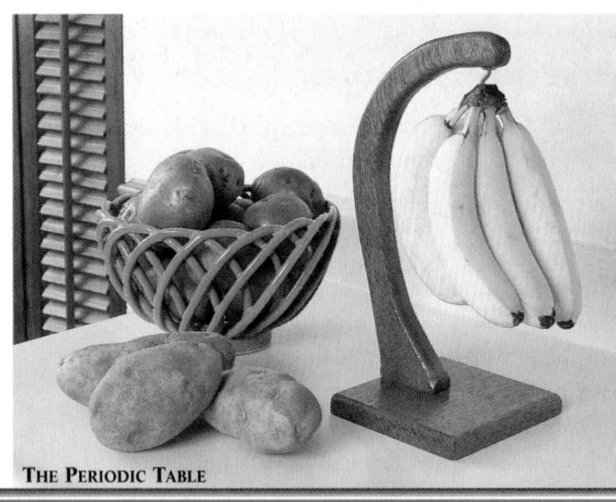

Cultural Diversity

That'll be two cowries and a whale's tooth. . . Coinage metals got their name from their use as money, but many things have been used as money. The Native Americans' wampum consisted of beads made from shells. Cowrie shells in India, whales' teeth in Fiji, and stone disks in Yap (a Pacific Island) have all served in monetary systems. The use of metals for exchange appeared around 7000 B.C. in the Middle East. Bronze was used first. Gold and silver began to be used because of their value. True coins, of standard weight and value, were probably first produced by the Lydians of Anatolia (modern-day Turkey) in 640 B.C. They used a naturally occurring alloy of gold and silver called electrum. Eventually, the purity and weight of gold and silver in coins was certified by the government.

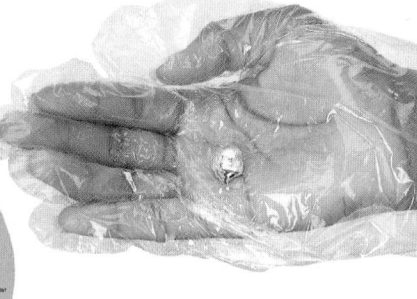

Reading Check ✓

Construct a chart that shows what each symbol in an element key represents. What other feature could be indicated with a symbol?

ELEMENTS IN GROUPS 13–18

Aluminum, the most common metal in Earth's crust, has many uses. Carbon is found in two common forms—diamond and graphite. Nitrogen, oxygen, sulfur, and phosphorus are essential for life. Ammonia and sulfuric acid are important chemicals in manufacturing. Silicon is a metalloid used as a semiconductor in electronics. The halogens combine with other elements to form a variety of substances such as table salt and sodium fluoride. The noble gases have many uses that depend upon the fact that they do not combine with other elements. ***What are the two groups of elements that together form common salts?***

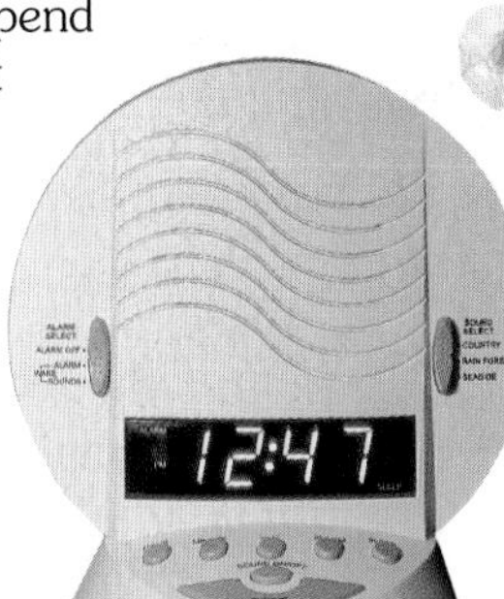

3-3 TRANSITION ELEMENTS

Iron is the most important transition element because of its strength and durabilty, but it must be protected from corrosion. Magnets contain elements from the iron triad. The coinage metals are fairly unreactive, malleable elements. The uses of copper depend upon its superior ability to conduct heat and electricity. Substances containing silver are in the coating on photographic film. Platinum is used as electrodes and as a catalyst. The lanthanides are naturally occurring elements with similar properties. The actinides are radioactive elements. All actinides except thorium, proactinium, and uranium are synthetic. ***Why is it dangerous to handle the mercury that is spilled when a thermometer or barometer breaks?***

Answers to Questions

Section 3-1

Periodicity Both types of families have common traits and characteristics.

Section 3-2

Alkali and Alkaline Earth Metals Aluminum is mixed with magnesium.

Elements in Groups 13–18 Group 1 and Group 17 form common salts.

Section 3-3

Transition Elements Mercury is a poisonous metal that can be absorbed through the skin.

GLENCOE TECHNOLOGY

CD-ROM

Glencoe Science Voyages Interactive CD-ROM

Chapter Summaries and Quizzes

Have students read the Chapter Summary and then take the Chapter Quiz to determine whether they have mastered chapter content.

Assessment

Portfolio Encourage students to place in their portfolios one or two items of what they consider to be their best work. Examples include:

- Assessment, pp. 65, 71
- Multiple Learning Styles, pp. 68, 78
- Science Journal, pp. 74, 86
- Across the Curriculum, p. 77
- Activity 3-2, pp. 90–91 P

Performance Additional performance assessments may be found in **Performance Assessment** and **Science Integration Activities.** Performance Task Assessment Lists and rubrics for evaluating these activities can be found in Glencoe's **Performance Assessment in the Science Classroom.**

Using Vocabulary

1. A group is a vertical column of elements on the periodic table. A period is a horizontal row.
2. Metalloids are elements with properties intermediate between metals and nonmetals. Because they are slightly conductive, they act as semiconductors.
3. Alloys are mixtures of elements, one of which is a metal. Metals and alloys have the properties of metals.
4. nonmetal, metalloid, metal
5. Like a metal, a metalloid conducts electricity but not as well. A metalloid has some of the properties of metals as well as some of the properties of nonmetals.

interNET CONNECTION To reinforce chapter vocabulary, use the **Study Guide for Content Mastery** booklet. Also available are activities for **Glencoe Science Voyages** on the Glencoe Science Web Site. **www.glencoe.com/sec/science**

Checking Concepts

6. C	11. A
7. B	12. D
8. B	13. C
9. D	14. D
10. A	15. A

Thinking Critically

16. Mercury is poisonous and can kill organisms that live in waterways.
17. Yes, because fluorine is the most reactive nonmetal.
18. Hydrogen can burn.
19. The hydrogen produced when an active metal reacts with water can cause a fire and an explosion.
20. They would be shorter.

Chapter 3 Assessment

Using Vocabulary

a. alloy
b. group
c. metal
d. metalloid
e. nonmetal
f. period
g. semiconductor

Answer the following questions about the Vocabulary words.

1. What is the difference between a group and a period?
2. What is the connection between a metalloid and a semiconductor?
3. How are a metal and an alloy alike?
4. Arrange the terms *nonmetal, metal,* and *metalloid* according to increasing electrical conductivity.
5. How is a metalloid like a metal? How is it different?

Checking Concepts

Choose the word or phrase that best answers the question.

6. Which of the following groups combines most readily with other elements?
   A) coinage metals
   B) alkaline earth metals
   C) alkali metals
   D) iron triad
7. Which element is located in Group 6, period 4?
   A) tungsten C) titanium
   B) chromium D) hafnium
8. Which element is **NOT** found uncombined in nature?
   A) gold C) silver
   B) calcium D) copper
9. Which group contains only nonmetals?
   A) Group 1 C) Group 2
   B) Group 12 D) Group 18
10. Which of the following elements is likely to be contained in a substance with a brilliant yellow color?
    A) chromium C) iron
    B) carbon D) tin
11. Which halogen is radioactive?
    A) astatine C) bromine
    B) chlorine D) iodine
12. Which of the following is unlikely to happen to zinc?
    A) It is rolled into sheets.
    B) It is used to coat a steel hull.
    C) It is used in a battery.
    D) It is used as an insulator.
13. Which of the following describes the element tellurium?
    A) alkali metal C) metalloid
    B) transition metal D) lanthanide
14. Which element has the highest melting point?
    A) bromine C) mercury
    B) iodine D) tungsten
15. Which of these elements is **NOT** essential for living organisms?
    A) strontium C) sodium
    B) sulfur D) selenium

Thinking Critically

16. Why is it important that mercury be kept out of streams and waterways?
17. If you were going to try to get the noble gas argon to combine with another element, would fluorine be a good choice for the other element? Explain.
18. Hydrogen, which is lighter than helium, used to be used in blimps that carried passengers. Why is helium a better choice?
19. Why is water **NOT** used for putting out some chemical fires?

20. It's possible that some of the actinides beyond uranium were once present in Earth's crust. If that is true, how would their half-lives compare with the half-life of uranium, which is 4.5 billion years?

Developing Skills

If you need help, refer to the **Skill Handbook.**

21. **Recognizing Cause and Effect:** Why do photographers work in low light when they develop film?
22. **Predicting:** How would life on Earth be different if the atmosphere were 80 percent oxygen and 20 percent nitrogen instead of the other way around?
23. **Making and Using Graphs:** Make a bar graph of the representative elements that shows how many of the elements are solids, liquids, and gases at room temperature.
24. **Concept Mapping:** Draw a concept map of the periodic table. Make the first division between representative elements and transition elements.
25. **Making and Using Tables:** The periodic table below shows the locations of a few elements. For each element shown, give the element's period and group number; whether the element is a metal or a nonmetal; and whether it is a solid, liquid, or gas at room temperature.

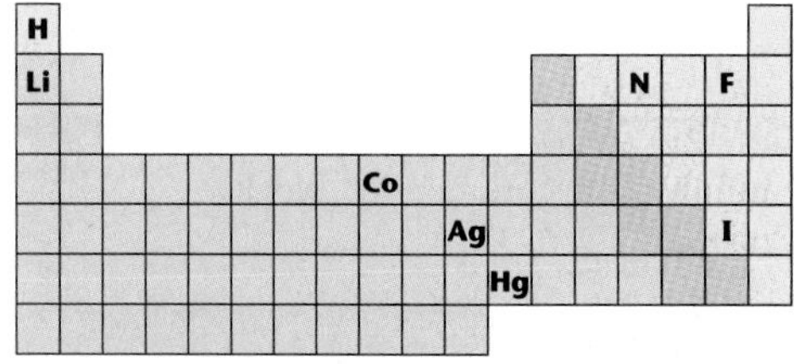

Test-Taking Tip

When Eliminating, Cross It Out List the answer choice letters on the scratch paper. Use your pencil to cross out choices you've eliminated. You'll stop yourself from choosing an answer you've mentally eliminated.

Test Practice

Use these questions to test your Science Proficiency.

1. Diamond is one of the hardest substances on Earth. Graphite is soft. Which is the best explanation for the difference in hardness?
   A) Graphite and diamond are made from different elements.
   B) Graphite is a mixture of elements.
   C) The atoms in diamond and graphite are arranged in different patterns.
   D) Diamond is made from carbon-14 atoms. Graphite contains mainly carbon-12 atoms.
2. Which is the best description of sulfur?
   A) period 2, Group 16, transition element, important industrial element
   B) period 3, oxygen family, representative element, biologically important
   C) period 5, oxygen family, representative element, poisonous
   D) period 6, inner transition element, radioactive, metal

Assessment Resources

The **Test Practice Workbook** provides students with practice in the format, concepts, and critical-thinking skills tested in standardized exams.

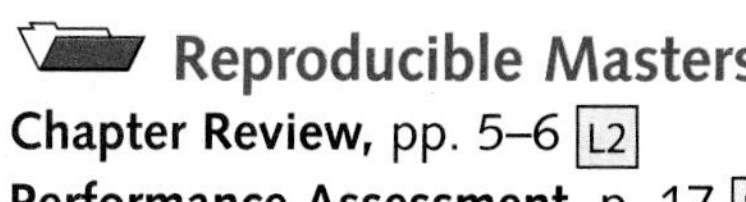

Reproducible Masters

Chapter Review, pp. 5–6 L2
Performance Assessment, p. 17 L2
Assessment, pp. 9–12 L2

Glencoe Technology

Chapter Review Software
Computer Test Bank
MindJogger Videoquiz

The Princeton Review Test Practice

The Test-Taking Tip was written by The Princeton Review, the nation's leader in test preparation.

1. C
2. B

Developing Skills

21. Until the film has been developed and the excess halogen compound removed, the film is still sensitive to light and the existing image could be destroyed.
22. Answers will vary but should include recognition of oxygen's ability to react with most elements.
23. Graphs should show that 32 are solid, one is a liquid, and 11 are gaseous.
24. Representative elements could be connected to the phrase *Groups 1, 2 and 13–18* and to the words *metals* and *nonmetals.* Transition elements should be connected to *Groups 2–12* and to the word *metals.*
25. H: 1, 1, nonmetal, gas
    Li: 2, 1, metal, solid
    Co: 4, 9, metal, solid
    Ag: 5, 11, metal, solid
    Hg: 6, 12, metal, liquid
    N: 2, 15, nonmetal, gas
    F: 2, 17, nonmetal, gas
    I: 5, 17, nonmetal, solid

Bonus Question

Although chromium, like selenium, is poisonous, it is needed in trace amounts in your diet. How does this information apply to the safe use of vitamin-mineral tablets containing chromium? *Care must be taken that the amount needed is not exceeded.*

Chapter 4 Chemical Bonds

Section	Objectives	Activities/Features
Chapter Opener		**Explore Activity:** Model the Energy of Electrons, p. 97
4-1 **Why do atoms combine?** 2½ Sessions 1½ Blocks	1. **Describe** the arrangement of electrons in an atom. 2. **Interpret** the arrangement of electrons in terms of their energy. 3. **Explain** the relationship between the arrangement of electrons in an atom and that atom's location in the periodic table.	**Using Math,** p. 100 **Using Math,** p. 101 **MiniLab:** Drawing Electron Dot Diagrams, p. 102 **Skill Builder:** Classifying, p. 103 **Using Math,** p. 103 **Activity 4-1:** Atomic Structure, pp. 104–105
4-2 **Ionic and Covalent Bonds** 3½ Sessions 1½ Blocks	4. **Describe** ionic and covalent bonds. 5. **Distinguish** polar and nonpolar covalent bonds. 6. **Use** chemical shorthand.	**Earth Science Integration,** p. 108 **MiniLab:** Constructing a Model for Methane, p. 109 **Problem Solving:** Beyond Diamond and Graphite, p. 110 **Using Math,** p. 113 **Skill Builder:** Predicting, p. 113 **Using Computers,** p. 113 **Activity 4-2:** Ionic Compounds, p. 114 **How It Works:** Metallic Bonding, p. 115

The number of recommended single-period sessions — The number of recommended blocks
One session and one-half block are allowed for chapter review and assessment.

Activity Materials

Explore	Activities	MiniLabs
p. 97 paper clips, magnet	pp. 104–105 magnetic board, rubber magnetic strips, paper, marker, grapes, candy-coated peanuts, coins p. 114 8 different-colored papers, 2 different-colored tacks, corrugated cardboard, scissors	p. 102 ruler, pencil, paper p. 109 circles of different-colored papers, scissors

Need Materials? Contact Science Kit at 1-800-828-7777 or at www.sciencekit.com on the Internet.
For alternate materials, see the activity on the listed page.

Standards		Reproducible Resources	Technology
National	State/Local	Test Practice Workbooks are available for use with each chapter.	English and Spanish audiocassettes are available for use with each section.
National Content Standards: UCP2, A1, A2, B1		**Activity Worksheets,** pp. 17–18, 21 **Enrichment,** p. 8 **Reinforcement,** p. 8 **Study Guide,** pp. 13–14	**Section Focus Transparency 8** **Teaching Transparency 7** **Teaching Transparency 8** **Glencoe Science Voyages Interactive Videodisc—Physical** **Internet Connection,** p. 100
National Content Standards: UCP1, A1, A2, B1, B3, D1, G3		**Activity Worksheets,** pp. 19–20, 22 **Critical Thinking/Problem Solving,** p. 4 **Enrichment,** p. 9 **Home Involvement,** p. 37 **Laboratory Manual,** pp. 17–20 **Laboratory Manual,** pp. 21–24 **Multicultural Connections,** pp. 7–8 **Reinforcement,** p. 9 **Study Guide,** pp. 15–16	**Section Focus Transparency 9** **Science Integration Transparency 4** **Glencoe Science Voyages Interactive CD-ROM** **Glencoe Science Voyages Interactive Videodisc—Physical** **Internet Connection,** p. 111 **The Infinite Voyage Series**

Key to Teaching Strategies

The following designations will help you decide which activities are appropriate for your students.

L1 Level 1 activities should be appropriate for students with learning difficulties.

L2 Level 2 activities should be within the ability range of all students.

L3 Level 3 activities are designed for above-average students.

ELL ELL activities should be within the ability range of English Language Learners.

COOP LEARN Cooperative Learning activities are designed for small group work.

P These strategies represent student products that can be placed into a best-work portfolio.

Multiple Learning Styles logos, as described on page 61T, are used throughout to indicate strategies that address different learning styles.

Assessment Resources

Chapter Review, pp. 7–8
Assessment, pp. 13–16
Performance Assessment in the Science Classroom (PASC)
MindJogger Videoquiz
Alternate Assessment in the Science Classroom
Performance Assessment, p. 18
Chapter Review Software
Computer Test Bank

Chapter 4 Chemical Bonds

This is a representation of key blackline masters available in the Teacher Classroom Resources. See Resource Manager boxes within the chapter for additional information.

Transparencies

Section Focus Transparencies

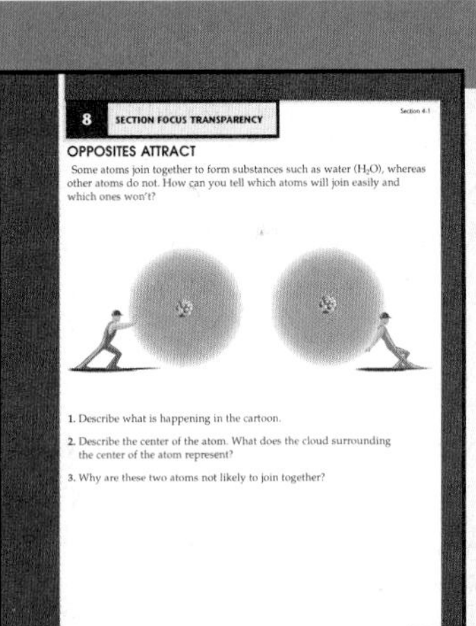

8 SECTION FOCUS TRANSPARENCY Section 4.1

OPPOSITES ATTRACT

Some atoms join together to form substances such as water (H_2O), whereas other atoms do not. How can you tell which atoms will join easily and which ones won't?

1. Describe what is happening in the cartoon.
2. Describe the center of the atom. What does the cloud surrounding the center of the atom represent?
3. Why are these two atoms not likely to join together?

L2

9 SECTION FOCUS TRANSPARENCY Section 4.2

THEY GO TOGETHER

Like peanut butter and jelly or ketchup and french fries, salt and popcorn just "go together." Salt itself is a combination of two things that often go together in nature. Table salt—sodium chloride—is made up of sodium and chlorine.

1. How many electrons does sodium have in its outer energy level?
2. How many electrons does chlorine have in its outer energy level?
3. Explain why sodium atoms and chlorine atoms are likely to combine.

L2

Science Integration Transparencies

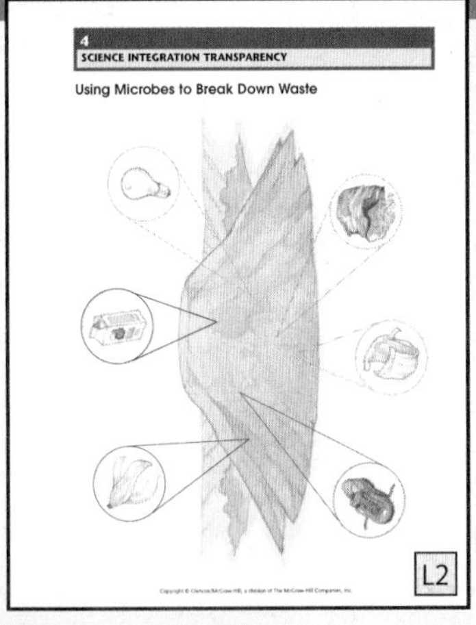

4 SCIENCE INTEGRATION TRANSPARENCY

Using Microbes to Break Down Waste

L2

Teaching Transparencies

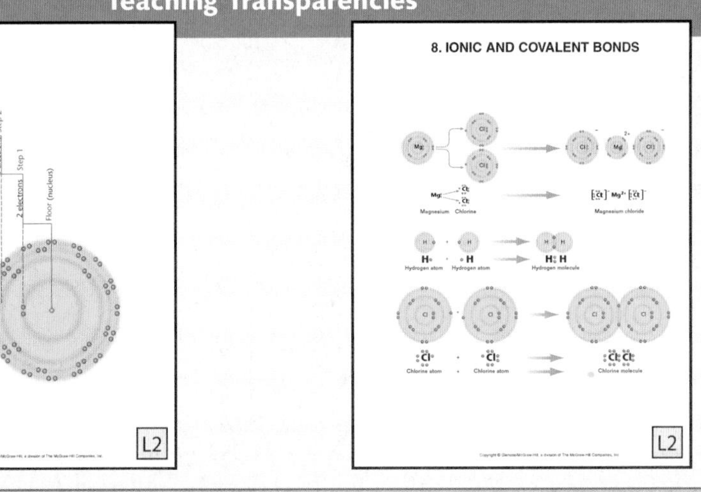

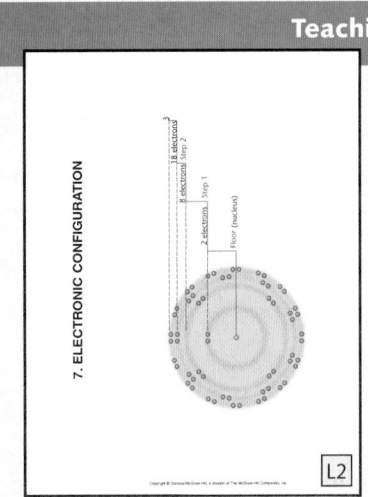

Meeting Different Ability Levels

Study Guide for Content Mastery

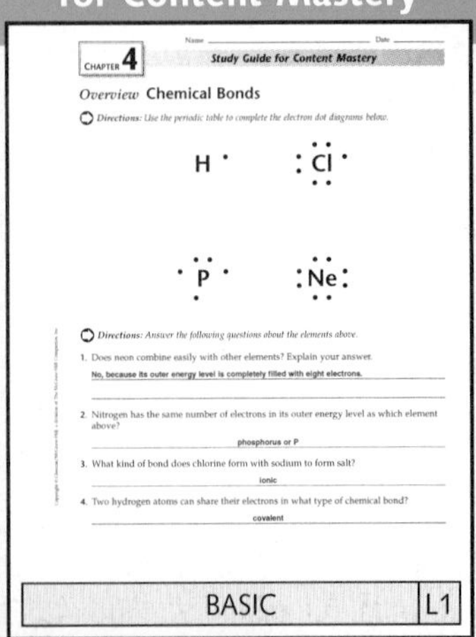

CHAPTER 4 Study Guide for Content Mastery

Name ______ Date ______

Overview Chemical Bonds

Directions: Use the periodic table to complete the electron dot diagrams below.

H· :Cl· ·P· :Ne:

Directions: Answer the following questions about the elements above.

1. Does neon combine easily with other elements? Explain your answer.
No, because its outer energy level is completely filled with eight electrons.
2. Nitrogen has the same number of electrons in its outer energy level as which element above?
phosphorus or P
3. What kind of bond does chlorine form with sodium to form salt?
ionic
4. Two hydrogen atoms can share their electrons in what type of chemical bond?
covalent

BASIC L1

Reinforcement

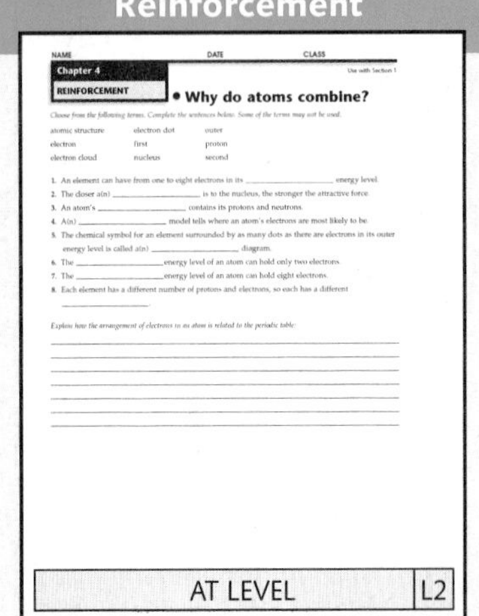

NAME ______ DATE ______ CLASS ______

Chapter 4 REINFORCEMENT

Use with Section 1

• Why do atoms combine?

Choose from the following terms. Complete the sentences below. Some of the terms may not be used.

atomic structure	electron dot	outer
electron	first	proton
electron cloud	nucleus	second

1. An element can have from one to eight electrons in its ______ energy level.
2. The closer a(n) ______ is to the nucleus, the stronger the attractive force.
3. An atom's ______ contains its protons and neutrons.
4. A(n) ______ model tells where an atom's electrons are most likely to be.
5. The chemical symbol for an element surrounded by as many dots as there are electrons in its outer energy level is called a(n) ______ diagram.
6. The ______ energy level of an atom can hold only two electrons.
7. The ______ energy level of an atom can hold eight electrons.
8. Each element has a different number of protons and electrons, so each has a different ______.

Explain how the arrangement of electrons in an atom is related to the periodic table:

AT LEVEL L2

Enrichment Worksheets

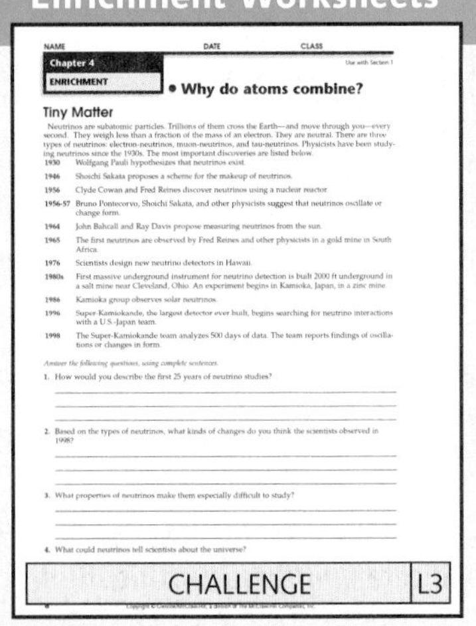

NAME ______ DATE ______ CLASS ______

Chapter 4 ENRICHMENT

Use with Section 1

• Why do atoms combine?

Tiny Matter

Neutrinos are subatomic particles. Trillions of them cross the Earth—and move through you—every second. They weigh less than a fraction of the mass of an electron. They are neutral. There are three types of neutrinos: electron-neutrinos, muon-neutrinos, and tau-neutrinos. Physicists have been studying neutrinos since the 1930s. The most important discoveries are listed below.

1930	Wolfgang Pauli hypothesizes that neutrinos exist.
1946	Shoichi Sakata proposes a scheme for the makeup of neutrinos.
1956	Clyde Cowan and Fred Reines discover neutrinos using a nuclear reactor.
1956-57	Bruno Pontecorvo, Shoichi Sakata, and other physicists suggest that neutrinos oscillate or change form.
1964	John Bahcall and Ray Davis propose measuring neutrinos from the sun.
1965	The first neutrinos are observed by Fred Reines and other physicists in a gold mine in South Africa.
1976	Scientists design new neutrino detectors in Hawaii.
1980s	First massive underground instrument for neutrino detection is built 2000 ft underground in a salt mine near Cleveland, Ohio. An experiment begins in Kamioka, Japan, in a zinc mine.
1986	Kamioka group observes solar neutrinos.
1996	Super-Kamiokande, the largest detector ever built, begins searching for neutrino interactions with a U.S.-Japan team.
1998	The Super-Kamiokande team analyzes 500 days of data. The team reports findings of oscillations or changes in form.

Answer the following questions, using complete sentences.

1. How would you describe the first 25 years of neutrino studies?
2. Based on the types of neutrinos, what kinds of changes do you think the scientists observed in 1998?
3. What properties of neutrinos make them especially difficult to study?
4. What could neutrinos tell scientists about the universe?

CHALLENGE L3

Hands-on Activities

Activity Worksheets

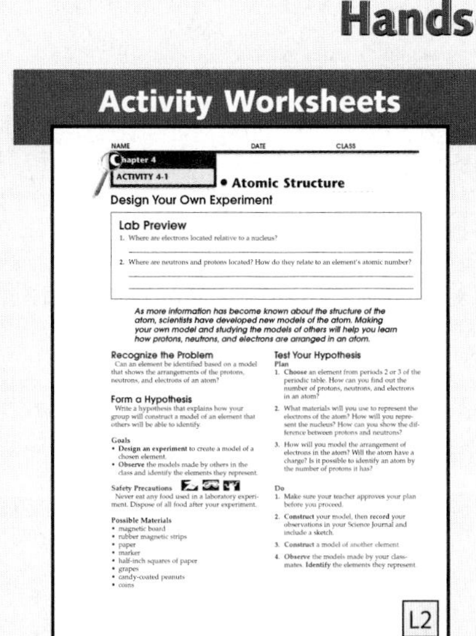
NAME DATE CLASS

Chapter 4
ACTIVITY 4-1
• Atomic Structure
Design Your Own Experiment

Lab Preview

L2

Lab Manual

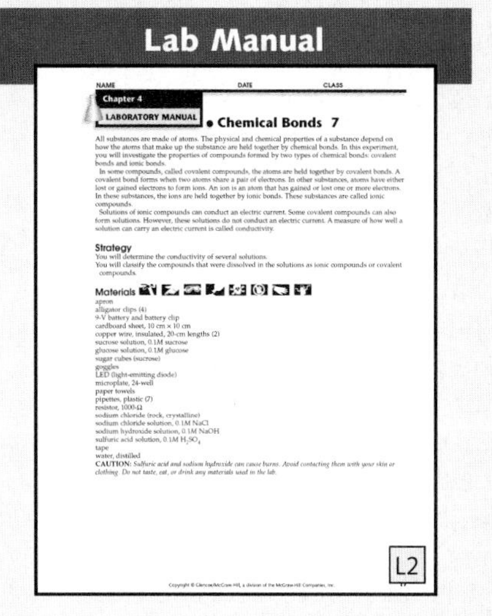
NAME DATE CLASS

Chapter 4
LABORATORY MANUAL
• Chemical Bonds 7

Strategy

Materials

L2

Accessibility

Spanish Resources

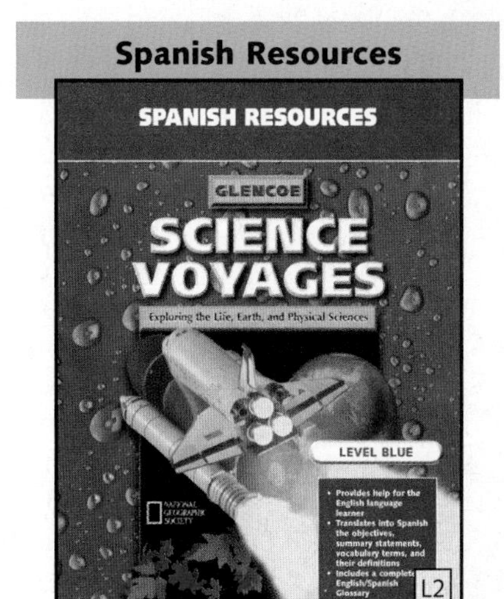

Assessment

Performance Assessment

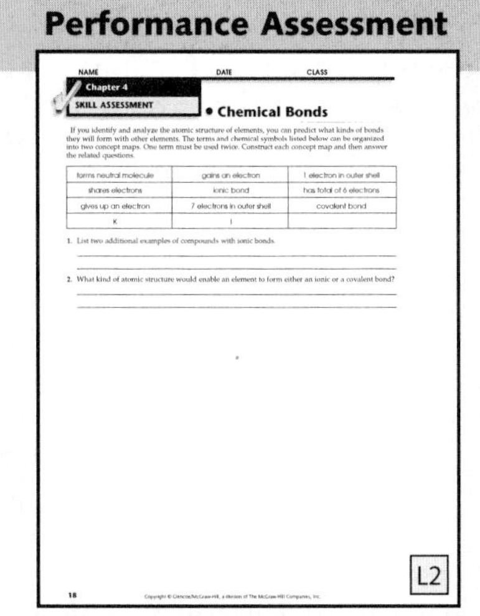
NAME DATE CLASS

Chapter 4
SKILL ASSESSMENT
• Chemical Bonds

forms neutral molecule	gains an electron	1 electron in outer shell
shares electrons	ionic bond	has total of 8 electrons
gives up an electron	7 electrons in outer shell	covalent bond
K	I	

L2

Chapter Review

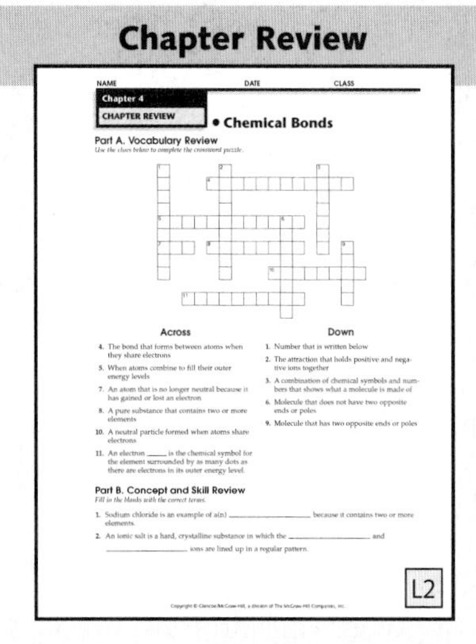
NAME DATE CLASS

Chapter 4
CHAPTER REVIEW
• Chemical Bonds

Part A. Vocabulary Review

Across

Down

Part B. Concept and Skill Review

L2

Assessment

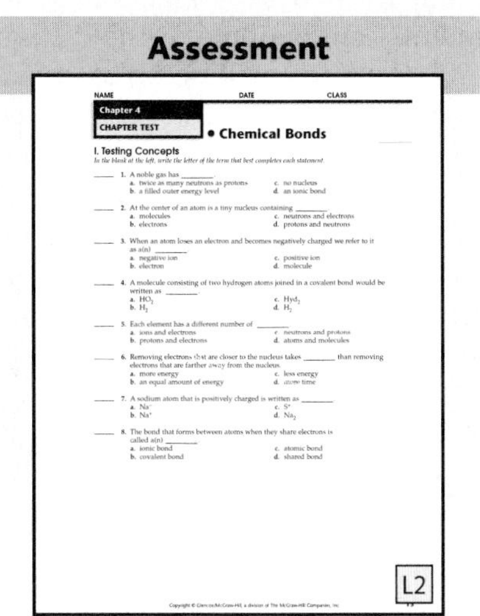
NAME DATE CLASS

Chapter 4
CHAPTER TEST
• Chemical Bonds

I. Testing Concepts

L2

Test Practice Workbook

Extending Content

Critical Thinking/ Problem Solving

Multicultural Connections

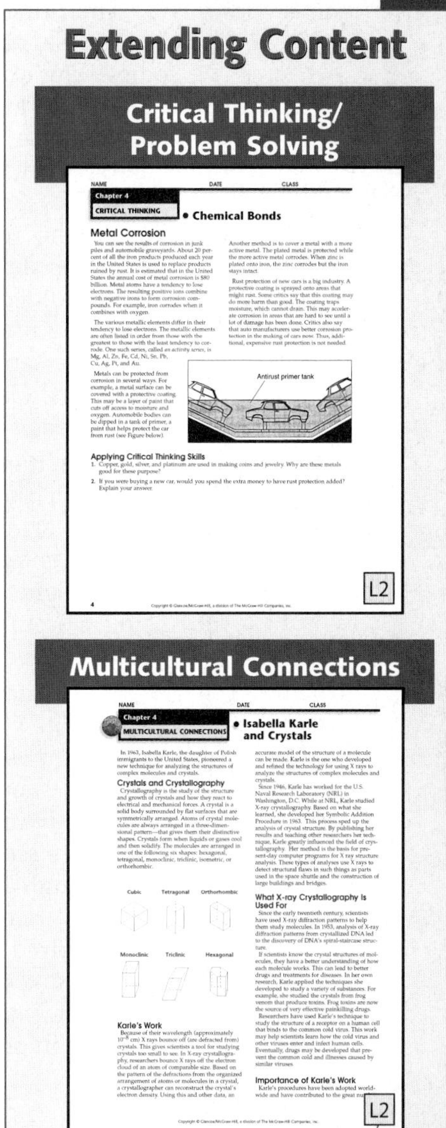
NAME DATE CLASS

Chapter 4
CRITICAL THINKING
• Chemical Bonds

Metal Corrosion

Antirust primer tank

Applying Critical Thinking Skills

L2

NAME DATE CLASS

Chapter 4
MULTICULTURAL CONNECTIONS
• Isabella Karle and Crystals

Crystals and Crystallography

Cubic Tetragonal Orthorhombic

Monoclinic Triclinic Hexagonal

What X-ray Crystallography Is Used For

Karle's Work

Importance of Karle's Work

L2

Helping You Prepare

How Many Electrons? (Section 4-1)

Students may ask how the maximum number of electrons per energy level is known. Each electron in an atom has a set of four quantum numbers, and no sets are identical. The energy level occupied by an electron is determined by its principal quantum number, n, which can have integral values beginning with 1. The values of n correspond to the energy levels shown in **Figure 4-3.** The number of electrons in each energy level can be calculated from the expression $2n^2$. If 1, 2, 3, and 4 are substituted, in turn, into the expression $2n^2$, the results correspond to the numbers of electrons shown at each of the four steps, or energy levels, in **Figure 4-3.** The steps are called principal quantum energy levels.

The principal energy levels are divided into sublevels, each with somewhat different energies. For example, an electron with principal quantum number 2, is in energy level 2. Its position is further defined by its sublevel within energy level 2. An electron's sublevel is determined by its second and third quantum numbers. The region of space around the atom, which is defined by the three quantum numbers and occupied by the electron, is called an orbital. An orbital can hold two electrons that have the same first, second, and third quantum numbers. However, the fourth quantum numbers of the two electrons must be different.

When there is more than one orbital in a sublevel, each of the orbitals has the same energy. When electrons are added to these orbitals, they always enter orbitals that are unoccupied and only begin to pair up when all orbitals are singly occupied. This is because the negatively charged electrons repel one another.

The diagrams of electrons in the energy level shown in **Figure 4-4** are drawn to reflect the way that electrons fill orbitals. Elements in Groups 1 and 2 are filling a sublevel that contains only one orbital, so beryllium's two electrons are shown as a pair. Elements in Groups 13 through 18 are filling a sublevel that has six orbitals. Nitrogen, for example, has two electrons paired in a sublevel that contains only one orbital, and three electrons in a sublevel that has three orbitals. Oxygen's eighth electron must pair up in one of the partially filled orbitals.

GLENCOE TECHNOLOGY

CD-ROM

Glencoe Science Voyages Interactive CD-ROM

Chapter Summaries

Use the Chapter Summary to introduce, teach, or review chapter material.

Electron Dot Diagrams (Section 4-1)

The electrons that are represented on electron dot diagrams are often called valence electrons. These are the electrons that are in an atom's outer energy level and are involved in the formation of chemical bonds. Although transition elements frequently undergo reactions that are controlled by the number of outer electrons the atoms contain, electron arrangements for these atoms are irregular. The electron dot diagrams for the transition elements, Groups 3–12, are not used for this age of student.

Chemical Bonds (Section 4-2)

The type of chemical bond formed in a chemical reaction is determined by the electronegativities of the elements involved. Electronegativity is a measurement of the relative attraction of an atom for electrons. In general, if two elements have electronegativity differences of 2.1 or more, the bond formed by a reaction between the two elements will be ionic. If the difference is 0.5 up to 2.1, the bond will be polar covalent. A difference less than 0.5 results in a nonpolar covalent bond.

Both the representative and transition metals have relatively low ionization energies, so they tend to lose all or some of their valence electrons to form positive ions. The nonmetals on the right side of the periodic table have almost a full complement of valence electrons and tend to gain electrons to form negative ions. Ionic bonds are always formed between a metal and a nonmetal.

Students can use electron dot diagrams to help them predict the ions that some of the lighter representative elements will form or the number of covalent bonds others will form. However, such predictions are not as clear cut for the transition elements and for the heavier representative elements because many of these elements are capable of forming more than one ion. For example, iron can lose either two or three electrons to form the common ions Fe^{2+} and Fe^{3+}.

It's important to recognize the distinction between a compound and a molecule. A compound is a substance that contains two or more elements. The elements may be joined by ionic or covalent bonds. A molecule is a substance that is bonded covalently. Molecules may contain only one element.

Polar and Nonpolar Molecules (Section 4-2)

Polar molecules cannot result from nonpolar bonds. But molecules containing polar bonds can be either polar or nonpolar, depending on the shape of the molecule. For example, carbon dioxide contains two polar bonds. But the molecule is linear, and each bond cancels out the effect of the other, producing a nonpolar molecule. A water molecule also contains two polar bonds. However, the water molecule is bent, producing a positive end and a negative end, so the water molecule is a polar molecule.

SCIENCE UPDATE

For current events or science in the news, access the Glencoe Science Web Site at **www.glencoe.com/sec/science**

Chemical Shorthand (Section 4-2)

Formulas for molecular compounds express the composition of one molecule. However, formulas for ionic compounds represent the relative numbers of each type of ion present in the compound. For example, the formula NaCl means that for every sodium ion present, one chloride ion is also present. It does not mean that one specific sodium ion forms a unit with one specific chloride ion. In referring to the formulas for ionic compounds, students should use the term *formula unit* rather than molecule. Thus, the formula NaCl means one formula unit of sodium chloride.

Teacher to Teacher

"Students need to talk while working together during labs, but the noise level can get loud. I solve this problem by playing music during the lab activity. If the students cannot hear the music, they know they are too loud. Believe it or not, this works!"

Catherine Walker
Catherine C. Walker, Teacher
Martin Middle School
Raleigh, NC

CHAPTER 4
Chemical Bonds

CHAPTER OVERVIEW

Section 4-1 Electron arrangement and how it relates to the periodic table are introduced. The importance of the amount of energy an electron has is also discussed.

Section 4-2 Chemical bonds, both ionic and covalent, are described. Polar covalent and nonpolar covalent bonds are compared and contrasted. Students learn the meaning of chemical formulas.

Chapter Vocabulary

electron dot diagram
chemical bond
ions
ionic bond
compound
formula
covalent bond
molecule

Theme Connection

Stability and Change Although certain electron arrangements in atoms are stable, changes that occur when bonds are formed lead to more stable arrangements of electrons.

If time does not permit teaching the entire chapter, use Reviewing Main Ideas on pp. 116–117.

CHAPTER
4 Chemical Bonds

Chapter Preview

Section 4-1
Why do atoms combine?

Section 4-2
Ionic and Covalent Bonds

Skills Preview

Skill Builders
- Classify
- Map Concepts

Activities
- Hypothesize
- Design an Experiment

MiniLabs
- Make and Use a Table
- Make a Model

Reading Check ✓

Before you read this chapter—and all the other ones—read the What You'll Learn feature at the beginning of each section. Explain why each section includes this feature.

96

Multiple Learning Styles

Look for the following logos for strategies that emphasize different learning modalities.

Linguistic Science Journal, p. 100; Using Science Words, p.107; Preview, p. 116

Logical-Mathematical Multiple Learning Styles, p. 111

Visual-Spatial Quick Demo, p. 99; MiniLab, p. 102; Activity, p. 112; Reteach, p. 116

Auditory-Musical Out of Time, p. 116

Kinesthetic Explore Activity, p. 97; Reteach, pp. 101, 112; Activity, pp. 104–105, 114; Go Further, p. 105; Inclusion Strategies, p. 108; MiniLab, p. 109

Interpersonal Discussion, p. 99; Activity, p. 101; Assessment, p. 113; Review, p. 116

Intrapersonal Assessment, p. 117

Explore Activity

It's time to clean out the garage and attic and get rid of stuff. Look at it all—stuff made out of wood, glass, plastic, metal, cloth, and even paper. Where do all the different materials that make up everyday things come from? There are fewer than 100 different kinds of naturally occurring atoms on Earth. They combine with each other in countless ways to make countless different substances. Why is this so? What makes elements combine with other elements? The answer is in their electrons.

Model the Energy of Electrons

1. Pick up a paper clip with a magnet. Touch the paper clip to another paper clip and pick it up.
2. Continue to pick up paper clips until you have a strand of them and no more will attach.
3. One by one, gently pull off the paper clips.

Science Journal

In your Science Journal, write down which paper clip was easiest to remove and which was hardest. Think of the magnet as if it were the nucleus of an atom. How do you suppose the magnet and the paper clips are a model for the nucleus and the electrons in an atom?

Explore Activity

Purpose

Kinesthetic Use the Explore Activity to help students discover that attractive forces decrease as distance increases. L2 ELL

Materials

magnet and 5 or 6 paper clips for each group

Teaching Strategies

- Use small, light paper clips and magnets that are strong enough to hold at least five paper clips.
- Do not use plastic-coated paper clips.

Science Journal The last paper clip attached was easiest to remove. The one attached to the magnet was the most difficult. The electrons farthest from the nucleus have the least attraction for the nucleus.

Assessment

Content To reinforce students' knowledge of the structure of the atom, have them sketch a cross section of a nitrogen atom, showing two electrons close to the nucleus and five more at a distance farther from the nucleus. Use **Performance Assessment in the Science Classroom,** p. 55.

Assessment Planner

Portfolio
Refer to p. 117 for suggested items that students might select for their portfolios.

Performance Assessment
See p. 117 for additional Performance Assessment options.
Skill Builder, pp. 103, 113
MiniLab, pp. 102, 109
Activity 4-1, pp. 104–105; 4-2, p. 114

Content Assessment
Section Assessment, pp. 103, 113
Chapter Assessment, pp. 118–119
Proficiency Prep, pp. 103, 113

SECTION 4 1

Prepare

Content Background

Refer to **How Many Electrons?** and **Electron Dot Diagrams** on p. 96E.

Preplanning

Refer to the **Chapter Organizer** on pp. 96A–B.

1 Motivate

Bellringer

Before presenting the lesson, display **Section Focus Transparency 8** on the overhead projector. Use the accompanying **Focus Activity** worksheet. L2 ELL

Section 4-1

8 SECTION FOCUS TRANSPARENCY

OPPOSITES ATTRACT

Some atoms join together to form substances such as water (H_2O), whereas other atoms do not. How can you tell which atoms will join easily and which ones won't?

1. Describe what is happening in the cartoon.
2. Describe the center of the atom. What does the cloud surrounding the center of the atom represent?
3. Why are these two atoms not likely to join together?

Caption Answer

Figure 4-1 *The electrons can be anywhere.*

4-1 Why do atoms combine?

What You'll Learn

- How the electrons are arranged in an atom
- The energy of electrons in atoms
- How the arrangement of electrons in an atom is related to the periodic table

Vocabulary
electron dot diagram
chemical bond

Why It's Important

- When you know about an atom's electrons, you can predict how the atom will behave.

Atomic Structure

At the center of an atom is a tiny nucleus containing the atom's protons and neutrons. The rest of the space in the atom is empty, except for the atom's electrons. The electrons are in constant motion around the nucleus. Scientists know that they cannot say exactly where the electrons are at any time. They use a model, the electron cloud model, which tells where the electrons are most likely to be. They are most likely to be clustered around the nucleus because their negative charges are attracted to the positively charged nucleus. But, the electrons could be anywhere. That's why the model for an electron cloud in **Figure 4-1** has a fuzzy outline.

How many electrons are in the electron cloud of an atom, and how are they arranged? Each element has a different number of protons and electrons, so each has a different atomic structure. For example, lithium has three protons in its nucleus, and three electrons move around lithium's nucleus.

The Periodic Table

When the elements are arranged in order of increasing atomic number, they fall into groups in which the members share common properties. Could those common properties depend upon similarities in the way electrons are arranged in the atoms?

Electron Arrangements and Energy

All the electrons in an atom are in the electron cloud, but within the cloud, some electrons are closer to the nucleus than others. How do scientists know this? Think about the Explore Activity. It took more energy on your part to pull off the paper clip closest to the magnet than it took to remove the one farthest away. That's because the closer a paper clip is to the magnet, the stronger

Figure 4-1 In the electron cloud model, the electrons are more likely to be in the heavily shaded area than in the lightly shaded area, but they could be anywhere. **Why is there no definite boundary for an atom?**

Resource Manager

The following **Teacher Classroom Resources** can be used with Section 4-1:

Reproducible Masters

Activity Worksheets, pp. 17–18, 21 L2
Enrichment, p. 8 L3
Reinforcement, p. 8 L2
Study Guide, pp. 13–14 L1 ELL

Transparencies

Teaching Transparency 7
Teaching Transparency 8

the magnet's attractive force on the clip. Scientists have found that the closer an electron is to the nucleus, the stronger the attractive force between the positively charged nucleus and the negatively charged electrons. So, removing electrons that are close to the nucleus takes more energy than removing those farther away from the nucleus. A diagram of how the electrons might be arranged in energy levels around the nucleus of an atom is shown in **Figure 4-2.** Notice that the electrons are arranged in spheres at different distances from the nucleus. That means that each sphere must represent a different energy.

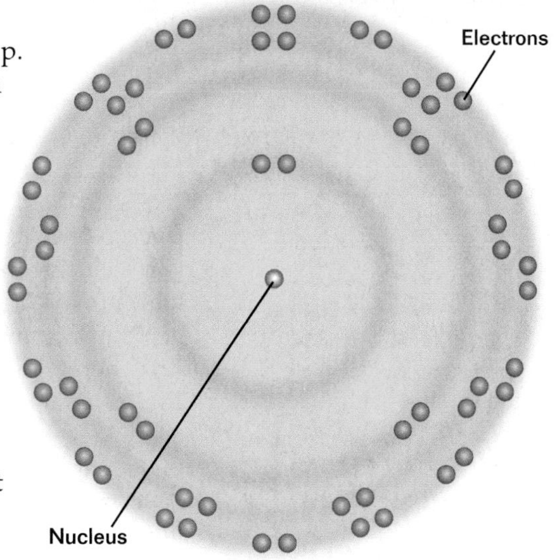

Figure 4-2 The energy of an electron is different depending upon which energy level it occupies.

An Energy Stairway

The stairway, shown in **Figure 4-3,** is a model for picturing the energy differences among electrons in the electron cloud. Think of the nucleus as being at floor level. The difference in heights of the steps represents the difference in energy between electrons on different steps. Electrons in the sphere closest to the nucleus are in the lowest energy level. They are on the first energy step. These electrons are held most tightly to the nucleus because they occupy the space closest to the nucleus. Electrons in the next sphere are on the second energy step. They are at a higher energy level because they are farther from the nucleus. Electrons in the outermost sphere have even higher energy because they are still farther from the attractive force of the positively charged nucleus.

VISUALIZING Energy Levels

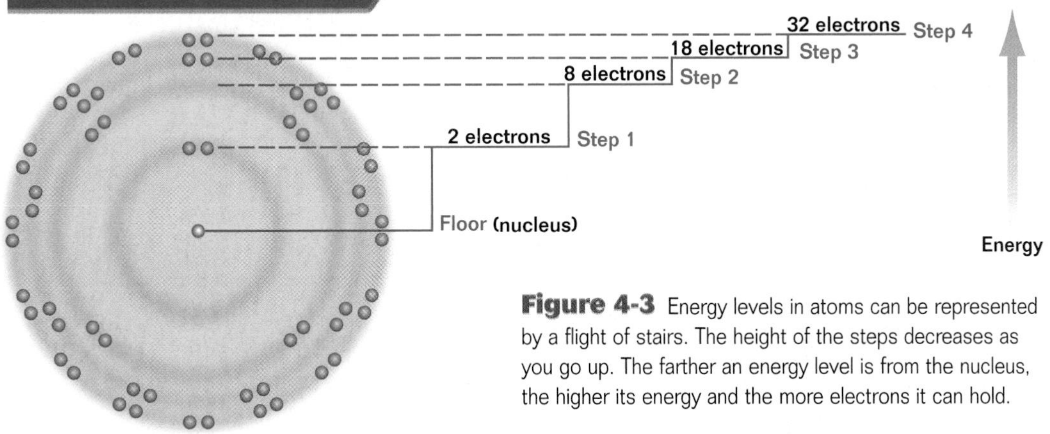

Figure 4-3 Energy levels in atoms can be represented by a flight of stairs. The height of the steps decreases as you go up. The farther an energy level is from the nucleus, the higher its energy and the more electrons it can hold.

Content Background

Elements in the periodic table exhibit properties that repeat in a regular pattern. Students should be familiar with other examples of periodicity. The yearly change of seasons, phases of the moon, and repetition of days, weeks, and months are all examples of periodic events.

VISUAL Learning

Figure 4-3 Point out to students that total energy increases as level increases, but the energy difference between adjacent levels decreases.

Tying to Previous Knowledge

Students are familiar with the structure of the atom. Now they will learn that the behavior of an atom is based on the location and arrangement of the electrons, not on the protons and neutrons.

2 Teach

Discussion

Interpersonal Show students an electric fan. Turn it on. From their observations, have students discuss how the fan represents an electron cloud. The blades are within the area defined by the "cloud" of the blades, but the locations of the individual blades at any one time can't be determined. L3

Quick Demo

Visual Spatial Show that electrons farther from the nucleus have higher energy. Securely fasten a large rubber stopper to one end of a sturdy string that is about 2 m long. Hold the string about 0.5 m from the stopper. Swing the string and stopper above your head, just fast enough to keep the stopper moving in a circle. Have students note the speed of the stopper. Then, hold the string about 1.5 m from the stopper and swing the string and stopper at the same level. Students should notice that the stopper swung in the larger circle travels faster and thus has more energy. **CAUTION:** *Be sure all students are at least 3 m from the demonstration.*

Using Math

Remind students that they should square the variable before they multiply by two. $2n^2 = 2 \times n^2$. *Total number of electrons in 5 levels* $= (2 \times 1^2) + (2 \times 2^2) + (2 \times 3^2) + (2 \times 4^2) + (2 \times 5^2) = 2 + 8 + 18 + 32 + 50 = 110$.

interNET CONNECTION

Internet Addresses

____

____

____

____

For Internet tips, see Glencoe's **Using the Internet in the Science Classroom.**

Caption Answer

Figure 4-4 *the third energy level*

GLENCOE TECHNOLOGY

Videodisc

Glencoe Science Voyages Interactive Videodisc—Physical

Side 1, Lesson 4 *Periodicity*

39981

40194

42222

Refer to Videodisc Teacher Guide for additional bar codes.

Using Math

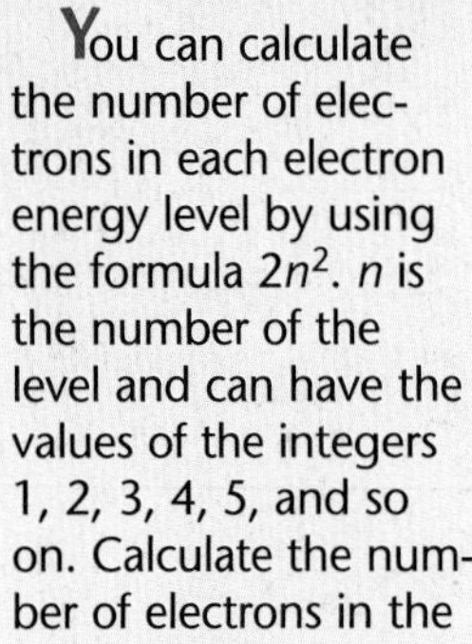

You can calculate the number of electrons in each electron energy level by using the formula $2n^2$. n is the number of the level and can have the values of the integers 1, 2, 3, 4, 5, and so on. Calculate the number of electrons in the first five energy levels.

interNET CONNECTION

Visit the Glencoe Science Web Site at **www.glencoe.com/sec/science** for more information about electrons in atoms.

How many electrons?

You can see in **Figure 4-3** that the farther an energy level is from the nucleus, the bigger its sphere. The bigger the sphere, the more electrons it can hold. **Figure 4-3** shows the maximum number of electrons that each of the first four energy levels can hold. The first energy level can hold only two electrons. Notice in the periodic table in **Figure 4-6** that there are two elements in the first period. The periods of the periodic table are the horizontal rows. Period 1 contains only hydrogen and helium. These elements have electrons only in the first energy level. Hydrogen has one electron. Helium has a completed outer energy level with two electrons. The second energy level holds eight electrons. In **Figure 4-4,** you can see that eight elements are in the second period. These elements have two electrons in the first energy level, plus different numbers of electrons in the second energy level. Starting with lithium, each element in the second period has one more electron in the second energy level than the element that comes before it. The final element in this period, neon, has a completed outer energy level with eight electrons.

Electron Arrangement and Groups

The elements in the same column of the periodic table are called a group or a family of elements. Fluorine, chlorine, and bromine are three members of Group 17, the halogen family. Just as people in a family may have similar smiles, noses, or eating habits, elements in the same family have similar properties. This is because they all have the same number of electrons in their outer energy levels. **Figure 4-5** shows the electron arrangements of sodium, Group 1, and chlorine, Group 17. Notice that sodium has one electron in its outer energy level and chlorine has seven. Compare the diagrams of these elements in **Figure 4-5** with the diagrams of lithium and fluorine in **Figure 4-4.** You can see that the Group 1 elements, lithium and sodium, have one electron in their outer energy levels. Fluorine and chlorine both have seven electrons in their outer energy levels. You know that bromine is in the same family as fluorine and chlorine, so

	1	2	13	14	15	16	17	18
2	Li	Be	B	C	N	O	F	Ne
3	Na	Mg	Al	Si	P	S	Cl	Ar

Figure 4-4 Lithium and carbon have their outermost electrons in the second energy level. **In what level do sodium and chlorine have theirs?**

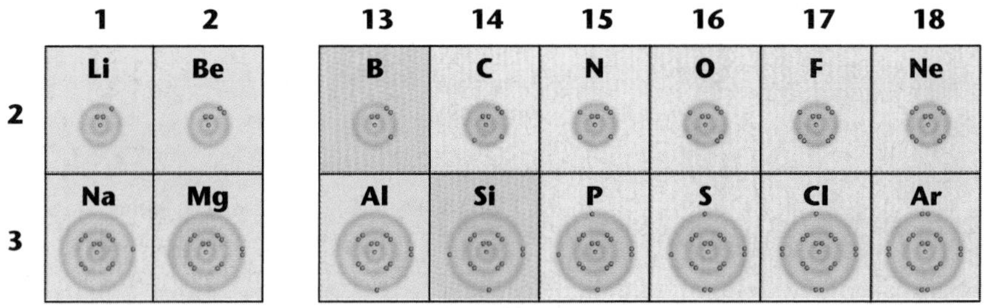

Science Journal

Noble Gases The noble gases used to be known as inert gases. Have students find out the meaning of the word *inert* and infer how calling them inert gases differs from calling them noble gases. Inert indicates that these gases do not react at all. Noble indicates that they do not react easily or frequently. L2

Caption Answer

Figure 4-5 *They have the same number of electrons in their outer energy levels.*

100 CHAPTER 4 CHEMICAL BONDS

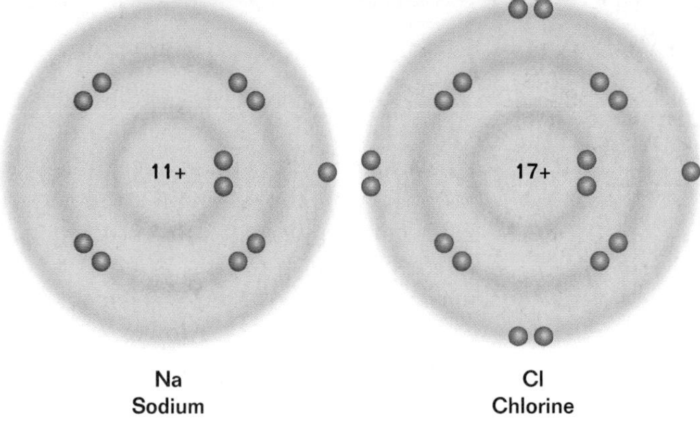

Figure 4-5 Compare the electron arrangements of sodium and chlorine with the electron arrangements of lithium and fluorine in Figure 4-4. **What can you conclude about elements that are in the same families?**

you can predict that bromine also has seven electrons in its outer energy level. The number of electrons in an atom's outer energy level determines how the element will combine with other elements. ☑

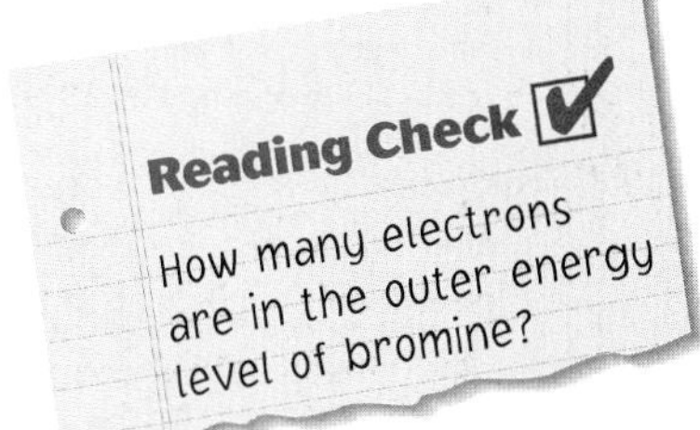

Look at the elements in Group 18 of the periodic table in **Figure 4-6.** The number of electrons in the outer energy level of each group is shown at the top of the column. The members of Group 18, the noble gases, have eight electrons in their outer energy levels. They do not combine easily with other elements. The noble gases are stable, which means that they resist change. The reason for their stability is that their outer energy levels are filled.

	1e⁻ 1	2e⁻ 2	3e⁻ 13	4e⁻ 14	5e⁻ 15	6e⁻ 16	7e⁻ 17	8e⁻ 18
1	Hydrogen **H** 1							Helium **He** 2
2	Lithium **Li** 3	Beryllium **Be** 4	Boron **B** 5	Carbon **C** 6	Nitrogen **N** 7	Oxygen **O** 8	Fluorine **F** 9	Neon **Ne** 10
3	Sodium **Na** 11	Magnesium **Mg** 12	Aluminum **Al** 13	Silicon **Si** 14	Phosphorus **P** 15	Sulfur **S** 16	Chlorine **Cl** 17	Argon **Ar** 18
4	Potassium **K** 19	Calcium **Ca** 20	Gallium **Ga** 31	Germanium **Ge** 32	Arsenic **As** 33	Selenium **Se** 34	Bromine **Br** 35	Krypton **Kr** 36
5	Rubidium **Rb** 37	Strontium **Sr** 38	Indium **In** 49	Tin **Sn** 50	Antimony **Sb** 51	Tellurium **Te** 52	Iodine **I** 53	Xenon **Xe** 54
6	Cesium **Cs** 55	Barium **Ba** 56	Thallium **Tl** 81	Lead **Pb** 82	Bismuth **Bi** 83	Polonium **Po** 84	Astatine **At** 85	Radon **Rn** 86
7	Francium **Fr** 87	Radium **Ra** 88						

Using Math

An atom of copper has an effective volume of 1.18×10^{-23} cm^3. The volume of a penny is 0.314 cm^3. Calculate the number of copper atoms in a pure copper penny.

Figure 4-6 You can see that the number of electrons (e^-) in the outer energy levels increases from one to eight across a period of these groups.

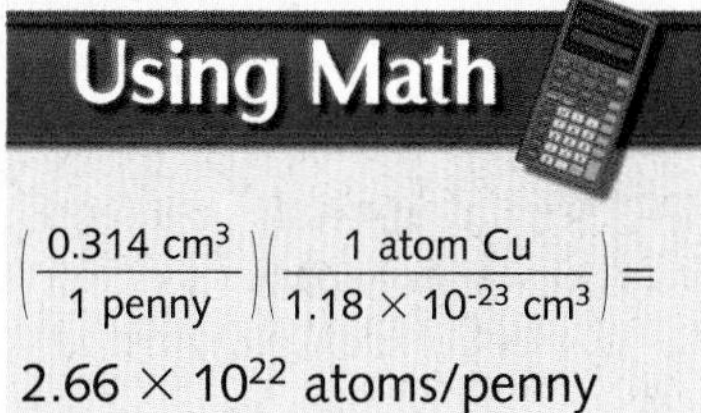

$$\left(\frac{0.314 \text{ cm}^3}{1 \text{ penny}}\right)\left(\frac{1 \text{ atom Cu}}{1.18 \times 10^{-23} \text{ cm}^3}\right) =$$

2.66×10^{22} atoms/penny

3 Assess

Check for Understanding

Activity

Have pairs of students write the symbols for the elements in Groups 1, 2, and 13–18 on cards. Shuffle the cards and divide them into two facedown stacks. Each student turns a card over at the same time. Using a periodic table for reference, determine which card has the greater number of electrons in its dot diagram. The student with this card gets both of them. If they are equal, each keeps his or her own card. The student who ends up with all the cards wins. L2 ELL COOP LEARN

Reteach

Kinesthetic Have students use different colors of modeling clay to make a cross-sectional model of an atom. The atom should contain different energy levels. L1 ELL

Guided Reading Strategy

Problem Solution Journal Have students divide a piece of paper in half. Label the left side "Problems" and the right side "Consequences of failing to resolve the problem." Through writing, the student identifies a problem, brainstorms possible alternatives, chooses a probable solution, anticipates stumbling blocks, and proposes arguments. Have students write a Problem Solution Journal related to this section. For example, students could write about how they would draw an energy level diagram for an atom that has five full energy levels. P

Extension

For students who have mastered this section, use the **Reinforcement** and **Enrichment** masters.

Purpose

Visual Spatial Students will observe patterns exhibited by electron dot diagrams. L2 ELL

Materials

paper, periodic table, pencil

Teaching Strategies

Have students compare their diagrams to make sure no elements are skipped in making the table.

Troubleshooting Be sure dots are dark enough to be easily seen.

Analysis

1. The numbers of outer electrons are the same.
2. Each element has one more electron than the element that precedes it.

Performance Have students use a thin layer of modeling clay and short pieces of drinking straws to model the above activity. The lengths of the straws should be proportional to the number of electrons in the electron dot diagram. Use **Performance Assessment in the Science Classroom,** p. 51. P

Drawing Electron Dot Diagrams

Procedure

1. Draw a periodic table that includes the first 18 elements. These are the elements from hydrogen through argon. Make each block a 3-cm square.
2. Fill in each block with the electron dot diagram of the element.

Analysis

1. What do you observe about the electron dot diagram of the elements in the same family?
2. Describe any changes you observe in the electron dot diagrams across a period.

Electron Dot Diagrams

As you're probably beginning to understand, the number of electrons in an element's outer energy level tells you a lot about the element's behavior. Different atomic structures result in different physical properties such as color; hardness; and whether an element is a solid, liquid, or gas. Atomic structure also determines the chemical properties of an element, such as how the element behaves with other elements. If you want to predict how atoms of one element will behave in the presence of atoms of another element, it would help to have an easy way to represent the atoms and show how many electrons are in their outer energy levels. You can do this with electron dot diagrams. An **electron dot diagram** is the chemical symbol for the element surrounded by as many dots as there are electrons in its outer energy level.

Writing Dot Diagrams

How do you know how many dots to make? For Groups 1, 2, and 13–18, you can use a periodic table. Group 1 has one outer electron. Group 2 has two. Group 13 has three, Group 14, four, and so on to Group 18, which has eight. Helium is an exception. It has only two electrons in its single energy level. How many electrons are in the outer energy level of the oxygen family? These elements are in Group 16, so the answer is six.

Figure 4-7 The electron dot diagram shows the symbol for phosphorus and the five electrons in its outer energy level.

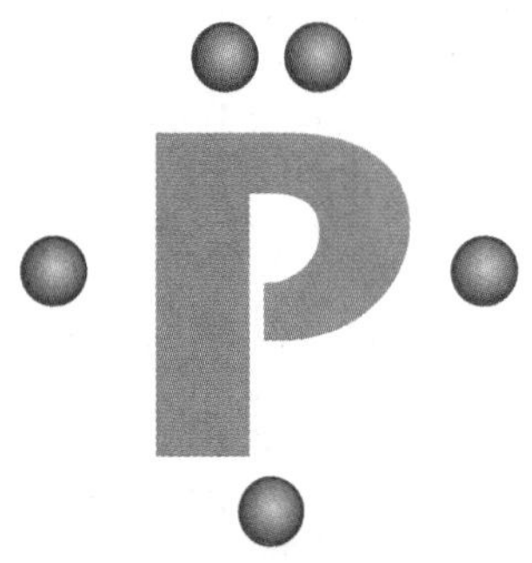

Phosphorus

How would you write a dot diagram for the element phosphorus? First, write the symbol for the element phosphorus—P. Then, find phosphorus in the periodic table. Next, ask what group it is in. It's in Group 15. This means that it has five electrons in its outer energy level. The completed dot diagram with the five electrons is shown in **Figure 4-7.**

What happens when atoms form chemical bonds with each other? A **chemical bond** is a force that holds two atoms together. Chemical bonds form when atoms combine in ways that give them eight electrons in their outer energy levels. When this happens, the atoms have outer energy levels that are filled, just like the noble gases. Each atom then has greater stability than before it interacted. A chemical

Content Background

In 1916, the American chemist G.N. Lewis invented the electron dot diagram, and so these diagrams are often called Lewis electron dot symbols. If there are four or fewer electrons in the outer energy level of an atom, the electrons are placed singly around the atomic symbol. A fifth electron is placed in a pair; a sixth forms a second pair, and so on. This way of representing the electrons reflects the way electrons fill orbitals in the atom. Because electrons repel each other, they do not pair up until there is no other space to occupy.

Figure 4-8 Chemical bonds hold atoms together like friends linking arms. **Why do atoms form chemical bonds?**

bond is like friends linking arms as in **Figure 4-8.** In the next section, you'll learn how gaining, losing, or sharing electrons provides the link that holds atoms together.

Section Assessment

1. How many electrons does nitrogen have in its outer energy level? How many does bromine have?
2. How many electrons does oxygen have in its first energy level? Second energy level?
3. Which electrons in oxygen have the higher energy, those in the first energy level or those in the second?
4. **Think Critically:** Atoms in a group of elements increase in size as you move down in the periodic table. Explain why this is so.
5. **Skill Builder**
   Classifying Use the periodic table to organize the following elements into families: K, C, Sn, Li, F, Na, Pb, and I. Then, write the electron dot diagram for each element and compare the diagrams in each family. What can you conclude? If you need help, refer to Classifying in the **Skill Handbook** on page 713.

If you need help, refer to Classifying in the Skill Handbook on page 713.

Using Math

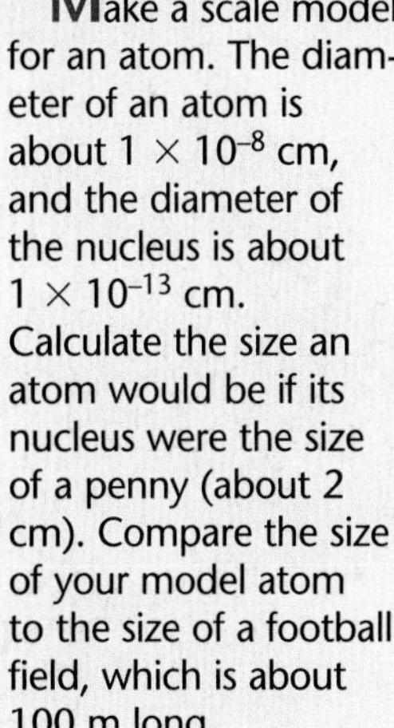

Make a scale model for an atom. The diameter of an atom is about 1×10^{-8} cm, and the diameter of the nucleus is about 1×10^{-13} cm. Calculate the size an atom would be if its nucleus were the size of a penny (about 2 cm). Compare the size of your model atom to the size of a football field, which is about 100 m long.

5. **Skill Builder**
   Classifying Li, Na, and K are in the same family, and each has one electron shown in its electron dot diagram. F and I have seven electrons shown. C, Sn, and Pb have four electrons shown.

Assessment

Content Have students make up a problem similar to the Skill Builder using elements whose dot diagrams show three, two, and five electrons. Use **Performance Assessment in the Science Classroom,** p. 19.

Caption Answer

Figure 4-8 *to obtain the stable outer electron arrangement of eight electrons*

4 Close

Proficiency Prep

Use this quiz to check students' recall of section content.

1. **What is the particle that controls the behavior of an atom?** *electron*
2. **What does the symbol in an electron dot diagram represent?** *the nucleus and inner level electrons*

Section Assessment

1. 5, 7
2. 2, 6
3. those in the second energy level
4. **Think Critically** A level of electrons is added to each period as you go down the periodic table.

Using Math

x is the diameter of the model atom.

$$\frac{x}{2 \text{ cm}} = \frac{1 \times 10^{-8} \text{ cm}}{1 \times 10^{-13} \text{ cm}}$$

$x = 2 \times 10^5 \text{ cm} = 2 \times 10^3 \text{ m}$

Compare the size of the model atom to a football field by dividing.

$$\frac{2 \times 10^3 \text{ m}}{100 \text{ m}} = 20 \text{ football fields}$$

Recognize the Problem

Purpose

Kinesthetic Students will develop a model of an atom.

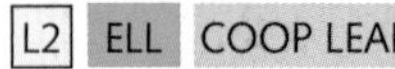
L2 ELL COOP LEARN

Process Skills

designing an experiment, predicting, forming a hypothesis, communicating, making a model

Time

45 minutes

Materials

Any small, round objects can be used to represent subatomic particles. Magnetic tape is sold at most craft and hobby stores.

Form a Hypothesis

Possible Hypotheses

Students might hypothesize that all atoms will have a central nucleus with electrons around it. The number of protons and electrons can be used to determine the identity of a neutral atom of the element represented.

Test Your Hypothesis

Possible Procedures

Use the periodic table to determine the number of each type of particle present in an atom of the chosen element. Choose one type of object to represent an electron, one type to represent a proton, and one type to represent a neutron. Attach each object to be used to a short magnetic strip. On the magnetic board, cluster the protons and neutrons together to form the nucleus. Place the appropriate number of electrons in each level around the nucleus.

Atomic Structure

As more information has become known about the structure of the atom, scientists have developed new models of the atom. Making your own model and studying the models of others will help you learn how protons, neutrons, and electrons are arranged in an atom.

Possible Materials

- Magnetic board
- Rubber magnetic strips
- Paper
- Marker
- Half-inch squares of paper
- Grapes
- Candy-coated peanuts
- Coins

Recognize the Problem

Can an element be identified based on a model that shows the arrangement of the protons, neutrons, and electrons of an atom?

Form a Hypothesis

Write a hypothesis that explains how your group will construct a model of an element that others will be able to identify.

Goals

- **Design an experiment** to create a model of a chosen element.
- **Observe** the models made by others in the class and identify the elements they represent.

Safety Precautions

Never eat any food used in a laboratory experiment. Dispose of all food after your experiment.

Test Your Hypothesis

Plan

1. **Choose** an element from periods 2 or 3 of the periodic table. How can you find out the number of protons, neutrons, and electrons in an atom?
2. What materials will you use to represent the electrons of the atom? How will you represent the nucleus? How can you show the difference between protons and neutrons?
3. How will you model the arrangement of electrons in the atom? Will the atom have a charge? Is it possible to identify an atom by the number of protons it has?

Do

1. Make sure your teacher approves your plan before you proceed.
2. **Construct** your model, then **record** your observations in your Science Journal and include a sketch.
3. **Construct** a model of another element.
4. **Observe** the models made by your classmates. **Identify** the elements they represent.

Analyze Your Data

1. What elements did you identify using your hypothesis?
2. In a neutral atom, **identify** which particles are always present in equal numbers.
3. **Predict** what would happen to the charge on an atom if one of the electrons were removed. What happens to an atom if one proton and one electron are removed?
4. **Compare and contrast** your model with the electron cloud model of the atom.

Draw Conclusions

1. What is the minimum amount of information you need to know to identify a neutral atom of an element?
2. If you made models of the isotopes boron-10 and boron-11, how would these models be different?

Teaching Strategies

- Be sure students understand that the models represent the arrangement of particles in the atom only and that the model is not to scale.
- Have students choose atoms from periods 2 and 3.

Expected Outcome

Students will determine that for a neutral atom, the number of either the protons or the electrons can determine the identity of an element.

Error Analysis

Have students trade models and check to make sure the number of electrons and protons is the same for each atom.

Analyze Your Data

1. Answers will vary. The number of protons or electrons determines the identity.
2. protons and electrons
3. The charge would become positive. The identity of the atom changes.
4. The model is two-dimensional. The electron cloud is three-dimensional. The model shows the electrons in definite positions, but in the electron cloud, the positions of the electrons are not determined.

Draw Conclusions

1. either the number of protons or the number of electrons
2. Boron-11 would contain one more neutron. Both atoms would contain the same numbers of electrons and protons.

GO Further

Kinesthetic Each energy level contains areas in which there is a high probability of finding electrons. These areas are called orbitals. Each orbital can contain two electrons. Use a high school chemistry text to find out more about orbitals. How many orbitals must there be in level 1? In level 2? In level 3?

Assessment

Performance In an energy level, electrons exist as pairs. Have students adjust their models so that the electrons exist as pairs. Use **Performance Assessment in the Science Classroom,** p. 51.

SECTION 4•2

Prepare

Refer to **Chemical Bonds, Polar and Nonpolar Molecules,** and **Chemical Shorthand** on pp. 96E–F.

Preplanning

Refer to the **Chapter Organizer** on pp. 96A–B.

1 Motivate

Bellringer

Before presenting the lesson, display **Section Focus Transparency 9** on the overhead projector. Use the accompanying **Focus Activity** worksheet. L2 ELL

Section 4-2

9 SECTION FOCUS TRANSPARENCY

THEY GO TOGETHER

Like peanut butter and jelly or ketchup and french fries, salt and popcorn just "go together." Salt itself is a combination of two things that often go together in nature. Table salt—sodium chloride—is made up of sodium and chlorine.

1. How many electrons does sodium have in its outer energy level?
2. How many electrons does chlorine have in its outer energy level?
3. Explain why sodium atoms and chlorine atoms are likely to combine.

Tying to Previous Knowledge

Students are familiar with materials that undergo change in identity, such as iron rusting and food spoiling. Bonds breaking and forming cause such changes.

4•2 Ionic and Covalent Bonds

What You'll Learn

- How to describe ionic and covalent bonds
- The difference between polar and nonpolar covalent bonds
- Chemical shorthand

Vocabulary

ion
ionic bond
compound
covalent bond
molecule
formula

Why It's Important

- Everything in the world is held together by bonds.

Ionic Bonds—Loss and Gain

Some metal atoms can obtain the stable atomic structure of a noble gas by losing an electron. This is easy for elements in Group 1. Think about sodium as an example. Sodium has one electron in its outer energy level. If a sodium atom loses that electron, the energy level occupied by the electron becomes empty as you can see in **Figure 4-9**. The energy level below that is filled. By losing one electron, sodium's atomic structure becomes the same as the stable noble gas neon.

Other nonmetal atoms can acquire the stable structure of a noble gas by gaining an electron. Elements in Group 17, such as chlorine and fluorine, have seven electrons in their outer energy levels. These elements readily gain an electron. In doing so, they fill their outer energy levels. For example, if an atom of chlorine gains an electron, its atomic structure becomes the same as the noble gas argon. The diagram in **Figure 4-9** shows the chlorine atom as it gains an electron.

Positive and Negative Ions

When a sodium atom loses an electron, the atom becomes positively charged because there is one electron less in the atom than there are protons in the nucleus. Similarly, when a chlorine atom gains an electron, it becomes negatively charged because there is one more electron in the atom than there are protons in the nucleus. An atom that is no longer neutral because it has lost or gained an electron is called an **ion** (I ahn). A sodium ion is represented by the symbol Na^+. A chlorine ion

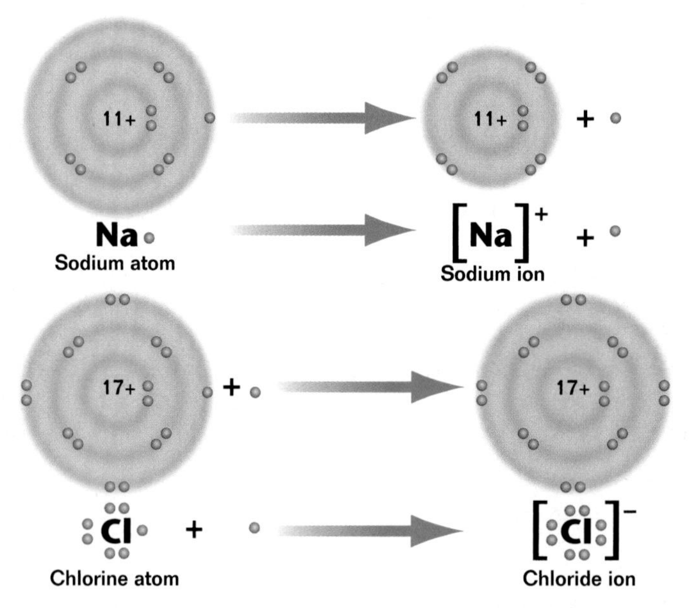

Figure 4-9 When sodium loses an electron and chlorine gains an electron, their outer energy levels become full.

Resource Manager

The following **Teacher Classroom Resources** can be used with Section 4-2:

Reproducible Masters

Activity Worksheets, pp. 19–20, 22 L2
Critical Thinking/Problem Solving, p. 4 L2
Enrichment, p. 9 L3
Home Involvement, p. 37 L2
Laboratory Manual, pp. 17–24 L2
Multicultural Connections, pp. 7–8 L2
Reinforcement, p. 9 L2
Study Guide, pp. 15–16 L1 ELL

Transparencies

Science Integration Transparency 4 L2

Figure 4-10 The symbols in brackets represent the sodium ion and the chloride ion. These ions form when sodium loses an electron and chlorine gains one. When sodium loses an electron and chlorine gains it, ordinary table salt, sodium chloride, is the result.

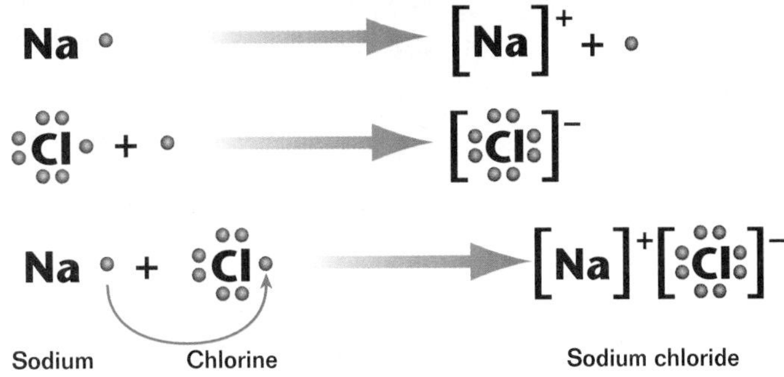

is represented by the symbol Cl^-. **Figure 4-10** shows dot diagrams for the formation of the two ions.

The positive sodium ion and the negative chlorine ion are attracted to each other. This attraction, which holds the ions close together, is a chemical bond called an **ionic bond.** In **Figure 4-10,** you can see that when sodium and chlorine ions form an ionic bond, the compound sodium chloride, ordinary table salt, is formed. A **compound** is a pure substance that contains two or more elements.

Ionic Salts

Sodium chloride, the stuff that comes out of your salt shaker, is an example of an ionic salt. An ionic salt is a hard, crystalline (KRIH stuh lihn) compound in which positive ions of metal atoms and negative ions of nonmetal atoms are lined up in a regular pattern as shown in **Figure 4-11.** When ionic salts are dissolved in water, the ions separate. A solution of an ionic salt will conduct an electric current because the charged particles can move through the solution. Pure water is a poor conductor of electric current.

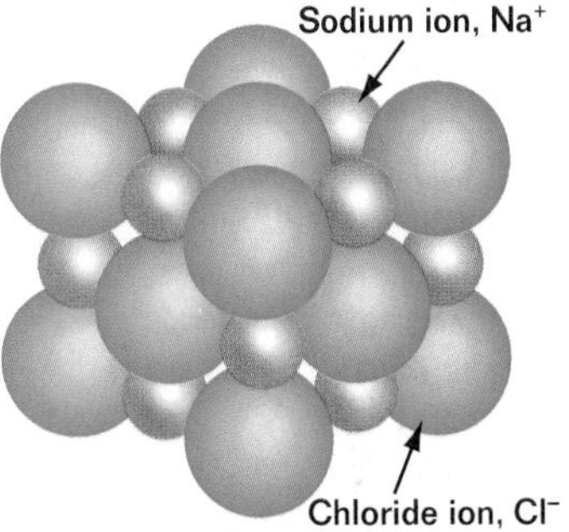

Figure 4-11 In ionic compounds such as sodium chloride, the positive and negative ions line up in regular fashion. Each positive ion is surrounded by negative ions, and each negative ion is surrounded by positive ions.

2 Teach

PHYSICS INTEGRATION

The attraction of positive and negative ions is an electrical attraction. Tell students that it is the same attraction shown by oppositely charged clothing coming out of a dryer on a cold day.

Using Science Words

Linguistic The symbols that show the charges on ions are called superscripts. *Super-* means "above," and *script* means "write," so a superscript is written above. Mention superscripts again when students use subscripts later in this chapter. Be sure they can distinguish between superscripts and subscripts.

Correcting Misconceptions

Students are used to a gain resulting in a larger number and a loss resulting in a smaller number. It is often difficult for students to understand that a gain of electrons results in a negative charge and a loss of electrons results in a positive charge. Use a visual to connect the charges to the particles in the atom. Start with the same number of electrons and protons. Then, take away and add electrons, each time asking students to determine the excess negative or positive charge.

Content Background

The negative pole in a battery or electrolysis setup is called the cathode because it attracts positive ions, which are called cations. The positive pole is the anode because it attracts negative ions, which are called anions.

Integrating the Sciences

Earth Science Limestone, a rock composed primarily of the ionic compound $CaCO_3$, is the most widely used building stone in the United States. The strength of limestone is due to the arrangement of its ions in its crystal structure. Marble, another rock used in buildings, is also $CaCO_3$, but it has different properties because its crystal structure is different.

Enrichment

Have interested students investigate the term *oxidation number.* Have them determine the oxidation number of each element in the following compounds: $AuCl_3$, P_2O_5, K_2CrO_4. **Hints:** The total charge on a compound is zero. The oxidation number for many elements can be found by using the element's electron arrangement.

Sample solution for $AuCl_3$: From the periodic table, Cl will gain one electron, so the oxidation number for Cl is 1–. Au + 3(1–) = 0; Au must be 3+.

Other answers: *P, 5+; O, 2–; K, 1+; Cr, 6+* L3 P

EARTH SCIENCE INTEGRATION

Minerals made up of a single element consist of elements that are relatively unreactive. Active elements always occur in nature as part of compounds. The most common elements in minerals are oxygen, silicon, aluminum, iron, calcium, sodium, potassium, and magnesium.

Teacher FYI

Hydrogen does not exhibit all the properties shown by other elements in Group 1. It is a gas at room temperature and forms covalent bonds with other elements. Some periodic tables place the hydrogen block slightly apart from Group 1 to indicate that hydrogen's properties put it in a class by itself.

Flex Your Brain

Use the Flex Your Brain activity to have students explore COVALENT BONDS.

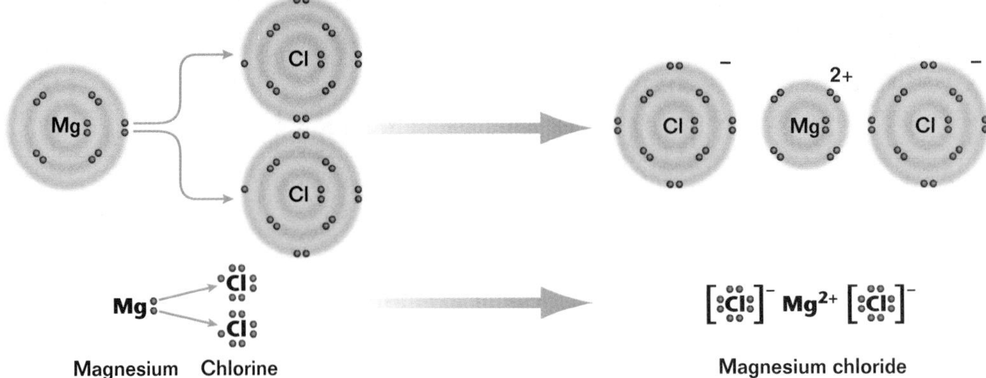

Figure 4-12 Magnesium divides up its two electrons between two chlorines to form $MgCl_2$, but it also could give two electrons to one atom, as it does in MgO.

EARTH SCIENCE INTEGRATION

Mineral Structure

Some minerals are made up of a single element, but most are compounds of different elements. The properties and appearance of a mineral occur because of how the atoms of its elements are arranged. Use an Earth science textbook or other source to find out the elements that make up the most common minerals.

Using the periodic table, you can predict that ionic salts similar to sodium chloride would form between all the elements of the alkali metals family and all of the halogens. Some examples are sodium fluoride, the anticavity ingredient in some toothpastes, and potassium iodide, which is frequently added to table salt to prevent iodine deficiency.

More Gains and Losses

You have seen what happens when elements gain or lose one electron. Now see what happens when elements gain or lose more than one. The element magnesium, Mg, in Group 2 has two electrons in its outer energy level. Magnesium can lose these two electrons and have the same structure as a stable neon atom. The two electrons can be gained by two chlorine atoms. As you can see in **Figure 4-12,** a single magnesium ion represented by the symbol Mg^{2+} and two chlorine ions are produced. The two negatively charged chlorine ions are attracted to the positively charged magnesium ion. The compound magnesium chloride is produced.

The two electrons released by magnesium could be gained by a single atom such as oxygen. When oxygen gains two electrons to form the ion O^{2-}, it can combine in a one-to-one ratio with a positive ion in Group 2. If the positive ion is Mg^{2+}, magnesium oxide (MgO) is formed.

Covalent Bonds—A Matter of Sharing

Some atoms of nonmetals are unlikely to lose or gain electrons. For example, carbon has six protons and six electrons. Four of the six electrons are in its outer energy level. To obtain a noble gas structure, carbon would either have to gain four electrons or lose four electrons. If carbon gained four electrons, that would mean that the carbon nucleus, with its charge of 6+, would have to hold its own six electrons plus four more—a total of ten negatively charged

Inclusion Strategies

Visually Impaired Students who are visually impaired will benefit from the manipulation of physical models to help them understand electron transfer or electron sharing. Have them use small magnets to represent electrons and larger magnets to represent nuclei. These magnets can be moved on a magnetic board. L2 ELL

108 CHAPTER 4 CHEMICAL BONDS

electrons. That would take too much energy. Too much energy also would be needed to remove four electrons. Each time an electron is removed, the nucleus holds the remaining electrons even more tightly. So, how do atoms of an element like carbon form bonds with other atoms?

The Covalent Bond

Atoms that do not gain or lose electrons become more stable by sharing electrons. The chemical bond that forms between atoms when they share electrons is called a **covalent** (koh VAY luhnt) **bond.** Shared electrons are attracted to the nuclei of two atoms at the same time. They move between the outer energy levels of each atom in the covalent bond so that each atom has a full outer energy level some of the time. The atoms in a covalent bond form a neutral particle, which means that the particle contains the same numbers of positive and negative charges. The neutral particle formed when atoms share electrons is called a **molecule** (MAH luh kyewl). You can see a model of electron sharing and molecule formation in **Figure 4-13.** Notice that no charged particles are involved because no electrons are gained or lost.

Constructing a Model for Methane

Procedure

1. Using circles of different colored paper to represent protons, neutrons, and electrons, build paper models of one carbon atom and four hydrogen atoms.
2. Use your models of atoms to construct a molecule of methane by forming covalent bonds. The methane molecule has four hydrogen atoms chemically bonded to one carbon atom.

Analysis

1. In the methane molecule, do the carbon and hydrogen atoms have the same arrangement of electrons as two noble gas elements? Explain.
2. Is the methane molecule charged?

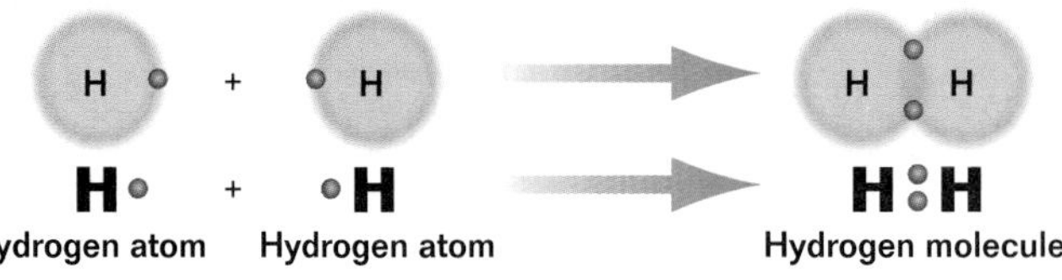

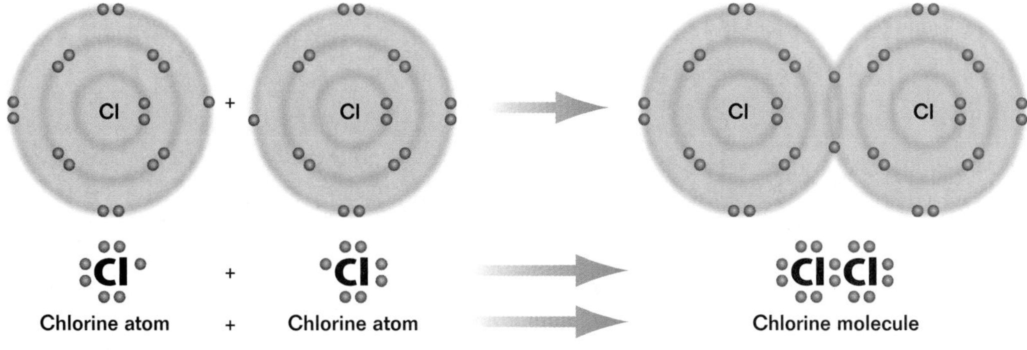

Figure 4-13 The sharing of electrons allows each atom to have a filled outer energy level. **Which noble gas is hydrogen similar to? Which is chlorine similar to?**

Caption Answer

Figure 4-13 *helium, argon*

For additional help doing this activity at home, see the corresponding pages in the **Home Involvement** booklet.

Purpose

Kinesthetic Students will model a methane molecule. L2 ELL

Materials

paper of three different colors, scissors

Teaching Strategies

- Students should make the protons and neutrons the same size. The electrons should be smaller.
- Be sure students understand that this model is two-dimensional and does not accurately represent the actual three-dimensional molecule.

Analysis

1. Yes; each hydrogen atom shares two electrons and thus has the same electron arrangement as helium. The carbon atom shares eight electrons and has the same electron arrangement as neon.
2. No; an equal number of electrons and protons are present.

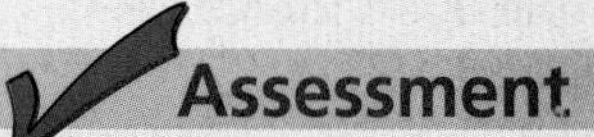

Performance For additional practice, have students revise their carbon atoms to represent nitrogen atoms and make models of ammonia, NH_3. Use **Performance Assessment in the Science Classroom**, p. 51. P

Across the Curriculum

History Even though molecules have a stable electron arrangement, sometimes they will react to form a more stable substance. For example, H_2 and O_2 both have stable arrangements, but they will react to form water, H_2O, which is even more stable. A tragic example of this reaction was seen in 1937 when the Hindenburg, a German airship, exploded. It was full of hydrogen because hydrogen is lighter than air and provided lift for the airship. The hydrogen reacted explosively with oxygen in the air. Thirty-six people were killed. However, when this reaction is controlled, the energy released can be useful. The reaction between H_2 and O_2 is currently used to power the space shuttle.

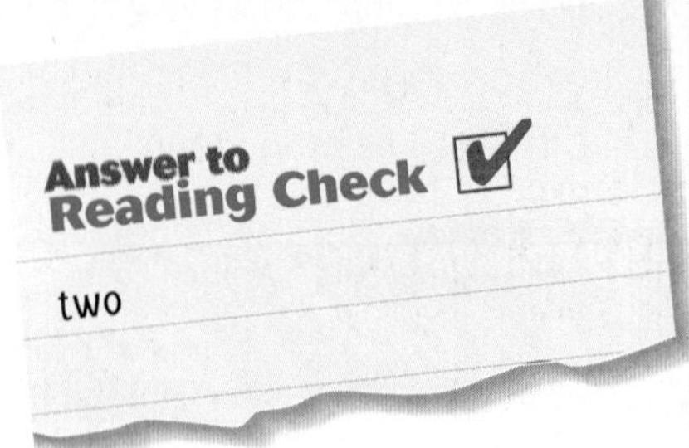

Problem Solving

Mixtures might be separated if one type of particle is small enough to enter the buckyball and the other particles are not.

Solve the Problem

Larger particles don't pass through the marbles, but the smaller particles do.

Think Critically

1. Larger particles remain on top while smaller ones pass through. The packing of the marbles resulted in holes too small for larger particles to pass through.
2. Smaller molecules would either pass through the buckyballs or be trapped inside them. Larger molecules would not.
3. Answers will vary.

GLENCOE TECHNOLOGY

Videodisc

Glencoe Science Voyages Interactive Videodisc—Physical

Side 2, Lesson 5 *Carbohydrates and Hydrocarbons*

3800

3963

Refer to Videodisc Teacher Guide for additional bar codes.

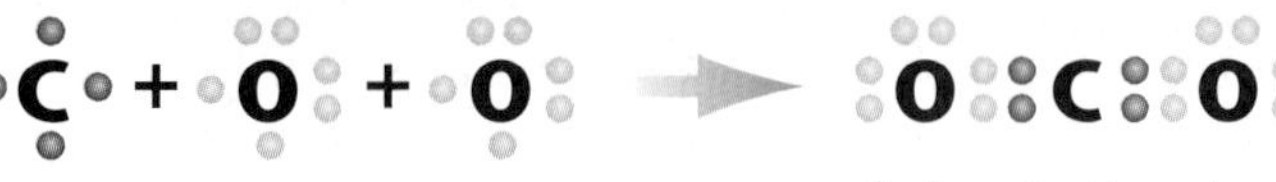

Carbon atom   Oxygen atoms   Carbon dioxide molecule

Figure 4-14 Convince yourself, by counting the electrons, that all of carbon's four electrons and all of the two oxygens' 12 electrons are present in the electron dot diagram of CO_2. **Does each atom in the two covalent compounds have eight electrons around it?**

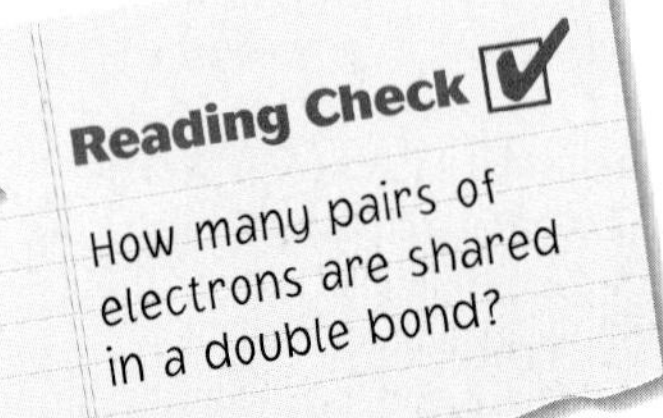

Reading Check
How many pairs of electrons are shared in a double bond?

Sometimes an atom shares more than one electron with another atom. In the molecule carbon dioxide, shown in **Figure 4-14,** each of the oxygen atoms shares two electrons with the carbon atom. When two pairs of electrons are involved in a covalent bond, the bond is called a double bond. **Figure 4-14** also shows the sharing of three pairs of electrons between two nitrogen atoms in the nitrogen molecule. When three pairs of electrons are shared by two atoms, the bond is called a triple bond. Nitrogen molecules make up about 80 percent of the air in the atmosphere.

Problem Solving

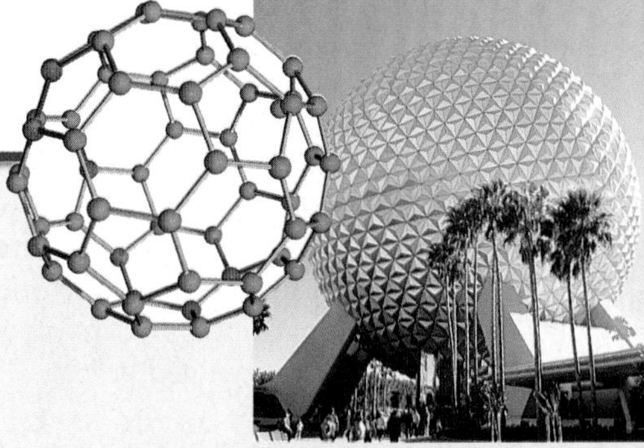

Beyond Diamond and Graphite

Is there no end to the variety of nature? Bursting onto the scene in 1985 came a new form of carbon. If you could see this new kind of carbon, you might say that it looks like a soccer ball. In fact, it's called a buckyball, which is a nickname for buckminsterfullerene. Buckminster Fuller is the architect who designed the first geodesic dome. The dome at right is located at EPCOT near Orlando, Florida. Buckminsterfullerene looks a lot like the dome created by its namesake. This amazing form of carbon is a molecule containing 60 carbon atoms bonded together in a hollow sphere.

In early 1990, *Science* magazine named buckminsterfullerene the "Molecule of the Year" because it held so much yet-to-be-developed promise. Medical applications were proposed in which disease-attacking agents would be attached to the outside of the molecule or radioactive isotopes would be carried inside the molecule. The molecule could then be injected into a patient. Another application concerned the separation of mixtures. How might that work?

Solve the Problem

1. Fill a tall, glass cylinder with glass marbles. The marbles will represent the spherical buckyballs. The mixture to be separated could be sand or salt mixed with barley or rice. These substances represent two different chemical compounds.
2. Pour the sand and barley mixture over the marbles and observe.

Think Critically

1. Did the mixture change as a result of being poured over the marbles? How do you think the packing of the marbles helped with the separation?
2. How might buckyballs be used to separate a mixture of chemical compounds?
3. Can you think of any other uses for buckyballs?

Caption Answer

Figure 4-14 *yes*

Figure 4-15 The balloon became electrically charged by rubbing it on someone's hair. Now, it attracts a stream of water. The two pairs of electrons in the two bonds between oxygen and hydrogen spend more time near the oxygen than near the hydrogen. This makes oxygen slightly negative and hydrogen slightly positive.

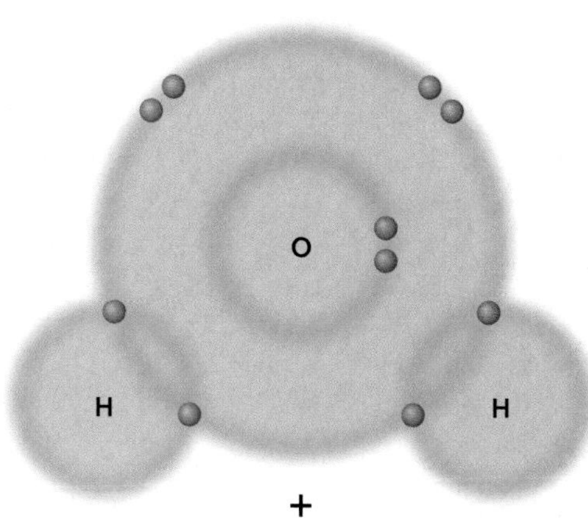

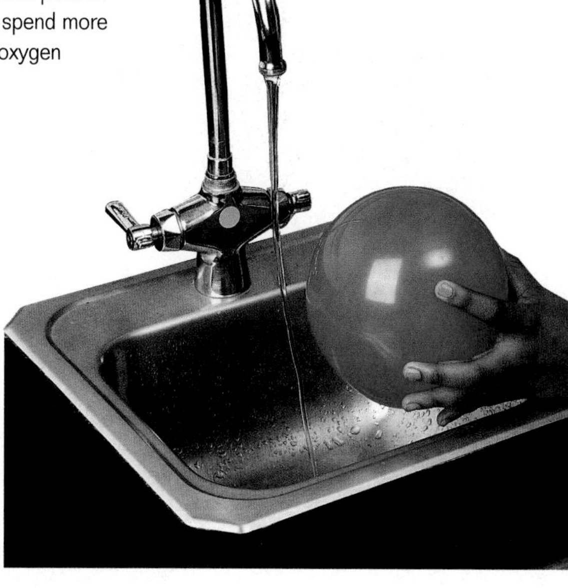

Polar and Nonpolar Molecules

You have seen that atoms often share electrons to become more stable. Do the atoms always share electrons equally? The answer is no. Some atoms have a greater attraction for electrons than others do. Oxygen, for example, attracts electrons more strongly than hydrogen does. When a covalent bond forms between hydrogen and oxygen, the shared pair of electrons tends to spend more time near the oxygen atom than the hydrogen atom.

The Polar Water Molecule

Water molecules are formed when hydrogen and oxygen share electrons. **Figure 4-15** shows evidence of the unequal sharing of electrons by hydrogen and oxygen in water. Because the oxygen atom has a greater share in the electron pair, the oxygen end of a water molecule has a slight negative charge, and the hydrogen end has a slight positive charge. This type of bond is a polar bond. *Polar* means having two opposite ends or poles. Often, one or more polar bonds result in a polar molecule such as the water molecule. Molecules that do not have these unbalanced charges are called nonpolar molecules. Because all atoms have different atomic structures, they all have different attractions for electrons, so the only truly nonpolar bonds are bonds between the same two atoms. The nitrogen molecule, which has two nitrogen atoms joined in a covalent bond, is an example of a nonpolar bond.

interNET CONNECTION

Visit the Glencoe Science Web Site at **www.glencoe.com/sec/science** for more information about polar molecules.

interNET CONNECTION

Internet Addresses

For Internet tips, see Glencoe's **Using the Internet in the Science Classroom.**

Using an Analogy

A covalent bond can be compared to a tug of war where the rope cannot be completely pulled to one side. The rope is analogous to a shared pair of electrons, and the people represent the nuclei. If the people pulling the rope exert an equal pull on both ends of the rope, an equal amount of rope stays on both sides. If one side has a stronger pull, more of the rope will be on that side.

GLENCOE TECHNOLOGY

Videodisc

The Infinite Voyage:

Insects: The Ruling Class

Chapter 14 *Prospecting for Healing Medicine from Insects* 6:30

Fires of the Mind

Chapter 3 *Positron Emission Tomography (PET)* 3:00

Refer to the Teacher Guide for bar codes and teaching strategies.

Multiple Learning Styles

Logical-Mathematical Have students use pennies and quarters to model formation of compounds from electron dot diagrams. For example, a quarter surrounded by six pennies would represent oxygen; a quarter and a single penny would represent hydrogen. Have them use similar models to determine the formulas for potassium bromide, KBr; magnesium chloride, $MgCl_2$; and aluminum sulfide, Al_2S_3.

GLENCOE TECHNOLOGY

CD-ROM

Glencoe Science Voyages Interactive CD-ROM

Explorations

Have students do the interactive exploration *How can you tell which elements form chemical bonds?*

3 Assess

Check for Understanding Activity

Visual-Spatial Have students draw the nuclei and electron clouds for a molecule of a covalent compound such as HCl. Have them draw arrows to show the attractions and repulsions found in the molecule. Arrows should show the attraction between both nuclei and both electron clouds and the repulsion between the nuclei and between the electron clouds. L2 ELL P

Reteach

Kinesthetic Have students use several Styrofoam balls of two different sizes to model the arrangement of the ions in an ionic solid. L1 ELL

Extension

For students who have mastered this section, use the **Reinforcement** and **Enrichment** masters.

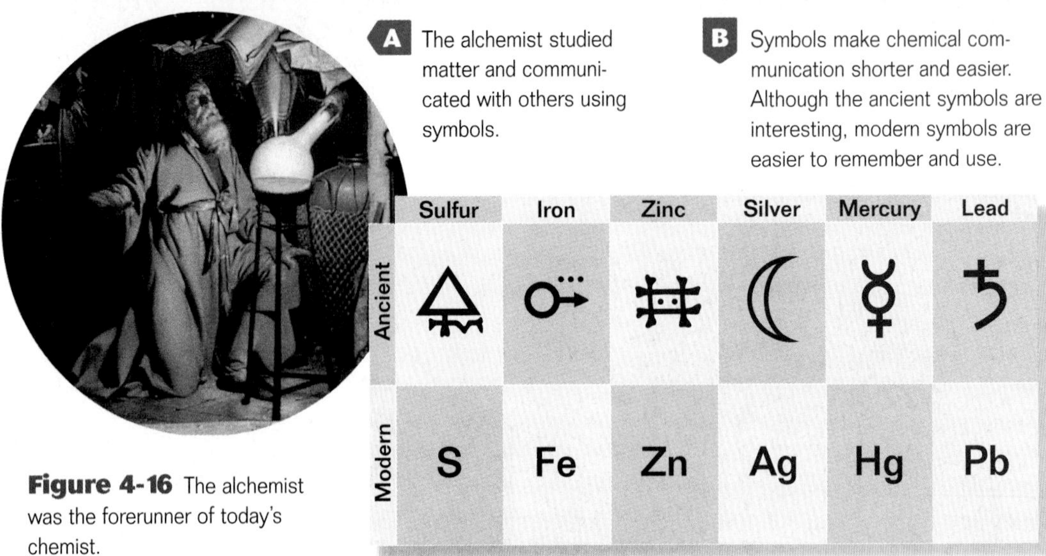

Sulfur
Iron
Zinc
Silver
Mercury
Lead
Ancient
Modern
S
Fe
Zn
Ag
Hg
Pb

A The alchemist studied matter and communicated with others using symbols.

B Symbols make chemical communication shorter and easier. Although the ancient symbols are interesting, modern symbols are easier to remember and use.

Figure 4-16 The alchemist was the forerunner of today's chemist.

Chemical Shorthand

The medieval alchemist (AL kuh mist) in **Figure 4-16A** looks quite different from a modern chemist, but like the ancient alchemists, today's chemist investigates matter, records results to share with others, and uses symbols to represent the elements. Some of the symbols used by alchemists are shown in **Figure 4-16B.** The modern chemist knows that the black tarnish that forms on silver is a compound made up of the elements silver and sulfur. She uses symbols to represent the compound: Ag_2S. If the alchemist knew the composition of tarnish, how might he have used his symbols to represent it? Modern symbols make it easy to write down chemical information and have other people understand it.

Formulas for Molecules

When you write Ag_2S, chemists everywhere know exactly what you mean. Chemical formulas allow scientists to communicate and share research. **Figure 4-17** shows a model of the way a hydrogen molecule is formed. Two hydrogen atoms join together in a covalent bond. The resulting molecule is represented by the chemical formula H_2. The small 2 after the H in the formula is called a subscript. *Sub-* means "below" and *script* means "write," so a subscript is a number that is written below. The subscript 2 means that two atoms of hydrogen are in the molecule.

Figure 4-17 Two hydrogen atoms make up one hydrogen molecule. The formula for the hydrogen molecule makes clear by placing the subscript 2 after the H.

H + H → H H

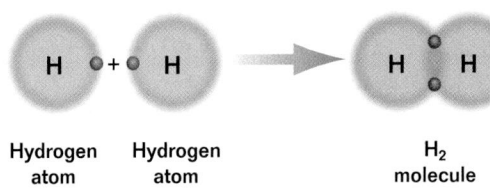

Hydrogen atom | Hydrogen atom | H_2 molecule

VISUAL Learning

Figure 4-16B Point out that the ancient symbols are complicated and might vary from alchemist to alchemist.

Figure 4-17 Tell students that molecules that consist of only two atoms of the same element are said to be diatomic. All of the gaseous elements, except the noble gases, exist as diatomic molecules. Have students write the formulas for other diatomic elements: nitrogen, oxygen, chlorine, fluorine, bromine, and iodine. *N_2, O_2, Cl_2, F_2, Br_2, I_2*

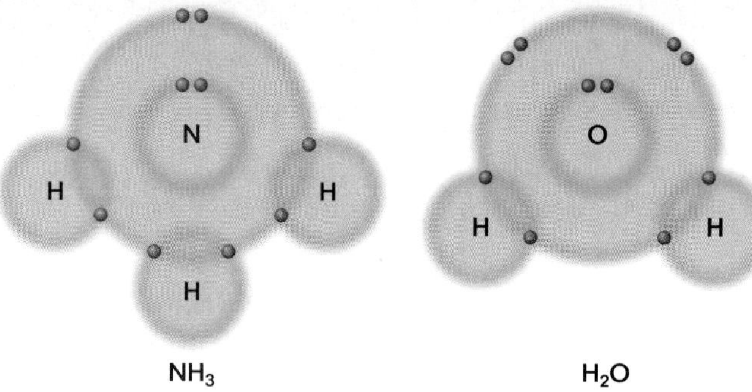

Figure 4-18 Ammonia has three hydrogen atoms and one nitrogen atom, so its formula is NH_3. The water molecule, H_2O, has two hydrogen atoms and one oxygen atom.

A chemical **formula** is a combination of chemical symbols of the elements that tells what elements are present in a molecule and how many atoms of each element are present. Similarly, the formula for the molecule containing two chlorine atoms is Cl_2. When there is no subscript, the number of atoms is understood to be one.

Covalently bonded molecules also can be compounds like ammonia and water shown in **Figure 4-18.** These molecules have more than one kind of atom joined together in covalent bonds. Ammonia has the formula NH_3, and the formula for water is H_2O. The formula for silver tarnish, Ag_2S, tells you that silver tarnish is a compound that contains two silver atoms and one sulfur atom.

Using Math

A container holds a gas made up of molecules that contain carbon and hydrogen. Of the atoms in the container, 20 percent are carbon. Determine the chemical formula of the gas molecules.

Section Assessment

1. Use the periodic table to decide whether lithium would form a positive or a negative ion. Would fluorine form a positive or a negative ion? Write the formula for the compound the two elements would form.
2. What is the difference between a polar and a nonpolar bond?
3. What does a chemical formula tell you?
4. **Think Critically:** Most laundry detergents are long molecules with one end that is soluble in grease and the other end soluble in water. What is the most probable type of molecule in detergents? Explain.
5. **Skill Builder**
   Predicting Scientists use what they have learned to predict what they think will happen. Do the **Chapter 4 Skill Activity** on page 745 to predict the type of bond that will form between elements.

Using Computers

Spreadsheet Design a table using spreadsheet software to compare and contrast ionic, polar covalent, and nonpolar covalent bonds. If you need help, refer to page 738.

Assessment

Oral Ask why ionic compounds are usually solid at room temperature, whereas covalent compounds are frequently gases or liquids. Ions are bonded to several other ions that hold them in a rigid structure. Molecules are attracted less to other molecules around them. Use **Performance Assessment in the Science Classroom,** p. 71.

Using Math

The ratio 20 C : 80 H can be reduced to 1 C : 4 H. The formula is CH_4.

4 Close

Proficiency Prep

Use this quiz to check students' recall of section content.

1. **What kind of chemical bond is formed because of the attraction between charged particles?** *ionic bond*
2. **How many atoms of carbon are in one molecule of C_2H_4?** 2

Section Assessment

1. Li^+, F^-; LiF
2. In a nonpolar bond, electrons are shared equally. In a polar bond, they are not.
3. A chemical formula tells you what elements are in the compound and their proportion.
4. **Think Critically** Polar bonds on one end are soluble in water and nonpolar bonds on the other end are soluble in grease.

Using Computers

For each bond type, student tables should include arrangement of electrons, basic particles, and any other information students think is important. Check tables for accuracy. P

Purpose

Kinesthetic Students will model ionic compounds and the process that forms them. L2

ELL COOP LEARN

Process Skills

observing and inferring, recognizing cause and effect, making models, using numbers

Time

30 minutes

Alternate Materials

Different colors of paper are not essential if disks are clearly labeled with symbols of the elements represented.

Safety Precautions

Be sure students use caution when handling scissors and thumbtacks.

Teaching Strategies

- It will be helpful for students to visualize the chemical symbol on each disc surrounded by a square. Each side of the square can contain two electrons.
- The symbols for the ions formed are: Li^{+}, S^{2-}, Mg^{2+}, O^{2-}, Ca^{2+}, N^{3-}, Al^{3+}, and I^{-}.
- You can provide templates or round objects for students to trace around to make the disks.

Answers to Questions

1. Diagrams should show each symbol surrounded by eight dots. Each ion should have the following charge: Li^{+}, S^{2-}, Mg^{2+}, O^{2-}, Ca^{2+}, N^{3-}, Al^{3+}, and I^{-}.
2. Li^{+}: He; S^{2-}, Ca^{2+}: Ar; Mg^{2+}, O^{2-}, N^{3-}, Al^{3+}: Ne; I^{-}: Xe
3. two
4. Eight electrons in an energy level is a stable arrangement. Atoms will not easily gain or lose electrons if they have eight electrons in their outer energy level.

Ionic Compounds

Materials

- Paper (8 different colors)
- Tacks (2 different colors)
- Corrugated cardboard
- Scissors

Metals in Groups 1 and 2 often lose electrons and form positive ions. Nonmetals in Groups 15, 16, and 17 often gain electrons and become negative ions. What are the possibilities for the formation of compounds between these five groups of elements?

What You'll Investigate

How do different atoms combine with each other to form compounds?

Goals

- **Construct** models of electron gain and loss.
- **Write** formulas for the ions that form when electrons are gained or lost.
- **Determine** the formulas of compounds formed between positive and negative ions.

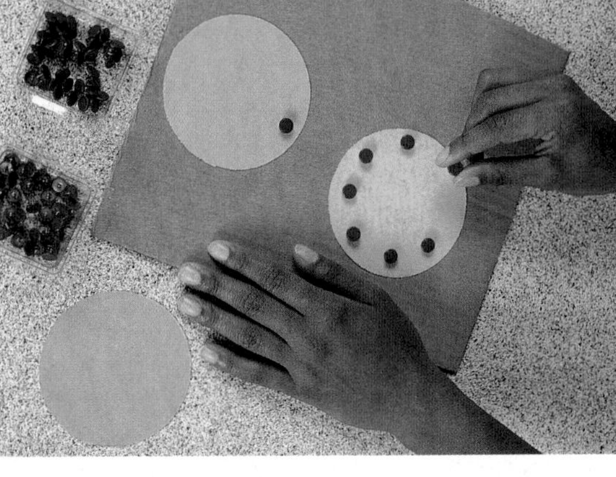

Procedure  

1. **Cut** three paper disks to represent each of these elements: Li, S, Mg, O, Ca, N, Al, and I. The disks should be about 7 cm in diameter. Use a different color of paper for each element.
2. On each disk, **write** the symbol of the element it represents.
3. Lay circles that represent an atom of lithium and an atom of sulfur side by side on a piece of corrugated cardboard.
4. **Choose** a color of thumbtack to represent the outer electron of lithium. Choose another color of thumbtack to represent the outer electrons of sulfur. **Place** one tack for each electron around the outside of each disk. Space the tacks evenly.
5. **Move** one or more electrons from the metallic atom to the nonmetallic atom so that both elements achieve a noble gas arrangement of electrons. If necessary, add more atoms of one or the other element.
6. Write the formulas for each of the ions in the ionic compound.
7. Repeat steps 3 through 6 for the remaining combinations of atoms: Mg and O, Ca and N, Al and I.

Conclude and Apply

1. **Draw** electron dot diagrams for all of the ions produced.
2. **Identify** the noble gas elements that have the same electron arrangements as the ions you produced.
3. How many lithium atoms combine with one sulfur atom?
4. Why did you have to use more than one atom in some cases? Why couldn't you just take more electrons from one metal atom or add extra ones to a nonmetal atom?

Assessment

Content For each pair of elements that make up a compound, have students multiply the number of each type of atom used by the charge of the resulting ion to show that the overall charge on a unit of the compound is zero. For example, for Li_2S, $2(1+) + 1(2-) = 0$. Use **Performance Assessment in the Science Classroom,** p. 29.

114 CHAPTER 4 CHEMICAL BONDS

How it Works

Metallic Bonding

Knowing the type of bonding in a substance can help you predict many of its physical properties. An ionic compound may form a solid with a high melting point that conducts electricity in the liquid state or when it is dissolved in water. Many covalent compounds are gases, liquids, or soft solids at room temperature. They do not conduct electricity or easily dissolve in water.

Bonding in metals is not due to the formation of compounds. Metallic bonding is the sharing of electrons between all the atoms in the metal. This type of bonding explains why some metals have the strength to support a high-rise office building (left), why other metals can be formed into the thin wire filaments within lightbulbs, and why still other metals can be rolled or shaped into soft drink cans or hammered into horseshoes.

IN METALLIC BONDING

1. The outer electrons of each atom in the metal are not held tightly to the nucleus. Instead, they are free to move from one nucleus to another.
2. The metal atoms are bonded together in a large network. A sea of electrons surrounds each positively charged nucleus.
3. The bonding in metals is not rigid. Each nucleus can slide through the sea of electrons to new positions and stay connected to the other nuclei. As a result, metals can be hammered into thin sheets or pulled into long, thin wires.
4. The electrons can easily flow through the metal to conduct electricity.

Thinking Critically

1. How does metallic bonding differ from ionic bonding? From covalent bonding?
2. Explain why a metal with three outer electrons would be a better conductor than a metal with one outer electron.

Career CONNECTION

Use the library to research the difference between a metallurgist and a metalsmith.

How it Works

Purpose

Students learn about the special bonding in metals.

Content Background

Typically, metals have low ionization energies. The orbitals of the outer, ionizable electrons overlap those of their neighbors making it possible for electrons to move throughout the metal crystal. Thus, the crystal is an array of positive nuclei in a sea of electrons. The more electrons in the outer energy level of an atom, the stronger the metallic bond.

VISUAL Learning

What would the diagram look like if the metal were not being hammered? *All the atoms would be lined up in rows and the electrons would be scattered around them.*

Teaching Strategies

- Hammer a piece of metal or a nail on a hard surface until it is deformed.
- Visit a blacksmith, if there are any in your area, or a metal-working factory.

Career CONNECTION

A metallurgist is knowledgeable about the science and technology of metals. A minimum of a bachelor's degree in metallurgy is required. A metalsmith works with metals, shaping and forming them. Two years of technical college and an apprenticeship could prepare a metalsmith.

Thinking Critically

1. In ionic bonding, an atom loses an electron and another atom gains it. In covalent bonding, two atoms share electrons. In metallic bonding, no ions are formed, and there is no direct sharing between individual pairs of atoms.
2. Each metal atom with three outer electrons would have three electrons in the sea of electrons. There would be more electrons to conduct electric charge.

Chapter 4 Reviewing Main Ideas

Reviewing Main Ideas can be used to preview, review, reteach, and condense chapter content.

Preview

Linguistic Have students try to answer the Reviewing Main Ideas questions in their Science Journals. Use student answers as a source for discussion throughout the chapter.

Review

Interpersonal Have students answer the questions on separate pieces of paper and compare their answers with those of other students in the class. COOP LEARN

Reteach

Visual-Spatial Have students look at the illustrations on these pages. Ask them to describe details that support the main ideas of the chapter found in the statement for each illustration.

00:00 OUT OF TIME?

Auditory-Musical If time does not permit teaching the entire chapter, use the information on these pages along with the chapter Audiocassettes to present the material in a condensed format.

Chapter 4 Reviewing Main Ideas

For a **preview** of this chapter, study this Reviewing Main Ideas before you read the chapter. After you have studied this chapter, you can use the Reviewing Main Ideas to **review** the chapter.

The Glencoe MindJogger, Audiocassettes, and CD-ROM provide additional opportunities for review.

Section 4-1 ELECTRON ARRANGEMENT

The electrons in the electron cloud of an atom are arranged in energy levels. Each energy level contains a definite number of electrons. The number of electrons in the outer energy level of the atom increases across any period of the periodic table. The noble gas elements are stable because they have filled outer energy levels. ***How many electrons are in the outer energy level of fluorine?***

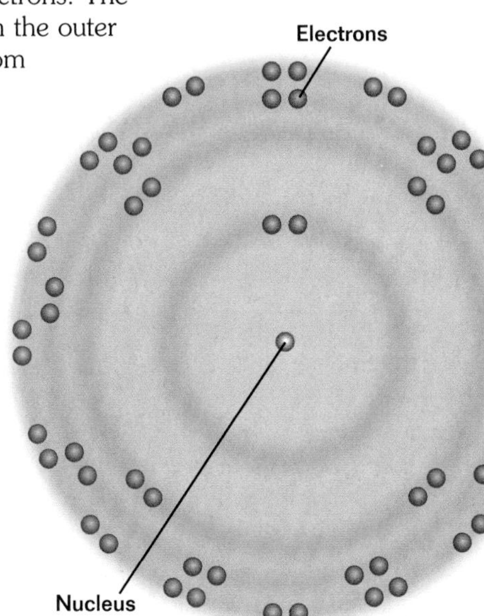

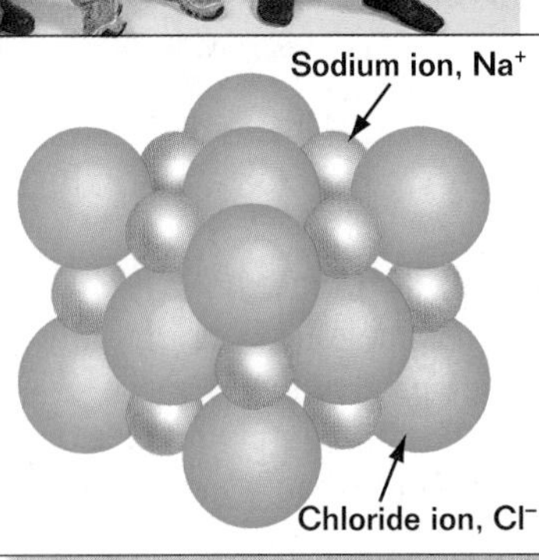

Section 4-2 IONIC AND COVALENT BONDS

Atoms can become more stable if they gain, lose, or share electrons until their outer energy level is filled with electrons. **Ionic bonds** are created when a metal atom loses one or more electrons and a nonmetal atom gains one or more electrons. **Covalent bonds** are created when nonmetal atoms share one or more electrons. The unequal sharing of electrons results in a polar covalent bond. ***How does the number of electrons in the outer energy level determine the type of bond that will be formed?***

Cultural Diversity

Salt of the Earth Long ago, Egyptians used it to prepare bodies for afterlife. In Arabia, people who ate it together were pledging their loyalty to one another. People of the Far East often rubbed newborn babies with it to ensure good health. They hung small bags of it around older children's necks to protect them from harm. What is it? It is salt, an ionic compound that is one of the most important minerals used by humans throughout history.

Salt was once used in one of the primary methods of food preservation, and so it was valuable. The Roman soldiers who built the famous Roman roads were often paid in salt. The English word for wages, *salary*, comes from the Latin word for these wages, *salarium*.

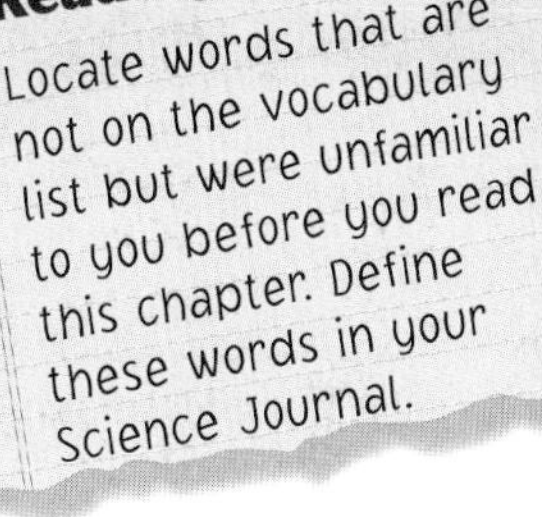

Reading Check
Locate words that are not on the vocabulary list but were unfamiliar to you before you read this chapter. Define these words in your Science Journal.

CHEMICAL SYMBOLS AND FORMULAS

In order to communicate clearly about elements and combinations of elements, chemists created chemical symbols and **formulas.** This chemical language tells what elements are in **molecules** and **compounds,** and how many atoms of each element are present. The formula for silver sulfide, Ag_2S, shows there are two silver atoms and one sulfur atom in every molecule of silver sulfide. ***How many hydrogen atoms and how many nitrogen atoms are in one molecule of ammonia, NH_3?***

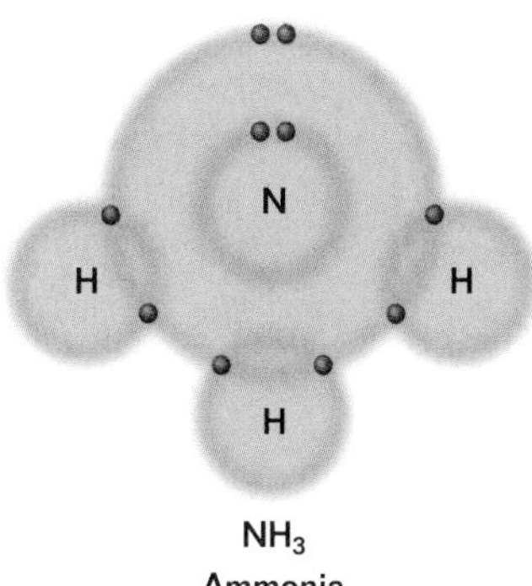

NH_3
Ammonia

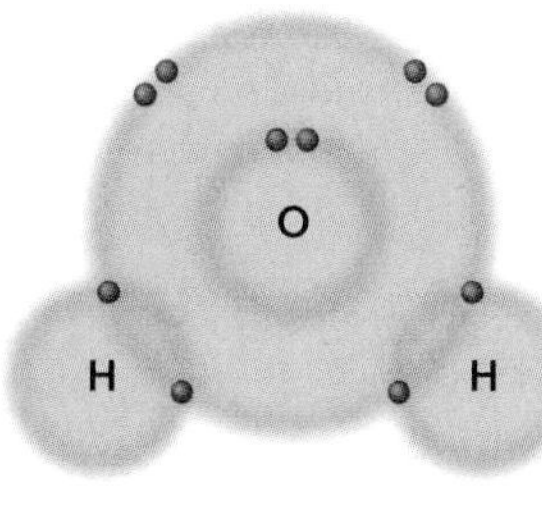

H_2O
Water

Career CONNECTION

Dr. Brenna Flaugher, Particle Physicist

As a particle physicist, Brenna Flaugher uses a supercollider to study the particles that make up protons and neutrons, and the forces that bind these particles together. Though these particles are small, they can help understand big things, like why matter has mass, why gravity works, and how the universe was formed. Brenna chose a career in particle physics because it represents an exciting scientific frontier. ***How does studying atoms help us understand chemical interactions?***

Answers to Questions

Section 4-1

Electron Arrangement The outer energy level of fluorine contains seven electrons.

Section 4-2

Ionic and Covalent Bonds Atoms with one or two electrons and those with six or seven can lose or gain electrons to form ionic bonds. Atoms with three, four, and five electrons are more likely to share electrons in covalent bonds.

Chemical Symbols and Formulas Ammonia contains three hydrogen atoms and one nitrogen atom.

Career CONNECTION

The atom is the basic unit in all substances, so its nature determines how it behaves in chemical reactions.

GLENCOE TECHNOLOGY

CD-ROM

Glencoe Science Voyages Interactive CD-ROM

Chapter Summaries and Quizzes

Have students read the Chapter Summary and then take the Chapter Quiz to determine whether they have mastered chapter content.

Assessment

Portfolio Encourage students to place in their portfolios one or two items of what they consider to be their best work. Examples include:

- Guided Reading Strategy, p. 101
- MiniLab, pp. 102, 109
- Enrichment, p. 108
- Activity, p. 112
- Using Computers, p. 113 P

Performance Additional performance assessments may be found in **Performance Assessment** and **Science Integration Activities.** Performance Task Assessment Lists and rubrics for evaluating these activities can be found in Glencoe's **Performance Assessment in the Science Classroom.**

Using Vocabulary

1. An ion is a charged particle and a molecule is neutral.
2. A molecule is a neutral particle formed when atoms share electrons. A compound is a pure substance that contains two or more elements.
3. An electron dot diagram is the symbol for an element surrounded by as many dots as there are electrons in it's outer energy level. A formula is a combination of chemical symbols of the elements that tell what elements are present in a molecule or compound and how many.
4. A formula uses symbols to portray the composition of molecules.
5. Ionic bonds are formed when opposite charges attract each other. Electron sharing results in covalent bonds.

interNET CONNECTION To reinforce chapter vocabulary, use the **Study Guide for Content Mastery** booklet. Also available are activities for **Glencoe Science Voyages** on the Glencoe Science Web Site. **www.glencoe.com/sec/science**

Checking Concepts

6. B
7. A
8. C
9. D
10. B
11. B
12. B
13. A
14. D
15. D

Chapter 4 Assessment

Using Vocabulary

a. chemical bond
b. compound
c. covalent bond
d. electron dot diagram
e. formula
f. ion
g. ionic bond
h. molecule

Distinguish between the terms in each of the following pairs.

1. ion, molecule
2. molecule, compound
3. electron dot diagram, formula
4. formula, molecule
5. ionic bond, covalent bond

Checking Concepts

Choose the word or phrase that best answers the question.

6. Which term is used to represent a molecule?
   A) equation
   B) formula
   C) chemical symbol
   D) number
7. Which of the following is a covalently bonded molecule?
   A) Cl_2
   B) air
   C) Ne
   D) salt
8. Which of the following is represented by the symbol Cl^-?
   A) an ionic compound
   B) a polar molecule
   C) a negative ion
   D) a positive ion
9. Which phrase describes what happens to electrons when a polar covalent bond forms?
   A) They are lost.
   B) They are gained.
   C) They are shared equally.
   D) They are shared unequally.
10. Which of the following compounds is unlikely to contain ionic bonds?
    A) NaF
    B) CO
    C) LiCl
    D) $MgBr_2$
11. Which term describes the units that make up compounds with covalent bonds?
    A) ions
    B) molecules
    C) salts
    D) acids
12. In the chemical formula CO_2, the subscript 2 shows which of the following?
    A) There are two oxygen ions.
    B) There are two oxygen atoms.
    C) There are two CO_2 molecules.
    D) There are two CO_2 compounds.
13. Which term describes the units that make up substances formed by ionic bonding?
    A) ions
    B) molecules
    C) acids
    D) atoms
14. Which is **NOT** true about the molecule H_2O?
    A) It contains two hydrogen atoms.
    B) It contains one oxygen atom.
    C) It is a polar covalent compound.
    D) It is an ionic compound.
15. What is the number of the group in which the elements have a filled outer energy level and are stable?
    A) 1
    B) 13
    C) 16
    D) 18

Thinking Critically

16. Groups 1 and 2 form many compounds with Groups 16 and 17. Explain.
17. What would you need to know about the atoms in a covalent bond in order to decide if the bond is polar?
18. When salt is dropped into a glass of water, the salt dissolves in the water and the sodium and chlorine ions are separated. Explain why this might occur.

Thinking Critically

16. Elements in Groups 1 and 2 lose electrons easily. Elements in Groups 16 and 17 gain electrons easily.
17. whether the attraction of each atom for the shared electrons is equal or not
18. The positive ends of polar water molecules are attracted to the chloride ions and pull them out of the solid. The negative ends of polar water molecules are attracted to the sodium ions and pull them out of the solid.
19. The outer electron in cesium is farther from the nucleus and is more easily removed from the atom.
20. The negative parts of water molecules are attracted to the positive parts of other water molecules. Because of these attractions, more energy is required to separate the molecules.

19. Cesium in period 6 is more reactive than lithium in period 2. Both elements are in the alkali metals family. Explain the difference in reactivity on the basis of the outer energy levels of the two atoms.
20. Use the fact that water is a polar molecule to explain why water has a much higher boiling point than other molecules of the same size.

Developing Skills

If you need help, refer to the Skill Handbook.

21. **Predicting:** Suppose that equal masses of CuCl and $CuCl_2$ are decomposed into their component elements, copper and chlorine. Predict which compound will yield more copper. Explain your answer.
22. **Concept Mapping:** Draw a concept map starting with the term *chemical bond* and use all the vocabulary words.
23. **Recognizing Cause and Effect:** A helium atom has only two electrons. Why does helium behave as a noble gas?
24. **Observing and Inferring:** Suppose you have a sample of an element. You identify it as iron. List observations that you made that allowed you to infer that it is iron.
25. **Making and Using a Table:** Fill in the second column of the table with the number of metal atoms in one unit of the compound. Fill in the third column with the number of atoms of the nonmetal in one unit.

Formulas of Compounds

Compound	Number of Metal Atoms	Number of Nonmetal Atoms
Cu_2O	2	1
Al_2S_2	2	2
NaF	1	1
$PbCl_4$	1	4

Test-Taking Tip

Your Answers Are Better Than the Test's When you know the answer, answer the question in your own words before looking at the answer choices. Often, more than one answer choice will look good, so arm yourself with yours before looking.

Test Practice

Use these questions to test your Science Proficiency.

1. Which of the following statements is true?
   A) A molecule also can be a compound.
   B) A compound can contain only two different kinds of atoms.
   C) A compound can contain only one kind of atom.
   D) A molecule can contain only one kind of atom.
2. Which statement below **BEST** explains why atoms react chemically with each other?
   A) When atoms react, they lose all of their electrons and become more stable.
   B) When atoms react, they lose, gain, or share electrons to reach a full outer energy level and are then more stable.
   C) When atoms react, they gain protons and are then more stable.
   D) When atoms react, they lose, gain, or share electrons and are then less stable.

Test Practice

The Test-Taking Tip was written by The Princeton Review, the nation's leader in test preparation.

1. A
2. B

Developing Skills

21. Copper(I) chloride (CuCl) will yield more copper. It has a lower percentage of chlorine.
22. Student concept maps might show that chemical bonds are ionic and covalent. The basic unit of an ionic bond is an ion, and that of a covalent bond is a molecule. Ions and molecules can be represented by electron dot diagrams and formulas.
23. The lowest energy level can contain only two electrons. If this energy level is the outer level, it is full with two electrons.
24. Observations might include its physical appearance, its reaction to a magnet, and its density.
25. See student page.

Bonus Question

Fluorine attracts electrons more strongly than chlorine does. Hydrogen fluoride and hydrogen chloride are both polar molecules. Which compound would have a higher boiling point? Explain your answer. *Hydrogen fluoride is more polar. It would have a higher boiling point because the negative and positive ends of different molecules would more strongly attract each other.*

Assessment Resources

The **Test Practice Workbook** provides students with practice in the format, concepts, and critical-thinking skills tested in standardized exams.

Reproducible Masters

Chapter Review, pp. 7–8 L2
Performance Assessment, p. 18 L2
Assessment, pp. 13–16 L2

Glencoe Technology

Chapter Review Software
Computer Test Bank
MindJogger Videoquiz

Chapter 5 Chemical Reactions

Section	Objectives	Activities/Features
Chapter Opener		**Explore Activity:** Observe a Chemical Reaction, p. 121
5-1 **Describing Chemical Reaction** 4 Sessions 2 Blocks	1. **Determine** whether a chemical reaction has occurred. 2. **Describe** how to read and understand a balanced equation. 3. **Distinguish** reactions that absorb energy from those that release energy.	**MiniLab:** Observing a Chemical Change, p. 124 **Earth Science Integration,** p. 127 **Skill Builder:** Comparing and Contrasting, p. 129 **Using Math,** p. 129 **Activity 5-1:** Exothermic or Endothermic?, pp. 130–131
5-2 **Rates of Chemical Reactions** 3 Sessions 1½ Blocks	4. **Describe** and **explain** how to describe and measure the speed of a chemical reaction. 5. **Explain** how chemical reactions can be speeded up or slowed down.	**Problem Solving:** Changing Rates of Reactions, p. 135 **MiniLab:** Uncovering Inhibitors, p. 136 **Using Math,** p. 136 **Skill Builder:** Observing and Inferring, p. 137 **Using Math,** p. 137 **Activity 5-2:** Speeding Up a Reaction, p. 138 **Science and Math:** Using Proportions, p. 139

The number of recommended single-period sessions — The number of recommended blocks
One session and one-half block are allowed for chapter review and assessment.

Activity Materials

Explore	Activities	MiniLabs
p. 121 baking soda, 50-mL graduated cylinder, vinegar, sealable plastic bag, twist tie	pp. 130–131 8 test tubes, test-tube rack, 3% hydrogen peroxide solution, raw liver, raw potato, thermometer, stopwatch, 25-mL graduated cylinder p. 138 2 test tubes, test-tube rack, 25-mL graduated cylinder, plastic spoon, hot plate, wooden splint, 3% hydrogen peroxide, manganese dioxide, beaker, hot water, lighter	p. 124 baking soda, evaporating dish, white vinegar, 10-mL graduated cylinder p. 136 ingredients labels for food products

Need Materials? Contact Science Kit at 1-800-828-7777 or at www.sciencekit.com on the Internet.
For alternate materials, see the activity on the listed page.

Standards		Reproducible Resources	Technology
National	State/Local	Test Practice Workbooks are available for use with each chapter.	English and Spanish audiocassettes are available for use with each section.
National Content Standards: UCP2, UCP3, A1, A2, B1, B3		**Activity Worksheets,** pp. 23–24, 27 **Enrichment,** p. 10 **Laboratory Manual,** pp. 25–28 **Reinforcement,** p. 10 **Study Guide,** pp. 17–18	**Section Focus Transparency 10** **Teaching Transparency 9** **Internet Connection,** p. 124 **Internet Connection,** p. 127 **Glencoe Science Voyages Interactive CD-ROM** **Glencoe Science Voyages Interactive Videodisc—Physical**
National Content Standards: UCP3, B1, B2, B3, C1		**Activity Worksheets,** pp. 25–26, 28 **Critical Thinking/Problem Solving,** p. 5 **Enrichment,** p. 11 **Home Involvement,** p. 35 **Laboratory Manual,** pp. 29–32 **Multicultural Connections,** pp. 9–10 **Reinforcement,** p. 11 **Study Guide,** pp. 19–20	**Section Focus Transparency 11** **Teaching Transparency 10** **Science Integration Transparency 5** **Glencoe Science Voyages Interactive Videodisc—Earth** **Glencoe Science Voyages Interactive Videodisc—Life**

Key to Teaching Strategies

The following designations will help you decide which activities are appropriate for your students.

L1 Level 1 activities should be appropriate for students with learning difficulties.

L2 Level 2 activities should be within the ability range of all students.

L3 Level 3 activities are designed for above-average students.

ELL ELL activities should be within the ability range of English Language Learners.

COOP LEARN Cooperative Learning activities are designed for small group work.

P These strategies represent student products that can be placed into a best-work portfolio.

Multiple Learning Styles logos, as described on page 61T, are used throughout to indicate strategies that address different learning styles.

Assessment Resources

Chapter Review, pp. 9–10
Assessment, pp. 17–20
Performance Assessment in the Science Classroom (PASC)
MindJogger Videoquiz
Alternate Assessment in the Science Classroom
Performance Assessment, p. 19
Chapter Review Software
Computer Test Bank

Chapter 5 Chemical Reactions

This is a representation of key blackline masters available in the Teacher Classroom Resources. See Resource Manager boxes within the chapter for additional information.

Transparencies

Section Focus Transparencies

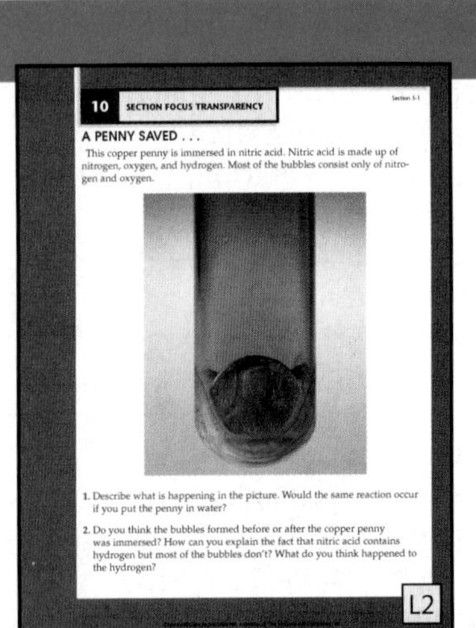
10 SECTION FOCUS TRANSPARENCY

Section 5-1

A PENNY SAVED . . .

This copper penny is immersed in nitric acid. Nitric acid is made up of nitrogen, oxygen, and hydrogen. Most of the bubbles consist only of nitrogen and oxygen.

1. Describe what is happening in the picture. Would the same reaction occur if you put the penny in water?
2. Do you think the bubbles formed before or after the copper penny was immersed? How can you explain the fact that nitric acid contains hydrogen but most of the bubbles don't? What do you think happened to the hydrogen?

L2

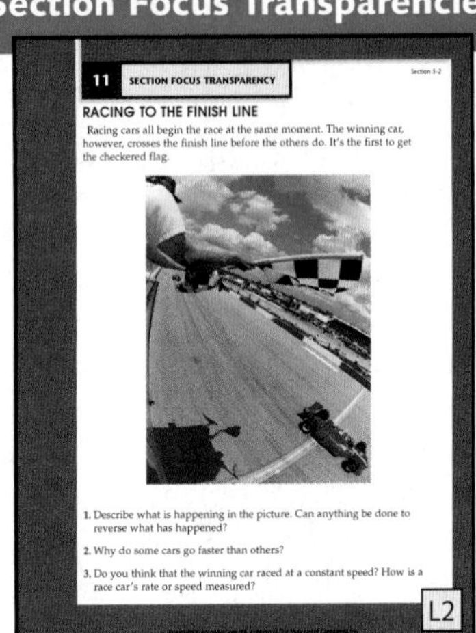
11 SECTION FOCUS TRANSPARENCY

Section 5-2

RACING TO THE FINISH LINE

Racing cars all begin the race at the same moment. The winning car, however, crosses the finish line before the others do. It's the first to get the checkered flag.

1. Describe what is happening in the picture. Can anything be done to reverse what has happened?
2. Why do some cars go faster than others?
3. Do you think that the winning car raced at a constant speed? How is a race car's rate or speed measured?

L2

Science Integration Transparencies

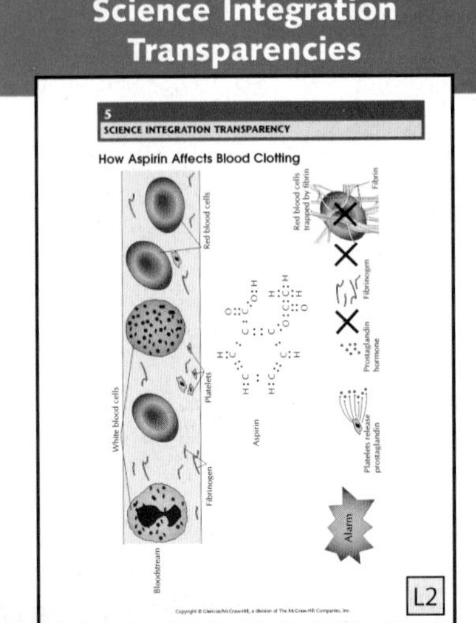
5 SCIENCE INTEGRATION TRANSPARENCY

How Aspirin Affects Blood Clotting

L2

Teaching Transparencies

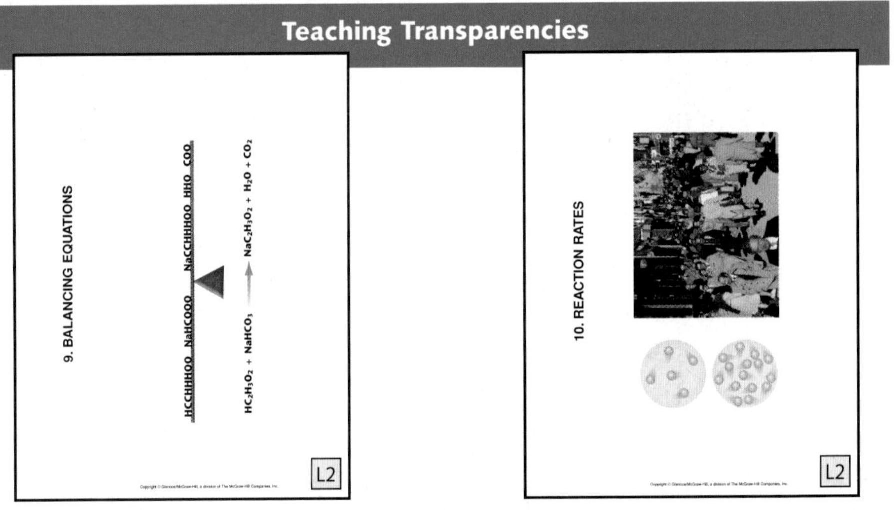

L2

L2

Meeting Different Ability Levels

Study Guide for Content Mastery

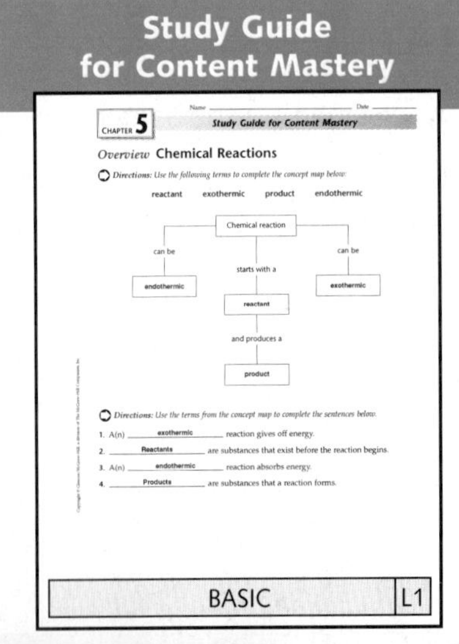
CHAPTER 5 Study Guide for Content Mastery

Overview Chemical Reactions

Directions: Use the following terms to complete the concept map below.

reactant exothermic product endothermic

Directions: Use the terms from the concept map to complete the sentences below.

1. A(n) exothermic reaction gives off energy.
2. Reactants are substances that exist before the reaction begins.
3. A(n) endothermic reaction absorbs energy.
4. Products are substances that a reaction forms.

BASIC L1

Reinforcement

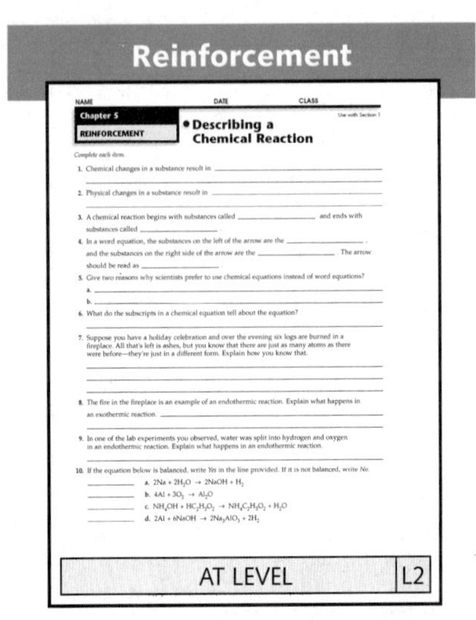
Chapter 5 REINFORCEMENT

• Describing a Chemical Reaction

1. Chemical changes in a substance result in
2. Physical changes in a substance result in
3. A chemical reaction begins with substances called ______ and ends with substances called
4. In a word equation, the substances on the left of the arrow are the ______ and the substances on the right side of the arrow are the ______. The arrow should be read as
5. Give two reasons why scientists prefer to use chemical equations instead of word equations.
6. What do the subscripts in a chemical equation tell about the equation?
7. Suppose you have a holiday celebration and over the evening six logs are burned in a fireplace. All that's left is ashes, but you know that there are just as many atoms as there were before—they're just in a different form. Explain how you know that.
8. The fire in the fireplace is an example of an endothermic reaction. Explain what happens in an exothermic reaction.
9. In one of the lab experiments you observed, water was split into hydrogen and oxygen in an endothermic reaction. Explain what happens in an endothermic reaction.
10. If the equation below is balanced, write Yes in the line provided. If it is not balanced, write No.
   a. $2Na + 2H_2O \rightarrow 2NaOH + H_2$
   b. $4Al + 3O_2 \rightarrow Al_2O$
   c. $NH_4OH + HC_2H_3O_2 \rightarrow NH_4C_2H_3O_2 + H_2O$
   d. $2Al + 6NaOH \rightarrow 2Na_3AlO_3 + 2H_2$

AT LEVEL L2

Enrichment Worksheets

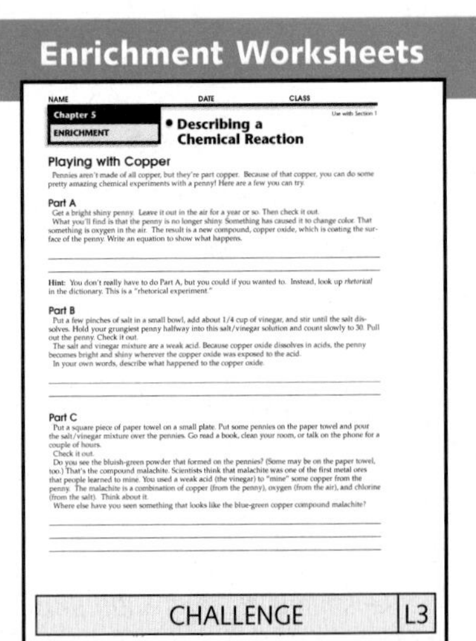
Chapter 5 ENRICHMENT

• Describing a Chemical Reaction

Playing with Copper

Pennies aren't made of all copper, but they're part copper. Because of that copper, you can do some pretty amazing chemical experiments with a penny! Here are a few you can try.

Part A

Part B

Part C

CHALLENGE L3

Resource Manager

Hands-on Activities

Activity Worksheets

Chapter 5 · ACTIVITY 5-1 • Exothermic or Endothermic?

Design Your Own Experiment

L2

Lab Manual

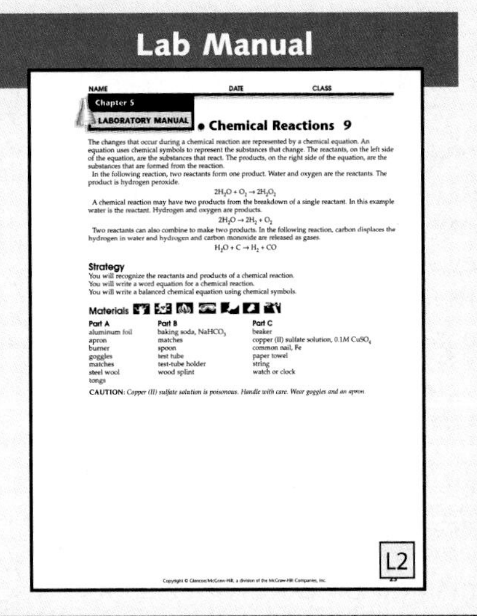
Chapter 5 · LABORATORY MANUAL • Chemical Reactions 9

L2

Accessibility

Spanish Resources

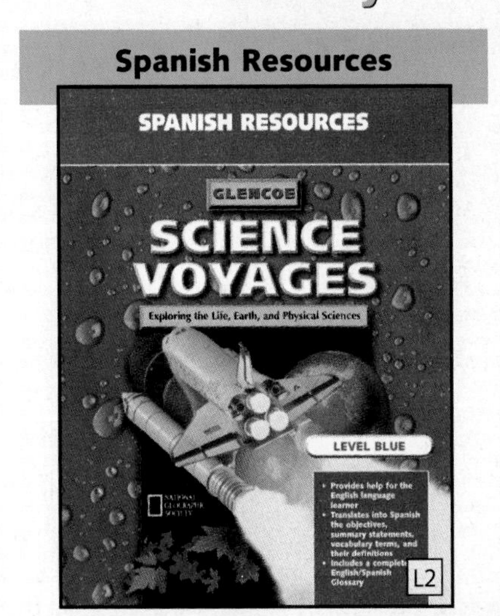

Assessment

Performance Assessment

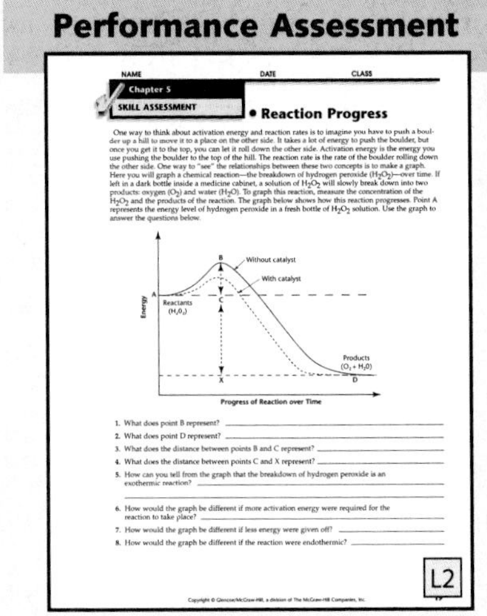
Chapter 5 · SKILL ASSESSMENT • Reaction Progress

L2

Chapter Review

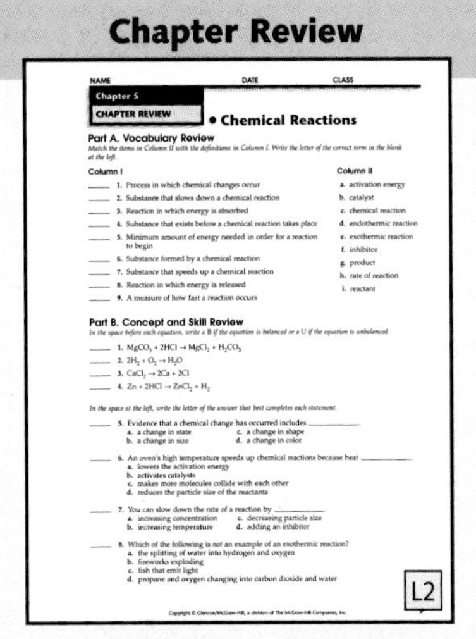
Chapter 5 · CHAPTER REVIEW • Chemical Reactions

L2

Assessment

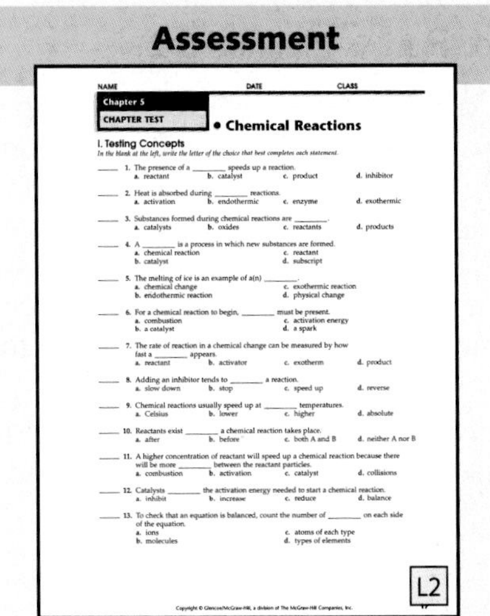
Chapter 5 · CHAPTER TEST • Chemical Reactions

L2

Test Practice Workbook

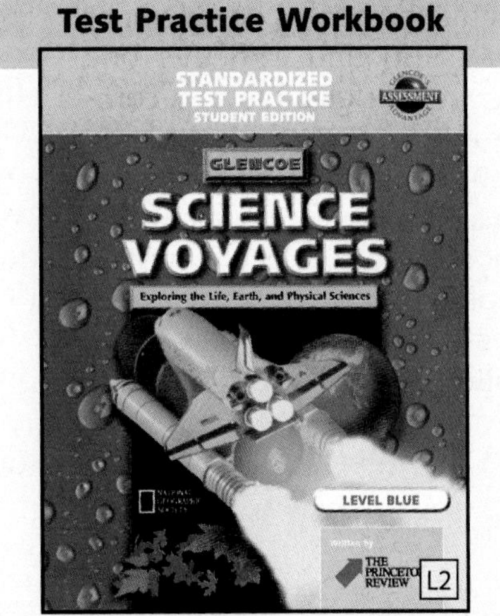

Extending Content

Critical Thinking/ Problem Solving

Chapter 5 · CRITICAL THINKING • Chemical Reactions

The Nitrogen Cycle

L2

Multicultural Connections

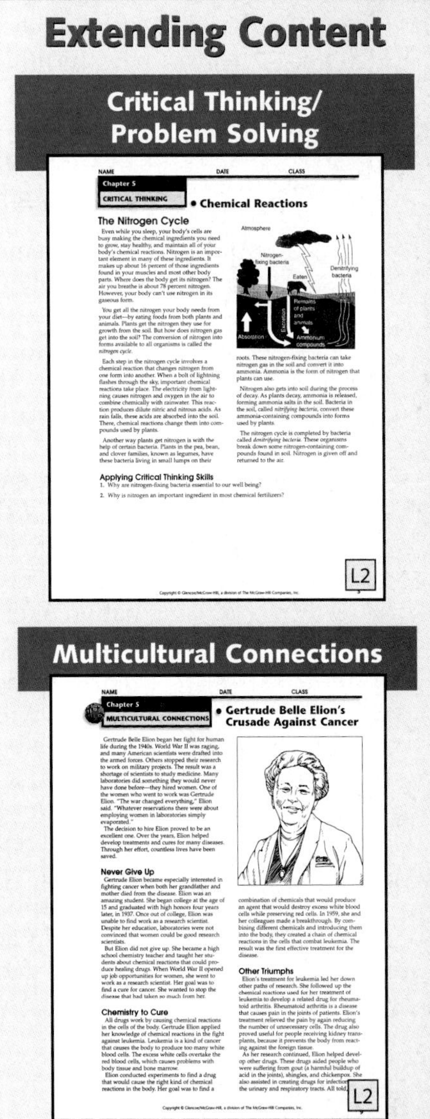
Chapter 5 · MULTICULTURAL CONNECTIONS • Gertrude Belle Elion's Crusade Against Cancer

L2

Helping You Prepare

Physical and Chemical Changes (Section 5-1)

A change in physical properties indicates a physical change. Many types of evidence indicate a chemical change. The key distinction between the two types of changes is whether the reactants change their chemical identities. If they do, the change is chemical.

Chemical Equations (Section 5-1)

A chemical equation must show the identities and relative amounts of the reactants and products. It is more complete when the physical states of the reactants and products are also included. Often equations show whether energy is released or absorbed and whether a catalyst is used. A chemical equation is not acurate unless the formulas are correct and the equation is balanced.

Types of Chemical Reactions (Section 5-1)

Most chemical reactions can be classified as one of the following five types.

In a synthesis reaction, simple reactants combine to form one product. Reactants in a synthesis reaction can be elements, compounds, or a combination of elements and compounds. An example of elements as reactants is hydrogen and oxygen, which react to form water.

In a decomposition reaction, one reactant breaks up into two or more products. The products can be elements, compounds, or a combination of elements and compounds.

In a single-displacement reaction, one element replaces another in a compound. Whether one element will displace another element in a compound is based on the relative activities of the elements. A more active element will replace a less active element in a compound. For example, zinc will replace iron. Iron will replace lead, and lead will replace copper. Activity is a measure of how readily an atom attracts or loses an electron. Trends in activity follow trends in electronegativity. In general, the activity of metals decreases as you go up and to the right on the periodic table. The activity of nonmetals decreases as you go down and to the left on the periodic table. For example, flourine is more active than chlorine, and chlorine is more active than bromine.

Double-displacement reactions occur only in solution and only if a precipitate or water is formed. When two solutions of soluble ionic salts are mixed, you can predict that a precipitate will form if one of the positive ions present in the mixture forms an insoluble compound with one of the negative ions.

A combustion reaction is one in which a substance combines with oxygen with the release of a significant amount of energy. The products of a combustion reaction are elements combined with oxygen. Typical combustion reactions are the burning of hydrocarbon fuels such as methane, propane and butane, all of which form the products CO_2 and H_2O. The burning of metals, such as magnesium and iron, is also an example of combustion, although this kind of reaction may also be considered synthesis.

Reaction Rate (Section 5-2)

In addition to temperature, concentration, particle size, and catalysts, reaction rate is determined by the nature of the reactants. Reactions that involve electron transfer or bond rearrangement generally take longer than reactions that do not involve these changes. Ionic reactions, such as double-displacement reactions, occur almost instantaneously.

The rate of a reaction is not constant throughout the course of the reaction because the rate is

GLENCOE TECHNOLOGY

 **CD-ROM**

Glencoe Science Voyages Interactive CD-ROM

Chapter Summaries

Use the Chapter Summary to introduce, teach, or review chapter material.

proportional to reactant concentration and the concentrations of reactants decrease as reactants are converted to products. For this reason, chemists report experimental results in different ways. Sometimes average rates of reaction are reported over a particular time period. Often the rate is measured at the start of the reaction and reported as an initial rate. Sometimes the rate is measured over the course of the reaction and the data are plotted. The slope of the curve at a particular time is the instantaneous rate.

Depending upon the reaction, rates may be measured using changes in the reaction medium. If a product is colored, the rate can be measured as a function of the intensity of color. If pH changes during the reaction, the rate can be measured by means of changes in pH. Similarly, the increase in the volume of a product gas measured at a particular temperature and pressure can be used to determine rate.

Activation Energy (Section 5-2)

In order to react, particles must collide with each other so that new bonds can form at the same time that old bonds are broken. Two conditions are necessary. The particles must have sufficient kinetic energy to overcome the repulsion between particles, and they must collide in an orientation such that the new bonds can form. Most collisions do not meet these criteria. When they do, an activiated complex is formed for a brief instant during which the old reactant bonds break and new product bonds form. The particles may also separate without reacting. The energy of the activated complex is called the activation energy, that is, the minimum amount of energy a system must possess in order for a reaction to occur.

SCIENCE UPDATE

For current events or science in the news, access the Glencoe Science Web Site at **www.glencoe.com/sec/science**

Catalysts (Section 5-2)

When a catalyst is used, it may be of two types—heterogeneous and homogeneous. Heterogeneous catalysts are in a different physical state from the reaction medium. For example, a catalyst may be a solid in a reaction occurring in the liquid or gas phase. Often a heterogeneous catalyst provides a surface upon which the reactants can react and this lowers the activation energy. The reaction of sulfur dioxide and oxygen gases occurs extremely slowly at room temperature, but if solid vanadium(V) oxide is added, the reaction speeds up.

Homogeneous catalysts are in the same state as the reactants and may actually enter into the reaction at some point by forming intermediate compounds. However, like all catalyst, they are recoverable at the end of the reaction.

Teacher to Teacher

"While discussing chemical reactions, you can illustrate the wide range of energies involved with various reactions by having the students compare the relatively small amounts of energy released in the combustion of wood or coal to the large amounts of energy released during a space shuttle launch."

Cathy Mariotti Ezrailson, Teacher
Oak Ridge High School
Conroe, TX

CHAPTER 5 Chemical Reactions

CHAPTER OVERVIEW

Section 5-1 Examples of evidence of a chemical reaction are described. Students learn to recognize a balanced equation and explain the role of energy in reactions.

Section 5-2 Factors that affect the rate of a chemical reaction are explained. The role of a catalyst and an inhibitor in a reaction is explored.

Chapter Vocabulary

chemical reaction
reactant
product
endothermic reaction
exothermic reaction
rate of reaction
inhibitor
catalyst

Theme Connection

Systems and Interactions The system of a chemical reaction includes the reactants that interact and the products they form.

If time does not permit teaching the entire chapter, use Reviewing Main Ideas on pp. 140–141.

CHAPTER 5 Chemical Reactions

Chapter Preview

Section 5-1
Describing a Chemical Reaction

Section 5-2
Rates of Chemical Reactions

Skills Preview

Skill Builders
- Predict
- Interpret Data

Activities
- Design an Experiment
- Make a Model

MiniLabs
- Observe and Infer
- Compare and Contrast

Reading Check

As you read, use context clues to figure out unfamiliar terms. For example, what clues help you understand the term *jostling* in the caption for Figure 5-12A? *Proteases* in the caption for Figure 5-13?

120

Multiple Learning Styles

Look for the following logos for strategies that emphasize different learning modalities.

Linguistic Across the Curriculum, p. 125; Enrichment, p. 125; Multiple Learning Styles, p. 126; Using Science Words, p. 128; Assessment, p. 138; Preview, p. 140

Logical-Mathematical Inclusion Strategies, p. 124; Activity, pp. 126, 130; Enrichment, p. 127; Assessment, p.137

Visual-Spatial Explore Activity, p. 121; Quick Demo, p. 123; MiniLab, pp. 124, 136; Science Journal. p. 133; Using an Analogy, p. 135; Reteach, pp. 137, 140; Activity, p. 138

Auditory-Musical Out of Time, p. 140

Kinesthetic Reteach, p. 128

Interpersonal Discussion, pp. 123, 135; Review, p. 140

Explore Activity

An unfortunate accident caused this awful scene. Dramatic changes are going on as chemical reactions rage. When the action stops, the matter that existed before the chemical reactions will not be the same as before. It may look different, smell different, have a different physical state, or have different chemical properties. A chemical reaction is a change in matter, sometimes complex, as in this photo, and sometimes simple, as you will see in this Explore Activity.

Observe a Chemical Reaction

1. Pour 50 mL of vinegar into the bottom of a small plastic bag with a zipper closing. Have your partner hold the bag open so that you can pour the vinegar without getting any on the sides of the bag.
2. Cinch the bag together in the middle and tie it off with a twist tie.
3. Put one teaspoonful of baking soda into the top of the bag. Force out as much air as possible and zip the bag.
4. Untie the tie and shake the baking soda down into the vinegar. Observe.

Science Journal

In your Science Journal, draw a sketch of what happened after you mixed the vinegar and baking soda. Write a paragraph explaining your picture.

✓ Assessment Planner

Portfolio
Refer to p. 141 for suggested items that students might select for their portfolios.

Performance Assessment
See p. 141 for additional Performance Assessment options.
Skill Builder, p. 129
MiniLab, pp. 124, 136
Activity 5-1, pp. 130–131; 5-2, p. 138

Content Assessment
Section Assessment, pp. 129, 137
Chapter Assessment, pp. 142–143
Proficiency Prep, pp. 129, 137

Explore Activity

Purpose

Visual-Spatial Use the Explore Activity so that students can observe a chemical reaction. L2 ELL COOP LEARN

Preparation

Protect lab tables from spills.

Materials

vinegar, baking soda, 50-mL graduated cylinder, sealable plastic bag, twist tie, teaspoon

Teaching Strategies

- If the vinegar gets on the side of the bag, wipe it off with a paper towel before using the twist tie.
- Be sure the bags are completely sealed before the baking soda and vinegar are mixed.

Sketches should show bubbles and the bag expanding from the released gas. Paragraphs will differ but could include that the increased amount of gas produces increased pressure and expands the bag.

✓ Assessment

Portfolio Have students write a paragraph relating the results of the activity to what happens when you bake a cake. *Gases that make the cake rise are produced.* Use **Performance Assessment in the Science Classroom,** p. 105. P

SECTION 5·1

Prepare

Refer to **Physical and Chemical Changes, Chemical Equations,** and **Types of Chemical Reactions** on p. 120E.

Preplanning

Refer to the **Chapter Organizer** on pp. 120A–B.

1 Motivate

Bellringer

Before presenting the lesson, display **Section Focus Transparency 10** on the overhead projector. Assign the accompanying **Focus Activity** worksheet. L2 ELL

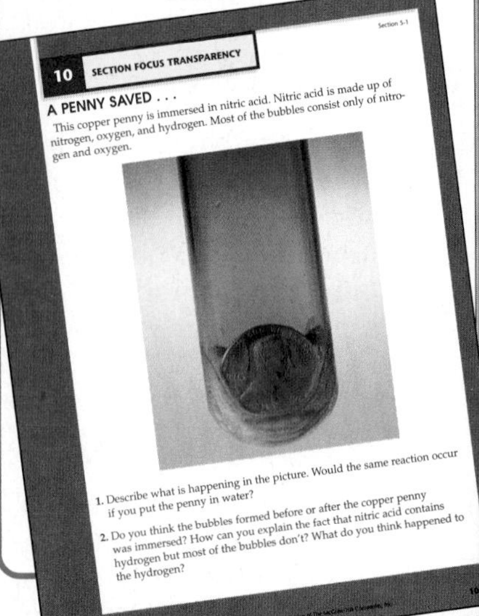

Section 5-1

10 SECTION FOCUS TRANSPARENCY

A PENNY SAVED . . .

This copper penny is immersed in nitric acid. Nitric acid is made up of nitrogen, oxygen, and hydrogen. Most of the bubbles consist only of nitrogen and oxygen.

1. Describe what is happening in the picture. Would the same reaction occur if you put the penny in water?
2. Do you think the bubbles formed before or after the copper penny was immersed? How can you explain the fact that nitric acid contains hydrogen but most of the bubbles don't? What do you think happened to the hydrogen?

10

Tying to Previous Knowledge

Students are already familiar with chemical reactions such as food spoiling, metals corroding, or fuels burning. Now they will learn how reactions are described.

5·1 Describing a Chemical Reaction

What You'll Learn

- Ways to tell whether or not a chemical reaction is occurring
- How to read and understand a balanced chemical equation
- That some reactions release energy and others absorb energy

Vocabulary
chemical reaction
reactant
product
endothermic reaction
exothermic reaction

Why It's Important

- Almost every important process in your life is a chemical reaction.

Evidence of Chemical Reactions

You can smell a rotten egg and the smoke from a campfire. These are signs of chemical reactions. It's easy to tell when these chemical reactions occur. They give off smoke or smell bad. Other reactions are less obvious, but you can usually tell they have occurred.

Physical and Chemical Changes

Matter undergoes two kinds of changes—physical changes and chemical changes. Physical changes in a substance are those that affect its physical properties, such as its size and shape or its state (solid, liquid, or gas). For example, when water is frozen into ice, its physical state changes from liquid to solid, but it's still water. Chemical changes in a substance result in the formation of new substances that have properties different from those of the original substance. For example, a chemical change has occurred when a spot of rust appears on the steel body of a car, when an egg is fried, or when the leaves turn red in the fall. A process in which chemical changes occur is called a **chemical reaction.**

The same substance can undergo both physical and chemical changes. Look at the newspaper shown in **Figure 5-1.** If you take a piece of newspaper in your hands and crumple it

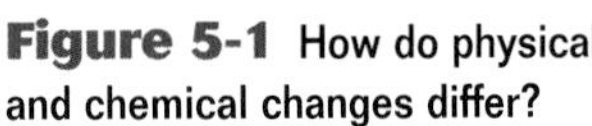

Figure 5-1 How do physical and chemical changes differ?

A Tearing or crumpling a piece of newspaper doesn't really change its substance. It's still newspaper, so only a physical change has occurred.

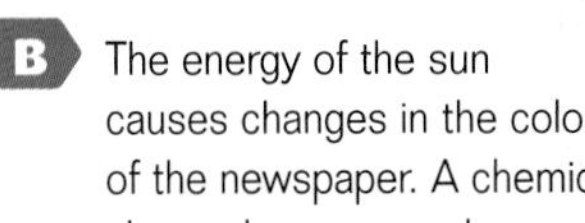

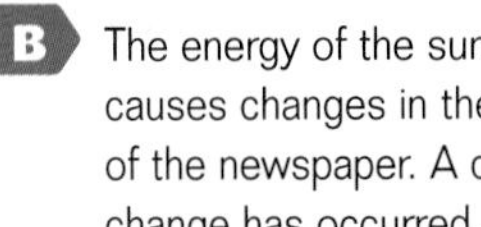

B The energy of the sun causes changes in the color of the newspaper. A chemical change has occurred.

Resource Manager

The following **Teacher Classroom Resources** can be used with Section 5-1:

Reproducible Masters

Activity Worksheets, pp. 23–24, 27 L2

Enrichment, p. 10 L3

Laboratory Manual, pp. 25–28 L2

Reinforcement, p. 10 L2

Study Guide, pp. 17–18 L1 ELL

Transparencies

Teaching Transparency 9 L2

VISUALIZING Chemical Reactions

Figure 5-2 Look for evidence of chemical change. It's all around you.

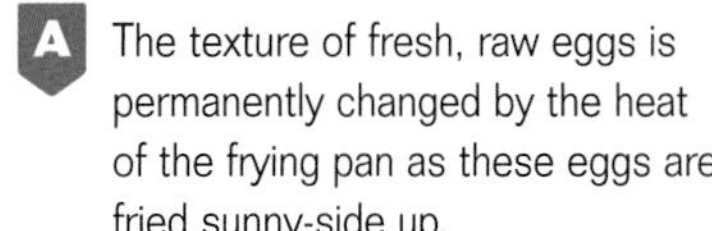

A The texture of fresh, raw eggs is permanently changed by the heat of the frying pan as these eggs are fried sunny-side up.

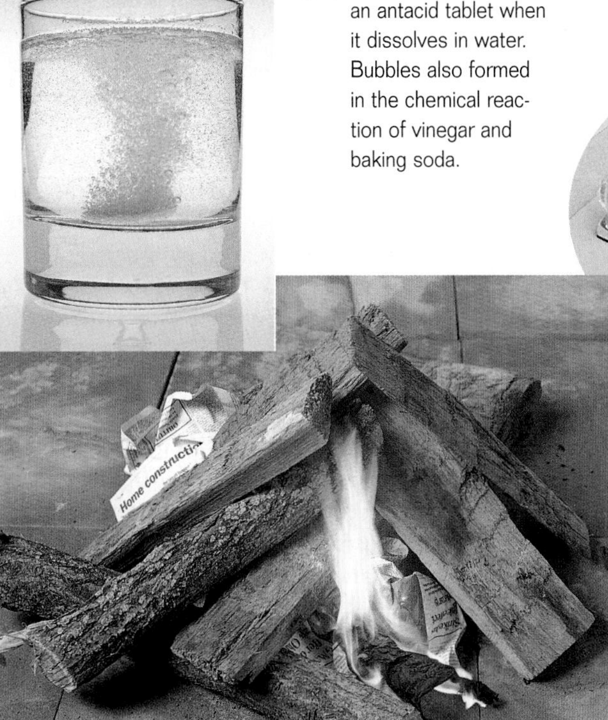

B Bubbles stream from an antacid tablet when it dissolves in water. Bubbles also formed in the chemical reaction of vinegar and baking soda.

C Soap scum is an example of a precipitate, which is sometimes a product of a chemical reaction.

D Smoke and ash are left after a newspaper burns as kindling for these logs. Heat is also evidence that a chemical reaction is occurring.

up, you change its size and shape, but you still have a piece of newspaper. Crushing the paper is a physical change. If you leave that piece of newspaper in sunlight for a long time, it will turn yellow. If you use it as kindling in a campfire and touch a match to it, it will burst into flames. These processes are chemical reactions. The final substances are chemically different from the starting substances. How can you tell that a chemical reaction has occurred? Sometimes it is obvious, sometimes not. **Figure 5-2** shows several clues to look for to determine whether or not a change is chemical.

2 Teach

Discussion

Interpersonal Discuss the following changes with students. As a class, decide whether each is a chemical change or a physical change.

a. growth of a tree
b. butter melting
c. use of foods in your body
d. gas escaping from soda
e. gasoline used in an auto
f. a lake freezing over

a, c, and e are chemical changes. L2 COOP LEARN

Quick Demo

Visual-Spatial Have students examine a piece of magnesium ribbon. Burn the ribbon. **CAUTION:** *Use tongs to hold the magnesium ribbon while burning it. The resulting light is bright. Do not allow anyone to observe it directly. Hold it in a coffee can in a dark room and observe it indirectly.* Ask students to put on goggles and examine the white powder that results. Have them name the signs of chemical change they observed. *Evidence could include a change in color and release of energy.* Ask students in what forms the energy was released. *heat and light*

Caption Answer

Figure 5-1 *A chemical change involves a change in identity of the reactants. A physical change does not affect the identity of the substance.*

VISUAL Learning

Figure 5-2D Ask students what the term *precipitate* means to them. Most will respond that rain, snow, and sleet are forms of precipitation. In weather, as in chemical reactions, precipitation is something that falls. In a chemical reaction, it falls because it is a solid formed in a liquid solution.

Purpose

Visual-Spatial Students will observe a chemical reaction.

Materials

baking soda, teaspoon, evaporating dish, vinegar, 10-mL graduated cylinder

Teaching Strategies

To speed up the drying process, evaporating dishes can be gently heated on hot plates.

Analysis

1. Bubbles indicated that a reaction occurred in step 1. No evidence of a reaction was present in step 4.
2. No; the baking soda reacted with the acid, but the residue did not.

Assessment

Content Have students explain why they were to use a nonmetal dish for the activity. *The acid might have reacted with a metal, interfering with the results.* Use **Performance Assessment in the Science Classroom,** p. 19.

interNET CONNECTION

Internet Addresses

____

____

____

____

For Internet tips, see Glencoe's **Using the Internet in the Science Classroom.**

Observing a Chemical Change

Procedure

1. Place about ¼ teaspoon of baking soda in an evaporating dish. Add 2 mL of white vinegar.
2. Allow the mixture to dry.
3. Examine the result and compare it with baking soda. Do they look the same?
4. To further investigate the residue, add 2 mL of vinegar and observe.

Analysis

1. Did a chemical reaction occur in step 1? In step 4? Explain.
2. Are the chemical properties of the residue the same as those of baking soda? Explain.

Visit the Glencoe Science Web Site at **www.glencoe.com/sec/science** for more information about chemical reactions.

Chemical Equations

In order to describe a chemical reaction, you must know what substances react. The substances that react, called the **reactants** (ree AK tunts), are substances that exist before the reaction begins. The substances that are formed by the reaction are called the **products.**

When you mix baking soda and vinegar, a vigorous chemical reaction occurs. Bubbles form. The reaction mixture foams up inside the container. Baking soda and vinegar are the common names for the reactants in this reaction. They also have chemical names. Baking soda is the compound sodium hydrogen carbonate, and vinegar is acetic (uh SEE tihk) acid in a water solution. These are the reactants. What are the products? You saw bubbles form when the reaction occurred, but is that enough of a description? There are many kinds of bubbles. Are bubbles the only product, or do some atoms from the vinegar and baking soda end up forming something else? What goes on in the chemical reaction may be more than what you can see with your eyes. Chemists try to find out everything that happens in a chemical reaction. Then, they record it in a shorthand known as a chemical equation.

Word Equations

One way to describe a chemical reaction is with an equation that uses words to describe the reactants and products. The reactants are listed on the left side of an arrow, separated from each other by plus signs. The products are placed on the right side of the arrow. They also are separated by plus signs. The arrow between the reactants and products represents the changes that occur during the chemical reaction. When reading the equation, the arrow is read *produces*. How would you write a word equation for the reactants and products in the chemical reaction between baking soda and vinegar, shown in **Figure 5-3?**

Inclusion Strategies

Learning Disabled Provide items of equal mass such as paper clips, coins, and washers to represent different atoms. Have students use a double pan balance to balance equations using the materials provided. They should find that to bring the scales into balance, the same number and kind of atom must be on both sides of the balance just as in a balanced chemical equation. Start with a simple equation such as $C + O_2 \rightarrow CO_2$, which is already balanced. Then, give them $H_2 + O_2 \rightarrow H_2O$ and $H_2O_2 \rightarrow H_2O + O_2$. Remind students of the law of conservation of mass, and have them use the balance to find the coefficients for the equations. The balanced equations are: $2H_2 + O_2 \rightarrow 2H_2O$ and $2H_2O_2 \rightarrow 2H_2O + O_2$. L2 ELL

Chemical names rather than common names are used in word equations. In the baking soda and vinegar reaction, you already know the chemical names of the reactants—sodium hydrogen carbonate and acetic acid. The names of the products are sodium acetate, water, and carbon dioxide gas. The word equation for the reaction is as follows.

acetic acid + sodium hydrogen carbonate → sodium acetate + water + carbon dioxide

Equations with Formulas

The word equation for the reaction of baking soda and vinegar is long. That's why chemists use chemical formulas to represent the chemical names of pure substances in the equation. You can convert a word equation into a chemical equation by substituting chemical formulas for the chemical names. For example, the chemical equation for the reaction between baking soda and vinegar can be written as follows.

$$HC_2H_3O_2 + NaHCO_3 \rightarrow NaC_2H_3O_2 + H_2O + CO_2$$

$HC_2H_3O_2$	$NaHCO_3$	$NaC_2H_3O_2$	H_2O	CO_2
acetic acid (vinegar)	sodium hydrogen carbonate (baking soda)	sodium acetate	water	carbon dioxide

Remember that in these formulas, the subscripts tell you the number of atoms of a particular element in that molecule. The subscript 2 in CO_2 means that each molecule of carbon dioxide has two oxygen atoms. If an atom has no subscript, it means that there is only one atom of that element in the molecule.

Figure 5-3 Observing a reaction is the first step toward writing a chemical equation to describe it.

Conservation of Mass

What happens to the atoms in the reactants when the reactants are converted into products? Do they disappear? No, they don't. According to the *law of conservation of mass,* the mass of the products of a chemical reaction is always the same as the mass of the reactants in that reaction.

In your math class, you have seen equations with equal signs. In these math equations, the right side of the equation is numerically equal to the left side. But, in a chemical equation, it is the number and kind of atoms that are equal on the two sides. Every atom that appears on the reactant side of the equation also appears on the product side.

Across the Curriculum

Mathematics Have students write a paragraph comparing and contrasting chemical and mathematical equations. Paragraphs should indicate that the arrow in a chemical equation is comparable to an equal sign and that the numbers of each kind of atom are equal on both sides of that sign. L2

Enrichment

Linguistic Have students write chemical equations for the following reactions. They may need help in writing the formulas for binary compounds. Show them that the total charges on the positive and negative ions in a binary compound must add up to zero. For example, for the compound $FeCl_3$, $(1 \times 3+) + (3 \times 1-) = 0$. Check the formulas at this time; do not balance the equations.

1. Sodium reacts with aluminum chloride to form sodium chloride and aluminum. $Na + AlCl_3 \rightarrow NaCl + Al$
2. Potassium bromide reacts with chlorine to produce potassium chloride and bromine. $KBr + Cl_2 \rightarrow KCl + Br_2$
3. Hydrogen peroxide breaks down into water and oxygen. $H_2O_2 \rightarrow H_2O + O_2$

Have students save their equations for the Activity on the following teacher page.

Flex Your Brain

Use the Flex Your Brain activity to have students explore CHEMICAL REACTIONS.

GLENCOE TECHNOLOGY

CD-ROM

Glencoe Science Voyages Interactive CD-ROM

Explorations

Have students do the interactive exploration *What properties do elements have?*

Caption Answer

Figure 5-4 *yes*

Activity

Logical-Mathematical Students can now balance the equations they wrote in the Enrichment on the previous teacher page.

1. $3Na + AlCl_3 \rightarrow 3NaCl + Al$
2. $2KBr + Cl_2 \rightarrow 2KCl + Br_2$
3. $2H_2O_2 \rightarrow 2H_2O + O_2$

VISUAL Learning

Figure 5-4 **How does the picture support the law of conservation of mass?** *Mass is not created or destroyed in a chemical reaction.*

Answer to Reading Check

It is balanced when an equal number of each type of atom is on both sides.

Making a Model

Have students use different colors or shadings to draw representations of a formula such as $MgCl_2$—one magnesium and two chlorine atoms bunched together. Repeat with other formulas such as H_2CO_3 and Al_2O_3. Then, on the chalkboard, draw representations of compounds such as H_2O_2 and CH_4 and have them write the formulas for the compounds. L1

Caption Answer

Figure 5-5 *The reactants and products become cooler.*

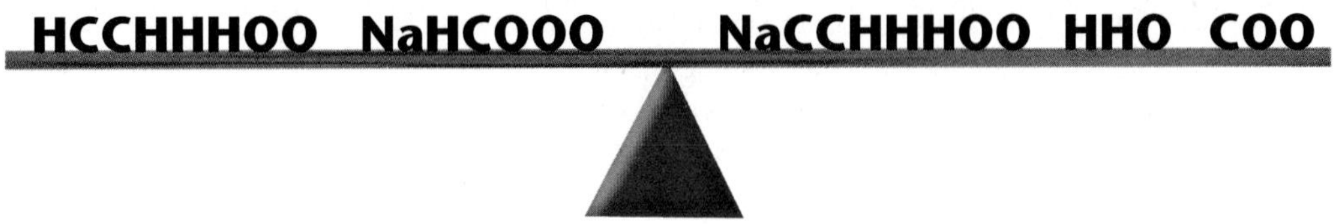

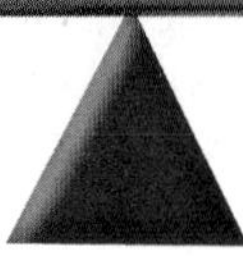

$$HC_2H_3O_2 + NaHCO_3 \rightarrow NaC_2H_3O_2 + H_2O + CO_2$$

Figure 5-4 Count all the carbon atoms, all the hydrogen atoms, all the oxygen atoms, and all the sodium atoms on each side of the balance. **Are there equal numbers of each kind of atom on each side?**

Atoms are not lost or created in a chemical reaction. They just change partners, as old chemical bonds in the reactants break and new chemical bonds form in the products.

Balancing Chemical Equations

When you write the chemical equation for a reaction, you must observe the law of conservation of mass. Sometimes, this is easy, as in the vinegar and baking soda reaction. All that you needed to do was write down the chemical formulas for the reactants and products. Look at **Figure 5-4.** It shows that when you count the number of carbon, hydrogen, oxygen, and sodium atoms on each side of the arrow in the equation, you find that the numbers of each kind of atom are equal, or balanced.

Reading Check

When is the equation for a chemical reaction balanced?

Not all chemical equations are balanced so easily. For example, here is the equation for the reaction that occurs when silver tarnishes.

$$Ag + H_2S \rightarrow Ag_2S + H_2$$

silver hydrogen sulfide silver sulfide hydrogen

Count the number of atoms of each type in the reactants and in the products. Two hydrogen atoms are on the reactant side, and two hydrogen atoms are on the product side. One sulfur atom is on the reactant side and one sulfur atom is on the product side. Notice that one silver atom is on the reactant side and two silver atoms are on the product side. The law of conservation of mass says this cannot be true. A chemical reaction cannot create a silver atom, so the equation as it is written does not represent the reaction correctly. The equation must show that two atoms of silver react. Check to see that the equation is balanced when it is written as follows with a 2 in front of the reactant Ag.

$$2Ag + H_2S \rightarrow Ag_2S + H_2$$

Multiple Learning Styles

Linguistic Ask students to consider the law of conservation of mass and the statement, "We are rapidly using up our natural resources." Have them write short essays that show that the law and the statement are not in conflict. Essays could include that we are using resources in the form in which they exist, but that because of the law of conservation of mass, atoms cannot be destroyed.

Energy in Chemical Reactions

Recall that atoms form chemical bonds because they become more stable by gaining, losing, or sharing electrons. When atoms become more stable, they have a lower total energy. This means that when atoms form bonds, energy is released. The reverse is also true. When bonds break, energy must be added. This energy is taken up by the atoms that form the products of such a reaction.

In a chemical reaction, some bonds in the reactant molecules break while new bonds in the products form, so changes in energy are a part of every chemical reaction. Noticeable amounts of energy often are released or absorbed during a chemical reaction, as you can see in the example of an energy-releasing reaction shown in **Figure 5-5.**

Energy Is Absorbed

In some chemical reactions, the energy needed to break the old bonds in the reactants is greater than the energy released when the new bonds form in the products. Energy must be absorbed if these reactions are to occur. A reaction in which energy is absorbed is called an **endothermic reaction.** In the equation for an endothermic (en duh THUR mihk) reaction, the word *energy* is sometimes written along with the reactants in the chemical equation. Think of energy as a necessary reactant in the reaction. An example of an endothermic reaction is the reaction that breaks down water into hydrogen and oxygen.

$$2H_2O + \text{energy} \rightarrow 2H_2 + O_2$$

water hydrogen oxygen

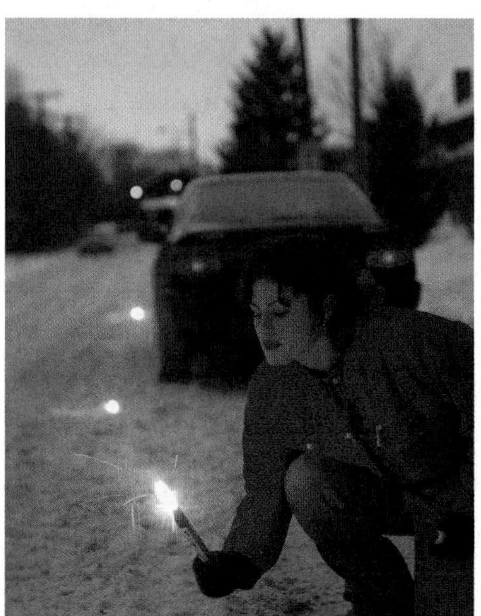

Figure 5-5 Energy is released immediately when a highway emergency flare is activated. **What observation might tell you that a reaction absorbs energy?**

interNET CONNECTION

Visit the Glencoe Science Web Site at **www.glencoe.com/sec/science** for more information about energy in chemical equations.

EARTH SCIENCE INTEGRATION

The Sun's Energy
Without energy from the sun, life on Earth, as we know it, could not exist. Infer whether the reactions that occur inside the sun are exothermic or endothermic.

EARTH SCIENCE INTEGRATION

The heat and light that radiates from the sun is evidence that the reactions that occur in the sun are exothermic. Almost all the energy on Earth comes from the sun. Only a tiny fraction derives from the cooling of Earth's core and radioactive sources in Earth's crust.

Correcting Misconceptions

Students may think that any change that involves a change in energy is a chemical reaction. The formation of some solutions also releases or absorbs energy. Many hot or cold packs are based on heat of solution.

Enrichment

Logical-Mathematical In a catalytic converter of a car, a reaction occurs when nitrogen monoxide gas, NO, reacts with hydrogen gas. Ammonia gas and water are formed. Have students write a balanced equation for the reaction. $2NO + 5H_2 \rightarrow 2NH_3 + 2H_2O$ L3 ELL

Internet Addresses

For Internet tips, see Glencoe's **Using the Internet in the Science Classroom.**

Content Background

Some energy changes are noticeable, such as when things burn, and some are not. Iron rusting does not involve an obvious energy change. The energy change is there; it's just too small to detect easily.

Integrating the Sciences

Life Science Photosynthesis is endothermic. Energy from the sun, in the presence of chlorophyll, is necessary for carbon dioxide and water to react to produce sugar and oxygen. The process of cellular respiration is exothermic. Energy is released when sugar and oxygen react to produce water and carbon dioxide.

Caption Answer

Figure 5-6B *the environment*

GLENCOE TECHNOLOGY

Videodisc

Glencoe Science Voyages Interactive Videodisc—Physical

Side 2, Lesson 6 *Chemical Detectives*

12969

13678

Refer to the Videodisc Teacher Guide for additional bar codes.

Caption Answer

Figure 5-7 *gasoline, coal, methane*

3 Assess

Check for Understanding

Using Science Words

Linguistic Other than *endothermic* and *exothermic,* elicit from students instances where *en-* means "in" and *ex-* means "out." Examples could include *entrance* and *exit* and *endoskeleton* and *exoskeleton.* L2

Reteach

Kinesthetic Have students use different coins or other objects to model balancing the chemical equations in the Section Assessment, Question 1. L1 ELL

Extension

For students who have mastered this section, use the **Reinforcement** and **Enrichment** masters.

Energy Is Released

If the energy needed to break the old bonds in the reactants is less than the energy released when the new bonds form in the products, then the reaction will release energy. A reaction in which energy is released is called an **exothermic reaction.** Some examples of reactions in which energy is being released or absorbed are shown in **Figure 5-6.** Can you identify each of them as exothermic or endothermic?

When writing a chemical equation for a reaction that releases energy, the word *energy* is sometimes written along with the products. An example of an exothermic (ek soh THUR mihk) reaction is the reaction that occurs when you burn propane in a gas grill.

$$\underset{\text{propane}}{C_3H_8} + \underset{\text{oxygen}}{5O_2} \rightarrow \underset{\text{carbon dioxide}}{3CO_2} + \underset{\text{water}}{4H_2O} + \text{energy}$$

But, it's not always necessary to include energy in a chemical equation. Usually, it's included only when it's important to know whether a reaction absorbs or releases energy. A fuel like propane, for example, is burned for the purpose of

Figure 5-6 Some reactions require energy or they won't happen. Others release energy as they take place.

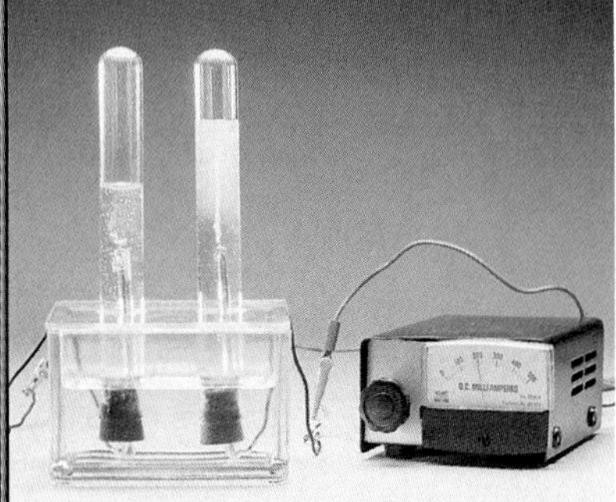

A Electrical energy is being used to break apart water molecules. The two gases, hydrogen and oxygen, are being collected in separate test tubes.

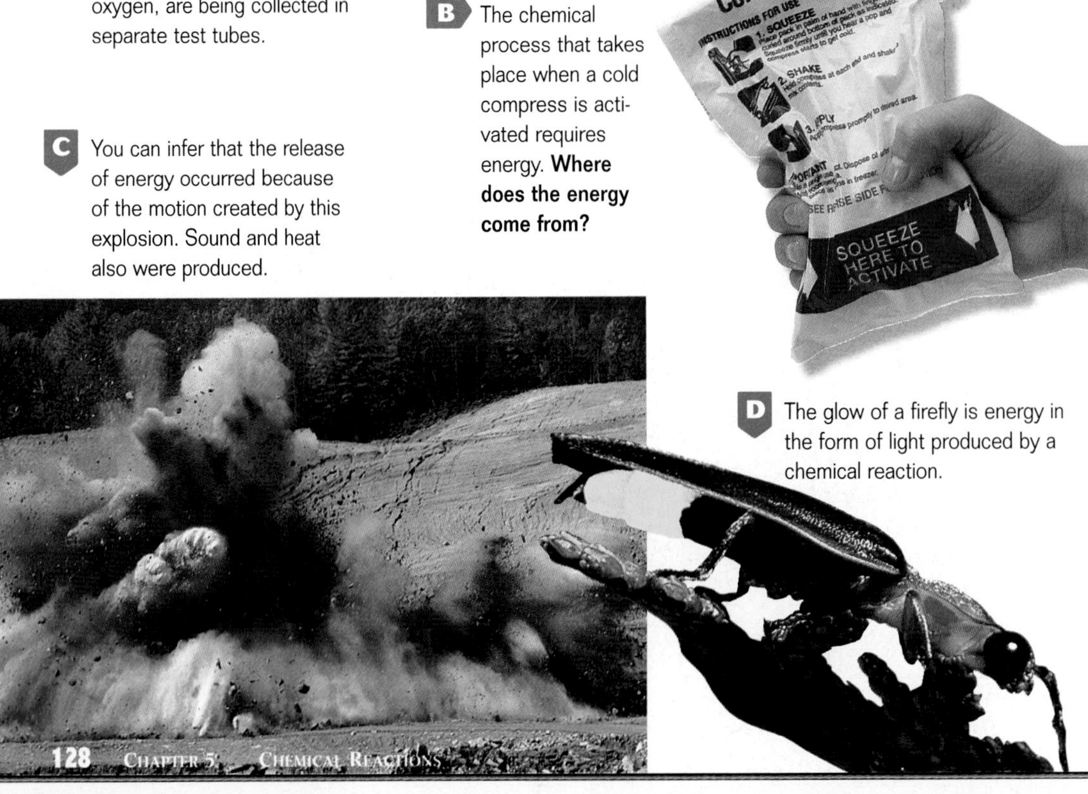

B The chemical process that takes place when a cold compress is activated requires energy. **Where does the energy come from?**

C You can infer that the release of energy occurred because of the motion created by this explosion. Sound and heat also were produced.

D The glow of a firefly is energy in the form of light produced by a chemical reaction.

Guided Reading Strategy

Double Bubble Map This strategy uses two bubble maps to compare concepts. Each cluster has qualities that are unique to that idea. In the middle, connecting ideas are similar to both cluster ideas. This technique helps students list common qualities and unique qualities before writing or discussing a topic. Have students design a Double Bubble Map for a concept such as exothermic and endothermic reactions. P

Sample map:

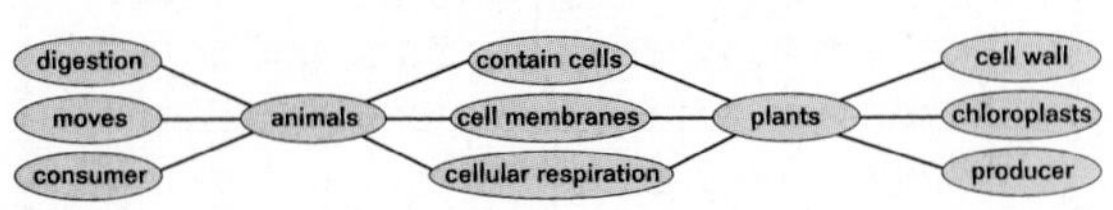

obtaining energy to cook food, as shown in **Figure 5-7.** Therefore, energy is included in the equation. For the breakdown of water, energy is included so that you know the reaction will not occur unless energy is provided. In a reaction such as the tarnishing of silver, energy may be released or absorbed, but because this is not the most useful thing to know about this reaction, energy is not included in the equation at this time.

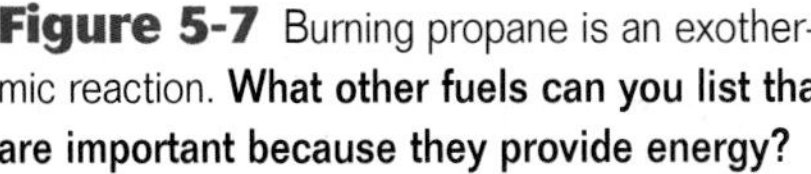

Figure 5-7 Burning propane is an exothermic reaction. **What other fuels can you list that are important because they provide energy?**

Section Assessment

1. Are the following chemical equations balanced? Why or why not?
   a. $Ca + Cl_2 \rightarrow CaCl_2$
   b. $Zn + Ag_2S \rightarrow ZnS + Ag$
   c. $Cl_2 + NaBr \rightarrow NaCl + Br_2$
2. What evidence might tell you that a chemical reaction has occurred?
3. What is the difference between an exothermic and an endothermic reaction?
4. **Think Critically:** After a forest fire, the ashes left over have less mass and take up less space than the trees that lived there before the fire. How can this be explained in terms of the law of conservation of mass?
5. **Skill Builder**
   Comparing and Contrasting
   The energy released when hydrogen and oxygen combine to form water can supply the energy that takes the space shuttle into orbit. The reaction is $2H_2 + O_2 \rightarrow 2H_2O$ + energy. When water is broken down into the elements H_2 and O_2, the reaction is $2H_2O$ + energy $\rightarrow 2H_2 + O_2$. Compare the energy released in the first equation with the energy absorbed in the second equation. If you need help, refer to Comparing and Contrasting in the **Skill Handbook** on page 720.

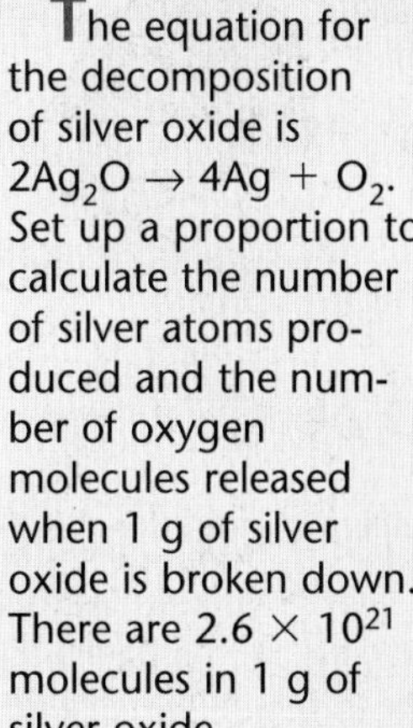

Using Math

The equation for the decomposition of silver oxide is $2Ag_2O \rightarrow 4Ag + O_2$. Set up a proportion to calculate the number of silver atoms produced and the number of oxygen molecules released when 1 g of silver oxide is broken down. There are 2.6×10^{21} molecules in 1 g of silver oxide.

5. **Skill Builder**
The amounts of energy are equal.

Assessment

Content Have students explain why they think equations are sometimes written with a double arrow, ⇄, instead of a single arrow. *The double arrow indicates that the reaction can proceed in either direction.* Use **Performance Assessment in the Science Classroom,** p. 21.

4 Close

Proficiency Prep

Use this quiz to check students' recall of section content.

1. **Water evaporates. What type of change is this?** *physical*
2. **Bubbles form when magnesium is added to an acid. What type of change is this?** *chemical*

Section Assessment

1. The first equation is balanced because an equal number of each type of atom is present on each side of the equation. The other two equations are not balanced.
2. a color change, the formation of bubbles, the formation of a precipitate, the evolution or absorption of heat, and a change in the identity of a substance
3. Energy is given off in an exothermic reaction and absorbed in an endothermic reaction.
4. **Think Critically** Gases were also given off.

Using Math

Using the coefficients in the balanced equation, twice as many atoms of silver, or 5.2×10^{21} atoms, are produced. Half as many, or 1.3×10^{21}, oxygen molecules are produced.

Activity 5·1 Design Your Own Experiment

Recognize the Problem

Purpose

Logical-Mathematical Students will design an experiment to determine whether a reaction is endothermic or exothermic. L2 ELL COOP LEARN

Process Skills

designing an experiment, classifying, making and using tables, observing and inferring, forming a hypothesis, interpreting data, measuring in SI, using numbers

Time

40 minutes

Materials

Be sure alcohol thermometers are used so that no exposure to mercury results if a thermometer is broken. Hydrogen peroxide can be purchased from a pharmacy or grocery store.

To dispose of the potato and liver, wrap in paper and put into the trash. The hydrogen peroxide can be flushed down the drain.

Form a Hypothesis

Possible Hypotheses

Students might hypothesize that you can tell whether a reaction is endothermic or exothermic by whether the temperature falls or rises during the reaction.

Design Your Own Experiment

Activity 5·1

Exothermic or Endothermic?

Possible Materials

- Test tubes (8)
- Test-tube rack
- Hydrogen peroxide solution (3%)
- Raw liver
- Raw potato
- Thermometer
- Stopwatch
  - * *clock with second hand*
- Graduated cylinder (25-mL)

* *Alternate Materials*

Energy is always a part of a chemical reaction. Some reactions must have energy supplied to them from the environment or they won't happen. An example is the cold packs you may have used when you were injured in sports. The endothermic reaction inside the cold pack cools you by taking energy away from you. Other reactions release energy into the environment.

Recognize the Problem

Does a reaction give off heat if it is exothermic or endothermic? What evidence can you find to show that a reaction between hydrogen peroxide and liver or potato is exothermic?

Form a Hypothesis

Think about the difference between endothermic and exothermic reactions. Consider the goals of the experiment and **make a hypothesis** that describes how you can use the reactions between hydrogen peroxide and liver or potato to determine if a reaction is exothermic or endothermic.

Goals

- **Design an experiment** to test whether a reaction is exothermic or endothermic.
- **Measure** the energy released in a chemical reaction.

Safety Precautions

Wear a lab apron and goggles at all times. Be careful when handling glass thermometers. Test tubes containing hydrogen peroxide should be placed and kept in racks. Dispose of materials as directed by your teacher. Wash your hands when you complete this activity. **CAUTION:** *Hydrogen peroxide can irritate skin and eyes and damage clothing.*

Test Your Hypotheses

Possible Procedures

Place the test tubes in the test-tube rack. In each, pour hydrogen peroxide until the tube is about half-full. Drop small pieces of liver into half the tubes and small pieces of potato into the other half. Immediately after adding the liver or potato, measure and record the temperature of the liquid in each tube. After a certain number of minutes, again measure and record each temperature. Average each group of temperatures.

Test Your Hypothesis

Plan

1. As a group, look at the list of materials. **Decide** (a) what procedure you will use to test your hypothesis, and (b) what measurements you will make.
2. **Decide** how you will measure the heat released to the environment while a reaction is going on. **Determine** how many measurements you will need to make during a reaction.
3. You will get more accurate data if you repeat each experiment several times. Each repeated experiment is called a trial. Use the average of all the trials as your data for supporting your hypothesis.
4. Copy the data table in your Science Journal before you begin your experiment.

Do

1. Make sure your teacher approves your plan and your data table before you proceed.
2. Carry out your plan.
3. **Record** your measurements immediately in your data table.

Analyze Your Data

1. Can you **infer** that a chemical reaction took place? If so, what evidence did you observe?
2. **Identify** the variables in this experiment.

Draw Conclusions

1. Do your observations allow you to distinguish between an exothermic reaction and an endothermic reaction? Use your data to **explain** your answer.
2. Where did the energy in this experiment come from?
3. Suppose you had used smaller pieces of liver and potato. **Predict** what changes you would have observed.

Temperature After Adding Liver/Potato

Trial	Temperature after adding liver (°C)		Temperature after adding potato (°C)	
	Starting	After ___ min	Starting	After ___ min
1				
2	Student data for both liver and potato			
3	should show an increase in tempera-			
4	ture. The reactions are exothermic.			
Total				
Average				

Teaching Strategies

- Interested students may ask what is happening during the reaction. Tell them that enzymes in the potato and liver are breaking down the hydrogen peroxide into water and oxygen.
- Students may want to use tongs to handle the liver.

Expected Outcome

Temperature will rise after the liver and potato are added, showing that the reactions are exothermic. The rise in temperature will be more pronounced for the liver.

Error Analysis

If a trial using potato does not show an increase in temperature, the piece of potato was probably too small. Have pairs of students read the thermometers to avoid human error in the readings.

Analyze Your Data

1. Yes, energy and a gas were released.
2. The item added to the hydrogen peroxide is the independent variable; temperature change is the dependent variable.

Draw Conclusions

1. Student answers will vary. The temperature increased in each case, so exothermic reactions must have taken place.
2. The energy was released by the liver, potato, and hydrogen peroxide as they reacted to form products.
3. There would have been smaller temperature changes.

GO Further

Have students use bar graphs to present their data. Their graphs should show temperature on the y-axis and trial number on the x-axis. Have them graph data for both potato and liver on the same graph, using different colors. Graphs should show higher bars for liver for each trial.

P

Assessment

Performance Repeat the activity using a slurry of carrots instead of liver or potato. Have students write a short paragraph analyzing their data. Use **Performance Assessment in the Science Classroom,** p. 33.

SECTION 5-2

Prepare

Refer to **Reaction Rate, Activation Energy,** and **Catalysts** on pp. 120E–F.

Preplanning

Refer to the **Chapter Organizer** on pp. 120A–B.

1 Motivate

Bellringer

Before presenting the lesson, display **Section Focus Transparency 11** on the overhead projector. Assign the accompanying **Focus Activity** worksheet. L2 ELL

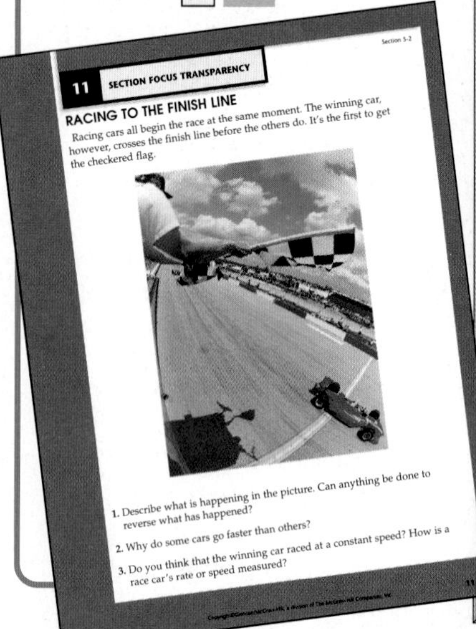

Section 5-2

11 SECTION FOCUS TRANSPARENCY

RACING TO THE FINISH LINE

Racing cars all begin the race at the same moment. The winning car, however, crosses the finish line before the others do. It's the first to get the checkered flag.

1. Describe what is happening in the picture. Can anything be done to reverse what has happened?
2. Why do some cars go faster than others?
3. Do you think that the winning car raced at a constant speed? How is a race car's rate or speed measured?

11

Tying to Previous Knowledge

From previous experience, students are aware that changing the temperature usually affects the rate of a chemical reaction. Chemical changes that occur during cooking and placing food in the refrigerator to prevent spoilage are common examples.

5-2 Rates of Chemical Reactions

What You'll Learn

- How to describe and measure the speed of a chemical reaction
- How chemical reactions can be speeded up or slowed down

Vocabulary
rate of reaction
inhibitor
catalyst

Why It's Important

- It helps to be able to speed up beneficial reactions and slow down destructive ones.

How fast?

Fireworks explode in the summer sky. A tree lies rotting in a forest. Two sets of chemical reactions are happening here—one fast and one slow. You've seen other examples of chemical reactions that take different amounts of time: the baking soda and vinegar reaction, a burning match, the gradual rusting of a car's fender. Why does one reaction in **Figure 5-8** take longer than the other? Can you measure how fast a reaction proceeds? Can anything be done to speed up or slow down a reaction?

Activation Energy

If a chemical reaction is to occur between two substances, the particles of those substances must bump into each other or collide. That makes sense, because to form new chemical bonds, atoms must be close together. But, not just any collision will do. The collision must be strong enough to cause a change to take place. This means that the reaction particles must smash into each other with a certain minimum amount of energy. Anything less, and the reaction will not occur. Why is this true? A reaction involves breaking bonds in the reactants and then recombining the atoms to form products. The process of breaking the bonds requires energy, so for the reaction to get underway, energy must be present at the beginning. This minimum amount of energy is called the activation energy of the reaction.

Figure 5-8 Some reactions are so slow you don't realize they are happening. Others happen explosively.

A It takes decades for the soft green coating to develop on copper statues. This coating is the result of exposure of copper to other elements in the air.

B The disappointing thing about fireworks is that these chemical reactions are over so quickly.

Resource Manager

The following **Teacher Classroom Resources** can be used with Section 5-2:

Reproducible Masters

Activity Worksheets, pp. 25–26, 28 L2
Critical Thinking/Problem Solving, p. 5 L2
Enrichment, p. 11 L3
Home Involvement, p. 35 L2
Laboratory Manual, pp. 29–32 L2
Multicultural Connections, pp. 9–10 L2
Reinforcement, p. 11 L2
Study Guide, pp. 19–20 L1 ELL

Transparencies

Teaching Transparency 10 L2
Science Integration Transparency 5 L2

What about exothermic reactions? Is there an activation energy for reactions that release energy? In both exothermic and endothermic reactions, enough energy must be present at the start to break the original bonds, so even exothermic reactions have an activation energy. Consider the exothermic reaction between gasoline and oxygen gas. You know that gasoline burns readily to provide a lot of energy to move vehicles such as cars and buses. But, if gasoline is spilled when a car's gas tank is being filled, the gasoline doesn't burst into flames when it is exposed to air. It just forms a puddle on the ground and, in time, evaporates. In this case, the necessary activation energy is not available. But, if someone ignores the No Smoking sign in **Figure 5-9** or leaves the car's ignition on so that it creates a spark, it could be enough to supply the necessary activation energy and start an explosive reaction. Then, the energy that the reaction releases is enough to keep the reaction going.

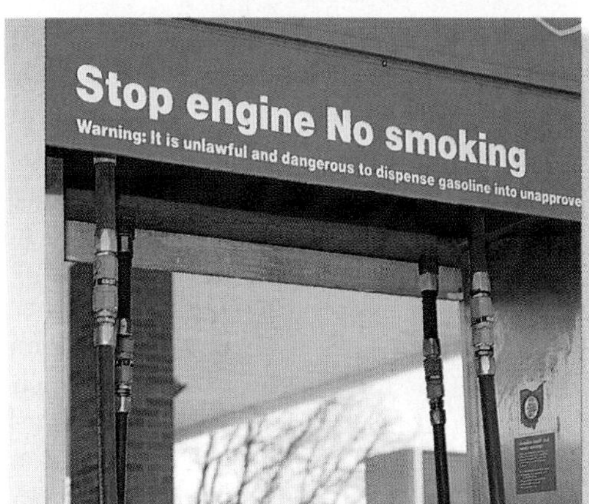

Figure 5-9 A spark from a car's ignition or a cigarette could supply the activation energy needed to ignite spilled gasoline.

Reaction Rate

Many physical quantities are measured in terms of a rate. A rate tells you how much something changes over time. For example, speed is the rate at which you might run or ride your bike. It's the amount of distance you move divided by the time during which you were moving. Maybe you jog at a rate of 8 km per hour. Chemical reactions have rates, too. The **rate of reaction** is a measure of how fast a reaction occurs.

To find the rate of a reaction, you can measure either how quickly one of the reactants is disappearing or how quickly one of the products is appearing, as in **Figure 5-10.** Both measurements tell how the amount of a substance changes per unit of time. Reaction rate is important because the faster the product can be made, the lower the cost. However, sometimes fast rates of reaction are not desirable. In the case of the spoilage of food, the slower the rate, the longer the food will stay edible. What conditions control the rate of a reaction, and what can be done to change the rate?

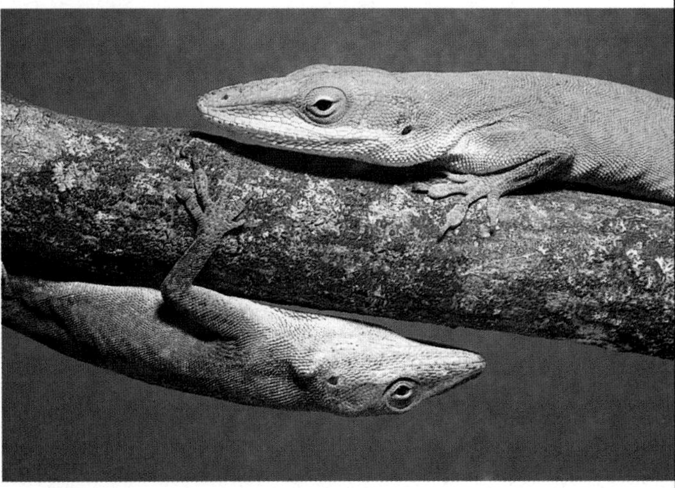

Figure 5-10 As a population of green chameleons turns red, the rate of appearance of red chameleons is equal to the rate of disappearance of green chameleons.

2 Teach

Using an Analogy

Have students relate activation energy to starting a business. No matter how much money the business will eventually make, an initial investment must be made. Similarly, even exothermic reactions require activation energy.

GLENCOE TECHNOLOGY

Videodisc

Glencoe Science Voyages Interactive Videodisc—Earth

Side 1, Lesson 2 *Mysteries of the Cave*

24043

Interactive Videodisc—Life

Side 1, Lesson 3 *Decomposers: Earth's Natural Recyclers*

32737

Refer to the Videodisc Teacher Guide for additional bar codes.

Content Background

Many reactions do not happen in a simple one-step process or mechanism. Two, three, four, or more steps may be involved in the process that eventually converts the reactants to products. Each step may occur at a different rate. The overall rate of reaction is the rate of the slowest step.

Science Journal

Reactions with Copper Have students examine some new pennies, some old pennies that have been used recently, and some old pennies that have not been used recently. Have them describe the pennies in their journals, explaining how they think chemical reactions relate to the appearance of the pennies. L2 P

Teacher FYI

Batteries and photographic film lose effectiveness over time because of chemical reactions that occur in them. Keeping unused batteries and film in the refrigerator helps them stay active for a longer period of time because it slows down the rates of the reactions. Storing them in the freezer keeps them fresh almost indefinitely.

Caption Answer

Figure 5-11 *Decreasing the temperature decreases the rate of spoilage. Increasing the temperature increases the rate.*

VISUAL Learning

Figure 5-12 What is the advantage of storing valuable historic documents in sealed cases with most of the air removed? *Any damaging reaction of the paper with substances in the air is minimized.*

Teacher FYI

People are often placed on oxygen when they have certain health problems. Increasing the concentration of oxygen in the body increases the rate of cellular respiration, providing needed energy.

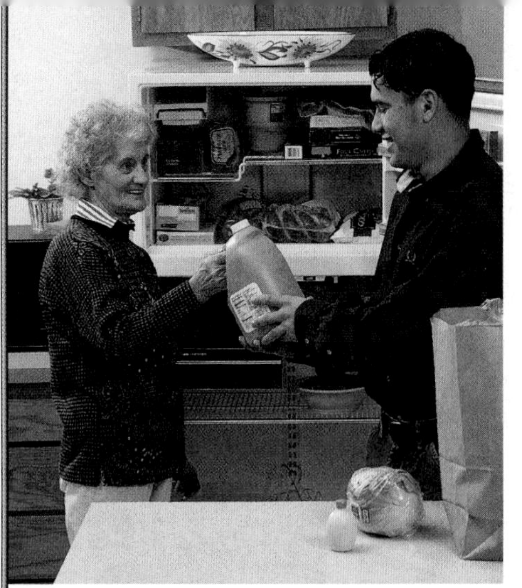

Figure 5-11 Some fresh foods can be stored for a week or more at the temperature of the refrigerator. Other foods are still edible after storing for six months or a year at freezing temperatures. **How does temperature affect spoilage?**

Temperature Makes a Difference

What can you do to keep the food you buy at the store from spoiling? You can put it in the refrigerator or the freezer, as in **Figure 5-11.** The spoiling of food is a chemical reaction, and the temperature of the food affects the rate of this reaction. Most chemical reactions speed up at higher temperatures. This is because atoms and molecules are always in motion and the higher the temperature, the faster they move. Faster molecules collide with each other more often and with greater energy than slower molecules, so collisions are more likely in which there is enough energy to break the old bonds. This energy is the activation energy. The high temperature inside an oven speeds up the chemical reactions going on as the liquid batter of a cake changes into a spongy product. Lowering the temperature slows down most reactions. For example, if you caught a fish in the summer and put it into the freezer, you could eat it in the winter.

Concentration Affects Rate

The more reactants that are present, the greater the chance of collisions between them and the faster the reaction rate. It's like the situation in **Figure 5-12.** When you try to walk along a street that is full of people hurrying here and there, you're

Figure 5-12 Reactions occur faster when there are more particles to collide with each other.

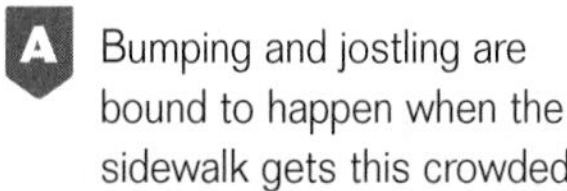

A Bumping and jostling are bound to happen when the sidewalk gets this crowded.

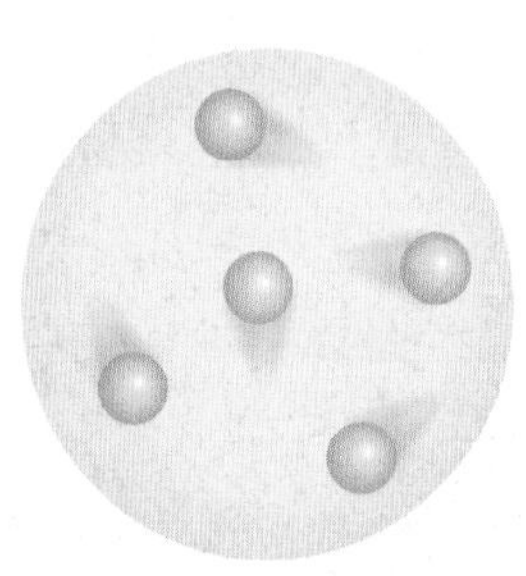

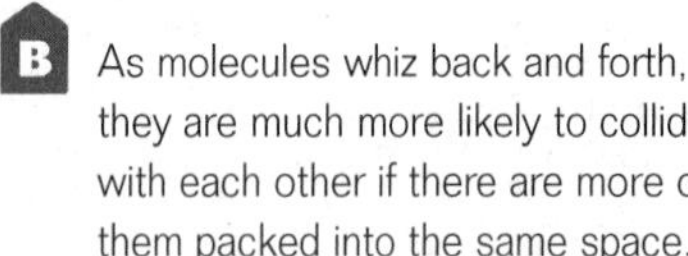

B As molecules whiz back and forth, they are much more likely to collide with each other if there are more of them packed into the same space.

Integrating the Sciences

Physics Rates play an important role in the study of motion. Speed is a rate that relates how distance changes over time. Common units of speed include mph (miles per hour), km/s, and cm/s. Instantaneous speed is a measure of the speed at any point in time. Average speed is obtained by dividing distance traveled by the time it took to travel the distance.

liable to bump into other people. The amount of substance present in a certain volume is called the concentration of the substance. If you increase the concentration, you increase the number of particles of a substance per unit of volume. The particles are more crowded, so more collisions occur, which increases the rate of reaction.

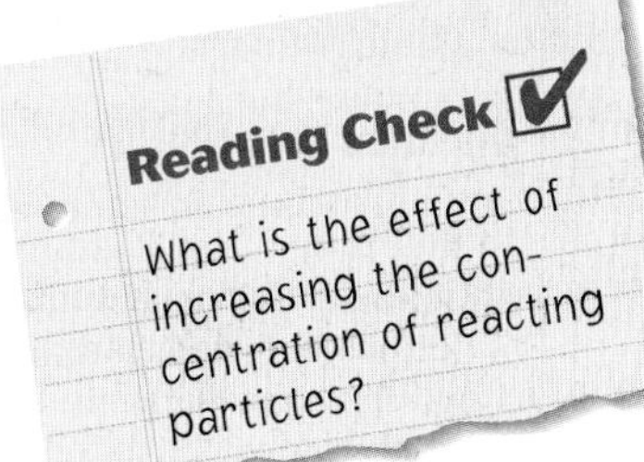

Reading Check
What is the effect of increasing the concentration of reacting particles?

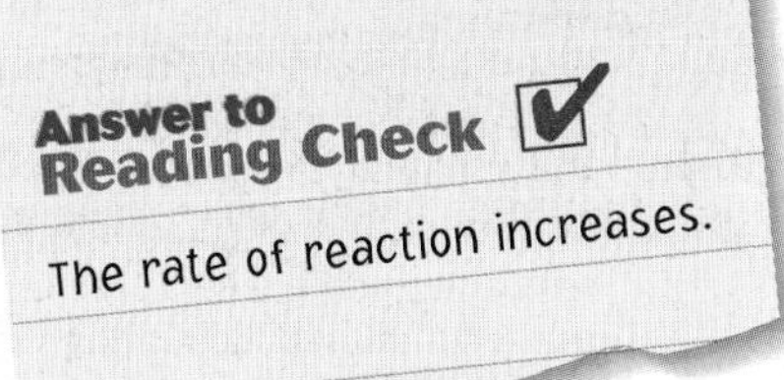

Answer to Reading Check
The rate of reaction increases.

Particle Size Can Change the Rate

The size of the reactant particles also affects how fast the reaction can occur. Only the atoms or molecules on the outside of the piece of reactant material are in contact with the other reactants and can take part in the reaction. If the particles are large, most of the atoms are stuck inside and can't participate in the reaction. If the particles are small, more of the reactant atoms are at the surface and can react. When more atoms can take part in the reaction, the rate of reaction increases. Think about how easily you can start a campfire with thin, dry twigs. Even a large pile of twigs will easily catch fire and burn completely in a few minutes. Could you start a fire if you just had large logs and no tinder to burn? Probably not, but once started, a campfire of logs will burn more slowly, and sometimes die down with one log still slowly smoldering.

Problem Solving

Changing Rates of Reaction

Chemists often try to make reactions go more quickly. The faster the reaction, the more product can be made in a given period of time and the lower the cost. In their search for faster reaction rates, chemists experiment with the conditions of the reaction such as the temperature, the concentration of the reactants, and the particle size of the reactants.

Examine the table that lists the conditions for two trials for each of the three reactions in column 1. List the factors that affect the rate of a reaction. Next, use your list to decide which of the trials for each reaction was faster.

Think Critically: In reaction 1, what additional change could be made in a third trial? Would it increase the reaction rate if the baking soda in reaction 2 were dissolved in water? In reaction 3, what more could the chemist do to get more oxygen gas from hydrogen peroxide more quickly? What could be done to slow down reaction 3? Explain your answers.

Conditions for Reactions

Chemical Reaction	Trial 1	Trial 2
1. Zinc reacts with hydrochloric acid.	The zinc is in chunks.	The zinc is powdered.
2. Baking soda reacts with acetic acid.	10% acetic acid is used.	5% acetic acid is used.
3. Three percent hydrogen peroxide breaks down into oxygen gas and water.	The reaction takes place at 50°C.	The reaction takes place at 25°C.

Content Background

How much you can increase reaction rate by increasing the concentration of one reactant is limited. If you have a high concentration of one reactant and a low concentration of another, the rate of reaction will be limited by the amount of the substance of low concentration.

Discussion

Interpersonal Have students revisit Activity 5-1, and discuss how the enzymes in the liver and potato serve as catalysts for the decomposition of hydrogen peroxide. COOP LEARN

Problem Solving

Reaction rate is affected by size of the reactant particles, concentration of reactant, temperature, and presence of a catalyst. The more successful trials are 2, 1, and 1, respectively.

Think Critically

Answers will vary but could include the following. The zinc could be in small pieces, or the temperature could be varied. Yes, the rate would increase. Further increase the temperature, or use a higher concentration of hydrogen peroxide. Further reduce the temperature.

3 Assess

Check for Understanding

Using an Analogy

Visual-Spatial Have students visualize catalysts as hands that hold molecules in the best possible position for the reaction to take place. By holding molecules in the best position, the catalyst reduces the activation energy.

Try at Home

Mini Lab

For additional help doing this activity at home, see the corresponding pages in the **Home Involvement** booklet.

Purpose

Visual-Spatial Students will investigate common inhibitors. L2 COOP LEARN

Materials

food packages

Teaching Strategies

Some food packages have a use by date, and some have a purchase by date. Ask what the wording might indicate about the freshness of the product.

Analysis

1. Answers will vary.
2. Less food is wasted, and there are fewer health risks from spoiled food.

Assessment

Process Have students compare the shelf life of dry products, such as crackers, to the shelf life of canned and bottled products and explain their conclusions. Use **Performance Assessment in the Science Classroom,** p. 43.

Using Math

$$\frac{66 \text{ g/L}}{50 \text{ s}} = 1.3 \text{ g/L/s}$$

Try at Home

Mini Lab

Uncovering Inhibitors

Procedure

1. Cereals and crackers would be stale soon after you bought them if it were not for some common inhibitors that increase the shelf life of these products. The long chemical names for three such inhibitors are usually shortened to BHT, TBHQ, and tocopherols. Look at the ingredient lists on packages on your kitchen shelves and list products that contain one of these inhibitors.
2. A date on the top of the box tells you how long the product is considered fresh. Compare that date with the approximate date when the product was purchased to estimate shelf life.

Analysis

1. What is the average estimated shelf life of the products you examined?
2. Why is increased shelf life important?

Using Math

At the beginning of a reaction, there is no CO_2 present. After 50 s, the concentration of CO_2 is 66 g per liter. Calculate the average rate of reaction during this time in units of grams per liter per second.

Inhibitors—Slowing Down

Sometimes, reactions occur too quickly. Food and medications, for example, undergo chemical reactions that cause them to spoil or lose their effectiveness. Can these reactions be slowed down? A substance that slows down a chemical reaction is called an **inhibitor.** An inhibitor doesn't completely stop a reaction, but it makes the formation of a certain amount of product take longer. The boxes in which many cereals are sold contain the compound butyl hydroxytoluene, BHT. The presence of BHT in the packaging material slows the spoiling of the cereal and increases shelf life.

Catalysts—Speeding Up

Is it possible to speed up a chemical reaction? You could add a catalyst (KAT uh lihst). A **catalyst** is a substance that speeds up a chemical reaction but doesn't appear in the chemical equation because it is not permanently changed or used up. A reaction using a catalyst will not produce more product than a reaction without a catalyst, but it will produce the same amount of product faster. How does a catalyst work? Visualize catalysts as hands that hold molecules in the best possible position for the reaction to take place. By holding molecules in the best position for the reaction, the catalyst reduces the activation energy needed to start the reaction. When the activation energy is reduced, the reaction rate increases.

Enzymes Are Catalysts

LIFE SCIENCE INTEGRATION

Some of the most effective catalysts are at work in your body. These catalysts, called enzymes, speed up reactions needed for efficient cell functioning. They help your body convert food to fuel, build bone and muscle tissue, and convert extra energy to fat.

These are complex reactions. Without enzymes, they would occur at rates that are

LIFE SCIENCE INTEGRATION

Lactose intolerance is a condition that occurs when an enzyme that breaks down the sugar lactose, which is found in dairy products, is not produced in a person's digestive system.

Integrating the Sciences

Life Science Meat tenderizers contain proteases, which act as catalysts to break down proteins. Proteases help break down tough connective tissue in meat and make the meat more tender. Meat tenderizers are often used to minimize the effect of insect stings because most animal venom is protein based.

too slow to measure or they would not occur at all. Enzymes make it possible for your body to function. Enzymes function as catalysts by positioning the reacting molecules so that their structures fit together properly. One class of enzymes called proteases (PROH tee ays es) functions within cells to break down proteins and recycle the materials. Proteins are large, complex molecules that perform many important functions in living things. Proteases are used in common products, such as meat tenderizer and contact lens-cleaning solution, as shown in **Figure 5-13.** Why do you think these products would need to break down proteins?

Figure 5-13 Proteins from the eye collect on contact lenses and can cloud your view. Proteases in lens-cleaning solutions speed up the decomposition of proteins so that they can be removed from a lens.

Section Assessment

1. How would you measure the rate of a reaction?
2. For the following general reaction, A + B + energy → C, where A and B are gases, what will be the effect on the reaction rate of the following?
   a. increasing the temperature
   b. increasing the pressure
   c. adding more of A without adding more of B
3. **Think Critically:** Jars of spaghetti sauce are stored on shelves at the grocery store waiting to be purchased. When you take a jar home and use it, you break the airtight seal on the top. These jars are labeled "refrigerate after opening." Explain why the jar can be stored on the shelf in the market but must be placed in the refrigerator after it is opened.
4. **Skill Builder**
   Observing and Inferring The rate of a reaction is affected by several factors. For example, the temperature of the reaction mixture can either speed up or slow down the reaction. Do the **Chapter 5 Skill Activity** on page 746 to investigate a chemical reaction. Then, infer the type of reaction you have observed and the effect temperature has on it.

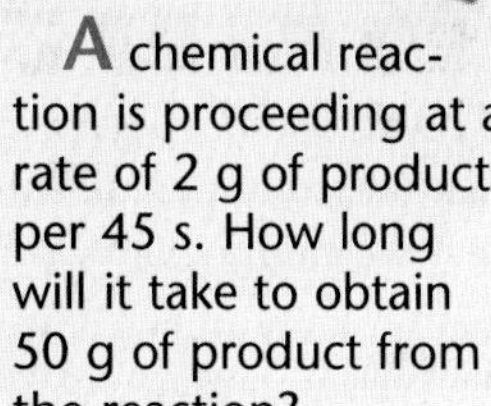

Using Math

A chemical reaction is proceeding at a rate of 2 g of product per 45 s. How long will it take to obtain 50 g of product from the reaction?

Reteach

Visual-Spatial Have students make up a crossword puzzle using the factors that affect reaction rate as the words in the puzzle and their descriptions as the clues. L2

Extension

For students who have mastered this section, use the **Reinforcement** and **Enrichment** masters.

4 Close

Proficiency Prep

Use this quiz to check students' recall of section content.

1. **What is the minimum amount of energy needed to start a reaction?** *activation energy*
2. **What tells you how much something changes over time?** *a rate*
3. **How does making the pieces of reactants smaller affect the reaction rate?** *It increases it.*

Section Assessment

1. Measure how much product forms or how much reactant is used up in a certain amount of time. Then, divide the amount of reactant or product by the time.
2. All increase reaction rate.
3. Critical Thinking Opening the jar exposes its contents to oxygen and other substances in the air that might react with the jar contents to spoil the food. Refrigeration slows down those reactions.

Assessment

Performance Have students design an experiment to determine rate of spoilage of two pieces of bread, one containing an inhibitor, such as BHT, and the other containing no inhibitor. If the experiment is actually done, be sure the procedure is approved first. Use **Performance Assessment in the Science Classroom,** p. 23. P

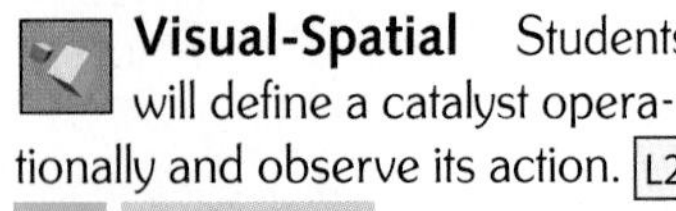

Purpose

Visual-Spatial Students will define a catalyst operationally and observe its action. L2 ELL COOP LEARN

Process Skills

observing, inferring, forming operational definitions, classifying, recognizing cause and effect

Time

30 minutes

Teaching Strategies

Have the glowing splint ready when the MnO_2 is placed in the solution. It should be glowing, not burning.

Troubleshooting The bottle of hydrogen peroxide should be freshly opened. Hydrogen peroxide can be purchased from a pharmacy or a grocery store.

Answers to Questions

1. Bubbles formed; a gas was released.
2. In the test tube containing the manganese dioxide; more bubbles were present.
3. It supported the burning of the splint but it did not burn, so it was oxygen.
4. Nothing remained in the tube without the catalyst. The MnO_2 remained in the other tube.
5. Yes, because it sped up the reaction but remained unchanged when the reaction was over.
6. Examples might include, "She was a catalyst on the committee because she made things happen."

Activity 5•2

Using Scientific Methods

Speeding Up a Reaction

The equation for a chemical reaction tells you nothing about how fast the reaction occurs. One slow reaction is the breakdown of hydrogen peroxide, H_2O_2, into oxygen gas, O_2, and water. Is there a way to make this reaction go faster?

Chemists measure the rate of a chemical reaction by observing how quickly the reactants are used up or the products are formed. Testing the production of oxygen is a handy way to observe the rate of a reaction. A glowing wooden splint will relight and burn brightly when placed in oxygen.

Materials

- Test tubes (2)
- Test-tube rack
  **beaker to hold test tubes*
- Graduated cylinder (25 mL)
- Small plastic spoon
- Hot plate
- Wooden splint
- Hydrogen peroxide, 3%, H_2O_2
- Manganese dioxide, MnO_2
- Beaker of hot water
- Bunsen burner
  **lighter*

**Alternate Materials*

What You'll Investigate

How is the rate of the breakdown of hydrogen peroxide affected when manganese dioxide, MnO_2, is added as a catalyst?

Goals

- **Observe** the decomposition of hydrogen peroxide.
- **Infer** how a catalyst changes the reaction rate.

Safety Precautions

CAUTION: *Hydrogen peroxide can irritate skin and eyes. Wear goggles, an apron, and gloves. Do not use more than 5 mL of hydrogen peroxide.*

Procedure

1. Pour 5 mL of hydrogen peroxide into each of two test tubes.
2. Place about ¼ teaspoonful of manganese dioxide in one of the test tubes.
3. Light the wooden splint. Blow out the flame and insert the glowing splint first into the test tube containing only hydrogen peroxide and then into the test tube containing the manganese dioxide.
4. Record your observations.
5. Place the two test tubes in a beaker of hot water and heat them on a hot plate until all the liquid has disappeared. Record your observations.

Conclude and Apply

1. **Describe** what happened when manganese dioxide was added to one of the test tubes.
2. In which test tube was gas produced more rapidly? How do you know?
3. How did you identify the gas?
4. What remained in the two test tubes after the liquid was driven off?
5. Does manganese dioxide fit the description of a catalyst? Give reasons for your answer.
6. The word *catalyst* is used in everyday conversation to describe special people. Write a sentence that illustrates what effect such people might have on others around them.

Assessment

Portfolio Have students define the term control. Then, using examples from the activity, have them write a description of the role of the control in helping them draw conclusions in an experiment. Use **Performance Assessment in the Science Classroom,** p. 17. P 

Using Proportions

The Mole

One job of a chemist is to determine the number of atoms needed to combine with other atoms or molecules to make new products. In real life, large numbers of atoms are involved in chemical reactions. So, chemists invented the mole to use as a counting unit, the way a baker uses the word *dozen*, meaning 12 of something. A mole of atoms contains 6.02×10^{23} atoms, and a mole of molecules contains 6.02×10^{23} molecules. This huge quantity is known as Avogadro's number. If you counted out 1 mole of peas, your pile would cover the United States to a depth of about 6 km. Let's see how chemists use the mole to solve problems.

Problem and Solution

Ammonia gas is made from nitrogen gas and hydrogen gas. This reaction is written as follows.

$$N_2 + 3H_2 \rightarrow 2NH_3$$

This balanced equation shows a chemist that 1 mole of nitrogen molecules reacts with 3 moles of hydrogen molecules and that 2 moles of ammonia molecules will be produced. If you wanted to produce 6 moles of ammonia from this reaction, how would you know how much hydrogen you needed?

1. From the balanced equation, you now know that the ratio of hydrogen molecules to ammonia molecules is 3:2.

2. The easiest way to find out your answer is to set up a proportion and calculate the cross product. Start with the ratio that is known. Set it equal to the ratio that has the unknown quantity. Then, solve the proportion.

$$\frac{3 \text{ moles } H_2}{2 \text{ moles } NH_3} = \frac{x}{6 \text{ mole } NH_3}$$

$$x = \frac{(3 \text{ moles } H_2)(6 \text{ moles } NH_3)}{2 \text{ moles } NH_3}$$

$$x = 9 \text{ moles } H_2$$

You would start with 9 moles of H_2 to produce 6 moles of NH_3.

Practice PROBLEMS

1. How many moles of N_2 would be needed to produce 9 moles of NH_3?
2. How many moles of NH_3 would you produce if 5 moles of N_2 were used?

NATIONAL GEOGRAPHIC

Science & Math

Content Background

- The mole is a convenient way of scaling up tiny molecules and atoms to dimensions that can be measured and manipulated in the laboratory. Students may be reading equations in terms of molecules of reactants and products; now they can read them as moles of reactants and moles of product, always recognizing that the relationships are exactly the same.
- The coefficients in a chemical equation reveal the ratios in which reactants combine with each other and the ratios of products to reactants. One mole of N_2 will always react with 3 moles of H_2 and one mole of N_2 will always produce two moles of NH_3. From such ratios, proportions can be made to find the moles of any of the three participants if you know the moles of the other two.

Teaching Strategies

- Help students recognize that they are setting two ratios equal. In one ratio, both quantities are known. In the other, one quantity is the unknown.
- Emphasize that the units or labeling on both sides of the proportion must be the same—moles of H_2 on the top, moles of NH_3 on the bottom. The proportion could have been set up with moles of NH_3 in the numerators of the two ratios, but the solution is easier if the unknown is placed on top.
- Review the solution of this algebraic equation. To solve for x, both sides are multiplied by 6 moles of NH_3.
- Ask students if the answer is reasonable. You want to make three times as much ammonia, so you must start with three times as much hydrogen.

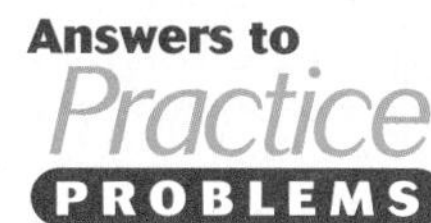

1. 4.5 moles of N_2
2. 10 moles of NH_3

Chapter 5 Reviewing Main Ideas

Reviewing Main Ideas can be used to preview, review, reteach, and condense chapter content.

Preview

Linguistic Have students try to answer the Reviewing Main Ideas questions in their Science Journals. Use student answers as a source for discussion throughout the chapter.

Review

Interpersonal Have students answer the questions on separate pieces of paper and compare their answers with those of other students in the class. COOP LEARN

Reteach

Visual-Spatial Have students look at the illustrations on these pages. Ask them to describe details that support the main ideas of the chapter found in the statement for each illustration.

00:00 OUT OF TIME?

Auditory-Musical If time does not permit teaching the entire chapter, use the information on these pages along with the chapter Audiocassettes to present the material in a condensed format.

Chapter  5 Reviewing Main Ideas

For a **preview** of this chapter, study this Reviewing Main Ideas before you read the chapter. After you have studied this chapter, you can use the Reviewing Main Ideas to **review** the chapter.

The Glencoe MindJogger, Audiocassettes, and CD-ROM provide additional opportunities for review.

Section

5-1 EVIDENCE FOR CHEMICAL REACTIONS

Reactions are always occurring all around you. Many observable signs show that **chemical reactions** have occurred, including changes in color or odor, the release or absorption of heat or light, and the release of a gas. Sometimes, a solid called a precipitate forms when two clear liquids are mixed. Observations of the changes that occur are the basis for writing equations that describe chemical reactions. ***Write down an example of a chemical reaction and describe the evidence that shows it has occurred.***

BALANCED CHEMICAL EQUATIONS

A chemical equation is a shorthand way of describing what happens in a chemical reaction. In a chemical equation, chemists use symbols to represent the **reactants** and **products** of a reaction. The reactants are placed on the left side of the equation with an arrow pointing toward the products on the right. The law of conservation of mass requires that chemical equations be balanced, meaning that the same number of atoms of each element must be found on each side of the equation. The chemical equation sometimes shows whether a reaction is **endothermic** or **exothermic.** ***What is the difference between an endothermic and an exothermic reaction?***

HCCHHHOO NaHCOOO NaCCHHHOO HHO COO

$$HC_2H_3O_2 + NaHCO_3 \rightarrow NaC_2H_3O_2 + H_2O + CO_2$$

Cultural Diversity

The sky is falling, or is it?. . . Punta Arenas, Chile, with 115 000 people, is the southernmost large city in the world. Unfortunately, it happens to be located under an ozone hole for part of the year. Although ozone, O_3, is a poisonous gas, it protects Earth's living beings from the harmful effects of high-energy radiation from the sun. Stripped of that protection at times, Punta Arenas is experiencing changes in reproductive patterns in local plants and animals. Plants are turning yellow, apparently burned by high levels of ultraviolet radiation. The vision of some rabbits has become poor. Scientists are concerned about the destruction of the ozone layer in Punta Arenas and elsewhere in the world and are studying such changes to see if there is a definite link to the ozone hole.

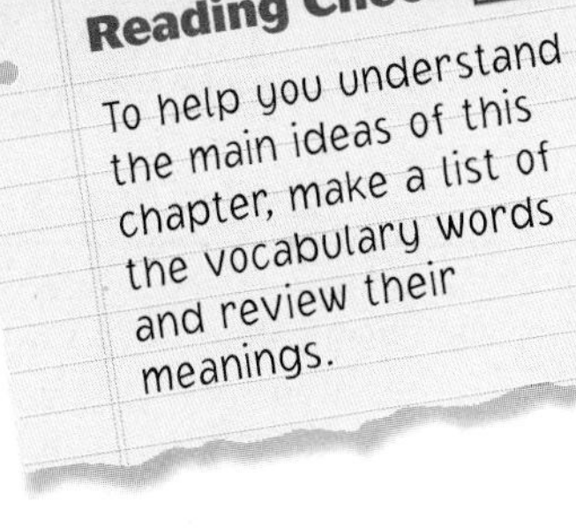

Reading Check
To help you understand the main ideas of this chapter, make a list of the vocabulary words and review their meanings.

Section 5-2 RATE OF REACTION

The **rate of reaction** is a measure of how quickly a reaction occurs. All reactions have an activation energy, which is a minimum amount of energy required to start the reaction. Reactions with low activation energies occur rapidly. Those with high activation energies occur slowly or not at all. Other factors that influence the rate of a chemical reaction are the temperature at which the reaction occurs, the concentration of the reactants, and the size of the particles of reactant. **Catalysts** are substances that can speed up a reaction without being used up. **Inhibitors** slow down the rate of reaction. ***Why do many reactions occur more quickly at higher temperatures?***

Career CONNECTION

Dr. Lynda Jordan, Biochemist

Dr. Lynda Jordan is a biochemist working at North Carolina Agricultural and Technical State University. Dr. Jordan studies the enzyme phospholipase, an enzyme isolated from the cells of the human placenta. She is interested in finding out about the structure and function of the enzyme. Many people have diseases, such as diabetes, that are associated with this enzyme, so understanding how the enzyme functions is important. ***How might an enzyme cause a disease in an organism?***

Answers to Questions

Section 5-1

Evidence for Chemical Reactions Answers will vary. Examples could include food spoiling resulting in color and odor changes, or a match burning resulting in gases being given off and the release of energy.

Balanced Chemical Equations An endothermic reaction absorbs energy, and an exothermic reaction releases energy.

Section 5-2

Rate of Reaction In order for reactions to take place, particles must collide with enough energy to react. Increasing temperature increases the speed of the particles and the chance that a collision will occur with sufficient energy to react.

Career CONNECTION

If an enzyme is absent or fails to function, some part of the organism's system will also malfunction. This is what is called disease.

GLENCOE TECHNOLOGY

CD-ROM

Glencoe Science Voyages Interactive CD-ROM

Chapter Summaries and Quizzes

Have students read the Chapter Summary and then take the Chapter Quiz to determine whether they have mastered chapter content.

Assessment

Portfolio Encourage students to place in their portfolios one or two items of what they consider to be their best work. Examples include:

- Explore Activity, p. 121
- Guided Reading Strategy, p. 128
- Go Further, p. 131
- Science Journal, p. 133
- Assessment, pp. 137, 138 P

Performance Additional performance assessments may be found in **Performance Assessment** and **Science Integration Activities.** Performance Task Assessment Lists and rubrics for evaluating these activities can be found in Glencoe's **Performance Assessment in the Science Classroom.**

Using Vocabulary

1. An exothermic reaction releases energy; an endothermic reaction absorbs energy.
2. A catalyst speeds up the rate of a reaction.
3. The reactants are what goes into the reaction. The products are what remain when the reaction is over.
4. Both affect the rate of a reaction. The catalyst makes the reaction go faster and the inhibitor makes it go slower.
5. A chemical reaction is a process in which the identities of the reactants are changed. The rate of a reaction is a measure of how fast a chemical reaction takes place.

interNET CONNECTION To reinforce chapter vocabulary, use the **Study Guide for Content Mastery** booklet. Also available are activities for **Glencoe Science Voyages** on the Glencoe Science Web Site. **www.glencoe.com/sec/science**

Checking Concepts

6. B	11. B
7. D	12. C
8. D	13. B
9. C	14. A
10. C	15. D

Thinking Critically

16. The pickling compounds inhibit spoiling of the pickles.
17. An exothermic process occurs because the tube becomes warm.
18. No chemical reaction occurs because there is no change in the identity of the water. The energy change that occurs comes from an external energy source.
19. No, both representations show one sulfur atom and two silver atoms, but in the second one, the atoms are combined in the compound silver sulfide. In the first one, they are individual atoms.

Chapter 5 Assessment

Using Vocabulary

a. catalyst
b. chemical reaction
c. endothermic reaction
d. exothermic reaction
e. inhibitor
f. product
g. rate of reaction
h. reactant

Explain the differences between terms in each of the following sets.

1. exothermic reaction, endothermic reaction
2. catalyst, rate of reaction
3. reactant, product
4. catalyst, inhibitor
5. chemical reaction, rate of reaction

Checking Concepts

Choose the word or phrase that best answers the question.

6. A balanced chemical equation must have the same number of atoms of each of these on both sides.
   A) atoms C) molecules
   B) elements D) compounds
7. Which is **NOT** a balanced equation?
   A) $CuCl_2 + H_2S \rightarrow CuS + 2HCl$
   B) $AgNO_3 + NaI \rightarrow AgI + NaNO_3$
   C) $2C_2H_6 + 7O_2 \rightarrow 4CO_2 + 6H_2O$
   D) $MgO + Fe \rightarrow Fe_2O_3 + Mg$
8. Which is a chemical change?
   A) Paper is shredded.
   B) Liquid wax turns solid.
   C) A raw egg is broken.
   D) Soap scum forms.
9. Reactions that release energy are which of the following?
   A) unbalanced C) exothermic
   B) balanced D) endothermic
10. Which is a false statement about the law of conservation of mass?
   A) The mass of reactants must equal the mass of products.
   B) All the atoms on the reactant side of an equation are also on the product side.
   C) It is not always necessary to have the same elements present on both sides of the equation.
   D) No atoms are lost, but only rearranged.
11. What is a way to decrease the rate of a chemical reaction?
   A) increase the temperature
   B) reduce the concentration of a reactant
   C) increase the concentration of a reactant
   D) add a catalyst
12. In order to slow down a chemical reaction, what should you add?
   A) catalyst C) inhibitor
   B) salt D) enzyme
13. Which is **NOT** evidence that a chemical reaction has occurred?
   A) The leaves turn red in fall.
   B) Steam condenses on a cold window.
   C) A strong odor comes from the exhaust pipe of a car.
   D) Bubbles of gas form when a tablet is placed in water.
14. What does **NOT** affect reaction rate?
   A) the law of conservation of mass
   B) activation energy
   C) particle size
   D) concentration
15. Which of the following does NOT describe a catalyst?
   A) It can be recovered after the reaction.
   B) It speeds up a reaction.
   C) It does not appear in the chemical equation.
   D) It can be used in place of an inhibitor.

Thinking Critically

16. Pickled cucumbers remain edible much longer than fresh cucumbers. Explain.
17. A test tube containing a substance becomes warmer when you add another substance to it. What can you infer from this observation?
18. A beaker of water standing in the sunlight becomes warm. Has a chemical reaction occurred? Explain.
19. Is $2Ag + S$ the same as Ag_2S? Explain.

Developing Skills

If you need help, refer to the Skill Handbook.

20. **Interpreting Data:** At 25°C, you measure the rate of a chemical reaction. You then increase the temperature to 100°C and find that the reaction rate is half as large as before. Does this reaction absorb or release energy? Explain.
21. **Interpreting Scientific Illustrations:** The two curves on the graph represent the concentrations of compounds A (blue) and B (red) during a chemical reaction.
    A) Which compound is a reactant?
    B) Which compound is a product?
    C) During what time period is the concentration of the reactant changing most rapidly?

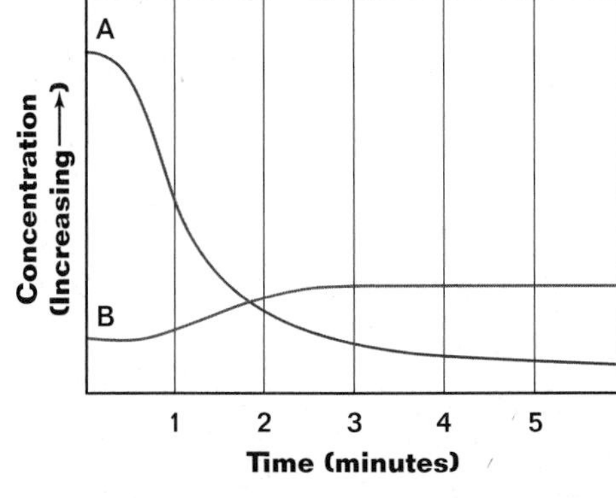

Test-Taking Tip

Plan Your Work and Work Your Plan
Set up a study schedule for yourself well in advance of your test. Plan your workload so that you do a little each day rather than a lot all at once. The key to retaining information is to repeatedly review and practice it.

Test Practice

Use these questions to test your Science Proficiency.

1. Which of the following is **NOT** true.
   A) All chemical reactions either release or absorb energy.
   B) In all chemical equations, energy must be included either on the reactant or the product side.
   C) Some reactions are important because they produce energy.
   D) Reactions that produce energy are called exothermic.
2. In a balanced equation for a chemical reaction, each side of the equation must have all of the following except one. Choose the one that should **NOT** be included.
   A) the same number and kind of elements
   B) the same number of each kind of atom
   C) the same number of molecules
   D) the same mass

THE PRINCETON REVIEW Test Practice

The Test-Taking Tip was written by The Princeton Review, the nation's leader in test preparation.

1. B
2. C

Developing Skills

20. It releases energy. If it absorbed energy, raising the temperature would increase the rate of reaction.
21. A) A is the reactant.
    B) B is the product.
    C) the first two minutes

Bonus Question

Which of the following equations for the formation of iron(III) chloride, $FeCl_3$, is correctly written and balanced? Explain what is wrong with each of the other two equations.

a. $Fe + 3Cl_2 \rightarrow Fe_2Cl_3$
The formula for iron(III) chloride is $FeCl_3$ and cannot be changed; 2 should go in front of the formula and in front of Fe.

b. $2Fe + 3Cl_2 \rightarrow 2FeCl_3$
correct as written

c. $Fe + Cl_3 \rightarrow FeCl_3$
The formula for chlorine is Cl_2 not Cl_3.

Assessment Resources

The **Test Practice Workbook** provides students with practice in the format, concepts, and critical-thinking skills tested in standardized exams.

Reproducible Masters

Chapter Review, pp. 9–10 L2
Performance Assessment, p. 19 L2
Assessment, pp. 17–20 L2

Glencoe Technology

Chapter Review Software
Computer Test Bank
MindJogger Videoquiz

UNIT 2

Forces and Motion

In this unit, students are introduced to kinematics, the study of motion, and dynamics, the study of the causes of motion. The relationship between motion and force is discussed in the context of Newton's three laws of motion. The unit concludes with a description of forces of attraction.

Unit Overview

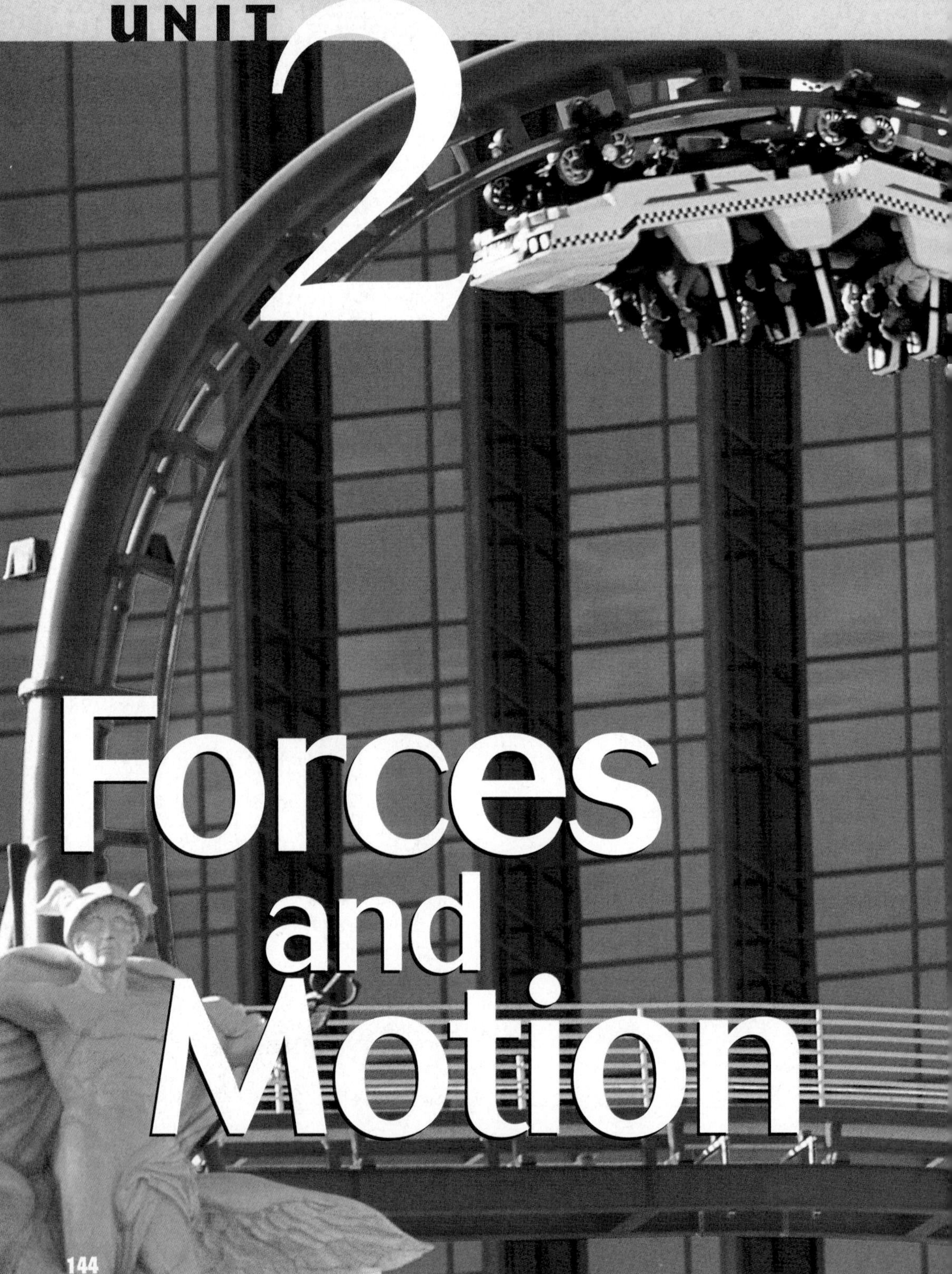

Science at Home

Measuring Motion Have students monitor TV and newspapers to find measurements of motion. Have them categorize the types of motion and the units used to measure motion.

NATIONAL GEOGRAPHIC

What's Happening Here?

What kind of motor propels this wild roller coaster ride as it loops down the track (left)? None at all. Once the train of cars leaves the highest point of the ride, nothing more than the force of gravity is in charge. What makes the roller coaster stop at the ride's end? Another force—friction. Only forces can cause motion, and only forces can stop it. In this unit, you will learn about these forces and how objects themselves play a role in whether the forces acting on them are weak or strong. You will also observe some things that are not quite what you might expect and things that you might not have noticed before. An engineer and inventor, Harold "Doc" Edgerton, took this famous 1957 photograph (below). Now part of the collection of the Museum of Modern Art in New York City, it reveals something about the laws of motion that your eye might miss—exactly what happens to a drop of milk after it strikes the top of a red cookie tin.

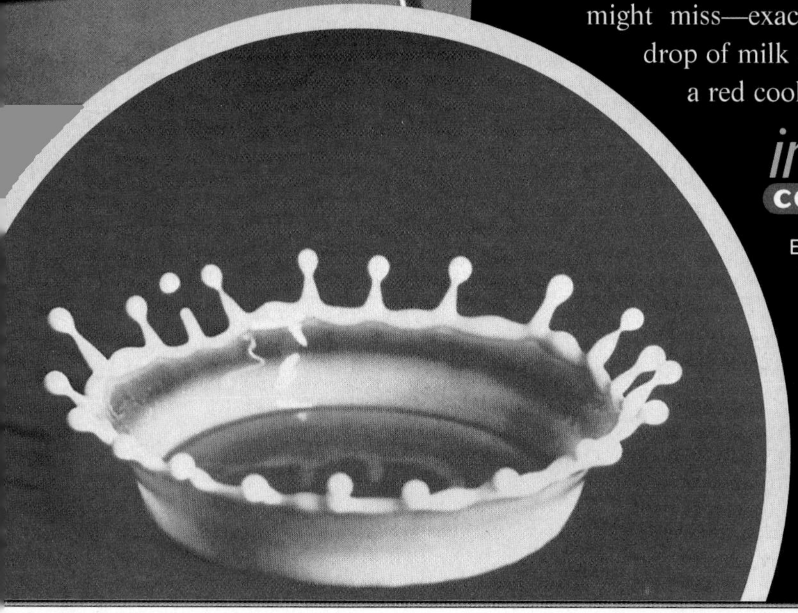

interNET CONNECTION

Explore the Glencoe Science Web Site at **www.glencoe.com/sec/science** to find out more about topics found in this unit.

interNET CONNECTION

Internet Addresses

____

____

____

Explore the Glencoe Science Web Site at **www.glencoe.com/sec/science** to find out more about topics found in this unit.

Introducing the Unit

What's happening here?

Have students read the text and examine the pictures. Ask why the height of a roller coaster is advertised by amusement parks. Ask what would happen if the roller coaster were built only a few meters from the ground.

Content Background

The energy driving the roller coaster comes from potential energy. This is the energy the roller coaster has at the high point of the track. When the roller coaster begins to fall, the potential energy is converted to kinetic energy, the energy of motion.

Previewing the Chapters

- Have students make a list of the sports, entertainment, and recreational activities depicted by photographs in this unit.
- Have students look at illustrations and photographs that depict different forms of energy.

Tying to Previous Knowledge

- Have students brainstorm words that describe different types of motion, such as swirling, tumbling, and gliding.
- Have students recall how the motion of their bodies changes as the motion of a vehicle in which they are riding changes.

Chapter 6 Motion

Section	Objectives	Activities/Features
Chapter Opener		**Explore Activity:** Compare Collisions, p. 147
6-1 **What is motion?** 3 Sessions 1½ Blocks	1. **Describe** how to calculate speed. 2. **Explain** how to calculate velocity and acceleration.	**MiniLab:** Calculating Acceleration, p. 152 **Skill Builder:** Measuring in SI, p. 155 **Using Math,** p. 155 **Activity 6-1:** The Tortoise and the Hare, pp. 156–157
6-2 **What is momentum?** 3 Sessions 1½ Blocks	3. **Describe** how to find and object's momentum. 4. **Explain** how to use the law of conservation of momentum to understand collisions.	**Earth Science Integration,** p. 160 **Problem Solving:** Observing Inertia, p. 162 **Chemistry Integration,** p. 163 **Skill Builder:** Interpreting Scientific Illustrations, p. 163 **Science Journal,** p. 163 **Activity 6-2:** Comparing Collisions, p. 164
6-3 **What is energy?** 2 Sessions 1 Block	5. **Define** what energy is and **describe** some of its forms. 6. **Describe** how to calculate kinetic gravitational potential energy. 7. **Explain** what the law of conservation of energy is and **describe** how to use it.	**MiniLab:** Observing Energy Transfer, p. 166 **Skill Builder:** Observing and Inferring, p. 168 **Using Computers,** p. 168 **Science and Society:** Discovery of the Neutrino, p. 169

The number of recommended single-period sessions The number of recommended blocks
One session and one-half block are allowed for chapter review and assessment.

Activity Materials

Explore	Activities	MiniLabs
p. 147 ruler, book, 2 marbles, paper	pp. 156–157 stopwatch, meterstick, graph paper, calculator p. 164 5 small marbles, 2 large marbles, 2 metersticks	p. 152 masking tape, meterstick p. 166 2 balls of different sizes

Need Materials? Contact Science Kit at 1-800-828-7777 or at www.sciencekit.com on the Internet.
For alternate materials, see the activity on the listed page.

Standards		Reproducible Resources	Technology
National	State/Local	Test Practice Workbooks are available for use with each chapter.	English and Spanish audiocassettes are available for use with each section.
National Content Standards: UCP2, UCP3, A2, B2, D3, E2		**Activity Worksheets,** pp. 29–30, 33 **Enrichment,** p. 12 **Laboratory Manual,** pp. 33–36 **Reinforcement,** p. 12 **Study Guide,** p. 21	**Section Focus Transparency 12** **Teaching Transparency 11** **Glencoe Science Voyages Interactive Videodisc—Physical**
National Content Standards: UCP2, UCP3, UCP4, B1, B2, D1, D3, E2, G3		**Activity Worksheets,** pp. 31–32 **Critical Thinking/Problem Solving,** p. 6 **Enrichment,** p. 13 **Laboratory Manual,** pp. 37–40 **Multicultural Connections,** pp. 11–12 **Reinforcement,** p. 13 **Study Guide,** p. 22	**Section Focus Transparency 13** **Science Integration Transparency 6** **Glencoe Science Voyages Interactive CD-ROM** **Glencoe Science Voyages Interactive Videodisc—Physical** **Internet Connection,** p. 162
National Content Standards: UCP3, B2, B3, G3, G4		**Activity Worksheets,** p. 34 **Enrichment,** p. 14 **Reinforcement,** p. 14 **Study Guide,** pp. 23–24	**Section Focus Transparency 14** **Teaching Transparency 12** **Internet Connection,** p. 168

Key to Teaching Strategies

The following designations will help you decide which activities are appropriate for your students.

L1 Level 1 activities should be appropriate for students with learning difficulties.

L2 Level 2 activities should be within the ability range of all students.

L3 Level 3 activities are designed for above-average students.

ELL ELL activities should be within the ability range of English Language Learners.

COOP LEARN Cooperative Learning activities are designed for small group work.

P These strategies represent student products that can be placed into a best-work portfolio.

Multiple Learning Styles logos, as described on page 61T, are used throughout to indicate strategies that address different learning styles.

Assessment Resources

Chapter Review, pp. 11–12
Assessment, pp. 23-26
Performance Assessment in the Science Classroom (PASC)
MindJogger Videoquiz
Alternate Assessment in the Science Classroom
Performance Assessment, p. 20
Chapter Review Software
Computer Test Bank

Chapter 6 Motion

This is a representation of key blackline masters available in the Teacher Classroom Resources. See Resource Manager boxes within the chapter for additional information.

Transparencies

Section Focus Transparencies

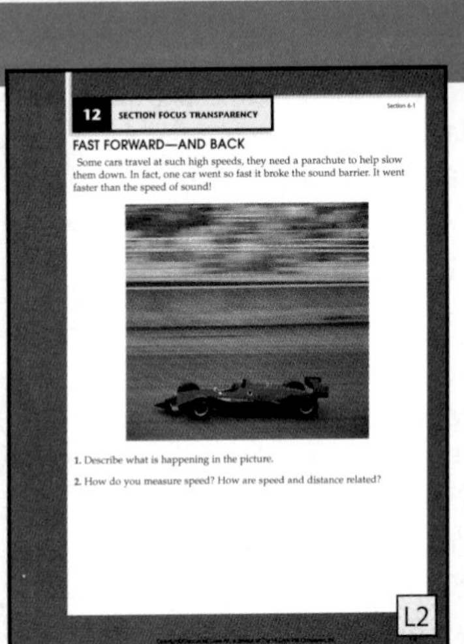

12 SECTION FOCUS TRANSPARENCY — Section 6-1

FAST FORWARD—AND BACK

Some cars travel at such high speeds, they need a parachute to help slow them down. In fact, one car went so fast it broke the sound barrier. It went faster than the speed of sound!

1. Describe what is happening in the picture.
2. How do you measure speed? How are speed and distance related?

L2

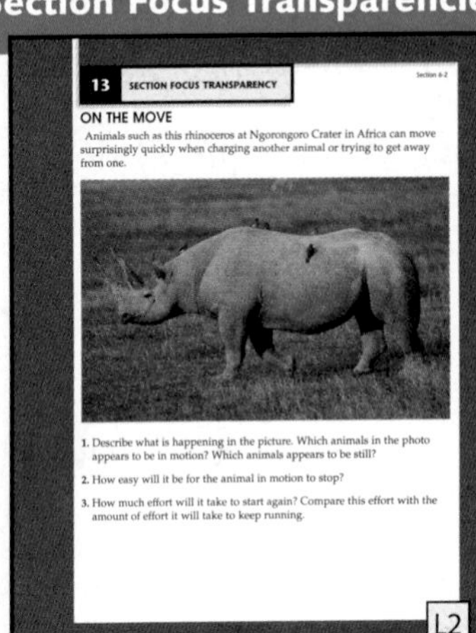

13 SECTION FOCUS TRANSPARENCY — Section 6-2

ON THE MOVE

Animals such as this rhinoceros at Ngorongoro Crater in Africa can move surprisingly quickly when charging another animal or trying to get away from one.

1. Describe what is happening in the picture. Which animals in the photo appears to be in motion? Which animals appears to be still?
2. How easy will it be for the animal in motion to stop?
3. How much effort will it take to start again? Compare this effort with the amount of effort it will take to keep running.

L2

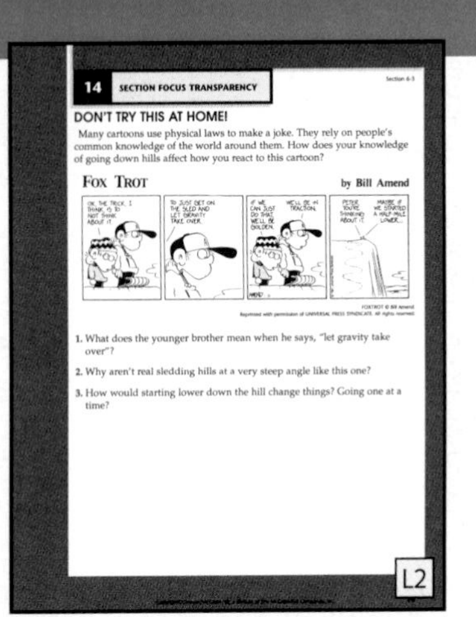

14 SECTION FOCUS TRANSPARENCY — Section 6-3

DON'T TRY THIS AT HOME!

Many cartoons use physical laws to make a joke. They rely on people's common knowledge of the world around them. How does your knowledge of going down hills affect how you react to this cartoon?

FOX TROT by Bill Amend

1. What does the younger brother mean when he says, "let gravity take over"?
2. Why aren't real sledding hills at a very steep angle like this one?
3. How would starting lower down the hill change things? Going one at a time?

L2

Science Integration Transparencies

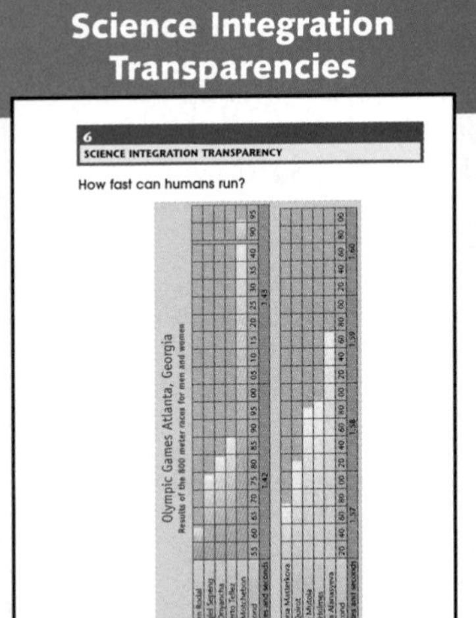

6 SCIENCE INTEGRATION TRANSPARENCY

How fast can humans run?

L2

Teaching Transparencies

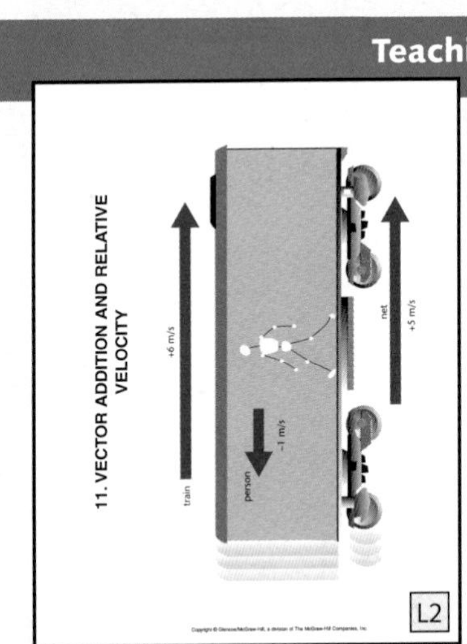

L2

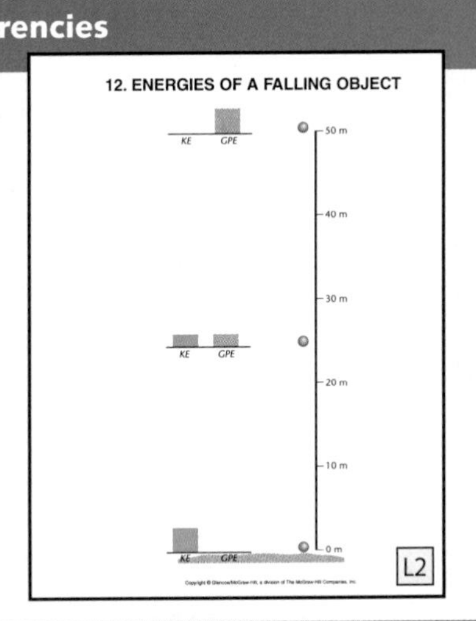

L2

Meeting Different Ability Levels

Study Guide for Content Mastery

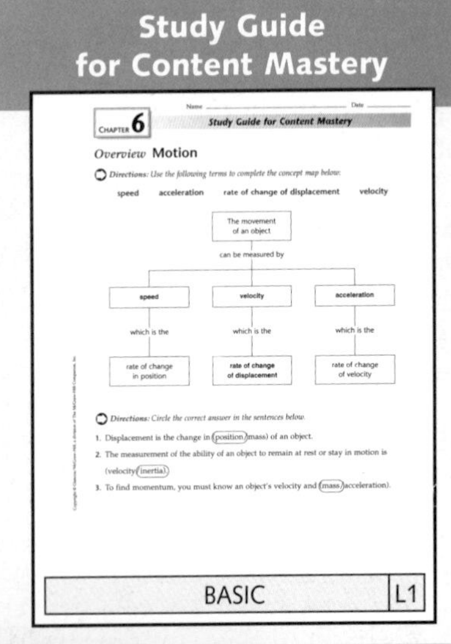

Name ______ Date ______

CHAPTER 6 — *Study Guide for Content Mastery*

Overview **Motion**

Directions: Use the following terms to complete the concept map below:

speed acceleration rate of change of displacement velocity

Directions: Circle the correct answer in the sentences below.

1. Displacement is the change in (position/mass) of an object.
2. The measurement of the ability of an object to remain at rest or stay in motion is (velocity/inertia).
3. To find momentum, you must know an object's velocity and (mass/acceleration).

BASIC L1

Reinforcement

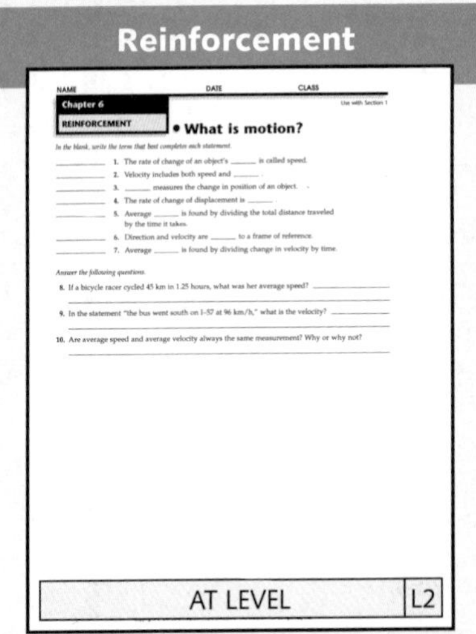

NAME DATE CLASS

Chapter 6 REINFORCEMENT — Use with Section 1

• What is motion?

In the blank, write the term that best completes each statement.

______ 1. The rate of change of an object's ______ is called speed.
______ 2. Velocity includes both speed and ______.
______ 3. ______ measures the change in position of an object.
______ 4. The rate of change of displacement is ______.
______ 5. Average ______ is found by dividing the total distance traveled by the time it takes.
______ 6. Direction and velocity are ______ to a frame of reference.
______ 7. Average ______ is found by dividing change in velocity by time.

Answer the following questions.

8. If a bicycle racer cycled 45 km in 1.25 hours, what was her average speed? ______
9. In the statement "the bus went south on I-57 at 96 km/h," what is the velocity? ______
10. Are average speed and average velocity always the same measurement? Why or why not?

AT LEVEL L2

Enrichment Worksheets

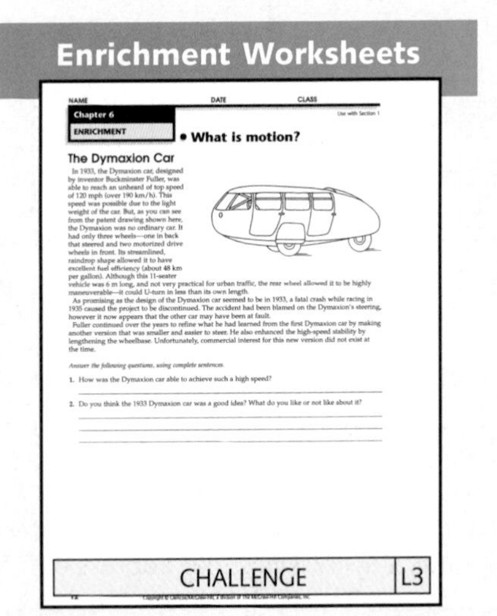

NAME DATE CLASS

Chapter 6 ENRICHMENT — Use with Section 1

• What is motion?

The Dymaxion Car

In 1933, the Dymaxion car, designed by inventor Buckminster Fuller, was able to reach an unheard of top speed of 120 mph (over 190 km/h). This speed was possible due to the light weight of the car. But, as you can see from the patent drawing shown here, the Dymaxion was no ordinary car. It had only three wheels—one in back that steered and two motorized drive wheels in front. Its streamlined, raindrop shape allowed it to have excellent fuel efficiency (about 48 km per gallon). Although this 11-seater vehicle was 6 m long, and not very practical for urban traffic, the rear wheel allowed it to be highly maneuverable—it could U-turn in less than its own length.

As promising as the design of the Dymaxion car seemed to be in 1933, a fatal crash while racing in 1935 caused the project to be discontinued. The accident had been blamed on the Dymaxion's steering, however it now appears that the other car may have been at fault.

Fuller continued over the years to refine what he had learned from the first Dymaxion car by making another version that was smaller and easier to steer. He also enhanced the high-speed stability by lengthening the wheelbase. Unfortunately, commercial interest for this new version did not exist at the time.

Answer the following questions, using complete sentences.

1. How was the Dymaxion car able to achieve such a high speed?
2. Do you think the 1933 Dymaxion car was a good idea? What do you like or not like about it?

CHALLENGE L3

Hands-on Activities

Activity Worksheets

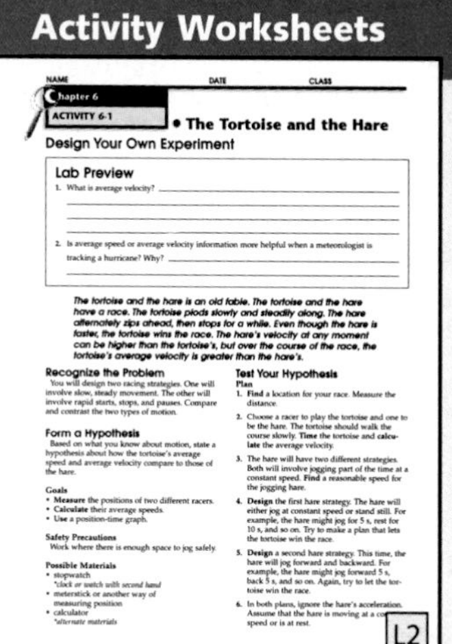

Chapter 6
ACTIVITY 6-1
The Tortoise and the Hare
Design Your Own Experiment

Lab Preview

The tortoise and the hare is an old fable. The tortoise and the hare have a race. The tortoise plods slowly and steadily along. The hare alternately zips ahead, then stops for a while. Even though the hare is faster, the tortoise wins the race. The hare's velocity at any moment can be higher than the tortoise's, but over the course of the race, the tortoise's average velocity is greater than the hare's.

Recognize the Problem
Form a Hypothesis
Goals
Safety Precautions
Possible Materials
Test Your Hypothesis

L2

Lab Manual

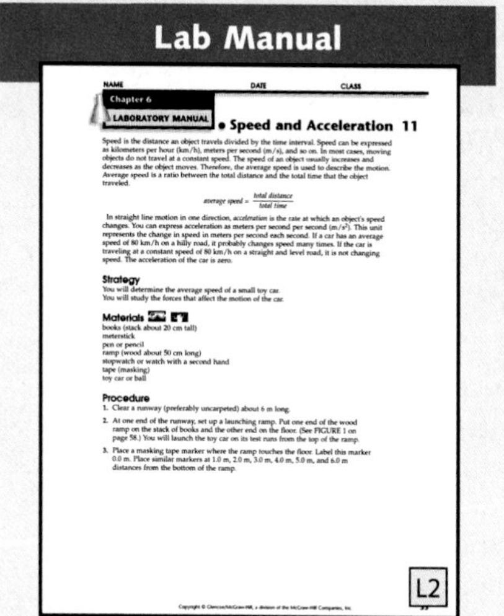

Chapter 6
LABORATORY MANUAL
Speed and Acceleration 11

Strategy
Materials
Procedure

L2

Accessibility

Spanish Resources

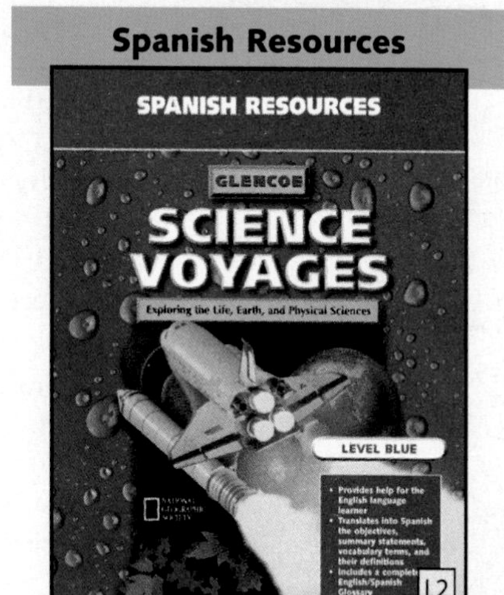

SPANISH RESOURCES
GLENCOE
SCIENCE VOYAGES
Exploring the Life, Earth, and Physical Sciences
LEVEL BLUE

- Provides help for the English language learner
- Translates into Spanish the objectives, summary statements, vocabulary terms, and their definitions
- Includes a complete English/Spanish Glossary

L2

Assessment

Performance Assessment

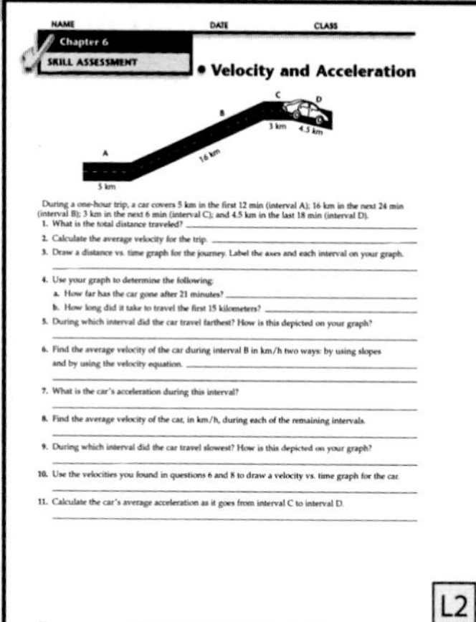

Chapter 6
SKILL ASSESSMENT
Velocity and Acceleration

L2

Chapter Review

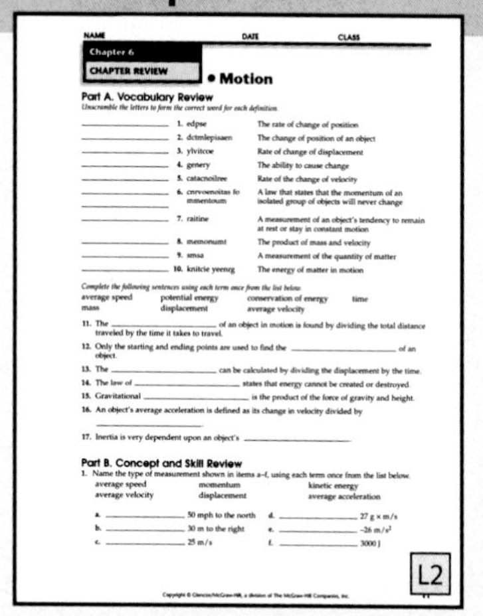

Chapter 6
CHAPTER REVIEW
Motion

Part A. Vocabulary Review
Part B. Concept and Skill Review

L2

Assessment

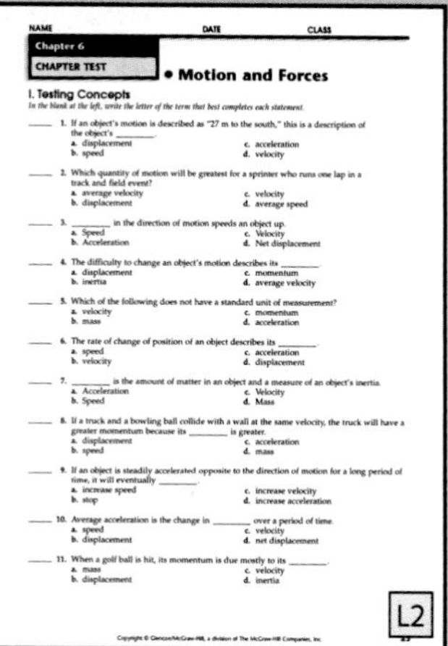

Chapter 6
CHAPTER TEST
Motion and Forces

I. Testing Concepts

L2

Test Practice Workbook

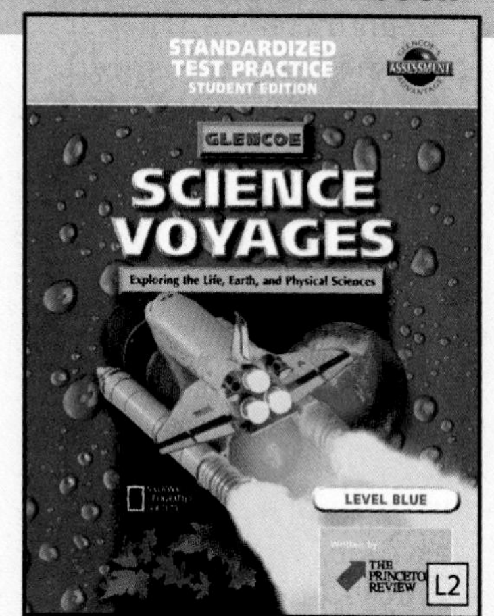

STANDARDIZED TEST PRACTICE
STUDENT EDITION
GLENCOE
SCIENCE VOYAGES
Exploring the Life, Earth, and Physical Sciences
LEVEL BLUE
THE PRINCETON REVIEW

L2

Extending Content

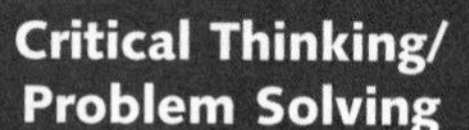

Critical Thinking/ Problem Solving

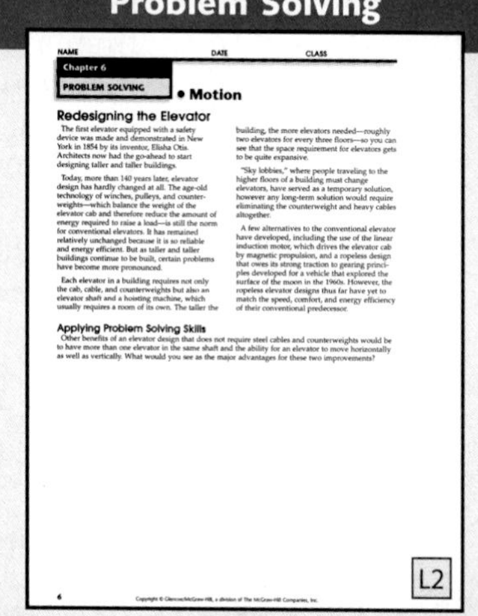

Chapter 6
PROBLEM SOLVING
Motion

Redesigning the Elevator
Applying Problem Solving Skills

L2

Multicultural Connections

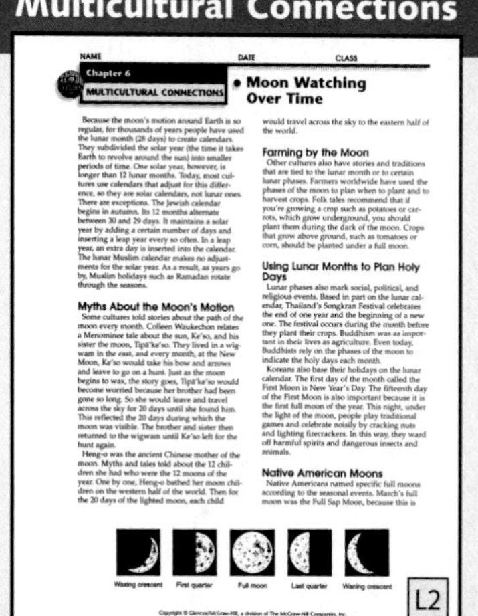

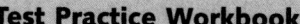

Chapter 6
MULTICULTURAL CONNECTIONS
Moon Watching Over Time

Farming by the Moon
Using Lunar Months to Plan Holy Days
Myths About the Moon's Motion
Native American Moons

L2

Helping You Prepare

Motion (Section 6-1)

Although early Greek scientists understood how levers, simple machines, and floating bodies behaved more than 2000 years ago, they had difficulty explaining motion. Aristotle was one of the first to clarify the concept. In his view, there were two kinds of motion: natural motion and violent motion.

Natural motion occurred when an object attempted to reach its proper location. A rock would fall to Earth when it was dropped because that was where it belonged; smoke would rise because it belonged to the air. Violent motion resulted when outside forces were imposed on an object. Pushing a cart or lifting a weight produced violent motion of those objects.

Following Aristotle's teachings led to contradictions. Over the years, scientists observed natural phenomena that did not fit Aristotle's view of the world. Galileo observed that when he dropped a light object and a heavy object from a tower at the same time, both objects hit the ground together. According to Aristotle's teaching, a stone that was twice as heavy would travel twice as fast and hit the ground in half the time. Wrestling with these contradictions led Galileo to modify Aristotle's thinking and propose new explanations of motion that did a better job of describing how things move.

Galileo broke with Aristotle's notion that the distance that separated an object from its proper place determined its natural motion. He introduced time as an important factor in describing motion. Using distance and time to describe motion, he defined speed, velocity, and acceleration. With these concepts, he was able to explain the motion of a ball on a plane. He noted that the speed of a ball increases when it rolls down an inclined plane, that the speed decreases when it rolls up the plane, and that the speed does not change when it rolls on a flat plane. Galileo called an object's tendency to resist changes in motion inertia.

Aristotle and Galileo each made major contributions to our understanding of motion. We still use many of their ideas when we teach students today. In some ways, students repeat the learning process these great thinkers used in developing their understandings of motion. Students come to the classroom with a view of how things move. By providing them with counterexamples that challenge their views, we encourage them to let go of the concepts that cannot explain contradictions in favor of concepts that provide more complete explanations.

GLENCOE TECHNOLOGY

CD-ROM

Glencoe Science Voyages Interactive CD-ROM

Chapter Summaries

Use the Chapter Summary to introduce, teach, or review chapter material.

Newton's Laws of Motion (Section 6-1)

Galileo's work was expanded on by Newton to explain the motion of a body. Newton's three laws of motion describe how forces affect an object's motion. The three laws are: An object will remain at rest or continue moving with constant velocity until it is acted upon by a net force. An object acted upon by a net force will accelerate in the direction of the force according to $a = F/m$. And, forces occur in equal but opposite pairs.

This chapter will discuss acceleration rather than force, but it may be helpful to keep in mind that any change (acceleration) in an object's motion is caused by a net force. Recall that force = (mass)(acceleration). Because mass is constant, the acceleration is proportional to the force.

Vectors (Section 6-1)

The quantities described in this section that have magnitude and direction, such as displacement, velocity, and acceleration, are called vector quantities. Other examples include momentum and force. A quantity with magnitude but no direction, such as mass or speed, is called a scalar.

One way to visualize a motion problem is with vectors, which are arrows that correspond in length to the magnitude and point in the direction of the quantity. For example, an arrow 2 cm long pointing to the left could represent a velocity of 2 m/s left. You can add vectors by drawing them tip-to-tail and then connecting the two ends of the chain with a sum vector.

This is easiest to see with displacements (try 1 m left + 3 m right + 2 m up, in any order) but it is true for any group of vectors. You can draw vectors to represent all the displacements, velocities, accelerations, or forces acting on an object. Add them to find the net value. Note that you cannot add vectors that represent different quantities, such as velocity to acceleration.

Momentum (Section 6-2)

Momentum is the product of the mass and velocity of an object. It measures how difficult it is to change the motion of an object. It is "inertia in motion." An object can have a large momentum if it has a large mass, a high velocity, or both.

When an object with a large momentum collides with an immovable object, like a wall, it undergoes a rapid change in velocity, which produces a force of impact on the wall. During the collision, the object colliding with the wall changes its momentum, and the force of impact imparted to the wall over the time of contact is equal to the object's change in momentum. The product of the force of impact and time is called impulse. So, simply put, impulse = change in momentum, or $F\Delta t = \Delta(mv)$. Δ means "change in," so $\Delta t = t_{final} - t_{initial}$. By increasing the time over which momentum changes, for example with a cushion on the wall, we can decrease the force of impact.

Energy
(Section 6-3)

Energy is a difficult concept for students to grasp because it is so abstract. Unlike mass, which you can touch and feel, energy only manifests itself in the change process. We know it is there because it reveals itself in certain changes. In this chapter, students are introduced to different forms of energy and the law of conservation of energy, which states that energy cannot be created or destroyed, merely transformed from one form to another.

This chapter also introduces gravitational potential energy and kinetic energy and shows the relationship between them in simple systems: a dropped object, a simple pendulum, and a bouncing ball. As the changes in each system occur, total energy is conserved, as gravitational potential energy is transformed to kinetic energy and in some cases back to gravitational potential energy. Because it is possible to use measurable quantities to calculate the gravitational potential and kinetic energies, it is possible to describe these energy transformations quantitatively.

SCIENCE UPDATE

For current events or science in the news, access the Glencoe Science Web Site at **www.glencoe.com/sec/science**

Teacher to Teacher

"I use the idea of a treasure map to illustrate how doing multiple displacements in any sequence will still lead to the 'treasure.' The distance from the origin to 'X' is the resultant of the multiple moves. To help students grasp the concept, I demonstrate at least two possible sequences."

John Burger

John Burger, Assistant Professor
New England Institute of Technology
Warwick, RI

CHAPTER 6
Motion

CHAPTER OVERVIEW

Section 6-1 Displacement, velocity, and acceleration are introduced and used to describe the motion of an object.

Section 6-2 This section defines momentum and demonstrates that it is conserved in a collision.

Section 6-3 This section defines kinetic and gravitational potential energy and discusses the law of conservation of energy.

Chapter Vocabulary

speed
displacement
velocity
acceleration
mass
inertia
momentum
law of conservation of momentum
energy
kinetic energy
law of conservation of energy
gravitational potential energy

Theme Connection

Stability and Change Motion is the change in the location of an object. Displacement, velocity, and acceleration describe how the location of an object changes over time. Total momentum is conserved when objects collide, but momentum can be transferred from one object to another. The energy of the universe is constant, although the forms of energy change.

If time does not permit teaching the entire chapter, use Reviewing Main Ideas on pp. 170–171.

CHAPTER 6

Motion

Chapter Preview

Skills Preview

Skill Builders
- Measuring in SI
- Observe and Infer

Activities
- Use Numbers
- Design an Experiment

MiniLabs
- Use Numbers
- Observe and Infer

Reading Check ✓

Before reading the chapter, list the vocabulary terms. Note what you think each word means. As you read, revise your definitions.

146

Multiple Learning Styles

Look for the following logos for strategies that emphasize different learning modalities.

Kinesthetic Explore Activity, p. 147; Multiple Learning Styles, p. 152; MiniLab, p. 152; Activity, pp. 154, 161

Visual-Spatial Multiple Learning Styles, p. 149; Visual Learning, pp. 153, 161; Activity, p. 164; Science Journal, p. 167; Reteach, pp. 162, 170

Interpersonal Integrating the Sciences, pp. 150, 153; Discussion, pp. 151, 162; Review, p. 170

Logical-Mathematical Tying to Previous Knowledge, p. 148; Multiple Learning Styles, p. 149; Discussion, p. 149; Enrichment, p. 150; MiniLab, p. 166; Assessment, p. 168

Linguistic Science Journal, p. 160; Quick Demo, p. 167; Enrichment, p. 167; Review, p. 170

Intrapersonal Tying to Previous Knowledge, p. 166

Explore Activity

It's your turn. You chalk up the end of your pool cue and take aim. If you make the break just right, the balls will scatter just how you want them to. You might have observed the collision of two or more balls when playing pool, croquet, or pinball. With practice and understanding, players learn to control the motions of the balls. Science can explain the motion.

Compare Collisions

1. Use a piece of paper with a fold in the middle to make a track and a ruler with a groove to make a ramp.
2. Lean the ruler against a binder or a book to give it a slope. Place the base of the ramp on the track.
3. Put a target marble at the bottom of the ramp. Mark its starting position.
4. Let a second marble, the shooter, roll down the ramp from about 10 cm up and hit the target marble. Mark on the paper where both marbles go.
5. Repeat the experiment, starting the shooter higher up the ramp.

In your Science Journal, describe your experiment and what you discovered. Did both marbles always move? When did they move farthest?

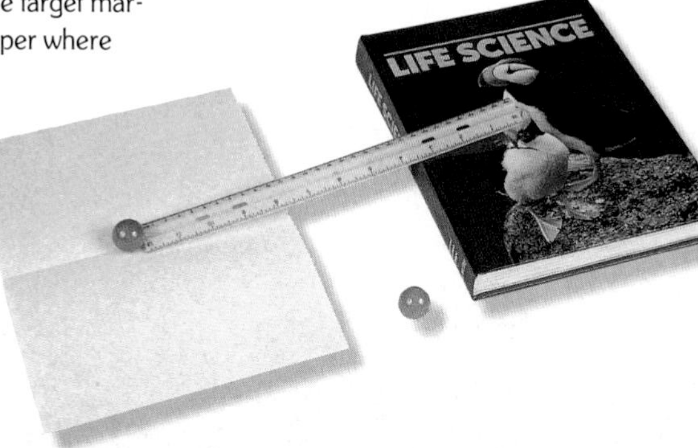

Assessment Planner

Portfolio
Refer to p. 171 for suggested items that students might select for their portfolios.

Performance Assessment
See p. 171 for additional Performance Assessment options.
Skill Builder, pp. 155, 163, 168
MiniLab, pp. 152, 166
Activity 6-1, pp. 156–157; 6-2, p. 164

Content Assessment
Section Assessment, pp. 155, 163, 168
Chapter Assessment, pp. 172–173
Proficiency Prep, pp. 155, 163, 168

Explore Activity

Purpose

Kinesthetic Use the Explore Activity to help students discover how momentum is transferred from one body to another. L2 ELL COOP LEARN

Preparation

Sort the marbles so that each group's marbles are about the same size.

Materials

two marbles, a ruler with a groove, paper, textbook

Teaching Strategies

Give each student group a large shooter marble and repeat the experiment.

Students will state that when the marbles collide, both marbles move. When the rolling marble starts higher on the ramp or is larger, the marble at the bottom of the ramp moves faster following the collision. When the rolling marble is larger, the marble at the bottom of the ramp also moves faster after the collision.

Assessment

Oral Ask students to describe what happens when someone who is skating fast collides with a skater who is standing still. *After the collision, both skaters move forward (if they don't fall down) at speeds less than the fast skater's speed before the collision.* Use **Performance Assessment in the Science Classroom,** p. 71.

SECTION 6-1

Prepare

Refer to **Motion, Newton's Laws of Motion,** and **Vectors** on pp. 146E–F.

Preplanning

Refer to the **Chapter Organizer** on pp. 146A–B.

1 Motivate

Bellringer

Before presenting the lesson, display **Section Focus Transparency 12** on the overhead projector. Use the accompanying **Focus Activity** worksheet. L2 ELL

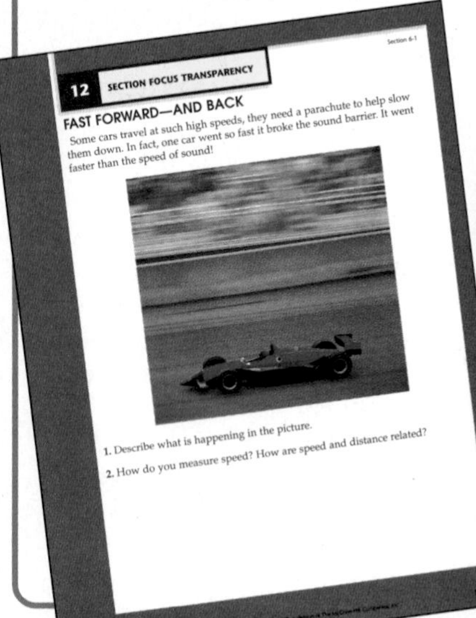

Tying to Previous Knowledge

Logical-Mathematical Have students review graphing techniques: establishing scales with equal increments, labeling axes with variable names and units, titling, and using colors to distinguish variables.

6-1 What is motion?

- How to calculate speed
- How to calculate velocity and acceleration

Vocabulary
speed
displacement
velocity
acceleration

- Most of the changes you observe are the result of matter in motion.

Change in Position

As you stand on a street corner, you can sense how fast all the vehicles and pedestrians are moving by watching them change position. If something is moving slowly, such as a snail crossing a wall, its slow motion is obvious. By observing for just a short time, you know it will take hours for it to change its position from one end of the wall to the other. At the other extreme, a race car changes its position in a flash. A car can be moving so fast that you have a hard time following it. By observing for a short time, you know it can cover a lot of track in a hurry. It is easy to get a rough idea of an object's motion from familiar experiences, as shown in **Figure 6-1.**

To better describe an object's motion, numbers are used. The rate of change of position is called **speed.** You can describe an object's motion with its speed at one instant, as police radar does. Or, you can describe the average speed for a journey. Average speed is found by dividing the total distance traveled by the time it takes.

$$\text{average speed} = \frac{\text{distance}}{\text{time}}$$

If you ran 50 m in 20 s, the average speed was as follows.

$$\frac{50\text{ m}}{20\text{ s}} = 2.5\text{ m/s}$$

Your average speed was 2.5 m/s.

In the example above, you might have started out slowly, at a steady speed, slowed to turn around, and

Figure 6-1 Speed is the rate of change of position.

A This rhinoceros beetle might walk 0.08 m in 10 s, for an average speed of 0.008 m/s.

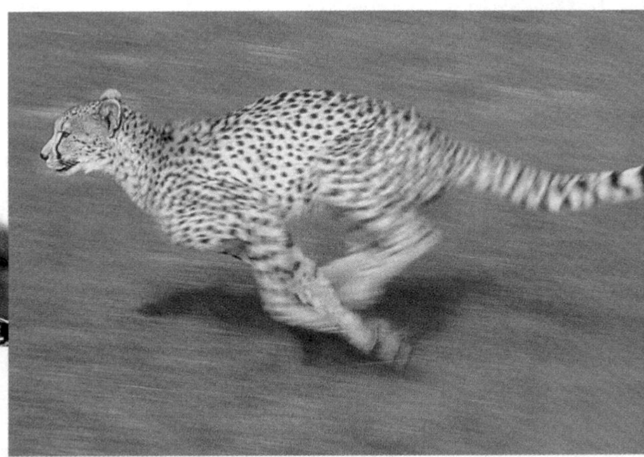

B This cheetah might run 300 m in 10 s, for an average speed of 30 m/s.

Resource Manager

The following **Teacher Classroom Resources** can be used with Section 6-1:

Reproducible Masters

Activity Worksheets, pp. 29–30, 33 L2
Enrichment, p. 12 L3
Laboratory Manual, pp. 33–36
Reinforcement, p. 12 L2
Study Guide, p. 21 L1 ELL

Transparencies

Teaching Transparency 11 L2

Graph A

Constant Speed

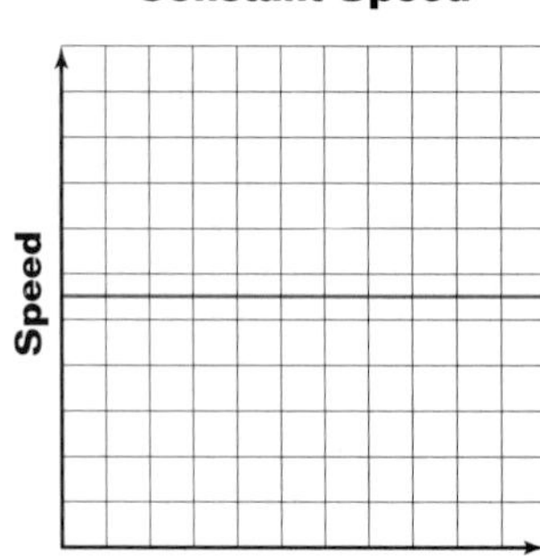

Graph B

Speed Changes at Constant Rate

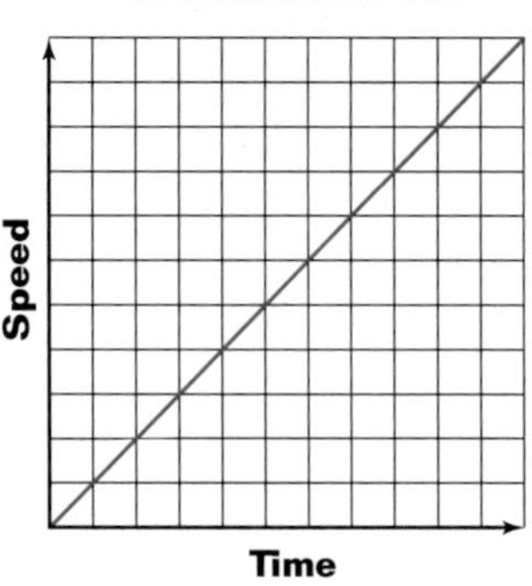

Graph C

Instantaneous Speed

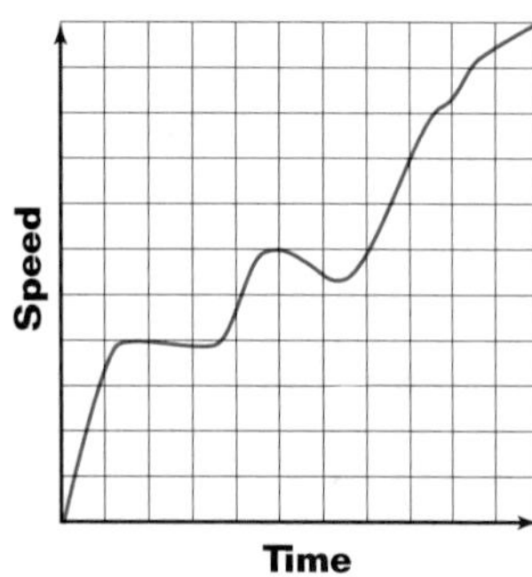

stopped suddenly to avoid hitting a wall. If you were concerned with the details of your motion, you might record your speed every few seconds over the course of the run. You might also record the direction at those times, tell where you ran, and indicate when you speeded up or slowed down. In this chapter, you will usually be concerned with average speed, or with speed that is increasing or decreasing in a steady, predictable way. You can compare the ways of describing motion in the graphs in **Figure 6-2.**

Figure 6-2 Graph A shows constant speed. When you use average speed to make calculations, you treat it as a constant speed. Constant acceleration is illustrated in Graph B. The actual speed increases over time. In this case, the average speed is the same as the constant speed in Graph A. Graph C shows the details of a speed changing over time. **Compare the initial and final speeds in Graphs B and C.**

Displacement

Saying you ran 2.5 m/s is often all you need to know. But where did you go? The direction of motion can be important. **Displacement** measures the change in position of an object. It includes direction. Only the starting and ending points are used to find displacement. This is illustrated in **Figure 6-3.** If you tell a friend you moved 20 m to the left, you are describing your displacement.

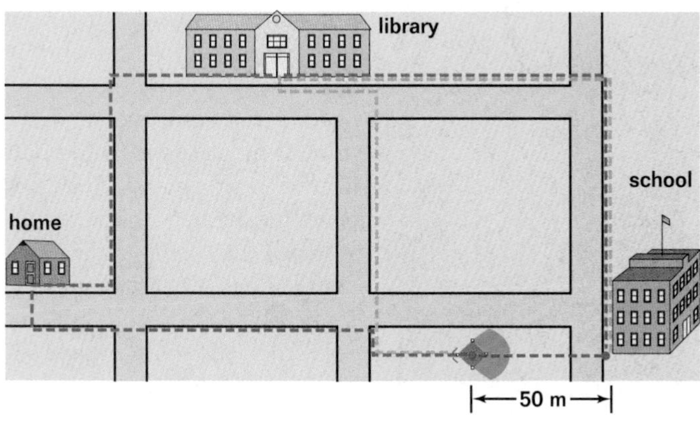

Figure 6-3 Three students (red line, blue line, orange line) walk from school to the ball diamond. In each case, the displacement is 50 m west. The distances traveled depend on the routes each student chose. **How does the distance traveled in each case compare to the displacement?**

2 Teach

Correcting Misconceptions

Students may confuse speed and average speed. A walk around the block with an average speed of 5 km/h could include many different instantaneous speeds—running to catch the walk signal, stopping to chat with a friend, and strolling slowly while watching a cat.

Discussion

Logical-Mathematical Lead the students to conclude that speed-time graphs have characteristic shapes for different types of motion. The speed-time graph of constant speeds will always be horizontal lines (where slope equals zero). The intercept of the line with the speed axis shows how fast the object is going. When the object is standing still, the speed is zero and the graph is the time axis. Positively accelerated motion always produces a graph with a positive slope, and negatively accelerated motion produces a graph with a negative slope. Ask the students to describe the motion represented in **Figure 6-2C.** L2

Caption Answers

Figure 6-2 *If scales are the same, the speeds are the same.*

Figure 6-3 *The red path has equal distance and displacement; in all others the distance is greater than displacement. (You cannot have displacement greater than distance.)*

Multiple Learning Styles

Logical-Mathematical To understand the speed-time graphs in **Figure 6-2,** some students will need to collect and plot speed and time data. Once they have drawn the graphs, they will be able to understand the relationships they describe.

Visual-Spatial Refer to **Figure 6-2.** On an overhead projector with a transparency marked off in equal increments, use a model car to illustrate moving slowly at a constant speed, moving quickly at a constant speed, standing still, moving with a constant positive acceleration, and moving with a constant negative acceleration.

Answer to Reading Check

Velocity describes how fast and in what direction an object is moving. Speed describes only how fast the object is moving.

Enrichment

Logical-Mathematical Ask students to determine the displacement of a hiker who walks west for two hours at a rate of 3 km/h and then walks north for four hours at a rate of 2 km/h. Draw a diagram that describes this hike. *The hiker goes 6 km west, then 8 km north. The displacement is 10 km in a direction a little north of northwest.* P

Using Science Words

A quantity that has a magnitude and a direction, such as displacement or velocity, is called a vector. The word *vector* is used in biology. In pathology, it describes an organism that carries a virus from one host to another (mosquitoes are a vector for malaria); in genetics, it describes an agent, such as a plasmid, that transfers genetic material from one location to another.

GLENCOE TECHNOLOGY

Videodisc

Glencoe Science Voyages Interactive Videodisc—Physical

Side 1, Lesson 1 *Motion*

1473

Refer to the Videodisc Teacher Guide for additional bar codes.

Velocity

The rate of change of displacement is **velocity** (vel AH seh TEE). Velocity includes both speed and direction. For example, you might say, "We drove west at 30 km/h." In this case, 30 km/h is the speed and west at 30 km/h is the velocity. *Velocity* is often used as a synonym for *speed,* but in science velocity and speed mean two different things.

$$\text{average velocity} = \frac{\text{displacement}}{\text{time}}$$

$$v = \frac{d}{t}$$

Reading Check What is the difference between velocity and speed?

In this equation, v stands for average velocity and d for displacement.

Average speed is not always equal to average velocity. For example, if you run around a 1-km track in six minutes (0.1 hour), your distance traveled is 1 km. However, your displacement for the whole trip around the track is 0 because you end up where you started. Your initial and final positions are identical. So, despite the fact that you ran the whole track, there is no change in position.

$$\text{average speed} = \frac{\text{distance}}{\text{time}} = \frac{1\text{ km}}{0.1\text{ h}} = 10\text{ km/h}$$

$$\text{average velocity} = \frac{\text{displacement}}{\text{time}} = \frac{0\text{ km}}{0.1\text{ h}} = 0\text{ km/h}$$

Your average speed is 10 km/h, but your average velocity is 0 km/h.

Velocity gives much more information than speed when measuring motion. The directional part is important. You have seen examples of velocity. For example, when weather reporters track a hurricane, they give its position and its velocity. The direction is needed for someone to determine if he or she is in the path of the hurricane and should leave the area.

When the *Pathfinder* spacecraft landed on Mars in 1997, it released a small robot named Sojourner, shown in **Figure 6-4.** The robot had to be guided

Figure 6-4 Controllers gave Sojourner careful instructions on how to roll away from the *Pathfinder* spacecraft after its cushioned landing on Mars. **Why was the robot's speed important? Why was its direction important?**

150 CHAPTER 6 MOTION

Integrating the Sciences

Earth Science Take the students to a stream and ask them to work in teams to determine the velocity of the water in the stream. Have them compare their measurements with those made by others in the class. Caution them to stay away from slippery banks, cars, and other hazards. Dropping a small twig or piece of bark on one side of a bridge, timing how long it takes to drift to the other side of the bridge, and then pacing off the width of the bridge would be one way to gather the data needed to complete this exercise. L2

ELL COOP LEARN

around large boulders and then moved up against rocks in order to study them. Sojourner could not carry out its mission without ground controllers on Earth knowing both its position and its velocity.

Relative Motion

Motion is always described relative to a frame of reference. For example, the *Sojourner* robot in **Figure 6-4** starts at the spacecraft *Pathfinder.* A displacement might be described as "4 m north of *Pathfinder.*" Another reference frame, such as the rock Scooby Doo, could have been chosen. People also must agree on directions. *Forward* and *left* can have different meanings, depending on which way you are facing.

For motion back and forth along a line, people sometimes use positive and negative numbers. For example, +3 would mean three steps forward, and –5 would mean five steps back. If you make both displacements, you will be two steps back from where you started, as shown in **Figure 6-5.** This is true no matter which order you do the displacements.

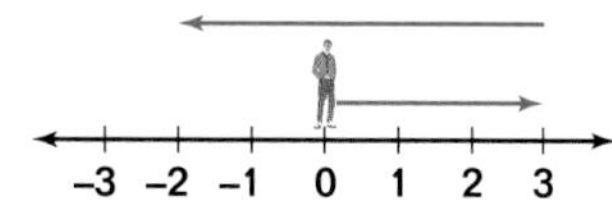

Figure 6-5 If you take 3 steps forward and 5 steps back, you will be 2 steps back from your starting point. **What happens if you take 4 steps left and 1 step right?**

Velocity is also relative. Imagine watching a train moving 20 km/h north relative to the ground. If you are standing on the sidewalk, the train appears to be moving at 20 km/h north. If you are riding in a car going north at 15 km/h, the train appears to be moving more slowly, at 5 km/h north. If you are riding in a car going south at 15 km/h, the train appears to zip by at 35 km/h. The motion of the train relative to the ground is the same in each case. Only your frame of reference changes.

Positive and negative numbers are used to indicate motion forward and backward or right and left. **Figure 6-6** shows an example of how to compute relative velocity.

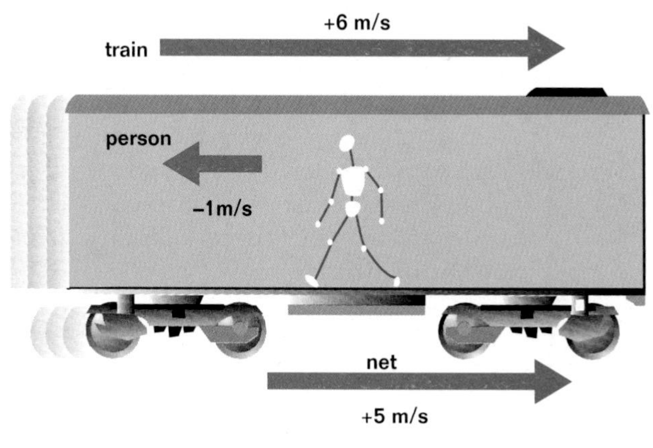

Figure 6-6 The velocity of the walker relative to the ground is 5 m/s forward.

Using an Analogy

If students have been to a large airport with moving sidewalks, they have some experience with relative motion. People standing still on the walkways are moving relative to the ground. Point out that people standing still on the ground are moving relative to people riding on the sidewalks. If someone walks the wrong way on a moving sidewalk at a high enough speed, he or she will be holding still relative to the ground. You can also point out that cars moving in the opposite direction on the highway appear to zip past because their speed relative to your car is very high. Whereas when you ride in a car that moves at 105 km/h to pass a car moving at 100 km/h, the motion of your car relative to the other appears slow.

Discussion

Interpersonal Ask students in groups of four or five to make a list of as many different modes of transportation as they can think of. Then ask them to estimate their speeds in SI units and arrange them in order from quickest to slowest. Ask the groups to share their findings. L2 COOP LEARN

Caption Answers

Figure 6-4 *Speed is important because if the robot goes too fast, it might get into trouble; direction is important so the robot goes to the right rock.*

Figure 6-5 *You will be 3 steps to the left of your starting point.*

Across the Curriculum

Physical Education **When you run laps around the track, would you rather have the coach record your average speed or average velocity?** *average speed* **Why?** *Because the track is a circular path, the displacement for any number of laps, and hence the average velocity, is zero. The average speed is a better measure of how fast you were running along the path.* L2

Purpose

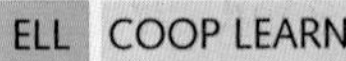

Kinesthetic Students will develop a kinesthetic sense of what it means to accelerate. L3

ELL COOP LEARN

Materials

meterstick, masking tape

Teaching Strategies

Students should take turns clapping and walking the course so that each gets a chance to experience accelerated motion.

Analysis

1. Frontward, your velocity increases. Backward, it decreases.
2. Your velocity and acceleration are listed in the table below.

t (claps)	d (m)	v (m/clap)	a (m/clap^2)
0	0		
1	0.1	0.1	
2	0.4	0.3	0.2
3	0.9	0.5	0.2
4	1.6	0.7	0.2
5	2.5	0.9	0.2
6	3.6	1.1	0.2

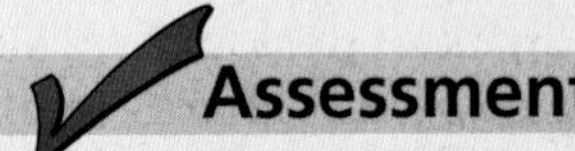

Assessment

Process Give students time-lapse photographs of a falling object or bouncing ball. You must tell them the interval between flashes. This is the time interval they will use. Ask them to measure the average velocity of the object or ball between locations. Then, ask them to estimate the acceleration of the object by calculating the change in the average velocities between locations. Use **Performance Assessment in the Science Classroom,** p. 29.

Acceleration

When you're riding in a car that takes off quickly from a stop sign, you feel your body press back against the seat. When you stop, your body is pushed forward against the seat belt. You can sense motion when you accelerate. **Acceleration** is the rate of change of velocity. Speeding up, slowing down, and turning are all forms of acceleration. To find the average acceleration, use the following formula.

$$\text{average acceleration} = \frac{\text{change in velocity}}{\text{time}}$$

$$a = \frac{v_2 - v_1}{t}$$

For example, if an object takes 2 s to go from velocity 0 to velocity +4 m/s, the average acceleration is found as follows.

$$\frac{4 \text{ m/s} - 0 \text{ m/s}}{2 \text{ s}} = +2 \text{ m/s}^2$$

The average acceleration is $+2$ m/s^2.

You can rearrange the formula to find the change in velocity given the acceleration and time, as illustrated in **Figure 6-7.** The direction of the acceleration is important.

When an object accelerates in the direction it is moving, the object speeds up, as shown in **Figure 6-7A.** If an object is moving to the right and you accelerate it to the right, it goes to the right at a greater velocity.

Acceleration in the direction opposite to its motion slows an object down, as shown in **Figure 6-7B.** If an object is moving forward and you accelerate it backward, its velocity decreases. For example, friction accelerates an object opposite to the direction of motion, slowing it down.

MiniLab

Calculating Acceleration

Procedure

1. Mark off a course. Place tape at the following number of meters from start: 0, 0.1, 0.4, 0.9, 1.6, 2.5, and 3.6.
2. Work with a partner. While one of you claps a slow, steady beat, the other should move along the course, stepping on one piece of tape for each clap.
3. Measure the time between claps.
4. Experience negative acceleration by moving through the course from 3.6 to 0 while your partner claps a steady beat.

Analysis

1. As you move through this course forward and backward, how does your velocity change?
2. Calculate the change in displacement (velocity) and the change in velocity (acceleration) for each time interval. For example, if your claps were about 3 s apart, then you would go from 0 to 0.1 m in 3 s for a velocity of 0.03 m/s, and the acceleration would be (0.03 m/s − 0)/(3 s) = 0.01 m/s^2.

Acceleration and Distance

When an object accelerates in the direction of motion, it covers more distance in each second than it did in the previous second. An object that starts at rest and accelerates at a for time t covers a distance given by the following formula.

$$\text{distance} = 0.5(\text{acceleration})(\text{time})^2$$

$$d = 0.5at^2$$

Multiple Learning Styles

Kinesthetic Students need an opportunity to experience acceleration to know what it feels like. The MiniLab on acceleration is designed to help them develop this sense.

Inclusion Strategies

Physically Challenged Use a wheelchair to help handicapped students complete the MiniLab on acceleration. Choose a reliable student to push the chair through the course while other students clap. For hearing-impaired students, use a strobe light to establish the cadence.

VISUALIZING Acceleration

Figure 6-7 Determine the direction of acceleration and velocity. Find the change in velocity. Then, find the new velocity.

A You are biking at 2 m/s and accelerate forward 0.3 m/s^2 for 2 s.
change in velocity = acceleration × time
= (0.3 m/s^2) (2 s)
= 0.6 m/s
Add the change in velocity to the initial velocity.
2 m/s + 0.6 m/s = 2.6 m/s
Your new velocity is 2.6 m/s forward. **What would your velocity be if you now accelerated at 0.1 m/s^2 for 5 s?**

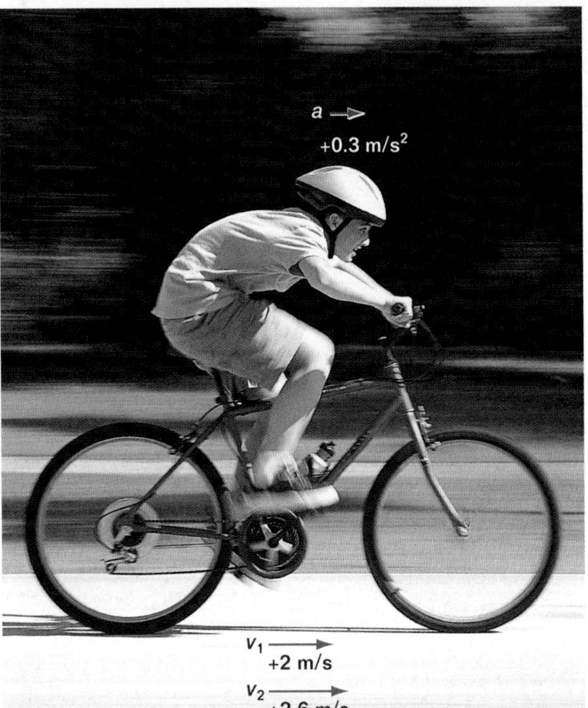

B You are biking at 2 m/s and accelerate backward (brake) at –0.5 m/s^2 for 2 s.
change in velocity = acceleration × time
= (–0.5 m/s^2) (2 s)
= –1 m/s
Add the change in velocity to the initial velocity.
2 m/s – 1 m/s = 1 m/s
Your new velocity is 1 m/s forward. **If you now accelerate at –0.3 m/s^2 for 1.5 s, what will your new velocity be?**

Quick Demo

Velocity describes both the speed and direction of an object. An object is accelerating when its speed or direction changes. Push a student sitting in a rolling chair across the room in a straight line at a constant speed. *Acceleration is zero because neither speed nor direction changed.* Place a penny on a record that is sitting on a turntable. As the record spins at a constant speed, ask the students whether the penny is accelerating. *Yes, although its speed does not change, its direction is constantly changing.*

Caption Answers

Figure 6-7A *2.6 m/s + (0.1 m/s²)(5 s) = 3.1 m/s*

Figure 6-7B *1 m/s + (−0.3 m/s²)(1.5 s) = 0.55 m/s*

VISUAL Learning

Figures 6-7A and 6-7B Ask students to draw velocity-time graphs for the motion shown. *Graph A shows initial velocity of 2 m/s and a line of positive slope climbing to 2.6 m/s at 2 s. Graph B shows initial velocity of 2 m/s and a line of negative slope falling to 1 m/s at 2 s.*

Integrating the Sciences

Biology Ask students to pair up and try to catch a ruler. The student dropping the ruler should hold it just above the catcher's fingers before letting it go. The student catching the ruler should observe how far the ruler fell before it was caught and use this distance (*d*) to calculate how long it fell (*t*) before it was caught. $d = 0.5gt^2$ where *g* is the acceleration due to gravity, 9.8 m/s^2. For example, if the ruler falls 10 cm (0.10 m) before it is caught, $t = \sqrt{2d/g}$ or 0.142 s. After students have calculated their reaction times, have them write them on the chalkboard so they can see how much reaction time varies in a group of people. L3 ELL COOP LEARN

Figures 6-8 and 6-9 Have students compare the shape of the graphs in each interval.

3 Assess

Check for Understanding

Activity

Kinesthetic Ask a volunteer to begin walking at a constant velocity in the classroom. Then ask students, one at a time, to call out changes in motion for the volunteer to perform. Ask the class to watch and raise their hands if they see the volunteer make a mistake. Let the person who called out the motion that stumped the volunteer become the new volunteer. Changes in motion might be: stop, move to the right with a constant speed, move forward with a positive acceleration, and move to the left with a negative acceleration. L2 COOP LEARN

Reteach

As you check the students' understanding, take the opportunity to correct their actions as needed. Make sure that the students demonstrate positive and negative displacement, velocity, and acceleration.

Extension

For students who have mastered this section, use the **Reinforcement** and **Enrichment** masters.

Table 6-1

Accelerating from Rest at 1 m/s^2		
Time (s)	Velocity (m/s) $v = at$	Distance (m) $d = 0.5at^2$
0	0	0.0
1	1	0.5
2	2	2.0
3	3	4.5
4	4	8.0

The velocity and distance of an object accelerating at a constant rate of 1 m/s^2 are given in **Table 6-1.** Note that if the acceleration is opposite to the direction of motion, the object will cover less and less distance in each time interval until it comes to a stop.

Graphing Motion

Graphs can help to explain motion. For example, the graph in **Figure 6-8** describes a bike ride along a street.

a. You start at rest.

b. You accelerate at 0.3 m/s^2 for 10 s.

c. You are now biking at 3 m/s. You maintain this speed for 30 s, until you come to a hill.

d. You start uphill. You slow down at –0.2 m/s^2 until you come to a stop. How long does this take?

e. You remain stopped for 5 s.

f. When you let off the brakes, you start to coast backward. You accelerate backward at –0.2 m/s^2 for 2 s.

g. You squeeze hard on the brakes with an acceleration of 0.4 m/s^2 until you come to a stop. Note that the acceleration is positive because it is opposite to a negative velocity.

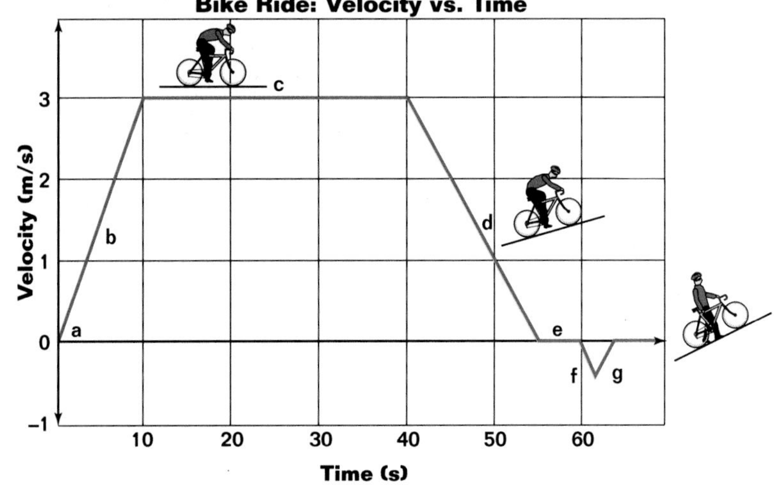

Figure 6-8 The graph shows velocity vs. time for a bike ride. **When is acceleration positive? When is it negative? When is it zero? How can you tell?**

Caption Answers

Figure 6-8 *positive: b, g; negative: d, f; zero: c, e, after g; by the slope of the graph*

Figure 6-9 *zero*

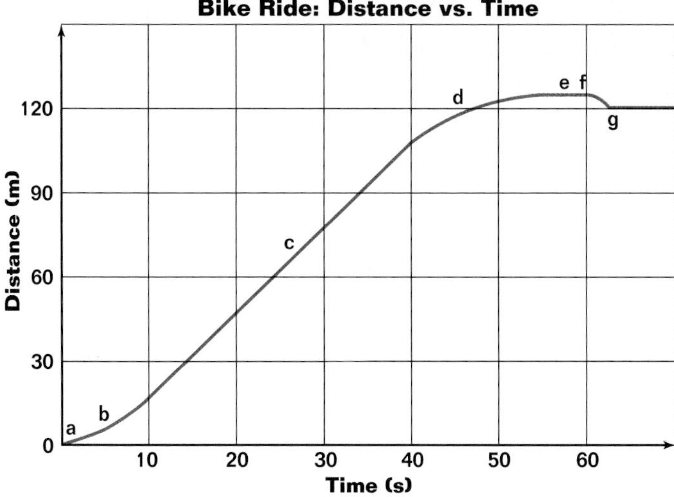

Figure 6-9 The information in **Figure 6-8** also can be conveyed in a distance-time graph, as shown here. Notice that when the acceleration is 0, the distance-time graph is a straight line. When you find the slope of the line (the rate of change of distance), you find the velocity. **What is the acceleration in part c of the graph?**

Compare the velocity-time graph in **Figure 6-8** with the distance-time graph in **Figure 6-9.** Both convey information about the same bike ride. The distance-time graph shows your displacement and how it changed (velocity). The velocity-time graph shows your speed and how it changed. Both describe your motion.

Section Assessment

1. Belayneh Dinsamo of Ethiopia set a world's record in the 1988 Rotterdam Marathon. He ran the 42.2-km course in 2.114 hours. What was his average speed?
2. A bicyclist starts at rest. She starts to pedal, and after 8 s she is traveling forward at 4 m/s. Find her acceleration, including the direction.
3. The bicyclist in question 2 continues to pedal at 4 m/s. Draw a velocity-time graph of her motion from 0 s to 15 s.
4. **Think Critically:** Suppose you are in-line skating forward at 1.5 m/s. Suddenly, another person bumps you, giving you an acceleration of 0.5 m/s^2 for 1 s. What other information do you need to determine your velocity after the push?
5. **Skill Builder**
Using Numbers Do the **Chapter 6 Skill Activity** on page 747 to calculate average velocity based on measurements from a scientific illustration.

Using Math

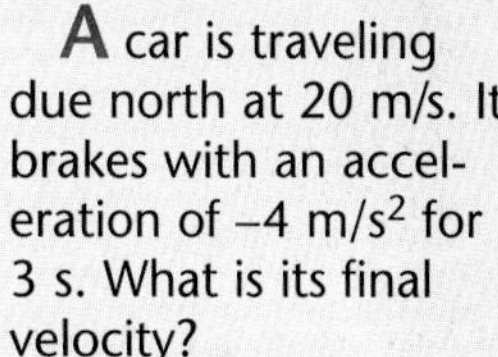

A car is traveling due north at 20 m/s. It brakes with an acceleration of –4 m/s^2 for 3 s. What is its final velocity?

4 Close

Proficiency Prep

Use this quiz to check students' recall of section content.

1. **What gives the direction and speed of an object in motion?** *velocity*
2. **If you are riding south in a car at 50 km/h, how fast do cars traveling with the same speed and direction appear to be moving? Cars traveling at 50 km/h in the opposite direction?** *0 km/h; 100 km/h north*

Section Assessment

1. His average speed is 20 km/h.
2. Her acceleration is 0.5 m/s^2 forward.
3. The graph starts at (0, 0) and goes diagonally to (8, 4). Then, it continues horizontally at 4 m/s^2 from 8 s to 15 s.
4. **Think Critically** You need to know what direction the person pushes you. If you are pushed forward, you will have a velocity of 2.0 m/s forward. If you are pushed backward, you will have a velocity of 1.0 m/s forward.

Using Math

$20 \text{ m/s} + (-4 \text{ m/s}^2)(3 \text{ s}) = 8 \text{ m/s}$

Its final velocity is 8 m/s north.

Assessment

Content Ask the students to determine which type of velocity-time graph most closely matches the motion of the falling ball. *It is constant acceleration, a straight line going diagonally up from (0, 0).* Use **Performance Assessment in the Science Classroom,** p. 41.

Activity 6-1 Design Your Own Experiment

Recognize the Problem

Purpose

Kinesthetic Students will observe (or experience) different types of motion involving constant speed. L2 ELL COOP LEARN

Process Skills

forming a hypothesis, comparing and contrasting, measuring in SI, interpreting data

Time

20 minutes to set up the racecourse, 45 minutes to run the races, 45 minutes to analyze the data and discuss the results

Materials

Have some of the students use masking tape on the floor to mark off eight or ten equal distances in two lanes. Tape numbers on the wall to identify the marks on the floor.

Safety Precautions

Students will need to stop and start quickly. Be sure the location is safe for the hare to jog.

Form a Hypothesis

Possible Hypothesis

Students might hypothesize that if the hare runs twice as fast as the tortoise, the hare will need to spend half the time resting to make his or her average velocity match that of the tortoise.

Test Your Hypothesis

Possible Procedures

Divide the class into teams of three or four. Have each team choose a tortoise and a hare. Experiment to determine reasonable speeds for the strolling tortoise and jogging hare in each group. Design a strategy for the hare in the first race. Consider allowing students to try the strategy for a mini-course. Then, design a strategy for the second race.

Design Your Own Experiment

Activity 6-1

The Tortoise and the Hare

Possible Materials

- Stopwatch
  - **clock or watch with second hand*
- Meterstick or another way of measuring position
- Calculator
  - **Alternate Materials*

The tortoise and the hare is an old fable. The tortoise and the hare have a race. The tortoise plods slowly and steadily along. The hare alternately zips ahead, then stops for a while. Even though the hare is faster, the tortoise wins the race. The hare's velocity at any moment can be higher than the tortoise's, but over the course of the race, the tortoise's average velocity is greater than the hare's.

Recognize the Problem

You will design two racing strategies. One will involve slow, steady movement. The other will involve rapid starts, stops, and pauses. Compare and contrast the two types of motion.

Form a Hypothesis

Based on what you know about motion, state a hypothesis about how the tortoise's average speed and average velocity compare to those of the hare.

Goals

- **Measure** the positions of two different racers.
- **Calculate** their average speeds.
- **Use** a position-time graph.

Safety Precautions

Work where there is enough space to jog safely.

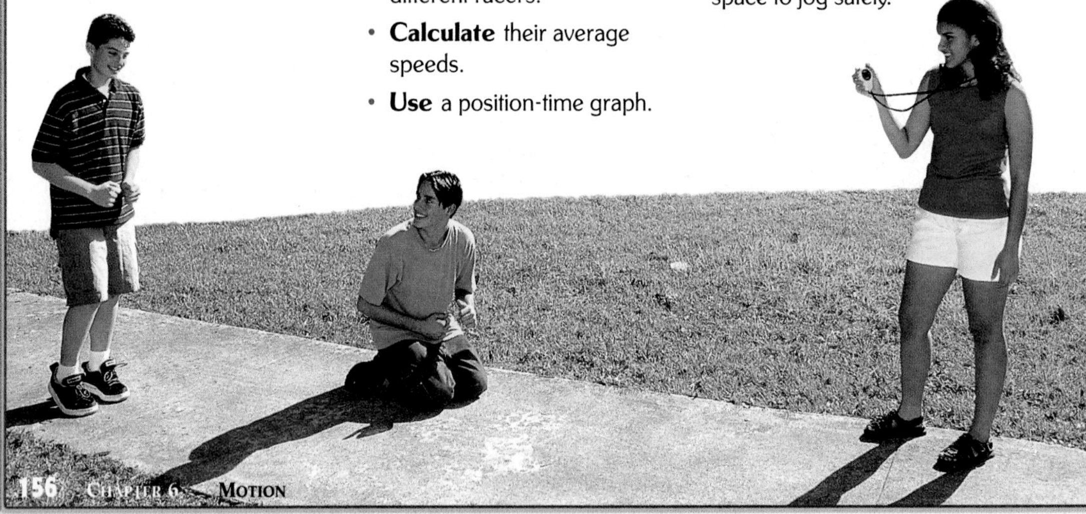

156 CHAPTER 6 MOTION

Teaching Strategies

- Once the data are collected, return to the classroom to perform the analysis or assign it as homework.

Expected Outcome

The faster the hare is relative to the tortoise, the more time he or she will need to spend resting for the first race. In the second race, the hare can spend the whole race trotting back and forth between two points, ultimately getting nowhere.

- Remind students that a champion sprinter (hare) might still do poorly in a marathon.

Test Your Hypothesis

Plan

1. **Find** a location for your race. Measure the distance.
2. Choose a racer to play the tortiose and one to be the hare. The tortoise should walk the course slowly. **Time** the tortoise and **calculate** the average velocity.
3. The hare will have two different strategies. Both will involve jogging part of the time at a constant speed. **Find** a reasonable speed for the jogging hare.
4. **Design** the first hare strategy. The hare will either jog at constant speed or stand still. For example, the hare might jog for 5 s, rest for 10 s, and so on. Try to make a plan that lets the tortoise win the race.
5. **Design** a second hare strategy. This time, the hare will jog forward and backward. For example, the hare might jog forward 5 s, back 5 s, and so on. Again, try to let the tortoise win the race.
6. In both plans, ignore the hare's acceleration. Assume that the hare is moving at constant speed or is at rest.

Do

1. Make sure your teacher approves your plan before you proceed.
2. **Run** the two races of hare vs. tortoise. One person should use a timer to call out *start, 5, 10,* and so on at 5-s intervals. (Longer intervals are fine if you have a long course.)
3. While doing the experiment, **record** your observations. Who won? When was the tortoise ahead? When was the hare ahead?

Analyze Your Data

1. **Calculate** the average velocity of each racer for both races.
2. **Calculate** the average speed of each racer for both races.
3. Use a distance-time graph to **compare and contrast** the distances the hare ran in the two races.

Draw Conclusions

1. If you know the speed of two racers at any moment, can you **predict** the outcome of a race? Explain.
2. **Compare and contrast** the different types of motion seen in the races.

Error Analysis

Ask students how they might make their speed measurements more precise. *They could make either the distance or time measurement more precise to improve the precision of the speed measurement.*

Analyze Your Data

1. average velocity $= \frac{\text{displacement}}{\text{time}}$
   For both races, the velocity is the length of the course divided by the time to run it for each.
2. average speed $= \frac{\text{distance}}{\text{time}}$
   For the first race, average speed is average velocity. For the second, the hare runs the entire course at his or her greater average speed.
3. The hare ran a much greater distance in the second race, even though displacement was the same in both races.

Draw Conclusions

1. No, as illustrated by the hare in both races; in the second race, the hare's instantaneous speed is always greater than the tortoise's.
2. The tortoise has a slow but constant velocity. In the first race, the hare's velocity is sometimes greater than the tortoise's and sometimes zero. In the second, the hare demonstrates high positive and negative velocities.

GO Further

Ask students to look up the Olympic records for the 100-m dash and the 100-m freestyle for men and women. Ask them to calculate the average speeds of the record holders in these races and compare them.

Assessment

Oral Explain how the tortoise might still win the race if the average *speed* of the hare always exceeds that of the tortoise. Use **Performance Assessment in the Science Classroom,** p. 71.

SECTION 6•2

Prepare

Refer to **Momentum** on p. 146F.

Preplanning

Refer to the **Chapter Organizer** on pp. 146A–B.

1 Motivate

Bellringer

Before presenting the lesson, display **Section Focus Transparency 13** on the overhead projector. Use the accompanying **Focus Activity** worksheet. L2 ELL

Section 6-2

13 SECTION FOCUS TRANSPARENCY

ON THE MOVE

Animals such as this rhinoceros at Ngorongoro Crater in Africa can move surprisingly quickly when charging another animal or trying to get away from one.

1. Describe what is happening in the picture. Which animals in the photo appears to be in motion? Which animals appears to be still?
2. How easy will it be for the animal in motion to stop?
3. How much effort will it take to start again? Compare this effort with the amount of effort it will take to keep running.

13

Tying to Previous Knowledge

Review the results of the Explore Activity at the beginning of this chapter with students. Momentum is transferred between the balls when they collide.

6•2 What is momentum?

What You'll Learn

- How to find an object's momentum
- How to use the law of conservation of momentum to understand collisions

Vocabulary

mass
inertia
momentum
law of conservation of momentum

Why It's Important

- The conservation of momentum explains collisions between objects, whether they are pool balls or atoms.

Mass and Inertia

The universe consists of matter in motion. **Figure 6-10** shows some familiar examples. The stars you see, the air you breathe, the ground you walk on, and the eyes you read with all are made of matter. The quantity of matter is measured as **mass.** The unit of mass is the kilogram. From the tiniest particles, such as atoms, to the largest objects, such as stars, all are made of matter.

Mass plays an important role when you study motion. In the 1600s, Galileo Galilei studied motion. He noticed that objects with a lot of mass were more difficult to move and, once moving, were just as difficult to stop. If you have ever had to help push a stalled car out of the road, you know just how difficult it can be to get it moving. Once it's moving, it's easy to keep it moving as long as the ground is flat. The effort to stop the car is just as great as the effort to get it moving.

Compared to pushing a car, pushing your bicycle is easy. It hardly takes any effort because the bicycle has a small mass. Galileo used the word inertia (in ER sha) to describe how easy or difficult it is to change an object's motion. **Inertia** measures an object's tendency to remain at rest or stay in constant motion. A measure of the inertia of an object is its mass. By pushing on different objects, you can compare their masses by seeing how easy they are to move.

Figure 6-10 Your world is filled with matter in motion.

A People can move their bodies, as well as objects such as this bat and ball.

B Steam lifts the lid off a pot.

Resource Manager

The following **Teacher Classroom Resources** can be used with Section 6-2:

 **Reproducible Masters**

Activity Worksheets, pp. 31–32 L2
Critical Thinking/Problem Solving, p. 6 L2
Enrichment, p. 13 L3
Laboratory Manual, pp. 37–40 L2
Multicultural Connections, pp. 11–12 L2
Reinforcement, p. 13 L2
Study Guide, p. 22

Transparencies

Science Integration Transparency 6 L2

Momentum

When Sir Isaac Newton began to organize his ideas to explain force and motion, he kept returning to the same two quantities—mass and velocity. He decided that these two quantities are the most important things to know when you want to understand an object's motion. He called the product of mass and velocity **momentum.** Momentum has the symbol p. Using m for mass, the formula is as follows.

$$\text{momentum} = \text{mass} \times \text{velocity}$$
$$p = mv$$

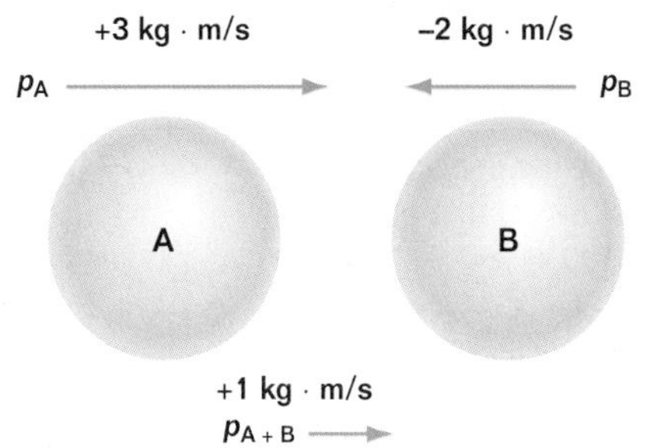

Figure 6-11 The momentum of this system, balls A and B, is the sum of the individual momentums.

Because momentum includes velocity, it has direction. Momentum points in the direction of motion, just like velocity. Positive and negative signs are used to indicate momentums in opposite directions. You can add momentums, as shown in **Figure 6-11.**

Momentum, Newton said, was the quantity of motion. If you know this quantity, then you can begin to understand exactly how objects move.

When a fast-moving baseball is zipping straight toward your head, you know you'd better duck! Moving at up to 200 km/h (56 m/s), the speeding ball could seriously injure you. Even if you caught the ball with a glove, your hand

C Natural processes control the movement of clouds and air, which we recognize as weather, and more dramatic movements, like earthquakes and volcanic eruptions.

D Satellites are in motion around Earth.

Flex Your Brain

Use the Flex Your Brain activity to have students explore INERTIA.

2 Teach

Using Science Words

When two objects collide and stick together after the collision, they undergo an inelastic collision. In such cases, momentum is conserved, just as it is in elastic collisions, where the objects bounce apart after the collision.

Teacher FYI

- A safety belt ties you to the car in which you are traveling. When the car stops suddenly, your inertia causes you to continue moving forward until you encounter a barrier: if not the seat belt, then the windshield or dashboard. When you are not wearing a seat belt, your momentum changes much more suddenly than it does when you are wearing a seat belt. This sudden change in momentum can cause injuries—concussions, whiplash, cuts, and bruises.
- An airbag prevents you from hitting the windshield or dashboard and allows your momentum to change over a longer period of time.

Guided Reading Strategy

Reflective Journal In this strategy, students identify activities and what they learned and record responses to the activities. Have students divide pieces of paper into several columns. Have them record their thoughts under headings such as "What I did," "What I learned," "What questions do I have," "What surprises did I experience," and "Overall response." Have students write a Reflective Journal for an activity in this section.

EARTH SCIENCE INTEGRATION

Because a meteor enters Earth's atmosphere at a high velocity, its momentum is much larger than that of a rock of the same size falling off a cliff. When it hits Earth, the meteor makes a larger crater than the rock. Near Flagstaff, Arizona, there is a crater more than 1 km in diameter made when a large meteor struck Earth millions of years ago.

GLENCOE TECHNOLOGY

CD-ROM

Glencoe Science Voyages Interactive CD-ROM

Explorations

Have students do the interactive exploration *How is momentum conserved in a vehicle collision?*

Videodisc

Glencoe Science Voyages Interactive Videodisc— Physical

Side 1, Lesson 2 *Machines and Forces*

17414

Refer to Videodisc Teacher Guide for additional bar codes.

EARTH SCIENCE INTEGRATION

Meteor Impact

A meteor that weighs only 100 kg and is about the size of a large footstool can create a large impact crater because it is moving at such high speed. A 100-kg rock falling off a cliff has a much smaller momentum.

would feel a sting when it hit. That ball has momentum. The momentum of a baseball with a mass of 0.125 kg moving at this speed is found using the momentum formula.

$$\text{momentum} = \text{mass} \times \text{velocity}$$
$$p = mv$$
$$= (0.125\text{ kg}) \times (56\text{ m/s})$$
$$= 7.0\text{ kg} \cdot \text{m/s}$$

The ball's momentum is 7.0 kg · m/s. An answer that includes direction might say the ball is moving toward the spectator in Section 1A, Row 7, Seat 23 with a momentum of 7.0 kg · m/s.

Momentum does not have a standard unit. You can use kg · m/s, g · m/s, kg · km/h, or whatever combination of mass and velocity units is most useful. (The symbol · means "times.") But, if you are making calculations with more than one momentum, be sure to use the same units for each.

Table 6-2 is a list of common objects that all have a momentum of 7 kg · m/s. Compare these objects with the speeding baseball. You can see that a mosquito with little mass needs a lot of velocity to have the same momentum. At the other extreme, a massive truck has the same momentum when barely moving. This is why, when you ride in a car on the highway, a collision with a truck is more dangerous than an insect colliding with your windshield.

Table 6-2

Common Objects with a Momentum of 7 kg · m/s

Object	Mass (kg)	Speed (m/s)
mosquito	0.000001	7 000 000
Ping-Pong ball	0.005	1 400
bullet	0.02	350
bowling ball	7	1
seventh grader	50	0.14
18-wheeler	12 000	0.0006

Major League Select any sport and consider the role that momentum plays in that sport. Think of five actions in the sport you have chosen and describe in your journal how momentum is transferred in each action. For example, describe how momentum is transferred when a basketball player shoots a free throw. L2

Caption Answer

Figure 6-12 *Before the collision, the white ball has all the momentum. For the 5-ball to gain momentum, the white ball must give some up, slowing down.*

Conservation of Momentum

When you hit a ball with a bat, you change the ball's motion. If the ball has a great deal of inertia, its velocity will not change quickly. For example, if you hit a bowling ball with a bat in the same way you would hit a baseball, the bowling ball's velocity will not change much. The baseball has much less inertia, so it's easier to change its motion. Newton discovered that in both cases, however, the momentum is the same. The two balls get the same quantity of motion from the bat as long as the action (or push) is the same and lasts for the same amount of time.

Once moving, which ball is easier to stop? It takes just as much force, applied for the same amount of time, to stop each ball. It would be like running a movie backward. Force applied in one direction gives a certain momentum, and force in the opposite direction during an equal amount of time stops that momentum.

Momentum is conserved. In every situation you can imagine, from atoms smashing in particle accelerators to stars exploding in a galaxy, the momentum of the collection of objects involved does not change. If no outside forces act on a group of objects, the momentum of the whole group will never change. This is called the **law of conservation of momentum.** If one object slows down, it's because it hit another object. The object it hit then moves faster. The one object lost just as much momentum as the other one gained, so there's no change overall. This law is illustrated in **Figure 6-12.** ☑

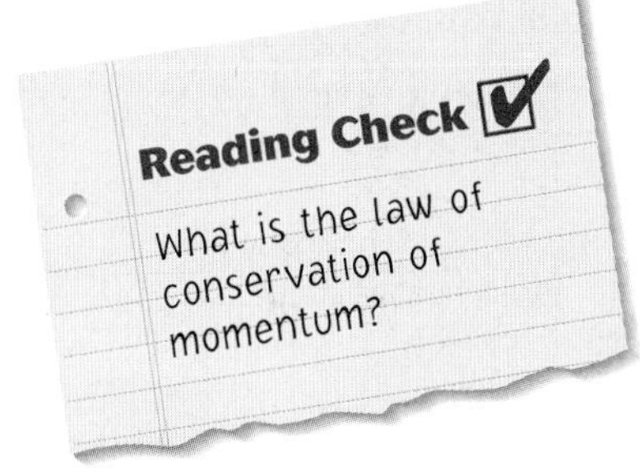

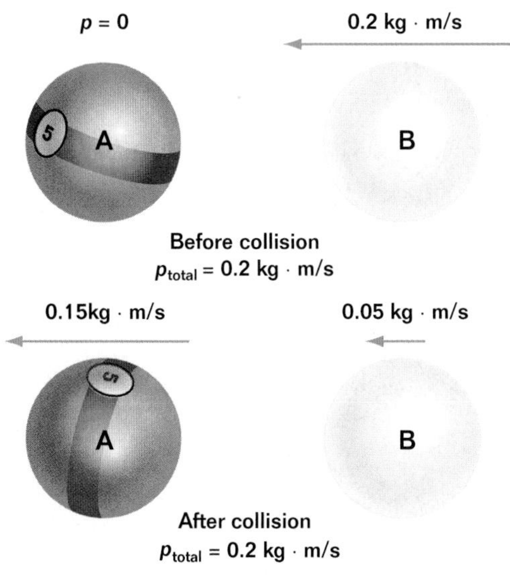

Figure 6-12 The total momentum is 0.2 kg · m/s before and after the balls collide because momentum is conserved. **How could you predict the white ball would slow down after the collision?**

VISUAL Learning

Figure 6-12 Have the students examine time-lapse photographs of billiard balls colliding. Ask them to measure the velocity of the balls before and after the collision, assuming that the time elapsed between images is 1 s. (So long as the time intervals are equal, it doesn't matter what they actually are.) **Is momentum conserved in these collisions?** *Yes, and because the balls are of equal mass, the sum of the velocities after the collision should be equal to the sum before the collision.* L2

Activity

Kinesthetic Give a volunteer a bowling ball and a meterstick. Ask the student to use the meterstick to move the bowling ball through a simple obstacle course that has several turns in it. Ask the student to repeat the task with a basketball. **Why is the task so much more difficult with the bowling ball?** *The bowling ball has much more inertia so it is more difficult to change the direction of its motion as the ball moves through the course.* L2

Answer to Reading Check ☑

This law states that the momentum of a system of objects will not change unless an outside force acts on the group.

Enrichment

Consider what happens when two train cars of equal mass are coupled in a train yard. To begin, the cars are located some distance apart on the track. The first car is pushed toward the second car that is sitting at rest. **If the first car is moving at 2 m/s when it bumps into the stationary car, what happens after the cars are coupled?** *They continue moving in the same direction but at half the speed (1 m/s).* **What happens if the first car is empty and the second car is twice as heavy?** *They continue moving at 0.67 m/s.* L2 P

Problem Solving

Review with the students what happened in the Explore Activity at the beginning of the chapter. The greater the mass of a ball is, the greater its inertia is, and the harder it is to change its motion. Hollow plastic balls (or eggs) that you fill would work well.

Think Critically

The target ball that moves furthest will be the one with the least mass and the ball that moves the shortest distance will have the most mass. You can make this experiment more accurate by performing it on an air track.

3 Assess

Check for Understanding

Discussion

Interpersonal Ask students to predict what will happen to a ball if it bounces off the bumper of an approaching car. *The ball will gain momentum because some of the car's momentum will be transferred to the ball.* L2

Reteach

Visual-Spatial Ask the students to describe the collision that will occur when you roll a bowling ball at a basketball. Perform the experiment. Repeat, this time rolling the basketball at the bowling ball. L2

Extension

For students who have mastered this section, use the **Reinforcement** and **Enrichment** masters.

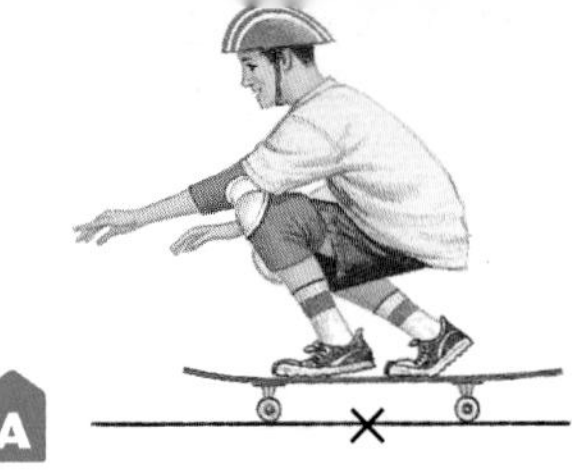

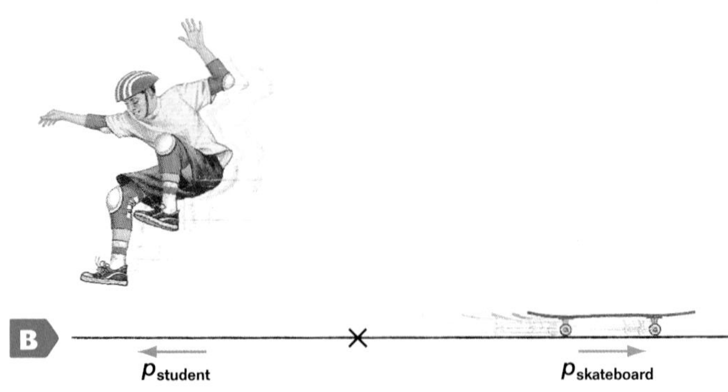

Figure 6-13 The student-skateboard systems in A and B have a momentum of 0. When the student jumps, the momentum of the system is conserved.

interNET CONNECTION

Visit the Glencoe Science Web Site at **www.glencoe.com/sec/science** for more information about meteors.

Examples of Momentum Conservation

The system of skateboard and rider in **Figure 6-13** has a momentum of 0 before and after the skateboarder jumps. In **Figure 6-13B,** the momentum of the person is equal and opposite to the momentum of the board, so they cancel. The opening pages of this chapter show a rack of pool balls being scattered by a cue ball. The shooter applies an outside force on the cue ball when he or she hits it. The cue ball gains momentum from the stick. When the cue ball hits the rack, it slows down as it collides with the other balls. The cue ball loses momentum as the other balls gain a nearly equal amount of momentum. In a perfect system, the balls would bounce around the table without stopping until an outside force acted. When you play pool, the outside force of friction causes the balls to slow down and eventually stop.

Problem Solving

Observing Inertia

Mass is usually measured with a beam balance or a spring scale. A beam balance compares a known mass to an unknown mass. A spring scale measures the pull (or push) of the mass on a spring. Sometimes, you need to measure mass without these simple lab tools. For example, scientists who study meteor craters can't weigh the meteor. Astronomers can't weigh a comet. They need other ways to determine mass.

Get a number of balls that are about the same size. Place them on a flat surface. Make a hypothesis about their relative masses without handling them. (For example, blue is heaviest, then red, then silver, and green is lightest.) Use one of the balls as a control ball. Place the other balls one at a time at the bottom of a ramp. Launch the control ball from the same point on a ramp to collide with each of these balls. (Launching from the same point ensures that the control ball will have approximately the same velocity each time.) Observe the collisions and the inertia of each ball.

Think Critically: How can you tell the mass order with this method? What can you do to make this more accurate?

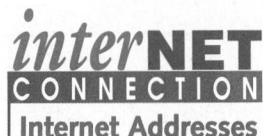

interNET CONNECTION

Internet Addresses

___

___

___

___

For Internet tips, see Glencoe's **Using the Internet in the Science Classroom.**

162 CHAPTER 6 MOTION

The law of conservation of momentum can help you figure out what happens in a collision. Using the break in pool as an example, you could calculate where every ball is going to go if you knew the momentum of the cue ball and the exact position of all the balls before the collision. You might need a computer to help with the calculations, but you would not need to know anything else.

The particles in a gas are sometimes modeled as tiny billiard balls. The particles have an average speed, which is determined by the temperature of the gas. But, individual particles might have speeds higher or lower than this value. If the system is at rest, the sum of the momentums of the individual particles is zero. In this model, momentum is conserved in each collision. When a fast particle hits a slow molecule, the momentum of each may change, but the total momentum for the pair remains constant. **Figure 6-14** illustrates how the collisions of the particles with the walls of the container provide the pressure of the gas.

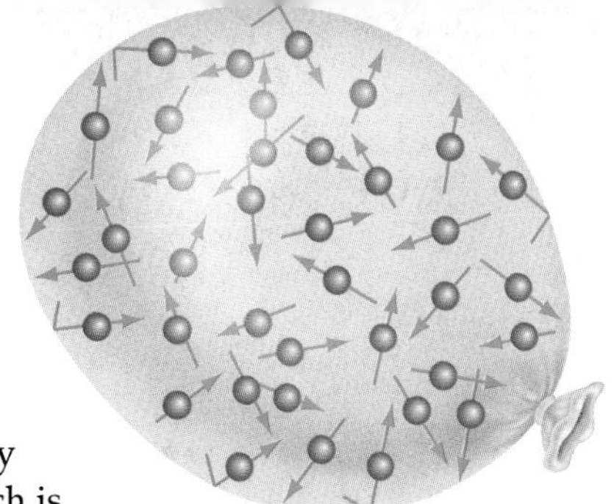

Figure 6-14 The particles in a gas can be modeled as colliding balls. When the particles collide with the balloon, they give the balloon its shape.

Section Assessment

1. A 140-kg lineman from your favorite team comes charging at you. He is running at full speed of 10 km/h. Suppose your mass is 50 kg. How fast must you be moving to stop his forward motion?
2. You see a film where one pool ball rolls forward and hits another. The first ball stops and the second moves off with the same momentum as the first ball. Can you tell whether the film is being run backward or forward?
3. **Think Critically:** Every day, Earth is hit by 1 million kg of matter from outer space. Most of this is in the form of grains of dust that hit Earth with an average speed of about 10 km/s. Give some reasons why we don't notice a change in the motion of Earth.
4. **Skill Builder** **Interpreting Scientific Illustrations** The illustration shows the momentums before and after a collision. What is the momentum of B after the collision? If you need help, refer to Interpreting Scientific Illustrations in the **Skill Handbook** on page 726.

Science Journal Explain how your momentum changes over the course of a bike ride around your block.

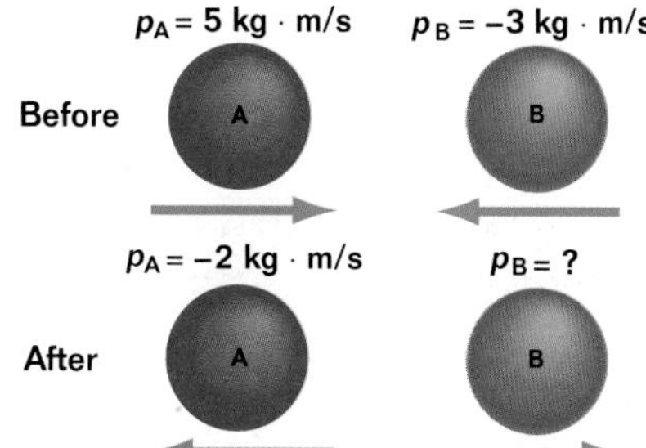

4. **Skill Builder** The total momentum before the collision will be equal to the total after.

$5 - 3 = -2 + p_B$, so $p_B = +4$ kg · m/s.

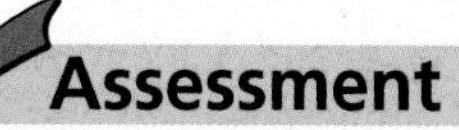

Assessment

Process One skater weighs 25 kg and is traveling at 2 m/s. Another weighs 75 kg and is traveling at −3 m/s. They collide but manage to hold onto each other and keep their footing. What is their velocity after the collision? *−1.75 m/s* Use **Performance Assessment in the Science Classroom,** p. 29.

CHEMISTRY INTEGRATION

When you increase the temperature of a gas, the molecules in the gas move more rapidly. The momentum of the gas molecules increases. When these molecules collide with the walls of a container, they push harder against the walls of the container, and the pressure of the gas is therefore higher.

4 Close

Proficiency Prep

Use this quiz to check students' recall of section content.

1. **What measures an object's inertia?** *its mass*
2. **When two balls collide, one can transfer what to the other?** *momentum*

Section Assessment

1. You must be moving at 28 km/h to stop him.
2. No, the balls could be moving either way.
3. **Think Critically** The dust comes at Earth from all different directions. The resulting change in Earth's momentum is zero so Earth does not appear to move. Also, 1 million kg is much less than Earth's mass.

Sample response: It is slow starting out, increasing as I get up to speed. At each corner, it is reduced when I slow down, changes direction when I go around the corner, and increases as I get back up to speed. I reduce my momentum down to 0 when I stop at the end.

Purpose

Visual-Spatial Students will observe how the mass and velocity of marbles before a collision affect their velocity after the collision. L2 ELL COOP LEARN

Process Skills

observing and inferring, making a hypothesis, comparing and contrasting, recognizing cause and effect, separating and controlling variables

Time

45 minutes

Safety Precautions

Make sure students pick up all of the marbles when they are finished so that none are left on the floor to cause accidents.

Teaching Strategies

Have students use metersticks to create tracks that confine the marbles' motion to one dimension. As an alternative, you might use a V-shaped molding strip as a track.

Answers to Questions

1. In steps 2 and 3, the target marble moves and the shooter stops in the track. In step 4, the target moves less than in steps 2 and 3 and the shooter may recoil. In step 5, the target moves further than in step 2 and the shooter may roll forward a little. In step 6, both marbles recoil after collision. In step 7, the small marble recoils further than the large marble. In step 8, the fourth marble moves forward and the others stop in the track.

Comparing Collisions

Materials

- Small marbles (5)
- Large marbles (2)
- Metersticks (2)

You've played games that involve bouncing balls against each other, the walls and floor, and various pieces of sports equipment. How do these collisions work?

What You'll Investigate

How do the masses and velocities of marbles before a collision affect the velocities of the marbles after a collision?

Goals

- **Make** a hypothesis about how momentum changes.
- **Compare and contrast** different collisions.

Procedure

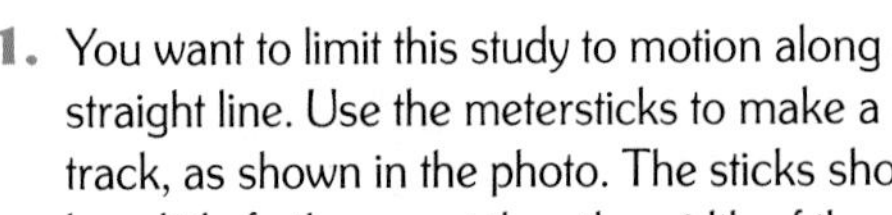

1. You want to limit this study to motion along a straight line. Use the metersticks to make a track, as shown in the photo. The sticks should be a little farther apart than the width of the largest marble you are using in each collision.
2. Set a small marble in the center of the track. Shoot another small marble as fast as you can down the track. Repeat. **Describe** the collision.
3. Repeat step 2 with two large marbles.
4. Repeat step 2 with a small shooter marble and a large target.
5. Repeat step 2 with a large shooter marble and a small target.
6. Repeat step 2 shooting two small marbles at each other.
7. Repeat step 2 shooting one small and one large marble at each other.
8. Repeat step 2 using four small, touching marbles as the target and one small marble as the shooter.

Conclude and Apply

1. **Compare and contrast** the various types of collisions.
2. How did you **separate and control variables?**

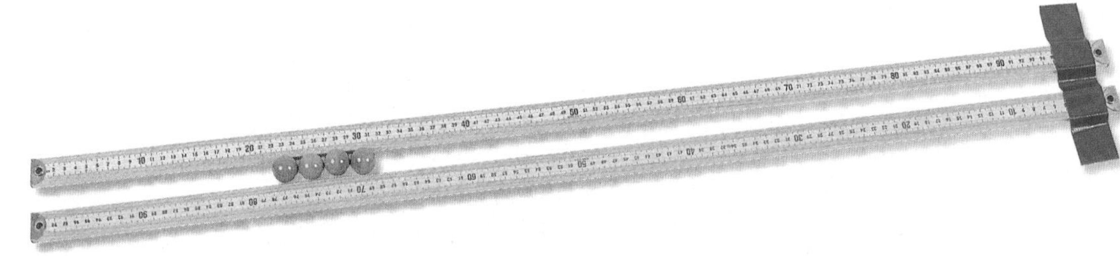

In steps 2, 3, 4, and 5, the mass of the marble is varied. Compare steps 6 and 2 to see what effect the direction of motion has on the collision. Compare steps 6 and 7 to see the effect of mass and then compare steps 4 and 7 to see the effect of direction. Compare steps 2 and 8 to see the effect of the number of marbles.

Assessment

Process A 200-g puck moving at 4.5 m/s across the ice hits an ice chip moving 2 m/s in the same direction. After the collision, the puck moves at 1 m/s and the ice chip travels at 16 m/s. What is the mass of the ice chip? *50 g* Use **Performance Assessment in the Science Classroom,** p. 29.

164 CHAPTER 6 MOTION

What is energy?

Energy

A final way to describe motion is with energy. **Energy** is the ability to cause change. If you look back at all the examples of motion in this chapter, you will see that all involve change.

The energy of matter in motion is **kinetic energy.** Where does kinetic energy come from? It comes from other forms of energy. Chemical energy is found in the bonds between atoms. You use it to move your body, as in **Figure 6-15.** Nuclear energy is contained in the bonds in the nucleus. Electromagnetic energy includes electricity, magnetism, and light. Heat is the transfer of thermal energy. All of these can cause change.

Energy can be transferred between objects. A soccer player has chemical energy in her muscles from the food she ate. The chemical energy is released as she accelerates her leg. Her leg now has kinetic energy. When her foot kicks the ball, the kinetic energy of her foot is used to accelerate the ball. Her foot and leg lose kinetic energy as the ball gains the same amount of kinetic energy. The ball soars downfield and eventually stops. The ball's kinetic energy turns to heat energy as it heats up the atoms and molecules of the ball, air, and ground. Eventually, these hot particles will bounce into other particles and spread the heat everywhere.

It can be difficult to follow the trail of energy. People became especially interested in defining and understanding energy when steam engines started to be used to do work. James Joule discovered the **law of conservation of energy,** which states that energy cannot be created or destroyed, but is only transformed from one form to another. ✓

What You'll Learn

- What energy is, and some of its forms
- How to find kinetic and gravitational potential energy
- What the law of conservation of energy is and how to use it

Vocabulary
energy
kinetic energy
law of conservation of energy
gravitational potential energy

Why It's Important

- Natural processes involve the transfer of energy.

Figure 6-15 Chemical energy is contained in your muscles. It is transformed to kinetic energy when you use your muscles to produce motion.

SECTION 6·3

Prepare

Refer to **Energy** on p. 146F.

Preplanning

Refer to the **Chapter Organizer** on pp. 146A–B.

1 Motivate

Bellringer

Before presenting the lesson, display **Section Focus Transparency 14** on the overhead projector. Use the accompanying **Focus Activity** worksheet. L2 ELL

14 SECTION FOCUS TRANSPARENCY

Section 6-3

DON'T TRY THIS AT HOME!

Many cartoons use physical laws to make a joke. They rely on people's common knowledge of the world around them. How does your knowledge of going down hills affect how you react to this cartoon?

FOX TROT by Bill Amend

FOXTROT © Bill Amend. Reprinted with permission of UNIVERSAL PRESS SYNDICATE. All rights reserved.

1. What does the younger brother mean when he says, "let gravity take over"?
2. Why aren't real sledding hills at a very steep angle like this one?
3. How would starting lower down the hill change things? Going one at a time?

Resource Manager

The following **Teacher Classroom Resources** can be used with Section 6-3:

 **Reproducible Masters**

Activity Worksheets, p. 34 L2

Enrichment, p. 14 L3

Reinforcement, p. 14 L2

Study Guide, pp. 23–24 L1 ELL

 **Transparencies**

Teaching Transparency 12 L2

Answer to Reading Check ✓

Energy is not created or destroyed, simply transformed from one form to another. The total energy of the universe is a constant.

Tying to Previous Knowledge

Intrapersonal Have students identify energy transformations that they have experienced in their daily lives. In each instance, ask them to identify the forms of energy and then to describe the change. L2

2 Teach

Purpose

Logical-Mathematical Students will observe the transfer of potential energy to kinetic energy in a pendulum. L2

ELL COOP LEARN P

Materials

weight, string, meterstick

Teaching Strategies

Students should be reminded to let the weight drop smoothly from waist height. They should be cautioned not to push it or swing it.

Analysis

1. Before the weight is released, the gravitational potential energy *(GPE)* is equal to *mgh.* The kinetic energy *(KE)* is 0 at this point.
2. at the bottom of the swing, at the top of the swing
3. As *GPE* decreased, *KE* increased, and vice versa. Because energy is conserved, the sum of *GPE* and *KE* is constant over the course of the swing.

Figure 6-16 Heat energy from the sun is transformed to chemical energy in the bamboo. When the animal eats the bamboo, it gains chemical energy, which it can transform to kinetic energy.

Mini Lab

Observing Energy Transfer

Procedure

1. Tie a weight to a long string. Hang the string and weight from the ceiling. Adjust the string until the weight is just above the floor.
2. Pull the weight to one side until it is 1 m high. Gently let go of the weight. Do not push it.
3. Observe the motion of the weight.

Analysis

1. Calculate the gravitational potential energy of the weight before it was released.
2. Where did the weight have the greatest kinetic energy? The least?
3. What happened as *GPE* decreased? Increased? Explain.

The total amount of energy in the whole universe never changes. Only the different forms in which energy appears change, as shown in **Figure 6-16.** As you study the flow of energy, as in the case of the soccer ball, you will eventually find that all the energy has been transformed into heat and seems to have disappeared. It really hasn't, but it has been lost from the object that had it at first.

To show how energy is transferred by friction, drop a basketball from shoulder height. After it bounces on the ground, it will not return to the height of your shoulders. When it bounces a second time, it won't return to the height of the first bounce. The bounces will keep getting shorter and shorter until the ball lies still on the ground. If there were no friction, the ball would bounce up and down from the same height forever.

Calculating Kinetic Energy

Kinetic energy is the energy an object has due to its motion. It depends on the object's mass and velocity. You can calculate the amount of kinetic energy using the following formula.

$$\text{kinetic energy} = \frac{1}{2}(\text{mass})(\text{velocity})^2$$

$$KE = \frac{1}{2}mv^2$$

KE represents kinetic energy; *m,* mass; and *v,* velocity. The unit of energy is the joule (J), 1 J = 1 kg · m²/s². It is named for James Joule.

Assessment

Performance Ask students to predict what will happen if they push the weight instead of dropping it. Will *KE* at the bottom of the swing be the same as before? *The weight starts with the same* GPE *but with more* KE, *so the total energy of the system is greater.* KE *at the bottom of the swing, when* GPE *= 0, will also be greater.* Use **Performance Assessment in the Science Classroom,** p. 21.

Potential Energy

Potential energy is the stored energy of position or condition. Many forces can store energy this way. A book on the edge of a desk has potential energy due to gravity. If you knock it off, it will accelerate toward the ground. A paper clip held near a magnet also has potential energy. If you let go of it, it will accelerate toward the magnet. The positive and negative charges in a battery have potential energy. When you run a wire between them, the negative charges move. A squashed spring has potential energy. If you release it, it will accelerate.

Anything that can fall has the ability to create change. **Gravitational potential energy,** or *GPE,* is the energy an object could change to kinetic energy if it falls. An object's *GPE* depends on its mass, *m,* and the height it can fall, *h.*

$$GPE = \text{(force of gravity)(height)}$$

$$GPE = mgh$$

The g represents the acceleration due to gravity, $9.8\ m/s^2$.

You have experience with gravitational potential energy. How many times have you held your arms over your head to protect it from something falling? The more massive the object or the farther it falls, the more you cringe, hoping it does not hit you on the head.

Figure 6-17 shows how energy changes when a ball is dropped. When you first release the ball, it has a certain gravitational potential energy, *mgh,* and no kinetic energy. Just before it hits the ground, its *GPE* is 0. All the *GPE* has been converted to kinetic energy. At any point along the way, it's part *GPE* and part *KE.* But everywhere the total amount of energy is the same.

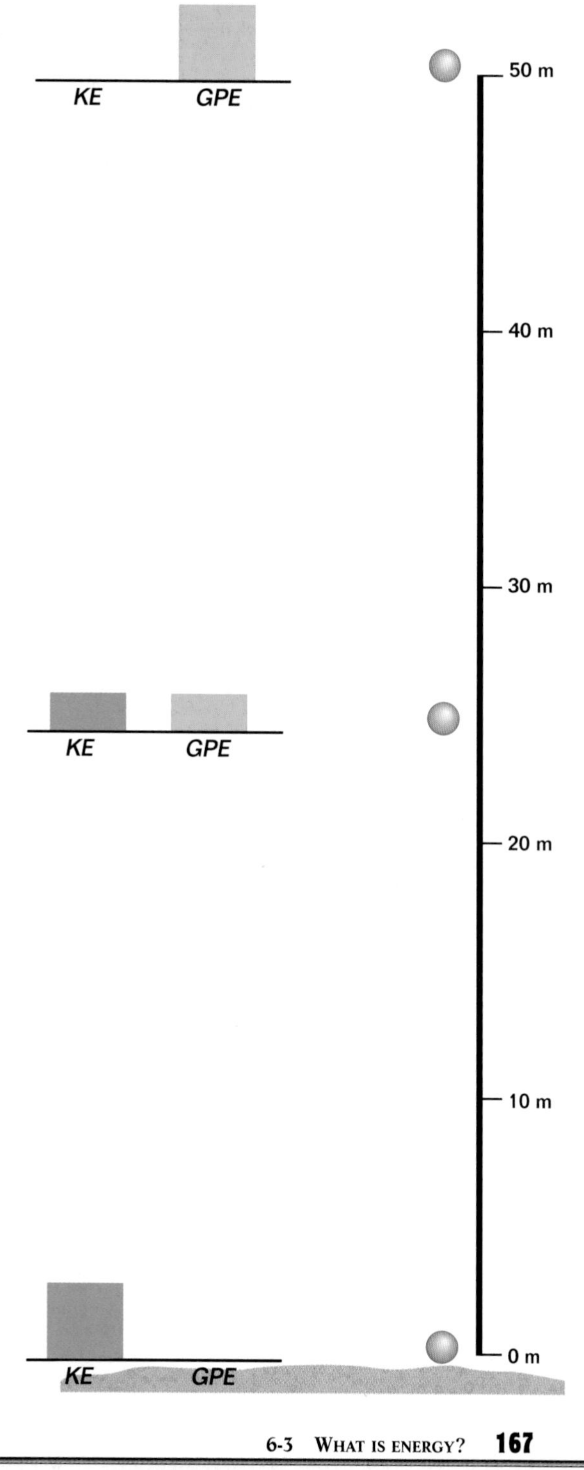

Figure 6-17 As the ball falls, gravitational potential energy is converted to kinetic energy.

Enrichment

Linguistic Space vehicles reentering Earth's atmosphere have a great deal of kinetic energy. Ask students to do research to identify the sources of this energy and how it is dissipated (transferred to other forms) so that the astronauts can land safely. How do the methods used in early spaceflights differ from those used on the space shuttle? L3 P

3 Assess

Check for Understanding

Quick Demo

Linguistic Ask students to describe the energy transformations that occur when you toss a basketball into the air and allow it to bounce on the floor before catching it. L2

Reteach

Ask students how much kinetic energy a 2-kg ball will have when it bounces on the floor after being thrown to a height of 4 m above the floor. $KE_{bottom} = GPE_{top} = mgh = (2\ kg)(9.8\ m/s^2)(4\ m) = 78\ J$ L2

Extension

For students who have mastered this section, use the **Reinforcement** and **Enrichment** masters.

Energy Transformations Ask students to find pictures in magazines that illustrate energy transformations. Ask each student to paste a picture into his or her Science Journal and then write a description identifying the energy transformations in the picture. L2

Caption Answer

Figure 6-18 *at the bottom; at the top; top; bottom; no*

*inter*NET CONNECTION

Internet Addresses

For Internet tips, see Glencoe's **Using the Internet in the Science Classroom.**

4 Close

Proficiency Prep

Use this quiz to check students' recall of section content.

1. **What is the energy of motion?** *kinetic energy*
2. **What is the gravitational potential energy of an object on the ground?** *0*

Section Assessment

1. $(0.5)(70\ kg)(10\ m/s)^2 = 3500\ kg \cdot m^2/s^2$
2. thermal energy in brake, tires, and the road
3. **Think Critically** Yes, the magnet has potential energy. When you release the magnet, it is attracted to the metal in the refrigerator door and moves toward the door. The potential energy in the magnetic attraction is converted to kinetic energy.

Using Computers

Perform an Internet search for energy sources. Use an Internet browser to search on *solar energy* or some other appropriate key word or words. P

Figure 6-18 Energy is transferred on a long slide. **Where is a rider's potential energy least? Greatest? Where is a rider's kinetic energy least? Greatest? Does the total energy change?**

*inter*NET CONNECTION

Visit the Glencoe Science Web Site at **www.glencoe.com/sec/science** for more information about energy.

Figure 6-18 shows a slide. As you ride down, potential energy is transferred to kinetic energy. When you climb back up, you use kinetic energy to gain potential energy. Because this is a real system, some energy is transferred to heat. But none is lost or gained: energy is conserved.

Section Assessment

1. Suppose you and your bicycle have a total mass of 70 kg. You are moving at 10 m/s. How much kinetic energy do you and the bicycle have?
2. When you bring your bicycle to a stop, where does the kinetic energy it had go?
3. **Think Critically:** Suppose you hold a strong magnet 1 cm away from the refrigerator door. Is there potential energy in this system? What happens when you let go of the magnet?
4. **Skill Builder**
   Observing and Inferring Use the conservation of energy to explain what happens when you drop a ball and it bounces back up. If you throw the ball downward instead of dropping it, do you expect it to bounce higher or lower than when you dropped it? Why? If you need help, refer to Observing and Inferring in the **Skill Handbook** on page 720.

Using Computers

Database Use on-line databases to investigate a particular source of energy, such as oil, solar, or alternative fuels. If you need help, refer to page 733.

4. **Skill Builder**
When you drop a ball, its *GPE* is converted to *KE* as it falls. When it hits the ground, some of its *KE* is lost to the ground as heat energy and some is transferred to *GPE* as it bounces up again. If you throw the ball down initially, it has more *KE* and bounces higher as *KE* is converted to *GPE*.

Assessment

Portfolio Ask students to think of other systems involving several forms of energy. Identify the forms of energy in each system and describe how energy is transformed. Use **Performance Assessment in the Science Classroom,** p. 105.

Discovery of the Neutrino

The law of conservation of momentum states that when no outside forces act on a system, the momentum of the system is conserved. The law of conservation of energy states that energy is not created or destroyed, only transferred from one object to another. These seemingly simple ideas are behind some of the most important scientific discoveries, including that of a tiny particle called a neutrino.

Tracking Particles

To find the momentum and energy of small particles, scientists study the tracks the particles leave in detectors (left). A track depends on the mass, charge, and initial momentum of the particle.

Around 1930, scientists discovered that one type of particle track (lower right) showed a sudden change of direction and speed. When the particle turned, it did not hit anything and no new outside force acted on it. Scientists predicted that a new particle, one they couldn't detect, was being ejected, carrying off momentum and energy. The new particle was called a neutrino, which means "little neutral particle."

The Mysterious Neutrino

Scientists thought the neutrino had no electric charge and no mass. Neutrinos leave no track in detectors. Direct evidence for the neutrino did not come until 1956. In 1998, scientists in Japan showed that neutrinos do have mass, though that mass has not yet been measured. Neutrinos are a topic of current research in science. Yet, they still obey the basic laws you learn in science class.

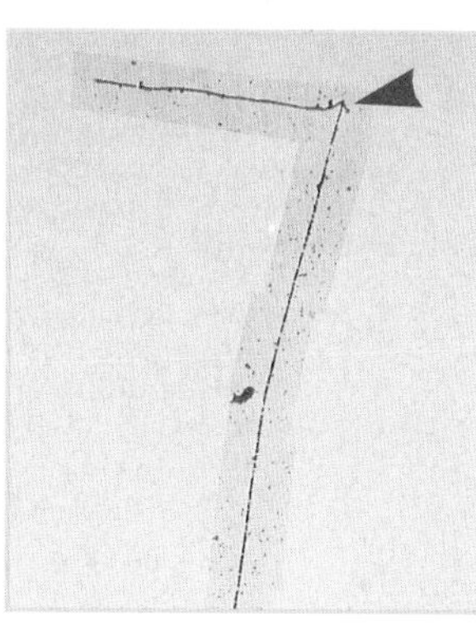

Science JOURNAL

The track at right was made by a particle in a high-energy accelerator. Scientists used the law of conservation of momentum to propose that the particle must have thrown off another particle, called a neutrino, which doesn't leave a track. In your Science Journal, explain why the conservation of momentum law suggests this is so.

Science & Society

Teaching Strategies

- Ask students if they have heard of neutrinos.
- Physics is often an intimidating subject for students. This demonstrates that simple concepts they have learned, such as the laws of conservation of momentum and energy, can be used to analyze advanced problems.

For More Information

- Gribbin, John, and Mary Gribbin. *Q is for Quantum: Particle Physics from A-Z.* New York: Free Press, 1999.
- Hoddeson, Lillian, and Laurie Brown, Michael Riordan, eds. *The Rise of the Standard Model: Particle Physics in the 1960s and 1970s.* New York: Cambridge University Press, 1997.
- Use an Internet search engine to search on *neutrino.*

The system of the particle should not change its momentum unless a force acts on it. Its momentum changed when it suddenly turned. It was not hit by an outside particle or accelerated by an outside force, so it must have emitted another particle, even though we can't see it. This is like a person jumping off a skateboard. Even if you can only see the skateboard, you know something must have happened for its motion to suddenly change.

Content Background

- The mass of the neutrino has long been a puzzle. By 1976, three different types of neutrino had been discovered. One type is produced in the sun. Scientists detected fewer of these arriving at Earth than they predicted. The solution was to assume the neutrino has mass; if this were true, it could change from one type to another. If some of the neutrinos produced in the sun changed type on their way to Earth, they wouldn't be detected. In 1998, scientists in Kamiokande, Japan, measured the difference in the number of neutrinos coming from the sky in the daytime and through Earth at night. Fewer come through Earth, so they must change to another type.

Chapter 6 Reviewing Main Ideas

Reviewing Main Ideas can be used to preview, review, reteach, and condense chapter content.

Preview

Linguistic Have students try to answer the questions in their Science Journals. Use student answers as a source for discussion throughout the chapter.

Review

Interpersonal Have students answer the questions on separate pieces of paper and compare their answers with those of other students in the class.

Reteach

Visual-Spatial Have students look at the illustrations on these pages. Ask them to describe details that support the main ideas of the chapter found in the statement for each illustration.

00:00 OUT OF TIME?

Auditory-Musical If time does not permit teaching the entire chapter, use the information on these pages along with the chapter Audiocassettes to present the material in a condensed format.

Chapter 6 Reviewing Main Ideas

For a **preview** of this chapter, study this Reviewing Main Ideas before you read the chapter. After you have studied this chapter, you can use the Reviewing Main Ideas to **review** the chapter.

The Glencoe MindJogger, Audiocassettes, and CD-ROM provide additional opportunities for review.

Section 6-1 VELOCITY AND ACCELERATION

An object's motion can be described by **velocity.** Velocity gives the rate of change of position, or **speed,** and the direction of motion. An object's change in motion is described with **acceleration,** the rate of change of velocity. Acceleration can act in the direction of motion, opposite to the direction of motion, or at an angle. ***How are speed and velocity related to position and time?***

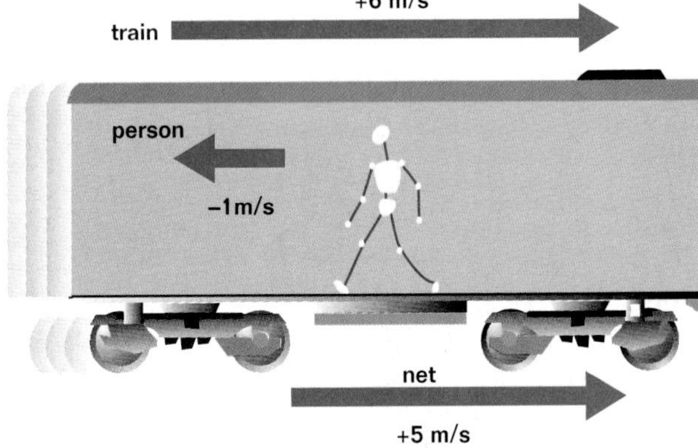

Section 6-2 MASS AND INERTIA

Mass is the amount of matter in an object and it is a measure of the object's **inertia.** ***How does the inertia of a freight train moving at 10 km/h compare with your inertia while you bicycle at the same speed?***

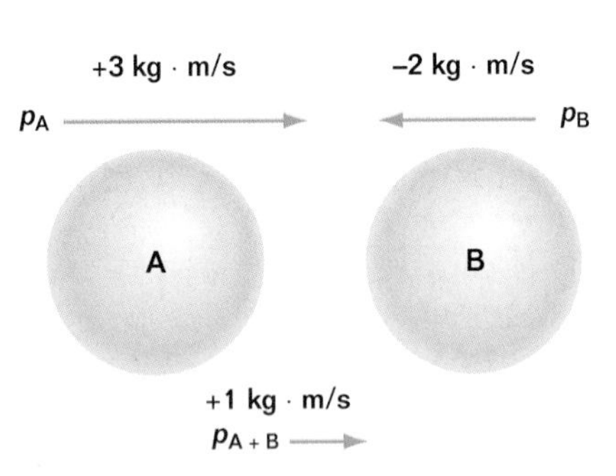

MOMENTUM

Momentum is the quantity of motion for an object. Knowing this value gives you an idea of how powerfully the object could collide with another object. ***If your mass is 60 kg and you travel in a car moving at 100 km/h, what is your momentum?***

Cultural Diversity

Earth's Slowing Rotation The slowing of Earth's rotation has been documented by Babylonian records of solar eclipses. The recorded dates of eclipses could have occurred only if Earth were rotating slightly faster in the past.

Reading Check

Explain how direction plays a role in the different concepts studied in this chapter.

CONSERVATION OF MOMENTUM

If no outside forces act on a group of objects, the momentum of the group will not change. The momentum of individual objects in the group may change, as collisions transfer momentum between objects, but the total momentum of the group remains unchanged. *What happens to the momentum of a small ball that strikes a large ball and stops?*

6-3 CONSERVATION OF ENERGY

Energy is the ability to cause change. It takes many forms. **Gravitational potential energy, kinetic energy,** and heat are familiar examples. Energy cannot be created or destroyed, only transferred from one form to another. *A bouncing ball eventually comes to a stop. Where did the kinetic energy go?*

Answers to Questions

Section 6-1

Velocity and Acceleration Speed and velocity measure change in position over time. Velocity also identifies the direction of motion, and it uses displacement rather than distance.

Section 6-2

Mass and Inertia The inertia of the freight train is much greater than your inertia because its mass is so much greater.

Momentum (60 kg)(100 km/h) = 6000 kg · km/h

Conservation of Momentum The momentum of the small ball is transferred to the large ball, causing it to move forward slowly.

Section 6-3

Conservation of Energy The energy was transformed into another form, heat.

GLENCOE TECHNOLOGY

CD-ROM

Glencoe Science Voyages Interactive CD-ROM

Chapter Summaries and Quizzes

Have students read the Chapter Summary then take the Chapter Quiz to determine whether they have mastered chapter content.

Assessment

Portfolio Encourage students to place in their portfolios one or two items of what they consider to be their best work. Examples include:

- Enrichment, pp. 150, 161, 167
- MiniLab, p. 166
- Using Computers, p. 168 P

Performance Additional performance assessments may be found in **Performance Assessment** and **Science Integration Activities.** Performance Task Assessment Lists and rubrics for evaluating these activities can be found in Glencoe's **Performance Assessment in the Science Classroom.**

Using Vocabulary

1. Mass is the measure of inertia.
2. Velocity is the rate of change of displacement.
3. Acceleration is the rate of change of velocity.
4. Kinetic energy and gravitational potential energy are two forms of energy. A falling object exchanges potential for kinetic energy.
5. Mass is a component of momentum; as mass increases and velocity is constant, momentum increases.

interNET CONNECTION To reinforce chapter vocabulary, use the **Study Guide for Content Mastery** booklet. Also available are activities for **Glencoe Science Voyages** on the Glencoe Science Web Site. **www.glencoe.com/sec/science**

Checking Concepts

6. D	**11.** D
7. A	**12.** D
8. B	**13.** B
9. C	**14.** A
10. A	**15.** C

Thinking Critically

16. The steel ball has a large mass. When it hits a wall, its momentum causes the wall to move a short distance off its foundation and collapse.
17. Chemical energy in the muscles is converted to mechanical energy of moving hands. Friction between your hands transforms some mechanical energy into heat.

Chapter  Assessment

Using Vocabulary

a. acceleration
b. displacement
c. energy
d. gravitational potential energy
e. inertia
f. kinetic energy
g. law of conservation of energy
h. law of conservation of momentum
i. mass
j. momentum
k. speed
l. velocity

For each set of terms below, explain the relationship that exists.

1. inertia, mass
2. displacement, velocity
3. velocity, acceleration
4. kinetic energy, gravitational potential energy
5. mass, momentum

Checking Concepts

Choose the word or phrase that best answers the question.

6. When an object accelerates, what can it do?
   A) speed up
   B) slow down
   C) change direction
   D) all of the above
7. What is the rate of change of position?
   A) velocity
   B) acceleration
   C) displacement
   D) momentum
8. Where is the kinetic energy of a falling object greatest?
   A) top of fall
   B) bottom of fall
   C) middle of fall
   D) it doesn't change
9. What is the rate of change of velocity called?
   A) momentum
   B) mass
   C) acceleration
   D) force
10. When no outside forces act on a system of objects, what do the objects do?
    A) conserve momentum
    B) do not conserve momentum
    C) come to rest
    D) continue with the same velocity
11. What is a possible unit of momentum?
    A) kg
    B) kg · m
    C) kg · m/s^2
    D) kg · m/s
12. What is the gravitational potential energy of a 3-kg object 8 m above the ground?
    A) 24 J
    B) 36 J
    C) 96 J
    D) 235 J
13. Which of the following is **NOT** conserved?
    A) mass
    B) acceleration
    C) energy
    D) momentum
14. What is the momentum of an object with mass 50 kg moving at 20 km/h?
    A) 1000 kg · km/h
    B) 2000 kg · km/h
    C) 5000 kg · km/h
    D) 20 000 kg · km/h
15. What is the kinetic energy of a 60-kg diver falling at 10 m/s?
    A) 300 J
    B) 600 J
    C) 3000 J
    D) 5880 J

Thinking Critically

16. When a wrecking ball hits a wall, it is usually moving at about 10 km/h, which is not very fast. Explain how this ball can knock down a solid wall.
17. When you rub your hands together, what energy was transformed to produce heat?
18. An 80-kg person decides to jump off the back end of a 30-kg canoe. His friend measures the speed of the canoe after he jumps to be 0.8 m/s. The canoe was initially at rest. What rule would you use to find the speed of the person who jumped?
19. If the canoe accelerates from 0 to 0.8 m/s in 0.2 s, what is the acceleration?

18. law of conservation of momentum
19. (0.8 m/s)(0.2 s) = 4 m/s^2
20. 180 J − 135 J = 45 J

Assessment

20. A ball has a potential energy of 180 J and a kinetic energy of 0 J. After falling 2 m, it has a potential energy of 135 J. What is its kinetic energy at this point?

Developing Skills

If you need help, refer to the **Skill Handbook.**

21. **Using Numbers:** An in-line skater is going north at 2 m/s. After accelerating smoothly for 9 s, she is going south at 1 m/s. What was her acceleration, including direction?
22. **Concept Mapping:** Complete the concept map with the following phrases: *kinetic energy, chemical energy (plant), chemical energy (animal),* and *solar energy.*

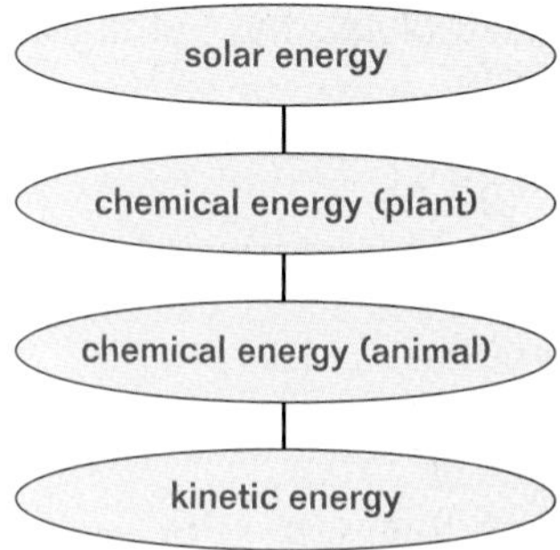

23. **Recognizing Cause and Effect:** Before a collision, a 1-kg ball is moving left at 0.4 m/s and a 2-kg ball is at rest. After the balls collide, only the 2-kg ball is in motion. What is its velocity? How do you know?
24. **Making and Using Graphs:** Make a distance-time graph for an object moving with constant velocity 4 m/s. Go from 0 s to 5 s.

Test-Taking Tip

Warm Up Before the Race On the day of your exam, arrive at the site early enough to relax, get settled, and go over your notes. It will give you time to relax and prepare your mind for the test.

Test Practice

Use these questions to test your Science Proficiency.

1. Before a collision, a system of three balls has a momentum of +8 kg · m/s. After the collision, one ball has a momentum of –2 kg · m/s and one ball has a momentum of +5 kg · m/s. What is the momentum of the third ball?
   A) +5 kg · m/s
   B) +13 kg · m/s
   C) +1 kg · m/s
   D) –1 kg · m/s
2. An object is displaced from a position 2 m north of you to a position 6 m south. The displacement takes 2 s. What is the velocity of the object?
   A) 1 m/s north
   B) 2 m/s north
   C) 3 m/s south
   D) 4 m/s south
3. A rock falls 10 m down a cliff. Where is its gravitational potential energy greatest?
   A) at the top of the fall
   B) at the bottom of the fall
   C) at the midpoint of the fall
   D) no change in *GPE*

THE PRINCETON REVIEW Test Practice

The Test-Taking Tip was written by The Princeton Review, the nation's leader in test preperation.

1. A
2. D
3. A

Developing Skills

21. The skater's acceleration is 0.33 m/s^2 south.
22. See student page.
23. 0.2 m/s to the left; The conservation of momentum states that the momentum of the system won't change, so the momentum of the first ball equals the momentum of the second ball.
24.

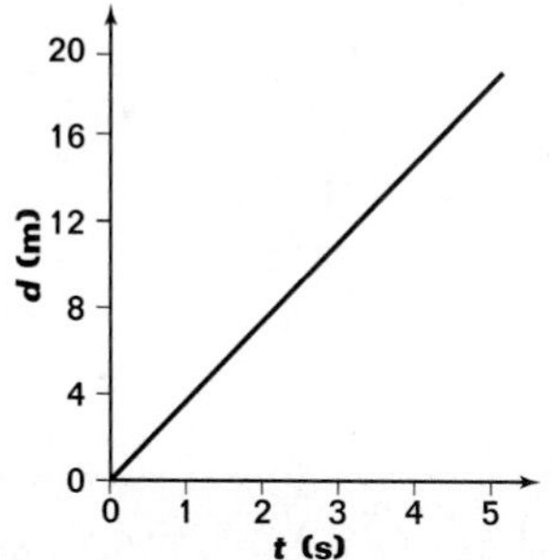

Bonus Question

Which has greater momentum, a falling raindrop or a truck at a stop light? *The raindrop has more momentum. A truck at rest has zero momentum.*

Assessment Resources

The **Test Practice Workbook** provides students with practice in the format, concepts, and critical-thinking skills tested in standardized exams.

Reproducible Masters

Chapter Review, pp. 11–12 L2
Performance Assessment, p. 20 L2
Assessment, pp. 23–26 L2

Glencoe Technology

Chapter Review Software
Computer Test Bank
MindJogger Videoquiz

Chapter 7 Force and Newton's Laws

Section	Objectives	Activities/Features
Chapter Opener		**Explore Activity:** Define Motion, p. 175
7-1 Newton's First Law 1 Session ½ Block	1. **Describe** how to recognize a force. 2. **Define** *balanced* and *net forces.* 3. **State** Newton's first law of motion. 4. **Explain** why friction works.	**Chemistry Integration,** p. 177 **MiniLab:** Defining Rolling Friction, p. 181 **Skill Builder:** Comparing and Contrasting, p. 182 **Using Computers,** p. 182
7-2 Newton's Second Law 3 Sessions 1½ Blocks	5. **State** Newton's second law of motion. 6. **Explain** why the direction of force is important.	**Using Math,** p. 184 **Using Math,** p. 185 **MiniLab:** Measuring Buoyant Force, p. 187 **Skill Builder:** Making and Using Tables, p. 188 **Using Math,** p. 188 **Science and Math:** Applying the Pythagorean Theorem, p. 189 **Activity 7-1:** Modeling Motion in Two Directions, pp. 190–191
7-3 Newton's Third Law 2 Sessions 1 Block	7. **State** Newton's third law of motion.	**Using Math,** p. 192 **Life Science Integration,** p. 194 **Skill Builder:** Using Numbers, p. 195 **Science Journal,** p. 195 **Activity 7-2:** Balloon Races, p. 196
7-4 Describing Motion 1 Session ½ Block	8. **Describe** how to use the law of conservation of momentum and Newton's laws of motion to describe and analyze motion.	**MiniLab:** Measuring Force Pairs, p. 199 **Problem Solving:** Modeling Motion in Space, p. 200 **Skill Builder:** Recognizing Cause and Effect, p. 201 **Using Math,** p. 201

The number of recommended single-period sessions — The number of recommended blocks
One session and one-half block are allowed for chapter review and assessment.

Activity Materials

Explore	Activities	MiniLabs
p. 175 meterstick, 3 books, marbles	p. 190–191 masking tape, timer, meterstick, paper, protractor, string, 2 spring scales, plastic lid, egg p. 196 balloons of different sizes and shapes, drinking straws, string, tape, meterstick, timer	p. 181 spring scale; stable, wheeled object p. 187 several small, heavy objects; spring scale; beaker; water p. 199 spring scales

Need Materials? Contact Science Kit at 1-800-828-7777 or at www.sciencekit.com on the Internet.
For alternate materials, see the activity on the listed page.

Chapter Organizer

Standards		Reproducible Resources	Technology
National	State/Local	Test Practice Workbooks are available for use with each chapter.	English and Spanish audiocassettes are available for use with each section.
National Content Standards: UCP4, B2, D1, D3, G1, G2, G3		**Activity Worksheets,** p. 39 **Enrichment,** p. 15 **Laboratory Manual,** pp. 41–44 **Reinforcement,** p. 15 **Study Guide,** pp. 25–26	Section Focus Transparency 15 Teaching Transparency 13 Glencoe Science Voyages Interactive Videodisc—Physical Internet Connection, p. 180
National Content Standards: UCP2, UCP3, B2, D3, G1, G3		**Activity Worksheets,** pp. 35–36, 40 **Enrichment,** p. 16 **Laboratory Manual,** pp. 45–48 **Reinforcement,** p. 16 **Study Guide,** p. 27	Section Focus Transparency 16 Glencoe Science Voyages Interactive CD-ROM
National Content Standards: UCP2, A1, B1, B2, C1, D3, G3		**Activity Worksheets,** pp. 37–38 **Enrichment,** p. 17 **Reinforcement,** p. 17 **Study Guide,** p. 26	Section Focus Transparency 17 Teaching Transparency 14 Science Integration Transparency 7 The Infinite Voyage Series Internet Connection, p. 193
National Content Standards: UCP3, B1, B2, E2, G1		**Activity Worksheets,** p. 41 **Critical Thinking/Problem Solving,** p. 7 **Enrichment,** p. 18 **Multicultural Connections,** pp. 13–14 **Reinforcement,** p. 18 **Study Guide,** p. 28	Section Focus Transparency 18 Glencoe Science Voyages Interactive Videodisc—Earth

Key to Teaching Strategies

The following designations will help you decide which activities are appropriate for your students.

L1 Level 1 activities should be appropriate for students with learning difficulties.

L2 Level 2 activities should be within the ability range of all students.

L3 Level 3 activities are designed for above-average students.

ELL ELL activities should be within the ability range of English Language Learners.

COOP LEARN Cooperative Learning activities are designed for small group work.

P These strategies represent student products that can be placed into a best-work portfolio.

Multiple Learning Styles logos, as described on page 61T, are used throughout to indicate strategies that address different learning styles.

Assessment Resources

Chapter Review, pp. 13–14
Assessment, pp. 27–30
Performance Assessment in the Science Classroom (PASC)
MindJogger Videoquiz
Alternate Assessment in the Science Classroom
Performance Assessment, p. 21
Chapter Review Software
Computer Test Bank

Chapter 7 Force and Newton's Laws

This is a representation of key blackline masters available in the Teacher Classroom Resources. See Resource Manager boxes within the chapter for additional information.

Transparencies

Section Focus Transparencies

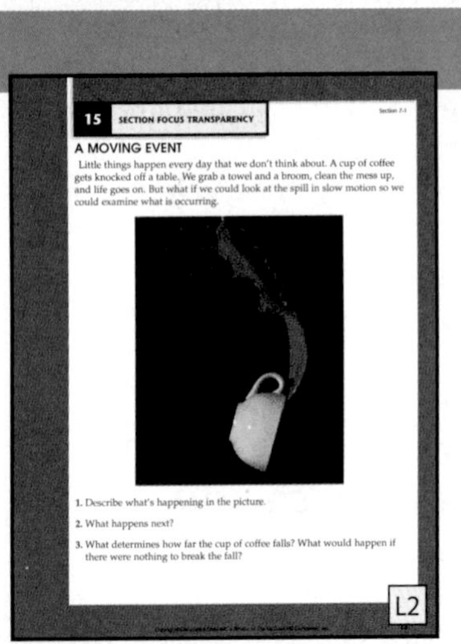
15 SECTION FOCUS TRANSPARENCY

A MOVING EVENT

Little things happen every day that we don't think about. A cup of coffee gets knocked off a table. We grab a towel and a broom, clean the mess up, and life goes on. But what if we could look at the spill in slow motion so we could examine what is occurring.

1. Describe what's happening in the picture.
2. What happens next?
3. What determines how far the cup of coffee falls? What would happen if there were nothing to break the fall?

L2

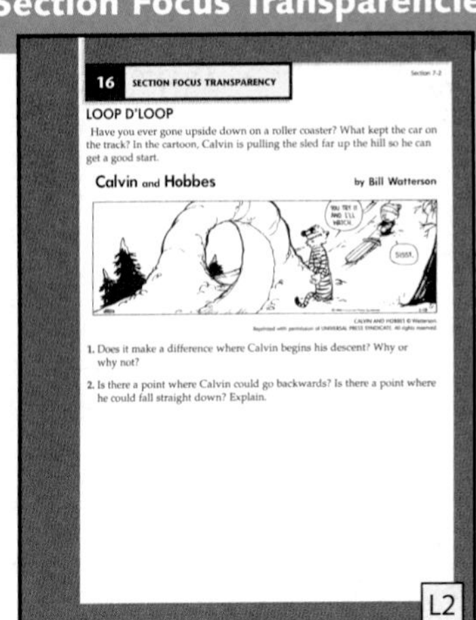
16 SECTION FOCUS TRANSPARENCY

LOOP D'LOOP

Have you ever gone upside down on a roller coaster? What kept the car on the track? In the cartoon, Calvin is pulling the sled far up the hill so he can get a good start.

1. Does it make a difference where Calvin begins his descent? Why or why not?
2. Is there a point where Calvin could go backwards? Is there a point where he could fall straight down? Explain.

L2

17 SECTION FOCUS TRANSPARENCY

RUN FOR FUN

People run for many reasons. Sometimes it's for exercise or for competition. Sometimes it's for the pure joy of running. And people run at different rates. Some people run fast. Others run slow or jog.

1. Look at the picture and also think of what happens when you run. In which direction does a person's body exert force?
2. Describe what might happen if a runner were racing across a thin wooden plank. What would likely happen if a group of runners ran arm in arm across the same plank? Can you account for the difference?

L2

Science Integration Transparencies

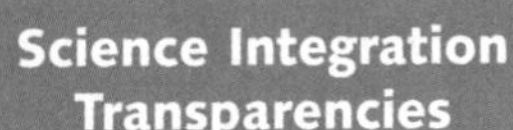

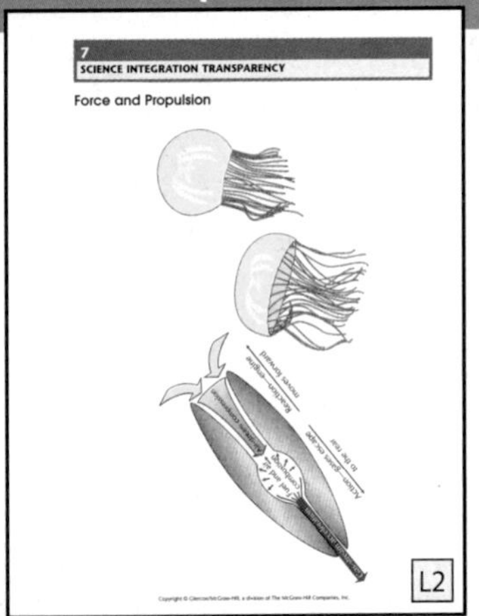

Teaching Transparencies

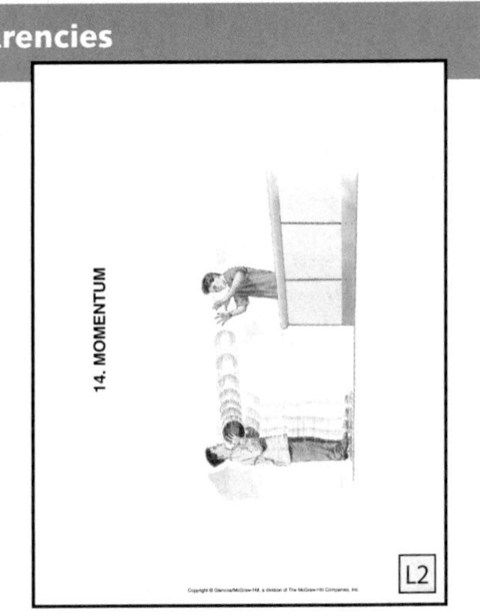

Meeting Different Ability Levels

Study Guide for Content Mastery

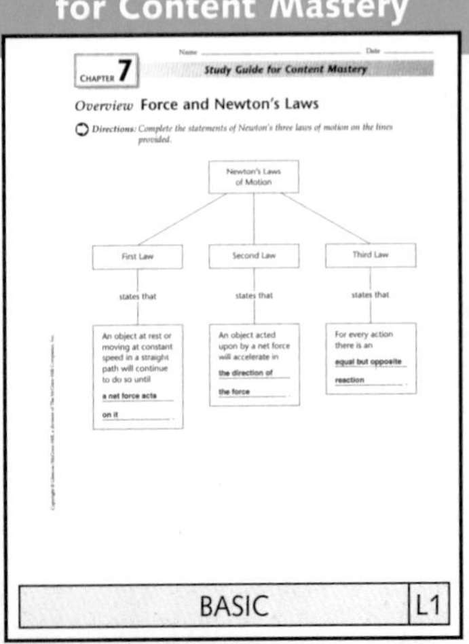
Chapter 7 Study Guide for Content Mastery

Overview Force and Newton's Laws

Directions: Complete the statements of Newton's three laws of motion on the lines provided.

Newton's Laws of Motion

First Law — states that — An object at rest or moving at constant speed in a straight path will continue to do so until **a net force acts on it**

Second Law — states that — An object acted upon by a net force will accelerate in **the direction of the force**

Third Law — states that — For every action there is an **equal but opposite reaction**

BASIC L1

Reinforcement

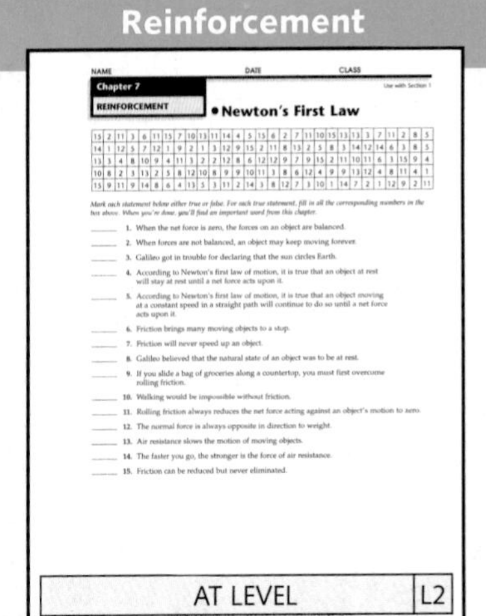
Chapter 7 REINFORCEMENT

• Newton's First Law

Mark each statement below either true or false. For each true statement, fill in all the corresponding numbers in the box above. When you're done, you'll find an important word from this chapter.

1. When the net force is zero, the forces on an object are balanced.
2. When forces are not balanced, an object may keep moving forever.
3. Galileo got in trouble for declaring that the sun circles Earth.
4. According to Newton's first law of motion, it is true that an object at rest will stay at rest until a net force acts upon it.
5. According to Newton's first law of motion, it is true that an object moving at a constant speed in a straight path will continue to do so until a net force acts upon it.
6. Friction brings many moving objects to a stop.
7. Friction will never speed up an object.
8. Galileo believed that the natural state of an object was to be at rest.
9. If you slide a bag of groceries along a countertop, you must first overcome rolling friction.
10. Walking would be impossible without friction.
11. Rolling friction always reduces the net force acting against an object's motion to zero.
12. The normal force is always opposite in direction to weight.
13. Air resistance slows the motion of moving objects.
14. The faster you go, the stronger is the force of air resistance.
15. Friction can be reduced but never eliminated.

AT LEVEL L2

Enrichment Worksheets

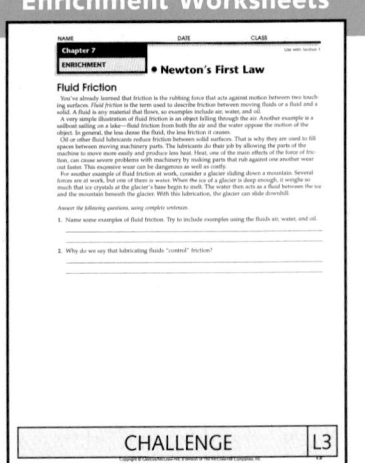

Chapter 7 ENRICHMENT

• Newton's First Law

Fluid Friction

CHALLENGE L3

Hands-on Activities

Activity Worksheets

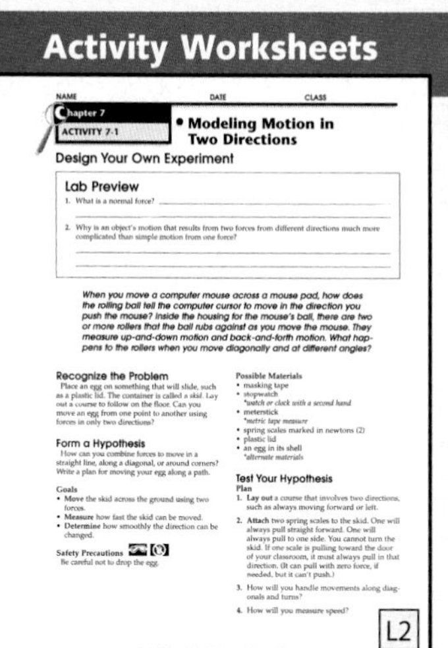
NAME DATE CLASS

Chapter 7 ACTIVITY 7-1 • Modeling Motion in Two Directions

Design Your Own Experiment

Lab Preview

L2

Lab Manual

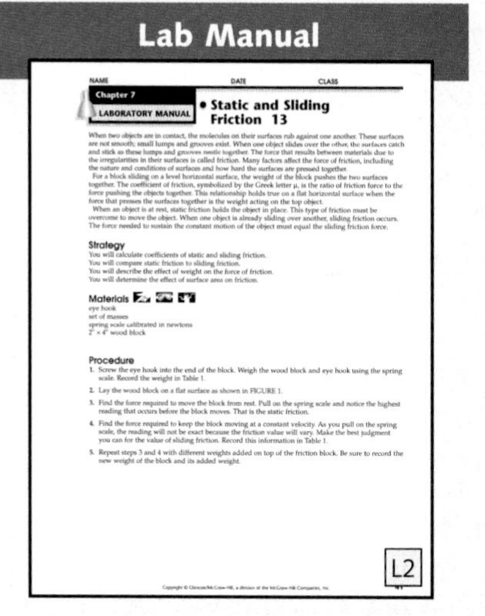
NAME DATE CLASS

Chapter 7 LABORATORY MANUAL • Static and Sliding Friction 13

Strategy

Materials

Procedure

L2

Accessibility

Spanish Resources

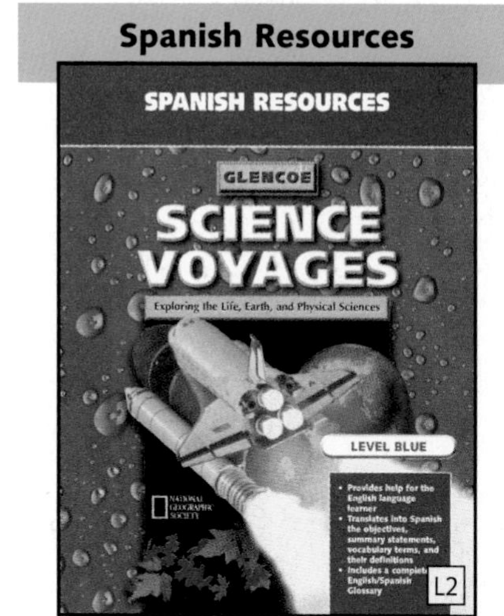

Assessment

Performance Assessment

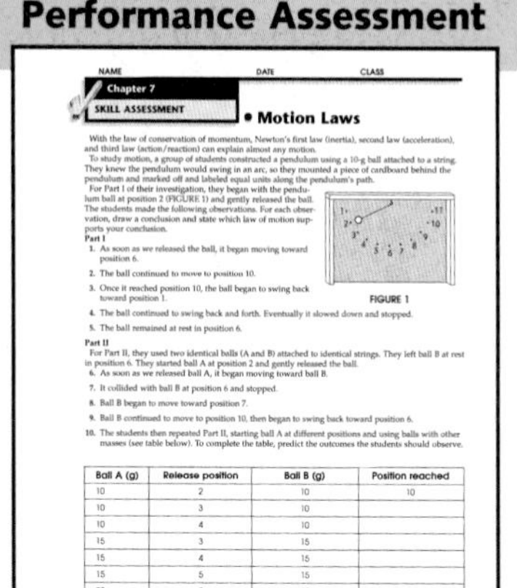
NAME DATE CLASS

Chapter 7 SKILL ASSESSMENT • Motion Laws

L2

Chapter Review

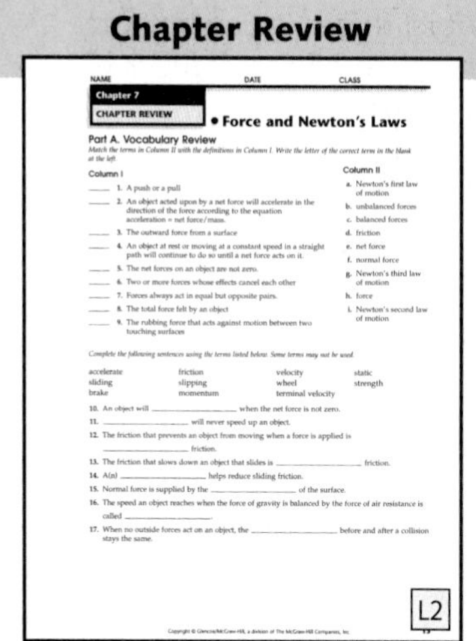
NAME DATE CLASS

Chapter 7 CHAPTER REVIEW • Force and Newton's Laws

Part A. Vocabulary Review

L2

Assessment

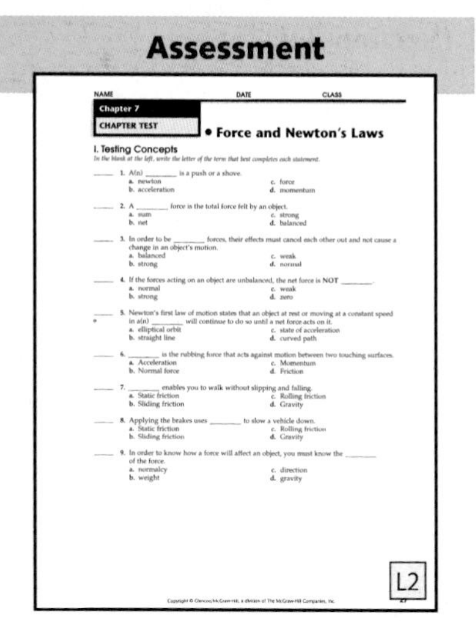
NAME DATE CLASS

Chapter 7 CHAPTER TEST • Force and Newton's Laws

I. Testing Concepts

L2

Test Practice Workbook

Extending Content

Critical Thinking/ Problem Solving

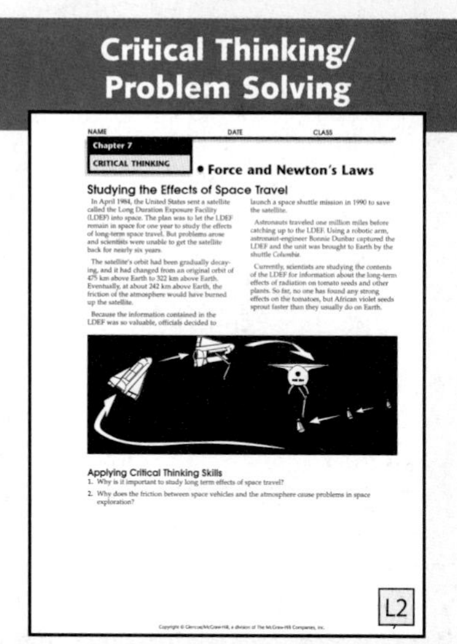
NAME DATE CLASS

Chapter 7 CRITICAL THINKING • Force and Newton's Laws

Studying the Effects of Space Travel

Applying Critical Thinking Skills

L2

Multicultural Connections

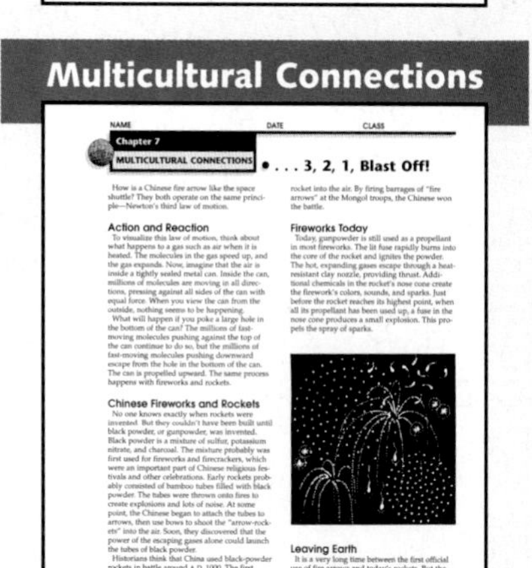
NAME DATE CLASS

Chapter 7 MULTICULTURAL CONNECTIONS • . . . 3, 2, 1, Blast Off!

Action and Reaction

Fireworks Today

Chinese Fireworks and Rockets

Leaving Earth

L2

Chapter 7 Force and Newton's Laws

Helping You Prepare

Force (Section 7-1)

A force is a push or a pull. Force is measured by the acceleration it gives a certain mass. If an object is accelerating, a net force must be acting on it. If you know one force is acting on an object, and the object is not accelerating, another force must be acting to balance the first force.

There are four fundamental forces. Gravity is the attraction between all matter. Electromagnetism is the attraction or repulsion due to electric and magnetic fields. The strong nuclear force holds neutrons and protons together in the nucleus. The weak nuclear force is involved in some types of radioactive decay—it can change a proton into a neutron and vice versa. These forces are fundamental because they can act at a distance through a field, and because they can be used to explain other forces.

The examples of force in this chapter are mostly gravity and contact forces. A contact force is a force that exists because of the contact between objects; it is electromagnetic in origin, because electromagnetism is behind the structure of materials. The normal force, friction, and the forces exerted by your hands and feet when you push a box or kick a ball are all contact forces.

Newton's Laws (Section 7-1)

Trying to understand the science of moving objects (classical mechanics) is one of the oldest scientific endeavors. The classical Greek idea that rest is natural, and an object in motion must have a force to keep it in motion, is intuitive to many people. Even some college physics students will start using this language when presented with a new type of problem. You might want to bring up examples such as a probe shot deep into space. If it doesn't come near any objects (to attract it gravitationally), it can keep going without an engine propelling it. This is something they may have seen presented on science fiction shows on television. If students report seeing fictional spaceships come to a dead stop whenever the engine has problems, ask them to explain why this is problematic.

Newton's First Law (Section 7-1)

Newton's first law of motion states that an object at rest or moving with constant velocity will continue in that state until acted on by a net force. The tendency of a body to remain at rest or in uniform linear motion is called inertia, and Newton's first law is sometimes called the law of inertia.

The fact that there is no difference between rest and uniform linear motion is a result of reference frames. If you are riding on a train at a constant velocity of 35 km/h west, to the passenger sitting opposite you, you appear to be holding still. To a passenger walking down the aisle at 1 m/s east, your relative motion is 1 m/s west. To a driver in a car outside, your velocity is different yet again, depending on the velocity of the car. In advanced physics courses, students choose a convenient reference frame to work in, often by defining the reference frame so that the body they are studying is still.

Suggest that students think about a cup of tea sitting on a table. The table might be in their house, on a train, or in a jet. They don't have to push on the cup as they travel. It continues moving relative to the ground as long as the train or plane does not suddenly speed up, slow down, or turn.

Friction (Section 7-1)

Aristotle identified the existence of friction, but it was not until Leonardo da Vinci that the basic rules of friction were discovered. The friction force depends on the nature of the surfaces—different surfaces have different coefficients of friction. Friction depends on the normal force exerted by a surface; it is not affected by the area of the surfaces in contact. (It can be affected by the true microscopic area of contact, but for practical purposes in the school lab there should not be a difference between, say, pushing a box on its large bottom surface and on a smaller side surface.) The study of friction is called tribology, and is of interest to theoretical and applied scientists.

GLENCOE TECHNOLOGY

 **CD-ROM**

Glencoe Science Voyages Interactive CD-ROM

Chapter Summaries

Use the Chapter Summary to introduce, teach, or review chapter material.

Newton's Second Law (Section 7-2)

The fundamental equation of classical mechanics is that the sum of the forces on an object equals the mass of the object times the acceleration, or $F_{net} = ma$. People often drop the "net" if a problem gives a force to be used in calculations; it is understood to be the net force.

Newton's first and second laws are often taught together. The first law applies if the forces on an object are balanced. The second law applies if the forces are unbalanced.

Newton's Third Law (Section 7-3)

Newton's third law states that for every force, there is an equal and opposite force. It is important to understand that the forces act on different objects. Students can easily mix action and reaction, in which there are two forces accelerating different objects, and balanced forces, in which no object accelerates. You can illustrate this in class with a ball. If two students push from opposite sides of the ball with the same force, it won't move. Both forces are applied to the same object. The same is true if they pull on the ball from opposite sides. If they toss the ball back and forth, there are action and reaction pairs between a student's hands and the ball when throwing and when catching. The push of the throw exerts a force on the ball and on the student.

Another reason for confusion with the third law is that Earth, or a similar large object, is often one of the objects. In the example above, a student is much more massive than a ball, and the student's shoes provide static friction with the floor, so that the ball's force is exerted on a large mass. The students can feel the force in their hands, but they won't move as visibly as they would throwing an object while standing on a low-friction surface. (Look at the two students in **Figure 7-22.**)

SCIENCE UPDATE

For current events or science in the news, access the Glencoe Science Web Site at **www.glencoe.com/sec/science**

Combining Laws (Section 7-4)

Newton's laws, along with laws such as the conservation of momentum and conservation of energy, are used to analyze motion problems. One powerful method for solving motion problems is to divide the problem into parts and determine what laws apply to each part. The laws of motion were used to understand the motion of celestial bodies, such as Earth, and the properties of gases.

Newton's laws of motion do not apply at relativistic speeds (close to the speed of light, 3×10^8 m/s). The relativistic laws of motion, however, reduce to Newton's laws for low speeds, the only ones students are likely to encounter at this level of study.

Teacher to Teacher

"Air resistance is a factor to consider with all moving objects on Earth. I have students identify where air resistance is purposefully increased or decreased as a result of design or function."

Kevin Finnegan

Kevin Finnegan, Teacher
McCord Middle School
Worthington, OH

CHAPTER 7 Force and Newton's Laws

CHAPTER OVERVIEW

Section 7-1 This section introduces force and describes how an object moves when there is no net force acting on it.

Section 7-2 This section describes how a net force on an object affects its motion.

Section 7-3 The interaction between an object supplying a force and one receiving a force is explored.

Section 7-4 Newton's laws of motion and the law of conservation of momentum are used to analyze motion.

Chapter Vocabulary

force
net force
balanced forces
unbalanced forces
Newton's first law of motion
friction
Newton's second law of motion
normal force
Newton's third law of motion

Theme Connection

Systems and Interactions Forces acting on objects affect how they move. Objects interacting with each other conform to Newton's laws of motion and the laws of conservation of momentum and energy.

00:00 OUT OF TIME?

If time does not permit teaching the entire chapter, use Reviewing Main Ideas on pp. 202-203.

CHAPTER 7 Force and Newton's Laws

Chapter Preview

Skills Preview

Skill Builders
- Concept Mapping

Activities
- Design an Experiment

MiniLabs
- Measure in SI

Reading Check ✓

As you read, make a chart of the examples used to help explain each of Newton's laws. Add one or two examples of your own for each law.

174

Multiple Learning Styles

Look for the following logos for strategies that emphasize different learning modalities.

Linguistic Discussion, p. 194; Visual Learning, p. 198; Preview, p. 202

Logical-Mathematical Enrichment, p. 181

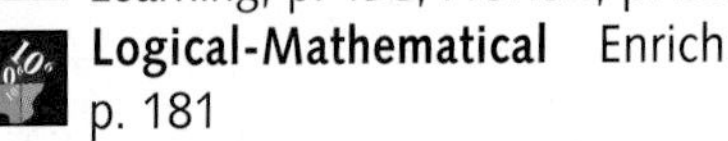

Visual-Spatial MiniLab, pp. 180, 187, 199; Using Science Words, p. 181; Activity, pp. 190–191; Reteach, pp. 194, 202

Auditory-Musical Out of Time, p. 202

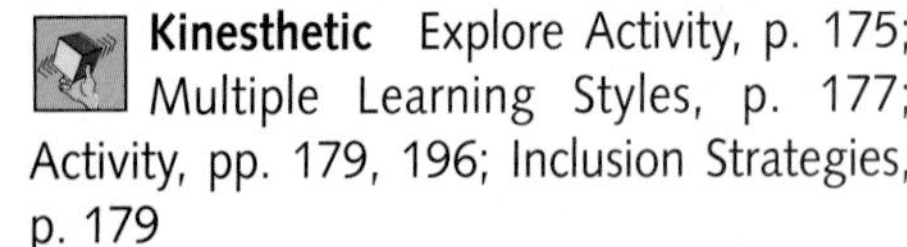

Kinesthetic Explore Activity, p. 175; Multiple Learning Styles, p. 177; Activity, pp. 179, 196; Inclusion Strategies, p. 179

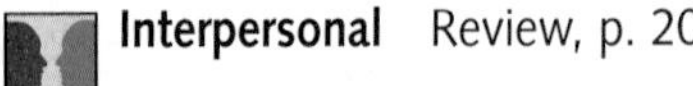

Interpersonal Review, p. 202

Explore Activity

Bobsleds go fast—very fast, as you know if you've ever watched one speed down its icy run. At the top of the run, the bobsledders exert a force on the sled to accelerate it. Then they jump in, and the force of gravity accelerates them down. The team members use their bodies as well as the brakes and steering mechanism to change the sled's motion, slowing it or turning it. The motion of the sled can be understood with Newton's laws of motion.

Define Motion

1. Lean one end of a meterstick on top of three books. This is your ramp. Put one side of the ramp against a wall so the marbles won't roll off.
2. Tap a marble so it rolls up the ramp. Measure how far up the ramp it travels before rolling back.
3. Repeat step 2 using two books, one book, and zero books. The same person should tap the marble each time, trying to keep the force constant.

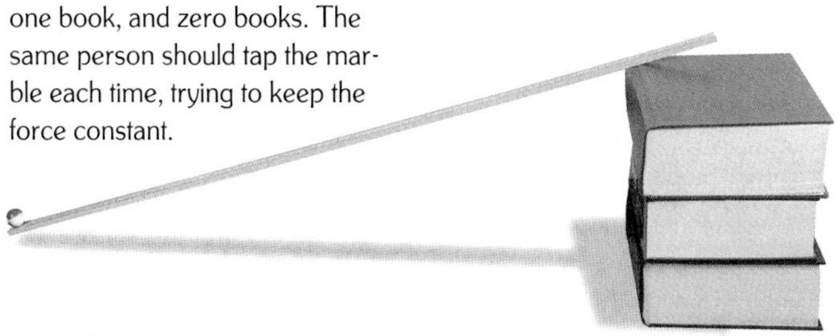

Science Journal

Make a table and record the motion of the marble for each ramp height. What do you think would happen if you could send a marble along a perfectly smooth, flat path?

175

Assessment Planner

Portfolio
Refer to p. 203 for suggested items that students might select for their portfolios.

Performance Assessment
See p. 203 for additional Performance Assessment options.
Skill Builder, pp. 182, 188, 195, 201
MiniLab, pp. 180, 187, 199
Activity 7-1, pp. 190–191; 7-2, p. 196

Content Assessment
Section Assessment, pp. 182, 188, 195, 201
Chapter Assessment, pp. 204–205
Proficiency Prep, pp. 182, 188, 195, 201

Explore Activity

Purpose

Kinesthetic Use the Explore Activity to help students see the effect that the steepness of the ramp has on the distance the marble travels up the ramp. L2 ELL COOP LEARN P

Preparation

Make sure that the books used are of similar thickness.

Materials

three books, a meterstick, and a marble for each group

Teaching Strategies

To make the initial velocity of the marble constant, you can use a flexible strip to make a launch ramp. Always release the marble from the same point on the ramp, and be sure there isn't a significant bump where the ramps join.

Science Journal Student will record data that show that the steeper the incline is, the shorter the distance traveled by the marble is. On a perfectly smooth, flat path, the marble would roll forever.

Assessment

Portfolio Show students a picture of a bobsled track, ski run, or slide. Ask students to identify the points where a rider would have maximum velocity. Ask students to defend their choices in a sentence or two. Use **Performance Assessment in the Science Classroom,** p. 105.

SECTION 7-1

Prepare

Refer to **Force, Newton's Laws, Newton's First Law,** and **Friction** on p. 174E.

Preplanning

Refer to the **Chapter Organizer** on pp. 174A–B.

1 Motivate

Bellringer

Before presenting the lesson, display **Section Focus Transparency 15** on the overhead projector. Use the accompanying **Focus Activity** worksheet. L2 ELL

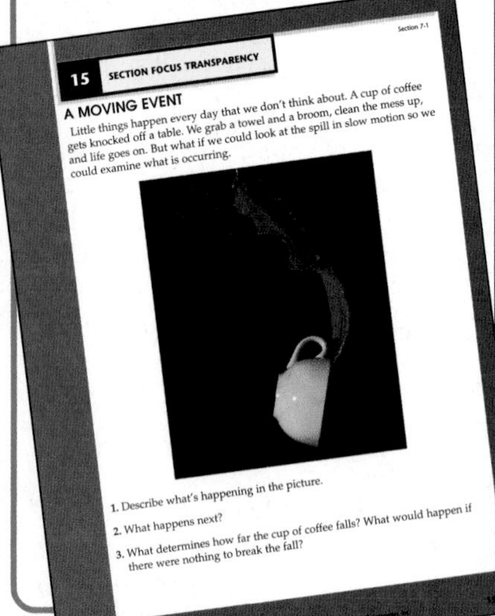

Section 7-1

15 SECTION FOCUS TRANSPARENCY

A MOVING EVENT

Little things happen every day that we don't think about. A cup of coffee gets knocked off a table. We grab a towel and a broom, clean the mess up, and life goes on. But what if we could look at the spill in slow motion so we could examine what is occurring.

1. Describe what's happening in the picture.
2. What happens next?
3. What determines how far the cup of coffee falls? What would happen if there were nothing to break the fall?

Tying to Previous Knowledge

Have students recall acceleration. In this section, they will learn what kinds of forces applied to objects cause them to accelerate.

7•1 Newton's First Law

What You'll Learn

- How to recognize a force
- What balanced and net forces are
- Newton's first law of motion
- How friction works

Vocabulary
force
net force
balanced forces
unbalanced forces
Newton's first law of motion
friction

Why It's Important

- Newton's first law is the basis of all motion, from a bike moving at constant speed to the motion of the planets.

Force

When an object accelerates, it changes its motion. It can speed up, slow down, or turn. If an object accelerates, a force must be acting on it. A **force** is a push or a pull. Some examples of forces are shown in **Figure 7-1.** For example, when you throw a ball, your hand exerts a force on the ball, and you accelerate the ball forward. After the ball leaves your hand, gravity exerts a force on it, causing its path to curve downward. When the ball hits the ground, the ground exerts a force, stopping the ball and perhaps bouncing it back up.

The force of a magnet can move a paper clip. Earth's gravitational field can also move the paper clip. Or, you can move the paper clip by picking it up. All of these are examples of forces acting on the paper clip.

Suppose you hold a paper clip near a magnet. You, the magnet, and gravity all exert forces on the clip. A **net force** is the total force felt by an object. The object will accelerate in the direction of the net force. The clip does not move because the net force is zero.

Figure 7-1 Each of these pictures shows a force working.

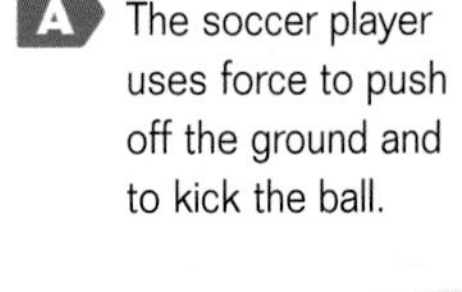

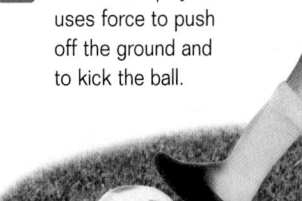

A The soccer player uses force to push off the ground and to kick the ball.

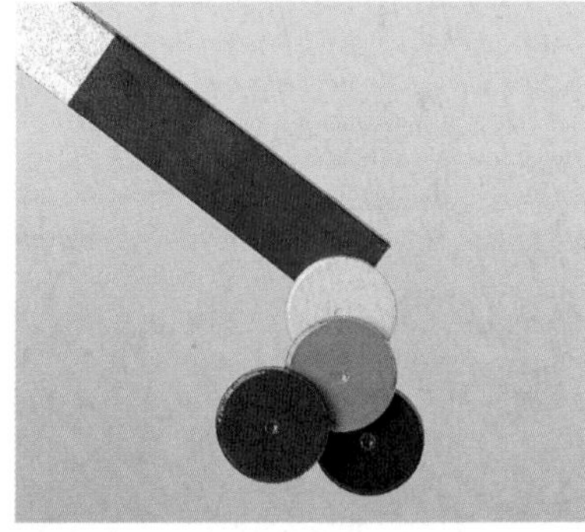

B The force of the magnet on the metal disks is strong enough to pull them off the table.

C The force stored in the spring will stop the door as it opens.

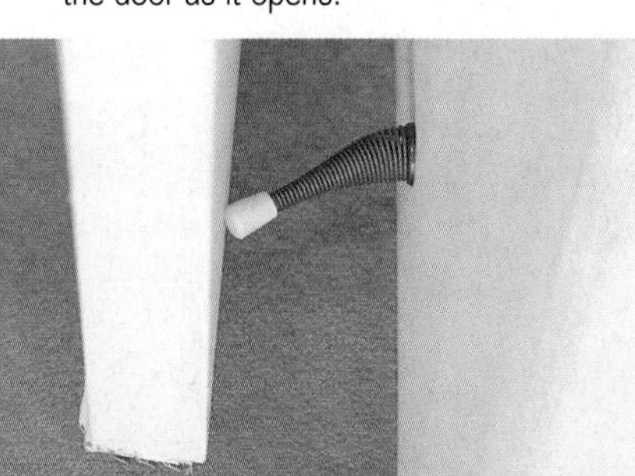

Resource Manager

The following **Teacher Classroom Resources** can be used with Section 7-1:

Reproducible Masters

Activity Worksheets, p. 39 L2

Enrichment, p. 15 L3

Laboratory Manual, pp. 41–44 L2

Reinforcement, p. 15 L2

Study Guide, pp. 25–26 L1 ELL

Transparencies

Teaching Transparency 13 L2

If you push gently on one side of the book in **Figure 7-2,** and a friend pushes hard on the other side, the net force is toward you, so the book will move toward you.

A force can act on an object without causing it to accelerate. Right now gravity is pulling you down and your chair is pushing you up. Your motion isn't changing, so the forces are *balanced.* Two or more forces are **balanced forces** if their effects cancel each other and they do not cause a change in an object's motion. An example is shown in **Figure 7-3.** If the forces on an object are balanced, the net force is zero. If the forces are **unbalanced forces,** the net force is not zero, and the object accelerates. An object can be in motion and have no net force acting on it. If you push a hockey puck across the ice, your hockey stick accelerates it by exerting a force. When you stop exerting that force, the puck keeps moving at constant speed across the ice until the force of friction slows it down. All the forces acting on the puck are balanced while its motion doesn't change.

Figure 7-2 The sum of all the forces acting on an object is the net force.

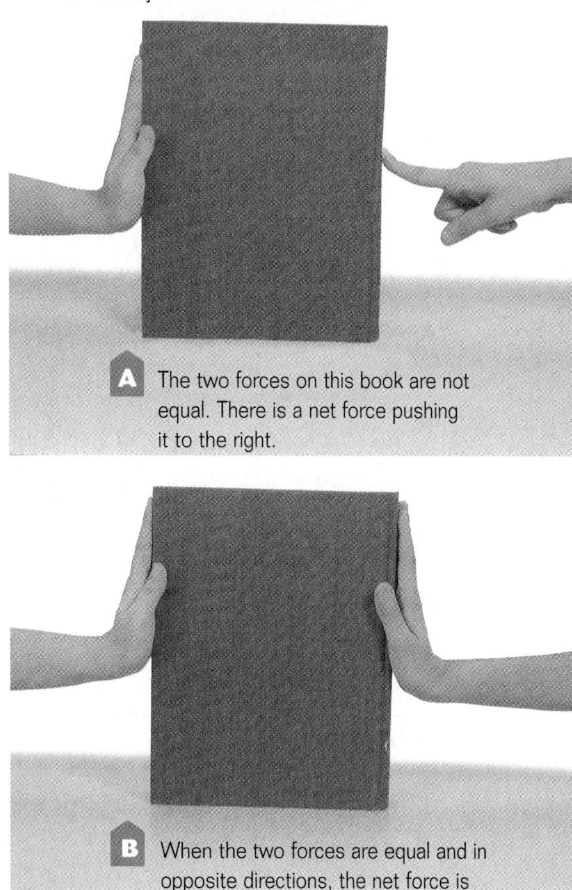

A The two forces on this book are not equal. There is a net force pushing it to the right.

B When the two forces are equal and in opposite directions, the net force is zero. The book does not move.

Figure 7-3 Acrobats exert forces to hold each other in position. All the forces are balanced, so the acrobats do not move. **What will happen if the forces become unbalanced?**

CHEMISTRY INTEGRATION

Electric Force
A neutral atom has balanced electric forces. An ion has charge and can accelerate other ions or electrons. It has a net electric force. When two negatively charged ions repel each other, is this an example of force? How do you know?

2 Teach

CHEMISTRY INTEGRATION

In a neutral atom, the number of protons in the nucleus equals the number of electrons distributed around the nucleus. In an ion, the number of electrons does not equal the number of protons. The result is a net charge. The net charge on an ion exerts an electric force capable of accelerating other charged particles. When two negatively charged ions repel, their motion changes, so a force is clearly at work.

Caption Answer

Figure 7-3 *The acrobats will accelerate, most likely by falling to the ground.*

GLENCOE TECHNOLOGY

Videodisc

Glencoe Science Voyages Interactive Videodisc—Physical

Side 1, Lesson 1 *Motion*

8141

Refer to Videodisc Teacher Guide for additional bar codes.

Content Background

When the forces acting on an object are balanced, the object may be at rest, but it need not be. The object may be moving at a constant velocity. When the forces acting on an object are not balanced, the object is always moving. In fact, it is always accelerating. It may be changing its speed, changing its direction, or both.

Multiple Learning Styles

Kinesthetic Push one book across the tabletop in 2 s. Repeat using two, three, and four books. How much force is required in each case? Can you feel the difference?

Content Background

Isaac Newton was born in the year Galileo died. Twenty-three years later, after studying Galileo's work, he developed the laws of motion that overthrew Aristotle's ideas, which had prevailed for 2000 years. Although these two men never met, they acted together to create a revolution in our understanding of the world around us.

Quick Demo

Place a cup of water on a skateboard and push it across the table to an assistant on the other side. Ask the assistant to stop the skateboard. **What happens to the cup of water?** *It keeps on moving and most likely spills.* Have paper towels handy.

Using an Analogy

The next time you are at a bowling alley, take a look at the ramp system that the pinsetter uses to return your ball. The ball is gently rolled along a horizontal track until it rolls down a ramp, along a track parallel to the alley, up a ramp, and along the horizontal rack next to the bowler. This ramp system is similar to the one used in Galileo's experiment. It works because there is little friction exerted by the track on the bowling ball. In Galileo's thought experiment, the ball would roll forever on the track beside the alley. You would be able to lengthen the alley forever and still return the ball.

Flex Your Brain

Use the Flex Your Brain activity to have students explore FRICTION.

Newton's First Law of Motion

In 1635, when Galileo Galilei was 70 years old, he was placed under house arrest for claiming that the planets, including Earth, orbit the sun and that Earth rotates once each day. His claim troubled many people. "How can Earth be moving?" they thought. "If it does, then our water glasses should fall over!" Galileo's view was revolutionary. He spent the remaining seven years of his life confined to his home. About thirty years later, Isaac Newton would build on Galileo's work and begin to change the way people thought about the world.

Galileo said the reason the water glass does not fall over is because Earth has always been moving around the sun and spinning on its axis in a smooth manner. If Earth suddenly stopped rotating, everything that is not strongly attached to the ground would spill. **Figure 7-4** gives another example.

Newton used Galileo's ideas about motion in what is now called **Newton's first law of motion.** It states, "An object will remain at rest or move with constant velocity until it is acted upon by a net force." This also is called Newton's law of inertia.

A Thought Experiment

Galileo discovered this scientific law by thinking about a ball rolling up a ramp, as in the Explore Activity. If the ramp is steep, the ball will not travel far before it stops. As the ramp

Figure 7-4 An object in motion remains in motion.

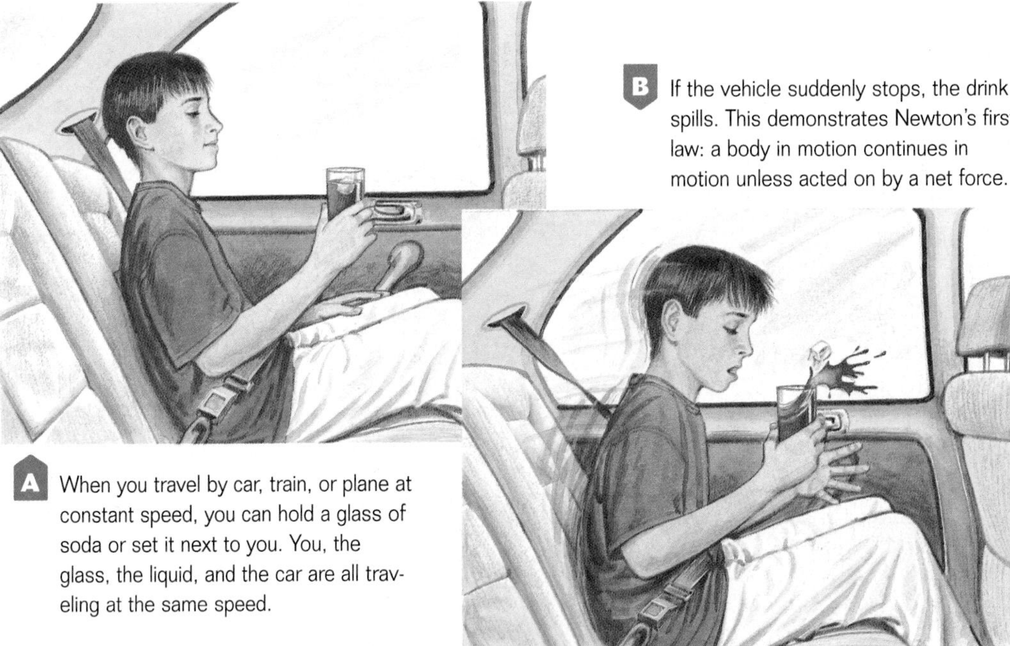

B If the vehicle suddenly stops, the drink spills. This demonstrates Newton's first law: a body in motion continues in motion unless acted on by a net force.

A When you travel by car, train, or plane at constant speed, you can hold a glass of soda or set it next to you. You, the glass, the liquid, and the car are all traveling at the same speed.

Guided Reading Strategy

Think-Pair Share This strategy encourages students to think first before discussing their ideas or thoughts about a topic. Students are asked to respond to a question by writing a response. After thinking for a few minutes, partners share responses to the question. Finally, the teacher asks the students to share responses with the class. Have students become involved in a Think-Pair Share about a topic in this section.

Across the Curriculum

Language Arts Bertold Brecht wrote the play *Galileo Galilei* about the arrest and trial of Galileo during the Inquisition. This play provides an interesting commentary on the relationship between science and the political climate in which it is studied. Some of your more advanced students might find this play of interest.

178 CHAPTER 7 FORCE AND NEWTON'S LAWS

A Without friction, the climber would slide down the slope.

Figure 7-5 Friction acts against the motion between objects.

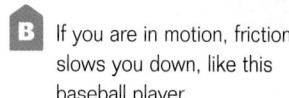

B If you are in motion, friction slows you down, like this baseball player.

is lowered closer and closer to level, the ball will go farther and farther up the ramp. If the ramp is then made perfectly smooth and level, the ball should continue moving forever if nothing disturbs it.

You can try this by rolling a bowling ball on a large, level surface, like your school gymnasium floor. A slight push will easily send the ball across the room at nearly constant speed.

What happens when you repeat the experiment on a rough or uneven surface, like grass or a thick carpet? The ball slows down. Something disturbs the ball's motion. A force must be acting on the ball.

Friction

Galileo said an object in motion remains in motion until a net (or unbalanced) force acts on it. The unbalanced force that brings nearly everything to a stop is **friction,** the rubbing force that acts against motion between two touching surfaces. There are a number of different forms of friction, but they all have one thing in common. They always act against an object's direction of motion, as shown in **Figure 7-5.** Friction will never speed up an object. If you rub your hand against a tabletop, you can feel the friction push against the direction your hand is moving. If you rub back the other way, you can feel the direction of friction change so it is again acting against your hand's motion. ☑

Quick Demo

Roll a bowling ball slowly across the floor in the classroom. Put down a piece of carpet and roll the ball giving it a push similar to the one used on the bare floor. **What happens?** *The ball does not roll as far or as quickly on the carpet.* **Why?** *Friction opposes the motion of the ball and slows it down.*

Activity

Kinesthetic Give students a child's building block, a piece of copy paper, and a piece of sandpaper. Ask them to place the block on the copy paper and use thumb and forefinger to flick it across the paper. Ask them to repeat using the block on the sandpaper. **What happens and why?** *The block moves further across the copy paper because the sandpaper exerts more friction on the block and keeps it from moving as far.*

Enrichment

Investigate the sport of curling. What is the object of this sport? What role does friction play in it? L2

Discussion

How does a hand brake on a bicycle work? How does it use friction to stop a bicycle? L2

Answer to Reading Check

Friction is a force that acts against the motion of two touching surfaces.

Inclusion Strategies

Physically Challenged If you have a student in your class who uses a wheelchair, ask the student to explain its braking system and the role friction plays in making it work. Ask students to compare pushing the chair with the brake off and on. L2

interNET CONNECTION

Visit the Glencoe Science Web Site at **www.glencoe.com/sec/science** for more information about the study of motion.

Older Ideas About Motion

It took a long time to understand force. People once thought the natural state of an object was rest. For an object to be in motion, something had to be continuously moving it. As soon as the force stopped, nature would bring the object to rest.

Galileo understood that constant motion is as natural as rest. If he could remove friction, an object would continue to move with constant motion. He did a series of experiments where he pushed an object across smoother and smoother surfaces and found that the object would go farther and farther. He reasoned that if he could make the surface perfectly smooth and flat, the object would never slow down. You can repeat this experiment yourself at home or at school.

Static Friction

Another experiment can demonstrate static friction. Place an eraser on your ruler. Start to tip the ruler, as shown in **Figure 7-6.** The eraser does not start to slide right away, but stays in place until the ruler reaches a certain angle. The friction that prevents an object from moving when a force is applied is called static friction. It is static friction that makes it possible to walk. Every step taken pushes against Earth. Without friction, you'd slip and fall.

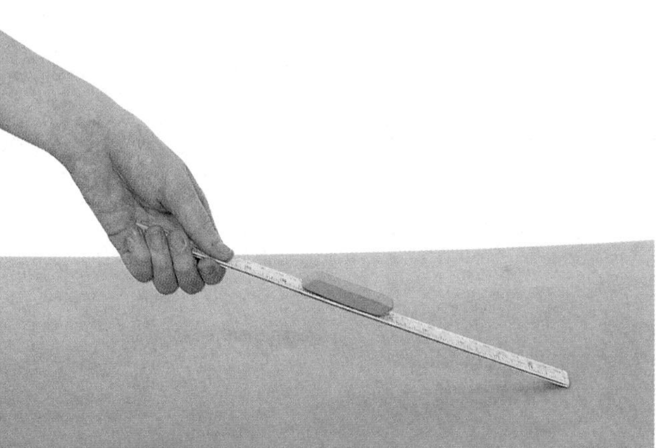

Figure 7-6 Static friction holds the eraser in place on the ruler. **What will happen when the net force due to gravity is greater than the force of static friction?**

Have you ever tried to push something heavy, like a refrigerator? When you begin to push, nothing happens. Static friction balances your force. As you push harder and harder, the object will suddenly give way and move. When the object begins to move, you are exerting a force too great for static friction to balance.

Sliding Friction

Static friction keeps an object at rest. Sliding friction slows down an object that slides. If you push an object across the room, there is sliding friction between the bottom of the object and the floor. You have to keep pushing to overcome the force of sliding friction. The brake pads in a car use sliding friction against the wheels to slow the car. Bicycle brakes, shown in **Figure 7-7A,** work the same way. Skidding tires, shuffling shoes, and rubbing hands are all common forms of sliding friction.

Teacher FYI

Vehicles traveling on icy roads require three to seven times more stopping distance than similar vehicles traveling on dry pavement. The ice reduces the friction between the tires and the road making it harder to stop.

Caption Answer

Figure 7-6 *The eraser will start to slide down the ruler.*

Purpose

Visual-Spatial Students will measure the force exerted by rolling friction on wheels. L2 ELL COOP LEARN

Materials

spring scale and skateboard for each group of students

Teaching Strategies

Explain to students that they are to observe the scale readings when the skateboard is at rest, when it just starts to move, as it continues to move with a constant speed, and as it stops.

Analysis

1. When the skateboard was at rest the scale read zero. As it started to move, the scale reading increased. As the skateboard reached a constant velocity, the scale reading decreased to a constant amount. As the skateboard slowed to a stop, the scale reading returned to zero.
2. the reading on the scale when the skateboard is moving at a constant speed

Assessment

Process Ask students to explain why they have to pedal their bikes continuously when they are traveling on level ground. *They have to overcome the rolling friction exerted by the pavement on the bicycle tires.* Use **Performance Assessment in the Science Classroom,** p. 71.

interNET CONNECTION

Internet Addresses

____

____

____

____

For Internet tips, see Glencoe's **Using the Internet in the Science Classroom.**

Figure 7-7 A bicycle uses sliding friction and rolling friction.

A Sliding friction is used to stop this bicycle tire. Friction between the brake pads and the wheel brings the wheel to a stop.

B Rolling friction with the ground pushes the bottom of the bicycle tire back so the wheel rolls forward.

Rolling Friction

The wheel helps reduce sliding friction, but even the best wheel cannot completely remove this force. In fact, another kind of friction, rolling friction, is needed to make a wheel turn. There is friction between the ground and the part of a bike tire in contact with the ground, as shown in **Figure 7-7B.** Rolling friction pushes back so that the tire rolls forward. Sometimes, when a bike hits a patch of ice or wet leaves, there is not enough friction between the tire and ground to spin the tire, and the bike skids.

Spin a wheel with your hand and you can feel the friction between your hand and the wheel. If the wheel were coated in oil, your hand would slip off and it would be difficult to get enough friction to start the wheel in motion.

Defining Rolling Friction

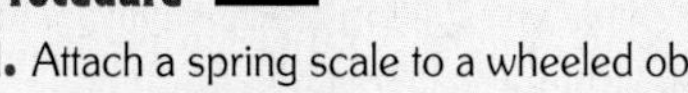

Procedure

1. Attach a spring scale to a wheeled object such as a skateboard.
2. Pull the skateboard across the room at a steady speed. Observe the reading on the spring scale.

Analysis

1. What did the spring scale read when you started? What did it read as you moved at constant speed? When you stopped?
2. What is the force of rolling friction in this example? (Assume air resistance is so small it can be ignored.)

Air Resistance

When you ride a bicycle, the air pushes your hair and clothes back. Whether you are biking, walking, or riding in a car, air pushes against you. This is air resistance. Air resistance acts on the forward moving part of an object, such as the front of a car. It acts against the direction of motion and gets stronger as an object goes faster.

When you first start to pedal, your legs provide the force to push the bicycle forward. The air resistance is low, and you can accelerate fairly quickly. As you go faster, the air resistance gets stronger. Eventually, the air resistance (and road friction) balance your pedaling force, so you move at constant velocity.

Friction Ask students to identify the type of friction involved in each of the following.

- bicycle tire on road *rolling friction*
- basketball player slipping on wet spot on floor *sliding friction*
- car stuck in mud *static friction*
- parachute slowing a fall *air resistance* L2

Enrichment

Logical-Mathematical Have students design parachutes and test them using a 20-g weight. Drop the weighted parachutes from the same height and determine which one keeps the weight in the air the longest. L3 COOP LEARN P

3 Assess

Check for Understanding

Using Science Words

Visual-Spatial Ask students to visualize a swing on a playground. One person is sitting in the swing and another is pushing it to make it swing at a constant height. Ask the students to identify all the forces on the swing/person system and how they combine to produce the observed motion. *Forces include weight of the swing and person, upward force of ropes supporting swing, friction and air resistance produced by swinging, and force exerted by person pushing the swing. Forces exerted by weight and ropes are balanced. Pushing balances the friction and air resistance to keep the swing moving back and forth at a constant height. Encourage students to identify the source of the forces in each case.* L2

Reteach

In the Check for Understanding, correct any mistakes in identification of forces and in use of language to describe them. L2

Extension

For students who have mastered this section, use the **Reinforcement** and **Enrichment** masters.

4 Close

Proficiency Prep

Use this quiz to check students' recall of section content.

1. **As long as the forces on an object are balanced, the object will tend to continue moving at what velocity?** *constant*
2. **What is the force that brings most objects to rest?** *friction*

Section Assessment

1. Yes, a force must act to change the car's motion (turn it).
2. Friction (a force) is almost always present, so it is almost impossible to verify that objects continue to move at a constant velocity in its absence.
3. **Think Critically** a. Unbalanced; speed is changing. b. Balanced; velocity is not changing. c. Unbalanced; speed is changing.

Using Computers

Student answers might include the wing design of the shuttle that permits rapid reentry and high-speed landings, and the heat shielding provided by the body flap.

Figure 7-8 Engineers design cars, bike helmets, and other items so that they have as little air resistance as possible.

Whatever type, friction plays a role in nearly every real-life situation, as shown in **Figure 7-8.** It is one key in understanding and applying Newton's laws. Friction is a force that is always present, though it can be reduced and sometimes ignored.

A When you bike, air resistance pushes against you to slow you down.

B When driving a car at high speed, overcoming the force of air resistance takes most of the energy used in gas.

Section Assessment

1. A car maintains a speed of 20 km/h as it turns to the left. Is a force acting on the car? Explain.
2. Explain why friction made it difficult to discover Newton's first law of motion.
3. **Think Critically:** In the following situations, are the forces balanced or unbalanced? How can you tell?
   a. You push a box of books until it is moving at 0.5 m/s.
   b. You continue to push the box of books across the floor at 0.5 m/s.
   c. You stop pushing the box, and it comes to a stop.
4. **Skill Builder**
   Comparing and Contrasting
   Compare and contrast static friction, sliding friction, and rolling friction. If you need help, refer to Comparing and Contrasting in the **Skill Handbook** on page 720.

Using Computers

Database Most of the meteors that reach Earth's atmosphere burn up on the way down. Friction between the meteor and the atmosphere produces a huge amount of heat. Research how the space shuttle is protected from friction when it reenters Earth's atmosphere. Report your findings in your Science Journal. If you need help, refer to page 733.

4. **Skill Builder**
Static friction is the force you must overcome to get an object to move. Sliding friction is the force you must overcome to keep a sliding object moving at a constant velocity. Rolling friction is the force you must overcome to keep a rolling object moving at a constant velocity.

Assessment

Oral Have students identify the forces on them as they complete a roller-coaster ride. *Students may identify weight, air resistance, restraining bar/seat belt, seat, and seat back as things that exert forces on them during the ride.* Use **Performance Assessment in the Science Classroom,** p. 71.

Newton's Second Law

7•2

Force and Acceleration

Are you ever afraid to share your ideas in class? Newton did not like to write about his discoveries because he was afraid he would be criticized. A fellow scientist encouraged Newton to publish his discoveries about motion. Newton reluctantly agreed and wrote *The Principia.*

The central theme for *The Principia* was Newton's description of forces and how they act, now called Newton's laws of motion. If you know how a force acts on an object, you can calculate anything you would like to know about its motion in the future as well as the past. Newton used the laws to calculate the motions of the planets.

Newton presented the answers to many complex problems. He calculated the orbits of the planets around the sun and the effect of Jupiter's gravity pulling on Saturn. He then asked an astronomer if he had noticed Saturn's motion change unexpectedly when it passed near Jupiter. The motion had changed and by just the amount Newton calculated. Newton's laws are still used to understand and predict motion today.

The change in Saturn's motion depended on the direction of Jupiter's force. As **Figure 7-9** shows, you must know the direction of a force to know what effect it will have.

Figure 7-9 The boy is moving at constant speed. When the girl gives him a gentle push, will he speed up, slow down, or turn to one side? You have to know the direction of a force to understand how it will affect motion.

What You'll Learn

- Newton's second law of motion
- Why the direction of force is important

Vocabulary
Newton's second law of motion
normal force

Why It's Important

- Newton's second law explains how any object, from a swimmer to a satellite, moves when any force acts on it.

SECTION 7 2

Prepare

Refer to **Newton's Second Law** on p. 174F.

Preplanning

Refer to the **Chapter Organizer** on pp. 174A–B.

1 Motivate

Bellringer

Before presenting the lesson, display **Section Focus Transparency 16** on the overhead projector. Use the accompanying **Focus Activity** worksheet. L2 ELL

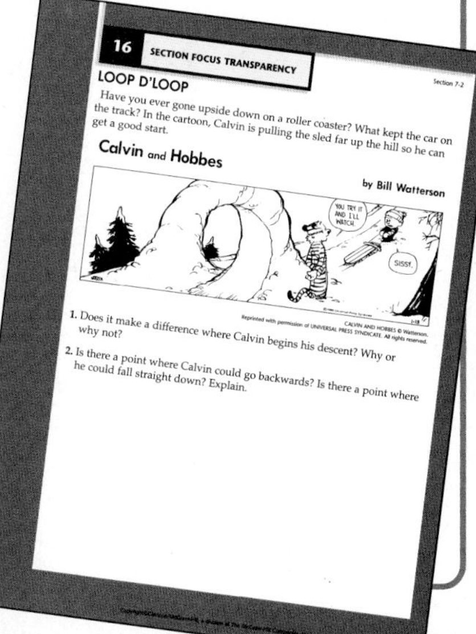

16 SECTION FOCUS TRANSPARENCY

Section 7-2

LOOP D'LOOP

Have you ever gone upside down on a roller coaster? What kept the car on the track? In the cartoon, Calvin is pulling the sled far up the hill so he can get a good start.

CALVIN AND HOBBES © Watterson. Reprinted with permission of UNIVERSAL PRESS SYNDICATE. All rights reserved.

1. Does it make a difference where Calvin begins his descent? Why or why not?
2. Is there a point where Calvin could go backwards? Is there a point where he could fall straight down? Explain.

Tying to Previous Knowledge

Have students recall acceleration. In this section, they will learn how force causes objects to accelerate.

Resource Manager

The following **Teacher Classroom Resources** can be used with Section 7-2:

Reproducible Masters

Activity Worksheets, pp. 35–36, 40 L2
Enrichment, p. 16 L3
Laboratory Manual, pp. 45–48 L2
Reinforcement, p. 16 L2
Study Guide, p. 27

2 Teach

Answer to Reading Check

Newton's second law states that an object undergoing a net force is accelerated in the direction of the force. The object's acceleration (*a*) is equal to the force (*F*) acting on it divided by its mass (*m*).
$a = F/m$

Using Math

$(30\ \text{N}) \div (6\ \text{kg}) = 5\ \text{m/s}^2$
$(0.5\ \text{kg})(9.8\ \text{m/s}^2) = 4.9\ \text{N}$

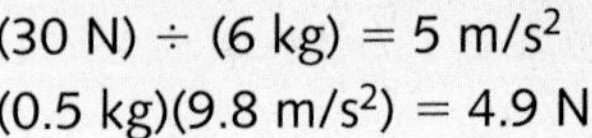

Caption Answer

Figure 7-10 *backward (opposite to direction of motion)*

Discussion

How does an air bag prevent injury in a car crash? *During a car crash, the driver's momentum carries him or her forward even as the car stops. The steering wheel and seat belt exert a force on the driver over a short period of time. An air bag reduces the forces on the driver by lengthening the time over which the momentum changes. Reducing the forces on the driver reduces the severity of injuries.*

Newton's first law of motion describes the motion of an object with no net force acting on it. **Newton's second law of motion** states, "An object acted upon by a net force will accelerate in the direction of the force according to the following equation."

$$\text{acceleration} = \frac{\text{net force}}{\text{mass}}$$

$$a = \frac{F_{net}}{m} \text{ or } F_{net} = ma$$

In this equation, a is the acceleration, m is the mass, and F_{net} is the net force. Force is measured in newtons, abbreviated N; $1\ \text{N} = 1\ \text{kg} \cdot \text{m/s}^2$. If force acts on a small mass and a large mass, the small mass accelerates more. For example, if you try to push an empty box across the floor, you can accelerate it faster than if the box is packed with books.

Using Math

A force of 30 N acts on a 6-kg mass. What is the acceleration? If a 0.5-kg mass accelerates at $9.8\ \text{m/s}^2$, what is the force?

Newton's Second Law and Momentum

Momentum is equal to mass times velocity. When a net force acts on an object, the object's momentum changes. For example, when the bicyclist in **Figure 7-10** brakes, he exerts a force to reduce his velocity. When he reduces his velocity, he reduces his momentum.

The longer a net force acts the greater the change in momentum. The change in momentum, $p_2 - p_1$, is the difference between the object's momentum before and after the force acts. This is described by the following formula.

$$\text{Force} \times \text{time} = \text{change in momentum}$$

$$Ft = p_2 - p_1$$

Because $p_1 = mv_1$ and $p_2 = mv_2$, you can substitute mv_1 and mv_2 in the equation above.

$$Ft = mv_2 - mv_1$$

Figure 7-10 This bicyclist uses the brakes to slow down. His velocity before and after he brakes is forward. **In what direction is the force?**

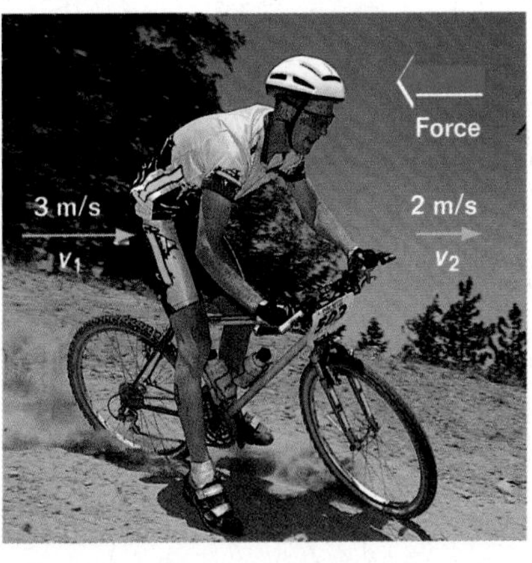

The force that acts on an object is related to the initial velocity, v_1, and final velocity, v_2, of the object.

Notice that the force can be positive or negative. Force is defined relative to a frame of reference. In the example in **Figure 7-10,** the positive direction is defined as forward. A force that slows the bike is directed backward, so such a force is negative.

Balanced Forces

While you are reading this sentence, you are probably sitting in a chair. Are forces acting on you now? Newton's first law says that if you're at rest, all the

Across the Curriculum

Health Seat belts, infant car seats, air bags, and helmets protect people using vehicles from hazards relating to inertia. Many states have laws relating to the use of safety equipment. Ask students to find out what the laws require in your state. Have students debate whether the use of safety equipment should be required. Reasons for requiring their use include saving lives and reducing personal injury. Reasons for not requiring safety equipment center on freedom of choice. L2 COOP LEARN

184 CHAPTER 7 FORCE AND NEWTON'S LAWS

forces acting on you are balanced. Gravity is pulling you down. Your chair is pushing you up. The outward force from a surface, such as the upward force provided by your chair, is called the **normal force.** *Normal* means at a right angle. On a flat surface, the normal force is straight up and balances your weight. The normal force is supplied by the strength of the surface—in this case, the chair. If you put a heavy weight on a rickety chair, the chair might not be able to provide enough normal force to balance the weight. Then, the chair breaks.

When the surface is tilted, the normal force is reduced, as shown in **Figure 7-11.** The normal force no longer balances the weight. If friction doesn't balance this net force (look back at **Figure 7-5A**), you will start moving downhill.

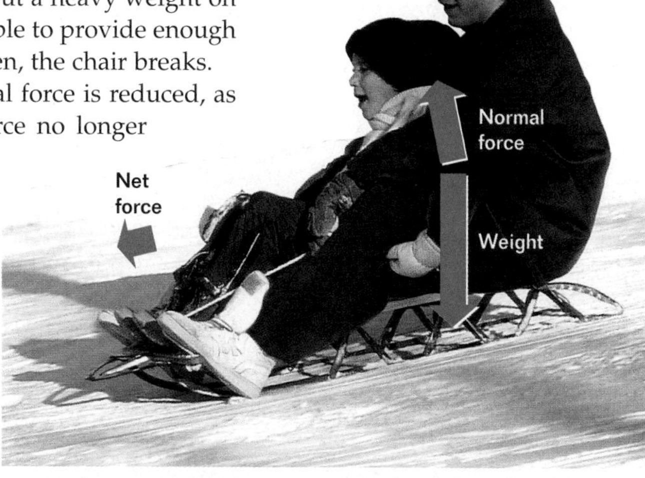

Figure 7-11 The normal force acts outward from a surface. On a hill, the normal force is less than your weight, and not opposite in direction. The forces are not balanced, so there is a net force parallel to the hill.

Using Math

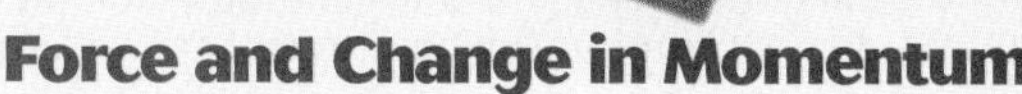

Force and Change in Momentum

Example Problem

A bicyclist exerts a net force of 24 N and accelerates from 2 m/s to 4 m/s. Find the time needed to do this if the bicycle and rider have a mass of 90 kg.

Problem-Solving Steps

1. What is known? velocity before and after, v_1 = 2 m/s and v_2 = 4 m/s, mass m = 90 kg, force F = –24 N
2. What is unknown? time t
3. Use the equation $Ft = mv_2 - mv_1$.
4. **Solution:**

$$Ft = mv_2 - mv_1$$
$$(24\text{ N})t = (90\text{ kg})(4\text{ m/s}) - (90\text{ kg})(2\text{ m/s})$$
$$(24\text{ kg}\cdot\text{m/s}^2)t = 180\text{ kg}\cdot\text{m/s}$$
$$t = 7.5\text{ s}$$

The bicyclist takes 7.5 s to reach the new speed.

Practice Problem

The same bicyclist exerts a force on the brakes to slow from 4 m/s to 0 m/s. This takes 12 s. What was the force?

Strategy Hint: Is the force positive or negative?

Quick Demo

Place a coin in the center of an index card on top of a glass with a smooth lip. Flick the card away suddenly. **What happens to the coin and why?** *The coin falls into the glass because the normal force exerted by the card is suddenly removed and the force of gravity on the coin makes it fall into the glass.*

Using Science Words

Have students consider the following moving objects and state whether or not the forces acting on them are balanced.

- leaf floating off a branch to the ground *balanced*
- driver of a car traveling at 60 km/h on the highway *balanced*
- blades of a windmill turning at constant speed *unbalanced*
- driver of a car turning a corner at 25 km/h *unbalanced*
- surfer riding a wave toward the beach *balanced*
- driver of a car pulling to a stop *unbalanced*
- child riding on a horse on a merry-go-round *unbalanced* L2

Using Math

$$Ft = mv_2 - mv_1$$
$$F(12\text{ s}) = (90\text{ kg})(0\text{ m/s} - 4\text{ m/s})$$
$$F(12\text{ s}) = -360\text{ kg}\cdot\text{m/s}$$
$$F = -30\text{ N}$$

Across the Curriculum

Language Arts We are all familiar with the story of Goldilocks and the Three Bears and what happened when Goldilocks tried out the bears' chairs. When she sat in Baby Bear's chair, she broke it to bits. Ask the students to explain what forces were acting on the chair and why the chair broke. *Goldilocks's weight was acting downward on the chair and the chair was exerting a normal force upward against Goldilocks. Unfortunately, the chair was not able to exert enough of a normal force to balance Goldilocks's weight, and the extra force broke the chair.* L2

7-2 NEWTON'S SECOND LAW **185**

GLENCOE TECHNOLOGY

CD-ROM

Glencoe Science Voyages Interactive CD-ROM

Explorations

Have students do the interactive exploration *What is Newton's second law of motion?*

Quick Demo

Take two coffee filters. Crumple one into a ball and leave the other open. Drop them. The greater air resistance on the open filter balances the force of gravity more quickly, so it reaches terminal velocity sooner.

Making a Model

Use a rubber band and a lead soldier to create a model of a bungee jumper. Describe what happens as the soldier falls. Identify the forces on the soldier and how they change during the jump. When are the forces balanced? *when it moves at constant velocity* When are the forces not balanced? *when its velocity changes* When is the soldier accelerating and when is it moving at constant velocity? *It is accelerating all the time and never moving at constant velocity.* L2

3 Assess

Check for Understanding

Discussion

Ask students to compare the forces required to stop a car traveling at 100 km/h when brakes are applied for 10 s and when the car hits a wall and stops in 0.1 s. *The force involved in braking is 1/100 of the force involved in the collision.* L2

Figure 7-12 The force of air resistance on these skydivers pushes them up. The force of gravity pulls them down. When the forces are equal, the skydivers fall at a constant speed. This speed is called terminal velocity.

Another example of balanced forces is an object moving at constant speed, such as the bicyclist in **Figure 7-8.** Even falling objects eventually reach a constant speed due to air resistance. *Terminal velocity* is the speed an object reaches when the force of gravity is balanced by the force of air resistance, as shown in **Figure 7-12.** When parachutists jump from an airplane, they will fall for a long time before opening the parachutes. As they accelerate downward, the air resistance against each parachutist's body gets stronger until terminal velocity is reached. If a jumper falls spread eagle, the terminal velocity is about 215 km/h. If a jumper falls in a jack knife, the terminal velocity could be 320 km/h. Although this is very fast, it is still constant. When the speed is constant, the forces acting must be balanced.

Once the parachute is opened, the upward force of air resistance on the open parachute is much greater than the downward force of gravity. The forces are unbalanced and the increased air resistance will slow the parachutist down to a safer terminal velocity of about 18 km/h.

Unbalanced Forces

When the forces acting on an object are not balanced, the object accelerates in the direction of the net force. It might speed up, slow down, or turn.

Figure 7-13 The force and acceleration are to the left. **If the puck has a mass of 0.2 kg and the hockey stick exerts a force of 100 N for 0.1 s, what is the final speed of the puck, v_2?**

Speeding Up

If you look back at all of the examples of objects speeding up, you'll notice there's something pushing or pulling the object in the direction it is moving. The direction of the push or pull is the direction of the force. It is also the direction of the acceleration. Force is in the same direction as the velocity if the object is speeding up, as shown in **Figure 7-13.**

For example, if an object is at rest or moving in a positive direction, and it is accelerated at +4 m/s^2, it will go +4 m/s faster every second the force acts. You accelerate like this when you fall. Your velocity increases downward by 9.8 m/s every second. This is a rapid change that

Science Journal

Skydiving Ask students to draw a picture and write a description of what happens from the time a sky diver jumps out of a plane until the time he or she lands on the ground. Ask them to use the following words in their descriptions: free fall, terminal velocity, air resistance, gravity, and acceleration due to gravity. Ask them to indicate when during the trip the forces on the sky diver are balanced and when they are unbalanced.

Figure 7-14 When you catch a ball, you exert a force opposite to the direction of the ball's motion. **If you exert a force of 40 N on a 0.5-kg ball moving at 10 m/s, how long does it take to stop the ball?**

produces high speeds in just seconds. If you have ever jumped off a high-diving platform, you know how quickly you speed up.

Slowing Down

To slow down an object you have to push or pull it against the direction it is moving. An example is given in **Figure 7-14.** This time the force is opposite to the velocity. If the velocity is positive, then the acceleration is negative and makes the velocity less and less.

When a platform diver hits the water, the water provides a large force that slows the diver down. If the diver doesn't have the correct form when entering the water, this force can hurt. You may have experienced this. Water normally seems easy to move around, but when you hit it quickly, its tendency is to remain at rest. It pushes up against you as you enter the water. The force of the water against your body can stop it about five times faster than the pull of gravity accelerated it.

Turning

Sometimes forces and motion are not in a straight line. If a net force acts at an angle to the direction of motion, an object will follow a curving path. Its velocity will change because the direction of motion changes. The object might be going slower, faster, or at the same speed after the turn.

If you jump straight forward from a diving board you will not continue straight across the pool at that height. The force of gravity accelerates you downward, at a right angle to your direction of motion.

Measuring Buoyant Force

Procedure 

1. Collect several small objects made of different materials. Weigh them on a spring scale and record the weights. If your scale measures in kilograms rather than newtons, multiply by $10\ m/s^2$ to get the force in newtons.
2. Now, attach each object to the spring scale and place the object in water. Compare the force reading on the scale with the weights you found in step 1.

Analysis

1. Compare the differences in the weights.
2. How would you find the buoyant force exerted upward on each object by the water?

MiniLab

Purpose

Visual-Spatial Students will observe the effect of buoyancy on the weights of objects. L2 ELL COOP LEARN

Materials

several weights made of different materials, spring scale, beaker of water for each group of students

Teaching Strategies

Make certain that the beakers will hold enough water so that the weights can be submerged completely.

Analysis

1. The weights of the objects in water are always less than the weights in air.
2. The buoyant force exerted upward on the object by the water is equal to the difference in the weight of the object in air and its weight in water.

Assessment

Process Ask students to compare the volume in cubic centimeters of each object with the difference in their masses in air and water measured in grams. The values should be equal. The buoyancy of an object in a fluid is equal to the weight of the fluid it displaces, and 1 cm^3 of water masses 1 g. (Archimedes' principle) Use **Performance Assessment in the Science Classroom,** p. 29.

Caption Answers

Figure 7-13 $Ft = mv_2 - mv,$
$(100\ N)(0.1\ s) = (0.2\ kg)v_2$
$v_2 = 50\ m/s$
Figure 7-14 $Ft = mv_2 - mv,$
$(-40\ N)t = (0.5\ kg)(0\ m/s) - (0.5\ kg)(10\ m/s)$
$t = 0.125\ s$

VISUAL Learning

Figure 7-12 Your local amusement park may have a gravity-drop ride that your students have experienced. Ask them to describe the experience.

Reteach

Have students identify the forces on them as they sit in a car that is coming to a stop. In addition to the force of gravity downward and the normal force of the seat upward, they should mention the force of the seat belt pulling them back. L2

Extension

For students who have mastered this section, use the **Reinforcement** and **Enrichment** masters.

4 Close

Proficiency Prep

Use this quiz to check students' recall of section content.

1. **When a force is applied to an object for a period of time, the object experiences a change in what?** *momentum or velocity*
2. **When an object is sitting at rest on a table, the force of gravity is balanced by what force?** *normal force*

Section Assessment

1. (6400 N) ÷ (80 kg) = 80 m/s^2; (80 m/s^2)(0.32 s) = 25.6 m/s
2. Weight and the normal force balance each other. Friction slows you. a = (−20 km/h) ÷ (60 s) = (−5.56 m/s) ÷ (60 s) = −0.09 m/s^2
3. Think Critically If an object picks up speed, the force is in the same direction it was moving; if it loses speed, the force is in the opposite direction. If the object changes direction, the force is at an angle to the path in which the object is moving.

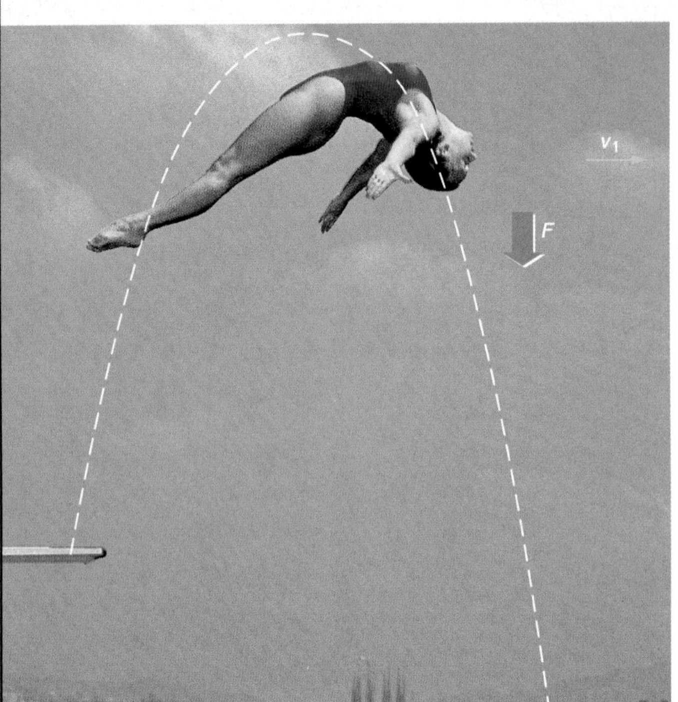

Your body follows a curving path in the air, as shown in **Figure 7-15.**

Acceleration makes motion exciting because you can feel the change. Pushing then pulling, fast then slow, up then down—these are the action words of force and acceleration. They are what make a day at the amusement park or the swimming pool so much fun.

Figure 7-15 When a diver jumps forward, she doesn't keep moving in a straight line. Gravity exerts a force perpendicular to her motion, turning her.

Section Assessment

1. A human cannonball with a mass of 80 kg is fired out of a cannon with a force of 6400 N. The force lasts for 0.32 s. Find the acceleration and final speed.
2. You are riding on your bicycle at a speed of 20 km/h when you decide to stop pedaling. Draw a simple picture of you on your bicycle. Using arrows to represent forces, draw and label all the forces acting on you as you coast along. If it takes you a minute to stop, at what rate did you accelerate?
3. **Think Critically:** Explain how you can determine the direction of a force by watching an object's change in motion.
4. **Skill Builder**
   Making and Using Tables The gravitational force on the surface of each planet in our solar system is different. Do the **Chapter 7 Skill Activity** on page 748 and use a table to find out what you would weigh on different planets.

Using Math

A ball of mass 5 kg is moving at 2 m/s. A force takes 4 s to stop the ball. Find the force.

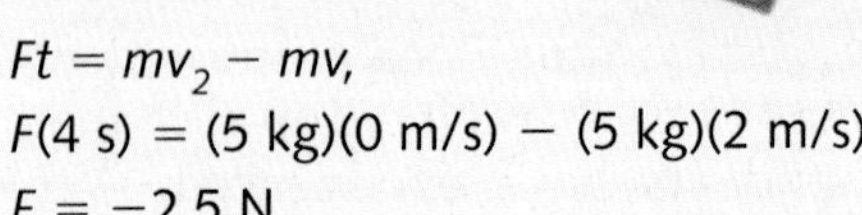

Using Math

$Ft = mv_2 - mv_1$

$F(4\text{ s}) = (5\text{ kg})(0\text{ m/s}) - (5\text{ kg})(2\text{ m/s})$

$F = -2.5\text{ N}$

The minus sign means that the force is pushing in the opposite direction of the ball's motion, and is slowing it down.

Assessment

Content When a diver dives into a pool, the water exerts an upward force that stops the diver's descent into the pool in one-fifth the time it takes to complete the dive. Compare the force exerted by the water with the force of gravity. *It is five times as great.* Use **Performance Assessment in the Science Classroom,** p. 29.

Science & Math

Applying the Pythagorean Theorem

One way to represent a force is with a vector. A vector is an arrow that points in the direction of the force and is proportional in length to the size of the force. For example, a 3-N force to the left can be represented on paper by a 3-cm arrow pointing left. Vectors also can represent other quantities that have number and direction, such as displacement, velocity, momentum, and acceleration.

Adding Vectors

You can represent all the forces acting on an object with vectors. When all the vectors are connected tip-to-tail, the vector for the total force is drawn from the end of the chain to the head, as follows.

Problem

A boat is moving east at 10 km/h relative to the water. The water is flowing south at 6 km/h relative to the shore. Find the velocity of the boat relative to the shore.

Solution

1. Make a sketch of the situation. Note that the vectors are at right angles.

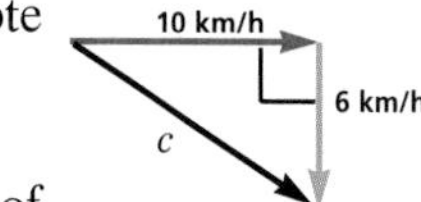

2. The two velocities form two sides of a right triangle. To find the boat's actual velocity, find the length of the hypotenuse. Use the Pythagorean theorem, $c^2 = a^2 + b^2$.

3. Substitute 10 and 6 for a and b, and solve for c.

$$c^2 = a^2 + b^2$$
$$= (10 \text{ km/h})^2 + (6 \text{ km/h})^2$$
$$= 136 \text{ (km/h)}^2$$
$$c = \sqrt{136 \text{ km}^2/\text{h}^2} = 11.7 \text{ km/h}$$

So, the boat is moving at about 12 km/h relative to the land.

Practice PROBLEMS

1. A plane is flying north at 500 km/h. A wind is blowing toward the east at a speed of 60 km/h. What is the actual speed of the plane?
2. You push on the front of a box with a force of 5 N. Your friend pushes on the left side of the box with a force of 12 N. What is the total force on the box? Use an arrow to show the direction of the force.
3. A ball is thrown with a forward velocity of 4 m/s and an upward velocity of 1 m/s. Find the total velocity of the ball.

Science & Math

Content Background

- Vectors are taught in detail in advanced math courses. This simple introduction to vectors can help students understand how different forces of motions combine.
- When students eventually study complicated motions, such as a projectile moving up and forward, vectors will be used to break the motion into manageable parts. Newton's first law is applied to the forward motion. Newton's second law is applied to the upward motion.

Teaching Strategies

- Refer to **Figure 7-2.** Vectors can be used to find the net force on an object when the different forces are not all in a line. Students could push on adjacent sides of the book, so that the resultant force is along a diagonal.
- When discussing motion in different frames of reference, vectors are one way to combine the relative motions. For example, if water is moving 4 m/s south relative to the shore, a boat is moving 7 m/s north relative to the water, and a person is walking 1 m/s north relative to the boat, all of these can be added to find the person's speed relative to the shore (4 m/s north).

Answers to Practice PROBLEMS

1. $\sqrt{(500 \text{ km/h})^2 + (60 \text{ km/h})^2} =$ 504 km/h relative to the ground
2. $\sqrt{(5 \text{ N})^2 + (12 \text{ N})^2} = 13 \text{ N}$
   The direction is away from you and to the right.
3. $\sqrt{(4 \text{ m/s})^2 + (1 \text{ m/s})^2} = 4.1 \text{ m/s}$
   The direction is up and foreward.

Activity 7-1 Design Your Own Experiment

Recognize the Problem

Purpose

Visual-Spatial Students will observe how to move an object from any point to another using forces at right angles to each other. L2 ELL COOP LEARN

Process Skills

observing, forming a hypothesis, designing an experiment, predicting, separating and controlling variables, recognizing cause and effect

Time

45 minutes

Materials

It would be a good idea to hard-boil the eggs before this experiment.

Form a Hypothesis

Possible Hypotheses

- Pull alternately in the two directions, moving along grid lines.
- Pull in both directions to move on diagonals.

Test Your Hypothesis

Possible Procedures

Pull on the skid in each direction and see how much force you need to apply to make the skid begin to move. Try accelerating the skid at increasing rates to see if there is a limit to how fast you can accelerate the skid. Try stopping the skid and observe what happens.

Design Your Own Experiment

Activity 7-1

Modeling Motion in Two Directions

When you move a computer mouse across a mouse pad, how does the rolling ball tell the computer cursor to move in the direction you push the mouse? Inside the housing for the mouse's ball, there are two or more rollers that the ball rubs against as you move the mouse. They measure up-and-down motion and back-and-forth motion. What happens to the rollers when you move diagonally and at different angles?

Possible Materials

- Masking tape
- Stopwatch
  - *watch or clock with a second hand
- Meterstick
  - *metric tape measure
- Spring scales marked in newtons (2)
- Plastic lid
- An egg in its shell

*Alternate Materials

Recognize the Problem

Place an egg on something that will slide, such as a plastic lid. The container is called a *skid.* Lay out a course to follow on the floor. Can you move an egg from one point to another using forces in only two directions?

Form a Hypothesis

How can you combine forces to move in a straight line, along a diagonal, or around corners? Write a plan for moving your egg along the path.

Goals

- **Move** the skid across the ground using two forces.
- **Measure** how fast the skid can be moved.
- **Determine** how smoothly the direction can be changed.

Safety Precautions

Be careful not to drop the egg.

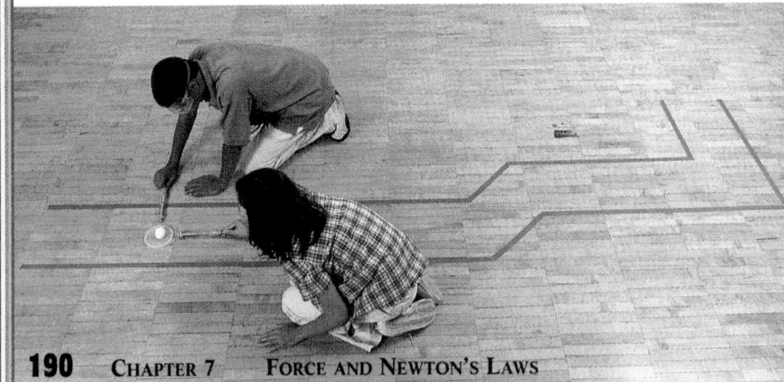

190 CHAPTER 7 FORCE AND NEWTON'S LAWS

Content Background

The motion of the boat is a combination of its own speed and the speed of the river. The combined downstream speed is the vector sum: ground speed = boat speed + river speed. The combined upstream speed is the vector difference: ground speed = boat speed − river speed. The boat cannot go upstream when the current is faster than the boat. The combined speed is the vector sum: ground speed = boat speed − river speed

Test Your Hypothesis

Plan

1. **Lay out** a course that involves two directions, such as the course shown in the photo.
2. **Attach** two spring scales to the skid. One will always pull straight forward. One will always pull to one side. You cannot turn the skid. If one scale is pulling toward the door of your classroom, it must always pull in that direction. (It can pull with zero force, if needed, but it can't push.)
3. How will you handle movements along diagonals and turns?
4. How will you measure speed?
5. **Experiment** with your skid. How hard do you have to pull to counteract sliding friction at a given speed? How fast can you accelerate? Can you stop suddenly without spilling the egg, or do you need to slow down?
6. **Write a plan** for moving your egg along the course by pulling only forward and to one side. Be sure you understand your plan and have considered all the details.

Do

1. Make sure your teacher approves your plan before you proceed.
2. **Try** moving your egg along the path.
3. **Modify** your plan, if needed.
4. **Organize** your data so it can be used to run your course.
5. **Test** your results with a new route.

Analyze Your Data

1. What was the difference between the two routes? How did this affect the forces you could use on the egg?
2. How did you **separate and control variables** in this experiment?
3. Was your hypothesis supported? Explain.

Draw Conclusions

1. What happens when you combine two forces at right angles?
2. If you could pull on all four sides (front, back, left, right) of your skid, could you move anywhere along the floor? **Make a hypothesis** to explain your answer.

Teaching Strategies

Suggest that students try moving the skid by applying forces in one direction followed by the other, and by applying forces in the two directions at the same time.

Expected Outcome

Students will find it much easier to move the skid by moving one direction at a time. Moving the skid in both directions simultaneously requires them to be more responsive to what they see happening as they perform the move.

Error Analysis

How does the surface of the course affect the force needed to pull the skid?

Analyze Your Data

1. Students should find a new route easier than the first as they learn from their experiences.
2. The variables were separated by measuring force in each direction.
3. Check students' explanations.

Draw Conclusions

1. Combining two forces at right angles produces a resultant force on a diagonal between the two.
2. Yes, because the four directions can be combined to move along any line.

GO Further

Refer to the Using Math on the previous spread. **If the skid has a force of 5 N applied toward the south and a force of 12 N applied toward the east, what is the resultant force on the skid?** Remember that force has both magnitude and direction. Be sure to provide both. *The force is 13 N at an angle (of 23°) south of east.*

Assessment

Performance Ask students to examine a computer mouse and determine how it measures directions moved. *Most have three trackers equally spaced around a circle. These three directions can be combined to produce any direction.* Use **Performance Assessment in the Science Classroom,** p. 29.

SECTION 7-3

Prepare

Refer to **Newton's Third Law** on p. 174F.

Preplanning

Refer to the **Chapter Organizer** on pp. 174A–B.

1 Motivate

Bellringer

Before presenting the lesson, display **Section Focus Transparency 17** on the overhead projector. Use the accompanying **Focus Activity** worksheet. L2 ELL

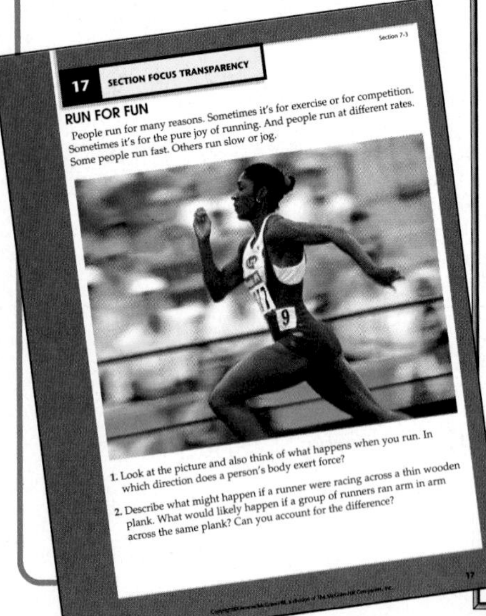

Section 7-3

17 SECTION FOCUS TRANSPARENCY

RUN FOR FUN

People run for many reasons. Sometimes it's for exercise or for competition. Sometimes it's for the pure joy of running. And people run at different rates. Some people run fast. Others run slow or jog.

1. Look at the picture and also think of what happens when you run. In which direction does a person's body exert force?
2. Describe what might happen if a runner were racing across a thin wooden plank. What would likely happen if a group of runners ran arm in arm across the same plank? Can you account for the difference?

17

Tying to Previous Knowledge

Have students recall Newton's first and second laws of motion. In this section, they will learn about the third law of motion.

7-3 Newton's Third Law

What You'll Learn

- Newton's third law of motion

Vocabulary

Newton's third law of motion

Why It's Important

- Newton's third law can help you understand motion from walking to launching rockets.

Action and Reaction

Newton's first two laws explain everything about the motion of a single object. If the forces acting on the object are balanced, the object will remain at rest or stay in motion with constant velocity. If the forces are unbalanced, the object will accelerate in the direction of the net force.

Newton's final law describes the connection between the object supplying the force and the object receiving the force. **Newton's third law of motion** states, "Forces always act in equal but opposite pairs." Another way of saying this is "For every action, there is an equal but opposite reaction." This means that one object can't supply a force (action) without the object it is acting on causing a return force (reaction), as shown in **Figure 7-16.**

Figure 7-16 When one ice-skater pulls on the second, the second pulls back just as hard. The forces are equal and opposite.

Resource Manager

The following **Teacher Classroom Resources** can be used with Section 7-3:

 **Reproducible Masters**

Activity Worksheets, pp.37–38 L2

Enrichment, p. 17 L3

Reinforcement, p. 17 L2

Study Guide, p. 26

 **Transparencies**

Teaching Transparency 14 L2

Science Integration Transparency 7 L2

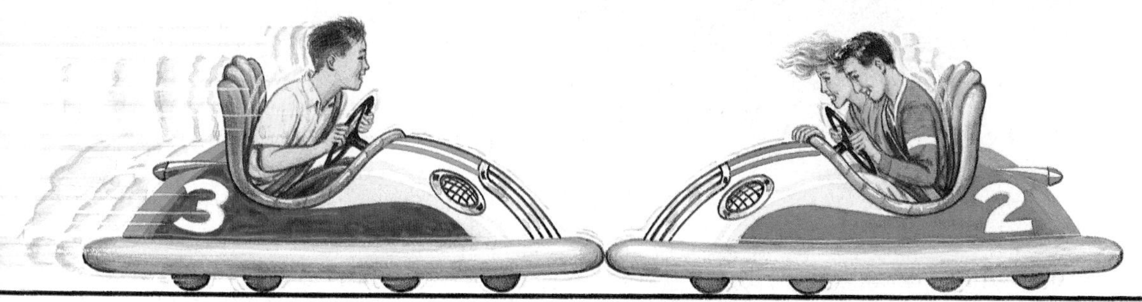

Figure 7-17 In this collision, the first car exerts a force on the second. The second exerts the same force in the opposite direction on the first car. **Which car do you think accelerates more?**

Fun with Newton

Imagine you're driving a bumper car and are going to ram into your two friends in another car, head-on, as shown in **Figure 7-17.** Initially, your friends are at rest. When your bumper meets theirs, its surface pushes against their bumper's surface. Their car accelerates in the direction you forced it to move—backwards. By Newton's third law, their car pushes you with an equal and opposite force, which is directed toward you. This causes your car to slow down because the force was against your motion. Action-reaction forces are always the same size but are in opposite directions and act on different objects.

There is no delay in time between the action and the reaction. They occur at the same time. If you touch your nose with your finger, your nose and finger sense the touch at exactly the same time. These are action-reaction forces. As soon as you remove your finger, the nerves in both your finger and nose will sense this. Also, when you touch your nose, your head moves in the direction of the finger's push, and the finger slows down as the nose pushes back. Why doesn't your head's motion change as drastically as your finger's motion?

Usually, you don't notice the action-reaction that goes on as you move about. You know how to use these forces from experience. You have been learning this since you learned to sit up or roll over. When you start looking, you notice action-reaction pairs all around you.

Using Math

Two students pull on each other. The 45-kg student has an acceleration of 0.2 m/s². What is the acceleration of the 50-kg student? Use action force = reaction force.

interNET CONNECTION

Visit the Glencoe Science Web Site at **www.glencoe.com/sec/science** for more information about the physics of living things.

2 Teach

Using Math

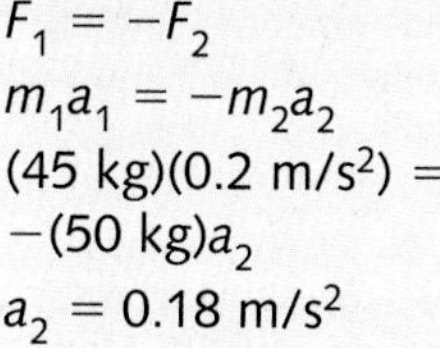

$F_1 = -F_2$

$m_1a_1 = -m_2a_2$

$(45\text{ kg})(0.2\text{ m/s}^2) = -(50\text{ kg})a_2$

$a_2 = 0.18\text{ m/s}^2$

The minus sign indicates that the force and acceleration of the second student are opposite in direction to those of the first student.

Answer to Text Question

Why doesn't your head's motion change as drastically as your finger's motion? *By Newton's third law of motion, if the mass of the head is larger than the mass of the finger, the change in velocity of the head must be smaller than that of the finger.*

GLENCOE TECHNOLOGY

Videodisc

The Infinite Voyage: Insects: The Ruling Class

Chapter 5 *Studying Insect Flight* 7:00

Refer to the Teacher Guide for bar codes and teaching strategies.

Caption Answer

Figure 7-17 *The car with one rider will accelerate more because the mass is smaller.*

interNET CONNECTION

Internet Addresses

For Internet tips, see Glencoe's **Using the Internet in the Science Classroom.**

Discussion

Ask students to identify action and reaction forces in a simple activity such as walking or jumping.

Answer to Reading Check

The reaction force is the pull of the diver on Earth.

Caption Answer

Figure 7-19 *the air or water*

INTEGRATION

Different species of birds use their wings in different ways in flight. Consider the hummingbird, the hawk, the swallow, and the Canada goose. All of them fly by pushing on the air with their wings, yet they use their wings differently to keep their bodies aloft. **What causes them to behave so differently?** *They must balance the downward force exerted by their weights against the net upward force exerted as they move their wings. Depending on their weights and the size and shape of their wings, they have to vary the frequency with which they move their wings.*

3 Assess

Check for Understanding

Discussion

Linguistic Ask students to describe how rowing a boat illustrates Newton's third law of motion. L2

Reteach

Visual-Spatial Ask students to cut sports pictures out of a magazine or newspaper and paste them into their journals. Then ask them to identify the force action and reaction pairs that appear in each picture. L2

Figure 7-18 The force of the ground on your foot is equal and opposite to the force of your foot on the ground. If you push down harder, the ground pushes up harder.

Large and Small

Another reason it's easy to miss the action-reaction pair is because one of the objects is often much more massive and appears to remain motionless when a force acts on it. It has so much inertia, or tendency to remain at rest, that it hardly accelerates. Walking is a good example. When you walk forward, you push backward on the ground. Your shoe pushes Earth backward, and Earth pushes your shoe forward, as shown in **Figure 7-18.** Earth has so much mass, it does not noticeably move when you push it. You have very little mass compared to Earth. Earth pushes you forward with enough acceleration to make you move. The forces are the same but in opposite directions. If you step on something that can move easily, like a skateboard, you can see it being pushed back.

One subtle example of action-reaction is falling to the ground after jumping off a diving board or a step. Earth's gravity pulls a diver down with an acceleration of 9.8 m/s^2. The reaction is the diver pulling Earth up. The forces are equal but opposite. Why don't you notice Earth being moved by this force? The person's mass is a tiny fraction of Earth's mass, so Earth's acceleration is a tiny fraction of the person's acceleration. ✔

Reading Check ✔

If the action force is the pull of Earth on a diver, what is the reaction force?

More Examples of Newton's Third Law

Have you ever stuck your hand out a car window and felt the wind push your hand back? Did it take a lot of strength to keep your hand steady? Why was it hard to hold your hand still? The answer is because air has mass. Your hand exerts a force forward on the air, and the air exerts an equal and opposite force back against your hand. The faster the car is going, the more force you have to exert to equal the force of the air.

When a bird flies, its wings push the air down and backward along a diagonal. In reaction, the air pushes the bird upward and forward, as shown in **Figure 7-19A.** If you could see the air, you would see it accelerate quickly as the bird pushes it. Air has little inertia. The bird is more massive than the air and does not accelerate as much.

When you paddle a canoe, there is little friction between the canoe and the water. To move the canoe forward, you push water back with your paddle. The paddle has a large enough surface to push a lot of water. Although it is hard to

Content Background

Unlike Newton's first and second law's of motion, which are used to describe the motion of a single object, Newton's third law of motion describes what happens when two objects interact with each other.

Figure 7-19 When a bat flies or a fish swims, they also push on the air or water around them. **What pushes back?**

A The bird's wings push down on the air, which pushes up on the wing. In a wind tunnel, you could see how the bird's wings push on the air. Without air to push on, the bird couldn't fly.

see the water move, you can see currents form on the surface as the water is pushed backwards, as in **Figure 7-19B.** The water accelerates backwards and reacts by pushing forward on the paddle. Because the paddle is attached to you and you are attached to the canoe, the canoe accelerates in the forward direction. The same thing happens when you use your arms to swim. Can you think of another example of action-reaction?

B The paddle pushes back on the water, and the water pushes forward on the paddle.

Section Assessment

1. You sit on the floor and push a skateboard with a force of 6 N. If your mass is 60 kg, what is the force the skateboard exerts on you? In what direction is the force?
2. A hockey puck is at rest on the ice. What two forces are acting on it? You now hit the puck across the ice. While you are hitting the puck, what forces act on it? What else has a change of motion when the puck is hit?
3. **Think Critically:** Suppose you are an astronaut on the space shuttle. What would happen if you pushed against a chair that was not bolted to the floor? Why is pushing against a chair that is bolted down different?
4. **Skill Builder**
   Using Numbers A person standing on a canoe throws a cement block over the side. The action force on the cement block is 60 N. The reaction force is on the person and canoe. Their total mass is 100 kg. What is their acceleration? If you need help, refer to Using Numbers in the **Skill Handbook** on page 731.

Science Journal

Some people have trouble understanding Newton's third law. They reason, "If every action has an equal and opposite reaction, nothing will ever move." Explain why objects can still move. (Consider whether the forces act on the same object or on different objects.)

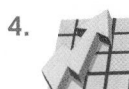

4. **Skill Builder**
   $F = ma$
   $60 \text{ N} = (100 \text{ kg})a$
   $a = 0.6 \text{ m/s}^2$

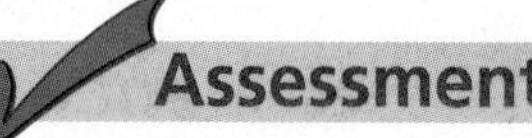

Assessment

Process Suppose the canoe masses 45 kg. **If the person now jumps out of the canoe, which will have a greater acceleration? Explain.** *the canoe, because it has less mass and the forces (ma) must be equal* Use **Performance Assessment in the Science Classroom,** p. 17.

Extension

For students who have mastered this section, use the **Reinforcement** and **Enrichment** masters.

4 Close

Proficiency Prep

Use this quiz to check students' recall of chapter content.

1. **What is the result of every action?** *an equal and opposite reaction*
2. **Which of Newton's laws of motion describes the relationship between the object supplying the force and the object receiving it?** *third*

Section Assessment

1. 6 N; opposite to the direction you pushed
2. Weight and normal force; weight, normal force, and push of hockey stick; the hockey stick slows down.
3. **Think Critically** It will move away from you. If you push against a chair bolted down, it is like pushing against the chair and the whole space shuttle. The combined system will barely move.

Science Journal

The action and reaction forces act on different objects, so it is possible for each object to have a net force, and thus a change in motion.

Activity 7·2

Purpose

Kinesthetic Students will use Newton's third law of motion to propel rockets across the classroom. L2 ELL COOP LEARN

Process Skills

observing and inferring, comparing and contrasting, recognizing cause and effect, controlling variables, measuring in SI, interpreting data

Time

45 minutes

Teaching Strategies

Ask students to set up the rocket paths and mark a starting point for their races. Suggest that one student handle the balloon while the other keeps the time. Students should consider what variables they want to control in this experiment.

Answers to Questions

1. Check student answers.
2. Students should note the time of travel for each race and then calculate the average speed of the balloon. Then they should conclude which balloon traveled fastest.
3. Students might discuss any of the following characteristics: thickness of the rubber, size when inflated, capacity for air, shape, or size of opening. Their inferences about distance traveled and speed should reflect their ability to separate variables.
4. Include weight, upward force of straw, force of escaping air, friction.
5. Escaping air pushes the balloon forward (third law) and balloon accelerates that way (second law). When it runs out of air it continues a short way (first law), then friction slows it (second law).

Activity 7·2

Using Scientific Methods

Balloon Races

Materials

- Balloons of different sizes and shapes
- Drinking straws
- String
- Tape
- Meterstick
- Stopwatch or clock

Going into space captures people's imaginations. Rockets use Newton's third law to propel them. In this experiment, you will compare different balloon rocket designs. The balloon rocket is powered by escaping air, using Newton's third law. Its motion is determined by Newton's first and second laws.

What You'll Investigate

How does Newton's third law accelerate different balloon rockets?

Goals

- **Measure** the speed of a balloon rocket.
- **Describe** how Newton's laws explain a rocket's motion.

Procedure 

1. Run a string across the classroom to make a rocket path. Leave one end loose so you can easily place the rockets on the string.
2. **Make** a balloon rocket according to the photo. Don't tie the balloon closed. Let it run down the track. **Measure** its distance and time.
3. Repeat step 2 with different balloons.

Conclude and Apply

1. **Compare and contrast** the distances traveled. Which rocket went the greatest distance?
2. **Calculate** the average speed for each rocket. **Compare and contrast** them. Which rocket has the greatest average speed?
3. **Infer** what aspects of these rockets made them travel far or fast.
4. **Draw** a diagram showing all the forces acting on a balloon rocket.
5. Use Newton's laws of motion to **explain** the motion of a balloon rocket from launch until it comes to a stop.

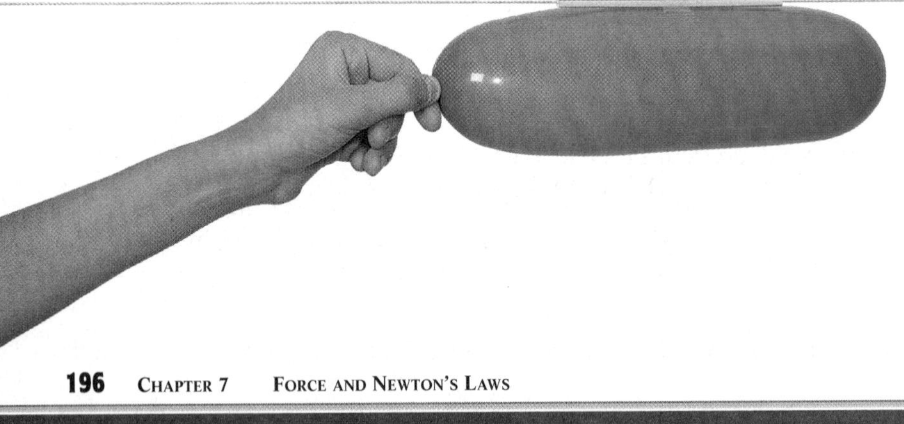

Assessment

Enrichment Ask students to design nozzles that control the flow of air out the back of the balloon. Using balloons of the same size, inflated to the same size, test the designs and award a prize for the best design. Use **Performance Assessment in the Science Classroom,** p. 23.

Describing Motion

The Laws of Motion

With Newton's laws and the law of conservation of momentum, summarized in **Table 7-1,** almost any motion problem can be solved. In most everyday problems, if you know an object's motion and all the forces acting on it, you can figure out how the object will move in the future and how it moved in the past. It can be exciting to make a prediction using Newton's laws and then see your prediction confirmed by experiment. **Figures 7-20** and **7-21** give examples of complex motions that can be analyzed with Newton's laws.

Table 7-1

The Laws of Motion	
Newton's first law	An object will remain at rest or continue moving with constant velocity until it is acted upon by a net force.
Newton's second law	An object acted upon by a net force will accelerate in the direction of the force according to the following equation. $a = \frac{F_{net}}{m}$
Newton's third law	Forces occur in equal but opposite pairs. (For every action, there is an equal but opposite reaction.)
Law of conservation of momentum	In a system where no outside forces act, the total momentum before and after a collision stays the same.

What You'll Learn

- How to use the law of conservation of momentum and Newton's laws of motion to describe and analyze motion

Why It's Important

- All the motion you observe, whether the moon in orbit or a fast-turning in-line skater, can be understood with these laws.

Figure 7-20 When the child pushes off the wall, the wall pushes against the child—Newton's third law. Conservation of momentum explains why the adult will be pushed back when she catches and slows the child. They glide back together. This demonstrates Newton's first law. Eventually friction with the water will slow them according to Newton's second law. **Can you find another example of Newton's third law?**

SECTION 7·4

Prepare

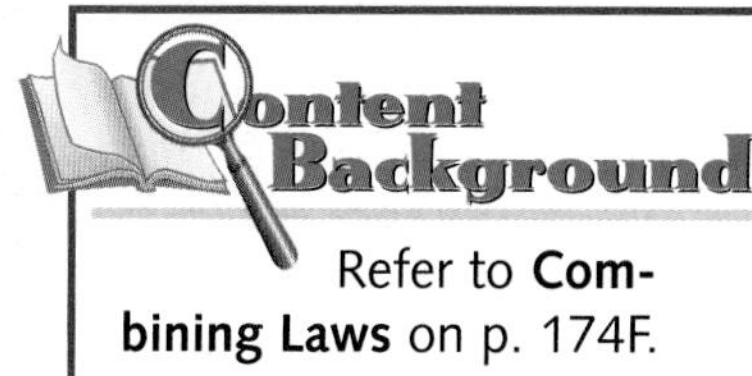

Refer to **Combining Laws** on p. 174F.

Preplanning

Refer to the **Chapter Organizer** on pp. 174A–B.

1 Motivate

Bellringer

Before presenting the lesson, display **Section Focus Transparency 18** on the overhead projector. Use the accompanying **Focus Activity** worksheet. L2 ELL

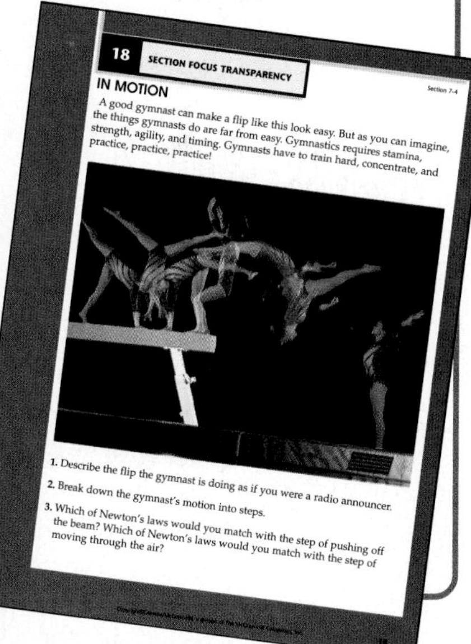
18 SECTION FOCUS TRANSPARENCY

Section 7-4

IN MOTION

A good gymnast can make a flip like this look easy. But as you can imagine, the things gymnasts do are far from easy. Gymnastics requires stamina, strength, agility, and timing. Gymnasts have to train hard, concentrate, and practice, practice, practice!

1. Describe the flip the gymnast is doing as if you were a radio announcer.
2. Break down the gymnast's motion into steps.
3. Which of Newton's laws would you match with the step of pushing off the beam? Which of Newton's laws would you match with the step of moving through the air?

Resource Manager

The following **Teacher Classroom Resources** can be used with Section 7-4:

 **Reproducible Masters**

Activity Worksheets, p. 41

Critical Thinking/Problem Solving, p. 7 L2

Enrichment, p. 18 L3

Multicultural Connections, pp. 13–14 L2

Reinforcement, p. 18 L2

Study Guide, p. 28 L1 ELL

Tying to Previous Knowledge

Have students recall Newton's laws of motion and the law of conservation of momentum. In this section, they will learn how to combine these principles in explaining complex motion.

2 Teach

Caption Answers

Figure 7-20 (See p. 197.) Sample Response: *When the child is caught, the child's weight pushes down and the adult pushes up; accept other reasonable answers.*

Figure 7-22 *Your speed would increase.*

GLENCOE TECHNOLOGY

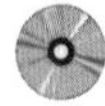

Videodisc

Glencoe Science Voyages Interactive Videodisc—Earth

Side 2, Lesson 8 *Space Exploration*

31216

Refer to Videodisc Teacher Guide for additional bar codes.

Correcting Misconceptions

Students will often use the third law of motion to explain the motion of a single object. In so doing, they confuse the force pairs discussed in the third law of motion with the balanced forces on an object that keep it at rest or moving at a constant velocity according to the first law of motion. Force pairs involve two objects and their interaction with each other. Balanced forces act on a single object.

VISUALIZING Newton's Laws

Figure 7-21 Athletes don't do calculations before they jump, run, or throw, but understanding how the laws of motion work can help you improve your game. Newton's laws are all seen on a bobsled run.

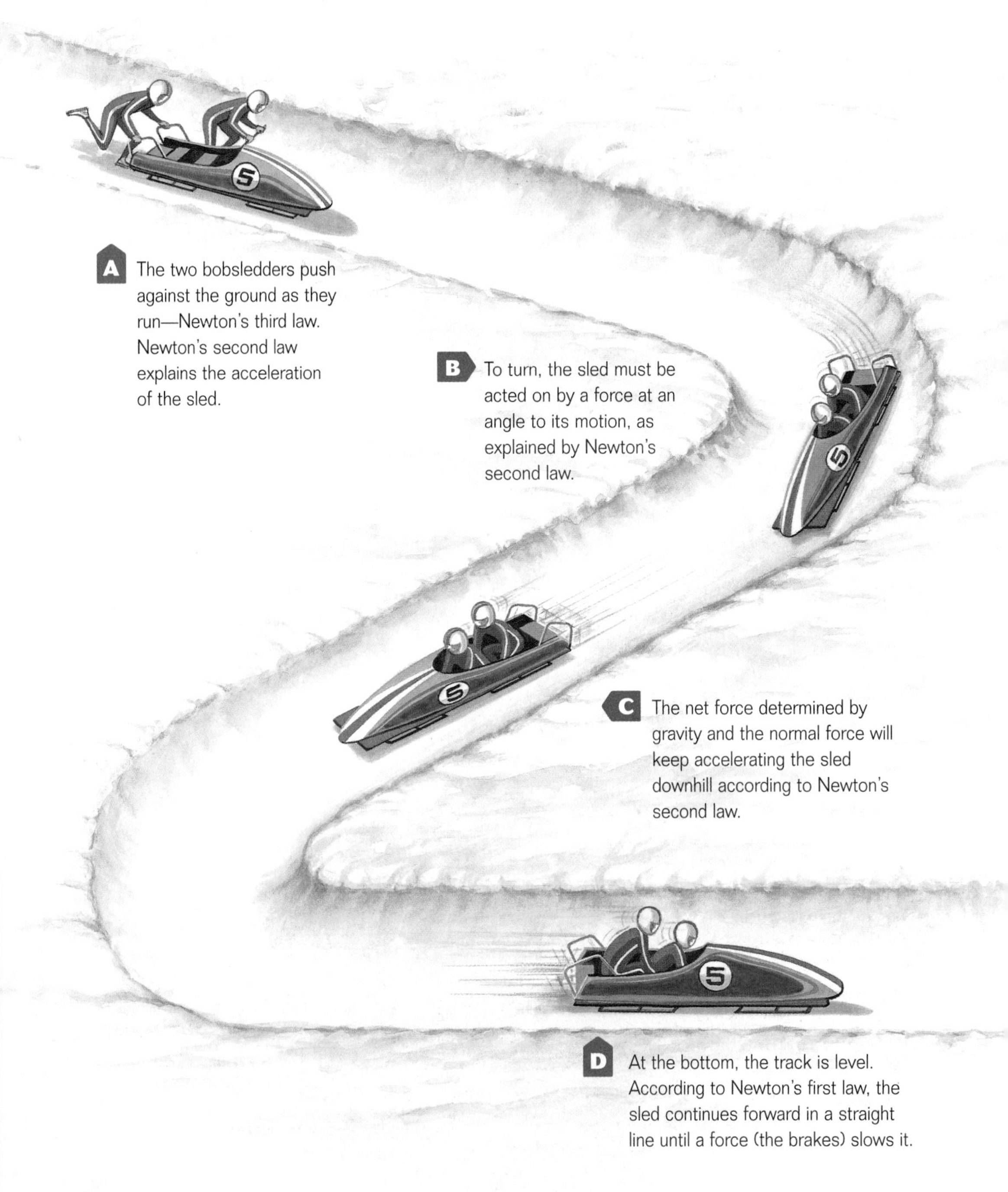

A The two bobsledders push against the ground as they run—Newton's third law. Newton's second law explains the acceleration of the sled.

B To turn, the sled must be acted on by a force at an angle to its motion, as explained by Newton's second law.

C The net force determined by gravity and the normal force will keep accelerating the sled downhill according to Newton's second law.

D At the bottom, the track is level. According to Newton's first law, the sled continues forward in a straight line until a force (the brakes) slows it.

VISUAL Learning

Figure 7-21 Have students write a journal entry that describes Newton's laws at work in the bobsled run. The figure captions provide an outline for their descriptions. The students need to provide particulars that show how each law applies in each case. L2

Inclusion Strategies

Visually Impaired If you have a student in your class who is unable to see the picture of the bobsled run, ask the student to take an elevator ride in a tall building and describe Newton's laws at work. What happens when the elevator starts up? While it is in the middle of its climb? As it slows to a stop?

Throwing and Catching a Ball

What happens when you can't use friction to hold yourself in one spot? Imagine you are standing on ice skates and the effect of friction is small. Suppose your friend exerts a forward force of 60 N for 1 s to throw a 15-kg ball, as shown in **Figure 7-22.** You can find the forward velocity of the ball.

$$\text{force} \times \text{time} = \text{mass} \times \text{velocity}$$
$$Ft = mv$$
$$(60\ \text{N})(1\ \text{s}) = (15\ \text{kg})(v)$$
$$60\ \text{kg} \cdot \text{m/s} = (15\ \text{kg})(v)$$
$$v = 4\ \text{m/s}$$

The ball is moving at 4 m/s.

What happens when you catch the ball? Use the law of conservation of momentum. Assume you have a mass of 50 kg.

$$\text{momentum before} = \text{momentum after}$$
$$\begin{matrix}\text{momentum of} \\ \text{ball before}\end{matrix} = \begin{matrix}\text{momentum of you} \\ \text{and ball after}\end{matrix}$$
$$m_1v_1 = m_2v_2$$
$$(15\ \text{kg})(4\ \text{m/s}) = (15\ \text{kg} + 50\ \text{kg})(v_2)$$
$$60\ \text{kg} \cdot \text{m/s} = (65\ \text{kg})(v_2)$$
$$v_2 = 0.9\ \text{m/s}$$

You and the ball go backward at about 0.9 m/s.

Measuring Force Pairs

Procedure

1. Work in pairs. Each person needs a spring scale.
2. Hook the two scales together. Each person should pull back on a scale. Record the two readings. Pull harder and record the two readings.
3. Continue to pull on both scales, but let the scales move toward one person. Do the readings change?
4. Try to pull in such a way that the scales have different readings.

Analysis

1. What can you conclude about the pair of forces in each situation?
2. Explain how this experiment demonstrates Newton's laws.

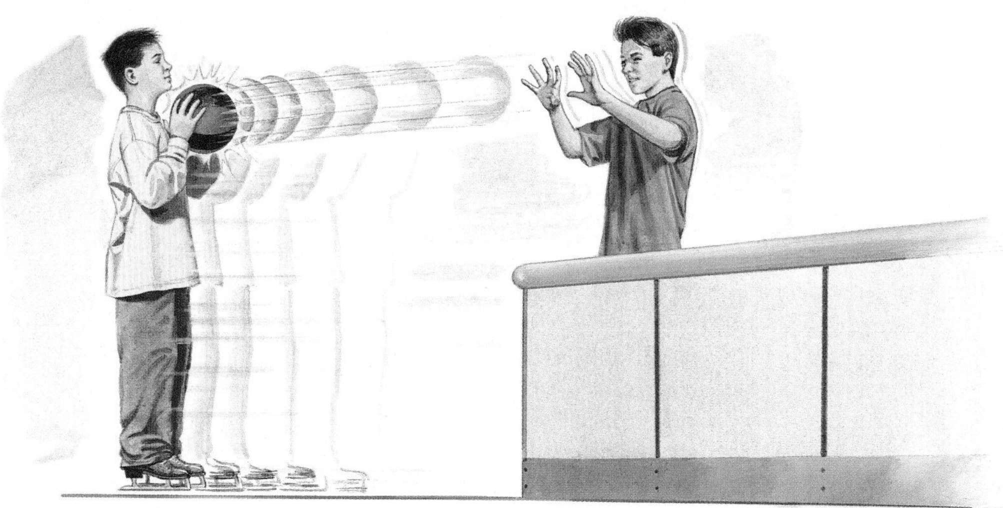

Figure 7-22 When you try to catch a ball without friction to hold you still, the law of conservation of momentum describes how you and the ball move backwards with the same momentum the ball alone had before the collision. **What would happen to your speed if you threw the ball back to your friend?**

Mini Lab

Purpose

Visual-Spatial Students will experience forces and measure them with a spring scale. L2 ELL COOP LEARN P

Materials

one spring scale for each student

Teaching Strategies

Make sure that the students try to let the forces on the scales become unbalanced and ask them to report what happens in that case.

Analysis

1. Unless the scales are accelerating (step 4) the forces are equal and opposite.
2. The forces on the two scales are equal and opposite, illustrating Newton's third law. If the forces are unbalanced, the scales accelerate (second law). If they are balanced, the scales are at rest or moving at constant speed (first law).

Assessment

Content Have students hang a weight from a spring scale that is hanging from a hook. Ask students to predict what will happen to the scale reading when the weight is pulled downward toward the table. *The force reading will increase.* Use **Performance Assessment in the Science Classroom,** p. 17.

Integrating the Sciences

Earth Science Newton's laws are used to explain the motion of the planets. For example, Earth's inertia would make it continue in a straight line (first law) but the force of the sun's gravity makes the orbit bend (second law). Earth pulls on the moon, but the moon also pulls on Earth (third law) as seen with the tides.

Problem Solving

Remind students of Newton's laws of motion. Indicate that Lovell used the phrase "zero gravity" when he actually meant free fall.

Think Critically

First: Once moving, you would continue until you could exert a force to stop. Second: Any slight push would move you and your tools. Third: When you try to push something it pushes you back.

3 Assess

Check for Understanding

Quick Demo

Blow up a balloon and let it go. **What makes it fly about the room?** *The gas escaping from the opening exerts a force on the balloon in the opposite direction making it move around the room with the opening behind.*

Reteach

Quick Demo

Push a ball across your desk, then let it roll. Apply Newton's laws—third and second to push, first to rolling.

Extension

For students who have mastered this section, use the **Reinforcement** and **Enrichment** masters.

4 Close

Proficiency Prep

Use this quiz to check students' recall of section content.

1. **What law can you use to explain the motion of objects before and after a collision?** *law of conservation of momentum*

Figure 7-23 If the engine compartment were closed, the gas inside would collide evenly with all sides, and it would stay at rest. But, the opening at the bottom of the engine lets the gas moving down escape. To get out, the gas must first bounce off the top of the compartment. The force down is equal to the force up.

Rocket Launch

The launching of the space shuttle is a spectacular use of Newton's third law. Three rocket engines supply the force of lift, called thrust. Just before launch, the shuttle's weight is about 20 million N. Nearly all of this is highly explosive rocket fuel.

When the rocket fuel is ignited, the burning creates a hot, fast-moving gas. Particles of gas push against the inside of the engine but can only escape out the bottom of the engine, as shown in **Figure 7-23.** The hard wall of the engine pushes the gas molecules downward when they bounce off of it. The upward push on the shuttle is the action. The downward push on the gas is the reaction. The forces are equal but opposite.

Problem Solving

Modeling Motion in Space

Astronaut Jim Lovell, who flew on *Gemini 7* and *12* and *Apollo 8* and *13,* explains how underwater training for astronauts started.

> The attempts to work outside a spacecraft on *Gemini* flights *9, 10,* and *11* were disasters. Every time the astronauts touched the spacecraft it seemed to repel them, and the astronauts became fatigued and hot, fighting to maintain position. We forgot Newton's third law of motion: "For every action there is an equal and opposite reaction." On Earth, gravity is so overwhelming that we don't notice the reaction. But in zero gravity the reaction is noticeable.
>
> . . . Someone had the brilliant idea that a person. . . underwater would be a good substitute for an astronaut in zero gravity . . . [With this technique] we established the proper handholds and footholds, tools, and movement techniques that are still used today.

Think Critically: Explain how each of Newton's laws would affect your motion working outside a spacecraft in orbit.

Integrating the Sciences

Chemistry When rocket fuels are ignited, chemical reactions occur. These reactions generate heat, light, and gaseous products. For example, when liquid hydrogen reacts with liquid oxygen, water is formed and a great deal of energy is released. The energy causes the water to become water vapor, which builds up pressure. As the hot gases are released at high speed through the rocket nozzle, they force the rocket to move forward.

Steering a Rocket

The space shuttle steers using the same principle that it does to launch. Little engines located all around its surface can fire in different directions. When the pilot wants to turn the shuttle's nose to the right, he or she will fire an engine on the front left and back right. The action-reaction is due to Newton's third law. According to Newton's second law, the reaction force will move the nose to the right and the tail to the left, as shown in **Figure 7-24A.**

The astronauts also have a backpack that works the same way, shown in **Figure 7-24B.** It uses cold rather than hot gas. Remember Newton's first law—once turning, how does an astronaut stop from turning?

Newton's laws are the keys to understanding motion. They aren't complicated, but you must think carefully to fully understand how they work. As you see how these laws are used to explain familiar motions, you can start to use them to analyze more complicated motions.

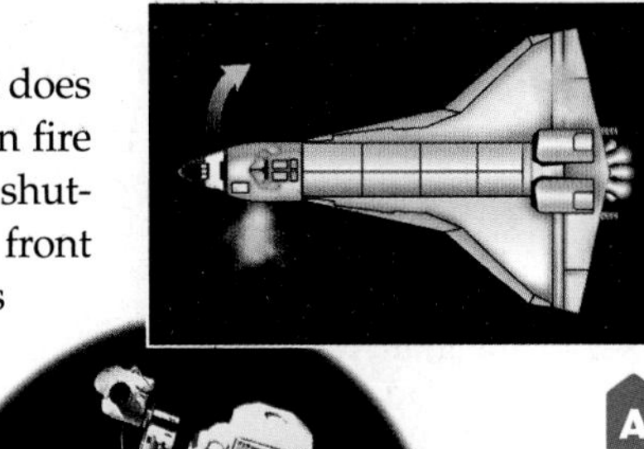

Figure 7-24 A stream of gas in one direction moves the shuttle (A) or astronaut (B) in the opposite direction.

Section Assessment

1. You catch a 0.2-kg baseball moving at 30 m/s. It takes you 0.4 s to bring it to a stop. What force did you use? If the ball is moving in a positive direction, is the force in a positive or negative direction?
2. A player throws a baseball. The ball flies forward and downward toward another player. The second player catches the ball. Explain how Newton's laws are involved in each of these three motions.
3. **Think Critically:** You can use the law of conservation of momentum to analyze a collision in which two balls roll together, collide, then roll apart. Explain what is happening in this collision using Newton's laws of motion.
4. **Skill Builder**
   Recognizing Cause and Effect Explain how cause and effect apply to Newton's second law. If you need help, refer to Recognizing Cause and Effect in the **Skill Handbook** on page 721.

Using Math

Look at **Figure 7-22.** Suppose the ball has a mass of 10 kg. Find its velocity if the throw is still 60 N for 1 s. Find your velocity after catching the ball.

2. **Which of Newton's laws of motion explains why an object accelerates in the direction of the force applied to it?** *second*

Section Assessment

1. $F = ma = m\left(\frac{v_2 - v_1}{t}\right) =$

   $(0.2 \text{ kg})\left(\frac{0 \text{ m/s} - 30 \text{ m/s}}{0.4 \text{ s}}\right)$

   $= 15$ N; negative
2. The first player applies a force to the ball for a short time to set it in motion (second law). The ball travels forward with a constant velocity resulting from the throw (first law) but the force of gravity makes it fall (second law). The second player applies a force to stop the ball when it is caught (second law).
3. **Think Critically** The two balls are moving with a constant velocity toward each other (first law). They collide and exert forces on each other (third law) and accelerate in the direction of the forces (second law).

Using Math

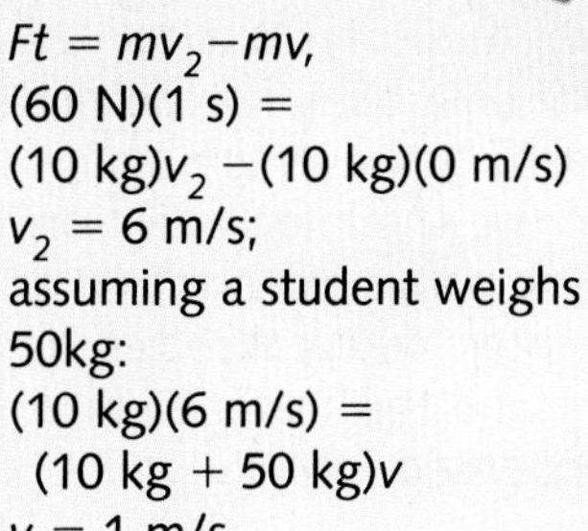
$Ft = mv_2 - mv_1$
$(60 \text{ N})(1 \text{ s}) =$
$(10 \text{ kg})v_2 - (10 \text{ kg})(0 \text{ m/s})$
$v_2 = 6$ m/s;
assuming a student weighs 50kg:
$(10 \text{ kg})(6 \text{ m/s}) =$
$(10 \text{ kg} + 50 \text{ kg})v$
$v = 1$ m/s

4. **Skill Builder**
   cause: a net force; effect: a change in motion in direction of the force

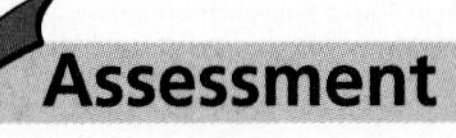

Assessment

Portfolio Have students use cause and effect as presented in the Skill Builder to identify instances in sports where forces are applied to objects in the course of play. Use **Performance Assessment in the Science Classroom,** p. 105. P

Reviewing Main Ideas can be used to preview, review, reteach, and condense chapter content.

Preview

Linguistic Have students try to answer the Reviewing Main Ideas questions in their Science Journals. Use student answers as a source for discussion throughout the chapter.

Review

Interpersonal Have students answer the questions on separate pieces of paper and compare their answers with those of other students in the class.

Reteach

Visual-Spatial Have students look at the illustrations on these pages. Ask them to describe details that support the main ideas of the chapter found in the statement for each illustration.

00:00 OUT OF TIME?

Auditory-Musical If time does not permit teaching the entire chapter, use the information on these pages along with the chapter Audiocassettes to present the material in a condensed format.

Chapter 7 Reviewing Main Ideas

For a **preview** of this chapter, study this Reviewing Main Ideas before you read the chapter. After you have studied this chapter, you can use the Reviewing Main Ideas to **review** the chapter.

The Glencoe MindJogger, Audiocassettes, and CD-ROM provide additional opportunities for review.

Section 7-1 FORCE

A **force** is a push or a pull. *How can you tell that a net force is acting on an object?*

NEWTON'S FIRST LAW

Newton's first law states that objects in motion tend to stay in motion and objects at rest tend to stay at rest unless acted upon by a **net force.** *Why don't we see objects in motion on Earth tending to stay in motion forever?*

Section 7-2 NEWTON'S SECOND LAW

Newton's second law states that an object acted upon by a net force will accelerate in the direction of this force according to the equation $a = F_{net}/m$. *If a baseball bat hits a bowling ball, why doesn't the bowling ball accelerate as quickly as a baseball that is hit just as hard?*

202 CHAPTER 7 FORCE AND NEWTON'S LAWS

Cultural Diversity

Inertia Although the law of inertia is called Newton's first law, Galileo is credited with formulating it. However, inertia was described in Chinese literature more than 2000 years ago. L1

And the Rocket's Red Glare. . . Centuries ago, the Chinese invented gunpowder. This new invention was first used during celebrations. Gunpowder, however, was quickly adapted to war purposes. By the 14th century, Chinese armies were using two-stage rockets in battles. These rockets would take a warhead over the enemy, where the warhead would release arrows.

Reading Check

List three questions someone might ask about force and the changes it causes. Then answer the questions.

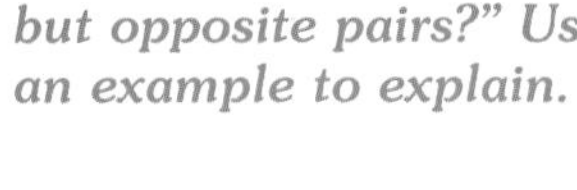

7-3 NEWTON'S THIRD LAW

Newton's third law states that forces are always applied in equal but opposite pairs between two objects. *What is meant by "equal but opposite pairs?" Use an example to explain.*

7-4 LAWS OF MOTION

The laws of motion can be used to completely describe and understand most of the motion you observe. *Explain how each of Newton's three laws is involved when you jump off a diving board into a pool.*

Answers to Questions

Section 7-1

Force The object accelerates.

Newton's First Law because the force of friction acts on them, slowing them down

Section 7-2

Newton's Second Law The bowling ball has more mass, so the acceleration produced must be less according to $a = F/m$.

Section 7-3

Newton's Third Law Equal and opposite pairs of forces occur when two objects interact with each other. For example, a book lying on a table exerts its weight downward on the table while the table exerts an equal force upward on the book.

Section 7-4

Laws of Motion When you jump off a diving board into a pool, you start at rest with the force of gravity on you balanced by the normal force of the board on you (first and third law). You dive by pushing off against the board, and the board exerts a force on you (third law) that accelerates you upward (second law). Once you lose contact with the board, the force of gravity accelerates you downward (second law). When you hit the water, the force of the water on you slows you.

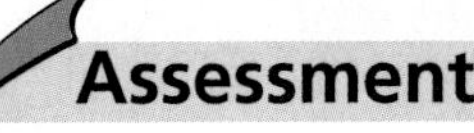

Assessment

Portfolio Encourage students to place in their portfolios one or two items of what they consider to be their best work. Examples include:

- Explore Activity, p. 175
- Enrichment, p. 181
- MiniLab, p. 199 P

Performance Additional performance assessments may be found in **Performance Assessment** and **Science Integration Activities.** Performance Task Assessment Lists and rubrics for evaluating these activities can be found in Glencoe's **Performance Assessment in the Science Classroom.**

Using Vocabulary

1. h
2. a
3. g
4. d
5. c

interNET CONNECTION To reinforce chapter vocabulary, use the **Study Guide for Content Mastery** booklet. Also available are activities for **Glencoe Science Voyages** on the Glencoe Science Web Site. **www.glencoe.com/sec/science**

Checking Concepts

6. A	11. A
7. B	12. B
8. C	13. C
9. D	14. C
10. A	15. D

Thinking Critically

16. Yes, it changed direction.
17. Because of Earth's large mass, we do not detect its acceleration when forces are applied to it. Therefore, we tend to overlook the role that Earth plays in force pairs.
18. Static friction: the car does not slide down the hill; sliding friction: brakes; rolling friction: car tires roll on road; air resistance: when driving at constant speed, must use gas to counter air resistance slowing car.
19. No; from the time the puck loses contact with the hockey stick and moves across the ice at constant speed, there is no net force applied to the puck. It stays in motion in accordance with Newton's first law.

Chapter 7 Assessment

Using Vocabulary

a. balanced forces
b. force
c. friction
d. net force
e. Newton's first law of motion
f. Newton's second law of motion
g. Newton's third law of motion
h. normal force
i. unbalanced forces

Each phrase below describes a science term from the list. Write the term that matches the phrase describing it.

1. the outward force a surface supplies to support an object
2. the forces acting on a body cancel each other
3. forces occur in equal and opposite pairs
4. the sum of the forces on an object
5. the force needed to turn a wheel

Checking Concepts

Choose the word or phrase that best answers the question.

6. How can Newton's third law be simply stated?
   A) action-reaction
   B) balanced-unbalanced
   C) inertia
   D) before-after
7. What is the rubbing when one surface moves against another surface called?
   A) terminal velocity
   B) friction
   C) normal force
   D) inertia
8. What is the combination of units for the newton?
   A) m/s^2
   B) $kg \cdot m/s$
   C) $kg \cdot m/s^2$
   D) kg/m
9. Which of the following has no direction?
   A) force
   B) acceleration
   C) momentum
   D) mass
10. What is a push or a pull a simple definition of?
    A) force
    B) momentum
    C) acceleration
    D) inertia
11. What is the type of friction important to walking?
    A) static friction
    B) sliding friction
    C) rolling friction
    D) air resistance
12. An object is accelerated by a net force in what direction?
    A) at an angle to the force
    B) in the direction of the force
    C) in the direction opposite to the force
    D) Any of these is possible.
13. If you exert a net force of 8 N on a 2-kg object for 3 s, what is the object's change in momentum?
    A) 12 kg · m/s
    B) 13 kg · m/s
    C) 24 kg · m/s
    D) 48 kg · m/s
14. You push against a wall with a force of 5 N. What is the force vector of the wall on your hands?
    A) 0 N
    B) 2.5 N
    C) 5 N
    D) 10 N
15. You are on a bike. Which of the following is an example of balanced forces?
    A) You pedal to speed up.
    B) You turn at constant speed.
    C) You coast to slow down.
    D) You pedal at constant speed.

Thinking Critically

16. A baseball is pitched east at 40 km/h. The batter hits it west at 40 km/h. Did the ball accelerate? Explain.
17. Frequently, we don't notice the pair of forces acting between two objects because one of the objects is Earth. How are the forces acting on Earth hidden?

20. When you kick a soccer ball, your foot collides with the ball. During the collision, the force exerted by your foot on the ball is equal and opposite to the force exerted by the ball on your foot.

18. A car is parked on a hill. The driver starts the car, accelerates until the car is driving at constant speed, drives at constant speed, then brakes to put the brake pads in contact with the spinning wheels. Explain how static friction, sliding friction, rolling friction, and air resistance are seen in this example.
19. You hit a hockey puck and it slides across the ice at constant speed. Is there a force keeping it in motion? Explain.
20. Newton's third law describes the forces between two colliding objects. Use this connection to explain the forces acting when you kick a soccer ball.

Developing Skills

If you need help, refer to the Skill Handbook.

21. **Making Models:** Explain why Galileo's thought experiment of rolling balls along a flatter and flatter ramp is a model of motion. Could the predicted motion ever be seen in a real experiment?
22. **Interpreting Scientific Illustrations:** Is there a net force acting on the object shown?

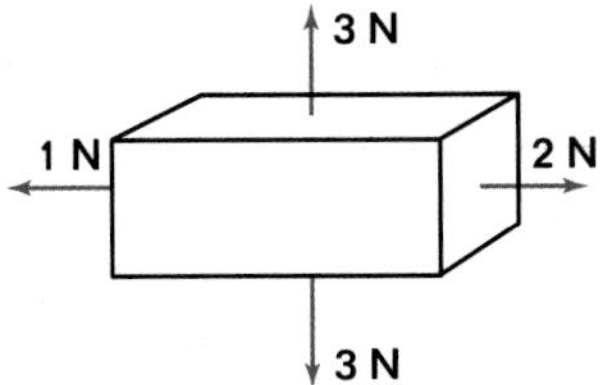

23. **Using Numbers:** An object of mass 0.4 kg accelerates at 2 m/s^2. Find the force.
24. **Recognizing Cause and Effect:** Use Newton's third law to explain why a rocket accelerates on takeoff.

Test-Taking Tip

Become an Expert on What You Fear Most If you think you can't remember all of the information, don't run away. Instead, consider it a challenge, meet the problem head-on, and you'll be surprised at how easy it is to conquer even the toughest concepts.

Test Practice

Use these questions to test your Science Proficiency.

1. Two students, Molly and Brian, are sitting in identical desk chairs with rollers. Molly weighs 40 kg and Brian weighs 60 kg. Brian quickly shoves Molly's chair, causing both chairs to move. During the push, while Brian's hand touched Molly's chair, which of the following is true?
   A) Neither student exerts a force on the other.
   B) Brian's force on Molly is larger.
   C) Molly's force on Brian is larger.
   D) Both students exert the same amount of force on each other.
2. You are standing in an elevator that is moving upward with constant velocity. What can you conclude about the forces acting on your body?
   A) The normal force of the floor is greater than the gravitational force.
   B) The normal force of the floor is less than the gravitational force.
   C) The normal force of the floor is equal to the gravitational force.
   D) No forces are acting.

Assessment Resources

The **Test Practice Workbook** provides students with practice in the format, concepts, and critical-thinking skills tested in standardized exams.

Reproducible Masters

Chapter Review, pp. 13–14 L2
Performance Assessment, p. 21 L2
Assessment, pp. 27–30 L2

Glencoe Technology

Chapter Review Software
Computer Test Bank
MindJogger Videoquiz

The Test-Taking Tip was written by The Princeton Review, the nation's leader in test preparation.

1. D
2. C

Developing Skills

21. It is a model of ideal motion—what would happen if friction didn't slow objects. A real experiment would have some friction.
22. Yes, 1 N to the right.
23. $(0.4\ kg)(2\ m/s^2) = 0.8\ N$
24. Before ignition, the weight of the rocket downward is balanced by the force of the launch pad upward. After ignition, the rocket expels hot combustion products downward with enough force to overcome the weight of the rocket and accelerate it upward. Newton's third law of motion explains the opposing forces in both cases.

Bonus Question

Two bats are swung with equal acceleration at baseballs of equal weight. Assuming that the bat and ball remain in contact for the same amount of time in each case and that the balls remain in the air for the same amount of time, which baseball will travel further if one bat weighs 1 kg and the other weighs 2 kg? *The ball hit by the 2-kg bat will travel further.*

UNIT 3

Earth's Interior

In this unit, students are introduced to the relationships among earthquakes, volcanoes, and plate tectonics and how forces within Earth are tied to these relationships. Movement of hot rock material inside Earth's mantle causes plates—sections of Earth's crust—to move. This movement causes vibrations (earthquakes) and allows molten material to reach Earth's surface through volcanoes.

Unit Overview

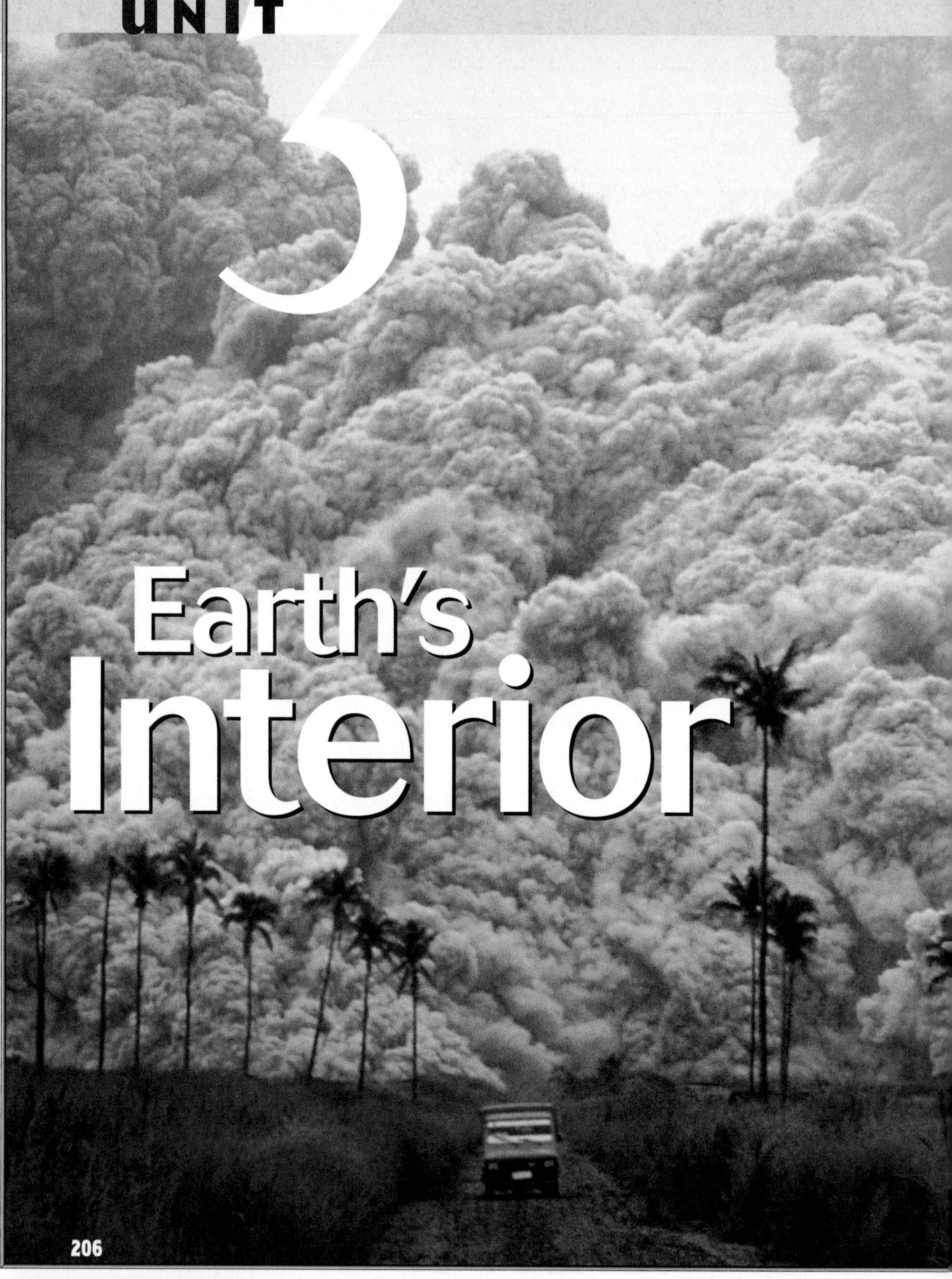

Science at Home

A World in Motion Have students monitor newspapers, news magazines, television news, and the Internet for stories about volcanic eruptions and earthquakes around the world.

NATIONAL GEOGRAPHIC

What's Happening Here?

The earth beneath your feet is not as solid as it feels. Earth's surface is, in fact, broken into massive, shifting plates. Along the edges of these plates, molten rock finds its way to the surface, creating volcanoes that can erupt with tremendous force. The people in this truck (left) narrowly escaped the explosion of Mount Pinatubo on the Philippine island of Luzon in 1991. Some 800 inhabitants of Luzon did not escape. When Mount Pinatubo awoke from its 600-year slumber, it spewed out more gas and debris than most other volcanic eruption of this century. Earth's internal processes also cause earthquakes. The twisted wreckage of a train in Kobe, Japan (below), illustrates the terrible destructive power unleashed by the quake of 1995. In this unit, you will learn how understanding the forces that originate deep within Earth helps us to predict the destruction they can cause.

interNET CONNECTION

Explore the Glencoe Science Web Site at **www.glencoe.com/sec/science** to find out more about topics found in this unit.

207

interNET CONNECTION

Internet Addresses

____

____

____

____

Explore the Glencoe Science Web Site at **www.glencoe.com/sec/science** to find out more about topics found in this unit.

Introducing the Unit

What's happening here?

Have students read the text and examine the pictures. Ask how volcanoes and earthquakes are similar. Point out to students that they will learn how forces inside Earth release great amounts of energy that can have devastating effects on Earth's surface.

Content Background

The explosive force of Mount Pinatubo sent ash as high as 30 km. This cloud of ash circled Earth for a year, scattering incoming sunlight and cooling the global climate. As far as 40 km from the volcano, ash accumulated on houses to a thickness of 30 cm. The collapse of these buildings caused most of the deaths.

Previewing the Chapters

- Have students look for pictures of the effects of earthquakes and volcanoes and compare and contrast them.
- Have students preview the chapter on plate tectonics and try to identify the continents.

Tying to Previous Knowledge

- Have students recall news stories about the damage done by earthquakes. Ask them to describe what they recall.
- Have students list the areas of the United States most susceptible to volcanic activity.
- Have students use a globe of Earth to hypothesize how the continents may once have fit together.

Chapter 8 Earthquakes

Section	Objectives	Activities/Features
Chapter Opener		**Explore Activity:** Modeling Rock Deformation, p. 209
8-1 **Forces Inside Earth** 1 Session ½ Block	1. **Explain** how earthquakes result from the buildup of energy in Earth's crust. 2. **Contrast** normal, reverse, and strike-slip faults.	**Physics Integration,** p. 211 **Physics Integration,** p. 213 **Skill Builder:** Concept Mapping, p. 214 **Using Computers,** p. 214
8-2 **Earthquake Information** 4 Sessions 2 Blocks	3. **Compare** and **contrast** primary, secondary, and surface waves. 4. **Explain** how an earthquake epicenter is located. 5. **Describe** the structure of Earth's interior.	**MiniLab:** Making and Using Tables and Graphs, p. 218 **Problem Solving:** Interpreting Data, p. 222 **Using Math,** p. 223 **Skill Builder:** Using Numbers, p. 223 **Science Journal,** p. 223 **Activity 8-1:** Epicenter Location, p. 224
8-3 **Destruction by Earthquakes** 3½ Sessions 1½ Blocks	6. **Define** *magnitude* and the *Richter scale*. 7. **List** ways to make your classroom and home more earthquake-safe.	**MiniLab:** Modeling Seismic-Safe Structures, p. 229 **Skill Builder:** Using Numbers, p. 230 **Using Math,** p. 230 **Reading and Writing in Science:** Why We Have Earthquakes—A Korean Folktale, p. 231 **Activity 8-2:** Earthquake Depths, pp. 232–233

The number of recommended single-period sessions The number of recommended blocks
One session and one-half block are allowed for chapter review and assessment.

Activity Materials

Explore	Activities	MiniLabs
p. 209 three individually colored pieces of clay	p. 224 string, metric ruler, globe, chalk, paper pp. 232–233 graph paper, pencil	p. 218 No materials needed. p. 229 building blocks, rubber bands

Need Materials? Contact Science Kit at 1-800-828-7777 or at www.sciencekit.com on the Internet.
For alternate materials, see the activity on the listed page.

Standards		Reproducible Resources	Technology
National	State/Local	Test Practice Workbooks are available for use with each chapter.	English and Spanish audiocassettes are available for use with each section.
National Content Standards: UCP1, UCP2, UCP4, B2, B3, D1		**Enrichment,** p. 19 **Reinforcement,** p. 19 **Study Guide,** pp. 29–30	**Section Focus Transparency 19** **Teaching Transparency 15** **National Geographic Society: STV** **The Infinite Voyage Series**
National Content Standards: UCP1, UCP2, A2, B2, B3, D1		**Activity Worksheets,** pp. 43–44, 47 **Enrichment,** p. 20 **Home Involvement,** pp. 26–27 **Laboratory Manual,** pp. 49–52 **Laboratory Manual,** pp. 53–56 **Reinforcement,** p. 20 **Study Guide,** p. 31	**Section Focus Transparency 20** **Science Integration Transparency 8** **Teaching Transparency 16** **Internet Connection,** p. 216 **Glencoe Science Voyages Interactive CD-ROM** **Glencoe Science Voyages Interactive Videodisc—Physical**
National Content Standards: UCP1, UCP3, A1, B2, B3, E1, E2, F1, F3, F5		**Activity Worksheets,** pp. 45–46, 48 **Critical Thinking/Problem Solving,** p. 8 **Enrichment,** p. 21 **Multicultural Connections,** pp. 15–16 **Reinforcement,** p. 21 **Study Guide,** pp. 31–32	**Section Focus Transparency 21** **The Infinite Voyage Series** **Internet Connection,** p. 228

Key to Teaching Strategies

The following designations will help you decide which activities are appropriate for your students.

L1 Level 1 activities should be appropriate for students with learning difficulties.

L2 Level 2 activities should be within the ability range of all students.

L3 Level 3 activities are designed for above-average students.

ELL ELL activities should be within the ability range of English Language Learners.

COOP LEARN Cooperative Learning activities are designed for small group work.

P These strategies represent student products that can be placed into a best-work portfolio.

Multiple Learning Styles logos, as described on page 61T, are used throughout to indicate strategies that address different learning styles.

Assessment Resources

Chapter Review, pp. 15–16
Assessment, pp. 33–36
Performance Assessment in the Science Classroom (PASC)
MindJogger Videoquiz
Alternate Assessment in the Science Classroom
Performance Assessment, p. 22
Chapter Review Software
Computer Test Bank

Chapter 8 Earthquakes

This is a representation of key blackline masters available in the Teacher Classroom Resources. See Resource Manager boxes within the chapter for additional information.

Transparencies

Section Focus Transparencies

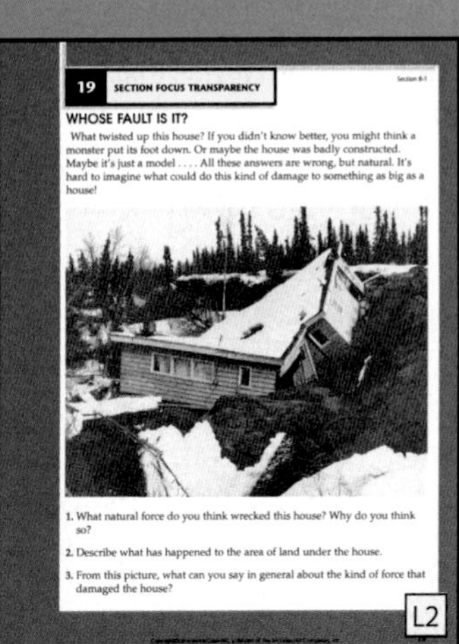
19 SECTION FOCUS TRANSPARENCY

WHOSE FAULT IS IT?

What twisted up this house? If you didn't know better, you might think a monster put its foot down. Or maybe the house was badly constructed. Maybe it's just a model . . . . All these answers are wrong, but natural. It's hard to imagine what could do this kind of damage to something as big as a house!

1. What natural force do you think wrecked this house? Why do you think so?
2. Describe what has happened to the area of land under the house.
3. From this picture, what can you say in general about the kind of force that damaged the house?

L2

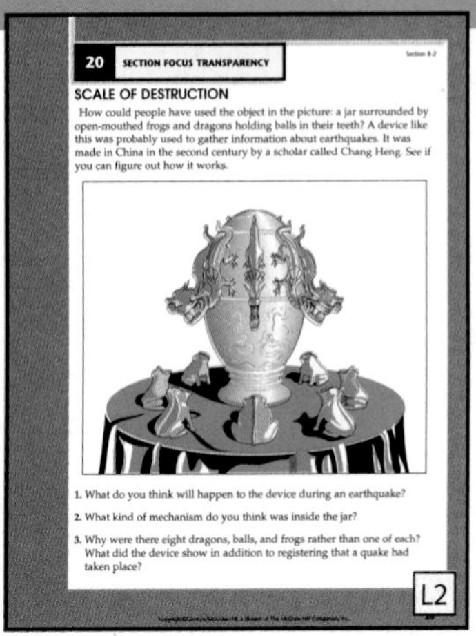
20 SECTION FOCUS TRANSPARENCY

SCALE OF DESTRUCTION

How could people have used the object in the picture: a jar surrounded by open-mouthed frogs and dragons holding balls in their teeth? A device like this was probably used to gather information about earthquakes. It was made in China in the second century by a scholar called Chang Heng. See if you can figure out how it works.

1. What do you think will happen to the device during an earthquake?
2. What kind of mechanism do you think was inside the jar?
3. Why were there eight dragons, balls, and frogs rather than one of each? What did the device show in addition to registering that a quake had taken place?

L2

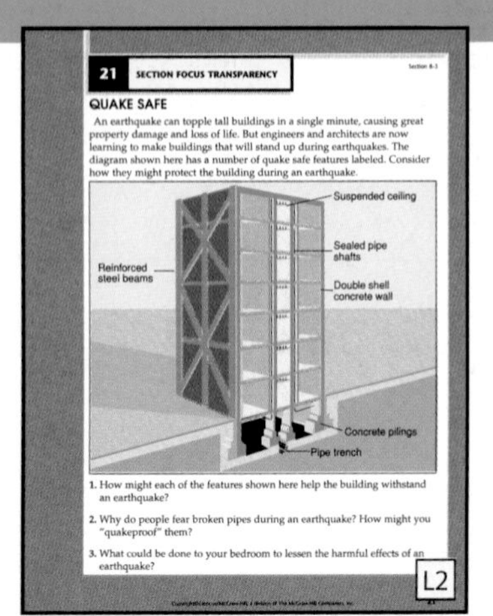
21 SECTION FOCUS TRANSPARENCY

QUAKE SAFE

An earthquake can topple tall buildings in a single minute, causing great property damage and loss of life. But engineers and architects are now learning to make buildings that will stand up during earthquakes. The diagram shown here has a number of quake safe features labeled. Consider how they might protect the building during an earthquake.

1. How might each of the features shown here help the building withstand an earthquake?
2. Why do people fear broken pipes during an earthquake? How might you "quakeproof" them?
3. What could be done to your bedroom to lessen the harmful effects of an earthquake?

L2

Science Integration Transparencies

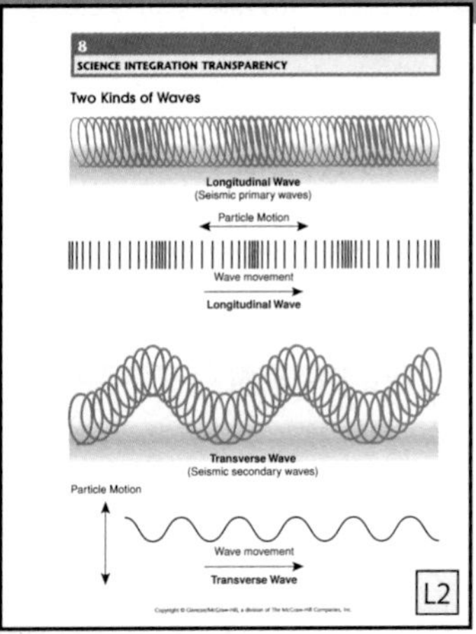
8 SCIENCE INTEGRATION TRANSPARENCY

Two Kinds of Waves

L2

Teaching Transparencies

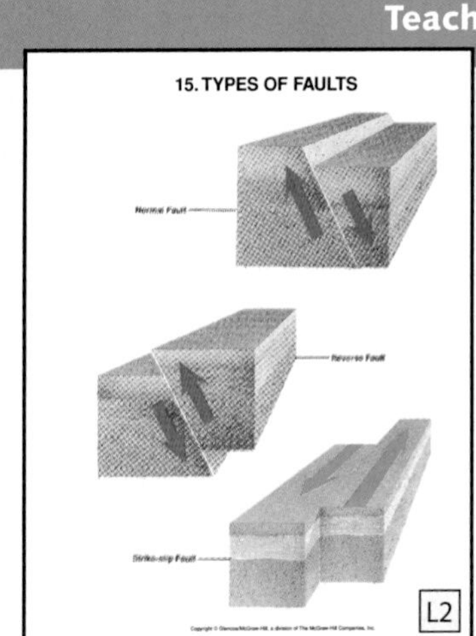

L2

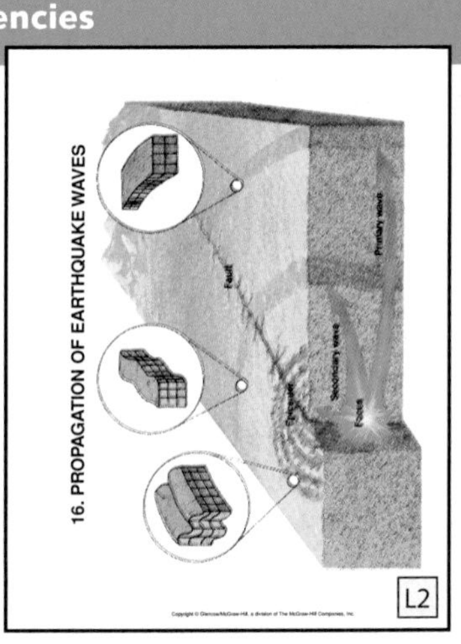

L2

Meeting Different Ability Levels

Study Guide for Content Mastery

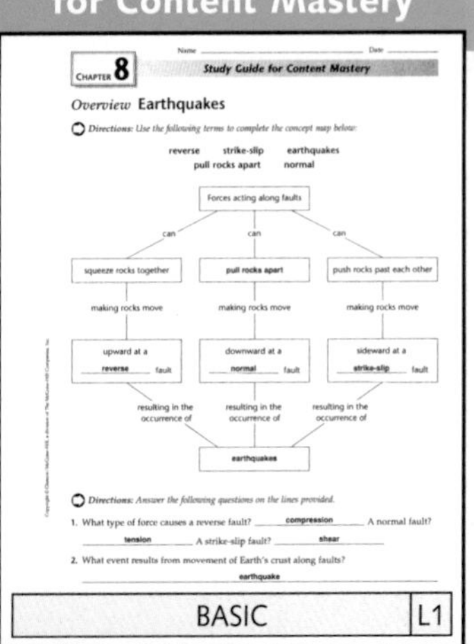
CHAPTER 8 Study Guide for Content Mastery

Overview Earthquakes

Directions: Use the following terms to complete the concept map below:

reverse, strike-slip, earthquakes, pull rocks apart, normal

Forces acting along faults — can: squeeze rocks together / pull rocks apart / push rocks past each other — making rocks move: upward at a reverse fault / downward at a normal fault / sideward at a strike-slip fault — resulting in the occurrence of earthquakes

Directions: Answer the following questions on the lines provided.

1. What type of force causes a reverse fault? compression A normal fault? tension A strike-slip fault? shear
2. What event results from movement of Earth's crust along faults? earthquake

BASIC L1

Reinforcement

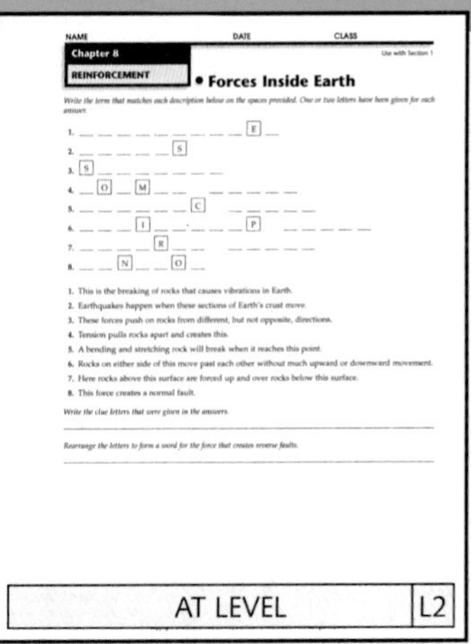
Chapter 8 REINFORCEMENT

• Forces Inside Earth

1. This is the breaking of rocks that causes vibrations in Earth.
2. Earthquakes happen when these sections of Earth's crust move.
3. These forces push on rocks from different, but not opposite, directions.
4. Tension pulls rocks apart and creates this.
5. A bending and stretching rock will break when it reaches this point.
6. Rocks on either side of this move past each other without much upward or downward movement.
7. How rocks above this surface are forced up and over rocks below this surface.
8. This force creates a normal fault.

AT LEVEL L2

Enrichment Worksheets

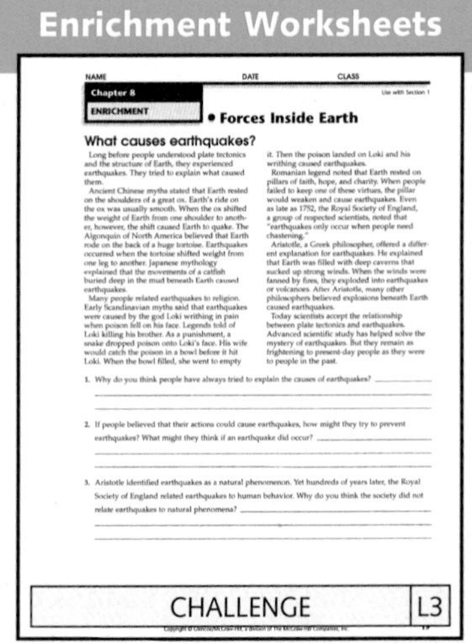
Chapter 8 ENRICHMENT

• Forces Inside Earth

What causes earthquakes?

1. Why do you think people have always tried to explain the causes of earthquakes?
2. If people believed that their actions could cause earthquakes, how might they try to prevent earthquakes? What might they think if an earthquake did occur?
3. Aristotle identified earthquakes as a natural phenomenon. Yet hundreds of years later, the Royal Society of England related earthquakes to human behavior. Why do you think the society did not relate earthquakes to natural phenomena?

CHALLENGE L3

Resource Manager

Hands-on Activities

Activity Worksheets

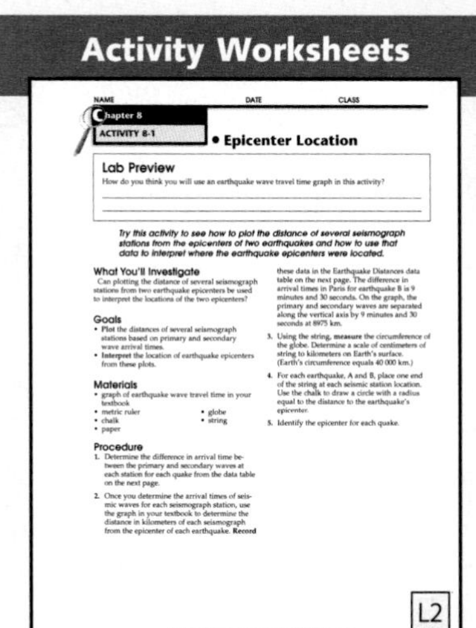
Chapter 8
ACTIVITY 8-1
• Epicenter Location

Lab Preview

L2

Lab Manual

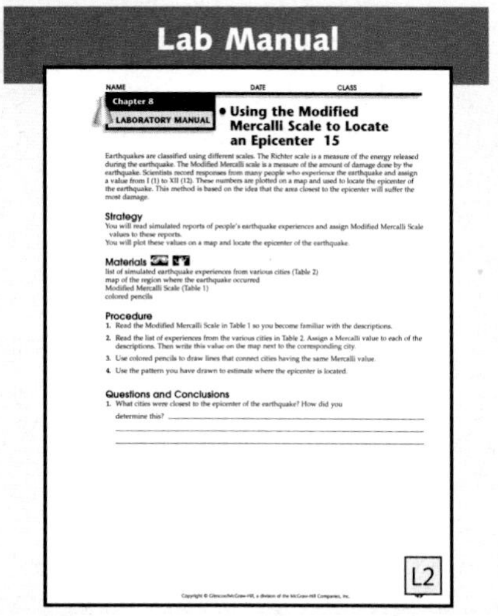
Chapter 8
LABORATORY MANUAL
• Using the Modified Mercalli Scale to Locate an Epicenter 15

Strategy

Materials

Procedure

Questions and Conclusions

L2

Accessibility

Spanish Resources

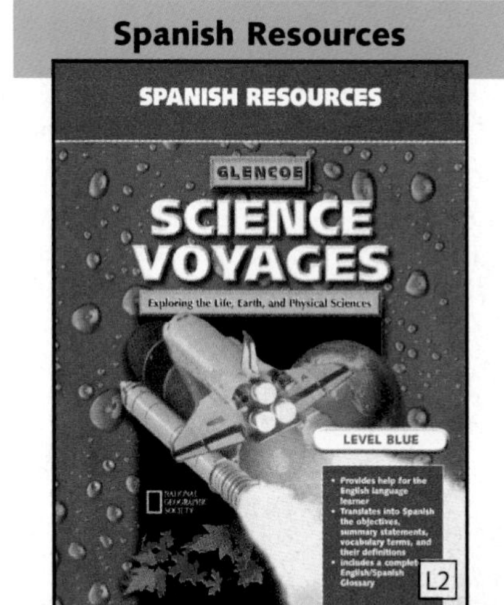

Assessment

Performance Assessment

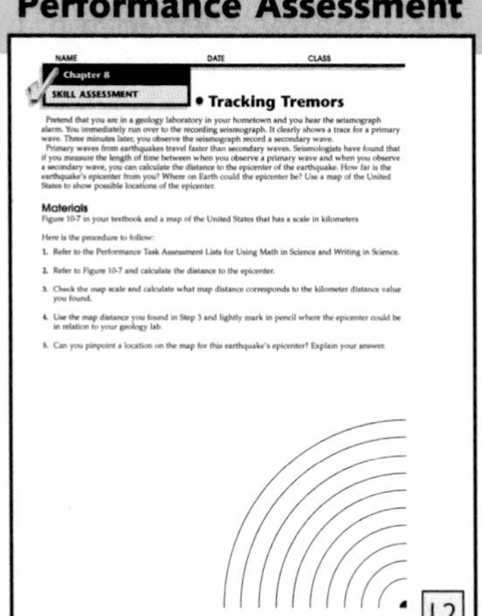
Chapter 8
SKILL ASSESSMENT
• Tracking Tremors

Materials

L2

Chapter Review

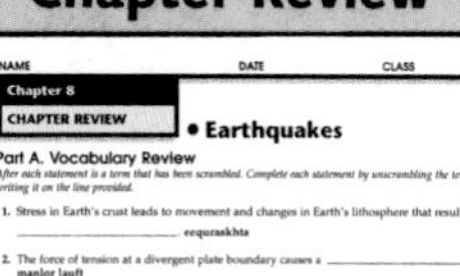
Chapter 8
CHAPTER REVIEW
• Earthquakes

Part A. Vocabulary Review

L2

Assessment

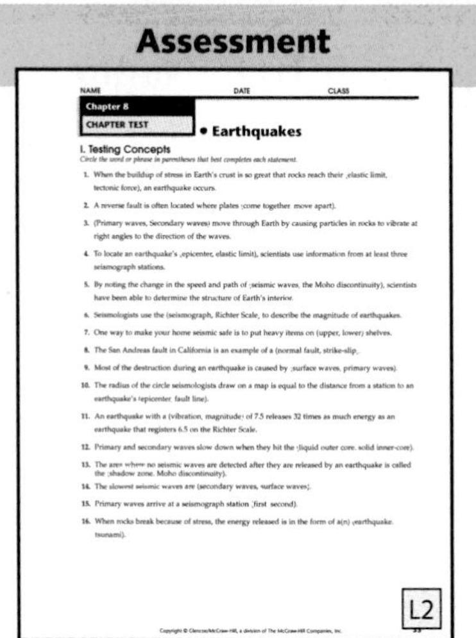
Chapter 8
CHAPTER TEST
• Earthquakes

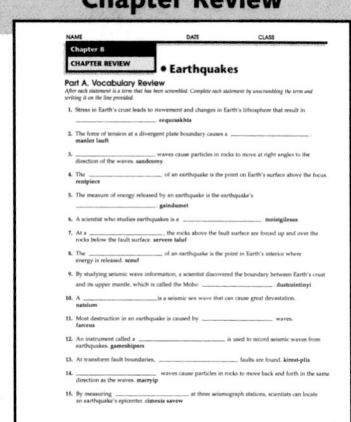

I. Testing Concepts

L2

Test Practice Workbook

Extending Content

Critical Thinking/ Problem Solving

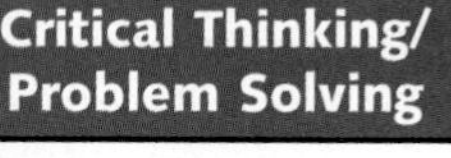
Chapter 8
CRITICAL THINKING
• Earthquakes

Can earthquakes be predicted?

Applying Critical Thinking Skills

L2

Multicultural Connections

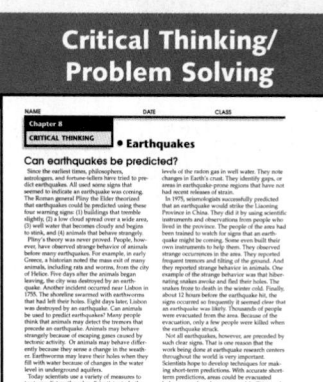

Chapter 8
MULTICULTURAL CONNECTIONS
• Tsunamis, Seiches, and Seismographs

Tsunami

Seiches

Other Effects of the Earthquake

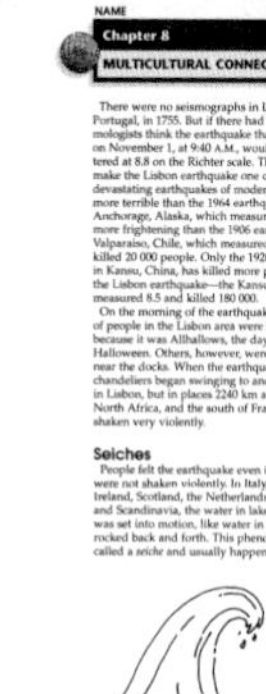

L2

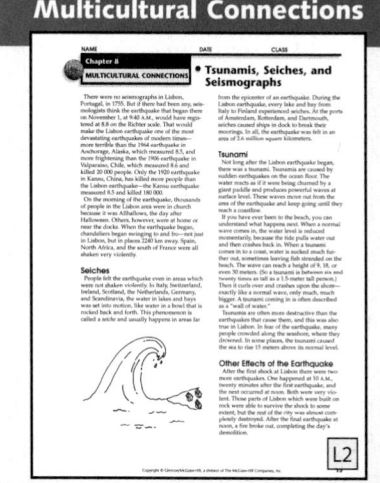

Helping You Prepare

Forces Inside Earth (Section 8-1)

Paleoseismology is the study of rock layers that have been disturbed by ancient earthquake activity. Studying earthquake history enables scientists to make predictions as to when large earthquakes are most likely to happen. In one area of the San Andreas Fault, paleoseismology has indicated that a major earthquake has occurred on the average of once every 140 to 150 years over the past 1400 years. The last major earthquake to hit this particular area of the San Andreas Fault occurred in 1857. Seismologists predict a 50 percent probability of a large 8.3 magnitude earthquake hitting the area within the next 30 years.

Earthquake Information (Section 11-2)

Primary waves are referred to as P-waves, secondary waves as S-waves, and some surface waves as L-waves.

P- and S-waves are called body waves. They can travel through Earth's interior. The behavior of P- and S-waves as they travel through Earth enables scientists to map Earth's interior.

Shallow-focus earthquakes occur where sections (plates) of Earth's crust and mantle are diverging and near the edges of plates that are converging. Intermediate- and deep-focus earthquakes occur where one plate subducts under another.

GLENCOE TECHNOLOGY

CD-ROM

Glencoe Science Voyages Interactive CD-ROM

Chapter Summaries

Use the Chapter Summary to introduce, teach, or review chapter material.

Seismology (Section 8-3)

Along the San Andreas Fault near Parkfield, California, a 6.0 magnitude earthquake has occurred about every 22 years since 1857. Seismologists predicted that another would occur sometime between 1988 and 1992. Instruments such as lasers, creep meters, survey alignment instruments, and other instruments were installed in the area as part of the Parkfield Earthquake Prediction Experiment. The year 1992 came and passed without the predicted earthquake of magnitude 6.0 or more.

Parkfield has been named the earthquake capital of the world by its residents, and it is likely that a moderate earthquake will hit there. Because of this, even though the five-year window of study has ended, instruments have been left in the area to monitor even the slightest amount of motion.

NATIONAL GEOGRAPHIC — **Teacher's Corner**

Products Available from Glencoe

To order the following products for use with this chapter, call Glencoe at 1-800-334-7344:

CD-ROM

NGS PictureShow: Dynamic Earth

Curriculum Kits

GeoKit: Dynamic Earth

GeoKit: Earth's Crust

Transparency Set

NGS PicturePack: Dynamic Earth

Videodisc

STV: Restless Earth

Products Available from National Geographic Society

To order the following products for use with this chapter, call National Geographic Society at 1-800-368-2728:

Videos

Changing Earth: Forces That Create, Forces That Destroy

Living on Our Changing Planet

Our Dynamic Earth

When the Earth Quakes

Another method that is used to help in predicting earthquakes is the study of seismic gaps. Seismic gaps are areas of a fault zone that have not produced a major earthquake for a period greater than 100 years. When a seismic gap area is located, researchers estimate how long it has been since the fault zone in question has experienced an earthquake. Using this information and knowledge of the average earthquake recurrence interval along the fault segment, they predict a time range over which the area could expect to experience a major earthquake.

Although much information is used in an attempt to predict earthquakes, success has been limited. Stress begins to build up in an area as soon as an earthquake has occurred. Without knowing how much stress can accumulate before rocks must shift, it is difficult to predict an earthquake with any amount of accuracy.

Earthquake Magnitude (Section 8-3)

The extent of the damage caused by an earthquake depends on distance to the epicenter, the type of bedrock in the area, the local soil or sediment types, and the number and type of structures subjected to the quake, among other factors.

During the 1985 Mexico City earthquake, the soft, unconsolidated sediments underlying Mexico City amplified earthquake vibrations. This resulted in the collapse of many buildings and the deaths of 10 000 people in Mexico City alone.

Seismic-Safe Structures

(Section 8-3)

Most loss of life in an earthquake occurs when people are trapped in and on crumbling structures, such as buildings, bridges, and highways. Making structures seismic-safe can reduce the loss of life in an earthquake. Seismic safe structures are resistant to vibrations that occur during an earthquake.

The two main strategies for building seismic-safe structures are shock absorption and reinforcement. The goals are to prevent structures from collapsing and to minimize falling debris.

Highways and buildings in earthquake-prone areas can be made seismic safe. Since 1971 in areas in California and Japan, stricter building codes have been enforced, and older buildings have been reinforced. Seismic-safe highways are supported by vertical steel rods wrapped with reinforcing rods encased in concrete.

Lives and property can be saved by replacing underground water and gas pipes with ones that will bend but not break during an earthquake. In some areas in Japan, electric power to trains is cut off when sensors note vibrations from an earthquake. Also, natural gas supplies are stopped as soon as vibrations are felt.

SCIENCE UPDATE

For current events or science in the news, access the Glencoe Science Web Site at **www.glencoe.com/sec/science**

Teacher to Teacher

"To avoid confusion during lab activities that require calculations, solve some practice math problems with the students prior to the activity. By doing this practice, they can become familiar with the calculations they will need to use."

Steve Manns, Teacher
Derry Area Middle School
Derry, PA

CHAPTER 8
Earthquakes

CHAPTER OVERVIEW

Section 8-1 The causes of earthquakes are described in this section. The three types of faults also are defined.

Section 8-2 Seismic waves and how they are used to locate an earthquake are discussed. A model of Earth's interior obtained from seismic data is presented.

Section 8-3 The destruction caused by earthquakes and methods of measuring earthquake magnitude and destruction are discussed. Earthquake safety also is introduced.

Chapter Vocabulary

fault	epicenter
earthquake	surface wave
normal fault	inner core
reverse fault	outer core
strike-slip fault	mantle
	crust
seismic wave	seismologist
focus	seismograph
primary wave	magnitude
secondary wave	tsunami

Theme Connection

Energy Forces inside Earth generate energy that is released during an earthquake as seismic waves.

If time does not permit teaching the entire chapter, use Reviewing Main Ideas on pp. 234–235.

CHAPTER 8
Earthquakes

Chapter Preview

Skills Preview

Skill Builders
- Compare and Contrast
- Make and Use a Table

Activities
- Interpret Data
- Make and Use a Graph

MiniLabs
- Interpret a Graph
- Make a Model

Reading Check

As you read Section 8-1 of this chapter, complete a chart with these three columns: type of fault, its cause, its effects.

208

Multiple Learning Styles

Look for the following logos for strategies that emphasize different learning modalities.

Linguistic Science Journal, pp. 213, 219, 222, 229; Tying to Previous Knowledge, p. 215; Across the Curriculum, p. 218; Quick Demo, p. 219; Inclusion Strategies, p. 226; Assessment, p. 233; Preview p. 234

Logical-Mathematical MiniLab, p. 218; Activity, pp. 224, 232

Visual-Spatial Quick Demo, p. 212; Assessment, p. 214; Across the Curriculum, p. 220; Multiple Learning Styles, p. 221; Activity, p. 221; Reteach, pp. 229, 234; Visual Learning, p. 230

Kinesthetic Explore Activity, p. 209; Activity, p. 212; Visual Learning, p. 220

Interpersonal Discussion, pp. 211, 213; Enrichment, p. 220; MiniLab, p. 228; Review, p. 234

Auditory-Musical Out of Time, p. 234

Explore Activity

You may have seen pictures of the damage from the 1995 Hanshin-Awaji (Kobe), Japan, earthquake. Have you ever thought about what caused this earthquake or wondered if it could happen where you live? As you read this chapter, you will explore how movement and forces inside Earth produce earthquakes.

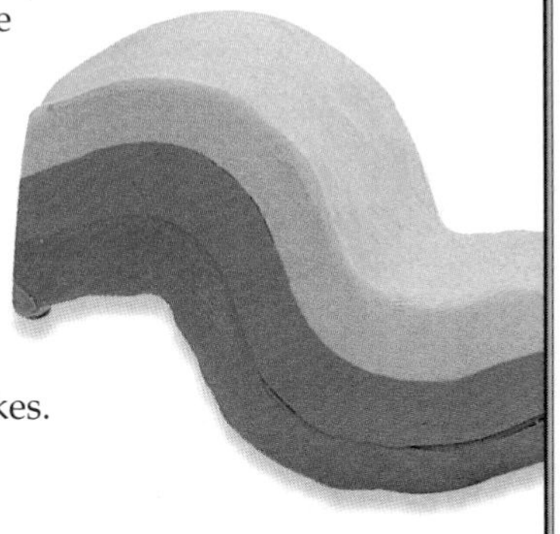

Model Rock Deformation

1. Place three layers of colored clay flat on a table.
2. Place your hands on opposite ends of the layers of clay.
3. Begin pushing your hands together, compressing the clay.
4. Now, hold another piece of layered clay in your hands.
5. Begin to apply tension by gradually pulling apart the clay.
6. Holding another piece of layered clay flat on the table, begin pushing so that one hand slides past the other hand.

Science Journal

What happens to clay layers when your hands compress them from directly opposite directions? What happens to the clay when you gradually pull it apart? Draw pictures of each of the deformed clay pieces in your Science Journal.

Assessment Planner

Portfolio
Refer to p. 235 for suggested items that students might select for their portfolios.

Performance Assessment
See p. 235 for additional Performance Assessment options.
Skill Builder, pp. 214, 223
MiniLab, pp. 218, 228
Activity, 8-1, p. 224; 8-2, pp. 232–233

Content Assessment
Section Assessment, pp. 214, 223, 230
Chapter Assessment, pp. 236–237
Proficiency Prep, pp. 214, 222, 229

Explore Activity

Purpose

Kinesthetic Use the Explore Activity to introduce students to forces that cause rocks to deform. Inform students that they will be learning how these forces can cause earthquakes. L2 ELL COOP LEARN

Materials

3 different colors of modeling clay (Use 10-cm × 5-cm × 1-cm slabs of clay for each group of four students.)

Teaching Strategies

- You may wish to have students work with the clay on waxed paper.
- Advise students to gradually apply compression and tension to the slabs of clay.

Students will notice that clay folds when compressed. Tension will cause the clay to stretch, thin, and eventually break.

Assessment

Content Ask students to relate what they have observed to structures they may be familiar with on Earth's surface. Use **Performance Assessment in the Science Classroom,** p. 71.

8•1 Forces Inside Earth

What You'll Learn

- To explain how earthquakes result from the buildup of stress in Earth's crust
- The differences between normal, reverse, and strike-slip faults

Vocabulary

fault
earthquake
normal fault
reverse fault
strike-slip fault

Why It's Important

- Studying the causes of earthquakes will help you tell where they can occur.

Causes of Earthquakes

Think about the last time you used a rubber band to hold a roll of papers together. You knew you could stretch the rubber band only so far before it would break. Rubber bands bend and stretch when you use force on them. Because they are elastic, they return to their original shape once the force is released. Plastic or play putty, as shown in **Figure 8-1,** acts in much the same way. With a certain amount of applied force, plastic will undergo elastic shape changes. But, then it returns to normal when the stress is removed. With additional stress, the plastic will undergo plastic deformation. This means that once it bends, it remains in the changed shape. Plastic deformation in putty is demonstrated by the student on the left in **Figure 8-1.**

Passing the Elastic Limit Causes Faulting

There is a limit to how far a rubber band will stretch or plastic will change shape. Once this elastic limit is passed, the rubber band or plastic remains deformed or breaks. Rocks act in much the same way. Up to a point, applied forces cause rocks to bend and stretch, undergoing elastic or plastic deformation. Once their elastic limit is passed, the rocks remain bent and may break. This is demonstrated in putty by the student on the right in **Figure 8-1.** Rocks break and move along surfaces called **faults.** Once a break happens, the rocks on either side of a fault move.

Figure 8-1
Play putty can be used to show how forces are used to change forms or shapes.

SECTION 8•1

Prepare

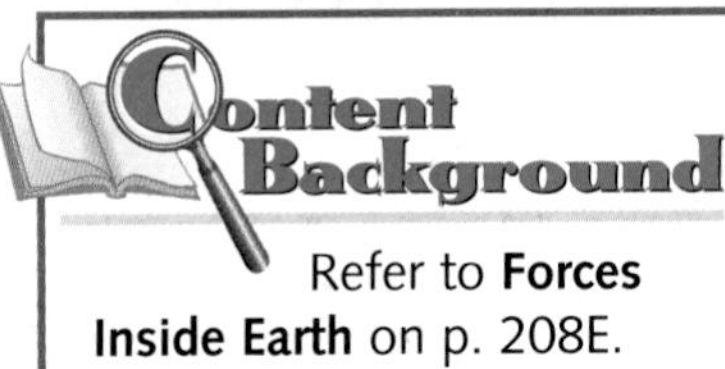
Content Background

Refer to **Forces Inside Earth** on p. 208E.

Preplanning

Refer to the **Chapter Organizer** on pp. 208A–B.

1 Motivate

Bellringer

Before presenting the lesson, display **Section Focus Transparency 19** on the overhead projector. Use the accompanying **Focus Activity** worksheet. L2 ELL

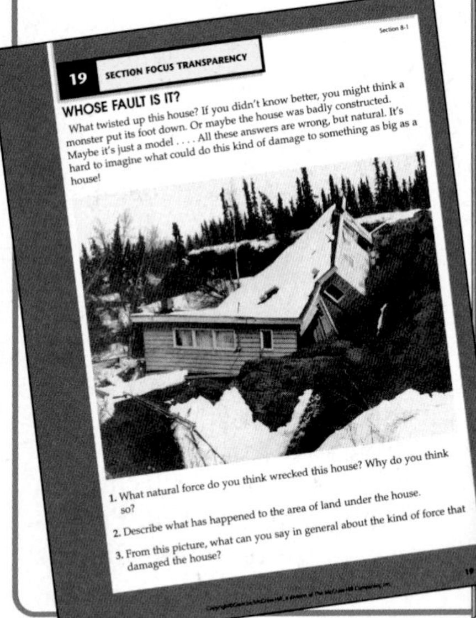
Section 8-1

19 SECTION FOCUS TRANSPARENCY

WHOSE FAULT IS IT?

What twisted up this house? If you didn't know better, you might think a monster put its foot down. Or maybe the house was badly constructed. Maybe it's just a model . . . . All these answers are wrong, but natural. It's hard to imagine what could do this kind of damage to something as big as a house!

1. What natural force do you think wrecked this house? Why do you think so?
2. Describe what has happened to the area of land under the house.
3. From this picture, what can you say in general about the kind of force that damaged the house?

19

Tying to Previous Knowledge

Help students recall recent earthquakes and discuss where they were located.

Resource Manager

The following **Teacher Classroom Resources** can be used with Section 8-1:

Reproducible Masters

Enrichment, p. 19 L3

Reinforcement, p. 19 L2

Study Guide, pp. 29–30 L1 ELL

Transparencies

Teaching Transparency 15 L2

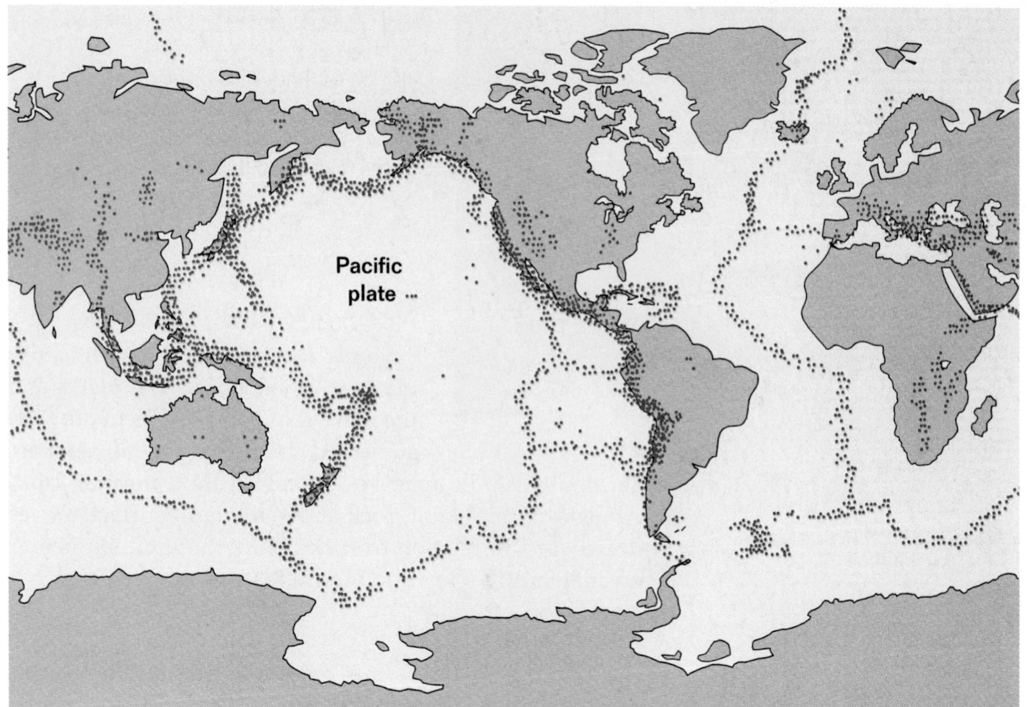

Figure 8-2 The dots represent the locations of major quakes over a ten-year period. Eighty percent of earthquakes occur along the edges of a section of Earth known as the Pacific plate.

What causes faults to form? Something must be forcing rocks to move. Otherwise, the rocks would just rest quietly. Earth's crust is in constant motion because of forces inside Earth. These forces cause sections of Earth's crust, called plates, to move, putting stress on rocks. To relieve this stress, rocks tend to bend, squeeze together, and stretch like putty, rubber bands, or the clay in the Explore Activity. But, if the force is great enough, rocks break. This breaking produces vibrations called **earthquakes. Figure 8-2** shows how the locations of earthquakes outline the sections of Earth's crust.

Types of Faults

Rocks go through several types of forces where sections or plates of Earth's crust and upper mantle meet. When you played with the layers of clay in the Explore Activity, you experimented with three forces—compression, tension, and shear. Compression is a force or stress that squeezes and compresses, while tension is the force that causes rocks to stretch and become longer. Shear is the force that causes rocks on either side of a fault to move past each other. Let's take a look at these three forces and the types of faults they create.

Content Background

Earthquake epicenters around the world mostly occur along Earth's plate boundaries. Vibrations in Earth occur because of the sudden movement of rock that has been storing potential energy in response to applied stress. When the energy is released, an earthquake occurs.

2 Teach

Discussion

Interpersonal Obtain photographs or articles featuring recent earthquakes, such as the 1995 earthquake in Kobe, Japan; the 1994 earthquake in Northridge, California; the 1993 Marharashtra, India, earthquake; or the 1985 Mexico City, Mexico, earthquake. *Time, Newsweek,* or *National Geographic* are excellent sources. Lead a discussion as to why earthquakes are able to cause such destruction.

Forces inside Earth—compression, tension, and shear—cause various structures to form in rocks. Normal faults are caused by tension; folds and reverse faults usually form due to compression; and shear forces produce strike-slip faults.

 **Videodisc**

STV: Restless Earth

Unit 3 *Spreading and Subduction* 7:21

37503-51201

Refer to the Teacher Guide for additional bar codes and teaching strategies.

Caption Answer

Figure 8-3 *tension, compression*

VISUAL Learning

Figure 8-3 Have students look at the block diagrams in the three parts of this figure and describe how movement along each of the three types of faults might affect the continuity of rock layers at Earth's surface.

Activity

Kinesthetic Different materials have different elastic and plastic limits. Have students bend these materials to see what happens as force is applied to each: a piece of cardboard; a plastic drinking straw; a wooden tongue depressor; a thin, steel wire; silicon putty; a thin sheet of slate or shale. Have students wear goggles during this activity. L2 ELL

Quick Demo

Visual-Spatial Prepare a large, triple-decker, peanut butter and jelly sandwich. Cut off the crusts so the individual layers can be seen. Construct a fault at about a 30° angle by cutting through the sandwich. Move the separate halves of the sandwich to demonstrate normal, reverse, and strike-slip faults.

GLENCOE TECHNOLOGY

Videodisc

The Infinite Voyage: Living with Disaster

Chapter 5 *Earthquakes: A Turbulence Beneath the Earth* 2:30

Refer to the Teacher Guide for bar codes and teaching strategies.

Tension forces

A When rock moves along a fracture caused by tension forces, the break is called a normal fault. Rock above the fault moves downward in relation to the rock below the fault surface. Normal faults can form mountains such as the Sierra Nevada, which border California on the east.

Figure 8-3 Rock layers are affected differently by tension, compression, and shear forces. **With which type of force would Earth's crust be stretched and thinned? With which type would Earth's crust be folded and thickened?**

Normal Faults

Some forces inside Earth cause plates to move apart. The plates and the rocks that compose them are then subjected to the force of tension. Tension can pull apart rocks and create a **normal fault.** Along a normal fault, rock above the fault surface moves downward in relation to rock below the fault surface. A normal fault is shown in **Figure 8-3A.**

Reverse Faults

Compression forces are present where Earth's plates move together. Compression pushes on rocks from opposite directions and causes them to bend and sometimes break. Once they break, the rocks continue to move along the fault surface. At a **reverse fault,** the rocks above the fault surface are forced up and over the rocks below the fault surface, as shown in **Figure 8-3B.**

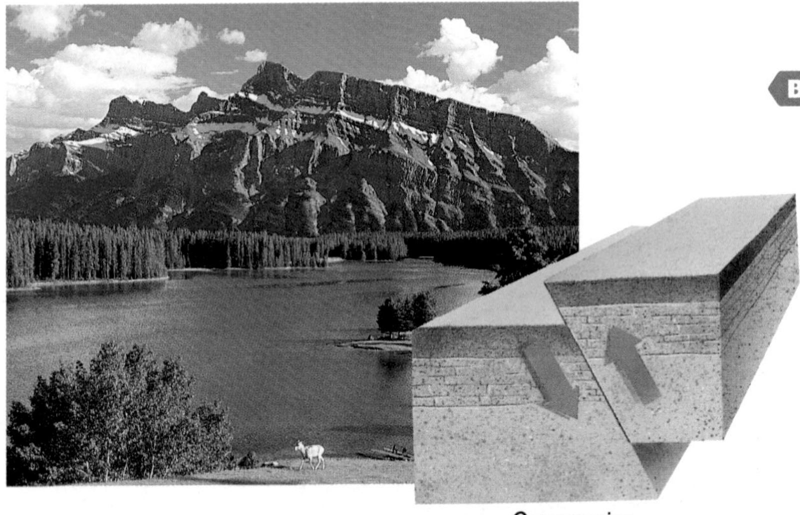

Compression forces

B When compression forces break rock, the rock above the fault surface moves upward in relation to the rock below the fault surface. The mountains shown, in Banff National Park in the Canadian Rocky Mountains, contain many reverse faults.

Integrating the Sciences

Physics Ask students the following questions about forces inside Earth. **What happens to rocks when compression is gradually applied?** *Gradual pushing from opposite directions tends to make rocks bend or fold.* **What will happen if compression is applied very quickly to rocks?** *Rocks will bend until their elastic limits are reached. Once this occurs, the rocks will remain bent and may break.*

Across the Curriculum

Mathematics The Sierra Nevada formed over a period of 10 million years. Mount Whitney is one of the many peaks in this range that stand 4000 m above sea level. Have students compute an average annual rate of uplift. *0.0004 m/yr* L2 ELL

C Shear forces push on rock in opposite, but not directly opposite, horizontal directions. When they are strong enough, these forces split rock and create strike-slip faults. There is relatively little vertical movement along a strike-slip fault. When movement is sudden along faults like the San Andreas Fault shown here, earthquakes occur.

Shear forces

Strike-Slip Faults

You have probably heard about the San Andreas Fault in California. At this fault, shown in **Figure 8-3C,** two of Earth's plates are moving sideways past each other because of shear forces. This type of fault is called a strike-slip fault. At a **strike-slip fault,** rocks on either side of the fault surface are moving past each other without much upward or downward movement. Compare the faults in **Figure 8-3.** How do they differ? ☑

As the rocks move past each other at a strike-slip fault, their ragged surfaces catch each other, and the rocks are twisted and strained. Not only do they change shape, but the catching of their surfaces prevents movement along the faults. As forces keep driving the plates to move, energy builds up and the rocks reach their elastic limit. When the rocks are stressed past their elastic limit, they may break and an earthquake may result.

Some earthquakes can be dramatic—even devastating—events, while others go almost unnoticed. Regardless of their sizes, most earthquakes result from plates moving over, under, and past each other. If these plates simply slid smoothly by each other, tension, compression, and shear forces would not build up energy. But, rocks do experience these stresses and energy builds up in them, causing small

Fault Forces
Explain what types of faults are produced by compression and by tension. How does the type of stress determine the nature of the fault in each case?

Compression causes reverse faults, whereas tension causes normal faults. Compression pushes one block of rock over another. Tension pulls on the rock allowing the block of rock above the fault to move downward.

Answer to Reading Check ☑

a fault in which rocks on either side of the fault surface move past each other without much upward or downward movement

NATIONAL GEOGRAPHIC

STV: Restless Earth
Unit 4 *Translation in California*
5:52

00001-10743
Refer to the Teacher Guide for additional bar codes and teaching strategies.

3 Assess

Check for Understanding

Discussion

Interpersonal Lead students in a discussion of the different causes of earthquakes.

Landers Quake After researching the 1992 Landers, California, earthquake, have students write a summary explaining why this earthquake is so important to the study of faults and earthquakes. *This quake may have triggered other earthquakes and may indicate that a new fault is being formed in the desert.* L2

Reteach

Have students use their hands or textbooks to demonstrate the movement that occurs along each of the three kinds of faults.

Extension

For students who have mastered this section, use the **Reinforcement** and **Enrichment** masters.

4 Close

Proficiency Prep

Use this quiz to check student's recall of section content.

1. **Which type of force causes a normal fault?** *tension*
2. **What is an example of a strike-slip fault?** *San Andreas Fault*

Section Assessment

1. shearing
2. reverse; when plates come together, compression forms reverse faults.
3. Energy is released, causing rocks to break and move along faults.
4. Think Critically Most earthquakes occur near plate boundaries. If earthquakes have occurred in an area in the past, they will probably occur again, but the exact timing of the quake cannot be predicted.

Using Computers

Student models should show appropriate motion of Earth for each of the fault types (normal, reverse, and strike-slip). Student models also should show how the forces that cause each fault differ.

Figure 8-4
Geologists use surface evidence like these cracks in Costa Rica when searching for dangerous hidden fractures or faults.

changes in shape. When rocks break, as shown in **Figure 8-4**, energy is released along fault surfaces, and we observe the effects in the form of earthquakes.

Section Assessment

1. What type of force usually generates strike-slip faults?
2. The Appalachian Mountains formed when two of Earth's plates collided. What type of faults would you expect to find in these mountains? Why?
3. What happens to rocks when an earthquake occurs?
4. **Think Critically:** Why might it be easier to predict *where* an earthquake will occur than it is to predict *when* it will occur?
5. **Skill Builder**
   Concept Mapping Make a cycle concept map that shows why many earthquakes occur along the San Andreas Fault. Use the following terms and phrases: *rocks, stress, bend and stretch, elastic limit reached,* and *earthquakes.* If you need help, refer to Concept Mapping in the **Skill Handbook** on page 714.

Using Computers

Graphics Use the graphics capabilities of a computer to make simple working models of the three types of faults: normal, reverse, and strike-slip. Have your computer model show how the forces that cause each fault differ. If you need help, refer to page 734.

5. **Skill Builder**
One possible solution is to draw a cycle concept map with the following captions:

Stress causes bending and stretching of rocks.

The elastic limit is reached.

Earthquake results. P

Assessment

Performance Use this Skill Builder to assess students' abilities to make a cycle concept map. Have students construct cycle concept maps to illustrate normal and reverse faults. Use **Performance Assessment in the Science Classroom,** p. 89. P 

Earthquake Information

Types of Seismic Waves

Have you ever seen a coiled-spring toy? When children play with a coiled-spring toy, they send energy waves through it. **Seismic** (SIZE mihk) **waves** made by an earthquake are like the waves of the toy. Where are seismic waves formed? How do they move through Earth, and how can we use the information that they carry? Let's investigate how scientists have answered these questions.

Earthquake Focus

As you have learned, when rocks move along a fault surface, energy is released and damage occurs, as seen in **Figure 8-5.** The point in Earth's interior where this energy release occurs is the **focus** of the earthquake. Seismic waves are produced at and travel outward from the earthquake focus.

What You'll Learn

- To compare and contrast primary, secondary, and surface waves
- How an earthquake epicenter is located
- The structure of Earth's interior

Vocabulary

seismic wave
focus
primary wave
secondary wave
epicenter
surface wave
inner core
outer core
mantle
crust

Why It's Important

- Seismic waves help scientists locate earthquakes and give information about Earth's interior.

Figure 8-5 This photograph shows buildings damaged during the 1989 Loma Prieta, California, earthquake. This earthquake was caused by the Pacific plate slipping past the North American plate by only 2 m.

Resource Manager

The following **Teacher Classroom Resources** can be used with Section 8-2:

 **Reproducible Masters**

Activity Worksheets, pp. 43–44, 47 L2

Enrichment, p. 20 L3

Home Involvement, pp. 26–27 L2

Laboratory Manual, pp. 49–52, 53–56 L2

Reinforcement, p. 20 L2

Study Guide, p. 31

 **Transparencies**

Science Integration Transparency 8 L2

Teaching Transparency 16 L2

SECTION 8-2

Prepare

Content Background

Refer to **Earthquake Information** on p. 208E.

Preplanning

Refer to the **Chapter Organizer** on pp. 208A–B.

1 Motivate

Bellringer

Before presenting the lesson, display **Section Focus Transparency 20** on the overhead projector. Use the accompanying **Focus Activity** worksheet. L2 ELL

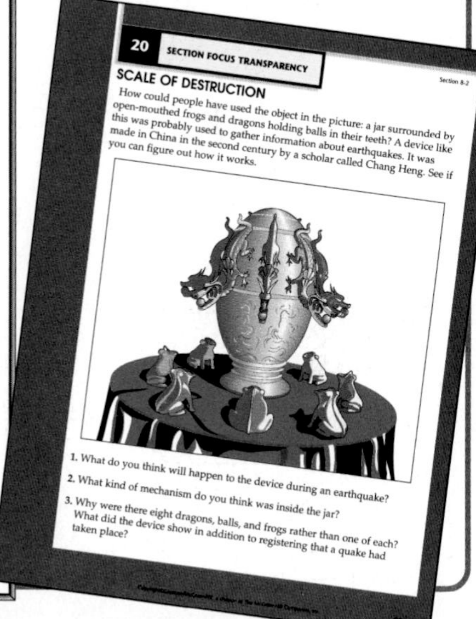

20 SECTION FOCUS TRANSPARENCY

Section 8-2

SCALE OF DESTRUCTION

How could people have used the object in the picture: a jar surrounded by open-mouthed frogs and dragons holding balls in their teeth? A device like this was probably used to gather information about earthquakes. It was made in China in the second century by a scholar called Chang Heng. See if you can figure out how it works.

1. What do you think will happen to the device during an earthquake?
2. What kind of mechanism do you think was inside the jar?
3. Why were there eight dragons, balls, and frogs rather than one of each? What did the device show in addition to registering that a quake had taken place?

Tying to Previous Knowledge

Linguistic Have students recall the use of the words *primary* and *secondary* in other subjects. Ask them to hypothesize as to which type of seismic wave—primary or secondary—travels through Earth faster.

2 Teach

VISUAL Learning

Figure 8-6 Have students describe the relative positions of the focus and epicenter. Have them identify the types of waves that travel through solid material.

Using Science Words

Intrapersonal For a week, have students look through newspapers or the Internet for news about earthquakes. They should identify and list chapter vocabulary they find in the articles. Have them bring their articles to class and discuss the meanings of the words they find. L2

Teacher FYI

Primary waves travel about 6.0 km/s through granite crust. Secondary waves travel about 3.5 km/s through the same material, whereas surface waves travel about 2.0 km/s.

interNET CONNECTION

Internet Addresses

____

____

____

____

For Internet tips, see Glencoe's **Using the Internet in the Science Classroom.**

interNET CONNECTION

Visit the Glencoe Science Web Site at **www.glencoe.com/sec/science** for more information about seismic waves.

Seismic Waves

Waves that cause particles in rocks to move back and forth in the same direction the wave is moving are called **primary waves.** If you squeeze together several coils on one end of a coiled-spring toy and then release them, they compress and then stretch as the wave travels through the toy. Particles in rocks also squeeze together and stretch apart as primary waves move through them.

Now, if you and a friend stretch the coiled-spring toy between you and then move one end up and down, a different type of wave will pass through the toy. The spring will move up and down as the wave moves along it. **Secondary waves** move through Earth by causing particles in rocks to vibrate at right angles to the direction of the wave.

VISUALIZING Seismic Waves

Figure 8-6 Primary and secondary waves travel outward from the focus. Surface waves move outward from the epicenter.

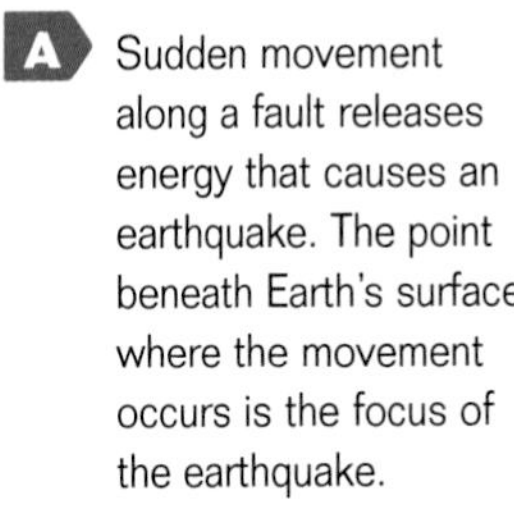

A Sudden movement along a fault releases energy that causes an earthquake. The point beneath Earth's surface where the movement occurs is the focus of the earthquake.

B Primary waves and secondary waves originate at the focus and travel outward in all directions. Primary waves travel faster than secondary waves.

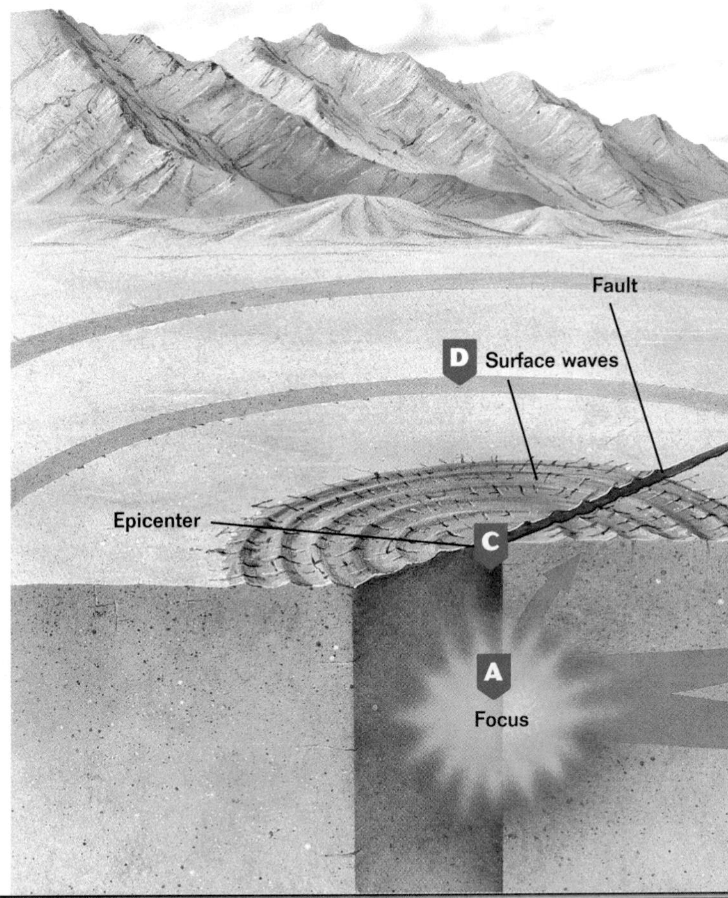

Content Background

Movement of rocks inside Earth releases strain energy that has built up. This energy is derived from strain that has accumulated in rocks undergoing stress. Tension, compression, and shear stress commonly generate strain in rocks. The released energy is transmitted through Earth by seismic body waves. Generation of primary and secondary waves at the earthquake focus enables seismologists to learn about rocks inside Earth based on how the different seismic waves are affected by Earth's interior.

The point on Earth's surface directly above an earthquake's focus is the **epicenter** (EP ih sent ur), as shown in **Figure 8-6.** Energy that reaches the surface of Earth makes waves that travel outward from the epicenter. These waves, called **surface waves,** move particles up and down and side to side in a swaying motion.

Surface waves cause most of the destruction during an earthquake. Because most buildings are stiff and hard, they begin to fall apart when surface waves pass. The waves cause different parts of a building to move in different directions. This is because part of the surface wave motion is up and down, and part of the motion is side to side. ☑

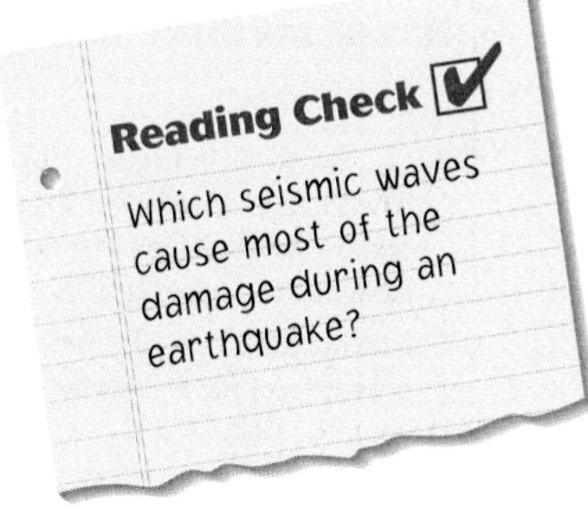

Reading Check
Which seismic waves cause most of the damage during an earthquake?

Locating an Epicenter

Primary, secondary, and surface waves don't travel through Earth at the same speed. Primary waves are the fastest. Surface waves are the slowest. Can you think of a way this information could be used to determine how far away an earthquake epicenter is? Think of the last time you and two friends rode your bikes to the store. You were fastest, so you arrived first. In fact, the longer you rode, the farther ahead of your friends you became. Scientists use the different speeds of seismic waves to find the distance to an earthquake epicenter.

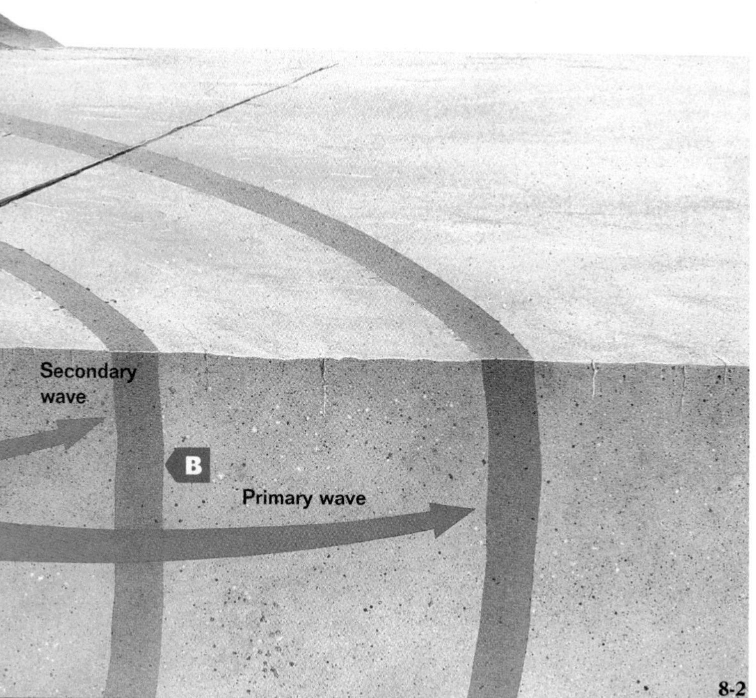

C The place on Earth's surface directly above the earthquake focus is called the epicenter. Surface waves radiate, or spread, outward from the epicenter in much the same way that ripples travel outward from a stone thrown into a pond.

D The amplitude, or height, of surface waves is greater than the amplitudes of primary and secondary waves. Surface waves cause the most damage during an earthquake.

Correcting Misconceptions

Many students think that all earthquakes begin at Earth's surface. Explain that earthquakes originate at the point where rocks break. This can occur near Earth's surface or deep inside Earth's crust or upper mantle.

Teacher FYI

Primary waves generated at the focus of an earthquake travel outward through Earth's interior. Sometimes these waves enter Earth's atmosphere and cause the loud noises associated with earthquakes.

GLENCOE TECHNOLOGY

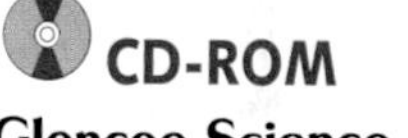

CD-ROM

Glencoe Science Voyages Interactive CD-ROM

Explorations

Have students do the interactive exploration *How do seismograph stations help determine an earthquake's epicenter?*

Inclusion Strategies

Hearing Impaired Obtain a coiled-spring toy and demonstrate each of the three types of seismic waves that have been discussed in class. Demonstrate primary waves by pushing the spring forward and then pulling it back. Demonstrate secondary waves by moving the spring from side to side. Surface waves can be demonstrated by causing the spring to move in an elliptical path while also moving the spring from side to side. Ask students to state which type of wave they think would cause more damage. L2 ELL

Try at Home MiniLab

For additional help doing this activity at home, see the corresponding pages in the **Home Involvement** booklet.

Purpose

Logical-Mathematical Students will realize that varying differences in arrival times of seismic waves can be used to determine distance to an epicenter. L2 P

Materials

graph paper labeled as shown in **Figure 8-7,** pencil, ruler

Teaching Strategies

- Use **Figure 8-7** to show students that epicenter distance can be determined if the arrival times of primary and secondary waves are plotted on a distance-time graph.
- Use a ruler held lengthwise parallel to the *y*-axis of **Figure 8-7** to help read differences in arrival times.

Analysis

1. The difference in times increases with distance to the earthquake epicenter.
2. Student distances will vary but should fit with interpretations in question 1.

Distance (km)	Difference in Arrival Time
1500	2 minutes, 50 s
2250	3 minutes, 40 s
2750	4 minutes, 20 s
3000	4 minutes, 45 s
4000	5 minutes, 45 s
7000	8 minutes, 15 s
9000	9 minutes, 40 s

Try at Home MiniLab

Making and Using Tables and Graphs

Procedure

1. Use the graph in **Figure 8-7** to determine the difference in arrival times for primary and secondary waves at the distances listed in the data table below. Two examples are provided for you.
2. Use the graph to determine the differences in arrival times for at least two other distances of your choice.

Analysis

1. Interpret what happens to the difference in arrival times as the distance from the earthquake increases.
2. Explain how the distances you chose fit with what you interpreted in question 1.

Arrival Times

Distance (km)	Difference in Arrival Time
1500	2 minutes; 50 s
2250	
2750	
3000	
4000	5 minutes; 45 s
7000	
9000	

Seismograph Stations

Based on their different speeds, primary waves arrive first at recording stations, secondary waves second, as shown in **Figure 8-7,** and surface waves last. This allows scientists to determine the distance to an earthquake epicenter. The farther apart the wave arrivals, the farther away the epicenter is. When epicenters are far from the seismograph station, the primary wave has more time to put distance between it and the secondary and surface waves.

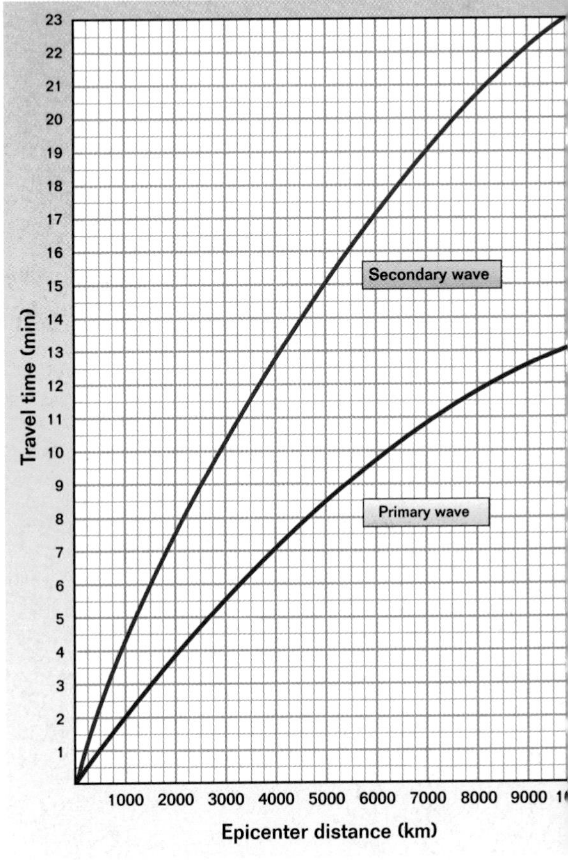

Figure 8-7 This graph shows the distance that primary and secondary waves travel over time. By measuring the difference in arrival times, a seismologist can determine the distance to the epicenter.

Assessment

Performance Have students determine distances to earthquakes whose primary and secondary wave arrival times are separated by 5 minutes and 7 minutes. Use **Performance Assessment in the Science Classroom,** p. 29.

Across the Curriculum

Language Arts Have students research the origin of the word *seismic*. Ask students to explain why primary, secondary, and surface waves are so named. *Primary waves travel fastest and arrive at seismograph stations first. Secondary waves arrive second. Surface waves are the slowest and move along Earth's surface.* L2

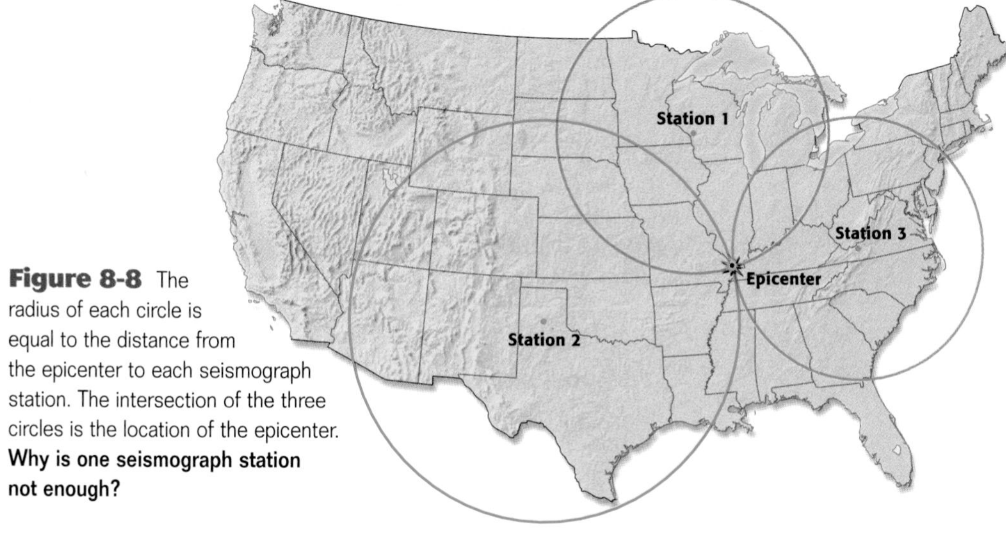

Figure 8-8 The radius of each circle is equal to the distance from the epicenter to each seismograph station. The intersection of the three circles is the location of the epicenter. **Why is one seismograph station not enough?**

Epicenter Location

If seismic wave information is recorded from at least three seismograph stations, the location of the epicenter can be determined, as shown in **Figure 8-8.** To locate an epicenter, scientists draw circles around each station on a map. The radius of each circle equals that station's distance from the earthquake epicenter. The point where all three circles meet is the location of the earthquake epicenter.

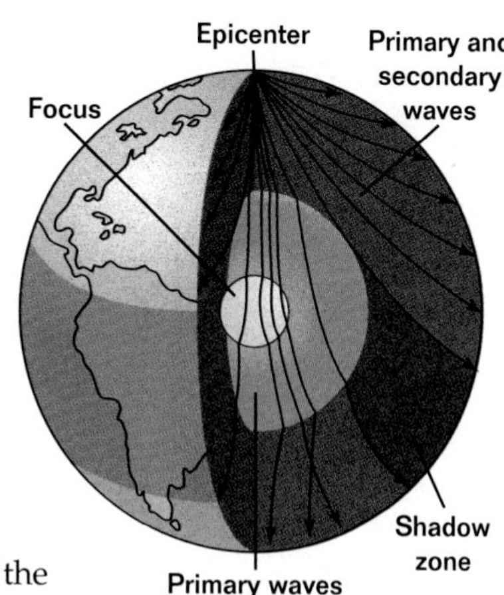

Figure 8-9 Primary waves bend when they contact the outer core (orange-red), and secondary waves are stopped completely. Primary waves also bend and speed up when they enter the inner core (yellow). In fact, as shown, seismic waves gradually bend and change speed as the density of rock changes.

Mapping Earth's Interior

Scientists have found that at certain depths within Earth, the speed and path of seismic waves change. These changes mark the boundaries of the layers in Earth with different densities. Recall that the density of a material is mass per unit volume. In general, material in Earth's layers becomes denser toward the core as pressures increase. Using information from seismic waves, scientists have learned about Earth's interior without ever having been there, as shown in **Figure 8-9.**

Structure of Earth

Seismic wave studies allow scientists to make a model of Earth's interior, as shown in **Figure 8-10.** At the very center of Earth is a solid, dense **inner core** made mostly of iron with some nickel and smaller amounts of oxygen, silicon, and sulfur. Above the solid inner core lies the liquid **outer core,** also made mainly of iron. Earth's **mantle** is the largest layer, lying directly above the outer core. It is made mostly of silicon, oxygen, magnesium, and iron. Earth's thinnest, outermost layer is the **crust.**

Caption Answer

Figure 8-8 *One station will tell the distance to the epicenter, and two will indicate two possible locations for the epicenter. An epicenter is located at the intersection of circles (radius equals distance to epicenter) from at least three seismographs.*

Quick Demo

Linguistic Place a large, flat pan of water in front of the class. Drop a small rock into the water. Have students observe the waves that are generated. Ask students to explain how the wave movement in the water is similar to the movement of certain types of earthquake waves at Earth's surface. L2

Teacher FYI

Earth's inner core may be growing very slowly as molten metal in Earth's outer core crystallizes in response to planetary cooling.

GLENCOE TECHNOLOGY

Videodisc

Glencoe Science Voyages Interactive Videodisc—Physical

Side 2, Lesson 7

Waves and Sound

21431

Refer to Videodisc Teacher Guide for additional bar codes.

Epicenter Connection Have students write short paragraphs in their Science Journals that explain the connection between earthquake epicenters and earthquake foci. They also might explain where the various types of seismic waves originate. L3

VISUAL Learning

Figure 8-10 Have students use information on these pages to make a model showing Earth's structure. They may wish to use modeling clay or other materials. Encourage students to be as creative as possible. Ask them to explain how scientists have obtained the data necessary to make their models.

 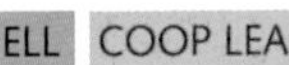

L2 ELL COOP LEARN

Enrichment

Interpersonal Have a small group of students research how Mohorovičić discovered the Moho discontinuity and present their findings to the rest of the class. *Mohorovičić noticed that seismographs at a certain distance from the epicenters of shallow earthquakes recorded two sets of P- and S-waves. He concluded that the first set represented waves that were bent so as to travel through denser, upper mantle and then reemerge at the surface to be recorded by a seismograph (P- and S-waves travel faster in denser, solid rock). The second set traveled directly from the earthquake's focus to the seismograph station through the less-dense crust (slower seismic waves). Mohorovičić reasoned that a boundary separated the less-dense crust from the denser rocks beneath. This boundary was named the Moho discontinuity in his honor.*

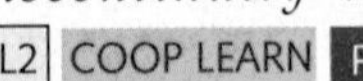

L2 COOP LEARN P

Compared to the mantle, the crust contains more silicon and aluminum and less magnesium and iron. The crust is separated from the mantle by the Moho discontinuity.

Moho Discontinuity

Seismic waves speed up when they reach the bottom of the crust. This boundary between the crust and the mantle is called the *Moho discontinuity* (dis kahnt un EW ut ee). The boundary was discovered by the Yugoslavian scientist Andrija Mohorovičić, who inferred that seismic waves speed up because they're passing into a denser layer of Earth.

This denser layer is called the upper mantle, as shown in **Figure 8-10.** It is made up of minerals that are denser, on average, than minerals found in the crust.

VISUALIZING Layers of Earth

Figure 8-10 This wedge shows the layers inside Earth from the inner core. The inner core, outer core, and mantle are shown at the correct scale, but the crust is shown much thicker than it actually is.

A The crust of Earth varies in thickness. It is greater than 60 km in some mountainous regions, and less than 5 km thick under some oceans.

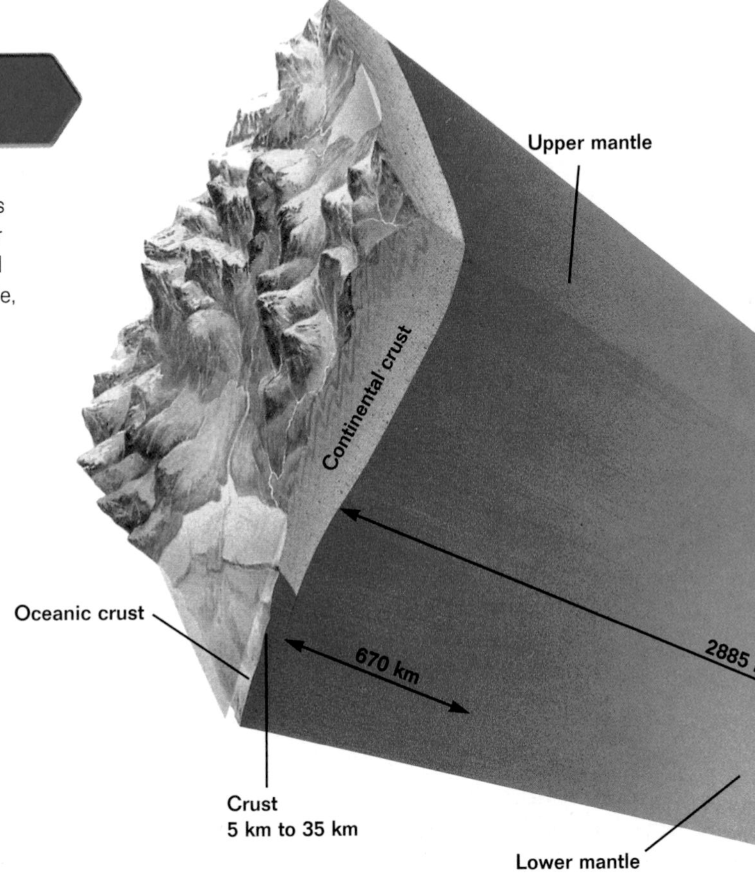

B There is a layer in the upper mantle where rock material is described as plasticlike. It is like a solid but also flows like a liquid when under pressure. Some parts of this layer are thought to be molten.

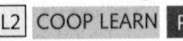

Across the Curriculum

Geography Review with students that earthquake P-waves are refracted, or bent, when they reach the core-mantle boundary. This causes a region on Earth's surface, between 105° and 140° from the focus, where no P-wave would reach a seismograph station. Have students draw a cross section of Earth that shows the location of an earthquake focus and epicenter. Students are to show on their cross sections where the P-wave shadow zone for the mapped earthquake would be. Students should identify specific locations on Earth that would be located within the earthquake's shadow zone. L2

Plasticlike Layer

Primary and secondary waves slow down when they hit a plasticlike layer that is part of the upper mantle. Then, seismic waves speed up again as they pass through the solid lower mantle. The denser the layer, the faster the seismic waves can travel through that layer.

Shadow Zone

An area exists on Earth where no seismic waves are detected after they are released by an earthquake. This area is called the *shadow zone.* Secondary waves don't pass through liquid, so they're stopped completely when they hit the liquid outer core. Primary waves are slowed and bent but not stopped by the liquid outer core. The bending of the primary waves and the stopping of the secondary waves create the shadow zone, as shown in **Figure 8-9.** These primary waves speed up again as they travel through the solid inner core.

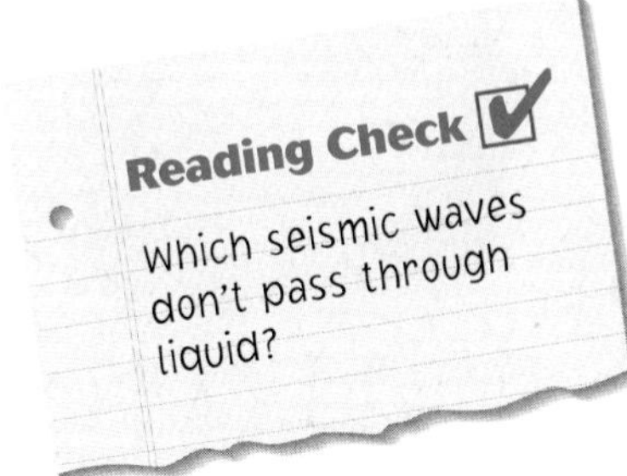

Reading Check
Which seismic waves don't pass through liquid?

Mantle Samples

You can see that scientists learn a lot about Earth's interior by studying the behavior of seismic waves. But, did you ever wonder if anyone has ever held a piece of Earth's mantle or core in his or her hands? Some volcanic materials are a window to Earth's interior, containing minerals that scientists suggest are pieces of the upper mantle. Magma can break off and bring up pieces of the mantle as it forces its way to the surface as lava.

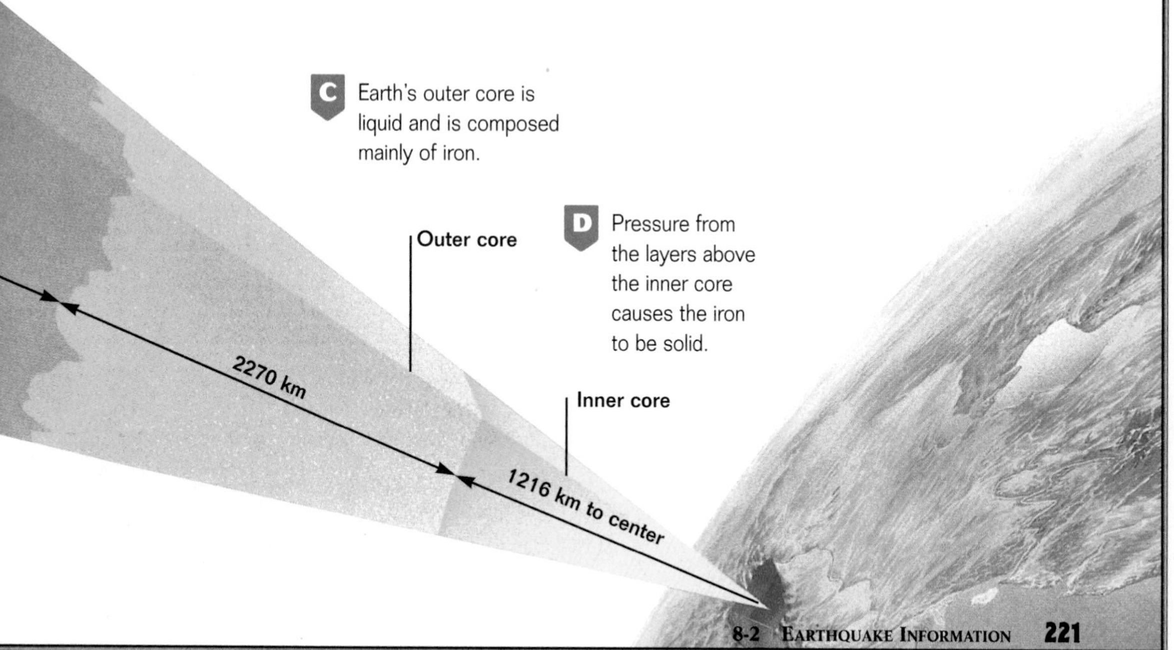

D Pressure from the layers above the inner core causes the iron to be solid.

1216 km to center

Using an Analogy

The internal structure of a peach can be used as an analogy of Earth's internal structure. The skin of the peach is like Earth's crust, the main part of the peach is like Earth's mantle, the pit of the peach is like Earth's outer core, and the seed of the peach inside the pit is like Earth's inner core. The roughness of the pit can be compared to the uneven boundary that separates Earth's mantle from its outer core.

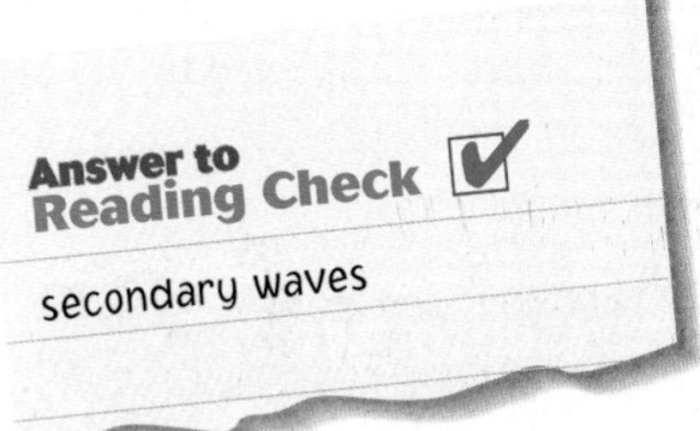

3 Assess

Check for Understanding Activity

Visual-Spatial Have students create a large table on the bulletin board or chalkboard summarizing the properties of Earth's layers. Include composition, thickness, and seismic wave behavior for each layer.

Reteach

Use a map, a ruler, a drawing compass, and the data for earthquake "A" from the teacher copy for Activity 8-1 to demonstrate how an epicenter is located.

Extension

For students who have mastered this section, use the **Reinforcement** and **Enrichment** masters.

Multiple Learning Styles

Visual-Spatial Help students visualize Earth's structure by building a model of the interior layers of Earth from modeling clay or modeling dough. First, make a ball of clay with a radius of 24 mm (the inner core). Cut this ball of clay in half and mold a different-colored clay around it. The second layer of clay (the outer core) should be 45 mm thick. Around this second layer, mold a 58-mm- thick layer (the mantle) of a different-colored clay. Mold a thin layer (the crust) of different-colored clay around this third layer. L2 ELL COOP LEARN

Problem Solving

This type of problem-solving task is what seismologists do when they try to hypothesize about Earth's interior without being able to observe it.

Think Critically

Answers will vary based on the contents of each box. Students should note that this problem-solving exercise is similar to the way seismologists have learned about Earth's interior. They have based their theories about Earth's structure on how seismic waves are affected by Earth's interior.

Using Math

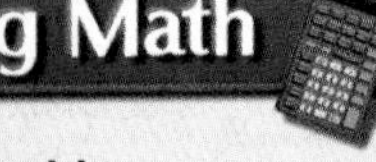

Practice Problem

$t = d/v$

$t = 600\ \text{km}/3.6\ \text{km/s}$

$t = 167\ \text{s}$ (2 min, 47 s)

4 Close

Proficiency Prep

Use this quiz to check students' recall of section content.

1. **What is the point on Earth's surface directly above an earthquake focus?** *epicenter*
2. **What are the first seismic waves to arrive at a seismograph station?** *primary*

Figure 8-11 Meteorites are made of minerals that are like those in different layers of Earth.

Meteorites

Samples of the deep mantle and core have never been collected. However, the rocky materials that make up our solar system, which includes Earth and meteorites, are thought to have formed at about the same time. Therefore, we can compare the composition of meteorites with that of Earth. Some meteorites have certain minerals that we know from rock formations and volcanic materials to be mantle minerals. Some meteorites are heavy and rich in iron, which studies show are the same materials in Earth's core. Scientists hypothesize that meteorites, such as the examples shown in **Figure 8-11,** contain samples that are like different parts of Earth's interior.

Problem Solving

Interpreting Data

Your teacher has placed five closed and sealed boxes in front of the class. The sizes of the five boxes are the same and equal to a sixth box that is empty. Your teacher has challenged you to complete problem-solving exercises in order to earn points. To earn all the points available, you must list at least three facts about the contents of each box. You are permitted to do anything you wish except open the boxes and look directly at the enclosed objects. The other rule is that you cannot damage any of the boxes in any way.

Determine what tests you will perform on each box that will reveal facts about its contents. You may wish to work with another student in case any of your tests require more than one person. In your Science Journal, make a table similar to the one above. Record all observations about the unknown box contents. List any inferences you have made concerning the contents of each box.

Box Interpretations

Box Number	Observations			Inferences
	Fact 1	Fact 2	Fact 3	
1				
2				
3				
4				
5				

Think Critically: Compare the facts you discovered with those listed by your teacher. How is the challenge presented by your teacher related to a study of seismic waves and mapping of Earth's interior?

Earthquake Epicenters Have students write a short story about what it would be like if they were living at the site of an earthquake epicenter. Encourage them to relate what might happen to buildings and bridges and whether they would see or feel seismic waves. L2 P

Using Math

Calculating Time

Example Problem: Primary waves travel at about 6 km/s through continental crust. The distance from Phoenix, Arizona, to Los Angeles, California, is about 600 km. How long would it take primary waves to travel between the two cities?

Problem-Solving Steps

1. What is known?
   distance, $d = 600$ km; average speed, $v = 6$ km/s
2. What is unknown? time, t
3. Use the equation, $t = d/v$
4. **Solution:** $t = d/v$
   $t = 600 \text{ km}/6 \text{ km/s} = 100$ s (1 minute, 40 s)

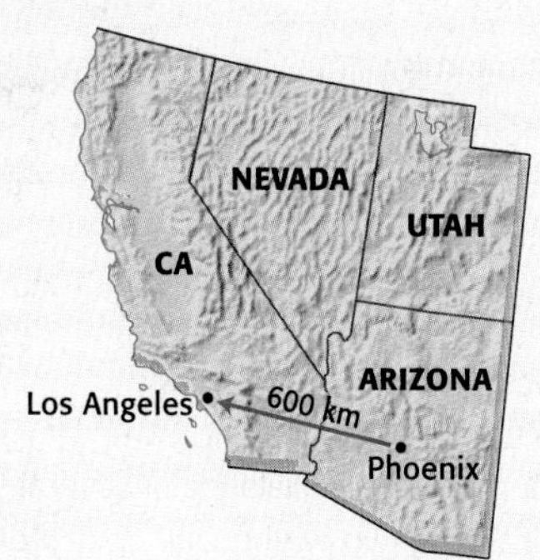

Practice Problem

Secondary waves travel at about 3.6 km/s through continental crust. How long would it take secondary waves to travel from Phoenix to Los Angeles?

Section Assessment

1. Which type of seismic wave does the most damage to property? Explain why.
2. Why is a seismic record from three locations needed to determine the position of an epicenter?
3. **Think Critically:** Suppose an earthquake occurs at the San Andreas Fault. What area on Earth would experience no secondary waves? Would China experience primary and secondary waves? Explain your answers.
4. **Skill Builder**
   Making and Using Graphs Use the data table below to make a graph of some travel times of earthquake waves. Which line represents primary waves? Which line represents secondary waves? If you need help, refer to Making and Using Graphs in the **Skill Handbook** on page 717.

Earthquake Wave Travel Times

Distance from Earthquake (km)	1500	2000	5000	5500	8600	10 000
Time (minutes)	5.0	2.5	14.0	7.0	11.0	23.5

When sound is produced, waves move through the air by pressing molecules together and then spreading them apart. Research sound waves and compare them to the types of seismic waves you have learned about. Relate what you learn to the fact that people report loud noise when earthquakes occur.

Section Assessment

1. Surface waves; as surface waves pass, structures try to move in an elliptical manner, with some back-and-forth sway. This will cause solid material to crack and crumble.
2. The circles drawn from two stations will intersect in two places, giving two possible epicenter locations. Data from a third station are needed to pinpoint which of those two possible points is the epicenter location.
3. **Think Critically** Hint: See Across the Curriculum, p. 220. No secondary waves would be recorded more than 105° from the epicenter. The eastern half of China lies in the P-wave shadow zone (105° to 140°) and would not receive direct arrivals of P- or S-waves. The rest of China would receive P-waves but not S-waves.

Primary seismic waves move by compressing and then stretching apart rock particles. This is the same way in which sound waves move through a material. Some of the noise associated with an earthquake may be caused by primary waves that enter the atmosphere.

4. **Skill Builder**
   The P-wave is represented by the points (2000, 2.5), (5500, 7.0), and (8600, 11.0). The other points represent the slower S-wave. Have students determine which data pairs correspond to P-waves and which correspond to S-waves. For example, the P-wave traveled 2000 km in less time than it took for the S-wave to travel 1500 km.

Assessment

Performance Use this Skill Builder to assess students' abilities to make and use graphs. Ask students to determine some travel times for earthquake waves at a distance of 3000 km, 4000 km, and 6000 km. Use **Performance Assessment in the Science Classroom,** p. 41.

Purpose

Logical-Mathematical Students will interpret data on an earthquake wave distance-time graph to determine the locations of earthquake epicenters.

 COOP LEARN 

Process Skills

using numbers, interpreting data, making and using tables, making and using graphs, comparing and contrasting

Time

50 minutes

Teaching Strategies

Be sure students understand how to use **Figure 8-7** before beginning this activity.

Answers to Questions

1. The difference in arrival time between P- and S-waves increases as the distance of the seismograph station from the earthquake increases. This time interval can be used to calculate the distance between the seismograph and the earthquake.
2. A: Mexico City, Mexico
   B: San Francisco, California
3. It takes a minimum of three seismograph stations to locate the epicenter of an earthquake.
4. Use a globe to demonstrate that these seismograph stations are within the shadow zone.

Epicenter Location

Materials

- **Figure 8-7**
- String
- Metric ruler
- Globe
- Chalk
- Paper

Try this activity to see how to plot the distance of several seismograph stations from the epicenters of two earthquakes and how to use these data to interpret where the earthquake epicenters were located.

What You'll Investigate

Can plotting the distance of several seismograph stations from two earthquake epicenters be used to interpret the locations of the two epicenters?

Goals

- **Plot** the distances of several seismograph stations based on primary and secondary wave arrival times.
- **Interpret** the location of earthquake epicenters from these plots.

Procedure

1. **Determine** the difference in arrival time between the primary and secondary waves at each station for each quake from the data table below.
2. Once you determine the arrival times of seismic waves for each seismograph station, use the graph in **Figure 8-7** to determine the distance in kilometers of each seismograph from the epicenter of each earthquake. **Record** these data in a data table provided by your teacher. The difference in arrival times in Paris for earthquake B is 9 minutes and 30 seconds. On the graph, the primary and secondary waves are separated along the vertical axis by 9 minutes and 30 seconds at 8975 km.
3. Using the string, **measure** the circumference of the globe. Determine a scale of centimeters of string to kilometers on Earth's surface. (Earth's circumference = 40 000 km.)
4. For each earthquake, A and B, place one end of the string at each seismic station location on the globe. Use the chalk to draw a circle with a radius equal to the distance from the earthquake's epicenter.
5. **Identify** the epicenter for each quake.

Conclude and Apply

1. How is the distance of a seismograph from the earthquake related to the arrival time of the waves?
2. What is the location of each earthquake epicenter?
3. How many stations were needed to accurately locate each epicenter?
4. **Predict** why some seismographs didn't receive secondary waves from some quakes.

Earthquake Wave Arrival Times

Location of Seismograph	Wave	Wave Arrival Times: Earthquake A	Wave Arrival Times: Earthquake B
(1) New York	P	2:24:05 P.M.	1:19:42 P.M.
	S	2:29:15 P.M.	1:25:27 P.M.
(2) Seattle	P	2:24:40 P.M.	1:14:37 P.M.
	S	2:30:10 P.M.	1:16:57 P.M.
(3) Rio de Janeiro	P	2:29:10 P.M.	—
	S	2:37:50 P.M.	—
(4) Paris	P	2:30:30 P.M.	1:24:57 P.M.
	S	2:40:10 P.M.	1:34:27 P.M.
(5) Tokyo	P	—	1:24:27 P.M.
	S	—	1:33:27 P.M.

Assessment

Performance Ask students to explain why data from two seismograph stations are not enough to locate an earthquake epicenter. Use **Performance Assessment in the Science Classroom,** p. 71. P

Earthquake Distances

Quake	Calculated distance to epicenter (km) from each seismograph location: (1)	(2)	(3)	(4)	(5)
A	(3425)	(3760)	(7700)	(9210)	—
B	(4140)	(1090)	—	(8975)	(8290)

224 CHAPTER 8 EARTHQUAKES

Destruction by Earthquakes

Measuring Earthquakes

On January 25, 1999, a major earthquake struck Colombia, South America, leaving over 1900 dead or missing. On February 4, 1998, and then again on May 30, 1998, major earthquakes of magnitudes 6.1 and 6.9 occurred at the Afghanistan-Tajikistan border. More than 6300 people were killed. On May 10, 1997, a magnitude-7.3 earthquake killed at least 1567 people in northern Iran. On January 17, 1995, a major earthquake occurred in Kobe, Japan, causing about $100 billion of property damage and 5502 deaths. On January 17, 1994, a major earthquake occurred in Northridge, California, causing billions of dollars of property damage, as seen in **Figure 8-12,** and 57 deaths. What determines the amount of damage done by an earthquake, and what can you do to protect yourself from the effects? With so many lives lost and such destruction, as shown in **Table 8-1,** it is important for scientists to learn as much as possible about earthquakes to try to reduce their damage.

What You'll Learn

- Definitions of *magnitude* and the *Richter scale*
- Ways to make your classroom and home more earthquake-safe

Vocabulary

seismologist
seismograph
magnitude
tsunami

Why It's Important

- People can prepare for earthquakes by building seismic-safe structures.

Figure 8-12
Several major highways were damaged in the January 17, 1994, earthquake in Northridge, California. **What happens during an earthquake that causes so much damage to highway overpasses?**

SECTION 8-3

Prepare

Content Background

Refer to **Seismology, Earthquake Magnitude,** and **Seismic-Safe Structures** on pp. 208E–F.

Preplanning

Refer to the **Chapter Organizer** on pp. 208A–B.

1 Motivate

Bellringer

Before presenting the lesson, display **Section Focus Transparency 21** on the overhead projector. Use the accompanying **Focus Activity** worksheet. L2 ELL

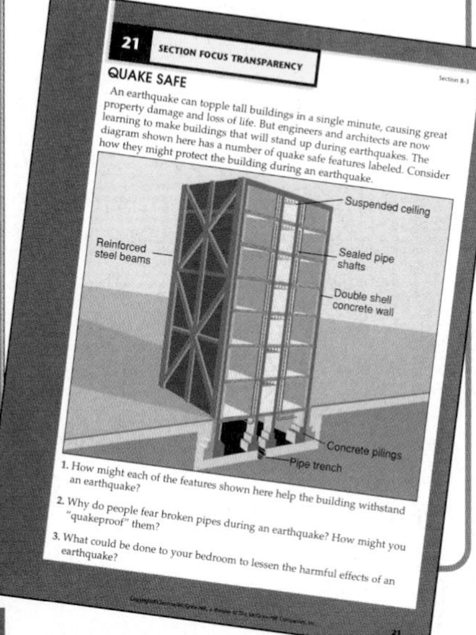

21 SECTION FOCUS TRANSPARENCY

Section 8-3

QUAKE SAFE

An earthquake can topple tall buildings in a single minute, causing great property damage and loss of life. But engineers and architects are now learning to make buildings that will stand up during earthquakes. The diagram shown here has a number of quake safe features labeled. Consider how they might protect the building during an earthquake.

1. How might each of the features shown here help the building withstand an earthquake?
2. Why do people fear broken pipes during an earthquake? How might you "quakeproof" them?
3. What could be done to your bedroom to lessen the harmful effects of an earthquake?

21

Resource Manager

The following **Teacher Classroom Resources** can be used with Section 8–3:

Reproducible Masters

Activity Worksheets, pp. 45–46, 48 L2

Critical Thinking/Problem Solving, p. 8 L2

Enrichment, p. 21 L3

Multicultural Connections, pp. 15–16 L2

Reinforcement, p. 21 L2

Study Guide, pp. 31–32 L1 ELL

Tying to Previous Knowledge

Help students recall photographs of the destruction caused by earthquakes they may have seen in newspapers or on television.

2 Teach

Content Background

The Modified Mercalli Scale is used to measure the intensity or amount of damage done by an earthquake. A rating of I to II is a low-intensity quake. An earthquake measuring VII causes negligible damage in buildings that are well designed and well constructed. An earthquake measuring XII designates total destruction of the area.

Making a Model

Tape a stiff sheet of paper to the side of a closed shoe box. Have a volunteer slowly draw a straight line from the top of the sheet to the bottom. Then, have the volunteer attempt the same feat as another student bounces a small rubber ball on the top of the box. Use this analogy to explain how a seismograph works.

Flex Your Brain

Use the Flex Your Brain activity to have students explore EARTHQUAKE PREDICTION.

Caption Answer

Figure 8-12 *Seismic waves generated by an earthquake shake structures. Brittle materials, such as concrete used in highway overpasses, are susceptable to breaking during vibrations.*

Seismology

Scientists who study earthquakes and seismic waves are **seismologists.** They use an instrument called a **seismograph** to record primary, secondary, and surface waves from earthquakes all over the world.

One type of seismograph has a drum holding a sheet of paper on a fixed frame. A pendulum with an attached pen is suspended from the frame. When seismic waves occur at the station, the drum vibrates but the pendulum remains at rest. The pen on the pendulum traces a record of the vibrations on a sheet of paper. The height of the lines traced on the paper is a measure of the energy released, or **magnitude,** of the earthquake.

Table 8-1

Large-Magnitude Earthquakes

Year	Location	Richter Value	Deaths
1556	Shensi, China	?	830 000
1737	Calcutta, India	?	300 000
1755	Lisbon, Portugal	8.8	70 000
1811–12	New Madrid, MO	8.3	few
1886	Charleston, SC	?	60
1906	San Francisco, CA	8.3	700–800
1920	Kansu Province, China	8.5	180 000
1923	Tokyo, Japan	8.3	143 000
1939	Concepción, Chile	8.3	30 000
1960	Southern Chile	8.6	5700
1964	Prince William Sound, AK	8.5	131
1970	Peru	7.8	66 800
1975	Laoning Province, China	7.5	few
1976	Tangshan, China	7.6	240 000
1985	Mexico City, Mexico	8.1	9500
1988	Armenia	6.9	28 000
1989	Loma Prieta, CA	6.9	63
1990	Iran	7.7	50 000
1990	Luzon, Philippines	7.8	1621
1993	Guam	8.1	none
1993	Marharashtra, India	6.4	30 000
1994	Northridge, CA	6.8	57
1995	Kobe, Japan	6.9	5502
1997	Northern Iran	7.3	>1500
1998	Afghanistan	6.1 & 6.9	>6300

Earthquake Magnitude

Not all seismographs measure vibrations in the same way. The Richter scale measures only local intensity on one kind of seismograph. However, seismologists also study magnitude in other ways.

The Richter magnitude is based on seismic waves that travel through Earth. It deals mainly with the strength of the break, not with the length or width of the fault. The Richter scale describes how much energy is released by the earthquake. For each increase of 1.0, the amplitude, or height, of the largest surface waves is ten times greater. However, about 32 times as much energy is released for every increase of 1.0 on the scale. For example, a magnitude-8.5 earthquake releases about 32 times as much energy as a magnitude-7.5

Inclusion Strategies

Learning Disabled Have students conduct research on major earthquakes that have occurred during recorded history. Have them construct time lines of the earliest to the most recent earthquakes. The magnitude of each earthquake should be included. Have students hypothesize why certain areas have more earthquakes than others. L2

earthquake. **Table 8-2** shows how often various magnitude earthquakes are expected to occur.

Another magnitude used by seismologists is based on Earth movement or surface waves. Seismologists also use a magnitude called the moment magnitude. It comes from multiplying the length of the fault break by the amount of rock movement and then again by the rock stiffness. The moment magnitude depends on the strength and size of fault movement.

Table 8-2

Earthquake Occurrences

Richter Magnitude	Number Expected per Year
1.0 to 3.9	> 949 000
4.0 to 4.9	6200
5.0 to 5.9	800
6.0 to 6.9	120
7.0 to 7.9	18
8.0 to 8.9	< 2

For an online update of this data, visit **www.glencoe.com/sec/science** and select the appropriate chapter.

Tsunamis

Most earthquake damage happens when surface waves cause buildings, bridges, and roads to collapse. People living near the seashore, however, have another problem. An earthquake under the sea causes a sudden movement of the ocean floor. The movement pushes against the water, causing a powerful wave that can travel thousands of kilometers in all directions, as shown in **Figure 8-13.** Far from shore, a wave caused by an earthquake is so long that a large ship may ride over it without anyone noticing. But, when one of these waves breaks on a shore, it forms a towering crest that can reach 30 m in height. Ocean waves caused by earthquakes are called seismic sea waves, or **tsunamis** (soo NAHM eez).

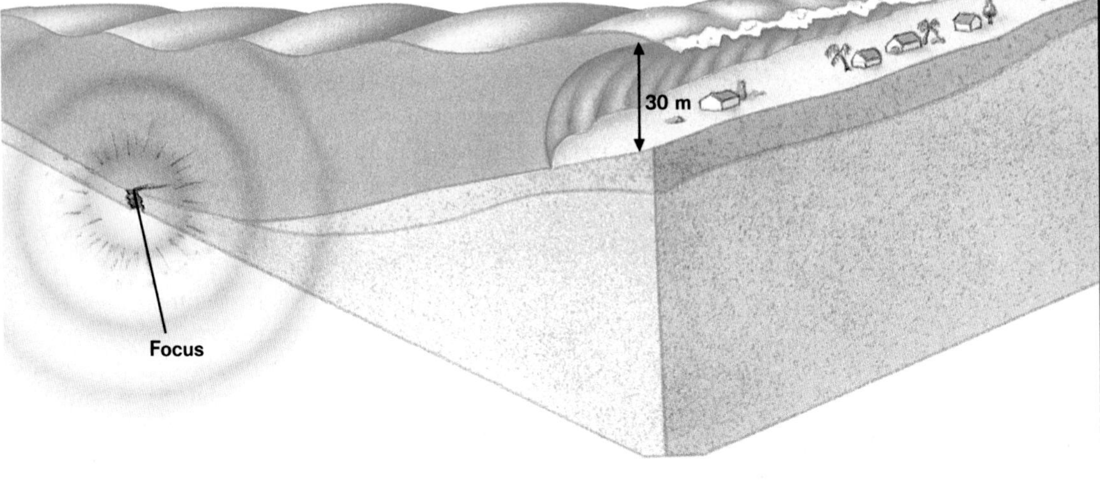

Figure 8-13 A tsunami begins over the earthquake focus. **What might happen to towns located near the shore?**

Teacher FYI

- Three of the strongest earthquakes in the United States occurred along the New Madrid fault system centered in Missouri.
- The Tsunami Warning System was developed by the United States in 1948 after a tsunami hit the Aleutian and Hawaiian Islands two years earlier. After a 1964 Alaskan wave took 103 lives, an improved Regional TWS was developed. Now GOES (Geostationary Operational Environmental Satellite) can issue warnings in as little as two minutes.
- More than one million earthquakes occur every year. Most are not directly observable by humans. However, on average, 20 earthquakes strong enough to be felt occur each day in California.

Caption Answer

Figure 8-13 *If an offshore earthquake occurs, towns near the shore could be destroyed by tsunamis.*

GLENCOE TECHNOLOGY

Videodisc

The Infinite Voyage: Living with Disaster

Chapter 6 *Predicting Earthquakes: The Parkfield Experiment*
10:00

Refer to the Teacher Guide for bar codes and teaching strategies.

Integrating the Sciences

Life Science Have students study **Table 8-1** and hypothesize why some strong earthquakes caused so much loss of life while others caused little. L2

Purpose

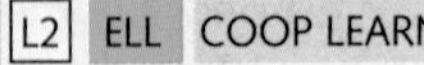

Interpersonal Students will use seismic-safe methods of construction.

L2 ELL COOP LEARN

Materials

blocks, rubber bands

Teaching Strategies

Safety Precautions When students are pounding on the tabletop, caution them to use a book or some other object to avoid harm to their hands.

Analysis

1. Structures with rubber bands around them are more likely to withstand the earthquake.
2. Concrete cement pillars could be wrapped with steel supports. The supports would decrease the chance that the pillars would break during an earthquake.

Assessment

Performance Have students build a model seismic-safe highway. Use **Performance Assessment in the Science Classroom,** p. 51.

GLENCOE TECHNOLOGY

Videodisc

The Infinite Voyage: Living with Disaster

Chapter 7 *Documenting Tragedy—Developing a Cure: Soviet Armenia* 4:00

Refer to the Teacher Guide for bar codes and teaching strategies.

Figure 8-14 On July 17, 1998, a powerful tsunami swept away trees and houses along the northern coast of Papua, New Guinea. At least 2000 people died.

Just before a tsunami crashes on shore, the water along a shoreline may move rapidly toward the sea, exposing a large portion that is normally underwater. This should be taken as an immediate warning sign that a tsunami could strike. **Figure 8-14** shows some damage that was caused by the tsunami that struck Papua, New Guinea, on July 17, 1998.

interNET CONNECTION

Visit the Glencoe Science Web Site at **www.glencoe.com/sec/science** for more information about tsunamis.

Earthquake Safety

You've seen the destruction that earthquakes can cause. However, there are ways to minimize the damage and loss of life.

One of the first steps in earthquake safety is to study the earthquake history of a region, such as the one illustrated in **Figure 8-16.** If you live in an area that's had earthquakes in the past, you can expect them to occur there in the future. As you know, most earthquakes happen along plate boundaries. **Table 8-1** shows where severe earthquakes have happened. Being prepared is an important step in earthquake safety.

Guided Reading Strategy

Think-Pair Share This strategy encourages students to think first before discussing their ideas or thoughts about a topic. Students are asked to write a response to a question. After thinking for a few minutes, partners share responses. Finally, the teacher asks the students to share responses with the class. Have students do a Think-Pair Share using the Reading & Writing in Science feature on p. 231.

Internet Addresses

For Internet tips, see Glencoe's **Using the Internet in the Science Classroom.**

Quake-Proofing Your Home

Make your home as earthquake-safe as possible. Take heavy objects down from high shelves and place them on lower shelves. Reduce the chance of fire from broken gas lines by checking that hot-water heaters and gas appliances are held securely in place. During an earthquake, keep away from windows and avoid anything that could fall on you. Watch for fallen power lines and possible fire hazards. Stay clear of rubble that could contain sharp edges.

Seismic-Safe Structures

Seismic-safe structures stand up to vibrations that occur during an earthquake. **Figure 8-15** shows how buildings can be built to resist earthquake damage.

Today in California, some new buildings are held together by flexible, circular moorings placed under the buildings. The moorings are arranged in layers of steel plates and rubber parts. The rubber acts like a cushion to absorb earthquake waves.

Modeling Seismic-Safe Structures

Procedure

1. Obtain a set of building blocks from your teacher.
2. On a tabletop, build one structure out of the blocks by simply placing one block on top of another.
3. Build a second structure by wrapping sections of three blocks together with rubber bands. Then, wrap larger rubber bands around the entire completed structure.
4. Set the second structure on the tabletop and pound on the side of the table with a steady rhythm.

Analysis

1. Which of your two structures was better able to withstand the "earthquake" caused by pounding on the table?
2. How might the idea of wrapping the blocks with rubber bands be used in construction of supports for elevated highways?

Figure 8-15 The rubber portions of this building's moorings absorb most of the wave motion of an earthquake. The building itself only sways gently. **What purpose does the rubber serve?**

3 Assess

Check for Understanding

Discussion

During a 1976 earthquake in Tang Shan, China, nearly a quarter of a million people were killed. Many of the people died because their homes were not constructed to be seismic safe. Ask students to review ways to make our homes and offices safer if an earthquake were to occur. L2

Reteach

Visual-Spatial Show pictures of the destruction from the 1906 earthquake in San Francisco. Ask students to speculate about what caused the almost total destruction of the city. Fires were a major factor. L1

Extension

For students who have mastered this section, use the **Reinforcement** and **Enrichment** masters.

4 Close

Proficiency Prep

Use this quiz to check students' recall of section content.

1. **How is the energy released by an earthquake measured?** *magnitude*
2. **What are seismic sea waves caused by earthquakes?** *tsunamis*

Caption Answer

Figure 8-15 *The rubber absorbs much of the motion, minimizing the shaking experienced by the building.*

Alaskan Earthquakes Have students write brief descriptions in their Science Journals of the damage done when tsunamis came ashore along the Pacific coast following the Alaskan earthquake of 1964. L2

Section Assessment

1. They absorb most of the wave motion of an earthquake.
2. Some scientists suggest that animals may be detecting changes in local magnetic fields, small tremors, gases released from the ground, or high-frequency sounds.
3. **Think Critically** In order to record vibrations, some point within the seismograph must remain at rest. Most seismographs consist of a frame that is attached to Earth. A pen records the seismic waves onto paper on a vibrating drum.

Using Math

Energy increases about 32 times as magnitude increases by one.

$7.5 - 5.5 = 2$ magnitude differences

$32^2 = 1024$ times more energy released

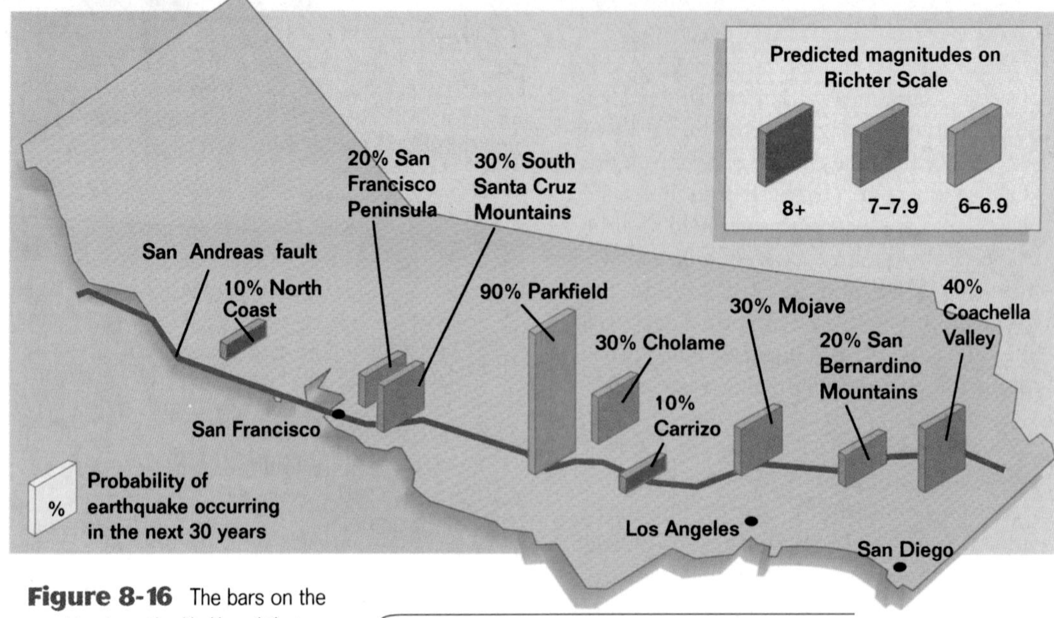

Figure 8-16 The bars on the graphic show the likelihood that an earthquake of a certain magnitude will strike these areas within the next 30 years. California residents are preparing for the major earthquakes predicted there.

For an online update of this data, visit **www.glencoe.com/sec/science** and select the appropriate chapter.

Figure 8-15 shows how they work. Tests have shown that buildings supported in this way should be able to withstand an earthquake measuring up to 8.3 on the Richter scale without major damage.

Section Assessment

1. How do rubber moorings in a building help minimize damage during an earthquake?
2. Research how animal behavior has been studied to predict earthquakes. What changes may be occurring in the environment to cause animals to act differently?
3. **Think Critically:** Explain why a seismograph wouldn't work if the pen vibrated along with the rest of the machine.
4. **Skill Builder** **Using Numbers** Have you ever wondered what you would need to have stored up at home in the event of an earthquake? To find out what's important, and how much it costs, do the **Chapter 8 Skill Activity** on page 731.

Using Math

Calculate the difference in energy released between an earthquake of Richter magnitude 7.5 and one of magnitude 5.5.

VISUAL Learning

Figure 8-16 Have students look at this figure and explain why some areas along the San Andreas Fault are assigned higher probabilities of experiencing an earthquake in the next 30 years than others.

Why We Have Earthquakes— A Korean Folktale

An earthquake is a shaking of Earth caused by the release of energy as rock suddenly breaks or shifts under stress. Most quakes happen along faults—breaks in Earth's crust along which rocks on either side can move. The Korean Peninsula is relatively stable compared to Japan, which is situated on a plate boundary. Of the nearly 2000 earthquakes that have been historically or scientifically recorded in Korea since 2 A.D., only 48 have been destructive.

Traditional Korean folktales, which have been passed on orally from generation to generation, explain natural events such as earthquakes. The tales also are told to teach moral lessons. Like the folktales and myths of other cultures throughout the world, Korean folktales reflect the peculiarities of the environment where they are told.

A Shoulder to Lean On

One Korean folktale tells of a time when one corner of Heaven began to sag. The King of Heaven took a gigantic pillar of red copper and placed one end on Earth and the other end under the sagging corner of Heaven.

The ground on Earth was soft, and, since Heaven was heavy, the pillar began to sink into Earth. The king sent the strongest man in Heaven to hold the pillar on his shoulder. This was the only way to keep the great weight of Heaven from sagging.

The man is still holding the pillar. He can't let it slip from his shoulder or all of Heaven will come crashing down. But, the great weight becomes painful for the man to hold on just one shoulder. So, from time to time, he shifts the pillar from one shoulder to the other. Every time the man shifts the weight of the pillar, the ground on Earth shakes with his efforts. According to the folktale, this is why we have earthquakes.

Science Journal

Using what you have learned about earthquakes in this chapter, write your own story to explain why earthquakes occur. Use your stories to explain things about earthquakes that are still not well understood. Read your classmates' stories to find out what questions they still have about earthquakes. Make a list of these questions in your Science Journal.

Teaching Strategies

Writing As a class project, students could write a play that explains why there are earthquakes. Students could include how they can ensure their personal safety and the safety of others if an earthquake should occur during the school day. L2 COOP LEARN

Reading Students should read myths of other cultures that explain earthquakes. One is the Japanese myth of the earthquake fish. Students could practice retelling these stories after they have read them to each other in small groups. L2 COOP LEARN

NATIONAL GEOGRAPHIC

Reading & Writing in Science

Content Background

- The telling of stories is a traditional way of teaching what many children today learn in schools, from television, radio, books, magazines and newspapers. Stories are told to teach moral lessons as well as to entertain and to pass on the wisdom of preceding generations. Often, stories are told to explain that which is unexplainable or is a cause for fear in a community.
- The Korean myth summarized in this feature encourages students to reflect on or ask questions about the structure of Earth and why we have earthquakes. It also implies that stresses imparted on Earth's surface are an explanation for earthquakes.
- The Korean peninsula lies on the Eurasian plate but is not far from the plate boundaries of the Philippine, Pacific and Eurasian plates. Seismologists have plotted epicenters of earthquakes and found that for the most part, they occur in narrow zones that define plate boundaries.

Science Journal As they write their stories, students should include ideas about the movement of plates and where they collide, move apart, and slide past one another.

For Additional Information

- So-Un, Kim. Translated by Setsu Higashi. *The Story Bag*. Rutland, VT. Charles E. Tuttle Co., 1955.

Activity 8·2

What You'll Investigate

Purpose

Logical-Mathematical Students will carry out an investigation to illustrate any relationship between the depth of earthquake foci and epicenter location or the movement of Earth's plates. L2 COOP LEARN P

Process Skills

observing and inferring, communicating, using numbers, interpreting data, hypothesizing, making and using tables, making and using graphs, comparing and contrasting, separating and controlling variables

Procedure

Time

45 minutes

Teaching Strategies

Discuss the three types of plate boundaries with students (convergent, divergent, and transform).

Troubleshooting Draw a blank version of the focus depth vs. distance graph shown on this page. Indicate to students the location of the coast of the continent on the graph. Help students begin by plotting the first two locations.

Activity 8·2

Materials

- Graph paper
- Pencil

Earthquake Depths

You learned earlier in this chapter that Earth's crust is broken into sections called plates. Stresses caused by movement of these plates generate energy within rocks that must be released. When this release is sudden and rocks break, an earthquake occurs.

What You'll Investigate

Can a study of the foci of earthquakes tell us anything about how strain builds up in rocks and how it may be released?

Goals

- **Observe** any connection between earthquake-focus depth and epicenter location using the data provided on the next page.
- **Describe** any observed relationship between earthquake-focus depth and the movement of plates at Earth's surface.

Procedure

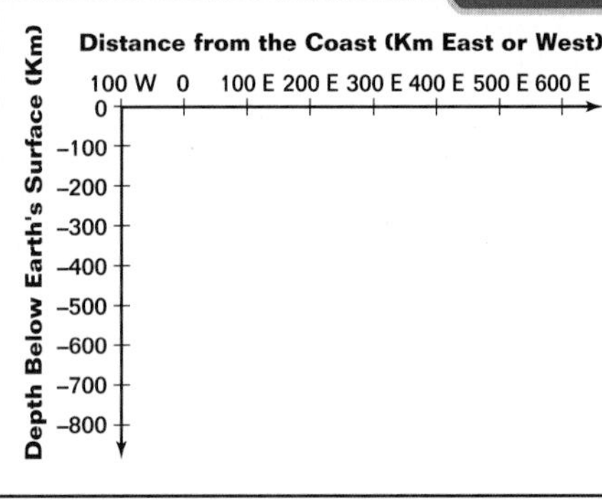

1. Use graph paper and the data table on the next page to make a line graph plotting the depths of earthquake foci and the distances from the coast of a continent for each earthquake epicenter.
2. **Place** "Distance from the coast" on the horizontal axis. Begin labeling at the far left with 100 km west. To the right of it should be 0 km, then 100 km east, 200 km east, 300 km east, and so on through 700 km east. What point on your graph would represent the coast?
3. Label the vertical axis "Depth below Earth's surface." **Label** the top of the graph 0 km to represent Earth's surface. **Label** the bottom of the vertical axis −800 km.
4. **Plot** the focus depths against the distance and direction from the coast for each earthquake in the table on the next page.

Inclusion Strategies

Visually Impaired Ask some of your students to prepare copies of the maps and charts being used in this activity in a manner useful to those who are visually impaired. Outline the locations under study with thick lines and identify earthquake foci by raised bumps on the maps. Students who are able could produce maps and charts using Braille. L2

Conclude and Apply

1. **Describe** any observed relation between the location of earthquake epicenters and the depth of earthquake foci.
2. Based on the graph you have completed, **hypothesize** what is happening to the plates at Earth's surface in the vicinity of the plotted earthquake foci.
3. **Infer** what process is causing the earthquakes you plotted on your graph paper.
4. **Hypothesize** why none of the plotted earthquakes occurred below 700 km.

Focus and Epicenter Data

Quake	Focus Depth	Distance of Epicenter from Coast (km)
A	−55 km	0
B	−295 km	100 E
C	−390 km	455 E
D	−60 km	75 E
E	−130 km	255 E
F	−195 km	65 E
G	−695 km	400 E
H	−20 km	40 W
I	−505 km	695 E
J	−520 km	390 E
K	−385 km	335 E
L	−45 km	95 E
M	−305 km	495 E
N	−480 km	285 E
O	−665 km	545 E
P	−85 km	90 W
Q	−525 km	205 E
R	−85 km	25 W
S	−445 km	595 E
T	−635 km	665 E
U	−55 km	95 W
V	−70 km	100 W

Expected Outcome

Students should realize that earthquake foci occur deeper farther inland from the shore. They should realize that this is because one section of Earth's crust is being subducted, causing earthquakes deeper and deeper inside Earth.

Error Analysis

Ask students which direction on their chart they have plotted earthquakes E and H. This will check whether students measure east and west of the coastline. Ask students what focus depth is measured from.

Conclude and Apply

1. The earthquakes near the coast are shallow-focus quakes. Moving inland, the earthquake foci become progressively deeper.
2. The two plates of Earth's crust are colliding. Stress is building up, generating earthquakes.
3. One section of Earth's crust (the ocean section) is sliding under another (the continent section). As one plate moves under the other, earthquakes occur deeper and deeper inside Earth.
4. The tremendous pressure and temperatures at this depth and below reduce the rigidity of solids. Generally, earthquakes occur because of the fracturing of solids. At a depth of 700 km, the rock material is plastic-like and stress is absorbed without fracturing. P

GO Further

Have students do research to find out where on Earth the distribution of earthquake foci might be similar to that in this activity. *the west coast of South America*

Assessment

Oral Ask students to explain why earthquake foci occur deeper and deeper the farther inland the epicenter is located from the shore. Use **Performance Assessment in the Science Classroom,** p. 71.

Reviewing Main Ideas can be used to preview, review, reteach, and condense chapter content.

Preview

Linguistic Have students try to answer the questions in their Science Journals. Use student answers as a source for discussion throughout the chapter.

Review

Interpersonal Have students answer the questions on separate pieces of paper and compare their answers with those of other students in the class.

Reteach

Visual-Spatial Have students look at the illustrations on these pages. Ask them to describe details that support the main ideas of the chapter found in the statement for each illustration.

00:00 OUT OF TIME?

Auditory-Musical If time does not permit teaching the entire chapter, use the information on these pages along with the chapter Audiocassettes to present the material in a condensed format.

Chapter 8 Reviewing Main Ideas

For a **preview** of this chapter, study this Reviewing Main Ideas before you read the chapter. After you have studied this chapter, you can use the Reviewing Main Ideas to **review** the chapter.

The Glencoe MindJogger, Audiocassettes, and CD-ROM provide additional opportunities for review.

Section 8-1 FORCES INSIDE EARTH

Plate movements put stress on rocks. To a point, the rocks bend and stretch. But, if the force is great enough and the rock's elastic limit is passed, the rocks will remain bent and may break. When the rocks break, they can move along surfaces called **faults.** Breaking rocks produce vibrations called **earthquakes.** ***How do rocks move relative to each other in a reverse fault?***

Tension forces

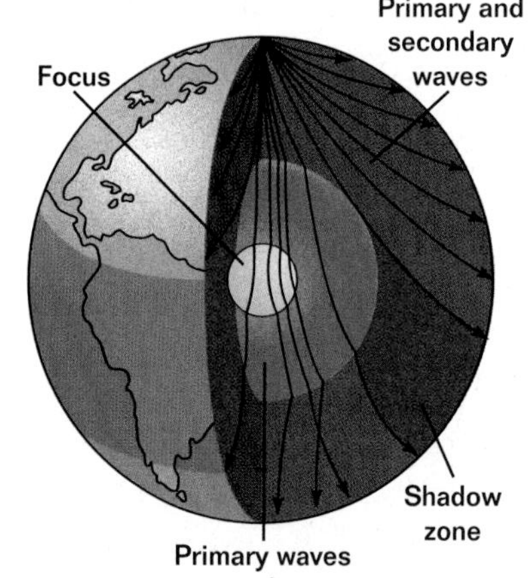

Section 8-2 EARTHQUAKE INFORMATION

Primary waves compress and stretch rock particles as the waves move. **Secondary waves** move by causing particles in the rocks to move at right angles to the direction of the waves. **Surface waves** move rock particles up and down and from side to side. Scientists can locate earthquake **epicenters** by measuring **seismic wave** speeds. By observing the speeds and paths of seismic waves, scientists are able to determine the boundaries among Earth's layers. ***What happens to the path and speed of seismic waves as they move from one layer to another inside Earth?***

Cultural Diversity

Tsunami! One of the earliest recorded tsunamis struck 1400 km off the Chilean coast in 1562. In 1674, one wave reaching 100 m in height struck Indonesia. Tsunamis can produce strange results. In 1868, a Civil War sidewheeler U.S.S. *Wateree,* in a Chilean port was deposited intact and unharmed 0.5 km inland, while 20 000 people onshore lost their lives. Thera, one of the Cyclades Islands, may be the remnant of a volcano that erupted, causing tsunamis that ended Minoan civilization on Crete. It has been compared to the explosion of Krakatau in 1883, in which the resulting wave killed 30 000 people in Java. In the last 20 years, 2.8 million lives have been lost to tsunamis. One in three tsunamis originates off the Chilean coast due to the movement of the Nazca Plate.

Reading Check

Write your own summary of Section 8-3 before reading the text on this page. Try to keep your summary within three to five sentences.

Section 8-3

DESTRUCTION BY EARTHQUAKES

Seismologists study **earthquakes** and the waves produced by earthquakes. The **magnitude** of an earthquake is a measure of the energy released by the earthquake. The Richter scale describes how much energy is released by an earthquake. For each difference of one on the Richter scale, an earthquake releases about 32 times more energy. *How much more energy is released by an earthquake of magnitude 8.5 than an earthquake of magnitude 6.5?*

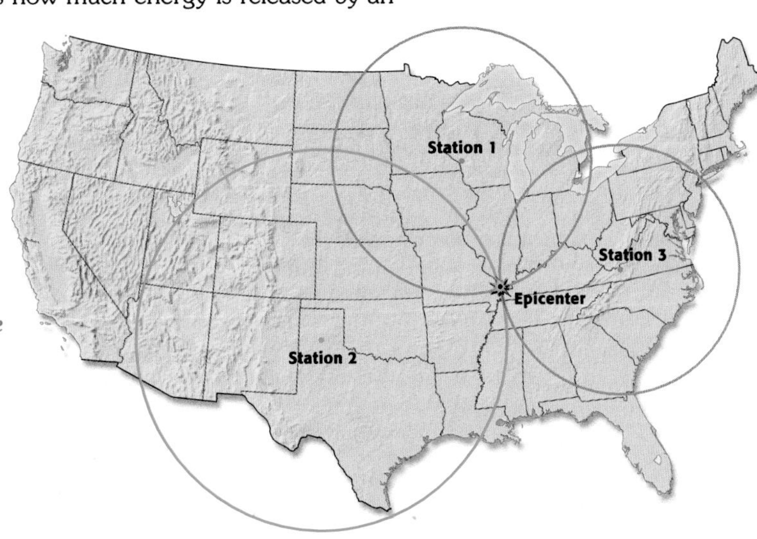

SEISMIC-SAFE STRUCTURES

Most lives lost during an earthquake are due to destruction of human-made structures. Seismic-safe structures are resistant to vibrations that occur during an earthquake. Buildings in areas with such structures are damaged during an earthquake but are less likely to collapse. *Give suggestions for how to quake-proof your home.*

CHAPTER 8 REVIEWING MAIN IDEAS 235

Answers to Questions

Section 8-1

Forces Inside Earth In a reverse fault, rocks above the fault surface move up relative to rocks below the fault surface.

Section 8-2

Earthquake Information The path and speed of seismic waves change as they move from one layer to another inside Earth. Differing densities in different layers will bend the path of seismic waves and either speed them up, slow them down, or stop them (S-waves are stopped by liquids).

Section 8-3

Destruction by Earthquakes For each increase of one magnitude, 32 times more energy is released by an earthquake. With a difference of 6.5 to 8.5 in magnitude (an increase of two magnitudes), 1024 (32 × 32) times more energy is released.

Seismic-safe Structures Do not place heavy objects on high shelves, and check to see that the water heater and gas appliances are well secured.

GLENCOE TECHNOLOGY

CD-ROM

Glencoe Science Voyages Interactive CD-ROM

Chapter Summaries and Quizzes

Have students read the Chapter Summary then take the Chapter Quiz to determine whether they have mastered chapter content.

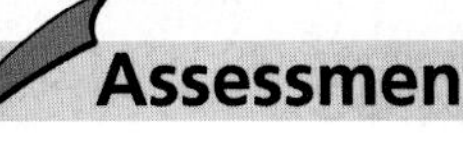

Assessment

Portfolio Encourage students to place in their portfolios one or two items of what they consider to be their best work. Examples include:

- MiniLab, p. 218
- Activity 8-1, p. 224
- Activity 8-2, pp. 232–233 P

Performance Additional performance assessments may be found in **Performance Assessment** and **Science Integration Activities.** Performance Task Assessment Lists and rubrics for evaluating these activities can be found in Glencoe's **Performance Assessment in the Science Classroom.**

Using Vocabulary

1. Surface waves are seismic waves that travel outward from the epicenter. A tsunami is a powerful ocean wave generated by an earthquake.
2. Faults are surfaces along which rocks move when forces cause them to break. A focus is the point in Earth's interior where rupture along a fault occurs, producing an earthquake.
3. In a normal fault, rocks above the fault surface move downward in relation to rocks below the fault surface. In a reverse fault, rocks above the fault surface are forced up and over the rocks below the fault surface.
4. A seismologist is a scientist who studies earthquakes and seismic waves. A seismograph is an instrument used to record seismic waves from earthquakes.
5. The inner core is the very center of Earth. The outer core surrounds the inner core.

interNET CONNECTION To reinforce chapter vocabulary, use the **Study Guide for Content Mastery** booklet. Also available are activities for **Glencoe Science Voyages** on the Glencoe Science Web Site. **www.glencoe.com/sec/science**

Checking Concepts

6. C	**11.** B
7. A	**12.** B
8. B	**13.** D
9. B	**14.** A
10. A	**15.** C

Chapter 8 Assessment

Using Vocabulary

a. crust
b. earthquake
c. epicenter
d. fault
e. focus
f. inner core
g. magnitude
h. mantle
i. normal fault
j. outer core
k. primary wave
l. reverse fault
m. secondary wave
n. seismic wave
o. seismograph
p. seismologist
q. strike-slip fault
r. surface wave
s. tsunami

Distinguish between the terms in each of the following pairs.

1. surface wave, tsunami
2. fault, focus
3. normal fault, reverse fault
4. seismologist, seismograph
5. inner core, outer core

Checking Concepts

Choose the word or phrase that best answers the question.

6. Earthquakes can occur when which of the following is passed?
A) tension limit
B) seismic limit
C) elastic limit
D) shear limit
7. When the rock above the fault surface moves down relative to the rock below the fault surface, what kind of fault forms?
A) normal
B) strike-slip
C) reverse
D) shearing
8. Primary and secondary waves move outward from which of the following?
A) epicenter
B) focus
C) Moho discontinuity
D) tsunami
9. What kind of waves stretch and compress rocks?
A) surface
B) primary
C) secondary
D) shear
10. What are the slowest seismic waves?
A) surface
B) primary
C) secondary
D) pressure
11. What is the fewest number of seismograph stations that are needed to locate the epicenter of an earthquake?
A) two
B) three
C) four
D) five
12. What happens to primary waves when they go from liquids into solids?
A) slow down
B) speed up
C) stay the same
D) stop
13. What part of a seismograph remains still?
A) sheet of paper
B) fixed frame
C) drum
D) pendulum
14. An earthquake of magnitude 7.5 has how much more energy than a quake of magnitude 6.5?
A) 32 times more
B) 32 times less
C) twice as much
D) about half as much
15. How are most lives lost during an earthquake?
A) tsunamis
B) primary waves
C) collapse of buildings
D) broken gas lines

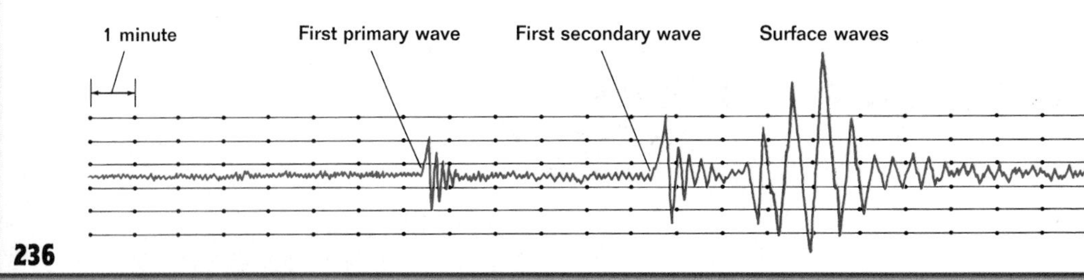

236

Thinking Critically

16. Tension along the Mid-Atlantic Ridge causes normal faults to form.
17. Tsunamis are caused by earthquakes that displace the ocean floor. Tides, on the other hand, are caused by the gravitational pull among the sun, the moon, and Earth.
18. The single-story, wood-frame house would be more stable because the wood is able to give more than the masonry building when surface waves travel through it.

Thinking Critically

16. What kind of faults would you expect to be most common along the Mid-Atlantic Ridge? Explain.
17. Tsunamis often are called tidal waves. Explain why this is incorrect.
18. Which would probably be more stable during an earthquake—a single-story wood-frame house or a brick building? Explain.

Developing Skills

If you need help, refer to the **Skill Handbook.**

19. **Interpreting Scientific Illustrations:** The illustration on the opposite page is a typical record of earthquake waves made on a seismograph. How many minutes passed between the arrival of the first primary wave and the first secondary wave?
20. **Concept Mapping:** Complete the concept map below showing what faults result from the three forces. Use the following terms: *tension, compression, shear, normal faults, reverse faults,* and *strike-slip faults.*

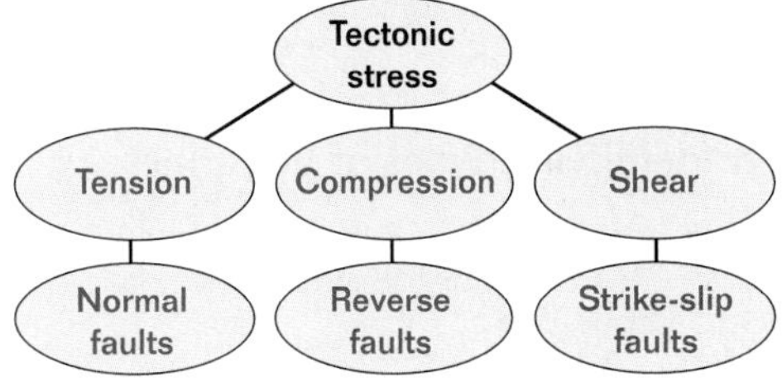

Test-Taking Tip

Work Weak Areas, Maintain Strong Ones It's sometimes difficult to focus on all the concepts needed for a test. So, ask yourself "What's my strongest area?" and "What's my weakest area?" Focus most of your energy on your weak areas. But, also put in some upkeep time in your best areas.

Test Practice

Use these questions to test your Science Proficiency.

1. Normal faults occur when tension is applied to rocks. Which of the following statements **BEST** supports this fact?
   A) As tension is applied, Earth's crust thins and can crack.
   B) When Earth's crust thins and cracks due to tension, the rock above the fault moves down relative to the rock below the fault.
   C) Tension causes Earth's crust to fold and eventually develop faults.
   D) When Earth's crust thins and cracks due to tension, the rock above the fault moves up relative to the rock below the fault.
2. Seismic records show that primary waves slow down and secondary waves stop when they reach Earth's outer core. What does this tell you about Earth's outer core?
   A) The density of Earth material increases in the outer core.
   B) Earth's outer core is solid.
   C) Earth's outer core is liquid and has a lower density than rock material at the bottom of the mantle.
   D) Earth's inner core is solid and more dense than the mantle.

THE PRINCETON REVIEW Test Practice

The Test-Taking Tip was written by The Princeton Review, the nation's leader in test preparation.

1. B
2. C

Developing Skills

19. 5 minutes
20. *Tension, compression,* and *shear* would branch from *tectonic stress; normal faults* would branch from *tension; reverse faults* would branch from *compression; strike-slip faults* would branch from *shear.*

Bonus Question

Would earthquake foci at divergent plate boundaries be deep, intermediate, or shallow? Explain your answer. *Earthquake foci at divergent plate boundaries would be shallow. Cracks and faults formed at a divergent plate boundary would occur at or near Earth's surface.*

Assessment Resources

The **Test Practice Workbook** provides students with practice in the format, concepts, and critical-thinking skills tested in standardized exams.

Reproducible Masters

Chapter Review, pp. 15–16 L2
Performance Assessment, p. 22 L2
Assessment, pp. 33–36 L2

Glencoe Technology

Chapter Review Software
Computer Test Bank
MindJogger Videoquiz

Chapter 9 Volcanoes

Section	Objectives	Activities/Features
Chapter Opener		**Explore Activity:** Model a Volcano, p. 239
9-1 **What causes volcanoes?** 2 Sessions 1 Block	1. **Describe** how volcanoes can affect people. 2. **Identify** conditions that cause volcanoes. 3. **Describe** the relationship between volcanoes and Earth's moving plates.	**Using Math,** p. 241 **Skill Builder:** Concept Mapping, p. 245 **Science Journal,** p. 245 **Activity 9-1:** Locating Active Volcanoes, pp. 246–247
9-2 **Types of Volcanoes** 1 Session ½ Block	4. **Relate** the explosiveness of a volcanic eruption to the silica and water vapor content of its lava. 5. **Identify** three forms of volcanoes.	**Physics Integration,** p. 249 **Life Science Integration,** p. 249 **Problem Solving:** Comparing Volcanic Rocks, p. 252 **MiniLab:** Modeling Volcanic Cones, p. 253 **Skill Builder:** Making and Using Graphs, p. 254 **Using Math,** p. 254
9-3 **Igneous Rock Features** 3 Sessions 1½ Blocks	6. **Explain** how intrusive igneous rock features form. 7. **Explain** how a volcanic neck and a caldera form.	**MiniLab:** Modeling Magma Movement, p. 256 **Physics Integration,** p. 257 **Using Math,** p. 259 **Skill Builder:** Comparing and Contrasting, p. 259 **Using Computers,** p. 259 **Activity 9-2:** Identifying Types of Volcanoes, p. 260 **Science and Society:** Predicting Volcanic Eruptions, p. 261

The number of recommended single-period sessions The number of recommended blocks
One session and one-half block are allowed for chapter review and assessment.

Activity Materials

Explore	Activities	MiniLabs
p. 239 modeling clay, baking soda, red food coloring, vinegar	pp. 246–247 world map, tracing paper, Figures 8-2, 9-3, 10-9 p. 260 Figure 9-1, paper, pencil	p. 253 sand or sugar, paper plate, plaster of paris, protractor p. 256 2 transparent plastic cups, colored cooking oil, water, dropper

Need Materials? Contact Science Kit at 1-800-828-7777 or at www.sciencekit.com on the Internet.
For alternate materials, see the activity on the listed page.

Standards		Reproducible Resources	Technology
National	State/Local	Test Practice Workbooks are available for use with each chapter.	English and Spanish audiocassettes are available for use with each section.
National Content Standards: UCP1, A1, B2, B3, D1, F3		**Activity Worksheets,** pp. 49–50 **Enrichment,** p. 22 **Laboratory Manual,** pp. 57–58 **Reinforcement,** p. 22 **Study Guide,** pp. 33–34	**Section Focus Transparency 22** **National Geographic Society: STV** **Glencoe Science Voyages Interactive Videodisc—Earth** **The Infinite Voyage Series**
National Content Standards: UCP1, UCP5, A1, B1, B2, F3		**Activity Worksheets,** p. 53 **Critical Thinking/Problem Solving,** p. 9 **Enrichment,** p. 23 **Laboratory Manual,** pp. 59–60 **Multicultural Connections,** pp. 17–18 **Reinforcement,** p. 23	**Section Focus Transparency 23** **Teaching Transparency 17** **Glencoe Science Voyages Interactive CD-ROM** **Glencoe Science Voyages Interactive Videodisc—Earth** **Internet Connection,** p. 252
National Content Standards: UCP1, UCP2, UCP5, A1, B2, E1, E2, F1, F4, F5		**Activity Worksheets,** pp. 51–52, 54 **Enrichment,** p. 24 **Reinforcement,** p. 24 **Study Guide,** pp. 34–36	**Section Focus Transparency 24** **Teaching Transparency 18** **Science Integration Transparency 9** **Glencoe Science Voyages Interactive Videodisc—Earth** **Internet Connection,** p. 261

Key to Teaching Strategies

The following designations will help you decide which activities are appropriate for your students.

L1 Level 1 activities should be appropriate for students with learning difficulties.

L2 Level 2 activities should be within the ability range of all students.

L3 Level 3 activities are designed for above-average students.

ELL ELL activities should be within the ability range of English Language Learners.

COOP LEARN Cooperative Learning activities are designed for small group work.

P These strategies represent student products that can be placed into a best-work portfolio.

Multiple Learning Styles logos, as described on page 61T, are used throughout to indicate strategies that address different learning styles.

Assessment Resources

Chapter Review, pp. 17–18
Assessment, pp. 37–40
Performance Assessment in the Science Classroom (PASC)
MindJogger Videoquiz
Alternate Assessment in the Science Classroom
Performance Assessment, p. 23
Chapter Review Software
Computer Test Bank

Chapter 9

Volcanoes

This is a representation of key blackline masters available in the Teacher Classroom Resources. See Resource Manager boxes within the chapter for additional information.

Transparencies

Section Focus Transparencies

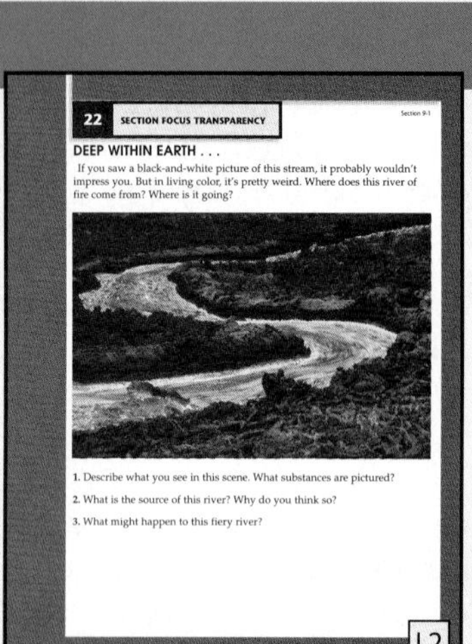

22 SECTION FOCUS TRANSPARENCY — Section 9-1

DEEP WITHIN EARTH . . .

If you saw a black-and-white picture of this stream, it probably wouldn't impress you. But in living color, it's pretty weird. Where does this river of fire come from? Where is it going?

1. Describe what you see in this scene. What substances are pictured?
2. What is the source of this river? Why do you think so?
3. What might happen to this fiery river?

L2

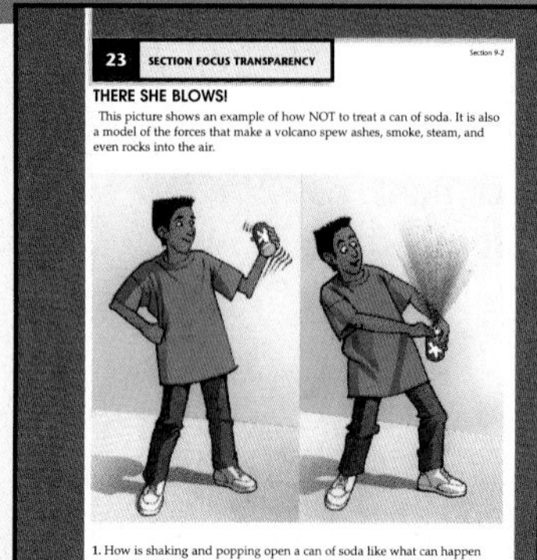

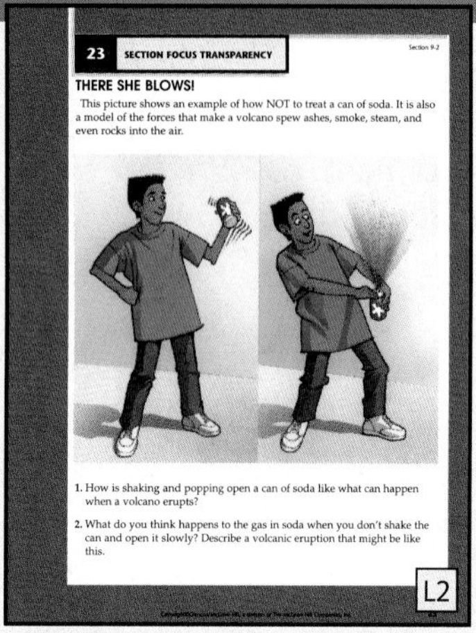

23 SECTION FOCUS TRANSPARENCY — Section 9-2

THERE SHE BLOWS!

This picture shows an example of how NOT to treat a can of soda. It is also a model of the forces that make a volcano spew ashes, smoke, steam, and even rocks into the air.

1. How is shaking and popping open a can of soda like what can happen when a volcano erupts?
2. What do you think happens to the gas in soda when you don't shake the can and open it slowly? Describe a volcanic eruption that might be like this.

L2

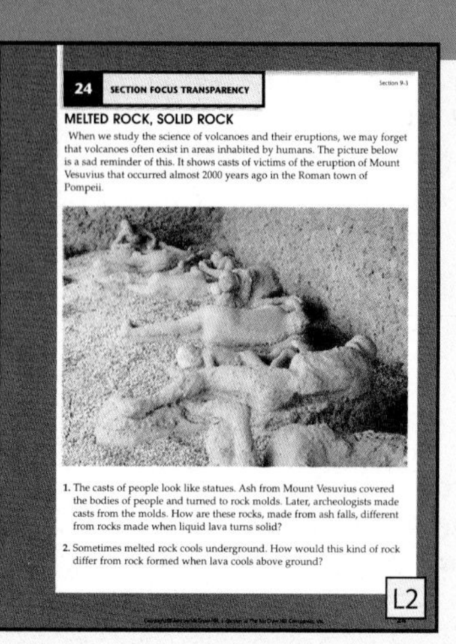

24 SECTION FOCUS TRANSPARENCY — Section 9-3

MELTED ROCK, SOLID ROCK

When we study the science of volcanoes and their eruptions, we may forget that volcanoes often exist in areas inhabited by humans. The picture below is a sad reminder of this. It shows casts of victims of the eruption of Mount Vesuvius that occurred almost 2000 years ago in the Roman town of Pompeii.

1. The casts of people look like statues. Ash from Mount Vesuvius covered the bodies of people and turned to rock molds. Later, archeologists made casts from the molds. How are these rocks, made from ash falls, different from rocks made when liquid lava turns solid?
2. Sometimes melted rock cools underground. How would this kind of rock differ from rock formed when lava cools above ground?

L2

Science Integration Transparencies

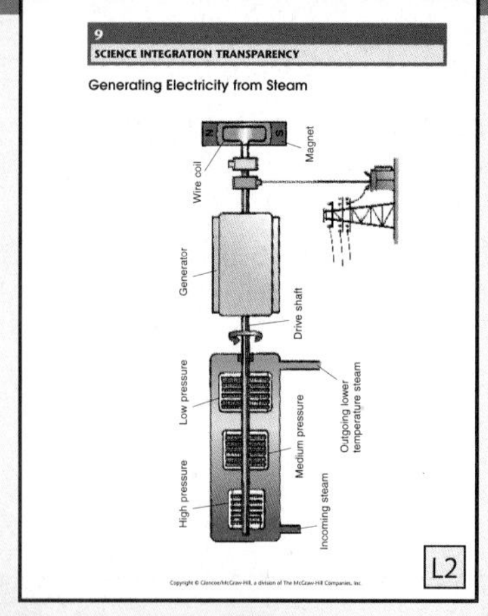

9 SCIENCE INTEGRATION TRANSPARENCY

Generating Electricity from Steam

L2

Teaching Transparencies

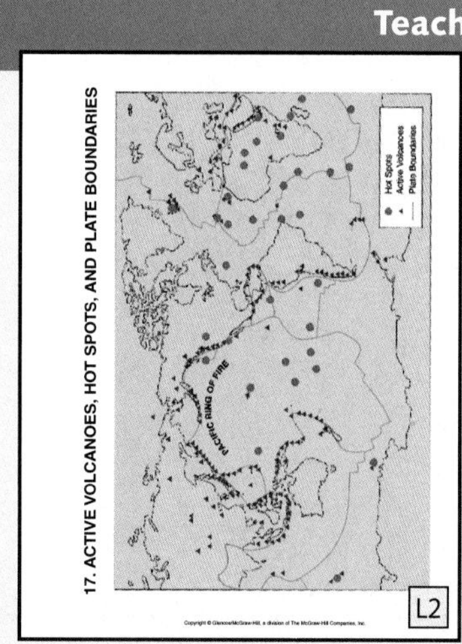

17. ACTIVE VOLCANOES, HOT SPOTS, AND PLATE BOUNDARIES

L2

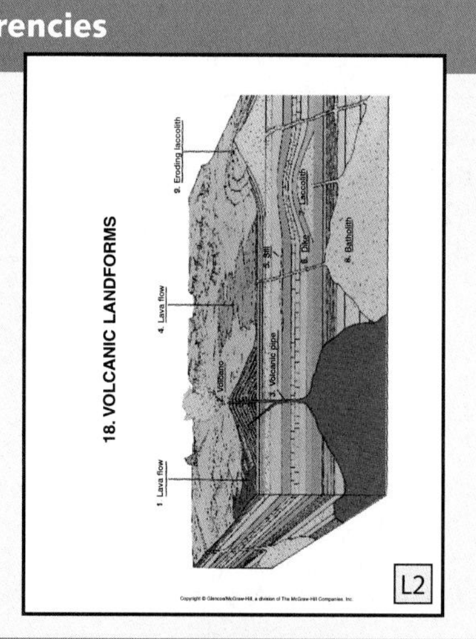

18. VOLCANIC LANDFORMS

L2

Meeting Different Ability Levels

Study Guide for Content Mastery

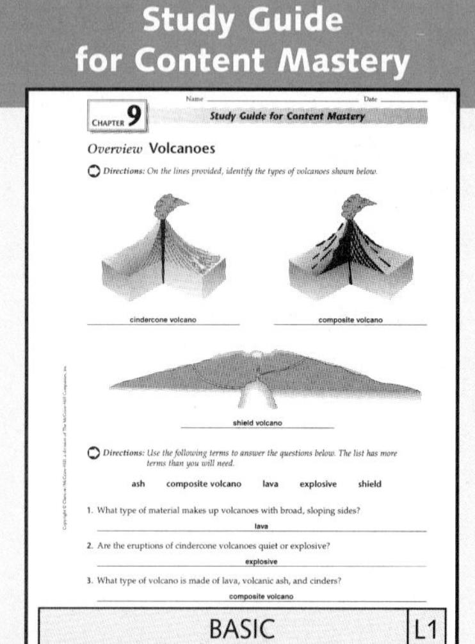

Name ______ Date ______

CHAPTER 9 — Study Guide for Content Mastery

Overview Volcanoes

Directions: On the lines provided, identify the types of volcanoes shown below.

Directions: Use the following terms to answer the questions below. The list has more terms than you will need.

ash composite volcano lava explosive shield

1. What type of material makes up volcanoes with broad, sloping sides? lava
2. Are the eruptions of cindercone volcanoes quiet or explosive? explosive
3. What type of volcano is made of lava, volcanic ash, and cinders? composite volcano

BASIC L1

Reinforcement

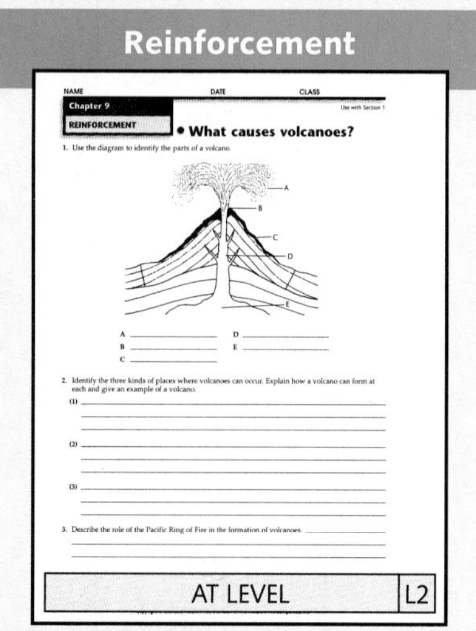

NAME DATE CLASS

Chapter 9 REINFORCEMENT — Use with Section 1

• What causes volcanoes?

1. Use the diagram to identify the parts of a volcano.

A ______ D ______
B ______ E ______
C ______

2. Identify the three kinds of places where volcanoes can occur. Explain how a volcano can form at each and give an example of a volcano.

(1) ______
(2) ______
(3) ______

3. Describe the role of the Pacific Ring of Fire in the formation of volcanoes. ______

AT LEVEL L2

Enrichment Worksheets

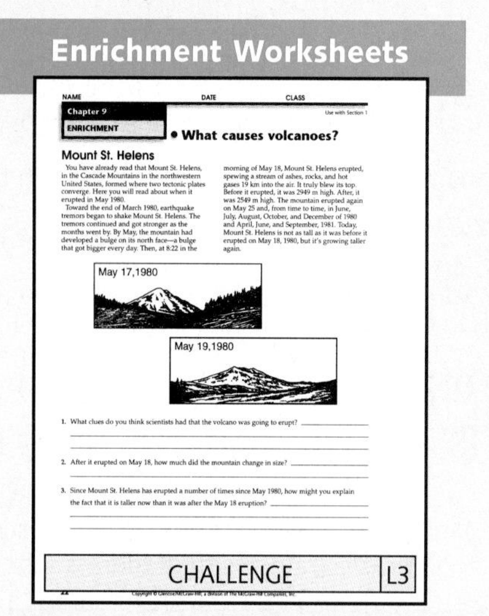

NAME DATE CLASS

Chapter 9 ENRICHMENT — Use with Section 1

• What causes volcanoes?

Mount St. Helens

You have already read that Mount St. Helens, in the Cascade Mountains in the northwestern United States, formed where two tectonic plates converge. Here you will read about when it erupted in May 1980.

Toward the end of March 1980, earthquake tremors began to shake Mount St. Helens. The tremors continued and got stronger as the months went by. By May, the mountain had developed a bulge on its north face—a bulge that got bigger every day. Then, at 8:22 in the morning of May 18, Mount St. Helens erupted, spewing a stream of ashes, rocks, and hot gases 19 km into the air. It truly blew its top. Before it erupted, it was 2949 m high. After, it was 2549 m high. The mountain erupted again on May 25 and, from time to time, in June, July, August, October, and December of 1980 and April, June, and September, 1981. Today, Mount St. Helens is not as tall as it was before it erupted on May 18, 1980, but it's growing taller again.

1. What clues do you think scientists had that the volcano was going to erupt? ______
2. After it erupted on May 18, how much did the mountain change in size? ______
3. Since Mount St. Helens has erupted a number of times since May 1980, how might you explain the fact that it is taller now than it was after the May 18 eruption? ______

CHALLENGE L3

Resource Manager

Hands-on Activities

Activity Worksheets

NAME DATE CLASS

Chapter 9
ACTIVITY 9-1
• Locating Active Volcanoes

Lab Preview

What are lines of latitude and longitude? ______

Have you ever wondered why volcanic eruptions occur in certain regions on Earth? Volcanoes form when hot, melted rock material is forced upward to Earth's surface. As the melted rock moves inside Earth, vibrations occur, which are felt as earthquakes. In this activity, you will see whether the locations of active volcanoes are correlated to the locations of recent earthquakes.

What You'll Investigate

Is there a correlation between the locations of active volcanoes and the locations of earthquake epicenters?

Goals

- **Plot** the locations of several active volcanoes.
- **Describe** any correlation you see between locations of volcanoes and locations of earthquake epicenters.

Materials

- Appendix G
- tracing paper
- figures in your textbook showing the locations of earthquakes and tectonic plate boundaries of active volcanos

Procedure

1. Use tracing paper to outline the continents on the world map in Appendix G. Include the lines of latitude and longitude on your tracing.

Volcano Locations

Volcano	Latitude	Longitude	Volcano	Latitude	Longitude
#1	64° N	19° W	#11	15° N	43° E
#2	28° N	34° E	#12	6° N	75° W
#3	43° S	172° E	#13	64° S	158° E
#4	35° N	136° E	#14	38° S	78° E
#5	18° S	68° W	#15	21° S	56° E
#6	25° S	114° W	#16	38° N	26° E
#7	20° N	155° W	#17	7° S	13° W
#8	54° N	167° W	#18	2° S	102° E
#9	16° N	122° E	#19	38° N	30° W
#10	28° N	17° W	#20	54° N	159° [illegible]
			#21	17° N	62° [illegible]

L2

Lab Manual

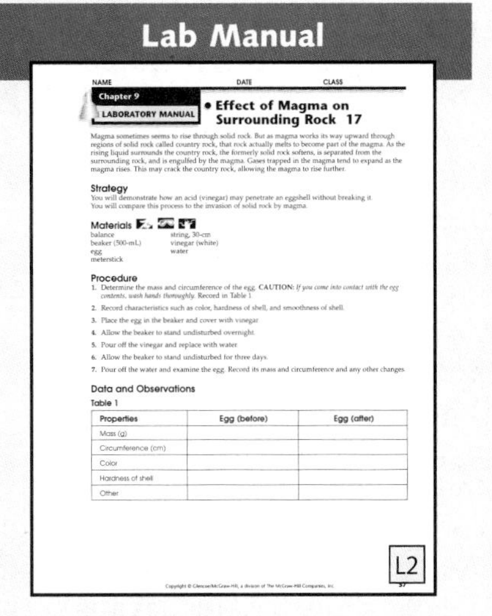
NAME DATE CLASS

Chapter 9
LABORATORY MANUAL
• Effect of Magma on Surrounding Rock 17

Strategy

Materials

Procedure

Data and Observations

Table 1

Properties	Egg (before)	Egg (after)
Mass (g)		
Circumference (cm)		
Color		
Hardness of shell		
Other		

L2

Accessibility

Spanish Resources

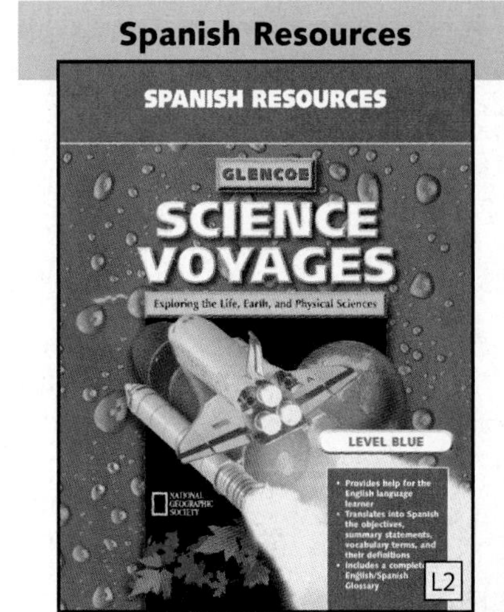

Assessment

Performance Assessment

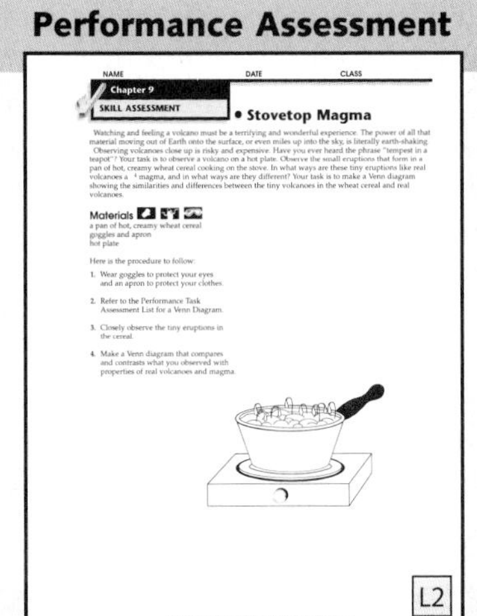
NAME DATE CLASS

Chapter 9
SKILL ASSESSMENT
• Stovetop Magma

Materials

L2

Chapter Review

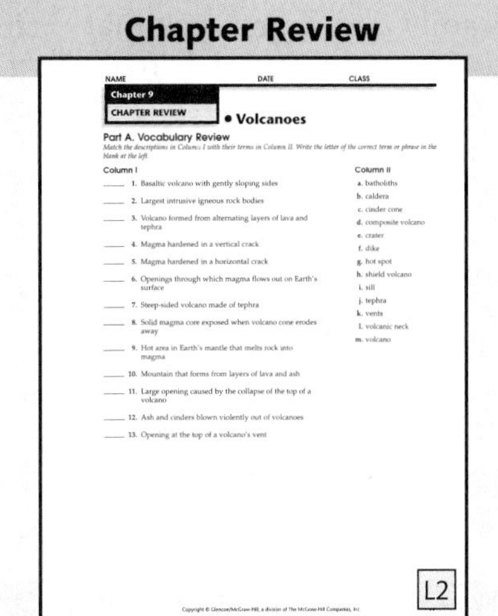
NAME DATE CLASS

Chapter 9
CHAPTER REVIEW
• Volcanoes

Part A. Vocabulary Review

L2

Assessment

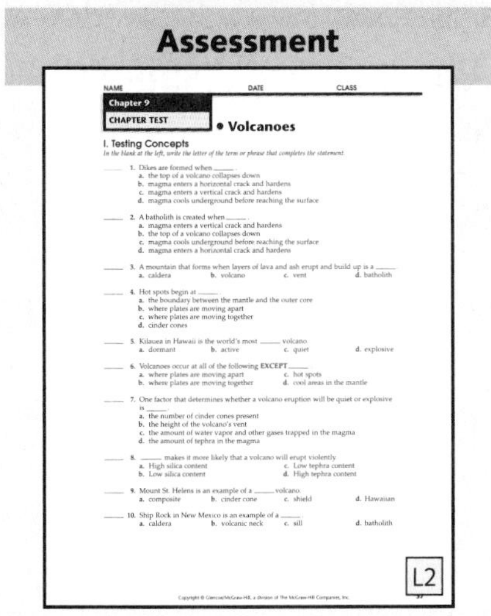
NAME DATE CLASS

Chapter 9
CHAPTER TEST
• Volcanoes

I. Testing Concepts

L2

Test Practice Workbook

Extending Content

Critical Thinking/ Problem Solving

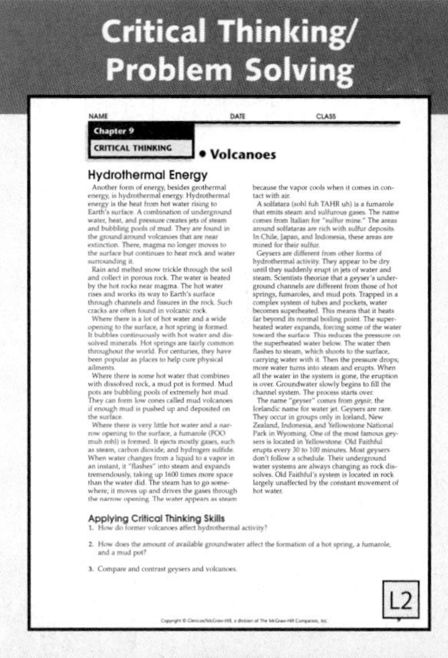
NAME DATE CLASS

Chapter 9
CRITICAL THINKING
• Volcanoes

Hydrothermal Energy

Applying Critical Thinking Skills

L2

Multicultural Connections

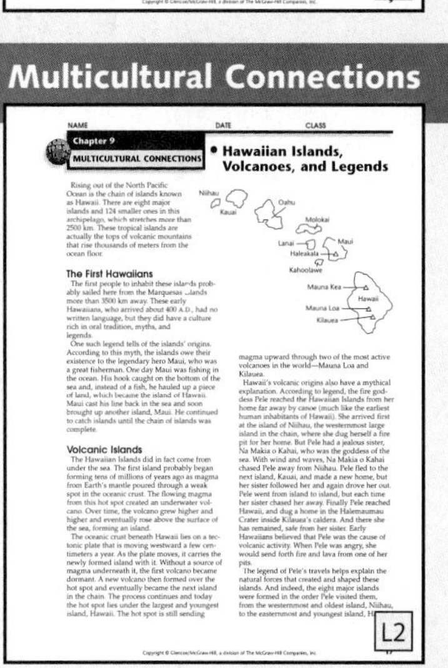
NAME DATE CLASS

Chapter 9
MULTICULTURAL CONNECTIONS
• Hawaiian Islands, Volcanoes, and Legends

The First Hawaiians

Volcanic Islands

L2

Volcanoes

Helping You Prepare

How do volcanoes form?
(Section 9-1)

The distribution of volcanoes on Earth's surface is related to the position and motion of Earth's plates. Volcanic eruptions occur where Earth's plates move apart (divergent boundaries) move together (convergent boundaries), and along regions on Earth not necessarily on plate boundaries, called hot spots. These regions form magma below Earth's surface that is less dense than surrounding rocks. This magma rises toward the surface and erupts as lava, forming volcanoes.

Lava from some volcanoes, such as those in Hawaii and Iceland, is basaltic. Basaltic lava is strongly associated with divergent plate boundaries and hot spot locations. This type of lava is relatively low in the compound silica (SiO_2) and enriched in the elements magnesium and iron. Basaltic lava flows readily and forms rock that is dense compared to those formed from granitic lava.

Granitic lava flows from volcanoes like Mount St. Helens in Washington, where Earth's plates move together. Granitic lava is high in silica and depleted in magnesium and iron. Granitic lava is viscous and resists flow. At convergent plate boundaries that form volcanoes, one plate is forced under another, and partial melting of the plate at depth occurs. Lava compositions between basaltic and granitic occur, and depend upon the type of plate boundary, the materials that originally melted to form magma, and mixing between more than one batch of magma.

GLENCOE TECHNOLOGY

 **CD-ROM**

Glencoe Science Voyages Interactive CD-ROM

Chapter Summaries

Use the Chapter Summary to introduce, teach, or review chapter material.

Styles of Eruption
(Section 9-2)

Material ejected from volcanoes includes lava, gases, and tephra (ejected lava fragments). Most of the gas released from volcanoes is water vapor. Gases make up between one and five percent of the total weight of most magmas. It is thought that water vapor from magmas was the source of the water in Earth's early oceans. Also, gases released by volcanoes may have contributed to the composition of Earth's early atmosphere.

Materials that comprise tephra are referred to as cinders when they are the size of peas and lapilli when they are the size of walnuts. Mate-

NATIONAL GEOGRAPHIC — **Teacher's Corner**

Products Available from Glencoe

To order the following products for use with this chapter, call Glencoe at 1-800-334-7344:

CD-ROM

NGS PictureShow: Dynamic Earth

Curriculum Kits

GeoKit: Dynamic Earth

GeoKit: Earth's Crust

Transparency Set

NGS PicturePack: Dynamic Earth

Videodisk

STV: Restless Earth

Products Available from National Geographic Society

To order the following products for use with this chapter, call the National Geographic Society at 1-800-368-2728:

Videos

Changing Earth: Forces That Create, Forces That Destroy

Living on Our Changing Planet

Our Dynamic Earth

Volcano!

rial larger than lapilli is called blocks or bombs when ejected in a semi-molten state. Volcanic ash is tephra that is smaller than 4 mm.

Volcanic eruptions that form at divergent plate boundaries and hot spots tend to expel basaltic lava. This lava flows readily, releases gas easily, and is associated with nonexplosive eruptions, like most of those in Hawaii. Eruptions along convergent boundaries produce lava that is richer in silica; this lava traps gas more easily and is associated with more dangerous, explosive eruptions, such as the 1980 eruption of Mount St. Helens.

Forms of Volcanoes (Section 9-2)

Shield volcanoes are the largest. Mauna Loa, for example, measures 9 km from top to base and about 200 km from side to side. Next in size are composite volcanoes. Mount Rainier, for example, measures 3 km from top to base and about 20 km from side to side. The smallest form of volcano is the cinder cone volcano. Sunset crater, for example, measures about 0.3 km from top to base and about 1.8 km from side to side.

Not all eruptions of lava come from volcanoes. Some lava is erupted through fissures (cracks) in Earth. The Columbia Plateau, located in the northwestern United States, formed from layer after layer of basaltic lava that extruded as fissure eruptions.

Viscous (thick) lava does not flow easily. As this type of lava is extruded, it often produces a dome-shaped mass of lava called a lava dome. Scientists study the growth of lava domes for signs of continued or renewed eruptions. Changes in growth rate of lava domes can indicate changes inside the volcano. Many lava domes form after explosive eruptions.

SCIENCE UPDATE

For current events or science in the news, access the Glencoe Science Web Site at **www.glencoe.com/sec/science**

Intrusive Features (Section 9-3)

Another name for intrusive igneous rock bodies is plutons. Plutons are described by position, shape, and/or size. Plutons that are flat and shaped similar to a tabletop are called tabular. Examples are dikes and sills. Others, such as batholiths, are large and massive. Plutons, such as sills, are concordant. This means they form between layers of surrounding rock. Others, such as dikes, are discordant in that they cut across surrounding rock layers.

Crater Lake, located in Oregon, formed about 7000 years ago when a volcano spewed 40 to 50 km^3 of volcanic material into the air. With the magma chamber then partly emptied, 1500 m of the original 3600-m cone collapsed. Rainwater filled the caldera to form a lake. Magma forced to the surface after the caldera formed built Wizard Island in the lake.

Teacher to Teacher

"The geographic locations of volcanoes is an important part of understanding plate tectonics. Have students plot the locations of volcanoes on a class map. This activity helps to either introduce or reinforce the concept of plates and plate boundaries."

Kevin Finnegan

Kevin Finnegan, Teacher
McCord Middle School
Worthington, OH

CHAPTER 9 Volcanoes

CHAPTER OVERVIEW

Section 9-1 Volcanoes, how they form, and how they can affect people are discussed. The link between volcanism and Earth's moving plates is presented.

Section 9-2 The relationship between lava composition and the explosiveness of a volcano is discussed. Three forms of volcanoes are described.

Section 9-3 This section compares and contrasts the mode of formation of several intrusive igneous rock features.

Chapter Vocabulary

volcano	composite volcano
vent	batholith
crater	dike
hot spot	sill
shield volcano	volcanic neck
tephra	caldera
cinder cone	

Theme Connection

Energy/Stability and Change The energy involved in the formation of magma, its movement upward toward the surface, and finally its flow onto the surface as lava should be focal points of the chapter. Stability and change is a secondary theme for this chapter when the evolution of volcanoes is presented.

If time does not permit teaching the entire chapter, use Reviewing Main Ideas on pp. 262–263.

CHAPTER 9 Volcanoes

Chapter Preview

Section 9-1
What causes volcanoes?

Section 9-2
Types of Volcanoes

Section 9-3
Igneous Rock Features

Skills Preview

Skill Builders
- Map Concepts

Activities
- Measure
- Interpret Data

MiniLabs
- Make a Model

Reading Check

Before you begin this chapter, look up the word origins of unfamiliar terms like *tephra, batholith,* and *caldera.* Knowing the origins will help you understand these words.

Multiple Learning Styles

Look for the following logos for strategies that emphasize different learning modalities.

Linguistic Across the Curriculum, pp. 241, 244, 250, 252; Science Journal, pp. 249, 258; Inclusion Strategies, p. 251; Using Science Words, p. 257; Preview, p. 262

Logical-Mathematical Activity, pp. 246–247

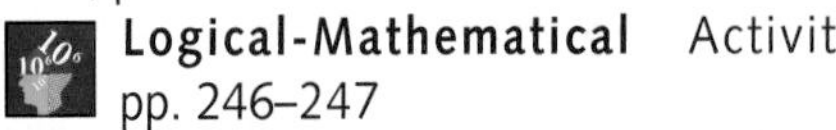

Visual-Spatial Quick Demo, p. 243; Reteach, pp. 244, 262; Visual Learning, p. 250; Activity, p. 258

Auditory-Musical Activity, p. 244; Out of Time, p. 262

Kinesthetic Explore Activity, p. 239; Multiple Learning Styles, p. 251; MiniLab, pp. 253, 256

Interpersonal Activity, p. 260; Review, p. 262

Explore Activity

The explosive eruptions of Soufrière Hills volcano on the Caribbean island of Montserrat began in July 1995 and have blanketed much of the island with volcanic ash. Clouds of ash rose to heights of 12 000 m and covered much of the capital city of Plymouth. Volcanoes can be spectacular and dangerous. Massive eruptions of volcanic ash into Earth's atmosphere can cause drastic changes in the environment. On a smaller scale, and definitely in the case of Montserrat island's population, volcanic eruptions affect humans in many ways. List harmful and also helpful effects that volcanoes have.

Model a Volcano

1. Use clay to make a small model volcano with a crater at the top.
2. Place a small amount of baking soda (less than 1/4 teaspoon) and a drop of red food coloring in the crater.
3. Add approximately 20 mL of vinegar to the baking soda in the crater.

Science Journal

In your Science Journal, write a paragraph that explains what happens to the baking soda and food coloring when the vinegar is added. Hypothesize how your model eruption is similar to an actual eruption and how it is different.

239

Assessment Planner

Portfolio
Refer to p. 263 for suggested items that students might select for their portfolios.

Performance Assessment
See p. 263 for additional Performance Assessment options.
Skill Builder, pp. 245, 259
MiniLab, pp. 253, 256
Activity 9-1, pp. 246–247; 9-2, p. 260

Content Assessment
Section Assessment, pp. 245, 254, 259
Chapter Assessment, pp. 264–265
Proficiency Prep, pp. 244, 254, 259

Explore Activity

Purpose

Kinesthetic Use the Explore Activity to introduce students to a study of volcanic eruptions. L1 ELL COOP LEARN

Materials

for one volcano: modeling clay, $\frac{1}{4}$ teaspoon baking soda, 1 drop red food coloring, 20 mL vinegar

Teaching Strategies

- Have each group place a small metal cup in the crater of the model volcano to hold the baking soda and vinegar.
- Cover work areas with plastic or newspaper.

Safety Precautions All students should wear safety goggles during the activity. Caution students to use only a small amount of baking soda.

Gases and other materials flow out of the volcano as it erupts. This is similar to how trapped gases can cause a real volcano to erupt. The difference is that in a real volcano, the force that causes the eruption comes from below Earth's surface. It is not caused by a reaction of surface materials.

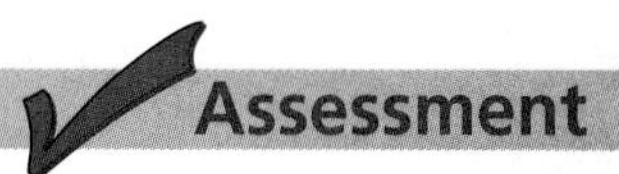

Process Have students write how the model volcano and the real volcano compare. Use **Performance Assessment in the Science Classroom,** p. 87.

SECTION 9•1

Prepare

Refer to **How do volcanoes form?** on p. 238E.

Preplanning

Refer to the **Chapter Organizer** on pp. 238A–B.

1 Motivate

Bellringer

Before presenting the lesson, display **Section Focus Transparency 22** on the overhead projector. Use the accompanying **Focus Activity** worksheet. L2 ELL

Section 9-1

22 SECTION FOCUS TRANSPARENCY

DEEP WITHIN EARTH . . .

If you saw a black-and-white picture of this stream, it probably wouldn't impress you. But in living color, it's pretty weird. Where does this river of fire come from? Where is it going?

1. Describe what you see in this scene. What substances are pictured?
2. What is the source of this river? Why do you think so?
3. What might happen to this fiery river?

Tying to Previous Knowledge

Have students recall how earthquakes occur where plates of Earth's surface move apart or move together.

9•1 What causes volcanoes?

What You'll Learn

- How volcanoes can affect people
- Conditions that cause volcanoes
- The relationship between volcanoes and Earth's moving plates

Vocabulary
volcano
vent
crater
hot spot

Why It's Important

- You'll understand why volcanoes are common in certain regions on Earth.

Volcanoes and You

A **volcano** is an opening in Earth's surface. It often forms a mountain when layers of lava and volcanic ash erupt and build up. Most of Earth's volcanoes are dormant, which means that they are not currently active, but more than 600 are active now. Active volcanoes sometimes erupt smoke, steam, ash, cinders, and flows of lava.

In 1980, Mount St. Helens in Washington state erupted. It was one of the largest recent volcanic eruptions in North America. Geologists warned people to leave the area surrounding the mountain. Most people left, but a few stayed. A total of 59 people were killed as a result of the eruption. Heat from the eruption melted snow, which also caused mudslides and flooding in the area.

Active Volcanoes

For centuries, the Kilauea volcano in Hawaii has been erupting, but not explosively. Most of the town of Kalapana Gardens was destroyed in May 1990. No one was hurt because the lava moved slowly. The most recent series of eruptions from Kilauea, as seen in **Figure 9-1,** began in January 1983.

Figure 9-1 Kilauea in Hawaii has been continually erupting since January 3, 1983, becoming the most active volcano on Earth. Living with volcanoes as active as Kilauea can create serious problems for home owners. Losses have reached 61 million dollars as at least 181 homes have been destroyed.

Resource Manager

The following **Teacher Classroom Resources** can be used with Section 9-1:

 **Reproducible Masters**

Activity Worksheets, pp. 49–50 L2

Enrichment, p. 22 L3

Laboratory Manual, pp. 57–58 L2

Reinforcement, p. 22 L2

Study Guide, pp. 33–34 L1 ELL

Figure 9-2 Volcanic ash covered several buildings in Iceland during an eruption in 1973. **Why might people continue to live close to a volcano despite the danger?**

Kilauea is the world's most active volcano. Iceland is also famous for its active volcanoes and is known as the land of fire and ice. An Icelandic eruption is shown in **Figure 9-2.**

Eruptions of the Century

The largest volcanic eruption of the twentieth century occurred on the Alaska Peninsula. Beginning on June 6, 1912, Mount Katmai erupted an estimated 30 times greater volume of material than was expelled during the 1980 eruption of Mount St. Helens. In June 1991, Mount Pinatubo erupted in the Philippines, killing nearly 900 people. The eruption is considered the largest of any volcano in more than half a century. Millions of tons of sulfur dioxide and ash were thrown into Earth's upper atmosphere. It's possible that this material was the cause of the lowered global temperatures and record ozone losses that were observed as recently as 1993.

Just prior to the eruption of Mount Pinatubo, Mount Unzen in Japan erupted. Forty-four people lost their lives, including several volcanologists who were studying the erupting volcano and producing an educational program.

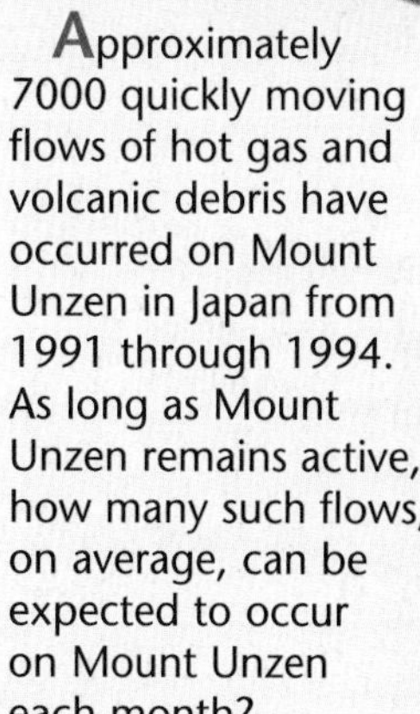

Using Math

Approximately 7000 quickly moving flows of hot gas and volcanic debris have occurred on Mount Unzen in Japan from 1991 through 1994. As long as Mount Unzen remains active, how many such flows, on average, can be expected to occur on Mount Unzen each month?

2 Teach

Caption Answer

Figure 9-2 *Answers will vary; possible answers include fertile soil or access to harbors.*

Teacher FYI

Pyroclastic flows and surges have been responsible for most deaths and injuries caused by volcanic eruptions in the twentieth century. A pyroclastic flow and surge caused almost all of the 29 000 deaths during Mount Pelée's eruption on the island of Martinique in 1902.

Using Math

The average number would equal 7000 ÷ 48 = 146.

NATIONAL GEOGRAPHIC

Videodisc

STV: Restless Earth

Unit 1 Introduction 7:22

00001–14511

Refer to the Teacher Guide for additional bar codes and teaching strategies.

Integrating the Sciences

Chemistry Eruptions of Kilauea are less explosive than those of many other volcanoes. Have students determine how the chemical composition of lava from Kilauea is different from other volcanoes and why this difference results in less explosive eruptions. *Lava from Kilauea is basaltic—a hot, easy flowing lava that does not trap gases.* L2

Across the Curriculum

Literature Have students read a book about famous eruptions, such as the 1902 eruption of Mount Pelée, the 1980 eruption of Mount St. Helens, or the continuing eruptions of Kilauea, and examine how they affected the people there. Ask volunteers to share what they learn with their classmates. L2

Caption Answer

Figure 9-3 *Active volcanoes occur at plate boundaries and at hot spots.*

Correcting Misconceptions

Some students may think only people living near an erupting volcano are affected. Inform them that winds can carry and deposit volcanic ash thousands of kilometers.

Answer to Reading Check
Magma is less dense than the surrounding rock.

GLENCOE TECHNOLOGY

Videodisc

Glencoe Science Voyages Interactive Videodisc—Earth

Side 1, Lesson 4

Volcanoes: Erupting Mountains

42392

42612

43091

44806

45260

45649

Refer to Videodisc Teacher Guide for additional bar codes.

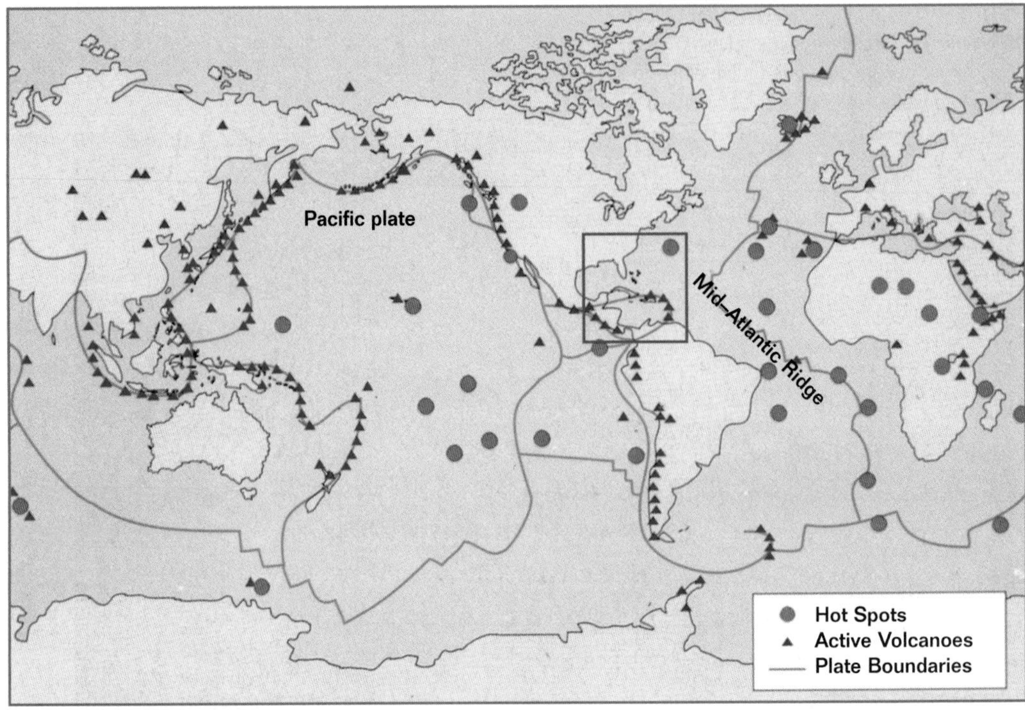

Figure 9-3 The diagram above shows the locations of active volcanoes, hot spots, and plate boundaries around the world. The squared-off area is shown in depth in **Figure 9-4B. How are the locations of active volcanoes related to the locations of hot spots and plate boundaries?**

Reading Check
Why is magma forced upward toward Earth's surface?

How do volcanoes form?

What happens inside Earth to create volcanoes? Why are some areas of Earth more likely to have volcanoes than others? Deep inside Earth, heat and pressure cause rock to melt and form magma. Some deep rocks already are melted. Others are hot enough that a small rise in temperature or drop in pressure can cause them to melt to form magma.

Magma Forced Upward

Magma is less dense than the rock around it, so it is slowly forced upward toward Earth's surface. You can see this process if you turn a bottle of cold syrup upside down. Watch the dense syrup force the less-dense air bubbles slowly toward the top of the bottle.

After many thousands or even millions of years, magma reaches Earth's surface and flows out through an opening called a **vent.** As lava flows out, it cools quickly and becomes solid, forming layers of igneous rock around the vent. The steep-walled depression around a volcano's vent is the **crater.**

Guided Reading Strategy

Flow Chart A flow chart helps students logically sequence events. Students will write major stages of the sequence in large ovals and write sub-stages in smaller ovals under the larger ovals. Have students design a Flow Chart for a concept in this section. Sample flow chart:

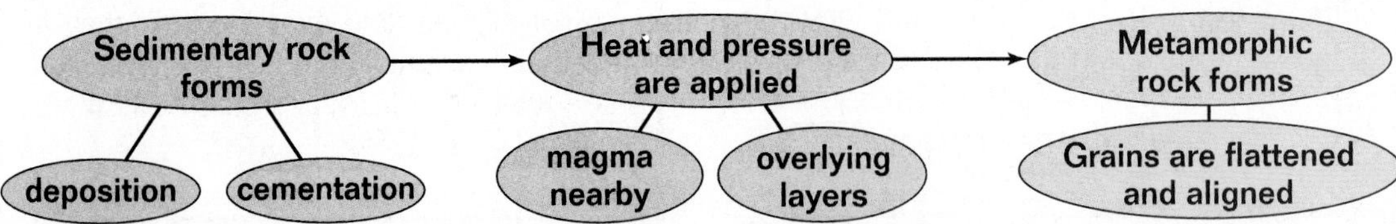

Where do volcanoes occur?

Volcanoes form in places that are directly related to the movement of Earth's plates. Volcanoes occur where plates are moving apart, where plates are moving together, and at locations called hot spots. You can find locations of active volcanoes along with plate boundaries and hot spots on the map in **Figure 9-3.** There are many examples of volcanoes around the world at these three different areas. Let's explore volcanoes in Iceland, the Caribbean island of Montserrat, and Hawaii.

Figure 9-4 The locations of volcanoes depend on the motion of Earth's plates.

Plates Moving Apart

Iceland is a large island in the North Atlantic Ocean. It is near the Arctic Circle and has some glaciers. But, as seen in **Figure 9-2,** it also has volcanoes. Iceland has volcanic activity because it sits on top of the Mid-Atlantic Ridge.

The Mid-Atlantic Ridge is an area where Earth's plates are moving apart. Where plates separate, they form long, deep cracks called rifts. Magma flows from rifts as lava and is quickly cooled by seawater. **Figure 9-4A** shows how magma rises at rifts to form new volcanic rock. As more lava flows, it builds up from the seafloor. Sometimes, the volcanoes and rift eruptions rise above sea level, forming islands such as Iceland.

A Volcanic activity occurs where Earth's plates move apart. **Why does Iceland have volcanoes?**

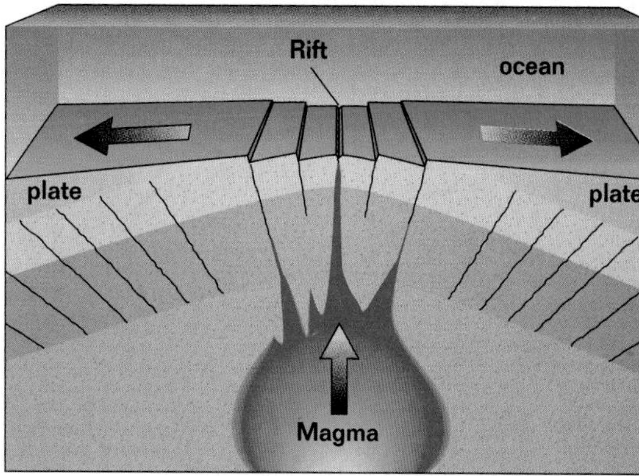

Plates Moving Together

Soufrière Hills volcano is located on the island of Montserrat, which is part of the Lesser Antilles islands of the Caribbean. Soufrière Hills volcano formed because it is located where Earth's plates move together as shown in **Figure 9-4B.** Here, the North and South American plates are forced under the less-dense Caribbean plate.

B Volcanoes form where the North and South American plates are forced below the Caribbean plate. **Why does magma form along this type of plate boundary?**

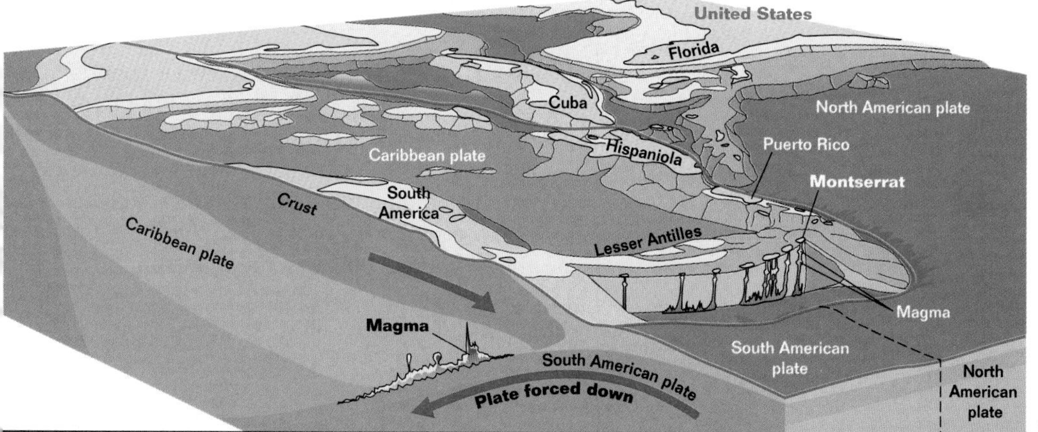

243

Caption Answer

Figure 9-4A *Iceland lies on the Mid-Atlantic Ridge.*

Figure 9-4B *The plate that is forced under another plate partially melts.*

Quick Demo

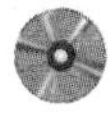

Visual-Spatial Attach an air pump to a balloon neck and place the balloon under a large piece of denim. As you inflate the balloon, explain that the bulge in the cloth represents magma that causes doming on the cloth volcano. Students should conclude that the volcano will eventually erupt. Inform them that bulging and earthquakes are often precursors to eruptions.

Using an Analogy

Show a lava lamp and explain that the rising globs of material inside the lamp are warmer and less dense than the surrounding material. The globs are forced upward, much the same as magma below Earth's surface.

GLENCOE TECHNOLOGY

Videodisc

The Infinite Voyage: To the Edge of the Earth

Chapter 3 *Exploring Volcanoes: To the Center of the Earth*
10:00

Refer to the Teacher Guide for bar codes and teaching strategies.

Integrating the Sciences

Biological Sciences Scientists have recently discovered communities, including giant clams and worms, living near mid-ocean ridges. These communities do not get their energy from sunlight. Bacteria start the food chain by oxidizing hydrogen sulfide brought into the ocean by plumes of very hot water (black smokers) streaming from the rock at various spots along the ridge.

Content Background

Volcanoes have formed all around the Pacific plate where it collides with other plates. This area is called the Pacific Ring of Fire. Volcanoes in this area include Mount Rainier, Mount Hood, Mount Jefferson, Crater Lake, Mount Shasta, and Mount St. Helens.

3 Assess

Check for Understanding

Activity

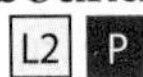

Auditory-Musical Have groups of students compose a short song describing the three geologic settings where volcanoes occur (divergent boundaries, convergent boundaries, and hot spots). L2 P

Reteach

Visual-Spatial Draw a cross section of an area where one of Earth's moving plates is forced under another. Explain how material from the lower plate melts due to changes in temperature. The melted material is less dense than the surrounding material and thus is forced upward toward Earth's surface to form volcanoes. L2

Extension

For students who have mastered this section, use the **Reinforcement** and **Enrichment** masters.

4 Close

Proficiency Prep

Use this quiz to check students' recall of section content.

1. **What is a crater?** *the opening at the top of a volcano's vent*
2. **What is Loihi?** *an underwater volcano extending off of the island of Hawaii*

Caption Answer

Figure 9-5B *The Pacific plate changed its direction of motion at some time. This change is indicated by a bend in the Hawaiian-Emperor Seamount System.*

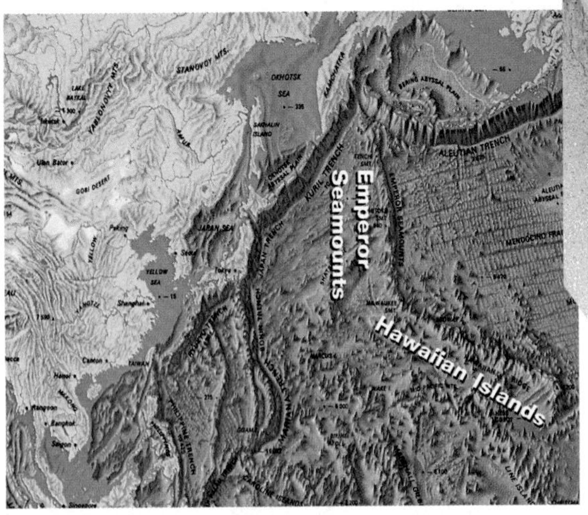

A This map of the ocean floor shows the Hawaiian Islands.

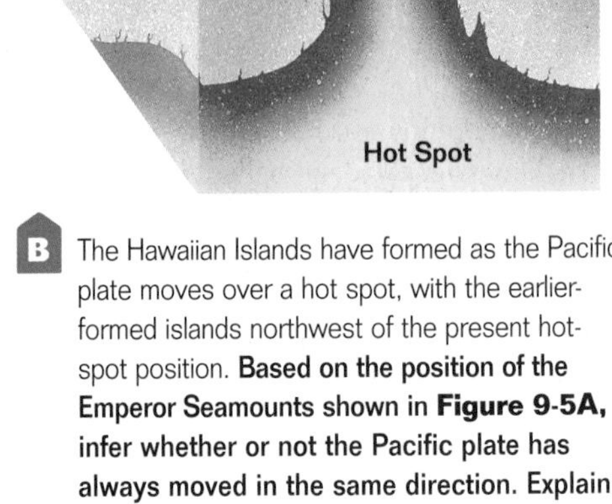

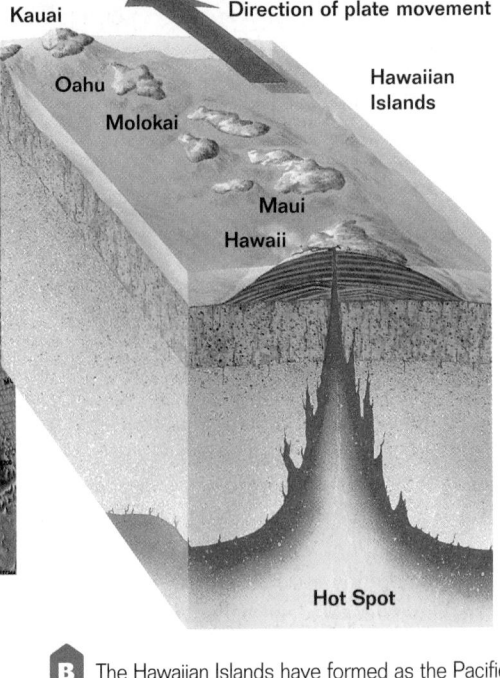

B The Hawaiian Islands have formed as the Pacific plate moves over a hot spot, with the earlier-formed islands northwest of the present hot-spot position. **Based on the position of the Emperor Seamounts shown in Figure 9-5A, infer whether or not the Pacific plate has always moved in the same direction. Explain your answer.**

Figure 9-5 Continued movement of the Pacific plate over a hot spot formed the islands of Kauai, Oahu, Molokai, Maui, and Hawaii over a period of about 5 million years. Scientists suggest that the Emperor Seamounts, which are extinct, underwater volcanoes, also formed in this way.

Magma forms when the plate being forced under the Caribbean plate gets deep enough and hot enough to partially melt. The magma is then forced upward to the surface, forming the volcanoes of the Lesser Antilles. **Figure 9-4B** shows how the North and South American plates are moving below the Caribbean plate.

Hot Spots

Like Iceland, the Hawaiian Islands are volcanic islands. But, unlike Iceland, they haven't formed at a plate boundary. The Hawaiian Islands are in the middle of the Pacific plate, far from its edges. What process could be forming them?

Geologists suggest that some areas in the mantle are hotter than other areas. Some geologists hypothesize that hot-spot magma begins at the boundary between the mantle and the outer core. These **hot spots** melt rock, which is then forced upward toward the crust as magma. The Hawaiian Islands sit on top of a hot spot under the Pacific plate. Magma from

Volcanoes and You Encourage students to visit the office of the city planner or other local government official to ask whether volcanic activity might affect their geographic location. Have them write in their Science Journals about what they discovered. L2

Across the Curriculum

Geography Display a map of the world. Have each student locate one active volcano on the map and place a pin with the name of the volcano at the proper position. Have the class note any patterns. Ask students to list countries that have a greater number of active volcanoes than most and explain why this is true. L2 P

C Computer image showing the island of Hawaii and Loihi, an underwater volcano. If Loihi reaches the surface, it will form a new island.

deep in Earth's mantle has melted through the crust to form several volcanoes. Those that rise above the water form the Hawaiian Islands, as shown in **Figure 9-5C.**

As you can see in **Figures 9-5A** and **9-5B,** the Hawaiian Islands are all in a line. This is because the Pacific plate is moving over the stationary hot spot. The island of Kauai is the oldest Hawaiian island and was once located where the big island of Hawaii is today. As the plate moved, Kauai moved away from the hot spot and became dormant. Continued movement of the Pacific plate formed Oahu, Molokai, Maui, and Hawaii over a period of about 5 million years.

Section Assessment

1. How are volcanoes related to Earth's moving plates?
2. As rock material melts, it becomes less dense. Explain what's happening to the atoms and molecules to cause this.
3. Why does lava cool rapidly along a mid-ocean ridge?
4. **Think Critically:** If the Pacific plate stopped moving, what would happen to the island of Hawaii?
5. **Skill Builder**
   Concept Mapping Make a concept map that shows how the Hawaiian Islands formed over a hot spot. Use the following terms and phrases: *volcano forms, plate moves, volcano becomes dormant,* and *new volcano forms.* If you need help, refer to Concept Mapping in the **Skill Handbook** on page 714.

Science Journal

Scientists were able to predict approximately when Mount Pinatubo in the Philippines would erupt. Research the changes in Earth's crust that were observed that led to this prediction. In your Science Journal, write a report on equipment used to predict volcanic eruptions.

Section Assessment

1. Volcanoes form when lava flows onto Earth's surface where plates are moving apart; one moving plate is forced under another and the magma formed reaches Earth's surface, or plates move over hot spots in Earth's mantle.
2. As matter changes state from a crystalline solid to a liquid, the atoms and molecules move over and around each other. More volume is required to contain the loosely arranged molecules. Thus, the material is usually less dense.
3. Most eruptions occur beneath the ocean. The water cools the lava quickly.
4. **Think Critically** As long as the hot spot provided magma, the island would grow larger and larger.

Science Journal

Answers will vary. Students' replies should include instruments such as tiltmeters, creep meters, lasers, seismographs, and instruments to measure gaseous content.

5. **Skill Builder**
   Possible solution: List the following vertically in a concept map: Volcano forms, Plate moves, Volcano becomes dormant, New volcano forms.

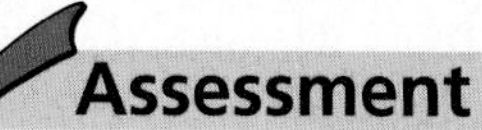

Assessment

Performance Assess students' abilities to make a concept map by having them share their maps with the class. Use **Performance Assessment in the Science Classroom,** p. 89.

Activity 9•1

What You'll Investigate

Purpose

Logical-Mathematical Carry out an investigation in which data interpretation will show the relationships among locations of active volcanoes, earthquakes, hot spots, and boundaries of Earth's plates. L2 COOP LEARN P

Process Skills

communicating, interpreting data, observing, hypothesizing, measuring in SI

Procedure

Time

40 minutes

Materials (optional)

a large, poster-sized world map (suitable for students to use for marking); cardboard backing for the map (so students can stick map pins into it); map pins

Safety Precautions

If the map is mounted for pinning, caution students to handle map pins with care.

Teaching Strategies

Once students finish individual work on their maps, encourage them to use a large, poster-sized map to display their data.

Tying to Previous Knowledge

Review how to determine locations on Earth using lines of latitude and longitude.

Activity 9•1

Locating Active Volcanoes

Materials

- World map
- Tracing paper (2 to 4 pieces)
- Data table on the following page
- **Figure 8-2**
- **Figure 9-3**
- **Figure 10-10**

Have you ever wondered why volcanic eruptions occur in certain regions on Earth? Volcanoes form when hot, melted rock material is forced upward to Earth's surface. As the melted rock moves inside Earth, vibrations occur, which are felt as earthquakes. In this activity, you will see whether the locations of active volcanoes relate to the locations of recent earthquakes.

What You'll Investigate

Is there a correlation between the locations of active volcanoes and the locations of earthquake epicenters?

Goals

- **Plot** the locations of several active volcanoes.
- **Describe** any correlation you see between locations of volcanoes and locations of earthquake epicenters.

Troubleshooting Have copies available, in the same scale, of maps showing active volcano locations, earthquake epicenter locations, and boundaries of Earth's moving plates.

Inclusion Strategies

Visually Impaired Provide your visually impaired students with three-dimensional relief maps that have raised latitude and longitude lines on the surface of the map. Match your visually impaired students with students who are not visually impaired. Encourage the team to use the relief map on which volcano locations can be seen and felt.

Procedure

1. Use tracing paper to outline the continents on a world map. Include the lines of latitude and longitude on your tracing.
2. Use the list of latitudes and longitudes of 21 active volcanoes to plot their locations on your tracing.
3. Compare your tracing with **Figure 8-2** and **Figure 9-3.**
4. In your Science Journal, and on a data table that you make, list the location of each volcano and indicate in a column whether an earthquake epicenter has been plotted close to the volcano. Also include three additional columns in your table to be used in step 5.
5. Using **Figure 10-10,** determine whether each volcano is located near a plate boundary or near a hot spot. Record this information in the extra three columns of your data table.

Volcano Locations

Volcano	Latitude	Longitude
#1	64° N	19° W
#2	28° N	34° E
#3	43° S	172° E
#4	35° N	136° E
#5	18° S	68° W
#6	25° S	114° W
#7	20° N	155° W
#8	54° N	167° W
#9	16° N	122° E
#10	28° N	17° W
#11	15° N	43° E
#12	6° N	75° W
#13	64° S	158° E
#14	38° S	78° E
#15	21° S	56° E
#16	38° N	26° E
#17	7° S	13° W
#18	2° S	102° E
#19	38° N	30° W
#20	54° N	159° E
#21	17° N	62° W

Conclude and Apply

1. **Describe** any patterns of distribution that active volcanoes form on Earth.
2. **Describe** any patterns of distribution of earthquake epicenters shown in **Figure 8-2.**
3. **Compare and contrast** any patterns that you observe with the locations of Earth's plate boundaries and hot spots shown in **Figures 9-3** and **10-10.**
4. **Write a hypothesis** to explain any patterns you observed for locations of active volcanoes, earthquake epicenters, tectonic plate boundaries, and hot spots. Suggest ways in which geologists might test your hypothesis.

Expected Outcome

Students should see a positive correlation between active volcano location and the locations of earthquake epicenters. They also should hypothesize about a relation between active volcano locations and Earth's moving plates.

Error Analysis

Ask students to propose possible reasons for not being able to see a clear relation between volcano locations and the locations of earthquake epicenters. If student correlations do not match expected outcomes, ask them to explain how measuring latitude and longitude could lead to error.

Conclude and Apply

1. Students may note that more volcanoes appear to be associated with the Pacific Ocean.
2. Most epicenters are located around the Pacific Ocean. Other locations fall into patterns along the mid-ocean ridges, in southern Europe, in the Middle East, and north of India.
3. Some hot spots occur along plate boundaries, such as Iceland; some hot spots occur within a plate such as Hawaii.
4. The hypothesis should reflect the relation among active volcanoes and earthquake epicenters around the Pacific Ocean and that earthquakes and active volcanoes also occur in the vicinity of Earth's plate boundaries and hot spots. Accept and discuss all proposals for testing hypotheses.

GO Further

Ask students why they should expect to see a correlation between active volcano locations and the location of earthquake epicenters. *Moving bodies of magma can produce earthquakes, and both earthquakes and volcanoes occur at divergent and convergent plate boundaries.*

Assessment

Performance Tell students that a large number of extinct volcanoes have been located in the midst of one of Earth's large, moving ocean plates. Ask them to explain what might have caused the volcanoes. Use **Performance Assessment in the Science Classroom,** p. 71.

9-1 WHAT CAUSES VOLCANOES? 247

SECTION 9-2

Prepare

Refer to **Styles of Eruption** and **Forms of Volcanoes** on pp. 238E–F.

Preplanning

Refer to the **Chapter Organizer** on pp. 238A–B.

1 Motivate

Bellringer

Before presenting the lesson, display **Section Focus Transparency 23** on the overhead projector. Use the accompanying **Focus Activity** worksheet. L2 ELL

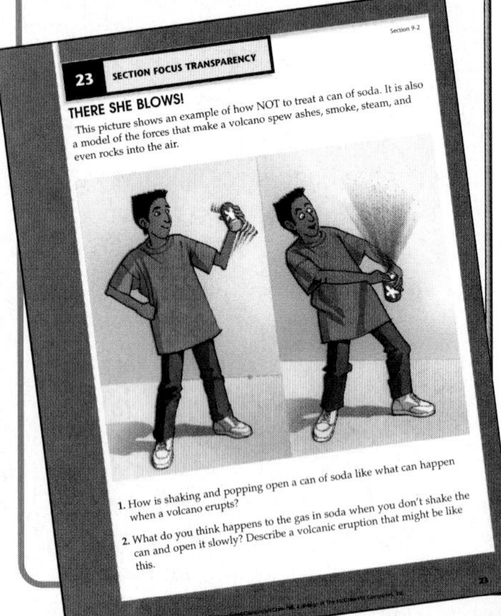
Section 9-2

23 SECTION FOCUS TRANSPARENCY

THERE SHE BLOWS!

This picture shows an example of how NOT to treat a can of soda. It is also a model of the forces that make a volcano spew ashes, smoke, steam, and even rocks into the air.

1. How is shaking and popping open a can of soda like what can happen when a volcano erupts?
2. What do you think happens to the gas in soda when you don't shake the can and open it slowly? Describe a volcanic eruption that might be like this.

Tying to Previous Knowledge

Gases in a warm carbonated beverage cause liquid to gush from the container when pressure is released. Similarly, water vapor and other gases are released during a volcanic eruption.

9-2 Types of Volcanoes

What You'll Learn

- How the explosiveness of a volcanic eruption is related to the silica and water vapor content of its magma
- Three forms of volcanoes

Vocabulary

shield volcano
tephra
cinder cone
composite volcano

Why It's Important

- You'll understand what makes a volcano dangerous.

Styles of Eruptions

Some volcanic eruptions are explosive and violent, like those from Soufrière Hills volcano, Mount Pinatubo, and Mount St. Helens. In others, the lava quietly flows from a vent, as in the Kilauea (kihl ah WAY ah) eruptions. What causes these differences?

Two important factors control whether an eruption will be explosive or quiet. One is the amount of water vapor and other gases that are trapped in the magma. The other factor is how much silica is present in the magma. Silica is a compound composed of the elements silicon and oxygen.

Trapped Gases

Have you ever shaken a soft-drink container and then quickly opened it? The pressure from the gas in the drink builds up and is released suddenly when you open the can, spraying the drink. In the same way, gases such as water vapor and carbon dioxide are trapped in magma by the pressure of the surrounding magma and rock. As magma nears

Figure 9-6 A calm day in Washington was suddenly interrupted when Mount St. Helens erupted at 8:32 A.M. on May 18, 1980, as shown in this sequence of photographs. **Why was the eruption so violent compared with eruptions of volcanoes like Kilauea?**

A 8:32 A.M.

B 38 seconds later

Resource Manager

The following **Teacher Classroom Resources** can be used with Section 9-2:

Reproducible Masters

Activity Worksheets, p. 53 L2
Critical Thinking/Problem Solving, p. 9 L2
Enrichment, p. 23 L3
Laboratory Manual, pp. 59–60 L2
Multicultural Connections, pp. 17–18 L2
Reinforcement, p. 23 L2

Transparencies

Teaching Transparency 17 L2

the surface, there is less pressure. This allows the gas to escape from the magma. Gas escapes easily from some magma during quiet eruptions. Gas that builds up to high pressures eventually causes explosive eruptions such as the one shown in **Figure 9-6.**

Magma Composition

The second major factor that affects the type of eruption is the composition of the magma. Magma that is relatively low in silica is fluid and produces quiet, nonexplosive eruptions such as those at Kilauea. This type of lava pours from volcanic vents and runs down the sides of a volcano. These quiet eruptions form volcanoes over hot spots such as Hawaii. They also flow from rift zones, which are long, deep cracks such as those in Iceland. Because the magma is fluid when it is forced upward in a vent, trapped gases can escape easily in a nonexplosive manner.

Silica-rich magma, on the other hand, produces explosive eruptions such as those at Mount St. Helens. This magma sometimes forms where Earth's plates are moving together and one plate is forced under another. When the lower plate gets deep and hot enough, a portion of it is melted. This melting portion is richer in silica than the solid plate. As the melted portion is forced upward, it comes in contact with the crust and becomes more enriched in silica. Silica-rich magma is thick and gas gets trapped, causing pressure to build up. When an explosive eruption occurs, the gases expand rapidly, often carrying pieces of lava in the explosion.

Devastating Eruptions

Whenever a volcano erupts, people who live in its vicinity are affected in many ways. If the eruption is unexpected, lives can be lost. If people know the volcano is about to erupt, they can evacuate. Either way, their lives may never be the same. Research how the continuing eruption of the Soufrière Hills volcano on the Lesser Antilles island of Montserrat has affected life on the island.

C 42 seconds later

D 53 seconds later

2 Teach

At depth, magma is under pressure from all directions (lithostatic pressure) due to the surrounding rock. Tell students that lithostatic pressure is like the pressure on an underwater diver.

Student answers will vary but should include that many of the inhabitants have been evacuated from more than two thirds of the island and that several cities, including the capital, Plymouth, have been covered by volcanic ash.

Caption Answer

Figure 9-6 *Magma found in Mount St. Helens contains more trapped gases and water and is of granitic composition, having a higher amount of silica.*

GLENCOE TECHNOLOGY

Glencoe Science Voyages Interactive CD-ROM

Explorations

Have students do the interactive exploration *How does the composition of magma affect the nature of a volcano's eruption?*

Science Journal

Magma Composition Inform students that as magma cools, different minerals crystallize at different temperatures. Ask students to research how the composition of magma determines its temperature and how the temperature of magma affects its ability to flow. Have them use what they learn to write a one-page report in their Science Journals about why some magmas are hotter than others. *The temperature of a magma is determined in part by the chemical composition of the magma. The hotter a magma is, the more easily it flows.* L2

VISUAL Learning

Figure 9-7 Provide students with photographs and descriptions of several unknown volcanoes. Ask students to use the information in this figure to help them determine the form of each volcano.

GLENCOE TECHNOLOGY

Videodisc

Glencoe Science Voyages Interactive Videodisc—Earth

Side 1, Lesson 4

Volcanoes: *Erupting Mountains*

46347

47866

49922

Refer to Videodisc Teacher Guide for additional bar codes.

Reading Check
What type of magmas produce violent eruptions?

Magma Water Content

Another factor that causes magma to erupt explosively is its high water content. The magma at some converging zones contains a lot of water vapor. This is because of water in the oceanic crust that is carried by one plate forced below another. The trapped water vapor in the magma causes explosive eruptions. Sometimes, gas causes lava fountains to form from basaltic magmas, as illustrated in **Figure 9-8.**

VISUALIZING Forms of Volcanoes

Figure 9-7 The form of a volcano is determined by the nature of its eruption.

A When hot, fluid lava flows from one or more vents without erupting violently, it builds a gentle slope when it cools. This creates a shield volcano such as Mauna Loa, in background, in Hawaii.

B Explosive eruptions throw rock and lava high into the air. The lava cools and hardens into tephra. When tephra falls to the ground, it forms a steep-sided, loosely packed cinder cone volcano. Pictured here is a cinder cone in Arizona.

Across the Curriculum

Geography Ask students to hypothesize why some people live so close to volcanoes knowing that eruptions can be dangerous. *Students' responses might include economics, the scenery, and the rarity of explosions.* L2

Economics Have a volunteer who listed economics as one reason people live so close to dangerous volcanoes explain what some of the economic reasons might be. *One idea students may describe involves the richness of volcanic soil for growing vineyards and other crops.* L2

Forms of Volcanoes

A volcano's form depends on whether it is the result of a quiet or an explosive eruption and the type of lava it is made of—silica-poor, silica-rich, or a composition somewhere in between. Volcanoes are of three basic forms—shield volcanoes, cinder cone volcanoes, or composite volcanoes, as shown in **Figure 9-7.**

Shield Volcano

Quiet eruptions spread out silica-poor lava in flat layers. The buildup of these layers forms a broad volcano with gently sloping sides called a **shield volcano.** Examples of shield volcanoes are the Hawaiian Islands.

Cinder Cone Volcano

Explosive eruptions throw lava and rock high into the air. Bits of rock or solidified lava dropped from the air are called **tephra** (TEFF ruh). Tephra varies in size from volcanic ash—the smallest—to cinders, to larger rocks called

Figure 9-8 Usually, the hot, thin lava flows of Kilauea in Hawaii are nonviolent eruptions. **What could be causing the lava fountain shown above?**

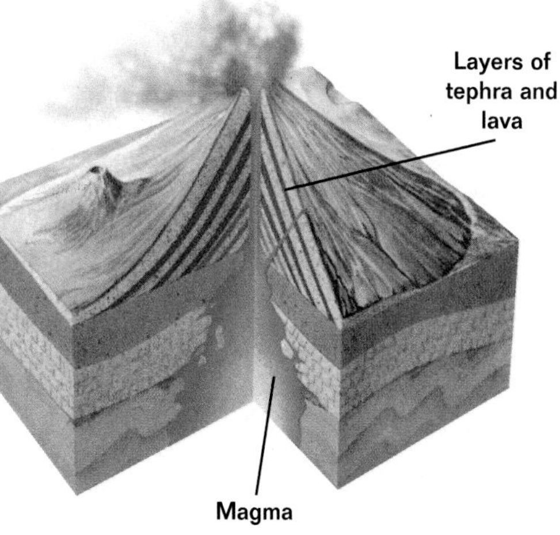

C Whenever volcanic eruptions vary between violent and quieter times, tephra layers alternate with lava layers. A volcano built by this layering of tephra and lava has a composite form, such as Mount Shasta in California, shown here, or Mount St. Helens.

Teacher FYI

Mauna Loa in Hawaii is the largest shield volcano in the Hawaiian chain. This shield volcano rises more than 9 km above the ocean floor.

Enrichment

Encourage students to research the massive mudflows that can occur during and after the eruption of some volcanoes. L2

Caption Answer

Figure 9-8 *gases escaping from the lava*

GLENCOE TECHNOLOGY

Videodisc

Glencoe Science Voyages Interactive Videodisc—Earth

Side 1, Lesson 1 *The Rock Cycle*

2252

2798

Refer to Videodisc Teacher Guide for additional bar codes.

Flex Your Brain

Use the Flex Your Brain activity to have students explore FORMS OF VOLCANOES.

Multiple Learning Styles

Kinesthetic Have students work in small groups to make clay models of shield volcanoes, cinder cone volcanoes, and composite volcanoes. Both lava and tephra should be represented. L3 ELL COOP LEARN

Inclusion Strategies

Gifted Have each student write a story about a volcanic eruption as told from the point of view of a human observer, or someone caught in the vicinity of the erupting volcano. The stories should include descriptions of the eruption in detail, from the early stages of development to the aftermath. Encourage creativity but insist on scientific accuracy. L3 P

Correcting Misconceptions

Most students think that volcanic eruptions occur only at the top of the mountain in the previously formed crater. Inform students that the initial eruption of Mount St. Helens in 1980 occurred on the flank of the mountain as well as at the top. Tremendous amounts of debris were forced laterally from the volcano, knocking down thousands of 60-m-high trees.

Problem Solving

Volcanic rocks that are dark in color are generally rich in iron and magnesium and low in silica. Volcanic rocks that are light in color are generally rich in silica and are iron/magnesium poor. An exception is obsidian, a black, volcanic glass that can be rich in silica.

Think Critically

Visible air pockets indicate the presence of gases. Some volcanic rocks, like pumice, float in water, confirming the presence of trapped gases.

interNET CONNECTION

Visit the Glencoe Science Web Site at **www.glencoe.com/sec/science** for more information on forms of volcanoes.

bombs and blocks. When tephra falls to the ground, it forms a steep-sided, loosely packed **cinder cone** volcano, as seen in **Figure 9-7B.**

A Mexican farmer learned about cinder cones one morning when he went to his cornfield. He noticed that a hole in his cornfield that had been there for as long as he could remember was giving off smoke that smelled like sulfur. Throughout the night, hot glowing cinders were thrown high into the air. In just a few days, a cinder cone several hundred meters high covered his cornfield. This is the volcano named Paricutín.

Composite Volcano

Some volcanic eruptions can vary between quiet and violent. An explosive period can release gas and ash, forming a tephra layer. Then, the eruption can switch over to a quiet period, erupting lava over the top of the tephra layer. When this cycle of lava and tephra is repeated over and over in alternating layers, a **composite volcano** is formed. Composite volcanoes are found mostly where Earth's plates come together

Problem Solving

Comparing Volcanic Rocks

During your study of volcanoes and the material that is ejected from volcanoes, you are given four different igneous rocks. Your task is to determine how the rocks formed and what elements they likely contain.

The rocks are fine-grained and some are full of holes. The holes were caused by escaping gases during the cooling of these rocks. The color of volcanic rocks can indicate what minerals each rock contains. Dark-colored rocks tend to contain minerals high in iron and magnesium, whereas light-colored rocks tend to have a higher concentration of silica-rich minerals.

Study the photograph. Based on the overall color of the rocks, what elements do you think each is likely to contain?

Think Critically:
Because some of these rocks are full of holes formed by gases as the rock cooled, it is possible that gases are also trapped inside these rocks. Is there a method to test the possible presence of trapped gas inside the rocks? Explain.

Across the Curriculum

History Have students find out about the eruptions of Vesuvius in Italy—in particular, the eruption of 79 A.D. and how it affected Pompeii and Herculaneum. Students' reports should include what has been learned about life in Pompeii since excavation of the city began in the 1800s. L3 P

interNET CONNECTION

Internet Addresses

For Internet tips, see Glencoe's **Using the Internet in the Science Classroom.**

Figure 9-9 Mount Pinatubo in the Philippines erupted violently in 1991.

and one plate is forced below the other. Mount St. Helens is an example. As you can see in **Table 9-1,** many things affect volcanic eruptions and the form of a volcano.

Mount St. Helens formed as the Juan de Fuca plate was forced beneath the North American plate. The ocean floor of the Juan de Fuca plate partially melted as it was forced downward. Successive eruptions of lava and tephra were produced. They formed the majestic composite volcano that towers above the surrounding landscape. Before the 1980 eruption, silica-rich magma rose and was trapped beneath the surface. An earthquake-triggered landslide took place that released pressure on the underlying magma. This started a series of explosive eruptions, as seen in **Figure 9-6.**

The action of Earth's plates coming together also caused the 1991 eruption of the composite volcano Mount Pinatubo, in the Philippines, as seen in **Figure 9-9.** Mount Pinatubo erupted violently after lying quiet for more than 600 years. The islands of the Philippines are a volcanic island arc, formed where the Philippine plate meets the Eurasian plate.

MiniLab

Modeling Volcanic Cones

Procedure

1. Pour dry sand or sugar onto one spot on a paper plate, forming a model of a cinder cone volcano. **CAUTION:** *Do not taste, eat, or drink any materials used in the lab.*
2. Mix a batch of plaster of paris and pour it onto one spot on another paper plate, forming a model of a shield volcano.
3. Allow the model of the shield volcano to dry. Use a protractor to measure the slope angles of the sides of the volcanoes.

Analysis

1. Which of your volcano models has steeper sides?
2. What form of volcano is represented by the model with steeper sides?
3. Infer why this is so.

3 Assess

Check for Understanding

Discussion

Have students discuss the dangers and the benefits of each type of eruption.

Reteach

Have students make tables listing the type of lava erupted, the shape, the explosiveness of eruption, and an example for each of the three kinds of volcanoes.

Extension

For students who have mastered this section, use the **Reinforcement** and **Enrichment** masters.

MiniLab

Purpose

Kinesthetic Students will make models of cinder cone and shield volcanoes to learn about their shapes.

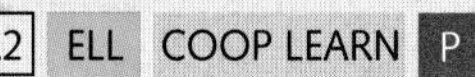

L2 ELL COOP LEARN P

Materials

sugar or sand, plaster of paris, paper plates, protractors

Teaching Strategies

Review how to measure angles with a protractor.

Analysis

1. the one made of sugar or sand
2. cinder cone volcano
3. Tephra piles up around the vent as steeply as gravity will allow. The fluid lava that erupts from shield volcanoes spreads out to form gentle slopes.

Content Background

The granitic magma inside Mount St. Helens is rich in silica and tends to trap gases. When an earthquake caused the north slope of Mount St. Helens to avalanche, pressure was released and the gases escaped in a sudden explosion.

Assessment

Content To further assess students' understanding of volcano shapes, have them draw a cross-sectional diagram of each type in their Science Journals. Use **Performance Assessment in the Science Classroom,** p. 55.

4 Close

Proficiency Prep

Use this quiz to check students' recall of section content.

1. **What is the composition of thick magma that contains a lot of silica?** *granitic*
2. **What are the three forms of volcanoes?** *shield, cinder cone, and composite*
3. **What is volcanic material ejected high into the air during explosive volcanic eruptions?** *tephra*

Section Assessment

1. water vapor and other gases in the magma and the composition of the magma
2. Granitic magmas are silica-rich. A high silica content makes magma thick. The more silica there is, the thicker the magma is.
3. **Think Critically** The lava from Krakatau was probably silica-rich because of the explosive nature of the eruption.

Using Math

Tambora gave off 60 times as much material as Mount St. Helens.

30 km³ ÷ 0.5 km³ = 60

The volume was 60 times larger.

Table 9-1

Thirteen Selected Eruptions in History

Volcano and Location	Year	Type	Eruptive Force	Magma Content: Silica	Magma Content: H_2O	Ability of Magma to Flow	Products of Eruption
Etna, Sicily	1669	composite	moderate	high	low	medium	lava, ash
Tambora, Indonesia	1815	cinder	high	high	high	low	cinders, gas
Krakatoa, Indonesia	1883	cinder	high	high	high	low	cinders, gas
Pelée, Martinique	1902	cinder	high	high	high	low	gas, ash
Vesuvius, Italy	1906	composite	moderate	high	low	medium	lava, ash
Katmai, Alaska	1912	composite	high	high	high	low	lava, ash, gas
Paricutín, Mexico	1943	cinder	moderate	high	low	medium	ash, cinders
Surtsey, Iceland	1963	shield	moderate	low	low	high	lava, ash
St. Helens, WA	1980	composite	high	high	high	low	gas, ash
Kilauea Iki, Hawaii	1989	shield	low	low	low	high	lava
Pinatubo, Philippines	1991	composite	high	high	high	low	gas, ash
Galeras, Colombia	1993	composite	high	high	high	low	gas, ash
Soufrière Hills, Montserrat	1995	composite	high	high	high	low	gas, ash, blocks

Section Assessment

1. Some volcanic eruptions are quiet and others are violent. What causes this difference?
2. Why are silica-rich magmas thicker than silica-poor magmas?
3. **Think Critically:** In 1883, Krakatoa in Indonesia erupted. Infer which kind of lava Krakatoa erupted: silica-rich or silica-poor? Support your inference using data in **Table 9-1.**
4.  **Skill Builder**
   Making and Using Graphs Have you ever wondered about how volcanic eruptions compare to one another? To find out more about the sizes of eruptions, do the **Chapter 9 Skill Activity** on page 750.

Using Math

When Mount St. Helens erupted in 1980, about 0.5 km³ of material were ejected from the volcano. Tambora in Indonesia gave off 30 km³ of material in 1815. How many times larger was the volume of material given off by Tambora?

Assessment

Performance Assess students' abilities to make and use graphs by having them make another type of graph to compare volcanic eruptions. Use **Performance Assessment in the Science Classroom,** p. 39.

Igneous Rock Features

Intrusive Features

We can observe volcanic eruptions because they are examples of igneous activity on the surface of Earth. But, far more igneous activity occurs underground because most magma never reaches the surface to form volcanoes. Intrusive rock forms when magma cools underground. What forms do intrusive igneous rocks take? You can look at some of these features in **Figure 9-10** and **Figure 9-11.**

Batholiths

The largest intrusive igneous rock bodies are **batholiths.** They can be many hundreds of kilometers wide and long and several kilometers thick. Batholiths form when magma cools underground before reaching the surface. However, not all of

What You'll Learn

- How intrusive igneous rock features form
- How a volcanic neck and a caldera form

Vocabulary

batholith, dike, sill, volcanic neck, caldera

Why It's Important

- Igneous activity formed many features you can observe on Earth's surface.

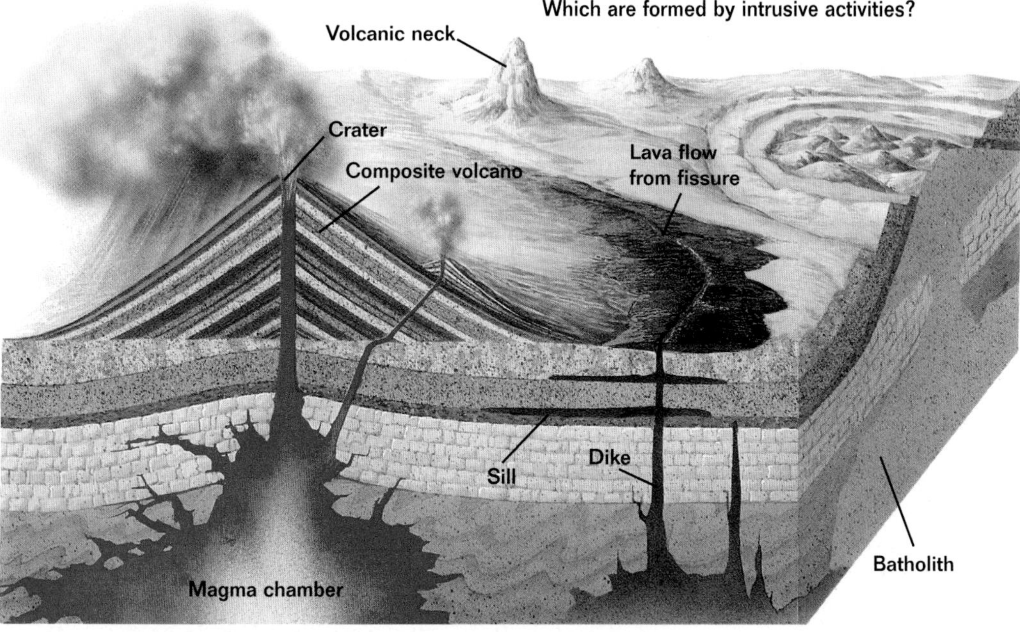

Figure 9-10 This diagram shows intrusive and other features associated with volcanic activity. **Which features shown are formed above ground? Which are formed by intrusive activities?**

SECTION 9·3

Prepare

Refer to **Intrusive Features** on p. 238F.

Preplanning

Refer to the **Chapter Organizer** on pp. 238A–B.

1 Motivate

Bellringer

Before presenting the lesson, display **Section Focus Transparency 24** on the overhead projector. Use the accompanying **Focus Activity** worksheet. L2 ELL

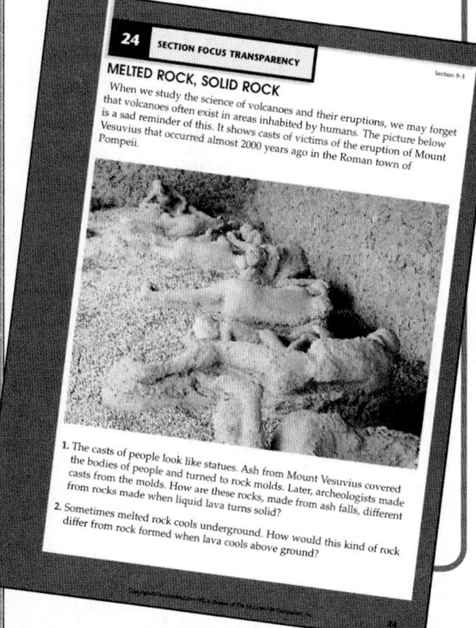

24 SECTION FOCUS TRANSPARENCY

Section 9-3

MELTED ROCK, SOLID ROCK

When we study the science of volcanoes and their eruptions, we may forget that volcanoes often exist in areas inhabited by humans. The picture below is a sad reminder of this. It shows casts of victims of the eruption of Mount Vesuvius that occurred almost 2000 years ago in the Roman town of Pompeii.

1. The casts of people look like statues. Ash from Mount Vesuvius covered the bodies of people and turned to rock molds. Later, archeologists made casts from the molds. How are these rocks, made from ash falls, different from rocks made when liquid lava turns solid?
2. Sometimes melted rock cools underground. How would this kind of rock differ from rock formed when lava cools above ground?

Caption Answer

Figure 9-10 *above ground: crater, composite volcano, lava flow; intrusive: dike, sill, batholith, volcanic neck*

Resource Manager

The following **Teacher Classroom Resources** can be used with Section 9-3:

Reproducible Masters

Activity Worksheets, pp. 51–52, 54 L2

Enrichment, p. 24 L3

Reinforcement, p. 24 L2

Study Guide, pp. 34–36 L1 ELL

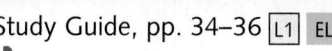

Transparencies

Teaching Transparency 18 L2

Science Integration Transparency 9 L2

2 Teach

MiniLab

Purpose

Kinesthetic Students will model the movement of magma toward Earth's surface. L2 ELL

Materials

2 transparent plastic cups, oil that is slightly colored (such as olive oil), dropper, enough water to fill one of the cups about $\frac{1}{3}$ full

Teaching Strategies

Have students squeeze oil from the submerged dropper as slowly as possible.

Analysis

1. The oil rises toward the surface of the water.
2. Oil is less dense than water, as magma is less dense than surrounding rock in Earth's crust.

Assessment

Content To further assess students' understanding of densities of different materials, have them research the densities of molten and solid rock of various compositions. Have them record these data in their Science Journals. Use **Performance Assessment in the Science Classroom,** p. 27.

VISUALIZING Igneous Features

Figure 9-11 Igneous features can form in many different sizes and shapes. Some of the most common are batholiths, dikes, sills, and volcanic necks. **Why are these features often exposed and jutting out at the surface?**

A Most of the bare rock visible in Yosemite National Park in California is a batholith that has been exposed by erosion.

B Ship Rock in New Mexico, seen in the background, is a volcanic neck.

MiniLab

Modeling Magma Movement

Procedure

1. Pour water into a transparent, plastic cup.
2. Pour a small amount of cooking oil in to a separate plastic cup. Use oil that is slightly colored, such as olive oil.
3. Extract a small amount of oil with a dropper.
4. Submerge the dropper tip into the water cup and slowly squeeze oil drops into the water.

Analysis

1. Describe what happened to the oil.
2. How do your observations compare with the movement of magma within Earth's crust?

them are hidden in Earth. Some batholiths have been exposed at Earth's surface by erosion. The granite domes of Yosemite National Park, as seen in **Figure 9-11A,** are the remains of a huge batholith that stretches across much of the length of California.

Dikes and Sills

Magma sometimes squeezes into cracks in rock below the surface. This is like squeezing toothpaste into the spaces between your teeth. Magma that is squeezed into a generally vertical crack

Tying to Previous Knowledge

Have students recall that molten rock material is forced upward toward Earth's surface. Some of this rising magma can cool to form intrusive igneous rock structures.

VISUAL Learning

Figure 9-11 **Are the igneous intrusions shown in this figure younger or older than the rocks they cut through?** *younger*

The horizontal sill shown here is located in Yellowstone National Park. It formed when magma squeezed between rock layers.

The vertical dikes shown here are located in Nevada. They formed when magma was squeezed into vertical cracks in the surrounding rock layers.

that cuts across rock layers and hardens is called a **dike.** Magma that is squeezed into a horizontal crack between rock layers and hardens is called a **sill.** These features are shown in **Figures 9-11C** and **9-11D.** Most dikes and sills run from a few meters to hundreds of meters long. Some magma that forms a sill may continue to push the rock layers upward.

Other Features

When a volcano stops erupting, the magma hardens inside the vent. Erosion begins to wear away the volcano. The cone is much softer than the solid igneous rock in the vent. Thus, the cone erodes away first, leaving behind the solid igneous core as a **volcanic neck.** Ship Rock, New Mexico, is a volcanic neck. It is just one of many volcanic necks in the southwestern United States.

Sometimes after an eruption, the top of a volcano can collapse. This produces a large opening called a **caldera,** as shown in **Figure 9-12.** Crater Lake in Oregon is a caldera that is now a lake. Crater Lake formed after the violent eruption and destruction of Mount Mazama about 7000 years ago.

PHYSICS INTEGRATION

Rising Magma

You have learned that large bodies of magma underground are gradually forced upward toward Earth's surface. What forces push the magma upward through solid rock?

Content Background

Igneous rock bodies either form deep inside Earth or at or near Earth's surface. When the igneous rock bodies form at depth, they crystallize slowly, allowing time for large crystals to form in the rock. However, if the igneous rock body forms at or near Earth's surface, crystals form quickly and do not have time to grow very large. Igneous rock bodies that form at depth include batholiths and stocks. Sills and dikes form near Earth's surface where magma squeezes in between rock layers or into cracks. Volcanoes and lava plateaus form on Earth's surface.

Caption Answer

Figure 9-11 *Intrusive igneous rocks are often more resistant to erosion than surrounding rocks.*

PHYSICS INTEGRATION

As magma forms, it becomes less dense than surrounding rocks. The denser rocks surrounding the magma push on it, forcing it to rise. The less-dense magma is forced upward through cracks in the overlying rock.

Using Science Words

Linguistic Have students find the origin of *lith* (Greek *lithos*). Have them find other words that contain *lith* and explain their meanings. L2

GLENCOE TECHNOLOGY

Videodisc

Glencoe Science Voyages Interactive Videodisc—Earth

Side 1, Lesson 1

The Rock Cycle

2485

3415

Side 1, Lesson 4

Volcanoes: Erupting Mountains

51915

Refer to Videodisc Teacher Guide for additional bar codes.

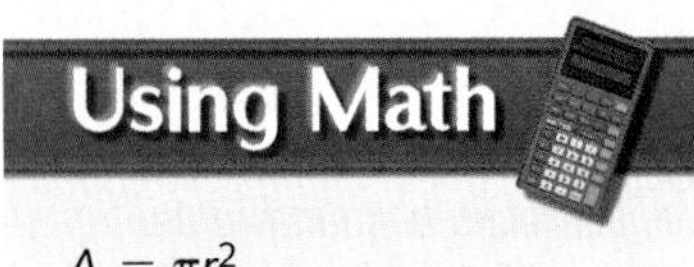

$A = \pi r^2$
$A = (3.14)(4.5\text{ km})^2$
$= 63.6\text{ km}^2$

Enrichment

Have students research when and how the Sierra Nevada batholith formed and how large it is thought to be.

3 Assess

Check for Understanding Activity

Visual-Spatial Provide each student with an unlabeled block diagram illustrating igneous bodies. Have the students identify and name each intrusive and extrusive feature. L2

Reteach

Make and use flash cards of the intrusive rock features. L1

Extension

For students who have mastered this section, use the **Reinforcement** and **Enrichment** masters.

Figure 9-12 Crater Lake in Oregon formed when the top of a volcano collapsed, forming a caldera as shown in the sequence below.

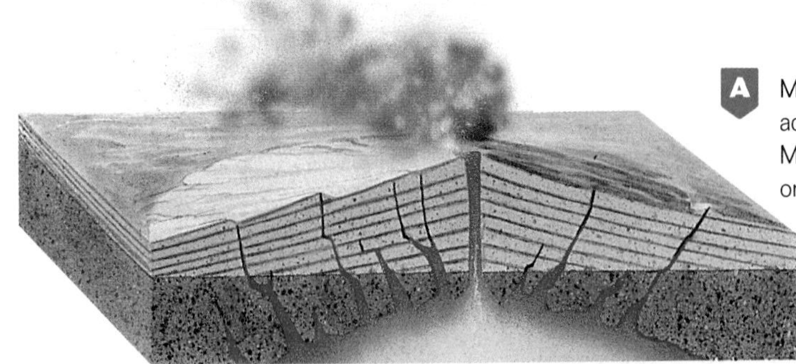

A Magma rises, causing volcanic activity of the former Mount Mazama. Magma is erupted onto the surface as lava.

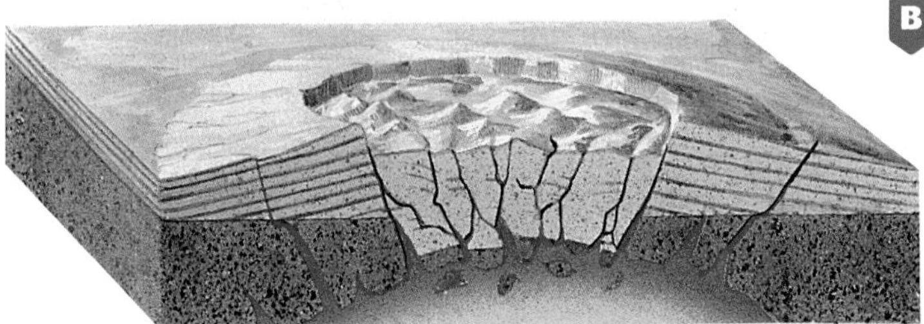

B Magma chamber partially empties, causing rock material to collapse down into the emptied chamber below the surface. This forms a circular-shaped caldera.

C Crater Lake formed when water collected into the circular space left when surface material collapsed.

Reading Check
What exposes igneous features that formed below the surface?

Igneous Features Exposed

You have learned in this chapter about one way that Earth's surface is continually built up and how it is worn down. The surface of Earth is built up by volcanoes. Also, igneous rock is formed when magma hardens below ground. Eventually, the processes of erosion wear down rock at the surface, exposing features like batholiths, dikes, and sills.

258 CHAPTER 9 VOLCANOES

Igneous Rocks Have students bring in igneous rock samples and write a paragraph in their Science Journal that explains how the igneous rock may have formed. If no igneous rock body exists in your area, ask a geologist to visit and discuss the location of the nearest one. L2

Figure 9-12 Tell students that after an 1883 eruption, the Indonesian island Krakatau collapsed into its magma chamber, largely disappearing beneath the ocean.

D Wizard Island in Crater Lake, in Oregon, is a cinder cone volcano that erupted after the formation of the caldera.

Using Math

Crater Lake in Oregon measures between 8 km and 10 km across. If you use the average width of 9 km and assume the lake is circular, you can approximate the area of the lake inside this caldera. Use the equation:

$$A = \pi r^2$$

where A = the area of a circle and r = the radius of a circle.

Section Assessment

1. What's the difference between a caldera and a crater?
2. What is a volcanic neck and how does it form?
3. Explain how calderas form.
4. **Think Critically:** Why are the dome features of Yosemite National Park actually intrusive volcanic features when they are exposed at the surface in the park?
5. **Skill Builder**
   Comparing and Contrasting
   Compare and contrast dikes, sills, batholiths, and volcanic necks. If you need help, refer to Comparing and Contrasting in the **Skill Handbook** on page 720.

Using Computers

Graphics Use the graphics software available on your computer to produce an illustration of igneous rock features based on **Figure 9-10.** Be sure to include both intrusive features and features that form above ground. If you need help, refer to page 734.

4 Close

Proficiency Prep

Use this quiz to check students' recall of section content.

1. **What are the largest intrusive igneous rock bodies?** *batholiths*
2. **What forms when the top of a volcano collapses?** *caldera*

Section Assessment

1. A caldera forms when the top of a volcano collapses. A crater is the steep-walled depression found around a volcano's vent.
2. the solid igneous core left behind when the outer layers erode
3. The magma chamber is partially emptied due to the eruption. Gravity then pulls down the top of the volcano.
4. **Think Critically** The dome features formed when magma cooled underground. Erosion later exposed the dome.

Using Computers

Student answers will vary but should include the major intrusive igneous rock bodies illustrated and described in **Figure 9-10.** P

5. **Skill Builder**
   All are intrusive igneous features. Dikes and sills are tabular in shape (like the top of a table). Dikes and sills are smaller than batholiths.

Assessment

Process Use this Skill Builder to assess students' abilities to compare and contrast. Ask students to explain in writing the difference between a sill and a dike. Use **Performance Assessment in the Science Classroom,** p. 87.

Purpose

Interpersonal Relate the physical and chemical properties of magma to the nature of the volcanic eruptions and the volcanic form. L2 ELL COOP LEARN

Process Skills

classifying, inferring, communicating, interpreting data, and hypothesizing

Time

40 minutes

Teaching Strategies

Troubleshooting Enlarge the figure to be used in this activity, and distribute copies onto which students are to plot the data given.

Answers to Questions

1. the greater the ability of the magma to flow, the lower the eruptive force of the volcano, and vice versa
2. a magma that flows easily
3. Volcanoes with magma that is low in silica and water tend to produce lavas that are more fluid. Magma and lava high in silica and water tend to produce cinders, ash, and superheated gases.
4. The ability of a magma or lava to flow is greater when the silica and water contents are low.
5. The silica content seems to have a greater effect than does the water content.
6. Shield volcanoes result from magma with relatively low amounts of silica and water. The lavas from cinder cone volcanoes have relatively high amounts of silica and water. Composite volcanoes erupt lava that is high in silica with variable water contents.

Identifying Types of Volcanoes

Materials

- **Table 9-1**
- Paper
- Pencil

You have learned that certain properties of magma are related to the type of eruption and the form of the volcano that will develop. Try this activity to see how to make and use a table that relates the properties of magma to the form of volcano that develops.

What You'll Investigate

Are the silica and water content of a volcano related to the form of volcano that develops?

Goals

- **Determine** any relation between the ability of magma to flow and eruptive force.
- **Determine** any relation between magma composition and eruptive force.

Procedure

1. **Copy** the graph shown at right.
2. Using the information from **Table 9-1, plot** the magma content data for each of the volcanoes listed by writing the name of the basic type of volcano in the appropriate spot on the graph.
3. When the plotting of all 13 volcanoes has been completed, **analyze** the patterns of volcanic types on the diagram to answer the questions.

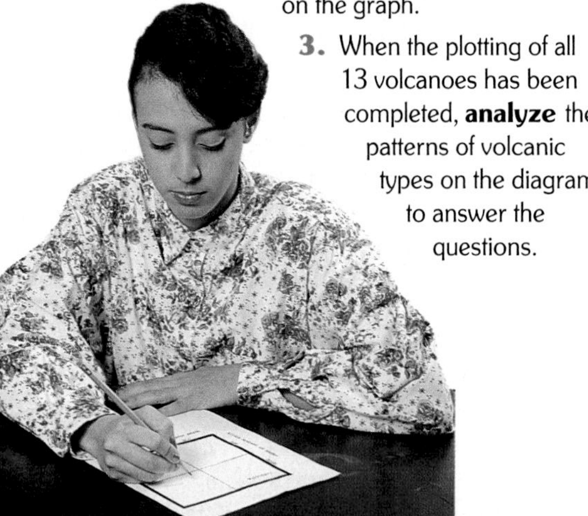

Conclude and Apply

1. What relation appears to exist between the ability of the magma to flow and the eruptive force of the volcano?
2. Which would be more liquidlike: a magma that flows easily or one that flows with difficulty?
3. What relation appears to exist between the silica or water content of the magma and the nature of the material ejected from the volcano?
4. How is the ability of a magma to flow related to its silica and water content?
5. **Infer** which of the two variables (silica or water content) appears to have the greater effect on the eruptive force of the volcano.
6. **Describe** the relation that appears to exist between the silica and water content of the magma and the type of volcano that is produced.

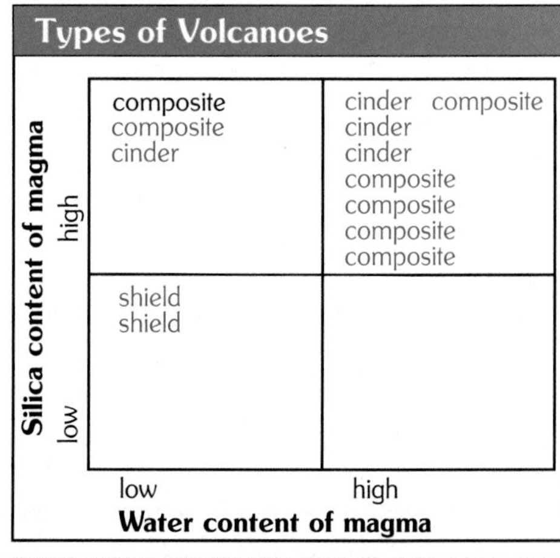

Assessment

Content To further assess students' understanding of volcano type identification, research the 1991 eruption of Mount Unzen in Japan and the 1982 eruption of El Chichón in Mexico and plot them on your table. Use **Performance Assessment in the Science Classroom,** p. 87.

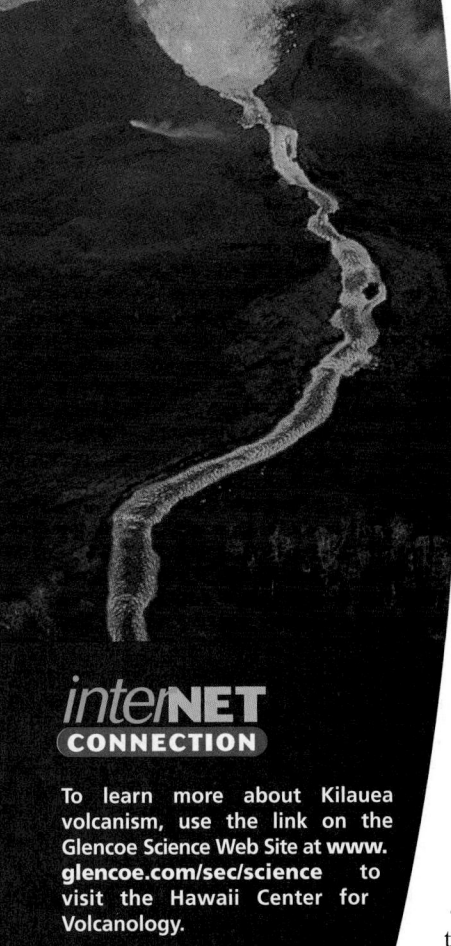

Predicting Volcanic Eruptions

Soufriére Hills volcano on the Caribbean island of Montserrat began erupting in July 1995 and continues to be very active. Although the volcano has killed 20 people in recent years, thousands of lives were saved because of advance warnings. Predicting eruptions doesn't protect buildings or roads, but it can save people and livestock. Scientists are now working on a worldwide volcano warning system.

Predicting Activity on Kilauea

The key to the volcano warning system is another system, the Global Positioning System (GPS), a collection of U.S. satellites orbiting Earth. The GPS makes it possible to take exact measurements of the Earth's surface and to pinpoint any location on the planet with great accuracy. It does this by measuring the distance between a receiver's position on Earth and at least three satellites orbiting Earth. GPS data can show whether the position being measured is moving. If the movement is associated with a volcanic eruption—such as moving magma—the information can be used to warn people about a coming eruption.

Giving Advanced Warning

This is exactly what a team of scientists from Stanford University hypothesized. They placed 13 receivers around a crater on Kilauea (left), a volcano on the island of Hawaii. On January 30, 1997, a new fissure eruption in and around the crater occurred. Eight hours before the eruption, the receivers showed that Kilauea's surface was moving. The volcano's summit was pulling apart, a movement that could have been caused by rising magma inside the volcano. Unfortunately, the volcano erupted before scientists received the information because data were only reported once every 24 hours. Research on this prediction method continues, however, and the Stanford team plans to put in place a better system that will report data continuously. This system will allow scientists to warn people before dangerous eruptions occur.

interNET CONNECTION

To learn more about Kilauea volcanism, use the link on the Glencoe Science Web Site at **www.glencoe.com/sec/science** to visit the Hawaii Center for Volcanology.

Teaching Strategies

- Have students research recent volcanic eruptions to determine whether any were predicted.
- Divide the class into groups according to the following methods of volcanic eruption prediction: the Global Positioning System; detection and analysis of gases emitted by volcanoes; detection of ground deformation by ground instruments such as tiltmeters; detection of earthquakes associated with volcanic activity. Have each group of students report their findings to the class orally. Reports should include a description of the method researched, and volcanic eruptions that were studied and possibly predicted using the method.

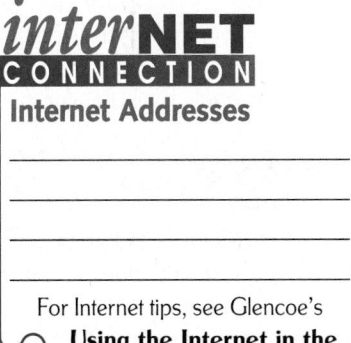

interNET CONNECTION

Internet Addresses

____

____

____

____

For Internet tips, see Glencoe's **Using the Internet in the Science Classroom.**

Content Background

The eruption of Pu`u`O`o, on Kilauea, Hawaii, has added more than 225 hectares of new land to the island of Hawaii. This continuous eruption, which began on January 3, 1983, has destroyed many human-built structures, including houses, roadways, and a National Park Service Visitor Center.

For More Information

Hawaii Center for Volcanology
Dept. of Geology and Geophysics
2525 Correa Rd.
Honolulu, HI 96822

Reviewing Main Ideas can be used to preview, review, reteach, and condense chapter content.

Preview

Linguistic Have students try to answer the questions in their Science Journals. Use student answers as a source for discussion throughout the chapter.

Review

Interpersonal Have students answer the questions on separate pieces of paper and compare their answers with those of other students in the class.

Reteach

Visual-Spatial Have students look at the illustrations on these pages. Ask them to describe details that support the main ideas of the chapter found in the statement for each illustration.

00:00 OUT OF TIME?

Auditory-Musical If time does not permit teaching the entire chapter, use the information on these pages along with the chapter Audiocassettes to present the material in a condensed format.

Chapter 9 Reviewing Main Ideas

For a **preview** of this chapter, study this Reviewing Main Ideas before you read the chapter. After you have studied this chapter, you can use the Reviewing Main Ideas to **review** the chapter.

The Glencoe MindJogger, Audiocassettes, and CD-ROM provide additional opportunities for review.

Kauai
Direction of plate movement
Oahu
Molokai
Hawaiian Islands
Maui
Hawaii
Hot Spot

Section

9-1 CAUSES OF VOLCANOES

Volcanoes can be dangerous to people, causing deaths and destroying property. Rocks in the crust and mantle melt to form magma, which is forced upward toward Earth's surface. When the magma flows through **vents,** it's called lava and forms volcanoes. Volcanoes form over hot spots when magma flows onto the seafloor. Sometimes, the lava builds up from the seafloor to form an island. Volcanoes over **hot spots** and rifts sometimes form on land. Volcanoes also form when Earth's plates pull apart or come together. ***What happens to the lower plate where two plates come together in order for a volcano to form?***

Section

9-2 TYPES OF VOLCANOES

Some lavas are thin and flow easily, producing quiet eruptions. Other lavas are thick and stiff, and thus produce violent eruptions. Water vapor in magma adds to its explosiveness. **Shield volcanoes** are mountains made of silica-poor lava that have gently sloping sides. **Cinder cones** are steep sided and are made of **tephra.** **Composite volcanoes,** made of lava and tephra, are steep sided. ***Why are eruptions of composite volcanoes so explosive?***

Cultural Diversity

Volcanoes and Earthquakes Have students collect photos and articles about volcanoes and earthquakes from around the world. Have students make collages of the photos and discuss the cultural effects each volcano or earthquake might have had on the people living in the area. Encourage students to study why people continue to live near large, explosive volcanoes like Vesuvius in Italy. L1

Reading Check ✓

Choose a topic in this chapter that interests you. Look it up in a reference book. Think of a way to share what you learn with others.

Section

9-3 IGNEOUS ROCK FEATURES

Intrusive igneous rock bodies such as batholiths, dikes, and sills form when magma solidifies underground. **Batholiths** are the most massive igneous rock bodies. **Dikes** form when magma squeezes into vertical cracks, cutting across rock layers. **Sills** form when magma squeezes in between rock layers. When a volcano stops erupting, the outer part of it erodes, leaving behind a **volcanic neck.** A **caldera** forms when the top of a volcano collapses, forming a large opening. ***What causes a volcano to collapse and form a caldera?***

Robert Ballard, Oceanographer

Not all volcanic activity takes place on land. Robert Ballard, an oceanographer, explores volcanic activity deep in the ocean. He conducted the first manned exploration of the mid-ocean ridge, which is a chain of underwater volcanic rifts that spans the globe. Robert also discovered the hydrothermal vents of the Galápagos Rift. These underwater vents spew out hot, briny water that is heated by magma deep beneath the ocean floor. ***Do you think that volcanoes might affect the chemistry of the ocean?***

Answers to Questions

Section 9-1

What causes volcanoes? Changes in pressure and temperature cause part of the lower plate to melt. The melted material is less dense than surrounding rock material and the magma is forced upward toward Earth's surface.

Section 9-2

Types of Volcanoes Lava that erupts from composite volcanoes contains higher concentrations of water and silica. The water vapor can be very explosive when pressure is released. The silica concentration makes the lava thick and sticky. Both factors tend to cause eruptions to be explosive.

Section 9-3

Igneous Rock Features When a magma chamber empties after an eruption, gravity forces the top of the volcano down into the empty chamber.

GLENCOE TECHNOLOGY

CD-ROM

Glencoe Science Voyages Interactive CD-ROM

Chapter Summaries and Quizzes

Have students read the Chapter Summary then take the Chapter Quiz to determine whether they have mastered chapter content.

Career CONNECTION

Yes; volcanic eruptions in ocean water will expel chemical elements and compounds into the water, thereby changing its chemical composition.

Assessment

Portfolio Encourage students to place in their portfolios one or two items of what they consider to be their best work. Examples include:

- Activity pp. 246–247
- MiniLab, p. 253
- Across the Curriculum, p. 244 P

Performance Additional performance assessments may be found in **Performance Assessment and Science Integration Activities.** Performance Task Assessment Lists and rubrics for evaluating these activities can be found in Glencoe's **Performance Assessment in the Science Classroom.**

Chapter 9 Assessment

Using Vocabulary

1. m
2. b
3. h
4. c
5. i

interNET CONNECTION To reinforce chapter vocabulary, use the **Study Guide for Content Mastery** booklet. Also available are activities for **Glencoe Science Voyages** on the Glencoe Science Web Site. **www.glencoe.com/sec/science**

Checking Concepts

6. C	11. A
7. B	12. B
8. A	13. D
9. C	14. C
10. C	15. D

Thinking Critically

16. Glaciers form at high elevations and high latitudes. Iceland is at a relatively high latitude. The Mid-Atlantic Ridge, of which Iceland is a part, is a volcanic feature on the ocean bottom related to Earth's moving plates. Because glaciers and volcanoes are caused by different processes, they can coexist.
17. The lava is very fluid. Because it flows easily, relatively quiet eruptions are produced.
18. Volcanoes form where Earth's plates move apart or collide. The enormous forces produced by plate movements can produce earthquakes.

Chapter 9 Assessment

Using Vocabulary

a. batholith	g. hot spot
b. caldera	h. shield volcano
c. cinder cone	i. sill
d. composite volcano	j. tephra
e. crater	k. vent
f. dike	l. volcanic neck
	m. volcano

Each phrase below describes a science term from the list. Write the term that matches the phrase describing it.

1. mountain made of lava and tephra
2. large opening formed by the collapse of a volcano
3. volcano with gently sloping sides
4. steep-sided volcano made of tephra
5. an igneous intrusion formed between rock layers

Checking Concepts

Choose the word or phrase that best answers the question.

6. What type of plate boundary forms composite volcanoes?
   A) plates moving apart
   B) plates sticking and slipping
   C) plates moving together
   D) plates sliding past each other
7. Why is Hawaii made of volcanoes?
   A) Plates are moving apart.
   B) A hot spot exists.
   C) Plates are moving together.
   D) Rift zones exist.
8. What kind of magmas produce violent volcanic eruptions?
   A) those rich in silica
   B) those that are fluid
   C) those forming shield volcanoes
   D) those rich in iron
9. Magma that is low in silica produces what kind of eruptions?
   A) thick C) quiet
   B) caldera D) explosive
10. What is made entirely of tephra?
   A) shield volcano C) cinder cone
   B) caldera D) composite volcano
11. What kind of volcano is Kilauea?
   A) shield volcano C) cinder cone
   B) composite volcano D) caldera cone
12. What is magma that squeezes into a vertical crack and then hardens?
   A) sill C) volcanic neck
   B) dike D) batholith
13. What is the largest igneous intrusive body?
   A) dike C) sill
   B) volcanic neck D) batholith
14. Which describes solid material erupted from a volcano?
   A) lava C) tephra
   B) sand D) sill
15. What is the process that formed Mount St. Helens?
   A) plates sticking and slipping
   B) caldera formation
   C) plates sliding sideways
   D) plates moving together

Thinking Critically

16. Explain how glaciers and volcanoes can exist on Iceland.
17. What kind of eruption is produced when lava that is low in silica flows from a volcano? Explain.
18. How are volcanoes related to earthquakes?
19. A mountain called Misti is a volcano in Peru. Peru is on the western edge of South America. How might this volcano have formed?

19. Students should be able to infer that the volcano, like those in the Cascades, formed as the result of one plate being forced under the other. Displaying a map of North and South America might be helpful in answering this question. Referring students to a map showing the boundaries of Earth's plates also would be useful.

20. A composite volcano is composed of alternating layers of tephra and lava. The layers of tephra are deposited by violent, explosive eruptions of the volcano. The layers of lava are deposited by less violent eruptions of the volcano. However, even the less violent eruptions of a composite volcano are often more violent than those of a shield volcano.

20. Describe in detail what a composite volcano is made of. Which parts represent violent eruptions?

Developing Skills

If you need help, refer to the Skill Handbook.

21. **Concept Mapping:** Make a network tree concept map that compares quiet eruptions with explosive eruptions. Use the following words and phrases: *Hawaii, high-silica, flows easily, quiet, explosive, composite, Mount St. Helens, shield, low-silica,* and *resists flow.*

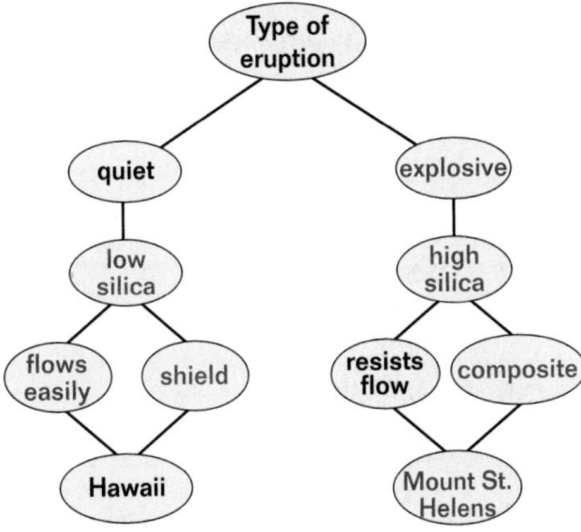

22. **Observing and Inferring:** A volcano erupted violently in Indonesia in 1883. What can you infer about the magma's composition? If people saw the eruption, what would they observe coming out of the volcano?
23. **Classifying:** Mount Fuji's steep sides are made of layers of silica-rich lava and ash. Classify Mount Fuji.
24. **Measuring in SI:** The base of the volcano Mauna Loa is about 5000 m below sea level. The total height of the volcano is 9170 m. What percentage of the volcano is above sea level? Below sea level?

Test-Taking Tip

All or None When filling in answer ovals, remember to fill in the entire oval. A computer will be scoring your answers. Don't give the right answer to a problem only to lose points on it because the computer couldn't read your oval.

Test Practice

Use these questions to test your Science Proficiency.

1. Not all volcanoes look or erupt the same. Which of the following statements **BEST** explains why this is true?
   A) Volcanoes form at different locations.
   B) Magmas of different compositions produce different forms of volcanoes because of the way they erupt.
   C) Magma compositions do not vary. Volcanoes form differently because of the latitude at which they form.
   D) The form of a volcano is related to the age of the volcano.
2. All Hawaiian Islands have formed in the same way. Which of the following statements **BEST** explains this?
   A) The Hawaiian Islands have formed over an area where one plate is forced under another.
   B) The Hawaiian Islands have formed over an area where plates are moving apart.
   C) Each Hawaiian Island is supplied by its own hot spot of magma.
   D) A hot spot provided magma for all islands as the Pacific plate slowly moved over the hot spot's location.

The Test-Taking Tip was written by The Princeton Review, the nation's leader in test preparation.

1. B
2. D

Developing Skills

21. See student page.
22. The eruption was violent; thus, the magma was silica rich and contained a lot of water. If people did observe the eruption (a few actually did), they would have seen tephra blown high into the atmosphere.
23. Fuji is a composite volcano.
24. Of the total height, 4170 m is above sea level. Thus, about 45 percent is above sea level and about 55 percent is below sea level.

Bonus Question

In Activity 9-1, you learned that the locations of active volcanoes are related to earthquakes, boundaries of Earth's moving plates, and hot spots. Based on what you have learned, what could be said about an area in the midst of a continent that shows evidence of a large number of ancient, extinct volcanoes? *This could indicate that the area was once located at a plate boundary or that a hot spot was once located under the continent.*

Assessment Resources

The **Test Practice Workbook** provides students with practice in the format, concepts, and critical-thinking skills tested in standardized exams.

Reproducible Masters

Chapter Review, pp. 17–18 L2
Performance Assessment, p. 23 L2
Assessment, pp. 37–40 L2

Glencoe Technology

- **Chapter Review Software**
- **Computer Test Bank**
- **MindJogger Videoquiz**

Chapter 10 Plate Tectonics

Section	Objectives	Activities/Features
Chapter Opener		**Explore Activity:** Re-form an Image, p. 267
10-1 **Continental Drift** 1 Session ½ Block	1. **Explain** the hypothesis of continental drift. 2. **Discuss** four pieces of evidence supporting the hypothesis of continental drift.	**MiniLab:** Interpreting Fossil Data, p. 270 **Skill Builder:** Comparing and Contrasting, p. 271 **Science Journal,** p. 271
10-2 **Seafloor Spreading** 2 Sessions 1 Block	3. **Describe** seafloor spreading. 4. **Relate** how age and magnetic clues support seafloor spreading.	**Using Math,** p. 273 **Physics Integration,** p. 274 **Chemistry Integration,** p. 275 **Skill Builder:** Concept Mapping, p. 275 **Using Math,** p. 275 **Activity 10-1:** Seafloor Spreading Rates, p. 276
10-3 **Plate Tectonics** 4 Sessions 2 Blocks	5. **Compare** and **contrast** different types of plates. 6. **Describe** how convection currents might be the cause of plate tectonics. 7. **Describe** the effects of plate tectonics found at each type of boundary.	**Problem Solving:** The Fit Isn't Perfect, p. 279 **MiniLab:** Modeling Convection Currents, p. 282 **Physics Integration,** p. 285 **Skill Builder:** Interpreting Scientific Diagrams, p. 286 **Using Computers,** p. 286 **Science and Math:** Finding and Using Rates, p. 287 **On the Internet:** Predicting Tectonic Activity, pp. 288–289 **Field Guide to Roadside Geology,** pp. 290–295

The number of recommended single-period sessions — The number of recommended blocks
One session and one-half block are allowed for chapter review and assessment.

Activity Materials

Explore	Activities	MiniLabs
p. 267 scissors, pictures from magazines	p. 276 metric ruler, pencil pp. 288–289 world map, tissue paper or plastic overlay	p. 270 clay, "fossils," such as macaroni, buttons, or paper clips p. 282 clear casserole dish, hot plate, thermal mitts, food color, water

Need Materials? Contact Science Kit at 1-800-828-7777 or at www.sciencekit.com on the Internet.
For alternate materials, see the activity on the listed page.

Standards		Reproducible Resources	Technology
National	State/Local	Test Practice Workbooks are available for use with each chapter.	English and Spanish audiocassettes are available for use with each section.
National Content Standards: UCP3, A1, A2, D1, D2		**Activity Worksheets,** p. 57 **Enrichment,** p. 25 **Home Involvement,** p. 31 **Laboratory Manual,** pp. 61–62 **Reinforcement,** p. 25 **Study Guide,** pp. 37–38	**Section Focus Transparency 25** **Science Integration Transparency 10** **Glencoe Science Voyages Interactive CD-ROM**
National Content Standards: UCP2, A1, A2, D1, D2		**Activity Worksheets,** pp. 55–56 **Critical Thinking/Problem Solving,** p. 10 **Enrichment,** p. 26 **Reinforcement,** p. 26	**Section Focus Transparency 26** **Internet Activity,** p. 288
National Content Standards: UCP1, UCP2, UCP3, A1, A2, B2, D1, D2, F3		**Activity Worksheets,** p. 58 **Enrichment,** p. 27 **Multicultural Connections,** pp. 19–20 **Reinforcement,** p. 27 **Study Guide,** pp. 39–40	**Section Focus Transparency 27** **Teaching Transparency 19** **Teaching Transparency 20** **Science Integration Transparency 10** **Glencoe Science Voyages Interactive Videodisc—Earth** **National Geographic Society: STV** **Internet Activity,** p. 281 **The Infinite Voyage Series**

Key to Teaching Strategies

The following designations will help you decide which activities are appropriate for your students.

L1 Level 1 activities should be appropriate for students with learning difficulties.

L2 Level 2 activities should be within the ability range of all students.

L3 Level 3 activities are designed for above-average students.

ELL ELL activities should be within the ability range of English Language Learners.

COOP LEARN Cooperative Learning activities are designed for small group work.

P These strategies represent student products that can be placed into a best-work portfolio.

Multiple Learning Styles logos, as described on page 61T, are used throughout to indicate strategies that address different learning styles.

Assessment Resources

Chapter Review, pp. 19–20
Assessment, pp. 41–44
Performance Assessment in the Science Classroom (PASC)
MindJogger Videoquiz
Alternate Assessment in the Science Classroom
Performance Assessment, p. 24
Chapter Review Software
Computer Test Bank

Chapter 10 Plate Tectonics

This is a representation of key blackline masters available in the Teacher Classroom Resources. See Resource Manager boxes within the chapter for additional information.

Transparencies

Section Focus Transparencies

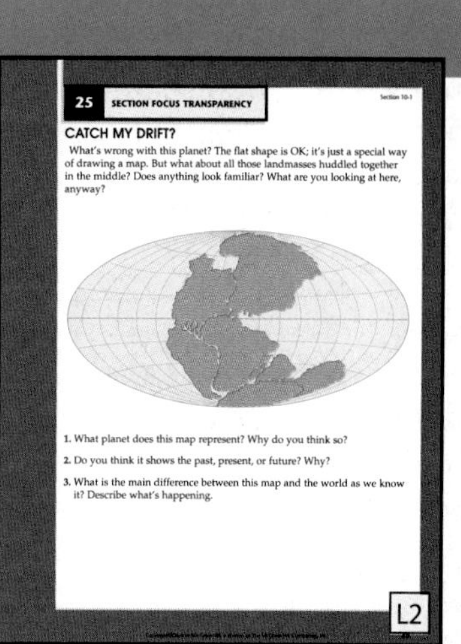

25 SECTION FOCUS TRANSPARENCY

CATCH MY DRIFT?

What's wrong with this planet? The flat shape is OK; it's just a special way of drawing a map. But what about all those landmasses huddled together in the middle? Does anything look familiar? What are you looking at here, anyway?

1. What planet does this map represent? Why do you think so?
2. Do you think it shows the past, present, or future? Why?
3. What is the main difference between this map and the world as we know it? Describe what's happening.

L2

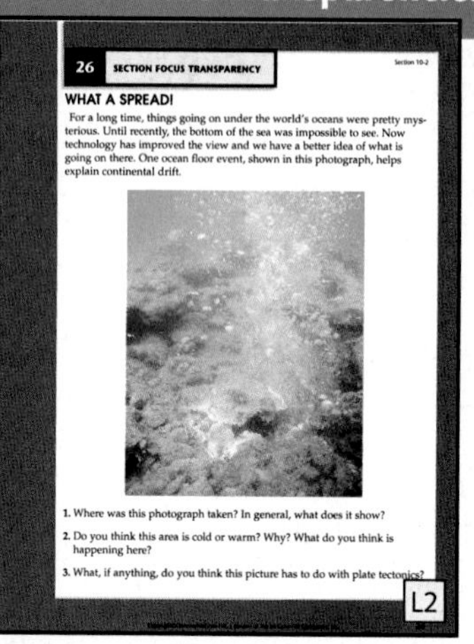

26 SECTION FOCUS TRANSPARENCY

WHAT A SPREAD!

For a long time, things going on under the world's oceans were pretty mysterious. Until recently, the bottom of the sea was impossible to see. Now technology has improved the view and we have a better idea of what is going on there. One ocean floor event, shown in this photograph, helps explain continental drift.

1. Where was this photograph taken? In general, what does it show?
2. Do you think this area is cold or warm? Why? What do you think is happening here?
3. What, if anything, do you think this picture has to do with plate tectonics?

L2

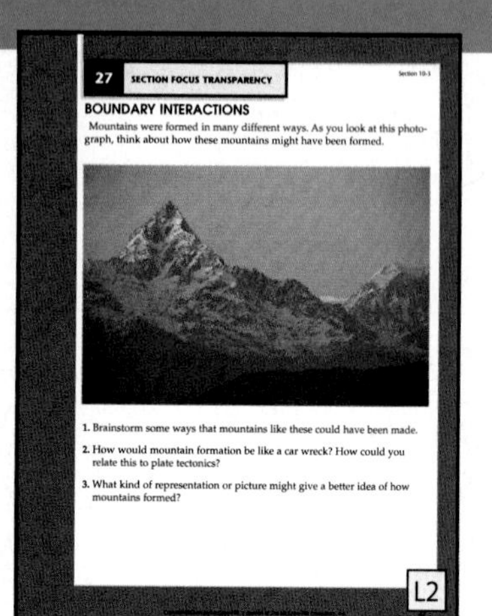

27 SECTION FOCUS TRANSPARENCY

BOUNDARY INTERACTIONS

Mountains were formed in many different ways. As you look at this photograph, think about how these mountains might have been formed.

1. Brainstorm some ways that mountains like these could have been made.
2. How would mountain formation be like a car wreck? How could you relate this to plate tectonics?
3. What kind of representation or picture might give a better idea of how mountains formed?

L2

Science Integration Transparencies

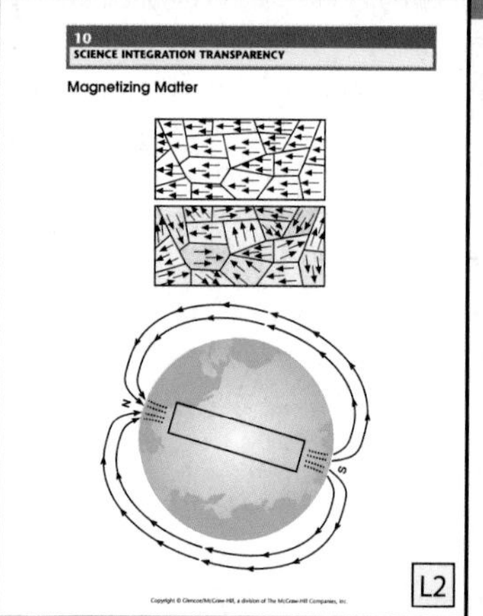

10 SCIENCE INTEGRATION TRANSPARENCY

Magnetizing Matter

L2

Teaching Transparencies

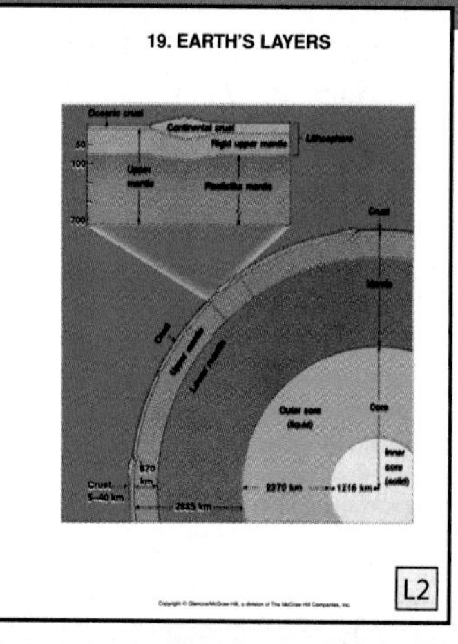

19. EARTH'S LAYERS

L2

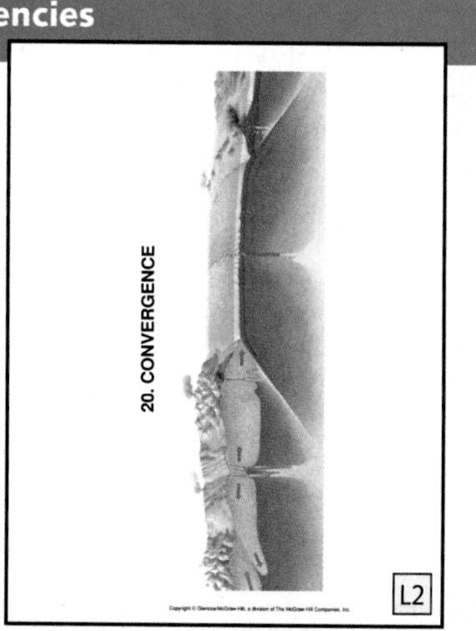

20. CONVERGENCE

L2

Meeting Different Ability Levels

Study Guide for Content Mastery

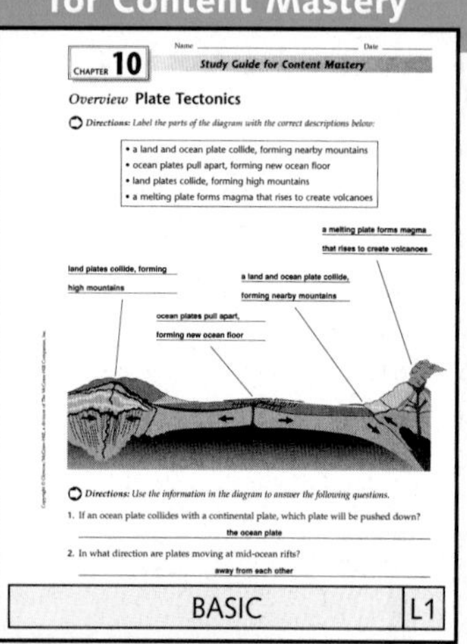

CHAPTER 10 Study Guide for Content Mastery

Overview Plate Tectonics

Directions: Label the parts of the diagram with the correct descriptions below.

- a land and ocean plate collide, forming nearby mountains
- ocean plates pull apart, forming new ocean floor
- land plates collide, forming high mountains
- a melting plate forms magma that rises to create volcanoes

Directions: Use the information in the diagram to answer the following questions.

1. If an ocean plate collides with a continental plate, which plate will be pushed down? the ocean plate
2. In what direction are plates moving at mid-ocean rifts? away from each other

BASIC L1

Reinforcement

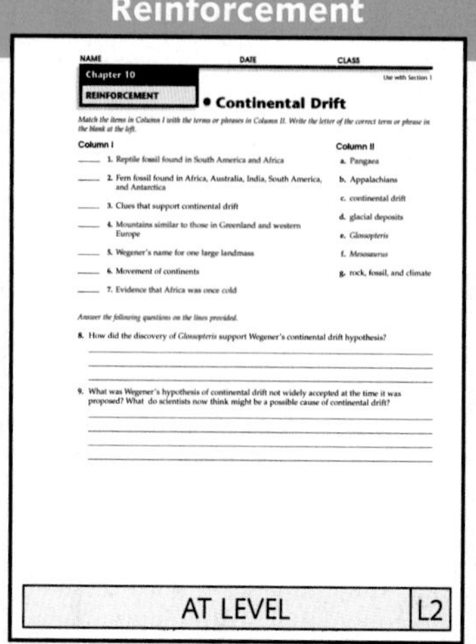

Chapter 10 REINFORCEMENT • Continental Drift

Match the items in Column I with the terms or phrases in Column II. Write the letter of the correct term or phrase in the blank at the left.

Column I	Column II
____ 1. Reptile fossil found in South America and Africa	a. Pangaea
____ 2. Fern fossil found in Africa, Australia, India, South America, and Antarctica	b. Appalachians
____ 3. Clues that support continental drift	c. continental drift
____ 4. Mountains similar to those in Greenland and western Europe	d. glacial deposits
____ 5. Wegener's name for one large landmass	e. Glossopteris
____ 6. Movement of continents	f. Mesosaurus
____ 7. Evidence that Africa was once cold	g. rock, fossil, and climate

Answer the following questions on the lines provided.

8. How did the discovery of *Glossopteris* support Wegener's continental drift hypothesis?
9. What was Wegener's hypothesis of continental drift not widely accepted at the time it was proposed? What do scientists now think might be a possible cause of continental drift?

AT LEVEL L2

Enrichment Worksheets

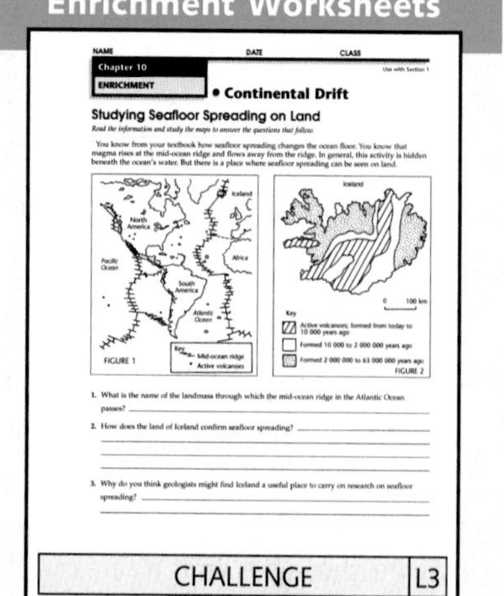

Chapter 10 ENRICHMENT • Continental Drift

Studying Seafloor Spreading on Land

1. What is the name of the landmass through which the mid-ocean ridge in the Atlantic Ocean passes?
2. How does the land of Iceland confirm seafloor spreading?
3. Why do you think geologists might find Iceland a useful place to carry on research on seafloor spreading?

CHALLENGE L3

Resource Manager

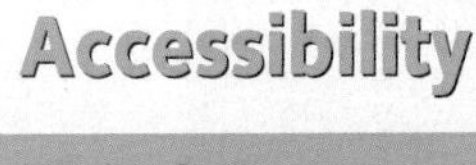

Hands-on Activities

Activity Worksheets

Chapter 10
ACTIVITY 10-1
• Seafloor Spreading Rates

L2

Lab Manual

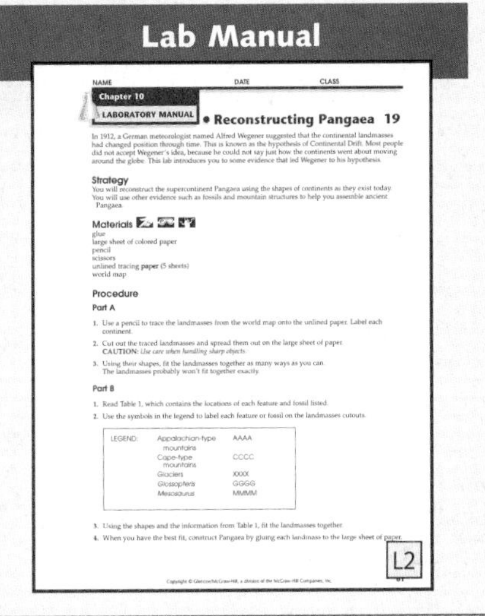

Chapter 10
LABORATORY MANUAL
• Reconstructing Pangaea 19

L2

Accessibility

Spanish Resources

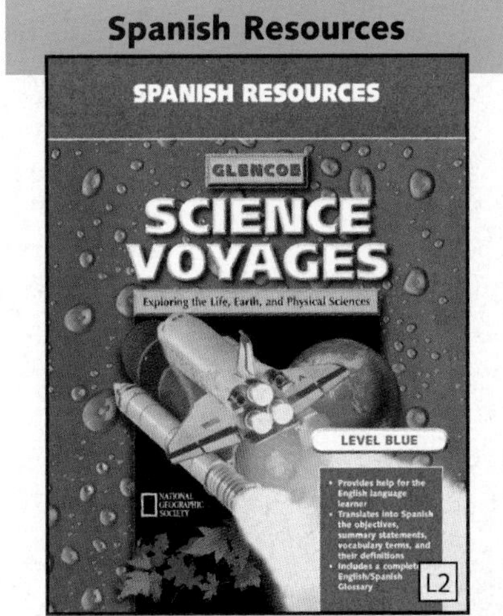

Assessment

Performance Assessment

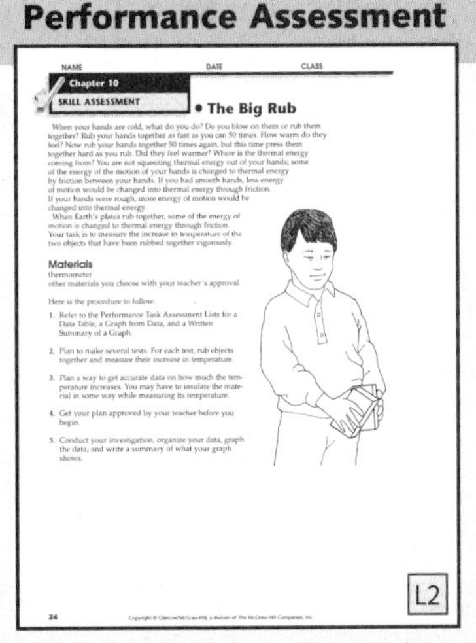

Chapter 10
SKILL ASSESSMENT
• The Big Rub

L2

Chapter Review

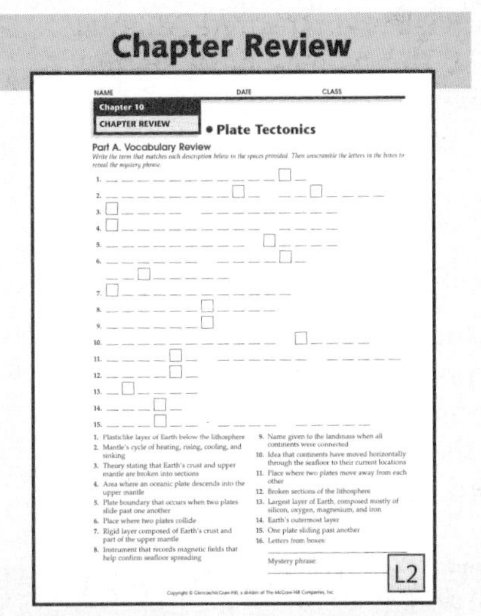

Chapter 10
CHAPTER REVIEW
• Plate Tectonics

L2

Assessment

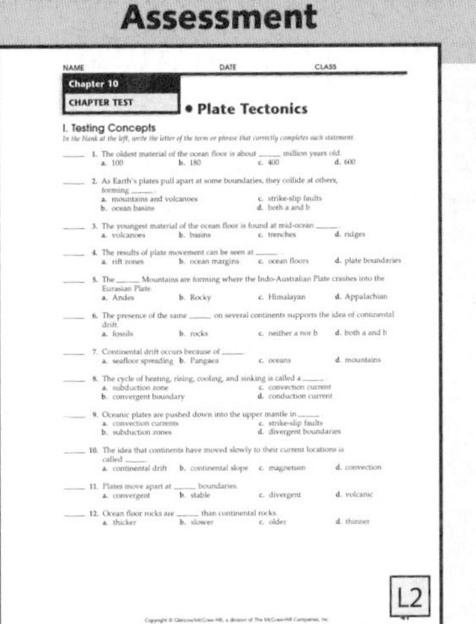

Chapter 10
CHAPTER TEST
• Plate Tectonics

L2

Test Practice Workbook

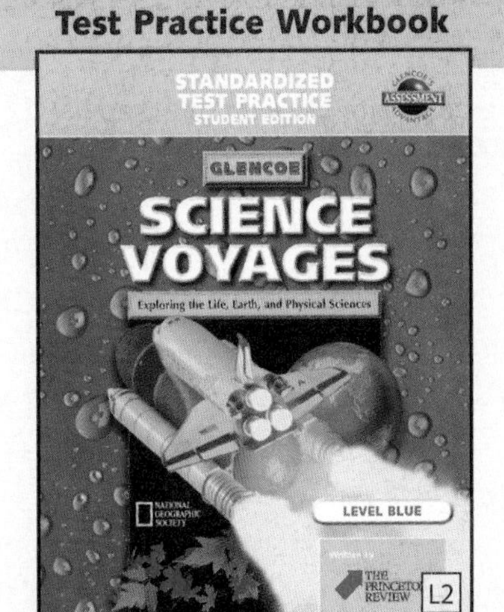

Extending Content

Critical Thinking/ Problem Solving

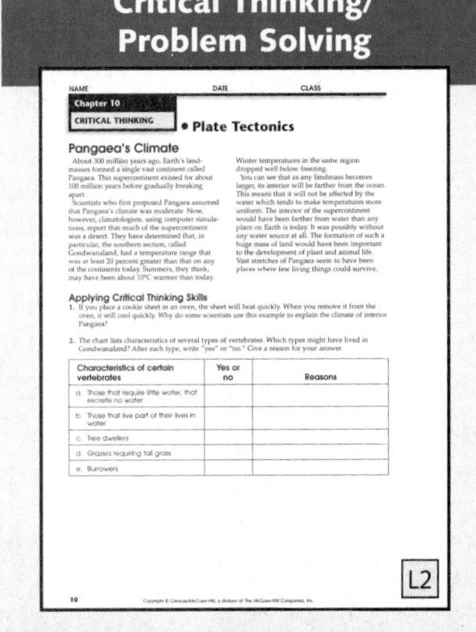

Chapter 10
CRITICAL THINKING
• Plate Tectonics

Pangaea's Climate

L2

Multicultural Connections

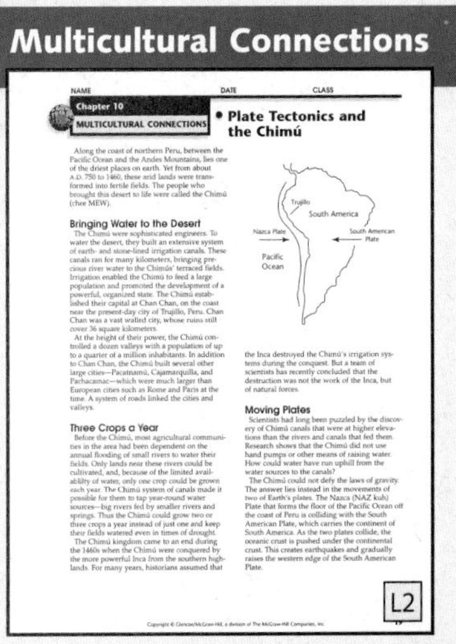

Chapter 10
MULTICULTURAL CONNECTIONS
• Plate Tectonics and the Chimú

L2

Helping You Prepare

Pangaea (Section 10-1)

About 200 million years ago, Pangaea covered about 40 percent of Earth's surface, while a large ocean, Panthalassa, covered the rest of the planet. Pangaea broke up to form Laurasia and Gondwanaland, which were separated by the Tethys Sea.

The study of ancient climates is called paleoclimatology. Alfred Wegener, a meteorologist, collected data about ancient climates in hopes of finding supporting evidence for his hypothesis. During his study of paleoclimates, he noted that glaciers covered much of the southern hemisphere between 220 million and 300 million years ago.

The Seafloor Moves (Section 10-2)

Certain species of green turtles swim from South America to Ascension Island in the mid-Atlantic to lay their eggs. The turtles may have started this trip when continents were much closer. As the seafloor spread, the instinctive trip became longer.

As the ocean floor slowly separates, new rocks form at a mid-ocean ridge. The spreading process moves older rocks on either side of the ridge farther apart. As the older rocks move apart, new rock material flows onto the seafloor and solidifies. Because of this motion, the oldest rocks are found farthest from the mid-ocean ridge.

GLENCOE TECHNOLOGY

 **CD-ROM**

Glencoe Science Voyages Interactive CD-ROM

Chapter Summaries

Use the Chapter Summary to introduce, teach, or review chapter material.

Paleomagnetism is the study of the magnetic properties of ancient rocks. When rock material is heated above the Curie point, magnetic minerals lose their magnetic properties. Once they cool down, they magnetically align with the current magnetic field. If Earth's magnetic field has reversed, the record of this reversal is shown in the magnetic characteristics of rocks formed at that time.

Plate Boundaries (Section 10-3)

Motion of Earth's plates is accommodated at plate edges. Boundaries between lithospheric plates may be divergent, convergent, or transform. The intersection of any three plate boundaries is called a triple junction.

Divergent plate boundaries often begin as continental rifts such as the modern-day

NATIONAL GEOGRAPHIC — **Teacher's Corner**

Products Available from Glencoe

To order the following products for use with this chapter, call Glencoe at 1-800-334-7344:

CD-ROM

NGS PictureShow: Dynamic Earth

Curriculum Kits

GeoKit: Dynamic Earth

GeoKit: Earth's Crust

Transparency Set

NGS PicturePack: Dynamic Earth

Videodisc

STV: Restless Earth

Products Available from National Geographic Society

To order the following products for use with this chapter, call National Geographic Society at 1-800-368-2728:

Videos

Changing Earth: Forces That Create, Forces That Destroy

Living on Our Changing Planet

Oceans in Motion

African Rift Valley. Tensional forces may stretch and thin the continental crust until a mid-ocean ridge develops, and oceanic crust forms. Once a mid-ocean ridge has formed, full-fledged seafloor spreading begins, and the continental fragments begin to separate.

In order for Earth to maintain a constant size, lithosphere produced at mid-ocean ridges must be consumed elsewhere. This occurs at convergent boundaries. At these boundaries, older, cooler, and denser oceanic plates are forced beneath less-dense plates in subduction zones. The denser plate descends into the mantle along a plane that may dip at angles ranging from 30° to 90°. This plane is defined by the foci of earthquakes associated with the subducting slab.

Transform boundaries may occur on land or on the seafloor. These faults most commonly connect offset segments of mid-ocean ridges. These ridge-to-ridge transform faults are a conspicuous feature of any mid-ocean ridge system. Transform faults also may connect a ridge to a trench or a trench to another trench.

Mountains, Arcs, and Volcanoes

(Section 10-3)

Most of the world's spectacular mountain ranges were formed at collision-type convergent plate boundaries. When two plates carrying continents collide, rocks are folded and faulted resulting in a thickened and uplifted continental crust. The Himalaya are classic examples of collision-type mountains. This range began to form about 50 million years ago as India began to collide with Tibet and the Eurasian plate. Even today, India is pushing northward into Tibet and the Himalaya continue to rise. The Appalachian Mountains also formed in a series of collisions. These collisions produced the folded rock layers of the Valley and Ridge Province and also produced large, low-angle reverse faults (thrust faults) along which slices of continental crust were carried tens or even hundreds of kilometers westward.

Mountains also can form along ocean-continent convergent boundaries. The Andes Mountains of South America are a modern-day example. The Andes have grown due to rock deformation and volcanism resulting from subduction of an oceanic plate (Nazca plate) under the South American plate. The ocean trench marking the subduction zone is named the Peru-Chile Trench after these two countries so strongly affected by their plate tectonic setting.

When one oceanic plate descends beneath another at an ocean-ocean convergent plate boundary, a volcanic island arc forms behind the ocean trench. Volcanic arcs form as a result of partial melting of the subducting plate and possibly some mantle rock above the descending plate. The Japanese and Philippine Islands are examples of volcanic island arcs.

SCIENCE UPDATE

For current events or science in the news, access the Glencoe Science Web Site at **www.glencoe.com/sec/science**

Teacher to Teacher

"To illustrate plate movement, I have students use graham crackers as plates and frosting as magma. Using the information they learned about convergent and divergent boundaries, have students re-create these movements using their materials. Remind students not to eat anything made or used in a laboratory."

Deborah P Huffine

Deborah Peters Huffine, Teacher
Noblesville Intermediate School
Noblesville, IN

CHAPTER 10
Plate Tectonics

CHAPTER OVERVIEW

Section 10-1 Fossil, climate, and rock clues that support continental drift and the existence of Pangaea are presented.

Section 10-2 An explanation of seafloor spreading is presented as more support for the movement of continents.

Section 10-3 Plate tectonics is explained in terms of divergent, convergent, and transform boundaries. Causes and effects of plate tectonics are presented.

Chapter Vocabulary

continental drift	plate
Pangaea	lithosphere
seafloor spreading	asthenosphere
plate tectonics	convection current

Theme Connection

Energy The transfer of energy in Earth's interior sets up massive convection currents in the mantle. These convection cells are thought to be the driving force that causes the movements of Earth's plates.

00:00 OUT OF TIME?

If time does not permit teaching the entire chapter, use Reviewing Main Ideas on pp. 296–297.

CHAPTER

10 Plate Tectonics

Chapter Preview

Section 10-1
Continental Drift

Section 10-2
Seafloor Spreading

Section 10-3
Plate Tectonics

Skills Preview

Skill Builders
- Compare and Contrast
- Interpret a Scientific Diagram

Activities
- Interpret Data
- Make a Prediction

MiniLabs
- Interpret Data
- Make a Model

Reading Check

As you read, list the prefixes you encounter such as *con-* or *sub-* and look up their meanings. Identify other words that begin with these prefixes.

266

Multiple Learning Styles

Look for the following logos for strategies that emphasize different learning modalities.

Linguistic Explore Activity, p. 267; Assessment, p. 271; Multiple Learning Styles, p. 278; Across the Curriculum, p. 279; Enrichment, p. 280; Science Journal, p. 285; Preview, p. 296

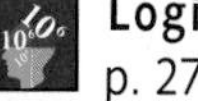

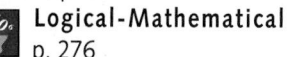

Logical-Mathematical Activity, p. 276

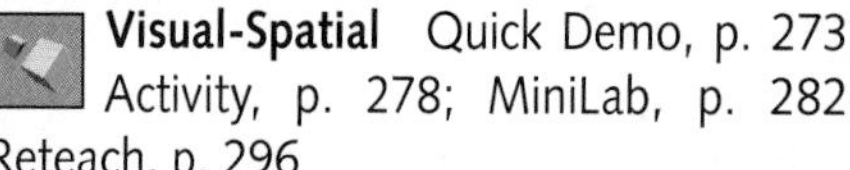

Visual-Spatial Quick Demo, p. 273; Activity, p. 278; MiniLab, p. 282; Reteach, p. 296

Auditory-Musical Out of Time, p. 296

Kinesthetic MiniLab, p. 270

Interpersonal Activity, p. 283; Review, p. 296

Explore Activity

This photograph of Earth is unique because the clouds have been removed using a computer. You can see the shapes of the continents just like on a map. Look closely at the general shapes of the continents. Do you see any relationship between continents? If this photograph of Earth were cut into pieces, could you fit the pieces back together? What clues might you use?

Re-Form an Image

1. Working with a partner, obtain photographs that are of interest to you from an old magazine. Do not look at each other's photographs.
2. You and your partner are each to cut one picture into small pieces.
3. Exchange picture pieces with your partner.
4. Using clues on surrounding pieces, re-form the image of the photograph your partner has cut into small pieces.

In your Science Journal, describe the characteristics of the cut-up photograph you used to re-form the image. Can you think of other examples in which characteristics of objects are used to match them up with other objects?

Assessment Planner

Portfolio
Refer to p. 297 for suggested items that students might select for their portfolios.

Performance Assessment
See p. 297 for additional Performance Assessment options.
Skill Builder, pp. 271, 275
MiniLab, pp. 270, 282
Activity, 10-1, p. 276; 10-2, pp. 288–289

Content Assessment
Section Assessment, pp. 271, 275, 286
Chapter Assessment, pp. 298–299
Proficiency Prep, pp. 271, 275, 286

Explore Activity

Purpose

Linguistic Use the Explore Activity to introduce students to continental drift. Briefly explain that the concept of continental drift states that Earth's continents have changed positions over time. L2 ELL COOP LEARN

Materials

scissors, photographs from an old magazine

Teaching Strategies

Have students compare their results with other students' results. Discuss differences and similarities.

Troubleshooting Explain that it is not necessary that the cut-up photograph outlines fit together perfectly, because students are trying to match only the general shapes.

Safety Precautions Caution students to handle scissors with care.

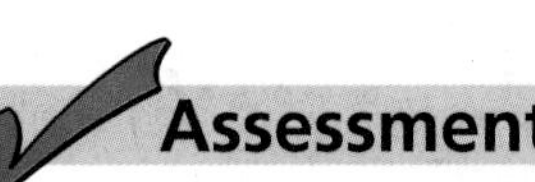

In general, the shapes and content of the photograph pieces enable students to guess how pieces may once have fit together. *jigsaw puzzles, broken archaeological artifacts, and continents*

Assessment

Process Ask students to explain in their Science Journals what characteristics of some photographs made them easier to fit together than others. Use **Performance Assessment in the Science Classroom,** p. 103.

SECTION 10-1

Prepare

Refer to **Pangaea** on p. 266E.

Preplanning

Refer to the **Chapter Organizer** on pp. 266A–B.

1 Motivate

Bellringer

Before presenting the lesson, display **Section Focus Transparency 25** on the overhead projector. Use the accompanying **Focus Activity** worksheet. L2 ELL

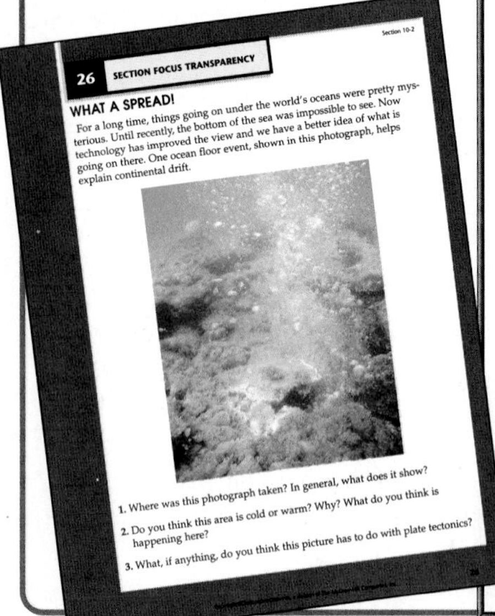

Section 10-2

26 SECTION FOCUS TRANSPARENCY

WHAT A SPREAD!

For a long time, things going on under the world's oceans were pretty mysterious. Until recently, the bottom of the sea was impossible to see. Now technology has improved the view and we have a better idea of what is going on there. One ocean floor event, shown in this photograph, helps explain continental drift.

1. Where was this photograph taken? In general, what does it show?
2. Do you think this area is cold or warm? Why? What do you think is happening here?
3. What, if anything, do you think this picture has to do with plate tectonics?

Tying to Previous Knowledge

Have students recall that overwhelming evidence must be presented in court to win many cases. Tell them that scientists also must prove their hypotheses.

10-1 Continental Drift

What You'll Learn

- The hypothesis of continental drift
- Four pieces of evidence supporting continental drift

Vocabulary

continental drift
Pangaea

Why It's Important

- The hypothesis of continental drift led to plate tectonics, a theory that explains many dynamic processes in Earth.

Evidence for Continental Drift

When you look at a map of Earth's surface, one thing is obvious. In **Figures 10-1** and **10-2,** you can see that the edges of some continents look as if they would fit together like a puzzle. In the early 1800s, as accurate maps of Earth's surface were first being developed, other people also noticed this fact.

Pangaea

Alfred Wegener (VEG nur) thought that the fit of the continents wasn't just a coincidence. He suggested that all the continents were joined together at some point in the past. In a 1912 lecture, he proposed the idea of continental drift. According to the hypothesis of **continental drift,** continents have moved slowly to their current locations. Wegener suggested that all continents were once connected as one large landmass that broke apart about 200 million years ago. He called this large landmass **Pangaea** (pan JEE uh), which means "all land."

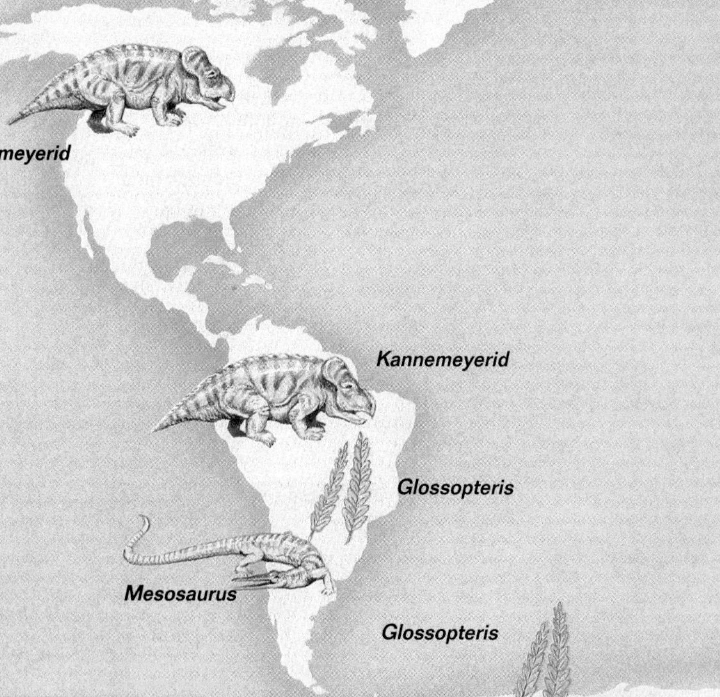

Figure 10-1
Glossopteris, *Mesosaurus*, and other organisms shown in this illustration lived in Pangaea.

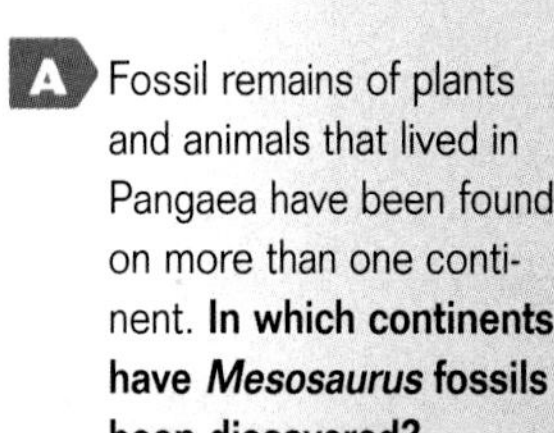

A Fossil remains of plants and animals that lived in Pangaea have been found on more than one continent. **In which continents have *Mesosaurus* fossils been discovered?**

Resource Manager

The following **Teacher Classroom Resources** can be used with Section 10-1:

Reproducible Masters

Activity Worksheets, p. 57 L2

Enrichment, p. 25 L3

Home Involvement, p. 31 L2

Laboratory Manual, pp. 61–62 L2

Reinforcement, p. 25 L2

Study Guide, pp. 37–38 L1 ELL

Transparencies

Science Integration Transparency 10 L2

Long after Wegener's death in 1930, his basic hypothesis, that the continents have moved, was accepted. The evidence Wegener had to support his idea hadn't been enough to convince many people during his lifetime. However, Wegener's early evidence has since been joined by other important observations. Let's explore both Wegener's clues and some newer ones.

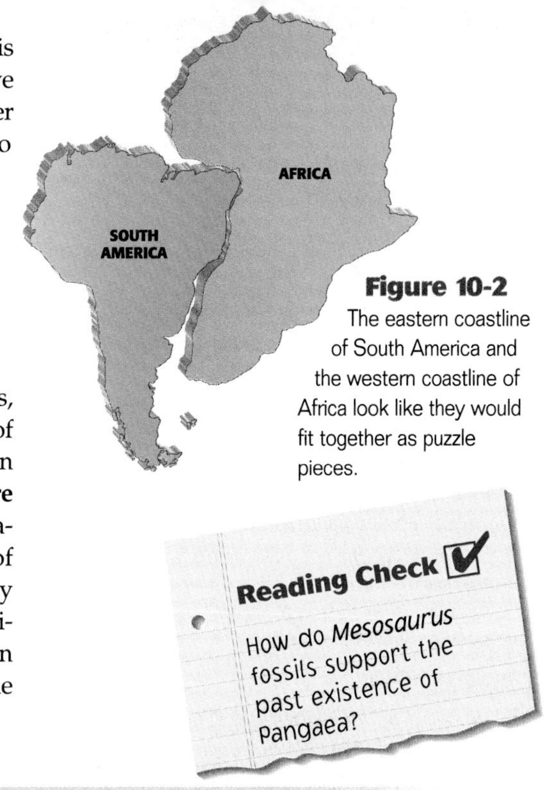

Figure 10-2 The eastern coastline of South America and the western coastline of Africa look like they would fit together as puzzle pieces.

Fossil Clues

Besides the puzzlelike fit of the continents, other clues were found from fossils. Fossils of the reptile *Mesosaurus* have been found in South America and Africa, as shown in **Figure 10-1.** This swimming reptile lived in freshwater and on land. How could fossils of *Mesosaurus* be found so far apart? It's unlikely that it could have swum between the continents. Wegener thought this reptile lived on both continents when they were joined as one giant landmass. ☑

Reading Check ☑

How do *Mesosaurus* fossils support the past existence of Pangaea?

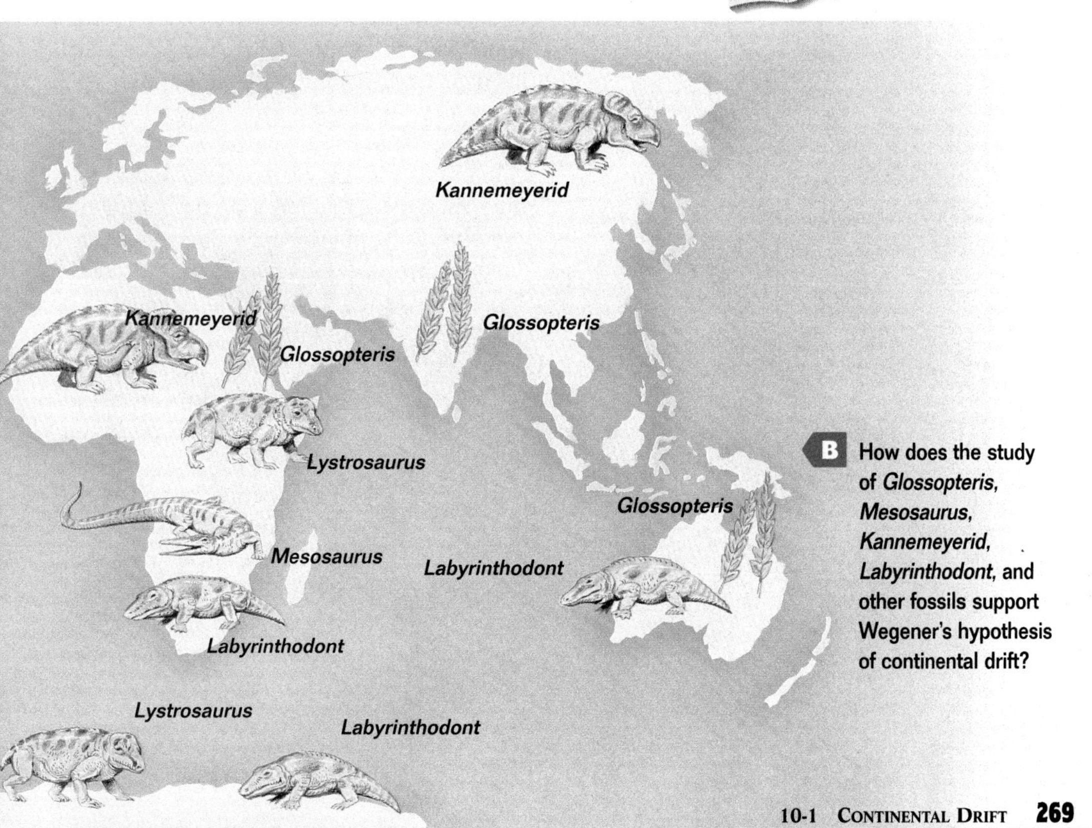

B How does the study of *Glossopteris, Mesosaurus, Kannemeyerid, Labyrinthodont,* and other fossils support Wegener's hypothesis of continental drift?

Across the Curriculum

History Have students research the life and scientific work of Alfred Wegener. Encourage students to read about his work in Greenland and how that research led him to formulate his hypothesis of continental drift. L2

Caption Answers

Figure 10-1A *South America, Africa*

Figure 10-1B *These animals and plants could not have crossed large oceans, so continents must have been close together for them to occur on different continents.*

2 Teach

Discussion

Discuss why Wegener's idea of continental drift was rejected. Wegener suggested that tidal forces caused continents to move over the oceanic crust or that the continents plowed through oceanic crust. Sir Howard Jeffreys explained that the tidal forces needed to move continents would be so great that Earth's rotation would be stopped.

Answer to Reading Check

Because *Mesosaurus* couldn't swim long distances, these fossils suggest that the continents were once connected.

3 Assess

Check for Understanding

Discussion

Review the evidence Wegener used to support his hypothesis of continental drift.

Reteach

Have students relate why some of the photographs used in the Explore Activity were easy to reconstruct to why some continents are easier to match up than others. L2

Extension

For students who have mastered this section, use the **Reinforcement** and **Enrichment** masters.

GLENCOE TECHNOLOGY

CD-ROM

Glencoe Science Voyages Interactive CD-ROM

Explorations

Have students perform the interactive exploration *What geologic evidence supports the existence of Pangaea?*

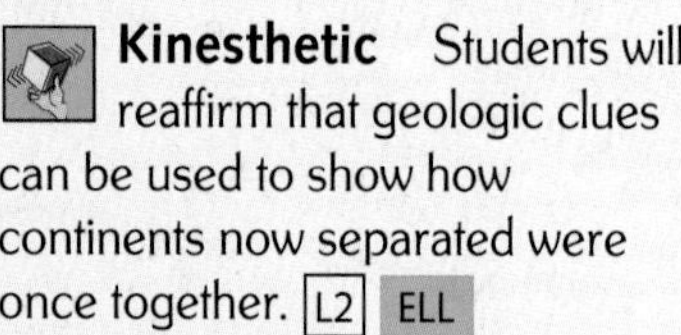

Try at Home MiniLab

For additional help doing this activity at home, see the corresponding pages in the **Home Involvement** booklet.

Purpose

Kinesthetic Students will reaffirm that geologic clues can be used to show how continents now separated were once together. L2 ELL

COOP LEARN P

Materials

modeling clay or modeling dough of various colors; objects such as macaroni, small buttons, or peanuts to use as fossils

Teaching Strategies

Prepare model fossils, continents, and landmasses prior to class. Position continents around the room prior to students entering.

Analysis

1. Students should be able to reconstruct at least some of the original clay landmass.
2. similar mountain forms, similar fossils, and similarly colored clay
3. Answers will vary but fossils and mountains may help with difficult continents.

Try at Home MiniLab

Interpreting Fossil Data

Procedure

1. Build a three-layer landmass using clay or modeling dough.
2. Mold the clay into mountain ranges.
3. Place similar "fossils" into the clay at various locations around the landmass.
4. Form five continents from the one landmass. Also, form two smaller landmasses out of different clay with different mountain ranges and fossils.
5. Place the five continents and two smaller landmasses around the room.
6. Students who did not make or place the landmasses will locate the drifted continents and reconstruct a model that shows how they were once positioned.

Analysis

1. Were you able to reconstruct all or part of the original clay landmass?
2. What clues, if any, were useful in reconstructing the original landmass?
3. How did you deal with continents that initially didn't seem to fit?

Another fossil that helps support the hypothesis of continental drift is *Glossopteris*. **Figure 10-3** shows this fossil fern, which has been found in Africa, Australia, India, South America, and most recently in Antarctica. The presence of this fern in so many areas led Wegener to suggest that all of these regions were once connected and had a similar climate.

Climate Clues

Fossils of warm-weather plants were found on the island of Spitzbergen in the Arctic Ocean. Wegener hypothesized that Spitzbergen drifted from the tropic regions. He also used glacial clues to support his theory.

Glacial deposits and grooved bedrock found in South America, Africa, India, and Australia show that these continents were once covered with glaciers. How could you explain why glacial deposits were found in areas where no glaciers exist today? Wegener thought that these continents were all connected and covered with ice near Earth's south pole at one time.

Rock Clues

If the continents were connected at one time, then rocks that make up the continents should be the same. Similar rock structures *are* found on different continents. Parts of the Appalachian Mountains of the eastern United States are similar to those found in Greenland and western Europe. If you were to travel to eastern South America and western Africa, you would find rock structures that are similar. Rock clues like these support the idea that the continents were once connected.

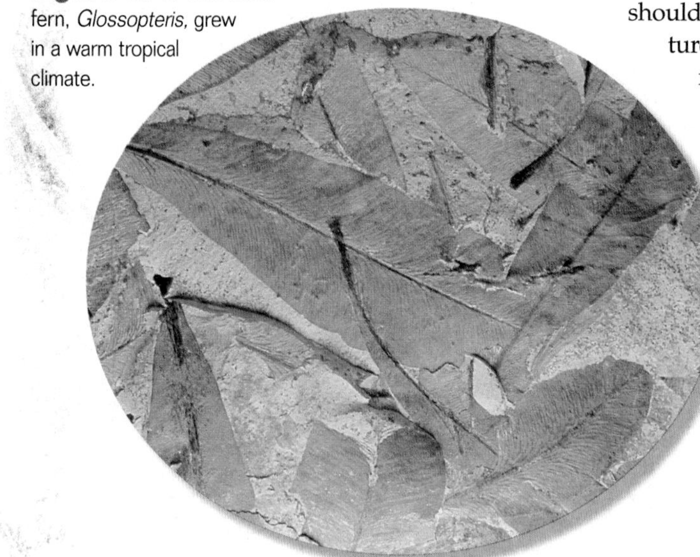

Figure 10-3 This fossil fern, *Glossopteris*, grew in a warm tropical climate.

Assessment

Oral Have students explain in their Science Journals what characteristics they used to reconstruct the original landmass. Then, call on them to read their answers in class. Use **Performance Assessment in the Science Classroom,** p. 71.

Science Journal

Continental Movement New evidence suggests that mountains in southwest South America match up with the older Appalachians. Have students speculate on how this could be true. *Accept all reasonable ideas. Before colliding with the African plate, the North American plate may have been positioned west of South America.*

250 million years ago 180 million years ago Present

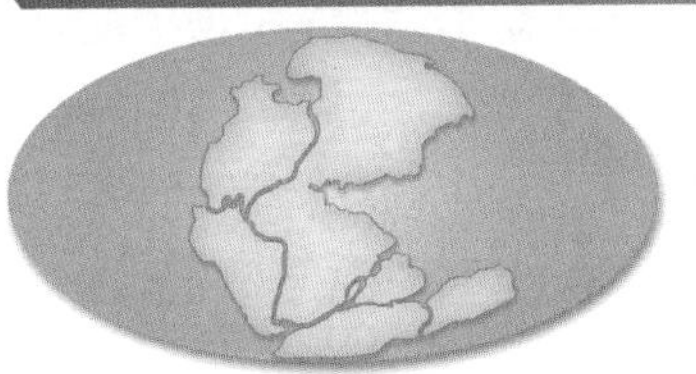

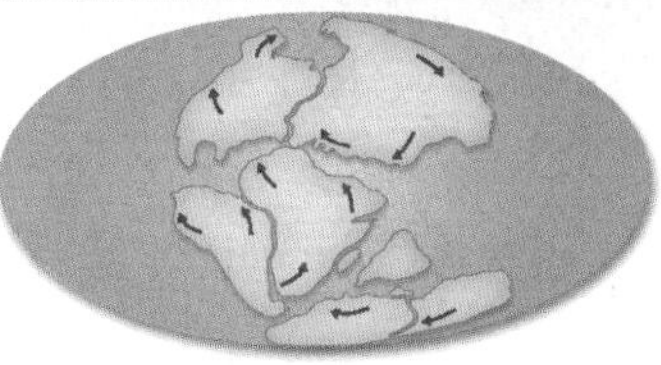

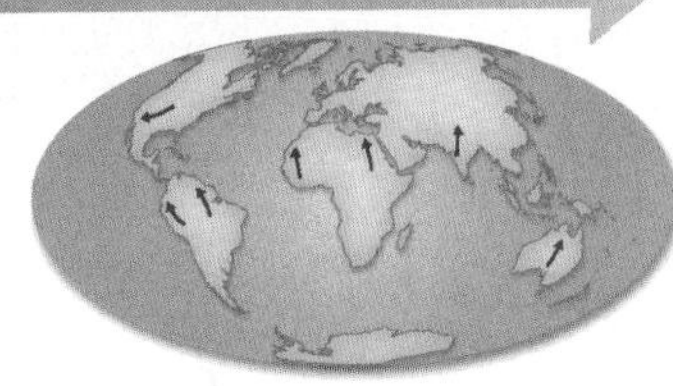

Figure 10-4 These computer models show the probable course that the continents have taken. On the far left is their position 250 million years ago. In the middle is their position 180 million years ago. At right is their current position. **Based on the diagrams, and assuming that the rate of movement will stay the same, what will happen to the Atlantic Ocean during the next 100 million years?**

How could continents drift?

Although Wegener provided evidence to support his hypothesis of continental drift, he couldn't explain how, when, or why these changes, shown in **Figure 10-4,** had taken place. Because other scientists at that time could not provide explanations either, Wegener's idea of continental drift was rejected. The idea was so different that most people closed their minds to it.

Rock, fossil, and climate clues were the main lines of evidence for continental drift. After Wegener's death, more clues were found and new ideas that supported continental drift were discovered. One of these new ideas, seafloor spreading, helped provide an explanation of how the continents could move.

Section Assessment

1. State one reason why Wegener's ideas about continental drift were not accepted.
2. How did Wegener use climate clues to support his hypothesis about continental drift?
3. **Think Critically:** Why would you expect to see similar rocks and rock structures on two landmasses that were connected at one time?
4. **Skill Builder**
   Comparing and Contrasting Compare and contrast the location of fossils of the tropical plant *Glossopteris,* as shown in **Figure 10-1,** with the climate that exists at each location today. If you need help, refer to Comparing and Contrasting in the **Skill Handbook** on page 720.

Science Journal

Imagine you are Alfred Wegener in the year 1912. In your Science Journal, write a letter to another scientist explaining your idea about continental drift. Try to convince this scientist that your hypothesis is correct.

Caption Answer

Figure 10-4 *It will widen.*

4 Close

Proficiency Prep

Use this quiz to check students' recall of section content.

1. **What hypothesis suggests that continents have moved over time?** *continental drift*
2. **What did Wegener call the large landmass that broke apart to form the continents?** *Pangaea*
3. **Fossils of what freshwater reptile found in both Africa and South America provided support for continental drift?** *Mesosaurus*

Section Assessment

1. Wegener could not explain how, when, or why the continents drifted.
2. He felt that fossils of warm-weather plants found on islands in the Arctic Ocean, as well as glacial deposits and grooved bedrock found in South America, Africa, India, and Australia, supported the idea of continental drift.
3. **Think Critically** Some rocks and rock structures would have formed on both landmasses when they were connected.
4. **Skill Builder** *Glossopteris* fossils are found in all continents in the southern hemisphere. The climates of each continent are different. Several of these continents are not tropical, yet *Glossopteris* was a tropical plant.

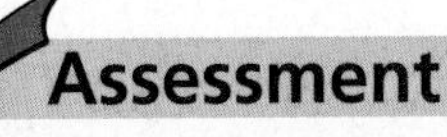

Assessment

Oral Ask students to explain how the location of *Glossopteris* fossils provides support for continental drift. *All locations where the fossils have been found may once have been connected and probably had a similar climate.* Use **Performance Assessment in the Science Classroom,** p. 17.

SECTION 10 2

Prepare

Refer to **The Seafloor Moves** on p. 266E.

Preplanning

Refer to the **Chapter Organizer** on pp. 266A–B.

1 Motivate

Bellringer

Before presenting the lesson, display **Section Focus Transparency 26** on the overhead projector. Use the accompanying **Focus Activity** worksheet. L2 ELL

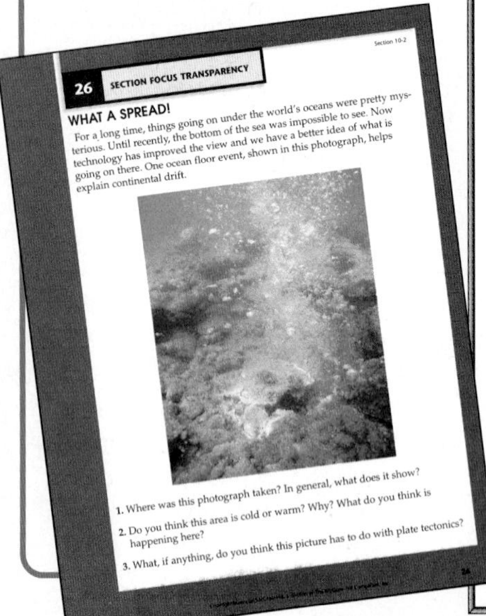

Section 10-2

26 SECTION FOCUS TRANSPARENCY

WHAT A SPREAD!

For a long time, things going on under the world's oceans were pretty mysterious. Until recently, the bottom of the sea was impossible to see. Now technology has improved the view and we have a better idea of what is going on there. One ocean floor event, shown in this photograph, helps explain continental drift.

1. Where was this photograph taken? In general, what does it show?
2. Do you think this area is cold or warm? Why? What do you think is happening here?
3. What, if anything, do you think this picture has to do with plate tectonics?

Tying to Previous Knowledge

Help students recall how lava moves whenever it erupts at Earth's surface through fissures. Remind them that lava flows outward in both directions, similar to the movement of Earth's crust on either side of a mid-ocean ridge.

10 2

Seafloor Spreading

What You'll Learn

- A description of seafloor spreading
- How age and magnetic clues support seafloor spreading

Vocabulary
seafloor spreading

Why It's Important

- Seafloor spreading helps explain how continents drift apart.

Clues on the Ocean Floor

Up until the early 1950s, little was known about the ocean floor. Scientists didn't have the technology needed to explore the deep oceans. But, the invention of echo-sounding devices allowed the development of accurate maps of the ocean floor. Soon, scientists discovered an ocean floor that had mountains and valleys just like on the continents. They also found a system of ridges and valleys in the Atlantic, the Pacific, and in other oceans around the world. The mid-ocean ridges form an underwater mountain range that stretches along the center of much of Earth's ocean floor. This discovery raised the curiosity of many scientists. What formed these mid-ocean ridges?

Age of ocean floor in millions of years

150–200	100–150	50–100	0–50	50–100	100–150	150–200

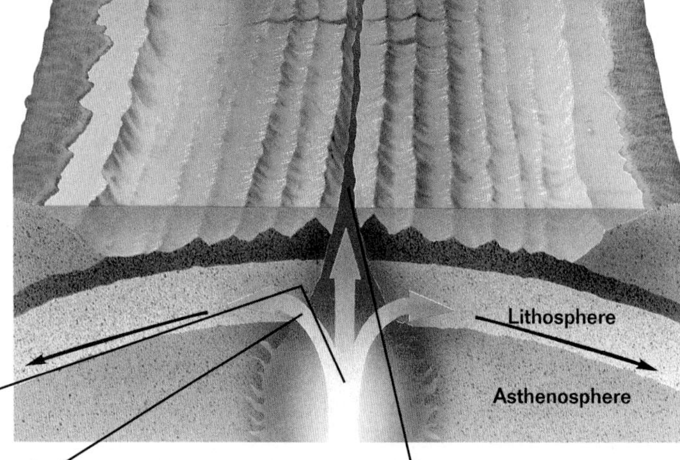

Figure 10-5 As the seafloor spreads apart at a mid-ocean ridge, new seafloor is created. The older seafloor moves away from the ridge in opposite directions. **If seafloor spreading is happening, what evidence should you expect to find by studying rocks taken from the seafloor?**

A Hot, less-dense, partially molten rock material from deep inside Earth is forced upward.

B As this hot material approaches the more rigid upper mantle, it is deflected, and the lithosphere moves along with it.

C Plates of Earth's lithosphere, which are composed of the crust and rigid upper mantle, are forced apart and moved in the direction of the moving hot rock material in the asthenosphere. A rift forms into which molten rock from the upper mantle is forced until it finally flows out onto Earth's surface as lava.

Resource Manager

The following **Teacher Classroom Resources** can be used with Section 10-2:

Reproducible Masters

Activity Worksheets, pp. 55–56 L2
Critical Thinking/Problem Solving, p. 10 L2
Enrichment, p. 26 L3
Reinforcement, p. 26 L2

The Seafloor Moves

In the early 1960s, Princeton University scientist Harry Hess suggested an explanation. His now-famous and accepted theory is known as **seafloor spreading.** Hess proposed that hot, less-dense material below Earth's crust is forced upward toward the surface at a mid-ocean ridge. Then, it turns and flows sideways, carrying the seafloor away from the ridge in both directions, as seen in **Figure 10-5.**

As the seafloor spreads apart, magma moves upward and flows from the cracks. It becomes solid as it cools and forms new seafloor. The seafloor that is carried away from the ridge cools, contracts, and becomes more dense than the material below it. Colder seafloor begins to sink downward. The theory of seafloor spreading was later shown to be correct by the following lines of evidence.

Using Math

Measure the distance between North America and Africa at three locations on a world map. Determine an average distance between the two continents. Assuming the oldest seafloor (180 million years old) formed when Pangaea first broke up, how fast have the two continents been moving apart since then? Use the equation *rate = distance/time.*

Age Evidence

In 1968, scientists aboard the research ship *Glomar Challenger* began gathering information about the rocks on the seafloor. The *Glomar Challenger,* as shown in **Figure 10-6,** was equipped with a drilling rig that allowed scientists to drill into the seafloor to obtain rock samples. The scientists began drilling to study the ages of rocks in the seafloor and made a remarkable discovery. They found no rocks older than 180 million years. In contrast, some continental rocks are almost 4 billion years old. Why are these seafloor rocks so young?

Figure 10-6 The research ship *Glomar Challenger* helped in the exploration of the world's oceans and the seafloor.

2 Teach

Flex Your Brain

Use the Flex Your Brain activity to have students explore SEAFLOOR SPREADING.

Quick Demo

Visual-Spatial Obtain a tectonic globe or build a map on which you can move continents. Use the globe or map to demonstrate continental movement as you teach this section and the next section.

Answer to Text Question

Why are these seafloor rocks so young? *Older seafloor has already been subducted.*

Using Math

If the distance between the two continents is 4500 km, then the rate of separation is 2.5 cm/year.

rate = distance/time

= 450 000 000 cm/ 180 000 000 years

Caption Answer

Figure 10-6 *Rocks get older away from the mid-ocean ridge.*

Visual Learning

Figure 10-6 The *Glomar Challenger* had a very sophisticated positioning system that kept the ship's drill rig directly above the hole being drilled in the seafloor.

Content Background

Moving rock in Earth's mantle drives seafloor spreading. Rising rock causes Earth's surface to bulge and split. As the rock turns and moves sideways, it carries Earth's plates. Continents do not plow through the ocean floor; the ocean floor moves along with the continents.

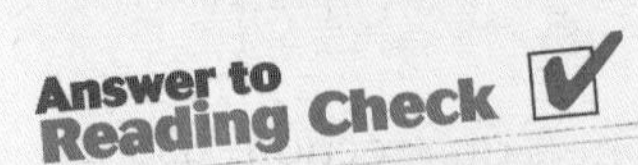

iron-bearing minerals in seafloor basalt

PHYSICS INTEGRATION

The study of dateable, magnetic volcanic rocks has allowed geologists to reconstruct when in the past Earth's magnetic field had normal polarity and when it had reverse polarity. Polarities of strips of ocean floor of known age have allowed scientists to construct a geomagnetic time scale.

CHEMISTRY INTEGRATION

The Curie point is the temperature at which iron minerals lose their magnetism. As lava cools on the ocean floor, the rocks acquire a magnetic field consistent with Earth's magnetic field. If rocks are reheated beyond the Curie Point, the magnetic signature they acquired at the time they formed is lost.

3 Assess

Check for Understanding

Activity

In a time line, have students include the scientific and technological advances that led to the theory of seafloor spreading. L2

A Black smokers along mid-ocean ridges give off hot water that is rich in metals.

B Echo-sounding allows scientists to discover seafloor features on a large scale like those shown here on the Atlantic Ocean floor.

Figure 10-7 Many new discoveries have been made on the seafloor.

Scientists also found that the youngest rocks are located at the mid-ocean ridges. The ages of the rocks become increasingly older farther from the ridges on both sides. The evidence for seafloor spreading was getting stronger. New seafloor features and life-forms were also discovered along mid-ocean ridges, as shown in **Figure 10-7.**

Magnetic Clues

Earth's magnetic field has a north and a south pole. Magnetic lines, or directions, of force leave Earth near the south pole and enter Earth near the north pole. During a *magnetic reversal,* the magnetic forces run the opposite way. Scientists have determined that Earth's magnetic field has reversed itself many times in the past. These reversals occur over thousands or even millions of years.

Reading Check
What materials on the seafloor record magnetic field reversals?

Iron-bearing minerals, such as magnetite, that are found in basalt record Earth's magnetic field direction when they form. If Earth's magnetic field reverses, new iron minerals being formed will reflect that magnetic reversal.

Scientists found that rocks on the ocean floor show many magnetic reversals. A magnetometer (mag nuh TAHM ut ur), a sensitive instrument that records magnetic data, is used. The magnetic alignment in the rocks reverses back and forth over time in strips parallel to the mid-ocean ridges, as shown in **Figure 10-8.**

Reteach

Have pairs of students construct three-dimensional models of rifting at a mid-ocean ridge. L2 COOP LEARN

Caption Answer

Figure 10-8 *The magnetic polarity patterns in oceanic rock show that new rock is forming at the mid-ocean ridges, and older rocks are found away from the ridges.*

This discovery provided strong support that seafloor spreading was indeed happening. The magnetic reversals showed that new rock was being formed at the mid-ocean ridges.

The ideas of Alfred Wegener and Harry Hess changed the way people think about Earth's crust. Fossil, rock, and climate evidence supporting the hypothesis of continental drift is too strong to be discounted. Seafloor spreading shows that ocean floors change, too. You'll soon see how these two ideas are closely related.

CHEMISTRY INTEGRATION

Curie Point

Find out what the Curie point is and describe in your Science Journal what happens to iron-bearing minerals when they are heated to the Curie point. Explain how this is important to studies of seafloor spreading.

Normal magnetic field

Reverse magnetic field

4 3 1 0 1 3 4

Age of ocean floor (millions of years)

Figure 10-8 Changes in Earth's magnetic field are preserved in rock that forms on both sides of mid-ocean ridges. The time line on this diagram shows how this happens over millions of years. **Why is this considered evidence for seafloor spreading?**

Section Assessment

1. How does the recording of Earth's magnetic field in iron-bearing minerals help support the theory of seafloor spreading?
2. What eventually happens to seafloor that is carried away from a mid-ocean ridge?
3. **Think Critically:** How is seafloor spreading different from continental drift?
4. **Skill Builder**
   Concept Mapping Make a concept map that discusses the evidence for seafloor spreading using the following terms and phrases: *ages increase away from ridge, pattern of magnetic field reversals, mid-ocean ridge, pattern of ages around ridge,* and *reverses back and forth.* If you need help, refer to Concept Mapping in the **Skill Handbook** on page 714.

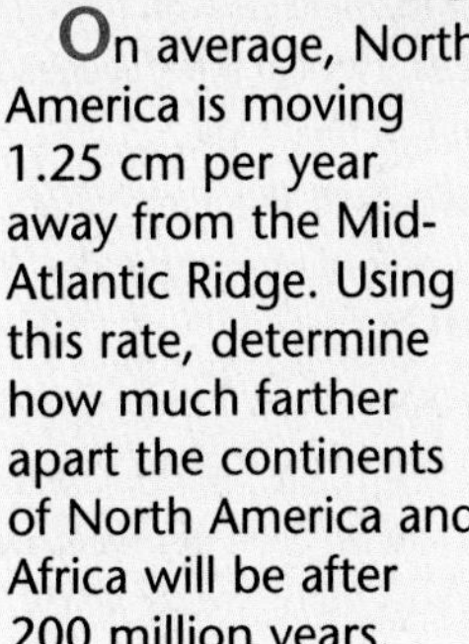

Using Math

On average, North America is moving 1.25 cm per year away from the Mid-Atlantic Ridge. Using this rate, determine how much farther apart the continents of North America and Africa will be after 200 million years.

Extension

For students who have mastered this section, use the **Reinforcement** and **Enrichment** masters.

4 Close

Proficiency Prep

Use this quiz to check students' recall of section content.

1. **Where is new seafloor created?** *mid-ocean ridge*
2. **How old are the oldest ocean-floor rocks?** *about 180 million years old*

Section Assessment

1. Iron-bearing minerals in ocean floor rocks record Earth's magnetic field when they form. Alternating magnetic field reversals parallel to mid-ocean ridges support the idea of seafloor spreading.
2. It cools, contracts, and becomes denser. It begins to sink downward away from a ridge.
3. **Think Critically** Seafloor spreading states that continents move with the seafloor. Continental drift proposed that the continents moved, but no reasonable mechanism for the motion was suggested.
4. **Skill Builder**
   Pattern of magnetic field reversals, and *pattern of ages around ridge* branch from *mid-ocean ridge,.* *Reverses back and forth* branches from *pattern of magnetic field reversals,* and *ages increase away from ridges* branches from *pattern of ages around ridge.*

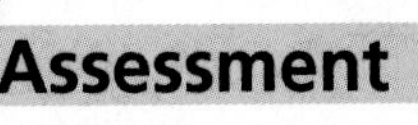

Assessment

Performance Assess students' abilities to make concept maps by having them work together as a class to produce the concept map. Use **Performance Assessment in the Science Classroom,** p. 89.

Using Math

If the North American plate is moving 1.25 cm per year away from the Mid-Atlantic Ridge, North America and Africa separate by 2.5 cm more each year. After 200 million years, they will be separated by 500 000 000 cm or 5000 km.

Purpose

Logical-Mathematical Students will interpret rock polarity data to determine the rate of seafloor spreading. L2

COOP LEARN P

Process Skills

communicating, sequencing, making and using tables, predicting, observing and inferring, measuring in SI, using numbers, interpreting data

Time

50 to 60 minutes

Teaching Strategies

The half-spreading rate shown by the data is about 1.25 cm/year. Divergence at some mid-ocean ridges is occurring at rates of up to 6.0 cm/year.

Troubleshooting Make sure students understand that they should use only the peaks above the baseline. In Step 6, make sure students use the normal polarity average for distance.

Answers to Questions

1. Rocks nearer the ridge are younger than rocks farther from the ridge.
2. about 192 million years ago, assuming a relatively constant rate of spreading
3. Points along coastlines on either side of a mid-ocean ridge could be used to determine when they were at the ridge. If the calculated times were consistent, then this would mark the time that at least part of Pangaea was intact.

Materials

- Metric ruler
- Pencil

Seafloor Spreading Rates

So far, you've learned a lot about seafloor spreading and magnetic field reversals. How can you use your knowledge to reconstruct Pangaea? Try this activity to see how you can determine where a continent may have been located in the past.

What You'll Investigate

Can magnetic clues, such as magnetic field reversals on Earth, be used to help reconstruct Pangaea?

Goals

- **Interpret** data about magnetic field reversals.
- **Use** these magnetic clues to reconstruct Pangaea.

Procedure

1. **Study** the magnetic field graph below. You will be working only with normal polarity readings, which are the peaks above the baseline in the top half of the graph.
2. **Place** the long edge of a ruler vertically on the graph. Slide the ruler so that it lines up with the center of **peak #1 west** of the Mid-Atlantic ridge.
3. **Determine** and **record** the distance and age that line up with the center of **peak #1 west.** Repeat this process for **peak #1 east** of the ridge.
4. **Calculate** the average age and distance for this pair of peaks: **peaks #1 west** and **east.**
5. **Repeat** steps 1 through 4 for each remaining pair of normal polarity peaks.
6. For the six pairs of peaks, **calculate** the rate of movement in cm/year. Use the formula *rate = distance/time* to **calculate** the rate. You must **convert** kilometers to centimeters.

For example, to calculate a rate using Normal polarity peak #5, West from the ridge:

$$\text{rate} = \frac{125\text{ km}}{10\text{ million years}} = \frac{12.5\text{ km}}{\text{million years}}$$

$$= \frac{1\,250\,000\text{ cm}}{1\,000\,000\text{ years}} = 1.25\text{ cm/year}$$

Conclude and Apply

1. Compare the age of igneous rock found near the mid-ocean ridge with that of igneous rock found farther away from the ridge.
2. If the distance from a point on the coast of Africa to the Mid-Atlantic Ridge is approximately 2400 km, **calculate** how long ago that point in Africa was at or near the Mid-Atlantic Ridge.
3. How could you use this method to reconstruct Pangaea?

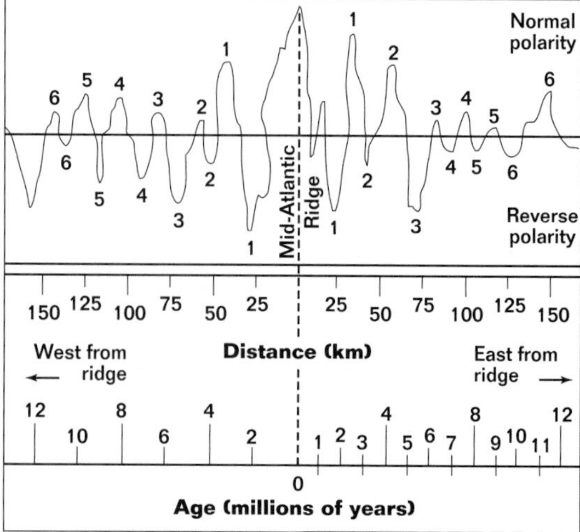

Assessment

Performance To further assess student's understanding of seafloor spreading, have them measure the distance between a point on the eastern coast of the United States and the mid-ocean ridge. Have students determine how long ago that point was near the mid-ocean ridge. Use **Performance Assessment in the Science Classroom,** p. 29.

Plate Tectonics

10-3

Plate Tectonics

The discovery of seafloor spreading helped scientists understand what was happening to Earth's crust and upper mantle. The idea of seafloor spreading showed that more than just continents were moving, as Wegener had thought. It was now certain to scientists that sections of the seafloor and continents move around in relation to one another.

Plate Movements

In the 1960s scientists developed a new theory that combined the main ideas of continental drift and seafloor spreading. According to the theory of **plate tectonics,** Earth's crust and upper mantle are broken into sections. These sections, called **plates,** move around on a special layer of the mantle. The plates can be thought of as rafts that float and move around on this layer.

Composition of Earth's Plates

Plates are made of the crust and a part of the upper mantle, as seen in **Figure 10-9.** These two parts together are called the **lithosphere** (LIHTH uh sfihr). This rigid layer is about 100 km thick and is less dense than material underneath. The plastic-like layer below the lithosphere is called the **asthenosphere** (as THEN uh sfihr).

What You'll Learn

- How to compare and contrast different types of plate boundaries
- How convection currents might be the cause of plate tectonics
- The effects of plate tectonics found at each type of boundary

Vocabulary
plate tectonics
plate
lithosphere
asthenosphere
convection current

Why It's Important

- Plate tectonics explains how many of Earth's features form.

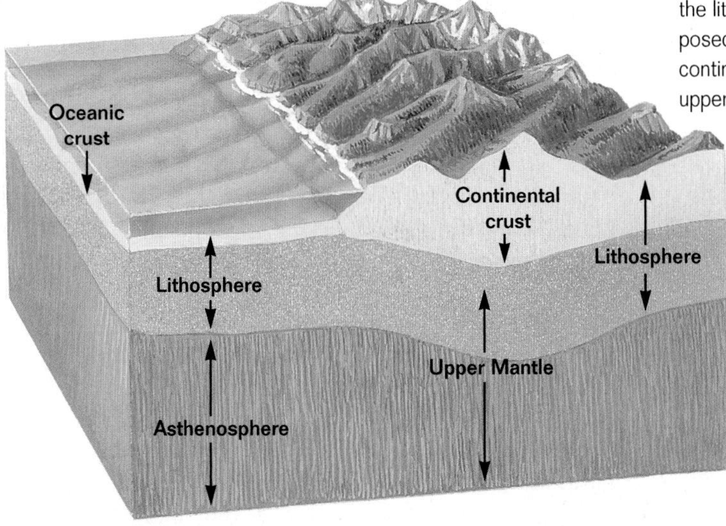

Figure 10-9 Plates of the lithosphere are composed of oceanic crust, continental crust, and rigid upper mantle.

Resource Manager

The following **Teacher Classroom Resources** can be used with Section 10-3:

 **Reproducible Masters**

Activity Worksheets, p. 58 L2

Enrichment, p. 27 L3

Multicultural Connections, pp. 19–20 L2

Reinforcement, p. 27 L2

Study Guide, pp. 39–40 L1 ELL

 **Transparencies**

Teaching Transparency 19, 20 L2

Science Integration Transparency 10 L2

SECTION 10 3

Prepare

Refer to **Plate Boundaries and Mountains, Arcs, and Volcanoes** on pp. 266E–F.

Preplanning

Refer to the **Chapter Organizer** on pp. 266A–B.

1 Motivate

Bellringer

Before presenting the lesson, display **Section Focus Transparency 27** on the overhead projector. Use the accompanying **Focus Activity** worksheet. L2 ELL

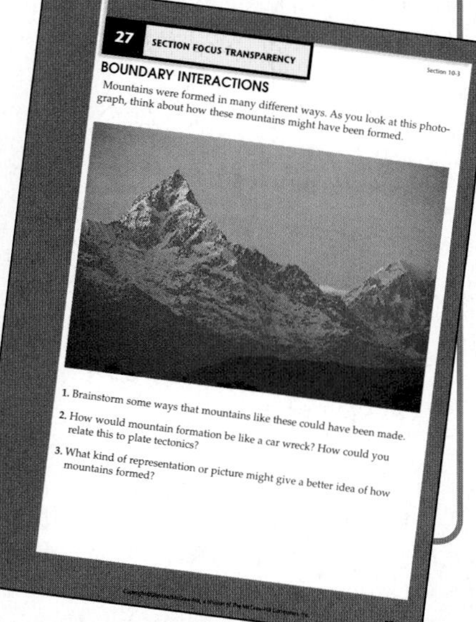
27 SECTION FOCUS TRANSPARENCY

BOUNDARY INTERACTIONS

Mountains were formed in many different ways. As you look at this photograph, think about how these mountains might have been formed.

1. Brainstorm some ways that mountains like these could have been made.
2. How would mountain formation be like a car wreck? How could you relate this to plate tectonics?
3. What kind of representation or picture might give a better idea of how mountains formed?

Tying to Previous Knowledge

Have students recall recent earthquakes. Plot the locations of the quakes on a map to show that most earthquakes occur in specific areas.

2 Teach

Using an Analogy

Tell students that Earth's plates move about as fast as their fingernails grow.

Flex Your Brain

Use the Flex Your Brain activity to have students explore PLATE TECTONICS.

Caption Answer

Figure 10-10 *The Nazca plate and the Pacific plate are moving away from each other.*

Activity

Visual-Spatial Show students a topographic map of the ocean floor, which is available from the National Geographic Society. Have students determine locations on the map where subduction is probably occurring. Have them also locate divergent plate boundaries.

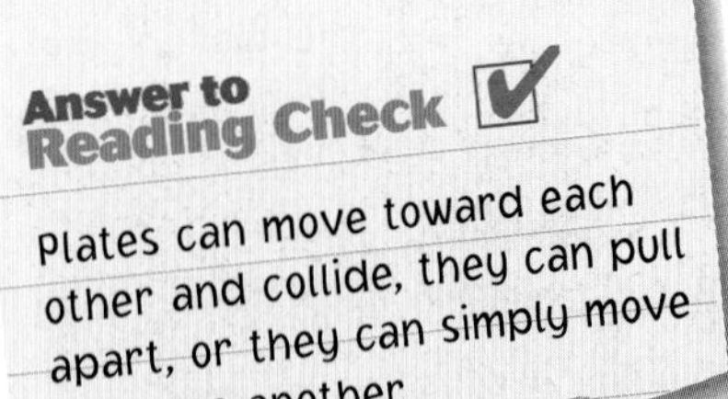

Enrichment

Have students find out about the geologic history of Iceland. Have them concentrate on the rifting of the island and its relationship to the Mid-Atlantic Ridge. L3

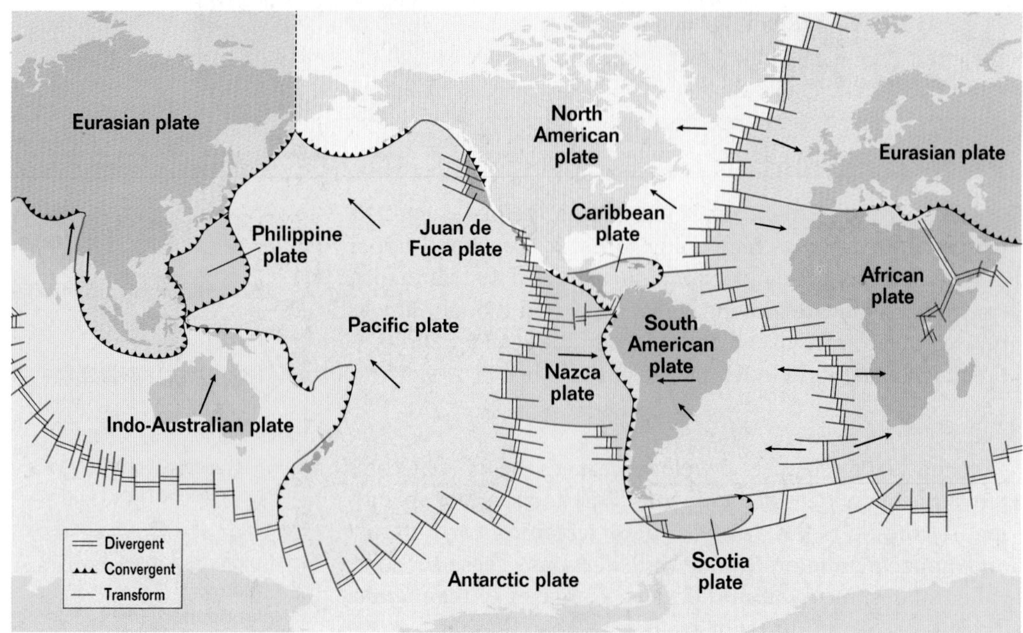

Figure 10-10 This diagram shows the major plates of the lithosphere, their direction of movement, and the type of boundary between them. **Based on what is shown in this figure, what is happening where the Nazca plate meets the Pacific plate?**

The rigid plates of the lithosphere "float" and move around on the asthenosphere. You can think of the plates on the asthenosphere as large, flat stones placed on top of putty. By applying force, you can easily slide the stones around on the putty.

Plate Boundaries

What happens when plates move? They can interact in three ways. They can move toward each other and collide, they can pull apart, or they can simply move past one another. When the plates interact, the result of their movement is seen at the plate boundaries, as in **Figure 10-10.**

Movement along any plate boundary means that changes must happen at other boundaries. What is happening to the Atlantic Ocean between the North American and African plates? Compare this with what is happening along the western margin of South America.

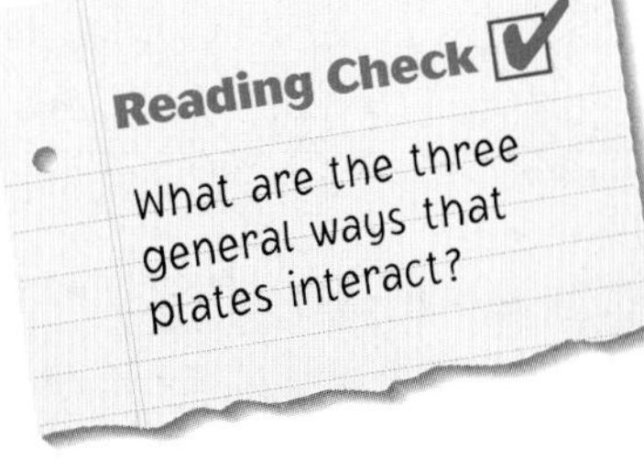

Reading Check
What are the three general ways that plates interact?

Plates Moving Apart

The boundary between two plates that are moving apart is called a *divergent boundary.* You learned about divergent boundaries when you read about seafloor spreading. In the Atlantic Ocean, the North American plate is moving away from the Eurasian and the African plates, as seen in **Figure 10-10.**

Multiple Learning Styles

Linguistic Inform students that many scientists other than Alfred Wegener and Harry Hess contributed ideas that led to plate tectonics. Some of them include A.L. Du Toit, S.K. Runcorn, Bruce Heezen, Arthur Holmes, J. Tuzo Wilson, Jack Oliver, Lynn R. Sykes, Fred Vine, D.H. Matthews, L.W. Morley, Robert Dietz, Allan Cox, Richard Doell, and Brent Dalrymple. Ask the school librarian or the librarian from your community library to visit class and bring books on plate tectonics in which students could read about contributions made by these scientists.

278 CHAPTER 10 PLATE TECTONICS

That divergent boundary is called the Mid-Atlantic Ridge. The Great Rift Valley in eastern Africa is another example of a divergent plate boundary. Here, a valley has formed where two continental plates are separating. **Figure 10-11B** shows a side view of what a rift valley might look like and the hot material that rises up where plates separate.

Plates Moving Together

If new crust is being added at one location, why doesn't Earth's surface keep expanding? As new crust is added in one place, it disappears at another. The disappearance of crust can occur when seafloor cools, becomes more dense, and sinks. This happens where two plates collide at what is called a *convergent boundary.*

There are three types of convergent boundaries. When an oceanic plate collides with a less-dense continental plate, the oceanic plate is forced under the continental plate. The area where an oceanic plate is pushed down into the upper mantle is called a *subduction zone.* Volcanoes occur above subduction zones.

Figure 10-11C shows how this type of convergent boundary creates a deep-sea trench where one plate is forced beneath the other. High temperatures and pressures cause

Problem Solving

The Fit Isn't Perfect

Recall the Explore Activity you performed at the beginning of this chapter. While you were trying to fit pieces of a cut-up photograph together, what clues did you use?

Take a copy of a map of the world and cut out each continent. Lay them out on a tabletop and try to fit them together, using techniques you used in the Explore Activity. You will find that the pieces of your Earth puzzle, the continents, do not fit together very well. Yet, several of the areas on some continents fit together extremely well.

Take out another world map—one that shows the continental shelves as well as the continents. Copy it and cut out the continents, this time including the continental shelves.

Think Critically: When the continents are pieced together with the continental shelves attached, almost all of them fit together well. Why did this slight change of including the continental shelves solve the problem of fitting the continents together? What is true about the continental shelves that indicates they should be included with maps of the continents?

Using Science Words

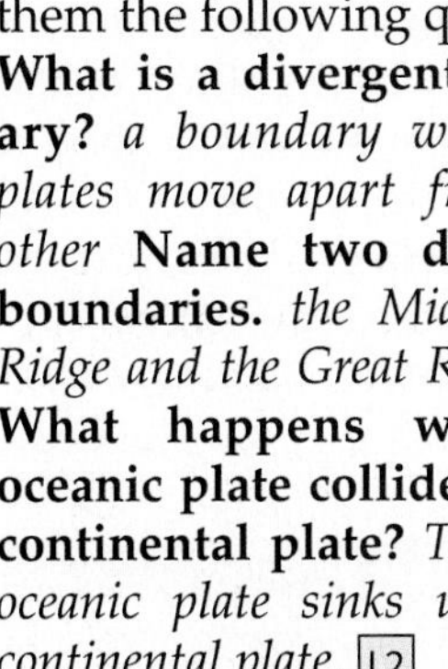

To help students improve in the use of science words, ask them the following questions. **What is a divergent boundary?** *a boundary where two plates move apart from each other* **Name two divergent boundaries.** *the Mid-Atlantic Ridge and the Great Rift Valley* **What happens when an oceanic plate collides with a continental plate?** *The denser oceanic plate sinks under the continental plate.* L2

Quick Demo

Obtain two pieces of flexible foam padding about 8 cm thick. Apply compression forces to demonstrate the folding that occurs when two continental plates converge. Also demonstrate the process of subduction that occurs when an oceanic plate and a continental plate converge or when an oceanic plate and another, less-dense oceanic plate converge.

Problem Solving

Showing just the part of the continents that are exposed above the water leaves off the continental shelves. Because the continental shelves are part of the continents, when they are included, the continents should fit together better.

Think Critically

The continental shelves are part of the continents. The present-day coastlines are the result of the modern sea level and do not represent the edges of continents.

Across the Curriculum

Language Arts Have students use dictionaries to define the terms *diverge* and *converge.* Once they have found the definitions of these terms, ask the following questions. **Why is the Mid-Atlantic Ridge classified as a divergent plate boundary?** *The seafloor is spreading apart at the Mid-Atlantic Ridge.* **What kinds of landforms result from the collision of two plates?** *Volcanic mountains form when oceanic and continental plates converge. Volcanic island arcs form where two oceanic plates converge. Folded mountain ranges develop when two continental plates converge.* L2

Enrichment

Linguistic Have students write reports in their Science Journals about the history of the study of the ocean floor. Reports should compare and contrast the work of Harry Hess and of crews aboard the ships *Glomar Challenger* and *JOIDES Resolution.* L3

GLENCOE TECHNOLOGY

Videodisc

Glencoe Science Voyages Interactive Videodisc—Earth

Side 1, Lesson 4

Volcanoes: Erupting Mountains

43091

43751

44253

Refer to Videodisc Teacher Guide for additional bar codes.

the subducted plate to melt as it descends under the other plate. The newly formed magma is forced upward along these plate boundaries, forming volcanic mountains. The Andes mountain system of South America contains many volcanoes. They were formed at the convergent boundary of the Nazca and the South American plates.

The second type of convergent boundary occurs when two oceanic plates collide, and when seafloor that has become more dense due to cooling begins to sink. In this type of plate collision, one plate bends and slides under the other, forming a subduction zone as shown in **Figure 10-11E.** A deep-sea trench is formed, and new magma that is produced rises to form an island arc of volcanoes. The islands of Japan are an island arc formed where two oceanic plates collide.

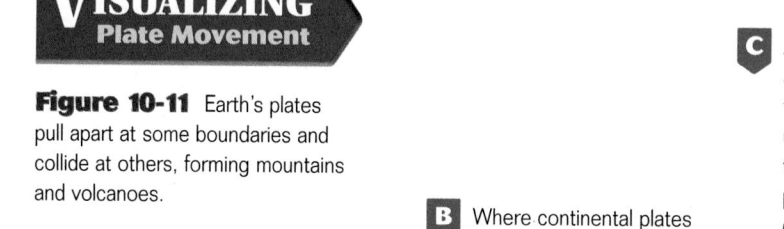

Figure 10-11 Earth's plates pull apart at some boundaries and collide at others, forming mountains and volcanoes.

A As one continental plate collides with another, lithosphere is pushed up at the boundary and mountains form.

B Where continental plates pull apart, a rift valley forms. If the rift valley separates further, it may flood and become an ocean.

C As an oceanic plate collides with a less-dense continental plate, the continental plate is forced upward and the oceanic plate is forced under the continental plate. As the oceanic plate descends, it starts to melt. The melted rock is less dense than surrounding rock and is forced upward, forming volcanoes.

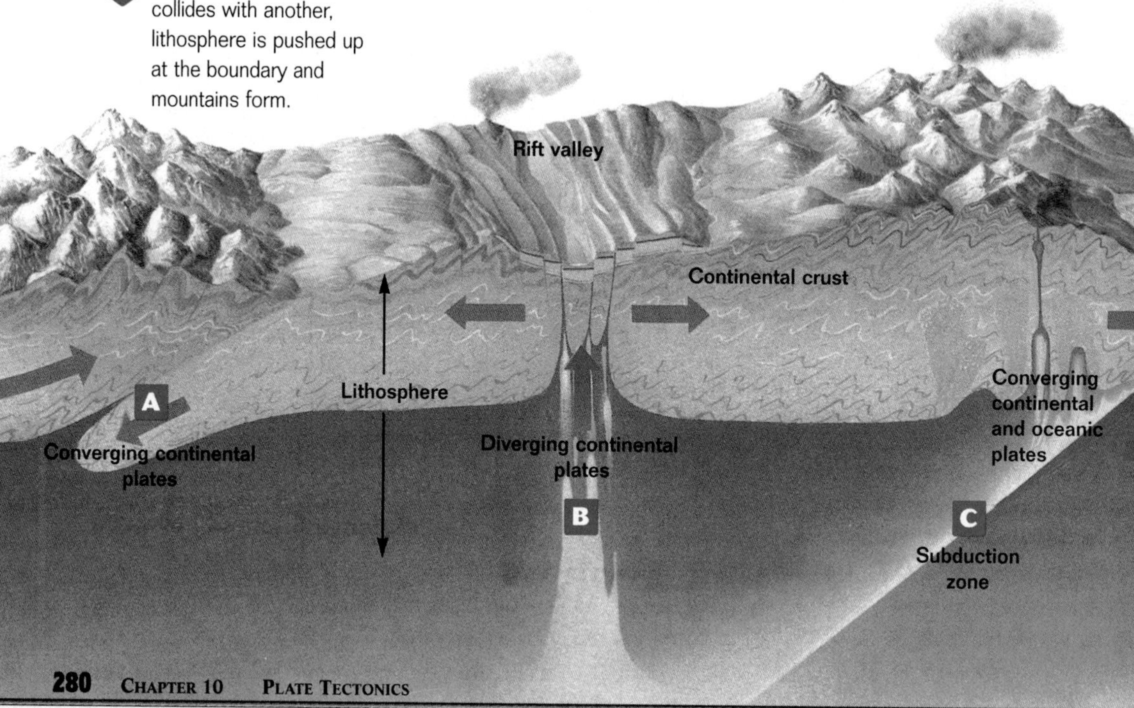

VISUAL Learning

Figure 10-11 After students study **Figure 10-11,** select three volunteers to illustrate the different types of convergent boundaries on the chalkboard, on the overhead projector, or on poster paper. Ask other students to do the same with divergent plate boundaries. L2

The third type of convergent boundary occurs when two continental plates collide as shown in **Figure 10-11A.** Because both of these plates are less dense than the material in the asthenosphere, usually no subduction occurs. The two plates just collide and crumple up, forming mountain ranges. Earthquakes are common at these convergent boundaries. But, volcanoes do not form because there is no subduction. The Himalaya in Asia are forming where the Indo-Australian plate crashes into the Eurasian plate.

Plates Sliding Past Each Other

The third type of plate boundary is called a *transform boundary.* Transform boundaries occur when two plates slide past one another. They move either in opposite directions or in the same direction at different rates. When one plate slips past another suddenly, earthquakes occur. The Pacific plate is sliding past the North American plate, forming the famous San Andreas Fault in California, as seen in **Figure 10-12.** The San Andreas Fault is part of a transform plate boundary. It has been the site of many earthquakes.

Visit the Glencoe Science Web Site at **www.glencoe.com/sec/science** for more information about types of plate boundaries.

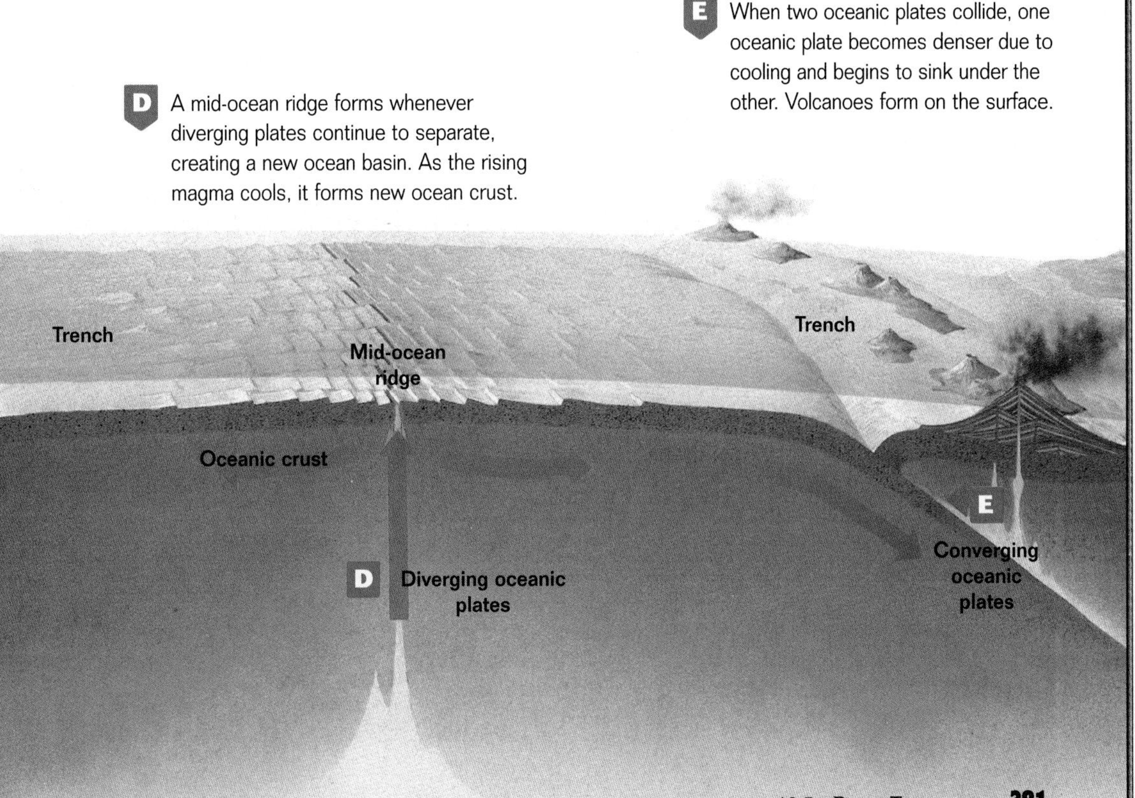

D A mid-ocean ridge forms whenever diverging plates continue to separate, creating a new ocean basin. As the rising magma cools, it forms new ocean crust.

E When two oceanic plates collide, one oceanic plate becomes denser due to cooling and begins to sink under the other. Volcanoes form on the surface.

Teacher FYI

The Pacific and North American plates, sliding past each other along the San Andreas Fault, each move an average of about 5 cm per year.

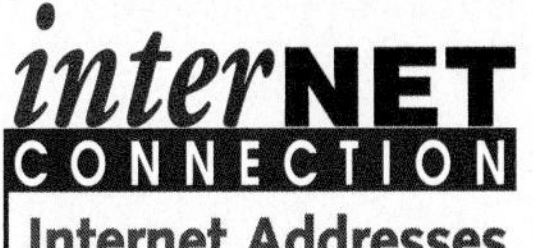

Internet Addresses

For Internet tips, see Glencoe's **Using the Internet in the Science Classroom.**

Correcting Misconceptions

Ask students to stand perfectly still. Then ask them whether or not they are moving. Explain that Earth movements such as rotation, revolution, and plate movements are not felt by humans. Have students find out the velocities at which each of the processes mentioned occurs. L3

Videodisc

STV: Restless Earth

Unit 4 *San Andreas Fault* 0:59

00001-01776

Refer to the Teacher Guide for additional bar codes and teaching strategies.

Integrating the Sciences

Physics Thermal energy is transferred from one place to another by three methods. One of these, convection, is thought to provide the energy needed to power the movement of Earth's plates. Ask students to research energy transfer by convection currents and then have them describe the driving mechanism of Earth's plates. *Hot, plasticlike material in the asthenosphere is forced upward toward the lithosphere. When the hot material reaches the lithosphere, it moves laterally and carries Earth's plates. As the material cools, it sinks. These huge convection currents in the mantle are the driving force of plate tectonics.* L3

MiniLab

Purpose

Visual-Spatial Students will observe convection currents and infer what causes them to form. L2 ELL

COOP LEARN P

Materials

food coloring; water; thermal mitts; clear, colorless glass container; hot plate

Teaching Strategies

Safety Precautions Have students wear thermal mitts to protect their hands.

Troubleshooting If students experience difficulty observing convection currents, instruct them to drop the food coloring into the water soon after turning on the hot plate.

Analysis

1. Answers will vary.
2. Transfer of thermal energy and the resulting density differences cause convection currents.
3. One possible solution is to begin heating the water only on one side.

Assessment

Oral To further assess students' understanding of convection currents, have them observe a heated pan of noodle soup. Ask students to explain what is happening. Use **Performance Assessment in the Science Classroom,** p. 17.

Modeling Convection Currents

Procedure

1. Fill a clear, colorless casserole dish with water to 5 cm from the top.
2. Center the dish on a hot plate and heat. **CAUTION:** *Wear thermal mitts to protect your hands.*
3. Add a few drops of food coloring to the water directly above the hot plate.
4. Looking from the side of the dish, observe what happens in the water.
5. In your Science Journal, describe what you observe. If possible, make an illustration.

Analysis

1. Determine whether any currents form in the water.
2. If so, infer what causes the currents to form.
3. If not, determine how to change the experiment in order to cause currents to form. Get permission from your teacher before you proceed.

Causes of Plate Tectonics

Many new discoveries have been made about Earth's crust since Wegener's day. But, one question still remains. What causes the plates to move and the seafloor to spread? Scientists now think they have a pretty good idea. They think that plates are moved by the same basic process that is used to heat some buildings.

Convection Currents

In a forced-air heating system, air is warmed in a furnace and a blower forces it into each room of the building. The warm air is forced upward through vents on the floor and heats the surrounding air. Cooler air, which is more dense, sinks to the floor of the room. It returns to the furnace through the cold air return and is reheated. This entire cycle of heating, rising, cooling, and sinking is called a **convection current.** This same process, occurring in the mantle, is thought to be the force behind plate tectonics.

Figure 10-12 The San Andreas Fault in California occurs along the transform plate boundary where the Pacific plate is sliding past the North American plate.

 This photograph shows an aerial view of the San Andreas Fault.

Content Background

Many scientists have speculated about whether Earth's plates are passive passengers carried by large convection cells or are actually active parts of the convection cells. At present, the active plate model seems to have gained favor among most geologists.

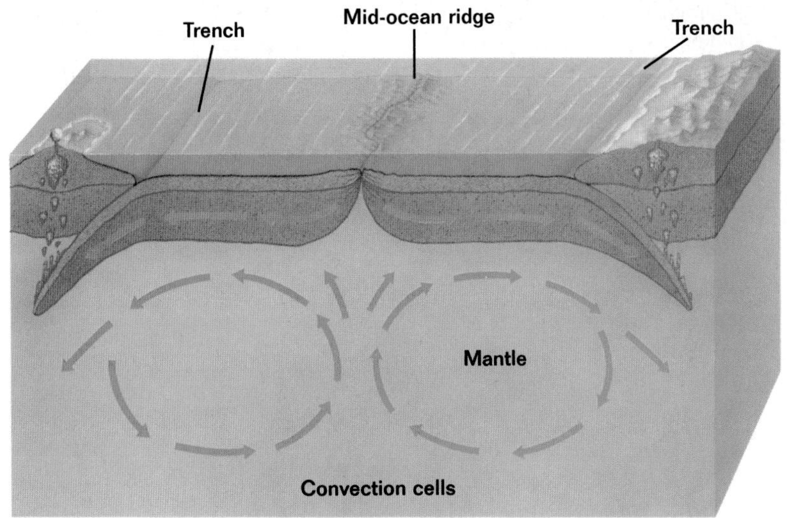

Figure 10-13 Pictured is one hypothesis of how convection currents (see arrows) are the driving force of plate tectonics. In this hypothesis, convection is limited to the upper mantle only. In another hypothesis, convection currents occur throughout the mantle.

Scientists suggest that differences in density cause hot, plasticlike rock to be forced upward toward the surface. When this material reaches Earth's lithosphere, it moves horizontally and carries plates of the lithosphere with it, as described earlier. As it cools, the plasticlike rock becomes more dense. It then sinks into the mantle, taking overlying lithosphere with it.

These huge convection currents provide the energy to move plates as shown in **Figure 10-13.** They are, therefore, the cause of many of Earth's surface features.

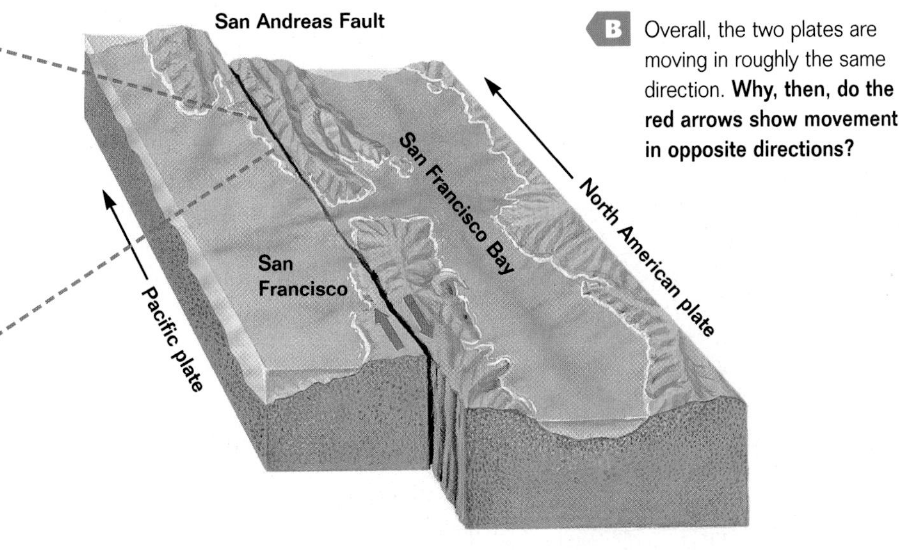

B Overall, the two plates are moving in roughly the same direction. **Why, then, do the red arrows show movement in opposite directions?**

Activity

Interpersonal Form four groups and assign each group one of the following topics to master and present to the class: convergent boundaries, divergent boundaries, transform boundaries, and the driving mechanism of plate tectonics. L2 COOP LEARN

Making a Model

Tape several sheets of paper together to make one long sheet of paper about 1 m in length. Fold the paper in half. Place two desks together and stick the fold of the paper down between the desks. Pull on the two ends of the paper and place them on the desk tops. Place rocks on each paper to represent islands or continents on the two plates. Gradually pull the ends of the paper sheet away from each other. This demonstrates the divergence of plates caused by seafloor spreading.

Caption Answer

Figure 10-12B *The western side (Pacific plate) of the fault is moving faster than the eastern side (North American plate).*

GLENCOE TECHNOLOGY

Videodisc

The Infinite Voyage: Living with Disaster

Chapter 6 *Predicting Earthquakes: The Parkfield Experiment* 10:00

Refer to the Teacher Guide for bar codes and teaching strategies.

Inclusion Strategies

Learning Disabled Have students place a piece of long, plastic tubing into the neck of a strong balloon and secure the tube so no air can escape from the balloon. Have them place the balloon at the bottom of an aquarium tank, with the tubing extending over the top. Add a layer of moist sand and then a layer of dry sand, each about 2 mm deep. Alternate layers several times. Have a student blow up the balloon slowly until the sand begins to crack to simulate an earthquake.

Gifted Gifted students may take this simulation one step further. Have those students build a model city on the top of the sand. A student can videotape the "earthquake" and students can prepare a documentary showing how the quake affected the "city." L2 COOP LEARN

Caption Answer

Figure 10-14 *tension*

Discussion

Use the following inquiry question to help students consider the relation between earthquakes and plate tectonics. **Earthquakes are associated with some plate boundaries. Why do you think this is so?** *Much force is involved with plate movements. As plates collide or slide past one another, energy is released as earthquakes occur.*

STV: Restless Earth

Unit 3 *Spreading in Africa* 1:58

37503-41049

Unit 3 *Rifting* 1:27

43941-46580

Refer to the Teacher Guide for additional bar codes and teaching strategies.

Internet Addresses

For Internet tips, see Glencoe's **Using the Internet in the Science Classroom.**

Figure 10-14 Fault-block mountains can form when Earth's crust is stretched by tectonic forces. The arrows indicate the directions that blocks have moved. **What type of force occurs when Earth's crust is pulled in opposite directions?**

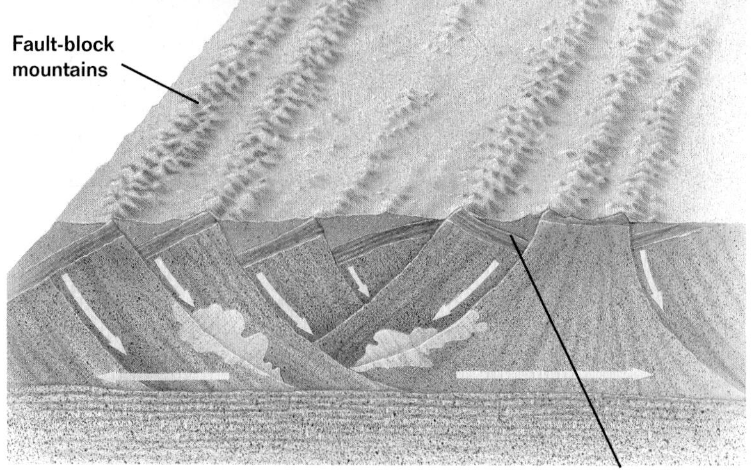

interNET CONNECTION

Visit the Glencoe Science Web site at **www.glencoe.com/sec/science** for more information about the Great Rift Valley in Africa.

Effects of Plate Tectonics

Earth is a dynamic planet with convection currents inside that power the movement of plates. As the plates move, they interact. The interaction of plates produces forces that build mountains, create ocean basins, and cause volcanoes. Whenever rocks in Earth's crust break and move, a fault forms and energy is released in the form of seismic waves. Humans feel this release as earthquakes. You can see some of the effects of plate tectonics in the **Field Guide to Roadside Geology** at the end of this chapter.

Normal Faults and Rift Valleys

Diverging plates cause tension forces that stretch Earth's crust. This causes large blocks of crust to break and tilt or slide down. Entire mountain ranges may form in the process, called fault-block mountains, as shown in **Figure 10-14.** Generally, the faults that form from tension are normal faults. Once the divergence causes a separation in Earth's crust, rift valleys can form. Examples of rift valleys are the Great Rift Valley in Africa, shown in **Figure 10-15,** and the valleys that occur in the middle of mid-ocean ridges. Examples include the Mid-Atlantic Ridge and the East Pacific Rise.

Figure 10-15 The Great Rift Valley of Africa will probably become an ocean basin as rifting continues.

Strike-Slip Faults

If one plate is sliding past another, the forces are not directly opposite. The plates stick and then slide along large strike-slip faults. One such example is

Guided Reading Strategy

Pair of Pairs This strategy encourages students as partners to respond to a question. They brainstorm together, recording their ideas on one paper. After a few minutes, they combine with another pair and share responses. Finally, the teacher asks the groups of four to share any responses. Have students use the Pair of Pairs strategy on a Think Critically question in a Section Assessment in this chapter.

Integrating the Sciences

Meteorology/Oceanography Inform students that convection currents play a role in circulation and the transfer of energy in other Earth systems. Convection currents transfer energy within the atmosphere. Density currents within Earth's oceans are also examples of convection currents. Have students study books on meteorology and oceanography to find other examples of convection currents. L2

the San Andreas Fault. When plates move suddenly, vibrations are generated inside Earth that are felt as an earthquake. Plate tectonics explains how activity inside Earth can affect Earth's crust differently in different locations. We have seen how plates have moved since Pangaea separated. What was Earth like before that?

Mountains, Arcs, and Volcanoes

Most of Earth's mountain belts, volcanoes, and earthquakes occur at convergent plate boundaries. Compression forces produce several effects where plates move together. When continental plates converge, the forces generated cause massive folding of rock layers into mountain ranges such as the Himalaya, shown in **Figure 10-16,** or the Appalachian Mountains. Reverse faults also may occur if the forces are great enough. If the two converging plates are oceanic plates, one plate slides under the other, melting occurs, and island arcs and volcanoes form.

If an oceanic plate converges with a continental plate, the oceanic plate slides under the continental plate, melting occurs, and volcanoes form. Entire mountain ranges can form at this type of convergent boundary. ☑

Tectonic Forces
In what directions are forces applied at convergent, divergent, and transform boundaries? Demonstrate these forces using wooden blocks or your hands.

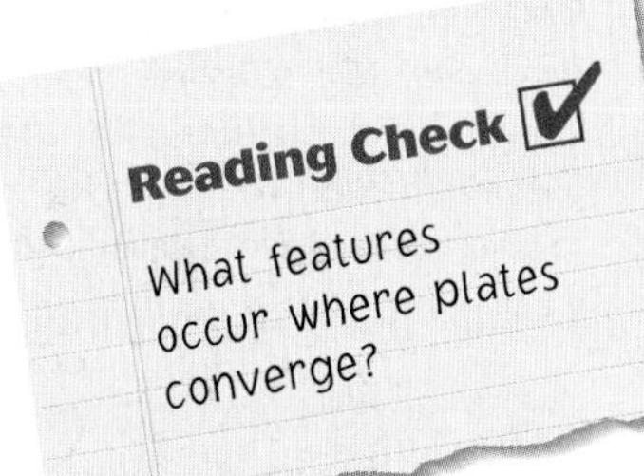

Reading Check
What features occur where plates converge?

Testing for Plate Tectonics

Until recently, the only tests scientists could use to check for plate movement were indirect. They could study the magnetic characteristics of rocks on the seafloor. They could study volcanoes and earthquakes. However, these methods only provided indirect evidence that the plates have moved and are still moving. They did not provide proof—only support of the idea.

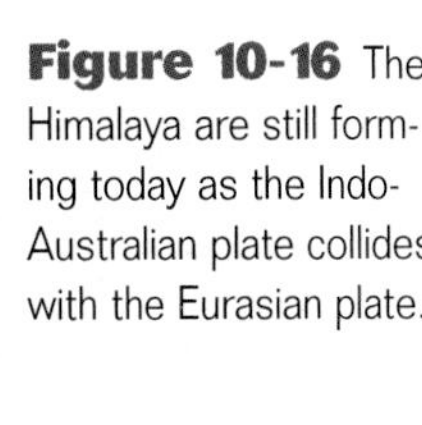

Figure 10-16 The Himalaya are still forming today as the Indo-Australian plate collides with the Eurasian plate.

PHYSICS INTEGRATION

Convergent boundary forces applied: → ←
Divergent boundary forces applied: ← →
Transform boundary forces applied: ↑ ↓

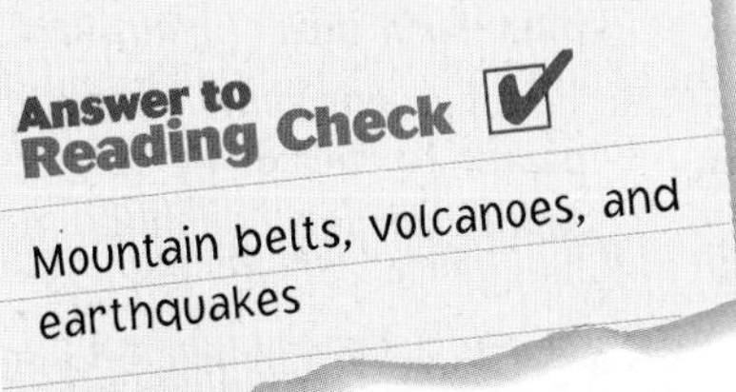

3 Assess

Check for Understanding

Discussion

Lead students in a discussion about how the three different types of plate boundaries together accommodate motion of Earth's plates.

Reteach

Using a supermarket conveyor belt as an analogy, explain how Earth's plates move.

Extension

For students who have mastered this section, use the **Reinforcement** and **Enrichment** masters.

Science Journal

Landers Earthquake Have students research the 1992 Landers, California, earthquake. In their Science Journals, have them write a brief summary explaining why this earthquake is so important to the study of plate tectonics and plate boundaries. *Being one of the largest earthquakes to hit California in 40 years, it may have triggered other earthquakes and may indicate that a new fault is forming in the desert. The plate boundary between the Pacific plate and the North American plate may be shifting eastward.* L2

4 Close

Proficiency Prep

Use this quiz to check students' recall of section content.

1. **What type of boundaries form when plates move apart?** *divergent*
2. **What happens when two continents collide?** *rocks are crumpled into mountains*
3. **What type of boundaries form when plates slide past each other?** *transform*
4. **What causes Earth's plates to move?** *convection in the mantle*

Section Assessment

1. Plates slide past one another.
2. Plates of the lithosphere diverge.
3. divergent, ocean-continent convergent, and ocean-ocean convergent
4. **Think Critically** Iceland is a portion of the Mid-Atlantic Ridge, which is a site of volcanic activity.

Using Computers

Student bar graphs should show that earthquakes with small Richter magnitudes occur much more often than those with large magnitudes.

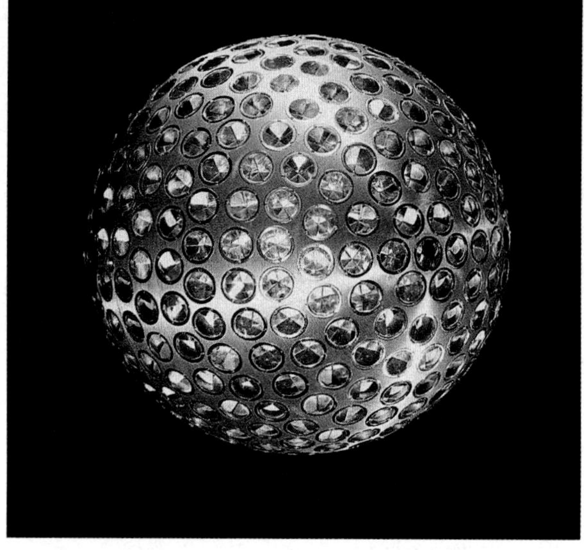

Figure 10-17 When using the Satellite Laser Ranging System, scientists on the ground shoot laser pulses at a satellite, shown here. The pulses reflect off the satellite and are used to determine an exact location on the ground.

Now, scientists can measure exact movements of Earth's plates of as little as 1 cm/year. New methods had to be discovered to be able to measure the small amounts of movement of Earth's plates. One method uses lasers and a satellite, as shown in **Figure 10-17.**

Current data from these methods show that Hawaii is moving toward Japan at a rate of about 8.3 cm/year. Also, Maryland is moving away from England at a rate of about 1.7 cm/year. The total range of data from the methods taken all over the world shows that lithospheric plates move between 1 to 12 cm/year relative to the positions of other plates.

Section Assessment

1. What happens to plates at a transform plate boundary?
2. What occurs at plate boundaries associated with seafloor spreading?
3. Describe three types of plate boundaries where volcanic eruptions can occur.
4. **Think Critically:** Using **Figure 10-10** and a world map, determine what natural disasters might be likely to occur in Iceland.
5. **Skill Builder**
   Interpreting Scientific Illustrations Plate tectonic activity causes many events that can be dangerous to humans. One of these events is an earthquake that occurs on the seafloor. This can form a seismic sea wave, or tsunami. Learn how scientists predict the arrival time of a tsunami in a coastal area. Do the **Chapter 10 Skill Activity** on page 751.

Using Computers

Graphics Research ten recent earthquakes of magnitude 3.0 or greater. Make a bar graph that plots the number of earthquakes on the *y*-axis and their Richter magnitudes on the *x*-axis. Make the first bar on the *x*-axis have a Richter range of 3–4, the second a range of 4–5, etc. If you need help, refer to page 734.

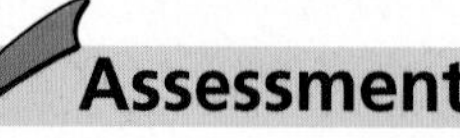

Assessment

Performance Have students draw a cross section showing how the wave height of a tsunami may increase from open ocean values of less than 1 m to values greater than 30 m upon entering shallow water and reaching land. Use **Performance Assessment in the Science Classroom,** p. 55.

Science & Math

Finding and Using Rates

A rate is a ratio of two measurements with different units. You are familiar with some rates, such as kilometers per hour. Kilometers per hour is also a unit rate because the denominator of the rate is one unit. Finding unit rates can help you solve problems about the movement of geologic features in Earth's crust, such as strike-slip faults.

Problem

A well-known strike-slip fault is the San Andreas Fault in California (see aerial view at left). The fault has moved about 600 km in 150 million years. Follow the steps below to answer two questions. What is the rate of movement per year of the San Andreas Fault? At this rate, how far will the fault move in 1000 years?

Solution

1. Think: 150 million is a large number, and 600 is a much smaller number. You will be dividing to find the rate, so convert 600 km to millimeters. Since 1 km = 1000 m and 1 m = 1000 mm, multiply 600 by 1000 to get meters and again by 1000 to get millimeters. $600 \times 1000 \times 1000 =$ 600 000 000; 600 km is 600 000 000 mm.

2. Find the unit rate: Write the rate as a fraction. Then, simplify the fraction to have a denominator of 1.

$$\frac{\text{mm}}{\text{years}} = \frac{600\,000\,000 \div 150\,000\,000}{150\,000\,000 \div 150\,000\,000} = \frac{4\text{ mm}}{1\text{ year}} = 4\text{ mm/year}$$

The unit rate is 4 mm per year.

3. To find the movement of the fault over 1000 years: Multiply the unit rate by 1000. $4 \times 1000 = 4000$. The movement in 1000 years is 4000 mm, or 4 m.

Practice PROBLEMS

1. The Great Glen Fault in Scotland moved 8 km in 220 million years. What is the rate of movement per year of this fault?
2. How many times faster than the Great Glen Fault is the San Andreas Fault moving?
3. During the last 90 years, the San Andreas Fault has been moving much faster than in previous years. During this time period, the rate has been about 4 cm per year. About how much has the fault moved in the last 90 years?

Content Background

- These problems also include converting metric units of measure and computation with decimals.
- The sample problem has two parts: finding a unit rate and solving a problem using that rate.
- Be sure students understand that what is calculated in the sample problem is an average rate. Sometimes faults move more quickly or slowly during certain periods of time. (See Practice Problem 3.)

Teaching Strategies

- Be sure students understand the conversion of kilometers to millimeters. Use a meterstick to show them the lengths of a meter, a centimeter, and a millimeter.
- The sample problem could be solved using kilometers. For example, $\frac{600}{150\,000\,000} = 0.000\,004$ km. Then, convert to millimeters by multiplying by 1000×1000. The result is 4 mm.
- Students could research other faults to find the distance moved over a period of time. Then, they could find the unit rates and compare them to the San Andreas and Great Glen faults.

Answers to Practice PROBLEMS

1. 0.036, or 0.036 mm/year
2. approximately 111 times faster
3. 360 cm or 3.6 m

Activity 10•2 On the Internet

Recognize the Problem

Objectives

- Students will plot earthquake epicenters and the locations of volcanic eruptions.
- Students will predict tectonically active locations based on their plot.

Form a Hypothesis

Internet Students will obtain the latitudes and longitudes of 20 recent earthquakes and 20 recent volcanic eruptions. Data can be accessed through the Glencoe Science Web Site at **www.glencoe.com/sec/science.** They will plot these locations on a map of the world. Once plotted, students will use the locations to determine areas of Earth that are tectonically active.

Non-Internet Sources Students will obtain maps of the world on which they will make their plots. They will use the plotted locations on the map to determine areas of Earth that are tectonically active.

Time Required

two 35- to 40-minute class periods or one block of 70 to 80 minutes

Activity 10•2

Predicting Tectonic Activity

Earthquakes occur every day on Earth. Many of them are too small to be felt by humans, but all of them can tell us something about our planet. Active volcanoes can do the same. Active volcanoes often form at plate boundaries. The movement of plates on Earth causes forces that build energy in rocks. The release of this energy can produce vibrations in Earth (earthquakes).

Recognize the Problem

Can tectonically active areas be predicted by plotting locations of earthquake epicenters and volcanic eruptions?

Form a Hypothesis

Think about where earthquakes and volcanoes have occurred in the past. **Make a Hypothesis** about whether the locations of earthquake epicenters and active volcanoes can be used to predict tectonically active areas.

Goals

- **Plot** earthquake epicenters and the locations of volcanic eruptions obtained from the Glencoe Science Web Site.
- **Predict** tectonically active locations based on a plot of the locations of earthquake epicenters and active volcanoes.

Data Sources

Visit the Glencoe Science Web Site at **www.glencoe.com/sec/science** for more information about earthquake and volcano sites. If you do not have access to the Internet, you can obtain the locations of earthquake epicenters and active volcanoes from the U.S. Geologic Survey or local newspapers.

Locations of Epicenters and Eruptions

Earthquake Epicenter/ Volcanic Eruption	Longitude	Latitude

interNET CONNECTION

Internet Addresses

____

____

____

____

For Internet tips, see Glencoe's **Using the Internet in the Science Classroom.**

Preparation

Internet Access the Glencoe Science Web Site at **www.glencoe.com/sec/science** to run through the steps the students will follow.

Non-Internet Sources If the Internet is not used, obtain tissue paper or sheets of plastic for the students to use to draw copies of maps showing the locations of recent earthquakes and volcanic eruptions. The locations of earthquake epicenters and volcanoes can be obtained from the U.S. Geological Survey or from local newspapers.

Test Your Hypothesis

Plan

1. **Make a data table** like the one shown on the opposite page.
2. **Collect data** for earthquake epicenters and volcanic eruptions for at least the past two weeks. Your data should include the longitude and latitude for each location. For help, refer to the **data sources** given on the opposite page.
3. **Plot the locations** of earthquake epicenters and volcanic eruptions on a map of the world. Use an overlay of tissue paper or plastic.

Do

1. Make sure your teacher approves your plan and your data table before you proceed.
2. After you have collected and plotted the locations of earthquake epicenters and volcanic eruptions from at least the past two weeks, it's time to predict tectonically active areas on Earth.
3. Using your data, **predict** what areas of the world are tectonically active.
4. **Compare** and **contrast** the areas that you predicted to be tectonically active with the plate boundary map shown in **Figure 10-10.**

Analyze Your Data

1. What areas on Earth do you **predict** to be the locations of tectonic activity?
2. How close did your prediction come to the actual location of tectonically active areas?

Draw Conclusions

1. How could you make your predictions closer to the locations of actual tectonic activity?
2. Would data from a longer period of time help? **Explain.**
3. What types of plate boundaries were close to your locations of earthquake epicenters? Volcanic eruptions?
4. **Explain** which types of plate boundaries produce volcanic eruptions. Be specific.

Test Your Hypothesis

Teaching Strategies

- Separate students into groups of two or three per computer.
- Encourage students to look for patterns shown by the plotted locations of earthquake epicenters and active volcanoes.

Have students work with other groups in the class and combine all location data on one map. Encourage them to look up as many as 50 more of each on the Internet. Note whether this increase in data changes any conclusions about tectonically active areas on Earth.

Analyze Your Data

1. Answers will vary, but students will likely predict some type of plate boundary.
2. Answers will depend on data collected; students will notice most occurrences along plate boundaries. Hot spot volcanic eruptions may not coincide with plate boundaries.

Draw Conclusions

1. Consider the specific type of plate boundary for earthquakes and volcanoes. Volcanoes generally occur along divergent boundaries and subduction zones; earthquakes can occur along any plate boundary.
2. Yes; more time would permit more data that could support student hypotheses.
3. Answers will vary.
4. divergent; ocean/ocean convergent; ocean/continent convergent

References

- Feather, Ralph M. Jr., and Susan Snyder. *Earth Science.* Columbus, OH: Glencoe/McGraw-Hill, 1999.
- Tarbuck, Edward J. and Frederick K. Lutgens. *Earth: An Introduction to Physical Geology.* Upper Saddle River, NJ, 1999.
- Thompson, Graham R. and Jonathan Turk. *Introduction to Physical Geology.* Fort Worth, TX: Saunders College Pub., 1998.

Assessment

Oral Have students formulate a hypothesis that could explain the relationship among the locations of earthquake epicenters and active volcanoes and Earth's tectonic activity. To assess the results of the project, use **Performance Assessment in the Science Classroom,** p. 21.

FIELD GUIDE

Using the Field Guide

- Use this field guide with student pages 277 to 285.
- A field guide enables the user to classify or identify a feature or concept.
- In using a field guide, students will apply steps of a scientific method as they observe, investigate, and draw conclusions.
- This field guide applies nationally; local and regional field guides are available for more specific local use. Two sources of regional information are listed at the bottom of this page.
- Encourage students to use this field guide outside.

FIELD ACTIVITY

Earth structures observed on a road trip will vary from region to region but may include faults, folds, caves, landslides, and sedimentary features. After completing the Field Activity, have students compare notes to further their understanding of Earth structures and the forces that produce them.

Tying to Previous Knowledge

Students have seen many of the Earth structures discussed in this field guide in the background of motion pictures, particularly westerns. Tell them that after studying this field guide, they will appreciate these movies even more.

FIELD GUIDE to Roadside Geology

FIELD ACTIVITY

Geologic forces slowly push and pull on Earth's crust, creating the surface features we can see around us. As you travel, look around you. The next time you drive along the road, whether on a personal journey or a field trip with your school, use this field guide to help you identify Earth structures you observe along the way. What forces are at work to form the structures you see? Record your observations and inferences about forces in your Science Journal.

Earthquakes! Landslides! Volcanic eruptions! These are some of the ways that Earth's surface can change quickly. However, most of the changes in Earth's crust are less spectacular and occur much more slowly. Because of the life span of humans, Earth's surface appears to change little. Features like mountains and rivers will not appear or disappear during a person's lifetime, but these features do change over much longer periods of time. In this field guide, you'll see some examples of how Earth's crust changes over time

Faults

- A fault is created when rocks move along a break or fracture.
- Faults can be small, with only centimeters of movement, or they can be large, stretching for hundreds of kilometers.
- There are three basic types of faults: normal faults, reverse faults, and strike-slip faults.

- Normal faults can form when tectonic forces pull on Earth's crust in opposite directions.

A Layers of rock have dropped downward along a normal fault.

B This normal fault located in Death Valley, California, shows a large amount of movement.

Other Field Guides to Roadside Geology

- The Roadside Geology series, Mountain Press Publishing Company, Missoula, Montana
- The Geological Highway Map Series, The American Association of Petroleum Geologists, Tulsa, Oklahoma

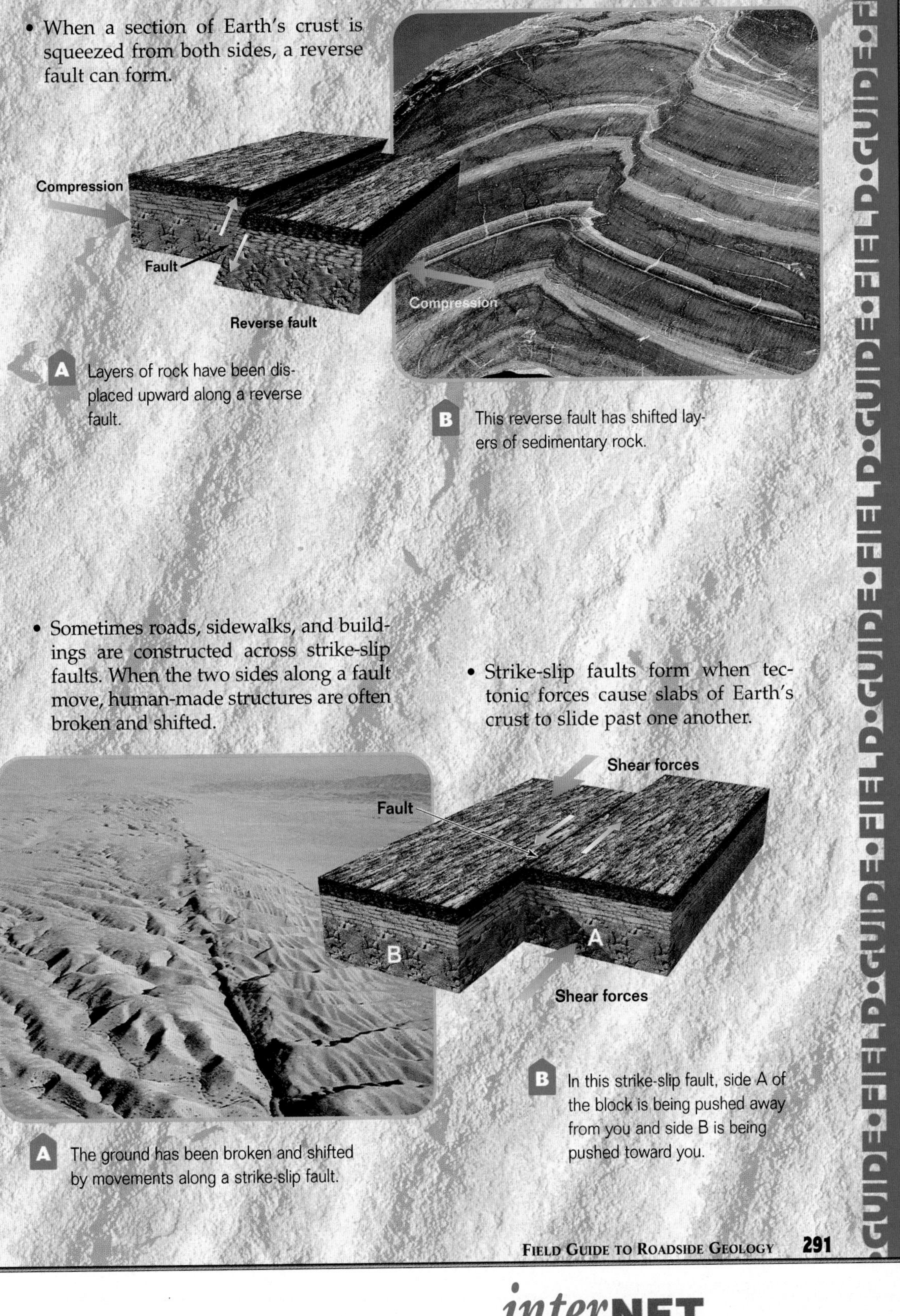

• When a section of Earth's crust is squeezed from both sides, a reverse fault can form.
Compression
Fault
Reverse fault
Compression
A Layers of rock have been displaced upward along a reverse fault.
B This reverse fault has shifted layers of sedimentary rock.
• Sometimes roads, sidewalks, and buildings are constructed across strike-slip faults. When the two sides along a fault move, human-made structures are often broken and shifted.
• Strike-slip faults form when tectonic forces cause slabs of Earth's crust to slide past one another.
Shear forces
Fault
B
A
Shear forces
B In this strike-slip fault, side A of the block is being pushed away from you and side B is being pushed toward you.
A The ground has been broken and shifted by movements along a strike-slip fault.
FIELD GUIDE • FIELD GUIDE • FIELD GUIDE • FIELD GUIDE • FIELD GUIDE • FIELD GUIDE • FIELD GUIDE • F
FIELD GUIDE TO ROADSIDE GEOLOGY 291

Teacher FYI

Reverse faults that dip at small angles are called thrust faults.

Making a Model

Have student groups use different-colored modeling clay to make three identical stacks of horizontal rock layers. Then, have students cut a normal fault in one clay stack, a reverse fault in another, and a strike-slip fault in the third with a spatula and move the blocks appropriately. Ask the students to use their spatulas to model the effects of erosion on their faulted terrains and then to observe the surface morphology and the surface arrangement of different rock layers for each terrain. L2

COOP LEARN

Activity

Obtain an interesting geologic map from a university library or your state geologic survey. Have students learn the map symbols for reverse, normal, and strike-slip faults and locate faults on the map. Students also should examine other features on the map. L2

interNET CONNECTION

Internet Addresses

____

____

____

____

For Internet tips, see Glencoe's **Using the Internet in the Science Classroom.**

Using Science Words

Have students investigate the meaning of the word *anticline* and the word *syncline;* both are derived from the Greek. After they have finished investigating these two words, ask them to speculate about the meaning of the word *monocline. The word* anticline *means "opposite inclined" and reflects the fact that the limbs of an anticline dip in opposite directions. The word* syncline *means "together inclined" and reflects the fact that the limbs of a syncline dip toward each other. A monocline is a fold with only one limb.* L2

Quick Demo

Fold a large sheet of paper back and forth many times as if to make a hand fan. Unfold the paper to show how anticlines and synclines alternate in folded rock layers.

Teacher FYI

Folds that are tilted forward or backward so that the hinge, or axis, of the fold is not horizontal are called plunging folds. Folds that are laid over on their side are called recumbent folds.

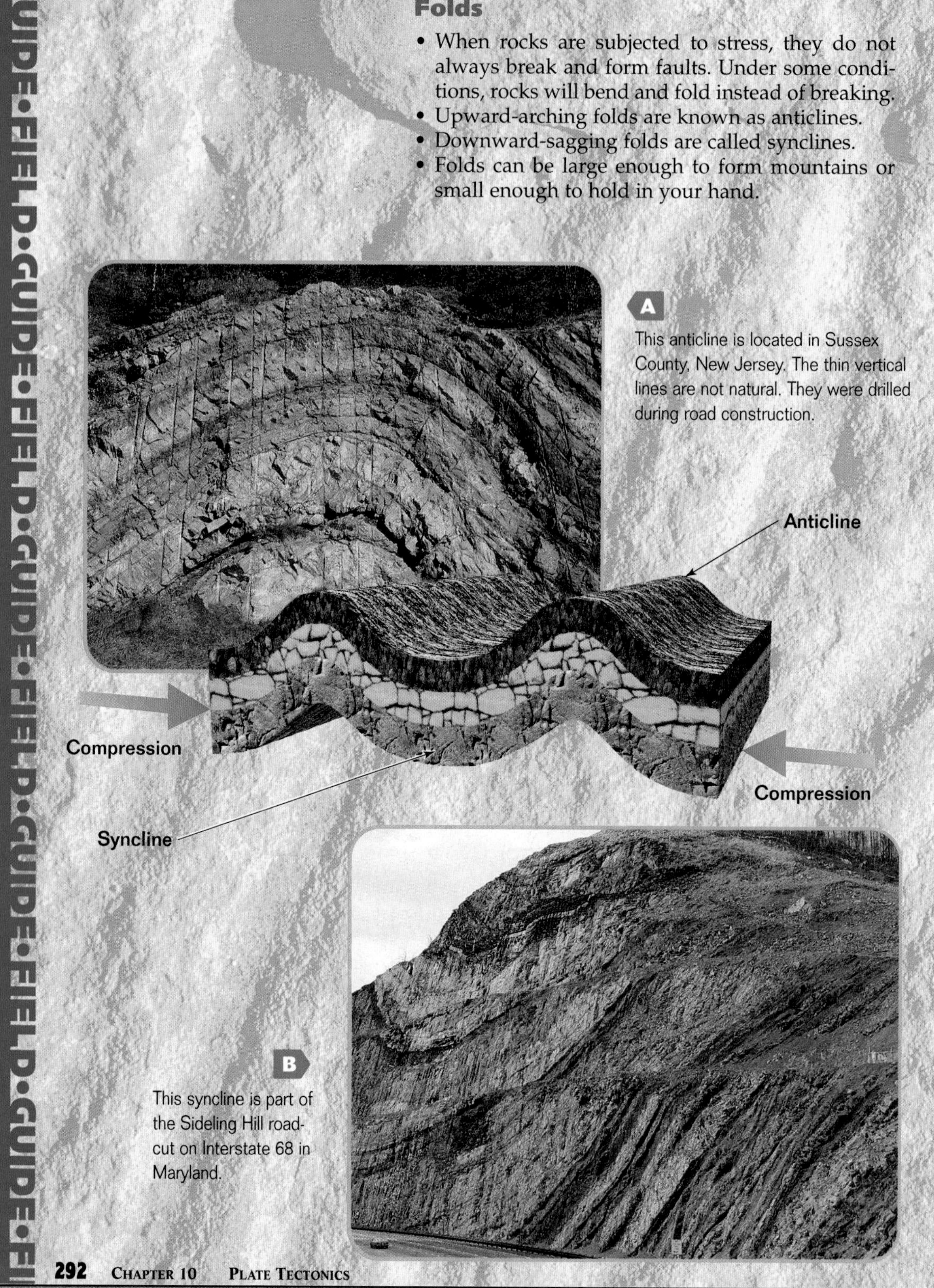

GUIDE•FIELD•GUIDE•FIELD•GUIDE•FIELD•GUIDE•FIELD•GUIDE•FI
Folds
• When rocks are subjected to stress, they do not always break and form faults. Under some conditions, rocks will bend and fold instead of breaking.
• Upward-arching folds are known as anticlines.
• Downward-sagging folds are called synclines.
• Folds can be large enough to form mountains or small enough to hold in your hand.
A
This anticline is located in Sussex County, New Jersey. The thin vertical lines are not natural. They were drilled during road construction.
Anticline
Compression
Compression
Syncline
B
This syncline is part of the Sideling Hill road-cut on Interstate 68 in Maryland.
292 CHAPTER 10 PLATE TECTONICS

Across the Curriculum

Geography The Valley and Ridge Province of the Appalachian Mountains consists of sedimentary rock layers deformed into a series of plunging anticlines and synclines. The ridges and valleys are sculpted by erosion. Resistant sandstone layers in the limbs of folds stand up to form ridges, and soft-shale layers are eroded into valleys. Explain to students how the Valley and Ridge Province formed, and have them help you draw a cross section across the province on the chalkboard.

Limestone Features

- Layers of limestone are common rock formations in Earth's crust.
- Water in nature is usually slightly acidic. When acidic water comes in contact with limestone, it reacts with the rock. Over time, the acidic water changes the rock into material that can then be washed away.
- Caves and sinkholes form when acidic water below Earth's surface slowly destroys the limestone.

A This cave in Luray Caverns, Virginia, is a hole left over after some limestone was removed by groundwater.

B This sinkhole in Winter Park, Florida, formed when limestone at Earth's surface collapsed into caves below.

Content Background

Caves result from the action of slightly acidic groundwater on soluble rocks like limestone. Therefore, caves result from the chemical weathering of rocks by groundwater. The water makes its way through limestone via cracks and other weaknesses, and dissolves minerals in limestone—primarily calcite and dolomite.

Discussion

Lead students in a discussion about how stalactites and stalagmites form in caves. *These features, together known as speleothems, form as calcite-bearing water drips from cave ceilings and onto cave floors. Air in caves is necessary for these features to form. When air interacts with the calcite-bearing water, carbon dioxide evolves from the water and solid calcite comes back out of the water as a new mineral deposit.*

VISUAL Learning

Obtain a topographic map of a region showing prominent karst topography. This will be an area containing prominent caves and sinkholes, such as Kentucky or Florida. The map should contain abundant circular-shaped depressions. Have students compare these map features with the photograph of the sinkhole in Winter Park, Florida.

Correcting Misconceptions

Students often do not appreciate the size and speed of some large landslides. Tell students that landslides can travel as much as 100 km from their point of origin and can have volumes of many cubic kilometers. These giant landslides may travel at speeds in excess of 100 km per hour.

Teacher FYI

Landslide is a general term that includes a wide variety of gravity-driven rock or soil movements such as falls, slumps, slides, and flows.

Using an Analogy

Ice skaters can skate faster on days when temperatures are near freezing than on days when it is very cold because a thin layer of water forms beneath the blade, thereby reducing friction. Tell students that heavy rains can trigger some landslides for the same reason. When rainwater seeps in between sloping layers of rock on a hillslope, the water buoys up the overlying rock layers, reducing friction and allowing sliding to occur.

Landslides

- A landslide happens when a mass of earth and rock moves downhill in response to gravity.
- Landslides often are triggered by heavy rains or sometimes by earthquakes.
- A landslide generally can be recognized by two surface features. A large curved depression, or scar, is left behind where the landslide started. A bumpy region of mixed-up rock and soil is formed where the landslide stops.

A This landslide in the Madison Range, in Montana, was triggered by an earthquake on August 17, 1959.

B This slump is a type of landslide that is common in oversteepened areas that are eroded by streams, lakes, and oceans. This slump is located in central California. The scar shows the area where the slump broke away from the slope.

Science Journal

Have students research and write about a large landslide. Students should discuss the nature of the landslide, its impact on the surrounding landscape, and its effect on people (if known). Some noteworthy landslides include the 1980 Mount St. Helens landslide; prehistoric landslides on Mt. Rainier and Mt. Shasta; and many recent landslides in California, the Andes, and the Alps.

Sedimentary Features

- Sediments are deposited in many different environments such as beaches, rivers, swamps, and mudflats. Leaf imprints, animal tracks, mud cracks, fossils, and even raindrop patterns have been preserved in sedimentary rocks.
- One type of sedimentary feature that is often observed in sandstone is ripple marks. When water flows over a sandy area, the sand forms a series of small ridges, or ripples.

A This region of ripples was formed by flowing water at a beach in St. Johns County, Florida.

- If a rippled layer is gently buried by more sediments, the ripples can be preserved in the rock. Careful observation of sandstone layers often reveals ripple marks.

B These ripple marks are preserved in a sandstone formation in Utah.

FIELD•GUIDE•FIELD•GUIDE•FIELD•GUIDE•FIELD•GUIDE•FIELD•GUIDE•FI

Content Background

Dunes and ripples migrate in the direction that the water or wind that forms them is moving. As these features move, sand climbs up the upstream side and avalanches down the downstream side. The avalanching on the downstream side produces sloping layers of sand. These sloping layers are called cross bedding. Whole ripples are preserved only occasionally in rock, but cross bedding is common.

Activity

Obtain some mud from along the banks of a slow-flowing river or other location. Put the mud in a plastic tub and add water until it is moist (a little laundry water softener mixed in the water will keep the mud from clumping). Have students use a dropper to form raindrop imprints. Have them bring in worms, small crustaceans, and crawling insects to see what type of marks they make in the mud. After examining the raindrop imprints and animal tracks, let the mud dry to form mud cracks. L2

GO Further

To further students' understanding of rock structures, have them draw a large landscape panorama including all of the structures covered in this field guide.

Chapter 10 Reviewing Main Ideas

Reviewing Main Ideas can be used to preview, review, reteach, and condense chapter content.

Preview

Linguistic Have students try to answer the questions in their Science Journals. Use student answers as a source for discussion throughout the chapter.

Review

Interpersonal Have students answer the questions on separate pieces of paper and compare their answers with those of other students in the class.

Reteach

Visual-Spatial Have students look at the illustrations on these pages. Ask them to describe details that support the main ideas of the chapter found in the statement for each illustration.

00:00 OUT OF TIME?

Auditory-Musical If time does not permit teaching the entire chapter, use the information on these pages along with the chapter Audiocassettes to present the material in a condensed format.

Chapter 10 Reviewing Main Ideas

For a **preview** of this chapter, study this Reviewing Main Ideas before you read the chapter. After you have studied this chapter, you can use the Reviewing Main Ideas to **review** the chapter.

The Glencoe MindJogger, Audiocassettes, and CD-ROM provide additional opportunities for review.

Section 10-1 CONTINENTAL DRIFT

The hypothesis of **continental drift** states that continents have moved to their present positions on Earth. Wegener believed that all continents were once connected into one large landmass he called **Pangaea.** The puzzlelike fit of the continents, fossils, climatic evidence, and similar rock structures supports Wegener's idea of continental drift. One problem with Wegener's idea was that he could not explain what process could be responsible for moving continents through the oceans. ***What is true of the fossils of* Mesosaurus *that Wegener felt supported the hypothesis of continental drift?***

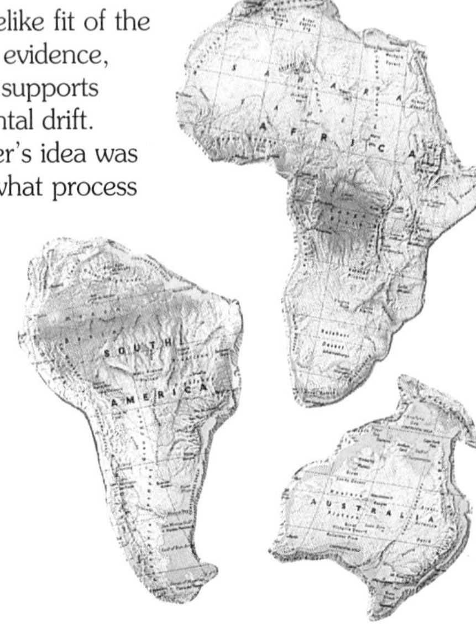

Section 10-2 SEAFLOOR SPREADING

Echo-sounding devices used to construct maps of the ocean floor showed underwater mountains and rift valleys. **Seafloor spreading** is the spreading apart of the seafloor at the mid-ocean ridges. The theory of seafloor spreading is supported by magnetic evidence in rocks and in the age of rocks on the ocean floor. The oldest rocks found on the ocean floor are 180 million years old. The youngest rocks are near the mid-ocean ridges, and the rocks become progressively older farther from the ridges. ***What type of magnetic evidence in rocks supports the theory of seafloor spreading?***

296 CHAPTER 10 PLATE TECTONICS

Cultural Diversity

Masai The Great Rift Valley extends through eastern Africa, creating a canyon more than 80 km wide. Along this rift valley, seminomadic pastoralists, the Masai, make their living. The focus of Masai life is cattle. Meat is not a normal part of the diet, as the Masai do not hunt. They believe it a sacrilege to break the earth, so they do not farm. They live from the produce of their herds, moving from one grazing land to another. Four to eight families and cattle live within a *kraal*, a circular area enclosed by a thornbush fence. The main organizing factor for Masai society is age sets. For example, each Masai male moves with his age set through a series of grades (including warrior grades), each lasting about 15 years. As one ages, one eventually becomes an elder who can make decisions for the tribe.

Reading Check ✓

Suggest one or two additional illustrations for this chapter and explain why they would be valuable.

Section **10-3 PLATE TECTONICS**

Plates move away from each other at divergent boundaries. Plates collide at convergent boundaries. At a transform boundary, two plates move horizontally past each other. Hot, plasticlike material from the mantle is forced upward to the **lithosphere,** moves horizontally, cools, and then sinks back into the mantle, causing **convection currents,** which are the driving force of **plate tectonics.** Most mountain belts, volcanoes, and earthquakes occur at convergent boundaries. Mid-ocean ridges and rift valleys occur at divergent boundaries. Major earthquakes occur at transform boundaries. ***At which type of plate boundary does subduction occur?***

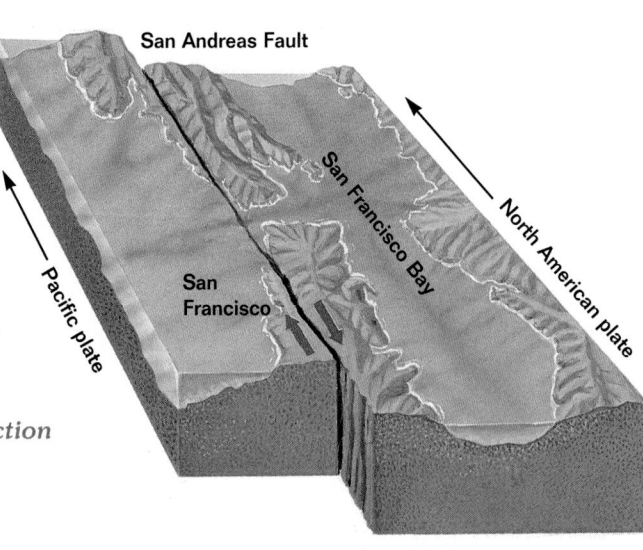

San Andreas Fault
San Francisco Bay
North American plate
San Francisco
Pacific plate

Career CONNECTION

Dr. Samuel B. Mukasa, Isotope Geochemist

As an isotope geochemist, Dr. Samuel Mukasa studies the elements that make up rocks. By comparing the concentrations of certain elements, he can figure out the date when a rock was actually formed. Dr. Mukasa then uses this information to understand the timing of the breakup and movement of continents in Earth's past. ***What information does a scientist need to figure out the rate at which continents have moved in the past?***

Answers to Questions

Section 10-1

Continental Drift Fossils of *Mesosaurus,* an animal that could not have crossed an ocean, were found in both Africa and South America.

Section 10-2

Seafloor Spreading Strips of seafloor basalt have similar patterns of alternating magnetic polarity on both sides of mid-ocean ridges.

Section 10-3

Plate Tectonics convergent plate boundaries

GLENCOE TECHNOLOGY

CD-ROM

Glencoe Science Voyages Interactive CD-ROM

Chapter Summaries and Quizzes

Have students read the Chapter Summary then take the Chapter Quiz to determine whether they have mastered chapter content.

the age of the rocks (time) and how far apart they are (distance)

Assessment

Portfolio Encourage students to place in their portfolios one or two items of what they consider to be their best work. Examples include:

- MiniLab analysis, pp. 270, 282
- Activity 10-1, p. 276 P

Performance Additional performance assessments may be found in **Performance Assessment** and **Science Integration Activities.** Performance Task Assessment Lists and rubrics for evaluating these activities can be found in Glencoe's **Performance Assessment in the Science Classroom.**

Chapter 10 Assessment

Using Vocabulary

1. a
2. b
3. e
4. h
5. c

*inter*NET CONNECTION To reinforce chapter vocabulary, use the **Study Guide for Content Mastery** booklet. Also available are activities for **Glencoe Science Voyages** on the Glencoe Science Web Site. **www.glencoe.com/sec/science**

Checking Concepts

6. B	11. C
7. D	12. B
8. C	13. D
9. D	14. C
10. A	15. B

Thinking Critically

16. Accept all reasonable answers. One possible answer is: In most continent-continent collisions, subduction zones do not form. As the Indo-Australian plate collides with the Eurasian plate to form the Himalaya, neither plate is forced into Earth deep enough for melting to occur. Therefore, no volcanism occurs.
17. Africa was once located near the south pole when all the continents were joined as a single landmass.
18. Alternating magnetic bands in seafloor rocks are symmetrical with respect to a mid-ocean ridge.

Chapter 10 Assessment

Using Vocabulary

a. asthenosphere	e. Pangaea
b. continental drift	f. plate
c. convection current	g. plate tectonics
d. lithosphere	h. seafloor spreading

Each phrase below describes a vocabulary term from the list. Write the term that matches the phrase describing it.

1. plastic-like layer below the lithosphere
2. idea that continents move on Earth's surface
3. large landmass made of all continents
4. process that forms new seafloor
5. driving force for plate movement

Checking Concepts

Choose the word or phrase that best answers the question.

6. Where is Earth's asthenosphere located?
   A) crust C) outer core
   B) mantle D) inner core
7. What type of plate boundary is the San Andreas Fault a part of?
   A) divergent boundary
   B) subduction boundary
   C) convergent boundary
   D) transform boundary
8. What hypothesis states that continents moved to their present positions?
   A) subduction
   B) seafloor spreading
   C) continental drift
   D) erosion
9. Which plate is subducting beneath the South American plate to form the Andes mountain system?
   A) North American C) Indo-Australian
   B) African D) Nazca
10. Evidence of which of the following features indicates that many continents were once near Earth's south pole?
    A) glaciers
    B) mid-ocean ridges
    C) volcanoes
    D) convection currents
11. What evidence in rocks supports the theory of seafloor spreading?
    A) plate movement
    B) subduction
    C) reversals of Earth's magnetic field
    D) convergence
12. Which type of plate boundary is the Great Rift Valley a part of?
    A) convergent C) transform
    B) divergent D) lithosphere
13. What theory states that plates move around on the asthenosphere?
    A) continental drift
    B) seafloor spreading
    C) subduction
    D) plate tectonics
14. What forms when one plate is forced under another plate?
    A) transform boundary
    B) divergent boundary
    C) subduction zone
    D) mid-ocean ridge
15. When oceanic plates collide, what volcanic landforms are made?
    A) folded mountains
    B) island arcs
    C) strike-slip faults
    D) mid-ocean ridges

Thinking Critically

16. Why are there few volcanoes in the Himalaya range but many earthquakes?
17. Glacial deposits often form at high latitudes near the poles. Explain why glacial deposits have been found in Africa.

19. The San Andreas Fault is a transform boundary. There is no subduction along such plate boundaries; thus, there is no volcanism.
20. Fossils of terrestrial organisms are used to support continental drift. Fish are found in oceans, and oceans surround all of the continents; therefore, most fossil fish aren't good evidence of continental drift.

18. How is magnetism used to support the theory of seafloor spreading?
19. Explain why volcanoes do not form along the San Andreas Fault.
20. Why wouldn't the fossil of an ocean fish found on two different continents be good evidence of continental drift?

Developing Skills

If you need help, refer to the Skill Handbook.

21. **Hypothesizing:** Mount St. Helens in the Cascade Mountain Range is a volcano. Use **Figure 10-10** and a U.S. map to hypothesize how it may have formed.
22. **Measuring in SI:** Movement along the African Rift Valley is about 2.1 cm per year. If plates continue to move apart at this rate, how much larger will the rift be (in meters) in 1000 years? In 15 500 years?
23. **Concept Mapping:** Make an events chain concept map that describes seafloor spreading along a divergent plate boundary. Choose from the following phrases: *magma cools to form new seafloor, magma rises, convection currents circulate hot material along boundary,* and *older seafloor is forced apart.*

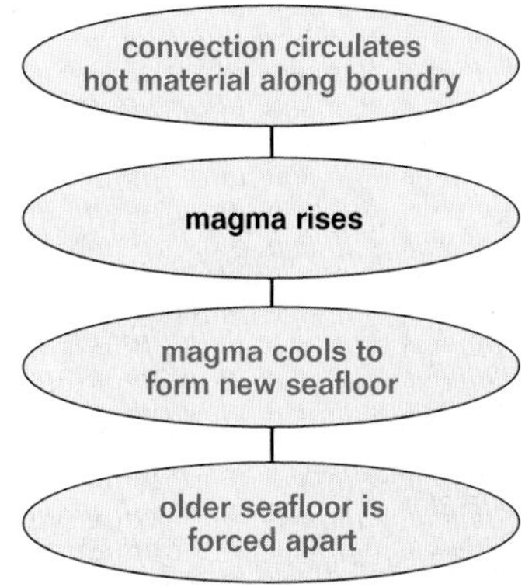
convection circulates hot material along boundry
magma rises
magma cools to form new seafloor
older seafloor is forced apart

THE PRINCETON REVIEW

Test-Taking Tip

The "Best" Answer Is Often the "Least Incorrect" If none of your answer choices look right, use the process of elimination to eliminate the *worst* ones. The one you've got left is the best choice.

Test Practice

Use these questions to test your Science Proficiency.

1. Alfred Wegener's original hypothesis of continental drift was not accepted by other scientists of his time. Which of the following statements **BEST** explains why this was true?
   A) Wegener had very little evidence to support his hypothesis.
   B) Wegener could not explain how continents move.
   C) Wegener was not a geologist.
   D) Wegener based his hypothesis only on the fossil record.
2. Island arcs form at convergent plate boundaries. Which of the following statements **BEST** explains this process?
   A) When two continental plates converge, subduction stops and mountains are built.
   B) When an oceanic plate converges on a continental plate, subduction leads to the formation of volcanoes.
   C) When two ocean plates diverge, magma is forced to Earth's surface, forming volcanoes.
   D) When two oceanic plates converge, subduction leads to the formation of volcanoes.

THE PRINCETON REVIEW

Test Practice

The Test-Taking Tip was written by The Princeton Review, the nation's leader in test preparation.

1. B
2. D

Developing Skills

21. The volcanoes in the Cascade Range formed as the Juan de Fuca plate subducted beneath the North American plate.
22. 21 m; 325.5 m
23. See student page.

Bonus Question

The record of magnetic reversals in rocks on either side of mid-ocean ridges supports the theory of seafloor spreading. **What additional information about the seafloor would add support to this theory?** *Student answers will vary. Students should indicate that the age of the ocean floor increases moving away from a mid-ocean ridge. Also, students may realize that scientists are now able to observe geologic processes as they occur at the mid-ocean ridge. Evidence of recent lava extrusion would offer support as well.*

Assessment Resources

The **Test Practice Workbook** provides students with practice in the format, concepts, and critical-thinking skills tested in standardized exams.

Reproducible Masters

Chapter Review, pp. 19–20 L2
Performance Assessment, p. 24 L2
Assessment, pp. 41–44 L2

Glencoe Technology

Chapter Review Software
Computer Test Bank

MindJogger Videoquiz

UNIT 4

Change Through Time

This unit introduces students to the record of Earth's past. Earth's evolutionary history and the development of the geologic time scale are presented. The unit describes how species change through natural selection. Students will learn how fossil records, cell structure, cell chemistry, and body structure provide evidence of evolution. A major concept developed in this unit is the measurement of geologic time units by changes in or extinctions of life-forms on Earth.

Unit Overview

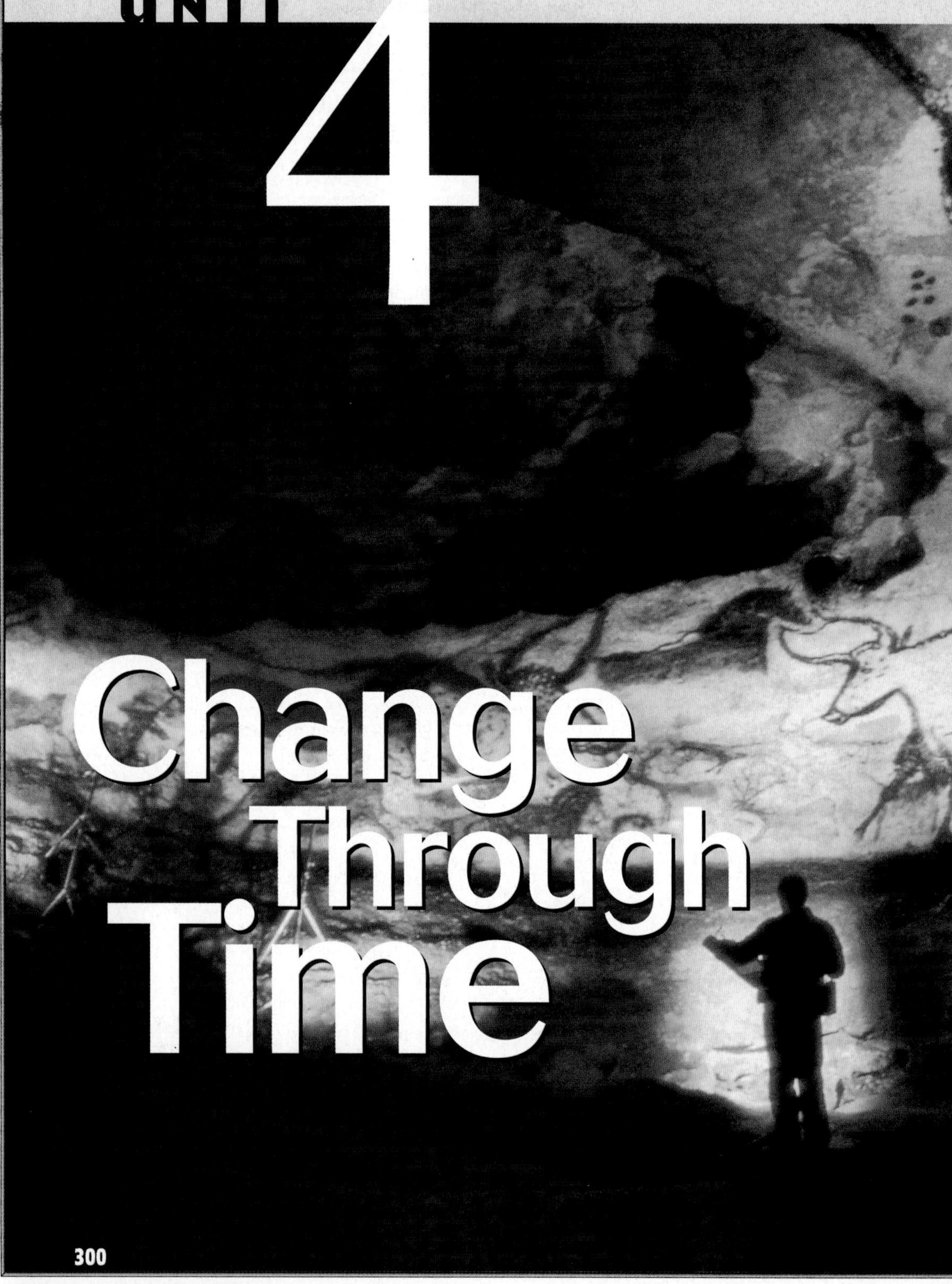

Science at Home

Fossil Collecting Have students bring in fossils they have collected. If they do not have any fossils, have them study rock exposures near their homes for evidence of fossils and draw a picture. Or students may use reference books to draw a picture of a fossil.

NATIONAL GEOGRAPHIC

What's Happening Here?

What traces of your existence will you leave for future generations to interpret? Long ago, someone painted these magnificent beasts on the walls of Lascaux (left), a cave in southern France. Archaeologists hypothesize that these drawings were created by Stone Age artists about 17 000 years ago. From the walls of this cave and others like it, scientists are piecing together the story of the ancestors of modern humans. While such drawings can help us interpret the human past, how can we figure out what happened before humans appeared on Earth? Even if you had been around and lived a long life, you could not have witnessed much of what happened. Why? Because like this glacier flowing into Prince William Sound, Alaska (below), many important changes happened too gradually to be seen. In this unit, you will learn about some of these slow changes and how to read the record these changes have left in the layers of Earth's crust.

interNET CONNECTION

Explore the Glencoe Science Web Site at **www.glencoe.com/sec/science** to find out more about topics found in this unit.

301

Introducing the Unit

What's happening here?

Have students read the text and examine the pictures. Ask students what the figure and the glacier have in common. Ask students how the information they leave behind is different.

Content Background

Unlike the fleeting tracks of recreational vehicles, ancient animal tracks help tell the story of evolution. For example, tracks show that primitive fish crawled on their bellies between pools. These short, broad tracks indicate that the animal could barely hold itself off the ground. The tracks of many dinosaurs through time showed that they developed longer strides, indicating that they became faster and faster.

Previewing the Chapters

- Have students look through photographs and illustrations for rocks and try to categorize them.
- Have students find pictures of plants and animals and guess from their appearance how they are adapted to their environment.

Tying to Previous Knowledge

Ask students to recall what they know about how traits are passed from generation to generation and how mutations occur.

interNET CONNECTION

Internet Addresses

Explore the Glencoe Science Web Site at **www.glencoe.com/sec/science** to find out more about topics found in this unit.

Chapter 11 Clues to Earth's Past

Section	Objectives	Activities/Features
Chapter Opener		**Explore Activity:** Model a Fossil, p. 303
11-1 **Fossils** 1 Session ½ Block	1. **Identify** the conditions necessary for fossils to form. 2. **Describe** processes of fossil formation. 3. **Explain** how fossil correlation is used to determine rock ages.	**MiniLab:** Predicting Fossil Preservation, p. 305 **Using Math,** p. 307 **Life Science Integration,** p. 310 **Skill Builder:** Concept Mapping, p. 311 **Science Journal,** p. 311
11-2 **Relative Ages of Rocks** 2 Sessions 1 Block	4. **Describe** several methods used to date rock layers relative to other rock layers. 5. **Describe** how to interpret gaps in the rock record. 6. **Give** an example of how rock layers may be correlated with other rock layers.	**Problem Solving:** Interpreting Scientific Illustrations, p. 317 **Skill Builder:** Observing and Inferring, p. 318 **Using Computers,** p. 318 **Activity 11-1:** Relative Age Dating, p. 319 **History of Science:** Extinction of Dinosaurs, p. 320
11-3 **Absolute Ages of Rocks** 2 Sessions 1 Block	7. **Contrast** absolute dating to relative dating. 8. **Describe** how half-lives of isotopes are used to determine the rock's age.	**Physics Integration,** p. 321 **MiniLab:** Sequencing Earth's History, p. 322 **Skill Builder:** Making and Using Tables, p. 325 **Science Journal,** p. 325 **Activity 11-2:** Radioactive Decay, pp. 326–327

The number of recommended single-period sessions — The number of recommended blocks
One session and one-half block are allowed for chapter review and assessment.

Activity Materials

Explore	Activities	MiniLabs
p. 303 small milk carton ($\frac{1}{2}$-pint), plaster of paris, leaf, shell, bone, petroleum jelly, water	p. 319 no materials needed pp. 326–327 shoebox with lid, 100 brass fasteners, 100 paper clips, graph paper, 100 pennies, 2 colored pencils	p. 305 no materials needed p. 322 no materials needed

Need Materials? Contact Science Kit at 1-800-828-7777 or at www.sciencekit.com on the Internet.
For alternate materials, see the activity on the listed page.

Standards		Reproducible Resources	Technology
National	State/Local	Test Practice Workbooks are available for use with each chapter.	English and Spanish audiocassettes are available for use with each section.
National Content Standards: UCP2, UCP3, UCP4, C5, D2		**Activity Worksheets,** p. 63 **Critical Thinking/Problem Solving,** p. 11 **Enrichment,** p. 28 **Home Involvement,** p. 28 **Laboratory Manual,** pp. 63–64 **Multicultural Connections,** pp. 21–22 **Reinforcement,** p. 28 **Study Guide,** pp. 41–42	**Section Focus Transparency 28** **Teaching Transparency 21** **The Infinite Voyage Series** **Glencoe Science Interactive Videodisc—Earth**
National Content Standards: UCP1, A1, A2, D2		**Activity Worksheets,** pp. 59–60 **Enrichment,** p. 29 **Laboratory Manual,** pp. 65–66 **Reinforcement,** p. 29 **Study Guide,** p. 43	**Section Focus Transparency 29** **Teaching Transparency 22** **Science Integration Transparency 11** **Internet Connection,** p. 313 **The Infinite Voyage Series**
National Content Standards: UCP1, A1, A2, D2		**Activity Worksheets,** pp. 61–62, 64 **Enrichment,** p. 30 **Reinforcement,** p. 30 **Study Guide,** p. 44	**Section Focus Transparency 30** **Glencoe Science Voyages Interactive CD-ROM** **Internet Connection,** p. 324

Key to Teaching Strategies

The following designations will help you decide which activities are appropriate for your students.

L1 Level 1 activities should be appropriate for students with learning difficulties.

L2 Level 2 activities should be within the ability range of all students.

L3 Level 3 activities are designed for above-average students.

ELL ELL activities should be within the ability range of English Language Learners.

COOP LEARN Cooperative Learning activities are designed for small group work.

P These strategies represent student products that can be placed into a best-work portfolio.

Multiple Learning Styles logos, as described on page 61T, are used throughout to indicate strategies that address different learning styles.

Assessment Resources

Chapter Review, pp. 21–22
Assessment, pp. 47–50
Performance Assessment in the Science Classroom (PASC)
MindJogger Videoquiz
Alternate Assessment in the Science Classroom
Performance Assessment, p. 25
Chapter Review Software
Computer Test Bank

Chapter 11 Clues to Earth's Past

This is a representation of key blackline masters available in the Teacher Classroom Resources. See Resource Manager boxes within the chapter for additional information.

Transparencies

Section Focus Transparencies

28 SECTION FOCUS TRANSPARENCY Section 11-1

ROCK OR WOOD?

If you were asked to identify the object in this picture, you'd probably say a log or part of a tree trunk. What's it made of? That's easy! Wood. Or is it? Look again and you'll come to another conclusion.

1. What led you to identify the object as a log or tree trunk?
2. What did you decide this log is made of? What led you to that conclusion?
3. How do you think the log came to be changed in this way?

L2

29 SECTION FOCUS TRANSPARENCY Section 11-2

RELATIVELY SPEAKING . . .

The bands of multicolored rock that take our breath away at sites like the Grand Canyon are more than just beautiful. They are tools that help us learn about the history of Earth. As you examine the spectacular contours of the canyon, think about what these layers tell us.

1. Do you think all the rock in the picture was formed at the same time? Why or why not?
2. If you think the rock formed at different times, which layers are the oldest and which are the youngest? Why do you think so?
3. How could knowing which layers of rock two fossils came from tell you their ages relative to each other?

L2

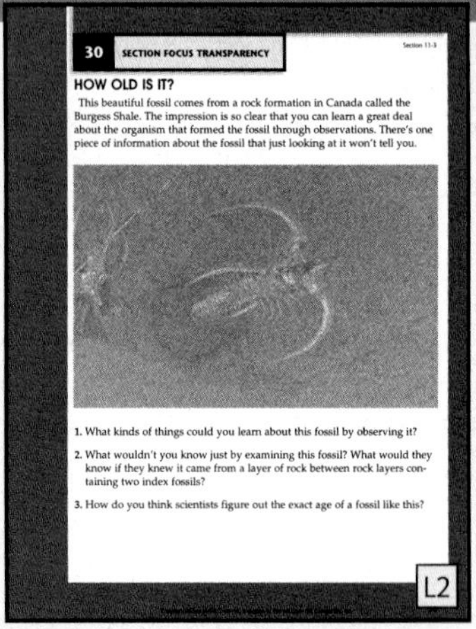

30 SECTION FOCUS TRANSPARENCY Section 11-3

HOW OLD IS IT?

This beautiful fossil comes from a rock formation in Canada called the Burgess Shale. The impression is so clear that you can learn a great deal about the organism that formed the fossil through observations. There's one piece of information about the fossil that just looking at it won't tell you.

1. What kinds of things could you learn about this fossil by observing it?
2. What wouldn't you know just by examining this fossil? What would they know if they knew it came from a layer of rock between rock layers containing two index fossils?
3. How do you think scientists figure out the exact age of a fossil like this?

L2

Science Integration Transparencies

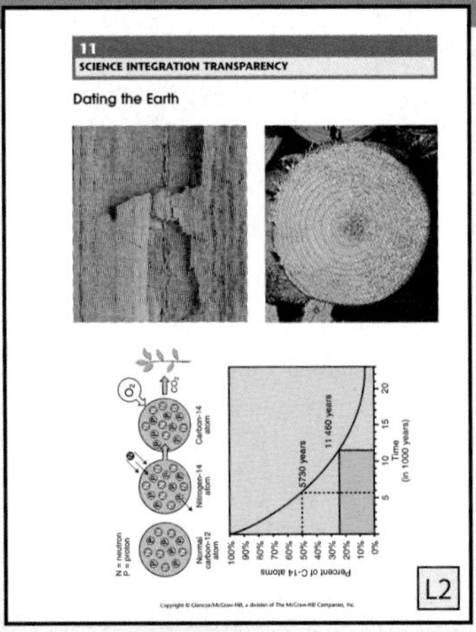

11 SCIENCE INTEGRATION TRANSPARENCY

Dating the Earth

L2

Teaching Transparencies

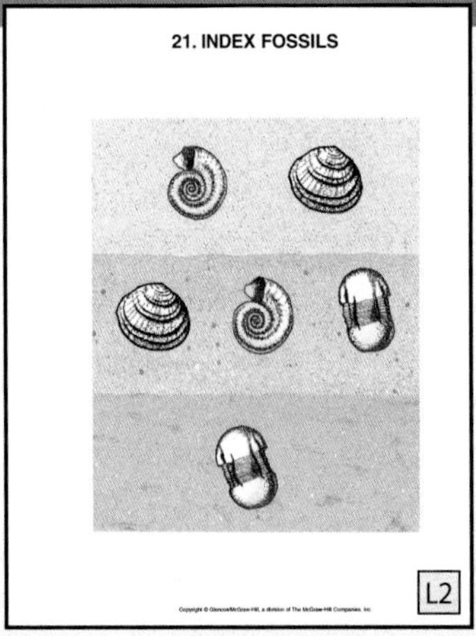

21. INDEX FOSSILS

L2

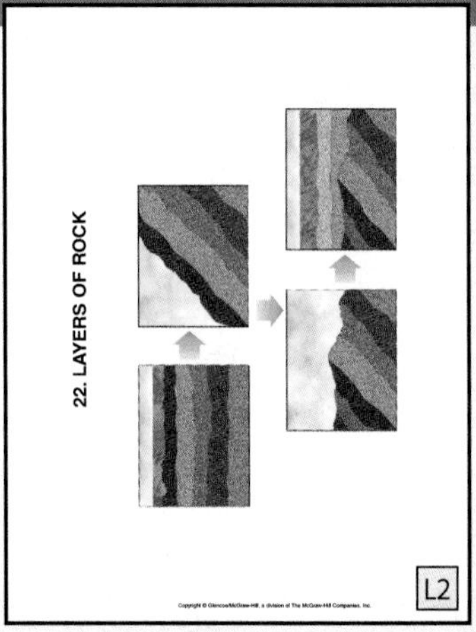

22. LAYERS OF ROCK

L2

Meeting Different Ability Levels

Study Guide for Content Mastery

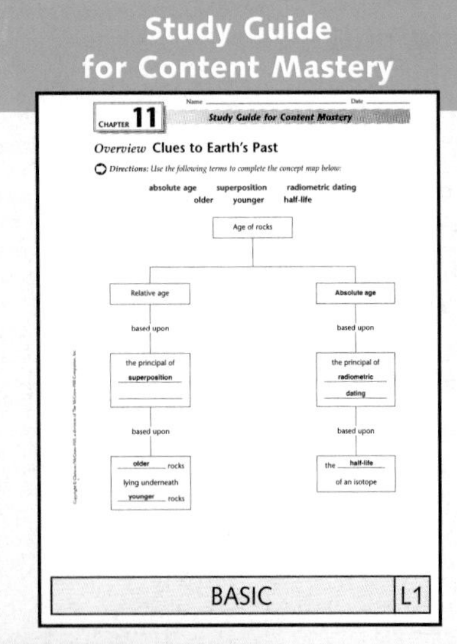

CHAPTER 11 Name Date

Study Guide for Content Mastery

Overview Clues to Earth's Past

Directions: Use the following terms to complete the concept map below:

absolute age, superposition, radiometric dating, older, younger, half-life

Age of rocks → Relative age, based upon the principal of superposition, based upon older rocks lying underneath younger rocks

Age of rocks → Absolute age, based upon the principal of radiometric dating, based upon the half-life of an isotope

BASIC L1

Reinforcement

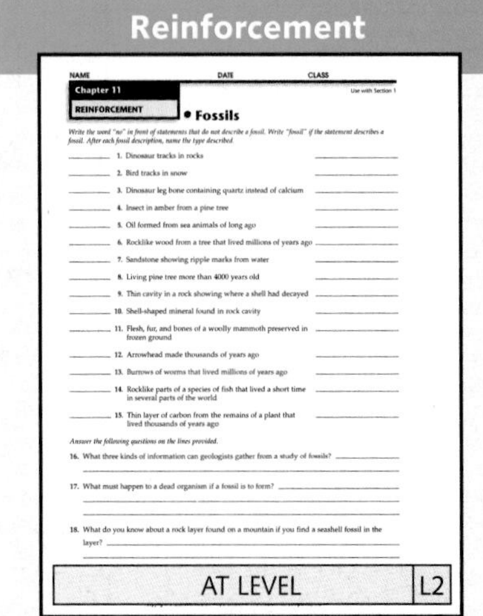

NAME DATE CLASS

Chapter 11 REINFORCEMENT • Fossils — Use with Section 1

Write the word "no" in front of statements that do not describe a fossil. Write "fossil" if the statement describes a fossil. After each fossil description, name the type described.

1. Dinosaur tracks in rocks
2. Bird tracks in snow
3. Dinosaur leg bone containing quartz instead of calcium
4. Insect in amber from a pine tree
5. Oil formed from sea animals of long ago
6. Rocklike wood from a tree that lived millions of years ago
7. Sandstone showing ripple marks from water
8. Living pine tree more than 4000 years old
9. Thin cavity in a rock showing where a shell had decayed
10. Shell-shaped mineral found in rock cavity
11. Flesh, fur, and bones of a woolly mammoth preserved in frozen ground
12. Arrowhead made thousands of years ago
13. Burrows of worms that lived millions of years ago
14. Rocklike parts of a species of fish that lived a short time in several parts of the world
15. Thin layer of carbon from the remains of a plant that lived thousands of years ago

Answer the following questions on the lines provided.

16. What three kinds of information can geologists gather from a study of fossils?
17. What must happen to a dead organism if a fossil is to form?
18. What do you know about a rock layer found on a mountain if you find a seashell fossil in the layer?

AT LEVEL L2

Enrichment Worksheets

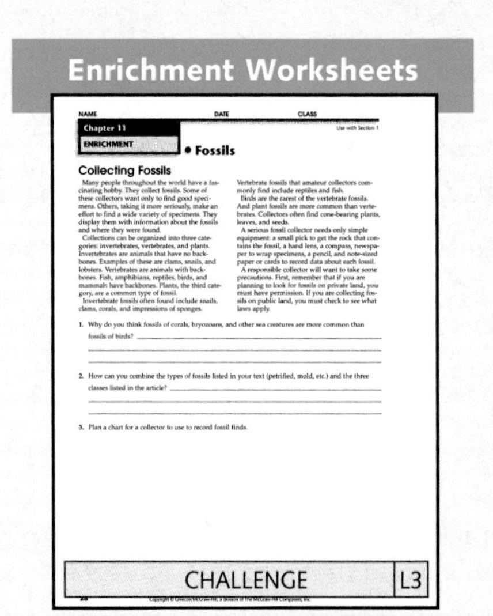

NAME DATE CLASS

Chapter 11 ENRICHMENT • Fossils — Use with Section 1

Collecting Fossils

Many people throughout the world have a fascinating hobby. They collect fossils. Some of these collectors want only to find good specimens. Others, taking it more seriously, make an effort to find a wide variety of specimens. They display them with information about the fossils and where they were found.

Collections can be organized into three categories: invertebrates, vertebrates, and plants. Invertebrates are animals that have no backbones. Examples of these are clams, snails, and lobsters. Vertebrates are animals with backbones. Fish, amphibians, reptiles, birds, and mammals have backbones. Plants, the third category, are a common type of fossil.

Invertebrate fossils often found include snails, clams, corals, and impressions of sponges. Vertebrate fossils that amateur collectors commonly find include reptiles and fish.

Birds are the rarest of the vertebrate fossils. And plant fossils are more common than vertebrates. Collectors often find cone-bearing plants, leaves, and seeds.

A serious fossil collector needs only simple equipment: a small pick to get the rock that contains the fossil, a hand lens, a compass, newspaper to wrap specimens, a pencil, and note-sized paper or cards to record data about each fossil.

A responsible collector will want to take some precautions. First, remember that if you are planning to look for fossils on private land, you must have permission. If you are collecting fossils on public land, you must check to see what laws apply.

1. Why do you think fossils of corals, bryozoans, and other sea creatures are more common than fossils of birds?
2. How can you combine the types of fossils listed in your text (petrified, mold, etc.) and the three classes listed in the article?
3. Plan a chart for a collector to use to record fossil finds.

CHALLENGE L3

Hands-on Activities

Activity Worksheets

Chapter 11
ACTIVITY 11-1
• Relative Age Dating

Lab Preview

Can you tell which of two rock layers is older? You don't need to know the exact ages of the layers to tell. Geologists can learn a lot about rock layers simply by studying their arrangement.

What You'll Investigate

Goals

Materials

Procedure

FIGURE A

FIGURE B

Granite — Limestone — Sandstone — Shale

L2

Lab Manual

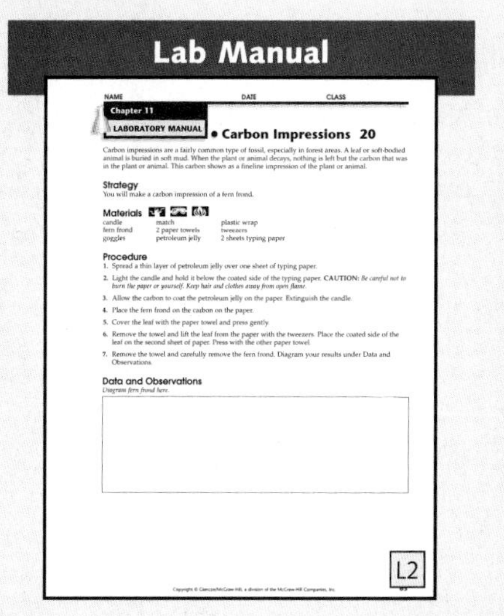

Chapter 11
LABORATORY MANUAL
• Carbon Impressions 20

Strategy

Materials

Procedure

Data and Observations

L2

Accessibility

Spanish Resources

SPANISH RESOURCES
GLENCOE
SCIENCE VOYAGES
Exploring the Life, Earth, and Physical Sciences
LEVEL BLUE
• Provides help for the English language learner
• Translates into Spanish the objectives, summary statements, vocabulary terms, and their definitions
• Includes a complete English/Spanish Glossary
L2

Assessment

Performance Assessment

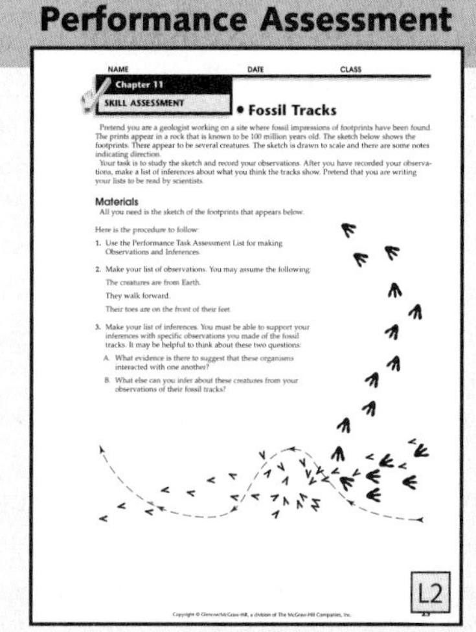

Chapter 11
SKILL ASSESSMENT
• Fossil Tracks

Materials

L2

Chapter Review

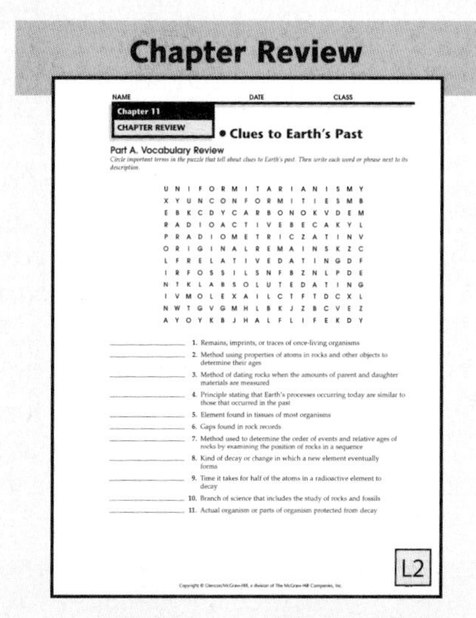

Chapter 11
CHAPTER REVIEW
• Clues to Earth's Past

Part A. Vocabulary Review

L2

Assessment

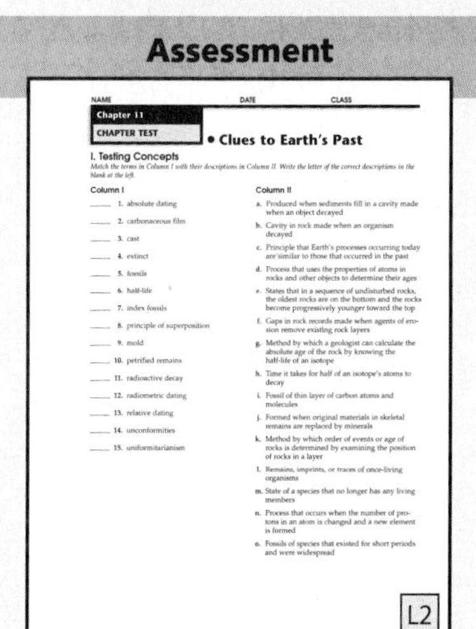

Chapter 11
CHAPTER TEST
• Clues to Earth's Past

I. Testing Concepts

Column I — Column II

L2

Test Practice Workbook

STANDARDIZED TEST PRACTICE
STUDENT EDITION
GLENCOE
SCIENCE VOYAGES
Exploring the Life, Earth, and Physical Sciences
LEVEL BLUE
THE PRINCETON REVIEW
L2

Extending Content

Critical Thinking/ Problem Solving

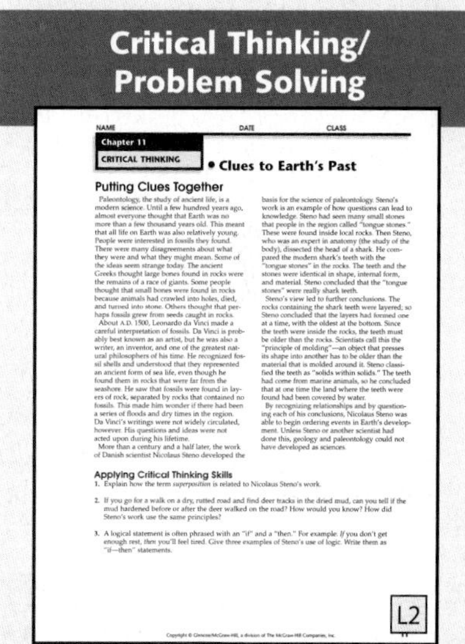

Chapter 11
CRITICAL THINKING
• Clues to Earth's Past

Putting Clues Together

Applying Critical Thinking Skills

L2

Multicultural Connections

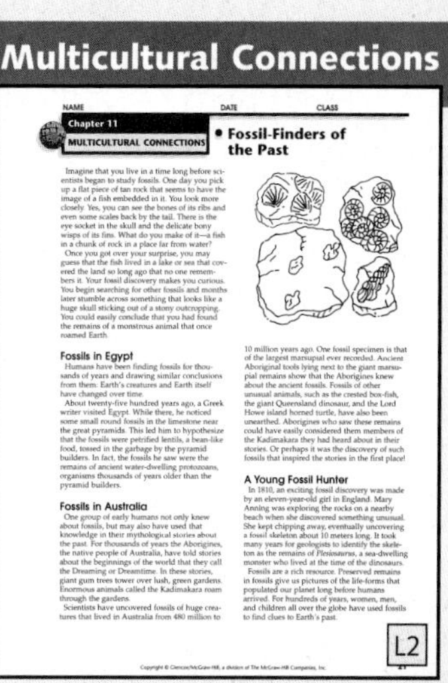

Chapter 11
MULTICULTURAL CONNECTIONS
• Fossil-Finders of the Past

Fossils in Egypt

Fossils in Australia

A Young Fossil Hunter

L2

Helping You Prepare

Fossils (Section 11-1)

Scientists think that certain reptiles swallowed stones to aid in digestion. When the organism died and decayed, the polished stones, called gastroliths, were left behind. Because gastroliths are traces of the original organism and not the organism itself, they are called trace fossils. Another trace fossil is a coprolite, or fossilized fecal material. Jewelry has been made from coprolites that have been cut and polished.

Facies fossils are the remains of organisms that were adapted to living in specific environments. The fossils are found only in rock types that were formed in those environments. Facies fossils enable paleontologists to reconstruct models depicting ancient climates. A stratigraphic facies contains rock layers that were generally deposited in the same environment of deposition. Seeing the environment in which a specific life-form lives during the present can help determine the environment in which similar ancient life-forms lived.

Fossil Formation (Section 11-1)

Some fossils consist of the original parts of the organism. Amber protects a trapped insect's body from decay. If the amber completely covers the insect's body, it will prevent bacteria, air, and water from reacting with the insect's body.

The skin and hair of some woolly mammoths have been found intact because they were protected from bacteria. These animals lived during the last ice age. When they became trapped within the ice, the low temperatures kept bacteria from developing and reproducing.

GLENCOE TECHNOLOGY

CD-ROM

Glencoe Science Voyages Interactive CD-ROM

Chapter Summaries

Use the Chapter Summary to introduce, teach, or review chapter material.

Fossil Preparation (Section 11-2)

When scientists locate an area thought to have fossils, large equipment and explosives are brought in to remove overlying rocks and soil. Once the excavation gets near the fossils, smaller tools are used. In the final phases of recovery, tiny picks and brushes are utilized to remove soil from the fossils.

Some fossils are fragile. In order to move them, they must be strengthened and protected. The fossils are first covered with layers of shellac. Next, strips of wet newspaper are molded onto the fossils. Finally, a plaster

NATIONAL GEOGRAPHIC — **Teacher's Corner**

Products Available from Glencoe

To order the following products for use with this chapter, call Glencoe at 1-800-334-7344:

Curriculum Kit

GeoKit: Earth's History

Products Available from National Geographic Society

To order the following products for use with this chapter, call National Geographic Society at 1-800-368-2728:

Video

Fossils: Clues to the Past

Index to National Geographic Magazine

The following articles may be used for research relating to this chapter:

"The Dawn of Humans: Redrawing Our Family Tree," by Lee Berger, August 1998.

"Africa's Dinosaur Castaways," by Paul C. Sereno, June, 1996.

"The Great Dinosaur Egg Hunt," by Phillip J. Currie, May 1996.

"Fossils: Annals of Life Written in Rock," by David Jeffery, August 1985.

mixture is used to coat burlap strips, that are then applied to the fossils. This final step produces a kind of cast that protects and supports the fossils. The reinforced fossils are then ready to be transported.

Relative Dating (Section 11-2)

The principle of faunal succession states that fossil organisms occur in rocks in a definite and determinable order. Thus, rocks formed during a particular interval of geologic time can be recognized by their fossils.

A geologic column is a composite diagram that shows the rocks of an area in the sequence in which they occur. Correlation of geologic columns from many locations enables geologists to construct geologic maps. Geologic maps show the relative age, distribution, and structural features of surface rocks.

Absolute Dating (Section 11-3)

A varve is a layer of sediment that is deposited over one year's time. A varve can be seen in a cross section of a rock layer. Because varves represent a specific amount of time, they can be counted and used to calculate the absolute age of lake deposits.

In order to correctly calculate the absolute age of a rock layer, a geologist must know the ratio of the number of radioactive parent isotopes to the number of daughter isotopes in the rock sample at present. It is assumed that no daughter product existed in the rock prior to decay, that none has been added, and that none has been removed.

Dealing with Errors

(Section 11-3)

Sometimes, daughter isotopes already exist in rocks and the calculated age of a rock could be wrong. However, for some isotopes, geologists are able to distinguish between original daughter product and product that forms from radioactive decay.

Other isotopes cannot be used because geologists cannot distinguish between original daughter isotopes and those that formed from radioactive decay of the parent isotope.

In order to cross-check their work in radiometric dating, geologists use several parent isotopes for the same age measurement. Because the different parent isotopes decay at different rates, using them for the same age measurement can ensure accuracy or expose errors.

It is assumed that no daughter product has leaked out of the object being dated. This does happen at times and can affect the validity of the calculated absolute age.

SCIENCE UPDATE

For current events or science in the news, access the Glencoe Science Web Site at **www.glencoe.com/sec/science**

Radiocarbon Dating (Section 11-3)

Radiometric dating that uses the radioactive isotope carbon-14 is referred to as radiocarbon dating. Cosmic rays strike atoms in Earth's upper atmosphere, releasing neutrons. The neutrons then strike atoms of nitrogen-14, producing carbon-14. Carbon-14 is continually being created in Earth's upper atmosphere.

Teacher to Teacher

"When most students think of fossils, they think of large dinosaur skeletons or other large vertebrate bones. I remind students that fossils come in all sizes. In class, we use binocular microscopes to examine the intricate microfossils that I've ordered from a scientific supply company."

Susan Leach Snyder

Susan Leach Snyder, Teacher
Jones Middle School
Upper Arlington, OH

CHAPTER 11 Clues to Earth's Past

CHAPTER OVERVIEW

Section 11-1 This section describes fossils and the conditions needed for them to form. Use of fossils as indicators of age and ancient environments concludes the section.

Section 11-2 This section explains how relative ages of rocks are determined. Methods used to correlate rocks also are described.

Section 11-3 This section contrasts absolute and relative dating. Radioactive decay also is described.

Chapter Vocabulary

fossil	relative dating
petrified remains	unconformity
carbonaceous film	absolute dating
mold	radioactive decay
cast	half-life
index fossil	radiometric dating
principle of superposition	uniformitarianism

Theme Connection

Stability and Change The evolution of life-forms throughout geologic time as shown by the fossil record should be a major focus of the chapter. The changes in life-forms on Earth can be used to obtain relative ages of rocks and to date geologic events.

00:00 OUT OF TIME?

If time does not permit teaching the entire chapter, use Reviewing Main Ideas on pp. 328–329.

CHAPTER 11 Clues to Earth's Past

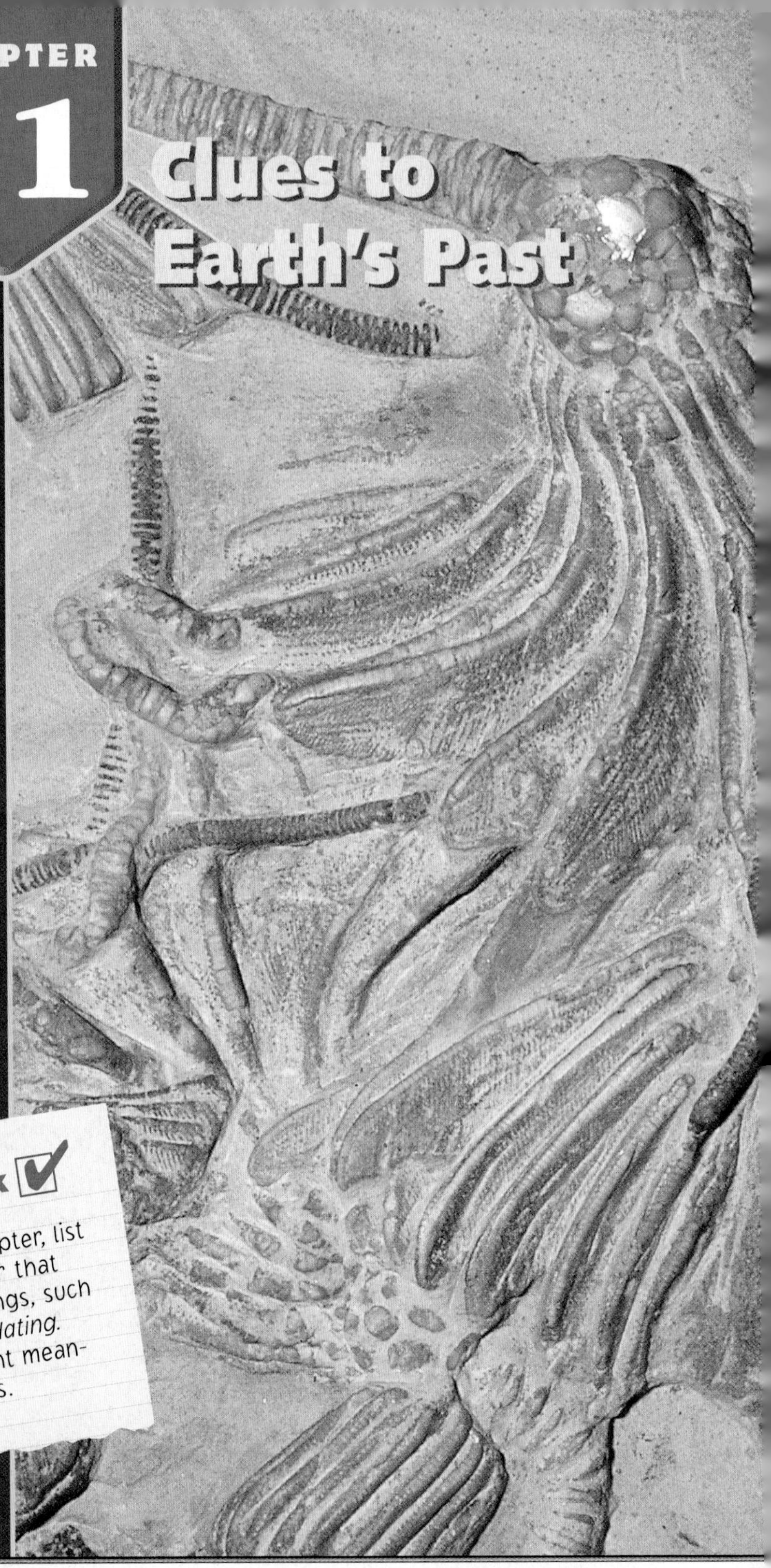

Chapter Preview

Section 11-1
Fossils

Section 11-2
Relative Ages of Rocks

Section 11-3
Absolute Ages of Rocks

Skills Preview

Skill Builders
- Interpret Data
- Make and Use a Table

Activities
- Interpret Data
- Analyze and Conclude

MiniLabs
- Observe
- Infer

Reading Check ✓

As you read this chapter, list words you encounter that have several meanings, such as *mold, cast,* and *dating.* Explain the different meanings of these terms.

302

Multiple Learning Styles

Look for the following logos for strategies that emphasize different learning modalities.

Linguistic Multiple Learning Styles, p. 305; Science Journal, p. 308; Preview, p. 328

Logical-Mathematical Using Math, p. 307; Activity, p. 319; MiniLab, p. 322; Assessment, p. 325

Visual-Spatial Explore Activity, p. 303; Assessment, pp. 318, 319; Quick Demo, p. 313; Reteach, p. 328

Auditory-Musical Out of Time, p. 328

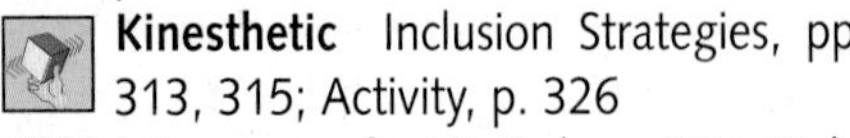
Kinesthetic Inclusion Strategies, pp. 313, 315; Activity, p. 326

Interpersonal MiniLab, p. 305; Making a Model, p. 308; Review, p. 328

Intrapersonal Assessment, p. 329

Naturalist Enrichment, p. 307

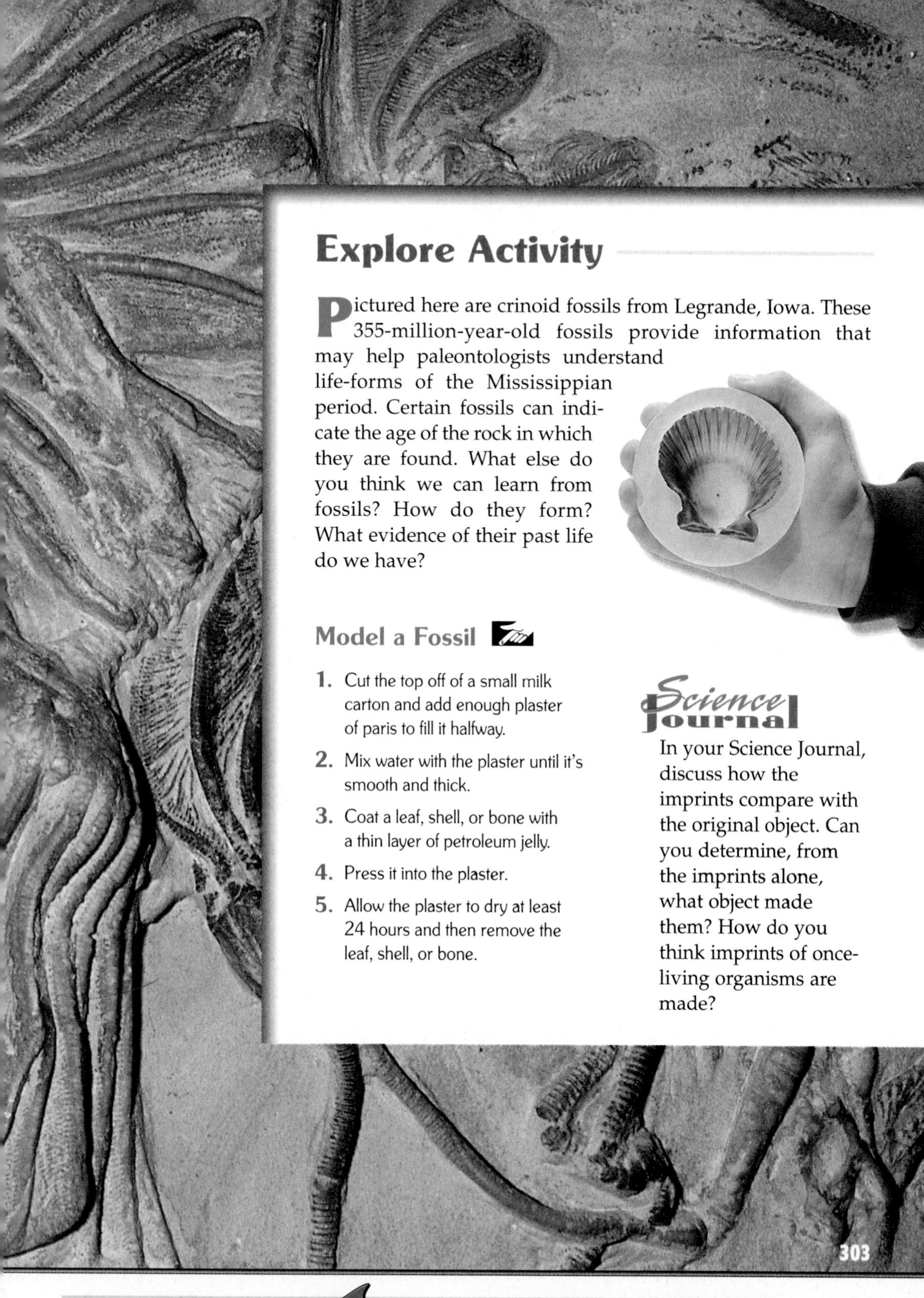

Explore Activity

Pictured here are crinoid fossils from Legrande, Iowa. These 355-million-year-old fossils provide information that may help paleontologists understand life-forms of the Mississippian period. Certain fossils can indicate the age of the rock in which they are found. What else do you think we can learn from fossils? How do they form? What evidence of their past life do we have?

Model a Fossil

1. Cut the top off of a small milk carton and add enough plaster of paris to fill it halfway.
2. Mix water with the plaster until it's smooth and thick.
3. Coat a leaf, shell, or bone with a thin layer of petroleum jelly.
4. Press it into the plaster.
5. Allow the plaster to dry at least 24 hours and then remove the leaf, shell, or bone.

Science Journal

In your Science Journal, discuss how the imprints compare with the original object. Can you determine, from the imprints alone, what object made them? How do you think imprints of once-living organisms are made?

303

Explore Activity

Purpose

Visual-Spatial Use the Explore Activity to introduce students to one method of fossil formation. L2 COOP LEARN

Preparation

Have students bring in small, clean, empty milk cartons, and leaves, shells, or clean meat bones.

Materials

one small milk carton ($\frac{1}{2}$ pint); plaster of paris (100 g); water; petroleum jelly; leaves, shells, or bones

Teaching Strategies

Have sample mold and cast fossils available for comparison.

Science Journal Student descriptions will vary, depending on how well they performed the activity. However, they should note that the fossil they make resembles the original object. For some fossils, students will be able to determine what object made them; for others, they may need additional information. Imprints may be made by footprints or resting traces.

Assessment

Performance Have students repeat the Explore Activity using prepared gelatin or jelly. Ask students whether it was as easy to produce a fossil of a soft object. Ask them how this is important to the study of the conditions necessary to form fossils. Use **Performance Assessment in the Science Classroom,** p. 33.

Assessment Planner

Portfolio
Refer to p. 329 for suggested items that students might select for their portfolios.

Performance Assessment
See p. 329 for additional Performance Assessment options.
Skill Builder, pp. 311, 325
MiniLab, pp. 305, 322
Activity, 11-1, p. 319; 11-2, pp. 326–327

Content Assessment
Section Assessment, pp. 311, 318, 325
Chapter Assessment, pp. 330–331
Proficiency Prep, pp. 311, 318, 325

SECTION 11-1

Prepare

Refer to **Fossils and Fossil Formation** on p. 302E.

Preplanning

Refer to the **Chapter Organizer** on pp. 302A–B.

1 Motivate

Bellringer

Before presenting the lesson, display **Section Focus Transparency 28** on the overhead projector. Use the accompanying **Focus Activity** worksheet. L2 ELL

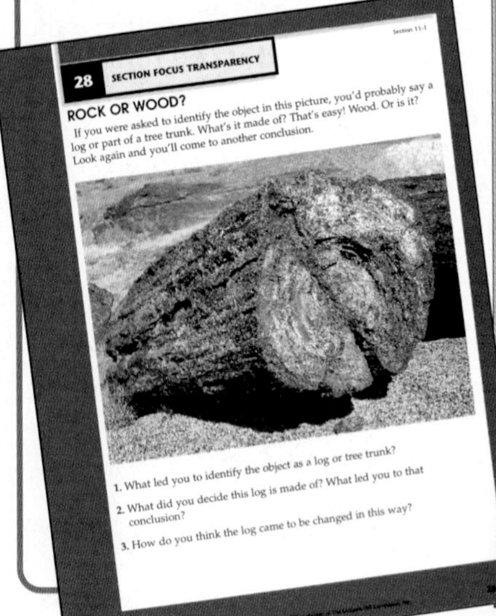

Section 11-1

28 SECTION FOCUS TRANSPARENCY

ROCK OR WOOD?

If you were asked to identify the object in this picture, you'd probably say a log or part of a tree trunk. What's it made of? That's easy! Wood. Or is it? Look again and you'll come to another conclusion.

1. What led you to identify the object as a log or tree trunk?
2. What did you decide this log is made of? What led you to that conclusion?
3. How do you think the log came to be changed in this way?

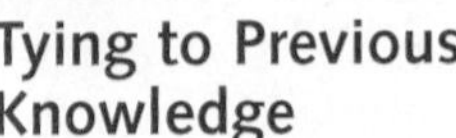

Tying to Previous Knowledge

Ask students to list what things they think can become fossils. In this section, they will learn that, under certain conditions, almost anything can become a fossil.

11•1 Fossils

What You'll Learn

- Conditions necessary for fossils to form
- Processes of fossil formation
- How fossil correlation is used to determine rock ages

Vocabulary

fossil
petrified remains
carbonaceous film
mold
cast
index fossil

Why It's Important

- Fossils can help you interpret how life on Earth has changed through time.

Traces from Our Past

The thick forest shakes as an *Allosaurus* charges forward in search of an evening meal. On the other side of the swamp, a herd of apatosaurs moves slowly and cautiously. The adults surround the young to protect them from predators. Soon, night will fall on this prehistoric day, 160 million years ago.

Does this story sound familiar to you? It's likely that you've read about dinosaurs and other past inhabitants of Earth. But, how do you know they really lived? What evidence do we have of past life on Earth? Scientists reconstruct what an animal looked like from its fossil remains, as in **Figure 11-1.**

Fossil Formation

In the Explore Activity, you made imprints of parts of organisms. Imprints are records, or evidence, of life. Evidence such as the remains, imprints, or traces of once-living organisms preserved in rocks are **fossils.** By studying fossils, geologists help solve mysteries of Earth's past.

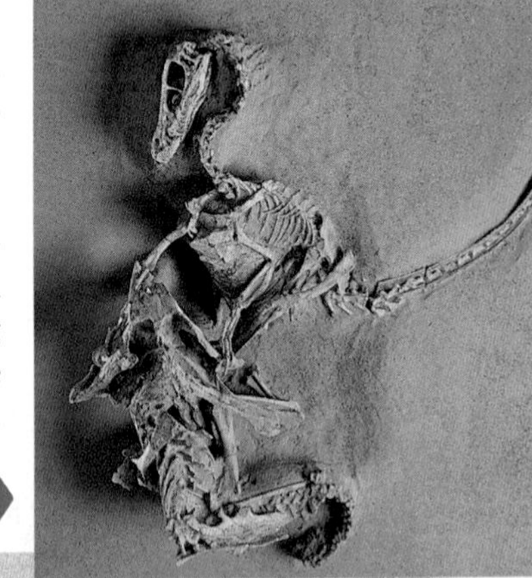

A

B

Figure 11-1 Scientists and artists can reconstruct what dinosaurs looked like using fossil remains. Two dinosaur fossils (A) were found in this position. Artists used the fossils to reconstruct a *Velociraptor* attacking a *Protoceratops* (B).

Resource Manager

The following **Teacher Classroom Resources** can be used with Section 11-1:

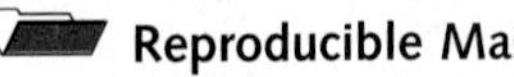

Reproducible Masters

Activity Worksheets, p. 63 L2
Critical Thinking/Problem Solving, p. 11 L2
Enrichment, p. 28 L3
Home Involvement, p. 28 L2
Laboratory Manual, pp. 63–64 L2
Multicultural Connections, pp. 21–22 L2
Reinforcement, p. 28 L2
Study Guide, pp. 41–42 L1 ELL

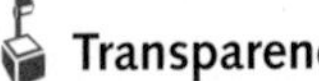

Transparencies

Teaching Transparency 21 L2

Fossils have helped geologists and biologists find out exactly when life began, when plants and animals first lived on land, and when certain types of organisms, such as the dinosaurs, disappeared. Fossils tell us not only *when* and *where* organisms once lived, but also *how* they lived.

Usually, the remains of dead plants and animals are quickly destroyed. Scavengers eat the dead organisms, or fungi and microorganisms cause them to decay. If you've ever left a banana on the shelf too long, you've seen this process begin. Compounds in the banana cause it to become soft and brown, and microorganisms move in and cause it to decay quickly. What keeps some plants and animals from decaying so that they become fossils?

Figure 11-2 The hard parts in plants, such as the cellulose in cell walls, made preservation of this fossil leaf possible.

Necessary Conditions

First of all, to become a fossil, the body of a dead organism must be protected from scavengers and microorganisms. One way this can occur is to have the body buried quickly by sediments. If a fish dies and sinks to the bottom of a pond, sediments carried into the pond by a stream will rapidly cover the fish. As a result, no animals or microorganisms can get to it. However, quick burial alone isn't enough to make a fossil.

Organisms have a better chance of being preserved if they have hard parts such as bones, shells, or teeth. As you may know, these hard parts are less likely to be eaten by other organisms, they decay more slowly, and they are less likely to weather away. Most fossils, such as the fossil leaf in **Figure 11-2,** are made of the hard parts of organisms. Fossils are most often found in sedimentary rocks. The heat and pressure involved in forming igneous and metamorphic rocks most often destroy fossil material.

Try at Home MiniLab

Predicting Fossil Preservation

Procedure

1. Take a brief walk outside and observe the area near your school or home.
2. Look around and notice what type of litter has been discarded on the school grounds. Note whether there is a paved road near your school. Note anything else that was made by humans.

Analysis

1. Predict what human-made or natural objects from our time might be preserved far into the future.
2. Explain what conditions would need to exist for these objects to be preserved as fossils.

Multiple Learning Styles

Linguistic Have students imagine they are fossils. Have them write their autobiographies and describe what they have seen and experienced. The stories should also include how the organism became a fossil and illustrations of what the fossil looks like. Encourage creativity. L2

2 Teach

Try at Home MiniLab

For additional help doing this activity at home, see the corresponding pages in the **Home Involvement** booklet.

Purpose

Interpersonal Students will think about what conditions would be necessary for objects from our time to become fossils. L2

Teaching Strategies

- Introduce this activity by asking students how we know about conditions that existed long ago on Earth's surface.
- If this activity is done in class, form problem-solving teams with four or five students per team. Ask for a consensus list from each team. Then write each team's list of five objects on the chalkboard. Have the class, on a consensus basis, infer which five are most likely to be preserved as fossils.

Analysis

1. This kind of activity is designed to make students think about conditions necessary for fossils to form. There are no right or wrong answers.
2. To be preserved, it is best if the object has hard parts and is buried quickly.

Assessment

Oral Have students explain why shark teeth are often found as fossils but impressions of jellyfish are rarely found. Use **Performance Assessment in the Science Classroom,** p. 27.

Discussion

Interpersonal Form cooperative groups. Each group is to be responsible for one of the five types of fossils discussed in this section. Once finished, each group is to direct the discussion on the type of fossil they were responsible for. [L2] COOP LEARN

Flex Your Brain

Use the Flex Your Brain activity to have students explore FOSSILS.

GLENCOE TECHNOLOGY

Videodisc

The Infinite Voyage: The Great Dinosaur Hunt

Chapter 10 *New Dinosaur Discoveries and Their Link with Today* (8:00)

Refer to the Teacher Guide for bar codes and teaching strategies.

Correcting Misconceptions

Some students might think that fossils form only from ancient life. Ask them what happens to organisms that die and settle to the bottom of a lake or ocean. Explain that these remains are buried quickly by sediments. Once buried, they begin the process of fossilization. In time, they may become fossils.

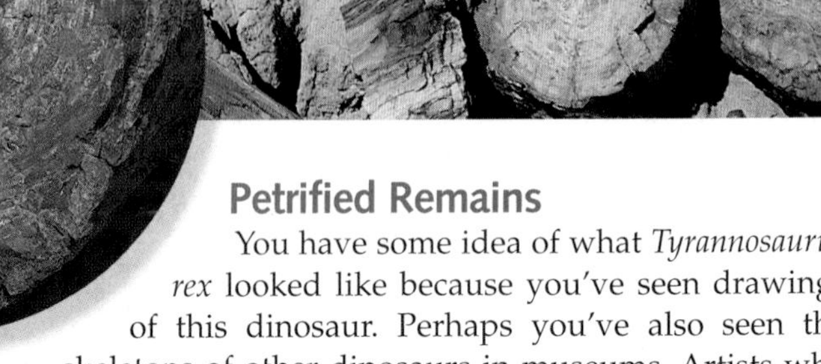

Figure 11-3 This pile of petrified wood is in the Petrified Forest National Monument in Arizona. Much of the original matter in these petrified plant remains has been replaced by quartz and other minerals. **Why have the fossils retained the shape of the original plant?**

Petrified Remains

You have some idea of what *Tyrannosaurus rex* looked like because you've seen drawings of this dinosaur. Perhaps you've also seen the skeletons of other dinosaurs in museums. Artists who draw *Tyrannosaurus rex* and other dinosaurs base their drawings on fossil bones. These bones are usually petrified.

Petrified (PEH truh fide) **remains** are hard and rocklike. Some or all of the original materials in the remains have been replaced by minerals. For example, a solution of water and dissolved quartz may flow through the bones of a dead organism. The water dissolves the calcium in the bone and deposits quartz in its place. Quartz is harder than calcium, so the petrified bone is rocklike.

We learn about past life-forms from bones, wood, and other remains that become petrified, like those in **Figure 11-3.** But, there are many other types of fossils to look at, too.

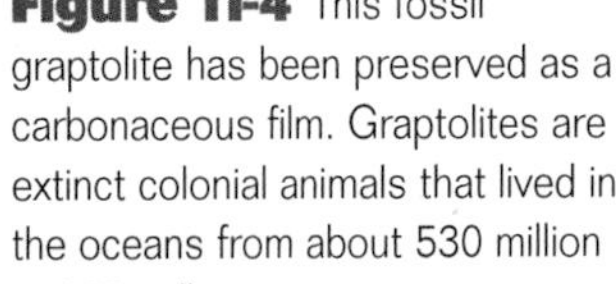

Figure 11-4 This fossil graptolite has been preserved as a carbonaceous film. Graptolites are extinct colonial animals that lived in the oceans from about 530 million to 320 million years ago.

Carbonaceous Films

The tissues of most organisms are made of compounds that contain carbon. Sometimes, the only fossil remains of a dead plant or animal is this carbon. As you know, fossils most often form when a dead organism is buried in sediments. As more and more sediments pile up, the organism is exposed to pressure and heat. These conditions force gases and liquids from the organism. A thin film of carbon is left, forming an outline of the original organism. This type of fossil is called

Across the Curriculum

Geography Have students research where petrified fossils have been found in the United States. Ask one student to locate the areas found by his or her classmates on a map of the United States. Students should determine how far away the closest find was. Ask students what is meant by the name *Petrified Forest.* [L2]

Caption Answer

Figure 11-3 *During the petrifaction process, original matter in an object is replaced by quartz and other minerals carried in solution. This preserves the original shape of the plant.*

306 CHAPTER 11 CLUES TO EARTH'S PAST

a **carbonaceous** (kar boh NAY shus) **film.** The process of chemically changing organic material is called carbonization. An example is shown in **Figure 11-4.**

In swamps and deltas, large amounts of plant matter accumulate. Over millions of years, these deposits become completely carbonized, forming the sedimentary rock coal. Coal is more important as a fuel than as a fossil because the makeup of the plant is most often lost when the coal forms.

Molds and Casts

Think again about the imprints in the plaster of paris you made earlier. In nature, such imprints are made when seashells or other hard parts of organisms fall into soft sediments such as mud. The object and sediments are then buried by more sediments. The sediments are squeezed and cemented together into rock. Holes in the rock let water and air reach the shell or hard part, causing it to dissolve, and leaving behind a hollow place in the rock called a **mold.** Later, other sediments may fill in the hollow place, harden into rock, and make a **cast** of the original organism, as shown in **Figure 11-5.**

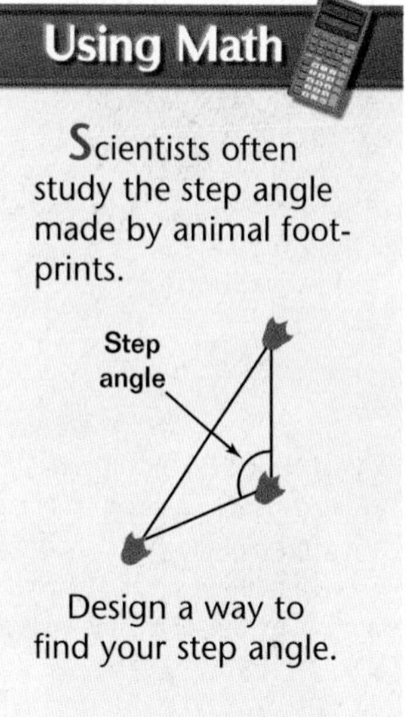
Using Math
Scientists often study the step angle made by animal footprints.
Step angle
Design a way to find your step angle.

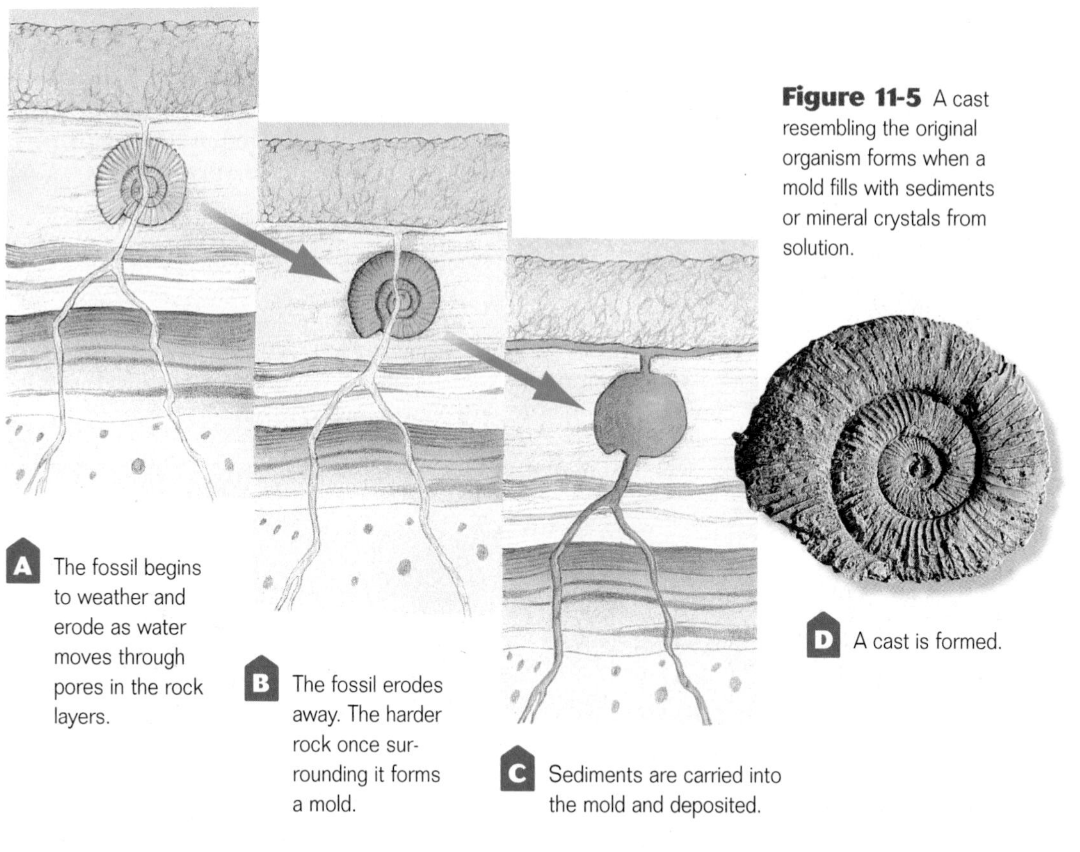
A The fossil begins to weather and erode as water moves through pores in the rock layers.
B The fossil erodes away. The harder rock once surrounding it forms a mold.
C Sediments are carried into the mold and deposited.

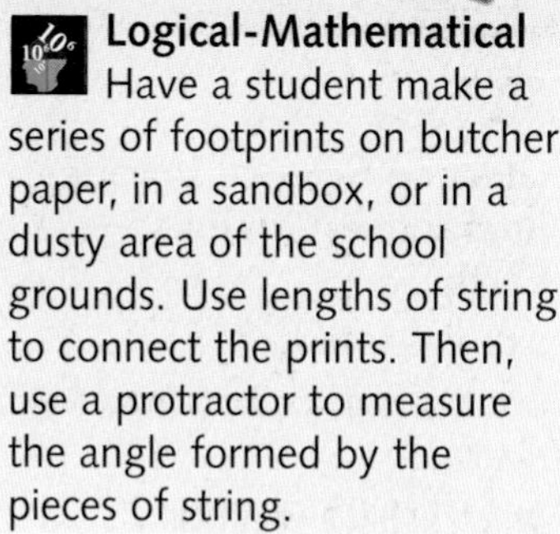
D A cast is formed.

Figure 11-5 A cast resembling the original organism forms when a mold fills with sediments or mineral crystals from solution.

Enrichment

Naturalist Ask students to bring in fossils they might have collected or received from others. Have the class determine the type of fossil and, if possible, the organism that produced each.

VISUAL Learning

Figure 11-5 Based on the figure, which of your fossils is a mold and which is a cast? *Answers will vary, but the mold should be the hollow or depression. The cast will be the bump.*

Using an Analogy

Ask whether any students in your class work with ceramics as a hobby. If so, have these students construct an analogy between the molds used in making ceramic statues and those formed in nature. Students may wish to use a statue to demonstrate why the internal structure of an organism is not preserved when casts are formed. L2 ELL

Using Math

Logical-Mathematical Have a student make a series of footprints on butcher paper, in a sandbox, or in a dusty area of the school grounds. Use lengths of string to connect the prints. Then, use a protractor to measure the angle formed by the pieces of string.

Guided Reading Strategy

News Summary This strategy helps students explain and make connections to their studies of science. Students are assigned the job of being television reporters. They are given several minutes to summarize or analyze their investigation for their "television" audience. Have students do a News Summary for an application of a concept from this chapter.

Across the Curriculum

Geology Invite a local collector of fossils from around the world to display some of his or her collection, tell about how the fossils were found and extracted from rock, and discuss from where the fossils were collected. If a collector is not available, arrange for a visit to the nearest museum that displays fossils from around the world.

Discussion

Use the following questions to initiate a discussion about trace fossils. **How do trace fossils differ from other types of fossils?** *Trace fossils are not formed from body parts. They are evidence of an organism's activity.* **What information about early life-forms can be obtained from the depth and separation of tracks left in sediment?** *The approximate size and mass of the organism that left them can be determined.* **What could you conclude about an organism if you found small, fossilized tracks that were far apart?** *Small tracks indicate a small organism. Therefore, if tracks are far apart, the organism was probably able to move swiftly or run.*

Making a Model

Interpersonal Encourage pairs of students to produce a model of a fossil that depicts one of the five methods of formation: petrified remains, carbonaceous films, molds and casts, original remains, or trace fossils. L2 ELL COOP LEARN

GLENCOE TECHNOLOGY

Videodisc

Glencoe Science Voyages Interactive Videodisc—Earth

Side 2, Lesson 5

Dinosaurs: Footprints in the Rock

5419

5966

Refer to Videodisc Teacher Guide for additional bar codes.

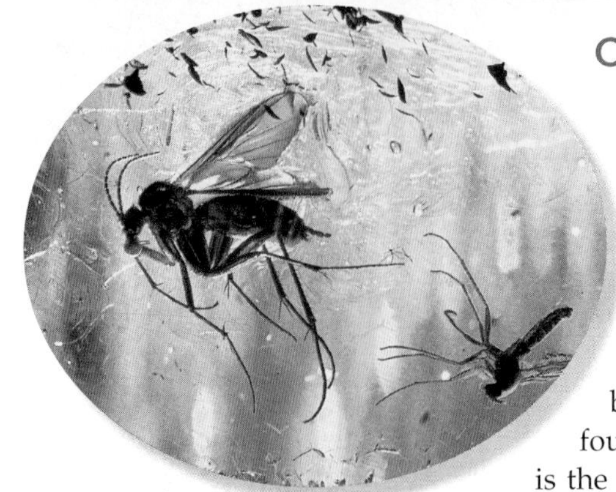

Figure 11-6 This 40-million-year-old insect was trapped in the sticky resin produced by a plant. Over time, the resin crystallized into amber, preserving the insect inside.

Original Remains

Sometimes the actual organism or parts of the organism are found. **Figure 11-6** shows an insect trapped in amber, a hard form of the sticky resin produced by some trees. The amber protects the insect's body from decay and petrification. Other organisms, such as woolly mammoths, have been found preserved in frozen ground. In 1991, the entire body of a man who lived 5300 years ago was found frozen in glacial ice in the southern Alps. It is the oldest complete human body ever discovered. Original remains have also been found in tar seeps such as the La Brea (BRAY ah) tar pits in California.

Trace Fossils

Fossilized tracks and other evidence of animal activity are called *trace fossils.* Perhaps your parents made your handprint or footprint in plaster of paris when you were born. If so, it's a record that tells something about you. From it, you can guess your size and maybe your weight at that age. Animals walking on Earth long ago have left similar tracks, such as those in **Figure 11-7.** In some cases, tracks can tell us more about how an organism lived than any other type of fossil. For example, the story described at the beginning of this chapter really took place.

Figure 11-7 Tracks made in soft mud, and now preserved in solid rock, can provide information about animal size, speed, and other behavior patterns. These tracks are located on the Navajo Reservation in Arizona (A) and in the Glenrose Rock Formation in Texas (B).

308 CHAPTER 11 CLUES TO EARTH'S PAST

Science Journal

Traces of the Past Encourage students to research what types of information can be learned about extinct animals from studying gastroliths and coprolites left by the organisms. Have students write a brief report of what they discover in their Science Journals. L3

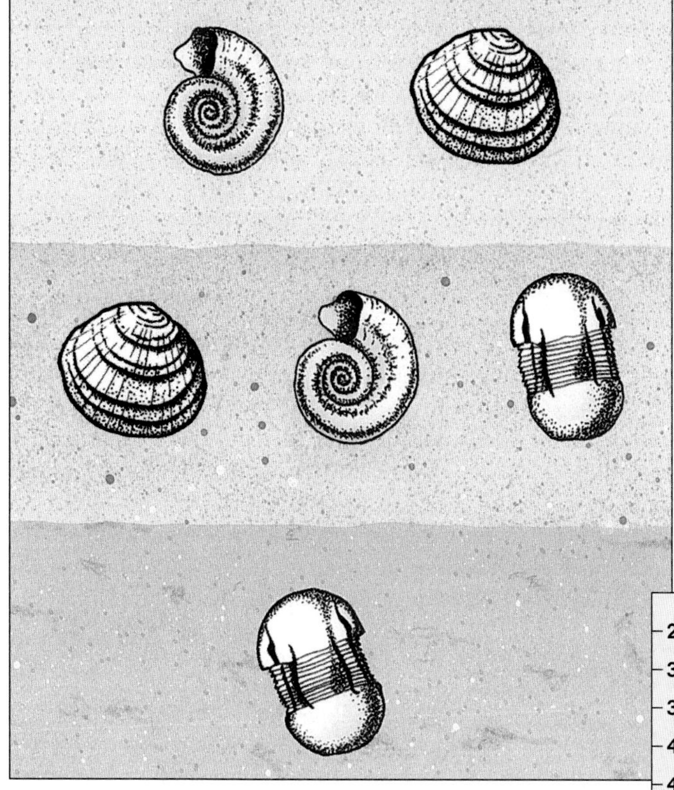

Figure 11-8 The sequence of sedimentary rock and the fossils each contains (A) can be used to date the rocks. The chart (B) shows when each organism inhabited Earth. **Why is it possible to say that the middle layer of rock had to be deposited between 438 and 408 million years ago?**

A Illustration of a sequence of rocks and the fossils they contain.

B Fossil Range Chart

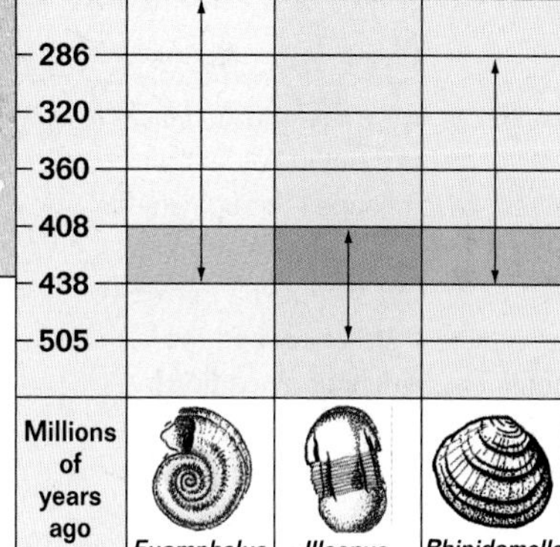

From a set of tracks at Davenport Ranch, Texas, we have learned something about the social life of *Apatosaurus,* one of the largest known dinosaurs. The largest tracks of the herd are on the outer edges and the smallest are on the inside. This suggests that the adult apatosaurs surrounded the young as they traveled—probably to protect them from enemies. In fact, a nearby set of allosaur tracks shows that one was stalking the herd.

Other trace fossils include worm holes and burrows made by marine animals. As you can see, a group of fossils can tell us a great deal about the individuals that lived on Earth before us. ☑

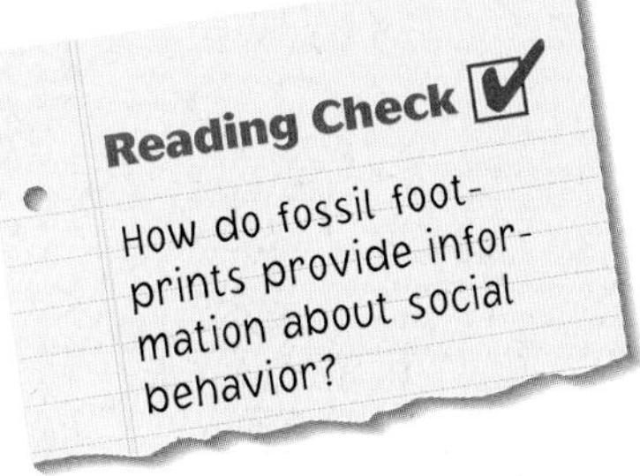

Reading Check
How do fossil footprints provide information about social behavior?

Index Fossils

The study of fossils tells that species are constantly changing, or evolving. Evidence shows that species live on Earth for a certain period of time before they evolve into new species or they die out completely. Some species of organisms inhabit Earth for long periods of time without changing much. Other species remain unchanged for only a short time. It is these organisms that make index fossils.

Using Science Words

Use the following question to assess whether students understand what is meant by the science term *index fossil.* **Why are index fossils useful to Earth scientists?** *Because the organisms that formed them existed for relatively short periods of time, the fossils are good indicators of the ages of the rocks in which they are found.*

GLENCOE TECHNOLOGY

Videodisc

The Infinite Voyage: The Search for Ancient Americans

Chapter 6 *The Windover Nomads* 4:30

Refer to the Teacher Guide for bar codes and teaching strategies.

Answer to Reading Check ☑

We can interpret where the adults and young ones stood or if one dinosaur was stalking another dinosaur.

Caption Answer

Figure 11-8 *The three fossils have ranges that overlap by between 438 and 408 million years. The age of the layer cannot be dated more accurately than that.*

Enrichment

Have an interested student research and report on the Tollund Man. The Tollund Man is the preserved body of a human found in Tollund Fen, Denmark. His remains were spectacularly well preserved in the shallow, oxygen-starved water of the fen. The Tollund Man was found with his leather cap still in place on his head. All of his facial hairs and the pores and wrinkles of his skin are easily visible. One of the things that makes this find particularly interesting is that Tollund Man has a rope noose around his neck. Scientists have inferred that he was hanged and then thrown into the fen approximately 2000 years ago. L2

LIFE SCIENCE INTEGRATION

Water will, at times, lie on top of tar seeps, and animals become trapped while drinking the water. Other animals become trapped when they attack trapped animals.

3 Assess

Check for Understanding

Discussion

How do molds and casts differ? *When an organism dies, it may become buried in sediment. As the sediments harden to form rocks, the organism slowly decays. When the organic material is completely gone, an impression, or mold, is left in the rock. If sediments later fill the cavity and then harden, a cast of the organism forms.*

Reteach

Divide students into groups of four. Assign the roles of reader, materials handler, fossil maker, and recorder. Have students determine which of the following types of sediments would best preserve fossils by pressing shells or bones into mixtures of sand and water, clay and water, and gravel and water. The recorder should report which mixture of sediments allowed the best imprint to be formed.

Extension

For students who have mastered this section, use the **Reinforcement** and **Enrichment** masters.

LIFE SCIENCE INTEGRATION

Trapped in Tar
You have learned that original remains of animals can be found in tar seeps. Hypothesize why so many animals became trapped in tar seeps. What would cause animals to walk into a tar pit?

Index fossils are species that lived on Earth for short periods of time, were abundant, and were widespread geographically. Scientists use index fossils to tell the age of rock layers. Because few fossils meet all the conditions to be an index fossil, groups of fossils are usually used to date rocks. This is how the rock layer in **Figure 11-8** was dated. Which fossil is the index fossil?

Fossils and Ancient Environments

Fossils also can be used to tell what the environment of an area was like long ago. For example, rocks in Antarctica contain fossils of tropical plants. As shown in **Figure 11-9,** the environment of Antarctica today isn't tropical, but we hypothesize that it was at the time these fossilized plants were living.

How would you explain the presence of fossilized brachiopods, animals that lived in shallow seas, in the rocks of the midwestern United States? **Figure 11-10** shows an example of

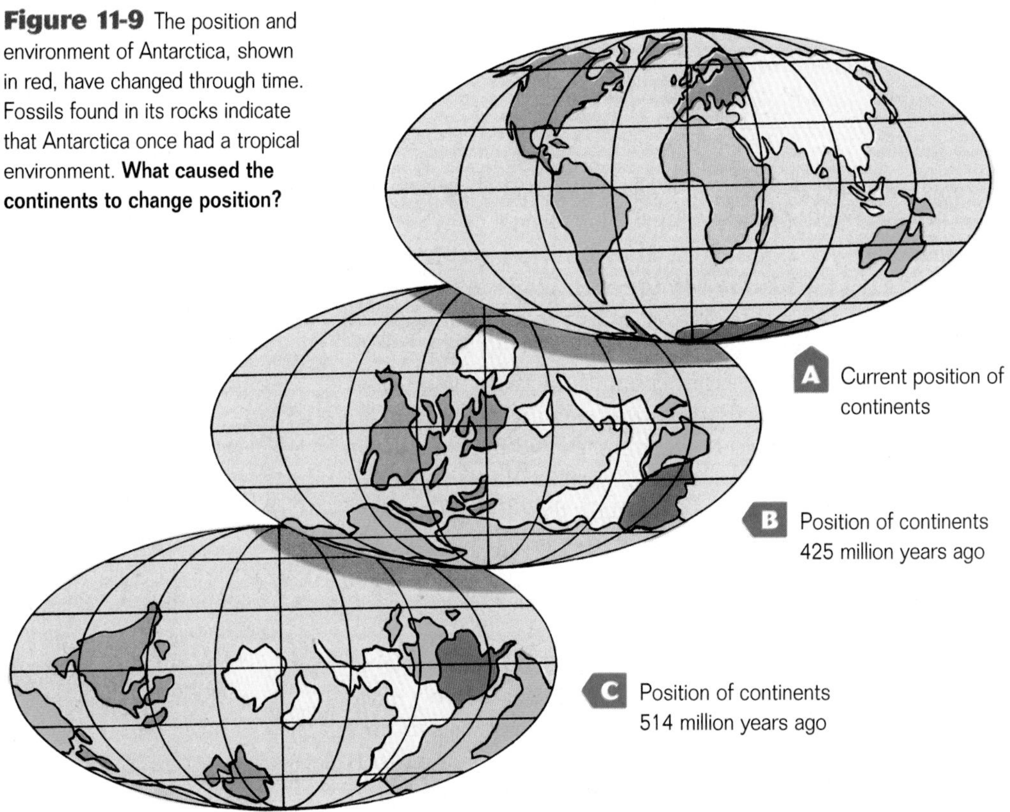

Figure 11-9 The position and environment of Antarctica, shown in red, have changed through time. Fossils found in its rocks indicate that Antarctica once had a tropical environment. **What caused the continents to change position?**

Caption Answers

Figure 11-9 *the movement of Earth's crust through plate tectonics*

Figure 11-10 *The waters along the Maine coast are colder today than they were in Silurian time.*

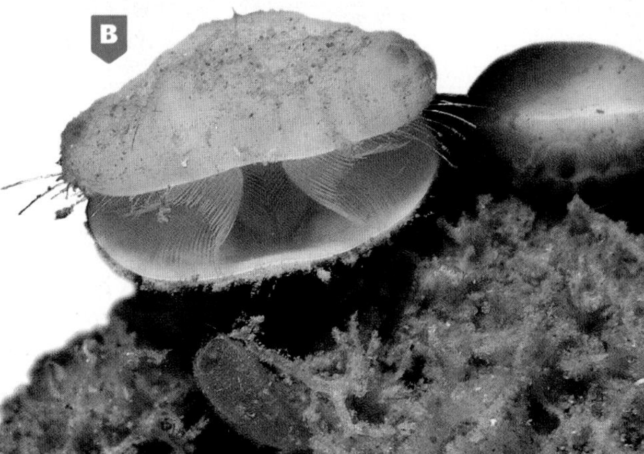

a modern brachiopod (BRACH kee uh pahd) and a fossil brachiopod. As shown in **Figure 11-9B** and **C,** North America was once found at the equator. The shallow seas that covered the central part of North America during some of this time were warm and hospitable to organisms such as brachiopods.

Fossils tell us not only about past life on Earth, but also about the history of the rock layers that contain them. Fossils can give information about environment, climate, and animal behavior, as well as dating the rocks.

Figure 11-10
(A) This Paleozoic-aged brachiopod lived in the warm shallow seas that once covered portions of North America.
(B) *Terebratulina septentrionalis* is a modern brachiopod. It lives off the coast of York, Maine. **How do the habitats of these brachiopods compare?**

Section Assessment

1. What conditions are needed for most fossils to form?
2. Describe how a mold-and-cast fossil might form.
3. Explain how index fossils are used.
4. **Think Critically:** What can be said about the ages of two geographically separated layers of rock that contain the same type of fossil?
5. **Skill Builder**
Concept Mapping Make a concept map that compares and contrasts petrified remains and original remains. Use the following terms and phrases: *types of fossils, original remains, evidence of former life, petrified remains, materials replaced by minerals,* and *actual parts of organisms.* If you need help, refer to Concept Mapping in the **Skill Handbook** on page 714.

Collect samples of fossils or visit a museum that has fossils on display. In your Science Journal, make an illustration of each fossil. Write a brief description, noting key facts about each. Also, write about how each fossil might have been formed.

4 Close

Proficiency Prep

Use this quiz to check students' recall of section content.

1. **What are remains or traces of once-living organisms preserved in Earth's rocks?** *fossils*
2. **What type of fossil forms when minerals replace an organism's original material?** *petrified remains*
3. **What are preserved tracks and traces of animal activity?** *trace fossils*

Section Assessment

1. quick burial and the presence of hard parts
2. An object buried in sediments later decays, leaving a cavity called a mold. Later, sediments may fill the cavity, harden, and produce a cast.
3. Because index fossils lived for a short period of time and were geographically widespread, they can be used to date specific layers of rocks.
4. Think Critically Both layers of rock formed during the period of time that the fossil-producing organism lived; the two layers of rock may be similar in age if the organism existed for only a short period of Earth's history.

5. **Skill Builder**
Begin with *Types of Fossils;* One branch might read: *original remains,* are composed of, *actual parts of organisms,* which are, *evidence of former life.* The other branch might read: *petrified remains,* are composed of, *materials replaced by minerals,* which are, *evidence of former life.*

Assessment

Performance Assess students' abilities to make concept maps by having them construct maps and then share them with other students. Encourage students to share their ideas and to modify their own maps. Use **Performance Assessment in the Science Classroom,** p. 89.

Answers will vary, depending on which fossils students use. Students should indicate that to be preserved as fossils, organisms need to be buried quickly and should contain hard parts.

SECTION 11-2

Prepare

Refer to **Fossil Preparation** and **Relative Dating** on pp. 302E–F.

Preplanning

Refer to the **Chapter Organizer** on pp. 302A–B.

1 Motivate

Bellringer

Before presenting the lesson, display **Section Focus Transparency 29** on the overhead projector. Use the accompanying **Focus Activity** worksheet. L2 ELL

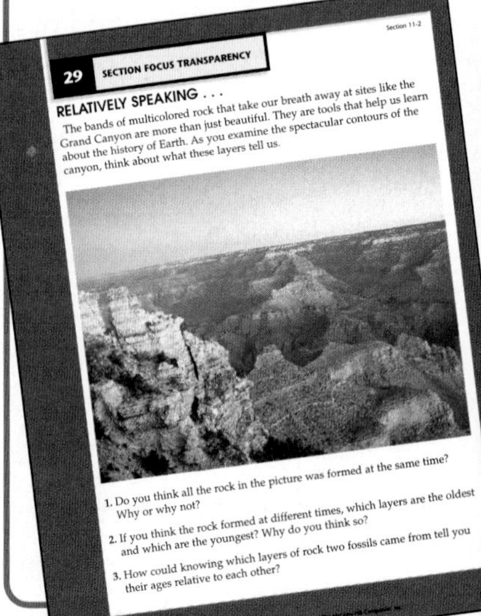
Section 11-2

29 SECTION FOCUS TRANSPARENCY

RELATIVELY SPEAKING . . .

The bands of multicolored rock that take our breath away at sites like the Grand Canyon are more than just beautiful. They are tools that help us learn about the history of Earth. As you examine the spectacular contours of the canyon, think about what these layers tell us.

1. Do you think all the rock in the picture was formed at the same time? Why or why not?
2. If you think the rock formed at different times, which layers are the oldest and which are the youngest? Why do you think so?
3. How could knowing which layers of rock two fossils came from tell you their ages relative to each other?

Tying to Previous Knowledge

Students experience superposition every day. Have students relate how sequences of sedimentary rocks are similar to the bricks in a building.

Relative Ages of Rocks

What You'll Learn

- Several methods used to date rock layers relative to other rock layers
- How to interpret gaps in the rock record
- An example of how rock layers may be correlated with other rock layers

Vocabulary
principle of superposition
relative dating
unconformity

Why It's Important

- Being able to determine the age of rock layers is important in constructing a history of how Earth has changed through time.

The Principle of Superposition

It's a hot summer day in July, and you're getting ready to meet your friends at the park. You put on your helmet and pads and grab your skateboard. But, the bearings in one of the wheels are worn, and the wheel isn't spinning freely. You remember reading an article in a skateboarding magazine about how to replace wheels, and you decide to look it up. In your room is a stack of magazines from the past year, as seen in **Figure 11-11.** You know that the article came out in the January edition, so it must be near the bottom of the pile. As you dig downward, you find the magazine from March, then February. You know that January must be next.

How did you know that the January issue of the magazine would be on the bottom? To find the older issue under newer ones, you used the principle of superposition.

Youngest Rocks on Top

The **principle of superposition** states that for undisturbed layers of rock, the oldest rocks are on the bottom and the rocks become younger and younger toward the top. Why is this the case? Is it always true?

As you know, sediments are often deposited in horizontal beds, forming layers of sedimentary rock. The first layer to form is usually on the bottom. Each additional layer forms on top of the previous one. Unless forces such as those made

Figure 11-11 This pile of magazines illustrates the principle of superposition. **Where would you look to find the oldest magazine? The youngest?**

The following **Teacher Classroom Resources** can be used with Section 11-2:

 **Reproducible Masters**

Activity Worksheets, pp. 59–60 L2

Enrichment, p. 29 L3

Laboratory Manual, pp. 65–66 L2

Reinforcement, p. 29 L2

Study Guide p. 43

 **Transparencies**

Teaching Transparency 22 L2

Science Integration Transparency 11 L2

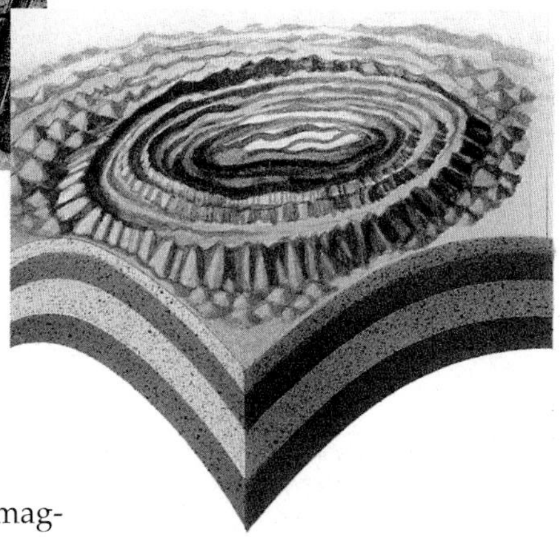

Figure 11-12 This illustration and photograph show a large-scale dome in sedimentary rocks with exposed rock layers in Wyoming. The oldest layers are folded up and exposed in the center. **Does the principle of superposition still apply here?**

by tectonic activity turn the layers upside down, the oldest rocks are found at the bottom. When layers have been turned upside down, geologists use other clues in the rock layers to tell their original positions.

Relative Dating

Suppose you now want to look for another issue of a magazine. You're not sure exactly how old it is—all you know is that it arrived after the January issue. You can find it in the stack by using relative dating.

Relative dating is used in geology to determine the order of events and the relative age of rocks by examining the position of rocks in a sequence. For example, if layers of sedimentary rock are offset by a fault, you know that the layers had to be there first before a fault could cut through them. The relative age of the rocks is older than the relative age of the fault. So, using the magazine example, how do you find the issue by relative dating?

Relative dating doesn't tell you anything about the exact age of rock layers. You don't know if a layer is 100 million or 10 000 years old—only that it's younger than the layers below it and older than the fault cutting through it.

Other Clues Help

Relative dating works well if rocks haven't been folded or overturned by tectonic processes. For example, look at **Figure 11-12.** Which layer is the oldest? In cases where rock layers have been disturbed, you may have to look for fossils and other clues to date the rocks. If you find a fossil in the top layer that's older than a fossil in a lower layer, you can hypothesize that layers have been turned upside down or faulted.

interNET CONNECTION

Visit the Glencoe Science Web Site at **www.glencoe.com/sec/science** to learn more about how the relative dating of rocks is done.

2 Teach

Quick Demo

Visual-Spatial Without explaining your actions to the students, place layer upon layer of five different-colored clays on top of your desk. Use a knife to cut a fault through all the layers. Now place a sixth layer on top of the faulted ones. Ask students to determine the relative ages of the layers and the fault. L2

Content Background

Several principles of geology help in understanding the relative history of Earth's rocks. The principles of superposition and original horizontality state that sedimentary rock layers are usually deposited in flat-lying, horizontal layers. The principle of cross-cutting relationships states that a rock layer or geologic feature that cuts across another layer or feature must be younger than the feature across which it cuts.

interNET CONNECTION

Internet Addresses

____

____

____

____

For Internet tips, see Glencoe's **Using the Internet in the Science Classroom.**

Inclusion Strategies

Visually Impaired Invite a geologist from your area to visit the class. Ask him or her to discuss how rock layers are oriented in your area. To help your visually impaired students, have the visitor orient a three-dimensional model in the same way so that students can feel how the layers are arranged.

Caption Answers

Figure 11-11 *You would look at the bottom; at the top.*

Figure 11-12 *Yes, they're bent but not overturned.*

Quick Demo

Use a set of books from an encyclopedia to demonstrate unconformities. Construct an angular unconformity by placing volumes 1, 2, 3, and 4 in numerical order, with volume 1 on the bottom. Tilt the books at an angle and then place volumes 7 and 8 horizontally on top of the tilted books. Demonstrate a disconformity by stacking volumes 1, 2, 3, and 4 in numerical order, with volume 1 on the bottom. Add volumes 7, 8, and 9 to the stack. Explain that the missing volumes in each case and the tilted beds in the first case create the unconformity.

VISUAL Learning

Figure 11-13 Have students examine the four parts of this figure. Ask the following question: **Why, if water is an agent of erosion, is the unconformity not recognized until part D?** *A gap in time cannot be recognized until a layer of sediment is deposited over the eroded surface marking the end of the erosional episode.*

Another clue you can use is the way the fossils are arranged in the layers. Most attached marine organisms grow upward, toward the sunlight. If you find a limestone formation with corals that are upright, you can infer that the rocks have not been tilted or overturned. Even something as simple as a hole in the rock can help. Sediments are always deposited horizontally at the bottom of a hole. If a hole looks like it is half filled from the top, the sample is upside down.

VISUALIZING Unconformity Formation

Figure 11-13 An angular unconformity results when horizontal layers overlie tilted layers.

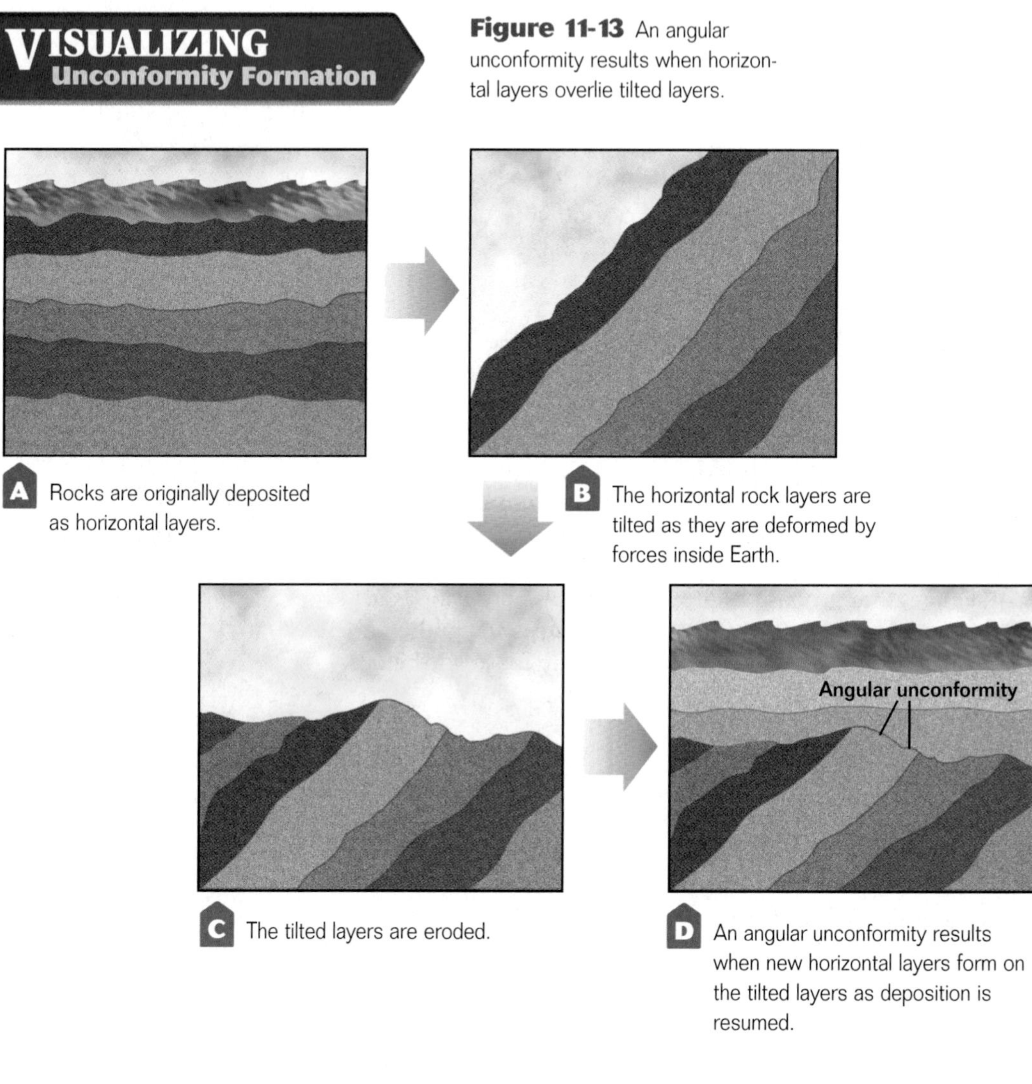

A Rocks are originally deposited as horizontal layers.

B The horizontal rock layers are tilted as they are deformed by forces inside Earth.

C The tilted layers are eroded.

D An angular unconformity results when new horizontal layers form on the tilted layers as deposition is resumed.

Integrating the Sciences

Physics Angular unconformities form when rock layers are uplifted, tilted, and eroded. Ask students what forces are necessary to produce angular unconformities. *Forces involved in the process of plate tectonics cause rock layers to be deformed. These forces include shear, compression, and tension. Forces caused by the agents of erosion wear away exposed rock surfaces.* L3

Unconformities

As you have seen, a layer of rock is a record of past events. But, most rock records are not complete—layers are missing. These gaps in rock layers are called **unconformities** (un kun FOR mihteez).

Unconformities develop when agents of erosion remove existing rock layers. They also form when a period of time passes without any new deposition occurring to form new layers of rock. ✔

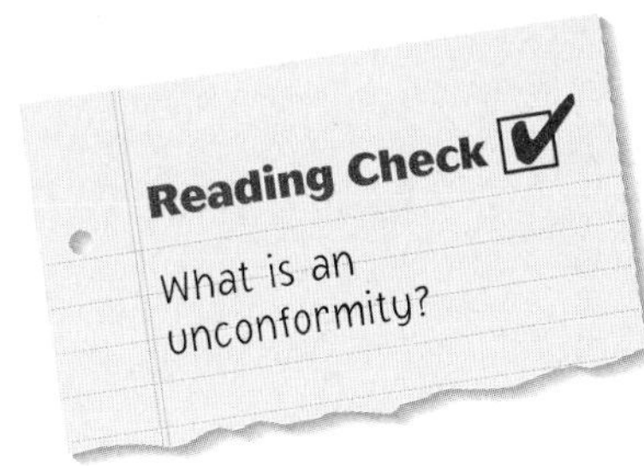

Angular Unconformities

Figure 11-13 illustrates one way an unconformity can form. Horizontal layers of sedimentary rock are tilted and uplifted, so that erosion and weathering wear them down. Eventually, younger sediment layers are deposited horizontally on top of the eroded and tilted layers. Such an unconformity is called an angular unconformity.

Disconformity

Suppose you're looking at a sequence of sedimentary rocks. They look complete, but layers are missing. If you look closely, you may find an old erosional surface. This records a time when the rocks were exposed and eroded. Later, younger rocks formed above the erosional surface when sediment deposition began again. Even though all the layers are horizontal, a gap still exists in the record. This type of unconformity, called a disconformity, is shown in **Figure 11-14.**

Figure 11-14 The buried erosional surface in the far right illustration is a disconformity. **How could you determine how much time and rock is missing?**

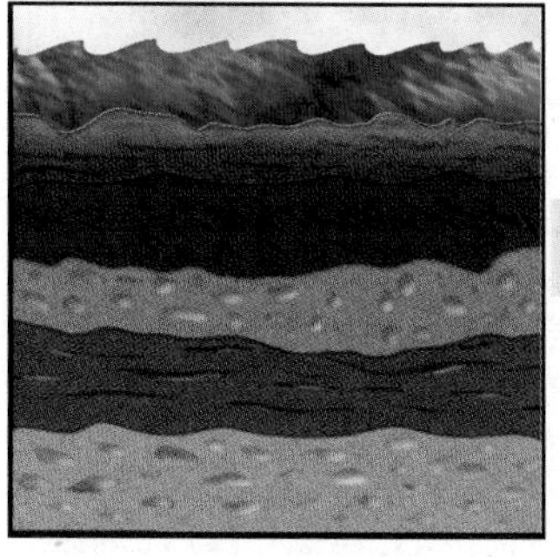

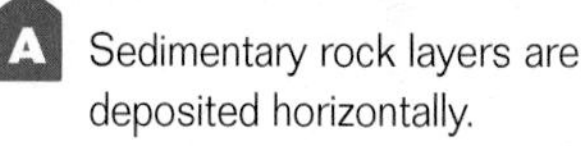

A Sedimentary rock layers are deposited horizontally.

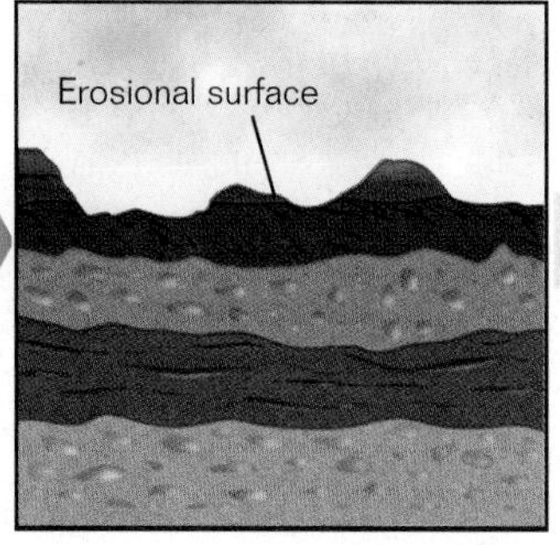

B The layers are uplifted, exposed, and eroded.

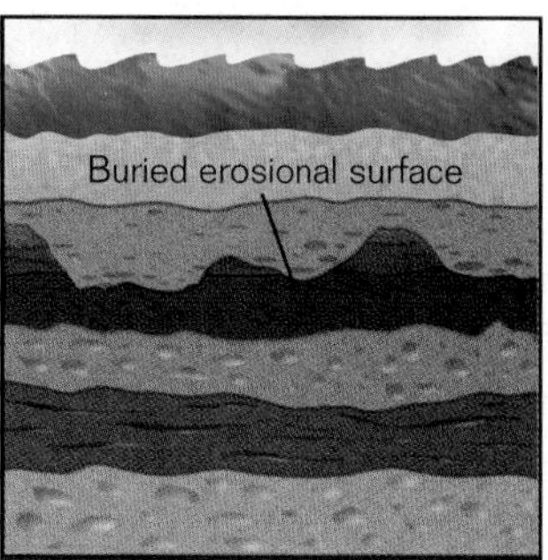

C When deposition resumes, younger horizontal sediments are deposited on the buried erosional surface.

Teacher FYI

When one type of rock is included in another, the included rock is called an inclusion. The rock with inclusions is younger than the rock from which the inclusions came. For example, if granite inclusions are found within a sedimentary rock layer, the sedimentary rock layer formed after the granite from which the inclusions came.

Answer to Reading Check ✔

a gap in the rock record representing a period of erosion or nondeposition

Discussion

Initiate a discussion of unconformities with students by asking the following questions. **What does an unconformity tell you about the geology of an area?** *At some time in the past, erosion removed some rock and/or time passed without any rock formation.* **How does an angular unconformity form?** *Horizontal rock layers are uplifted, tilted, or eroded. Horizontal layers of sediment are deposited on top of this new surface. The surface between these rocks and younger horizontal rocks is an angular unconformity.* **How might a disconformity form?** *Horizontal sedimentary rock layers are uplifted and eroded. Younger sedimentary rocks are deposited on this erosional surface to form a disconformity.*

Caption Answer

Figure 11-14 *Find a section that is complete and contains the same section of rock, and correlate rock units and/or fossils.*

Inclusion Strategies

Visually Impaired In order to help students participate in the discussion of unconformities, mold models of each type of unconformity from clay. Allow students to handle the unconformity models and to remove each of the layers step by step. Help visually impaired students produce mental models of the processes involved in the formation of each type of unconformity. L2

Problem Solving

When geologists correlate a rock layer from one location to the same rock layer at another location, they try to explain any differences noted in the thickness and other characteristics of the rock layers. Geologists use fossil content, orientation of the rock unit, the type of rock in each layer, and other information when trying to determine how one location might correlate with another.

At least three unconformities occur in the Westwater column; at least two are shown in the Green River column. Unconformities exist between sandstone (16) and underlying rock (sandstone (15) or shale (14)), between sandstone (8) and shale (5), and between shale (3) or shale (2) and schist or gneiss (1).

Think Critically

Deposition of rocks in the Green River area was interrupted by periods of erosion and/or nondeposition, as shown by the unconformities. Several hypotheses can explain why rocks are missing from the Westwater column. The rocks could have been deposited and later eroded. Or, they may never have been deposited in the area.

GLENCOE TECHNOLOGY

Videodisc

The Infinite Voyage: The Dawn of Humankind

Chapter 6 *Human Origins: Unexpected Finds in South Africa* 5:00

Refer to the Teacher Guide for bar codes and teaching strategies.

Nonconformity

Another type of unconformity, called a nonconformity, occurs when metamorphic or igneous rocks are uplifted and eroded. Sedimentary rocks are then deposited on top of this erosional surface. The surface between the two rock types is a nonconformity.

Correlating Rock Layers

Suppose you're studying a layer of sandstone in Bryce Canyon in Utah. Later, when you visit Canyonlands National Park, you notice that a layer of sandstone there looks just like the sandstone in Bryce Canyon, 250 km away. Above the sandstone in Canyonlands is a layer of limestone and then another sandstone layer. You return to Bryce Canyon and find the same sequence—sandstone, limestone, and sandstone. What do you infer? It's likely that you're actually looking at the same layer of rocks in two different locations. These rocks are parts of huge deposits that covered this whole area of the western United States, as seen in **Figure 11-15.** The sandstone and limestone you found at the two parks are the exposed surfaces of the same rock layers.

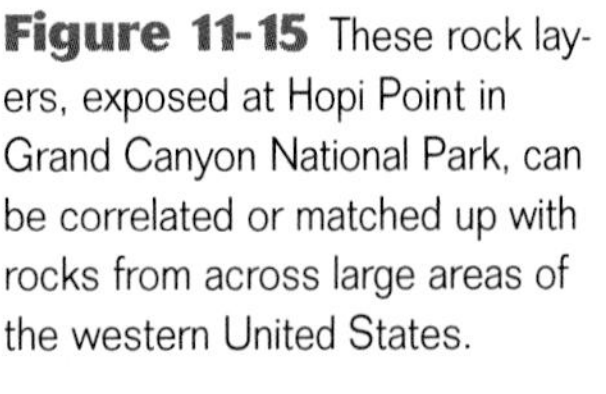

Figure 11-15 These rock layers, exposed at Hopi Point in Grand Canyon National Park, can be correlated or matched up with rocks from across large areas of the western United States.

Across the Curriculum

Geography Obtain state geologic maps of Colorado, Utah, Arizona, and New Mexico. Have students examine the maps and note that when they are arranged geographically, many of the rock units extend across state boundaries. Have students research the geologic history of this area during the Mesozoic and Cenozoic eras. L3

Evidence Used for Correlation

Geologists match up, or correlate, layers of rocks over great distances, as seen in **Figure 11-16.** It's not always easy to say that a rock layer exposed in one area is the same as a rock layer exposed in another area. Sometimes it's possible to walk along the layer for kilometers and prove that it's a continuous layer. In other cases, such as at Canyonlands and Bryce Canyon, the rock layers are exposed only where rivers have cut through overlying layers of rock and sediment. How can you prove that the limestone sandwiched between the two layers of sandstone in Canyonlands is the same limestone as at Bryce Canyon? One way is to use fossil evidence. If the same types of fossils are found in both outcrops of limestone, it's likely that the limestone at each place is the same age, and therefore, one continuous deposit. ✓

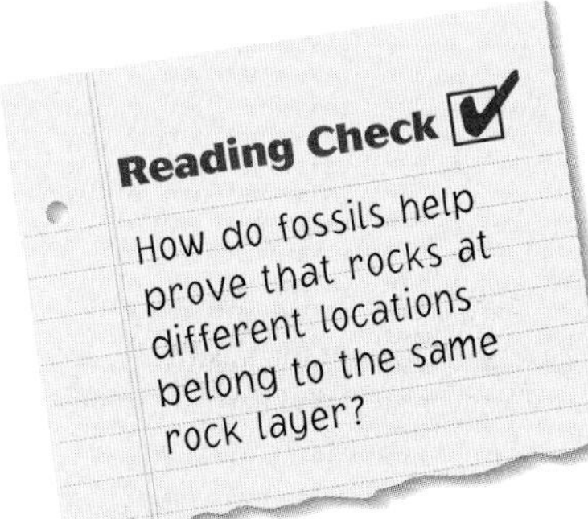

Reading Check
How do fossils help prove that rocks at different locations belong to the same rock layer?

Problem Solving

Interpreting Scientific Illustrations

When geologists study the rock outcrops in an area, they obtain rock samples from, measure the thickness of, and record a description of each rock layer. For example, one report might describe a 1-m-thick, massive sandstone of medium-brown color.

Once the descriptions are recorded for each layer of rock that is observed in one location, geologists draw a column that shows each of the rock layers. They then try to correlate or match up a rock column from one location to rock columns from other locations. A geologist can tell much about the geologic history of an area from a study of rock column correlations.

The rock column shown on the left is from Green River, Utah. The rock column on the right is from Westwater, Colorado. Using the rock columns, reconstruct the geologic history of the area. Correlate similar rock layers between the two locations. An example of how to correlate the rock columns is shown for rock layer 1. How many unconformities, and what types, can you recognize in each column?

Think Critically: Explain the geologic history of the Green River area in terms of erosion and deposition. Why are some layers missing from the Westwater column?

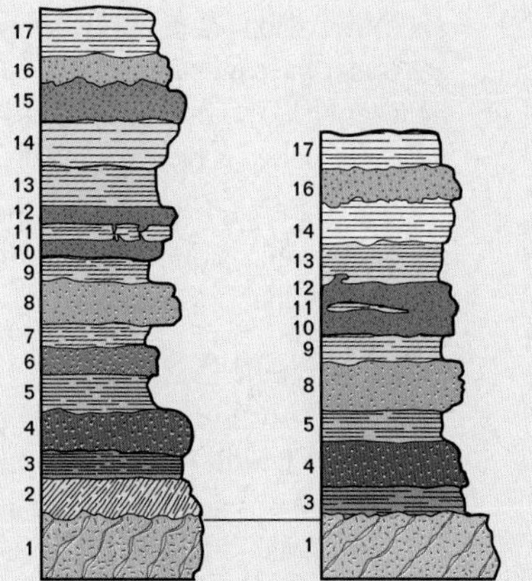

Answer to Reading Check ✓

If the fossils are the same type or can be shown to be the same age, they prove that the rocks are part of the same layer.

Teacher FYI

The basic unit of layered rocks is the formation. Named for convenience, a formation only has to be a mappable unit of rock. A formation is named for basic characteristics such as rock type, color and fossil content, all of which are readily observed under normal working conditions. A group consists of more than one formation, stacked on top of each other. A member is a subdivision of a formation. It is designated by a specific characteristic within it. Such characteristics might be abundance of fossils or an abundance of a particular mineral.

3 Assess

Check for Understanding Activity

Visual-Spatial Obtain a geologic map and correlation chart for an area that includes your state. Invite students to examine the charts and explain how the rock layers are correlated.

Integrating the Sciences

Chemistry Ask students why so few fossils are found in igneous and metamorphic rocks. *Heat, changes of state, and the forces involved with increased pressure would destroy fossils as the rock changes by metamorphism. Melting of rock material would also melt any organic material that existed before the igneous rocks began forming.*

Reteach

Use an overhead projector and a transparency to reconstruct the geologic columns in the Problem Solving activity. Start at the bottom of each column and explain the geologic processes involved as you move upward through the rock layers. L2 ELL

Extension

For students who have mastered this section, use the **Reinforcement** and **Enrichment** masters.

11-2 RELATIVE AGES OF ROCKS 317

Caption Answer

Figure 11-16 *Navajo SS, Entrada SS*

4 CLOSE

Proficiency Prep

1. **What is the principle of superposition?** *In an undisturbed rock sequence, the oldest rocks are at the bottom of the sequence.*
2. **What technique determines the ages of rocks as compared with one another?** *relative dating*

Section Assessment

1. Older papers would be closer to the bottom of the locker according to the principle of superposition.
2. An angular unconformity is a physical boundary in which tilted rocks are overlain by horizontal rocks. In a disconformity, all the rocks are relatively horizontal.
3. The shale is the oldest layer. It contains the oldest fossils of the three layers.
4. **Think Critically** The igneous intrusion is younger than the sedimentary rocks being domed upward. Sedimentary layers are almost always deposited horizontally. The layers would not be deposited in a domed, or arched, formation.

Assessment

Performance Assess students' abilities to interpret data by illustrating this Skill Builder on the chalkboard and having them interpret relative ages. Assume the fossils have not been moved. Use **Performance Assessment in the Science Classroom,** p. 55.

Are there other ways to correlate layers of rock? Sometimes relative dating isn't enough, and other dating methods must be used. In the next section, you'll see how the actual age of rocks can be determined and how geologists have used this information to determine the age of Earth.

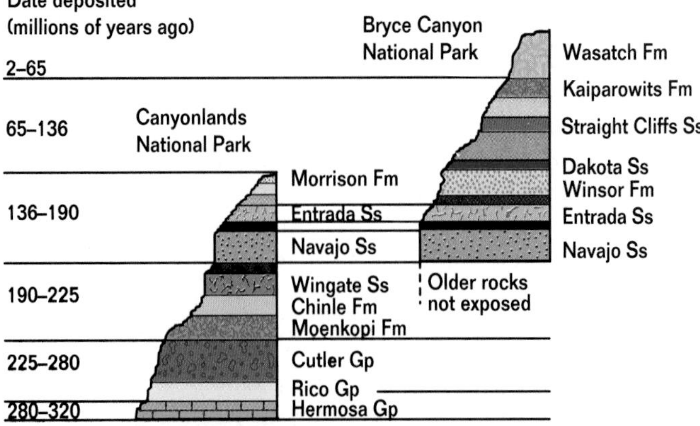

Figure 11-16 The many rock layers, or formations, in Canyonlands and Bryce Canyon have been dated and named. Some formations have been correlated between the two canyons. (NOTE: Fm = formation, Ss = sandstone, Gp = group.) **Which layers are present at both canyons?**

Section Assessment

1. Suppose you haven't cleaned out your locker all year. Where would you expect to find papers from the beginning of the year? What principle in geology would you use to find these old papers?
2. Why is it more difficult to recognize a disconformity than an angular unconformity?
3. A geologist finds a series of rocks. The sandstone contains a fossil that is 400 million years old. The shale contains fossils that are between 500 million and 550 million years old. The limestone, which lies under the sandstone, contains fossils that are between 400 million and 500 million years old. Which rock bed is oldest? Explain.
4. **Think Critically:** What are the relative ages of an igneous intrusion and overlying sedimentary rock layers that dome upward? Explain.
5. **Skill Builder**
   Observing and Inferring Do the **Chapter 11 Skill Activity** on page 752 to find out how fossils are used to interpret environments.

Using Computers

Spreadsheet Use the information about unconformities in Section 11-2 to prepare an electronic spreadsheet listing the types of unconformities, their differences, and their similarities. Use graphics software to generate illustrations of each type of unconformity. If you need help, refer to page 738.

Using Computers

Types of Unconformities	Similarities	Differences
Angular Unconformity	All represent gaps in the rock record.	horizontal layers over tilted layers
Disconformity	All indicate times of erosion and/or no deposition.	horizontal layers over older horizontal layers with layers missing and erosional surface visible
Nonconformity	sedimentary rock layers over eroded metamorphic or igneous rock layers	

Activity 11•1

Relative Age Dating

Can you tell which of two rock layers is older? You don't need to know the exact ages of the layers to tell. Geologists can learn a lot about rock layers simply by studying their arrangement.

Materials

- Paper
- Pencil

What You'll Investigate

Can the relative ages of rocks be determined by studying the rock layers and structures?

Goals

- **Determine** the relative order of events by interpreting illustrations of rock layers.

Procedure

1. Study **Figures A** and **B**. The legend will help you interpret the figures.
2. Determine the relative ages of the rock layers, unconformities, igneous dikes, and fault in each figure.

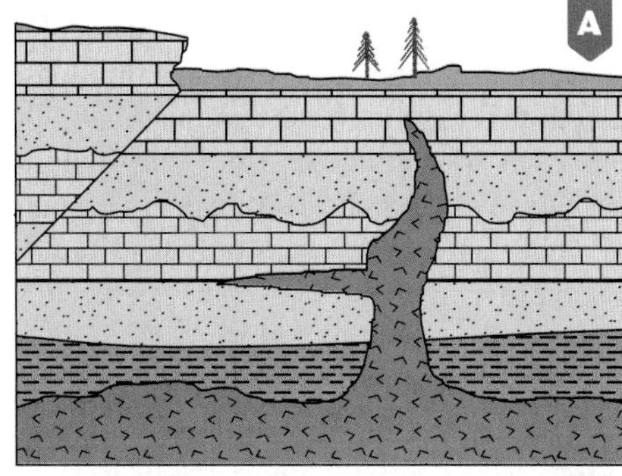

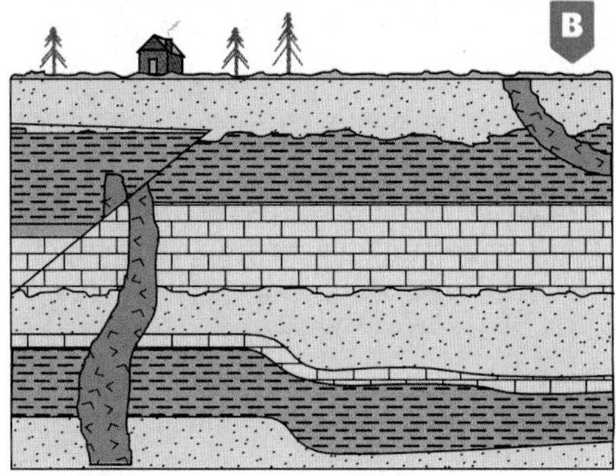

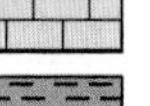

Conclude and Apply

Figure A

1. Were any layers of rock deposited after the igneous dike formed? Explain.
2. What type of unconformity is shown? Is it possible that there were originally more layers of rock than are shown here? Explain.
3. What type of fault is shown?
4. Explain how to determine whether the igneous dike formed before or after the fault occurred?

Figure B

5. What type of fault is shown?
6. Is the igneous dike on the left older or younger than the unconformity near the top? Explain.
7. Are the two igneous dikes shown the same age? How do you know?
8. Which two layers of rock may have been much thicker at one time than they are now?

Interpreting Scientific Illustrations

1. Make a sketch of Figure A. On it, **identify** the relative age of each rock layer, igneous dike, fault, and unconformity. For example, the shale layer is the oldest, so mark it with a *1.* Mark the next-oldest feature with a *2,* and so on.
2. Repeat the procedure in question 1 for Figure B.

Activity 11•1

Purpose

Logical-Mathematical Students will determine the relative order of events by interpreting geologic cross sections.
L2 ELL COOP LEARN P

Process Skills

interpreting data, formulating models, recognizing and using spatial relationships, sequencing, interpreting scientific illustrations

Time

40 to 45 minutes

Teaching Strategies

Have each group examine the two cross sections and make inferences based on the clues provided and their knowledge of superposition, unconformities, faulting, and igneous intrusions.

Answers to Questions

1. No, because the dike intrudes every layer, it must be the youngest feature.
2. A disconformity; yes, other rock could have existed and been eroded.
3. a reverse fault
4. The fault and the igneous dike cut across the youngest limestone but do not cut across each other. It is uncertain which of the two is younger.
5. a normal fault
6. the dike is offset by the fault but the unconformity is not, the dike is older.
7. No, the dike on the right intrudes the sandstone and the dike that has been offset by the fault is older than the sandstone.
8. The sandstone and shale exhibit erosional disconformities at their upper surfaces.

Interpreting Scientific Illustrations

1. (1) shale, (2) sandstone, (3) limestone, (4) disconformity, (5) sandstone, (6) limestone, (7) fault, (8) igneous intrusion; note that another possible solution is (7) igneous intrusion, (8) fault
2. (1) sandstone, (2) shale, (3) limestone, (4) sandstone, (5) disconformity, (6) limestone, (7) shale, (8) igneous intrusion (left), (9) fault, (10) disconformity, (11) sandstone, (12) igneous intrusion (right)

Assessment

Performance Based on what was learned about relative ages of rock layers, have students draw a block diagram similar to those in Activity 11-1. Tell them to include all four rock types. Have students exchange and interpret their diagrams. Use **Performance Assessment in the Science Classroom,** p. 55.

Content Background

- Except for those caused by human activities, extinctions occur over long periods of time relative to the range of a species.
- The layer of rock that marked the boundary between the Cretaceous and Paleocene periods is known as the K-P boundary. It marked a period in Earth's history about 66 million years ago when almost half of all known species suddenly disappeared, including dinosaurs.
- Scientists have found large quantities of sulfur around the Yucatan Peninsula crater. When the asteroid hit, it would have thrown this sulfur into the air, forming the cloud of darkness.

Teaching Strategies

- Have student groups research separate theories of extinction. Are these theories valid? Hold a debate and discuss the theories.
- Make a model meteorite bombing range by using marbles of different sizes and a large baking dish or box filled with about an inch of flour. Try dropping the marbles from different angles and at different speeds and see what type of patterns develop.
- Have students research other impact sites such as the Hoba West of South Africa, Lake Bosumtwi in Ghana, and Lake Elgygytgyn in northeast Siberia.

NATIONAL GEOGRAPHIC History of Science

Extinction of Dinosaurs

What killed the dinosaurs?

The fossil record indicates that dinosaurs appeared between 230 and 220 million years ago. As time passed, dinosaurs multiplied, diversified, and came to inhabit every continent on Earth. Then quite abruptly, in geologic terms, the dinosaurs disappeared. This happened about 66 million years ago. Left behind were only fossilized tracks, teeth, and bones (right) as proof of their existence. What caused this dramatic extinction? No one really knows yet, but scientists have proposed several hypotheses to explain the disappearance of the dinosaurs.

One early hypothesis suggested that egg-eating mammals interfered with dinosaur reproduction, so that the dinosaurs eventually died out. However, this hypothesis did not explain why many other animals also became extinct when dinosaurs did.

In the early 1980s, several scientists proposed that a large asteroid collided with Earth some 66 million years ago. According to this hypothesis, the asteroid vaporized rocks and seawater on impact and sent clouds of dust and acidic gases into the atmosphere. The dust clouds would have blocked out so much sunlight that plants were unable to carry out photosynthesis. As vegetation withered, plant-eating dinosaurs died, leaving their meat-eating relatives to starve as well. Other researchers suggest that the asteroid impact led to widespread wildfires, acid rain, or global warming that caused the dinosaur extinction.

Other Hypotheses

Another hypothesis proposes that intense volcanic activity spewed enormous quantities of dust and gases into the ancient atmosphere and led to global cooling. Animals unable to adapt died out, including the dinosaurs. Any hypothesis regarding dinosaur extinction must take into account that many other species perished when the dinosaurs did, and yet many mammals survived. Scientists continue to search for evidence that will determine what event, or combination of events, ended the age of dinosaurs.

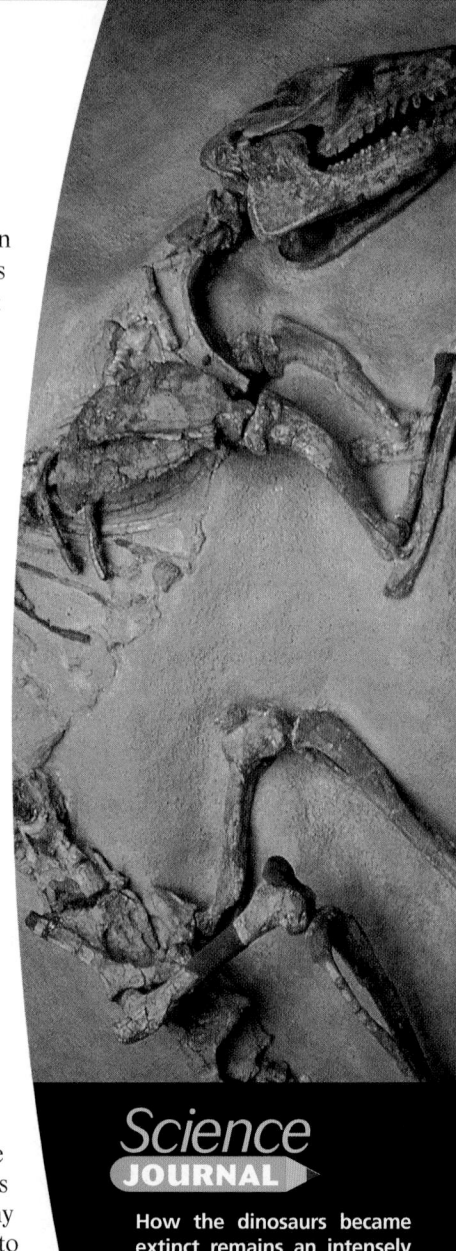

Science JOURNAL

How the dinosaurs became extinct remains an intensely debated topic. In your Science Journal, write an essay that discusses how one of the hypotheses could be supported and why.

Students may choose any theory they wish. They should be able to back up their choice. Some students may also combine theories into one.

For Additional Information

- Gore, R. 1989. Extinctions. National Geographic, pp. 662–699.
- Gore, R. 1993. Dinosaurs. National Geographic, pp. 2–53.
- Hecht, J. 1993. Vanishing Life: The Mystery of Mass Extinction. New York. Charles Scribner's Sons.
- Univerisity of California Museum of Paleontology.

Absolute Ages of Rocks

Absolute Dating

Remember the stack of magazines? As you continue to shuffle through them, looking for articles about wheels and bearings, you decide you need to restack them into a neat pile. By now, they're a mess and no longer in the order of their relative ages, as shown in **Figure 11-17.** How can you stack them so the oldest are on the bottom and the newest on top? Fortunately, magazines have their dates printed on their covers. Thus, stacking magazines in order is a simple process. Unfortunately for geologists, rocks don't have their ages stamped on them. Or do they?

Absolute dating is a method used to determine the age, in years, of a rock or other object. Absolute dating is a process that uses the properties of atoms in rocks and other objects to find their ages.

What You'll Learn

- How absolute dating differs from relative dating
- How the half-lives of isotopes are used to determine a rock's age

Vocabulary
absolute dating
radioactive decay
half-life
radiometric dating
uniformitarianism

Why It's Important

- Determining the absolute age of rocks and minerals allows scientists to calculate the exact age of Earth.

Radioactive Decay

An element can have atoms with different numbers of neutrons in their nuclei. These are called isotopes. Some of these isotopes undergo a process called **radioactive decay.** When an atom of some isotopes decays, one of its neutrons breaks down into a proton and an electron. The electron leaves the atom as a beta particle. The nucleus loses a neutron but gains a proton. Other isotopes give off two protons and two neutrons in the form of an alpha particle, as seen in **Figure 11-18.** As you know, when the number of protons in an atom is changed, as it is in radioactive decay, a new element is formed. For example, when an atom of the radioactive isotope uranium-238 decays, it eventually forms an atom of lead-206. Lead-206 isn't radioactive, so it does not decay any further.

PHYSICS INTEGRATION

Figure 11-17 The magazines that have been shuffled through no longer illustrate the principle of superposition.

Prepare

Refer to **Absolute Dating, Dealing with Errors,** and **Radiocarbon Dating** on p. 302F.

Preplanning

Refer to the **Chapter Organizer** on pages 302A–B.

1 Motivate

Bellringer

Before presenting the lesson, display **Section Focus Transparency 30** on the overhead projector. Use the accompanying **Focus Activity** worksheet. L2 ELL

11 SECTION FOCUS TRANSPARENCY

Section 4.1

ALL THAT GLITTERS. . .

If you were prospecting for gold and came upon this rock, what would you think? Most people would be delighted, thinking they had found gold. But the rock is really iron sulfide, or pyrite, otherwise known as fool's gold.

1. List the properties of pyrite that you can determine from the picture. For example, is it a solid, liquid, or gas? What color is it? Does it have crystals?
2. In what ways is pyrite similar to gold? Can you think of ways it might be different?

11

Resource Manager

The following **Teacher Classroom Resources** can be used with Section 11-3:

Reproducible Masters

Activity Worksheets, pp. 61–62, 64 L2
Enrichment, p. 30 L3
Reinforcement, p. 30 L2
Study Guide, p. 44 L1 ELL

Tying to Previous Knowledge

Have students recall that atoms of the same element with different numbers of neutrons are called isotopes. Radioactive isotopes are used in absolute dating.

Caption Answer

Figure 11-18 *Yes, heat is released along with alpha and beta particles during this process.*

Purpose

Logical-Mathematical Students will determine relative and absolute dates of events in Earth's history. L2 P

Materials

adding machine tape, meterstick, pencil

Teaching Strategies

- Suggest a scale of 1 mm for each 1 million years. This will require a 4.6-m (or longer) piece of adding machine tape.
- If a different scale is used, have students calculate the length of tape needed before starting.

Analysis

1.

Event	Years Before Present
Earth forms	4.6 B
oldest known fossils	3.5 B
1st many-celled organisms	1.25 B
1st many-celled animals	600 M
1st plants on land	439 M
1st amphibians	370 M
1st mammals	225 M
dinosaurs extinct	66 M
1st human ancestors	4.4 M

2. opportunity for self-assessment
3. Presence of humans amounts to about 1 percent of Earth's age.

Performance To further assess students' understanding of relative and absolute dating, have them determine the relative and absolute ages of students in the classroom. Use **Performance Assessment in the Science Classroom,** p. 27.

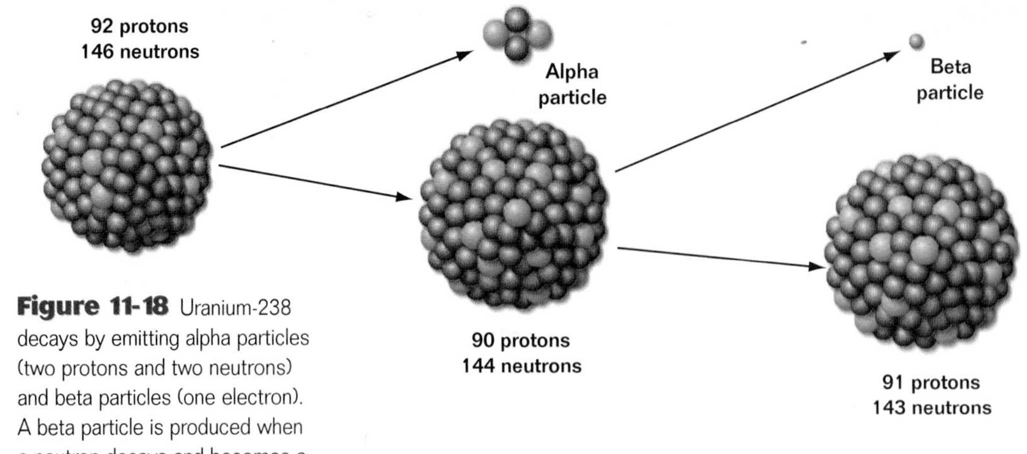

Figure 11-18 Uranium-238 decays by emitting alpha particles (two protons and two neutrons) and beta particles (one electron). A beta particle is produced when a neutron decays and becomes a proton. **Is any energy released during this process? If so, what?**

Sequencing Earth's History

Procedure

1. Sequence these events in Earth's history in relative order: Earth forms, first many-celled organisms, first land plants, first mammals, dinosaurs become extinct, first amphibians, first human ancestors, oldest known fossils, first many-celled animals.
2. Make a time line using these dates: 4.6 billion years, 3.5 billion years, 1.25 billion years, 600 million years, 439 million years, 408 million years, 225 million years, 66 million years, and 4.4 million years ago.
3. Match each event with the absolute date on your time line.

Analysis

1. Check your time line with your teacher.
2. Did you correctly list the events in relative order?
3. How does the age of Earth compare with the presence of humans on the time line?

In the case of uranium decaying to lead, uranium-238 is known as the parent material and lead-206 as the daughter product. Another example of a parent material is carbon-14, which decays to its daughter, nitrogen-14. Each radioactive parent material has a certain rate at which it decays to its daughter product. This rate is known as its half-life.

Half-Life

The **half-life** of an isotope is the time it takes for half of the atoms in an isotope to decay. For example, the half-life of carbon-14 is 5730 years. So it will take 5730 years for half of the carbon-14 atoms in an object to decay to nitrogen-14.

You might guess that in another 5730 years, all of the remaining carbon-14 atoms will have decayed to nitrogen-14. However, this is not the case. Only half of the atoms of carbon-14 remaining after the first 5730 years will decay during the second 5730 years. So, after two half-lives, one-fourth of the original carbon-14 atoms still remain. Half of the remaining carbon-14 will decay during another 5730 years. After many half-lives, such a small amount of the parent material remains that it may not be measurable.

322 CHAPTER 11 CLUES TO EARTH'S PAST

Radiometric Dating

To a geologist, the decay of radioactive isotopes is like a clock ticking away. The clock is keeping track of time that's passed since rocks have formed. As time passes, the amount of parent material in a rock decreases as the amount of daughter product increases, as seen in **Figure 11-19.** By measuring the amounts of parent and daughter materials in a rock and by knowing the half-life of the parent, a geologist can calculate the absolute age of the rock. This process is called **radiometric dating.**

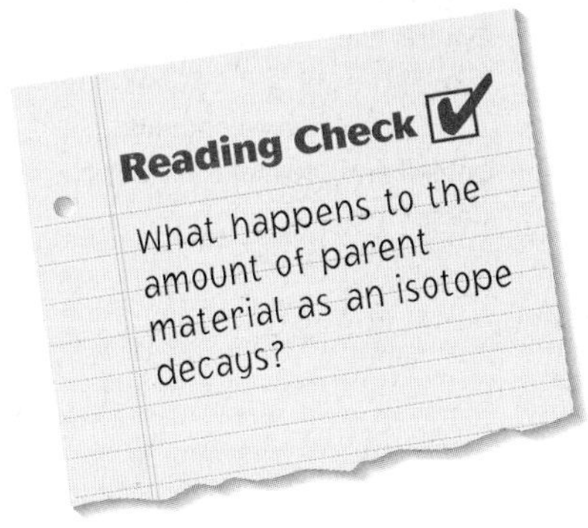

A scientist must decide which parent and daughter materials to measure when dating a rock or fossil. If the object to be dated is very old, then an isotope with a long half-life must be used. For example, if a fossil is 1 billion years old, there would be no measurable amount of carbon-14 left. However, the half-life of uranium-238 is 4.5 billion years. Enough of the parent material would still be present, as well as enough daughter material, to measure the rock or fossil's age.

Radiocarbon Dating

Carbon-14 is useful for dating fossils, bones, and wood up to 75 000 years old. Organisms take in carbon from the environment to build tissues in their bodies. The amount remains constant throughout their lives. After the organism dies, the carbon-14 slowly decays and escapes as nitrogen-14 gas. The amount of carbon-14 remaining can be measured to determine the age of the fossil or when humans used a fire site, as in **Figure 11-20.**

Figure 11-19 After each half-life, one-half the amount of parent material remains. Eventually, such a small amount of the parent material is left that it may not be measurable. **How much parent material is left after a fifth half-life?**

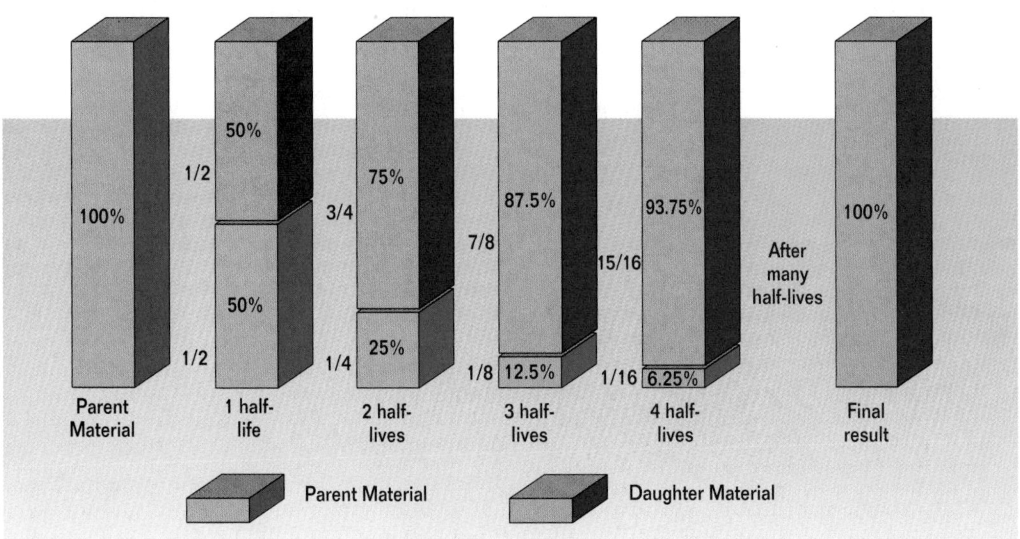

Activity

Ask students to imagine that a sheet of paper represents the amount of parent radioactive isotope in a rock. The half-life of the parent isotope is 20 s. After 20 s, ask students to tear the sheet of paper in half and to set one half aside. The half set aside represents the daughter isotope. Have students repeat the process every 20 s with the paper that remains. Ask students to describe what has happened to the amount of parent isotope. L2 ELL

The amount of parent isotope decreases during decay.

Caption Answer

Figure 11-19 *1/32 or 3.125%*

Content Background

The half-life of carbon-14 is about 5730 years. This value is rather short compared to the half-lives of other isotopes. The half-life of uranium-238 in the uranium-238 to lead-206 decay is 4.5 billion years (nearly the age of Earth). By contrast, the half-life of uranium-235 in the uranium-235 to lead-207 decay is 713 million years.

Integrating the Sciences

Chemistry Integrate chemistry into this lesson by asking the following questions and performing the activity on this page.

Why is radiometric dating often more useful to geologists than relative dating? *It enables geologists to determine the exact ages of rocks. Relative dating produces a sequence of geologic events based on the relationships among the events.*

How do geologists use radioactive decay to determine the absolute age of a rock? *The rate of decay, called the half-life, is the time it takes for half of the parent isotope to decay into the daughter isotope. The rate of decay together with the amounts of parent and daughter isotopes remaining in a rock are used to determine its absolute age.*

11-3 Absolute Ages of Rocks 323

Answer to Text Question

What is another process on Earth that illustrates uniformitarianism? *glaciers and ice, wave action, river erosion, wind erosion, sediment transport*

Caption Answer

Figure 11-20 *Forest fires or any fire in which organic remains containing carbon are burned could leave charcoal behind and provide radiocarbon dates.*

3 Assess

Check for Understanding

Using Science Words

Have students explain the two different usages in this chapter of the word *decay*. In Section 11-1, decay describes what happens to organic material when exposed to microorganisms and bacteria. In Section 11-3, decay describes the breakdown of radioactive isotopes.

Reteach

Have students determine the age of an object containing 1/32 of the radium-206 originally in the object. The half-life of radium-206 is 1600 years. *After five half-lives (8000 years), 1/32 of the original isotope remains.* L2 ELL

Figure 11-20 Human activity, like this campfire, also can be dated with carbon-14. **What other events could leave charcoal behind and provide radiocarbon dates?**

Rocks that can be radiometrically dated are mostly igneous although some metamorphic rocks can be used too. Sedimentary rocks cannot be dated by this method because only the absolute age of the sediment grains in the rock can be determined, not the rock itself. Radiometric dating has been used to date the oldest rocks found on Earth. These rocks are 3.96 billion years old. In western Australia sandstones, zircon mineral grains have been dated to about 4.1 to 4.3 billion years. Scientists have estimated the age of Earth at 4.6 billion years.

Source for Error

How sure can scientists be that the dates they calculate are accurate? First, they must make sure that no parent material is added to the rock after decay has begun and no daughter product is removed after forming. This can be difficult when elements such as potassium (K) and argon (Ar) are being analyzed, as shown in **Figure 11-21.** Second, care must be taken if the rocks have been metamorphosed. Remember that metamorphism changes minerals. This resets the decay clock.

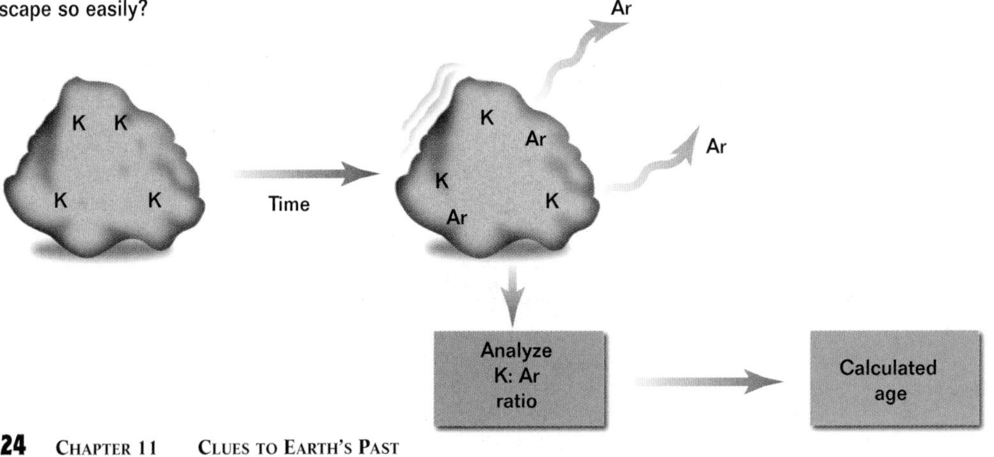

Figure 11-21 Over time, the potassium in the rock decays to argon. The argon escapes, making the ratio of potassium to argon decrease. **Why does Argon (Ar) escape so easily?**

GLENCOE TECHNOLOGY

CD-ROM

Glencoe Science Voyages Interactive CD-ROM

Explorations

Have students do the interactive exploration *How can fossil and rock data determine when an organism lived?*

Extension

For students who have mastered this section, use the **Reinforcement** and **Enrichment** masters.

Caption Answer

Figure 11-21 *Argon is a gas and easily leaves a rock.*

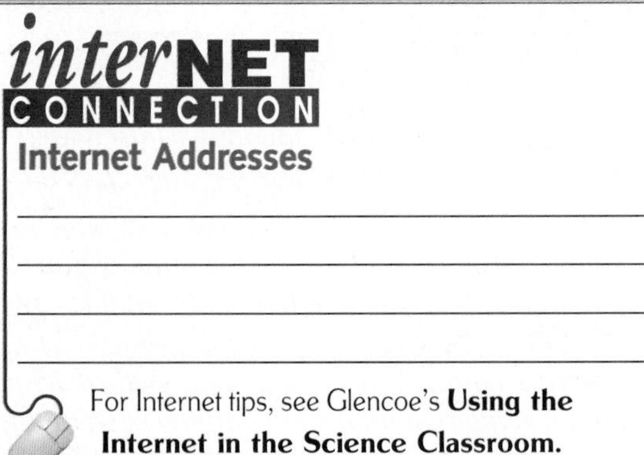

interNET CONNECTION

Internet Addresses

For Internet tips, see Glencoe's **Using the Internet in the Science Classroom.**

What effect would this have on the calculated age? Scientists avoid wrong ages by using more than one radioactive isotope, by running more than one check, and by using fresh, unweathered samples.

Uniformitarianism

Before radiometric dating was known, many people had estimated the age of Earth to be only a few thousand years old. But in the 1700s, Scottish scientist James Hutton estimated that Earth was much older. He used the principle of **uniformitarianism** (yew nih for mih TAHR ee ah nizm). This principle states that Earth processes taking place today are similar to those that took place in the past. Observing that the processes that changed the rocks and land around him were slow, he inferred that these processes had been just as slow throughout Earth's history. Hutton hypothesized that it took much longer than a few thousand years to form the rock layers around him and to erode mountain peaks to hills. John Playfair advanced Hutton's theories, but an English geologist, Sir Charles Lyell, is given the most credit for advancing uniformitarianism. What is another process on Earth that shows uniformitarianism?

Visit the Glencoe Science Web Site at **www.glencoe.com/sec/science** for more information about the ages of rocks.

Section Assessment

1. You discover three undisturbed rock layers. The absolute age of the middle layer is 120 million years. What can you say about the ages of the layers above and below it?
2. How old would a fossil be if it had only one-eighth of its original carbon-14 content remaining?
3. **Think Critically:** Suppose you radiometrically date an igneous dike running through only the bottom two layers in question 1. The dike is cut off by the upper rock layer. The dike is 70 million years old. What can you say about the absolute age of the upper layer?
4. **Skill Builder**
Making and Using Tables Make a table that shows the amounts of parent and daughter materials left of a radioactive element after four half-lives if the original parent material had a mass of 100 g. If you need help, refer to Making and Using Tables in the **Skill Handbook** on page 716.

Research Sir Charles Lyell in a geology book or encyclopedia. In your Science Journal, write a one-page report about his contribution to uniformitarianism.

4 CLOSE

Proficiency Prep

Use this quiz to check students' recall of section content.

1. **Which method of dating determines the age of a rock in years?** *absolute dating*
2. **What is one of the daughter isotopes of uranium-238?** *lead-206*
3. **What is the time it takes for half of a radioactive isotope to decay called?** *half-life*

Section Assessment

1. The top layer is less than 120 million years old; the bottom layer is more than 120 million years old. You can't determine their absolute ages.
2. After three half-lives, 1/8 of the original carbon-14 would remain. Thus, the fossil would be 17 190 years old.
3. **Think Critically** The upper layer is younger than 70 million years.

Sir Charles Lyell is given the most credit for advancing uniformitarianism. One reason was that his written works were easier to read. Encourage students to provide more details.

4. **Skill Builder**

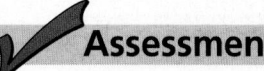

Half-Life	Parent	Daughter
0	100 g	0 g
1	50 g	50 g
2	25 g	75 g
3	12.5 g	87.5 g
4	6.25 g	93.75 g

Assessment

Performance Assess students' abilities to make and use tables and graphs by having them plot the data in their table. Half-lives should go on the horizontal axis, while the percentage of parent or daughter material should appear on the vertical axis. Use **Performance Assessment in the Science Classroom,** p. 39.

Activity 11·2

What You'll Investigate

Purpose

Kinesthetic Students will create a model and carry out an experiment that uses the model of radioactive half-lives in absolute age determination. L2 ELL COOP LEARN P

Process Skills

communicating, using numbers, interpreting data, formulating models, observing and inferring, making and using tables, making and using graphs, collecting and organizing data

Procedure

Time

one class period

Materials

shoebox with lid (1), brass fasteners (100), paper clips (100), pennies (100), colored pencils (2), graph paper (1 sheet)

Teaching Strategies

Tying to Previous Knowledge Help students recall that the half-life of a radioactive isotope is a measure of time that is definite and determinable.

Troubleshooting You may need to suggest shaking the shoe box as a model of half-life.

- For consistancy, instruct students to remove only the brass fasteners that are pointing to the X at an angle of 45° or less.
- To remove all fasteners, students may need to shake the box more than 15 times.
- Note that by beginning with 100 objects for the first shake, the number of objects remaining will be the percentage of original objects remaining.

Activity 11·2

Radioactive Decay

Materials

- Shoe box with lid
- Brass fasteners (100)
- Paper clips (100)
- Graph paper
- Pennies (100)
- Colored pencils (2)

Radioactive isotopes, elements that contain atoms with different numbers of neutrons, decay into their daughter elements in a specific amount of time. The rate of decay varies for each individual isotope. This rate can be used to determine the age of rocks that contain the isotopes under study. In this activity, you will develop a model that demonstrates how the half-life of certain radioactive isotopes can be used to determine absolute ages.

What You'll Investigate

What materials can be used to model age determination using radioactive half-lives?

Goals

- **Model** radioactive half-lives using listed materials.
- **Model** absolute age determination using the half-lives of radioactive isotopes.

Safety Precautions

Hold the lid of the box on tight to avoid having objects flying out of the box.

Procedure

1. Place 100 pennies into the shoe box with all heads up.
2. Place the lid on the box and shake it one time.
3. Remove the lid. Replace the pennies that are now tails up with paper clips. Record the number of pennies remaining in the box in a data table similar to the one shown on the next page.
4. Repeat steps 2 and 3 until all the pennies have been removed.

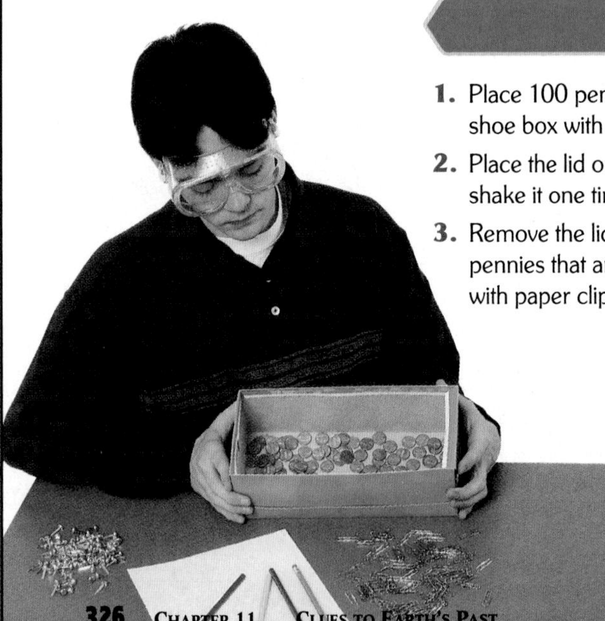

Inclusion Strategies

Visually Impaired Provide alternate materials that students can use to safely determine a change after each shake of the box. Suggestions include bent straws or pipe cleaners. Also, visually impaired students could be responsible for demonstrating the half-lives (shakes of the shoe box).

Expected Outcome

Students should be able to determine which materials are used as models of parent and daughter isotopes. Students should be able to determine the ratio of parent material remaining to daughter product produced during each half-life.

Error Analysis

Which objects were considered as parent isotopes? They should have been the items originally placed in the box. How was the ratio of parent isotope remaining to daughter product produced determined?

5. Remove the paper clips from the box. Put an "X" on one of the shorter sides of the box. Place 100 fasteners in the box, all pointed away from the "X".
6. Repeat step 2.
7. Remove the lid. Replace the fasteners that point toward the "X" with paper clips. Record the number of fasteners remaining in the box in a data table similar to the one shown at right.
8. Repeat steps 2 and 7 until all the fasteners have been removed.
9. Plot both sets of data on the same graph. Graph the "shake number" on the horizontal axis and the "number of pennies or fasteners remaining" on the vertical axis. Be sure to use a different colored pencil for each set of data.

Half-life Data

Shake Number	Number Remaining	
	Pennies	Fasteners

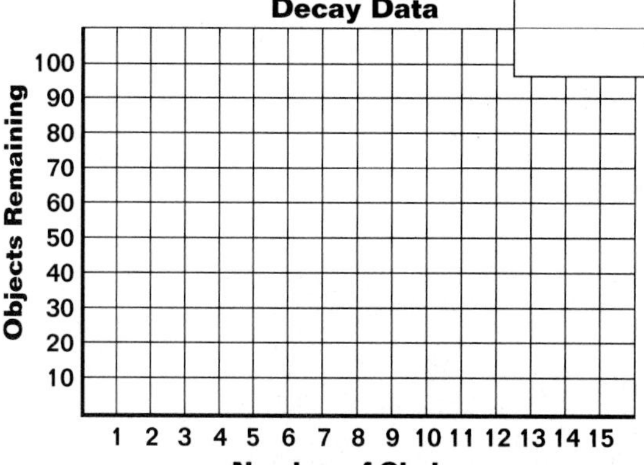

Conclude and Apply

1. In this model of radioactive decay, what do the coins and fasteners represent? The paper clips? The box? Each shake?
2. What was the half-life of the pennies? The fasteners?
3. How does the difference between the two objects affect the half-life? Compare the objects to the differences among radioactive elements.
4. Suppose you could make only one shake in 100 years. How many years would it take to have 25 coins and 75 paper clips remaining? To have 25 fasteners and 75 paper clips remaining?
5. How can absolute age of rocks be determined?

Conclude and Apply

1. The coins and fasteners represent radioactive parent isotopes, paper clips represent the stable daughter products, the box represents the rock in which decay occurs, and each shake represents a time interval.
2. Answers will vary. The number of shakes it takes to have half of each set of objects replaced is one half-life.
3. Answers will vary. The two types of objects have different probabilities of landing either heads down or pointing toward the X. Different elements have different half-lives because their atomic structures differ.
4. It would take two half-lives. Assuming the sample data shown, it would take two shakes (200 years) for the pennies and seven shakes (700 years) for the fasteners.
5. First, determine the percentage of original radioactive material remaining in the rock as compared to the daughter material into which it decays. Then multiply the number of half-lives that have occurred by the length of time required for each half-life.

GO Further

If the half-life of an isotope is 2000 years, what is the absolute age of a rock that contains only the stable daughter product? *Because all of the parent isotope has decayed, the absolute age of the rock cannot be determined.*

Assessment

Performance To further assess students' understanding of radioactive decay, have them repeat this activity using another material to represent the radioactive parent isotope. Use **Performance Assessment in the Science Classroom,** p. 33.

Chapter 11 Reviewing Main Ideas

Reviewing Main Ideas can be used to preview, review, reteach, and condense chapter content.

Preview

Linguistic Have students try to answer the questions in their Science Journals. Use student answers as a source for discussion throughout the chapter.

Review

Interpersonal Have students answer the questions on separate pieces of paper and compare their answers with those of other students in the class.

Reteach

Visual-Spatial Have students look at the illustrations on these pages. Ask them to describe details that support the main ideas of the chapter found in the statement for each illustration.

OUT OF TIME?

Auditory-Musical If time does not permit teaching the entire chapter, use the information on these pages along with the chapter Audiocassettes to present the material in a condensed format.

Chapter 11 Reviewing Main Ideas

For a **preview** of this chapter, study this Reviewing Main Ideas before you read the chapter. After you have studied this chapter, you can use the Reviewing Main Ideas to **review** the chapter.

The Glencoe MindJogger, Audiocassettes, and CD-ROM provide additional opportunities for review.

Section

11-1 FOSSILS

Fossils are more likely to form if hard parts of the dead organisms are buried quickly. Some fossils form when original materials that made up the organisms are replaced with minerals. Other fossils form when remains are subjected to heat and pressure, leaving only a **carbonaceous film** behind. When an organism is buried, decays, and leaves a cavity in the rock that is later filled with sediment, a **mold** and **cast** fossil forms. Some fossils are merely the tracks or traces left by former organisms. As a rule, a rock layer can be no older than the age of the fossils embedded in it. ***What type of fossil forms when original remains have been replaced with minerals?***

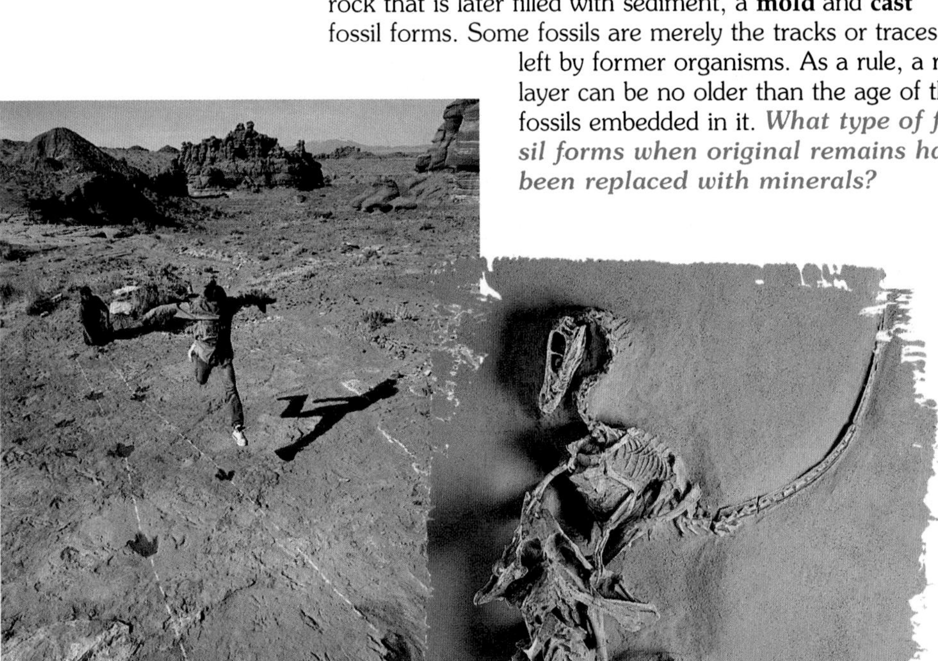

Cultural Diversity

The Copper Man of the Alps On September 19, 1991, a German couple hiking in the Alps came across a 5000-year-old traveler, naturally mummified in a small depression covered by glacial ice. The Iceman is now known to be one of the oldest and best preserved mummified humans. Grains on his clothing suggest that he came from lowland South Tirol. He wore finely stitched skin clothing, a woven grass cape, and boots. A deerskin quiver holds 2 arrows tipped with flint, and 12 unfinished ones. He carried two antibiotic fungi, a backpack, a half-finished longbow, high-quality flint, and a flint dagger. One of his most intriguing possessions was an ax, originally thought to be bronze but now known to be copper. It is flanged in a style not found anywhere nearby until nearly 800 years later.

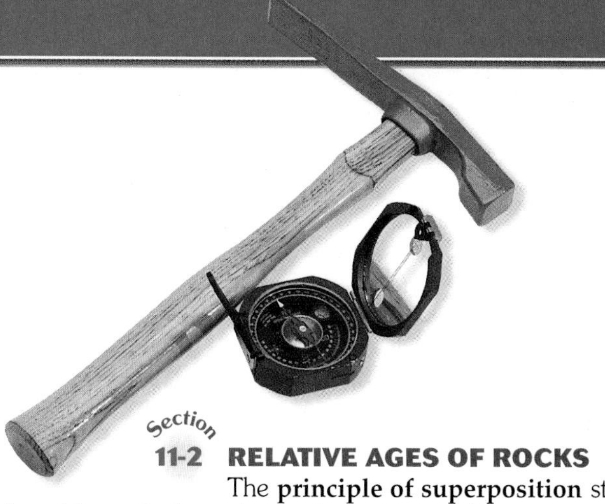

Reading Check

List any questions you still have about the chapter content. Review the chapter and try to answer them.

Section 11-2 RELATIVE AGES OF ROCKS

The **principle of superposition** states that older rocks lie underneath younger rocks in areas where the rocks haven't been disturbed. Faults are always younger than the rocks they cut across. Relative ages indicate if one layer of rock is younger or older than another. They do not indicate the layer's exact age in years. **Unconformities,** or gaps in the rock record, are due to erosion, nondeposition, or both. Three different types of unconformities can occur: angular unconformities, disconformities, and nonconformities. Fossils and rock types are often helpful when correlating similar rock bodies. ***What process or processes occur to form a disconformity?***

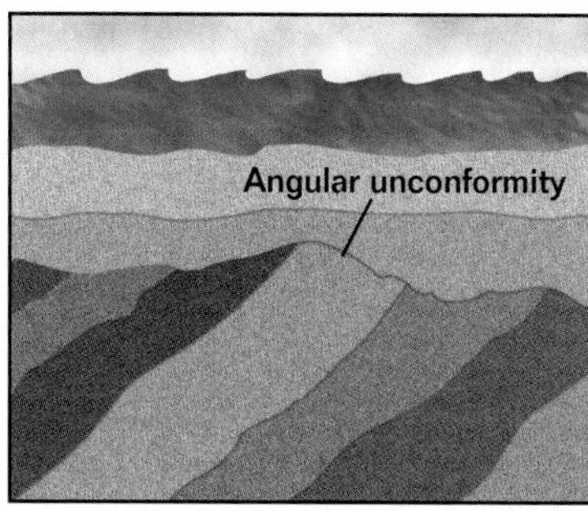

Section 11-3 ABSOLUTE AGES OF ROCKS

Unlike relative dating of rocks, **absolute dating** gives geologists a method by which they can determine the exact age in years of a rock or other object. The **half-life** of a radioactive isotope is the time it takes for half of the atoms in the isotope to decay. One half of the carbon-14 present in an object will decay to nitrogen-14 over a period of 5730 years. Because half-lives are constant, absolute ages of rocks containing radioactive elements can be determined. ***How are geologists able to determine a rock layer's age due to radiometric dating?***

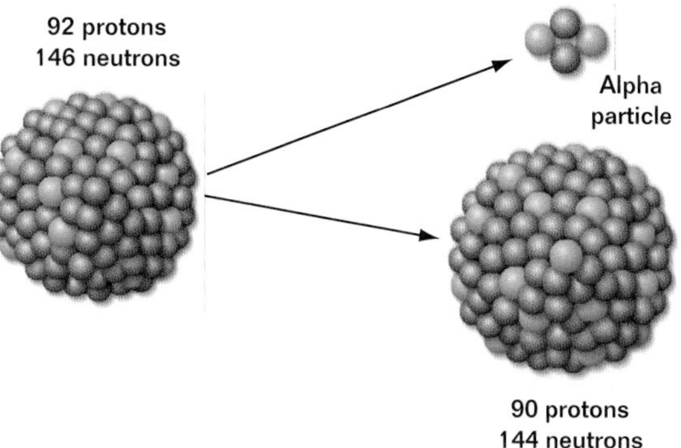

Answers to Questions

Section 11-1

Fossils petrified remains

Section 11-2

Relative Ages of Rock Present sedimentary rock layers are exposed and eroded. Later, younger rocks form above the erosional surface when sediment deposition begins again. The cross section of rock layers may look complete, but close inspection shows an erosional surface, or disconformity.

Section 11-3

Absolute Ages of Rock First, they determine the percentage of original radioactive material remaining in samples from the rock layer as compared to the daughter material into which it decays. Using these data, they determine the number of half-lives that have passed. They then multiply the number of half-lives that have occurred by the length of time required for each half-life.

GLENCOE TECHNOLOGY

CD-ROM

Glencoe Science Voyages Interactive CD-ROM

Chapter Summaries and Quizzes

Have students read the Chapter Summary then take the Chapter Quiz to determine whether they have mastered chapter content.

Assessment

Portfolio Encourage students to place in their portfolios one or two items of what they consider to be their best work. Examples include:

- Activity 11-1, p. 319
- MiniLab, p. 322
- Activity 11-2, pp. 326–327 P

Performance Additional performance assessments may be found in **Performance Assessment** and **Science Integration Activities.** Performance Task Assessment Lists and rubrics for evaluating these activities can be found in **Glencoe's Performance Assessment in the Science Classroom.**

Chapter 11 Assessment

Using Vocabulary

1. casts
2. index fossils
3. Principle of superposition
4. absolute dating
5. half-life

interNET CONNECTION To reinforce chapter vocabulary, use the **Study Guide for Content Mastery** booklet. Also available are activities for **Glencoe Science Voyages** on the Glencoe Science Web Site. **www.glencoe.com/sec/science**

Checking Concepts

6. B	11. A
7. D	12. C
8. C	13. B
9. A	14. D
10. D	15. D

Thinking Critically

16. The fossil record is incomplete because erosion and decay can destroy evidence of life if it's not buried quickly and protected from oxygen and moisture. Deeply buried remains are frequently destroyed by metamorphism.
17. Because the lava contains radioactive elements, an absolute age for the flow can be determined. This age can then be used to determine relative ages for the rocks above and below the flow.

Chapter 11 Assessment

Using Vocabulary

a. absolute dating
b. carbonaceous film
c. cast
d. fossil
e. half-life
f. index fossil
g. mold
h. petrified remains
i. principle of superposition
j. radioactive decay
k. radiometric dating
l. relative dating
m. unconformity
n. uniformitarianism

The sentences below include terms that have been used incorrectly. Change the incorrect terms so that the sentence reads correctly.

1. Rocklike fossils made of minerals are called *petrified remains.*
2. *Correlation fossils* are fossils of species that existed for a short time and were abundant and widespread.
3. The *principle of uniformitarianism* explains the fact that younger rock layers overlie older rock layers.
4. *Relative dating* allows geologists to determine the exact age of rocks and fossils.
5. *Radiometric dating* is the time it takes for half of the atoms of a radioactive isotope to decay.

Checking Concepts

Choose the word or phrase that completes the sentence.

6. What are remains of organisms in rocks called?
   A) half-lives C) unconformities
   B) fossils D) extinctions
7. What conditions allow dead organisms to change into fossils?
   A) slow burial C) soft parts present
   B) exposure to microorganisms D) hard parts present
8. What are cavities left in rocks called when a shell or bone decays?
   A) casts C) molds
   B) petrified remains D) carbon films
9. Which of the following is evidence of animal activity, such as fossilized tracks?
   A) a trace fossil C) original remains
   B) petrified remains D) carbonaceous film
10. "The present is the key to the past" is an explanation of which principle?
    A) superposition C) radioactivity
    B) succession D) uniformitarianism
11. A fault can be used to find what kind of age of a group of rocks?
    A) relative C) index
    B) radiometric D) absolute
12. What is an unconformity between horizontal rock layers called?
    A) fault C) disconformity
    B) angular unconformity D) nonconformity
13. During which process are new elements formed?
    A) superposition C) evolution
    B) radioactive decay D) uniformitarianism
14. In one type of radioactive decay, what breaks down, releasing an electron?
    A) alpha particle C) beta particle
    B) proton D) neutron
15. According to radiometric dating, how many years old is Earth?
    A) 2000 C) 3.5 billion
    B) 5000 D) 4.6 billion

Thinking Critically

16. We don't have a complete fossil record of life on Earth. Give some reasons why.

18. The distance between the foot imprints enables geologists to estimate the length of the dinosaur's legs. Once the foot and leg size are known, the overall size of the animal can be hypothesized. Once the overall size of the dinosaur is estimated, changes in the separation of the footprints can indicate when the animal was walking or running, and estimates of speed can be determined.
19. It's likely that any layer of shale containing volcanic dust is part of the same shale deposit. The dust-rich shale can act as a marker.
20. The half-life of carbon-14 is too short. All of the original carbon-14 in a fossil that's 2 million years old would have decayed. There would be no carbon-14 left to measure.

17. Suppose a lava flow were found between two sedimentary rock layers. How could the lava flow be used to date the rocks? (Hint: Most lava contains radioactive isotopes.)
18. A set of dinosaur tracks, as in **Figure 11-7,** is found. How might the tracks be used to determine how tall the dinosaur was or how fast it was moving?
19. Suppose you're correlating rock layers in the western United States. You find a layer of shale that contains volcanic dust deposits. How can this layer help you in your correlation over a large area?
20. Why is carbon-14 not suitable for dating fossils formed about 2 million years ago?

Developing Skills

If you need help, refer to the **Skill Handbook.**

21. **Concept Mapping:** Make a concept map listing the following possible steps in the process of making a cast of a fossil: *replacement by minerals, organism dies, mineral crystals form from solution, burial, fossil erodes away, protection from scavengers,* and *bacteria.*

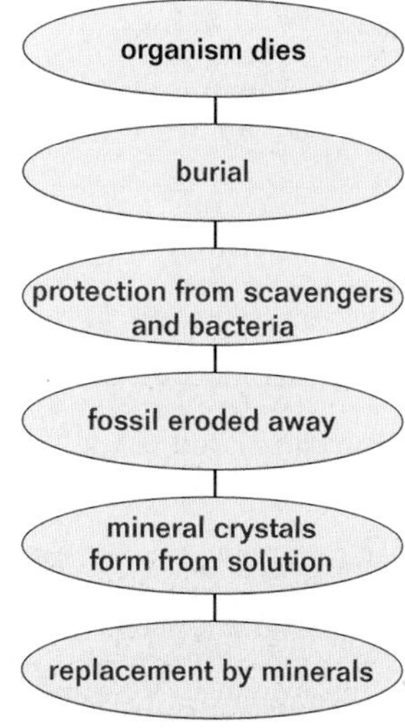

Test-Taking Tip

Make Yourself Comfortable When you take a test, try to make yourself as comfortable as possible. You will then be able to focus all your attention on the test.

Test Practice

Use these questions to test your Science Proficiency.

1. Many small fossil tracks of one type of animal are found surrounded by larger tracks of the same type of animal. What might this indicate about their social structure?
   A) Larger animals were attacking the smaller ones.
   B) Animals of different sizes were playing in a group.
   C) Large animals were surrounding the smaller ones for protection.
   D) Large animals run faster and therefore move to the outside of the herd.
2. An object was radiometrically dated and determined to be 90 000 years old. The half-life of the parent isotope is 30 000 years. Which statement **BEST** explains how this date was determined?
   A) In the object, 87.5 percent of the parent isotope and 12.5 percent of the daughter isotope are present.
   B) In the object, 50 percent of the parent isotope and 50 percent of the daughter isotope are present.
   C) In the object, 25 percent of the parent isotope and 75 percent of the daughter isotope are present.
   D) In the object, 12.5 percent of the parent isotope and 87.5 percent of the daughter isotope are present.

The Test-Taking Tip was written by The Princeton Review, the nation's leader in test preparation.

1. C
2. D

Developing Skills

21. possible solution: organism dies, burial, protection from scavengers and bacteria, fossil erodes away, mineral crystals form from solution, replacement by minerals

Bonus Question

Three igneous rock layers have been dated using radioactive isotopes. The top layer is 200 million years old, the middle layer is 150 million years old, and the bottom layer is 100 million years old. **Based on what you know about the principle of superposition, how would you explain this arrangement of rock ages?** *Because the relative ages of the rock layers are inverted, the rock layers have evidently been overturned since they were deposited.*

Assessment Resources

The **Test Practice Workbook** provides students with practice in the format, concepts, and critical-thinking skills tested in standardized exams.

Reproducible Masters

Chapter Review, pp. 21–22 L2
Performance Assessment, p. 25 L2
Assessment, pp. 47–50 L2

Glencoe Technology

- Chapter Review Software
- Computer Test Bank
- MindJogger Videoquiz

Chapter 12 Change Through Time

Section	Objectives	Activities/Features
Chapter Opener		**Explore Activity:** Model Camouflage, p. 333
12-1 **Mechanisms of Evolution** 4 Sessions 2 Blocks	1. **Compare** and **contrast** Lamarck's theory of evolution and Darwin's theory of evolution. 2. **Explain** the importance of variations in organisms. 3. **Relate** how gradualism and punctuated equilibrium describe the rate of evolution.	**Problem Solving:** When can some fish be sold? p. 337 **Using Math,** p. 338 **MiniLab:** Relating Evolution to Species, p. 339 **Skill Builder:** Making and Using Graphs, p. 341 **Using Math,** p. 341 **Activity 12-1:** Recognizing Variation in a Population, pp. 342–343
12-2 **Evidence for Evolution** 3 Sessions 1½ Blocks	4. **Describe** the importance of fossils as evidence of evolution. 5. **Explain** how relative and radiometric dating are used to date fossils. 6. **Give** examples of five types of evidence for evolution.	**Using Math,** p. 346 **Earth Science Integration,** p. 349 **Skill Builder:** Making and Using Tables, p. 351 **Using Computers,** p. 351 **History of Science:** Footprints in Geologic Time, p. 352 **Activity 12-2:** A Model of Natural Selection, p. 353
12-3 **Primate Evolution** 2 Sessions 1 Block	7. **Describe** the differences in living primates. 8. **Describe** the adaptations of primates. 9. **Trace** the evolutionary history of primates.	**MiniLab:** Living Without Thumbs, p. 355 **Earth Science Integration,** p. 355 **Skill Builder:** Concept Mapping, p. 357 **Science Journal,** p. 357

The number of recommended single-period sessions — The number of recommended blocks
One session and one-half block are allowed for chapter review and assessment.

Activity Materials

Explore	Activities	MiniLabs
p. 333 classified ads from a newspaper, hole punch, black paper, white paper, stopwatch or clock, pencil, graph paper	pp. 342–343 leaves, flower, and seeds from one species of plant; metric ruler; magnifying glass; graph paper p. 353 red beans, white beans, paper bag, pencil, paper	p. 339 pencil, paper p. 355 tape

Need Materials? Contact Science Kit at 1-800-828-7777 or at www.sciencekit.com on the Internet.
For alternate materials, see the activity on the listed page.

Standards		Reproducible Resources	Technology
National	State/Local	Test Practice Workbooks are available for use with each chapter.	English and Spanish audiocassettes are available for use with each section.
National Content Standards: UCP2, UCP3, UCP4, A1, A2, C5, D2, G1, G2, G3		**Activity Worksheets,** pp. 65–66, 69 **Enrichment,** p. 31 **Laboratory Manual,** pp. 69–74 **Laboratory Manual,** pp. 70–74 **Reinforcement,** p. 31 **Study Guide,** pp. 45–46	**Section Focus Transparency 31** **Teaching Transparency 23** **Teaching Transparency 24** **Glencoe Science Voyages Interactive CD-ROM** **Internet Connection,** p. 337 **Glencoe Science Voyages Interactive Videodisc—Life** **The Infinite Voyage Series**
National Content Standards: UCP2, UCP3, UCP4, A2, C5, D2		**Activity Worksheets,** pp. 67–68 **Enrichment,** p. 32 **Multicultural Connections,** pp. 23–24 **Reinforcement,** p. 32 **Critical Thinking/Problem Solving,** p. 12 **Study Guide,** p. 47	**Section Focus Transparency 32** **Science Integration Transparency 12** **Internet Connection,** p. 345 **Internet Connection,** p. 348 **Glencoe Science Voyages Interactive Videodisc—Earth** **Glencoe Science Voyages Interactive CD-ROM**
National Content Standards: UCP2, UCP3, UCP4, C5, D2		**Activity Worksheets,** p. 70 **Enrichment,** p. 33 **Home Involvement,** p. 28 **Reinforcement,** p. 33 **Study Guide,** p. 48	**Section Focus Transparency 33** **Glencoe Science Voyages Interactive CD-ROM**

Key to Teaching Strategies

The following designations will help you decide which activities are appropriate for your students.

L1 Level 1 activities should be appropriate for students with learning difficulties.

L2 Level 2 activities should be within the ability range of all students.

L3 Level 3 activities are designed for above-average students.

ELL ELL activities should be within the ability range of English Language Learners.

COOP LEARN Cooperative Learning activities are designed for small group work.

P These strategies represent student products that can be placed into a best-work portfolio.

Multiple Learning Styles logos, as described on page 61T, are used throughout to indicate strategies that address different learning styles.

Assessment Resources

Chapter Review, pp. 23–24
Assessment, pp. 51–54
Performance Assessment in the Science Classroom (PASC)
MindJogger Videoquiz
Alternate Assessment in the Science Classroom
Performance Assessment, p. 26
Chapter Review Software
Computer Test Bank

Chapter 12 Change Through Time

This is a representation of key blackline masters available in the Teacher Classroom Resources. See Resource Manager boxes within the chapter for additional information.

Section Focus Transparencies

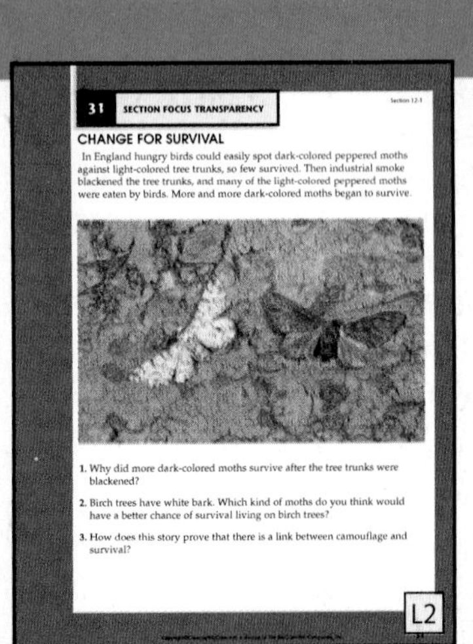

31 SECTION FOCUS TRANSPARENCY

Section 12-1

CHANGE FOR SURVIVAL

In England hungry birds could easily spot dark-colored peppered moths against light-colored tree trunks, so few survived. Then industrial smoke blackened the tree trunks, and many of the light-colored peppered moths were eaten by birds. More and more dark-colored moths began to survive.

1. Why did more dark-colored moths survive after the tree trunks were blackened?
2. Birch trees have white bark. Which kind of moths do you think would have a better chance of survival living on birch trees?
3. How does this story prove that there is a link between camouflage and survival?

L2

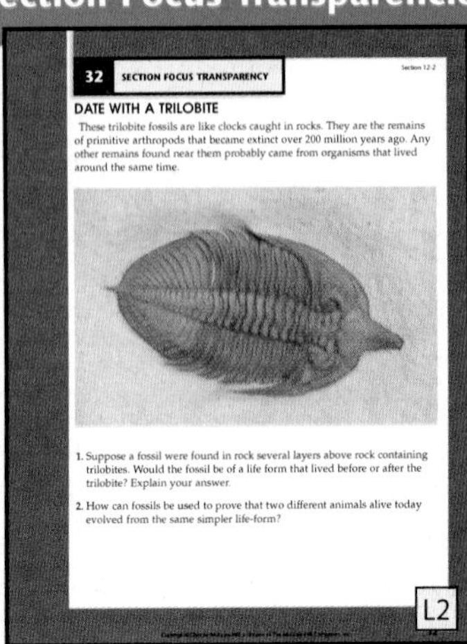

32 SECTION FOCUS TRANSPARENCY

Section 12-2

DATE WITH A TRILOBITE

These trilobite fossils are like clocks caught in rocks. They are the remains of primitive arthropods that became extinct over 200 million years ago. Any other remains found near them probably came from organisms that lived around the same time.

1. Suppose a fossil were found in rock several layers above rock containing trilobites. Would the fossil be of a life form that lived before or after the trilobite? Explain your answer.
2. How can fossils be used to prove that two different animals alive today evolved from the same simpler life-form?

L2

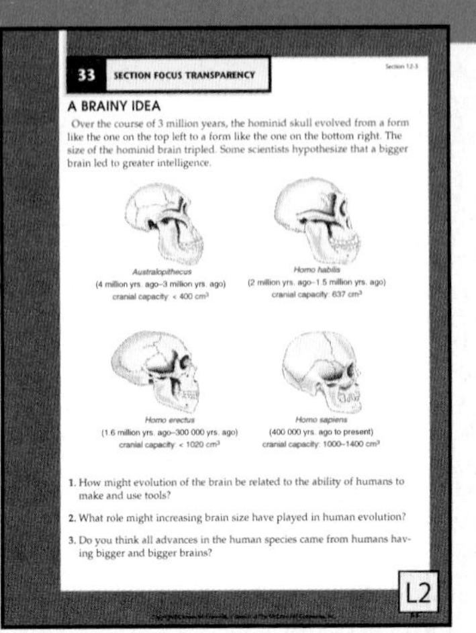

33 SECTION FOCUS TRANSPARENCY

Section 12-3

A BRAINY IDEA

Over the course of 3 million years, the hominid skull evolved from a form like the one on the top left to a form like the one on the bottom right. The size of the hominid brain tripled. Some scientists hypothesize that a bigger brain led to greater intelligence.

1. How might evolution of the brain be related to the ability of humans to make and use tools?
2. What role might increasing brain size have played in human evolution?
3. Do you think all advances in the human species came from humans having bigger and bigger brains?

L2

Science Integration Transparencies

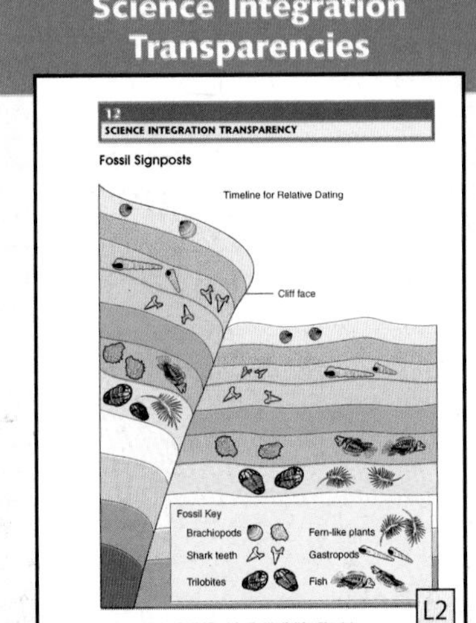

12 SCIENCE INTEGRATION TRANSPARENCY

Fossil Signposts

L2

Teaching Transparencies

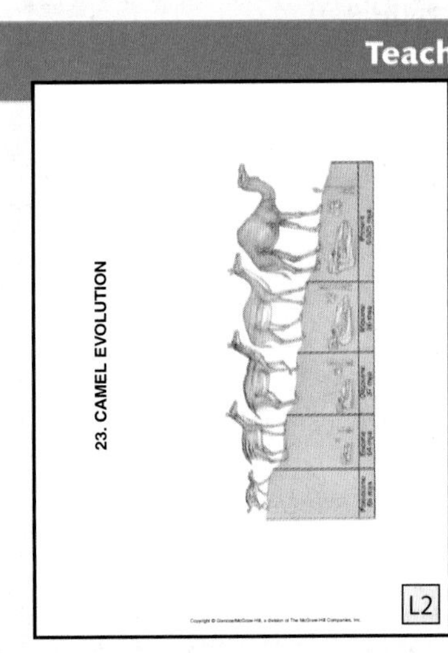

23. CAMEL EVOLUTION

L2

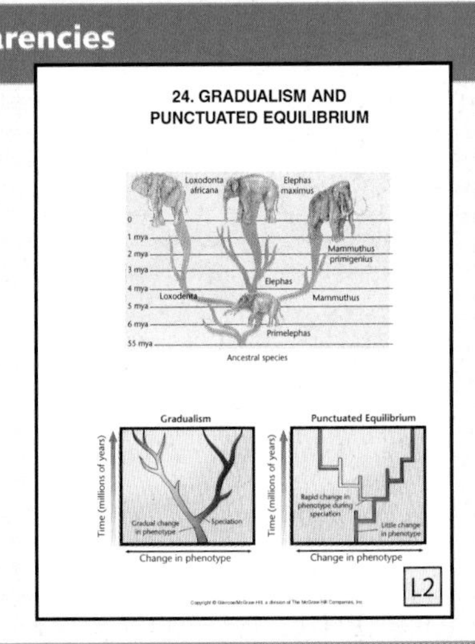

24. GRADUALISM AND PUNCTUATED EQUILIBRIUM

L2

Meeting Different Ability Levels

Study Guide for Content Mastery

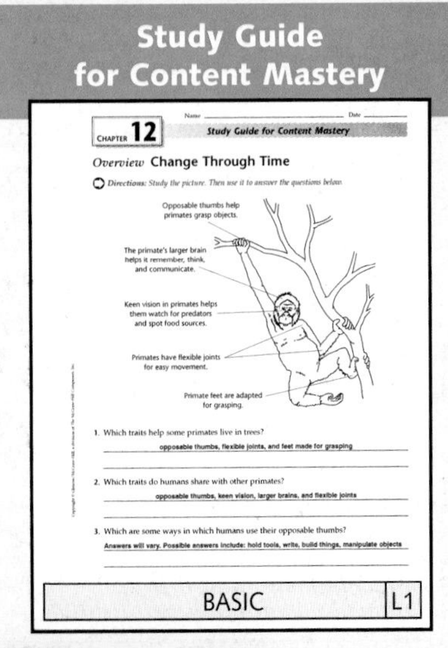

CHAPTER 12 Name ______ Date ______

Study Guide for Content Mastery

Overview Change Through Time

Directions: Study the picture. Then use it to answer the questions below.

1. Which traits help some primates live in trees?
opposable thumbs, flexible joints, and feet made for grasping
2. Which traits do humans share with other primates?
opposable thumbs, keen vision, larger brains, and flexible joints
3. Which are some ways in which humans use their opposable thumbs?
Answers will vary. Possible answers include: hold tools, write, build things, manipulate objects

BASIC L1

Reinforcement

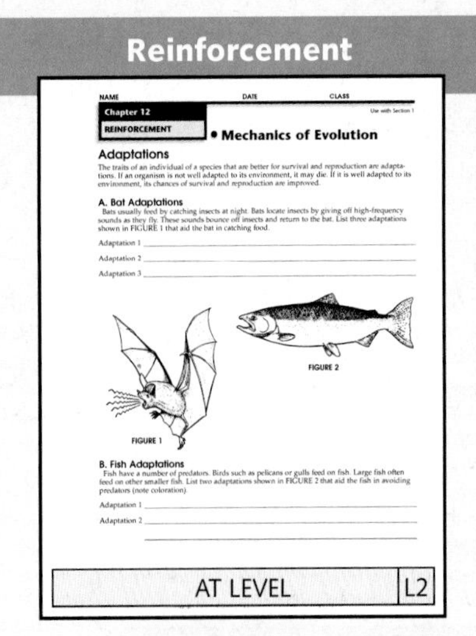

NAME DATE CLASS

Chapter 12 REINFORCEMENT • Mechanics of Evolution

Use with Section 1

Adaptations

The traits of an individual of a species that are better for survival and reproduction are adaptations. If an organism is not well adapted to its environment, it may die. If it is well adapted to its environment, its chances of survival and reproduction are improved.

A. Bat Adaptations

Bats usually feed by catching insects at night. Bats locate insects by giving off high-frequency sounds as they fly. These sounds bounce off insects and return to the bat. List three adaptations shown in FIGURE 1 that aid the bat in catching food.

Adaptation 1 ______

Adaptation 2 ______

Adaptation 3 ______

FIGURE 1

FIGURE 2

B. Fish Adaptations

Fish have a number of predators. Birds such as pelicans or gulls feed on fish. Large fish often feed on other smaller fish. List two adaptations shown in FIGURE 2 that aid the fish in avoiding predators (note coloration).

Adaptation 1 ______

Adaptation 2 ______

AT LEVEL L2

Enrichment Worksheets

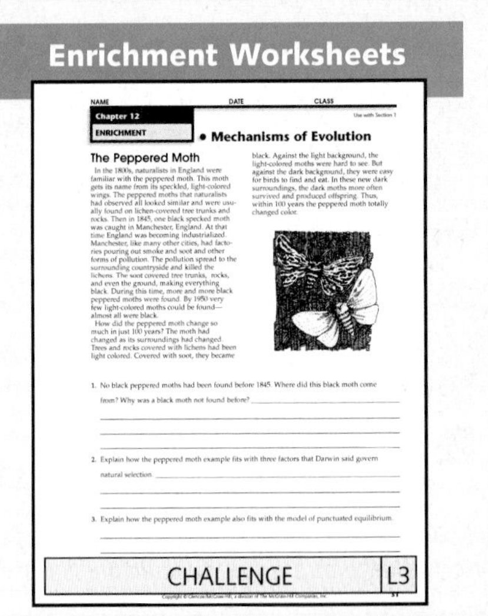

NAME DATE CLASS

Chapter 12 ENRICHMENT • Mechanisms of Evolution

Use with Section 1

The Peppered Moth

In the 1800s, naturalists in England were familiar with the peppered moth. This moth gets its name from its speckled, light-colored wings. The peppered moths that naturalists had observed all looked similar and were usually found on lichen-covered tree trunks and rocks. Then in 1845, one black specked moth was caught in Manchester, England. At that time England was becoming industrialized. Manchester, like many other cities, had factories pouring out smoke and soot and other forms of pollution. The pollution spread to the surrounding countryside and killed the lichens. The soot covered tree trunks, rocks, and even the ground, making everything black. During this time, more and more black peppered moths were found. By 1950 very few light-colored moths could be found—almost all were black.

How did the peppered moth change so much in just 100 years? The moth had changed as its surroundings had changed. Trees and rocks covered with lichens had been light colored. Covered with soot, they became black. Against the light background, the light-colored moths were hard to see. But against the dark background, they were easy for birds to find and eat. In these new dark surroundings, the dark moths more often survived and produced offspring. Thus, within 100 years the peppered moth totally changed color.

1. No black peppered moths had been found before 1845. Where did this black moth come from? Why was a black moth not found before? ______
2. Explain how the peppered moth example fits with three factors that Darwin said govern natural selection. ______
3. Explain how the peppered moth example also fits with the model of punctuated equilibrium. ______

CHALLENGE L3

Hands-on Activities

Activity Worksheets

Chapter 12

ACTIVITY 12-1

• Recognizing Variation in a Population

Design Your Own Experiment

Lab Preview

L2

Lab Manual

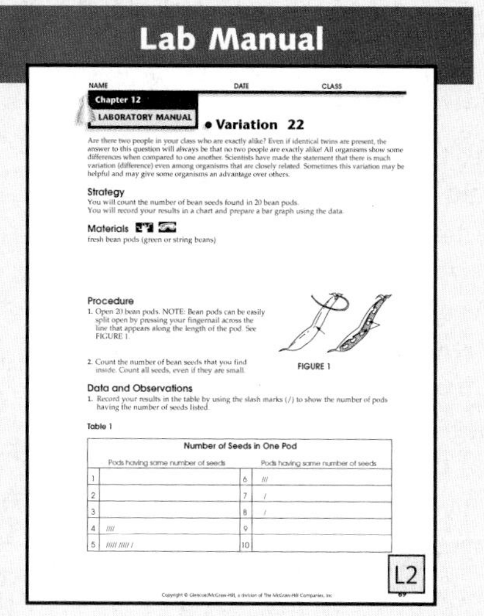

Chapter 12

LABORATORY MANUAL

• Variation 22

Strategy

Materials

Procedure

Data and Observations

Number of Seeds in One Pod

L2

Accessibility

Spanish Resources

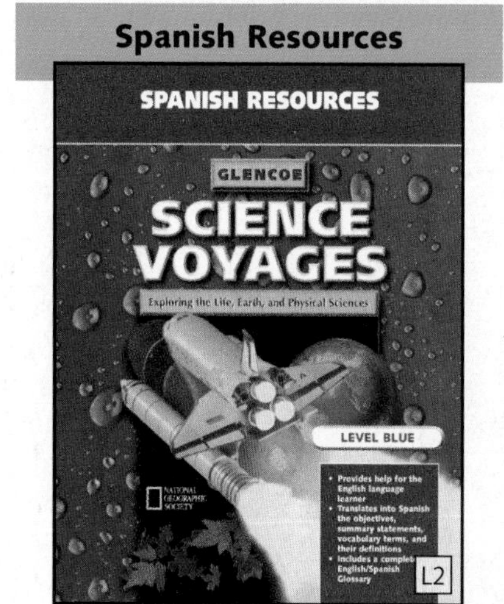

Assessment

Performance Assessment

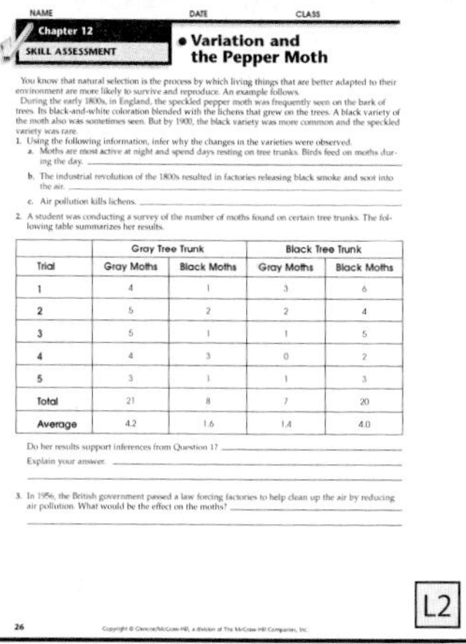

Chapter 12

SKILL ASSESSMENT

• Variation and the Pepper Moth

L2

Chapter Review

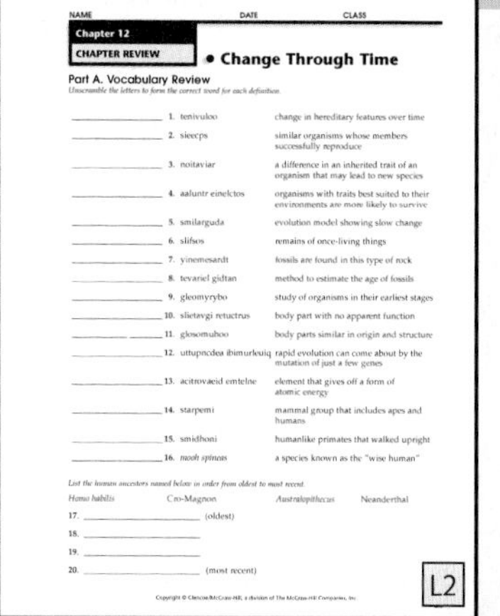

Chapter 12

CHAPTER REVIEW

• Change Through Time

Part A. Vocabulary Review

L2

Assessment

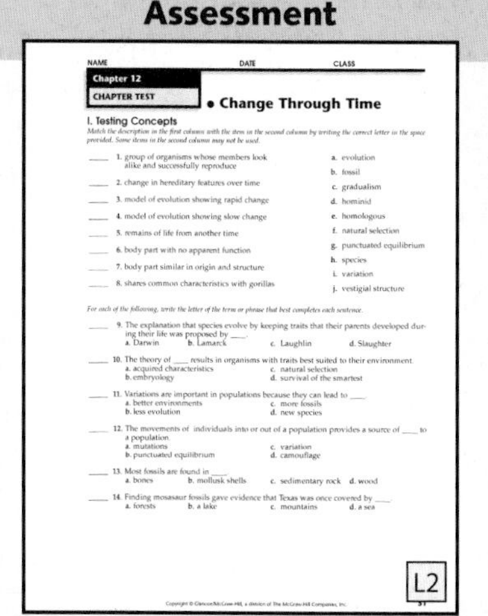

Chapter 12

CHAPTER TEST

• Change Through Time

I. Testing Concepts

L2

Test Practice Workbook

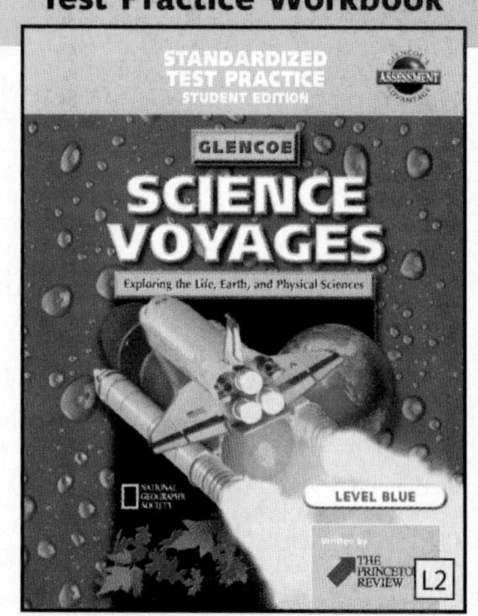

Extending Content

Critical Thinking/ Problem Solving

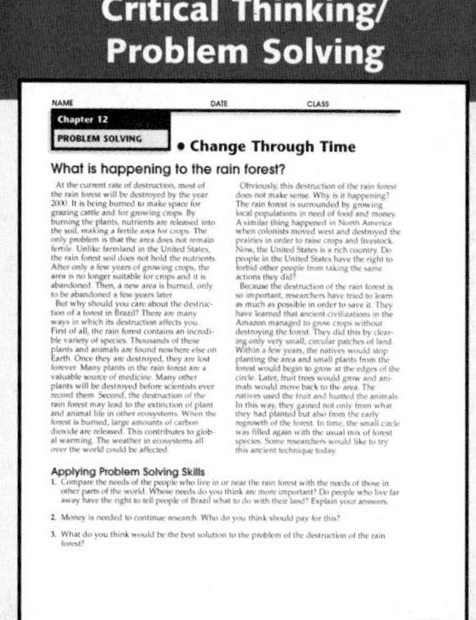

Chapter 12

PROBLEM SOLVING

• Change Through Time

What is happening to the rain forest?

Applying Problem Solving Skills

L2

Multicultural Connections

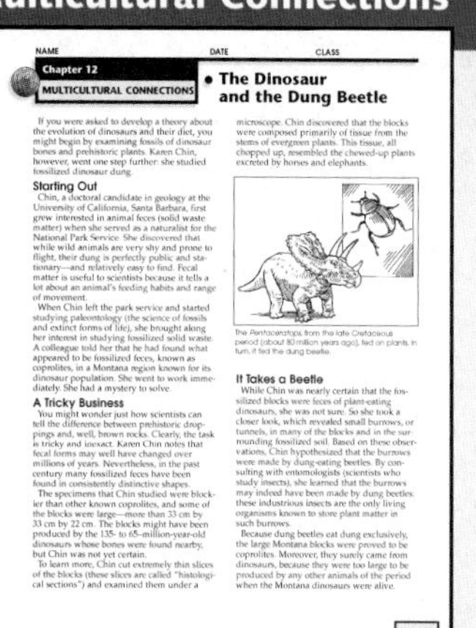

Chapter 12

MULTICULTURAL CONNECTIONS

• The Dinosaur and the Dung Beetle

Starting Out

A Tricky Business

It Takes a Beetle

L2

Chapter 12 Change Through Time

Helping You Prepare

Early Thoughts About Evolution (Section 12-1)

Plato and Aristotle, two Greek philosophers, held views that species were essentially perfect. Because species were considered to be well adapted, there was no discussion needed on evolution. Special Creation with all species fixed was the prevailing view. In addition, Carolus Linnaeus, father of taxonomy, organized the diversity of living things into a hierarchy of taxonomic categories that did not imply evolution.

Evolution by Natural Selection (Section 12-1)

Charles Darwin and Alfred Wallace provided enough evidence in 1859 to convince many scientists that evolution occurs. They differed from the prevailing view of their time in two important ways—species change, or evolve, and natural selection is the mechanism by which this evolution occurs.

An important point about the discussions on natural selection and evolution is that Darwin's observations were not limited to those made during his trip around the world on the HMS *Beagle.* Even as a young boy, Darwin was an avid collector of beetles and other information about natural history. By the time he became the ship's naturalist, he was already in agreement with his grandfather, Erasmus Darwin, that organisms evolve.

Teacher's Corner

Products Available from National Geographic Society

To order the following products, call National Geographic Society at 1-800-368-2728:

Videos

Energy: The Fuels and Man

Energy: The Problems and the Future

Index to National Geographic Magazine

The following article may be used:

"Can We Harness the Wind?" by Roger Hamilton, December 1975.

GLENCOE TECHNOLOGY

CD-ROM

Glencoe Science Voyages Interactive CD-ROM

Chapter Summaries

Use the Chapter Summary to introduce, teach, or review chapter material.

Evolution is the accumulated change in allelic frequencies of populations. These frequencies change as a result of selection pressure by the environment on variations that are inherited in a population. Natural selection is the name given to this differential success in reproduction by well-adapted members of a population.

Adaptation and Variation (Section 12-1)

Variability, the raw material of evolution, is of concern to evolutionary biologists. Mutation is the primary source of variability. Evolution is the change in variation as a result of interbreeding of individuals within a population.

High levels of variability are found in nearly all populations. It remains difficult to measure the exact amount of genetic variability within a population because every gene within the population cannot be sampled. Genetics and biochemical studies are the primary sources for directly measuring evolution within a population.

Fossil Evidence (Section 12-2)

Information about evolution is indirectly available from the fossil record. From petrified wood, for example, paleontologists can tell the species of many kinds of trees and even their ages when they died. Also, the environment in which an organism lived, the diet of the organism, and the makeup of communities within ancient ecosystems can often be inferred from fossils.

The Fossil Record (Section 12-2)

Superposition of sedimentary rocks allows us to determine relative ages of rock layers and the fossils within them. Similar fossils, called index fossils can often correlate rock strata from one location to another.

Radiometric dating involves the measurement of quantities of radioactive isotopes and their decay products. Radioactive isotopes have half-lives that are not affected by environmental factors such as temperature or atmospheric pressure. Because the length of half-lives for radioactive isotopes of elements is known, an age can be assigned to many rocks or fossils.

The evidence of evolution of species from their fossils is compatible with other types of evidence for evolution. Transitional fossils have been located for some species, and species such as echinoderms have extensive fossil records that appear complete.

Other Evidence for Evolution (Section 12-2)

The geographical distribution of closely related species is one example of evidence for evolution. For example, two closely related squirrel species have diverged on opposite sides of the Grand Canyon. Similar geographical separations have occurred in animals and plants of South America, Africa, and Australia.

Biochemical evidence provides some of the best evidence of evolution. Changes in allelic frequencies, mutation rates, and similar changes at the molecular level indicate that organisms are presently evolving.

SCIENCE UPDATE

For current events or science in the news, access the Glencoe Science Web Site at **www.glencoe.com/sec/science**

Primates (Section 12-3)

Primates are the order of mammals most closely related to humans. The first primates appear to have been small, arboreal insectivores. Present day prosimians such as the loris, tarsier, and potto are primitive primates that probably resemble the ancestral species of the late Cretaceous period.

Primate Classification (Section 12-3)

Anthropoid primates include monkeys, apes, and humans. Monkeys are separated into New World and Old World species based on biogeography. Unlike their African cousins, New World monkeys possess prehensile tails. Apes include gibbons, gorillas, and chimpanzees and are confined to the Old World. Humans live worldwide.

Teacher to Teacher

"Make a giant time line out of butcher or computer paper. Pre-mark the major eras on the paper. Have students attach 5" × 7" cards with information and pictures about the plants and animals characteristic of that era. Add cards as you progress in your study."

Maureen E. Allen

Maureen Allen, Science Resource Specialist
Brywood School
Irvine, CA

CHAPTER 12 Change Through Time

CHAPTER OVERVIEW

Section 12-1 Lamarck's and Darwin's theories of evolution are compared and contrasted in relation to observed variation. Gradualism and punctuated equilibrium are discussed as modifications of Darwin's theory.

Section 12-2 The evidence for evolution by natural selection is presented. Relative and radiometric dating are compared.

Section 12-3 The possibility of evolution of primates from a common ancestor and the evolutionary history of humans are described.

Chapter Vocabulary

species	radioactive element
evolution	homologous
natural selection	vestigial structure
variation	embryology
gradualism	primates
punctuated equilibrium	hominids
sedimentary rock	*Homo sapiens*

Theme Connection

Stability and Change Changes that occur during evolution bring about stability by increasing variation within a population.

OUT OF TIME?

If time does not permit teaching the entire chapter, use Reviewing Main Ideas on pp. 358–359.

CHAPTER 12 Change Through Time

Chapter Preview

Skills Preview

Skill Builders
- Make a Table
- Map Concepts

Activities
- Collect and Organize Data
- Formulate a Model

MiniLabs
- Make a Model
- Infer

Reading Check

Before reading this chapter, list the kinds of images you expect to see. Compare this list with the images you find as you read.

Multiple Learning Styles

Look for the following logos for strategies that emphasize different learning modalities.

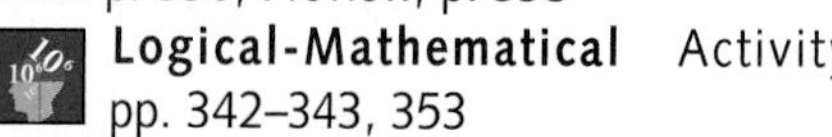

Linguistic Using Science Words, p. 350; Preview, p. 358

Logical-Mathematical Activity, pp. 342–343, 353

Visual-Spatial Explore Activity, p. 333; Inclusion Strategies, p. 335; Quick Demo, p. 337; MiniLab, p. 339; Across the Curriculum, p. 347; Activity, p. 349; Assessment, pp. 351, 357; Reteach, p. 358

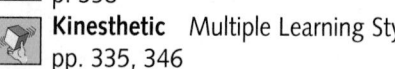

Auditory-Musical Out of Time, p. 358

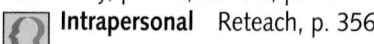

Kinesthetic Multiple Learning Styles, pp. 335, 346

Interpersonal Discussion, p. 340; Activity, p. 346; Review, p. 358

Intrapersonal Reteach, p. 356

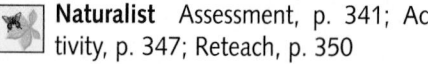

Naturalist Assessment, p. 341; Activity, p. 347; Reteach, p. 350

Explore Activity

The Central Indian Tiger is a fierce hunter. It preys mostly on large mammals, including lions and other tigers. If injured or unable to get food, tigers have even been known to eat humans. Because tigers can run swiftly only for a short distance, they must conceal themselves so they can spring on their prey and kill it before it gets away. Tigers are camouflaged according to their natural environment. The tiger on the opposite page is colored perfectly for its surroundings. Its stripes blend in with the tall grass, making it almost invisible as it stalks its prey.

Model Camouflage

1. Spread a sheet of classified ads from a newspaper on the floor.
2. Using a hole punch, punch out 100 circles each from sheets of white paper, black paper, and classified ads.
3. Scatter the paper circles on the spread-out sheets of classified ads. Pick up as many paper circles as possible for 10 s. Have a partner time you.
4. Count each kind of paper circle that you picked up. Then, pour the circles back on the newspaper pages.
5. Repeat steps 3 and 4 three times. Graph your data.

Science Journal

In your Science Journal, describe which paper circles were most difficult to find. What can you infer from this activity?

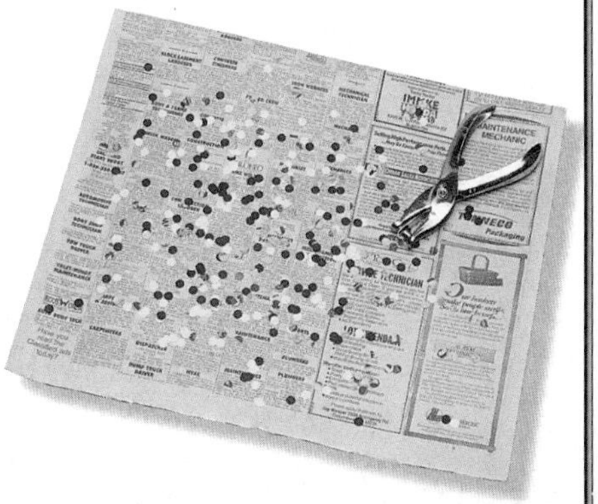

Explore Activity

Purpose

Visual-Spatial Use the Explore Activity to show students that organisms must have adaptations, such as camouflage coloration, for survival. L2 ELL COOP LEARN

Preparation

Accumulate classified ads from the newspaper.

Materials

newspaper classified ads, black and white paper, stopwatch or clock, pencil, graph paper, hole punch

Teaching Strategies

- In general, students should pick up far more of the white and black circles than the newsprint circles.
- If you find that students are picking up most of the circles within the time limit, add more circles or use less time.

Students should indicate that circles of classified ads were more difficult to find. You can infer that patterns help conceal organisms from predators in their environments.

Assessment

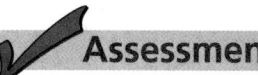

Process Provide students with photographs of animals that exhibit concealing coloration or patterns and have them describe how each is beneficial to the animal. Use **Performance Assessment in the Science Classroom,** p. 71.

Assessment Planner

Portfolio

Refer to p. 359 for suggested items that students might select for their portfolios.

Performance Assessment

See p. 359 for additional Performance Assessment options.
Skill Builder, pp. 351, 357
MiniLab, pp. 339, 355
Activity 12-1, pp. 342–343; 12-2, p. 353

Content Assessment

Section Assessment, pp. 341, 351, 357
Chapter Assessment, pp. 360–361
Proficiency Prep, pp. 341, 351, 357

SECTION 12 1

Prepare

Refer to **Early Thoughts About Evolution, Evolution by Natural Selection,** and **Adaptation and Variation** on p. 332E.

Preplanning

Refer to the **Chapter Organizer** on pp. 332A–B.

1 Motivate

Bellringer

Before presenting the lesson, display **Section Focus Transparency 31** on the overhead projector. Use the accompanying **Focus Activity** worksheet. L2 ELL

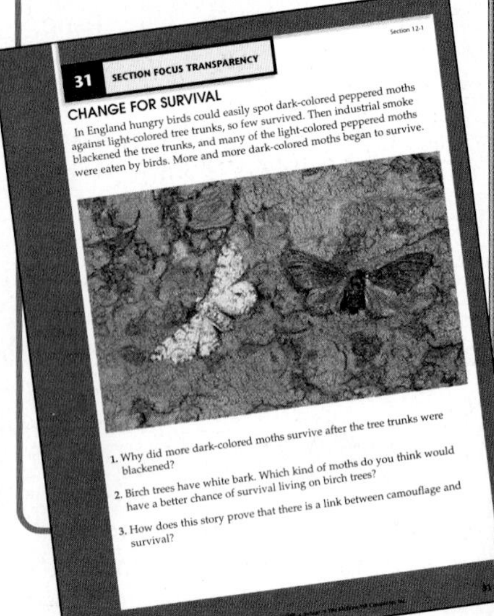

Section 12-1

31 SECTION FOCUS TRANSPARENCY

CHANGE FOR SURVIVAL

In England hungry birds could easily spot dark-colored peppered moths against light-colored tree trunks, so few survived. Then industrial smoke blackened the tree trunks, and many of the light-colored peppered moths were eaten by birds. More and more dark-colored moths began to survive.

1. Why did more dark-colored moths survive after the tree trunks were blackened?
2. Birch trees have white bark. Which kind of moths do you think would have a better chance of survival living on birch trees?
3. How does this story prove that there is a link between camouflage and survival?

31

12•1 Mechanisms of Evolution

What You'll Learn

- Lamarck's explanation of evolution and Darwin's theory of evolution
- The importance of variations in organisms
- How gradualism and punctuated equilibrium describe the rate of evolution

Vocabulary

species
evolution
natural selection
variation
gradualism
punctuated equilibrium

Why It's Important

- The theory of evolution explains why living things are different and predicts changes that will occur.

Early Thoughts About Evolution

On Earth today, there are millions of different types of organisms. Among these organisms are different species of plants, animals, bacteria, fungi, and protists. A **species** is a group of organisms with members that reproduce among themselves in their natural environment. Have any of these species of organisms changed since they first appeared on Earth? Are they still changing today? Evidence from observation of fossils indicates that living things have changed through time and are still changing. Change in the hereditary features of a species over time is **evolution.** For example, **Figure 12-2** shows how the camel has changed over time.

In 1809, Jean Baptiste de Lamarck, a French scientist, proposed one of the first explanations as to how species evolve or change. Lamarck hypothesized that species evolve by keeping traits that their parents develop during their lives. Characteristics that are not used are lost from the species. According to Lamarck's theory of evolution, if the parents lift weights, their children will be born with muscles stronger or larger than children of nonweight lifters. Lamarck's explanation of evolution is often called the theory of acquired characteristics.

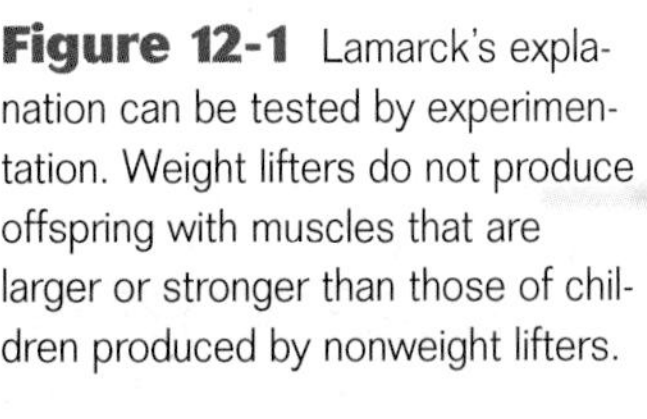

Figure 12-1 Lamarck's explanation can be tested by experimentation. Weight lifters do not produce offspring with muscles that are larger or stronger than those of children produced by nonweight lifters.

Resource Manager

The following **Teacher Classroom Resources** can be used with Section 12-1:

Reproducible Masters

Activity Worksheets, pp. 65–66, 69 L2
Enrichment, p. 31 L3
Laboratory Manual, pp. 69–74 L2
Reinforcement, p. 31 L2
Study Guide, pp. 45–46 L1 ELL

Transparencies

Teaching Transparency 23, 24 L2

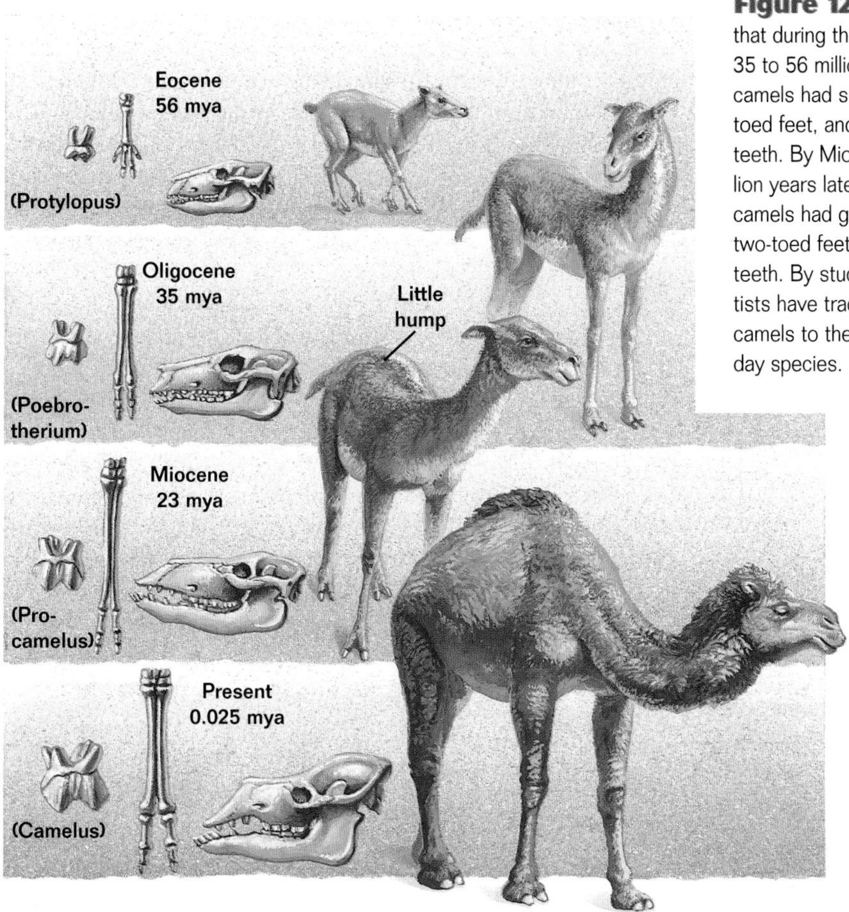

Figure 12-2 Fossils indicate that during the Eocene epoch, 35 to 56 million years ago, camels had small body size, four-toed feet, and low-crowned teeth. By Miocene times, 33 million years later, species of camels had grown larger and had two-toed feet and high-crowned teeth. By studying fossils, scientists have traced the evolution of camels to the forms of present-day species.

Genes on chromosomes control the inheritance of traits. The traits that develop during an organism's life, such as large muscles, as shown in **Figure 12-1,** are not inherited. After scientists collected large amounts of information on the inheritance of characteristics, Lamarck's explanation was rejected. The data showed that characteristics an organism develops or acquires during its lifetime aren't passed on to its offspring.

Reading Check
What was Lamarck's explanation of evolution?

Evolution by Natural Selection

In the mid-1800s, Charles Darwin came up with the theory of evolution that is still accepted today. At the age of 22, Darwin became the ship's naturalist aboard HMS *Beagle*. The *Beagle* was on a trip to survey the east and west coasts of South America. The ship sailed from England in December 1831. Darwin's work was to record facts about all the plants and animals he observed during the journey.

Tying to Previous Knowledge

Reinforce the differences between the terms *hypothesis* and *theory*. Explain that a theory is more than a hypothesis. It is an accepted explanation based on a large number of tests.

2 Teach

VISUAL Learning

Figure 12-1 Ask students why weight lifters do not produce offspring with muscles that are stronger or larger. *The DNA is unaffected by lifting weights.*

Figure 12-2 Have students list all the differences and likenesses they observe in the camel and the camel ancestors. Discuss how these changes might have come about.

Flex Your Brain

Use the Flex Your Brain activity to have students explore EVOLUTION.

Answer to Reading Check
that evolution occurred when organisms inherited acquired traits

Inclusion Strategies

Gifted Students can create their own species. They can draw it, describe its habitat and diet, and give the species a history. They should describe the changes that may have occurred within the species. Have students make a time line showing major physical changes and ecological events that coincided with changes in the species. The species may be from the past or the future. L3

Multiple Learning Styles

Kinesthetic Have students make clay impressions (secretly) of various items of daily use. Plaster of paris can be poured into the impression to form a fossil. Have students analyze the objects as if they were paleontologists in the year 3000 A.D. L2 COOP LEARN

Discussion

How are genetics and the theory of evolution related? *Genetics provides the mechanism for evolution to work in a population. If traits were not inherited, there could be no evolution.*

Correcting Misconceptions

Ask students to list the inadequacies of Lamarck's theory. Students may agree with Lamarck until they critically examine the failures of his explanation. L2

Discussion

What is meant by the term *survival of the fittest*? *The fittest are those whose adaptations match their environments; their offspring inherit these traits and thus are more likely to survive.*

Content Background

Much attention has been given to Darwin's visit to the Galápagos Islands. But, before he ever began his tour on the HMS *Beagle*, he suspected the process of evolution.

VISUAL Learning

Figure 12-3 Ask students to describe how Darwin's observations while aboard HMS *Beagle* could have led him to his theory of evolution by natural selection. *He observed similar species of organisms, separated by different kinds of barriers.*

Darwin's Observations

Darwin collected many plants, animals, and fossils from stops all along his route, which is shown in **Figure 12-3.** He was amazed by the variety of plants and animals he found in the Galápagos Islands. The Galápagos Islands are off the coast of Ecuador. The plants and animals Darwin saw in these islands must have come from Central and South America, yet on these 19 small islands, he found many species that he had not seen before. He observed giant cactus trees, 13 species of finches, and huge land tortoises, but he saw few other reptiles, only nine mammal species, and no amphibians at all. Darwin became particularly interested in the finches. He wondered how so many different, but closely related, species of finches could live on islands just a few miles apart.

For 20 years after the voyage, Darwin continued studying his collections. He thought about his observations and made further studies. He collected evidence of variations among species by breeding pigeons for racing. He also studied breeds of dogs and varieties of flowers. Darwin knew that people selected traits they wanted in plant and animal offspring by breeding parents that had those traits.

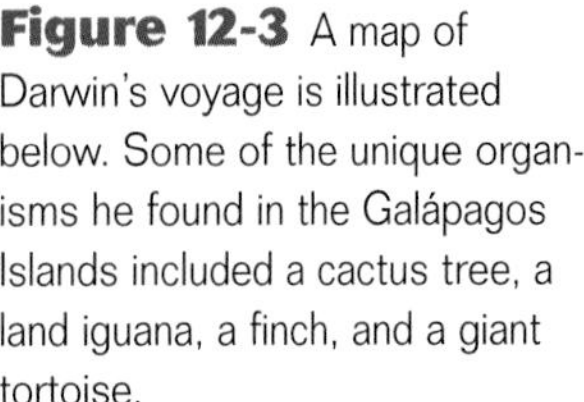

Figure 12-3 A map of Darwin's voyage is illustrated below. Some of the unique organisms he found in the Galápagos Islands included a cactus tree, a land iguana, a finch, and a giant tortoise.

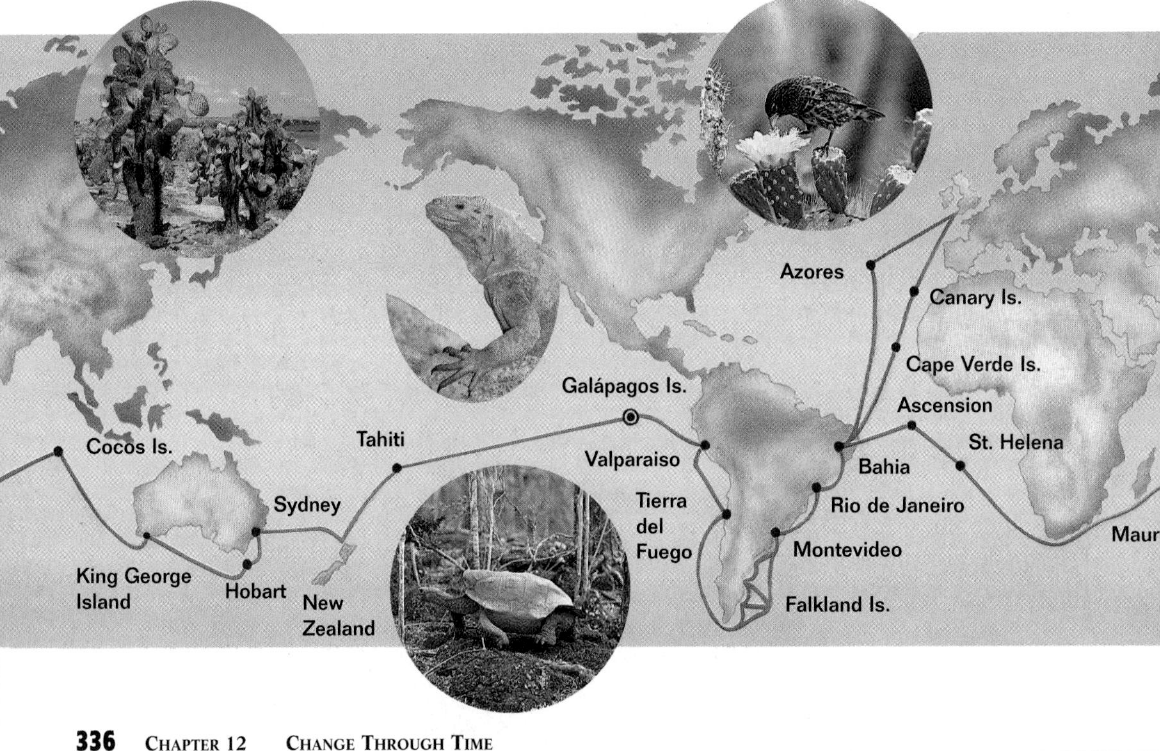

Science Journal

Darwin and Wallace Have students research and describe how the work of Alfred Wallace complemented that of Charles Darwin. Darwin and Wallace came to the same conclusion about evolution. Darwin proposed the mechanism of natural selection to account for the conclusion. Wallace worked in Malaysia. Darwin and Wallace's work was presented in 1858. L3

336 CHAPTER 12 CHANGE THROUGH TIME

Principles of Natural Selection

Darwin's observations suggested that organisms with traits most favorable for their environment survived and passed these traits on to their offspring. After many experiments, Darwin's hypothesis became the theory of evolution by natural selection. **Natural selection** means that organisms with traits best suited to their environment are more likely to survive and reproduce. The factors identified in natural selection are as follows.

1. Organisms produce more offspring than can survive.
2. Variations are found among individuals of a species.
3. Variations are passed on to offspring.
4. Some variations allow members of a population to survive and reproduce better than others.
5. Over time, offspring of individuals with helpful variations make up more and more of a population.

Darwin wrote a book describing his theory of evolution by natural selection. His book, *On the Origin of Species by Means of Natural Selection,* was published in 1859. Some changes have been made to Darwin's theory as new information has been gathered. However, his theory remains one of the most important ideas in the study of life science.

interNET CONNECTION

Visit the Glencoe Science Web Site at **www.glencoe.com/sec/science** for more information about the finches Darwin observed.

Problem Solving

When can some fish be sold?

Alejandro has decided to raise tropical fish as a hobby and to sell his extra fish to a local store to make some spending money. In his research, Alejandro learned that each tropical fish requires one gallon of water. Eventually, they will produce more young than can be kept in his 30-gallon aquarium. He knew that he wanted to keep his most beautiful fish and sell the others. Alejandro realized that selecting fish in this way would be similar to Charles Darwin's theory of evolution by natural selection.

Solve the Problem

1. Assume Alejandro buys one pair of adult fish that just produced young. The species of fish Alejandro bought produce equal numbers of males and females. Each adult pair of fish begins to breed when they are two months old and produce ten young every subsequent two months. Also assume that all of the young survive to reproduce. How many fish will Alejandro have after two months?
2. If Alejandro continues to raise fish, how long will it be before he must sell some fish or get another aquarium?

Think Critically: How does Alejandro's problem relate to the first factor that governs natural selection as listed at the top of this page?

Problem Solving

All organisms have the capacity to produce more offspring than can survive. If some fish were not removed, the aquarium would become overpopulated, and some fish would die.

Solve the Problem

1. A pair of adult fish produce 10 young in 2 months, so the total is 12.
2. He must sell some fish after 4 months.

Think Critically The first factor that governs natural selection is that every species overproduces offspring. Alejandro's fish eventually produce more young than can be supported by his aquarium.

Quick Demo

 **Visual-Spatial** Show students photographs of different organisms. Let the students list the adaptations they think were selected for in each organism. L2

GLENCOE TECHNOLOGY

CD-ROM

Glencoe Science Voyages Interactive CD-ROM

Explorations

Have students do the interactive exploration *How can natural selection be modeled?*

interNET CONNECTION

Internet Addresses

For Internet tips, see Glencoe's **Using the Internet in the Science Classroom.**

Using Math

The events are equally likely, but that is not what happens. Because the classified ad circles are camouflaged, fewer are chosen.

Teacher FYI

Albinism occurs in almost all species of mammals and has also been observed in other groups of animals and plants.

GLENCOE TECHNOLOGY

Videodisc

Glencoe Science Voyages Interactive Videodisc—Life

Side 1, Lesson 2

Evolution: Patterns of Change

15195

17849

22558

23064

25056

Refer to the Videodisc Teacher Guide for additional bar codes.

Using Math

Use the data from the Explore Activity. The experimental probability of picking up a white circle is as follows.

Probability = white circles ÷ total circles

Find the probability of picking up white, black, and classified ad circles. Are these events equally likely? Is that what actually happened?

Adaptation and Variation

One of the points in Darwin's theory is that differences are found among individuals of a species. These differences are called variations. A **variation** is an inherited trait that makes an individual different from other members of the same species. Variations can be small, such as differences in the shape of human hairlines, or large, such as an albino squirrel in a population of gray squirrels, or fruit without seeds. Variations are important in populations of organisms. A population is a group of organisms of one species that live in an area. If enough variations occur in a population as it produces new offspring, a new species may evolve from the existing species. It may take hundreds, thousands, or even millions of generations for a new species to evolve.

The Sources of Variations

Some variations are more helpful than others. An adaptation is any variation that makes an organism better suited to its environment. The variations that result in adaptation can be in an organism's color, shape, behavior, or chemical makeup. Camouflage is an adaptation that lets an organism blend into its environment, as shown in **Figure 12-4A.** An organism that can camouflage itself is more likely to survive and reproduce. These types of variations result from mutations, which are changes in an organism's DNA.

What other factors bring about evolution? The movement of individuals of the same species into or out of an area brings in or removes new genes and variations. Have you ever had an exchange student come to your school? The student

Figure 12-4 Variations may be beneficial, harmful, or neutral in a population.

Camouflage causes some organisms to blend into their environment. **How does camouflage coloration give this spider an advantage in survival?**

B Variations that result in a disadvantage, such as albinism, tend to decrease in a population over time. **What would likely happen to an albino squirrel in its natural environment?**

VISUAL Learning

Figure 12-4 Have students discuss other examples of variations that could be beneficial, harmful, or neutral in a population of organisms.

338 CHAPTER 12 CHANGE THROUGH TIME

probably brought new ideas, maybe a new style of dress, and even a new language. When new individuals come into an existing population, they can bring in new genes and variations in much the same way. Some organisms are separated from others by geography and changes in climate. This isolation can result in evolutionary change, as you can see in **Figure 12-5.** Each of these factors affects how fast evolution occurs.

How fast does evolution occur?

Scientists do not agree on the answer to this question. Many scientists hypothesize that evolution occurs slowly, perhaps taking tens or hundreds of millions of years. Other scientists hypothesize that evolution may occur quickly. As you study evolution, you will see that evidence supports both of these models.

MiniLab

Relating Evolution to Species

Procedure

1. On a piece of paper, print the alphabet in lowercase letters.
2. Order the letters into three groups. Put all of the vowels in the first group. Place all of the consonants that do not drop below the line into the second group and all of the consonants that do drop below the line in the third group.

Analysis

1. How are the three groups of letters similar to each other?
2. If the letters were organisms, how would scientists know how closely related the letters were to each other?

Figure 12-5 The Tana river in Kenya separates two populations of giraffes. Over time, these two populations have become distinct. **Do these giraffes have different appearances? What does this tell you about their genetic makeup?**

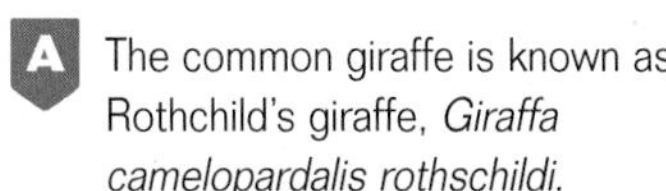

A The common giraffe is known as Rothchild's giraffe, *Giraffa camelopardalis rothschildi.*

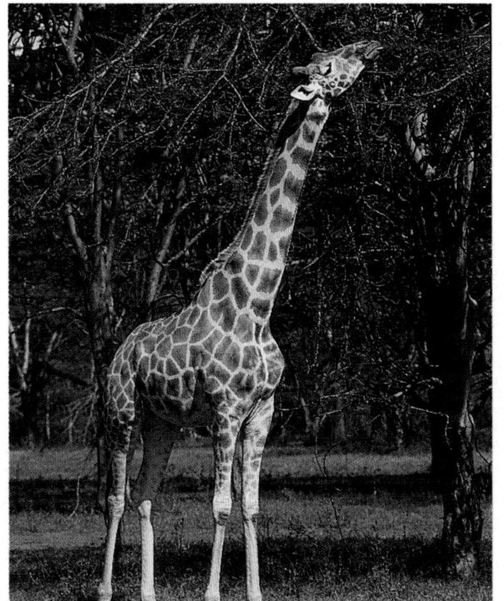

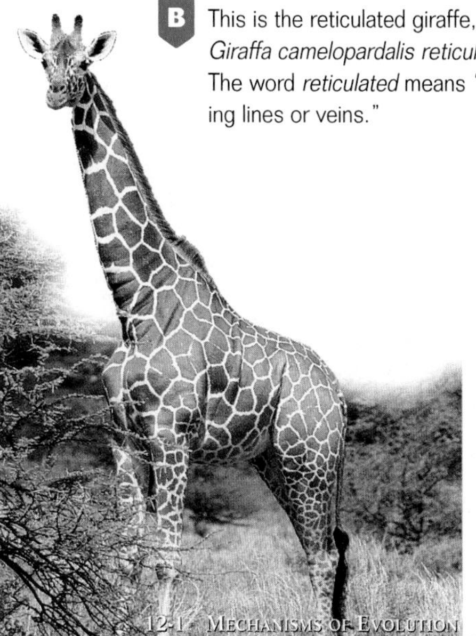

B This is the reticulated giraffe, *Giraffa camelopardalis reticulata.* The word *reticulated* means "having lines or veins."

Caption Answers

Figure 12-4A *The spider is not easily seen by birds or other predators.*

Figure 12-4B *It would be selected against and probably be killed by a predator because it is too easy to see.*

Figure 12-5 *Yes; they must also have different genotypes.*

MiniLab

Purpose

Visual-Spatial Students will practice classifying letters and sequencing changes. L2

Materials

paper and pencil

Teaching Strategies

Explain to students that the letters of the alphabet have changed over time. You may research and show the evolution of the letters *f* and *s* in particular. Tell how this type of evolution is different from evolution in living things.

Analysis

1. Answers will vary. Students may indicate that they are all letters of the alphabet or are all lowercase letters.
2. Letters with a characteristic in common would be the most closely related (i.e. letters that are dotted). Letters with similar characteristics would be the next closest relations (i.e. dotted letters and tall letters). Letters with no similar characteristics would be distantly related.

Assessment

Performance To further assess students' understanding of evolution, have them make up and explain another hypothetical evolutionary schema using whatever shapes or materials they choose. **Use Performance Assessment in the Science Classroom,** p. 49.

3 Assess

Check for Understanding

Discussion

Interpersonal Have students discuss why Darwin was impressed with the ability of humans to produce new breeds of plants and animals through artificial selection. He saw this as an analogy to the mechanism of evolution—natural selection. COOP LEARN

Reteach

Have students list similarities between artificial selection and natural selection. L2

Extension

For students who have mastered this section, use the **Reinforcement** and **Enrichment** masters.

GLENCOE TECHNOLOGY

Videodisc

The Infinite Voyage: The Great Dinosaur Hunt

Chapter 9 *Communication Theories* 5:30

Refer to the Videodisc Teacher Guide for bar codes and teaching strategies.

Gradualism

Darwin hypothesized that the rate of evolution was steady, slow, and ongoing. The model that describes evolution as a slow change of one species to another, new species is known as **gradualism.** According to the gradualism model, continued mutations and variations will result in a new species over time. According to this model, there should be intermediate forms of all species. Evolution involves a change in the phenotype, or appearance, of a species as its hereditary features change. Look back at **Figure 12-1,** showing evolution of the camel. Fossil evidence shows gradual changes between the camel as it first appeared and how it looks today. Camels appear to have evolved gradually over millions of years. Fossil evidence shows the gradual evolution of many present-day species.

Punctuated Equilibrium

But gradualism doesn't explain the evolution of some species, especially those in which there is a gap in the fossil record because few intermediate forms have been discovered. The **punctuated equilibrium** model, as seen in **Figure 12-6,** shows that rapid evolution can come about by the mutation of just a few genes, resulting in the appearance of a new species. How fast is evolution by this model? New species could appear as quickly as every few million years and sometimes even more rapidly than that. For example, bacteria that cause illness in humans can sometimes be killed by antibiotics such as penicillin. Penicillin has been available only since 1940, yet some species of bacteria are now resistant to this drug. How did this happen so quickly? As in any population, some of the bacteria had variations that allowed them to keep from being

Figure 12-6 Evolution can occur slowly, as in gradualism, or rapidly, as in punctuated equilibrium. In the diagrams below, branches of different colors represent different species. Branches that do not continue to the top of the graph represent species that are extinct and, therefore, are no longer evolving. A change in the phenotype of a species is a change in its appearance.

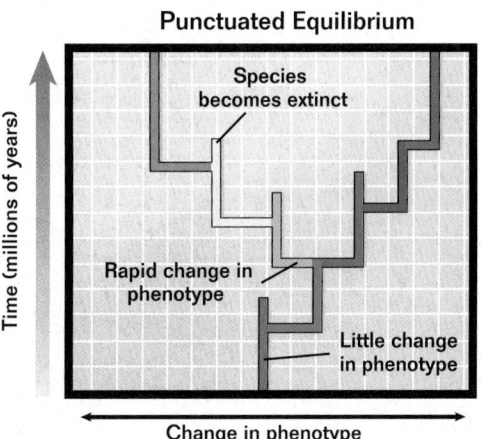

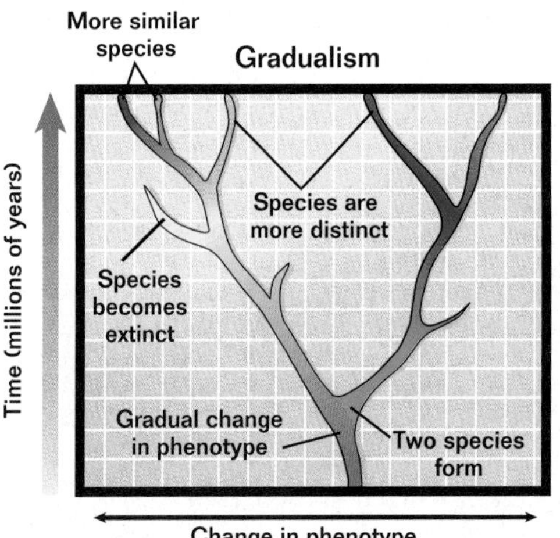

VISUAL Learning

Figure 12-6 Have students compare the graphs that explain gradualism and punctuated equilibrium. Explain that both types of evolution are observed in the fossil record.

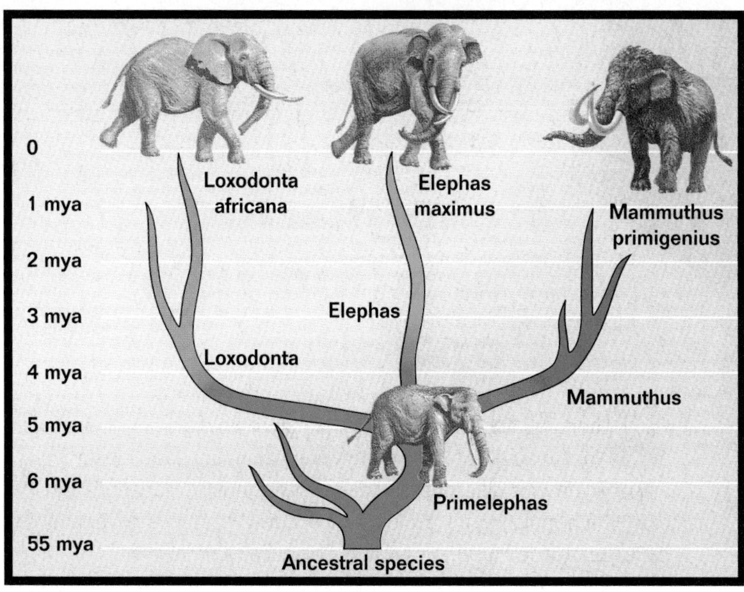

Figure 12-7 The evolution of the elephant illustrates how punctuated equilibrium usually occurs. Notice that three distinct species evolved over 1 million years—a relatively short amount of time. This same change would have taken several million years to occur in gradualism.

killed by penicillin. When the drug was used to kill bacteria, the few individuals with this variation lived to reproduce. Over a short period of time, the entire population of bacteria became resistant to penicillin. The bacteria had evolved quickly—an example of punctuated equilibrium. In this step-like pattern, large changes take place in a short period of time. The fossil record also gives examples of this type of evolution, as you can see in **Figure 12-7.** Punctuated equilibrium and gradualism are compared in **Figure 12-6.**

Section Assessment

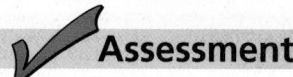

1. Compare Lamarck's and Darwin's ideas of evolution.
2. How are variations important in a population?
3. Define what an adaptation is and give an example.
4. **Think Critically:** Explain how the gradualism model of evolution differs from the punctuated equilibrium model.
5. **Skill Builder**
   Making and Using Graphs
   Do the **Chapter 12 Skill Activity** on page 753 to learn how to make and use a graph.

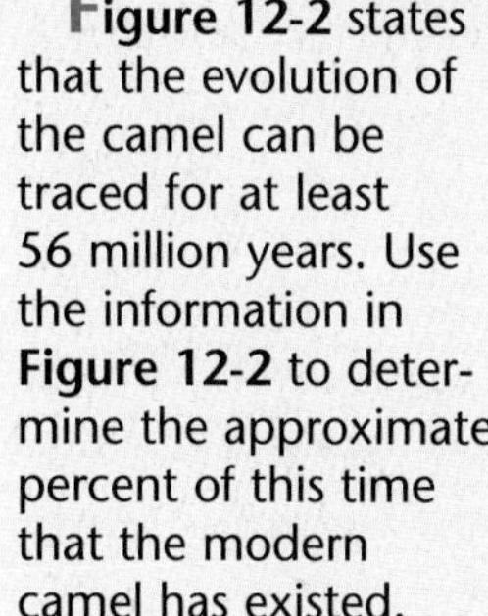

Using Math

Figure 12-2 states that the evolution of the camel can be traced for at least 56 million years. Use the information in **Figure 12-2** to determine the approximate percent of this time that the modern camel has existed.

4 Close

Proficiency Prep

Use this quiz to check students' recall of section content.

1. **What is a group of organisms with members that reproduce among themselves?** *a species*
2. **What is a group of organisms of one species that live in an area?** *a population*

Section Assessment

1. Lamarck thought acquired traits were passed to offspring. Darwin concluded that only certain traits were inherited and passed to offspring.
2. Some variations are advantageous for survival and reproduction.
3. An adaptation is any variation that makes an organism better suited to its environment. An example is color camouflage in a spider.
4. **Think Critically** Gradualism supports the hypothesis that an ancestral species slowly evolves to become another species. The punctuated equilibrium model explains that species tend to remain constant for millions of years and, suddenly, in the span of one or a few million years, become two or more species.

Using Math

$\frac{\text{2 million years}}{\text{56 million years}} \times 100\% =$ approximately 4%

Assessment

Performance To assess students' abilities to classify organisms by their variations, ask them to classify two species of birds that eat different types of foods. Use **Performance Assessment in the Science Classroom,** p. 49.

Recognize the Problem

Purpose

Logical-Mathematical Students will design and carry out an experiment to show the variation in a population. L2 ELL COOP LEARN

Process Skills

forming a hypothesis, measuring in SI, using numbers, interpreting data, communicating, making and using tables, designing an experiment, separating and controlling variables

Time

45 minutes to plan the investigation, 45 minutes to complete the investigation

Materials

Contact local florists about availability of plant parts. Do not choose seeds that are too small to accurately measure their size.

Safety Precautions

Caution students not to put any materials into their mouths. Be sure students are not allergic to any plants used.

Form a Hypothesis

Possible Hypotheses

Student hypotheses will vary. Possible hypotheses might be: "A sample of sunflowers will exhibit variations in number of leaves," or "A sample of sunflower seeds will exhibit variations in length."

Test Your Hypothesis

Possible Procedures

Procedures will vary. Most students will choose width or length to measure. Others may choose volume, number of petals, or some other variable they notice in seeds, leaves, or flowers.

Sample Data Table

Seed number	Length (mm)
1	8
2	9
3	8
4	6
5	5
6	8

Design Your Own Experiment

Recognizing Variation in a Population

Possible Materials

- Leaves, flowers, and seeds from one species of plant
- Metric ruler
- Magnifying glass
- Graph paper

When you first see a group of plants or animals of one species, they may all look alike. However, when you look closer, you will notice minor differences in each characteristic. Variations must exist in a population for evolution to occur. What kinds of variations have you noticed among species of plants or animals?

Recognize the Problem

How can you measure variation in a plant or animal population?

Form a Hypothesis

Make a hypothesis about the amount of variation in seeds, leaves, or flowers of one species of plant.

Goals

- **Design an experiment** that will allow you to collect data about variation in a population.
- **Observe, measure,** and **analyze** variations in a population.

Safety Precautions

Do not put any seeds, flowers, or plant parts in your mouth. Wash your hands after handling plant parts.

342 CHAPTER 12 CHANGE THROUGH TIME

Test Your Hypothesis

Plan

1. As a group, agree upon and write out the hypothesis statement.
2. List the steps you need to take to **test your hypothesis.** Be specific. Describe exactly what you will do at each step. List your materials.
3. Decide what characteristic of seeds, leaves, or flowers you will study. For example, you could **measure** the length of seeds, the width of leaves, or the number of petals on the flowers of plants.
4. **Design a data table** in your Science Journal to collect data about one variation. Use the table to record the data your group collects as you complete the experiment.
5. **Identify** any constants, variables, and controls of the experiment.
6. How many seeds, leaves, or flowers will you examine? Will your data be more accurate if you examine larger numbers?
7. **Summarize** the data in a graph or chart.

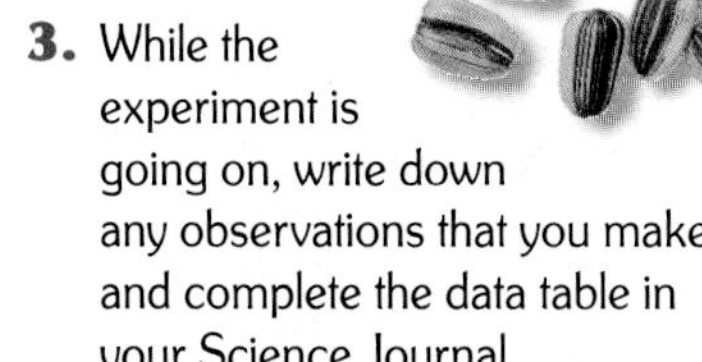

Do

1. Make sure your teacher approves your plan before you proceed.
2. Carry out the experiment as planned.
3. While the experiment is going on, write down any observations that you make and complete the data table in your Science Journal.

Analyze Your Data

1. **Compare** your results with those of other groups.
2. How did you determine the amount of variation present?

The *range* of a set of data is the difference between the greatest measurement and the smallest measurement. The *mean* is the sum of all the data divided by the sample size.

Draw Conclusions

1. **Graph** your results, placing the *range* of variation on the *x*-axis and the number of organisms that had that measurement on the *y*-axis.
2. **Calculate** the *mean* and *range* of variation in your experiment.

Teaching Strategies

- Guide students as they decide which trait to measure. Length or width of plant parts will be most easily measured with the materials suggested.
- For most students, larger seeds will be easier to work with. Sunflower seeds, lima beans, pinto beans, and peas are large enough.

Expected Outcome

Most students will collect data that result in a bell-shaped curve when graphed.

Error Analysis

Have students who measure the same trait share their results and explain any differences they observe.

Analyze Your Data

1. Results should be similar for the same measured variables.
2. The range of measurements determines the amount of variation.

Draw Conclusions

1. Graphs will be a bell-shaped curve for most variables.
2. Mean and range will vary depending on the plant parts used and the variables measured.

GO Further

Discuss the variations observed by the class. Have students think of reasons why some variations are more advantageous than others.

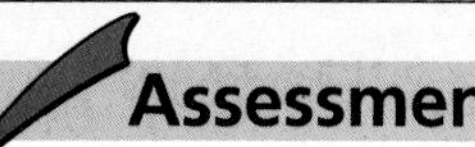

Assessment

Performance Have students measure variations in pieces of the same kind of fruit. Use **Performance Assessment in the Science Classroom,** p. 25. P

SECTION 12·2

Prepare

Content Background

Refer to **Fossil Evidence, The Fossil Record** and **Other Evidence for Evolution** on pp. 332E–F.

Preplanning

Refer to the **Chapter Organizer** on pages 332A–B.

1 Motivate

Bellringer

Before presenting the lesson, display **Section Focus Transparency 32** on the overhead projector. Use the accompanying **Focus Activity** worksheet. L2 ELL

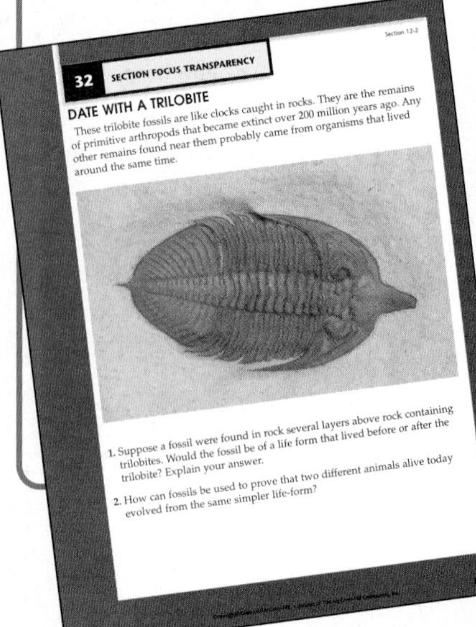

Section 12-2

32 SECTION FOCUS TRANSPARENCY

DATE WITH A TRILOBITE

These trilobite fossils are like clocks caught in rocks. They are the remains of primitive arthropods that became extinct over 200 million years ago. Any other remains found near them probably came from organisms that lived around the same time.

1. Suppose a fossil were found in rock several layers above rock containing trilobites. Would the fossil be of a life form that lived before or after the trilobite? Explain your answer.
2. How can fossils be used to prove that two different animals alive today evolved from the same simpler life-form?

12·2 Evidence for Evolution

What You'll Learn

- The importance of fossils as evidence of evolution
- How relative and radiometric dating are used to date fossils
- Examples of five types of evidence for evolution

Vocabulary

sedimentary rock
radioactive element
homologous
vestigial structure
embryology

Why It's Important

- Valid scientific theories must be backed up by observable or testable evidence.

Fossil Evidence

On a hot day in July 1975, in northern Texas, two people were walking along the shores of Lake Lavon. They came across some odd-looking rocks sticking up from the muddy shore. They noticed that the rocks seemed different from the surrounding limestone rocks. They took a few of the rocks to a scientist who studies reptiles and amphibians. The rocks were skull pieces of a fossil mosasaur, an extinct lizard that had lived in salt water.

A group of scientists returned to the site and carefully dug up the rest of the fossil mosasaur. This find indicates that about 120 million years ago, the northern Texas area—now more than 500 km from the Gulf of Mexico—was covered by a shallow sea. Fossils such as those found on the shores of Lake Lavon are studied by scientists called paleontologists (pay lee ahn TAHL uh justs), shown in **Figure 12-8.**

Figure 12-8 Digging for fossils requires careful work. Paleontologists, scientists who study the past by examining fossils, sift tons of earth and rock to find tiny bones. They may use dental equipment such as dental picks and toothbrushes to remove dirt as they work to uncover larger bones, such as these dinosaur bones found in Thailand.

Resource Manager

The following **Teacher Classroom Resources** can be used with Section 12-2:

Reproducible Masters

Activity Worksheets, pp. 67–68 L2
Enrichment, p. 32 L3
Multicultural Connections, pp. 23–24
Reinforcement, p. 32 L2
Critical Thinking/Problem Solving, p. 12 L2
Study Guide, p. 47

Transparencies

Science Integration Transparency 12 L2

VISUALIZING Fossils

Figure 12-9 Three examples of fossils are shown. **Which of these would most likely be found in a layer of sedimentary rock?**

A This is an imprint fossil made by a leaf.

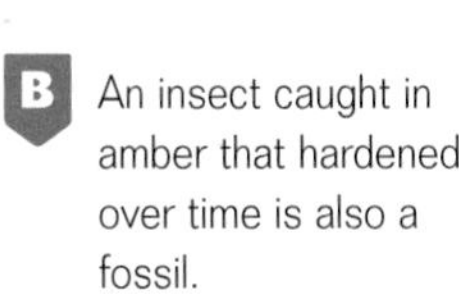

B An insect caught in amber that hardened over time is also a fossil.

C This is the cast fossil of an ammonite, an extinct marine organism.

Kinds of Fossils

The most evidence for evolution comes from fossils like those found on the shore of Lake Lavon in Texas. A fossil is any evidence of life from an earlier geological time, such as those illustrated in **Figure 12-9.** Examples of fossils include the following.

1. the imprint of a leaf, feather, or organism in rock
2. a cast made of minerals that filled in the hollows of an animal track, mollusk shell, or other parts of an organism
3. a piece of wood or bone replaced by minerals
4. an organism frozen in ice
5. an insect or other organism trapped in amber

Sedimentary rock contains the most fossils. **Sedimentary rock** is a rock type formed from particles of preexisting rocks. These particles can be deposited by water, wind, gravity, or ice. Limestone, sandstone, and shale are all examples of sedimentary rock. Fossils are found more often in limestone than in any other kind of sedimentary rock.

interNET CONNECTION

Visit the Glencoe Science Web Site at **www.glencoe.com/sec/science** for more information on fossils.

Tying to Previous Knowledge

Review the structure and function of DNA with students while they study the evidence for evolution.

Content Background

The fossil record has always been incomplete because most organisms never become fossils. They are either decomposed or eaten before they have an opportunity to become fossilized.

Caption Answer

Figure 12-9 *All of these fossils are found in sedimentary rock. Like the amber, fossils are also sometimes eroded from rock and found in streambeds.*

Activity

Have students research the Scopes trial and other legislation and court cases concerning the teaching of evolution. They may report their findings to the class.

interNET CONNECTION

Internet Addresses

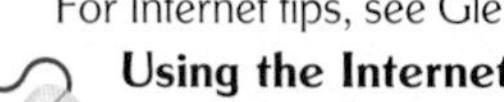

For Internet tips, see Glencoe's **Using the Internet in the Science Classroom.**

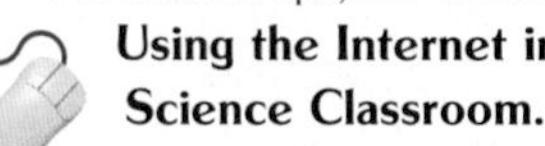

Integrating the Sciences

Earth Science Types of sedimentary rock include shale, limestone, sandstone, and conglomerate. Almost all fossils are found in one of these kinds of sedimentary rock. Nearly 75 percent of Earth's surface is covered by sedimentary rock. In some places, the sedimentary layers are almost a mile thick. Many sedimentary rocks lack the radioactive elements needed for radiometric dating.

Using Math

$\frac{66\,000\,000 \text{ years}}{4\,600\,000\,000 \text{ years}} \times 100\% =$
1.4%

EARTH SCIENCE INTEGRATION

Fossils are usually found in sedimentary rock because it is the least disturbed kind of rock. Igneous rock is produced by solidifying lava and never had organisms living in it. Metamorphic rock has undergone changes due to pressure and melting that destroys most fossils.

VISUAL Learning

Table 12-1 Explain the vastness of geological time. A million years is only 0.02 percent of the total.

Enrichment

Visit a natural history museum to observe fossil collections.

Activity

Interpersonal Have groups of students collect rocks and fossils from your area. Allow them to research the types of rocks and fossils they find. If students will donate their finds to the school, you can quickly build a school collection of fossils and rocks to display. L2 ELL COOP LEARN

Table 12-1

Geologic Time Scale							
Era	Cenozoic		Mesozoic			Paleozoic	
Period	Quaternary	Tertiary	Cretaceous	Jurassic	Triassic	Permian	Pennsylvanian
Millions of years ago							
	1.6	66	146	208	245	290	

EARTH SCIENCE INTEGRATION

Using Math

The Cenozoic era represents approximately 66 million years of Earth's 4.6-billion-year history. Approximately what percent of Earth's total history does this era represent?

The Fossil Record

You learned that the mosasaur fossil found in Texas was 120 million years old. How did scientists come up with this date? Scientists have divided Earth's history into eras and periods. These divisions make up the geologic time scale as shown in **Table 12-1.** Unique rock layers and fossils give information about the geology, weather, and life-forms of each time period. There are two basic methods for reading the record of past life. When these methods are used together, estimates of the ages of certain rocks and fossils can be made.

Relative Dating

One way to find the approximate age of a rock layer, or fossils within the layer, is relative dating. Relative dating is based on the idea that in undisturbed areas, older rock layers lie below younger rock layers, as shown in **Figure 12-10.** Therefore, fossils found in lower layers of rock are older than those in upper layers. Relative dating cannot give the exact age of a fossil. It can give only an estimate of how old the fossil might be.

Radiometric Dating

Scientists can give a more accurate age to a rock layer using radioactive elements. A **radioactive element** gives off radiation due to an unstable nucleus. As radioactive elements give off radiation, they eventually change to more stable products. The radiation is given off at a steady rate

Multiple Learning Styles

Kinesthetic Have students make a model showing relative dating using clear plastic or glass containers and sand, dirt, salt, cornmeal, or other materials. Several "fossils" should be placed in the model to explain their relative ages. Have each student present his or her model to the group. L2 ELL

Paleozoic					Precambrian
Mississippian	Devonian	Silurian	Ordovician	Cambrian	
					4600

323 362 408 439 510 543

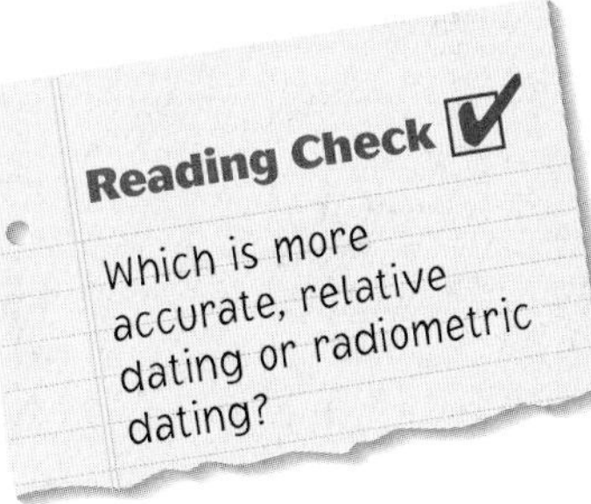

that is different for each element. Scientists can estimate the age of the rock by comparing the amount of radioactive element with the amount of nonradioactive element in the rock. However, many times this method of dating gives inconsistent dates because the original amount of radioactive element in the rock is never completely certain.

Figure 12-10 Fossils found in lower layers of sedimentary rock are usually older than the fossils found in upper layers.

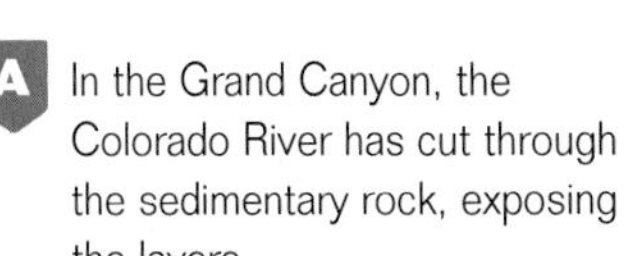

A In the Grand Canyon, the Colorado River has cut through the sedimentary rock, exposing the layers.

B Paleontologists can date fossils by the age of the rock layer in which they occur.

Discussion

Could relative dating be used to date fossils in rock layers that have been uplifted or disturbed in other ways? *No, radiometric dating would have to be used to obtain an age for the fossils.*

Activity

Naturalist Have students locate fossils in walls of local buildings and research the locations from which the building materials came. Most of the fossils will be of marine creatures in limestone that may come from other states in the United States or other countries. L3

Using an Analogy

Use a clock to put geological time in perspective. If a 12-hour period represents the total length of time since Earth formed, humans appeared in the last fraction of a second. If a 4.5-m time line is used, humans appeared in the last millimeter.

Discussion

Have students research and discuss alternative theories of evolution.

Across the Curriculum

Geography Have students use a geology text, geological map of the United States, or similar resources to describe the locations of different sedimentary rock types. L2

Caption Answer

Figure 12-11 *These fuels are formed from the buried remains of ancient organisms; fossils are the evidence of ancient organisms.*

GLENCOE TECHNOLOGY

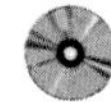 **Videodisc**

Glencoe Science Voyages Interactive Videodisc—Earth

Side 2, Lesson 5

Dinosaurs: Footprints in the Rock

1250

8794

Refer to the Videodisc Teacher Guide for additional bar codes.

Figure 12-11 In the Pennsylvanian period, 300 million years ago, amphibians and land plants were the dominant life-forms on Earth. Many of the plants of this period eventually became peat and coal. **Why do we call these fossil fuels?**

Fossils Show Evolution Occurred

Fossils are a record of organisms that lived in the past. But, the fossil record has gaps, much like a book with pages missing. Because every living thing doesn't or can't become fossilized, the record will never be complete. By looking at fossils, scientists conclude that many simpler forms of life existed earlier in Earth's history, and more complex forms of life appeared later. The oldest fossil bacteria appeared 3.5 billion years ago. Invertebrates with hard shells appeared in the Cambrian period, about 540 million years ago. The first land plants did not appear until the Silurian period, 439 million years ago. Dinosaurs were common on Earth during the Jurassic and Cretaceous periods, from 208 to 66 million years ago. The first mammals and birds did not appear until the Jurassic period, about 200 million years ago. **Figure 12-11** shows an artist's drawing of a scene of 300 million years ago. The fossil record gives scientists direct evidence that living things evolved. There are also other types of ideas that support the theory of evolution.

Integrating the Sciences

Earth Science By examining change over time, scientists can determine which traits were most favorable to survival in a particular environment.

Other Evidence for Evolution

Besides fossils, what other evidence is there for evolution? Scientists have found more evidence by looking at similarities in chemical makeup such as DNA, development, and embryological structure among organisms. You know that the functions of a dolphin's flipper, a bat's wing, and a bird's wing are different. Yet, as you can see in **Figure 12-12,** each of these structures is made up of the same kind of bones. Each has about the same number of muscles and blood vessels. Each of these limbs developed from similar tissues. Body parts that are similar in origin and structure are called **homologous** (huh MAHL uh gus). Homologous structures indicate that two or more species might share common ancestors.

EARTH SCIENCE INTEGRATION

Importance of Fossils
Many organisms have a history that has been preserved in sedimentary rock. Fossils of animals such as horses and whales have bones that have become reduced in size or number over geologic time as species have evolved. Explain what information can be understood from changes in structures over time.

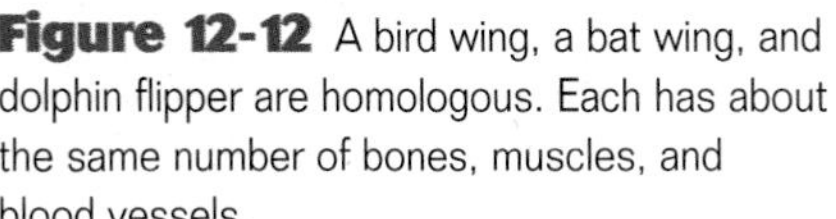

Figure 12-12 A bird wing, a bat wing, and dolphin flipper are homologous. Each has about the same number of bones, muscles, and blood vessels.

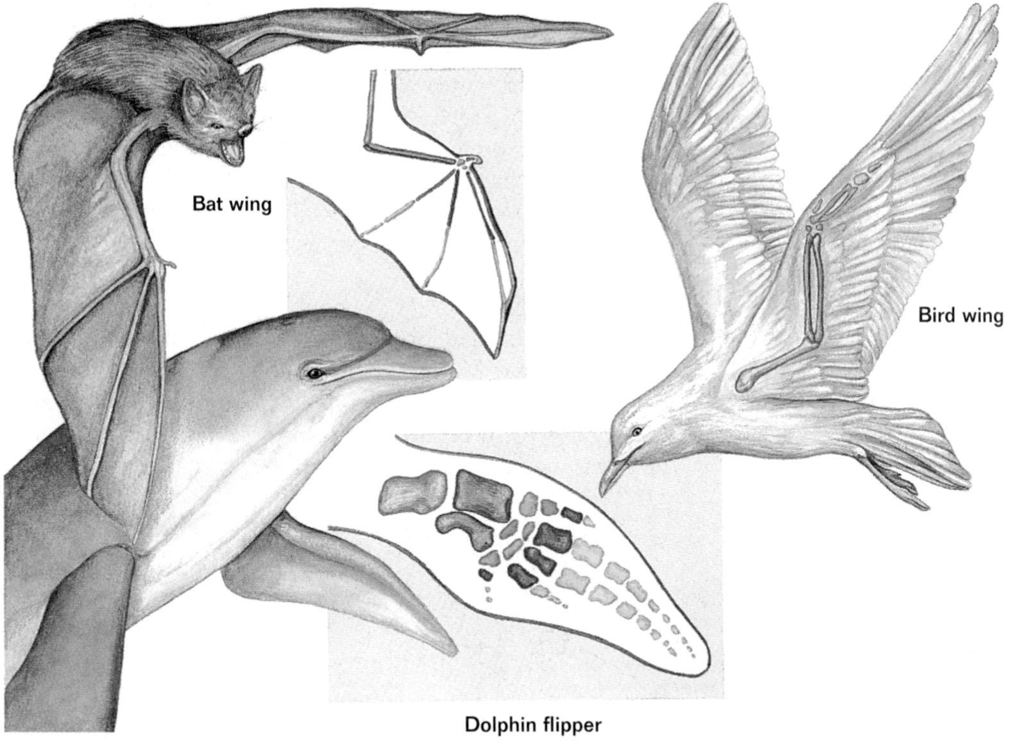

Content Background

Transitional forms can be seen by studying homologous structures. An example is the ancestral camel, which has slowly evolved from a small form without a hump to the present-day camel.

Activity

Visual-Spatial Have students compare the wing of a bat and the flipper of a sea lion. Ask students what relationship these similar structures have. L2

EARTH SCIENCE INTEGRATION

The past functions of present vestigial structures can be inferred from fossils that indicate what the structures were like in the past.

GLENCOE TECHNOLOGY

Videodisc

The Infinite Voyage: The Great Dinosaur Hunt

Chapter 7 *Newborns: Examining Dinosaur Eggs* 8:30

Refer to the Videodisc Teacher Guide for bar codes and teaching strategies.

Guided Reading Strategy

Supporting Idea Chart This strategy examines the relationship between a whole and its parts. Write the name of the whole object on the single line at the left. On the next set of lines to the right, write the major parts of the object. Finally, write the sub-parts of each major part. Have students design a Supporting Idea Chart for a concept in this section.

Sample Chart:

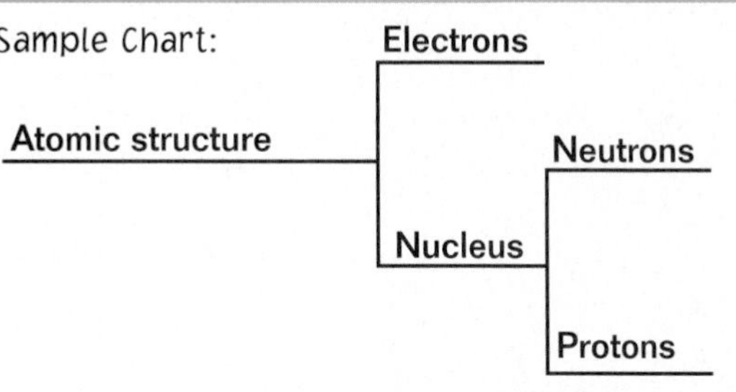

Caption Answer

Figure 12-14 *In the early stages of development, you cannot tell just by observation.*

Teacher FYI

Pesticide resistance in insects, antibiotic resistance in bacteria, and observed differences in salamanders and birds are all examples of direct evidence for evolution.

3 Assess

Check for Understanding

Using Science Words

Linguistic Have students determine the meaning of the prefix and suffix making up the word *homologous.* L2

Reteach

Naturalist Present examples of as many kinds of fossils as possible. Show students imprints, petrified wood, casts, molds, and amber. Have students identify each fossil. L2

Extension

For students who have mastered this section, use the **Reinforcement** and **Enrichment** masters.

4 Close

Proficiency Prep

Use this quiz to check students' recall of section content.

1. **What are remains of life from an earlier time called?** *fossils*
2. **Most fossils are contained in what type of rock?** *sedimentary*
3. **What are elements with atoms that give off radiation called?** *radioactive elements*

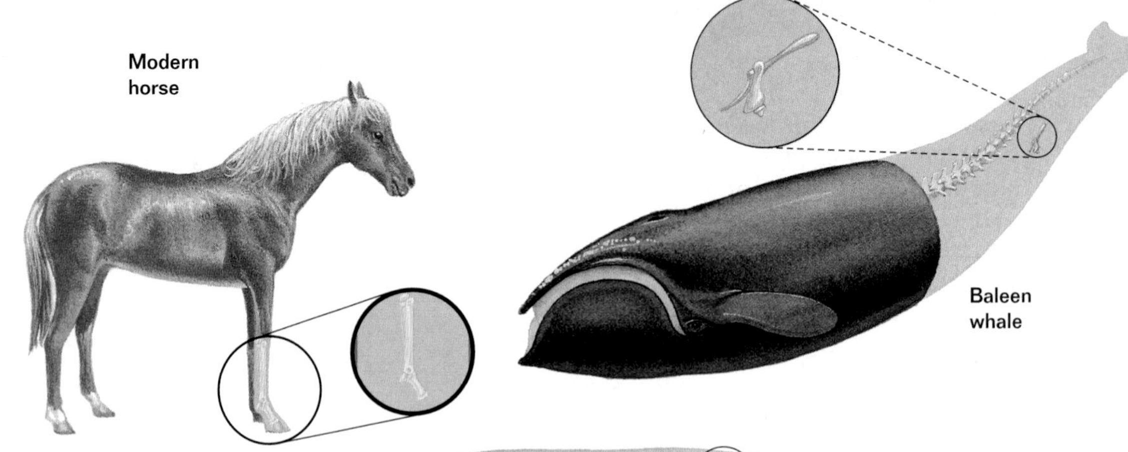

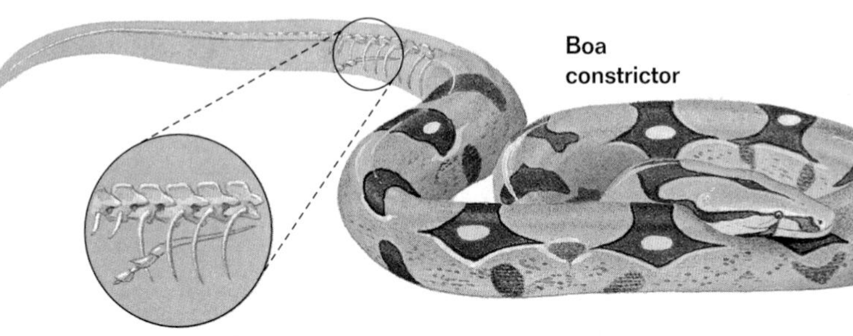

Figure 12-13 Do whales or snakes have back legs? You can see that they don't, yet both animals have vestigial hipbones and leg bones where legs may once have existed. Horses once had four functional toes. Now, they walk on just one toe. The others are no longer functional.

Vestigial Structures

Vestigial structures also give evidence for evolution. A **vestigial** (veh STIHJ ee ul) **structure** is a body part that doesn't seem to have a function. For example, manatees no longer have back legs, but they still have pelvic bones. Scientists hypothesize that vestigial structures are parts that once functioned in an ancestor, as seen in **Figure 12-13.**

Embryology

The study of development in organisms is called **embryology** (em bree AHL uh jee). An embryo is an organism in its earliest stages of development. Compare the embryos of the organisms in **Figure 12-14.** In the early stages of development, the embryos of fish, reptiles, birds, and mammals

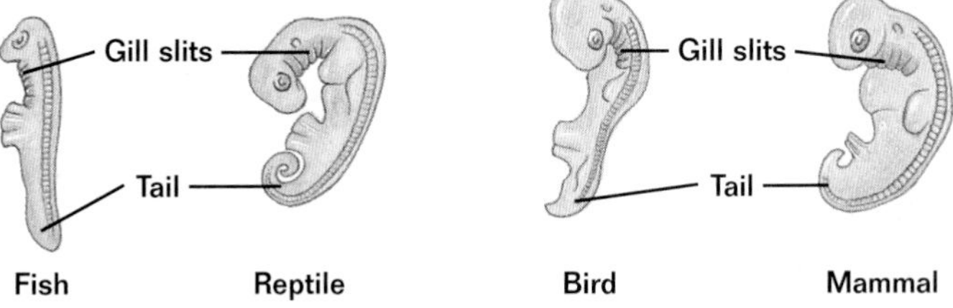

Figure 12-14 Similarities in the embryos of fish, reptiles, birds, and mammals suggest evolution. Many of the same features are found in all of these organisms. **How can you tell which organism's embryo is which?**

have a tail and gills or gill slits. Fish keep their gills, but the other organisms lose them as their development continues. Fish, birds, and reptiles keep their tails, but mammals may lose theirs. These similarities suggest an evolutionary relationship among all vertebrate species.

DNA

DNA is the molecule that controls heredity. It is contained on chromosomes and directs the development of every organism. Scientists can determine whether or not organisms are closely related by looking at their DNA. Organisms that are close relatives have similar DNA. By studying DNA, scientists have determined that dogs are the closest relatives of bears. You would not be surprised to learn that primates, such as gorillas, bonobos, and chimpanzees, like the one shown in **Figure 12-15,** also have DNA that is similar.

Genetic evidence also supports the view that primates all evolved from a common ancestor. Primates share many of the same proteins, including hemoglobin. Hemoglobin is a protein in red blood cells that carries oxygen. Many primates have hemoglobin that is nearly the same.

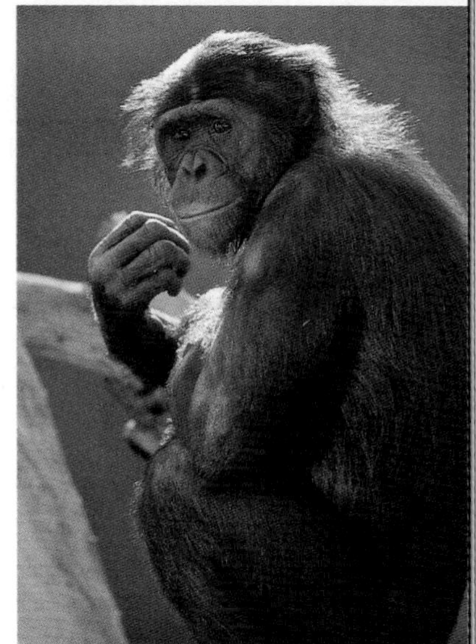

Figure 12-15 The DNA of humans and chimpanzees is similar in many ways.

Section Assessment

1. How are relative and radiometric dating used to interpret the fossil record?
2. How are fossils important evidence of evolution? List the different kinds of fossils.
3. How can DNA provide evidence of evolution?
4. **Think Critically:** Compare and contrast the five types of evidence for evolution.
5. **Skill Builder** **Making and Using Tables** Use **Table 12-1,** the geologic time scale, to answer the following questions. Which was the longest period of the Paleozoic era? Which was the shortest? What period began 1.6 million years ago? If you need help, refer to Making and UsingTables in the **Skill Handbook** on page 716.

Using Computers

Spreadsheet Prepare a spreadsheet that contains the name of each era and its corresponding length expressed in millions of years. Use the spreadsheet to make a chart that shows the information graphically. What information becomes more evident from a graphical presentation? If you need help, refer to page 738.

Section Assessment

1. Radiometric dating is used to date rocks by measuring relative amounts of radioactive elements and their stable products. Relative dating is used to find the approximate age of a rock layer by its position relative to other layers.
2. Fossils provide evidence for how simpler forms of life changed over time to more complex forms. Organisms can be frozen in ice or trapped in amber. Wood or bone can be replaced by minerals. There are also cast fossils and imprint fossils.
3. Organisms that are close relatives have similar DNA.
4. **Think Critically** Make sure answers are consistent with information in the text.

Using Computers

The graph produced from the spreadsheet will indicate that approximately 90 percent of the time scale occurs during the Precambrian and only about 3 percent during the Cenozoic.

4.  **Skill Builder** Ordovician; Silurian; Quaternary

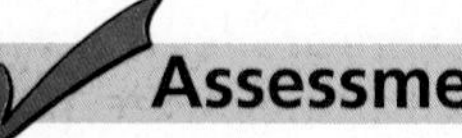

Assessment

Performance Have students prepare a poster showing the time periods in which fishes, amphibians, reptiles, birds, and mammals first appeared. Use **Performance Assessment in the Science Classroom,** p. 73. P

- The Laetoli footprints occur as two sets of tracks made by three hominids. One set of tracks consists of single imprints made by a smaller individual. The other set of tracks consists of double imprints made by two individuals walking one behind the other. The second individual seems to have intentionally placed his or her feet in the tracks made by the first individual.
- Mary Leakey and others also have collected fossil material, including jaw bones, from the Laetoli site. This fossil material seems to belong to the genus *Australopithecus.*

Teaching Strategies

- Have students research the location of the Laetoli site as well as other important archeological sites such as Olduvai Gorge. Students should then plot the sites on a map of Africa.
- Have students examine footprints made by barefooted individuals at the beach or other locations. Ask students to try to estimate the height, weight, and pace of the people who made the footprints.

For Additional Information

Hay, R.L., and Leakey, M.D., The fossil footprints of Laetoli: *Scientific American,* volume 246, 1982, pp. 50-57.

NATIONAL GEOGRAPHIC

History of Science

Footprints in Geologic Time

In 1978, a team led by renowned archaeologist Mary Leakey (shown in inset) made an astounding discovery in the Laetoli area of northern Tanzania in Africa. Amid the ancient tracks left by prehistoric giraffes, elephants, and rhinoceros were the fossilized footprints of three hominids—thought to be early ancestors of *Homo sapiens*. Preserved in volcanic ash, the Laetoli footprints (right) are estimated to be some 3.4 million years old.

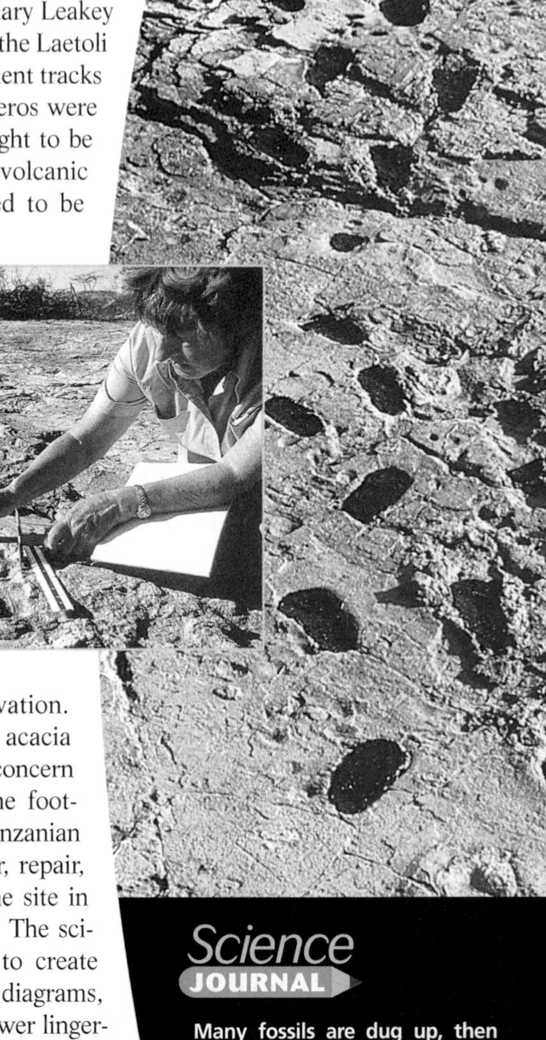

Settling the Debate

In the minds of many, Leakey's discovery laid to rest the debate as to when our ancestors began to walk upright. The depth and spacing of the footprints indicated that these early hominids, nearly 3.4 million years ago, had erect posture and walked like modern humans. Leakey, who spent more than six decades conducting research in East Africa, considered the find her greatest achievement.

Preserving the Past

After studying the footprints, Leakey's team buried the fossils in sand for preservation. Unknown to them, the sand contained seeds of acacia trees, which soon sprouted. Scientists expressed concern that eventually the tree roots would damage the footprints. In 1994, scientists working with the Tanzanian government began a two-year project to uncover, repair, and then re-cover the footprints. They buried the site in sand, soil, and materials to prevent root growth. The scientists also photographed the footprints again to create more detailed diagrams of each imprint. The diagrams, accurate to within half a millimeter, may help answer lingering questions about the hominids who made the footprints, such as whether they were male or female.

In 1996, Mary Leakey attended an event held at Laetoli by the Masai, a local tribe. Knowing the significance of the site, the Masai have agreed to help protect it.

Science JOURNAL

Many fossils are dug up, then stored in museums for further study and safekeeping. Research why scientists decided not to dig up the Laetoli footprints. Write your findings in your Science Journal.

Science JOURNAL There are several reasons the footprints were not dug up and removed from the site. Among these, students should discover that to move the footprints would be contrary to the widely accepted ethic of conservation in context. Additional reasons include the cultural significance of the site, and the risk of damage during removal.

A Model of Natural Selection

Natural selection has been observed in a variety of organisms in nature. Studying natural selection takes a long time because natural selection occurs in populations that may take years to produce a new generation. However, the process occurs in a way that can be explained by a simple model.

Materials

- Red beans and white beans (10 each)
- Paper bag
- Pencil and paper

What You'll Investigate

What is the result of natural selection?

Safety Precautions

CAUTION: *Do not taste or eat any material used in the lab.*

Procedure

1. Take a paper bag and write "Rabbit Gene Pool" on it.
2. Place ten red beans and ten white beans in the bag.
3. **Make a table** that you can use to record the genetics in the population. **Assume** that the pairs of beans are rabbits. A pair of red beans make a brown rabbit. A red bean and a white bean make a gray rabbit, and a pair of white beans make a white rabbit.
4. Without looking into the bag, take out two beans to represent an offspring. Write the colors of beans in the table.
5. Continue taking beans out of the bag two at a time and writing the results.
6. To model selection, predators eat all of the white rabbits and half of the gray rabbits. For each brown rabbit, place six baby rabbits (two red beans for each rabbit) in the bag along with its parents. For each remaining gray rabbit, do the same thing (one red bean and one white bean for each rabbit).
7. Repeat steps 4 and 5 two more times.

Conclude and Apply

1. How did the rabbit gene pool change during the activity?
2. What eventually happens to the white rabbits?
3. Describe how this model is similar to the way natural selection occurs in nature.
4. How is this model unlike the way natural selection occurs in nature?

Rabbit Offspring

Rabbit #	Bean Colors	
1	red	white
2	red	red
3	white	red
4	white	white
5	red	red
6	red	white
7	red	white
8	white	red
9	white	white
10	red	white
11	red	red
12	red	white
13	red	red
14	red	red
15	red	white

Assessment

Performance Have students design their own model to mimic natural selection. Use **Performance Assessment in the Science Classroom,** p. 51.

Purpose

Logical-Mathematical Students will make and use a model to explain natural selection and infer similarities between the model and natural selection. L2 ELL COOP LEARN

Process Skills

making models, communicating, forming operational definitions, interpreting data, observing and inferring

Time

45 minutes

Teaching Strategies

- Explain to students that the reason there are two beans per rabbit is that one gene for color is inherited from each parent.
- Similar size white and red beans should be used.

Answers to Questions

1. The number of white beans in the gene pool decreased. The number of red beans increased, and the overall number of rabbits increased.
2. The white rabbits died out as a result of natural selection by predators.
3. The model is similar to natural selection because there is an overproduction of rabbits (the population continued to grow even with predation). Predation removed certain individuals but not others.
4. The model is unlike natural selection because the predation was completely against white rabbits and not at all against brown rabbits. This does not usually occur in nature. Also, in nature some populations tend to remain fairly stable and do not continue to increase.

SECTION 12-3

Prepare

Content Background

Refer to **Primates** and **Primate Classification** on p. 332F.

Preplanning

Refer to the **Chapter Organizer** on pp. 332A–B.

1 Motivate

Bellringer

Before presenting the lesson, display **Section Focus Transparency 33** on the overhead projector. Use the accompanying **Focus Activity** worksheet. L2 ELL

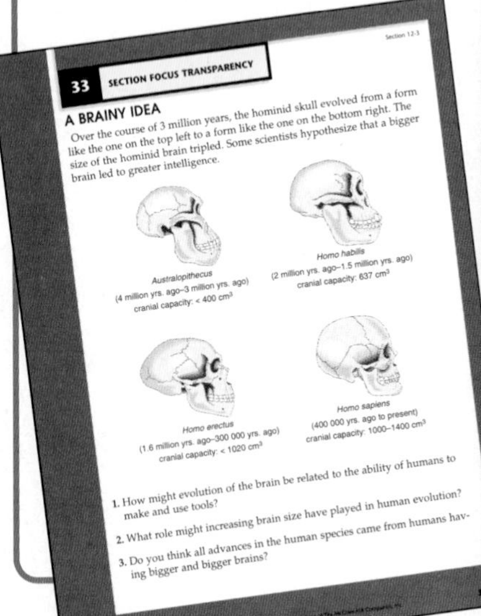

Section 12-3

33 SECTION FOCUS TRANSPARENCY

A BRAINY IDEA

Over the course of 3 million years, the hominid skull evolved from a form like the one on the top left to a form like the one on the bottom right. The size of the hominid brain tripled. Some scientists hypothesize that a bigger brain led to greater intelligence.

Australopithecus
(4 million yrs. ago–3 million yrs. ago)
cranial capacity: < 400 cm^3

Homo habilis
(2 million yrs. ago–1.5 million yrs. ago)
cranial capacity: 637 cm^3

Homo erectus
(1.6 million yrs. ago–300 000 yrs. ago)
cranial capacity: < 1020 cm^3

Homo sapiens
(400 000 yrs. ago to present)
cranial capacity: 1000–1400 cm^3

1. How might evolution of the brain be related to the ability of humans to make and use tools?
2. What role might increasing brain size have played in human evolution?
3. Do you think all advances in the human species came from humans having bigger and bigger brains?

33

12-3 Primate Evolution

What You'll Learn

- The differences in living primates
- The adaptations of primates
- The evolutionary history of modern primates

Vocabulary

primates
hominids
Homo sapiens

Why It's Important

- Studying primate evolution will help you appreciate the differences between humans and other primates.

Primates

Monkeys, apes, and humans belong to the group of mammals called **primates.** The primates share several characteristics that lead scientists to think that all primates may have evolved from a common ancestor. All primates have opposable thumbs that allow them to reach out and grasp things, as shown in **Figure 12-16.** Having an opposable thumb allows you to cross your thumb over your palm and touch your fingers. Think of the problems you might have if you didn't have this type of thumb.

Primates also have binocular vision. Binocular vision permits a primate to judge depth or distance with its eyes. All primates have flexible shoulders and rotating forelimbs. These allow tree-dwelling primates to swing easily from branch to branch and allow you to swing on a jungle gym. Each of these characteristics suggests that all primates may share common ancestry.

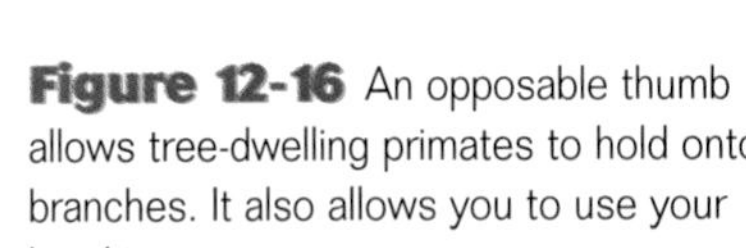

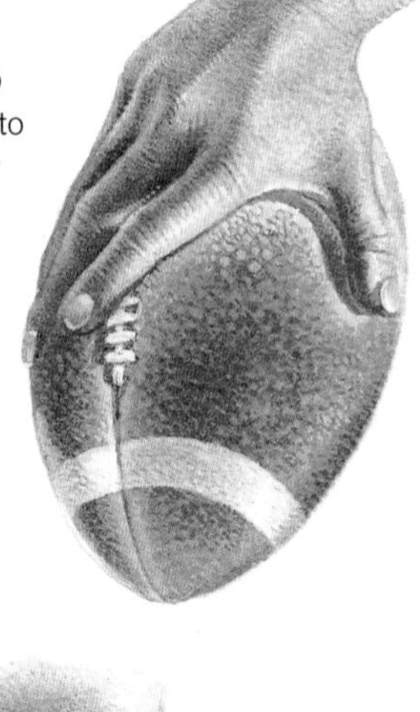

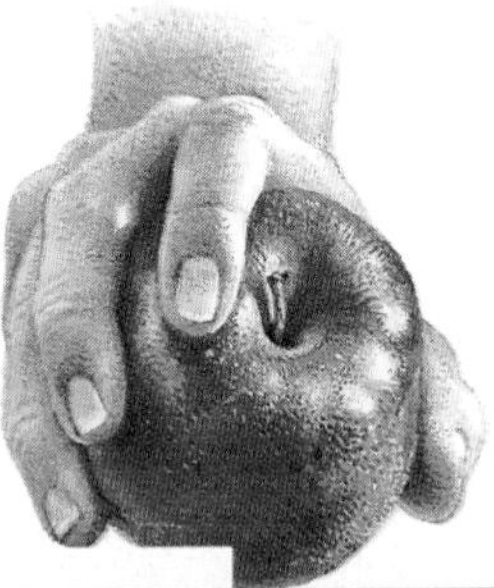

Figure 12-16 An opposable thumb allows tree-dwelling primates to hold onto branches. It also allows you to use your hand in many ways.

Resource Manager

The following **Teacher Classroom Resources** can be used with Section 12-3:

Reproducible Masters

Enrichment, p. 33 L3
Activity Worksheets, p. 70
Reinforcement, p. 33 L2
Study Guide, p. 48 L1 ELL

Content Background

Primates are thought to have evolved during the Eocene epoch. There are presently about 200 species of primates. Genetic studies indicate that the chimpanzee, bonobo, and gorilla are more closely related to humans than to any other primates.

Primate Classification

Primates are divided into two major groups. The first group includes organisms such as lemurs and tarsiers, the prosimians, as shown in **Figure 12-17.** These animals are active at night and have large eyes and excellent hearing. The second group of primates includes monkeys, apes, and humans.

Hominids

About 4 to 6 million years ago, our earliest ancestors branched off from the other primates. These ancestors, called **hominids,** were humanlike primates that ate both meat and vegetables and walked upright on two feet. Hominids shared some common characteristics with gorillas, orangutans, and chimpanzees, but a larger brain size separated them from these other great apes.

African Origins

In the early 1920s, Raymond Dart, a South African scientist, discovered a fossil skull in a quarry in South Africa. The skull had a small space for the brain, but humanlike jaw and teeth. Dart named his discovery *Australopithecus.* He chose the name *Australopithecus* for one of the earliest hominid

Figure 12-17 Tarsiers belong to a subgroup of primates called the prosimians, which means "before apes." They are commonly found in the rain forests of Southeast Asia.

EARTH SCIENCE INTEGRATION

African Rift Valley

Many fossils from hominids and early humans have been found in the African Rift Valley. This area of Africa is where two tectonic plates of Earth's crust are moving past one another. Do research on this area and draw a map of it in your Science Journal. Write a paragraph that explains why you might expect to find many fossils there.

Try at Home MiniLab

Living Without Thumbs

Procedure

1. Tape your thumb securely to your hand. Do this for both hands.
2. Leave your thumbs taped down for at least two hours. During this time, do the following activities: eat a meal, change clothes, and brush your teeth. Be careful not to try anything that could be dangerous.
3. Write about your experiences in your Science Journal.

Analysis

1. Did not having usable thumbs significantly affect the way you did things? Explain.
2. Infer how having opposable thumbs may have influenced primate evolution.

EARTH SCIENCE INTEGRATION

Fossils might be exposed in this area because of earthquakes and shifting rock layers.

GLENCOE TECHNOLOGY

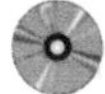 **Videodisc**

The Infinite Voyage: The Search for Ancient Americans

Chapter 3 *Ancient Weapons for Hunters* 4:00

Chapter 8 *Mayan Culture: Deciphering Heiroglyphics* 5:00

Refer to the Videodisc Teacher Guide for bar codes and teaching strategies.

Try at Home MiniLab

For additional help doing this activity at home, see the corresponding pages in the **Home Involvement Booklet.**

Purpose

Students will observe the difficulties of life without opposable thumbs, and infer how having opposable thumbs may have influenced primate evolution.

Materials

tape

Teaching Strategies

Tell students it will be easier for them to tape both thumbs down if they use a roll of tape, rather than tape in a dispenser.

Safety Precautions

Remind students not to try anything that could be dangerous with impaired manual dexterity (ie. riding a bike) during this experiment.

Analysis

1. Answers will vary.
2. Have students explain their responses. Accept all reasonable answers.

Across the Curriculum

Geography Use the information about fossil sites in Africa to increase students' awareness of African geography and the rich cultural heritage found there. Students should research sites such as Olduvai Gorge in Tanzania. They can also find out about other fossil sites in Europe and Asia. L3

Assessment

Have students design a house with features that could be easily used by someone without thumbs. Use **Performance Assessment in the Science Classroom,** p. 51.

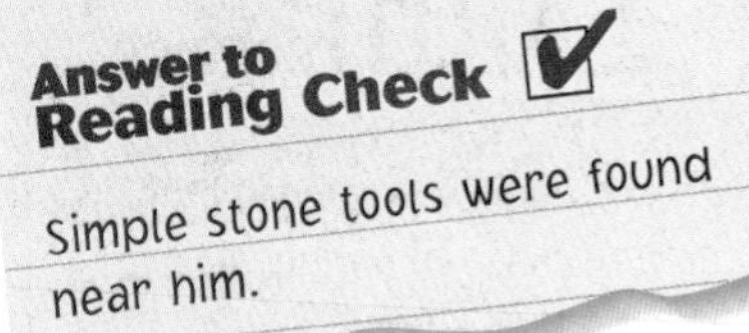

Answer to Reading Check

Simple stone tools were found near him.

Caption Answer

Figure 12-19 *Answers will vary*

GLENCOE TECHNOLOGY

 **Videodisc**

The Infinite Voyage: The Dawn of Humankind

Chapter 2 *Evolution of Early Man* 6:00

Chapter 7 *DNA Studies Create a Controversy* 3:30

Chapter 8 *"Out of Africa" vs. Multiregional Debates on Origination of Modern Man* 6:00

Refer to the Videodisc Teacher Guide for bar codes and teaching strategies.

3 Assess

Check for Understanding

Activity

Using what they know about Neanderthals, have students write an advertisement in their Science Journals for *The Neanderthal News* for a modern product that they think Neanderthals might have been able to use. Student ads should emphasize tools for hammering and cutting. L2

Reteach

Intrapersonal Have students prepare a list of the characteristics common to humans and other primates. L1

Extension

For students who have mastered this section, use the **Reinforcement** and **Enrichment** masters.

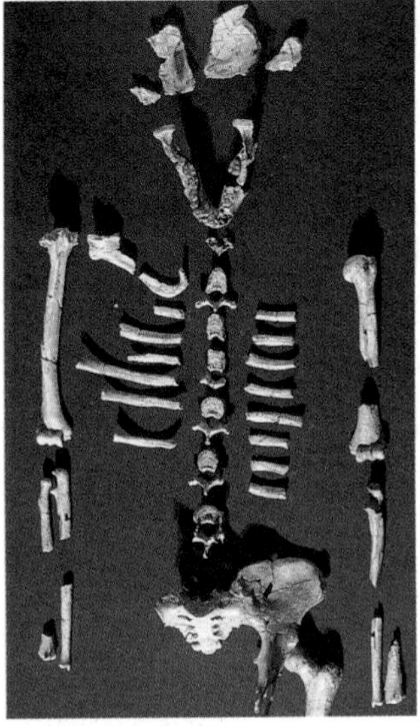

Figure 12-18 The fossil remains of Lucy, a hominid, are estimated to be 2.9 to 3.4 million years old.

Reading Check

Why was *Homo habilis* given that name?

groups discovered because it means "southern ape." In 1974, an almost-complete skeleton of *Australopithecus,* as shown in **Figure 12-18,** was discovered by American scientist Donald Johanson and his coworkers. They named the fossil Lucy. Lucy had a small brain but is thought to have walked upright. This fossil is important because it indicates how modern hominids may have evolved.

About 40 years after the discovery of *Australopithecus,* a discovery was made in East Africa by Louis, Mary, and Richard Leakey. The Leakeys discovered a fossil more like present-day humans than *Australopithecus.* They named this hominid *Homo habilis,* the "handy man," because they found simple stone tools near him. Scientists estimate *Homo habilis* to be 1.5 to 2 million years old.

Based upon many fossil comparisons, anthropologists have suggested that *Homo habilis* gave rise to another species about 1.6 million years ago, *Homo erectus. Homo erectus* had a larger brain than *Homo habilis.* This hominid moved out of Africa about 1 million years ago. *Homo habilis* and *Homo erectus* both are thought to be ancestors of humans because they had larger brains and were more like humans than *Australopithecus.*

Modern Humans

Our species is named ***Homo sapiens,*** meaning "wise human." The fossil record indicates that the human species evolved about 400 000 years ago. By about 125 000 years ago, two early groups of *Homo sapiens,* Neanderthals and Cro-Magnon humans, probably lived at the same time in parts of Africa and Europe.

Neanderthals had short, heavy bodies with thick bones; small chins; and heavy browridges, as you can see in **Figure 12-19.** The Neanderthals lived in family groups in caves and

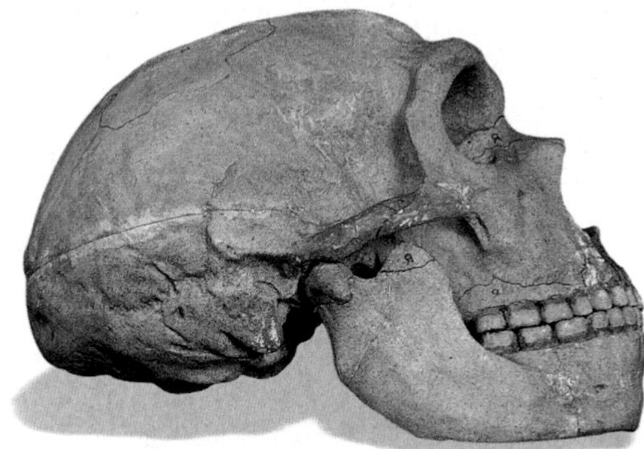

Figure 12-19 In this photograph, the skull of a Neanderthal, right, can be compared with the skull of a Cro-Magnon, left. **What differences can you see between these two skulls?**

Content Background

During discussion of this section, stress that Neanderthals and Cro-Magnons were *Homo sapiens,* the same as members of our species today.

Inclusion Strategies

Visually Impaired Provide skulls for students to learn about the structures you describe in class such as browridges, jaws, teeth, and so on. Casts can be purchased from biological supply houses.

356 CHAPTER 12 CHANGE THROUGH TIME

hunted mammoths, deer, and other large animals, with well-made stone tools. For reasons that are not clear, Neanderthals disappeared from the fossil record about 35 000 years ago. Most scientists think Neanderthals were a side branch of human evolution but are not direct ancestors of modern humans.

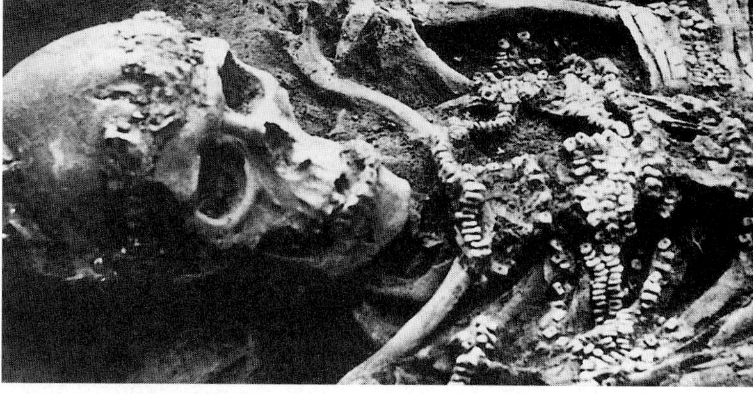

Figure 12-20 This grave contained objects thought to be placed there by Cro-Magnon humans. In addition to graves such as this, tools and paintings on cave walls have led scientists to hypothesize that Cro-Magnon humans had a well-developed culture.

Cro-Magnon fossils have been found in Europe, Asia, and Australia. These fossils are dated from 40 000 to about 10 000 years old. The oldest recorded art dates from the caves of France where Cro-Magnon humans first painted bison, horses, and spear-carrying people. Cro-Magnon humans lived in caves, made stone carvings, and buried their dead, as seen in **Figure 12-20.** Standing about 1.6 m to 1.7 m tall, the physical appearance of Cro-Magnon people was almost the same as that of modern humans. Cro-Magnon humans are thought to be direct ancestors of modern humans.

Section Assessment

1. Describe at least three kinds of evidence that suggest all primates may have shared a common ancestor.
2. What is the importance of *Australopithecus?*
3. Describe the differences among Neanderthals, Cro-Magnon humans, and modern humans.
4. **Think Critically:** Propose a hypothesis about why teeth represent the most abundant available fossils of hominids.
5. **Skill Builder**
   Concept Mapping Using information in this section, make a concept map to show the sequence of hominids. Use the following terms: Neanderthal, *Homo habilis, Australopithecus,* modern *Homo sapiens,* and Cro-Magnon human. If you need help, refer to Concept Mapping in the **Skill Handbook** on page 714.

Science Journal Write a story in your Science Journal about what life would be like for you if you did not have thumbs.

4 Close

Proficiency Prep

Use this quiz to check students' recall of section content.

1. **What group do monkeys, apes, and humans belong to?** *primates*
2. **What species were Cro-Magnons members of?** Homo sapiens, *modern humans*

Section Assessment

1. Homologous structures, similar DNA, and fossils suggest a common ancestry for primates.
2. *Australopithecus,* an early hominid, had a small brain case but humanlike jaws and teeth.
3. Neanderthals had short bodies with massive bones and heavy browridges. Cro-Magnons were taller, invented art, made stone carvings, and buried their dead. Cro-Magnons were almost identical to modern humans.
4. **Think Critically** Teeth are the hardest parts of the organism.
5. **Skill Builder** The events chain should be in the following order: *Australopithecus, Homo habilis,* Neanderthals, Cro-Magnons, and modern *Homo sapiens.*

Science Journal

The story should include activities that would be more difficult to perform.

Assessment

Portfolio Have students add any other events or developments they think are important to their concept maps. Use **Performance Assessment in the Science Classroom,** p. 89. P

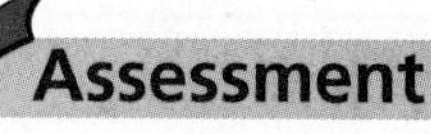

Chapter 12 Reviewing Main Ideas

Reviewing Main Ideas can be used to preview, review, reteach, and condense chapter content.

Preview

Linguistic Have students try to answer the questions in their Science Journals. Use student answers as a source for discussion throughout the chapter.

Review

Interpersonal Have students answer the questions on separate pieces of paper and compare their answers with those of other students in the class. COOP LEARN

Reteach

Visual-Spatial Have students look at the illustrations on these pages. Ask them to describe details that support the main ideas of the chapter found in the statement for each illustration.

OUT OF TIME?

Auditory-Musical If time does not permit teaching the entire chapter, use the information on these pages along with the chapter Audiocassettes to present the material in a condensed format.

Chapter 12 Reviewing Main Ideas

For a **preview** of this chapter, study this Reviewing Main Ideas before you read the chapter. After you have studied this chapter, you can use the Reviewing Main Ideas to **review** the chapter.

The Glencoe MindJogger, Audiocassettes, and CD-ROM provide additional opportunities for review.

Section 12-1 MECHANISMS OF EVOLUTION

Evolution is one of the central ideas of biology. It explains how living things changed in the past and provides predictions for how they may change in the future. Charles Darwin developed the theory of evolution by **natural selection** to explain how these changes account for the diversity of organisms. The factors that control natural selection are as follows.

1. Organisms produce more offspring than can survive.
2. **Variations** are found among individuals of a **species.**
3. Variations are passed on to offspring.
4. Some variations allow members of a population to survive and reproduce better than others.
5. Over time, offspring of individuals with helpful variations make up more and more of a population.

How did Darwin's theory differ

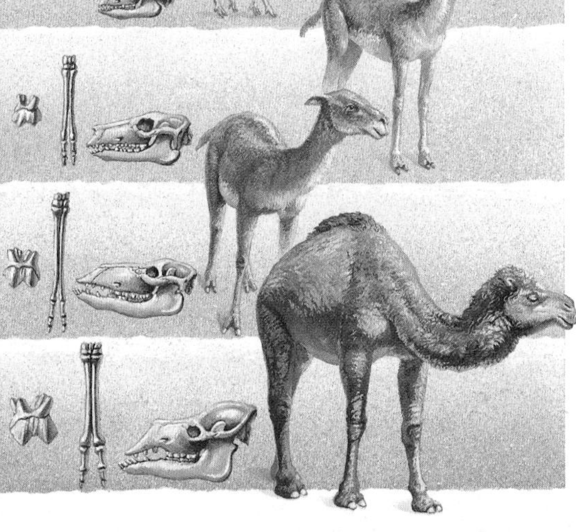

Cultural Diversity

Evolving Viruses The flu is an example of a sickness caused by a virus with DNA that evolves in order for the virus to survive. Every major flu epidemic has come from South China, where ducks, pigs, and humans are brought into daily contact. An avian flu transfers to pigs, as does a human flu variety. The viruses exchange pieces of genetic code to create a new flu strain. When it reinfects humans, it is different enough that antibodies created against the first form do not stop the new virus. That is why flu shots protect only against last year's flu, and not the current year's variety. One variant produced a flu epidemic in 1918–1919 that killed 20 million people worldwide. Healthy individuals could die within 48 hours of feeling ill.

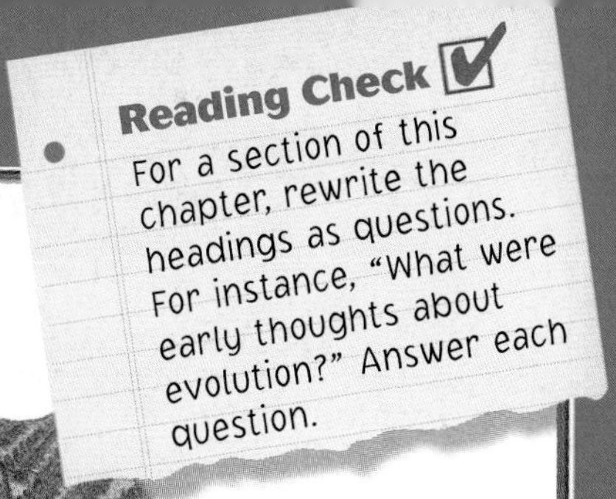

Reading Check

For a section of this chapter, rewrite the headings as questions. For instance, "What were early thoughts about evolution?" Answer each question.

Section 12-2 EVIDENCE FOR EVOLUTION

Fossils are one of the main sources of evidence for evolution. They are tested using relative dating and radiometric dating to estimate how old they are. Other evidence includes comparative **embryology, homologous** structures, **vestigial structures,** and chemical similarities. ***How are chemical similarities evidence of evolution?***

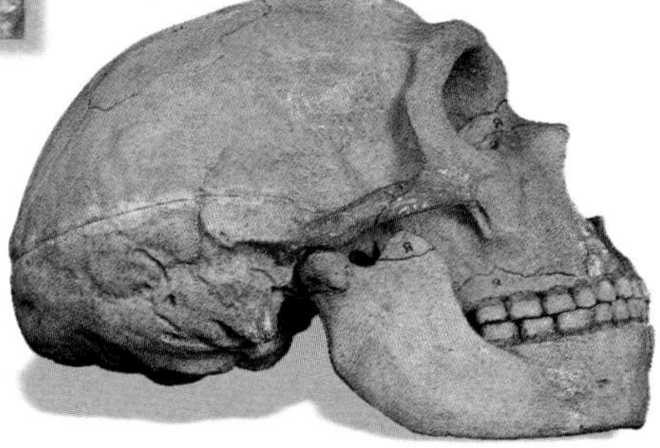

Section 12-3 PRIMATE EVOLUTION

Primates include monkeys, apes, and humans. **Hominids** are humanlike primates. The earliest known hominid is *Australopithecus.* Modern humans are thought to have evolved at least 400 000 years ago. ***What are the common characteristics of primates?***

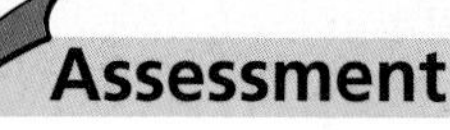

Assessment

Portfolio Encourage students to place in their portfolios one or two items of what they consider to be their best work. Examples include:

- Activity 12-1, pp. 342–343
- Using Computers, p. 351 P

Performance Additional performance assessments may be found in the **Performance Assessment** and **Science Integration Activities.** Performance Task Assessment Lists and rubrics for evaluating these activities can be found in **Glencoe's Performance Assessment in the Science Classroom.**

Answers to Questions

Section 12-1

Mechanisms of Evolution Darwin realized that only hereditary features are passed on to the next generation, not acquired features as Lamarck suggested.

Section 12-2

Evidence for Evolution Similarities in DNA, RNA, and proteins suggest ancestral relationships.

Section 12-3

Primate Evolution All primates have opposable thumbs, binocular vision, flexible shoulders, and rotating forelimbs.

GLENCOE TECHNOLOGY

CD-ROM

Glencoe Science Voyages Interactive CD-ROM

Chapter Summaries and Quizzes

Have students read the Chapter Summary then take the Chapter Quiz to determine whether they have mastered chapter content.

Using Vocabulary

1. c
2. n
3. l
4. e
5. h

interNET CONNECTION To reinforce chapter vocabulary, use the **Study Guide for Content Mastery** booklet. Also available are activities for **Glencoe Science Voyages** on the Glencoe Science Web Site. **www.glencoe.com/sec/science**

Checking Concepts

6. C	11. D
7. B	12. B
8. D	13. A
9. C	14. D
10. A	15. B

Thinking Critically

16. **Lamarck:** Ducks have webbed feet for swimming. The ducklings acquired the webbed feature. **Darwin:** A variation in a duck's feet was an advantage to survival in the environment. This was a feature that was passed on to the offspring.
17. Geographical isolation as a result of a volcanic eruption can divide a population. Two species may form.
18. Chameleons blend into their environment. This ability to change color helps protect them from predators.
19. The layer of rock where it was formed would be noted. Radiometric dating would be done. Comparisons to other fossils would be made.

Chapter 12 Assessment

Using Vocabulary

a. embryology
b. evolution
c. gradualism
d. hominids
e. homologous
f. *Homo sapiens*
g. natural selection
h. primates
i. punctuated equilibrium
j. radioactive element
k. sedimentary rock
l. species
m. variation
n. vestigial structure

Each phrase below describes a science term from the list. Write the term that matches the phrase describing it.

1. model of evolution showing slow change
2. structure with no obvious use
3. similar organisms that successfully reproduce
4. body structures that are similar in origin
5. group containing monkeys, apes, and humans

Checking Concepts

Choose the word or phrase that best answers the question.

6. What is an example of adaptation?
   A) a fossil
   B) a homologous structure
   C) camouflage
   D) gradualism
7. How can the most accurate age of a fossil be estimated?
   A) natural selection
   B) radiometric dating
   C) relative dating
   D) camouflage
8. What do homologous structures, vestigial structures, and fossils all provide evidence of?
   A) gradualism
   B) food choice
   C) species populations
   D) evolution
9. What is a factor that controls natural selection?
   A) inheritance of acquired traits
   B) unused traits become smaller
   C) organisms produce more offspring than can survive
   D) the size of an organism
10. What may a series of helpful variations in a species result in?
    A) adaptation
    B) fossils
    C) embryology
    D) climate change
11. What describes organisms that are adapted to their environment?
    A) homologous
    B) not reproducing
    C) forming fossils
    D) surviving and reproducing
12. Which model of evolution shows rapid change?
    A) embryology
    B) punctuated equilibrium
    C) gradualism
    D) adaptation
13. What are opposable thumbs and binocular vision characteristics of?
    A) all primates
    B) hominids
    C) humans only
    D) monkeys and apes
14. What is the study of an organism's early development?
    A) adaptation
    B) relative dating
    C) natural selection
    D) embryology
15. A fossil has the same number of bones in its hand as a gorilla. What type of evidence for evolution does this represent?
    A) DNA
    B) homologous structures
    C) vestigial structures
    D) embryology

Thinking Critically

16. How would Lamarck and Darwin have explained the webbed feet of a duck?

20. Answers could include that animals with protective coloration would survive better. A rabbit that lives in a cold climate and is white in the winter and brown in the summer will survive better than rabbits with different coloration.

17. Using an example, explain how a new species of organism could evolve.
18. How is the color-changing ability of chameleons an adaptation to their environment?
19. Describe the processes a scientist would use to figure out the age of a fossil.
20. Explain how a species could adapt to its environment. Give an example.

Developing skills

If you need help, refer to the **Skill Handbook.**

21. **Observing and Inferring:** Observe the birds' beaks pictured below. Describe each. Infer the types of food each would eat and explain why.

22. **Interpreting Data:** The chemicals present in certain bacteria were studied. Each letter below represents a different chemical found in the bacteria. Use this information to determine which of the bacteria are closely related.

Chemicals Present	
Bacteria 1	A, G, T, C, L, E, S, H
Bacteria 2	A, G, T, C, L, D, H
Bacteria 3	A, G, T, C, L, D, P, U, S, R, I, V
Bacteria 4	A, G, T, C, L, D, H

Test-Taking Tip

Make Yourself Comfortable When you take a test, try to make yourself as comfortable as possible. You will then be able to focus all your attention on the test.

Test Practice

Use these questions to test your Science Proficiency.

1. Which of the following statements **BEST** describes how evolution happens?
   - **A)** An insect with an adaptation for surviving insecticide lives to reproduce after being sprayed. Its offspring inherit the trait.
   - **B)** Two Great Danes have their ears cropped. They have a litter of puppies that also need to have their ears cropped.
   - **C)** Two excellent musicians have a baby. After years of practice, the child learns to play instruments as well as the parents.
   - **D)** After generations of stretching their necks to get leaves, all giraffes now have long necks.
2. Which of the following would **BEST** explain the punctuated equilibrium model of evolution?
   - **A)** A mountain range is built up over millions of years due to tectonic plates colliding.
   - **B)** During 54 million years of evolution, the camel evolved to its present form.
   - **C)** Many species become extinct after a meteor strikes Earth, causing darkness for many months.
   - **D)** Two populations become separated because of a flood, each evolving to look very different from the other.

Assessment Resources

The **Test Practice Workbook** provides students with practice in the format, concepts, and critical-thinking skills tested in standardized exams.

Reproducible Masters

Chapter Review, pp. 23–24 L2
Performance Assessment, p. 26 L2
Assessment, pp. 51–54 L2

Glencoe Technology

- Chapter Review Software
- Computer Test Bank
- MindJogger Videoquiz

Test Practice

The Test-Taking Tip was written by The Princeton Review, the nation's leader in test preparation.

1. A
2. C

Developing Skills

21. The hummingbird's beak is long and thin for sipping nectar. The bird of prey has a curved, sharp beak for eating prey. The duck has a wide, flat beak for dabbling in the mud. The pelican has a long beak with storage for scooping food.
22. Bacteria 2 and 4 have the same chemicals and are, therefore, most closely related.

Bonus Question

What relationship is implied by the statement that monkeys, apes, and humans belong to the group of mammals called primates? *The implication is that all of these organisms may share a common ancestor.*

Chapter 13 Geologic Time

Section	Objectives	Activities/Features
Chapter Opener		**Explore Activity:** Make a Time Scale of Your Life, p. 363
13-1 **Life and Geologic Time** 2 Sessions 1 Block	1. **Explain** how geologic time is divided into units. 2. **Explain** how changes in trilobites relate to the passage of geologic time. 3. **Describe** how plate tectonics influences changes in species.	**Life Science Integration,** p. 368 **Using Math,** p. 368 **Skill Builder:** Making and Using Graphs, p. 371 **Science Journal,** p. 371
13-2 **Early Earth History** 3 Sessions 1½ Blocks	4. **Identify** dominant life-forms in Precambrian time and the Paleozoic Era. 5. **Draw** conclusions about how organisms adapted to changing environments in Precambrian time and the Paleozoic Era. 6. **Describe** changes in Earth and its life-forms at the end of the Paleozoic Era.	**Chemistry Integration,** p. 373 **MiniLab: Interpreting Rock Layers,** p. 375 **Problem Solving:** Skull Structure, p. 376 **Skill Builder:** Recognizing Cause and Effect, p. 378 **Using Computers,** p. 378 **Activity 13-1:** Changing Species, p. 379 **Science and Society:** Fast Track to Extinction, p. 380
13-3 **Middle and Recent Earth History** 3 Sessions 1½ Blocks	7. **Compare** and **contrast** dominant life-forms in the Mesozoic and Cenozoic Eras. 8. **Explain** how changes caused by plate tectonics afected the evolution of life during the Mesozoic Era. 9. **Identify** when humans first appeared on Earth.	**MiniLab:** Measuring Seafloor Spreading, p. 385 **Skill Builder:** Sequencing, p. 387 **Using Math,** p. 387 **On the Internet:** Discovering the Past, pp. 388–389

The number of recommended single-period sessions   The number of recommended blocks
One session and one-half block are allowed for chapter review and assessment.

Activity Materials

Explore	Activities	MiniLabs
p. 363 8 index cards, scissors, pens	p. 379 deck of playing cards	p. 375 illustrations of fossil-bearing rock layers. p. 385 globe or world map, metric ruler, string

Need Materials? Contact Science Kit at 1-800-828-7777 or at www.sciencekit.com on the Internet.
For alternate materials, see the activity on the listed page.

Standards		Reproducible Resources	Technology
National	State/Local	Test Practice Workbooks are available for use with each chapter.	English and Spanish audiocassettes are available for use with each section.
National Content Standards: UCP1, UCP4, C5, D1, D2		**Enrichment,** p. 34 **Reinforcement,** p. 34 **Study Guide,** pp. 49–50	Section Focus Transparency 34 Teaching Transparency 25 Teaching Transparency 26 Science Integration Transparency 13 The Infinite Voyage Series Glencoe Science Voyages Interactive Videodisc—Life Glencoe Science Voyages Interactive Videodisc—Earth
National Content Standards: UCP4, A1, A2, C5, D1, D2		**Activity Worksheets,** pp. 71–73 **Enrichment,** p. 35 **Home Involvement,** p. 36 **Laboratory Manual,** pp. 71–76 **Reinforcement,** p. 35	Section Focus Transparency 35 **Internet Connection,** p. 377
National Content Standards: UCP4, A1, A2, C4, C5, D1, D2, F2, G3		**Activity Worksheets,** p. 74 **Critical Thinking/Problem Solving,** p. 13 **Enrichment,** p. 36 **Multicultural Connections,** pp. 25–26 **Reinforcement,** p. 36 **Study Guide,** pp. 51–52	Section Focus Transparency 36 Glencoe Science Voyages Interactive CD-ROM Glencoe Science Voyages Interactive Videodisc—Life **Internet Connection,** p. 388

Key to Teaching Strategies

The following designations will help you decide which activities are appropriate for your students.

L1 Level 1 activities should be appropriate for students with learning difficulties.

L2 Level 2 activities should be within the ability range of all students.

L3 Level 3 activities are designed for above-average students.

ELL ELL activities should be within the ability range of English Language Learners.

COOP LEARN Cooperative Learning activities are designed for small group work.

P These strategies represent student products that can be placed into a best-work portfolio.

Multiple Learning Styles logos, as described on page 61T, are used throughout to indicate strategies that address different learning styles.

Assessment Resources

Chapter Review, pp. 25–26
Assessment, pp. 55–58
Performance Assessment in the Science Classroom (PASC)
MindJogger Videoquiz
Alternate Assessment in the Science Classroom
Performance Assessment, p. 27
Chapter Review Software
Computer Test Bank

Chapter 13 Geologic Time

This is a representation of key blackline masters available in the Teacher Classroom Resources. See Resource Manager boxes within the chapter for additional information.

Transparencies

Section Focus Transparencies

34 SECTION FOCUS TRANSPARENCY

TRILOBITE TEACHERS

You can learn a lot from trilobites. Look at the ones in the picture. They are different ages. They show that trilobites, like other lifeforms, change over time.

1. Which trilobite do you think is the oldest? Why?
2. Why do you think trilobites changed over time?

L2

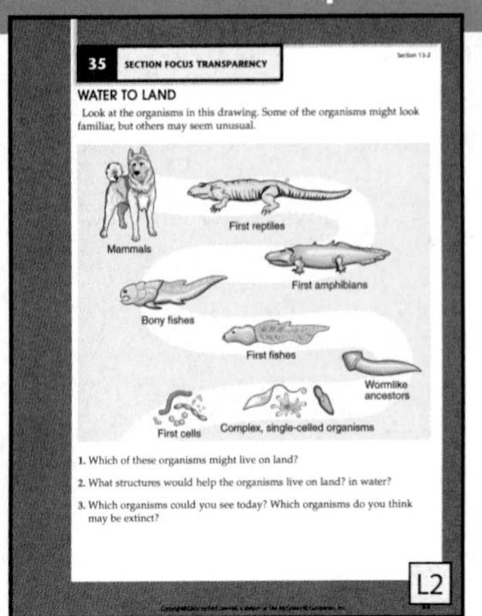
35 SECTION FOCUS TRANSPARENCY

WATER TO LAND

Look at the organisms in this drawing. Some of the organisms might look familiar, but others may seem unusual.

1. Which of these organisms might live on land?
2. What structures would help the organisms live on land? in water?
3. Which organisms could you see today? Which organisms do you think may be extinct?

L2

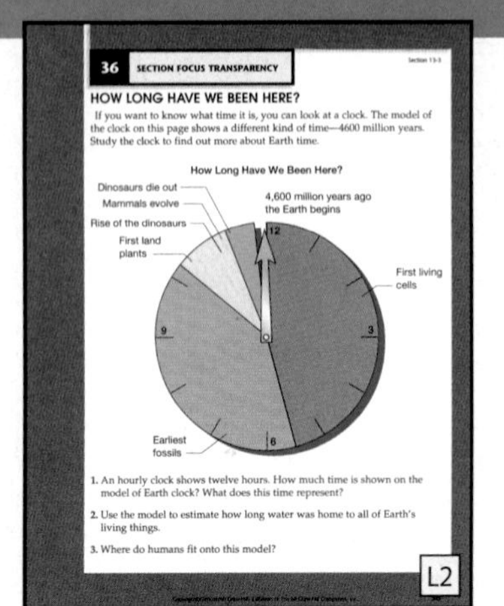
36 SECTION FOCUS TRANSPARENCY

HOW LONG HAVE WE BEEN HERE?

If you want to know what time it is, you can look at a clock. The model of the clock on this page shows a different kind of time—4600 million years. Study the clock to find out more about Earth time.

1. An hourly clock shows twelve hours. How much time is shown on the model of Earth clock? What does this time represent?
2. Use the model to estimate how long water was home to all of Earth's living things.
3. Where do humans fit onto this model?

L2

Science Integration Transparencies

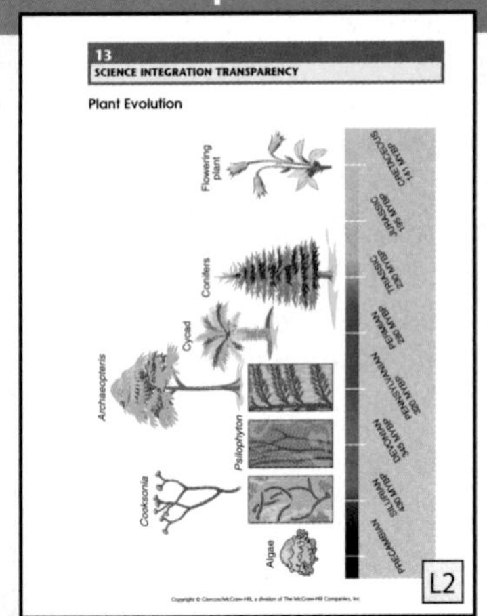
13 SCIENCE INTEGRATION TRANSPARENCY

Plant Evolution

L2

Teaching Transparencies

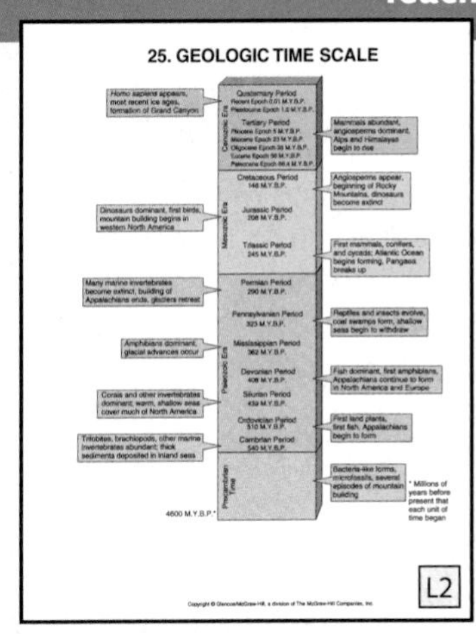
25. GEOLOGIC TIME SCALE

L2

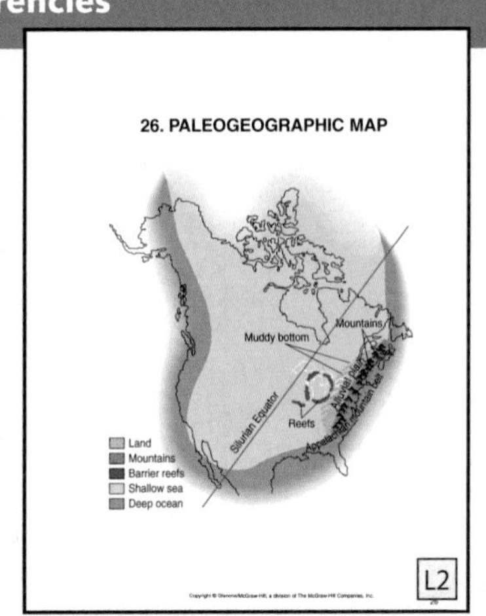
26. PALEOGEOGRAPHIC MAP

L2

Meeting Different Ability Levels

Study Guide for Content Mastery

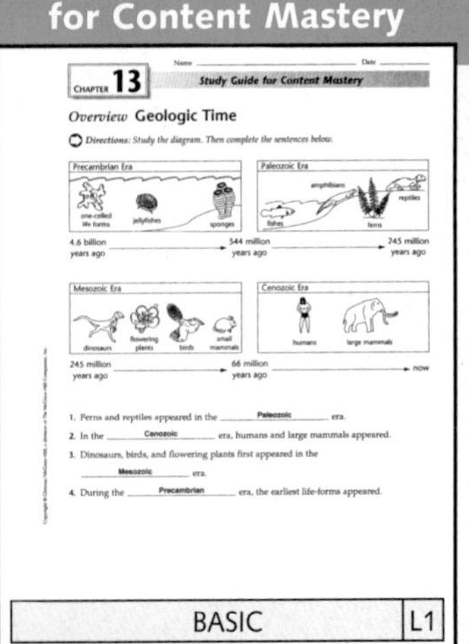
Chapter 13 Study Guide for Content Mastery

Overview Geologic Time

Directions: Study the diagram. Then complete the sentences below.

1. Ferns and reptiles appeared in the Paleozoic era.
2. In the Cenozoic era, humans and large mammals appeared.
3. Dinosaurs, birds, and flowering plants first appeared in the Mesozoic era.
4. During the Precambrian era, the earliest life-forms appeared.

BASIC L1

Reinforcement

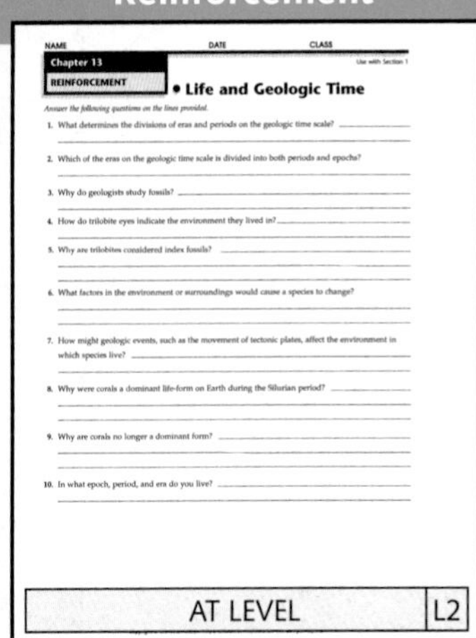
Chapter 13 REINFORCEMENT • Life and Geologic Time

1. What determines the divisions of eras and periods on the geologic time scale?
2. Which of the eras on the geologic time scale is divided into both periods and epochs?
3. Why do geologists study fossils?
4. How do trilobite eyes indicate the environment they lived in?
5. Why are trilobites considered index fossils?
6. What factors in the environment or surroundings would cause a species to change?
7. How might geologic events, such as the movement of tectonic plates, affect the environment in which species live?
8. Why were corals a dominant life-form on Earth during the Silurian period?
9. Why are corals no longer a dominant form?
10. In what epoch, period, and era do you live?

AT LEVEL L2

Enrichment Worksheets

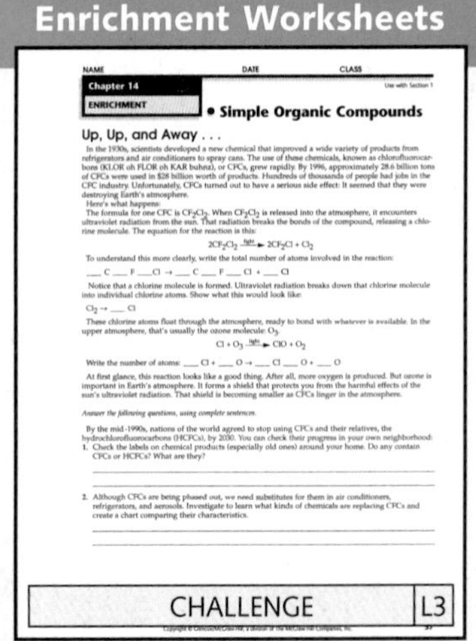
Chapter 14 ENRICHMENT • Simple Organic Compounds

Up, Up, and Away . . .

CHALLENGE L3

Hands-on Activities

Activity Worksheets

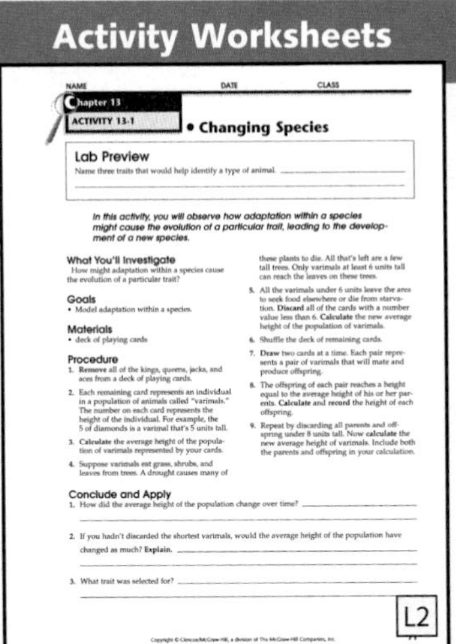

Lab Manual

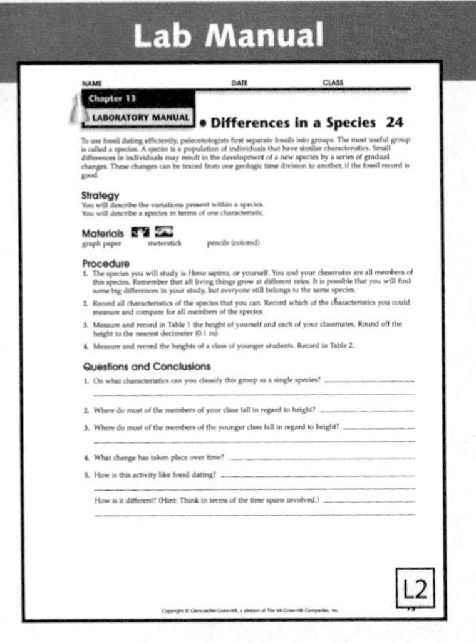

Accessibility

Spanish Resources

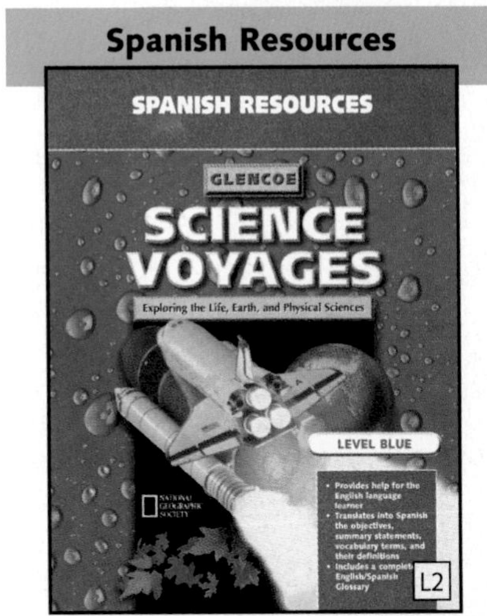

Assessment

Performance Assessment

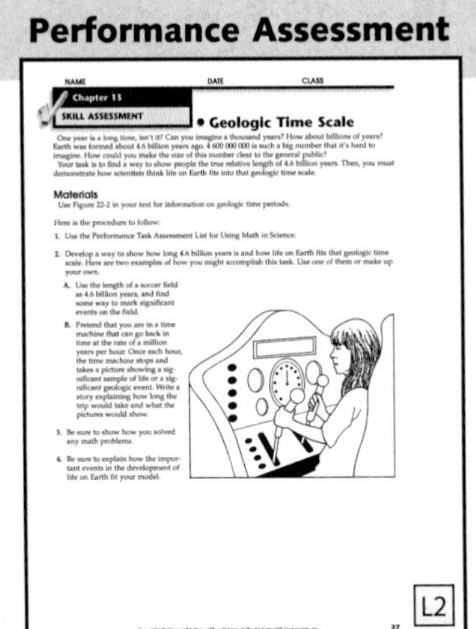

Chapter Review

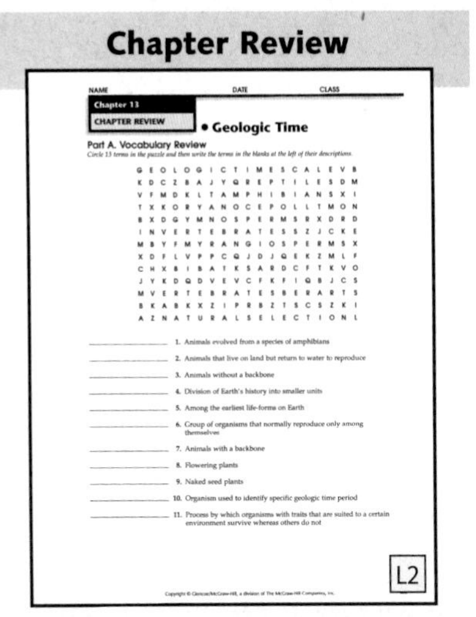

Assessment

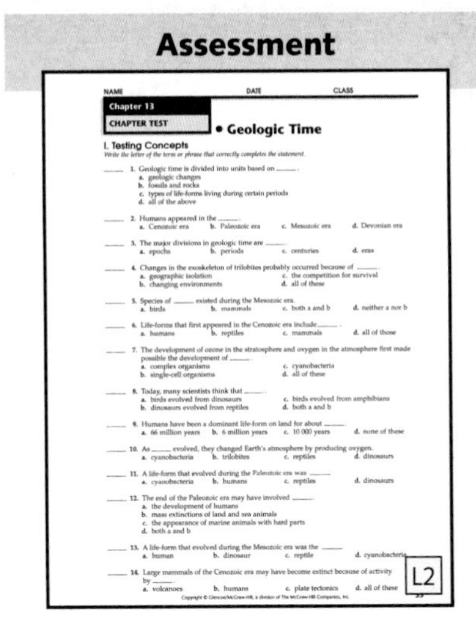

Test Practice Workbook

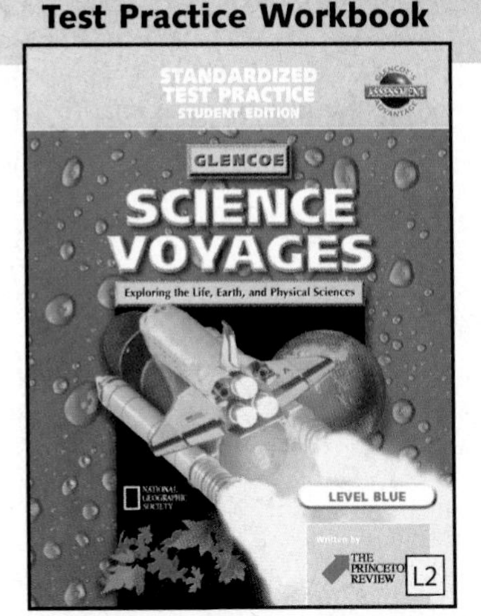

Extending Content

Critical Thinking/ Problem Solving

Multicultural Connections

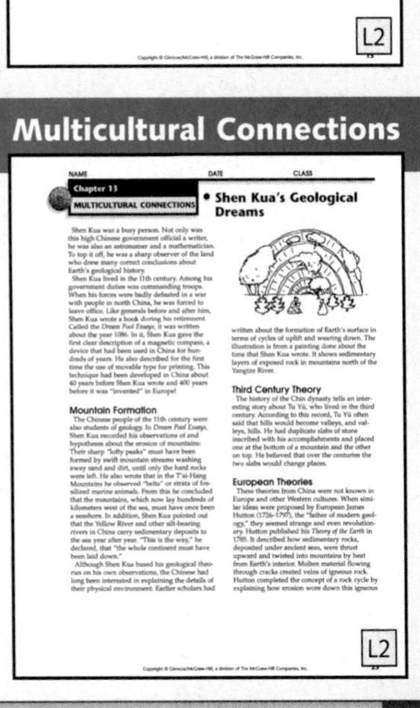

Helping You Prepare

Life and Geologic Time

(Section 13-1)

Nicholaus Steno (1638–1687) visited rock quarries and studied rock layers in Italy. Based on his studies, he proposed several principles of historical geology still used today. The principle of superposition states that in undisturbed beds of rock, older beds are located under younger beds of rock. The principle of original horizontality states that sedimentary rock layers are originally deposited in horizontal layers. The principle of original lateral continuity states that rock layers extend laterally in all directions until they thin out, end suddenly, or gradually change into a different type of sedimentary rock.

These principles are basic to stratigraphy. Stratigraphy is a division of geology in which texture, composition, arrangement, and correlation of sedimentary rock layers are studied.

In 1799, William Smith, an English surveyor and geologic hobbyist, noted that rock layers in any local section could be distinguished readily from those above and below them by the sorts of fossils they contained. Smith's discovery was a turning point in the development of the geologic time scale.

Two scientists in France, Baron Georges Leopold Cuvier (1769–1832) and Alexander Brongniart (1770–1847) also studied succession of fossils. Through their studies of fossils, the basics of vertebrate paleontology were established.

GLENCOE TECHNOLOGY

 **CD-ROM**

Glencoe Science Voyages Interactive CD-ROM

Chapter Summaries

Use the Chapter Summary to introduce, teach, or review chapter material.

Geologic history is based on the study of sedimentary rocks and their fossils. Although the geologic time scale was originally based on relative dating, absolute dating methods have enabled geologists to determine absolute dates of many rocks and some geologic events.

The Geologic Time Scale

(Section 13-1)

Subdivisions of geologic time can be determined from the fossil content of rock layers. Early geologic time is divided into three eons: the Hadean eon is the time period for which no rock record exists; the Archean eon begins with the age of the oldest known rocks; the Proterozoic eon began about 2.5 billion years ago and ends with the beginning of the Phanerozoic eon, about 540 million years ago. The Phanerozoic eon is further separated into the Paleozoic era, the Mesozoic era, and the Cenozoic era.

NATIONAL GEOGRAPHIC — **Teacher's Corner**

Products Available from Glencoe

To order the following products for use with this chapter, call Glencoe at 1-800-334-7344:

CD-ROM

NGS PictureShow: Age of Dinosaurs

Curriculum Kit

GeoKit: Earth's History

Transparency Set

NGS PicturePack: Age of Dinosaurs

Products Available from National Geographic Society

To order the following products for use with this chapter, call National Geographic Society at 1-800-368-2728:

Video

Dinosaurs: Then and Now

Index to National Geographic Magazine

The following articles may be used for research relating to this chapter:

"Dinosaur Embryos," by Luis Chiappe, December 1998.

Early Earth History (Section 13-2)

Trilobites are a common marine fossil from the Cambrian period. They were widespread and diverse. They are index fossils for the Paleozoic era.

The largest of all mass extinctions occurred at the end of the Permian period (Paleozoic era). Some evidence suggests that a huge volcanic eruption occurred in what is known as Siberia. The eruption would have released large concentrations of poisonous gases. The release of these gases, along with global changes in climates associated with the volcanic eruptions could have been the cause of the mass extinction.

Other evidence suggests the cause may have been a global turnover of ocean water. The upwelling of deep ocean water would have brought huge amounts of carbon dioxide to the surface. Some would have been released into the atmosphere. Too much carbon dioxide in the blood of animals can cause acidification of the blood, which can lead to the animal's death. Carbon dioxide is also a greenhouse gas. Added to the atmosphere in high enough quantities, the gas could have led to a global rise in temperatures.

Middle and Recent Earth History (Section 13-3)

The Triassic period is named for three related units of rock first studied in Germany. The Jurassic period is named after the Jura Mountains located between France and Switzerland, where this age of rock was first studied. The Cretaceous period, is named for the Latin word for chalk, creta. The white chalk cliffs of Dover, England, are of this age.

The KP (Cretaceous/Paleogene) boundary is the point in the geologic time scale that separates the Mesozoic era from the Cenozoic era. This boundary contains evidence for the extinction of the dinosaurs. An iridium-rich clay layer found at this boundary led to the theory that a collision with an asteroid was the final blow to the already dying dinosaur population.

Geologic evidence indicates that humans and their direct ancestors make up a group of animals called hominids. The earliest definite hominids were of the genus *Australopithecus.* Australopithecines were bipedal and had rounded jaws. They lived in the open grasslands of what is now eastern and southern Africa. Australopithecines were smaller than modern humans. Standing less than 1.5 m tall, they weighed about 20 kg. Their brains were half the size of present-day humans' brains. Fossil evidence indicates these early human ancestors used tools made of bone.

SCIENCE UPDATE

For current events or science in the news, access the Glencoe Science Web Site at **www.glencoe.com/sec/science**

Teacher to Teacher

"Create a time line of the geologic time scale where 1 cm of yarn represents 1 million years. On index cards, have students write an event, the time it occurred in millions of years, and the distance on the yarn. Using paper clips, attach the cards to the yarn. Attach the time line to the ceiling, spiraling toward the center."

Rebecca S. Buckingham

Rebecca Buckingham, Teacher
Lisbon Central School
Lisbon, NY

CHAPTER 13 Geologic Time

CHAPTER OVERVIEW

Section 13-1 This section presents the division of Earth's history into the geologic time scale. The development of trilobites through geologic time is discussed. Changes in the characteristics of trilobites is presented. The effect of plate tectonics on Earth history is described.

Section 13-2 Earth history during Precambrian time and the Paleozoic era is described in this section. Changes in Earth and its life-forms in each of the two ages are presented.

Section 13-3 This section describes changes in Earth and its life-forms during the Mesozoic and Cenozoic eras.

Chapter Vocabulary

geologic time scale	cyanobacteria
era	Paleozoic era
period	amphibian
epoch	reptile
trilobite	Mesozoic era
Precambrian time	gastrolith
	Cenozoic era

Theme Connection

Stability and Change Organic evolution (changes in life-forms), as it is used in dividing Earth's history into the geologic time scale, should be a major focus of all sections in this chapter.

00:00 OUT OF TIME?

If time does not permit teaching the entire chapter, use Reviewing Main Ideas on pp. 390–391.

CHAPTER 13 Geologic Time

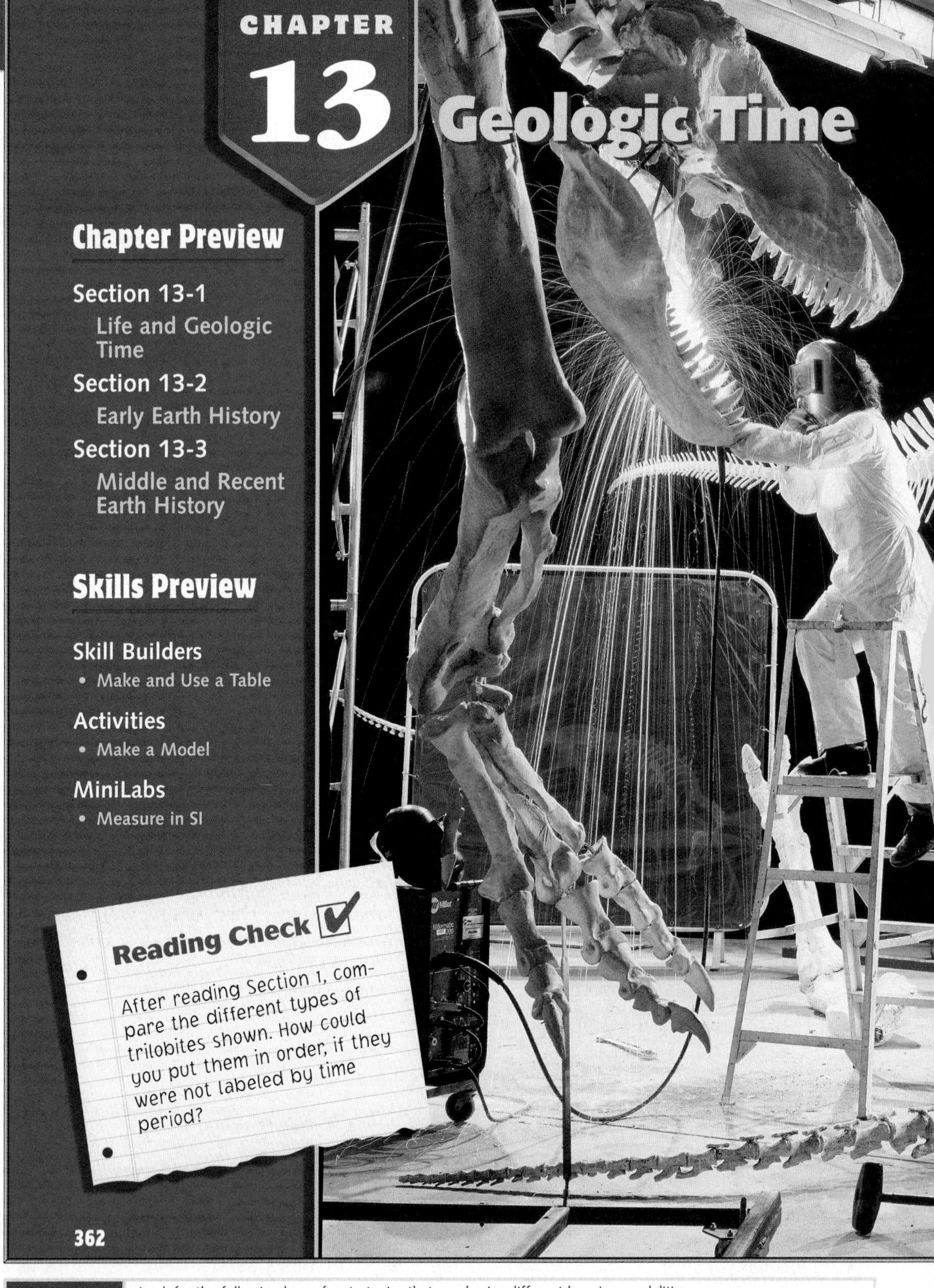

Chapter Preview

Skills Preview

Skill Builders
- Make and Use a Table

Activities
- Make a Model

MiniLabs
- Measure in SI

Reading Check ✓

After reading Section 1, compare the different types of trilobites shown. How could you put them in order, if they were not labeled by time period?

362

Multiple Learning Styles

Look for the following logos for strategies that emphasize different learning modalities.

Linguistic Science Journal, pp. 367, 377, 384; Quick Demo, p. 370; Integrating the Sciences, p. 373; Enrichment, p. 383; Preview, p. 390

Logical-Mathematical Multiple Learning Styles, p. 368; MiniLab, p. 385

Visual-Spatial Activity, p. 367; Assessment, p. 371; MiniLab, p. 375; Enrichment, p. 376; Reteach, p. 390

Auditory-Musical Out of Time, p. 390

Kinesthetic Explore Activity, p. 363; Inclusion Strategies, p. 373

Interpersonal Using an Analogy, p. 365; Activity, pp. 366, 379; Inclusion Strategies, pp. 382; Review, p. 390

Intrapersonal Activity p. 388–389

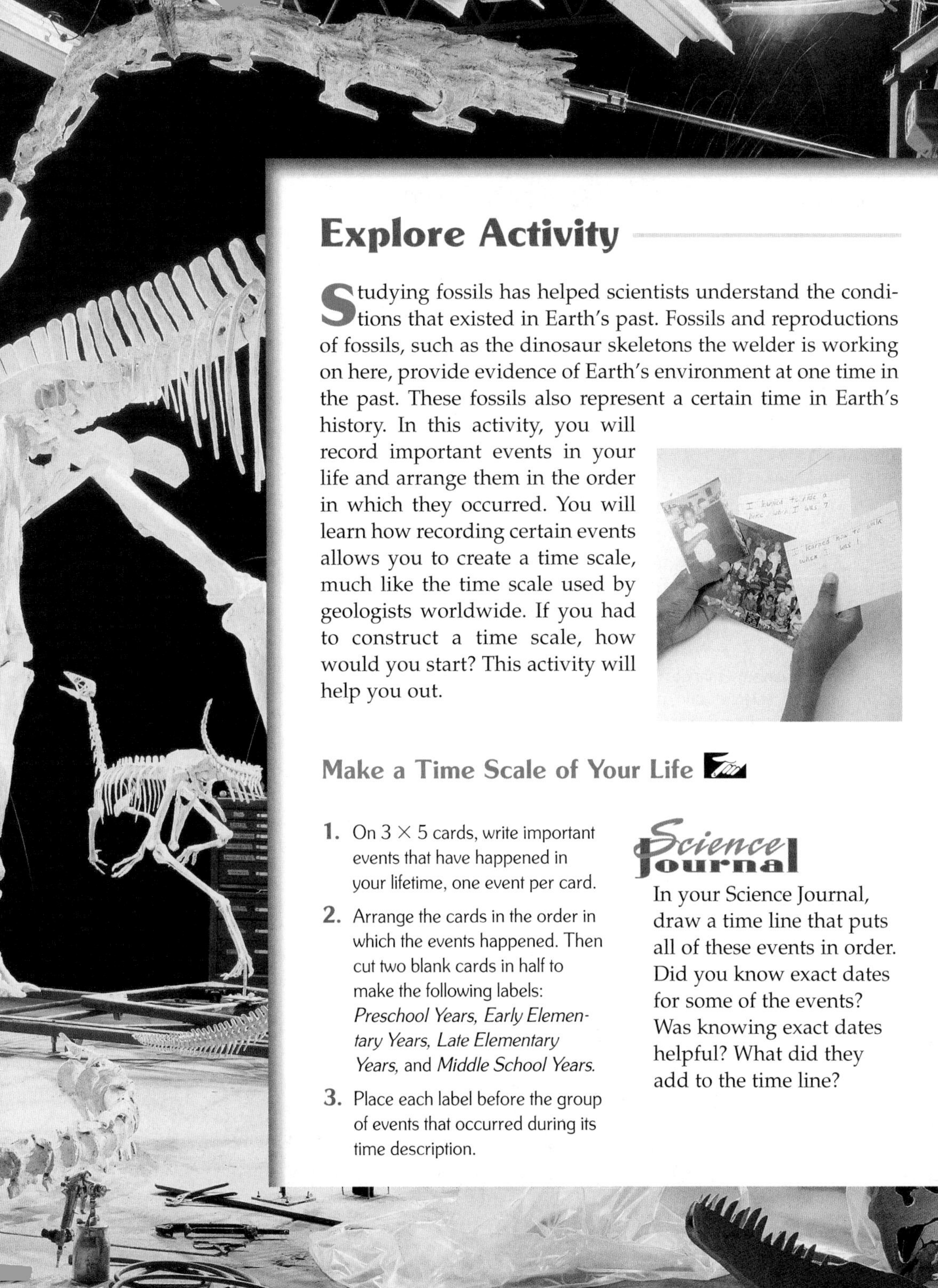

Explore Activity

Studying fossils has helped scientists understand the conditions that existed in Earth's past. Fossils and reproductions of fossils, such as the dinosaur skeletons the welder is working on here, provide evidence of Earth's environment at one time in the past. These fossils also represent a certain time in Earth's history. In this activity, you will record important events in your life and arrange them in the order in which they occurred. You will learn how recording certain events allows you to create a time scale, much like the time scale used by geologists worldwide. If you had to construct a time scale, how would you start? This activity will help you out.

Make a Time Scale of Your Life

1. On 3 × 5 cards, write important events that have happened in your lifetime, one event per card.
2. Arrange the cards in the order in which the events happened. Then cut two blank cards in half to make the following labels: *Preschool Years, Early Elementary Years, Late Elementary Years,* and *Middle School Years.*
3. Place each label before the group of events that occurred during its time description.

Science Journal

In your Science Journal, draw a time line that puts all of these events in order. Did you know exact dates for some of the events? Was knowing exact dates helpful? What did they add to the time line?

Explore Activity

Purpose

Kinesthetic Use the Explore Activity to introduce students to the concept of history and important events in time. Inform students that they will be learning about events in Earth's history and the changes in Earth and its lifeforms through time. L2

Materials

index cards (8 per group), scissors, pens or markers

Teaching Strategies

Encourage students to think back as far as they can.

Safety Precautions

Caution students to handle the scissors with care.

Science Journal Time scales will vary. However, students are likely to divide events similarly. Students should conclude that knowing exact dates made it easier to place events on the time line.

Assessment

Process Ask students what they learned about their lives from placing events on a time line. Many students may notice patterns they hadn't been aware of before. Use **Performance Assessment in the Science Classroom,** p. 17.

Assessment Planner

Portfolio

Refer to p. 391 for suggested items that students might select for their portfolios.

Performance Assessment

See p. 391 for additional Performance Assessment options.
Skill Builder, pp. 371, 378, 387
MiniLab, pp. 375, 385
Activity 13-1, p. 379; 13-2, pp. 388–389

Content Assessment

Section Assessment, pp. 371, 378, 387
Chapter Assessment, pp. 392–393
Proficiency Prep, pp. 371, 378, 387

SECTION 13-1

Prepare

Refer to **Life and Geologic Time** and **The Geologic Time Scale** on p. 362E.

Preplanning

Refer to the **Chapter Organizer** on pp. 362A–B.

1 Motivate

Bellringer

Before presenting the lesson, display **Section Focus Transparency 34** on the overhead projector. Use the accompanying **Focus Activity** worksheet. L2 ELL

34 SECTION FOCUS TRANSPARENCY

Section 13-1

TRILOBITE TEACHERS

You can learn a lot from trilobites. Look at the ones in the picture. They are different ages. They show that trilobites, like other lifeforms, change over time.

1. Which trilobite do you think is the oldest? Why?
2. Why do you think trilobites changed over time?

Tying to Previous Knowledge

Many students are familiar with the horseshoe crab. The horseshoe crab has a body structure related to the trilobite.

13•1 Life and Geologic Time

***What* You'll Learn**

- How geologic time is divided into units
- How trilobites from different periods of the Paleozoic era may have evolved through geologic time
- How plate tectonics affects changes in species

Vocabulary
geologic time scale
era
period
epoch
trilobite

***Why* It's Important**

- Because organisms change through time, scientists can describe Earth history using the Geologic Time Scale.

Geologic Time

A group of students went digging for fossils with their teacher. They knew that paleontologists study geologic history by collecting and studying fossils of organisms that lived long ago. The students were hoping to find some fossils from the Paleozoic era and, in particular, trilobites (TRI luh bites). They were told that they would be looking in rocks that are about 510 million years old.

Some examples of what they found are shown in **Figure 13-1.** The fossils are small and appear to have segments over much of their bodies. Some of them seem to be curled into a ball. What are they? Are these the trilobites their teacher told them about? Finding out about Earth's history will help you determine if these fossils are trilobites.

The Geologic Time Scale

The appearance and disappearance of types of organisms throughout Earth's history give scientists data to mark important changes or geologic occurrences in time. We can divide Earth's history into smaller units based on the types of lifeforms living during certain periods. The division of Earth's history into smaller units makes up the **geologic time scale.** All the divisions in the geologic time scale are based on changes in fossil organisms. Changes in the fossils can be caused by geologic events such as changes in sea level or mountain building.

Figure 13-1 The physical appearance of many types of organisms, such as the trilobites shown here, has changed throughout geologic time.

A *Modocia typicales* is from Cambrian rocks in Utah.

B *Isotelus maximus* is from Ordovician rocks in Ohio.

Resource Manager

The following **Teacher Classroom Resources** can be used with Section 13-1:

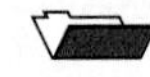 **Reproducible Masters**

Enrichment, p. 34 L3

Reinforcement, p. 34 L2

Study Guide, pp. 49–50 L1 ELL

 **Transparencies**

Teaching Transparency 25 L2

Teaching Transparency 26 L2

Science Integration Transparency 13 L2

The geologic time scale is a record of Earth's history, starting with Earth's formation about 4.6 billion years ago. Each period of time is named. When the ages of fossils and rock layers are determined, scientists can assign them to a specific place on the geologic time scale.

Subdivisions of Geologic Time

Geologic time is divided into three subdivisions: eras, periods, and epochs. **Eras** are major subdivisions of the geologic time scale based on differences in life-forms. There are three named eras—the Paleozoic, which means ancient life, the Mesozoic, or middle life, and the Cenozoic, or recent life. As you can see in **Figure 13-2** on the next page, the Mesozoic era began about 245 million years ago. Its end is marked by the extinction of the dinosaurs and many other organisms about 66 million years ago. When did trilobites first appear? Were the students looking in rocks of the correct age to find trilobites?

Eras are subdivided into **periods.** Periods are based on the types of life that existed at the time. Periods are divided into smaller units of time called **epochs.** Generally, only the Cenozoic era is shown subdivided further into epochs as seen in **Figure 13-2.** The epochs of the other periods are usually called early, middle, and late. Why is this so? The fossil record is more complete in these recent rock layers. As a result, geologists have more data with which to divide the time scale.

interNET CONNECTION

Visit the Glencoe Science Web Site at **www.glencoe.com/sec/science** to find out more about fossils.

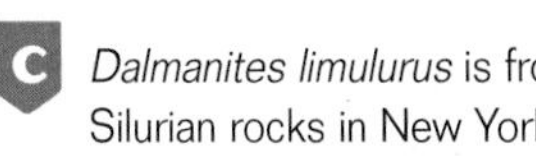

C *Dalmanites limulurus* is from Silurian rocks in New York.

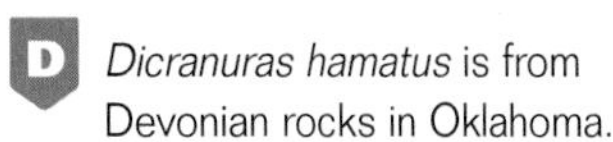

D *Dicranuras hamatus* is from Devonian rocks in Oklahoma.

2 Teach

Using an Analogy

Interpersonal Have student groups discuss and list, from earliest to latest, events that have occurred during the school year. Ask students to describe the number of events and the details they can remember from early in the year and compare these to events later in the year. Students should notice that events that have occurred recently are remembered in greater detail. Relate this analogy to the fact that the record of geologic events in recent periods is much more detailed that the record of events from periods long ago.

GLENCOE TECHNOLOGY

Videodisc

The Infinite Voyage: Life in the Balance

Chapter 1 *Understanding Mass Extinction* 6:00

Refer to the Teacher Guide for bar codes and teaching strategies.

interNET CONNECTION

Internet Addresses

For Internet tips, see Glencoe's **Using the Internet in the Science Classroom.**

Across the Curriculum

Geography Inform students that periods on the geologic time scale are often named for geographic regions where the rocks of that age were first studied. Ask them to determine where rocks of the Pennsylvanian and Mississippian periods were first studied. Rocks of the Pennsylvanian period are found exposed in Pennsylvania. Rocks of the Mississippian period are exposed along the Mississippi River. Ask students to determine which period on the geologic time scale represents rocks first studied in the Jura Mountains between France and Switzerland. L2

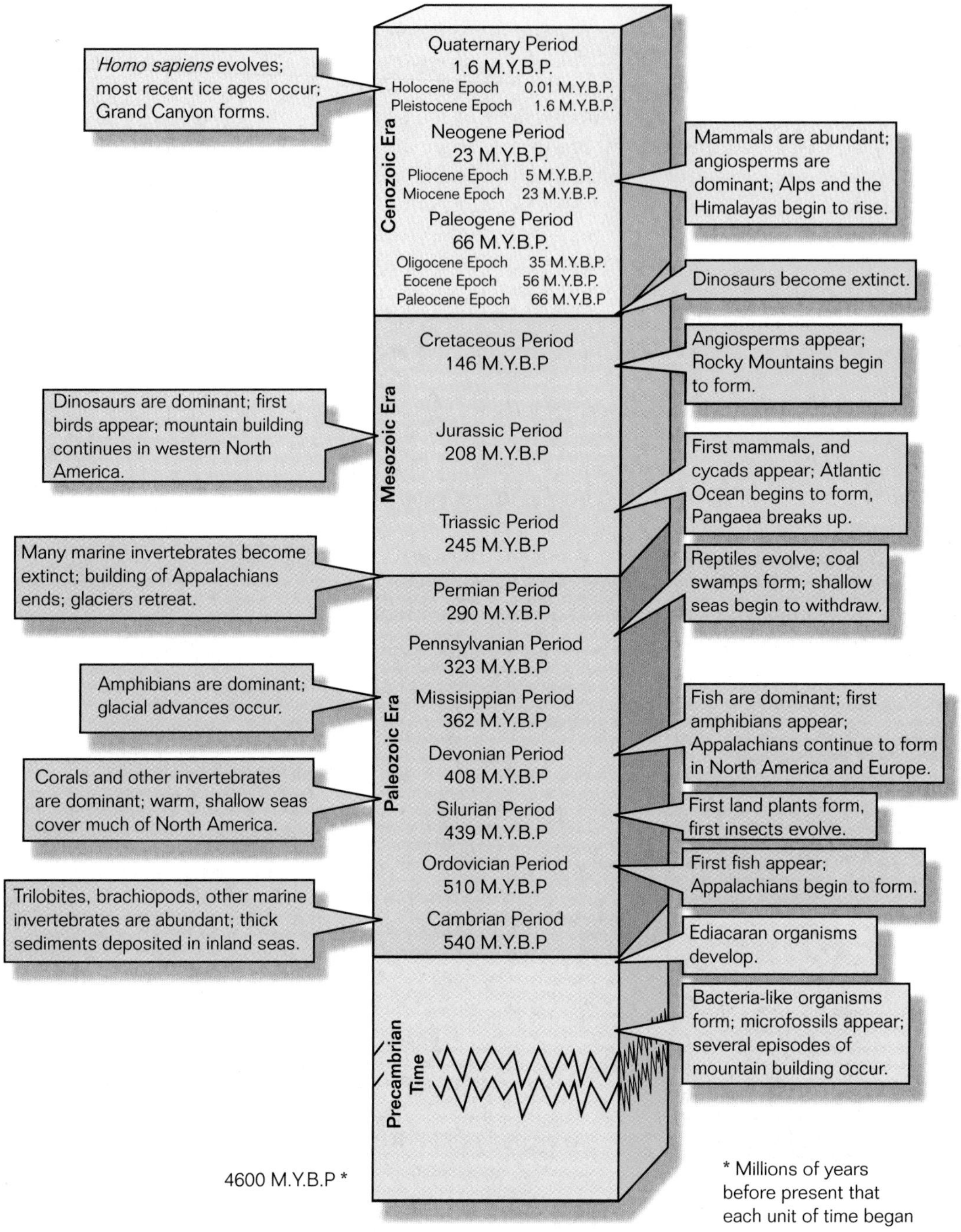

Activity

Interpersonal Provide groups of students with geologic maps of your area. Ask students to determine the age of rocks located near the school or their homes. Bring in samples of rock from a local exposure and have students determine what type of rock it is. Inform them of where you obtained the rocks and have them locate the area on their maps. L2 COOP LEARN

Correcting Misconceptions

Many students will think that scientists have obtained a complete record of Earth's past from fossils contained in the rocks. Explain that little is known about the first 4 billion years because much of the fossil record has been destroyed. Gaps in the fossil record exist in more recent rocks because of erosion.

Caption Answer

Figure 13-2 *Answers will vary.*

GLENCOE TECHNOLOGY

Videodisc

Glencoe Science Voyages Interactive Videodisc—Life

Side 2, Lesson 6 *Eyeing Evolution*

12743

Refer to Videodisc Teacher Guide for additional bar codes.

VISUALIZING Geologic Time

Figure 13-2 The geologic time scale is divided into subunits based on the appearance and disappearance of types of organisms. The numbers listed show the beginning of each subunit. **Beginning at the bottom, which events do you think were most important in Earth history?**

Cenozoic Era
Quaternary Period 1.6 M.Y.B.P.
Holocene Epoch 0.01 M.Y.B.P.
Pleistocene Epoch 1.6 M.Y.B.P.
Homo sapiens evolves; most recent ice ages occur; Grand Canyon forms.
Neogene Period 23 M.Y.B.P.
Pliocene Epoch 5 M.Y.B.P.
Miocene Epoch 23 M.Y.B.P.
Mammals are abundant; angiosperms are dominant; Alps and the Himalayas begin to rise.
Paleogene Period 66 M.Y.B.P.
Oligocene Epoch 35 M.Y.B.P.
Eocene Epoch 56 M.Y.B.P.
Paleocene Epoch 66 M.Y.B.P
Dinosaurs become extinct.

Mesozoic Era
Cretaceous Period 146 M.Y.B.P
Angiosperms appear; Rocky Mountains begin to form.
Jurassic Period 208 M.Y.B.P
Dinosaurs are dominant; first birds appear; mountain building continues in western North America.
First mammals, and cycads appear; Atlantic Ocean begins to form, Pangaea breaks up.
Triassic Period 245 M.Y.B.P
Many marine invertebrates become extinct; building of Appalachians ends; glaciers retreat.

Paleozoic Era
Permian Period 290 M.Y.B.P
Reptiles evolve; coal swamps form; shallow seas begin to withdraw.
Pennsylvanian Period 323 M.Y.B.P
Mississippian Period 362 M.Y.B.P
Amphibians are dominant; glacial advances occur.
Devonian Period 408 M.Y.B.P
Fish are dominant; first amphibians appear; Appalachians continue to form in North America and Europe.
Silurian Period 439 M.Y.B.P
Corals and other invertebrates are dominant; warm, shallow seas cover much of North America.
First land plants form, first insects evolve.
Ordovician Period 510 M.Y.B.P
First fish appear; Appalachians begin to form.
Cambrian Period 540 M.Y.B.P
Trilobites, brachiopods, other marine invertebrates are abundant; thick sediments deposited in inland seas.
Ediacaran organisms develop.

Precambrian Time
Bacteria-like organisms form; microfossils appear; several episodes of mountain building occur.
4600 M.Y.B.P *

* Millions of years before present that each unit of time began

Inclusion Strategies

Gifted Have students interview a grandparent or other senior citizen. They should ask what major changes in the world the senior has observed. Changes could be in inventions, transportation, communication, the environment, health, and political and philosophical issues. Students should develop a time line of some of these major events in this person's "era." L2

Answer to Text Question

When did trilobites first appear? *in the Cambrian period* **Were the students looking in rocks of the correct age to find trilobites?** *Yes, trilobites could be found in rocks that are between 245 and 544 million years old.* (See p. 365)

Geologic Time and Fossils

Geologists study fossils to help describe Earth's past environments, to interpret how extinct organisms lived, and to document changes in organisms through time. A brief study of trilobites illustrates how this is done.

When people look for fossils, they like to find trilobites. **Trilobites** (TRI luh bites) were organisms that lived hundreds of millions of years ago. They crawled on the seafloor and occasionally swam through the water. They ranged in size from 6 mm to 75 cm in length, with most between 2 cm and 7 cm in length and between 1 cm and 3 cm in width.

Trilobites first appeared during the Cambrian period and existed on Earth throughout the Paleozoic era. They became extinct at the end of the Permian period. Numerous species of trilobites lived on Earth for more than 300 million years. Although trilobites existed throughout Paleozoic time, they did not all look the same. The characteristics of trilobites changed with time.

The name *trilobite* is derived from an interesting fact about the structure of its exoskeleton. The exoskeleton of each trilobite is divided into three lobes that run the length of the body. Just as with insects, the trilobite's body was divided into three sections: the head (cephalon), the body (thorax), and the tail (pygidium). These are shown in **Figure 13-3.** ✓

Reading Check ✓

From what characteristic did trilobites get their name?

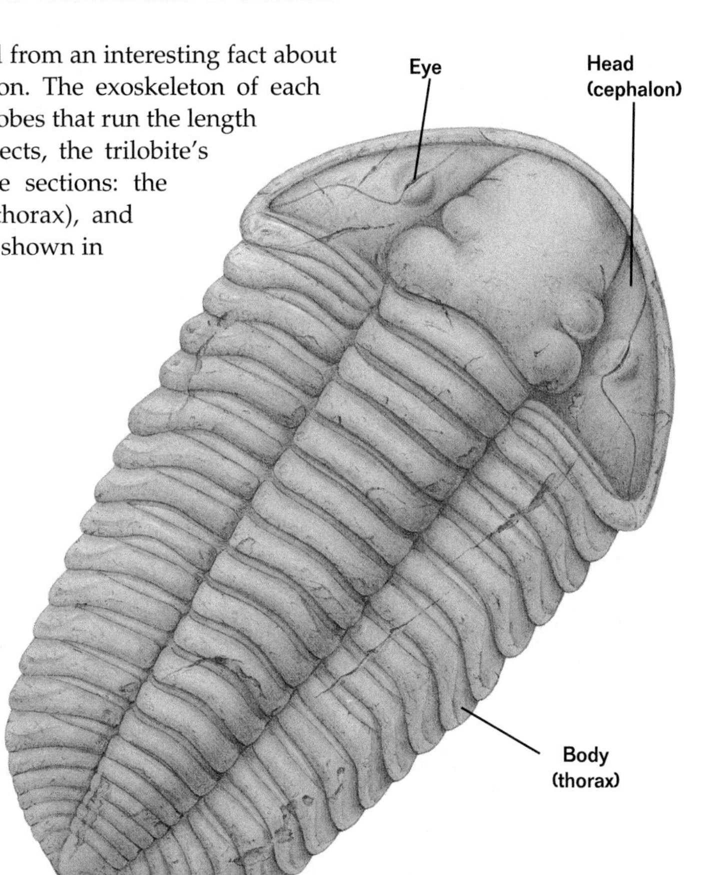

Figure 13-3 This illustration shows the parts of a typical trilobite.

Activity

Visual-Spatial Give students a geologic time scale and have them identify the eras by coloring their headings with a colored pencil. Have students identify periods and epochs by coloring their headings with two different-colored pencils. L1

Answer to Reading Check ✓

The name trilobite comes from the fact that a trilobite's exoskeleton was divided into three lobes.

Activity

Visual-Spatial Have students make a network tree concept map of the geologic time scale. Students' maps should show the hierarchy among the divisions of time. L2

GLENCOE TECHNOLOGY

Videodisc

Glencoe Science Voyages Interactive Videodisc—Earth

Side 1, Lesson 4 *Volcanoes: Erupting Mountains*

43091

Refer to Videodisc Teacher Guide for additional bar codes.

Science Journal

Theory of Organic Evolution Have students do some research in a historical geology book or biology text. In their Science Journals, have them define the terms *gradualism* and *punctuated equilibrium.* Encourage students to relate each of these terms to the study of the theory of organic evolution and the evolution of trilobites. L2

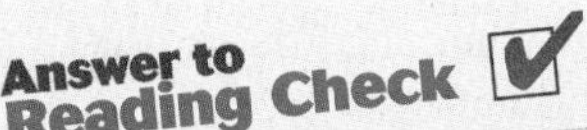

Using Math

Portions of the circle graph should represent the following percentages:
Permian (15.2%),
Pennsylvanian (11.2%),
Mississippian (13.2%),
Devonian (15.6%),
Silurian (10.5%),
Ordovician (24.1%), and
Cambrian (10.2%).
The longest period was the Ordovician and the shortest period was the Cambrian.

Caption Answers

Figure 13-4 *fewer segments, shortening or lengthening of glabella, complete disappearance of segments*

Figure 13-4c *the glabella is highly rounded, globe-shaped*

Gradual changes through time in organisms such as the trilobite, is the main concept of the theory of organic evolution. The explanation about how organisms change over time was developed about 150 years ago. This theory of organic evolution is used as a basis for scientific work on the development of life because, at the present time, it fits most of the evidence.

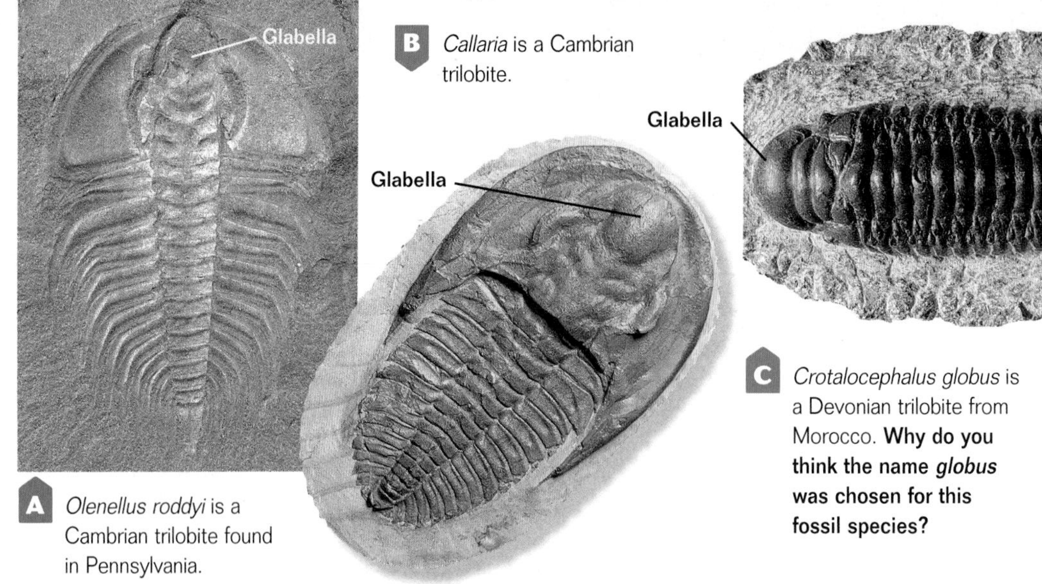

A *Olenellus roddyi* is a Cambrian trilobite found in Pennsylvania.

B *Callaria* is a Cambrian trilobite.

C *Crotalocephalus globus* is a Devonian trilobite from Morocco. **Why do you think the name *globus* was chosen for this fossil species?**

Figure 13-4 The *glabella* is a part of the trilobite's head. **Describe how the glabella changed through time.**

Changing Characteristics of Trilobites

Trilobites were common during the Cambrian period. Some species of trilobites became extinct at the close of the Cambrian period, others at the close of the Devonian period. Some species, however, survived until the end of the Permian period. Species of trilobites that lived during one period of the Paleozoic era show characteristics different from species of other periods. The different characteristics are used to show a gradual change of trilobites through geologic time as shown in **Figures 13-1** and **13-4.** Additionally, trilobites lived over large areas of the world during the Paleozoic era. They are considered an index fossil of the Paleozoic era. Index fossils are fossils that pinpoint a particular time in geologic history. In order to be an index fossil, the organism must have been geographically widespread, have lived for a relatively short period of time, and have distinct characteristics that help it stand out from other fossils. Because of physical changes through time, many species can be used as index fossils for specific geologic periods, such as the Cambrian period.

Using Math

Make a circle graph comparing the periods of the Paleozoic era. Sections of the circle graph should represent the lengths of the various periods of the Paleozoic era. Based on the circle graph, which period is the longest? Which period is the shortest?

Trilobite Eyes

Trilobites may have been the first organisms with true eyes and the capability to look out on their world. The position of the eyes on a trilobite fossil tells much about where the organism lived. If the eyes are located toward the front of the head, the organism was probably an active swimmer. If the eyes are located toward the back of the head, the organism might have been an ocean bottom dweller. In most species,

Multiple Learning Styles

Logical-Mathematical Have students study the chart, "The Victims and Survivors," from the article "Extinctions," by Rick Gore in *National Geographic*, June 1989, pages 662–699. Have pairs of students make circle graphs that show the percentage of extinctions that occurred at the end of the Ordovician period (70 percent of all species), the Devonian period (70 percent of all invertebrate species), the Permian period (more than 90 percent of all species), and the Cretaceous period (all dinosaurs and about 70 percent of all other animal species). The extinction event at the end of the Permian period is regarded as the greatest. L2 COOP LEARN

368 CHAPTER 13 GEOLOGIC TIME

Figure 13-5 Changes in trilobite eyes allowed species to adapt to their environment. (A) *Modocia typicalis* had long, crescent-shaped eyes; (B) *Calymene granulosa's* eyes were reduced in size; (C) *Peronopsis interstrictus* had no eyes and was blind; (D) The eyes of *Phacops rana* were compound like many modern-day insects.

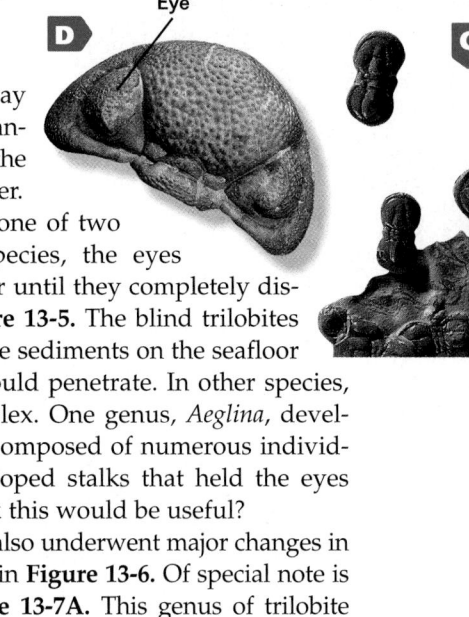

the eyes were located midway on the head—ideal for an organism that both crawled on the seafloor and swam in the water.

Trilobite eyes changed in one of two ways. In many trilobite species, the eyes became progressively smaller until they completely disappeared, as shown in **Figure 13-5.** The blind trilobites might have burrowed into the sediments on the seafloor or lived deeper than light could penetrate. In other species, the eyes became more complex. One genus, *Aeglina*, developed large compound eyes composed of numerous individual lenses. Some eyes developed stalks that held the eyes upward. Where do you think this would be useful?

The trilobite body and tail also underwent major changes in form through time as shown in **Figure 13-6.** Of special note is *Olenellus*, as shown in **Figure 13-7A.** This genus of trilobite from the Lower Cambrian period has pronounced spines. Although the exact use of the spines is not understood, the appearance of them is limited to earlier species. No spines are found in fossils between the Mississippian to the Permian periods. These differences also help identify different species and can be used to infer how and where they lived.

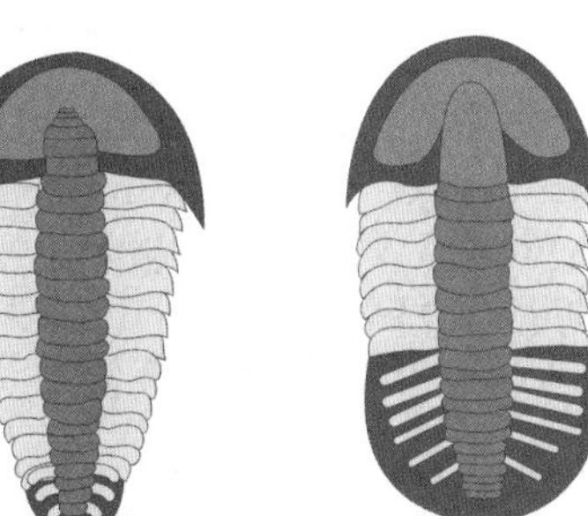

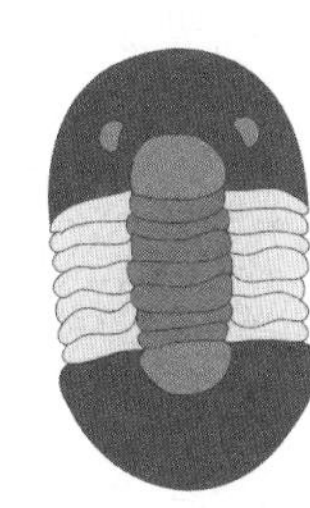

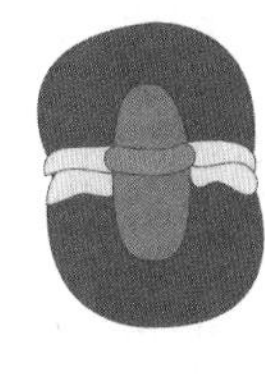

Figure 13-6 The physical features of trilobites changed throughout the Paleozoic era. **Which environments do you think each of these trilobites was adapted for?**

Flex Your Brain

Use the Flex Your Brain activity to have students explore ADAPTATION.

Enrichment

Have students research the work of early geologists in the construction of the geologic time scale. Scientists who students should research are Nicholaus Steno (1638–1687), James Hutton (1726–1797), William "Strata" Smith (1769–1838), and Charles Lyell (1797–1875). L3

Using Science Words

Help students develop better understanding and use of science words by asking the following inquiry questions. **Why were trilobites more likely to be preserved as fossils than many of the animals that lived in Precambrian time?** *Trilobites had developed hard parts and could be quickly buried under sediment.* **How can the position of eyes on fossilized trilobites help indicate the environment in which trilobites lived?** *The location of eyes on some fossilized trilobites was midway on the head, indicating an organism that crawled on the seafloor and swam in the water.*

Caption Answer

Figure 13-6 *The first, third, and fourth probably swam and crawled on the ocean floor. The second and fifth most likely lived on the ocean floor in deeper water.*

Guided Reading Strategy

ReQuest To improve listening skills, have students listen carefully as the teacher reads an interesting piece or story aloud. After the reading, have students construct questions to be discussed with the teacher. The teacher can assign students to read the story and participate in the questioning with other students. Have students participate in a ReQuest with the chapter feature or another interesting piece related to chapter content.

Content Background

In many trilobites, the eyes were probably one of the most important sensory organs. Trilobites had simple eyes, compound eyes, or no eyes at all. Some trilobites developed stalked eyes. Perhaps it was an adaptation that provided better visual sensitivity.

3 Assess

Check for Understanding

Quick Demo

Linguistic List the three most recent eras of geologic time on the chalkboard. Using illustrations, models, or both, identify which organisms are thought to have evolved, existed, and/or become extinct in each era. Have students write a brief one-paragraph summary in their Science Journals of the concepts demonstrated in class. L2

Answers to Text Question

What effect might these changes have had on the trilobite population? *Habitats would have been destroyed; the climate changed; ocean temperatures may have changed due to changes in circulation. If they were not able to adapt, they would die.*

Reteach

Demonstrate how lifeforms change through geologic time by showing students samples of trilobites from the Cambrian period and then from later periods in the Paleozoic era. Conclude by showing samples or photographs of a horseshoe crab, a present-day organism with characteristics similar to trilobites.

Extension

For students who have mastered this section, use the **Reinforcement** and **Enrichment** masters.

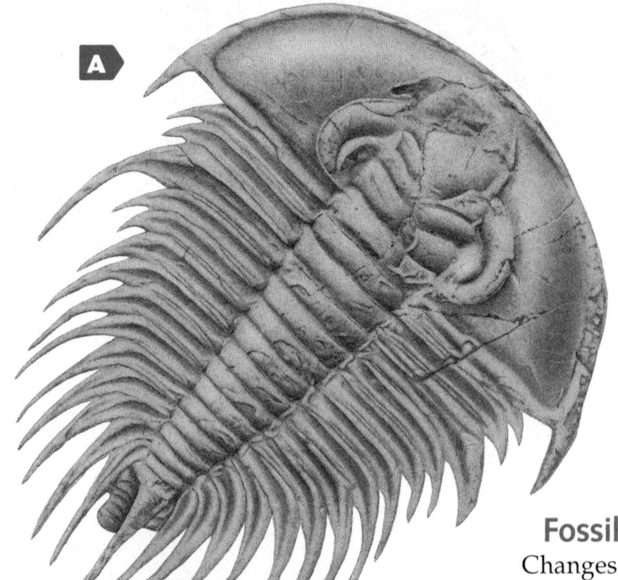

B

Figure 13-7 (A) This illustration shows an Olenellus trilobite. Trilobite spines can help determine a fossil's age. (B) *Kettneraspis williamsmi* is a spiny trilobite from the Devonian of Oklahoma.

Fossils Show Changes

Changes in the exoskeleton of trilobites probably occurred at least in part because they were adapting to changing environments, geographic isolation, how they lived, and the competition for survival. You have learned how paleontologists use the physical features of individual fossil species to interpret their life modes and environments. As you read through the rest of this chapter, you will see how studies such as the trilobite example helped enable geologists to interpret Earth history and create the geologic time scale.

The Effect of Plate Tectonics

Plate tectonics is one process that causes changing environments on Earth. As plates on Earth's surface moved over time, continents collided with and separated from each other many times. Continental collisions caused mountain building and the draining of seas. Continental separations caused deeper seas to develop between continents. This rearranging of land and sea still causes changes in climates today.

If species adapt to the changes, or evolve, they survive. If a species doesn't have individuals with characteristics needed to survive in the changing environment, the species becomes extinct. Trilobites lived in the oceans. As the supercontinent Pangaea came together at the end of the Paleozoic era, much of the ocean environment where trilobites lived was either changed or destroyed. What effect might these changes have had on the trilobite population? **Figure 13-8** illustrates the effect plate tectonics had on another ocean organism, coral.

Integrating the Sciences

Life Science As plates move across Earth's mantle, continents collide and separate many times. Continental collisions result in the formation of mountains. Mountain ranges can separate species that normally live together. Also, environments and climate change and oceans deepen or become shallow as landmasses move. Based on the theory of organic evolution, it is thought that the environmental changes result in the evolution of traits within species and the evolution of new species.

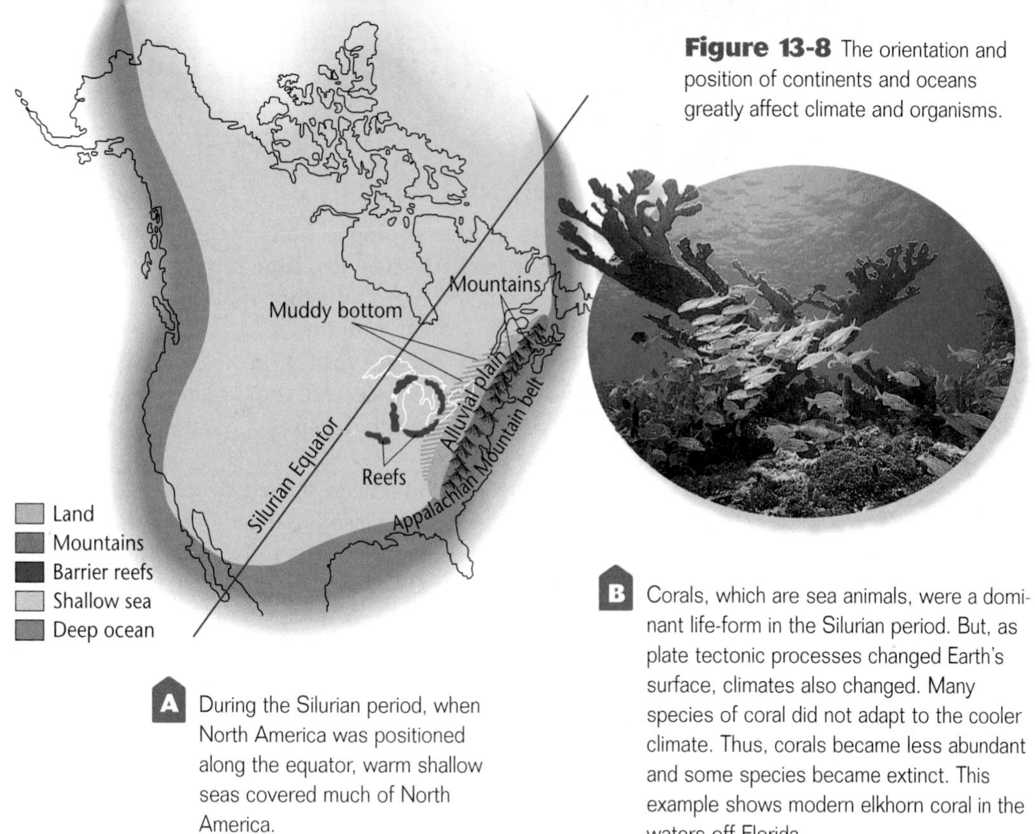

Figure 13-8 The orientation and position of continents and oceans greatly affect climate and organisms.

A During the Silurian period, when North America was positioned along the equator, warm shallow seas covered much of North America.

B Corals, which are sea animals, were a dominant life-form in the Silurian period. But, as plate tectonic processes changed Earth's surface, climates also changed. Many species of coral did not adapt to the cooler climate. Thus, corals became less abundant and some species became extinct. This example shows modern elkhorn coral in the waters off Florida.

Section Assessment

1. What are the major subdivisions of the geologic time scale based on?
2. Compare and contrast trilobite eyes and the type of environment they might have been adapted to.
3. How might plate tectonics affect all life on Earth?
4. **Think Critically:** How might movement of the continents have affected trilobite survival?
5. **Skill Activity**
   Interpreting Data Do the **Chapter 13 Skill Activity** on page 754 to interpret data about the age relationships between different dinosaurs.

Write a paragraph in your Science Journal that explains how various characteristics of trilobites from different periods of geologic time provide evidence that organisms belonging to the same genus or family change physically through time.

Assessment

Performance Assess students' abilities to observe and infer by having them look at photographs of giraffes and hypothesize why giraffes have such long necks. Use **Performance Assessment in the Science Classroom,** p. 21. 

Answers will vary, but expect students to include reference to changes in eye complexity. For example, one genus may have adapted to living in an area of low or no light by developing progressively smaller eyes.

4 Close

Proficiency Prep

Use this quiz to check students' recall of section content.

1. **What are the divisions of geologic time scale based on?** *the types of life-forms existing during certain times; the geologic changes that have occurred*
2. **What organism first appeared during the Cambrian period and became extinct at the end of the Permian period?** *trilobite*

Section Assessment

1. differences in the types of life that existed at that time
2. no eyes—deep water, burrower in sediment; complex eyes—many lenses, able to see in many directions; stalked eyes—possible burrower; eyes toward front of head—swimmer; eyes toward back of head—bottom dweller
3. As landmasses move across Earth, climates change dramatically. Only individuals suited to the changes survive and reproduce. They pass their traits to their offspring. Over many generations, the species has evolved so that it can survive in the changed environment.
4. **Think Critically** Because trilobites were marine animals, if continental movement resulted in ocean shallowing, change in currents, temperature, decrease of habitat or even destruction, trilobites would not have been able to survive.

Prepare

Content Background

Refer to **Early Earth History** on p. 362F.

Preplanning

Refer to the **Chapter Organizer** on pages 362A–B.

1 Motivate

Bellringer

Before presenting the lesson, display **Section Focus Transparency 35** on the overhead projector. Use the accompanying **Focus Activity** worksheet. L2 ELL

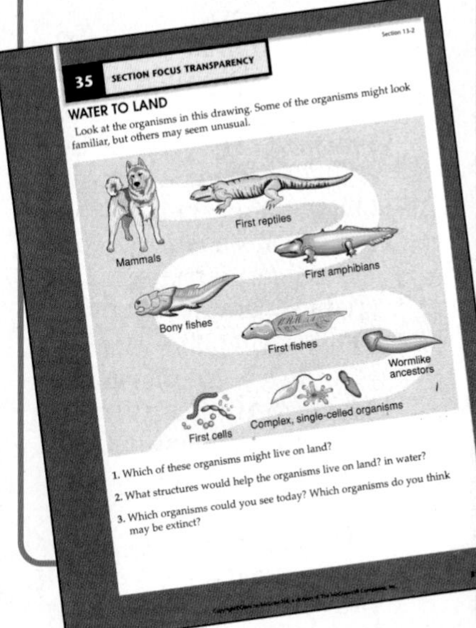

35 SECTION FOCUS TRANSPARENCY

WATER TO LAND

Look at the organisms in this drawing. Some of the organisms might look familiar, but others may seem unusual.

1. Which of these organisms might live on land?
2. What structures would help the organisms live on land? in water?
3. Which organisms could you see today? Which organisms do you think may be extinct?

Caption Answer

Figure 13-9 *They are well adapted to their particular environment.*

13•2 Early Earth History

What You'll Learn

- Dominant life-forms in Precambrian time and the Paleozoic era
- How organisms adapted to changing environments in Precambrian time and the Paleozoic era
- Changes in Earth and its life-forms at the end of the Paleozoic era

Vocabulary

Precambrian time
cyanobacteria
Paleozoic era
amphibian
reptile

Why It's Important

- The world you know today was created by physical and biological changes that occurred in the Mesozoic and early Cenozoic eras.

Precambrian Time

Look again at the geologic time scale in **Figure 13-2. Precambrian** (pree KAM bree un) **time** represents the longest geologic time unit of Earth's history. This time lasted from 4.6 billion to about 540 million years ago. Although the Precambrian was the longest unit of geologic time, relatively little is known about Earth and the organisms that lived during this time. Why is the fossil record from Precambrian time so sparse?

Precambrian rocks have been buried deeply and changed by heat and pressure. They also have been eroded more than younger rocks. These changes affect not only the rocks, but the fossil record, as well. Most fossils can't withstand the metamorphic and erosional processes that most Precambrian rocks have undergone.

Figure 13-9 In some conditions, cyanobacteria produce mound-shaped layers of calcium carbonate called stromatolites. Stromatolites were common about 2.8 billion years ago and are still being formed today. **What does this imply about the life-form cyanobacteria?**

A Stromatolites have changed little throughout geologic time. These modern ones in Australia look much like ancient stromatolites.

Resource Manager

The following **Teacher Classroom Resources** can be used with Section 13-2:

 **Reproducible Masters**

Activity Worksheets, pp. 71–73 L2

Enrichment, p. 35 L3

Home Involvement, p. 36 L2

Laboratory Manual, pp. 71–76 L2

Reinforcement, p. 35 L2

Early Life

It wasn't until fossilized cyanobacteria forming layered mats, called stromatolites, were found that scientists could begin to unravel Earth's complex history. Stromatolites are shown in **Figure 13-9.** Cyanobacteria first appeared on Earth about 3.5 billion years ago. **Cyanobacteria** are thought to be one of the earliest forms of life on Earth. They contain chlorophyll and as they photosynthesize, they give off oxygen. As these organisms evolved, they contributed to changes in Earth's atmosphere. During the few billion years following the appearance of cyanobacteria, oxygen became a major gas in Earth's atmosphere. The ozone layer in the stratosphere also began to develop, shielding Earth from ultraviolet rays. These major changes in the air allowed species of single-celled organisms to evolve into more complex organisms.

Animals without backbones, called invertebrates, developed near the end of Precambrian time. Imprints of jellyfish and marine worms have been found in late Precambrian rocks. However, because these early invertebrates were soft-bodied, they weren't easily preserved as fossils. This is another reason the Precambrian fossil record is so sparse.

CHEMISTRY INTEGRATION

Bacteria and Air

Cyanobacteria are thought to have been one of the mechanisms by which Earth's early atmosphere became richer in oxygen. Research the composition of Earth's early atmosphere. Describe where these gases originated.

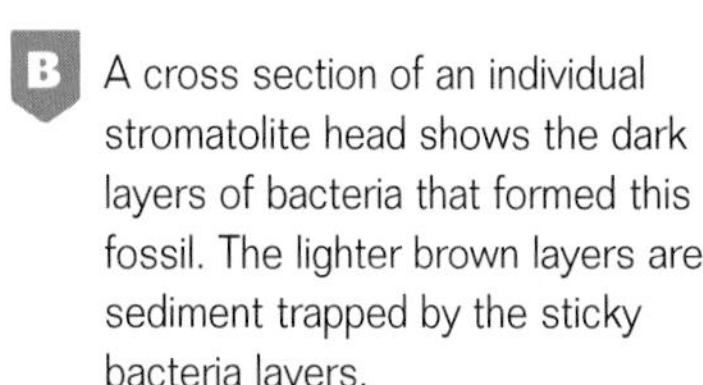

B A cross section of an individual stromatolite head shows the dark layers of bacteria that formed this fossil. The lighter brown layers are sediment trapped by the sticky bacteria layers.

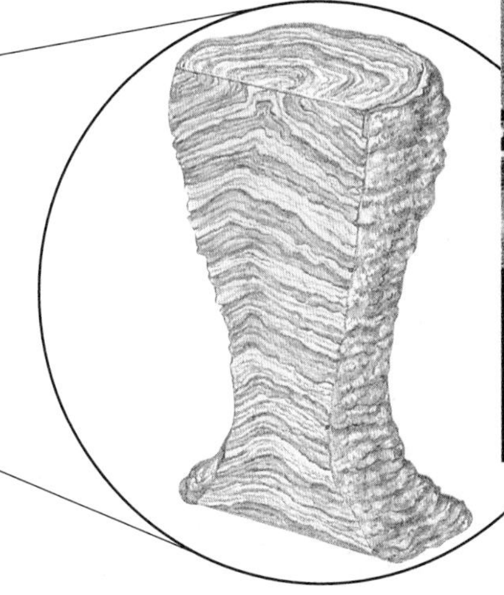

Tying to Previous Knowledge

Help students recall the importance of ozone to life on Earth. Inform students that ozone is made of three oxygen atoms (O_3) bonded together. When discussing the production of molecular oxygen (O_2) by cyanobacteria, relate the fact that ozone is produced when energy (such as that supplied by the sun or by lightning) is added to molecular oxygen.

2 Teach

Discussion

Why was the development of single-celled cyanobacteria so important to the organic evolution of more complex organisms? *As they evolved, cyanobacteria helped change Earth's atmosphere. They exchanged oxygen for other atmospheric gases. The amount of oxygen in the atmosphere increased, allowing an ozone layer to develop. The ozone layer shielded Earth's surface from harmful ultraviolet radiation from the sun. Complex life-forms were able to evolve in the changed environment.*

CHEMISTRY INTEGRATION

Gases in Earth's original atmosphere may have been in the original material that formed Earth. The gases were emitted during volcanic eruptions or derived from comet impacts. This early atmosphere was probably composed of water vapor, carbon dioxide, and nitrogen.

Inclusion Strategies

Visually Impaired Use plastic, plaster, or clay models of important fossils of animals and plants that lived during the Paleozoic period. Choose models that exhibit small details of the fossils. Being able to handle the fossils will help students picture their shapes, sizes, and details. Detailed and complete examples of an actual fossil may also be used for this purpose.

Integrating the Sciences

Life Science Have students research the role cyanobacteria played in transforming Earth's early atmosphere into one containing free molecular oxygen (O_2). In their Science Journals, ask them to hypothesize how life might be different if cyanobacteria had not transformed Earth's atmosphere. L2

Correcting Misconceptions

Ask students to hypothesize when sharks appeared on Earth. Many students will consider sharks to be modern-day animals because they are still around. Explain that it is thought that sharks evolved during the Devonian period about 408 million years ago. See *Earth and Life Through Time,* Steven M. Stanley, W.H. Freeman and Company, 1986.

VISUAL Learning

Figure 13-10 Examine the drawings. Are the organisms plants or animals? Explain your reasoning. *Answers will vary.* Encourage the students to think of the environment and mode of life in formulating their answers.

Content Background

Because life-forms first found in the Ediacaran hills of Australia are so different from what came next in the geologic time scale, the time when these organisms were alive on Earth can be thought of as a new period, the Ediacaran period, existing from about 600 to 540 million years ago. This period is placed at the end of Precambrian time and before the Cambrian period of the Paleozoic era.

Figure 13-10 These fossils are some of the first soft-bodied organisms preserved. They were first found in the Ediacara Hills in Australia.

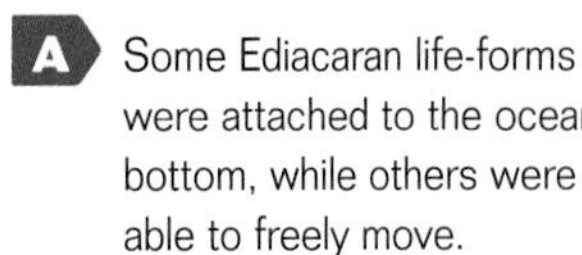

A Some Ediacaran life-forms were attached to the ocean bottom, while others were able to freely move.

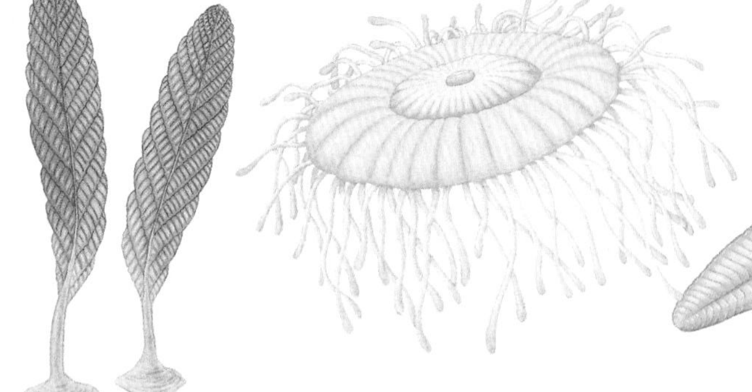

B *Dickinsonia* was a worm-like organism.

Unusual Life-Forms

Also developing at this time was a group of soft-bodied animals, first found in the Ediacara Hills of southern Australia. This group of organisms has become known as the *Ediacaran fauna.* Examples of these organisms are shown in **Figure 13-10.** Some paleontologists hypothesize that these organisms are the soft-bodied ancestors of many of the life-forms that developed during the Cambrian period. Other paleontologists hypothesize that these organisms were a completely different, now-extinct life-form. Some consider that the Ediacaran fossils are of organisms that were neither animal nor plant.

The Paleozoic Era

Fossils are more likely to form if organisms have hard parts. The beginning of the **Paleozoic** (pay lee uh ZOH ihk) **era** is marked by the presence of the first organisms with hard parts. Organisms were then more easily preserved.

The Paleozoic era, or era of ancient life, began about 544 million years ago. Warm, shallow seas covered much of Earth's surface during early Paleozoic time. Because of this, most of the life-forms were marine, meaning they lived in the ocean. Trilobites were common. Brachiopods (BRAH kee uh pahdz) and crinoids (KRI noyds), which still exist today, were also common. Although these animals may not be familiar to you, one type of animal you are familiar with—fish—evolved during this era, as well.

Content Background

A new discovery of early embryos has led to a change in understanding of the conditions that existed during the Cambrian period. It had been thought that the Cambrian period was a time conducive for the development of life. Eggs of some Cambrian organisms show evidence in support of large yolks. Large yolks usually exist when conditions are rather harsh, thus the organism hatches fully nourished and ready to fight for survival. New information such as this may lead to a change in understanding the evolution of life during the Cambrian period.

The Paleozoic era is broken into seven periods. The Cambrian period marks the appearance of marine animals with hard parts or skeletons. The most conspicuous and well known of these are trilobites. The start of the Ordovician period is marked by the beginning of the Appalachian Mountain–building process. This was probably caused by the collision of the Eurasian or African continental plate with the North American plate.

The first vertebrates, animals with backbones, developed during the Ordovician period. Plant life evolved on land during the Silurian period. Fish became dominant in the Devonian period, as seen in **Figure 13-11.** By this time, animals began to move onto land with the plants.

Interpreting Rock Layers

Procedure

1. Draw a sequence of three sedimentary rock layers.
2. Number the rock layers 1 through 3, bottom to top.
3. Identify the fossils in each layer as follows: Layer 1, contains fossils B and A; layer 2 contains fossils A, B, and C; layer 3 contains only fossil C.
4. Assign each of the fossils to one or more geologic periods. For example, fossil A lived from the Cambrian through the Devonian periods. Fossil C lived from the Devonian through the Permian periods, and so on.
5. Analyze the fossils' occurrence in each layer to help you determine the ages of each rock layer.

Analysis

1. Which layer or layers were you able to date to a specific period?
2. Why isn't it possible to determine during which specific period the other layers formed?
3. What is the age or possible age of each layer?

Figure 13-11 The giant fish, *Dunkleosteus,* which grew to more than 9 m long, lived during the Devonian period. This fossilized skull was found in Ohio. **What can you infer about the environment in Ohio during the Devonian?**

Caption Answer

Figure 13-11 *It was covered by a shallow sea.*

Try at Home
Mini Lab

For additional help doing this activity at home, see the corresponding pages in the **Home Involvement** booklet.

Purpose

Visual-Spatial Students will use fossils to determine the age of rock layers. L2 COOP LEARN

Teaching Strategies

- Have students construct a chart like the one shown.
- For each rock layer, list the periods during which it could have formed.

Troubleshooting Have students select fossil ages that match the chart below.

	A	B	C
Permian			
Pennsylvanian			
Mississippian			
Devonian			
Silurian			
Ordovician			
Cambrian			

Analysis

1. for this example, layer 2 because it contains fossils from A and C, from the Devonian period
2. Absence of a specific fossil does not necessarily mean that it did not exist; it may not have been found.
3. For this example, layer 1 could be Ordovician, Silurian, or Devonian. Layer 2 is Devonian. Layer 3 could have formed anytime from the Devonian through the Permian.

Assessment

Performance Tell students that a rock layer containing fossils B and C has been found directly above a rock layer containing fossil A. Have them hypothesize when the rock may have formed. Use **Performance Assessment in the Science Classroom,** p. 21.

13-2 Early Earth History **375**

Answer to Reading Check

The egg had a membrane that protected it from drying out.

Enrichment

Visual-Spatial Have students research the Pennsylvanian period's coal swamps, where much of the coal used today was formed. Show students samples of peat, lignite (palm coal), bituminous coal, and anthracite coal. Describe the process that must occur for plant remains to change into coal. L2

Problem Solving

New fossils from China including *Caudipteryx zoui* provide support for the idea that birds evolved from dinosaurs. *Caudipteryx zoui* fossils more than 120 million years old show clear presence of feathers. It has been difficult finding fossil evidence about the origin of birds because their physical structure (thin, hollow bones and feathers) limits fossil formation. Analysis of bone structure, including the skull, has also indicated a connection between birds and dinosaurs.

Think Critically

The skull of the bird looks most like the fossil skull. Based on the evidence from the skulls, the bird could have evolved from dinosaurs. P

Caption Answer

Figure 13-12 *a protective membrane*

Life on Land

One type of fish evolved a lung that enabled it to survive out of water. This fish had fins that allowed it to move across land. Other animals that left the water for life on land were amphibians. **Amphibians** live on land and breathe air, but they must return to water to reproduce. Their eggs must be kept moist in water. They first appeared during the Devonian period and became the dominant form of vertebrate life on land by the Mississippian period.

Over time, amphibians evolved an egg with a strong outer shell that protected it from drying out. The egg also contained a nutritious yolk for the embryo. Because of this, they no longer needed to return to water to reproduce. By the Pennsylvanian period, reptiles had evolved, probably from the same ancestor as amphibians. **Reptiles** do not need to return to water to reproduce, as shown in **Figure 13-12.** Reptiles have skin with hard scales that prevent loss of body fluids. This adaptation enables them to survive farther from water. They can survive in relatively dry climates, whereas amphibians with their thin, moist skins, cannot.

Reading Check

What developed that allowed amphibians to reproduce away from water?

Problem Solving

Skull Structures

Scientists study the structure of bones and other preserved fossil parts in an attempt to determine which organisms are related. Bones, or the way bones are connected at joints, in related organisms show similar structures or connections. For example, if the skull from a modern organism shows similar eye openings and a similar structure of the nasal passages to the fossil skull of an animal from Earth's past, the two organisms may be related. Some scientists might even hypothesize that the modern animal evolved from the earlier animal.

The photographs show the shape and structure of four different organisms. One of the skulls is a fossil of an ancient, now-extinct life-form. The other three skulls are from modern-day organisms: an iguana, a bird, and a muskrat. Compare and contrast the shape and structure of the four skulls.

Think Critically: Which of the modern skulls looks most like the fossil skull? Hypothesize about which of the modern animals may have evolved from the ancient life-form.

376 CHAPTER 13 GEOLOGIC TIME

Integrating the Sciences

Life Science To help students realize how each science is integrated with and dependent on other sciences, use the following questions to initiate a discussion on the history of life on Earth. **Why were most life-forms during the Paleozoic era marine life-forms?** *Warm, shallow seas covered much of Earth's surface.* **Why are brachiopod fossils considered good indicators of ancient marine environments?** *They were common during the Paleozoic era, when shallow seas covered much of Earth's surface, and are still found today in marine environments.* **What might have caused the mass extinctions that occurred at the end of the Paleozoic era?** *The environment changed, perhaps as a result of plate tectonics, because at this time all continental plates were coming together.* L2

Figure 13-12 Unlike frogs, salamanders, and other amphibians, reptiles such as these snakes can lay their eggs on land. This allows them to survive in relatively dry environments. **What characteristic of reptile eggs prevents the developing embryos from drying out?**

Many of the coal deposits mined today began forming during the Pennsylvanian period. Inland seas were cut off from the oceans. These freshwater seas covered much of the land. Swamps similar to those found in the Florida Everglades formed. When the swamp vegetation died, it was deposited in layers and quickly buried. This material later changed to today's coal beds. **Figure 13-13** shows what a forest might have looked like in the Pennsylvanian period.

Figure 13-13 The plants that make up the coal layers in the United States once lived in swampy areas.

A This illustration reconstructs what a Pennsylvanian-period forest might have looked like 300 million years ago.

B The plants end up as layers, or seams, of coal, as seen in this strip mine in southeastern Montana.

3 Assess

Check for Understanding

VISUAL Learning

Figure 13-13 Describe the changes that occurred from the healthy forest in A to the coal seams in B. *The trees and plants died, fell into the swamp and were buried beneath the water. More layers built up. Pressure and heat converted the plant layers to coal.*

Reteach

Have pairs of students list or search magazines for photographs that show the characteristics of amphibians that make them different from fish and the characteristics of reptiles that make them different from amphibians. Have partners test each other on the differences.

Extension

For students who have mastered this section, use the **Reinforcement** and **Enrichment** masters. L1 COOP LEARN

interNET CONNECTION

Internet Addresses

____

____

____

____

For Internet tips, see Glencoe's **Using the Internet in the Science Classroom.**

Integrating the Sciences

Life Science Inform students that coal begins to form when swamp plants die and partially decay. Plants are made up of molecules that contain atoms of carbon, hydrogen, and oxygen. Decay occurs when bacteria break apart these molecules, releasing oxygen and hydrogen gases and leaving carbon and impurities like sulfur behind.

Science Journal

Coal Formation Ask students to continue reviewing the production of coal by researching coal formation and writing a short report in their Science Journals explaining the stages that occur before coal is formed. L2 

4 Close

Proficiency Prep

Use this quiz to check students' recall of section content.

1. **What events may have caused climatic change in the Paleozoic?** *mountain building, glaciation, or continental movement*
2. **The fact that some species of amphibians evolved eggs with membranes supports the idea that amphibians and what other organisms evolved from the same ancestor?** *reptiles*

Section Assessment

1. mountain building, continental movement, drainage of seas, formation of deserts
2. Environments changed and many life-forms could not adapt quickly enough. Life-forms that were once separated were brought together. Competition for food increased. These conditions could have led to the extinction of some organisms.
3. Precambrian organisms had no hard parts.
4. Oxygen gas became a major component.
5. **Think Critically** ability to breathe air, scales or skin to prevent drying, ability to reproduce on land

Using Computers

Illustrations and descriptions will vary. Accept any general statements that describe students' illustrations. Trilobites, brachiopods, and crinoids are all marine invertebrate animals.

End of an Era

Mass extinctions of many land and sea animals have occurred. One mass extinction occurred at the end of the Paleozoic era. The cause of mass extinctions may have been changes in the environment following movement of continents through plate tectonics. Near the end of the Permian period, all continental plates came together to form the single landmass Pangaea, and major glaciers formed.

The slow, gradual collision of continental plates caused mountain building. Mountain-building processes caused seas to drain away, and interior deserts spread over parts of the United States and Europe. Climates changed from mild and warm to cold and dry. Many species, especially marine organisms, weren't able to adapt to these and other changes and became extinct.

interNET CONNECTION

Visit the Glencoe Science Web Site at **www.glencoe.com/sec/science** for more information on mass extinctions.

Section Assessment

1. What geologic events occurred at the end of the Paleozoic era?
2. How might geologic events at the end of the Paleozoic era have caused the mass extinctions that occurred?
3. Why is the Precambrian fossil record so sparse?
4. What major change occurred in the atmosphere during the Precambrian?
5. **Think Critically:** What adaptations were needed for life to move onto the land?
6. **Skill Builder**
   Recognizing Cause and Effect Describe the cause-and-effect relationship between amphibians, reptiles, and the eggs they use in reproduction. If you need help, refer to Recognizing Cause and Effect in the **Skill Handbook** on page 721.

Using Computers

Using a Database Research trilobites, brachiopods, and crinoids in a computer database of historical geology. Write a paragraph in your Science Journal describing each of these organisms and its habitat. Include hand-drawn illustrations, and compare them with the illustrations in the computer database of historical geology. If you need help, refer to page 733.

6. 

Skill Builder

Amphibians and reptiles lay eggs. Amphibian eggs must remain in water. The development of a strong outer shell allowed reptiles to lay eggs out of the water. The effect is the ability to reproduce on land.

Assessment

Oral Assess students' abilities to make and use tables by asking them the following question, "During which era did dinosaurs exist on Earth?" Use **Performance Assessment in the Science Classroom,** p. 71.

Activity 13•1

Changing Species

Materials

- Deck of playing cards

In this activity, you will observe how adaptation within a species might cause the evolution of a particular trait, leading to the development of a new species.

What You'll Investigate

How might adaptation within a species cause the evolution of a particular trait?

Goals

- **Model** adaptation within a species.

Procedure

1. **Remove** all of the kings, queens, jacks, and aces from a deck of playing cards.
2. Each remaining card represents an individual in a population of animals called "varimals." The number on each card represents the height of the individual. For example, the 5 of diamonds is a varimal that's 5 units tall.
3. **Calculate** the average height of the population of varimals represented by your cards.
4. Suppose varimals eat grass, shrubs, and leaves from trees. A drought causes many of these plants to die. All that's left are a few tall trees. Only varimals at least 6 units tall can reach the leaves on these trees.
5. All the varimals under 6 units leave the area to seek food elsewhere or die from starvation. **Discard** all of the cards with a number value less than 6. **Calculate** the new average height of the population of varimals.
6. Shuffle the deck of remaining cards.
7. **Draw** two cards at a time. Each pair represents a pair of varimals that will mate and produce offspring.
8. The offspring of each pair reaches a height equal to the average height of his or her parents. **Calculate** and **record** the height of each offspring.
9. Repeat by discarding all parents and offspring under 8 units tall. Now **calculate** the new average height of varimals. Include both the parents and offspring in your calculation.

Conclude and Apply

1. How did the average height of the population change over time?
2. If you hadn't discarded the shortest varimals, would the average height of the population have changed as much? **Explain.**
3. What trait was selected for?
4. Why didn't every member of the original population reproduce?
5. If there had been no varimals over 6 units tall in step 5, what would have happened to the population?
6. If there had been no variation in height in the population before the droughts occurred, would the species have been able to evolve into a taller species? **Explain.**
7. How does this activity **demonstrate** that traits evolve in species?

Activity 13•1

Purpose

Interpersonal Students will formulate a model showing the role of natural selection in creating variations within a species. L2 COOP LEARN P

Process Skills

formulating models, using numbers, interpreting data, forming operational definitions, recognizing cause and effect, communicating

Time

30 minutes

Teaching Strategies

To save time prior to class time, remove the cards that will not be used in this activity. This will eliminate step 1 of the procedure.

Answers to Questions

1. It increased.
2. No; the average would remain at about 6.
3. height; specifically, the ability to reach food above the ground
4. Some of the original varimals weren't able to obtain enough food to survive and, therefore, weren't able to reproduce.
5. This particular population would have become extinct.
6. Probably not; if all of the individuals would have been the same height, no group of individuals would have had an advantage in reaching the high food. In that case, any evolution of the varimal population would likely have occurred from some variation of a trait other than height.
7. By creating the variation of a trait within the varimal population, in this case height, the model demonstrates how the species was able to evolve into one capable of reaching food high above the ground.

Assessment

Oral To further assess students' understanding of evolution, ask them whether any individual varimal increased in height because of natural selection. Encourage students to explain their answers. *No; individuals do not evolve inheritable adaptations.* **Use Performance Assessment in the Science Classroom,** p. 71.

Teaching Strategies

- Discuss the fact that more than 80 percent of all deforestation of Amazonian rain forests has occurred since 1980.
- Have students discuss the significance of the fact that one fourth of all pharmaceuticals are derived from rain forest plants. Students should realize that the destruction of a habitat so rich in species has serious philosophical and economic ramifications.
- Show pictures of deforestation in South America and Asia. Explain that destruction of rain forests is permanent. Also explain that soil in a tropical rain forest supports farming for only a few years before new areas must be cleared.

Some scientists hypothesize that up to 20 000 species are becoming extinct each year. A large percentage of these extinctions occur in tropical rain forests.

Rain forest plants provide atmospheric oxygen and remove atmospheric carbon dioxide. Increased levels of carbon dioxide could lead to global warming.

NATIONAL GEOGRAPHIC

Science & Society

Fast Track to Extinction

Human Impact

Extinctions—the loss of all members of a species—have occurred throughout Earth's history. In past millennia, extinctions were due to changes in the environment or competition for resources. Some extinctions may have been caused by early humans. Today, humans are causing extinctions at a much higher rate. See the chart below.

When members of a species die out faster than they reproduce, so that only few of its members are living, a species is considered endangered. If the population continues to decline, the species will become extinct.

Humans contribute to extinction directly by overhunting and overcollecting and indirectly by changing a species' habitat—where the species lives. If that habitat is altered or destroyed and the species cannot adapt, that species will die.

Time	Rates of Extinction
70 000 000 years ago (disappearance of the dinosaurs)	1 species/1000 years
1 A.D. to 1650	1 species (mammal or bird)/82 years
1650 to 1850	1 species (mammal or bird)/5 years
1850 to 1900	1 species (mammal or bird)/9.5 months
1900 to 1950	1 species (mammal or bird)/8 months
1992	All plant & animal life, 1 to 6 species/day
2000	All plant & animal life, 1 species/hour

For an online update of this data, visit **www.glencoe.com/sec/science** and select the appropriate chapter.

Rain Forests

In the past decade, people cleared tropical rain forests for farming, logging, and other industries at an unprecedented rate. At right, a charred tree still burns as a farmer clears more land. Destroying rain forest eliminates habitats for many plants and animals. It is estimated that the destruction of all rain forests could result in a 90 percent loss of Earth's biodiversity, the variety of species on Earth.

Development with Habitat Protection

To slow or prevent loss of habitat, governments can restrict construction to allow both development and preservation. Development can include plans for preserving habitats or disturbing them as little as possible. Ecotourism (tourism that minimizes ecological impact), replanting efforts, and cultivating renewable crops are all ways to protect the world's rain forests.

interNET CONNECTION

Many organizations are working to slow the rate of extinction of animals and plants. Visit the Glencoe Science Web Site at www.glencoe.com/sec/science to learn more about the preservation of wildlife. What is being done to help endangered species? Do you think this type of effort is effective? Why or why not?

For More Information

Visit the Glencoe Science Web Site at *www.glencoe.com/sec/science* for related web sites.

Internet Addresses

For Internet tips, see Glencoe's **Using the Internet in the Science Classroom.**

Middle and Recent Earth History

The Mesozoic Era

Some of the most fascinating life-forms ever to live on Earth evolved during the Mesozoic era. One group of organisms you're probably familiar with—the dinosaurs—appeared during this geologic era.

The Breakup of Pangaea

The **Mesozoic** (mez uh ZOH ihk) **era,** or era of middle life, began about 245 million years ago. At the beginning of the Mesozoic era, all continents were joined as a single land-mass. This landmass was called Pangaea, as shown in **Figure 13-14.** Pangaea separated into two large landmasses during the Triassic period. The northern mass was *Laurasia,* and *Gondwana* was in the south. As the Mesozoic era continued, *Laurasia* and *Gondwana* broke up and formed the present-day continents.

Species that survived the mass extinctions of the Paleozoic era adapted to new environments. Recall that the hard scales of a reptile's skin help to retain body fluids. This trait, along with the hard shell of their eggs, enabled them to adapt to the drier climate of the Mesozoic era. They became the dominant animal life-form in the Jurassic period. Some of the reptiles evolved into archosaurs, suggested as being the common ancestor of crocodiles, dinosaurs, and birds.

What You'll Learn

- How dominant life-forms in the Mesozoic and Cenozoic eras compare and contrast
- How changes caused by plate tectonics affected the evolution of life during the Mesozoic era
- When humans probably first appeared on Earth

Vocabulary

Mesozoic era
gastrolith
Cenozoic era

Why It's Important

- As Earth's environments, plants, and animals changed through time, Earth became suitable for human life.

Figure 13-14 The supercontinent Pangaea formed at the end of the Paleozoic era. It began to break up at the end of the Triassic period. **Based on the position of the equator, describe the climate as tropical, temperate, or cold on each major landmass.**

Resource Manager

The following **Teacher Classroom Resources** can be used with Section 13-3:

 **Reproducible Masters**

Activity Worksheets, p. 74 L2

Critical Thinking/Problem Solving, p. 13 L2

Enrichment, p. 36 L3

Multicultural Connections, pp. 25–26 L2

Reinforcement, p. 36 L2

Study Guide, pp. 51–52 L1 ELL

SECTION 13-3

Prepare

Content Background

Refer to **Middle and Recent Earth History** on p. 362F.

Preplanning

Refer to the **Chapter Organizer** on pp. 362A–B.

1 Motivate

Bellringer

Before presenting the lesson, display **Section Focus Transparency 36** on the overhead projector. Use the accompanying **Focus Activity** worksheet. L2 ELL

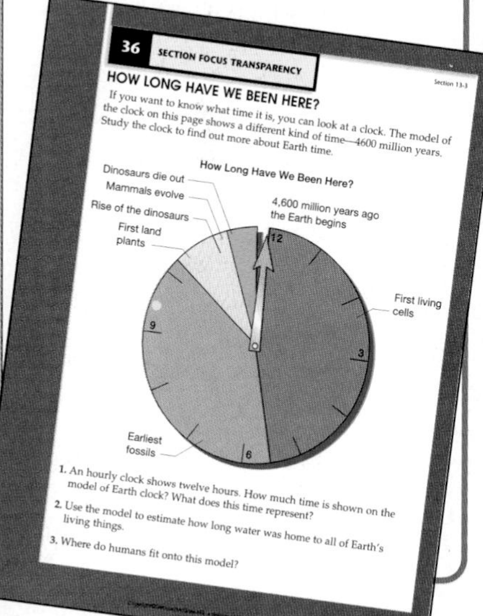
36 SECTION FOCUS TRANSPARENCY

Section 13-3

HOW LONG HAVE WE BEEN HERE?

If you want to know what time it is, you can look at a clock. The model of the clock on this page shows a different kind of time—4600 million years. Study the clock to find out more about Earth time.

1. An hourly clock shows twelve hours. How much time is shown on the model of Earth clock? What does this time represent?
2. Use the model to estimate how long water was home to all of Earth's living things.
3. Where do humans fit onto this model?

Tying to Previous Knowledge

Help students recall what they have read or heard about the idea that a large asteroid colliding with Earth may have led to the extinction of the dinosaurs.

2 Teach

Flex Your Brain

Use the Flex Your Brain activity to have students explore APATOSAURUS.

Correcting Misconceptions

Students may be familiar with the term Brontosaurus. This term is no longer used to refer to these large dinosaurs. Apatosaurs were among the largest dinosaurs, with masses up to 36 metric tons. They had long necks and tails supported by massive bodies.

Content Background

One explanation of how the asteroid that may have killed off the dinosaurs caused such widespread damage to Earth's ecology concerns the angle at which it struck Earth. The asteroid is thought to have collided with Earth on what is now the Yucatan Peninsula at a shallow angle. This would have sent large amounts of white-hot debris to distances of thousands of miles over much of what is now the North American continent.

Figure 13-15 Fossil evidence suggests that some dinosaurs, such as *Maiasaura*, may have nurtured their young. Fossil nests contain newly hatched and juvenile young. **What type of evidence might support this idea?**

Dinosaurs

What were dinosaurs like? Dinosaurs ranged in height from less than 1 m to enormous creatures such as *Apatosaurus,* which grew to 30 m in length, and *Tyrannosaurus,* which grew to 6 m in height. Some dinosaurs ate meat, whereas others ate only plants.

The first dinosaurs were small, and they appeared during the Triassic period. Larger species appeared during the Jurassic and Cretaceous periods. Throughout the Mesozoic era, new species of dinosaurs evolved as other species became extinct.

Good Mother Dinosaurs

The fossil record indicates that some dinosaurs nurtured their young and traveled in herds in which the adults surrounded their young. One such dinosaur is *Maiasaura,* shown in **Figure 13-15.** This dinosaur built nests in which it laid its eggs and raised its offspring. Nests have been found in clusters, indicating that more than one family of dinosaurs built in the same area. Some fossils of hatchlings have been found close to the adult animal. This has led some scientists to hypothesize that some dinosaurs nurtured their young. In fact, *Maiasaura* hatchlings may have stayed in the nest while they grew in length from about 35 cm to more than 1 m.

Inclusion Strategies

Learning Disabled Have pairs of students identify characteristics of meat- and plant-eating dinosaurs. Supply students with drawings or models of six different dinosaurs. Have them determine whether the dinosaurs were meat- or plant-eaters. Have students describe what characteristics were useful for their analysis. L2 COOP LEARN

Caption Answer

Figure 13-14 *tropical: northern South America, northern Africa, Southern North America; temperate: portions of North America, Asia, South America, Africa, India; polar: Northern Asia, Antarctica, Australia*

Reptile or Mammal?

Dinosaurs were reptiles. Recent studies indicate that dinosaurs may not have been cold-blooded, as are present-day reptiles. Tracks left in the mud by individual reptiles are usually close together. Tracks close together indicate that an animal moves slowly. Some dinosaur tracks that have been found indicate that they were much faster than most reptiles. This faster speed would be expected of warm-blooded animals, which need speed to be successful in hunting. *Gallimimus* was 4 m long and from its tracks, it is known that it could reach speeds of 80 km/h—as fast as a modern racehorse.

Other evidence that leads scientists to hypothesize that dinosaurs may have been warm-blooded has to do with their bone structure. Cross sections of the bones of cold-blooded animals exhibit rings similar to growth rings in trees. The bones of some dinosaurs don't show this ring structure. Instead, they are similar to bones found in birds and mammals. These observations indicate that dinosaurs may have been warm-blooded, fast-moving, nurturing animals somewhat like present-day mammals and birds. They may have been quite different from present-day reptiles.

Birds

Scientists have concluded that birds evolved from dinosaurs. Some scientists have even suggested that birds are dinosaurs, evolved from the advanced theropod called *Troodon,* shown in **Figure 13-16.** Theropods form a group of meat-eating dinosaurs that walked mainly on their hind legs.

Figure 13-16 A highly evolved dinosaur called *Troodon* had a birdlike stance, much like a modern ostrich.

Correcting Misconceptions

Ask students if humans were alive when dinosaurs lived on Earth. Some students will think they were because of seeing cartoons, movies, and videos on television. Explain that human ancestors appeared about 5 million years ago, long after the last dinosaurs became extinct about 66 million years ago.

Enrichment

Linguistic Have pairs of students read an article of their choice from *Natural History,* June 1995 or *The Planetary Report,* July/August 1996, or "The Day the Dinosaurs Died," *Weatherwise,* July/August 1998, or some other article about dinosaurs or their extinction. Have students discuss the key concepts of each article and then work together to write a summary of the main ideas of their particular article. L3

Caption Answer

Figure 13-15 *fossils of newly hatched and juvenile young in the nests*

GLENCOE TECHNOLOGY

CD-ROM

Glencoe Science Voyages Interactive CD-ROM

Explorations

Have students do the interactive exploration *What was Earth like throughout geologic time?*

Integrating the Sciences

Life Science It's important to note that plants coevolve with the other organisms in their environment. Plants aren't "passive bystanders" in the process of natural selection. Plants select thorns, tough bark, and poisons to thwart predators. For more information, direct students to *The Dinosaur Heresies,* by Robert T. Bakker, William Morrow and Company, Inc., New York, 1986.

13-3 Middle and Recent Earth History **383**

Teacher FYI

- Endotherms have a constant body temperature and are often said to be "warm-blooded."
- By some estimates, more than three fourths of all species on Earth died off at the end of the Mesozoic era.

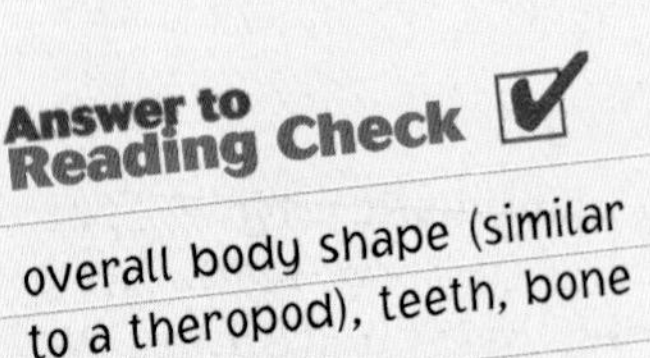

Caption Answer

Figure 13-17 *birdlike—feathered wings; dinosaurlike—teeth and claws*

GLENCOE TECHNOLOGY

Videodisc

Glencoe Science Voyages Interactive Videodisc—Life

Side 2, Lesson 9 *Ecosystems: Wetlands*

44405

Refer to Videodisc Teacher Guide for additional bar codes.

Figure 13-17 Fossils of *Archaeopteryx* that are about 150 million years old show both birdlike features and dinosaurlike features. **What birdlike and dinosaurlike features can you recognize?**

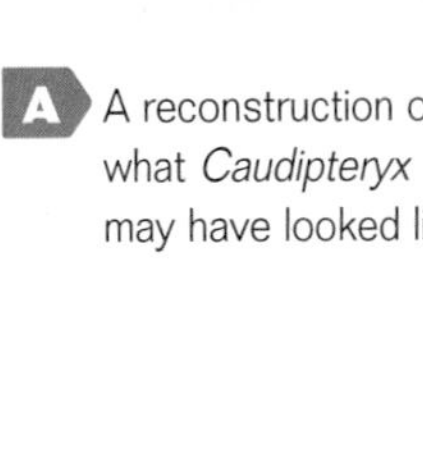

A A reconstruction of what *Caudipteryx* may have looked like.

B Considered the world's most priceless fossil, *Archaeopteryx* was found in a limestone quarry in Germany in 1861.

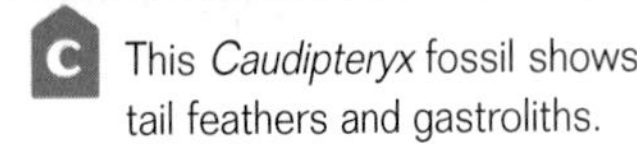

C This *Caudipteryx* fossil shows tail feathers and gastroliths.

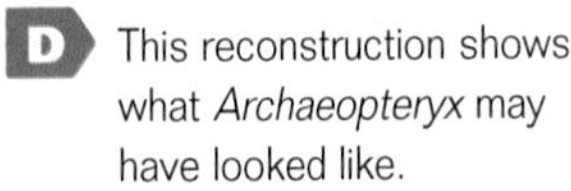

D This reconstruction shows what *Archaeopteryx* may have looked like.

Evidence for this is found in fossils of the first birds. They appeared during the Jurassic period of the Mesozoic era, as seen in **Figure 13-17.** The animal *Archaeopteryx* had wings and feathers like a bird but teeth and claws like a meat-eating dinosaur. *Archaeopteryx* may not have been a direct ancestor of today's birds. But, modern birds and *Archaeopteryx* probably share a common ancestor.

A new discovery in China is a fossil of an earlier birdlike organism with dinosaurlike characteristics. It has been named *Caudipteryx*. Imprints of feathers were found on the fossil, shown in **Figure 13-17C.** *Caudipteryx* shows different teeth from those shown by *Archaeopteryx*. The teeth point outward toward the front of the organism. The teeth were positioned such that they could fit easily into a beak, similar to that of a bird's. Also, the shape of the organism's body was more like a theropod, a meat-eating dinosaur, than like *Archaeopteryx*.

Reading Check
What characteristics link archaeopteryx to dinosaurs?

Science Journal

Dinosaurs Freestyle Give students 15 minutes to write freestyle about anything they can concerning dinosaurs. Afterward, form teams to share their results and questions. From this, they will be able to write a report on what their group knows or still wants to know about dinosaurs. L2 COOP LEARN

Also found associated with the fossil were **gastroliths,** stones swallowed to help with digestion. These can be found in the gizzards of modern birds. Fossils of *Caudipteryx* demonstrate strong evidence that this animal is related to the earliest birds, yet it looks more like a small, meat-eating dinosaur from that age.

Gymnosperms

During the Cretaceous period, seas expanded inland and species of plants, animals, and other organisms continued to adapt to new environments. Gymnosperms (JIHM nuh spurmz), which first appeared in the Paleozoic era, continued to adapt to their changing environment. The seeds of gymnosperms are not produced inside a fruit, as are the seeds of flowering plants. Pines, sequoias, and firs are gymnosperms.

Angiosperms

A new type of plant, called angiosperms (AN jee uh spurmz), evolved in the early Cretaceous period. Angiosperms, or flowering plants, produce seeds inside a fruit. Common angiosperms are magnolias and willows.

Many angiosperms survived while non-seed plants did not because their seeds were enclosed and protected in a fruit, allowing them to develop in varied environments. Angiosperms are so adaptive that they remain the dominant land plant today. A flower from an angiosperm is shown in **Figure 13-18.** Present-day angiosperms that evolved during the Mesozoic era include maple and oak trees.

MiniLab

Measuring Seafloor Spreading

Procedure

1. On a globe or world map, measure the distance in kilometers between a point near the east coast of South America and a corresponding point on the west coast of Africa.
2. Assuming that the rate of spreading has been about 3.5–4.0 cm per year, calculate how many years it took to create the present Atlantic Ocean if the continents were once joined.
3. Measure the distance across the Atlantic Ocean in several other locations and calculate the average of your results.
4. Check your calculations with the information provided in **Figure 13-2.**

Analysis

1. Did the values used to obtain your average value vary much?
2. How close did your average value come to the accepted estimate for the beginning of the breakup of Pangaea?

Figure 13-18 Angiosperms and pollinating insects coevolved, or evolved at the same time. The sweet nectar produced by many flowers attracts insects in search of food. The pollen of the flower sticks to the insect, which carries it to another flower. Some angiosperms wouldn't be able to reproduce without a particular species of insect.

MiniLab

Purpose

Logical-Mathematical Students will use the rate of seafloor spreading to calculate the age of the Atlantic Ocean. L3 COOP LEARN P

Materials

globe or world map, metric ruler, string (for measuring on the curved globe), paper, pencil

Teaching Strategies

This spreading rate is an average for a number of points along the Mid-Atlantic Ridge.

Analysis

1. Values used to obtain the average value for the age of the Atlantic Ocean will vary. Expect answers in the range of 160 to 210 million years.
2. Student answers will vary, depending on the points on each continent they choose for their measurements. Separations of 6000 to 7000 kilometers would take from 160 to 200 million years to achieve. As an example, at a 3.5 cm/year rate of spread, 700 000 000 cm ÷ 3.5 cm/year = 200 000 000 years.

Assessment

Content To further assess students' understanding of the formation of the Atlantic Ocean, have them hypothesize how environments might change near the East-African Rift Valley, where separation may eventually form a new sea. Use **Performance Assessment in the Science Classroom,** p. 21.

Across the Curriculum

Biology Have students compare and contrast marsupial wolves, rabbits, squirrels, and bears that evolved in Australia to their placental counterparts that evolved in similar environments in Europe and America. Students should note similarities in natural selection despite differences between placental and marsupial evolution caused by the isolation of the life-forms. L3

Content Background

Discuss the path of possible human evolution. Relate that there is much controversy among anthropologists as to how many species of *Australopithecus* existed, but many agree that there were at least four. It's not known which gave rise to our genus, *Homo.*

Content Background

Homo habilis may have evolved from *Australopithecus afarensis*. *Homo habilis* may have given rise to *Homo erectus* before becoming extinct about 1.5 million years ago. It is widely believed that *Homo erectus* was the direct ancestor of our species, *Homo sapiens*.

3 Assess

Check for Understanding

Discussion

Ask students the following question to help initiate a class discussion. **What evidence supports the hypothesis that birds evolved from dinosaurs?** Archaeopteryx *had wings and feathers like a bird but teeth and claws like a meat-eating dinosaur. Teeth in* Caudipteryx *point in such a way that they could fit easily into a beak. Present-day birds and extinct dinosaurs share other characteristics as well.*

Reteach

Obtain a book on early humans that shows paintings or drawings of humans on a hunting trip for the woolly mammoth and other Pleistocene mammals. Explain how overhunting can lead to extinction. Relate this to the near extinction of the American buffalo by overhunting in the early West. L2

Extension

For students who have mastered this section, use the **Reinforcement** and **Enrichment** masters.

VISUALIZING Cenozoic Life

Figure 13-19 Many prehistoric North American animals became extinct during the ice ages in the Pleistocene epoch.

Woolly mammoth

Horses

Camels

Dire wolves

Irish elk

Saber-toothed tiger

Pangaea broke up during the Mesozoic era, and continents continued to move toward their present positions. Landmasses were breaking up and seas were draining from the land. There also was increased volcanic activity. Many life-forms, including the dinosaurs, became extinct. These extinctions probably were caused by changing environments. Scientists still are investigating what caused the environments to change.

The Cenozoic Era

The **Cenozoic** (sen uh ZOH ihk) **era,** or era of recent life, began about 66 million years ago when dinosaurs and many other life-forms became extinct. Many of the mountain ranges throughout North and South America began to form at this time.

During the Cenozoic era, the climate became cooler and ice ages occurred. The Cenozoic era is subdivided into three periods. The present-day period is the Quaternary. We live in the Holocene epoch, which began after the last ice age. Many changes on Earth, its climate, and its life-forms, shown in **Figure 13-19,** occurred in the Cenozoic era. The two other periods (Neogene and Paleogene) were previously listed together as the Tertiary period.

Times of Mountain Building

The Alps formed when the African plate collided with the Eurasian plate. The Himalayas started to form when the Indo-Australian plate collided with the Eurasian plate.

As the number of flowering plants increased, their pollen and fruit provided food for the many insects and small, plant-eating mammals. The plant-eating mammals provided food for meat-eating mammals.

Inclusion Strategies

Visually Impaired In order to include all students in discussions of life-forms that exist today and have existed throughout the Mesozoic and Cenozoic periods, begin the discussion with detailed descriptions of certain dinosaurs and mammals like the woolly mammoth.

VISUAL Learning

Figure 13-19 **Where would a modern counterpart of each of these animals live? Is it different from their Cenozoic environment?** *Answers will vary. Students may suggest that an elephant is a woolly mammoth's counterpart. Its African and Indian environment differs greatly from the cold regions that Mammoths inhabited.*

Further Evolution of Mammals

Many kinds of mammals evolved into larger life-forms. The first mammals were most likely small insect eaters that developed about the same time as the dinosaurs. Not all mammals remained on land. Fossil evidence shows that ancestors of the present-day whales and dolphins once lived on land.

As Australia and South America separated from Antarctica in the continuing breakup of Pangaea, many life-forms became isolated. They evolved separately from life-forms in other parts of the world. Evidence of this can be seen today with the dominance of marsupials in Australia. Marsupials are mammals that carry their young in a pouch, as seen in **Figure 13-20.**

Our species, *Homo sapiens,* probably appeared about 500 000 years ago but became a dominant animal only about 10 000 years ago. As the climate remained cool and dry, many of the larger mammals became extinct. Some scientists hypothesize that the appearance of early humans may have led to the extinction of these mammals. Fossil records indicate that early humans were hunters. As their numbers grew, humans competed for food that other animals relied upon. They may have contributed to extinctions by overkill.

Figure 13-20 Kangaroos are marsupials that live in Australia and carry their young (a joey) in a pouch.

Section Assessment

1. In which era, period, and epoch did *Homo sapiens* first appear?
2. How did the development of hard seeds enable angiosperms to survive in a wide variety of climates?
3. What evidence indicates that dinosaurs were warm-blooded?
4. **Think Critically:** What is the connection between plate tectonics and the occurrence of marsupials?
5. **Skill Builder**
   Sequencing Arrange these organisms in sequence according to when they first appeared on Earth: *mammals, reptiles, dinosaurs, fish, ediacaran fauna, angiosperms, birds, insects, amphibians, first land plants,* and *bacteria.* If you need help, refer to Sequencing in the **Skill Handbook** on page 714.

Using Math

Make a graph comparing the periods of time that make up the Mesozoic and Cenozoic eras. Express how long dinosaurs were dominant compared with the time humans have been dominant.

4 Close

Proficiency Prep

Use this quiz to check students' recall of section content.

1. **During which era were dinosaurs the dominant life-form?** *Mesozoic era*
2. **Why are mammals able to survive in many different environments?** *Females produce milk to feed the young. They are warm-blooded and have hair or fur to insulate them from extremely cold temperatures. Because they move, they can escape extremely warm temperatures.*

Section Assessment

1. Cenozoic era, Quaternary period, Pleistocene epoch
2. The hard coating on the seeds protected them.
3. The spacing of their tracks indicates that they were slower walkers. Reptiles move faster and their tracks are closer together.
4. **Think Critically** When the continents separated, animal populations couldn't migrate as far as before; groups evolved along separate paths resulting in new species. The marsupials and placentals are one example.

Using Math

A bar graph might show percentage of time versus Mesozoic and Cenozoic. The mesozoic makes up 4 percent and the Cenozoic makes up 1.4 percent of Earth's history.

Dinosaurs were dominant for 62 million years, whereas humans have only been dominant for 10 000 years. Dinosaurs existed for 179 million years.

5. **Skill Builder**
Students should use **Figure 13-2** to answer this question. The sequence is bacteria, ediacaran fauna, fish, land plants, amphibians, insects, reptiles, mammals, dinosaurs, birds, and angiosperms.

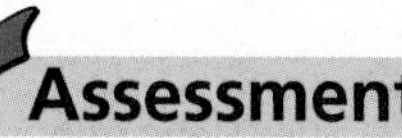

Assessment

Performance Assess students' abilities at sequencing by having them perform the Skill Builder and by comparing their sequences with **Figure 13-2.** Use **Performance Assessment in the Science Classroom,** p. 87.

Activity 13·2 On the Internet

Recognize the Problem

Intrapersonal Students will search for, gather, and analyze information from the Internet, library, and natural history museums on fossils. They will use this data to infer what North America looked like during the geologic past. They will present their results to the class.

Form a Hypothesis

Internet Students will gather data from Internet sites that can be accessed through the Glencoe Science Web Site. Students can post their data on the site and get data from other schools around the country. Click on the geologic time period you are interested in. This will open a database of fossil and paleogeographic data for that time. The site provides links to sites where fossil and paleogeographic data are available. Maps and data tables are also provided on the Web Site. Students can print them out or use them as a guide.

Non-Internet Sources If you do not have access to the Internet, use historical geology references in a library or natural history museum. Use a map of North America with an overlay to reconstruct the environment during the time period. Record data in a table such as the one shown.

Time Required

one week of data collection, one week for the data interpretation

Activity 13·2

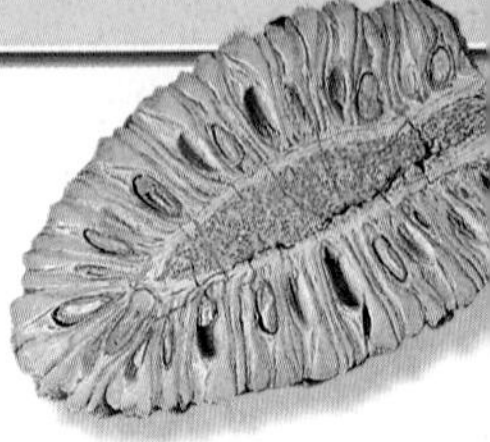

Discovering the Past

Imagine how the world looked millions of years ago. What animals might have been roaming around the spot where you are now sitting? You might be having trouble picturing the prehistoric world. Fortunately, the animals and plants of the past left a record of their existence—fossils. Scientists use fossils to find out what Earth looked like in the past. Fossils can help determine whether an area used to be dry land or an ocean. They also can help scientists determine what the climate in the past was like. Using the resources of the Internet and sharing data with your peers, you can start to discover how North America has changed through time.

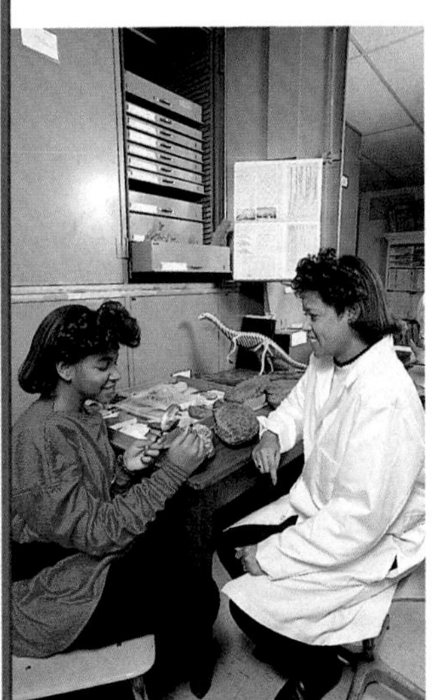

Recognize the Problem

How has your area changed over geologic time?

Form a Hypothesis

How might the area where you are now living have looked thousands or millions of years ago? Do you think the types of animals and plants have changed much over time? **Form a hypothesis** concerning the change in organisms and geography from long ago to the present day in your area.

Goals

- **Gather and communicate** details about fossils found in your areas.
- **Synthesize** information from various sources to make conclusions about the fossil record and the changes in your area over time.
- **Form conclusions** about the fossil record and changes in your area over time based on information from various sources.

Data Sources

Go to the Glencoe Science Web Site at **www.glencoe.com/sec/science** to find links to data on the Internet and hints on how to locate information. You also can visit a local natural history museum or library to gather information on fossils.

388 CHAPTER 13 GEOLOGIC TIME

Preparation

Internet Access the Glencoe Science Web Site at **www.glencoe.com/sec/science** to run through the steps the students will follow.

Non-Internet Sources Obtain a large map of North America and a thin paper or clear plastic overlay. Have some fossil reference books available. Have students visit or write to a natural history museum.

interNET CONNECTION

Internet Addresses

For Internet tips, see Glencoe's **Using the Internet in the Science Classroom.**

Test Your Hypothesis

Plan

1. **Choose** one of the following geologic time periods to research: the Pleistocene epoch, the Cretaceous period, the Pennsylvanian period, or the Ordovician period.
2. **Gather information** from the links on the Glencoe Science Web Site or the library about the fossil plants and animals found in your area during one of these geologic time periods. Find information on where and how the fossil organisms lived.

Do

1. Obtain descriptions of other fossils in your area from the sites listed on the Glencoe Science Web Site.
2. Complete a data table in your Science Journal like the one below. Add any additional information that you think is important. One example has been given.
3. Post the information on the data table for this activity on the Glencoe Science Web Site.

Analyze Your Data

1. Is there a present-day relative of your prehistoric animals or plants?
2. How have the organisms in your area changed over time? Is your hypothesis supported?

Draw Conclusions

1. **Infer** from the fossil organisms found in your area what the geography and climate were like during the geologic time period you chose.
2. Using information posted on the Glencoe Science Web Site, write a report about what North America looked like during one of the geologic time periods listed.

Fossil Data

Fossil Name	Location	Period or Epoch	How or Where Fossil Lived	Additional Information
snail or gastropod	Kansas City, Kansas	Cretaceous period	lived in a shallow ocean, climate was tropical	had thick shell and spines to protect it from predators

Test Your Hypothesis

Teaching Strategies

- This activity will allow students to discover what their area and the rest of North America looked like in the past. The main goal is to use the fossil record to determine the paleoclimate and paleogeography of North America during the four selected geologic time periods.
- Make sure students research where the fossils they find lived—either on land or in a freshwater or ocean environment.

References

- Dott, R.H., Jr. and D.R. Prothero. *Evolution of the Earth.* McGraw-Hill, Inc, 1994.
- Ausich, W.I. and N.G. Lane. *Life of the Past.* Macmillan Publishing, 1999.
- S.M. Stanley. *Earth and Life Through Time.* W. H. Freeman and Company, 1993.

GO Further

Students may obtain data from art in books and in museums that illustrate scientist's reconstructions of the different geologic times.

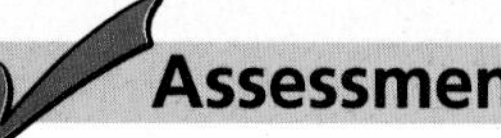

Assessment

Performance Have students mount their data tables on posterboard. Display them around the room. Provide time for each group to present their findings to the class. Use **Performance Assessment in the Science Classroom,** p. 73.

Chapter 13 Reviewing Main Ideas

Reviewing Main Ideas can be used to preview, review, reteach, and condense chapter content.

Preview

Linguistic Have students try to answer the questions in their Science Journals. Use student answers as a source for discussion throughout the chapter.

Review

Interpersonal Have students answer the questions on separate pieces of paper and compare their answers with those of other students in the class.

Reteach

Visual-Spatial Have students look at the illustrations on these pages. Ask them to describe details that support the main ideas of the chapter found in the statement for each illustration.

OUT OF TIME?

Auditory-Musical If time does not permit teaching the entire chapter, use the information on these pages along with the chapter Audiocassettes to present the material in a condensed format.

Chapter 13 Reviewing Main Ideas

For a **preview** of this chapter, study this Reviewing Main Ideas before you read the chapter. After you have studied this chapter, you can use the Reviewing Main Ideas to **review** the chapter.

The Glencoe MindJogger, Audiocassettes, and CD-ROM provide additional opportunities for review.

Section 13-1 LIFE AND GEOLOGIC TIME

Geologic time is divided into **eras, periods,** and **epochs.** Divisions within the geologic time scale are based on major evolutionary changes in organisms. The fossil record indicates that life-forms have changed over time. These changes include the physical appearance of organisms. Plate movements cause changes in Earth's climate that affect changes in organisms. ***Why is the Cenozoic era the only one in which periods are separated into named epochs on the geologic time scale?***

Cenozoic Era

Quaternary Period 1.6 M.Y.B.P.
Holocene Epoch 0.01 M.Y.B.P.
Pleistocene Epoch 1.6 M.Y.B.P.

Neogene Period 23 M.Y.B.P.
Pliocene Epoch 5 M.Y.B.P.
Miocene Epoch 23 M.Y.B.P.

Paleogene Period 66 M.Y.B.P.
Oligocene Epoch 35 M.Y.B.P.
Eocene Epoch 56 M.Y.B.P.
Paleocene Epoch 66 M.Y.B.P

Homo sapiens evolves; most recent ice ages; Grand Canyon forms.

Mammals are abundant; angiosperms are dominant; Alps and the Himalayas begin to rise.

Dinosaurs become extinct.

Section 13-2 EARLY EARTH HISTORY

Cyanobacteria were an early form of life that evolved during **Precambrian time. Trilobites,** brachiopods, fish, and corals were abundant during the **Paleozoic era.** Through time, bacteria evolved into higher life-forms, which evolved into many marine invertebrates during the early Paleozoic era. Plants and animals began to move onto land once a protective ozone layer had been established. During the Paleozoic era, glaciers advanced and seas withdrew from the continents. Many marine invertebrates became extinct. ***What was different between life-forms of Precambrian time and life-forms of the Cambrian period that allowed a better fossil record to be preserved?***

Reading Check

After you read this Reviewing Main Ideas, choose a sentence in each section that you feel best represents the main idea of that section.

Section

13-3 MIDDLE AND RECENT EARTH HISTORY

Reptiles and gymnosperms were dominant land life-forms in the **Mesozoic era.** All continents were together as one landmass called Pangaea at the beginning of the Mesozoic era. Pangaea separated into two landmasses during the Triassic period. While animals and birds evolved during the Jurassic period, dinosaurs continued to dominate throughout the Jurassic and Cretaceous. Angiosperms evolved in the early Cretaceous. They were dominant throughout the Cretaceous and continue to be dominant today. Mammals also began to dominate the land in the Cenozoic era. Plate tectonic changes in the Mesozoic era caused climates to become drier and seas to expand. *Homo sapiens* evolved during the Pleistocene epoch. ***What caused a change in Earth's climate during the Mesozoic era?***

Answers to Questions

Section 13-1

Life and Geologic Time The Cenozoic era represents the most recent division of geologic time. Because of this, the fossil record and the record of geologic events is more complete in these recent rock layers. Thus, geologists have more markers with which to divide the time scale.

Section 13-2

Early Earth History Organisms of the Cambrian period had developed hard parts.

Section 13-3

Middle and Recent Earth History The breakup of Pangaea and the movement of plates led to changes in the climate of the Mesozoic era.

GLENCOE TECHNOLOGY

CD-ROM

Glencoe Science Voyages Interactive CD-ROM

Chapter Summaries and Quizzes

Have students read the Chapter Summary then take the Chapter Quiz to determine whether they have mastered chapter content.

Assessment

Portfolio Encourage students to place in their portfolios one or two items of what they consider to be their best work. Examples include:

- Problem Solving, p. 376
- Activity 13-1, p. 379
- MiniLab, p. 385 P

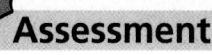

Performance Additional performance assessments may be found in **Performance Assessment** and **Science Integration Activities.** Performance Task Assessment Lists and rubrics for evaluating these activities can be found in **Glencoe's Performance Assessment in the Science Classroom.**

Chapter 13 Assessment

Using Vocabulary

1. g
2. k
3. l
4. b
5. f

interNET CONNECTION To reinforce chapter vocabulary, use the **Study Guide for Content Mastery** booklet. Also available are activities for **Glencoe Science Voyages** on the Glencoe Science Web Site. **www.glencoe.com/sec/science**

Checking Concepts

6. D	11. B
7. D	12. B
8. C	13. A
9. A	14. C
10. D	15. B

Thinking Critically

16. Too much ultraviolet radiation from the sun reached Earth's surface prior to the establishment of the ozone layer. UV light causes harmful mutations in the cells of plants.
17. Trilobites were widespread and existed for a limited segment of geologic time before becoming extinct. Thus, they can be used to accurately date the rocks in which their fossils are found.
18. Organisms of the Precambrian lacked the hard parts that evolved at the beginning of the Paleozoic.

Chapter 13 Assessment

Using Vocabulary

a. amphibian
b. Cenozoic era
c. cyanobacteria
d. epoch
e. era
f. gastrolith
g. geologic time scale
h. Mesozoic era
i. Paleozoic era
j. period
k. Precambrian time
l. reptile
m. trilobite

Each phrase below describes a science term from the list. Write the term that matches the phrase describing it.

1. record of events in Earth history
2. geologic time with poorest fossil record
3. probably evolved from the same ancestor as amphibians
4. the geologic era in which we live
5. used by dinosaurs and birds to help digest food

Checking Concepts

Choose the word or phrase that best answers the question.

6. How many millions of years ago did the era in which you live begin?
   A) 650 C) 1.6
   B) 245 D) 66
7. What is one of the most important fossils for determining age from the Paleozoic era?
   A) dinosaur C) fish
   B) angiosperm D) trilobite
8. Which is the longest division of geologic time?
   A) the Paleozoic era
   B) the Cenozoic era
   C) Precambrian time
   D) the Mesozoic era
9. What is the next-smaller division of geologic time after the era?
   A) period C) epoch
   B) stage D) eon
10. During which period was the most recent ice age?
   A) Pennsylvanian C) Paleogene
   B) Triassic D) Quaternary
11. What was one of the earliest forms of life on Earth?
   A) gymnosperm C) angiosperm
   B) cyanobacterium D) dinosaur
12. Which had the same ancestors as amphibians?
   A) trilobites C) angiosperms
   B) lungfish D) gymnosperms
13. In which era did the dinosaurs live?
   A) Mesozoic C) Miocene
   B) Paleozoic D) Cenozoic
14. What has seeds without protective coverings?
   A) angiosperms C) gymnosperms
   B) flowering plants D) magnolias
15. What evolved to become the dominant land plant during the Cenozoic era?
   A) gymnosperms C) ginkgoes
   B) angiosperms D) algae

Thinking Critically

16. Why couldn't plants move onto land prior to the establishment of an ozone layer?
17. Why are some trilobites classified as index fossils?
18. What is the most significant difference between Precambrian and Paleozoic life-forms?
19. How might the extinction of plant species from a tropical rain forest affect animals that live in the forest?

19. Plants are at the base of most food chains. They make their own food via photosynthesis and are themselves food for certain animals. These animals, in turn, are food for other animals. If the edible plant becomes extinct, extinctions of other organisms may occur.
20. Modern birds often swallow stones to help digest their food. Dinosaur skeletons have been found with gastroliths (stones in the stomach region) suggesting that they too used them as a digestive aid.

20. Explain why the discovery of gastroliths supports the theory that dinosaurs are ancestors of birds.

Developing Skills

If you need help, refer to the Skill Handbook.

21. **Observing and Inferring:** Use the outlines of the present-day continents to make a sketch of the Mesozoic supercontinent Pangaea.
22. **Hypothesizing:** Why did trilobites become extinct at the end of the Paleozoic era?
23. **Interpreting Data:** Fernando found what he thought was a piece of coral in a chunk of coal. Was he right? Explain.
24. **Interpreting Scientific Illustrations:** The circle graph below represents geologic time. Determine which era of geologic time is represented by each portion of the graph.

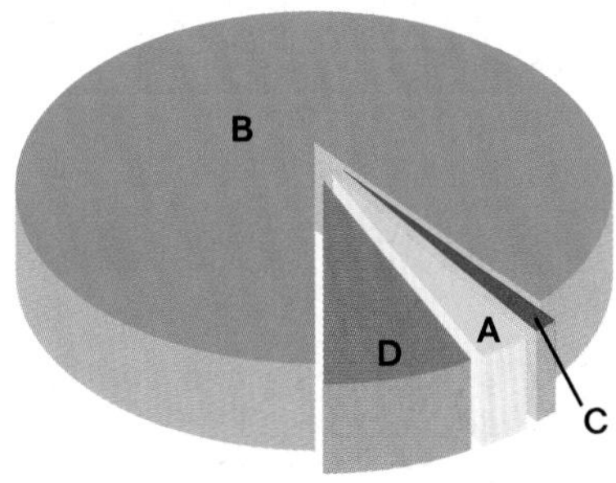

25. **Interpreting Scientific Illustrations:** The Cenozoic era has lasted 66 million years. What percentage of Earth's 4.6-billion-year history is that? How many degrees on the pie graph represent the Cenozoic era?

Test-Taking Tip

Use the Buddy System Study in a group. A small gathering of people works well because it allows you to draw from a broader base of skills and expertise. Keep it small and keep on target.

Test Practice

Use these questions to test your Science Proficiency.

1. The fossil record increased greatly around 544 million years ago. What one fact about organisms alive at that time **BEST** explains the change in the fossil record?
   A) Organisms became more mobile.
   B) Organisms had developed hard parts.
   C) Organisms were composed mostly of soft parts.
   D) Organisms moved onto land.
2. The fossil record is limited for Precambrian time. What does this tell you about the life-forms from that age?
   A) Organisms from Precambrian time did not have hard parts and were not preserved well.
   B) Few life-forms existed then.
   C) Precambrian life-forms were too small for fossilization.
   D) Precambrian time is too long for fossils to remain.

Assessment Resources

The **Test Practice Workbook** provides students with practice in the format, concepts, and critical-thinking skills tested in standardized exams.

Reproducible Masters

Chapter Review, pp. 25–26 L2
Performance Assessment, p. 27 L2
Assessment, pp. 55–58 L2

Glencoe Technology

- **Chapter Review Software**
- **Computer Test Bank**
- **MindJogger Videoquiz**

The Test-Taking Tip was written by The Princeton Review, the nation's leader in test preparation.

1. B
2. A

Developing Skills

21. should be similar to the figure of Pangea in this chapter
22. Accept all reasonable answers. Responses might include plate tectonic processes, withdrawal of shallow seas, or cooler climates.
23. No, corals are marine animals. Coal forms from dead plants in freshwater swamps.
24. A—Mesozoic era
    B—Precambrian time
    C—Cenozoic era
    D—Paleozoic era
25. The Cenozoic era represents approximately 1.4 percent of Earth's history (66 000 000 × 4 600 000 000 years = 0.014). This is represented by 5° on the graph (360° × 0.014 = 5°).

Bonus Question

Concept Mapping

Using Figure 13-2, create a concept map of either the Paleozoic era, the Mesozoic era, or the Cenozoic era. *Student concept maps should at least include all data listed for each era on* ***Figure 13-2.*** *They should also include additional details of the life and geology of the era chosen.*

UNIT 5

Foundations of Life

The unit begins with a discussion of the common structures and characteristics of organic and biological compounds. The unit continues with a description of asexual and sexual reproduction in plants, including reproduction by spores, cones, and flowers. Students will describe plant responses, including tropisms and photoperiodism. The processes of photosynthesis and respiration are discussed. The unit concludes with students identifying the structures used by plants for sexual reproduction and exploring key factors in seed development and dispersal.

Unit Overview

Science at Home

Plant Growth Rates Have students grow plants in various places inside their homes—by a sunny window, in a dark closet, or by a window that receives indirect sunlight. Make sure each student grows the same type of plant in each location and gives the plants the same amounts of water. Have students explain what happened to the plants. *Only plants that receive the appropriate amount of light thrive.*

NATIONAL GEOGRAPHIC

What's Happening Here?

It's a morning like any other. You gulp down some orange juice, grab your notebook, and catch the bus to school. What do all these activities have in common? They all depend on plants and on the carbon-containing molecules that plants produce. Without plants and certain other organisms, life's foundations would crumble. That's because plants, like the sunflowers at left, have the ability to manufacture carbon-containing molecules using only three simple ingredients: water, energy, and the gas carbon dioxide. When you pop a handful of sunflower seeds into your mouth or eat fruits and vegetables, you are eating plant-manufactured carbon compounds essential for life. Those contained in foods like milk, cheese, and meat come to you from animals that eat plants. Some of those carbon-containing molecules provide energy to move, breathe, and think. Others are the stuff of cells and enzymes and of the spiraling molecules of DNA (inset) which contain the "blueprints" needed to make you.

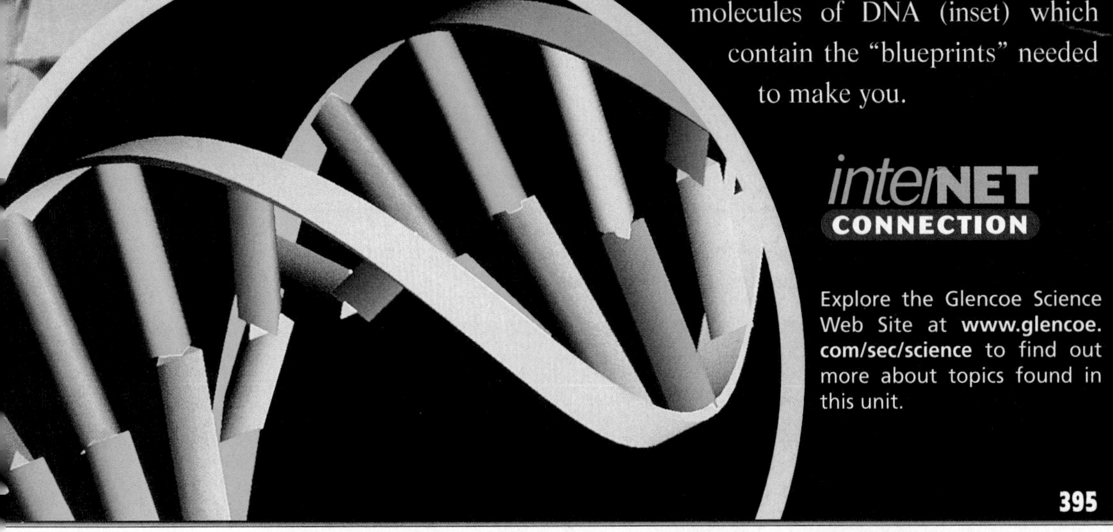

interNET CONNECTION

Explore the Glencoe Science Web Site at **www.glencoe.com/sec/science** to find out more about topics found in this unit.

interNET CONNECTION

Internet Addresses

Explore the Glencoe Science Web Site at **www.glencoe.com/sec/science** to find out more about topics found in this unit.

Introducing the Unit

What's happening here?

Have students read the text and examine the pictures. Show students a blueprint and ask them to compare it to the DNA model shown. Lead them to conclude that both models determine the outcome of the product, based on what is represented by the model.

Content Background

Nucleic acids are polymers that control the activities and reproduction of cells. DNA, which is one type of nucleic acid, codes and stores genetic information. With the genetic code, DNA controls the production of RNA, another nucleic acid. RNA controls the production of proteins, including enzymes.

Previewing the Chapters

- Have students identify instances in the text or pictures where the symbol for carbon is used.
- Have students look at photographs and illustrations and identify plant structures with which they are familiar.

Tying to Previous Knowledge

- Have students recall the atomic structure of carbon. Review the arrangement of electrons and how covalent bonds are formed.
- Have students name common plants. Ask them to name plants that have seeds.

Chapter 14 Carbon Chemistry

Section	Objectives	Activities/Features
Chapter Opener		**Explore Activity:** Infer Carbon Bonding, p. 397
14-1 **Simple Organic Compounds** 1½ Sessions 1 Block	1. **Explain** why carbon is able to form many compounds. 2. **Distinguish** saturated and unsaturated hydrocarbons. 3. **Identify** isomers of organic compounds.	**Earth Science Integration,** p. 400 **MiniLab:** Modeling Isomers, p. 402 **Skill Builder:** Making and Using Graphs, p. 403 **Using Math,** p. 403
14-2 **Other Organic Compounds** 3 Sessions 1½ Blocks	4. **Explain** how new compounds are formed by substituting hydrocarbons. 5. **Describe** the classes of compounds that result from hydrocarbon substitution.	**Skill Builder:** Making Models, p. 407 **Using Computers,** p. 407 **Activity 14-1:** Conversion of Alcohols, p. 408 **Science and Society:** Nature's Medicines and the Organic Chemist, p. 409
14-3 **Biological Compounds** 4 Sessions 2 Blocks	6. **Describe** how large organic molecules are made. 7. **Explain** the roles of organic molecules in the body. 8. **Explain** why eating the recommended amounts of certain foods is important for maintaining health.	**Life Science Integration,** p. 411 **MiniLab:** Summing Up Proteins, p. 411 **Problem Solving:** Comparing Sweetness, p. 413 **Using Math,** p. 415 **Skill Builder:** Forming a Hypothesis, p. 417 **Science Journal,** p. 417 **Activity 14-2:** Detecting Fats and Starches, pp. 418–419

The number of recommended single-period sessions — The number of recommended blocks
One session and one-half block are allowed for chapter review and assessment.

Activity Materials

Explore	Activities	MiniLabs
p. 397 toothpicks, raisins, gumdrops, grapes, clay	p. 408 test tube and stopper, potassium permanganate solution, sodium hydroxide solution, ethanol, dropper, pH test paper, 10-mL graduated cylinder, test-tube rack pp. 418–419 paper grocery bag, iodine solution, dropper bottle, marker, scissors, liquid cooking oil, bread, raw potato, cooked bacon, cheese, cracker, cooked egg white, potato chip	p. 402 toothpicks, two colors of clay p. 411 pencil, paper

Need Materials? Contact Science Kit at 1-800-828-7777 or at www.sciencekit.com on the Internet.
For alternate materials, see the activity on the listed page.

Standards		Reproducible Resources	Technology
National	**State/Local**	Test Practice Workbooks are available for use with each chapter.	English and Spanish audiocassettes are available for use with each section.
National Content Standards: B1, C1, D1, D2, E2, G3		**Activity Worksheets,** p. 79 **Enrichment,** p. 37 **Home Involvement,** p. 37 **Reinforcement,** p. 37 **Study Guide,** pp. 53–54	**Section Focus Transparency 37** **Teaching Transparency 27** **Glencoe Science Voyages Interactive Videodisc—Physical** **Glencoe Science Voyages Interactive CD-ROM**
National Content Standards: B1, C1, E2, F1		**Activity Worksheets,** pp. 75–76 **Enrichment,** p. 38 **Reinforcement,** p. 38 **Study Guide,** p. 55	**Section Focus Transparency 38** **Teaching Transparency 27** **Internet Connection,** p. 405 **The Infinite Voyage Series**
National Content Standards: UCP2, B1, B3, C1, F1, F4		**Activity Worksheets,** pp. 77–78, 80 **Critical Thinking/Problem Solving,** p. 14 **Enrichment,** p. 39 **Laboratory Manual,** pp. 77–82 **Laboratory Manual,** pp. 83–86 **Multicultural Connections,** pp. 27–28 **Reinforcement,** p. 39 **Study Guide,** pp. 55–56	**Section Focus Transparency 39** **Teaching Transparency 28** **Science Integration Transparency 14** **Glencoe Science Voyages Interactive Videodisc—Physical** **Internet Connection,** p. 415 **The Infinite Voyage Series**

Key to Teaching Strategies

The following designations will help you decide which activities are appropriate for your students.

L1 Level 1 activities should be appropriate for students with learning difficulties.

L2 Level 2 activities should be within the ability range of all students.

L3 Level 3 activities are designed for above-average students.

ELL ELL activities should be within the ability range of English Language Learners.

COOP LEARN Cooperative Learning activities are designed for small group work.

P These strategies represent student products that can be placed into a best-work portfolio.

Multiple Learning Styles logos, as described on page 61T, are used throughout to indicate strategies that address different learning styles.

Assessment Resources

Chapter Review, pp. 27–28
Assessment, pp. 61–64
Performance Assessment in the Science Classroom (PASC)
MindJogger Videoquiz
Alternate Assessment in the Science Classroom
Performance Assessment, p. 28
Chapter Review Software
Computer Test Bank

Chapter 14 Carbon Chemistry

This is a representation of key blackline masters available in the Teacher Classroom Resources.
See Resource Manager boxes within the chapter for additional information.

Transparencies

Section Focus Transparencies

37 SECTION FOCUS TRANSPARENCY

A COMMON ELEMENT

The picture shows a scene you would expect to see, perhaps, in the Northwest, in Canada, or in Alaska. You can look at the picture in a number of ways. One way is to determine which elements in the picture are related to one another.

1. Categorize the elements in the picture into living and nonliving things.
2. All living things have an element in common—and in this sentence the word *element* refers to an element in the periodic table. What element do you think it might be, and why?

L2

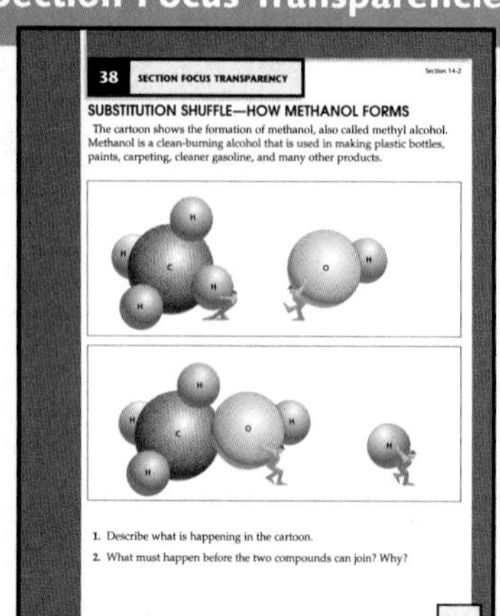

38 SECTION FOCUS TRANSPARENCY

SUBSTITUTION SHUFFLE—HOW METHANOL FORMS

The cartoon shows the formation of methanol, also called methyl alcohol. Methanol is a clean-burning alcohol that is used in making plastic bottles, paints, carpeting, cleaner gasoline, and many other products.

1. Describe what is happening in the cartoon.
2. What must happen before the two compounds can join? Why?

L2

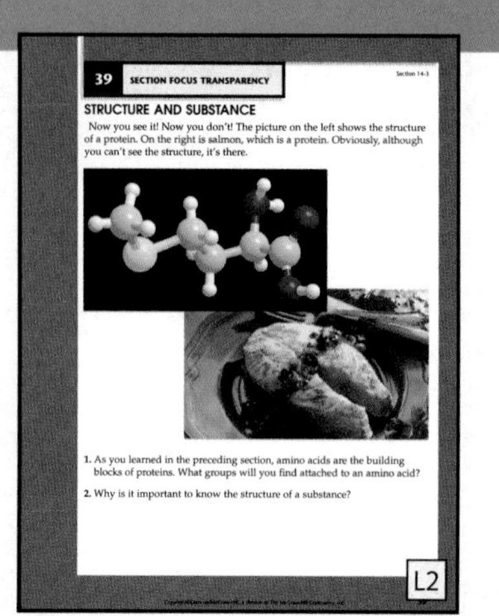

39 SECTION FOCUS TRANSPARENCY

STRUCTURE AND SUBSTANCE

Now you see it! Now you don't! The picture on the left shows the structure of a protein. On the right is salmon, which is a protein. Obviously, although you can't see the structure, it's there.

1. As you learned in the preceding section, amino acids are the building blocks of proteins. What groups will you find attached to an amino acid?
2. Why is it important to know the structure of a substance?

L2

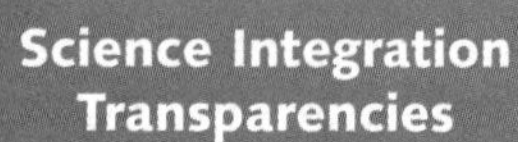

Science Integration Transparencies

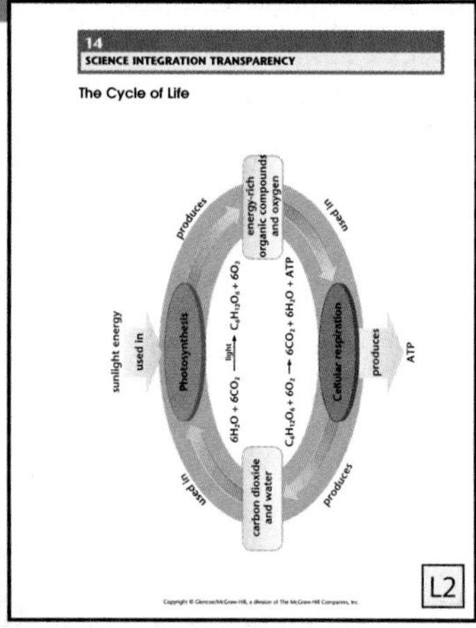

14 SCIENCE INTEGRATION TRANSPARENCY

The Cycle of Life

L2

Teaching Transparencies

L2

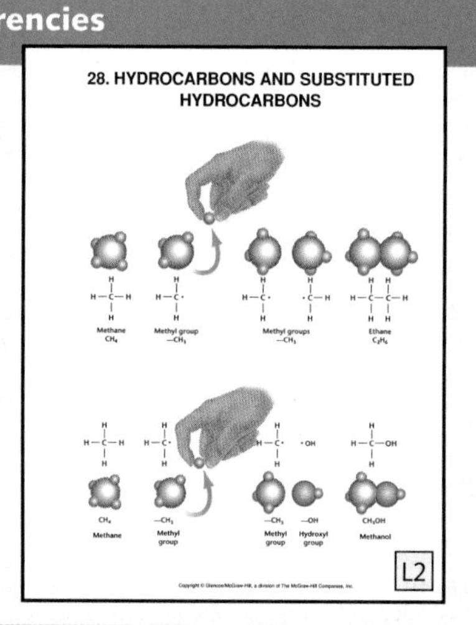

L2

Meeting Different Ability Levels

Study Guide for Content Mastery

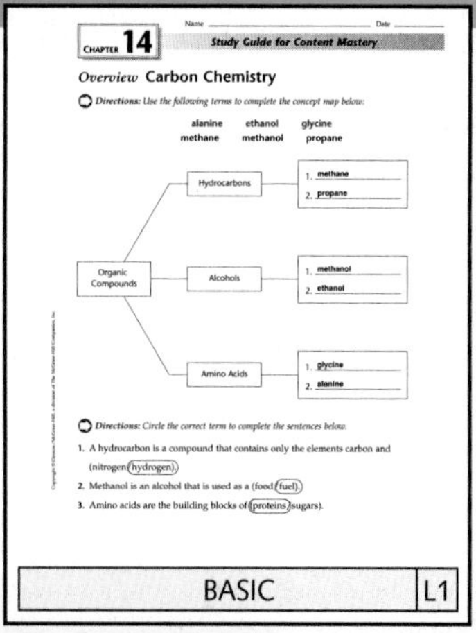

Chapter 14 Study Guide for Content Mastery

Overview Carbon Chemistry

Directions: Use the following terms to complete the concept map below.

alanine, ethanol, glycine, methane, methanol, propane

Organic Compounds — Hydrocarbons: 1. methane 2. propane; Alcohols: 1. methanol 2. ethanol; Amino Acids: 1. glycine 2. alanine

Directions: Circle the correct term to complete the sentences below.

1. A hydrocarbon is a compound that contains only the elements carbon and (nitrogen, hydrogen).
2. Methanol is an alcohol that is used as a (food, fuel).
3. Amino acids are the building blocks of (proteins, sugars).

BASIC L1

Reinforcement

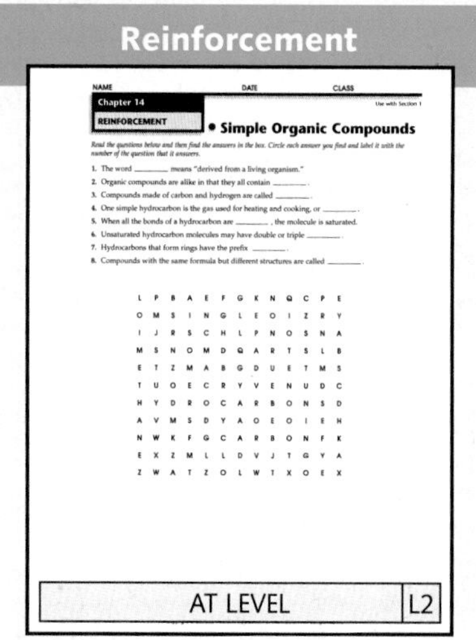

Chapter 14 REINFORCEMENT • Simple Organic Compounds

1. The word ______ means "derived from a living organism."
2. Organic compounds are alike in that they all contain ______.
3. Compounds made of carbon and hydrogen are called ______.
4. One simple hydrocarbon is the gas used for heating and cooking, or ______.
5. When all the bonds of a hydrocarbon are ______, the molecule is saturated.
6. Unsaturated hydrocarbon molecules may have double or triple ______.
7. Hydrocarbons that form rings have the prefix ______.
8. Compounds with the same formula but different structures are called ______.

AT LEVEL L2

Enrichment Worksheets

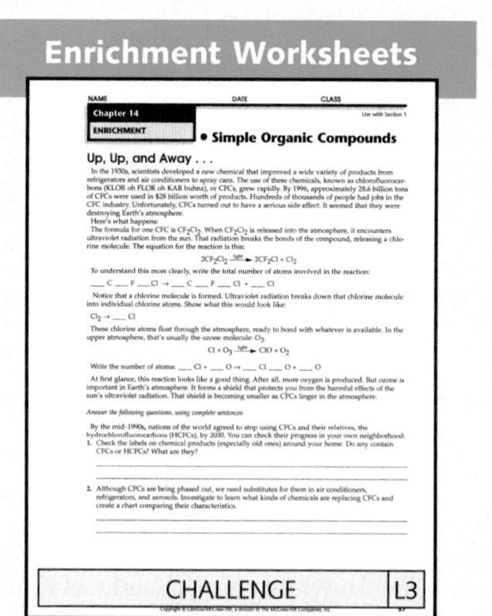

Chapter 14 ENRICHMENT • Simple Organic Compounds

Up, Up, and Away . . .

CHALLENGE L3

Hands-on Activities

Activity Worksheets

NAME DATE CLASS

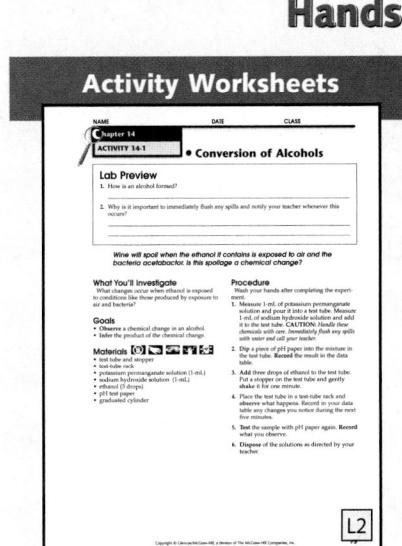

Chapter 14
ACTIVITY 14-1

• Conversion of Alcohols

Lab Preview

1. How is an alcohol formed?

2. Why is it important to immediately flush any spills and notify your teacher whenever this occurs?

Wine will spoil when the ethanol it contains is exposed to air and the bacteria acetobacter. Is this spoilage a chemical change?

What You'll Investigate

Goals

Materials

Procedure

L2

Lab Manual

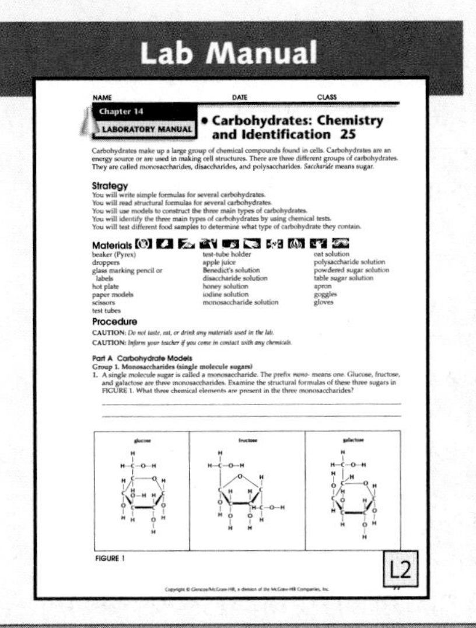
NAME DATE CLASS

Chapter 14
LABORATORY MANUAL

• Carbohydrates: Chemistry and Identification 25

Strategy

Materials

Procedure

Part A Carbohydrate Models

FIGURE 1

L2

Accessibility

Spanish Resources

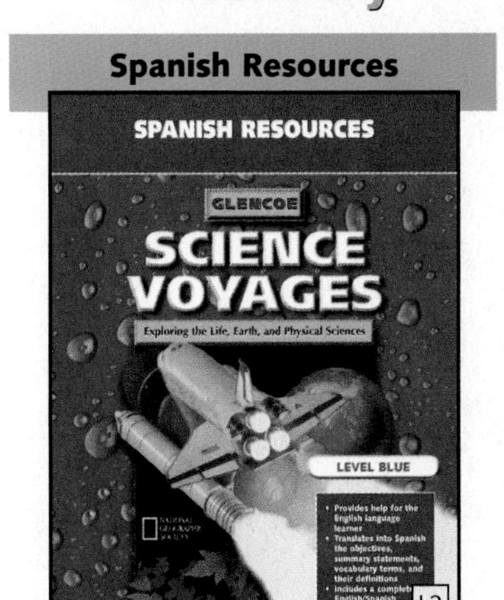
SPANISH RESOURCES

GLENCOE

SCIENCE VOYAGES

Exploring the Life, Earth, and Physical Sciences

LEVEL BLUE

• Provides help for the English language learner
• Translates into Spanish the objectives, summary statements, vocabulary terms, and their definitions
• Includes a complete English/Spanish Glossary

L2

Assessment

Performance Assessment

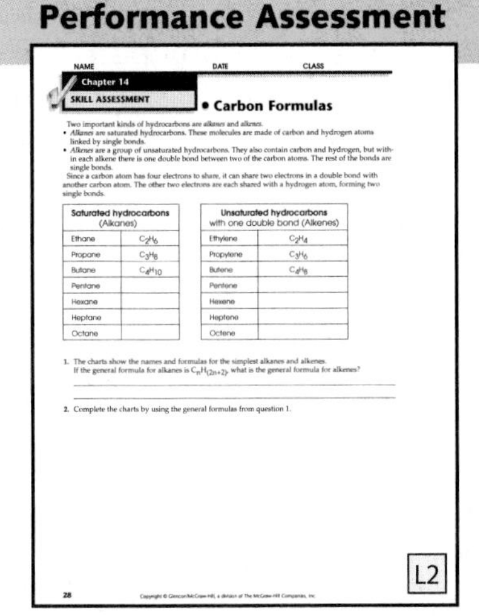
NAME DATE CLASS

Chapter 14
SKILL ASSESSMENT

• Carbon Formulas

Saturated hydrocarbons (Alkanes)	
Ethane	C_2H_6
Propane	C_3H_8
Butane	C_4H_{10}
Pentane	
Hexane	
Heptane	
Octane	

Unsaturated hydrocarbons with one double bond (Alkenes)	
Ethylene	C_2H_4
Propylene	C_3H_6
Butene	C_4H_8
Pentene	
Hexene	
Heptene	
Octene	

2. Complete the charts by using the general formulas from question 1.

L2

Chapter Review

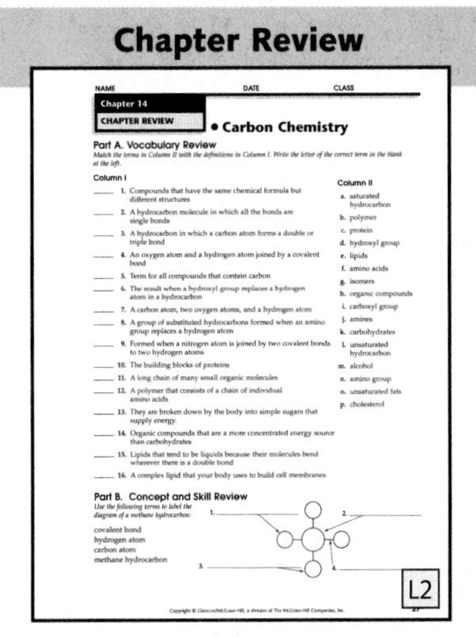
NAME DATE CLASS

Chapter 14
CHAPTER REVIEW

• Carbon Chemistry

Part A. Vocabulary Review

Part B. Concept and Skill Review

L2

Assessment

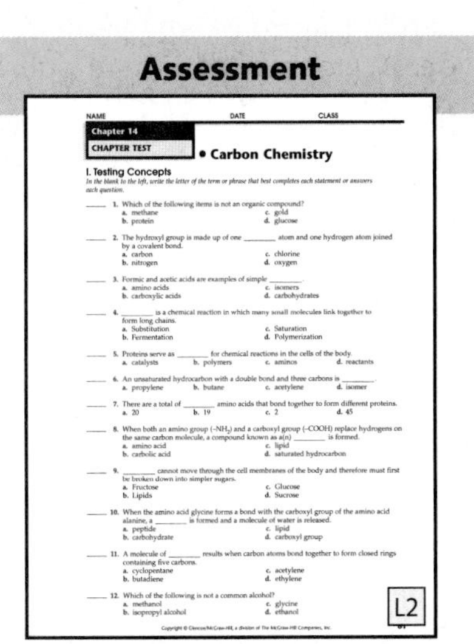
NAME DATE CLASS

Chapter 14
CHAPTER TEST

• Carbon Chemistry

I. Testing Concepts

L2

Test Practice Workbook

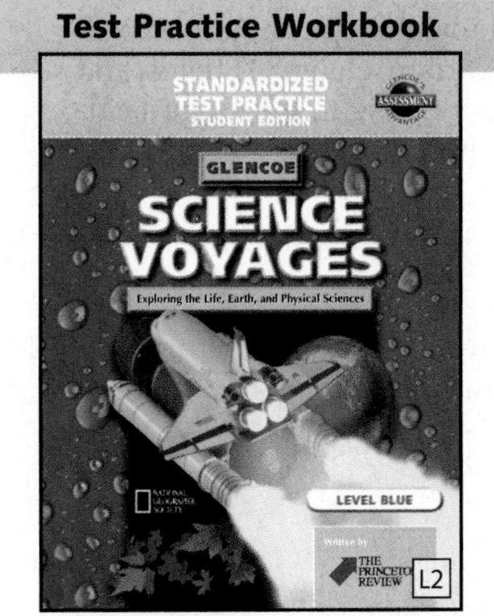
STANDARDIZED TEST PRACTICE
STUDENT EDITION

GLENCOE

SCIENCE VOYAGES

Exploring the Life, Earth, and Physical Sciences

LEVEL BLUE

THE PRINCETON REVIEW

L2

Extending Content

Critical Thinking/ Problem Solving

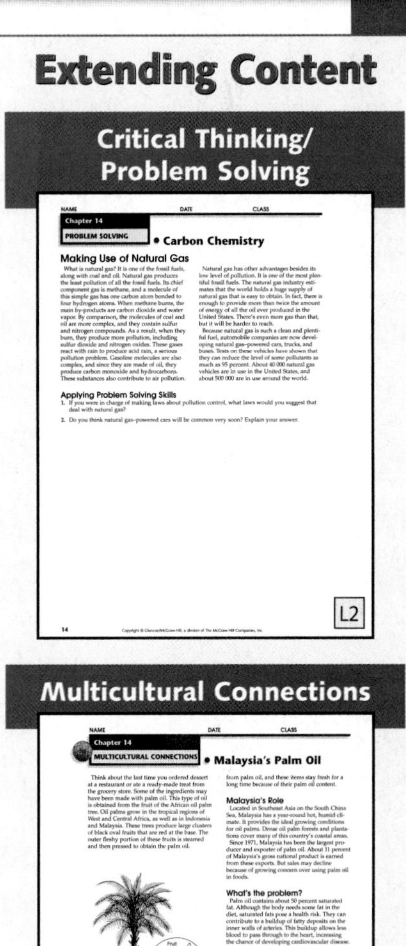
NAME DATE CLASS

Chapter 14
PROBLEM SOLVING

• Carbon Chemistry

Making Use of Natural Gas

Applying Problem Solving Skills

L2

Multicultural Connections

NAME DATE CLASS

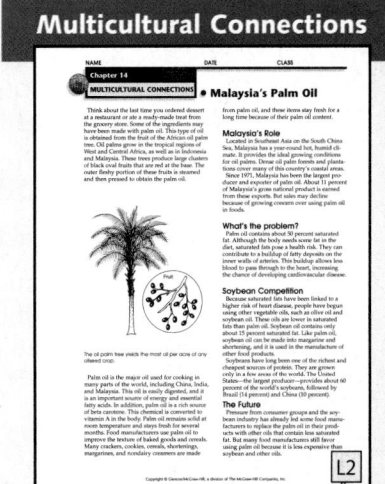

Chapter 14
MULTICULTURAL CONNECTIONS

• Malaysia's Palm Oil

Malaysia's Role

What's the problem?

Soybean Competition

The Future

L2

Helping You Prepare

Hydrocarbons (Section 14-1)

The terms *saturated* and *unsaturated,* as applied to hydrocarbons, came into use by chemists even before they knew how the bonding in the two types of hydrocarbons differed. They found from experience that some hydrocarbons took up hydrogen in the presence of a catalyst. When the substance stopped taking up hydrogen, it was said to be saturated. Hydrocarbons that would take up hydrogen were said to be unsaturated. Now chemists know that unsaturated hydrocarbons contain double or triple bonds. For an unsaturated hydrocarbon to be converted to a saturated hydrocarbon, each double bond must add two atoms of hydrogen and each triple bond must add four atoms of hydrogen.

Saturated hydrocarbons are known as alkanes. They are named by using a prefix to indicate the number of carbon atoms present and the suffix *-ane*. For example, C_5H_{12} is pentane. The general formula for a straight-chain alkane is C_nH_{2n+2}.

Unsaturated hydrocarbons with one or more double bonds are known as alkenes. They are named by using a prefix to indicate the number of carbon atoms present and the suffix *-ene*. For example, C_5H_{10} is pentene. The general formula for a straight-chain alkene with one double bond is C_nH_{2n}.

Unsaturated hydrocarbons with one or more triple bonds are known as alkynes. They are named by using a prefix to indicate the number of carbon atoms present and the suffix *-yne*. For example, C_5H_8 is pentyne. The general formula for a straight-chain alkyne containing one triple bond is C_nH_{2n-2}.

Any of these types of hydrocarbons can have branches. Branched alkanes are named according to the longest carbon chain. Alkenes and alkynes are named according to the longest carbon chain that contains all multiple bonds.

Substituted Hydrocarbons (Section 14-2)

Other substituted hydrocarbons exist in addition to those described in the section. Several of them are described here.

GLENCOE TECHNOLOGY

Glencoe Science Voyages Interactive CD-ROM

Chapter Summaries

Use the Chapter Summary to introduce, teach, or review chapter material.

When a carboxylic acid and an alcohol react, water and an ester form. The reaction is similar to the reaction of a carboxylic acid and an amine. Esters are used in the manufacture of polyester fabrics and as fragrances and flavorings. Many natural fragrances and flavors of flowers and fruits result from esters.

In an ether, two hydrocarbon parts are connected by an oxygen atom. Diethyl ether is the most common ether. It was formerly used as an anesthetic, but this use has been discontinued because of its flammability and because it causes nausea.

Aldehydes and ketones contain carbonyl groups. A carbonyl group is a carbon atom double bonded to an oxygen atom. If the carbonyl group is on the end of the carbon chain, the compound is an aldehyde. If the carbonyl group is not at the end of the chain, the compound is a ketone. Both types of compounds are reactive and have distinctive odors. Examples of aldehydes include vanillin, which provides the flavor and fragrance of vanilla, and formaldehyde. Acetone, used in nail polish remover, is a ketone.

Closely related to amines are amides, which contain an amino group bonded to a carbonyl group, $—CONH_2$. Many amines and amides, such as putrescine and cadaverine, have distinctive, often unpleasant, odors. When amino acids combine to form protein molecules, the linkage between the amino acid is an amide, also called a peptide.

What's a polymer? (Section 14-3)

Sometimes, the terms *plastic* and *polymer* are used synonymously, but not all polymers are plastics. Plastics are polymers that can be molded into different shapes.

Some plastics are thermoplastic, which means that they will soften and harden repeatedly as they are heated and cooled. Thermoplastics are easy to recycle because each time they are heated, they can be formed into new products.

Other plastics are thermosetting, which means that they harden permanently when they are molded. This permanent hardening usually results from cross-linking of the polymer strands. Cross-linking connects many polymers together, adding strength. These plastics actually become harder when heated. Although they are difficult to recycle, they are durable.

Polymerization Processes (Section 14-3)

Although all polymers are large molecules formed by combining small molecules, or monomers, they are formed in two different ways. The method of formation depends on the structure of the monomer used. Examples of each method are found in the section content.

In one polymerization process, one bond of a double bond is broken in two monomers, and the monomers bond together in this location. Because the monomers are basically added to each other, this process is called addition polymerization. In this process, all atoms contained in the monomers are present in the polymers.

The second polymerization process is called condensation polymerization because portions of the monomers are removed, or condensed when the polymer is formed. Usually, these portions form water.

Another process that happens frequently during a polymerization process is cross-linking. For example, when latex from rubber trees is heated, the polymer strands cross-link, forming solid rubber.

SCIENCE UPDATE

For current events or science in the news, access the Glencoe Science Web Site at **www.glencoe.com/sec/science**

Cholesterol (Section 14-3)

Medical experts often disagree about the health effects of cholesterol. The ideal serum, or blood, cholesterol level differs, depending on the source of the information. Frequently, a desirable serum cholesterol count is less than 200 mg/dL.

However, total cholesterol count is not as important as the ratio of the two different types of cholesterol present. LDL is a low-density lipid, and it is the one that clogs arteries. HDL is a high-density lipid and does not cause the vascular problems that LDL does. HDL actually helps prevent the damage that LDL can do. The most important information about serum, or blood, cholesterol is the ratio of HDL to LDL.

Teacher to Teacher

"After introducing the nomenclature for organic compounds, I have students work in pairs to build models of a number of progressively difficult compounds using a kit. You can also use small, different-colored marshmallows and toothpicks."

Tom McCarthy, Ph.D., Teacher
Saint Edward's School
Vero Beach, FL

CHAPTER 14
Carbon Chemistry

CHAPTER OVERVIEW

Section 14-1 Carbon chemistry, including hydrocarbons, saturation, and isomers, is investigated.

Section 14-2 Organic compounds that result from substituting other elements or groups for a hydrogen atom in a hydrocarbon are introduced.

Section 14-3 Organic polymers, especially biological compounds such as proteins, carbohydrates, and lipids, are discussed.

Chapter Vocabulary

organic compound
hydrocarbon
saturated hydrocarbon
unsaturated hydrocarbon
isomer
hydroxyl group
carboxyl group
amino group
amino acid
polymer
protein
carbohydrate
lipid

Theme Connection

Scale and Structure Although the size of organic molecules is on the micro level, their structures determine their properties on the macro level.

00:00 OUT OF TIME?

If time does not permit teaching the entire chapter, use Reviewing Main Ideas on pp. 420–421.

CHAPTER 14
Carbon Chemistry

Chapter Preview

Section 14-1
Simple Organic Compounds
Section 14-2
Other Organic Compounds
Section 14-3
Biological Compounds

Skills Preview

Skill Builders
- Sequence
- Make and Use a Graph

Activities
- Form a Hypothesis

MiniLabs
- Make a Model

Reading Check

Review or find out the meanings of these word parts so you will better understand this chapter: *carbo–, hydro–, iso–, poly–, –mer, –ane, –ene.*

396

Multiple Learning Styles

Look for the following logos for strategies that emphasize different learning modalities.

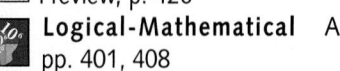

Linguistic Science Journal, p. 405; Preview, p. 420

Logical-Mathematical Activity, pp. 401, 408

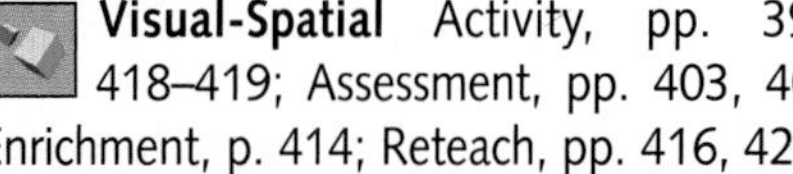

Visual-Spatial Activity, pp. 399, 418–419; Assessment, pp. 403, 407; Enrichment, p. 414; Reteach, pp. 416, 420

Auditory-Musical Out of Time, p. 420

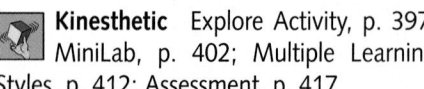

Kinesthetic Explore Activity, p. 397; MiniLab, p. 402; Multiple Learning Styles, p. 412; Assessment, p. 417

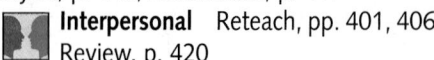

Interpersonal Reteach, pp. 401, 406; Review, p. 420

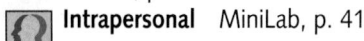

Intrapersonal MiniLab, p. 411

Explore Activity

This family is going on a picnic, and they're taking along a lot of stuff. Besides the picnic basket full of food, there are the baseball gloves, tennis rackets, towels and blankets, and the beach chairs. Different as they are, these items all share one thing in common—they contain the element carbon. Even many parts of the minivan are made of compounds that contain carbon. What is special about carbon that allows it to form so many different compounds?

Infer Carbon's Bonding

CAUTION: *Do not eat foods used in your activity.*

1. Insert four toothpicks into a small clay or plastic foam ball so that the toothpicks are evenly spaced around the sphere. The ball represents a carbon atom. The toothpicks represent chemical bonds.
2. Use raisins to represent hydrogen atoms, grapes to represent chlorine atoms, and gumdrops to represent fluorine atoms. Make models of molecules by adding any combination of raisins, grapes, and gumdrops to the toothpicks.
3. Compare your models with those of other class members.

Science Journal

Draw each model and write the formula for it. Did you make all the models that were possible with the materials you had? Did the class make all that were possible? What can you infer about the number of compounds a single carbon atom can form with only three kinds of atoms?

397

Explore Activity

Purpose

Kinesthetic Use the Explore Activity to help students discover why carbon forms so many compounds. L2 ELL COOP LEARN

Materials

raisins (4), grapes (4), gumdrops (4), pointed toothpicks (4), modeling clay or plastic foam ball for each group

Teaching Strategies

Allot a certain amount of time for students to make as many models as possible. Have them draw a diagram of each molecule as it is completed.

Safety Precautions

Caution students to not eat anything in a laboratory setting.

Science Journal Student entries should emphasize that carbon forms a multitude of compounds with other elements. P

Assessment

Performance Have groups of students draw electron dot diagrams of each of the compounds formed in the activity. Use **Performance Assessment in the Science Classroom,** p. 55. P

Assessment Planner

Portfolio

Refer to p. 421 for suggested items that students might select for their portfolios.

Performance Assessment

See p. 421 for additional Performance Assessment options.
Skill Builder, pp. 403, 417
MiniLab, pp. 402, 411
Activity 14-1, p. 408; 14-2, pp. 418–419

Content Assessment

Section Assessment, pp. 403, 407, 417
Chapter Assessment, pp. 422–423
Proficiency Prep, pp. 403, 407, 416

SECTION 14•1

Prepare

Refer to **Hydrocarbons** on p. 396E.

Preplanning

Refer to the **Chapter Organizer** on pp. 396A–B.

1 Motivate

Bellringer

Before presenting the lesson, display **Section Focus Transparency 37** on the overhead projector. Use the accompanying **Focus Activity** worksheet. L2 ELL

Section 14-1

37 SECTION FOCUS TRANSPARENCY

A COMMON ELEMENT

The picture shows a scene you would expect to see, perhaps, in the Northwest, in Canada, or in Alaska. You can look at the picture in a number of ways. One way is to determine which elements in the picture are related to one another.

1. Categorize the elements in the picture into living and nonliving things.
2. All living things have an element in common—and in this sentence the word *element* refers to an element in the periodic table. What element do you think it might be, and why?

37

Tying to Previous Knowledge

Students probably are familiar with the simple hydrocarbons used for fuel. Examples include methane (natural gas), propane (used in torches and for heating and cooking), and butane (lighters).

14•1 Simple Organic Compounds

What You'll Learn

- Why carbon is able to form many compounds
- How saturated and unsaturated hydrocarbons differ
- How to identify isomers of organic compounds

Vocabulary
organic compound
hydrocarbon
saturated hydrocarbon
unsaturated hydrocarbon
isomer

Why It's Important

- Plants, animals, and most of the things that are part of your life are made of organic compounds.

Organic Compounds

One way to classify the substances that are a part of your life is shown in **Figure 14-1.** Some substances are made by living organisms, for example, leaves and wood. Other substances, such as most rocks and minerals, are not and have never been alive. Most of the substances associated with living things contain the element carbon. Scientists used to think that this group of substances could be produced only by living plants and animals, so these carbon-containing substances were called organic compounds. The word *organic* means "derived from a living organism." But, in 1828, a German scientist formed the organic compound urea from substances that were not organic compounds. Scientists then realized that living organisms are not necessary to form organic compounds. Now, most compounds that contain carbon are called **organic compounds.**

Atoms form chemical bonds and thus obtain the stability of a noble gas with eight electrons in their outer energy level. A carbon atom has four electrons in its outer energy level, so it forms four covalent bonds with as many as four other atoms. A single covalent bond is a pair of electrons that is shared between two atoms. One of carbon's most frequent partners in covalent bonds is hydrogen.

Figure 14-1 Organic substances contain carbon.

A Most of the substances in the photo are organic. Although some are, or were, alive, others were manufactured.

B The substances in this photo are mostly composed of elements other than carbon.

Resource Manager

The following **Teacher Classroom Resources** can be used with Section 14-1:

 **Reproducible Masters**

Activity Worksheets, p. 79 L2

Enrichment, p. 37 L3

Home Involvement, p. 37 L2

Reinforcement, p. 37 L2

Study Guide, pp. 53–54 L1 ELL

 **Transparencies**

Teaching Transparency 27 L2

Hydrocarbons

Many compounds are made of carbon and hydrogen alone. A compound in which the only elements are carbon and hydrogen is called a **hydrocarbon.** The simplest hydrocarbon is methane, sometimes called natural gas. If you have a gas stove or gas furnace in your home, the fuel that may be burned in these appliances is methane. It consists of a single carbon atom covalently bonded to four hydrogen atoms. Methane's formula is CH_4. **Figure 14-2** shows a model of the methane molecule and its structural formula. In a structural formula, the lines between one atom and another atom represent pairs of electrons shared between the atoms. A single line represents one pair of electrons.

Now, visualize one of the hydrogen atoms being plucked from a methane molecule, as in **Figure 14-3A.** A fragment of the molecule called a methyl group, $-CH_3$, would remain. The methyl group can then form a single bond with another methyl group. If two methyl groups bond with each other, the result is the two-carbon hydrocarbon ethane, C_2H_6, which is shown with its structural formula in **Figure 14-3B.**

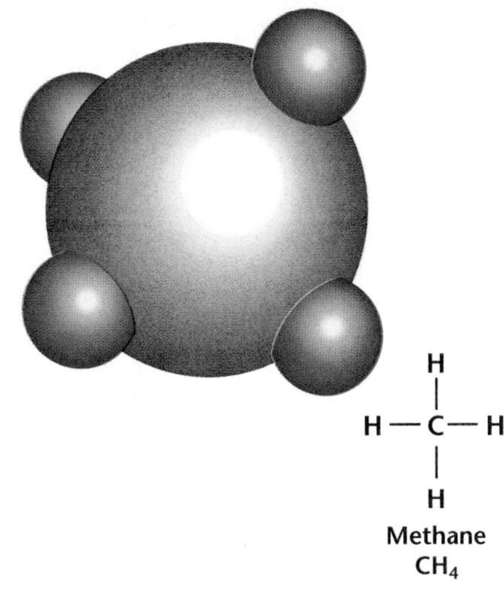

Figure 14-2 This simple molecule is the first of a long list of hydrocarbon molecules.

Figure 14-3 Here's a way to visualize the building up of larger hydrocarbons. **Would it matter which hydrogen atom was plucked off?**

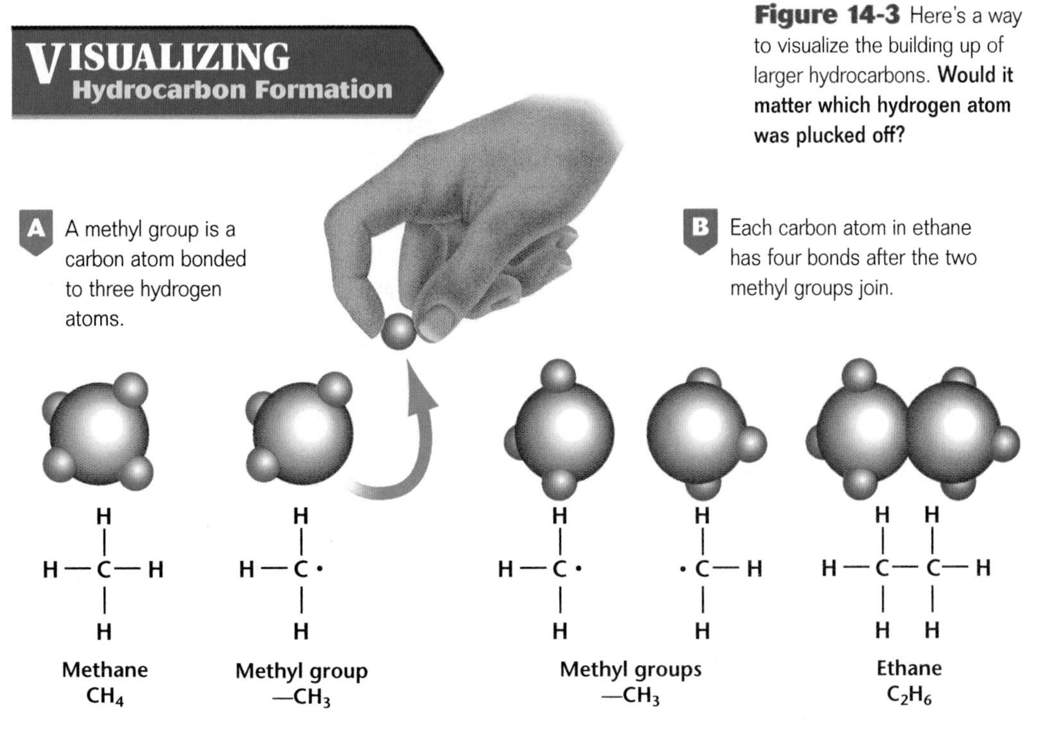

VISUALIZING
Hydrocarbon Formation
A A methyl group is a carbon atom bonded to three hydrogen atoms.
B Each carbon atom in ethane has four bonds after the two methyl groups join.
Methane
CH_4
Methyl group
$-CH_3$
Methyl groups
$-CH_3$
Ethane
C_2H_6

Content Background

Not all substances that contain carbon are organic. Carbon itself, carbon oxides, carbides, and carbonates are inorganic.

Teacher FYI

Methane is odorless. As a safety factor, small amounts of compounds with objectionable odors are added to natural gas so that gas leaks can be detected.

Caption Answer

Figure 14-3 *No, they are identical.*

VISUAL Learning

Figure 14-3 Be sure students see that when a hydrogen is removed from two methyl groups, the two groups can then form a bond with each other.

Activity

Visual-Spatial Make sure students understand that each line connecting the atoms in the structural formulas for hydrocarbon molecules represents a pair of electrons. Have them draw electron dot diagrams that represent what is happening in **Figure 14-3.** Have them compare their diagrams with the structural formulas for methane and ethane. P

Guided Reading Strategy

Synthesis Journal In this strategy, students reflect on a project, a paper, or a performance in light of their own experiences and plan for personal application. Have each student divide a piece of paper into three sections. Have them record "What I did," "What I learned," and "How I can use it." Have students write a Synthesis Journal related to an activity in this section.

Using an Analogy

Show students several examples where the term *saturated* means that it can't hold more and *unsaturated* means that it can hold more. One example would be a damp sponge. The sponge is unsaturated because it could hold more water, just as an unsaturated hydrocarbon can hold more hydrogen. A saturated sponge is holding all the water it can, just as a saturated hydrocarbon holds all the hydrogen it can.

Correcting Misconceptions

Students may think of gasoline as a compound derived from petroleum, not a mixture of hydrocarbons.

Petroleum is separated into its components by a process called fractional distillation. In fractional distillation, separation is possible because the components have different boiling points. When the present supply of petroleum has been used up, it will take hundreds of millions of years to produce more, if the conditions are right.

GLENCOE TECHNOLOGY

Videodisc

Glencoe Science Voyages Interactive Videodisc—Physical

Side 2, Lesson 5 *Carbohydrates and Hydrocarbons*

2836

5089

Refer to the Videodisc Teacher Guide for additional bar codes.

Figure 14-4 Propane and butane are two useful fuels.

A When propane burns, it releases energy for cooking food and warmth. It's the fuel used in camp stoves and heaters.

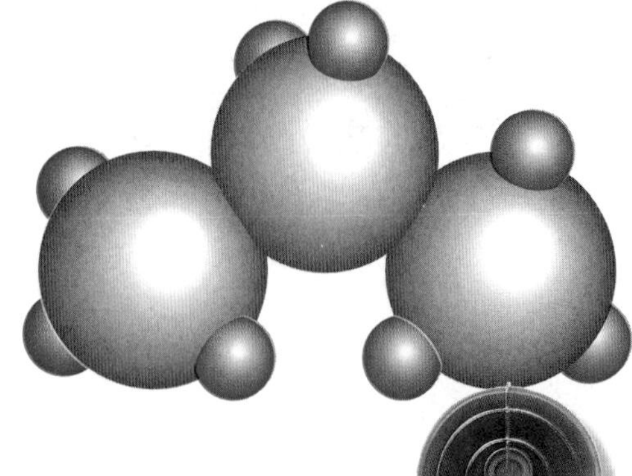

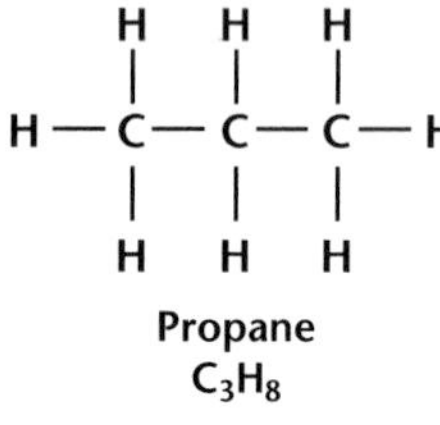

```
     H   H   H
     |   |   |
 H — C — C — C — H
     |   |   |
     H   H   H
```

Propane
C_3H_8

B In addition to its use as lighter fuel, butane is used in making many products.

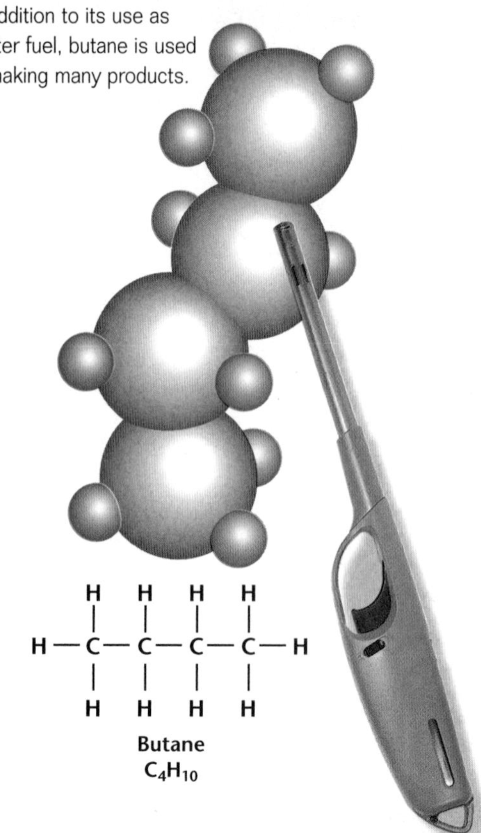

```
     H   H   H   H
     |   |   |   |
 H — C — C — C — C — H
     |   |   |   |
     H   H   H   H
```

Butane
C_4H_{10}

Petroleum from Dinosaurs
Petroleum is a mixture of hydrocarbons that was formed from aquatic plants and animals–perhaps even dinosaurs–that lived hundreds of millions of years ago. With the right temperature and pressure, dead plant and animal matter, buried deep under Earth's surface, is decomposed to form petroleum. Why is petroleum a nonrenewable resource?

Saturated Hydrocarbons

Methane and ethane are the first two members of a family of molecules in which carbon and hydrogen atoms are joined by single covalent bonds. When all the bonds in a hydrocarbon are single bonds, the molecule is called a **saturated hydrocarbon.** You can visualize the formation of larger hydrocarbons in the same way you visualized the formation of ethane. A hydrogen atom is removed from ethane and replaced by a $-CH_3$ group. Propane is the third member of the series. Butane, with four carbon atoms, is the fourth.

These short hydrocarbon chains have low boiling points, so they evaporate and burn easily. That makes methane a good fuel for your stove or furnace. Propane is used in gas grills and in hot-air balloons. Butane is a fuel for camp stoves and lighters. You can see the structures of these hydrocarbons in **Figure 14-4.** Some long-chain hydrocarbons have more than 50 carbon atoms. Longer hydrocarbons are used as oils, waxes, or in asphalt. **Table 14-1** lists the names and the chemical formulas of a few of the smaller saturated hydrocarbons.

Across the Curriculum

Math The hydrocarbons in gasoline are rated on their ability to burn smoothly, or not knock, in an engine. A scale was developed upon which pure isooctane, which knocks little, is rated 100, and heptane, which has a strong tendency to knock, is rated 0. The octane rating found on a gas pump places the gasoline mixture at the correct place on the rating scale.

Unsaturated Hydrocarbons

Carbon also forms hydrocarbons with double and triple bonds. In a double bond, two pairs of electrons are shared between two atoms, and in a triple bond, three pairs of electrons are shared. Hydrocarbons with double or triple bonds are called **unsaturated hydrocarbons.** Ethene, or ethylene, the simplest unsaturated hydrocarbon, has two carbon atoms joined by a double bond. Propene, or propylene, is an unsaturated hydrocarbon with three carbons. Some unsaturated hydrocarbons have more than one double bond. Butadiene has four carbon atoms and two double bonds. The structures of ethylene, propylene, and butadiene are shown in **Figure 14-5.**

Table 14-1

The Structures of Hydrocarbons

Name	Structural Formula	Chemical Formula
Methane	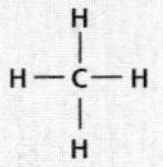 $H-\overset{H}{\underset{H}{C}}-H$	CH_4
Ethane	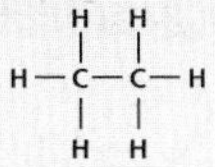 $H-\overset{H}{\underset{H}{C}}-\overset{H}{\underset{H}{C}}-H$	C_2H_6
Propane	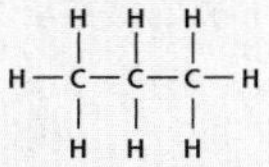 $H-\overset{H}{\underset{H}{C}}-\overset{H}{\underset{H}{C}}-\overset{H}{\underset{H}{C}}-H$	C_3H_8
Butane	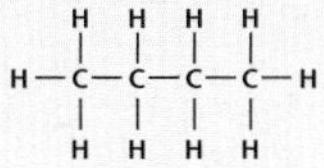 $H-\overset{H}{\underset{H}{C}}-\overset{H}{\underset{H}{C}}-\overset{H}{\underset{H}{C}}-\overset{H}{\underset{H}{C}}-H$	C_4H_{10}
Hexane	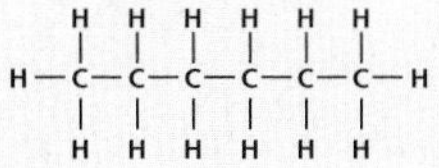 $H-\overset{H}{\underset{H}{C}}-\overset{H}{\underset{H}{C}}-\overset{H}{\underset{H}{C}}-\overset{H}{\underset{H}{C}}-\overset{H}{\underset{H}{C}}-\overset{H}{\underset{H}{C}}-H$	C_6H_{14}

Figure 14-5 You'll find unsaturated hydrocarbons in many of the products you use every day.

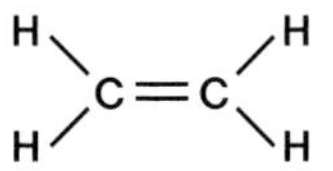

$H_2C=CH_2$

Ethylene
C_2H_4

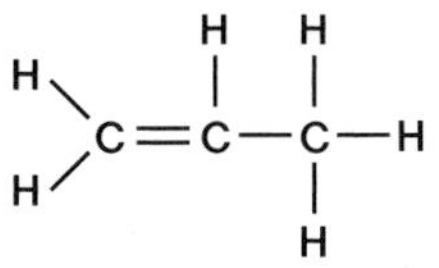

$H_2C=\overset{H}{C}-\overset{H}{\underset{H}{C}}-H$

Propylene
C_3H_6

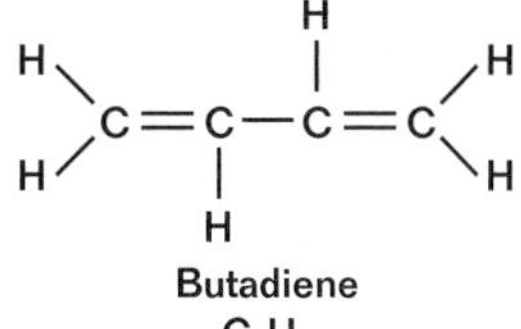

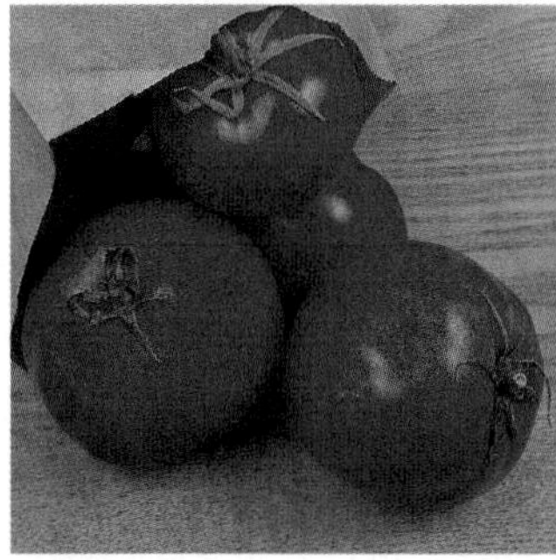

A Ethylene helps ripen fruits and vegetables. It's also used to make milk and soft-drink bottles.

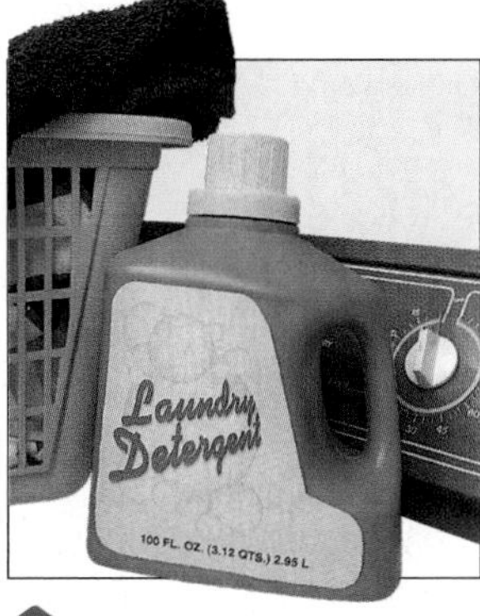

B This detergent bottle contains the tough plastic polypropylene made from propylene.

C Butadiene made it possible to replace natural rubber with synthetic rubber.

GLENCOE TECHNOLOGY

CD-ROM

Glencoe Science Voyages Interactive CD-ROM

Explorations

Have students do the interactive exploration *How can you build models of carbon compounds?*

3 Assess

Check for Understanding Activity

Logical-Mathematical Provide students with several examples of structural formulas of simple hydrocarbons. For each, have them write the molecular formula and determine whether the compound is saturated or unsaturated. L2 P

Reteach

Interpersonal Have students work in pairs to list objects in the classroom that contain organic materials. Objects could include anything made from wood or plastic or anything alive. On the chalkboard, compile a classroom list of those objects that most students agree contain organic compounds. L1 COOP LEARN

Extension

For students who have mastered this section, use the **Reinforcement** and **Enrichment** masters.

Integrating the Sciences

Life Science Cyclopropane compounds are rare in nature because their bonds are strained. However, a group of them known as pyrethrins are found in chrysanthemums. They act as a potent natural insecticide. Scientists are studying these compounds with hopes of using them on other plants, thereby reducing the amount of synthetic pesticides used.

14-1 SIMPLE ORGANIC COMPOUNDS **401**

Figure 14-6 In the welder's torch, ethyne (acetylene) is combined with oxygen to form a mixture that burns, releasing intense light and heat. The two carbon atoms in ethyne are joined by a triple bond. **Why is the oxygen important?**

$$H-C\equiv C-H$$

Ethyne or Acetylene
C_2H_2

Unsaturated hydrocarbons also may have triple bonds, as you can see in the structure of ethyne (ETH ine) shown in **Figure 14-6.** Ethyne, commonly called acetylene, is a gas used for welding because it produces high heat as it burns in a mixture with oxygen in the welding torch.

Hydrocarbon Isomers

Suppose you want to redecorate your room but you can't get new furniture or posters for the walls. One thing you can do is rearrange all of the things that you already have. Even though your room contains the same items, it is different from before. The atoms in an organic molecule also can have different arrangements but still have the same formula. Compounds that have the same chemical formula but different structures are called **isomers** (I suh murz). Two isomers, butane and isobutane, are shown in **Figure 14-7.** Notice that their formulas are the same. But, because of their different structures, they

Try at Home MiniLab

Modeling Isomers

Procedure

1. Construct a model of pentane, C_5H_{12}. Use toothpicks for covalent bonds and small balls of different colored clay for carbon atoms and hydrogen atoms.
2. Using the same collection of atoms, build a molecule with a different arrangement of the atoms. Are there any other possibilities?
3. Make a model of hexane, C_6H_{14}.
4. Arrange the atoms of hexane in different ways.

Analysis

1. How many isomers of pentane did you build? How many isomers of hexane?
2. Do you think there are more isomers of heptane, C_7H_{16}, than hexane? Why or why not?

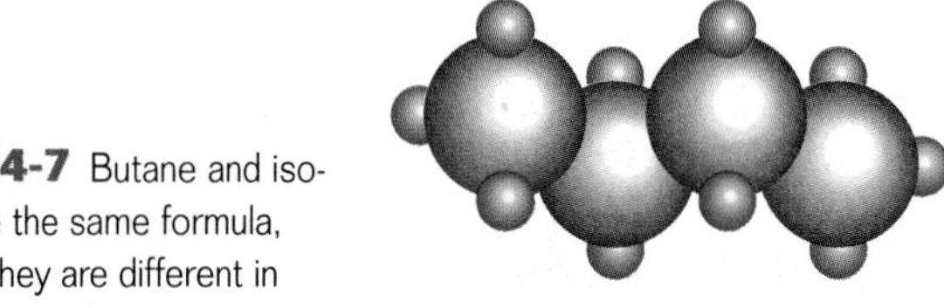

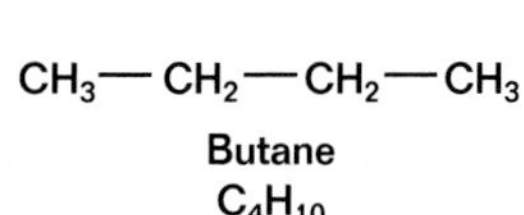

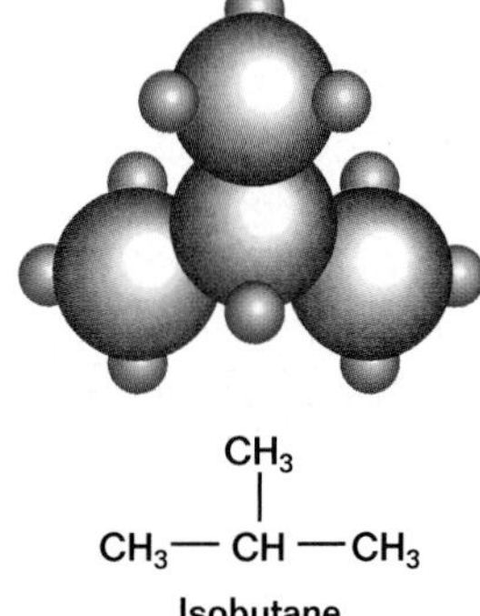

Figure 14-7 Butane and isobutane have the same formula, C_4H_{10}, but they are different in their structure and properties.

Caption Answers

Figure 14-6 *Combustion, or burning, is the combining of oxygen with another substance.*

Figure 14-8 *Cyclohexane contains two fewer hydrogen atoms.*

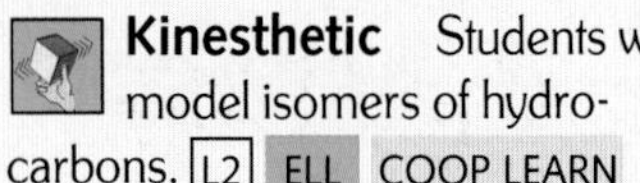

Try at Home MiniLab

Purpose

Kinesthetic Students will model isomers of hydrocarbons. L2 ELL COOP LEARN

Materials

round toothpicks (16) and enough modeling clay to make 17 small balls for each group

Teaching Strategies

- Have students sketch each isomer as they model it so that they don't model the same isomer more than once.
- Tell students that the chains of carbon atoms can bend, molecules can be flipped, and the longest chain is the parent chain. The following structures are all the same isomer.

```
CH3—CH2—CH—CH3
         |
         CH3

         CH3
         |
CH3—CH2—CH—CH3

CH3
|
CH—CH2—CH3
|
CH3
```

Analysis

1. There are three isomers of pentane and five of hexane.

Isomers of pentane:

```
CH3—CH2—CH2—CH2—CH3

              CH3
              |
     CH3—CH2—CH—CH3

   CH3
   |
CH3—C—CH3
   |
   CH3
```

Isomers of hexane:

```
CH3—CH2—CH2—CH2—CH2—CH3

              CH3
              |
     CH3—CH2—C—CH3
              |
              CH3

                  CH3
                  |
CH3—CH2—CH2—CH—CH3

         CH3
         |
CH3—CH2—CH—CH2—CH3

          CH3
          |
CH3—CH—CH—CH3
      |
      CH3
```

2. Yes, because there are more carbon atoms.

Process Have students compare isomers and make a final list of structures. Use **Performance Assessment in the Science Classroom,** p. 97.

have different chemical and physical properties. As the size of a hydrocarbon molecule increases, the possibilities for isomers also increase.

Reading Check

What is the same about isomers? What is different?

Answer to Reading Check

Their formulas are the same. Their structures are different.

Hydrocarbons in Rings

You may be thinking that all hydrocarbons are chains of carbon atoms with two ends. But, no rule states that a molecule must have two ends. Just as a rope can be tied together to form a loop, some molecules can occur in rings. You can see the structures of two different molecules in **Figure 14-8.** The carbon atoms bond together to form closed rings containing five and six carbons. The prefix *cyclo-* in their names tells you that the molecules are cyclic or ring shaped.

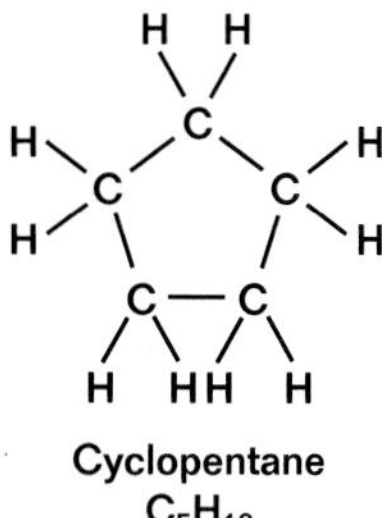

Cyclopentane
C_5H_{10}

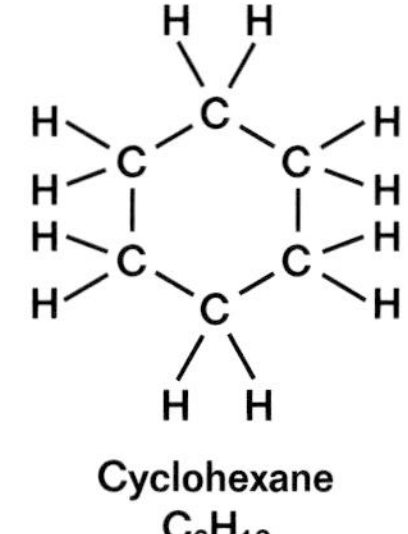

Cyclohexane
C_6H_{12}

Figure 14-8 Visualize a hydrogen plucked from the carbon atoms on both ends of a pentane or hexane chain. Then, the two end carbons form a bond with each other. **How does the formula for cyclohexane differ from the formula for hexane?**

Section Assessment

1. Explain the difference between a saturated hydrocarbon and an unsaturated hydrocarbon, and give an example of each.
2. From the structure of the carbon atom, explain the large number of compounds that can be formed by carbon.
3. **Think Critically:** Are propane and cyclopropane isomers? Use diagrams and formulas to explain your answer.
4. **Skill Builder**
Making and Using Graphs Make a graph using the information in **Table 14-1.** For each compound, plot the number of carbon atoms on the *x*-axis and the number of hydrogen atoms on the *y*-axis. Use your graph to predict the formula for the saturated hydrocarbon that has 11 carbon atoms. If you need help, refer to Making and Using Graphs in the **Skill Handbook** on page 717.

Using Math

The general formula for saturated hydrocarbons is C_nH_{2n+2} where *n* can be any whole number except zero. Use the general formula to determine the formula for a saturated hydrocarbon with 25 carbon atoms.

4. **Skill Builder**
Student graphs will result in a straight line. Locating 11 carbon atoms on the *x*-axis results in a corresponding *y* value of 24. The formula is $C_{11}H_{24}$. P

Assessment

Process Have students use their graphs to predict the formulas for the saturated hydrocarbons that contain five and seven carbon atoms. *C_5H_{12}, C_7H_{16}* Use **Performance Assessment in the Science Classroom,** p. 41.

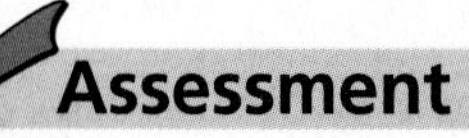

4 Close

Proficiency Prep

Use this quiz to check students' recall of section content.

1. **Most compounds that contain carbon are what type of compound?** *organic*
2. **What type of compound contains only carbon and hydrogen?** *hydrocarbon*
3. **What does the prefix *cyclo-* mean?** *ring-shaped*

Section Assessment

1. A saturated hydrocarbon, such as ethane, contains only single bonds. An unsaturated hydrocarbon, such as ethene, contains at least one double or triple bond.
2. Carbon atoms contain four outer-level electrons and will form four covalent bonds with other elements.
3. No, their formulas are different—C_3H_8 and C_3H_6.

Using Math

For $n = 25$,
$2n + 2 = 2(25) + 2 = 52.$
The formula is $C_{25}H_{52}$.

SECTION 14-2

Prepare

Refer to **Substituted Hydrocarbons** on p. 396E.

Preplanning

Refer to the **Chapter Organizer** on pp. 396A–B.

1 Motivate

Bellringer

Before presenting the lesson, display **Section Focus Transparency 38** on the overhead projector. Use the accompanying **Focus Activity** worksheet. L2 ELL

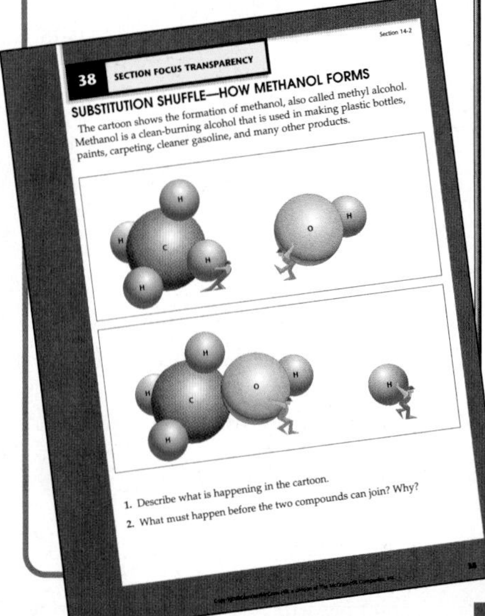

Section 14-2

38 SECTION FOCUS TRANSPARENCY

SUBSTITUTION SHUFFLE—HOW METHANOL FORMS

The cartoon shows the formation of methanol, also called methyl alcohol. Methanol is a clean-burning alcohol that is used in making plastic bottles, paints, carpeting, cleaner gasoline, and many other products.

1. Describe what is happening in the cartoon.
2. What must happen before the two compounds can join? Why?

Tying to Previous Knowledge

Students are familiar with a substitute being a replacement for what was originally there. Forming substituted hydrocarbons is a similar process.

14-2 Other Organic Compounds

What You'll Learn

- How new compounds are formed by substituting hydrocarbons
- The classes of compounds that result from substitution

Vocabulary
hydroxyl group
carboxyl group
amino group
amino acid

Why It's Important

- Many organic compounds that you use every day have been made by chemists.

Substituted Hydrocarbons

Suppose you pack an apple in your lunch every day. One day, you have no apples, so you substitute a pear. When you eat your lunch, you'll notice a difference in the taste and texture of your fruit. Chemists make substitutions, too. They change hydrocarbons to make compounds called substituted hydrocarbons. To make a substituted hydrocarbon, one or more hydrogen atoms are taken off and replaced by atoms such as the halogens, or by groups of atoms. Such changes result in compounds with chemical properties different from the original hydrocarbon. When one or more chlorine or fluorine atoms are added to methane in place of hydrogens, new compounds are formed like the ones in **Figure 14-9.**

Figure 14-9 Chlorine can replace from one to four of methane's hydrogen atoms.

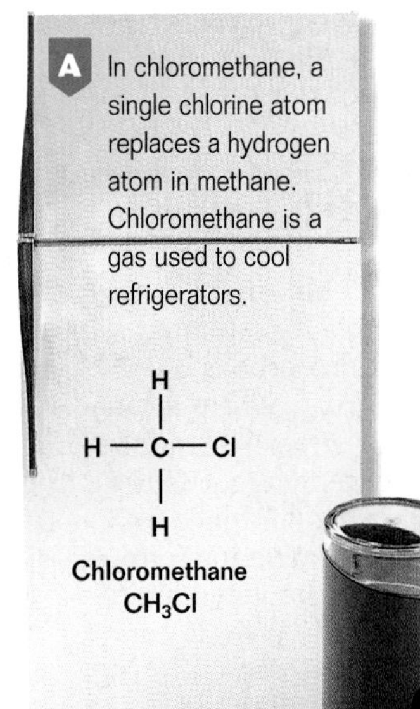

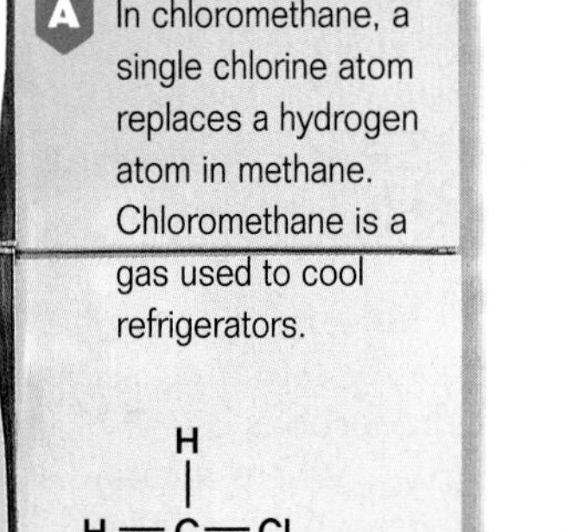

A In chloromethane, a single chlorine atom replaces a hydrogen atom in methane. Chloromethane is a gas used to cool refrigerators.

Chloromethane
CH_3Cl

C The trichloromethane, or chloroform, molecule has three chlorine atoms that replace hydrogen atoms in methane. Chloroform is used as a veterinary anesthetic

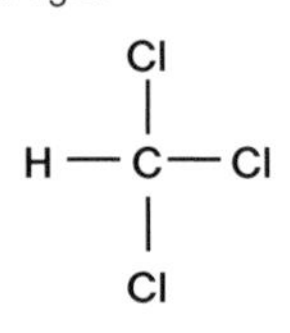

Trichloromethane or chloroform
$CHCl_3$

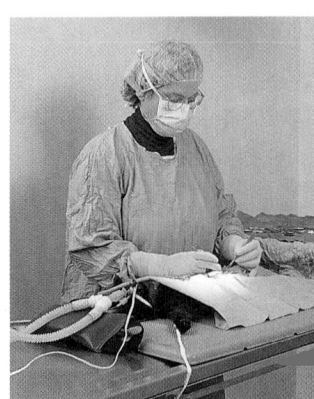

B Dichloromethane forms when two hydrogen atoms are replaced by chlorine atoms. Dichloromethane is a liquid used in manufacturing decaffeinated coffee.

Dichloromethane
CH_2Cl_2

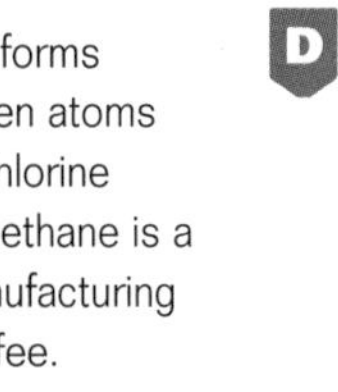

D Carbon tetrachloride is a fully substituted methane molecule. It is a poisonous substance that was formerly used as a dry-cleaning solvent.

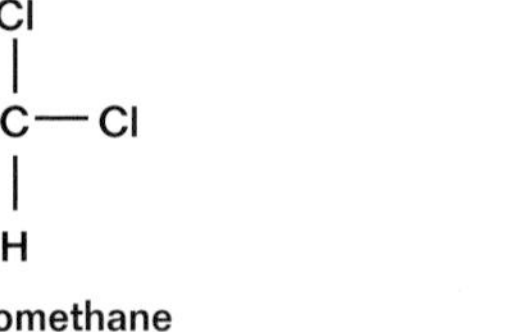

Carbon tetrachloride
CCl_4

Resource Manager

The following **Teacher Classroom Resources** can be used with Section 14-2:

 **Reproducible Masters**

Activity Worksheets, pp. 75–76 L2

Enrichment, p. 38 L3

Reinforcement, p. 38 L2

Study Guide, p. 55

 **Transparencies**

Teaching Transparency 27 L2

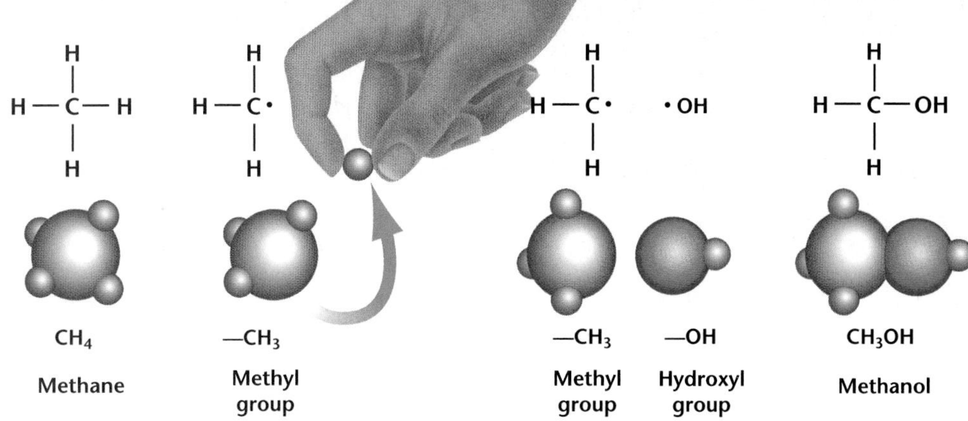

Alcohols

Groups of atoms also can be added to hydrocarbons to make different compounds. The **hydroxyl group** (hi DROX ul) is made up of an oxygen atom and a hydrogen atom joined by a covalent bond. It is represented by the formula –OH. When a hydroxyl group replaces a hydrogen atom in a hydrocarbon, an alcohol forms. **Figure 14-10** shows the formation of the alcohol methanol as a hydrogen in the methane molecule is replaced by a hydroxyl group.

Larger alcohol molecules are formed by adding more carbon atoms to the chain. Ethanol is an alcohol produced naturally when sugar in corn, grains, and fruit ferments. It is a combination of ethane and an –OH group. Isopropyl alcohol forms when the hydroxyl group is substituted for a hydrogen on the middle carbon of propane rather than one of the end carbons. You've probably used isopropyl alcohol to disinfect injuries. **Table 14-2** lists several alcohols with their structures and uses.

Figure 14-10 After the methane molecule loses one of its hydrogens, it has an extra electron to share, as does the hydroxyl group. **What kind of bond do they form?**

internet CONNECTION

Visit the Glencoe Science Web Site at **www.glencoe.com/sec/science** for more information about substituted hydrocarbons.

Table 14-2

Three Common Alcohols			
	Methanol	Ethanol	Isopropyl Alcohol
	H H—C—OH H	H H H—C—C—OH H H	H H H H—C—C—C—H H OH H
Uses			
Fuel	yes	yes	no
Cleaner	yes	yes	yes
Disinfectant	no	yes	yes
Manufacturing chemical	yes	yes	yes

2 Teach

Caption Answer
Figure 14-10 *covalent*

Flex Your Brain

Use the Flex Your Brain activity to have students explore ALCOHOL.

Content Background

Carboxylic acids were among the first groups of organic chemicals studied. Their common names were derived from their sources, not their structures. For example, formic acid (Latin *formica*, ant) is found in ant secretions and stings. Butyric acid (Latin *butyrum*, butter) is the acid that causes the smell of rancid butter. The six-, eight-, and ten-carbon acids were all discovered in goat fat and were given the names caproic, caprylic, and capric acids (Latin *caper*, goat).

internet CONNECTION

Internet Addresses

For Internet tips, see Glencoe's **Using the Internet in the Science Classroom.**

Science Journal

Functional Groups Tell students that the groups that can substitute for a hydrogen atom in a hydrocarbon are called functional groups. Have them investigate the meaning of the word *functional* and write a paragraph in which they infer why these groups were given this name. Function relates to use. Substituted hydrocarbons differ in use because they differ in properties. L2 P 

14-2 OTHER ORGANIC COMPOUNDS 405

GLENCOE TECHNOLOGY

Videodisc

The Infinite Voyage: Insects: The Ruling Class

Chapter 14 *Prospecting for Healing Medicine from Insects*

6:30

Refer to the Teacher Guide for bar codes and teaching strategies.

3 Assess

Check for Understanding

Discussion

Discuss with students the role of amines in the nitrogen cycle. All decaying animal tissues release amines into the environment. Ask students to explain how this release affects life. Amines provide essential nitrogen needed by plants and animals in a form they can use. L2

Reteach

Interpersonal Have groups of students prepare one set of index cards with names of types of substituted hydrocarbons and another set of cards with examples of formulas from the different groups. Have them play a game by laying down all the cards upside down. Each player turns over two cards and tries to match the name and formula for each group. If the two cards don't match, turn them back over, and it's the next person's turn. If they do match, the person who turned them over keeps the cards. When all the cards are gone, the player with the most cards wins. L1

COOP LEARN

Extension

For students who have mastered this section, use the **Reinforcement** and **Enrichment** masters.

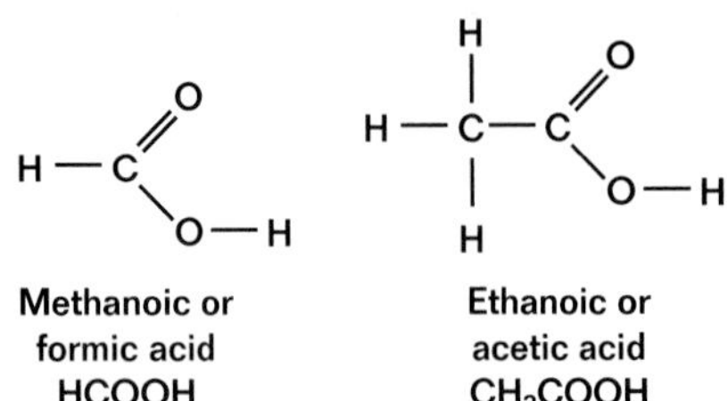

Figure 14-11 Ants make the simplest carboxylic acid, formic (methanoic) acid. **How do the structures of formic acid and acetic acid differ?**

Carboxylic Acids

Remember the reaction between vinegar and baking soda? The reactant in vinegar is acetic acid. You can think of acetic acid as the hydrocarbon methane with a carboxyl group substituted for a hydrogen. A **carboxyl group** (car BOX ul) consists of a carbon atom, two oxygen atoms, and a hydrogen atom. Its formula is –COOH. When a carboxyl group is substituted in a hydrocarbon, the substance formed is called a carboxylic acid. The simplest carboxylic acid is methanoic acid, commonly called formic acid. Formic acid consists of a single hydrogen atom and a carboxyl group. You can see the structures of formic acid and acetic acid in **Figure 14-11.** Some ants produce formic acid naturally. When they sting you, they inject formic acid into your skin.

You can probably guess that many other carboxylic acids are formed from longer hydrocarbons. Many carboxylic acids occur in foods. Citric acid is found in citrus fruits such as oranges and grapefruit. Lactic acid is present in milk.

Amines

Amines are a group of substituted hydrocarbons formed when an amino group replaces a hydrogen atom. An **amino group** (uh ME no) is a nitrogen atom joined by covalent bonds to two hydrogen atoms. It has the formula $-NH_2$. Methylamine, shown in **Figure 14-12,** is formed when one of the hydrogens in methane is replaced with an amino group. A more complex amine that you may have experienced is the novocaine your dentist uses to numb the pain of dental work. Amino groups are important because they are a part of many biological compounds.

Figure 14-12 Complex amines account for the strong smells of cheeses such as these, as well as the odor of other decaying organic matter.

Methylamine
CH_3NH_2

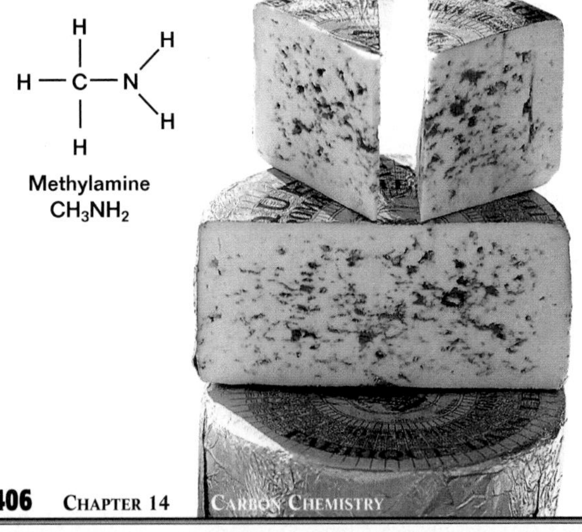

Amino Acids

You have seen that a group can be substituted onto one end of a chain to change the molecule. It's also possible to substitute groups on both ends of the chain, and even to replace hydrogen atoms bonded to carbon atoms in the middle of the chain. When both an amino group ($-NH_2$) and a carboxyl group (–COOH) replace hydrogens on the same carbon atom in a molecule, a

Caption Answer

Figure 14-11 *Acetic acid has a methyl group in place of a hydrogen atom in formic acid.*

special type of compound known as an amino acid is formed. **Amino acids** are the building blocks of proteins, which are an important class of biological molecules needed by living cells. Twenty different amino acids bond together in different combinations to form the variety of proteins that are needed in the human body. Glycine and alanine are shown in **Figure 14-13.** Glycine is the simplest amino acid. It is a methane molecule in which one hydrogen atom has been replaced by an amino group and another has been replaced by a carboxyl group. The other 19 amino acids are formed by replacing the highlighted hydrogen atom with different groups. For example, in alanine, the hydrogen atom is replaced by a methyl ($-CH_3$) group.

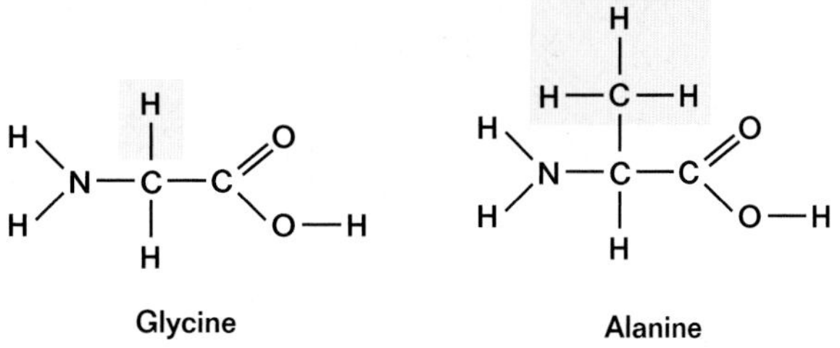

Glycine

Alanine

Figure 14-13 The amino acids glycine and alanine are the simplest building blocks of proteins.

Section Assessment

1. The nonstick coating found on some pots and pans is made from tetrafluoroethylene, a substituted hydrocarbon in which all four of the hydrogen atoms of ethylene are replaced by fluorine. Draw the structural formula for this molecule.
2. In what way is an amino acid different from a carboxylic acid?
3. How do the 20 amino acids differ from each other?
4. **Think Critically:** Both of the substituted hydrocarbons, chloromethane and dichloromethane, result from the replacement of hydrogen atoms with chlorine atoms. Predict which of these compounds will have the lower boiling point. Explain.
5. **Skill Builder**
Making Models A substituted hydrocarbon can be made by removing a hydrogen atom from a carbon and putting another atom or group in its place. Do the **Chapter 14 Skill Activity** on page 755 to make models of substituted hydrocarbons.

Using Computers

Word Processing Use the table function in a word processing program to make a table listing the classes of substituted hydrocarbons in this section: halogen-substituted hydrocarbons, alcohols, carboxylic acids, amines, and amino acids. List the substituted group(s) for each class and give the name and formula of a molecule that belongs in each class. If you need help, refer to page 732.

Using Computers

Classes of substituted hydrocarbons	Substituted group	Name of an example	Formula of an example
Halogen-substituted hydrocarbons	–F, –Cl, –Br, or –I	chloroethane	CH_3Cl
Alcohols	–OH	methanol	CH_3OH
Carboxylic acids	–COOH	methanoic acid	HCOOH
Amines	$-NH_2$	methylamine	CH_3NH_2
Amino acids	$-NH_2$, –COOH	glycine	CH_2NH_2COOH

4 Close

Proficiency Prep

Use this quiz to check students' recall of section content.

1. **What is a substituted hydrocarbon containing the hydroxyl group?** *an alcohol*
2. **What two groups does an amino acid contain?** *amino, carboxyl*
3. **What are the building blocks of proteins?** *amino acids*

Section Assessment

1. 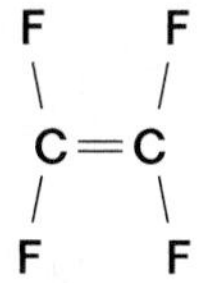 F₂C=CF₂ structure:

F F
C=C
F F

2. An amino acid has an amino group replacing a hydrogen atom; a carboxylic acid does not.
3. They differ in the hydrocarbon group attached to the carbon atom that has the acid and amino groups bonded to it.
4. **Think Critically** Chloromethane will have the lower boiling point because it has less mass.

Assessment

Process Have students compare their formulas and make a labeled display of one of each type of molecule. Use **Performance Assessment in the Science Classroom,** p. 51. P

Activity 14•1

Purpose

Logical-Mathematical Students will recognize changes that can occur in an organic compound. L2 ELL COOP LEARN

Process Skills

observing and inferring, measuring in SI, recognizing cause and effect, classifying

Time

30 minutes

Safety Precautions

Caution students against spilling, skin contact, or inhaling fumes of any chemicals used. If a spill does occur, immediately rinse with water.

Solutions with a pH between 6.0 and 8.0 may be poured down a drain. If pH is below 6.0 add NaOH until pH 7.0 is reached.

Dilute $KMnO_4$ solution with water before pouring down the drain.

Teaching Strategies

- Prepare 0.01 *M* $KMnO_4$ solution by dissolving 0.16 g $KMnO_4$ in 100 mL of distilled water.
- Prepare 6.0*M* NaOH solution by dissolving 24 g of solid NaOH in 100 mL of distilled water. The NaOH solution becomes hot during its preparation. Prepare it only in a heat-resistant glass container. Prepare well ahead of use so that it has time to cool.
- Dispense NaOH in dropper bottles. Tell students how many drops equal 1 mL.
- Use at least 90 percent ethanol. Ninety percent ethanol can be purchased in most pharmacies. If 70 percent ethanol is used, increase the amount.
- If students have difficulty getting the pH paper into the liquid, have them dip a glass stirring rod into the mixture and touch it to the paper.

Activity 14•1 Using Scientific Methods

Conversion of Alcohols

Materials

- Test tube and stopper
- Test-tube rack
- Potassium permanganate solution (1 mL)
- Sodium hydroxide solution (1 mL)
- Ethanol (3 drops)
- pH test paper
- Graduated cylinder

Wine will spoil when the ethanol it contains is exposed to air and the bacteria *Acetabactor.* Is this spoilage a chemical change?

What You'll Investigate

What changes occur when ethanol is exposed to conditions like those produced by exposure to air and bacteria?

Goals

- **Observe** a chemical change in an alcohol.
- **Infer** the product of the chemical change.

Procedure

Wash your hands after completing the experiment.

1. Measure 1 mL of potassium permanganate solution and pour it into a test tube. Measure 1 mL of sodium hydroxide solution and add it to the test tube. **CAUTION:** *Handle these chemicals with care. Immediately flush any spills with water and call your teacher.*
2. **Dip** a piece of pH paper into the mixture in the test tube. **Record** the result in your Science Journal.
3. **Add** three drops of ethanol to the test tube. Put a stopper on the test tube and gently **shake** it for one minute.
4. Place the test tube in a test-tube rack and **observe** what happens. Record any changes you notice during the next five minutes.
5. **Test** the sample with pH paper again. **Record** what you observe.
6. **Dispose** of the solutions as directed by your teacher.

Conclude and Apply

1. Did a chemical reaction take place? What leads you to **infer** this?
2. Alcohols may undergo a chemical reaction to form carboxylic acids in the presence of potassium permanganate. If the alcohol used is ethanol, what would you **predict** to be the chemical formula of the acid produced?

Alcohol Conversion

Procedure Step	Observations
Step 2	pH is greater than 7.
Step 4	Purple color fades.
Step 5	pH is less than 7.

- Point out to students that the pH measurements showed that the solution was basic but became acidic.

Answers to Questions

1. The color changes from purple to green to brown, indicating a chemical reaction.
2. CH_3COOH

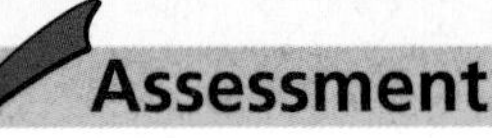

Assessment

Oral If the formulas of an acid and an alcohol are written as C_3H_8O and $C_3H_6O_2$, have students explain how to determine which formula is for the acid and which is for the alcohol. *Organic acids all must have at least two oxygen atoms.* Use **Performance Assessment in the Science Classroom,** p. 17.

NATIONAL GEOGRAPHIC

Science & Society

Nature's Medicines and the Organic Chemist

Nature's Medicine Chest

Plants have long been used as sources of medicine. Ancient Egyptian, Chinese, and Indian writings describe many plant-based treatments for diseases of the eyes, skin, and internal organs. In the inset, a thirteenth-century Arabic manuscript shows six healing herbs. Sap of both the piñon pine (left) and ponderosa pine tree was used by Native Americans to prevent infection in wounds.

Tree Bark to Drugstore

A chemical compound called quinine is found in the bark of the Cinchona tree. Long before Europeans arrived in the New World, native people in the Andes mountain region of South America used Cinchona bark to treat malaria, a disease that still afflicts millions of people worldwide. Around 1630, Jesuit priests in Peru learned from their native neighbors how to grind the bark and mix it with water to make an effective malaria remedy. For centuries, Cinchona bark was the world's only weapon against malaria.

Advances in organic chemistry have made it possible to synthesize, or put together, many medicinal compounds obtained from plants. In 1908, chemists identified the chemical formula of quinine as $C_{20}H_{24}N_2O_2$, but it wasn't until 1944 that quinine was synthesized in the laboratory.

The Search Continues

Today, the search goes on for new medicines derived from plants. When a plant compound shows promise in treating a disease, chemists often use computer models to help figure out its structure. Then, they try to synthesize that compound in the laboratory. The new medicine must then be tested for safety and effectiveness—a process that can take many years before the medicine reaches your local drugstore.

interNET CONNECTION

Visit the Glencoe Science Web Site at **www.glencoe.com/sec/science** to find more information about taxol, aspirin, and codeine. Prepare a presentation that includes the identity of the natural remedy and the medicine's uses.

Teaching Strategies

- Have students use library and Internet resources to find information about medicinal herbs such as ginseng, echinacea, and wolfbane. Have them list some of the uses of the herbs they find and present their findings as a poster.
- Have students investigate the discovery of penicillin in 1928, which ushered in the age of antibiotics. Have them write a paragraph summarizing their findings.
- Bacteria are becoming more and more resistant to antibiotics because antibiotics are being used too often, sometimes when they are not needed. Discuss what the increasing virulence of some bacteria could mean and what might be done to ensure that doctors have the means to stop infections. Students may suggest that organic chemists need to be constantly looking for new, more effective antibiotics and doctors need to prescribe an antibiotic only when there is a need.

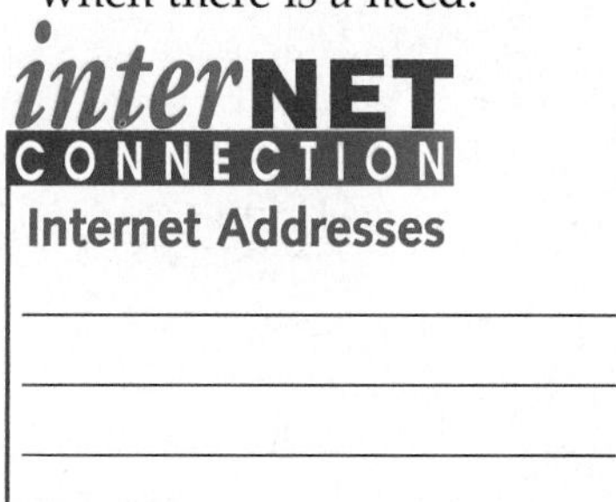

interNET CONNECTION

Internet Addresses

For Internet tips, see Glencoe's **Using the Internet in the Science Classroom.**

Content Background

Organic chemists worked 25 years to synthesize quinine and, thereby, confirm its structure. Commercial synthesis of quinine proved too difficult to be feasible, so chemists used the quinine structure as a model for synthesizing other molecules with similar features. Some of these synthesized molecules are even more effective than quinine because they eliminate the parasite that causes malaria throughout the body. Quinine reaches only the parasites in red blood cells and, consequently, relapses are common for patients treated with quinine only.

For More Information

Food and Drug Administration
5600 Fishers Lane
Rockville, MD 20857

Prepare

Refer to **What's a polymer?, Polymerization Processes,** and **Cholesterol** on p. 396F.

Preplanning

Refer to the **Chapter Organizer** on pp. 396A–B.

1 Motivate

Bellringer

Before presenting the lesson, display **Section Focus Transparency 39** on the overhead projector. Use the accompanying **Focus Activity** worksheet. L2 ELL

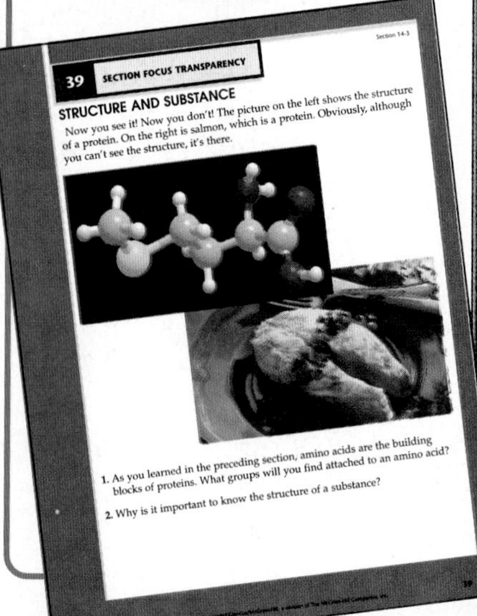

Tying to Previous Knowledge

Students are familiar with proteins, carbohydrates, and fats. They will learn the differences in the compositions of these compounds.

14-3 Biological Compounds

What You'll Learn

- How large organic molecules are made
- The roles of organic molecules in the body
- Why eating the recommended amounts of certain foods is important for maintaining health

Vocabulary

polymer, carbohydrate, protein, lipid

Why It's Important

- Your diet may affect how you feel.

What's a polymer?

Now that you know about some simple organic molecules, you can begin to learn about more complex biological molecules. These are organic substances found in milk, muscle, and blood, and some common materials such as the nonstick coating on a frying pan or the nylon in your jacket. All of these substances contain large molecules called polymers. A **polymer** is a molecule made up of many small organic molecules that link up with each other to form a long chain. The name polymer comes from the Greek words *poly,* which means "many," and *meros,* which means "part."

In **Figure 14-14,** you can see what happens in the polymerization of ethylene. Polymerization (pah lih mer i ZAY shun) is a chemical reaction that occurs between many small molecules when they link to form long chains. The ethylene molecule, C_2H_4, is an unsaturated hydrocarbon, so there is a double bond between the carbon atoms. One of the bonds in the double bond breaks in each ethylene molecule. The two carbon atoms then form new bonds with carbon atoms in other ethylene molecules. This process goes on as a chain reaction that results in the formation of a much larger molecule called polyethylene. It is a polymer that is used to make many products, such as plastic bottles. Polyethylene is an example of a synthetic polymer, but many polymers occur naturally. Some of them play important roles in keeping your body healthy.

Figure 14-14 Small molecules link into long chains to form polymers.

A The carbon atoms that were joined by the double bond each have an electron to share with another carbon in another molecule of ethylene.

B The process goes on until a huge molecule is formed.

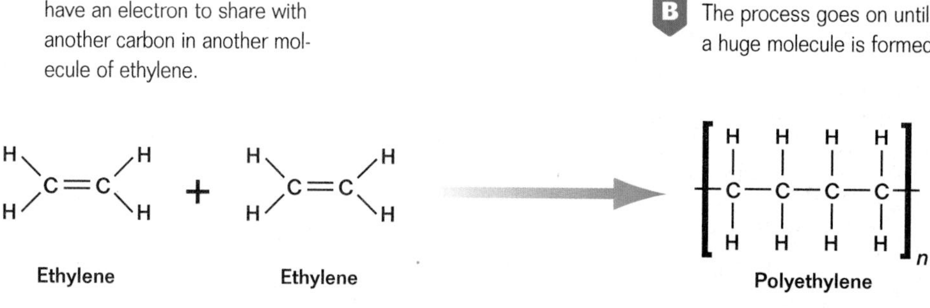

Resource Manager

The following **Teacher Classroom Resources** can be used with Section 14-3:

Reproducible Masters

Activity Worksheets, pp. 77–78, 80 L2
Critical Thinking/Problem Solving, p. 14 L2
Enrichment, p. 39 L3
Laboratory Manual, pp. 77–86 L2
Multicultural Connections, pp. 27–28 L2
Reinforcement, p. 39 L2
Study Guide, pp. 55–56 L1 ELL

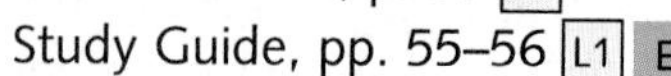

Transparencies

Teaching Transparency 28 L2
Science Integration Transparency 14 L2

Proteins Are Polymers

You've probably heard about proteins when you've been urged to eat healthy foods. A **protein** is a polymer that consists of a chain of individual amino acids linked together. Your body cannot function properly without them. Proteins serve as catalysts and speed up chemical reactions in cells. Some proteins make up the structural materials in ligaments, tendons, muscles, cartilage, hair, and fingernails. Hemoglobin, which carries substances through the blood, is a protein.

The different functions in your body are performed by different proteins. Your body makes many of these proteins by assembling 20 amino acids in different ways. Eight of the amino acids that are needed to make proteins cannot be produced by your body. These amino acids, which are called essential amino acids, must come from the food you eat. That's why you need to eat a diet containing protein-rich foods, like those in **Figure 14-15.**

Try at Home

MiniLab

Summing Up Protein

Procedure

1. Make a list of the foods you ate during the last 24 hours.
2. Use the data your teacher gives you to find the total number of grams of protein in your diet for the day. Multiply the grams of protein in one unit of food by the number of units of food you ate.

Analysis

1. The recommended daily allowance (RDA) of protein for girls, 11 to 14 years old, is 46 g per day. For boys, 11 to 14 years old, the RDA is 48 g per day. Was your total greater or less than the RDA?
2. Which of the foods you ate supplied the largest amount of protein? What percent of the total did that food supply?

Figure 14-15 Your body can't make eight of the amino acids needed for making proteins. **How can you be sure that you aren't missing any proteins?**

Approximately one-half of our non-water mass consists of proteins. One-half of these proteins is enzymes.

Caption Answer

Figure 14-15 *Eat a varied diet.*

Try at Home

MiniLab

For additional help doing this activity at home, see the corresponding pages in the **Home Involvement** booklet.

Purpose

Intrapersonal Students will determine whether their diets for the day provided them with the Recommended Daily Amount of protein. L3 ELL

Materials

table of protein-containing foods

Food	Protein
1 ounce meat, poultry, fish, or cheese	7 g
1 egg	7 g
1 cup milk or yogurt	8 g
½ cup peas or beans	6 g
2 tablespoons peanut butter	9 g
1 cup rice or pasta	6 g
1 potato, baked with skin	5 g
1 cup cooked vegetables	4 g
1 slice bread	3 g

Assessment

Content Have groups of students make up poems or songs about the power of protein to keep them healthy. Use **Performance Assessment in the Science Classroom,** p. 25.

Teaching Strategies

- The day before the MiniLab, have students make a list of the foods they eat and how much.
- Help them estimate the size of portions. Tell them a hamburger patty is about 3 ounces of beef.

Analysis

1. Student responses will vary.
2. Student responses will vary.

Caption Answers

Figure 14-16 *water*

Figure 14-17 *Carbohydrates contain a lot of energy that can be stored to provide energy for the race.*

Answer to Reading Check

The amino group of the one amino acid molecule bonds with the carboxyl group of another amino acid molecule, and a molecule of water is released.

Quick Demo

Show that carbohydrates are basically atoms of carbon and the atoms of water molecules bonded together. Place a 250-mL beaker in an operating fume hood. Add approximately 50 mL of sucrose (table sugar) to the beaker. Slowly add about 25 mL of concentrated sulfuric acid. Sulfuric acid is a dehydrating agent, which is a material that will remove water from another substance. The acid removes the water from the sugar, and carbon remains. Students will observe clouds of steam escaping and a column of black carbon forming in the beaker. After the reaction, allow students to have a close look at the carbon, but without touching. **CAUTION:** *Wear goggles, apron, and protective gloves. Be sure students are at least 3 m from the demonstration.*

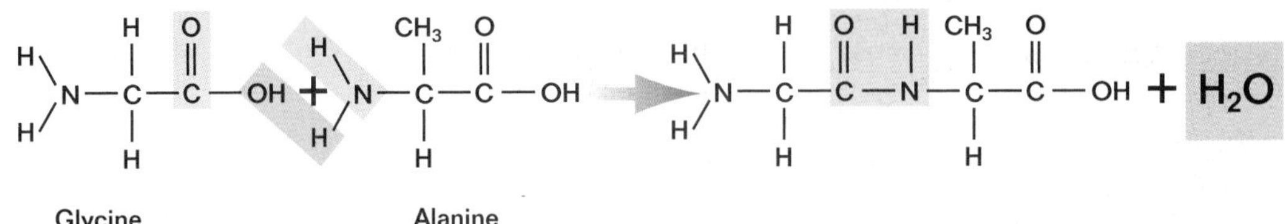

Figure 14-16 Both ends of an amino acid can link with another amino acid. **What molecule is released in the process?**

The process by which your body converts amino acids to proteins is shown in **Figure 14-16.** In this reaction, the amino group of the amino acid alanine forms a bond with the carboxyl group of the amino acid glycine, and a molecule of water is released. Each end of this new molecule can go on to form similar bonds with another amino acid. The process continues in this way until the amino acid chain, or protein, is complete.

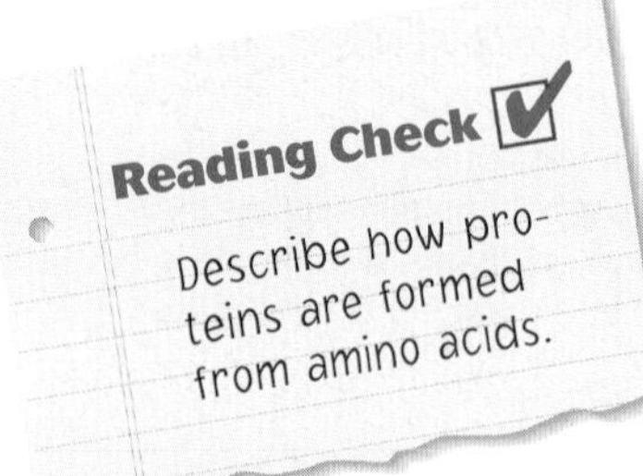

Reading Check
Describe how proteins are formed from amino acids.

Carbohydrates

The day before a race, marathon runners like the ones in **Figure 14-17** often eat large amounts of pasta. What's in pasta and other foods like bread and fruit that makes them good choices for prerace eating? These foods contain sugars and starches, which are members of the family of organic compounds called carbohydrates. A **carbohydrate** is an organic compound that contains only carbon, hydrogen, and oxygen in a ratio of two hydrogen atoms to one oxygen atom and one carbon atom. In the body, carbohydrates are broken down into simple sugars that the body can use for energy. In effect, the marathon runners are storing energy for the next day's race.

Figure 14-17 These athletes are eating a meal high in carbohydrates. **How will this help them in the next day's race?**

Multiple Learning Styles

Kinesthetic To help students see the relationship between a polymer and a monomer, have students clip one spring-type clothespin onto the leg of another one. Continue this process to form a polymer chain. If clothespins are not available, paper clips can be used.

412 CHAPTER 14 CARBON CHEMISTRY

Sugars

If you like chocolate-chip cookies or ice cream, then you're familiar with sugars. They are the substances that make both fresh fruit and candy sweet. Simple sugars are carbohydrates containing five, six, or seven carbon atoms arranged in a ring. The structures of glucose and fructose, two common simple sugars, are shown in **Figure 14-18.** Glucose forms a six-carbon ring. It is found in many naturally sweet foods, such as grapes.

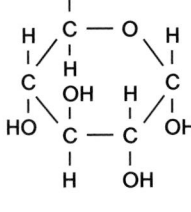

Glucose

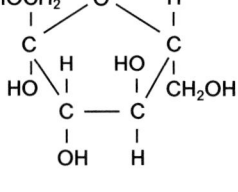

Fructose

Figure 14-18 Glucose and fructose are simple six-carbon carbohydrates found in many fresh foods and in packaged foods. **Name some products that contain these sugars.**

Problem Solving

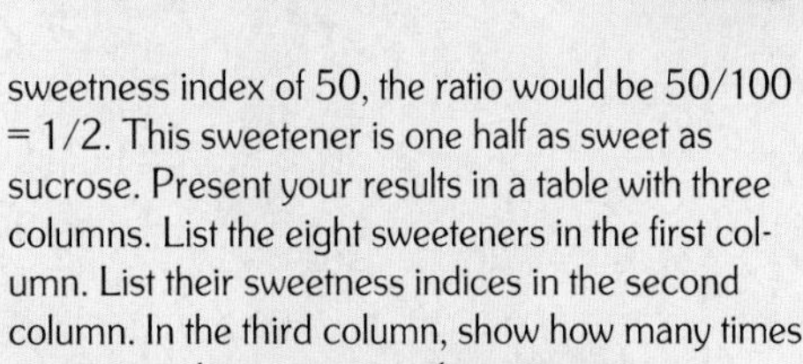

Comparing Sweetness

There are natural sugars, and there are artificial sweeteners. Natural sugars include sucrose, glucose, fructose, maltose, and lactose. Artificial sweeteners are compounds unrelated to sugars. They include saccharin, aspartame, and acesulfame. They are not all equally sweet. If you taste equal amounts of aspartame and sucrose, the aspartame will taste 200 times sweeter than sucrose. Assume sucrose has a sweetness index of 100. A sweetness index is a measure of how sweet a compound is. Compared with sucrose, other sweeteners have the following sweetness indices: glucose, 70; fructose, 170; maltose, 30; lactose, 16; saccharin, 40 000; aspartame, 20 000; acesulfame, 20 000.

Solve the Problem

1. Determine how many times sweeter than sucrose each sweetener is. You can figure this out by taking the ratio of the sweetness index of any sweetener to the sweetness index of sucrose. For example, aspartame's sweetness index is 20 000. The ratio of 20 000/100 = 200, so aspartame is 200 times sweeter than sucrose. For a sweetener with a sweetness index of 50, the ratio would be 50/100 = 1/2. This sweetener is one half as sweet as sucrose. Present your results in a table with three columns. List the eight sweeteners in the first column. List their sweetness indices in the second column. In the third column, show how many times sweeter each sweetener is than sucrose.
2. Make a bar graph that compares the sweetness indices of the sweeteners.
3. Which sugar is the sweetest? Which artificial sweetener is the sweetest?
4. How much maltose would match the sweetness of one teaspoon of sucrose?

Think Critically: Why might a person choose to use an artificial sweetener rather than a natural sugar?

Integrating the Sciences

Life Science Chitin is a structural carbohydrate that makes up the tough outer skeletons of arthropods such as lobsters, beetles, and other insects. Chitin is one of the most abundant natural polymers on Earth because of the large number of insects that produce it. The basic unit of chitin is similar to glucose but has a side chain containing an amide group like the connecting link between amino acids in proteins.

Caption Answer

Figure 14-18 *Answers might include some ice cream and soft drinks. Read product labels.*

Problem Solving

1.

Sweetener	Sweetness index	Sweetness compared to sucrose
Sucrose	100	1
Glucose	70	$\frac{7}{10}$
Fructose	170	$1\frac{7}{10}$
Maltose	30	$\frac{3}{10}$
Lactose	16	$\frac{4}{25}$
Saccharin	40 000	400
Aspartame	20 000	200
Acesulfame	20 000	200

2. Student graphs should show that the sweetness indexes of the sugars are so low compared to those of artificial sweeteners that they don't even show on the graph.
3. fructose, saccharin
4. $3\frac{1}{3}$ teaspoons

Think Critically

Student answers might include that some people, such as diabetics and hypoglycemics, are restricted in the amount of sugar they can eat. Also, artificial sweeteners contain fewer Calories for those people who need to limit the number of Calories ingested.

Caption Answer

Figure 14-19 *water*

Teacher FYI

The chief form in which carbohydrates are stored in plants is starch. In animals, it is glycogen.

Using Science Words

Point out to students that the chemical formula for each carbohydrate is a multiple of the formula CH_2O, or carbon plus water. This formula is the basis of the word *carbohydrate.*

Enrichment

Visual-Spatial Have students examine food labels and compile a list of the sugars they find. Sugars can be recognized by an *-ose* suffix. Students will probably find maltose or lactose that they were unaware were sugars. Discuss the following questions. Did any labels state "no added sugar," yet contain sugars? How could such labeling be dangerous for someone with a sugar control problem, such as diabetes? L2

GLENCOE TECHNOLOGY

Videodisc

Glencoe Science Voyages Interactive Videodisc—Physical

Side 2, Lesson 5 *Carbohydrates and Hydrocarbons*

994

1643

Refer to the Videodisc Teacher Guide for additional bar codes.

Sucrose

Figure 14-19 Sucrose is a molecule of glucose combined with a molecule of fructose. **What small molecule must be added to sucrose when it separates to form the two six-carbon sugars?**

Fructose is the sweet substance found in ripe fruit and honey. It is often made into corn syrup and added to many foods as a sweetener. The sugar you probably have in your sugar bowl or use in baking a cake is sucrose. Sucrose, shown in **Figure 14-19,** is a combination of the two simple sugars glucose and fructose. In the body, sucrose cannot move through cell membranes. It must be broken down into glucose and fructose to enter cells. Inside the cell, these simple sugars are broken down further to provide energy for cell functions.

Starches

Starches are large carbohydrates that exist naturally in grains such as rice, wheat, and corn. Starches are polymers of glucose molecules in which hundreds or thousands of sugar molecules may be joined together. Because each sugar molecule releases energy when it is broken down, starches are sources of large amounts of energy.

Figure 14-20 Your body cannot break down long cellulose fibers on celery, but your health can benefit from eating a certain amount of fiber.

Other Glucose Polymers

Two other important polymers that are made up of glucose molecules are cellulose and glycogen. Cellulose is a polymer that consists of long chains of glucose units linked together. This structure results in long, stiff fibers that make up the walls of plant cells, like the strands that pull off the celery stalk in **Figure 14-20.** Glycogen is a polymer that also contains chains of glucose units, but the chains are highly branched. Glycogen molecules are found in animal tissue where their function is to store energy. Although starch, cellulose, and glycogen are all polymers of glucose, humans can't use all of them as sources of energy. The human digestive system can't convert cellulose into sugars. Grazing animals, such as cows, have special digestive systems that allow them to break down cellulose polymer into sugars.

Content Background

Starch and cellulose differ in the orientation of the bond between the glucose subunits. Animals can't break the bonds in cellulose. However, microorganisms in the digestive tracts of cattle can digest cellulose. The presence of these microorganisms allows these animals to use cellulose as an energy source.

Lipids

Many of the foods you eat contain lipids, for example, butter, salad dressings, ice cream, cheese, meat, and potato chips. A **lipid** is an organic compound that contains the same elements as carbohydrates—carbon, hydrogen, and oxygen—but in different proportions. They are composed of three long-chain carboxylic acids bonded to an alcohol called glycerol that has three –OH groups. Lipids are commonly called fats and oils, but they also are found in greases and waxes like the beeswax in **Figure 14-21.**

Lipids Store Energy

Lipids store energy in their bonds, just as carbohydrates do, but they are a more concentrated source of energy than carbohydrates. If you eat more food than your body needs to supply the energy for your usual activities, the excess energy from the food is stored by producing lipids.

How can energy be stored in a molecule? The chemical reaction that produces lipids is endothermic. An endothermic reaction is one in which energy is absorbed. That means that energy is stored in the chemical bonds of lipids. When your body needs energy, the bonds are broken and energy is released. This process protects your body in times when you need extra energy or in times when you may not be able to eat. If you regularly eat more food than you need, large amounts of lipids will be produced and stored as permanent fat on your body.

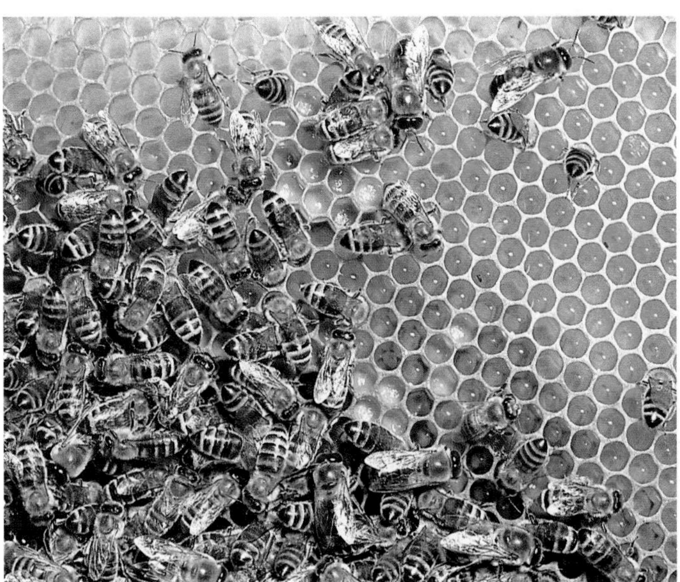

Figure 14-21 Fats and oils are not the only kinds of lipids. Wax is a lipid that is harder than fat. Bees secrete wax from a gland in the abdomen to form beeswax, which is part of the honeycomb.

interNET CONNECTION

Visit the Glencoe Science Web Site at **www.glencoe.com/sec/science** for more information about lipids.

Using Math

One gram of carbohydrates releases 4 Calories of energy and 1 g of lipids releases 9 Calories. If your daily diet provides 400 g of carbohydrates and 100 g of lipids, how many Calories of energy will be available to you?

Using Math

(400 g × 4 Cal/g) + (100 g × 9 Cal/g) = 1600 Cal + 900 Cal = 2500 Cal

Content Background

Unsaturated fats can be turned into saturated fats by a process known as hydrogenation. Nickel is often the catalyst used for this reaction.

interNET CONNECTION

Internet Addresses

For Internet tips, see Glencoe's **Using the Internet in the Science Classroom.**

GLENCOE TECHNOLOGY

Videodisc

The Infinite Voyage: A Taste of Health

Chapter 3 *Consequences of a Fatty Diet* 3:00

Refer to the Teacher Guide for bar codes and teaching strategies.

Inclusion Strategies

Gifted Pheromones are chemicals used for communication among animals of the same species. Have students use library or Internet sources to investigate pheromones. **What are some examples of animals using pheromones to communicate?** *ants leaving a trail to food and communication among bees* **How do pheromones relate to polymers?** *Many pheromones are formed from polymers.* L3

3 Assess

Check for Understanding

Discussion

Explain to students that the bodies of caribou, which are arctic animals, contain fats that are saturated. However, the lower parts of their legs contain many unsaturated fats. **Why is it beneficial for the caribou's lower legs to contain unsaturated, rather than saturated, fat?** *Unsaturated fats remain liquid at low temperatures. They allow the caribou's feet and legs to function properly at low temperatures.*

Reteach

Visual-Spatial Show students a copy of a food pyramid. Discuss with them why certain types of foods are present in the quantities and locations found in the pyramid. L2

Extension

For students who have mastered this section, use the **Reinforcement** and **Enrichment** masters.

4 Close

Proficiency Prep

Use this quiz to check students' recall of section content.

1. **What three elements make up lipids and carbohydrates?** *C, H, O*
2. **What group of compounds consists of sugars and starches?** *carbohydrates*
3. **What kind of molecule is formed by polymerization of amino acids?** *protein*

Saturated and Unsaturated Lipids

Not all lipids are the same. Remember the difference between saturated and unsaturated hydrocarbons? Unsaturated molecules have one or more double or triple bonds between carbon atoms. Lipid molecules may be saturated or unsaturated. As you can see in **Figure 14-22A,** when a lipid is saturated, the acid chains are straight because all the bonds are single bonds. They are able to pack together closely. A compact arrangement of the molecules is typical of a solid. These solid lipids are called saturated fats.

When a lipid is unsaturated, as in **Figure 14-22B,** the molecule bends wherever there is a double bond. This prevents the chains from packing close together, so these lipids tend to be liquid oils. They are called unsaturated fats.

Scientists and doctors have observed that people who eat a diet high in saturated fats have a high rate of cardiovascular problems such as heart disease. Fortunately, many foods containing both saturated and unsaturated fats are available so that you can choose the foods you want to include in your diet.

Figure 14-22 Whether a lipid is a liquid or a solid depends on the type of bonds.

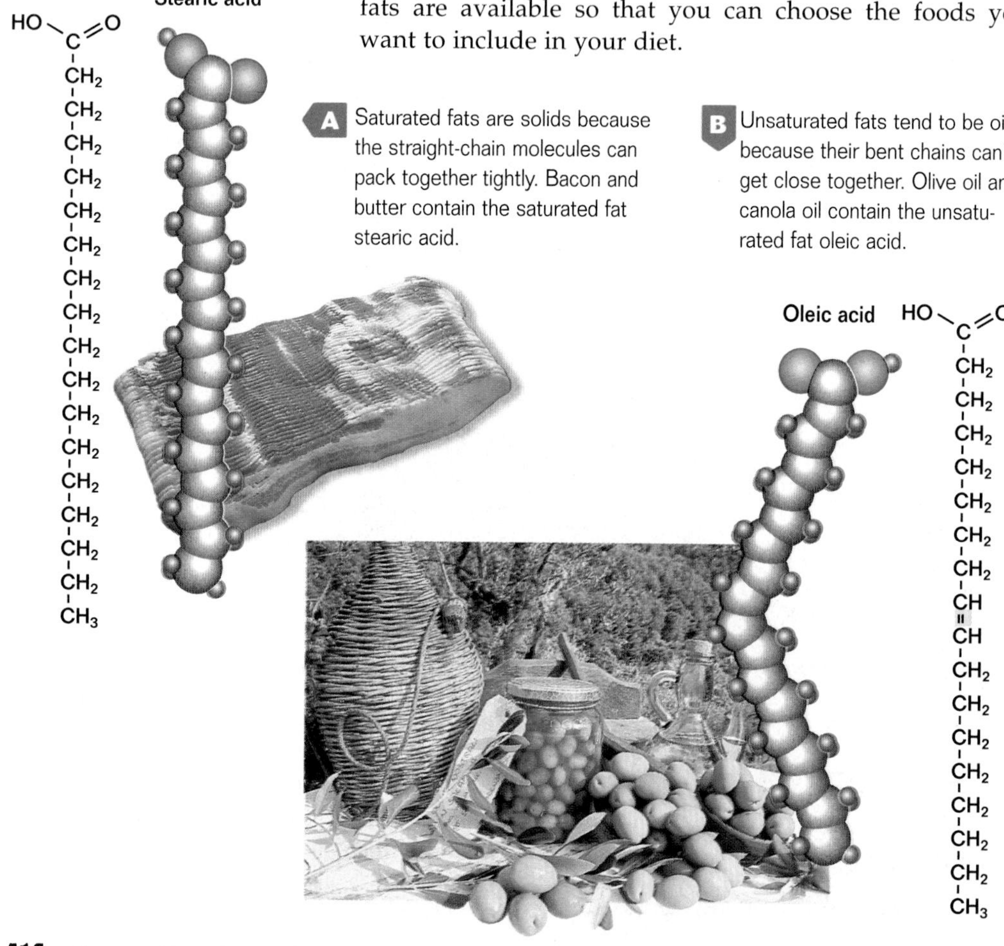

A Saturated fats are solids because the straight-chain molecules can pack together tightly. Bacon and butter contain the saturated fat stearic acid.

B Unsaturated fats tend to be oils because their bent chains can't get close together. Olive oil and canola oil contain the unsaturated fat oleic acid.

416 CHAPTER 14 CARBON CHEMISTRY

Cholesterol

Cholesterol is a complex lipid present in foods that come from animals, such as fatty meat, butter, eggs, and cheese. Even if you don't eat foods containing cholesterol, your body makes its own supply. Your body needs cholesterol for building cell membranes. Cholesterol is not found in plants, so oils derived from plants are free of cholesterol. However, the body can convert fats in these oils to cholesterol.

High cholesterol levels in the blood can lead to the buildup of deposits of cholesterol on the inside walls of arteries. This condition, known as atherosclerosis, is shown in **Figure 14-23.** When arteries become clogged, the flow of blood is restricted, which results in high blood pressure. This, in turn, can lead to heart disease. Eating less saturated fat and cholesterol can help to lower cholesterol levels in the blood and reduce the risk of heart problems.

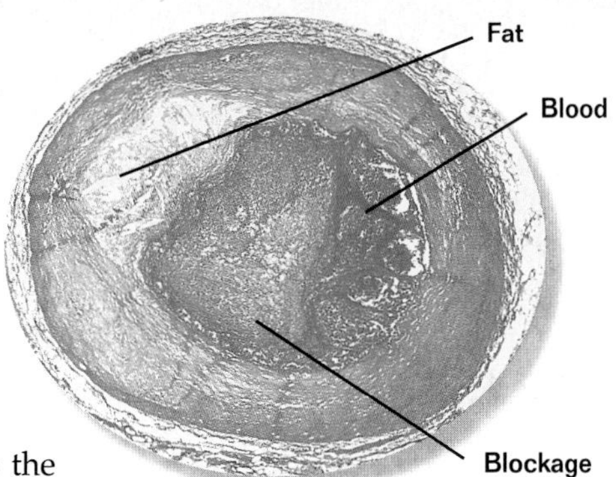

Figure 14-23 This view of an artery shows atherosclerosis, a dangerous condition in which arteries in the body become clogged. Deposits build up on the walls of the artery leaving less room for blood to flow.

Section Assessment

1. Describe the process by which large organic molecules such as proteins are made. What other product is formed along with a protein molecule?
2. Identify some of the roles of carbohydrates, proteins, and lipids in the functioning of your body.
3. How are cellulose and glycogen different from sugars and starches?
4. **Think Critically:** Explain why even people who eat a healthy diet may gain weight if they don't get enough exercise.
5. **Skill Builder**
   Forming a Hypothesis A chemist who planned to do experiments on refrigerants opened a valve on a tank that was supposed to contain the gas tetrafluoroethylene. He was surprised to find that no gas was released. When he opened the tank, he found a waxy, white solid. Form a hypothesis about how this white solid came to be inside the tank and what happened to the gas. If you need help, refer to Forming a Hypothesis in the **Skill Handbook** on page 722.

In your Science Journal, make a record of all the foods you eat during one day. Write a paragraph identifying the foods that contain proteins, carbohydrates (identify both starches and sugars), and lipids.

Section Assessment

1. The amino group from one amino acid combines with the carboxyl group from another amino acid to form a protein. Water is also formed.
2. Carbohydrates are broken down into simple sugars that the body can use for energy. Proteins serve as catalysts in chemical reactions in cells; make up structure in ligaments, tendons, muscles, cartilage, hair, and fingernails; and form hemoglobin. Lipids store energy until it is needed and are used for building cell membranes.
3. Cellulose and glycogen are more complex and more difficult to break down and use.
4. **Think Critically** If more food energy is taken in than is used, the person will gain weight.

Students could need additional help identifying what is contained in various foods. Emphasize that many foods will contain more than one category.

5. **Skill Builder**
   Student hypotheses could include that the gas underwent a polymerization reaction, forming a polymer that is a waxy, white solid.

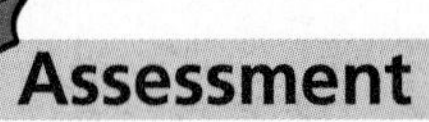

Assessment

Performance Have students use gumdrops and toothpicks to model the polymerization reaction mentioned in the Skill Builder. Use one color of gumdrop for carbon atoms and another color for fluorine atoms. Use **Performance Assessment in the Science Classroom,** p. 51.

Activity 14·2 Design Your Own Experiment

Recognize the Problem

Purpose

Visual-Spatial Students will test various foods for the presence of fat and starch.

Process Skills

predicting, making and using tables, observing and inferring, recognizing cause and effect, forming a hypothesis, designing an experiment

Time

40 minutes

Materials

If possible, use a variety of breads and crackers—some that contain fat and some that do not.

To prepare iodine solution, dissolve 5 g iodine and 10 g potassium iodide in 500 mL of distilled water.

Safety Precautions

The iodine solution is poisonous and an irritant.

Use 100 volumes of water to one volume of iodine solution before disposal.

Form a Hypothesis

Possible Hypotheses

Placing iodine on foods will indicate the presence of starch if the iodine turns blue. Foods containing fat will leave a grease spot on a brown paper bag.

Test Your Hypothesis

Possible Procedures

Place a sample of each food to be tested on brown paper for several minutes. Remove the food from the paper and check for a grease spot. Drop iodine solution on each food sample. If the iodine turns dark blue, starch is present. Record results.

Design Your Own Experiment

Activity 14·2

Detecting Fats and Starches

It's important to know what's in the foods you eat. Simple tests can show which foods contain carbohydrates and which contain fats. When rubbed on brown paper, foods that contain fats leave a grease spot, just as they make your hands feel greasy. When a drop of iodine solution is placed on foods containing starches, they turn dark blue.

Possible Materials

- Paper grocery bag
- Iodine solution in dropper bottle
- Marker
- Scissors
- Liquid cooking oil
- Bread
- Raw potato slice
- Cooked bacon
- Cheese
- Cracker
- Cooked egg white
- Potato chip

Recognize the Problem

How will you find out which foods contain starch? Which contain fat?

Form a Hypothesis

How will you and your group use procedures that you know to test foods to determine which foods contain starch, fat, or both?

Goals

- **Predict** which foods contain starch and which contain fat.
- **Observe** the tests on each food to determine the presence of starch and fat.

Safety Precautions

CAUTION: *Iodine is poisonous.* Do NOT eat food used in a laboratory experiment. Dispose of all food after your experiment.

Teaching Strategies

- Bread and crackers both contain carbohydrates, but they may or may not contain fats. Although they are less common, fat-free cheese and potato chips also are available. Be sure students know not to make generalizations based entirely on the results of the activity.
- Be sure the egg white is cooked in a manner that does not add fat.

Test Your Hypothesis

Plan

1. **Predict** which foods contain starch and which contain fat.
2. Reread the opening paragraph of the experiment. How can you use that information to plan your experiment? You know that cooking oil is a fat and bread contains starch. Testing these foods will result in a positive test. Can you use these positive tests as a comparison to other tests?
3. **Write** the procedure you will use to test your hypothesis.
4. **Copy** the data table in your Science Journal.

Do

1. Make sure your teacher approves your plan and your data table before you begin your experiment.
2. Make your predictions and then carry out your plan.
3. Immediately **record** all your observations and results in your data table.

Analyze Your Data

1. **Describe** the evidence that allowed you to **infer** that fat was present in the food.
2. **Describe** the evidence that showed that starch was present.

Draw Conclusions

1. Which of the foods you tested contain carbohydrates? Which contain fat?
2. Did any foods contain both carbohydrates and fat?
3. Were your predictions correct?

Sample data

Predictions and Tests for Fat and Starch

Food	Prediction	Paper Bag	Iodine
oil	fat	grease spot	no reaction
bread	starch	very little spot	blue color
potato	starch	no spot	blue color
bacon	fat	grease spot	no reaction

Expected Outcome

See the Sample Data in the Data Table on the student page. Those samples that turned the iodine blue contain starch, and those that left grease spots contain fat.

Error Analysis

One possible source of error is that moisture from the sample may be interpreted as a grease spot. If the spot is left exposed to the air for several minutes, moisture will evaporate, but a grease spot will remain.

Analyze Your Data

1. Those samples that left grease spots contain fat.
2. Those samples that turned the iodine blue contain starch.

Draw Conclusions

1. Bread, potato, and cracker contain starch. Oil, bacon, cheese, and potato chip contain fat. Bread and cracker could contain fat. Evaluate student responses on the samples used.
2. The potato chip contains both. Bread and cracker could contain both, depending on the samples used.
3. Answers will vary. See student Data Tables.

GO Further

Other types of carbohydrates can be detected by different means. Obtain sugar test paper. Glucose is present when the paper turns green. Have the students dilute 1 part honey or molasses with 5 parts water. Test the solution for glucose.

Assessment

Oral After completing the activity, discuss with students any results they had that were surprising to them. For example, students may think that all parts of an egg contain fat. Emphasize that foods can have a wide range of contents. Use **Performance Assessment in the Science Classroom,** p. 71.

Chapter 14 Reviewing Main Ideas

Reviewing Main Ideas can be used to preview, review, reteach, and condense chapter content.

Preview

Linguistic Have students try to answer the Reviewing Main Ideas questions in their Science Journals. Use student answers as a source for discussion throughout the chapter.

Review

Interpersonal Have students answer the questions on separate pieces of paper and compare their answers with those of other students in the class. COOP LEARN

Reteach

Visual-Spatial Have students look at the illustrations on these pages. Ask them to describe details that support the main ideas of the chapter found in the statement for each illustration.

OUT OF TIME?

Auditory-Musical If time does not permit teaching the entire chapter, use the information on these pages along with the chapter Audiocassettes to present the material in a condensed format.

Chapter 14 Reviewing Main Ideas

For a **preview** of this chapter, study this Reviewing Main Ideas before you read the chapter. After you have studied this chapter, you can use the Reviewing Main Ideas to **review** the chapter.

The Glencoe MindJogger, Audiocassettes, and CD-ROM provide additional opportunities for review.

Section 14-1 COMPOUNDS OF CARBON AND HYDROGEN

Hydrocarbons are compounds containing only carbon and hydrogen. If a hydrocarbon has only single bonds, it is called a **saturated hydrocarbon.** A hydrocarbon chain can be lengthened by substituting a methyl group for a hydrogen. **Isomers** are compounds with the same chemical formula but different structures, and so they have different properties. ***Draw the structural formulas of butane and isobutane.***

UNSATURATED HYDROCARBONS

Unsaturated hydrocarbons have one or more double or triple bonds. The simplest unsaturated hydrocarbons are ethylene and propylene. Each has one double bond and is used to form useful polymers. Butadiene has two double bonds and is used to make synthetic rubber. ***Draw the structural formula for an unsaturated hydrocarbon with five carbon atoms and two double bonds.***

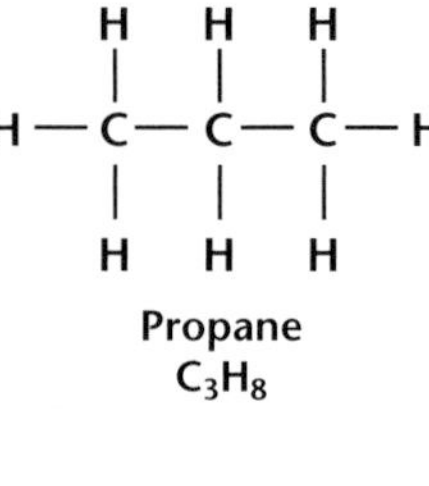

Propane
C_3H_8

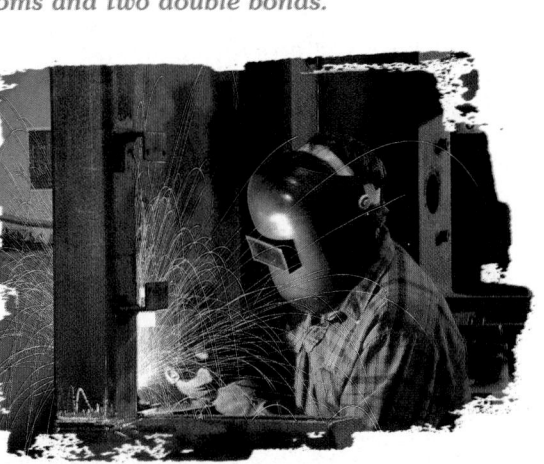

Ethyne or Acetylene
C_2H_2

Cultural Diversity

Hold the Cheese! Lactase is an enzyme that allows humans to break down lactose, the sugar in milk. Normally, human infants produce lactase, but lactase production stops in most humans as they age. This decrease causes a condition known as lactose intolerance. If a person lacks lactase, digesting milk products is difficult.

Only 18 percent of adult Americans of northern European ancestry are lactose intolerant, but 80 percent of African-American adults and 60 percent of Mexican-American adults do not produce lactase. In some Asian populations, such as Thai, 98 percent of the adults are lactose intolerant.

Scientists suggest that populations that have used dairy farming as an important food resource for thousands of years have adapted by retaining the ability to produce lactase.

Reading Check ✓

Choose a major illustration, such as **Figure 14-4**, and explain three things you learned from it.

Section 14-2 SUBSTITUTED HYDROCARBONS

Hydrocarbons may be substituted with other atoms such as the halogens, or with groups of atoms. An alcohol is formed when a **hydroxyl group** is substituted for a hydrogen in a hydrocarbon. A carboxylic acid is made when a **carboxyl group** is substituted. An amine is formed when an **amino group** is substituted. An **amino acid** contains both an amino group and a carboxyl group substituted on the same carbon atom. Substituted hydrocarbons have different physical and chemical properties from the unsubstituted hydrocarbons. ***List three functional groups and give their chemical formulas.***

Section 14-3 MOLECULES OF LIFE

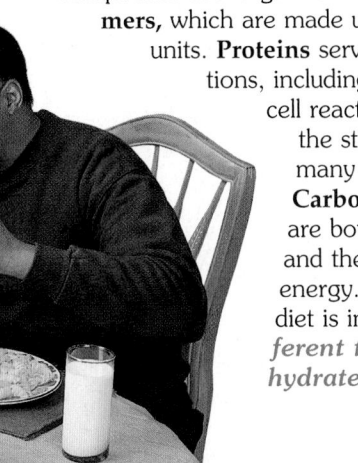

Biological compounds are complex, substituted hydrocarbons that make up living things. Many biological compounds are large molecules called **polymers,** which are made up of small repeating units. **Proteins** serve a variety of functions, including catalyzing many cell reactions and providing the structural material for many parts of the body. **Carbohydrates** and **lipids** are both energy sources and the means of storing energy. Eating a healthy diet is important. ***List different types of carbohydrates.***

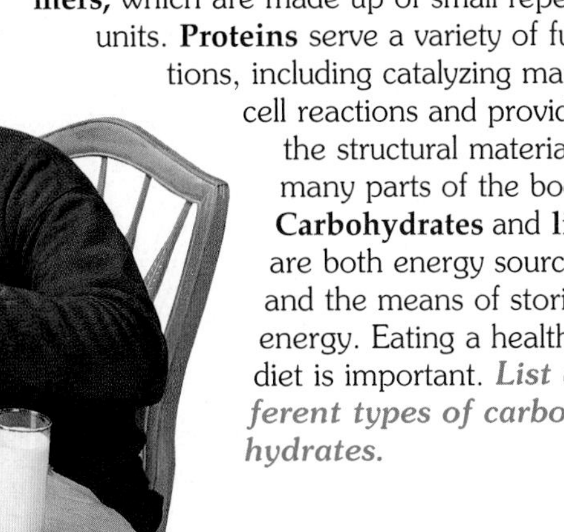

Answers to Questions

Section 14-1
Compounds of Carbon and Hydrogen

Butane

```
    H   H   H   H
    |   |   |   |
H — C — C — C — C — H
    |   |   |   |
    H   H   H   H
```

Isobutane

```
    H   H   H
    |   |   |
H — C — C — C — H
    |   |   |
    H H-C-H H
        |
        H
```

Unsaturated Hydrocarbons

Sample structure:

```
    H       H       H
    |       |       |
H — C = C — C = C — C — H
        |       |
        H       H
```

Section 14-2
Substituted Hydrocarbons

hydroxyl (–OH),
carboxyl (–COOH),
amino ($-NH_2$)

Section 14-3
Molecules of Life Carbohydrates can be starches, sugars, glycogen, or cellulose.

✓ Assessment

Portfolio Encourage students to place in their portfolios one or two items of what they consider to be their best work. Examples include:

- Science Journal, pp. 397, 405
- Assessment, pp. 397, 407
- Activity, pp. 399, 401
- Skill Builder, p. 403 P

Performance Additional performance assessments may be found in **Performance Assessment** and **Science Integration Activities.** Performance Task Assessment Lists and rubrics for evaluating these activities can be found in Glencoe's **Performance Assessment in the Science Classroom.**

GLENCOE TECHNOLOGY

CD-ROM

Glencoe Science Voyages Interactive CD-ROM

Chapter Summaries and Quizzes

Have students read the Chapter Summary then take the Chapter Quiz to determine whether they have mastered chapter content.

Using Vocabulary

1. An amino group is $-NH_2$. An amino acid contains both an amino group and a carboxyl group, $-COOH$.
2. A hydroxyl group is $-OH$, and a carboxyl group is $-COOH$.
3. The atoms are arranged differently.
4. A protein is a type of polymer.
5. Both are made from carbon, hydrogen, and oxygen and both store energy.

interNET CONNECTION To reinforce chapter vocabulary, use the **Study Guide for Content Mastery** booklet. Also available are activities for **Glencoe Science Voyages** on the Glencoe Science Web Site. **www.glencoe.com/sec/science**

Checking Concepts

6. B	11. C
7. D	12. C
8. C	13. A
9. A	14. C
10. D	15. C

Thinking Critically

16. They are the same as long as the same atoms are arranged in the same way in the molecules.
17. Yes; ethanol is a substituted hydrocarbon.
18. water and carbon dioxide
19. Answers could include that no oxygen is present in ethylene.

Chapter 14 Assessment

Using Vocabulary

a. amino acid
b. amino group
c. carbohydrate
d. carboxyl group
e. hydrocarbon
f. hydroxyl group
g. isomer
h. lipid
i. organic compound
j. polymer
k. protein
l. saturated hydrocarbon
m. unsaturated hydrocarbon

Answer the following questions about the Vocabulary words.

1. Explain the difference between an amino group and an amino acid.
2. How does a hydroxyl group differ from a carboxyl group?
3. How can an organic compound be an isomer?
4. What is the connection between a polymer and a protein?
5. What do carbohydrates and lipids have in common?

Checking Concepts

Choose the word or phrase that best answers the question.

6. A certain carbohydrate molecule has ten oxygen atoms. How many hydrogen atoms does it contain?
   A) five C) ten
   B) 20 D) 16
7. Which is **NOT** a group that can be substituted in a hydrocarbon?
   A) amino C) hydroxyl
   B) carboxyl D) lipid
8. Which chemical formula represents an alcohol?
   A) CH_3COOH C) CH_3OH
   B) CH_3NH_2 D) CH_4
9. Which can build up in arteries and lead to heart disease?
   A) cholesterol C) glucose
   B) fructose D) starch
10. What is an organic molecule that contains a triple bond called?
    A) polymer
    B) saturated hydrocarbon
    C) isomer
    D) unsaturated hydrocarbon
11. What is the name of the substituted hydrocarbon with the chemical formula CH_2F_2?
    A) methane C) difluoromethane
    B) fluoromethane D) trifluoromethane
12. Excess energy is stored in your body as which of the following?
    A) proteins C) lipids
    B) isomers D) saturated hydrocarbons
13. What are produced by reactions between carboxylic acids and glycerol?
    A) lipids C) sugars
    B) proteins D) carbohydrates
14. Which is a chemical formula that represents an amino acid?
    A) CH_3COOH C) NH_2CH_2COOH
    B) CH_3NH_2 D) CH_4
15. Which is a ring-shaped molecule?
    A) acetone C) cyclopentane
    B) Freon D) dichloroethane

Thinking Critically

16. Some drugs that were obtained from trees and plants are now manufactured. Do you think these manufactured drugs can be the same as the natural products? Explain.
17. Ethanol is used as a fuel for cars. Would you have predicted that ethanol would burn and produce energy? Explain.

18. Candle wax is one of the longer hydrocarbons. What do you think are the products of the burning of candle wax?
19. In the polymerization of proteins, water molecules are produced as part of the reaction. But, in the polymerization of ethylene, no water is produced. Explain.

Developing Skills

If you need help, refer to the **Skill Handbook.**

20. **Recognizing Cause and Effect** Marathon runners go through a process known as hitting the wall. They have used up all their stored glucose and start using stored lipids as fuel. What is the advantage of eating lots of complex carbohydrates the day before a race?
21. **Using a Graph** The graph shows the boiling points of some saturated hydrocarbons with from one to five carbon atoms. How does boiling point depend upon the number of carbon atoms? What would you predict would be the approximate boiling point of hexane, a hydrocarbon with six carbon atoms?

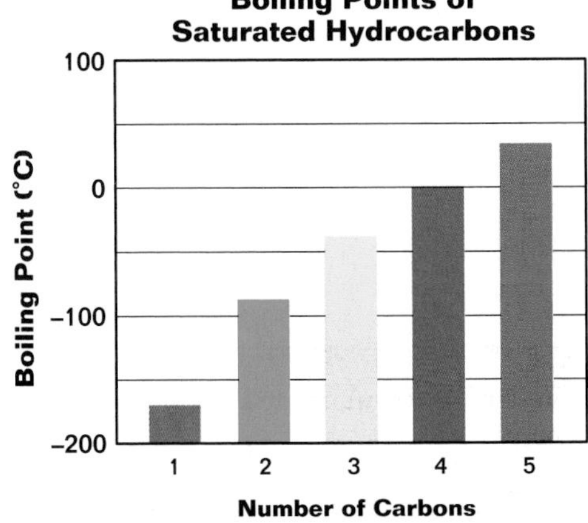

Test-Taking Tip

Study in Quiet It's best to study in an environment similar to the one in which you'll be tested. Blaring stereos, video game machines, chatty friends, and beepers are not allowed in the classroom during test time. So, why get used to them when you study?

Test Practice

Use these questions to test your Science Proficiency.

1. Which of the following is an unsaturated hydrocarbon?
   A) propane
   B) hexane
   C) ethene
   D) methane
2. When biological compounds are digested by the human body, which of the following processes does **NOT** occur?
   A) Carbohydrates are broken down into simple sugars.
   B) Excess energy released from food is stored as lipids.
   C) Proteins are broken down into lipids.
   D) Sugars are broken down to provide energy to cells.
3. Which of the following describes isomers?
   A) They contain a hydroxyl group.
   B) They occur in rings.
   C) They have the same formula but different structures.
   D) They have different formulas but the same structures.

Test Practice

The Test-Taking Tip was written by The Princeton Review, the nation's leader in test preparation.

1. C
2. C
3. C

Developing Skills

20. Excess sugars have not had time to be stored as lipids. They are still in the blood and are available for energy.
21. The boiling point increases as the number of carbon atoms increases. Students may estimate hexane's boiling point to be between 50° C and 100° C. Hexane's actual boiling point is 69° C.

Bonus Question

If n carbon atoms exist in a straight-chain hydrocarbon that contains one double bond, how many hydrogen atoms are present? $2n$ If students need a hint, advise them to find the formulas for several specific straight-chain hydrocarbons that contain one double bond and determine the numerical relationship between the number of carbon atoms and the number of hydrogen atoms for each of them.

Assessment Resources

The **Test Practice Workbook** provides students with practice in the format, concepts, and critical-thinking skills tested in standardized exams.

Reproducible Masters

Chapter Review, pp. 27–28 L2
Performance Assessment, p. 28 L2
Assessment, pp. 61–64 L2

Glencoe Technology

Chapter Review Software
Computer Test Bank
MindJogger Videoquiz

Chapter 15 Plant Processes

Section	Objectives	Activities/Features
Chapter Opener		**Explore Activity:** Observe Plants, p. 425
15-1 **Photosynthesis and Respiration** 4 Sessions 2 Blocks	1. **Describe** the process of gas exchange in plants. 2. **Explain** the process and importance of photosynthesis and respiration. 3. **Describe** the relationship between photosynthesis and respiration.	**Using Math,** p. 427 **MiniLab:** Observing Plant Use of Carbon Dioxide, p. 429 **Earth Science Integration,** p. 431 **MiniLab:** Demonstrating Respiration in Yeast, p. 432 **Skill Builder:** Comparing and Contrasting, p. 434 **Using Math,** p. 434 **Activity 15-1:** Stomata in Leaves, p. 435
15-2 **Plant Responses** 2 Sessions 1 Block	4. **Explain** the relationship between stimuli and tropisms in plants. 5. **Differentiate** between long-day and short-day plants. 6. **Explain** the relationship between plant hormones and responses.	**Problem Solving:** Predicting Plant Responses, p. 438 **Earth Science Integration,** p. 439 **Skill Builder:** Comparing and Contrasting, p. 440 **Science Journal,** p. 440 **How It Works:** Carnivorous Plants, p. 441 **Activity 15-2:** Plant Tropisms, pp. 442–443

The number of recommended single-period sessions The number of recommended blocks
One session and one-half block are allowed for chapter review and assessment.

Activity Materials

Explore	Activities	MiniLabs
p. 425 resealable bags, seedling plants in pots	p. 435 lettuce, dish, water, coverslip, microscope, microscope slide, salt solution, forceps pp. 442-443 petri dish, tape, string, corn seeds, bean seeds, paper towels, water	p. 429 bromothymol blue, test tubes, test-tube holder, tap water, carbonated water, *Elodea* sprig, dropper p. 432 bromothymol blue, yeast suspension, sugar solution, test tube

Need Materials? Contact Science Kit at 1-800-828-7777 or at www.sciencekit.com on the Internet.
For alternate materials, see the activity on the listed page.

Standards		Reproducible Resources	Technology
National	State/Local	Test Practice Workbooks are available for use with each chapter.	English and Spanish audiocassettes are available for use with each section.
National Content Standards: A2, A5, B2, C1, C3, D1, D3, D4		**Activity Worksheets,** pp. 81–82, 85, 86 **Enrichment,** p. 40 **Home Involvement,** p. 23 **Laboratory Manual,** pp. 87–88 **Reinforcement,** p. 40 **Study Guide,** pp. 57–58	**Section Focus Transparency 40** **Teaching Transparency 29** **Teaching Transparency 30** **Science Integration Transparency 15** **Internet Connection,** p. 430 **Glencoe Science Voyages Interactive Videodisc—Life** **National Geographic Society: STV**
National Content Standards: A4, B1, D3, D5		**Activity Worksheets,** pp. 83–84 **Critical Thinking/Problem Solving,** p. 15 **Enrichment,** p. 41 **Laboratory Manual,** pp. 89–92 **Multicultural Connections,** pp. 29–30 **Reinforcement,** p. 41 **Study Guide,** pp. 59–60	**Section Focus Transparency 41** **Internet Connection,** p. 437 **The Infinite Voyage Series**

Key to Teaching Strategies

The following designations will help you decide which activities are appropriate for your students.

L1 Level 1 activities should be appropriate for students with learning difficulties.

L2 Level 2 activities should be within the ability range of all students.

L3 Level 3 activities are designed for above-average students.

ELL ELL activities should be within the ability range of English Language Learners.

COOP LEARN Cooperative Learning activities are designed for small group work.

P These strategies represent student products that can be placed into a best-work portfolio.

Multiple Learning Styles logos, as described on page 61T, are used throughout to indicate strategies that address different learning styles.

Assessment Resources

Chapter Review, pp. 29–30
Assessment, pp. 65–68
Performance Assessment in the Science Classroom (PASC)
MindJogger Videoquiz
Alternate Assessment in the Science Classroom
Performance Assessment, p. 29
Chapter Review Software
Computer Test Bank

Chapter 15 Plant Processes

This is a representation of key blackline masters available in the Teacher Classroom Resources. See Resource Manager boxes within the chapter for additional information.

Transparencies

Section Focus Transparencies

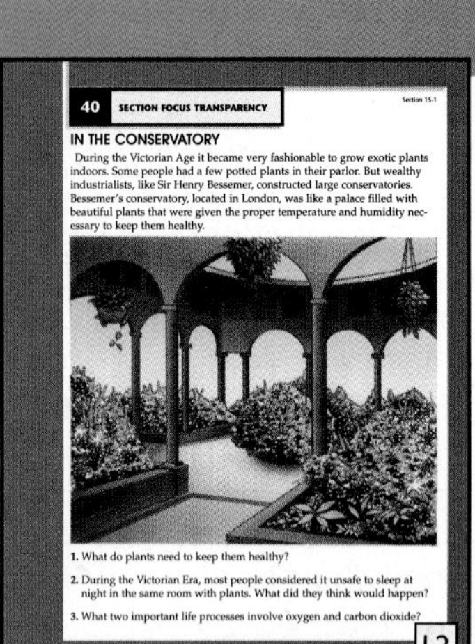
40 SECTION FOCUS TRANSPARENCY

Section 15-1

IN THE CONSERVATORY

During the Victorian Age it became very fashionable to grow exotic plants indoors. Some people had a few potted plants in their parlor. But wealthy industrialists, like Sir Henry Bessemer, constructed large conservatories. Bessemer's conservatory, located in London, was like a palace filled with beautiful plants that were given the proper temperature and humidity necessary to keep them healthy.

1. What do plants need to keep them healthy?
2. During the Victorian Era, most people considered it unsafe to sleep at night in the same room with plants. What did they think would happen?
3. What two important life processes involve oxygen and carbon dioxide?

L2

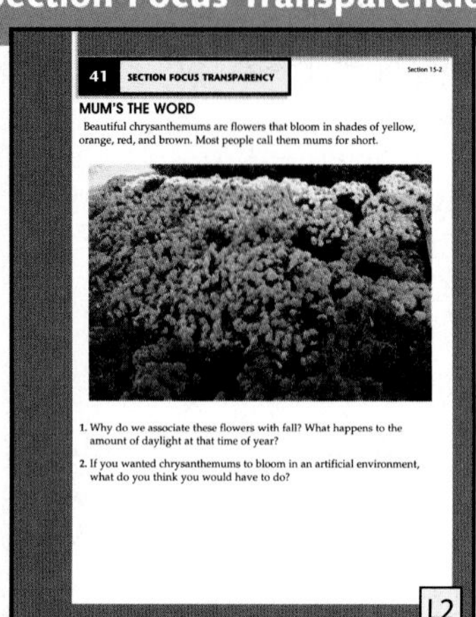
41 SECTION FOCUS TRANSPARENCY

Section 15-2

MUM'S THE WORD

Beautiful chrysanthemums are flowers that bloom in shades of yellow, orange, red, and brown. Most people call them mums for short.

1. Why do we associate these flowers with fall? What happens to the amount of daylight at that time of year?
2. If you wanted chrysanthemums to bloom in an artificial environment, what do you think you would have to do?

L2

Science Integration Transparencies

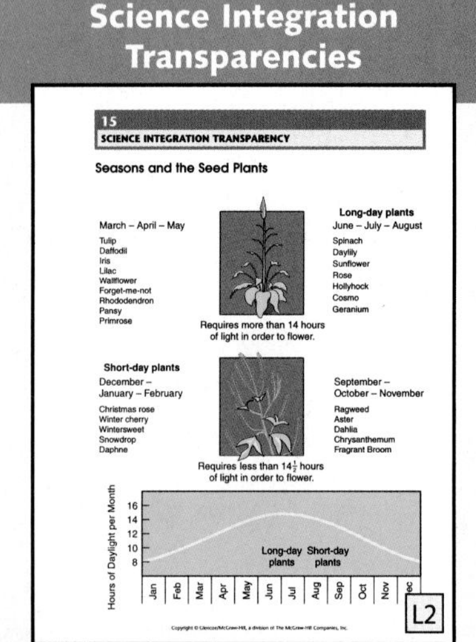
15 SCIENCE INTEGRATION TRANSPARENCY

Seasons and the Seed Plants

L2

Teaching Transparencies

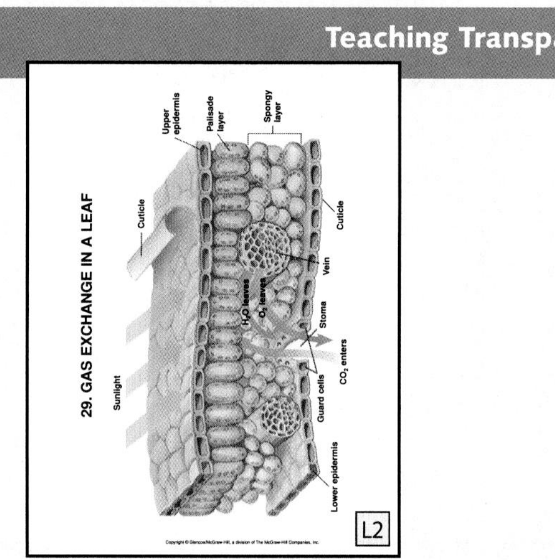

L2

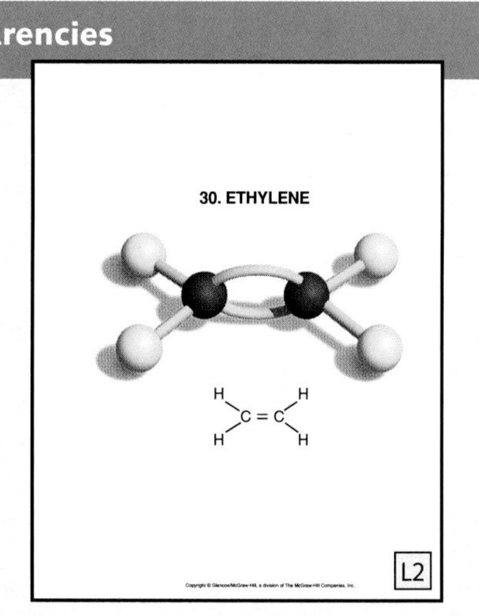

L2

Meeting Different Ability Levels

Study Guide for Content Mastery

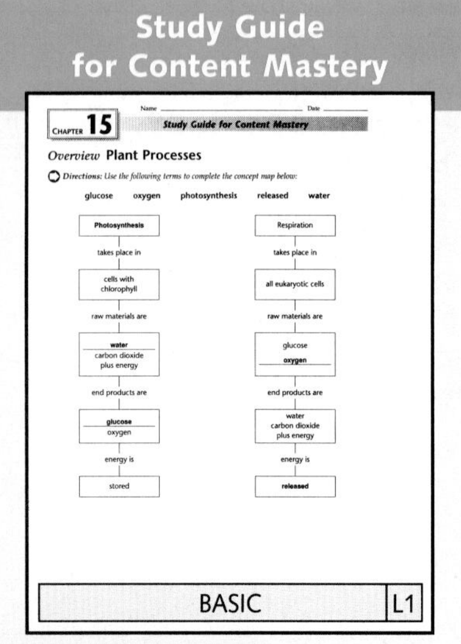
Name Date

CHAPTER 15 Study Guide for Content Mastery

Overview Plant Processes

Directions: Use the following terms to complete the concept map below:

glucose oxygen photosynthesis released water

BASIC L1

Reinforcement

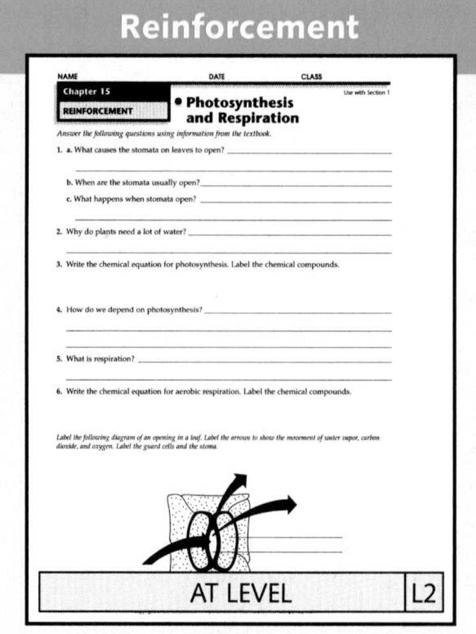
NAME DATE CLASS

Chapter 15 REINFORCEMENT

• Photosynthesis and Respiration

Use with Section 1

Answer the following questions using information from the textbook.

1. a. What causes the stomata on leaves to open?
   b. When are the stomata usually open?
   c. What happens when stomata open?
2. Why do plants need a lot of water?
3. Write the chemical equation for photosynthesis. Label the chemical compounds.
4. How do we depend on photosynthesis?
5. What is respiration?
6. Write the chemical equation for aerobic respiration. Label the chemical compounds.

Label the following diagram of an opening in a leaf. Label the arrows to show the movement of water vapor, carbon dioxide, and oxygen. Label the guard cells and the stoma.

AT LEVEL L2

Enrichment Worksheets

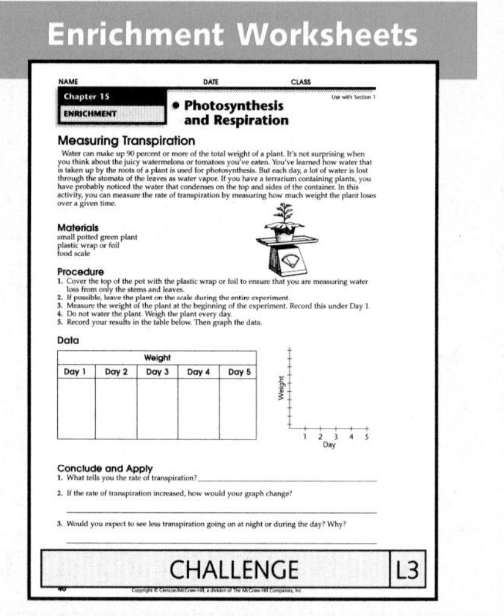
NAME DATE CLASS

Chapter 15 ENRICHMENT

• Photosynthesis and Respiration

Use with Section 1

Measuring Transpiration

Water can make up 90 percent or more of the total weight of a plant. It's not surprising when you think about the juicy watermelons or tomatoes you've eaten. You've learned how water that is taken up by the roots of a plant is used for photosynthesis. But each day, a lot of water is lost through the stomata of the leaves as water vapor. If you have a terrarium containing plants, you have probably noticed the water that condenses on the top and sides of the container. In this activity, you can measure the rate of transpiration by measuring how much weight the plant loses over a given time.

Materials

small potted green plant
plastic wrap or foil
food scale

Procedure

1. Cover the top of the pot with the plastic wrap or foil to ensure that you are measuring water loss from only the stems and leaves.
2. If possible, leave the plant on the scale during the entire experiment.
3. Measure the weight of the plant at the beginning of the experiment. Record this under Day 1.
4. Do not water the plant. Weigh the plant every day.
5. Record your results in the table below. Then graph the data.

Data

Weight				
Day 1	Day 2	Day 3	Day 4	Day 5

Conclude and Apply

1. What tells you the rate of transpiration?
2. If the rate of transpiration increased, how would your graph change?
3. Would you expect to see less transpiration going on at night or during the day? Why?

CHALLENGE L3

Hands-on Activities

Activity Worksheets

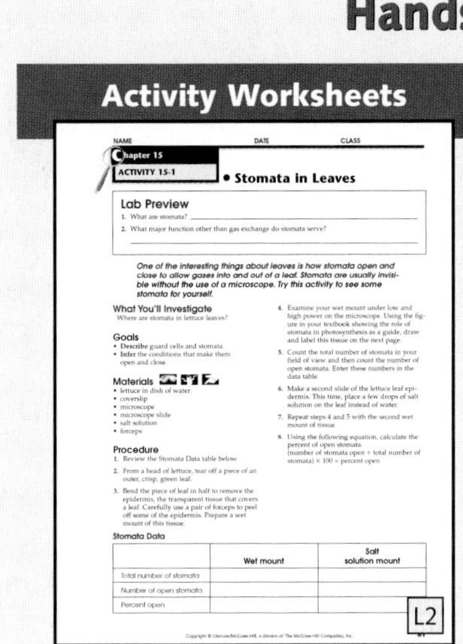

NAME DATE CLASS

Chapter 15
ACTIVITY 15-1
• Stomata in Leaves

Lab Preview

1. What are stomata?
2. What major function other than gas exchange do stomata serve?

One of the interesting things about leaves is how stomata open and close to allow gases into and out of a leaf. Stomata are usually invisible without the use of a microscope. Try this activity to see some stomata for yourself.

What You'll Investigate

Goals

Materials

Procedure

Stomata Data

	Wet mount	Salt solution mount
Total number of stomata		
Number of open stomata		
Percent open		

L2

Lab Manual

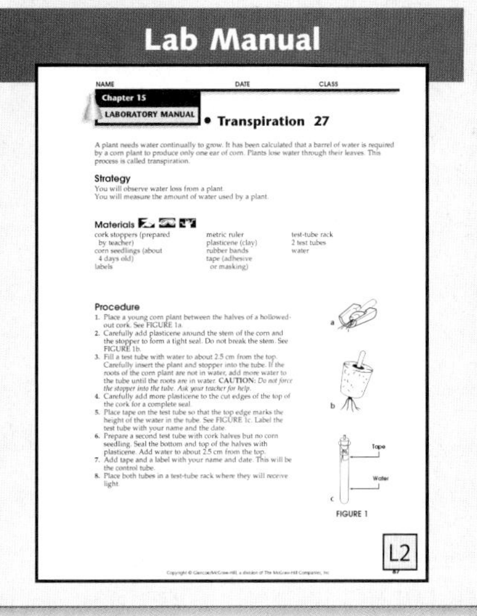

NAME DATE CLASS

Chapter 15
LABORATORY MANUAL
• Transpiration 27

Strategy

Materials

Procedure

FIGURE 1

L2

Accessibility

Spanish Resources

SPANISH RESOURCES

GLENCOE

SCIENCE VOYAGES

Exploring the Life, Earth, and Physical Sciences

LEVEL BLUE

L2

Assessment

Performance Assessment

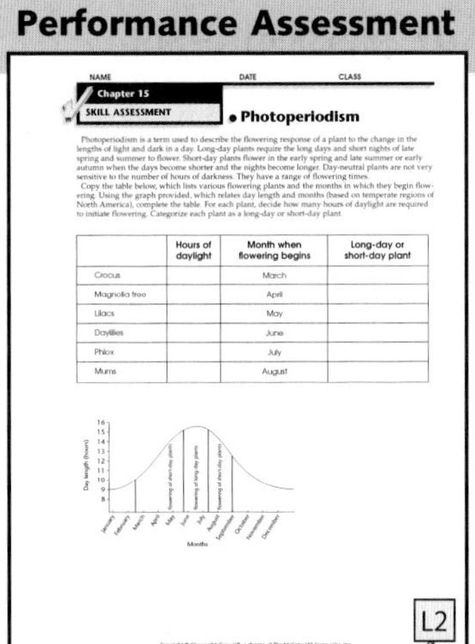

NAME DATE CLASS

Chapter 15
SKILL ASSESSMENT
• Photoperiodism

	Hours of daylight	Month when flowering begins	Long-day or short-day plant
Crocus		March	
Magnolia tree		April	
Lilacs		May	
Davilles		June	
Phlox		July	
Mums		August	

Months

L2

Chapter Review

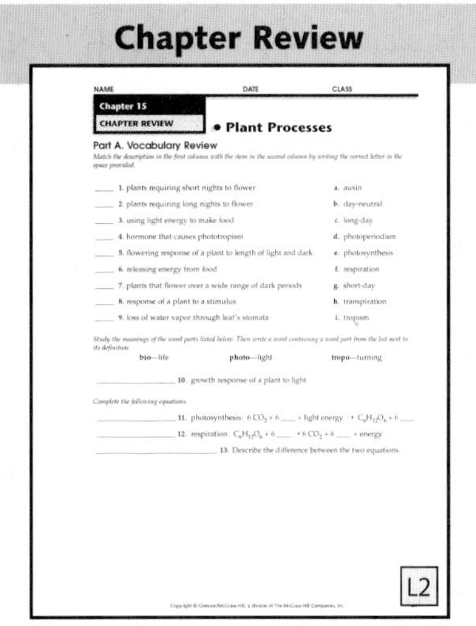

NAME DATE CLASS

Chapter 15
CHAPTER REVIEW
• Plant Processes

Part A. Vocabulary Review

L2

Assessment

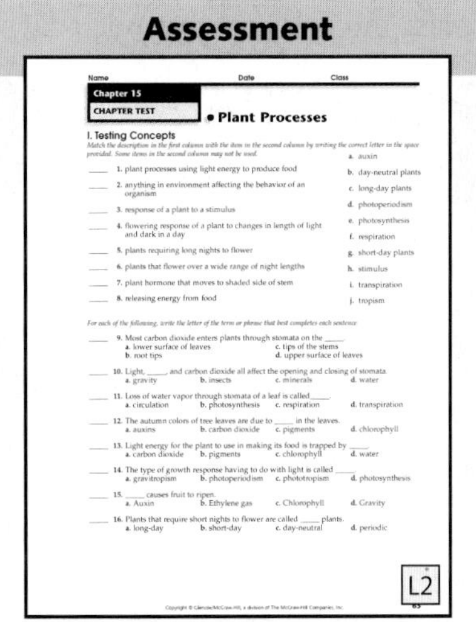

Name Date Class

Chapter 15
CHAPTER TEST
• Plant Processes

I. Testing Concepts

L2

Test Practice Workbook

STANDARDIZED TEST PRACTICE
STUDENT EDITION

GLENCOE

SCIENCE VOYAGES

Exploring the Life, Earth, and Physical Sciences

LEVEL BLUE

THE PRINCETON REVIEW

L2

Extending Content

Critical Thinking/ Problem Solving

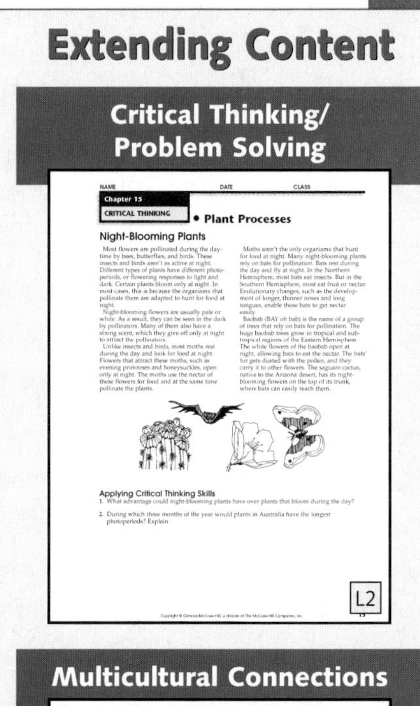

NAME DATE CLASS

Chapter 15
CRITICAL THINKING
• Plant Processes

Night-Blooming Plants

Applying Critical Thinking Skills

L2

Multicultural Connections

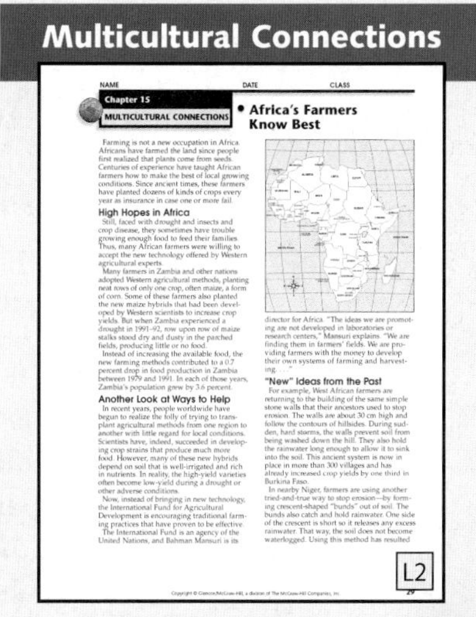

NAME DATE CLASS

Chapter 15
MULTICULTURAL CONNECTIONS
• Africa's Farmers Know Best

High Hopes in Africa

Another Look at Ways to Help

"New" Ideas from the Past

L2

Helping You Prepare

Gas Exchange in Plants
(Section 15-1)

Stomata (singular, *stoma*) allow gas exchange in plants. Each one is usually surrounded by two guard cells, but other arrangements of additional guard cells do exist. Water and solutes diffuse into and out of guard cells. This process relies on photosynthesis, carbon dioxide availability, temperature, and other complex internal factors in plant cells.

Most stomata are open during the day and closed at night. Plants growing in arid regions have their stomata open at night and closed during the day. Carbon dioxide is concentrated at night in cells with chloroplasts and released during the day to carry out photosynthesis. This adaptation reduces water loss.

Most plants have fewer stomata on the upper surface of the leaf than on the lower side of the leaf. On floating aquatic plants, stomata are only on the upper surface of the leaf. Submerged plants have no stomata but have evolved other mechanisms for gas exchange.

Photosynthesis (Section 15-1)

Photosynthesis happens in two sets of reactions. One series of reactions is dependent on light and the other is not.

The light reactions are complex. Many reactions and enzymes are involved. Light striking chlorophyll causes electrons to gain energy and leave chlorophyll molecules. Eventually, electrons along with hydrogen ions from water are added to $NADP^+$ a form of stored chemical energy to produce NADPH + H^+. NADPH is the one source of energy for the light-independent reactions.

GLENCOE TECHNOLOGY

CD-ROM

Glencoe Science Voyages Interactive CD-ROM

Chapter Summaries

Use the Chapter Summary to introduce, teach, or review chapter material.

During the light-independent reactions, NADPH and ATP, two forms of energy, are used to synthesize carbohydrates from carbon dioxide. Most plants use a process called the Calvin cycle. This process is extremely important in both aquatic and terrestrial ecosystems.

Respiration (Section 15-1)

Respiration is the mechanism by which energy from stored fuel is released. All respiration is preceded by glycolysis. Glycolysis is a series of chemical reactions that occurs in the cytoplasm of every cell. The process breaks down a glucose molecule into two molecules of pyruvic acid. This process is inefficient and produces only a small amount of ATP.

If respiration is occurring in organisms that do not require oxygen or if oxygen is unavailable, the process continues as anaerobic reactions. This results in the production of either lactic acid or alcohol. When alcohol is produced, the process is called fermentation. These two processes extract only a small portion of the energy from each molecule of pyruvic acid.

NATIONAL GEOGRAPHIC — **Teacher's Corner**

Products Available from Glencoe
To order the following products for use with this chapter, call Glencoe at 1-800-334-7344:

CD-ROMs: *NGS PictureShow: Plants: What It Means to Be Green*

Curriculum Kit: *GeoKits: Plants*

Transparency Set: *NGS PicturePack: Plants: What It Means to Be Green*

Videodisc: *STV: Plants*

Products Available from National Geographic Society
To order the following products for use with this chapter, call National Geographic Society at 1-800-368-2728:

Video: *Photosynthesis: Life Energy*

Aerobic respiration, which is respiration that uses oxygen, releases all the energy in the chemical bonds of pyruvic acid. The end products of this process are carbon dioxide, water, and energy. All eukaryotic cells use aerobic respiration. Some cells can shift into anaerobic respiration when oxygen supplies are low but only for short periods of time.

What are plant responses?

(Section 15-2)

Plants respond to their external and internal environments. Some responses are rapid while others occur slowly.

Responses to external stimuli, called tropisms, are slow, permanent, directed growth movements. Plant responses to internal stimuli are faster and reversible. One response is the sudden drooping of *Mimosa pudica* leaves when the plant is touched.

Plant Hormones (Section 15-2)

Plant hormones are chemicals produced in small amounts in specific plant cells. Hormones are then transported to other sites in the plant where they cause physiological changes.

Auxin, the first discovered plant hormone, is produced in the cells of the apical or stem-tip meristem and other young, mitotically-active plant tissue. Its effect depends on its concentration. The presence of auxin causes cell walls to become more elastic and stretch during active cell growth. As a result of this differential growth, the plant bends. Auxins also control suppression of lateral bud growth and prevent leaf abscission or leaf drop.

Ethylene regulates ripening of fruits. Abscisic acid is a plant hormone produced mainly in leaves and fruits. One of its effects is that it causes buds to become dormant.

SCIENCE UPDATE

For current events or science in the news, access the Glencoe Science Web Site at **www.glencoe.com/sec/science**

Photoperiods (Section 15-2)

Plants initiate the flowering process when the dark period reaches a critical length. Short-day plants flower when the nights are longer than the critical length. Conversely, long-day plants flower when the dark period is shorter than the critical length. Intermediate plants have two critical photoperiods and will not flower when the dark period is too long or too short. Day-neutral plants will flower given a minimum number of daylight hours.

A plant pigment called phytochrome mediates photoperiodism. In addition to this pigment, the hormone florigen is probably involved. However, in more than 50 years of searching, no hormone related directly to the flowering response has been isolated.

Teacher to Teacher

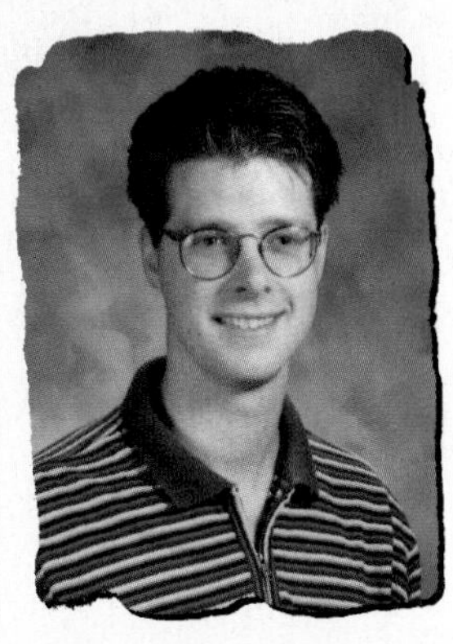

"Place slides on a number of microscopes without focusing them or locking the diaphragms and revolving nosepieces into place. Set up a different problem at each of several stations so students can see how quickly they can fix the problem as they move from microscope to microscope."

Steve Manns, Teacher
Derry Area Middle School
Derry, PA

CHAPTER 15
Plant Processes

CHAPTER OVERVIEW

Section 15-1 The processes and importance of photosynthesis and aerobic respiration are discussed in this section. Gas exchange is explained as a process that is needed in plants and animals.

Section 15-2 The relationship between stimuli and tropisms in plants is explained. Flowering responses of plants are discussed and examples are presented. Plant hormones are discussed in terms of the responses they produce in plants.

Chapter Vocabulary

stomata
transpiration
photosynthesis
respiration
tropism
auxin
photoperiodism
long-day plant
short-day plant
day-neutral plant

Theme Connection

Systems and Interactions Particular emphasis is placed on photosynthesis and respiration as homeostatic mechanisms and on the role of energy in these processes.

00:00 OUT OF TIME?

If time does not permit teaching the entire chapter, use Reviewing Main Ideas on pp. 444–445.

CHAPTER
15 Plant Processes

Chapter Preview

Section 15-1
Photosynthesis and Respiration

Section 15-2
Plant Responses

Skills Preview

Skill Builders
- Compare and Contrast
- Observe and Infer

Activities
- Predict
- Design an Experiment

MiniLabs
- Observe and Infer
- Measure in SI

Reading Check

Before you read the chapter, make a list of all the vocabulary words. Next to each word, write what you think it means. Then, as you read, change your definitions if necessary.

424

Multiple Learning Styles

Look for the following logos for strategies that emphasize different learning modalities.

Linguistic Science Journal, p. 431; Using Science Words, p. 433; Preview, p. 444

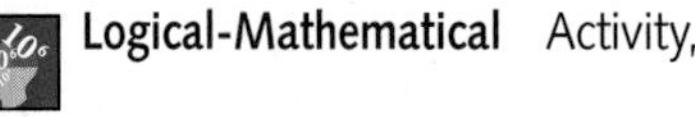

Logical-Mathematical Activity, p. 442

Visual-Spatial Activity, pp. 428, 435; MiniLab, pp. 429, 432; Reteach, pp. 433, 444; Across the Curriculum, p. 438; Quick Demo, p. 439

Auditory-Musical Multiple Learning Styles, p. 432; Out of Time, p. 444

Kinesthetic Explore Activity, p. 425

Interpersonal Review, p. 444

Explore Activity

Plants are similar to other living things. They are made of cells, reproduce, make and use substances, and need water. If someone forgot to water the petunias shown in the photograph, what do you think would happen? From your own experience, you probably know they would wilt. Do the following activity to discover the relationship between plants and water. Find out how water goes in and out of a plant. In this chapter, you will learn about other plant processes.

Observe Plants

1. Obtain a resealable plastic bag and a small potted plant from your teacher.
2. Place the potted plant in the plastic bag.
3. Seal the bag and place it in a sunny window.
4. Look at the plant at the same time every day for a few days.

Science Journal

In your Science Journal, describe what happens in the bag. If enough water is lost by a plant and not replaced, predict what will happen to the plant.

Explore Activity

Purpose

Kinesthetic Use the Explore Activity to introduce students to plant processes. Inform students that they will be learning more about plant processes as they read the chapter. L2

ELL COOP LEARN

Preparation

Obtain the materials needed. The seedlings should be large enough to show transpiration.

Materials

resealable bags, seedling plants in pots

Teaching Strategies

Have students record their hypotheses about what will happen when the plastic bags are placed over the seedlings.

Students should explain that water came from the soil and the plant. The plant will wilt or even die if it loses too much water.

Assessment

Process Have students diagram the pathway of water using as much terminology as they know from previous study (i.e., *roots, stems, vascular tissue, xylem,* etc.). Use **Performance Assessment in the Science Classroom,** p. 55.

Assessment Planner

Portfolio

Refer to p. 445 for suggested items that students might select for their portfolios.

Performance Assessment

See p. 445 for additional Performance Assessment options.
Skill Builder, p. 440
MiniLab, pp. 429, 432
Activity 15-1, p. 435; 15-2, pp. 442–443

Content Assessment

Section Assessment, pp. 434, 440
Chapter Assessment, pp. 446–447
Proficiency Prep, pp. 434, 440

SECTION 15-1

Prepare

Refer to **Gas Exchange in Plants, Photosynthesis,** and **Respiration** on pp. 424E–F.

Preplanning

Refer to the **Chapter Organizer** on pp. 424A–B.

1 Motivate

Bellringer

Before presenting the lesson, display **Section Focus Transparency 40** on the overhead projector. Use the accompanying **Focus Activity** worksheet. L2 ELL

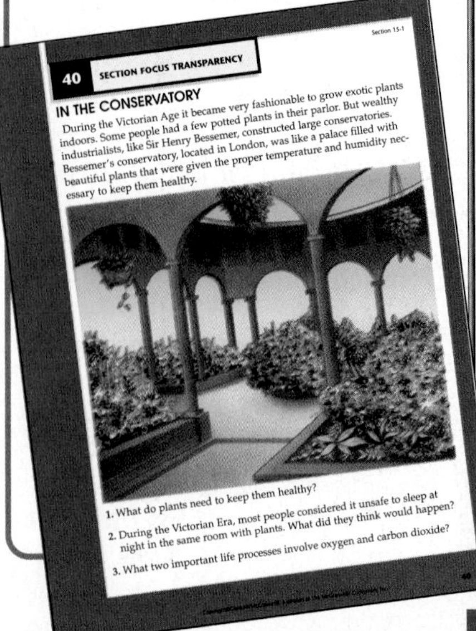

Section 15-1

40 SECTION FOCUS TRANSPARENCY

IN THE CONSERVATORY

During the Victorian Age it became very fashionable to grow exotic plants indoors. Some people had a few potted plants in their parlor. But wealthy industrialists, like Sir Henry Bessemer, constructed large conservatories. Bessemer's conservatory, located in London, was like a palace filled with beautiful plants that were given the proper temperature and humidity necessary to keep them healthy.

1. What do plants need to keep them healthy?
2. During the Victorian Era, most people considered it unsafe to sleep at night in the same room with plants. What did they think would happen?
3. What two important life processes involve oxygen and carbon dioxide?

Tying to Previous Knowledge

Explain to students that plants are green because they have chlorophyll, a pigment that traps most of light's energy but reflects green wavelengths of light.

Photosynthesis and Respiration

What You'll Learn

- How plants take in and give off gases
- Why photosynthesis and respiration are important
- Why photosynthesis and respiration are related

Vocabulary
stomata
transpiration
photosynthesis
respiration

Why It's Important

- Understanding photosynthesis and respiration in plants will help you understand their importance to life on Earth.

Gas Exchange in Plants

When you breathe, you take in and release mixtures of gases. You inhale air, a mixture of nitrogen, oxygen, carbon dioxide, and other gases. The mixture of gases that you exhale is mostly nitrogen, carbon dioxide, and water vapor. Gas exchange is one of the ways living cells obtain raw materials and get rid of waste products. For most organisms, carbon dioxide and water vapor are waste products of cell processes.

In plants, water and carbon dioxide are two of the raw materials needed for survival. Plant roots or rootlike structures absorb most of the water and it moves up through the plant to where it is needed. Water leaves a plant as water vapor. It may leave cells by diffusion and then be released through openings called **stomata** (sing., *stoma*). Stomata are on the surface(s) of a leaf or leaflike structure.

Stomata

How does carbon dioxide enter a leaf? Each stoma is surrounded by two guard cells that control the size of the opening. Water moves into and out of guard cells by osmosis. As water moves into guard cells, they swell and change shape,

Figure 15-1 Stomata open when guard cells absorb water (A). They close when water is lost (B). **Would a buildup of salt in the soil around a plant make the stomata open or close?**

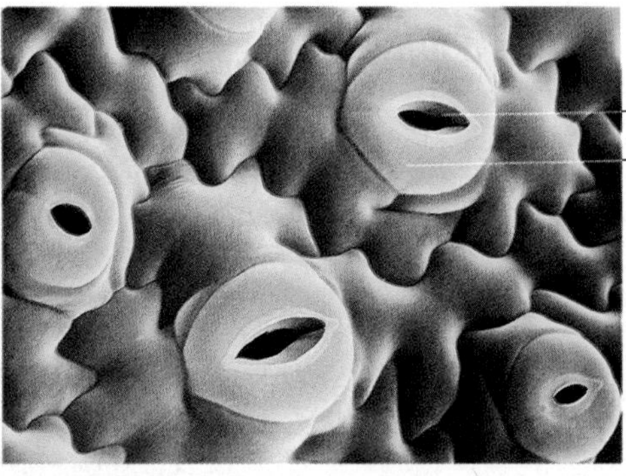

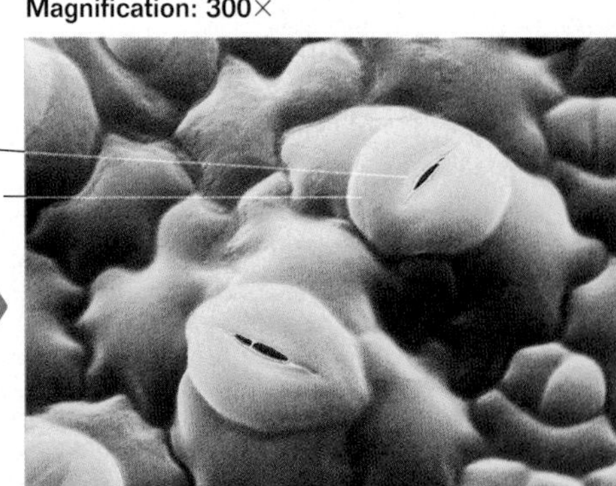

Resource Manager

The following **Teacher Classroom Resources** can be used with Section 15-1:

 **Reproducible Masters**

Study Guide, pp. 57–58 L1 ELL
Home Involvement, p. 23 L2
Activity Worksheets, pp. 81–82, 85–86 L2
Laboratory Manual, pp. 87–88 L2
Enrichment, p. 40 L3
Reinforcement, p. 40 L2

 **Transparencies**

Teaching Transparency 29 L2
Teaching Transparency 30 L2
Science Integration Transparency 15 L2

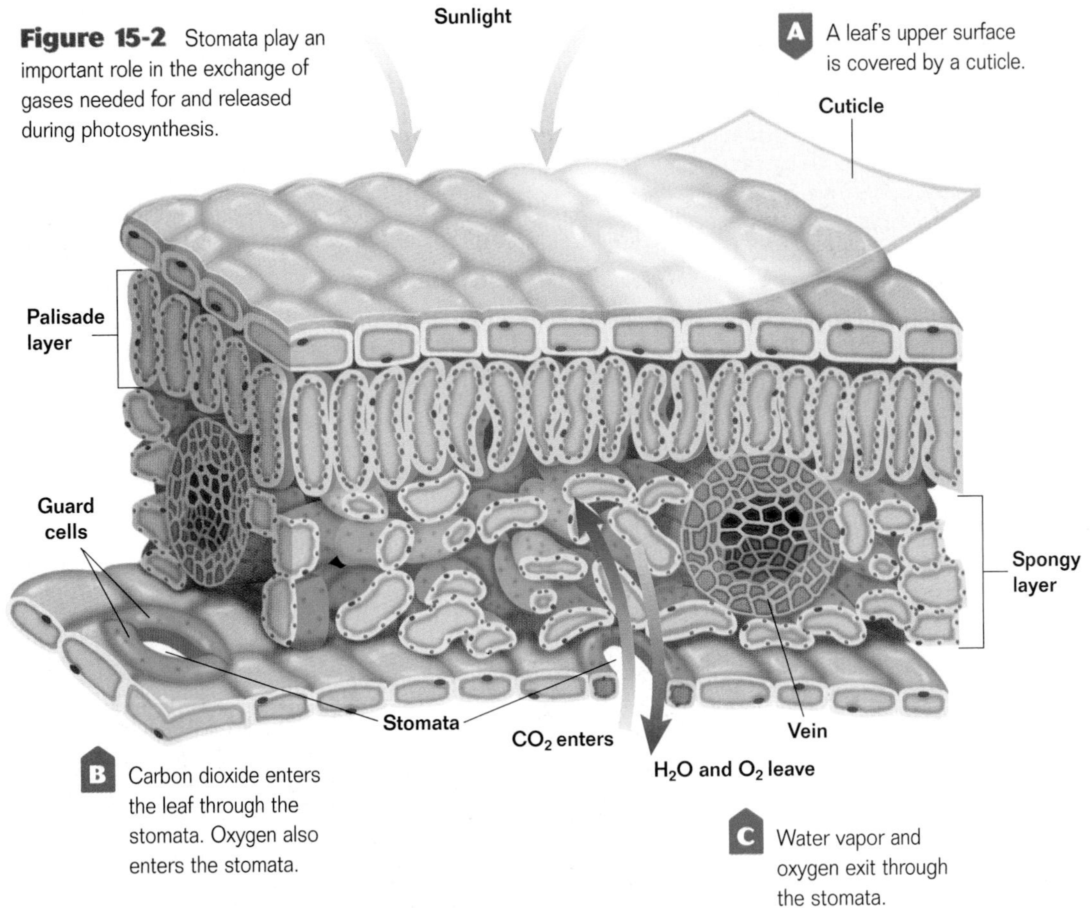

Figure 15-2 Stomata play an important role in the exchange of gases needed for and released during photosynthesis.

creating a stoma. Carbon dioxide enters the leaf through the stoma and water vapor may escape during this process. When guard cells lose water, they deflate and change shape again. This action closes the stoma. **Figure 15-1** shows open and closed stomata.

Light, water, and carbon dioxide all affect the opening and closing of stomata. Stomata usually are open during the day and closed at night. Less carbon dioxide enters and less water vapor escapes from the leaf when stomata are closed. Because leaves usually have more stomata on the lower surface, more carbon dioxide reaches the spaces around the spongy layer, as shown in **Figure 15-2.** Water vapor also is found in the air spaces of the spongy layer.

If you did the Explore Activity for this chapter, you saw that water vapor condensed on the inside of the plastic bag. Loss of water vapor through stomata of a leaf is called **transpiration.** Far more water is lost by transpiration than is used during the food-making process of photosynthesis.

Using Math

A corn plant transpires about 15 L of water per week. How much water will it transpire in a 100-day growing season?

Caption Answer

Figure 15-1 *Adding salt to soil around a plant would cause stomata to close. Water from plant cells would eventually diffuse into the soil. Water would leave guard cells too, and they would close the stoma.*

2 Teach

Correcting Misconceptions

Tell students that not all cells of plants contain chlorophyll. Those deep within the plant where light does not penetrate and the ones in underground plant parts, have no chlorophyll.

Using an Analogy

The following demonstration shows how guard cells change shape. Place a strip of cellophane tape along the length of an oblong balloon. Blow up the balloon. Show students that when the balloon is inflated, its shape changes just like a guard cell's does when it swells with water.

Making a Model

Using two oblong balloons with cellophane tape along one side, inflate them to model how guard cells form a stoma.

Using Math

(100 days ÷ 7 days) × 15 L = 71.4 L

VISUAL Learning

Figure 15-2 Make sure students understand that the primary function of the stomata is to allow carbon dioxide into the plant. Release of water and oxygen are other functions of the stomata.

Teacher FYI

Photosynthesis accounts for more than 99 percent of the energy used by living organisms on Earth.

VISUAL Learning

Figure 15-3 Some students may investigate which plant pigments provide which colors in the plant. Allow students to review which trees turn particular colors in your area of the country. L1

Activity

Visual-Spatial Place a prism in a bright light source. As the colors of white light are separated, point out that objects show only the colors that are reflected. All other colors are absorbed. Chlorophyll absorbs every color but green. Green light waves are reflected and not used in photosynthesis. Show a series of objects of different colors and have students tell which colors are absorbed and which are reflected. L2

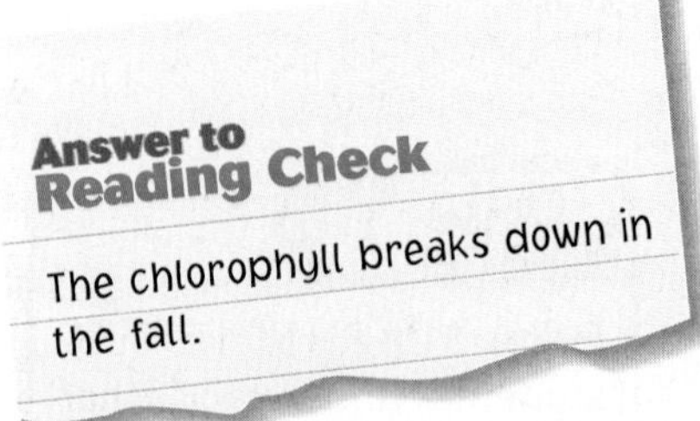
Answer to Reading Check

The chlorophyll breaks down in the fall.

GLENCOE TECHNOLOGY

CD-ROM

Glencoe Science Voyages Interactive CD-ROM

Explorations

Have students do the interactive exploration *What colors of the light spectrum are most important for plant growth?*

Figure 15-3 Light and chlorophyll are both essential parts of photosynthesis.

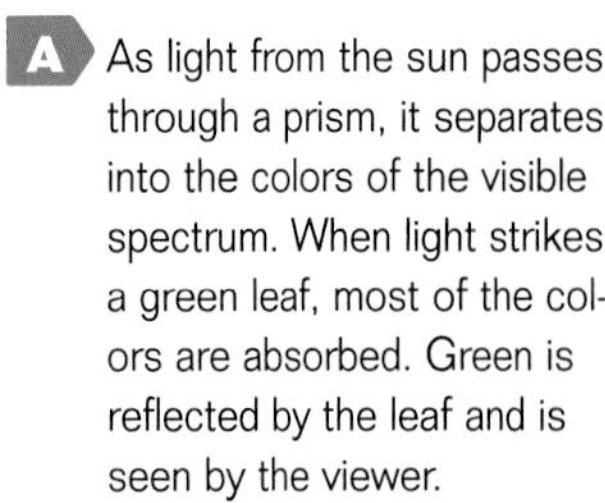
A As light from the sun passes through a prism, it separates into the colors of the visible spectrum. When light strikes a green leaf, most of the colors are absorbed. Green is reflected by the leaf and is seen by the viewer.

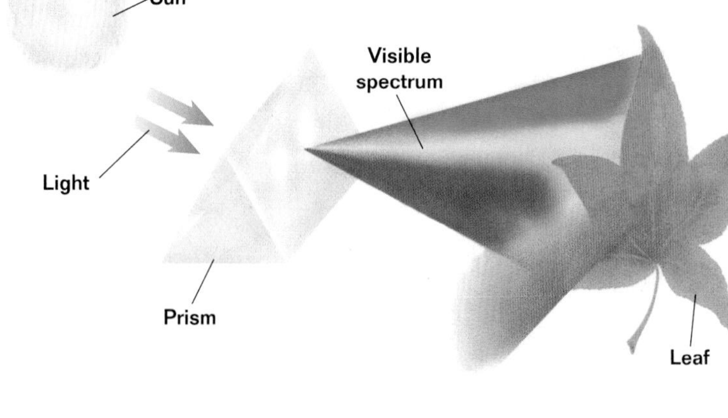

B Leaves of some trees, such as those on this sweet gum, change color in the autumn.

Spring

Summer

Fall

Photosynthesis

Why aren't all the leaves of the trees in **Figure 15-3B** green? If you live in a place that has changing seasons, you may see trees in the fall like in the photograph on the far right. In some places, many trees and bushes change color as the days get shorter and the weather grows colder. Leaves may change from green to red, brown, yellow, or orange. Some plants may even have leaves of different colors at the same time. These colors are the result of pigments in leaves. A pigment is a substance that reflects a particular part of the visible spectrum and absorbs the rest. In the spring and summer, there is so much green pigment chlorophyll in most leaves that it hides all other pigments. In the fall, chlorophyll breaks down and the other pigments become visible. ✓

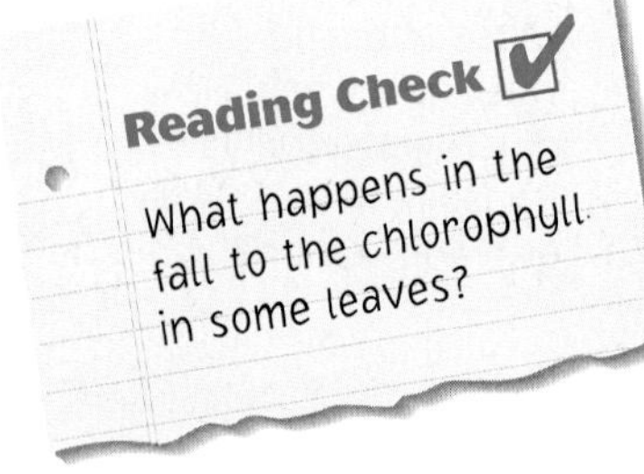
Reading Check ✓

What happens in the fall to the chlorophyll in some leaves?

Integrating the Sciences

Physics In physics, light is studied as energy in the form of particles and waves. The amount of energy increases as the wavelengths decrease. Ask students to research which colors of light have the shortest wavelengths and which have the longest. L2

Content Background

High internal pressure from water can be withstood in plants because they have a cell wall that prevents the cell from bursting.

As shown in **Figure 15-3A,** light from the sun contains all colors. When you see a green leaf, orange carrot, or red rose, you are seeing the reflected color. In plant cells, pigments absorb the other colors and trap light energy.

The Food-Making Process

Chlorophyll is a pigment in plants that traps light energy. Plants use this energy to make food. **Photosynthesis,** illustrated in **Figure 15-4,** is the process in which plants use light energy to produce food.

What do plants use besides light to make food? Carbon dioxide and water are the raw materials for photosynthesis. Some of the light energy trapped in the chlorophyll is used to split water molecules. Light energy is then used to join hydrogen from the water to carbon dioxide molecules. The new molecule formed is a simple sugar called glucose. The chemical bonds of glucose contain the energy a plant uses for growth and maintenance.

MiniLab

Observing Plant Use of Carbon Dioxide

Procedure

1. Pour 5 mL of tap water into a clean test tube.
2. Add 10 drops carbonated water and 20 drops of bromothymol blue indicator to the tap water. Place the test tube in a holder.
3. Write the color of the solution in your Science Journal.
4. Repeat steps 1 and 2. Then, add a sprig of *Elodea* to this test tube.
5. Write the color of this test tube's solution in your Science Journal.
6. Place the two test tubes in sunlight for 30 minutes. Observe the test tubes every five minutes. If using artificial lights, increase the time to one hour.

Analysis

1. In your Science Journal, describe and compare the two test tubes of solution before and after the 15 minutes.
2. What gas did you add to the solution?
3. Relate your observations to photosynthesis.

VISUALIZING Photosynthesis

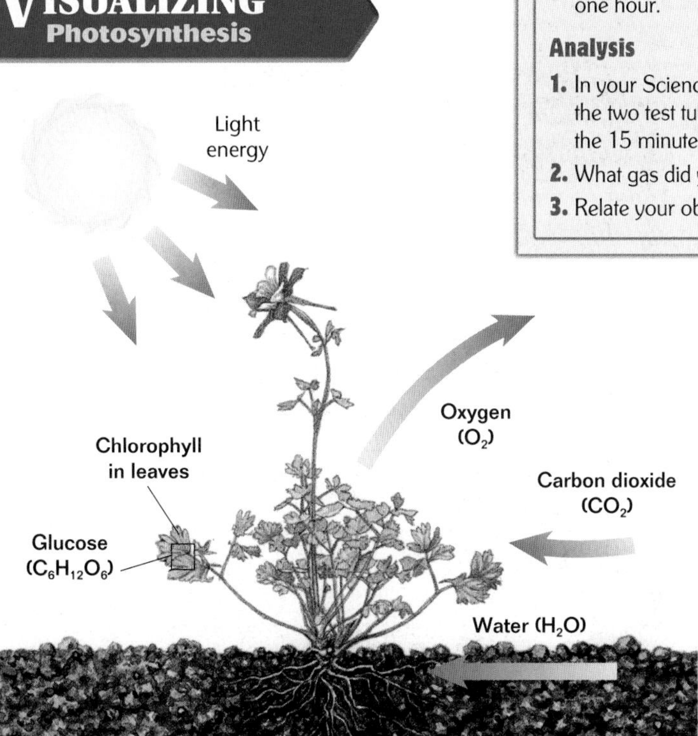

Figure 15-4 During photosynthesis, carbon dioxide from the air, water from the soil, and light energy react to form glucose and oxygen.

MiniLab

Purpose

Visual-Spatial Students will relate the use of carbon dioxide in photosynthesis by observing a chemical change.

Materials

bromothymol blue (20 mL), test tubes (2), test-tube holder or beaker, tap water (10 mL), carbonated water (10 mL), *Elodea* sprig, dropper

Teaching Strategies

Test this activity before class to be sure the color changes are apparent.

Analysis

1. The solution in the test tube without the *Elodea* stayed yellow. The solution in the test tube with *Elodea* changed to blue around the plant.
2. carbon dioxide
3. When *Elodea* is added and light is provided, the plants begin photosynthesis. This removes carbon dioxide, causing a change from yellow to blue in the test tube.

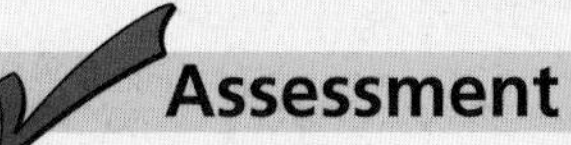

Assessment

Oral To further assess students' understanding of laboratory methods used to detect carbon dioxide, have students hypothesize how they could determine the amount of carbon dioxide used by plants in photosynthesis. Use **Performance Assessment in the Science Classroom,** p. 21.

Integrating the Sciences

Earth Science Have students research how the buildup of carbon dioxide in the atmosphere might affect photosynthesis. *Increased carbon dioxide may correlate to increased photosynthesis in certain localities such as rain forests and marine environments with large amounts of plankton.* L2

Flex Your Brain

Use the Flex Your Brain activity to have students explore PHOTOSYNTHESIS.

Enrichment

Explain to students that photosynthesis consists of two sets of reactions. One set of reactions makes energy directly available to the plant and the other stores energy. Emphasize that the beginning products of photosynthesis are carbon dioxide and water and the ending products are sugar and oxygen. This will help students understand the significance of respiration as the reverse of photosynthesis.

Using Math

six carbon dioxide molecules for every glucose molecule

interNET CONNECTION

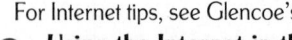

Internet Addresses

____

____

____

____

For Internet tips, see Glencoe's **Using the Internet in the Science Classroom.**

Caption Answer

Figure 15-5 *If there were enough plants, they would supply oxygen to the city's organisms and remove excess carbon dioxide.*

Photosynthesis is illustrated in the following equation:

$$6CO_2 + 6H_2O + \text{light energy} \xrightarrow{\text{chlorophyll}} C_6H_{12}O_6 + 6O_2$$

carbon dioxide, water, glucose, oxygen

A plant needs six molecules of carbon dioxide (CO_2) and six molecules of water (H_2O) to make one molecule of glucose ($C_6H_{12}O_6$). Six molecules of oxygen gas (O_2) are also produced during photosynthesis. Light energy is used in photosynthesis, then stored in the chemical bonds that hold the glucose molecule together.

What happens to the products of photosynthesis? Most of the oxygen from photosynthesis is released through stomata. But some of it is used to break down food molecules and release the energy stored in the chemical bonds of the food molecules. This energy is used for all of the plant's life processes such as growth and reproduction. Glucose is the main form of food for plant cells. A plant usually produces more glucose than it can use. Excess glucose is stored in plants as other sugars and starches. When you eat beets, carrots, potatoes, or onions, you are eating stored food. Glucose is also the basis of a plant's structure. The cellulose in plant cell walls is made from glucose.

Besides glucose, what other sugars do plants produce? Visit the Glencoe Science Web Site at **www.glencoe.com/sec/science** for more information about plant sugars.

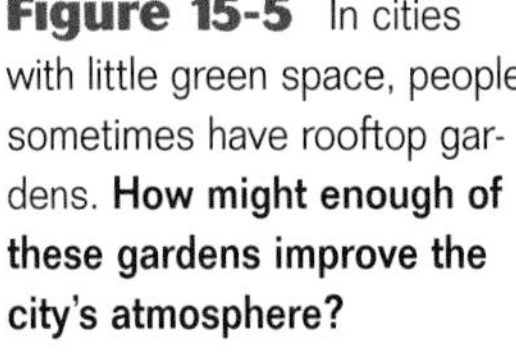

Figure 15-5 In cities with little green space, people sometimes have rooftop gardens. **How might enough of these gardens improve the city's atmosphere?**

Inclusion Strategies

Gifted Have students form an acrostic using the letters of the word *photosynthesis* to describe the process. L3

Importance of Photosynthesis

Why is photosynthesis important to living things? First, photosynthesis is food production. Organisms that carry on photosynthesis provide food for nearly all the other organisms on Earth. Second, photosynthetic organisms, like the plants in **Figure 15-5,** use carbon dioxide and release oxygen. This removes carbon dioxide from the atmosphere and replaces the oxygen most organisms, including humans, need to stay alive. As much as 90 percent of the oxygen entering our atmosphere today is a result of photosynthesis.

In most algae and photosynthetic bacteria, photosynthesis occurs in every cell. However, in green plants, only cells with chloroplasts carry on photosynthesis.

Photosynthesis and Earth's Air

Earth's atmosphere had no oxygen before the evolution of organisms that carry on photosynthesis. In the last 2 billion years, the relative amount of oxygen in Earth's atmosphere has increased more than 50 times. What might happen if photosynthesis suddenly stopped?

Respiration

Look at the photographs in **Figure 15-6.** Do these organisms have anything in common? Both of these organisms are similar in that they break down food to release energy.

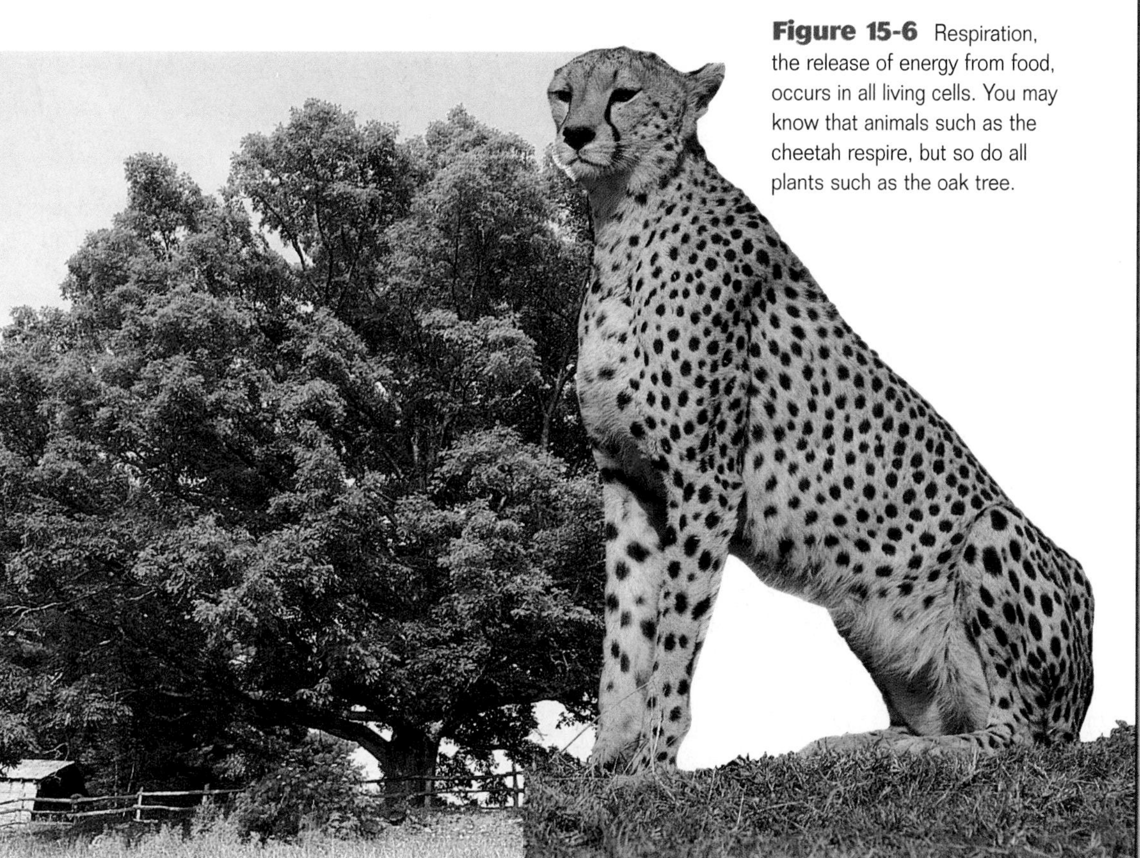

Figure 15-6 Respiration, the release of energy from food, occurs in all living cells. You may know that animals such as the cheetah respire, but so do all plants such as the oak tree.

EARTH SCIENCE INTEGRATION

The balance of CO_2 and O_2 in the atmosphere would be changed. The CO_2 would build up and poison the atmosphere.

VISUAL Learning

Figure 15-5 If you live in an urban area, ask students whether they have plants growing on their roofs. Have them discuss why or why not.

GLENCOE TECHNOLOGY

Videodisc

Glencoe Science Voyages Interactive Videodisc—Life

Side 1, Lesson 4

Photosynthesis and Cellular Respiration

43809

44334

Refer to the Videodisc Teacher Guide for additional bar codes.

Oxygen Supply In temperate forests, trees lose their leaves in winter. Have students research to discover what keeps the world supplied with oxygen during this time. In their Science Journals, have them write what they learned about one-celled, photosynthetic organisms in marine biomes. L2

Purpose

Visual-Spatial Students will record and analyze data that illustrate respiration in yeast. L2 ELL COOP LEARN P

Materials

bromothymol blue (10 mL), yeast suspension (20 drops), sugar solution (10 drops), test tube

Teaching Strategies

- Try the activity several times to gauge the amount of color change after 5, 10, and 15 minutes.
- Prepare the yeast suspension according to directions on the container of yeast.
- Dissolve 5 g of white sugar in a liter of water to make the sugar solution.

Analysis

1. The color gradually changes from blue to green.
2. Yeast carries on respiration, adding carbon dioxide to the solution.
3. Similar results should have occurred.

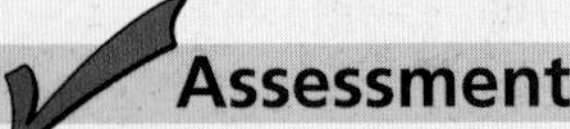

Assessment

Performance To further assess students' understanding of bromothymol blue as an indicator, design an experiment to test a hypothesis stating that respiration takes place in plants at night. Use **Performance Assessment in the Science Classroom,** p. 23.

Demonstrating Respiration in Yeast

Procedure

1. Pour 10 mL of bromothymol blue into a clean test tube.
2. Add 20 drops of yeast suspension and 10 drops of sugar solution.

Analysis

1. Record in your Science Journal any color change observed after five minutes, ten minutes, and 15 minutes.
2. What caused the color change you observed?
3. Compare the results of this MiniLab with those from the one earlier in the chapter.

Respiration is a series of chemical reactions by which all organisms break down food to release energy. The breakdown of food may or may not require oxygen. For organisms that are only one prokaryotic cell—a cell without a nucleus or other organelles—respiration takes place in the cytoplasm of the cell. For organisms made of one or more eukaryotic cells—cells that have a nucleus and other organelles—respiration involves organelles called mitochondria (sing., *mitochodrion*), as shown in **Figure 15-7.** Respiration that uses oxygen to chemically break down food is called aerobic respiration. The overall chemical equation for aerobic respiration is as follows.

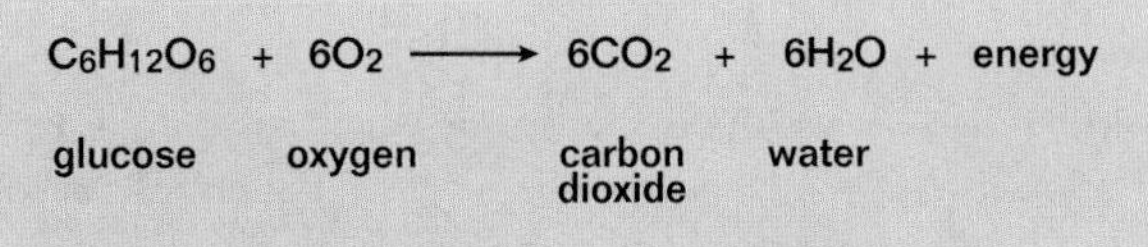

$$C_6H_{12}O_6 + 6O_2 \longrightarrow 6CO_2 + 6H_2O + \text{energy}$$

glucose, oxygen → carbon dioxide, water

Is the equation for aerobic respiration familiar? How does it relate to the chemical equation for photosynthesis? If you look closely, you can see that aerobic respiration is the reverse of photosynthesis. Photosynthesis combines carbon dioxide and water by using light energy. The end products are glucose (food) and oxygen. During photosynthesis, energy is stored in food. Photosynthesis occurs only in cells that contain chlorophyll, such as those in the leaves of plants. Aerobic respiration

Table 15-1

Comparing Photosynthesis and Aerobic Respiration

	Energy	Raw materials	End products	Where
Photosynthesis	stored	water and carbon dioxide, plus energy	glucose, oxygen	cells with chlorophyll
Aerobic respiration	released	glucose, oxygen	water and carbon dioxide, plus energy	all eukaryotic cells

Caption Answer

Figure 15-7 *water vapor and carbon dioxide*

Multiple Learning Styles

Auditory-Musical Have students make up songs that include the equations of photosynthesis and respiration. Then have them sing their songs to the class. L2 COOP LEARN

VISUAL Learning

Figure 15-7 Have students trace the pathways in a mitochondrion of the reactants and products of respiration.

combines oxygen and food to release the energy in the chemical bonds of the food. The end products of aerobic respiration are energy, carbon dioxide, and water. Aerobic respiration occurs in cells with mitochondria. It provides the energy needed by the cell and the entire organism. **Table 15-1** compares the processes of photosynthesis and aerobic respiration.

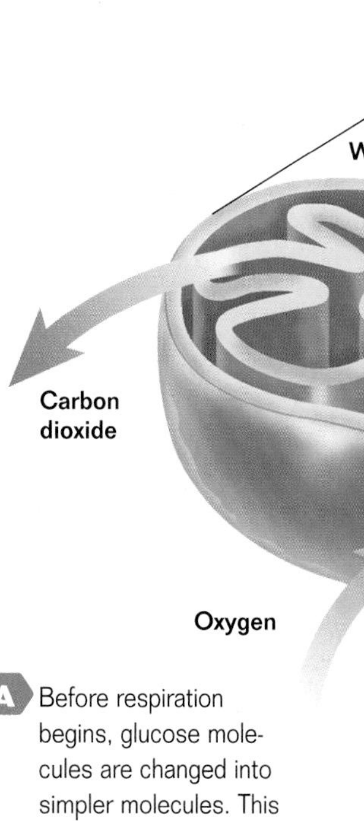

Figure 15-7 Respiration takes place in the mitochondria of eukaryotic cells.

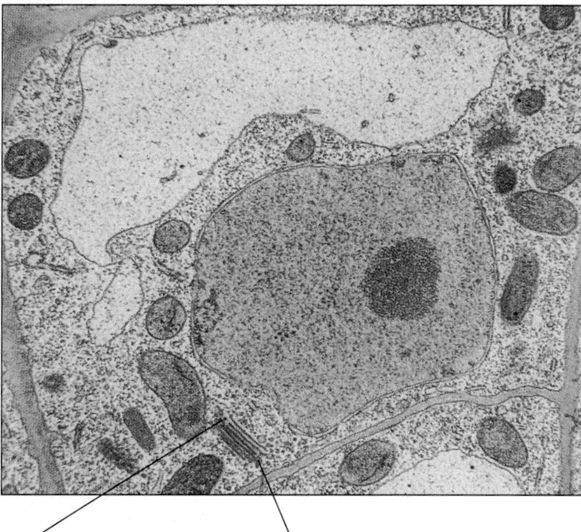

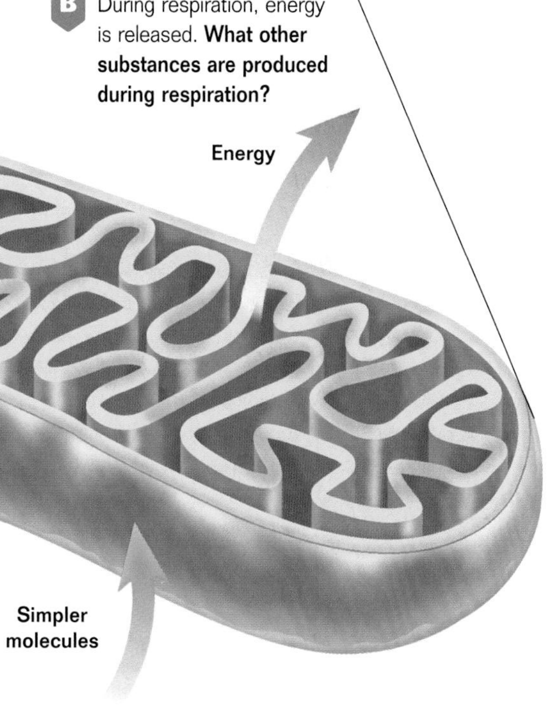

A Before respiration begins, glucose molecules are changed into simpler molecules. This takes place in the cytoplasm. These molecules then enter a mitochondrion, where they react with oxygen.

B During respiration, energy is released. **What other substances are produced during respiration?**

3 Assess

Check for Understanding

Using Science Words

Linguistic Have students look up the words *photo* and *synthesis* in a dictionary. Have them relate the definitions to photosynthesis. *Photo* means light and *synthesis* means the combining of parts to make a whole. L2

Reteach

Visual-Spatial Place one plant in the light and another in a dark area. Keep all other variables constant. Observe the changes in the two plants for a week. Have students explain why the changes occur. L2

Extension

For students who have mastered this section, use the **Reinforcement** and **Enrichment** masters.

Videodisc

STV: Plants

Unit 5 *What is a leaf?*

Photosynthesis 3:30

29400-35535

Refer to the Videodisc Teacher Guide for additional bar codes and teaching strategies.

Guided Reading Strategy

Pair of Pairs This strategy encourages students as partners to respond to a question. They brainstorm together, recording their ideas on one paper. After a few minutes, they share responses with another pair. Finally, the teacher asks the groups of four to share any responses with the class. Have students use the Pair of Pairs strategy on a Thinking Critically question in a Section Assessment in this chapter.

4 Close

Proficiency Prep

Use this quiz to check students' recall of section content.

1. **By what processes are carbon dioxide and water vapor exchanged through the stomata on leaf surfaces?** *diffusion*
2. **What is the loss of water vapor through the stomata of a leaf called?** *transpiration*
3. **What is the process in which plants use energy from light to produce food?** *photosynthesis*
4. **Where does aerobic respiration occur in a cell?** *mitochondria*

Section Assessment

1. Carbon dioxide and water vapor are exchanged by diffusion through the stomata on leaf surfaces.
2. Photosynthesis and respiration form a cycle of energy capture, release, and use.
3. Food molecules in the cytoplasm are broken down into simpler molecules.
4. **Think Critically** Transpiration contributes water vapor to the air.

Using Math

For every sugar molecule respired, six carbon dioxide molecules are produced. There are 36 molecules of carbon dioxide produced from 6 molecules of sugar, $6 \times 6 = 36$.

Importance of Respiration

If food, like the items in **Figure 15-8,** contains energy, why do cells carry out the process of respiration? The energy in food molecules is in a form that cannot be used by cells. During respiration, the food energy is changed into a form all cells can use. This energy drives the life processes used by almost all organisms on Earth. Even the process of photosynthesis uses some of this energy. Aerobic respiration returns carbon dioxide to the atmosphere, where it may again be used by photosynthetic organisms.

Figure 15-8 Humans and other animals depend on the glucose produced by plants during photosynthesis. Animals use the glucose to produce energy through respiration.

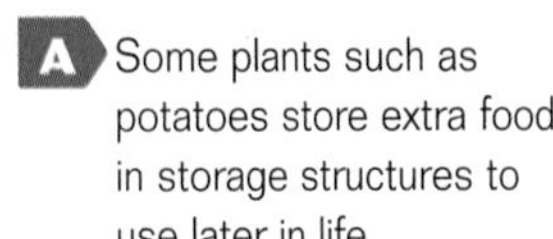

A Some plants such as potatoes store extra food in storage structures to use later in life.

B Wheat and rice are important sources of food for much of the world's population.

Section Assessment

1. Explain how carbon dioxide and water vapor are exchanged by a leaf.
2. Why are photosynthesis and respiration important?
3. What must happen to food molecules before respiration begins?
4. **Think Critically:** Humidity is water vapor in the air. How do plants contribute to humidity?
5. **Skill Builder**
   Observing and Inferring To learn how observation is a good scientific tool, do the **Chapter 15 Skill Activity** on page 756.

Using Math

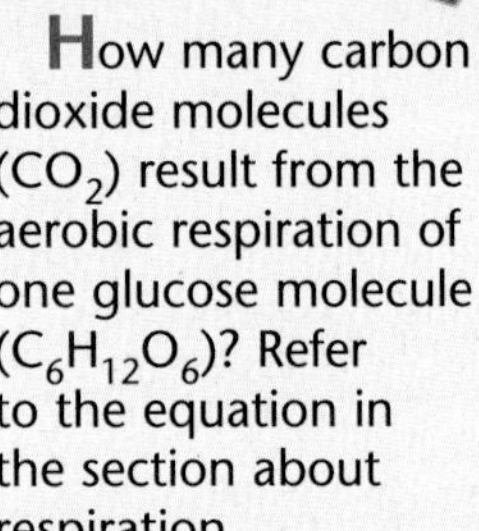

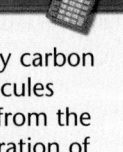

How many carbon dioxide molecules (CO_2) result from the aerobic respiration of one glucose molecule ($C_6H_{12}O_6$)? Refer to the equation in the section about respiration.

Assessment

Performance Using molecular model kits, have groups of students make the reactants of either photosynthesis or aerobic respiration. Exchange reactants between opposite groups and have them create the products of those reactants. Students should discover that the reactants of one are the products of the other. Use **Performance Assessment in the Science Classroom,** p. 97.

Stomata in Leaves

One of the interesting things about leaves is how stomata open and close to allow gases into and out of a leaf. Stomata are usually invisible without the use of a microscope. Try this activity to see some stomata for yourself.

What You'll Investigate

Where are stomata in lettuce leaves?

Goals

- **Describe** guard cells and stomata.
- **Infer** the conditions that make them open and close.

Materials

- Lettuce in dish of water
- Coverslip
- Microscope
- Microscope slide
- Salt solution
- Forceps

Procedure

1. Copy the Stomata Data table into your Science Journal.
2. From a head of lettuce, tear off a piece of an outer, crisp, green leaf.
3. Bend the piece of leaf in half to remove the epidermis, the transparent tissue that covers a leaf. Carefully use a pair of forceps to peel off some of the epidermis. Prepare a wet mount of this tissue.
4. Examine your wet mount slide under low and high power on the microscope. Using **Figure 15-2** as a guide, draw and label this tissue in your Science Journal.
5. Count the total number of stomata in your field of view and then count the number of open stomata. Enter these numbers in the data table.
6. Make a second slide of the lettuce leaf epidermis. This time, place a few drops of salt solution on the leaf instead of water.
7. Repeat steps 4 and 5 with the second wet mount of tissue.
8. Using the following equation, calculate the percent of open stomata.

   (number of stomata open $\div$ total number of stomata) $\times$ 100 = percent open

Stomata Data

	Wet mount	Salt solution mount
Total number of stomata		
Number of open stomata		
Percent open		

Conclude and Apply

1. How are guard cells different from the other cells of the leaf epidermis?
2. **Infer** why fewer stomata were open in the salt solution mount.
3. Which slide preparation had a greater percent of open stomata?
4. What can you **infer** about the function of stomata in a leaf?

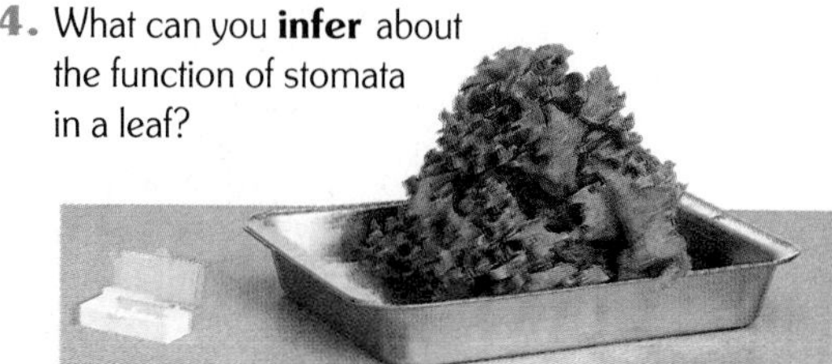

Purpose

Visual-Spatial Students will observe the activity of stomata in green plants. L2 ELL COOP LEARN P

Process Skills

observing and inferring, comparing and contrasting, recognizing cause and effect

Time

45 minutes

Alternate Materials Other leaf tissues that may be substituted for lettuce include onion and celery epidermis.

Teaching Strategies

Remind students that osmosis is diffusion of water through a semipermeable membrane.

Troubleshooting If an alternative leaf tissue is used, try the activity beforehand to make sure observations will be the same.

Answers to Questions

1. The guard cells are the only cells in the epidermis that have chloroplasts.
2. Salt water causes water to leave the guard cells, causing them to become limp and close.
3. The wet mount with plain water had a greater percentage of open stomata.
4. Stomata provide an entry into the leaf for carbon dioxide from the atmosphere.

Assessment

Performance To further assess students' understanding of stomata, have them use one of the materials from the alternate materials list and describe the outcome. Use **Performance Assessment in the Science Classroom,** p. 25.

SECTION 15•2

Prepare

Refer to **What are plant responses?, Plant Hormones,** and **Photoperiods** on p. 424F.

Preplanning

Refer to the **Chapter Organizer** on pp. 424A–B.

1 Motivate

Bellringer

Before presenting the lesson, display **Section Focus Transparency 41** on the overhead projector. Use the accompanying **Focus Activity** worksheet. L2 ELL

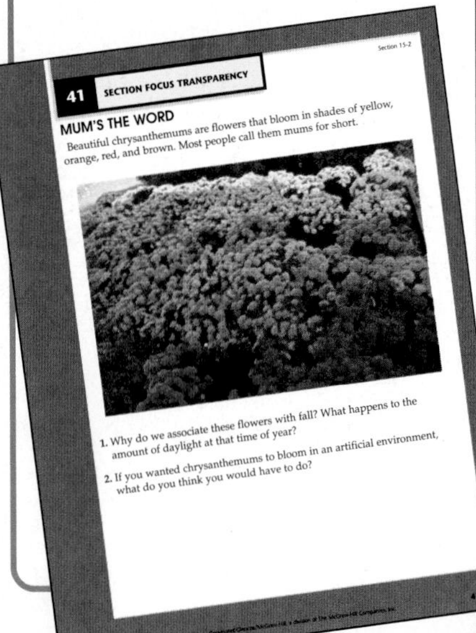

Section 15-2

41 SECTION FOCUS TRANSPARENCY

MUM'S THE WORD

Beautiful chrysanthemums are flowers that bloom in shades of yellow, orange, red, and brown. Most people call them mums for short.

1. Why do we associate these flowers with fall? What happens to the amount of daylight at that time of year?
2. If you wanted chrysanthemums to bloom in an artificial environment, what do you think you would have to do?

41

Tying to Previous Knowledge

Review plant parts such as roots, stems, and leaves with students. Have them name the functions of each part.

15•2 Plant Responses

What You'll Learn

- The relationship between stimuli and tropisms in plants
- Differences between long-day and short-day plants
- How plant hormones and responses are related

Vocabulary

tropism
auxin
photoperiodism
long-day plant
short-day plant
day-neutral plant

Why It's Important

- You will be a better gardener if you understand how plants respond to certain stimuli.

What are plant responses?

It's dark. You're alone in a room watching a horror film on television. Suddenly, the telephone near you rings. You jump, and your heart begins to beat faster. Did you know that you've just responded to a stimulus? A stimulus is anything in the environment that causes a change in the behavior of an organism. The organism's change in behavior is called a response. A stimulus may come from outside or inside the organism. The ringing telephone is an example of an outside stimulus. It caused you to jump, a response. Inside stimuli include chemical reactions and hormones. Hormones are substances made by cells for use somewhere else in the organism. Your beating heart is a response to inside stimuli. All living organisms, including plants, respond to stimuli. Plants respond to outside and inside stimuli. The response of a plant to an outside stimulus is a **tropism.** A tropism may be seen as movement or a change in growth. Tropisms can be positive or negative. For example, plants might grow toward or away from a stimulus.

Tropisms

Touch is one stimulus that results in a change in a plant's behavior. The pea plants in **Figure 15-9** show a response to touch. The response to touch is thigmotropism, from the Greek

Figure 15-9
The pea plant's tendrils respond to touch by coiling around things. The response to touch is called *thigmotropism.*

Resource Manager

The following **Teacher Classroom Resources** can be used with Section 15-2:

 **Reproducible Masters**

Activity Worksheets, pp. 83–84 L2

Laboratory Manual, pp. 89–92 L2

Enrichment, p. 41 L3

Reinforcement, p. 41 L2

Critical Thinking/Problem Solving, p. 15 L2

Multicultural Connections, pp. 29–30 L2

Study Guide, pp. 59–60 L1 ELL

436 CHAPTER 15 PLANT PROCESSES

Figure 15-10 Plants also show phototropism. This plant is obviously growing toward the light, an example of positive phototropism. **What do you think would happen if the plant were turned halfway around?**

word *thigma,* meaning "touch." Plants also respond to the stimuli of light, gravity, temperature, and amount of water.

Did you ever see a plant leaning toward a window? Light is an important stimulus to plants. When a plant responds to sunlight, the cells on the side of the plant opposite the light get longer than those facing the light. This causes the plant to bend toward the light. The response of a plant to light is called phototropism. A plant growing toward light is called a positive phototropism, as shown in **Figure 15-10.**

The response of an organism to gravity is called gravitropism. The downward growth of plant roots is a positive gravitropism. A stem growing upward is a negative gravitropism.

Plant Hormones

When you visit a supermarket or fruit stand, have you ever noticed that oranges are all about the same size and color? In nature, orange trees flower and produce fruit over a period of time. How do growers get fruits to respond so that most of it is ripe when it reaches the market? One way that growers do this is by using plant hormones.

Auxin and Ethylene

Plant hormones are chemical substances that affect growth. An **auxin** is a type of plant hormone. One of the ways auxin affects plants is that it causes plant stems and leaves to exhibit positive phototropism. When light shines on a plant from one side, the auxin moves to the shaded side of the stem. The auxin causes cells on the shaded side of the stem to increase in length. This causes the stem to curve toward the light.

interNET CONNECTION

Auxin and ethylene are just two of the hormones found in plants. Visit the Glencoe Science Web Site at www.glencoe.com/sec/science for more information about other plant hormones.

2 Teach

VISUAL Learning

Figure 15-10 Use this figure to introduce plant responses. Point out that tropisms are slow growth responses. Other responses may be quick and not involve growth.

Caption Answer

Figure 15-10 *The plant would grow the other direction, straightening then bending again.*

Activity

Grow a pea plant from a seed. Place a stick in the pot and the stem and tendrils will respond to touch by growing around the stick.

interNET CONNECTION

Internet Addresses

____

____

____

____

For Internet tips, see Glencoe's **Using the Internet in the Science Classroom.**

Flex Your Brain

Use the Flex Your Brain activity to have students explore PHOTOPERIODISM.

Content Background

Ewiti Kurosawa, a Japanese scientist, discovered the plant hormone gibberellin while investigating the cause of "foolish rice disease." He discovered that rice seedlings grew extremely tall after being infected with a fungus that secreted this substance. He named the substance gibberellin after the genus of the fungus, *Gibberella fujikuroi.* Later, two other Japanese scientists, Yabuta and Sumiki, purified the hormone.

Quick Demo

Use an activity kit for rapid-growing plants of the genus *Brassica,* available from biological supply houses, to demonstrate plant responses to hormones. These plants go from seed to flower in about 30 days.

Enrichment

Visit a commercial greenhouse as a field trip to find out how plant growers encourage plants to flower at times other than their normal flowering season.

VISUAL Learning

Figure 15-11 Point out that hormones may be simple molecules that cause complex responses in organisms.

Problem Solving

Solve the Problem

Auxin is the hormone primarily responsible for gravitropism. Therefore, auxin likely played the largest role in the response of the plant.

Think Critically

Jason would find that the roots were growing in a direction opposite to that of the stem's growth.

GLENCOE TECHNOLOGY

Videodisc

The Infinite Voyage: The Living Clock

Chapter 4 *Circadian Rhythm and the Biological Clock* 5:00

Refer to the Videodisc Teacher Guide for bar codes and teaching strategies.

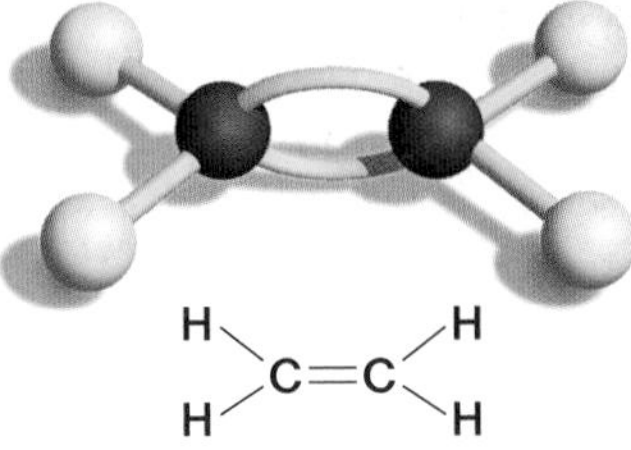

Figure 15-11 Ethylene, C_2H_4, is the plant hormone responsible for fruit ripening, such as these grapes.

Many plants produce the hormone ethylene, a chemical of carbon and hydrogen, as illustrated in **Figure 15-11.** Ethylene causes different plant responses. One response is that it causes fruit to ripen.

Today, fruit growers and shippers use this knowledge to get ripe fruit to market. Fruits such as oranges, grapes, and bananas are picked when they are still green. Green fruit is easier to handle because it does not bruise like ripe fruit does. During shipping, green fruit is exposed to ethylene gas. When the fruit arrives at the store, most of it has ripened.

Problem Solving

Predicting Plant Responses

Jason and his family returned from their two-week vacation and found that several potted plants on the patio were on their sides. After unpacking the car, Jason began to set up the potted plants. To his surprise, the plants looked like they were growing sideways. Later that day, Jason's grandmother telephoned. Jason told her about the plants. She told him not to worry because the plants would soon start to grow upright again.

Solve the Problem

1. Explain why the plants grew as they did.
2. What hormone may have played a part in this plant response?

Think Critically: Predict what Jason might find if he removed a plant's pot and looked at its roots. Explain.

Across the Curriculum

Geography Have students research the place of origin for different plants. Then, have them plot the locations on a world map. P

Photoperiods

Sunflowers bloom in the summer, and cherry trees flower in the spring. Some plant species produce flowers at specific times during the year. **Photoperiodism** is a plant's response to the number of hours of daylight and darkness it receives daily.

Earth makes one revolution around the sun every year. As it moves in its orbit about the sun, Earth also rotates. One rotation takes 24 hours. Because Earth is tilted about 23.5° from a line perpendicular to its orbit, the hours of daylight and darkness vary with the seasons. You may have noticed that the sun sets later in summer than in winter. These changes in lengths of daylight and darkness affect plant growth.

Most plants require a specific length of darkness to begin the flowering process. Generally, plants that require less than ten to 12 hours of darkness are called **long-day plants.** You may be familiar with long-day plants such as spinach, lettuce, and beets. Those plants that need 12 or more hours of darkness are called **short-day plants.** Some short-day plants are poinsettias, strawberries, and ragweed. **Figure 15-12** shows both long-day plants and short-day plants.

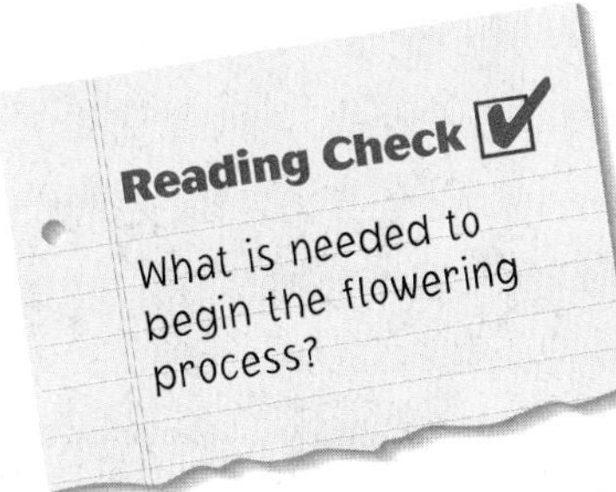

Figure 15-12 Long-day plants such as zinnias (A) and short-day plants such as primroses (B) flower in response to specific periods of darkness.

EARTH SCIENCE INTEGRATION

Latitude and season determine the hours of daylight. In latitudes near both poles, the hours of daylight vary from none to 24. As expected, midlatitudes are in between the two extremes. At the equator, daylight is always about 12 hours. The reason for this is the tilt of Earth as it revolves around the sun.

Answer to Reading Check

a certain number of hours of darkness

3 Assess

Check for Understanding

Quick Demo

Visual-Spatial After cutting two stems of *Coleus*, apply a rooting hormone to one stem, then plant both stems. After several days, have students observe the roots of both stems. Ask them to explain the results.

Reteach

Use different plants to demonstrate various tropisms. For example, use a morning glory to show a thigmotropism, or a plant that leans toward the light to show a phototropism. L2 ELL

Extension

For students who have mastered this section, use the **Reinforcement** and **Enrichment** masters.

Figure 15-13 Day-neutral plants, as seen in this garden, produce flowers all summer long.

Other plants like the marigolds shown in **Figure 15-13** are day-neutral. **Day-neutral plants** have no specific photoperiod, and the flowering process can begin within a range of hours of darkness.

In nature, photoperiodism is one factor that affects where flowering plants can grow and produce fruit. Even if the proper temperature and other growing conditions for a plant are in a particular environment, the plant will not flower and produce fruit without the correct photoperiod. Sometimes, the photoperiod of a plant has a narrow range. For example, some soybeans will flower with 14.5 hours of daylight but will not flower with only 14 hours of daylight. Farmers must choose the variety of soybeans with a photoperiod that matches the hours of daylight where they plant their crop.

Today, greenhouse growers can provide any length of artificial daylight or darkness. This means that all types of flowers are available year-round. You can buy short-day plants during the summer and long-day plants during the winter.

Section Assessment

1. Describe the difference between a response and a tropism.
2. Compare photoperiodism and phototropism.
3. Some red raspberries produce fruit in late spring, then again in the fall. What term describes their photoperiod?
4. **Think Critically:** What is the relationship between plant hormones and tropisms?
5. **Skill Builder**
   Comparing and Contrasting Different plant parts exhibit positive and negative tropisms. Compare and contrast the responses of roots, stems, and leaves to light. If you need help, refer to Comparing and Contrasting in the **Skill Handbook** on page 720.

Science Journal

For three years, a farmer in Costa Rica grew healthy strawberry plants. But, each year he was disappointed because the plants never produced any fruit. In your Science Journal, explain why this happened.

4 Close

Proficiency Prep

Use this quiz to check students' recall of section content.

1. **What is anything in the environment that affects the behavior of an organism?** *stimulus*
2. **When the plant responds to light by growing toward it, what term is used for this response?** *phototropism*
3. **What is the flowering response of plants to the change in the length of the period of darkness?** *photoperiodism*

Section Assessment

1. A response may include any reaction to environmental change, but a tropism is a plant-growth response to an external stimulus.
2. Photoperiodism is the plant-flowering response to the length of the period of darkness, but phototropism is any growth response to light.
3. short-day
4. **Think Critically** Plant hormones are responsible for tropisms.

Students might indicate that the environment is right for berries to grow. However, if they'd learned about photoperiodism, they would know that strawberries are short-day plants. Because Costa Rica is near the equator, the days are about the same length as the nights.

5. **Skill Builder**
Roots tend to grow away from light, while leaves and stems tend to grow toward light.

Assessment

Oral Use this Skill Builder to assess students' abilities to compare and contrast the responses of roots, stems, and leaves to light by having them explain their results to you. Use **Performance Assessment in the Science Classroom,** p. 71.

440 CHAPTER 15 PLANT PROCESSES

How it Works

Carnivorous Plants

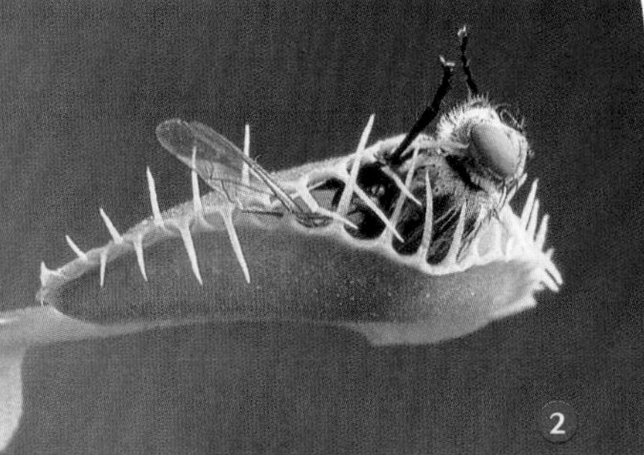

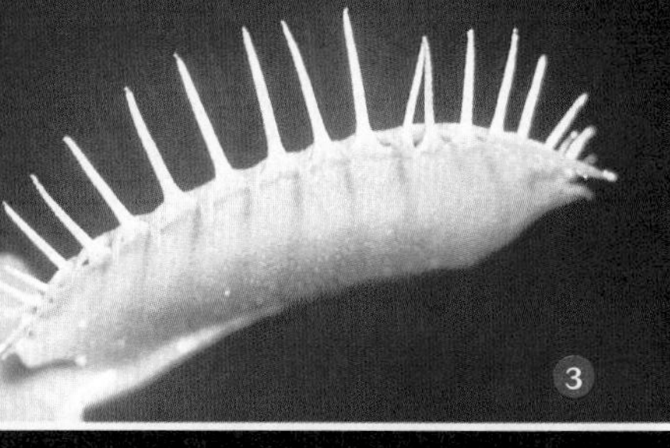

Carnivorous plants grow in soils that lack or are low in certain nutrients, particularly nitrogen. Over time, these plants have evolved ways to secure the nutrients they need. A Venus's-flytrap is one kind of carnivorous plant. It is currently on the list of endangered species. The ones available in stores are grown in nurseries because collecting Venus's-flytraps in the wild is illegal.

EATING HABITS OF A VENUS'S-FLYTRAP

1. The leaves form a hinged trap. Each half of the trap has three trigger hairs (see arrow) in a triangular arrangement.
2. When an insect or other small animal touches two of these hairs in quick succession, it causes a series of reactions that snap the trap shut within 0.4 s.
3. Stiff hairs along the outer edges of the leaf interlock, preventing the animal's escape.
4. Glands on the leaf secrete enzymes that help digest the prey. The glands are stimulated as the prey struggles to get free.
5. Digestion takes about ten days. During this time, the plant absorbs the digested nutrients. The leaf opens again when digestion and absorption are complete. The insect remains are then blown away.

Think Critically

1. Insects and other small animals provide carnivorous plants with nitrogen compounds. From what other sources do these plants get nutrients?

2. A pitcher plant is another carnivorous plant. Look again at the name of this plant. How do you think this plant traps its prey?

Career CONNECTION

Knowing about soils is important when growing Venus's-flytraps or any plants. Soil science is called *agronomy*. An agronomist studies the biological, chemical, and physical components and properties of soil. Research this career, and then make a list of jobs that require a degree in agronomy or knowledge of soil science.

NATIONAL GEOGRAPHIC

How it Works

Purpose

Students learn how a Venus's-flytrap uses its modified leaves to trap small prey.

The digestion of prey by carnivorous plants is analogous to digestion in animals in that both involve complex chemical processes. Unlike animals, however, plants do not have digestive organs.

The rapid closure of a Venus's-flytrap depends mainly on air temperature. It is thought that the closure is due to the loss of turgor in mesophyll cells at the leaf base. It is known that a decrease in ATP occurs each time the leaves close.

VISUAL Learning

Help students find the trigger hairs on each leaf.

Teaching Strategies

Have small groups of students demonstrate how a Venus's-flytrap catches and eventually consumes its prey. Allow students to make simple props and costumes.

Thinking Critically

1. from the soil and photosynthesis
2. Rainwater fills the pitcherlike leaf that has a slippery surface. Insects and other small animals that are attracted to the plants slip and fall into the water and drown.

Career CONNECTION

An agronomist earns at least a bachelor's degree at a four-year college. Some two-year colleges offer associate degrees in agronomy. There are many careers that require knowledge of agronomy. For more information, contact the nearest office of the U.S. Department of Agriculture, Soil Conservation Service.

Activity 15·2 Design Your Own Experiment

Recognize the Problem

Purpose

 **Logical-Mathematical** Students will design and carry out an experiment to observe plant tropisms in plant seedlings. L2 ELL COOP LEARN P

Process Skills

observing and inferring, communicating, making and using tables, comparing and contrasting, recognizing cause and effect, forming a hypothesis, designing an experiment, separating and controlling variables, interpreting data, using numbers

Time

1 period to set up; 10 minutes per day for up to two weeks

Materials

petri dish, tape, string, corn seeds, bean seeds, paper towel, water, ring stand

Safety Precautions

Some kinds of seeds are poisonous. Do not let students put any seeds in their mouths.

Form a Hypothesis

Possible Hypotheses

Student hypotheses will vary. Possible hypotheses for this activity are "Corn seedling roots will show positive gravitropism," "Corn seedling stems will show negative gravitropism," and "Corn seedlings will not show any tropisms."

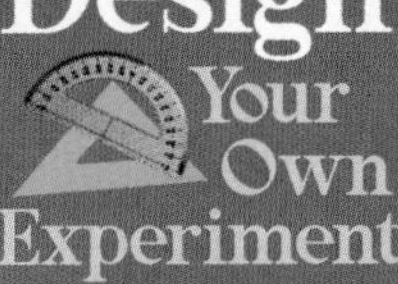

Activity 15·2

Plant Tropisms

Possible Materials

- Petri dish
- Tape
- String
- Corn seeds
- Bean seeds
- Paper towels
- Water

Have you ever seen a Venus's-flytrap's leaves close around an insect? Its movement was a response to a stimulus. In this case, the stimulus was the movement of the insect against sensitive, hairlike structures on the leaves. Tropisms are specific plant responses to stimuli outside of the plant. They can be positive or negative. What stimuli will cause responses by plants?

Recognize the Problem

How do plants respond to stimuli?

Form a Hypothesis

Based on your knowledge of tropisms, state a hypothesis about how the plant will respond to a stimulus.

Goals

- **Design** an experiment that tests the effects of a variable.
- **Observe** and analyze a plant response to a stimulus.

Safety Precautions

Some kinds of seeds are poisonous. Do not put any seed in your mouth.

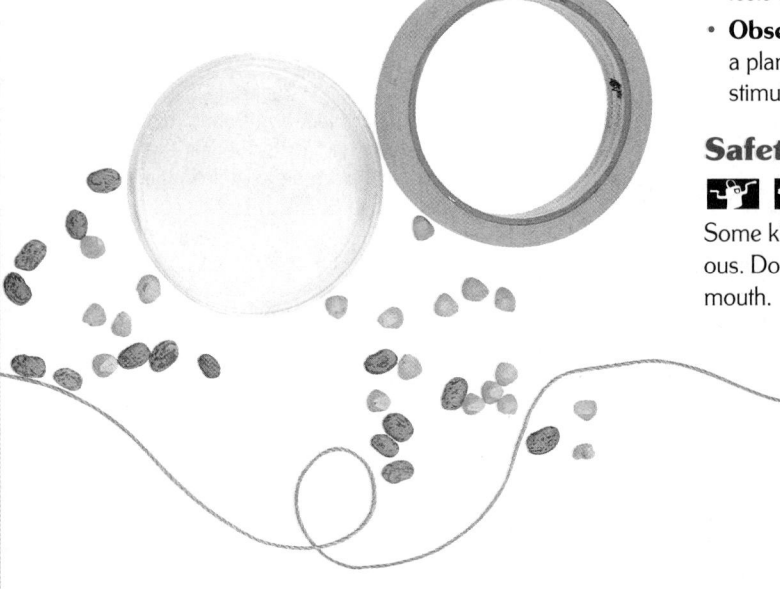

Test Your Hypothesis

Possible Procedures

Procedures will vary depending on the stimulus chosen by the student. Students should set up a control group and an experimental group. Only the experimental group is exposed to the stimulus. Stimuli may be any of those discussed in the chapter or chosen by students. Observe the experiment for several days. Record any observations and data.

Test Your Hypothesis

Plan

1. As a group, agree upon and write out a hypothesis statement.
2. As a group, **list** the steps needed to test your hypothesis. Be specific, describing exactly what you will do at each step. **List** your materials.
3. It is important to keep the seeds moist during the experiment. **Devise a method** to keep your seeds moist.
4. **Read** over your entire experiment to make sure that all your steps are in a logical order.
5. **Identify** any constants, variables, and controls of the experiment.
6. Is it necessary to run any tests more than one time?
7. If you need a data table, design one in your Science Journal so that it is ready to use as your group collects data.
8. Will the data be summarized in a graph? If yes, what kind of graph would be most useful?

Do

1. Make sure your teacher approves your plan before you proceed.
2. Carry out the experiment as planned.
3. While you are conducting the experiment, write down any observations that you make and complete the data table in your Science Journal.

Analyze Your Data

1. **Compare** your results with those of other groups.
2. **Identify** how the plants responded to the stimulus.

Draw Conclusions

1. What name would you give to the response you observed?
2. **Classify** the responses as positive or negative.
3. Infer why many plant growers sprout seeds under artificial light from lamps that are placed just a short distance above the soil.

Teaching Strategies

- Be sure that students have a hypothesis that can be tested during the time available.
- If students decide to test a germinating seedling's response to gravity in a petri dish, be sure that the dish is kept vertical with seeds oriented in different directions.
- Be sure students understand that the same stimulus may elicit a positive tropism in one part of the plant and a negative tropism in another part.
- Be sure students use a reasonable number of plants in each group.

Expected Outcome

Outcomes will vary, depending on the stimulus chosen. For instance, plant stems and leaves react negatively to gravity but positively to light, while roots should have the opposite reactions.

Error Analysis

Have students who chose the same hypothesis compare their results and explain any differences.

Analyze Your Data

1. Groups with similar experimental designs should have similar results.
2. Depending on the stimulus, response may be positive or negative.

Draw Conclusions

1. The responses will be tropisms. The particular tropism depends on the experiment.
2. The tropism will be positive or negative, depending on the experiment.
3. to keep stems straight and strong

GO Further

Students should produce an experimental design similar to the one for the original activity that will test a separate stimulus.

Assessment

Portfolio Have students make a labeled poster of their experimental results and share it with the class. Use **Performance Assessment in the Science Classroom,** p. 73. P

Chapter 15 Reviewing Main Ideas

Reviewing Main Ideas can be used to preview, review, reteach, and condense chapter content.

Preview

Linguistic Before reading this chapter, have students try to answer the questions in their Science Journals. Use student answers as a source for discussion throughout the chapter.

Review

Interpersonal Have students compare their answers with those of other students in the class.

Reteach

Visual-Spatial Ask students to look at the illustrations on these pages and describe details that support the main ideas of the chapter.

OUT OF TIME?

Auditory-Musical If time does not permit teaching the entire chapter, use the information on these pages along with the chapter Audiocassettes to present the material in a condensed format.

Chapter 15 Reviewing Main Ideas

For a **preview** of this chapter, study this Reviewing Main Ideas before you read the chapter. After you have studied this chapter, you can use the Reviewing Main Ideas to **review** the chapter.

The Glencoe MindJogger, Audiocassettes, and CD-ROM provide additional opportunities for review.

Section

15-1 PHOTOSYNTHESIS AND RESPIRATION

Gases like carbon dioxide and water vapor enter and leave a plant through openings called **stomata.** Stomata are usually found in the epidermis covering a leaf. Two guard cells surround each stoma. Water diffusing into and out of the guard cells causes stomata to open and close. ***What role do stomata play in transpiration?***

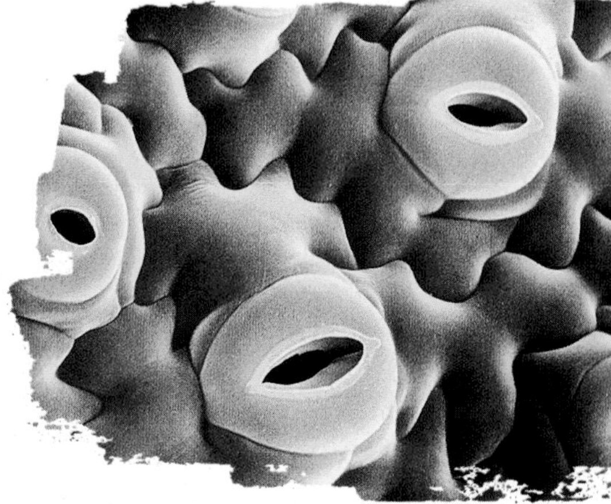

PHOTOSYNTHESIS

In plants, food is produced during the process of **photosynthesis.** Photosynthesis takes place in the chloroplasts of plant cells. Light energy is trapped by chlorophyll, the green pigment in chloroplasts. This energy is used to produce glucose and oxygen from carbon dioxide and water. The energy is stored in the chemical bonds of glucose. Photosynthesis provides the food for most organisms on Earth. ***Why are plants called producers?***

Cultural Diversity

Severo Ochoa Have students research the efforts of Spanish-American biochemist Severo Ochoa (1905–1993) toward the modern understanding of the citric acid cycle and photosynthesis. Ochoa showed how the oxidation of one glucose molecule could yield 36 ATP molecules. He also elucidated the mechanisms of the citric acid cycle and photosynthesis by identifying the function of key enzymes. Ochoa's research in cellular respiration in the 1930s and 1940s ultimately resulted in the discovery of the mechanisms of RNA and DNA synthesis, for which Ochoa and colleague Arthur Kornberg recieved a Nobel prize in 1959.

Reading Check ✓

What approach to reading is most helpful to you? Is it asking yourself questions, outlining, or something else? Share your approach with another student.

RESPIRATION

All organisms use **respiration** to release the energy stored in food molecules. The process begins in the cytoplasm of cells. First, food molecules are broken down into simpler forms. In prokaryotic cells, the process continues in the cytoplasm and some energy is released. Eukaryotic cells generally use oxygen to complete respiration. The release of energy occurs in the mitochondria. Carbon dioxide and water vapor are also products of respiration in eukaryotic cells. ***What are the three products of respiration for most eukaryotic cells?***

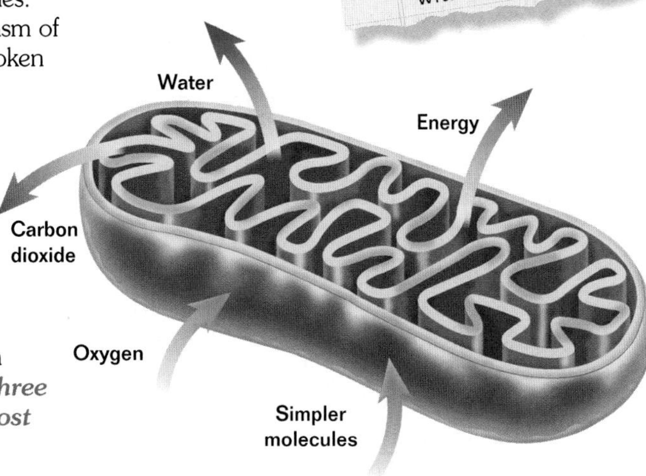

Section **15-2 PLANT RESPONSES**

Plants respond to stimuli. The response may be a movement, change in growth, or the beginning of some process, such as flowering. A stimulus from outside the plant is called a **tropism.** Outside stimuli include such things as light, gravity, and touch. The lengths of daylight and darkness each day may affect flowering times of plants. Hormones are stimuli from inside plants. These chemicals affect plants in many ways. **Auxin** and ethylene are two plant hormones. ***What things may act as outside stimuli for plants?***

Answers to Questions

Section 15-1

Photosynthesis and Respiration Stomata provide an opening through which water vapor may leave a plant's leaves.

Photosynthesis Plants are called producers because they produce usable energy as food for all organisms.

Respiration Aerobic respiration produces carbon dioxide, water, and energy.

Section 15-2

Plant Responses Light, gravity, and touch are some outside stimuli of plants.

GLENCOE TECHNOLOGY

CD-ROM

Glencoe Science Voyages Interactive CD-ROM

Chapter Summaries and Quizzes

Have students read the Chapter Summary then take the Chapter Quiz to determine whether they have mastered chapter content.

Assessment

Portfolio Encourage students to place in their portfolios one or two items of what they consider to be their best work. Examples include:

- MiniLab, p. 432
- Activity 15-1, p. 435
- Across the Curriculum, p. 438
- Activity 15-2, pp. 442–443 P

Performance Additional performance assessments may be found in the **Performance Assessment and Science Integration Activities.** Performance Task Assessment Lists and rubrics for evaluating these activities can be found in Glencoe's **Performance Assessment in the Science Classroom.**

Using Vocabulary

1. a
2. e
3. i
4. g
5. f

interNET CONNECTION To reinforce chapter vocabulary, use the **Study Guide for Content Mastery** booklet. Also available are the activities in the Interactive Tutor for **Glencoe Science Voyages** on the Glencoe Science Web Site. **www.glencoe.com/sec/science**

Checking Concepts

6. C	11. B
7. B	12 D
8. D	13. C
9. C	4. D
10. D	15. A

Thinking Critically

16. If bananas are picked when they are ripe, they bruise when handled and may be overripe by the time they arrive at a store. Green bananas do not easily bruise, and they ripen when exposed to ethylene.
17. (A) positive phototropism or negative gravitropism; (B) positive gravitropism; (C) positive phototropism; (D) positive thigmotropism
18. Oxygen is a by-product of photosynthesis. Until organisms that used carbon dioxide for photosynthesis existed, little oxygen was available.
19. Crabapple trees bloom in the spring when the days are short and nights are long. The number of daylight hours during the summer exceeds a crabapple's photoperiod.
20. Day-neutral plants will flower anywhere if they receive a minimum number of hours of sunlight and other environmental conditions are right. Long-day plants require the number of hours of daylight that occurs near the equator.

Chapter 15 Assessment

Using Vocabulary

a. auxin	f. respiration
b. day-neutral plant	g. short-day plant
c. long-day plant	h. stomata
d. photoperiodism	i. transpiration
e. photosynthesis	j. tropism

Match each phrase with the correct term from the list of Vocabulary words.

1. a plant hormone
2. using light to make glucose and oxygen
3. loss of water through stomata
4. plant that requires long nights to flower
5. releases energy from food

Checking Concepts

Choose the word or phrase that best answers the question.

6. What enters a plant when stomata open?
   A) sugar C) carbon dioxide
   B) water D) light
7. Which of these is a product of respiration?
   A) CO_2 C) C_2H_4
   B) O_2 D) H_2
8. Water, carbon dioxide, and energy are all products of what plant process?
   A) cell division C) growth
   B) photosynthesis D) respiration
9. What type of plant needs short nights to flower?
   A) day-neutral C) long-day
   B) short-day D) nonvascular
10. What do you call such things as light, touch, and gravity that cause plant responses?
   A) tropisms C) responses
   B) growth behaviors D) stimuli
11. What is a plant's response to gravity called?
   A) phototropism C) thigmotropism
   B) gravitropism D) hydrotropism
12. What are plant substances that affect plant growth called?
   A) tropisms C) germination
   B) glucose D) hormones
13. Leaves change colors because what substance breaks down?
   A) hormone C) chlorophyll
   B) carotenoid D) cytoplasm
14. What is a function of stomata?
   A) photosynthesis
   B) to guard the interior cells
   C) to allow sugar to escape
   D) to permit the release of oxygen
15. What are the products of photosynthesis?
   A) glucose and oxygen
   B) carbon dioxide and water
   C) chlorophyll and glucose
   D) carbon dioxide and oxygen

Thinking Critically

16. Growers of bananas pick green bananas, then treat them with ethylene during shipping. Why?
17. Identify each response as a positive or negative tropism.
   a. stem grows up
   b. roots grow down
   c. plant grows toward light
   d. a vine grows around a pole
18. Scientists who study sedimentary rocks and fossils suggest that oxygen did not occur on Earth until plantlike protists appeared. Why?
19. Explain why crab apple trees bloom in the spring but not in the summer.
20. Why do day-neutral and long-day plants grow best in countries near the equator?

Developing Skills

If you need help, refer to the Skill Handbook.

21. **Hypothesizing:** Make a hypothesis about when guard cells open and close in desert plants.
22. **Designing an Experiment to Test a Hypothesis:** Design an experiment to test your hypothesis from question 21.
23. **Observing and Inferring:** Based on your knowledge of plants, infer how the number and location of stomata differ in land and water plants.
24. **Classifying:** Make a chart that classifies these plants according to their photoperiod: flower year-round—corn, dandelion, tomato; flower in the spring, fall, or winter—chrysanthemum, rice, poinsettia; flower in summer—spinach, lettuce, petunias.
25. **Comparing and Contrasting:** Compare and contrast the action of auxin and the action of ethylene on a plant.
26. **Concept Mapping:** Complete the following concept map using the terms and plants in question 24.

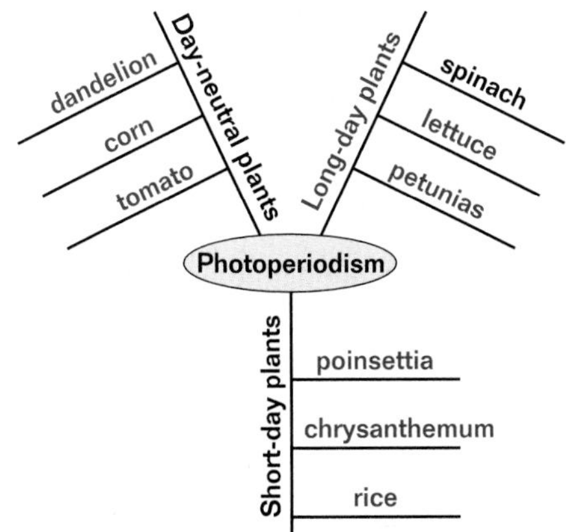

Test-Taking Tip

You Are Smarter Than You Think
Nothing on the science tests you will take this year is too difficult for you to understand. You can learn to master any of it. Be self-confident, and just keep practicing.

Test Practice

Use these questions to test your Science Proficiency.

1. What diffuses into and out of guard cells, causing them to open and close?
   A) carbon dioxide
   B) ethylene
   C) water
   D) glucose
2. What does respiration provide for every cell?
   A) energy
   B) food
   C) oxygen
   D) water
3. What is a plant's change in behavior to an outside stimulus called?
   A) hormone
   B) tropism
   C) transpiration
   D) reactant
4. What term is used for a plant's response to the number of hours of daylight and darkness it receives daily?
   A) gravitropism
   B) thigmotropism
   C) transpiration
   D) photoperiodism

Test Practice

The Test-Taking Tip was written by The Princeton Review, the nation's leader in test preparation.

1. C
2. A
3. B
4. D

Developing Skills

21. Desert plants' stomata might open and close opposite to most other plants in order to conserve moisture.
22. Floating water plants have stomata on upper leaf surfaces, whereas most land plants have more stomata on lower leaf surfaces than on upper leaf surfaces.
23. Short-day plants include iris, chrysanthemums, rice, and poinsettias. Day-neutral plants include corn, tomatoes, and dandelions. Long-day plants include lettuce, spinach, and petunias.
24. auxin—stem grows toward light; ethylene—fruit ripens
25. See student page.

Bonus Question

Some roses bloom more in spring and fall than during the summer. What type of photoperiod is this? *short-day*

Assessment Resources

The **Test Practice Workbook** provides students with practice in the format, concepts, and critical-thinking skills tested in standardized exams.

Reproducible Masters

Chapter Review, pp. 29–30 L2
Performance Assessment, p. 29 L2
Assessment, pp. 65–68 L2

Glencoe Technology

- **Chapter Review Software**
- **Computer Test Bank**
- **MindJogger Videoquiz**

Chapter 16 Plant Reproduction

Section	Objectives	Activities/Features
Chapter Opener		**Explore Activity:** Observe the Inside of a Seed, p. 449
16-1 **Introduction to Plant Reproduction** 3 Sessions 1½ Blocks	1. **Describe** the two types of plant reproduction. 2. **Describe** the two stages in a plant's life cycle. 3. **Describe** and compare the life cycles of a moss and a fern.	**Using Math,** p. 452 **Skill Builder:** Classifying, p. 455 **Using Math,** p. 455 **Activity 16-1:** Comparing Mosses, Liverworts, and Ferns, p. 456 **Science and Math:** Using Similar Triangles to Solve Problems, p. 457
16-2 **Seed Plant Reproduction** 5½ Sessions 2½ Blocks	4. **Sequence** the stages in the life cycles of typical gymnosperms and angiosperms. 5. **Describe** the structure and function of a flower. 6. **Describe** methods of seed dispersal in seed plants and give examples of each.	**MiniLab:** Observing Gymnosperm Cones, p. 459 **Physics Integration,** p. 460 **Problem Solving:** Using Numbers to Test Seeds, p. 463 **Physics Integration,** p. 464 **MiniLab:** Identifying How Seeds Disperse, p. 465 **Skill Builder:** Forming a Hypothesis, p. 467 **Science Journal,** p. 467 **Activity 16-2:** Germination Rate of Seeds, pp. 468–469 **Field Guide to Cones,** pp. 470–473

The number of recommended single-period sessions — The number of recommended blocks
One session and one-half block are allowed for chapter review and assessment.

Activity Materials

Explore	Activities	MiniLabs
p. 449 lima bean	p. 456 live mosses, liverworts, and ferns with gametophytes and sporophytes, hand lens, forceps, dropper, microscope slide, coverslip, microscope, dissecting needle, pencil with eraser p. 468 seeds, distilled water, salt, potting soil, plant trays, thermometer, graduated cylinder, beakers	p. 459 hand lens, gymnosperm cone, paper towel p. 465 pencil, paper, plant reference books

Need Materials? Contact Science Kit at 1-800-828-7777 or at www.sciencekit.com on the Internet.
For alternate materials, see the activity on the listed page.

Standards		Reproducible Resources	Technology
National	State/Local	Test Practice Workbooks are available for use with each chapter.	English and Spanish audiocassettes are available for use with each section.
National Content Standards: A1, C2		**Activity Worksheets,** pp. 87–88 **Enrichment,** p. 42 **Reinforcement,** p. 42 **Study Guide,** pp. 61–62	**Section Focus Transparency 42** **Teaching Transparency 31** **Internet Connection,** p. 451 **Glencoe Science Voyages Interactive CD-ROM**
National Content Standards: UCP1, UCP5, A1, A2, C1, C2, C5		**Activity Worksheets,** pp. 89–92 **Critical Thinking/Problem Solving,** p. 16 **Enrichment,** p. 43 **Laboratory Manual,** pp. 93–98 **Multicultural Connections,** pp. 31–32 **Reinforcement,** p. 43 **Study Guide,** pp. 63–64	**Section Focus Transparency 43** **Teaching Transparency 32** **Science Integration Transparency 16** **Glencoe Science Voyages Interactive CD-ROM** **National Geographic Society: STV** **Internet Connection,** p. 463

Key to Teaching Strategies

The following designations will help you decide which activities are appropriate for your students.

L1 Level 1 activities should be appropriate for students with learning difficulties.

L2 Level 2 activities should be within the ability range of all students.

L3 Level 3 activities are designed for above-average students.

ELL ELL activities should be within the ability range of English Language Learners.

COOP LEARN Cooperative Learning activities are designed for small group work.

P These strategies represent student products that can be placed into a best-work portfolio.

Multiple Learning Styles logos, as described on page 61T, are used throughout to indicate strategies that address different learning styles.

Assessment Resources

Chapter Review, pp. 31–32
Assessment, pp. 69–72
Performance Assessment in the Science Classroom (PASC)
MindJogger Videoquiz
Alternate Assessment in the Science Classroom
Performance Assessment, p. 30
Chapter Review Software
Computer Test Bank

Chapter 16 Plant Reproduction

This is a representation of key blackline masters available in the Teacher Classroom Resources. See Resource Manager boxes within the chapter for additional information.

Transparencies

Section Focus Transparencies

42 SECTION FOCUS TRANSPARENCY

IT'S RAINING, IT'S SPORING

Suppose you grew a favorite flower or vegetable, and you wanted to grow it again next summer. You might wait until it produced a flower and then produced seeds. You would pick the seeds and plant them in the spring. The moss pictured below doesn't produce flowers, and so it doesn't produce seeds. Yet it can reproduce itself.

1. Describe what is happening in the picture.
2. The moss is releasing material called spores. Why do you think it has produced so many of them?
3. More than 1200 varieties of moss live in North America. What might that tell you about how successfully they can reproduce themselves?

L2

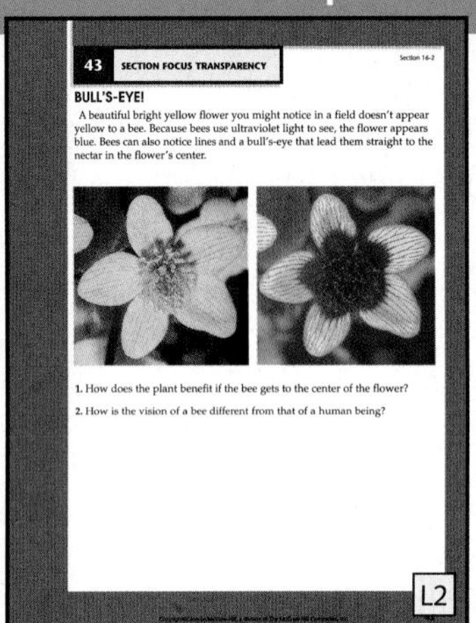

43 SECTION FOCUS TRANSPARENCY

BULL'S-EYE!

A beautiful bright yellow flower you might notice in a field doesn't appear yellow to a bee. Because bees use ultraviolet light to see, the flower appears blue. Bees can also notice lines and a bull's-eye that lead them straight to the nectar in the flower's center.

1. How does the plant benefit if the bee gets to the center of the flower?
2. How is the vision of a bee different from that of a human being?

L2

Science Integration Transparencies

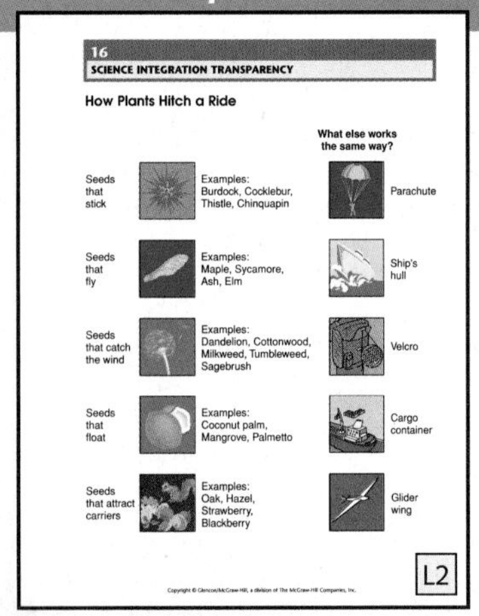

16 SCIENCE INTEGRATION TRANSPARENCY

How Plants Hitch a Ride

What else works the same way?

		Examples	What else works the same way?
Seeds that stick		Burdock, Cocklebur, Thistle, Chinquapin	Parachute
Seeds that fly		Maple, Sycamore, Ash, Elm	Ship's hull
Seeds that catch the wind		Dandelion, Cottonwood, Milkweed, Tumbleweed, Sagebrush	Velcro
Seeds that float		Coconut palm, Mangrove, Palmetto	Cargo container
Seeds that attract carriers		Oak, Hazel, Strawberry, Blackberry	Glider wing

L2

Teaching Transparencies

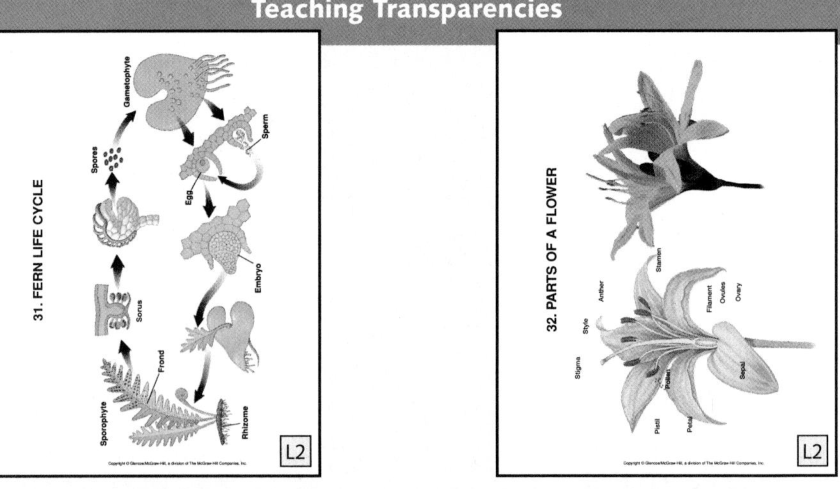

Meeting Different Ability Levels

Study Guide for Content Mastery

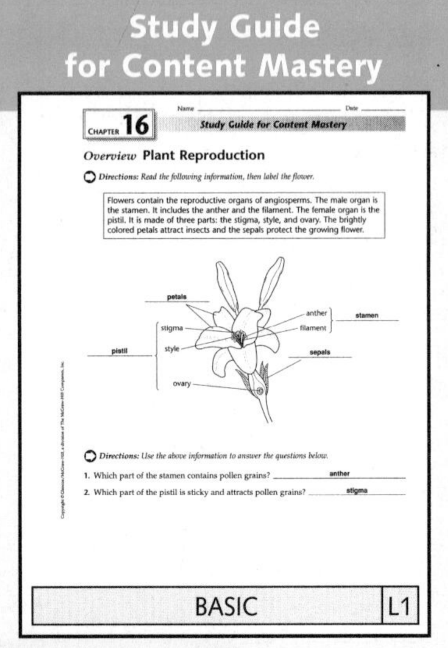

CHAPTER 16 Study Guide for Content Mastery

Overview Plant Reproduction

Directions: Read the following information, then label the flower.

Flowers contain the reproductive organs of angiosperms. The male organ is the stamen. It includes the anther and the filament. The female organ is the pistil. It is made of three parts: the stigma, style, and ovary. The brightly colored petals attract insects and the sepals protect the growing flower.

Directions: Use the above information to answer the questions below.

1. Which part of the stamen contains pollen grains? anther
2. Which part of the pistil is sticky and attracts pollen grains? stigma

BASIC L1

Reinforcement

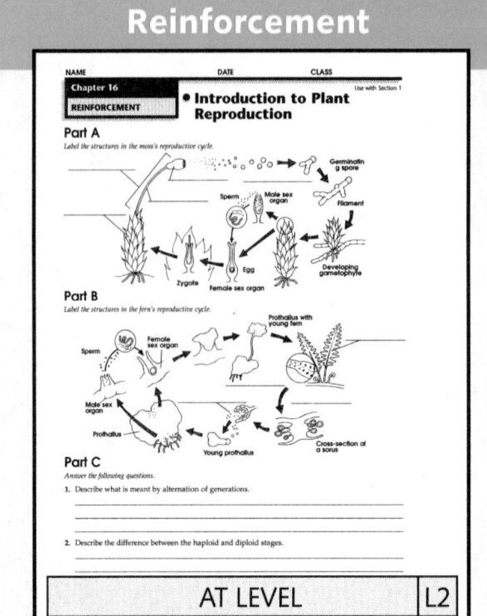

Chapter 16 REINFORCEMENT

Introduction to Plant Reproduction

Part A

Part B

Part C

1. Describe what is meant by alternation of generations.
2. Describe the difference between the haploid and diploid stages.

AT LEVEL L2

Enrichment Worksheets

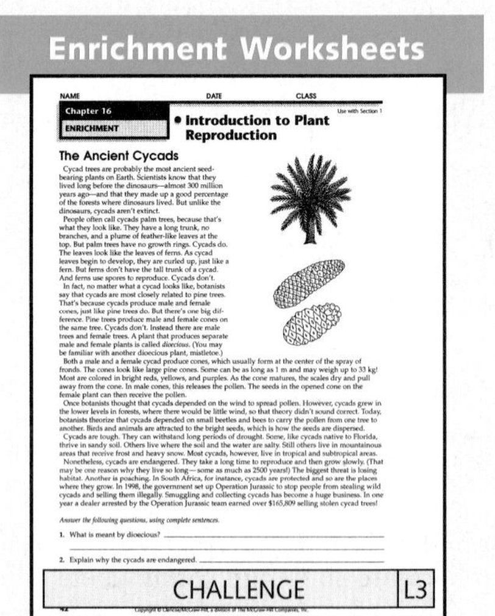

Chapter 16 ENRICHMENT

Introduction to Plant Reproduction

The Ancient Cycads

1. What is meant by dioecious?
2. Explain why the cycads are endangered.

CHALLENGE L3

Hands-on Activities

Activity Worksheets

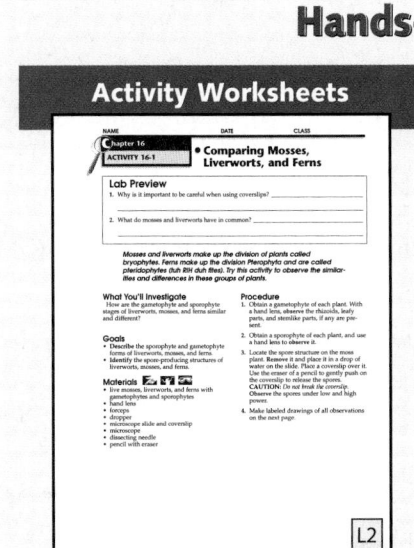

Chapter 16
ACTIVITY 16-1
Comparing Mosses, Liverworts, and Ferns

L2

Lab Manual

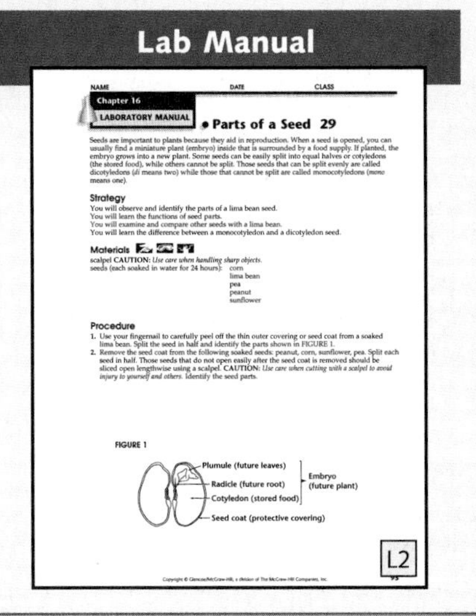
Chapter 16
LABORATORY MANUAL
Parts of a Seed 29

L2

Accessibility

Spanish Resources

Assessment

Performance Assessment

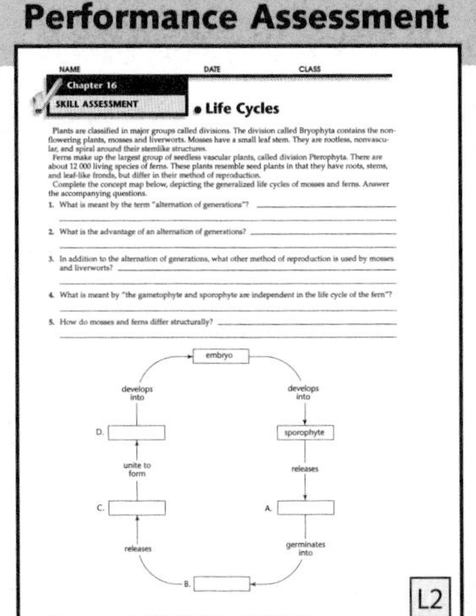
Chapter 16
SKILL ASSESSMENT
Life Cycles

L2

Chapter Review

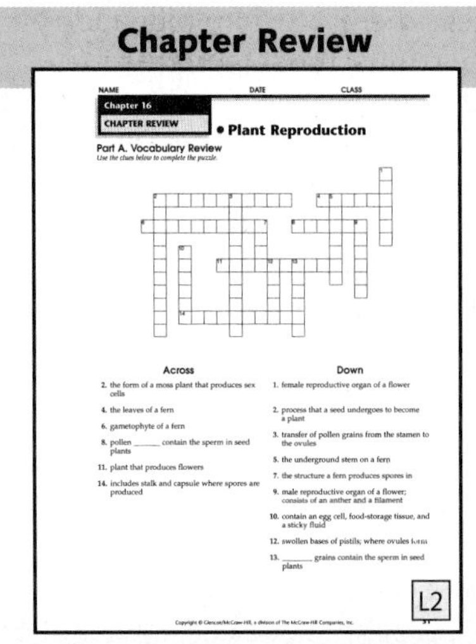
Chapter 16
CHAPTER REVIEW
Plant Reproduction

L2

Assessment

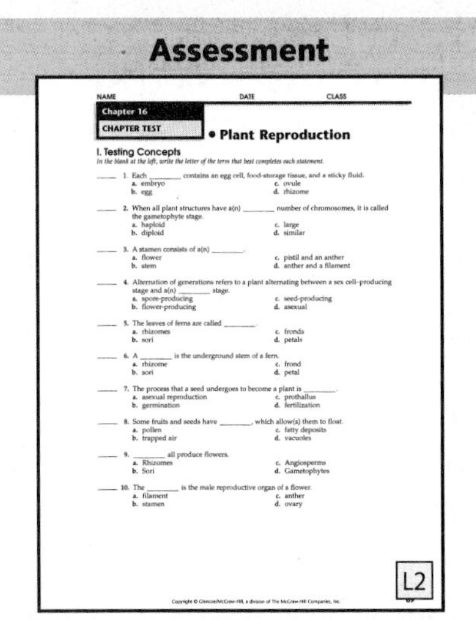
Chapter 16
CHAPTER TEST
Plant Reproduction

L2

Test Practice Workbook

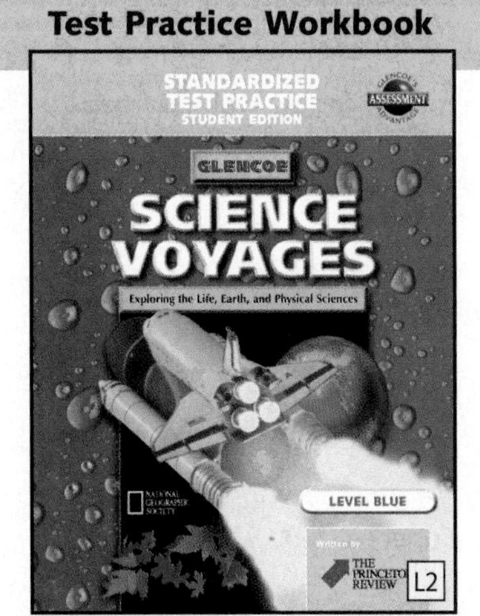

Extending Content

Critical Thinking/ Problem Solving

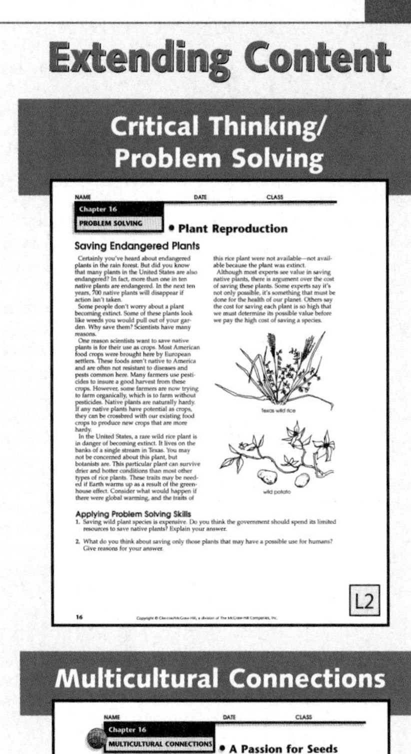
Chapter 16
PROBLEM SOLVING
Plant Reproduction
Saving Endangered Plants

L2

Multicultural Connections

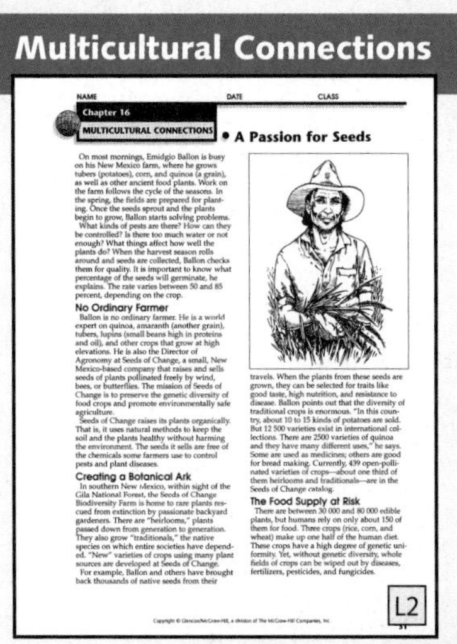
Chapter 16
MULTICULTURAL CONNECTIONS
A Passion for Seeds

L2

Chapter 16 Plant Reproduction

Helping You Prepare

Types of Reproduction (Section 16-1)

Asexual reproduction is a common method of reproduction in plants. Asexual reproduction works best in appropriate environments that change little over long periods of time. The advantage of asexual reproduction is the ability to produce large numbers of offspring that have the same genetic makeup as the parent plant. Such asexual reproduction is cloning. Many commercially grown plants such as orchids and African violets are routinely cloned.

The genetic diversity of plants is increased through sexual reproduction. Sexual reproduction allows plants to evolve and invade new habitats or adapt when the environment changes.

Haploid and Diploid Stages (Section 16-1)

In all plant life cycles, there are haploid and diploid stages. In some plants, the stages are separate and unique and referred to as an alternation of generations. Alternation of generations evolved with the ancestors of the plant kingdom, the ancient Chlorophyta, or green algae. A diploid sporophyte ($2n$) generation alternates with a haploid gametophyte generation (n). *Sporophyte* means "spore-producing" and *gametophyte* means "gamete-producing." These terms indicate the reproductive function of the plant. In some plants these are distinct organisms but, in others, they make up a larger organism.

GLENCOE TECHNOLOGY

CD-ROM

Glencoe Science Voyages Interactive CD-ROM

Chapter Summaries

Use the Chapter Summary to introduce, teach, or review chapter material.

Meiosis occurs in specialized cells of the sporophyte, the spore mother cells, and results in the production of spores. Spores produce the multicellular gametophyte by mitosis. In time, gametophytes produce haploid gametes. A male and a female gamete fuse to form a diploid zygote, the first cell in the multicellular sporophyte.

Seedless Plants (Section 16-1)

In mosses, liverworts, and hornworts, the gametophyte is the familiar plant that makes its own food by photosynthesis. The sporophyte generation in mosses is found at the tip of the gametophyte and consists of a stalk with a capsule in which spores are produced by meiosis.

Fern spores germinate into a filamentous plant that eventually grows into an inconspicuous heart-shaped gametophyte called a prothallus. The gametophyte is independent and carries on photosynthesis. Fern

NATIONAL GEOGRAPHIC — Teacher's Corner

Products Available from Glencoe

To order the following products for use with this chapter, call Glencoe at 1-800-334-7344:

CD-ROM: NGS PictureShow: *Plants: What It Means to Be Green*

Transparency Set: NGS PicturePack: *Plants: What It Means to Be Green*

Products Available from National Geographic Society

To order the following product for use with this chapter, call National Geographic Society at 1-800-368-2728:

Video: *Pollination*

Index to National Geographic Magazine

The following articles may be used for research relating to this chapter:

"Bats—The Cactus Connection," by Merlin D. Tuttle, June, 1991.

"Hummingbirds: The Nectar Connection," by Paul W. Ewald, February 1982.

"The Exquisite Orchids," by Luis Marden, April 1971.

"The Wasp That Plays Cupid to a Fig," by Robert F. Sisson, November 1970.

"Crossroads of the Insect World," by J. W. MacSwain, December 1966.

sporophytes have leaves called fronds. Fronds produce spores in specialized packets called sori (singular, *sorus*) that are often misidentified as a plant disease.

Gymnosperm Reproduction

(Section 16-2)

Gymnosperms are unique among seed plants because the ovules of their seeds are not completely enclosed by tissue produced by the sporophyte.

The sporophyte, or $2n$ generation of gymnosperms, are familiar trees and shrubs like pines, junipers, and spruces. At the end of separate stems, ovulate cones and pollen-bearing cones are produced. The female cones of gymnosperms vary from the familiar woody cones to fleshy, berry like cones. Berry like cones are often colorful such as the red ones on yews and the bluish ones on junipers. Many gymnosperm cones complete their life cycle in one year, but some take two or three years for maturation.

Angiosperm Reproduction

(Section 16-2)

Members of the phylum Anthophyta, often called flowering plants or angiosperms, are distinguished from gymnosperms by their production of flowers. Flowers contain the specialized reproductive structures. Flowers may be small and inconspicuous or large and showy.

The pistil of a flower consists of the stigma, style, and ovary. Inside the ovary are the ovules, in which a megaspore mother cell is produced. The megaspore mother cell undergoes meiosis, producing four haploid cells. These cells undergo mitosis to form an 8-nucleate embryo sac.

The male reproductive structure is the stamen. It consists of a filament and anther. Inside anthers, microspore mother cells undergo meiosis to produce microspores. Microspores develop into pollen grains with two haploid nuclei that become two sperm.

When the pollen grains of angiosperms reach the stigma, a pollen tube grows down through the style and into the ovary through an opening called the micropyle. One sperm fertilizes the egg, and the other sperm fuses with the polar nuclei to produce the nutritive tissue that occurs in the seeds of angiosperms. This process, called double fertilization, is unique to the angiosperms. The seeds are completely enclosed by sporophyte tissue.

SCIENCE UPDATE

For current events or science in the news, access the Glencoe Science Web Site at **www.glencoe.com/sec/science**

Development of Seeds

(Section 16-2)

All but about 35 000 of the 235 000 species of plants today are characterized by their production of seeds.

Seed Dispersal **(Section 16-2)**

Seeds are efficient units of dispersal for plants, and many have elaborate adaptations for moving away from the parent plant.

Teacher to Teacher

"In studying the role that insects play in plant reproduction, I have students compare the relationship of an airplane and an airport to that of an insect and a flower."

Leonard G. Rodríguez

Leonard G. Rodríguez, Assistant Principal
First Avenue Middle School
Pasadena, CA

CHAPTER 16 Plant Reproduction

CHAPTER OVERVIEW

Section 16-1 Sexual and asexual reproduction are discussed and compared. Sexual reproduction of nonvascular and seedless vascular plants is emphasized in this section.

Section 16-2 Reproduction of gymnosperms and angiosperms is discussed in this section. The structure and function of the flower are described, and methods of seed dispersal are given.

Chapter Vocabulary

gametophyte stage	sori
sporophyte stage	prothallus
alternation of generations	ovule
rhizome	pollen grain
frond	stamen
	pistil
	ovary
	pollination

Theme Connection

Systems and Interactions This chapter emphasizes the mechanisms and systems of reproduction in plants.

00:00 OUT OF TIME?

If time does not permit teaching the entire chapter, use Reviewing Main Ideas on pp. 474–475.

CHAPTER 16 Plant Reproduction

Chapter Preview

Section 16-1
Introduction to Plant Reproduction

Section 16-2
Seed Plant Reproduction

Skills Preview

Skill Builders
- Classify
- Hypothesize

Activities
- Compare and Contrast
- Design an Experiment to Test a Hypothesis

MiniLabs
- Observe
- Identify

Reading Check

List ten questions that a young child might ask about plant reproduction. After you read the chapter, underline the questions that were answered in the chapter.

448

Multiple Learning Styles

Look for the following logos for strategies that emphasize different learning modalities.

Linguistic Science Journal, p. 451; Using Science Words, p. 452; Enrichment, p. 454; Check for Understanding, p. 454; Activity, p. 460; Preview, p. 474

Logical-Mathematical Activity, p. 468

Visual-Spatial Explore Activity, p. 449; Activity, pp. 453, 456; MiniLab, p. 459; Reteach, p. 474

Auditory-Musical Out of Time, p. 474

Interpersonal Discussion, p. 452; Reteach, p. 454; Across the Curriculum, p. 461; Review, p. 474

Kinesthetic Inclusion Strategies, p. 461; Multiple Learning Styles, p. 464; MiniLab, p. 465

Naturalist Reteach, p. 466

Explore Activity

It's almost spring! The shelves in the garden center are overflowing with seed packets. Many familiar plants, like some of the plants you see here, grow from seeds. Some seeds come from flowers and others from cones. Seeds are just one way plants reproduce. To find out more about seeds, try the activity below. Then, in the chapter that follows, learn about the different ways plants reproduce.

Observe the Inside of a Seed

1. Obtain a lima bean or other large seed.
2. If the seed is hard and dry, place it in water overnight.
3. Observe the seed and describe it in your Science Journal.
4. Remove the paperlike covering from the seed and carefully pull apart the seed halves.
5. Look for the parts of the immature plant on one side of the seed.

Science Journal

In your Science Journal, identify the different parts of the immature plant.

449

Explore Activity

Purpose

Visual-Spatial Use the Explore Activity to introduce students to the parts of seeds. Inform students that they will learn more about the plants that make seeds in this chapter.

Preparation

Purchase dried lima beans from a grocery store. Soak seeds overnight.

Materials

Each student will need one lima bean.

Teaching Strategies

As you teach the parts of the seed, use the scientific names for the parts. The shell is a dried ovary; lima beans are seeds; seed leaves are cotyledons, etc.

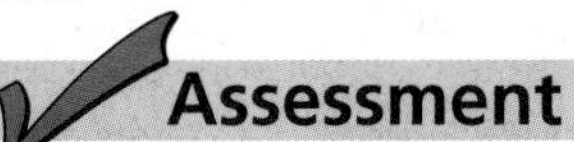

Students should identify the embryo, its leaves, stem, and root. They also should indicate the presence of the seed covering and the stored food.

Assessment

Performance To further assess students' understanding of seed parts, have them draw and label the embryo, stem, roots, and cotyledon of the seed. Use **Performance Assessment in the Science Classroom,** p. 55.

Assessment Planner

Portfolio
Refer to p. 475 for suggested items that students might select for their portfolios.

Performance Assessment
See p. 475 for additional Performance Assessment options.
Skill Builder, p. 467
MiniLab, pp. 459, 465
Activity 16-1, p. 456; 16-2, pp. 468–469

Content Assessment
Section Assessment, pp. 455, 467
Chapter Assessment, pp. 475–477
Proficiency Prep, pp. 454, 466

SECTION 16-1

Prepare

Refer to **Types of Reproduction, Haploid and Diploid Stages,** and **Seedless Plants** on pp. 448E–F.

Preplanning

Refer to the **Chapter Organizer** on pp. 448A–B.

1 Motivate

Bellringer

Before presenting the lesson, display **Section Focus Transparency 42** on the overhead projector. Use the accompanying **Focus Activity** worksheet. L2 ELL

Section 16-1

42 SECTION FOCUS TRANSPARENCY

IT'S RAINING, IT'S SPORING

Suppose you grew a favorite flower or vegetable, and you wanted to grow it again next summer. You might wait until it produced a flower and then produced seeds. You would pick the seeds and plant them in the spring. The moss pictured below doesn't produce flowers, and so it doesn't produce seeds. Yet it can reproduce itself.

1. Describe what is happening in the picture.
2. The moss is releasing material called spores. Why do you think it has produced so many of them?
3. More than 1200 varieties of moss live in North America. What might that tell you about how successfully they can reproduce themselves?

42

16-1 Introduction to Plant Reproduction

What You'll Learn

- The two types of plant reproduction
- The two stages in a plant's life cycle
- The life cycles of a moss and a fern

Vocabulary

gametophyte stage
sporophyte stage
alternation of generations
frond
rhizome
sori
prothallus

Why It's Important

- You'll be aware that you can grow new plants without using seeds.

Types of Reproduction

You and the garden plants shown in **Figure 16-1** are living organisms. But, you don't have leaves or roots, and a plant doesn't have a heart or a brain. Despite your differences, you are alike in many ways. You both can make similar copies of yourselves. This process is called reproduction. In this chapter, you'll learn how plants reproduce.

Sexual Reproduction

Plant sexual reproduction is similar to animal sexual reproduction. Both require fertilization, which is the combining of an egg and a sperm. Like animals, the plant's egg is produced in the female reproductive organs, and sperm are produced in male reproductive organs. The process of meiosis forms these sex cells. Meiosis is two divisions of a reproductive cell's nucleus. Meiosis results in four sex cells. Sex cells are haploid cells. That means that each sex cell has half the chromosomes of the original cell.

Male and female reproductive organs of plants may be on the same plant or on separate plants. For example, holly plants are referred to as male or female. A female holly, as shown in **Figure 16-2,** has flowers that have only female reproductive structures. Most plants have both sexes on one

Figure 16-1 Plants are living organisms that have all the characteristics of life.

Resource Manager

The following **Teacher Classroom Resources** can be used with Section 16-1:

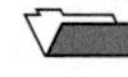 **Reproducible Masters**

Activity Worksheets, pp. 87–88 L2

Enrichment, p. 42 L3

Reinforcement, p. 42 L2

Study Guide, pp. 61–62 L1 ELL

 **Transparencies**

Teaching Transparency 31 L2

Figure 16-2 Holly berries develop after the egg is fertilized.

plant and can reproduce by themselves. Plants, such as apples and pears, have flowers with both sexes, but it takes another plant for fertilization to happen.

Many plants depend on animals or environmental factors to help get the egg and sperm together. For most plants, a seed develops following fertilization. A spore develops in some plants, such as mosses and ferns.

interNET CONNECTION

Visit the Glencoe Science Web Site at **www.glencoe.com/sec/science** for more information on plants that are male and female like holly.

Asexual Reproduction

Have you ever eaten seedless oranges and grapes? If these plants do not produce seeds, how do growers get new plants? Growers can produce new plants by asexual reproduction. Because most plant cells have the ability to grow into other cell types, a new plant can be produced from just part of a plant. For example, roots and leaves can grow from just a portion of the stem. The begonia shown in **Figure 16-3** is being asexually reproduced. A plant produced by asexual reproduction is genetically identical to the original plant. The plant part(s) used for asexual reproduction varies from species to species. People have used these methods of reproducing plants for centuries. You or someone you know may grow plants this way.

Figure 16-3 Leaf cuttings are one way that plants are asexually reproduced.

Tying to Previous Knowledge

Ask students to indicate where they may have seen mosses or ferns growing. Most will indicate that they have seen these plants growing in damp places in wooded areas.

2 Teach

Correcting Misconceptions

Many students assume that plants fertilize themselves. Point out that many plants must be cross-pollinated in order to reproduce.

Quick Demo

Show students *Coleus* or other plants that have been produced by asexual reproduction. You may also exhibit a strawberry plant that has runners.

interNET CONNECTION

Internet Addresses

____

____

____

____

For Internet tips, see Glencoe's **Using the Internet in the Science Classroom.**

Content Background

Self-pollinating plants usually produce flowers that are either not attractive to insects or have structures that hinder the movement of pollen from one plant to another. Genetic recombination in self-pollinating plants generally is not as extensive as in cross-pollinated plants.

Science Journal

Asexual Reproduction Have students research cloning as it relates to asexual reproduction of plants and write about how cloning of plants is an important activity in tree farming. L3

Answer to Text Question

How much of a plant's life cycle is spent in each stage? *Nonvascular plants and ferns spend about the same proportion of their life cycles in each stage. Vascular plants spend most of their life cycle in the sporophyte stage.*

Using Science Words

Linguistic Have students research the meanings of the prefixes and suffixes that make up the words *sporophyte* and *gametophyte.* L2

Using Math

17 chromosomes in the gametophyte and 34 chromosomes in the sporophyte

Discussion

Interpersonal Ask students to discuss how tissue culture is a useful cloning technique. Many plants may be grown from one plant with a desirable trait, more quickly than other asexual techniques. Another reason this technique is used is that it produces disease-free plants. The cells used for this procedure are not contaminated with pathogens that may be present in other cells of the plant. Plants that are routinely cloned this way include orchids, tobacco, chrysanthemums, potatoes, strawberries, asparagus, and gladiolas.

Enrichment

If there is a university nearby, arrange a field trip to see a tissue-culture laboratory. Large-scale plant growers may also have such facilities.

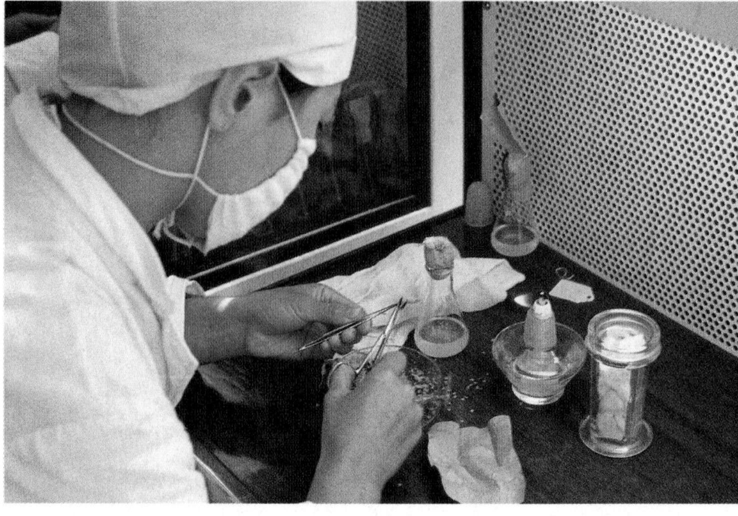

Figure 16-4 Many plants can be produced from just a few plant cells when grown using tissue culture techniques. Many orchids are reproduced by tissue culture.

Tissue culture is a form of asexual reproduction that uses a cluster of young cells to produce plants. This technology allows many identical plants to be produced from just a small portion of one plant. However, tissue culture requires special laboratory equipment and procedures, as in **Figure 16-4.**

Haploid and Diploid Stages

Every plant has a life cycle that contains two stages. The gametophyte (guh MEET uh fite) stage begins when cells in reproductive organs undergo meiosis. The cells formed are haploid (n). This means they contain half the number of chromosomes of a reproductive diploid cell. These haploid cells undergo mitosis to form plant structures. When all plant structures are made of haploid cells, it is called the **gametophyte stage.** Fertilization is the beginning of the sporophyte (SPOR uh fite) stage. Because cells in this stage are formed after fertilization, they have pairs of chromosomes, or are diploid. In the **sporophyte stage,** plant structures are made of cells with the diploid number ($2n$) of chromosomes. As you will learn in this chapter, these stages are different for different plant groups.

Using Math

A diploid apple has 34 chromosomes. How many chromosomes do cells in the gametophyte stage and cells in the sporophyte stage have?

Seedless Plants

Have you ever walked in a cool, damp, shaded forest or woods and noticed that only leafy plants like ferns were growing near the ground? Sometimes, mosses cover the ground or grow on logs. Ferns and mosses are two types of seedless plants. They reproduce sexually by spores, not by seeds.

Across the Curriculum

History Have students determine how moss gametophytes were used historically. One historic use was that they were used as bandages during wars because of their absorbancy and antiseptic properties. L2

The Moss Life Cycle

The life cycle of a moss is shown in **Figure 16-5.** You may know mosses as green, low-growing masses of plants. This is the gametophyte stage that produces the sex cells. Sometimes, a gametophyte moss plant has just male or female reproductive structures. Usually, both are on the same plant. For mosses, water is needed for fertilization. During a heavy dew or rain, water carries the sperm from the male reproductive structure to the female reproductive structure. Sperm swim to the eggs and fertilization occurs. A diploid cell forms, called a zygote. This is the beginning of the sporophyte stage. The zygote undergoes mitosis and develops into an embryo. The embryo grows into the mature sporophyte.

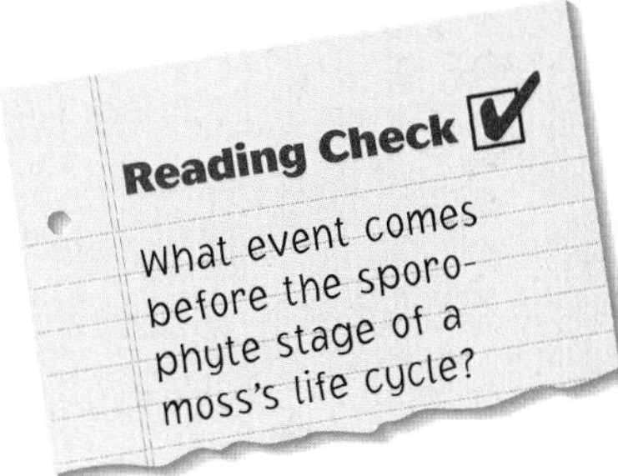

Reading Check
What event comes before the sporophyte stage of a moss's life cycle?

A moss sporophyte usually grows from the tip of the gametophyte. The sporophyte is not green and cannot carry on photosynthesis. It depends on the gametophyte for water and nutrients. The sporophyte consists of a stalk and a capsule. Inside the capsule, many cells undergo meiosis and form hundreds of haploid spores. When environmental conditions are just right, the capsule opens and releases the spores. If a spore lands on wet soil or rocks, it may grow into a green, threadlike structure. New moss gametophytes grow from this structure and the cycle begins again. When a plant's life cycle alternates between a sex-cell producing stage and a spore-producing stage, it is called **alternation of generations.** Liverworts have similar life cycles.

Figure 16-5 The life cycle of a moss alternates between gametophyte and sporophyte stages. **What is produced by the gametophyte stage?**

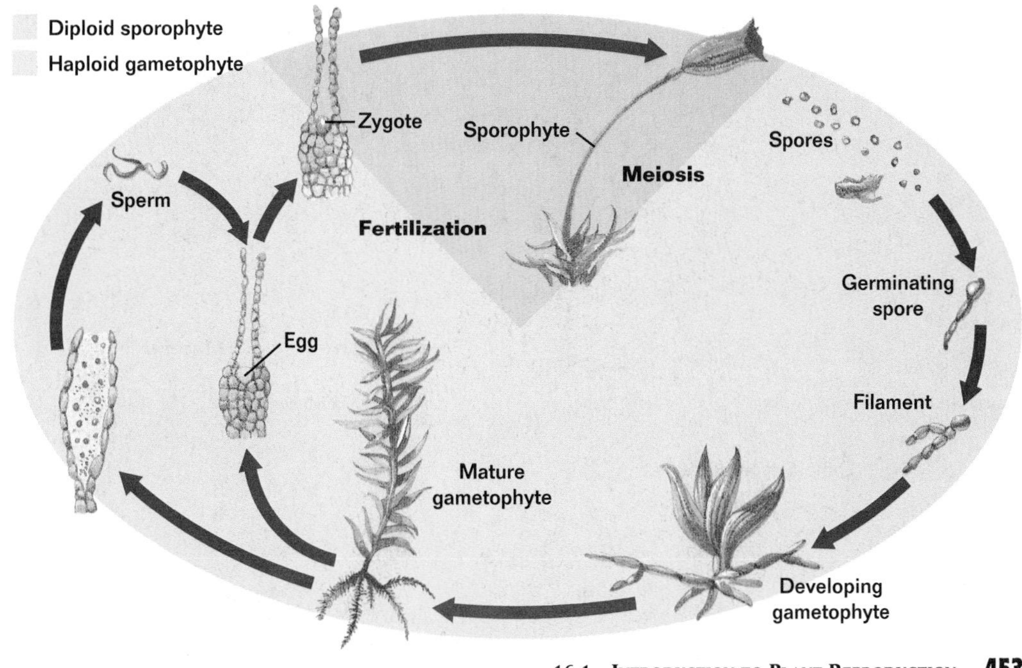

Teacher FYI

A single moss capsule may release 50 million spores.

Activity

Visual-Spatial Have students collect mosses from areas near their homes. Have them identify the gametophyte and sporophyte stages. L2 ELL

Answer to Reading Check

Fertilization is the formation of a zygote—the beginning of a sporophyte.

Caption Answer

Figure 16-5 *sex cells*

Using an Analogy

Use the recycling of a glass container as an analogy of the life cycle of a plant. *The glass is returned to a form that is changed (ground and remelted) and then returned to the original form to be used again.*

GLENCOE TECHNOLOGY

CD-ROM

Glencoe Science Voyages Interactive CD-ROM

Explorations

Have students do the interactive exploration *What is the life cycle of a simple plant?*

Frond is the name given to leaves of ferns and palms. Have students look in a dictionary to find the derivation and meaning of the word and then write a paragraph in their Science Journals to suggest why the word is used for both leaves.

Enrichment

Linguistic Have students write an essay that describes, compares, and contrasts the life cycles of mosses and ferns.

3 Assess

Check for Understanding Activity

Linguistic Provide each student with a list of terms used in this section. Have students identify the term as part of the moss life cycle, fern life cycle, or both life cycles. L2

Reteach

Interpersonal Give pairs of students drawings of the stages of moss and fern life cycles on 3 × 5 cards. Have students arrange and label the drawings. L2 ELL COOP LEARN

Extension

For students who have mastered this section, use the **Reinforcement** and **Enrichment** masters.

4 Close

Proficiency Prep

Use this quiz to check students' recall of section content.

1. **What is the generation of a moss that produces spores?** *sporophyte*
2. **What are produced by meiosis in the gametophyte generation of plants?** *Sperm and eggs*

Mosses and liverworts may reproduce asexually. If a piece of a moss gametophyte plant breaks off, it may grow into a new plant. Liverworts reproduce asexually by forming small balls of cells on the surface of the gametophyte plant. These are carried away by water and may grow into new gametophyte plants.

The Fern Life Cycle

Like mosses, ferns have alternation of generations. The life cycle of a fern is illustrated in **Figure 16-6.** The fern plants that you see in nature or as houseplants are fern sporophyte plants. The leaves, called **fronds,** grow from an underground stem called a **rhizome.** Roots grow from the rhizome, anchor the plant, and absorb water and nutrients. Fern sporophytes make their own food.

Spores are produced in structures called **sori** (sing., *sorus*) on the underside of the fronds. Sori usually look like crusty rust-, brown-, or blackish-colored bumps. When a sorus opens, it exposes the spore cases. Inside each spore case, cells have undergone meiosis to form spores. Thousands of fern spores are ejected when spore cases open.

If fern spores land on damp soil or rocks, they can grow into small, green, heart-shaped gametophyte plants. The fern gametophyte is called a **prothallus** (proh THAL us). It can

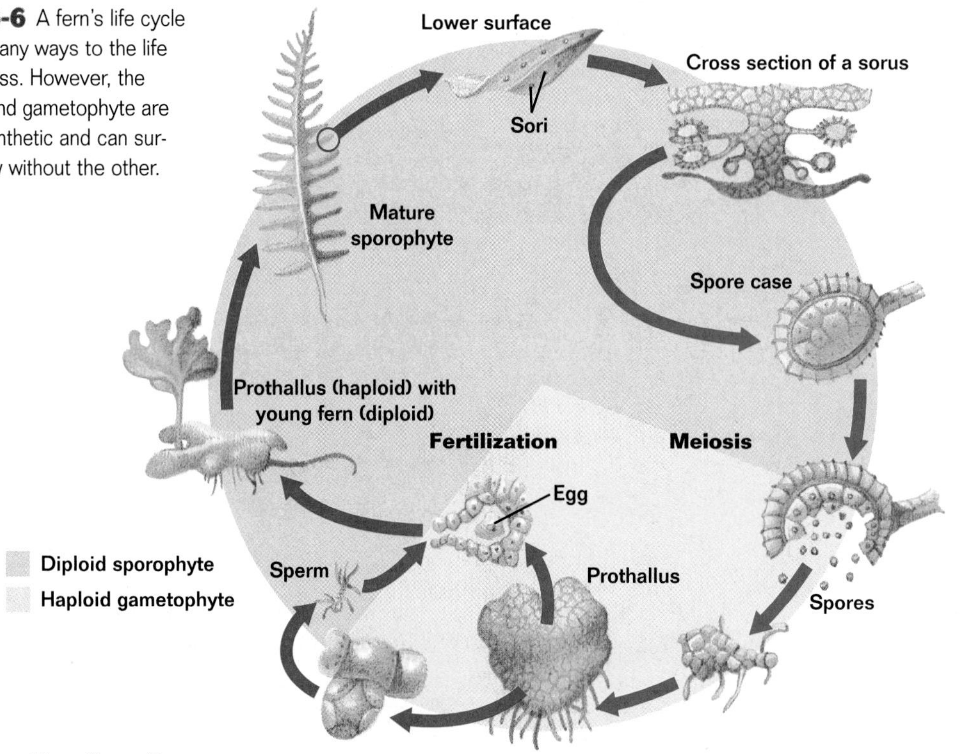

Figure 16-6 A fern's life cycle is similar in many ways to the life cycle of a moss. However, the sporophyte and gametophyte are both photosynthetic and can survive and grow without the other.

VISUAL Learning

Figure 16-6 All plants have an alternation of generations. Either have students outline the life cycle of a moss in their Science Journal, or discuss the reason for such an adaptation in class. L2

make its own food and absorb water and nutrients from the soil. The prothallus has both male and female reproductive structures. Sex cells form, and water is needed to bring them together. The zygote forms by fertilization. It grows into the familiar fern plant.

Ferns may reproduce asexually, also. Fern rhizomes grow and form branches. New fronds develop from each branch as shown in **Figure 16-7.** The new rhizome branch and fronds can be separated from the main plant. It can grow on its own and form more fern plants.

Figure 16-7 New plants grow from the rhizome of a fern.

Section Assessment

1. Describe the life cycle of mosses.
2. Explain the stages in the life cycle of a fern.
3. **Think Critically:** You see a plant that you like and want to grow an identical one. What type of plant reproduction would you use? Why?
4. **Skill Builder**
   Sequencing The life cycle of a plant is a sequence of events. Do the **Chapter 16 Skill Activity** on page 757 to learn about the events in the life cycle of a fern and those in the life cycle of a pine.

Using Math

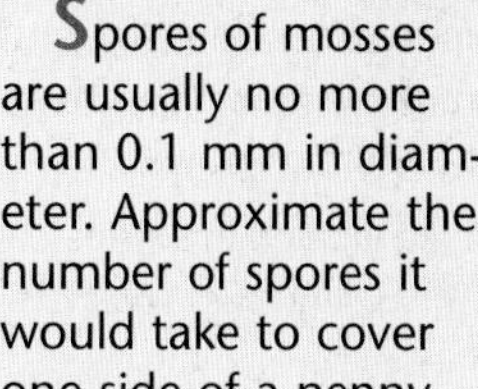

Spores of mosses are usually no more than 0.1 mm in diameter. Approximate the number of spores it would take to cover one side of a penny.

Assessment

Performance Hand students 3 × 5 cards that have descriptions of fern structures written on them. You may use moss structures instead. Have students identify the structure then move into two groups depending upon whether the structure is part of the sporophyte stage or gametophyte stage of the fern or moss life cycle. Then have students arrange themselves to create the plant's life cycle. Use **Performance Assessment in the Science Classroom,** p. 97.

Section Assessment

1. Spores land on the ground and grow into upright leafy gametophytes. Sex cells are produced on gametophytes. Sperm swim in water to reach the egg. When united, the zygote is produced. The zygote grows into a spore-producing sporophyte.
2. A spore grows into a heart-shaped gametophyte. The gametophyte produces sex cells that unite to form a zygote. A zygote grows into a sporophyte.
3. **Think Critically** A type of asexual reproduction (stem, leaf, or tip cutting) occurs because plants produced are identical to the parent plant. Seed-grown plants generally are not like the parent plant.

Using Math

area of the penny ÷ area of a spore = number of spores to cover one side of a penny

Area of a circle = πr^2

$\pi = 3.14$; $r = \frac{1}{2}$ diameter

area of a 0.1-mm spore = $3.14 \times (0.05)^2 = 0.00785$ mm^2

Diameter of a penny is 19 mm

area of a penny = $3.14 \times (9.5 \text{ mm})^2 = 283.385 \text{ mm}^2$

$283.385 \text{ mm}^2 \div 0.00785 \text{ mm}^2 = 36\,100$

About 36 100 spores/penny

Emphasize that this is only an approximation. The actual number is less because the spores cannot be broken up and there will be gaps between them.

Activity 16•1

Purpose

Visual-Spatial Students will observe the stages in the life cycles of liverworts, mosses, and ferns. L2 ELL COOP LEARN P

Process Skills

observing, classifying, comparing and contrasting

Time

50 minutes

Safety Precautions

Remind students not to eat any plant parts and to be careful when using microscopes.

Teaching Strategies

Troubleshooting

If moss spores are not liberated using water, add an equal amount of glycerin to the water. This mixture allows the spores to come out of the capsule more easily.

Answers to Questions

1. The gametophyte of a moss is a green, low-growing structure with leaves in a whorl around a stalk; that of the liverwort is a green, flat, leaflike form. Sporophytes of mosses are a nongreen stalk with a capsule containing spores at the top of the gametophyte. In liverworts, the sporophytes form on the gametophyte as nongreen umbrella-like structures with spores in cases underneath. Fern gametophytes are green, heart-shaped structures. Fern sporophytes are familiar green plants.
2. Spores, leaflike structures, and rootlike structures are common to all three.
3. Many spores do not land where conditions are right for growth. The greater the number of spores produced, the greater the chances that some will grow.

Activity 16•1 Using Scientific Methods

Comparing Mosses, Liverworts, and Ferns

Materials

- Live mosses, liverworts, and ferns with gametophytes and sporophytes
- Hand lens
- Forceps
- Dropper
- Microscope slide and coverslip
- Microscope
- Dissecting needle
- Pencil with eraser

Mosses and liverworts make up the division of plants called Bryophyta. Ferns make up the division Pterophyta and are called pteridophytes (tuh RIH duh fites). Try this activity to observe the similarities and differences in these groups of plants.

What You'll Investigate

How are the gametophyte and sporophyte stages of liverworts, mosses, and ferns similar and different?

Goals

- **Describe** the sporophyte and gametophyte forms of liverworts, mosses, and ferns.
- **Identify** the spore-producing structures of liverworts, mosses, and ferns.

Procedure   

1. Obtain a gametophyte of each plant. With a hand lens, **observe** the rhizoids, leafy parts, and stemlike parts, if any are present.
2. Obtain a sporophyte of each plant and use a hand lens to **observe** it.
3. Locate the spore structure on the moss plant. **Remove** it and place it in a drop of water on the slide. Place a coverslip over it. Use the eraser of a pencil to gently push on the coverslip to release the spores. **CAUTION:** *Do not break the coverslip.* **Observe** the spores under low and high power.
4. Make labeled drawings of all observations in your Science Journal.

Conclude and Apply

1. For each plant, **compare** the gametophyte's appearance to the sporophyte's appearance.
2. List the structure(s) common to all three plants.
3. **Form a hypothesis** about why each plant produces a large number of spores.

Assessment

Performance Assess students' understanding of the parts of mosses and ferns by having them identify parts of living specimens and by describing the functions of each. **Use Performance Assessment in the Science Classroom, p. 97.**

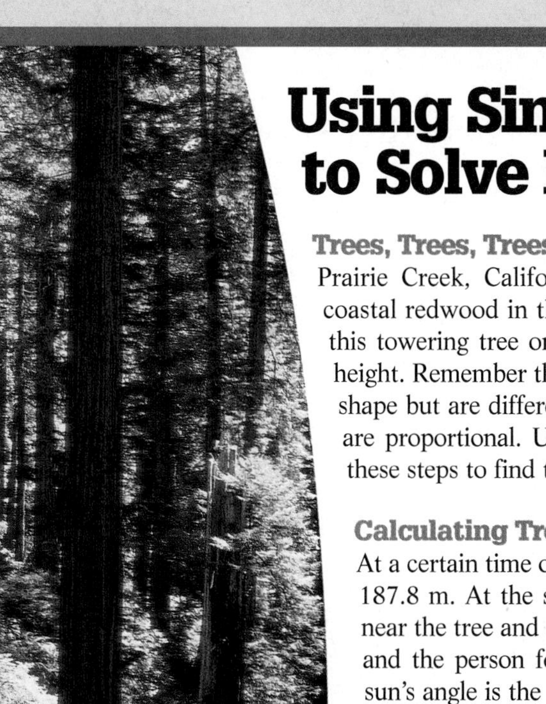

Using Similar Triangles to Solve Problems

Trees, Trees, Trees

Prairie Creek, California, is home to the largest known coastal redwood in the United States. If you stood next to this towering tree on a sunny day, you could calculate its height. Remember that two similar triangles have the same shape but are different sizes. The sides of similar triangles are proportional. Using this relationship, you can follow these steps to find the tree's height.

Calculating Tree Height

At a certain time of day, the redwood's shadow measures 187.8 m. At the same time, a person 1.5 m tall stands near the tree and casts a shadow 3 m long. Both the tree and the person form 90° angles with the ground. The sun's angle is the same for both the tree and the person. Because the triangles formed by each shadow, each object, and the sun's angle are proportional, the height of the tree can be calculated.

1. Write a proportion comparing the heights of objects to lengths of shadows (all measurements are in meters):

$$\frac{\text{height of person}}{\text{height of tree}} = \frac{\text{length of person's shadow}}{\text{length of tree's shadow}}$$

$$\frac{1.5}{h} = \frac{3}{187.8}$$

2. Find the cross products of the proportion:

$$1.5 \times 187.8 = 3 \times h$$
$$281.7 = 3 \times h$$

3. To find the value of h, divide both sides of the equation by 3:

$$\frac{281.7}{3} = \frac{3h}{3} \qquad 93.9 = h$$

The height of the tree is about 93.9 m.

Practice PROBLEMS

1. The largest American elm tree grows in Louisville, Kansas. When the elm casts a shadow of 17.4 m, a nearby, 0.9 m fence post has a 0.6 m shadow. Find the height of the American elm.
2. Cuba, New Mexico, is home to the largest piñon pine. When it casts a shadow of 27.6 m, a nearby, 0.45 m shrub casts a shadow of 0.6 m. Find the height of the piñon pine.
3. Try this method on a tall object in your neighborhood at two different times on the same day. Did the time of day affect your calculations?

Teaching Strategies

- Be sure that students understand the triangles used in the sample problem are similar.
- Help students identify corresponding angles and sides of triangles.
- Similar items of a proportion must be in the same unit of measure.

Answers to Practice PROBLEMS

1. $\frac{17.4\text{ m}}{x} = \frac{0.6\text{ m}}{0.9\text{ m}}$
   $x = 26.1\text{ m}$
2. $\frac{27.6\text{ m}}{x} = \frac{0.6\text{ m}}{0.45\text{ m}}$
   $x = 20.7\text{ m}$
3. The time of day should not affect the calculation.

Content Background

Two triangles are similar if corresponding angles are congruent (have equal measurements). Corresponding angles of two triangles are the angles formed by sides that are corresponding lengths. If the shortest and longest sides of one triangle form an angle, the shortest and longest sides of second triangle form the corresponding angle. If triangles are similar, the lengths of corresponding sides are proportional.

The two triangles used to find the height of the tree are similar because corresponding angles are congruent. The angle each object forms with the ground is considered to be 90°. The sun forms the same angle with each object if shadows are measured at the same location and at the same time of the same day. Because the sum of the three angles of any triangle is 180°, this means that the remaining angle of each triangle is the same number of degrees.

Using similar triangles and the length of shadows is called using indirect measurement. The unknown height is found by writing and solving a proportion using the relationships found in similar triangles. The trees used in this activity are actually listed in a National Champion list.

SECTION 16·2

Prepare

Refer to **Gymnosperm Reproduction, Angiosperm Reproduction, Development of Seeds,** and **Seed Dispersal** on p. 448F.

Preplanning

Refer to the **Chapter Organizer** on pp. 448A–B.

1 Motivate

Bellringer

Before presenting the lesson, display **Section Focus Transparency 43** on the overhead projector. Use the accompanying **Focus Activity** worksheet. L2 ELL

Section 16-2

43 SECTION FOCUS TRANSPARENCY

BULL'S-EYE!

A beautiful bright yellow flower you might notice in a field doesn't appear yellow to a bee. Because bees use ultraviolet light to see, the flower appears blue. Bees can also notice lines and a bull's-eye that lead them straight to the nectar in the flower's center.

1. How does the plant benefit if the bee gets to the center of the flower?
2. How is the vision of a bee different from that of a human being?

Tying to Previous Knowledge

Ask students to recall a time they dispersed seeds. One answer may be when they were eating a watermelon.

16·2 Seed Plant Reproduction

What You'll Learn

- The life cycles of typical gymnosperms and angiosperms
- The structure and function of the flower
- Methods of seed dispersal in seed plants

Vocabulary

ovule
pollen grain
stamen
pistil
ovary
pollination

Why It's Important

- Learning about cones and flowers will help you understand where seeds come from.

Gymnosperm Reproduction

Have you ever collected pine cones or used them in a craft project? If you have, you probably noticed that there are many shapes and sizes of pine cones. Cones are the reproductive structures on plants called gymnosperms (JIHM nuh spurmz). Each gymnosperm species has a different cone.

Pines are typical gymnosperms. Each pine produces male cones and female cones on the sporophyte plant. A mature female cone consists of a spiral of woody scales on a short stem. At the base of each scale are two ovules. Each **ovule** contains an egg cell, food-storage tissue, and a sticky fluid. **Pollen grains** develop on the smaller male cone. Two sperm eventually form in each pollen grain. As seen in **Figure 16-8,** a cloud of pollen grains is released from each male cone.

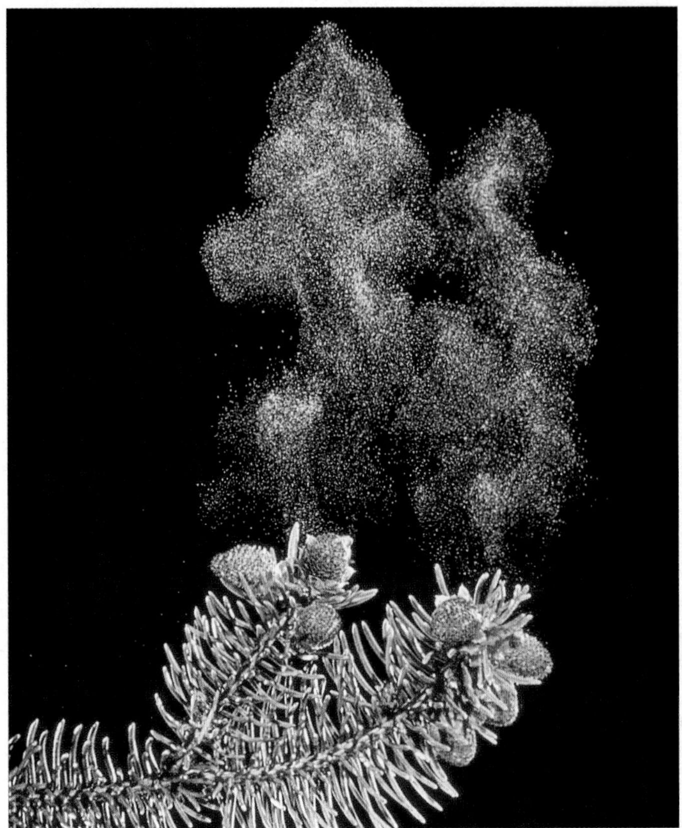

Figure 16-8 Male cones of a Norway spruce release clouds of tiny pollen grains.

Resource Manager

The following **Teacher Classroom Resources** can be used with Section 16-2:

 **Reproducible Masters**

Activity Worksheets, pp. 89–92 L2
Critical Thinking/Problem Solving, p. 16 L2
Enrichment, p. 43 L3
Laboratory Manual, pp. 93–98 L2
Multicultural Connections, pp. 31–32 L2
Reinforcement, p. 43 L2
Study Guide, pp. 63–64 L1 ELL

 **Transparencies**

Teaching Transparency 32 L2
Science Integration Transparency 16 L2

VISUALIZING Seed Formation in Gymnosperms

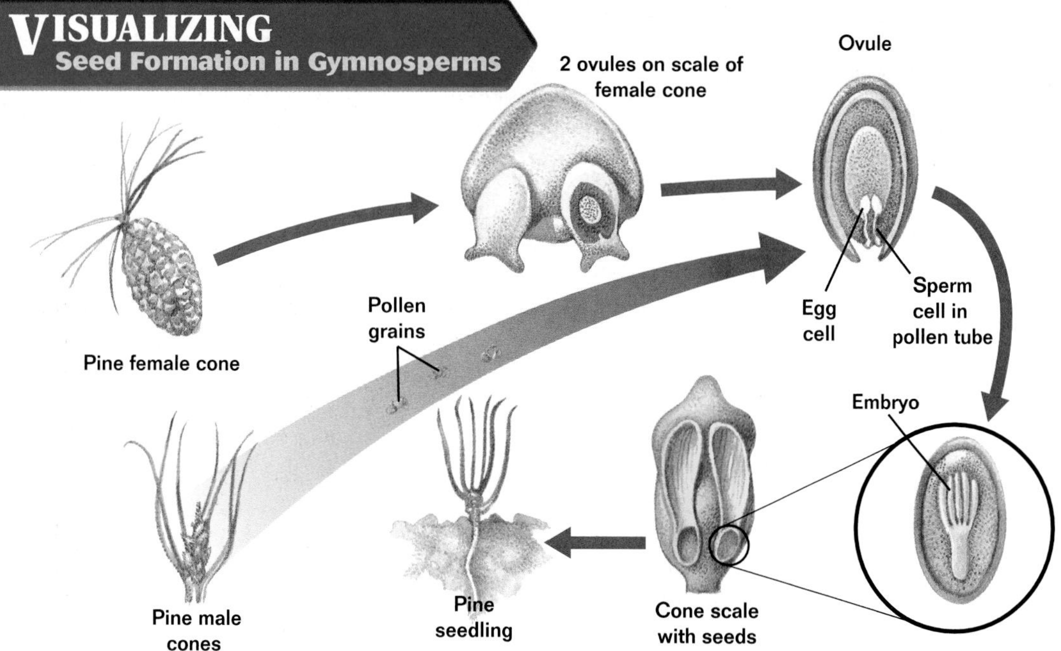

Figure 16-9 It may take two or three years for the seed of a female cone to form. **Where would you find the seed?**

Wind carries the pollen to female cones. However, most of the pollen falls on other plants, the ground, and bodies of water. If a pollen grain is blown between the scales of a female cone, it may be trapped in the sticky fluid secreted by the ovule. When the pollen grain and female cone are the same species, a pollen tube grows from the pollen grain toward the ovule. Fertilization may happen as much as 15 months later. The two sperm move down the pollen tube. One fertilizes the egg cell, and the other breaks down. As a result, a zygote forms that develops into an embryo. **Figure 16-9** illustrates this process.

Female cones of pines mature, open, and release their seeds, usually during the fall or winter months. It may take a long time for seeds to be released from a pine cone. From the moment a pollen grain falls on the female cone until the time the seeds are released may take two or three years. Released seeds are carried away, eaten, or buried by animals. Under favorable conditions, the buried seeds will grow into new pines.

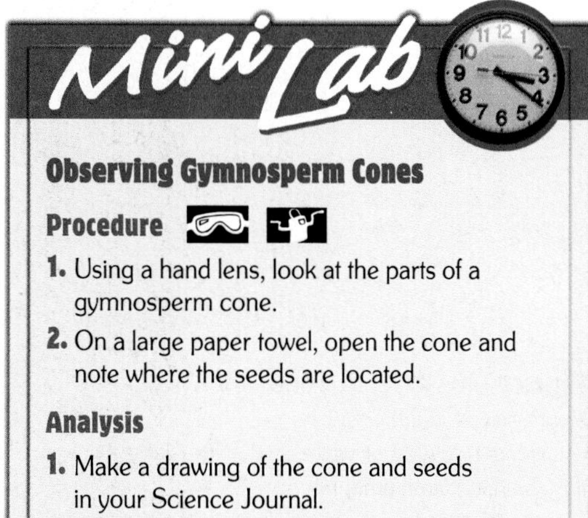

MiniLab

Observing Gymnosperm Cones

Procedure

1. Using a hand lens, look at the parts of a gymnosperm cone.
2. On a large paper towel, open the cone and note where the seeds are located.

Analysis

1. Make a drawing of the cone and seeds in your Science Journal.
2. Where are the seeds located?
3. Predict how this location is an advantage for the tree species.

VISUAL Learning

Figure 16-8 Relate that some gymnosperms produce so much pollen that it may form a yellow layer on things.

2 Teach

Caption Answer

Figure 16-9 *The seed is on a cone scale near the center of the cone.*

MiniLab

Purpose

Visual-Spatial Students will observe woody cone structures and identify parts. L2

ELL COOP LEARN

Materials

cones with seeds, paper towels, hand lens; at least one cone per two students

Teaching Strategies

Cones may shed their seeds. You may want to glue some seeds to the scales so that you know which seeds go with which cones.

Analysis

1. Drawings will vary.
2. Seeds are found at the base of a woody scale near the center of the cone.
3. Because these seeds are not inside a fruit, this location insures that they are protected until released from the cone.

Assessment

Performance To further assess students' understanding of gymnosperm cones, have students place several cones in the refrigerator overnight, then examine them on removal and several hours later. Have students state how cone activity might be an advantage to gymnosperms. Use **Performance Assessment in the Science Classroom,** p. 17.

Caption Answer

Figure 16-10 *moths and some mammals*

Flowers may be perfect or imperfect. Perfect flowers possess both stamens and pistils. Imperfect flowers may be either male (if they have only stamens) or female (if they have only pistils).

PHYSICS INTEGRATION

All molecules are in constant motion. For one to detect a scent, its molecules must be of a particular concentration. When the wind blows, the molecules are diffused rapidly. **Answer:** *On a windless day, the scent molecules would remain more concentrated in the air near the flower.*

Activity

Linguistic Have students write a description of a cone for someone who is visually impaired. After reading all the descriptions, share the best two or three with the class. P

PHYSICS INTEGRATION

Flower Aromas

The scents produced by flowers are compounds that evaporate quickly and move into the air. Infer why you would be able to detect the odor of a group of flowers better on a windless day than a windy one.

Angiosperm Reproduction

Angiosperms all produce flowers. Flowers are important because they contain the reproductive organs. When you think of a flower, you probably imagine something with a pleasant aroma and colorful petals. Although many such flowers do exist, some flowers are drab and have no aroma. Have you ever looked at the flowers of wheat, rice, or grass? Why do you think there is such variety among flowers?

The Flower

A flower's appearance may tell you something about the life of the plant it is part of. Large flowers with bright-colored petals often attract insects and other animals. These animals may eat the flower, its nectar, or pollen. As they move about the flower, the animals may get pollen on their wings, legs, or other body parts. As a result, these animals may spread the flower's pollen to other plants that they visit. Other flowers depend on wind, rain, or gravity to spread their pollen. Their petals may be small or absent. Flowers that open only at night, as seen in **Figure 16-10,** often have strong scents to attract animals.

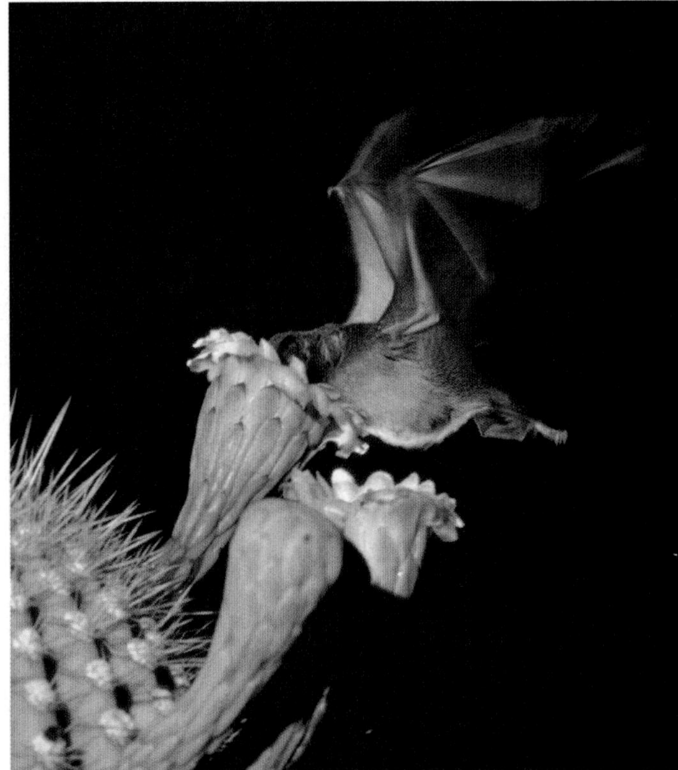

Figure 16-10 Some flowers bloom only at night. They are usually light colored or white, and they produce large amounts of scent molecules, nectar, and pollen. **Aside from bats, what other animals might pollinate night-blooming plants?**

Integrating the Sciences

Earth Science Gymnosperms are the dominant plant of the taiga biome that is south of the arctic tundra. In North America, most of this area is located between 45° and 60° north latitude.

Across the Curriculum

Geography Ask students to identify countries where taiga is a primary biome and the climatic conditions of these areas. *Canada, Norway, Sweden, Russia, etc.; harsh winters and short summers* L2

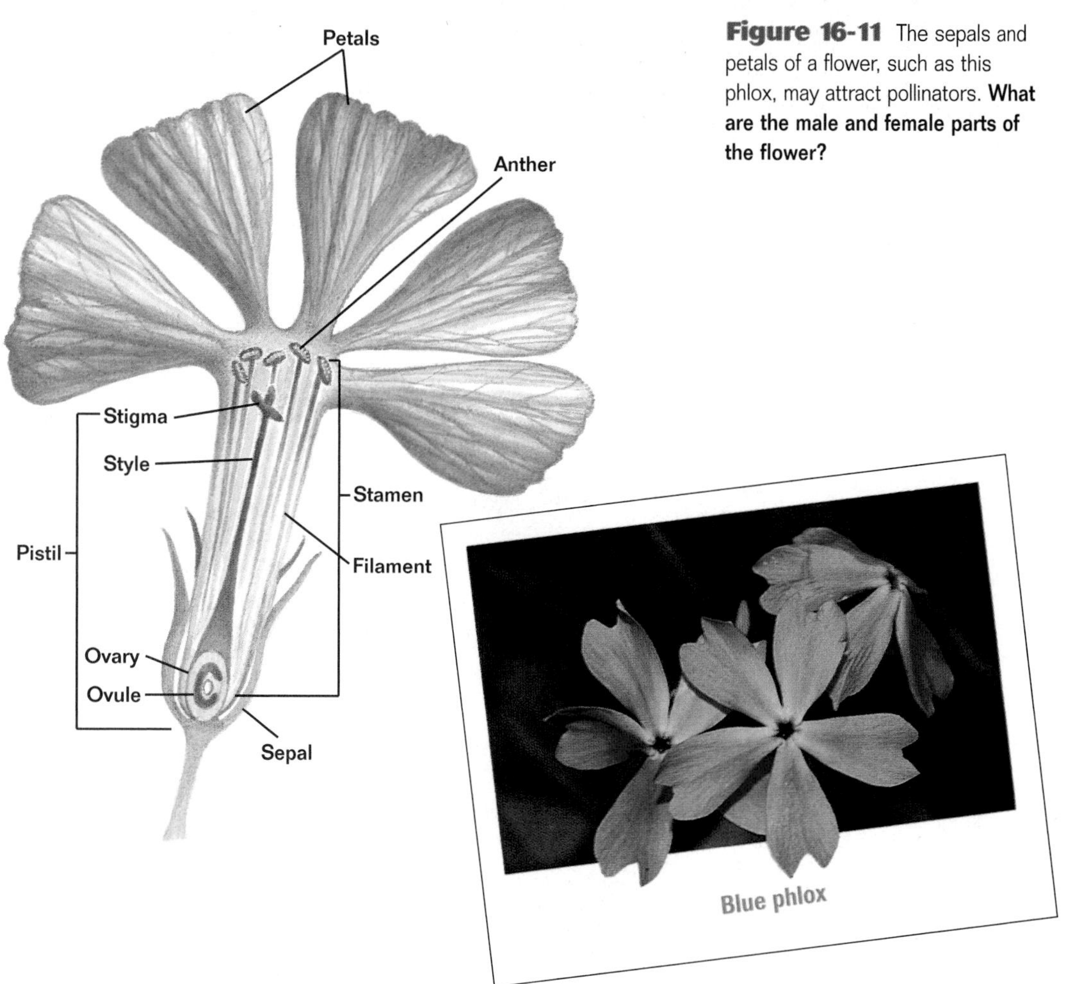

Figure 16-11 The sepals and petals of a flower, such as this phlox, may attract pollinators. **What are the male and female parts of the flower?**

Generally, the colored parts of a flower are the petals. Outside the petals are usually leaflike parts called sepals. Sepals are easy to see when a flower is still a bud. Sepals form the outside of the bud and cover the petals. In some flowers, the sepals are as colorful as the petals.

Inside the flower are the reproductive organs of the plant. The **stamen** is the male reproductive organ. A stamen consists of a filament and an anther. Pollen grains form inside the anther. The sperm develop in each pollen grain.

The **pistil** is the female reproductive organ. A pistil consists of a sticky stigma where the pollen grains land, a long stalklike style, and an ovary. The **ovary** is the swollen base of the pistil where ovules are formed. Eggs are produced inside the ovule as it develops. You can see the parts of a typical flower in **Figure 16-11.**

Reading Check
Where do pollen grains land in flowers?

Using a Model

A flower model can be used to show students the structures discussed in this section.

Flex Your Brain

Use the Flex Your Brain activity to have students explore FLOWERS.

Answer to Reading Check
Pollen grains land on the stigma of the pistil.

Caption Answer

Figure 16-11 *stamen and pistil*

Inclusion Strategies

Visually Impaired Students who are visually impaired should be provided models to identify the structures of flowers. Allow them to smell the scents of as many different flowers as possible to enrich their experience.

Across the Curriculum

Literature Have students work in teams to write a short story about a particular kind of flower and its pollination mechanism. The story should include a day in the life of a flower. L2 COOP LEARN

Enrichment

Take a field trip to a botanical garden to identify the plants from your area and from other areas of the world. If one is close by, extend the trip to an art museum to observe how many pieces of art contain flowers or other plant parts.

VISUAL Learning

Figure 16-12 Reinforce the process of pollination by having students trace the events using this illustration.

Figure 16-13 Ask students to recall the Explore Activity at the beginning of this chapter as they study this illustration. Use this illustration for review before students begin Activity 16-2.

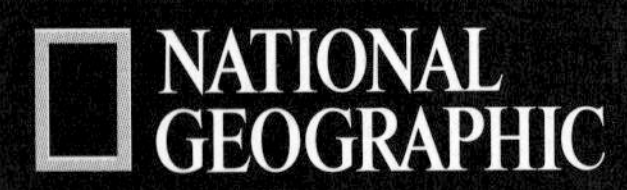

Videodisc

STV: Plants

Unit 2 *What Is a Flower, Reproduction* 4:00

32529-39550

Pollination 2:45

39859-44901

From Flower to Seed 2:00

45047-48746

Refer to the Teacher Guide for additional bar codes and teaching strategies.

Figure 16-12 The pollination process involves the transfer of pollen grains from the stamen to the stigma.

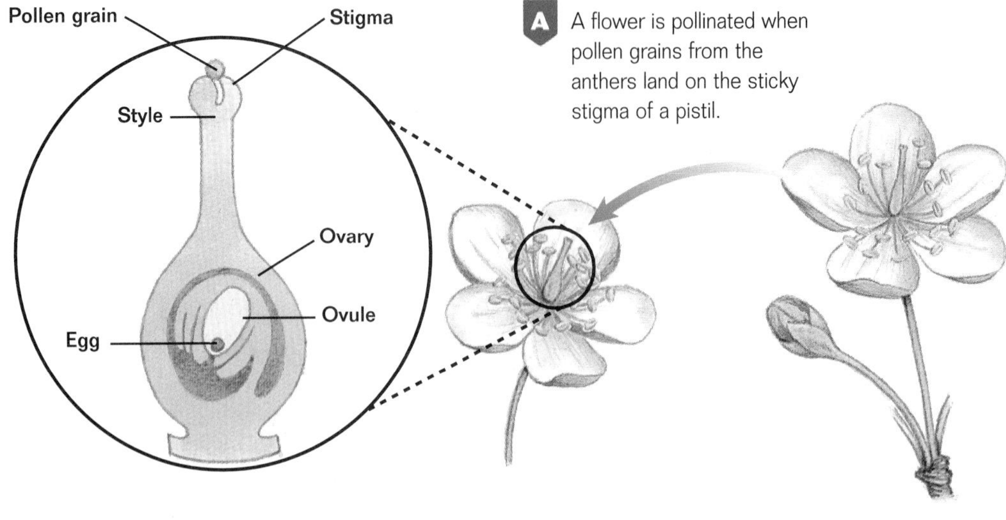

A A flower is pollinated when pollen grains from the anthers land on the sticky stigma of a pistil.

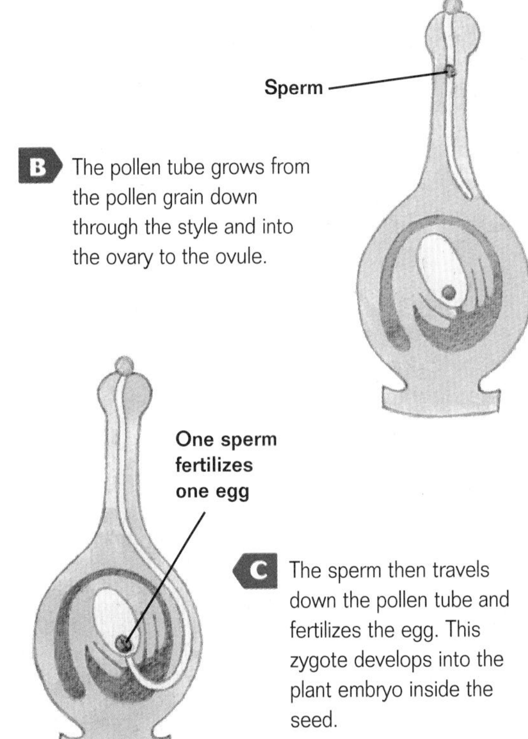

B The pollen tube grows from the pollen grain down through the style and into the ovary to the ovule.

C The sperm then travels down the pollen tube and fertilizes the egg. This zygote develops into the plant embryo inside the seed.

Development of a Seed

How does a seed develop? **Figure 16-12** illustrates this process. Pollen grains reach the stigma in a variety of ways. Pollen is carried by wind, rain, or animals such as insects, birds, and mammals. A flower is pollinated when pollen grains land on the sticky stigma. The transfer of pollen grains from the stamen to the stigma is the process of **pollination.** A pollen tube grows from the pollen grain down through the style. It enters the ovary and reaches an ovule. The sperm then travels down the pollen tube and fertilizes the egg. A zygote forms and grows into the plant embryo, which is inside the seed.

A seed is a mature ovule. It is surrounded by a protective seed coat. Inside the seed is the embryo. An embryo consists of an immature plant and stored food. The immature plant has structures that will eventually produce the plant's

Guided Reading Strategy

Problem Solution Journal Have students divide a piece of paper in half. Label the left side "Problems" and the right side "Consequences of failing to resolve the problem." Through writing, the student identifies a problem, brainstorms possible alternatives, chooses a probable solution, anticipates stumbling blocks, and proposes arguments. Have students write a Problem Solution Journal related to this section.

stem, leaves, and roots. In some plants, like beans and peanuts, the food is stored in structures called cotyledons. Other seeds like corn and wheat have food stored in a tissue called endosperm. This food provides the energy used by the seed as it sprouts. It also supplies energy for the immature plant's growth. You can see examples of these two seed types in **Figure 16-13.**

Figure 16-13 Seeds of land plants are capable of surviving unfavorable environmental conditions.

1. **Immature plant**
2. **Cotyledon(s)**
3. **Seed coat**
4. **Endosperm**

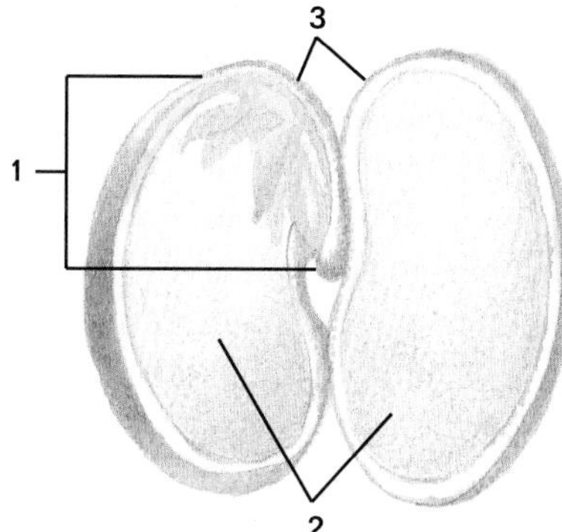

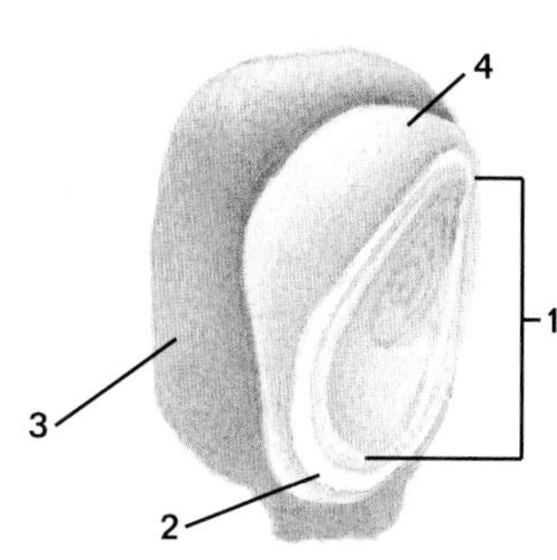

What is a seed bank? Visit the Glencoe Science Web Site at **www.glencoe.com/sec/science** for more information about seed banks.

Problem Solving

Using Numbers to Test Seeds

While purchasing seeds to plant in his vegetable garden, Ling noticed that each seed packet had useful information on it. On each packet, he found a seed count, planting instructions, and germination rate for the seeds inside. The packet he chose stated that it contained about 200 carrot seeds. The planting instructions were to plant seeds about 5 cm apart and 6 mm deep. It also claimed that 95 percent of the seeds would germinate. Ling decided that he would test the seed company's claims.

Think Critically: What should Ling do to determine whether the claims are true? How could Ling use the weight of the seeds to determine the number of seeds in the packet?

*inter*NET CONNECTION

Internet Addresses

For Internet tips, see Glencoe's **Using the Internet in the Science Classroom.**

Problem Solving

Consumer testing is rarely done because most commercial claims are actually understated. Seed companies test thousands of seeds before making any claims of viability. To test a claim, one must follow directions precisely.

Think Critically

1. Ling could count the number of seeds in the packet. He could plant 20 seeds according to package directions and see if 95 percent, or 19, germinate.
2. Ling could weigh all of the seeds and record this number. He could count out 20 seeds and weigh them. Dividing the total weight by the weight of 20 seeds and multiplying that answer by 20 will give an approximate number of seeds in the package.

Integrating the Sciences

Physics *Force* may be defined as a push or pull. Some dry fruits open with such great force when ripe, that their seeds are dispersed some distance from the plants. Witch hazel seeds may be propelled more than 12 m by the force of its splitting, ripe fruit.

16-2 SEED PLANT REPRODUCTION 463

Caption Answer

Figure 16-14A *Seeds of maples, dandelions, elms, pines, cottonwoods, and other plants are dispersed by wind.*

Teacher FYI

It would take more than ten million orchid seeds to equal the mass of a single coconut.

Ultimately, gravity is the reason all seeds reach the ground. Over 400 years ago, Galileo discovered that in a vacuum, gravity affects all objects in the same way. They fall at the same rate of acceleration—9.8 m/s^2. Apollo 15 commander David R. Scott demonstrated this on the moon in 1971. He simultaneously dropped a feather and hammer onto the moon's surface. They landed at the same time. However, on Earth other forces affect how objects fall, such as the atmosphere and the object's form.

Using an Analogy

The way many seeds attach themselves to passing animals is like the way that the two pieces of Velcro stick together. In fact, Velcro's invention was inspired by cockleburs stuck to the inventor's clothes.

Seed Dispersal

Most seeds grow only when placed on or in the ground. But, how do seeds naturally get from a plant to the ground? For many seeds, gravity is the answer.

Have you ever noticed how some plants just seem to appear in lawns, gardens, or the cracks of sidewalks? How did they get there? They probably grew from a seed, but where did the seed come from? In nature, seeds may travel great distances from the plants they grew on. Wind, water, and animals spread seeds. Some plants even have ways of ejecting their seeds. **Figure 16-14** shows ways that seeds are dispersed.

Wind dispersal happens usually because a seed has a structure attached to it that allows it to move with air currents. Dandelion, milkweed, and maple seeds are dispersed by the wind. Sometimes, seeds are so small that they become airborne when released by the plant.

Animals, including humans, disperse many seeds. Some seeds are eaten with fruits and dispersed as animals move from place to place. Often, for a seed to germinate, it must pass through an animal's digestive system. Hitchhiking on fur, feathers, and clothing is another way that animals disperse seeds. The fruit or seed may have a hooklike structure(s) or be coated with a sticky substance that allows it to stick to a passing animal. Humans often carry seeds without knowing it. Seeds wedge in the bottoms of shoes, drop into pockets or pant cuffs, and travel in our belongings.

Figure 16-14 Seeds can be dispersed by various methods.

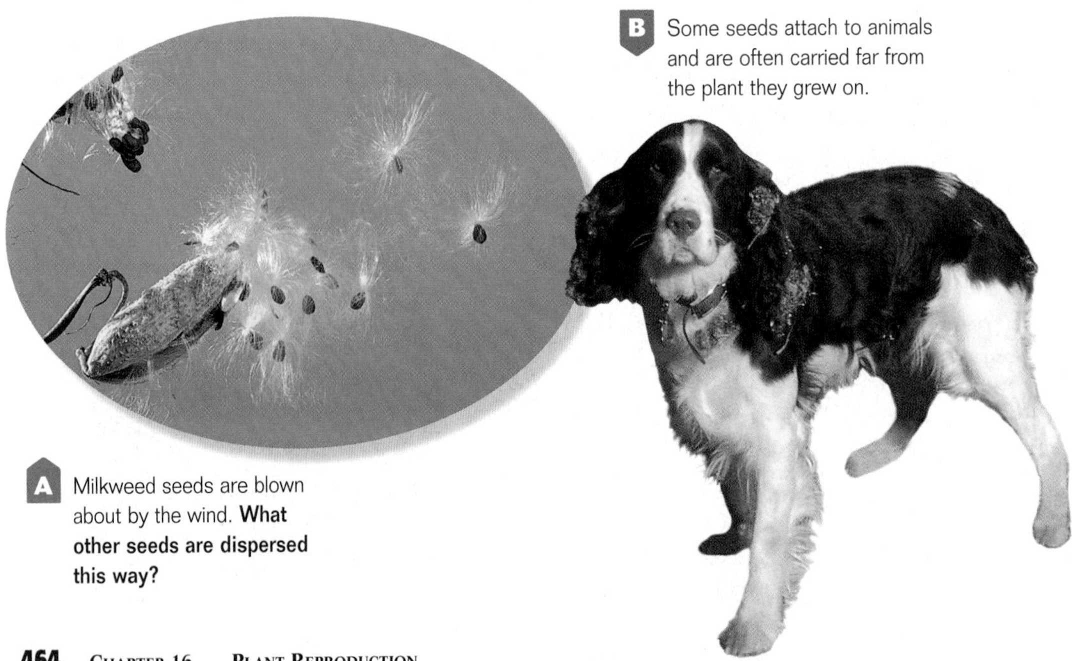

B Some seeds attach to animals and are often carried far from the plant they grew on.

A Milkweed seeds are blown about by the wind. **What other seeds are dispersed this way?**

Multiple Learning Styles

Kinesthetic Have students devise a wind carrier for a seed from a piece of paper ($8\frac{1}{2} \times 11$). Provide students with bean seeds to test their carrier.

Water also disperses seeds. Raindrops may knock seeds out of a dry fruit. Some fruits and seeds contain trapped air, which allows them to float on water. They also may have waxy coatings that delay water absorption. Floating seeds may travel great distances. The coconut palm's seed shown in **Figure 16-14C** has been dispersed hundreds of kilometers on ocean currents.

Have you ever touched the seedpod of an impatiens flower and watched as it exploded? The tiny seeds are ejected and spread some distance from the plant. This is another way that some plants disperse seeds.

Germination

Some seeds sprout or germinate in just a few days and other seeds take weeks or months to grow. Seeds will not sprout until environmental conditions are right. Some seeds can stay in a resting stage for hundreds of years. In 1982, seeds of the East Indian lotus sprouted after 466 years!

Identifying How Seeds Disperse

Procedure

1. Make a list of ten different seeds, including those pictured in **Figure 16-14.**
2. Research each of the ten seeds to determine how they are dispersed.

Analysis

1. How are the seeds of each plant on your list dispersed—by wind, water, insects, birds, or mammals?
2. Identify features that tell you how each kind of seed is dispersed.

D The plant may disperse seeds by ejecting them.

C This coconut seed floats in the surf.

MiniLab

Purpose

 **Kinesthetic** Students will infer dispersal mechanisms. L2 

Materials

botany texts, encyclopedias, or similar research materials

Teaching Strategies

- If possible, demonstrate seed dispersal by making models of various seed shapes.
- Purchase several kinds of seeds from a garden center or feed store. Allow students time to study these seeds before they make their list.

Analysis

1. Answers will vary depending on the seeds listed.
2. Features will vary but may include parachutes, wings, or similar features.

Assessment

Performance Perform the activity listed above with different seeds. Use **Performance Assessment in the Science Classroom,** p. 33.

 **Videodisc**

STV: Plants

Unit 4 *What Is A Seed, Dispersing Seeds* 4:00

Refer to the Teacher Guide for additional bar codes and teaching strategies.

3 Assess

Check for Understanding

Activity

Have students draw and label from memory a typical flower and seed. L2 ELL

Reteach

Naturalist Bring in plants, flowers, and seeds to demonstrate the parts of a plant's life cycle. Have students sequence a plant's life cycle by using the plants and plant parts. Reproductive structures can be obtained by dissecting a flower. A hand lens may be needed to see the flower's reproductive parts. Have students write a paragraph that details the sequence of the plant's life cycle. L2

Extension

For students who have mastered this section, use the **Reinforcement** and **Enrichment** masters.

4 Close

Proficiency Prep

Use this quiz to check students' recall of section content.

1. **What are produced on top of each cone scale?** *ovules*
2. **What develops in the male cone?** *Pollen grains*
3. **What is the female reproductive organ of the flower?** *pistil*

Figure 16-15 Germination is different in dicots and monocots.

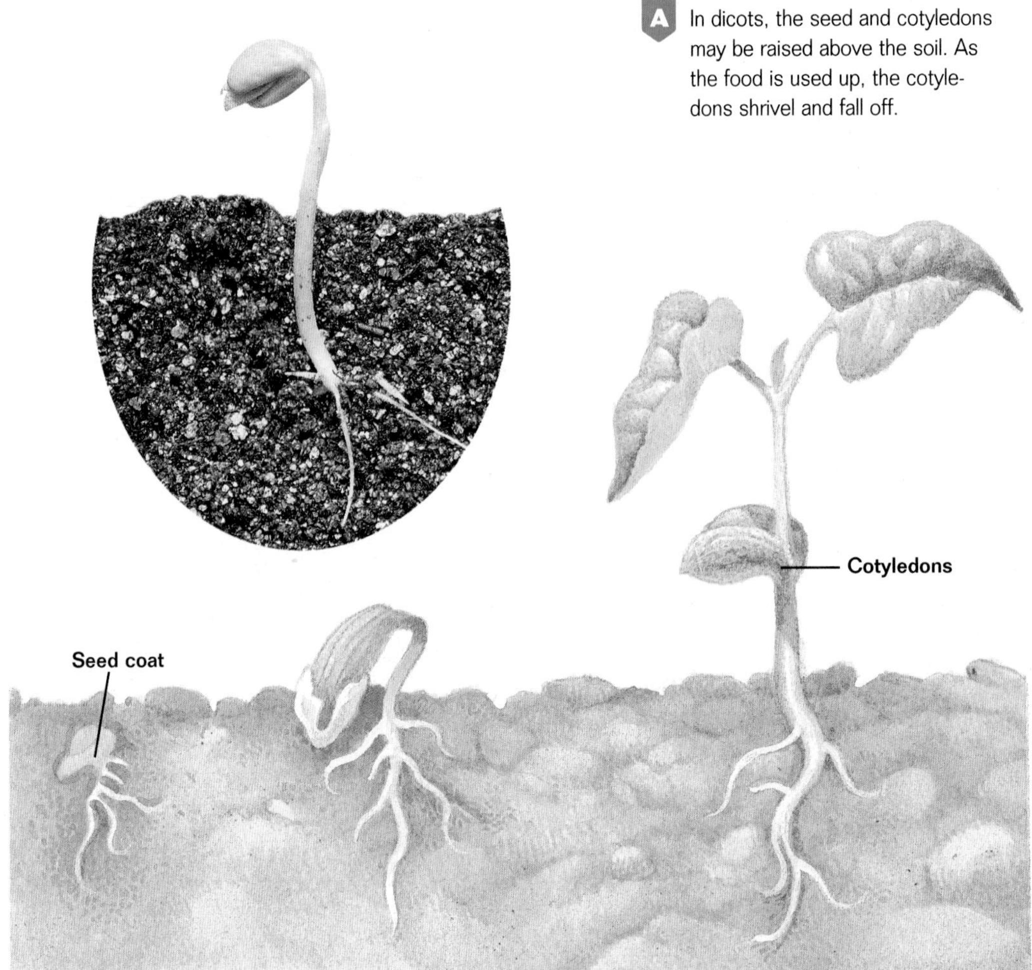

A In dicots, the seed and cotyledons may be raised above the soil. As the food is used up, the cotyledons shrivel and fall off.
Cotyledons
Seed coat

Germination, as shown in **Figure 16-15,** is a series of events that results in the growth of a plant from a seed. Temperature, the presence or absence of light, availability of water, and amount of oxygen present may affect germination. If the right combination of factors occurs, the seed will germinate. Germination begins when seed tissues absorb water. This causes the seed to swell. Then, a series of chemical reactions happens that releases energy from the stored food in the cotyledons or endosperm. Eventually, a root grows from the seed, followed by a stem and leaves. Once the plant is out of the soil, photosynthesis begins. Photosynthesis provides food and energy for the plant.

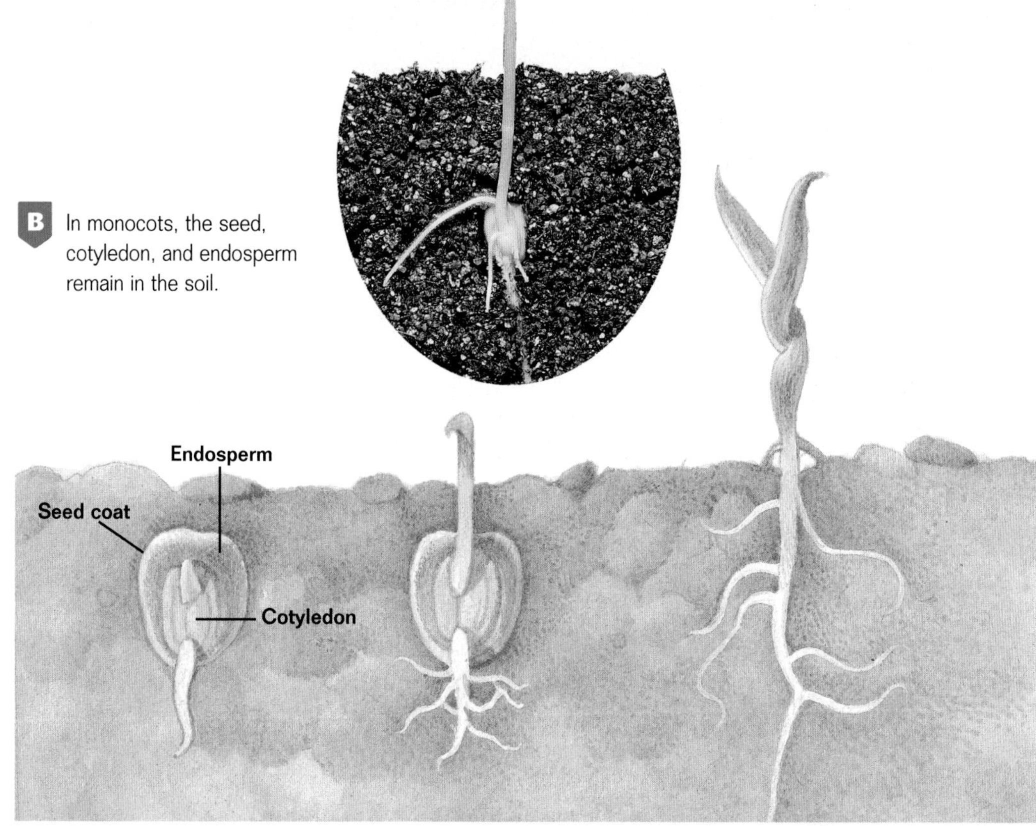

B In monocots, the seed, cotyledon, and endosperm remain in the soil.

Section Assessment

1. **Compare** life cycles of angiosperms and gymnosperms.
2. Diagram a flower and label its parts.
3. List three methods of seed dispersal in plants.
4. **Think Critically:** Some conifers have female cones on the top half of the tree and male cones on the bottom half. Why do you think this arrangement of cones is important?
5. **Skill Builder**
   Forming a Hypothesis A corn plant produces thousands of pollen grains on top of the plant in flowers that have no odor or color. The pistils grow from the cob lower down on the plant. Hypothesize how a corn plant is probably pollinated. If you need help, refer to Forming a Hypothesis in the **Skill Handbook** on page 722.

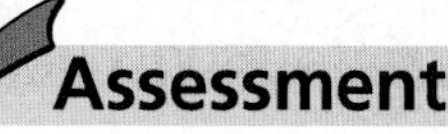

Science Journal Observe live specimens of several different types of flowers. In your Science Journal, describe their structures. Include numbers of petals, sepals, stamens, and pistil.

Section Assessment

1. The life cycles of angiosperms and gymnosperms are similar, except that the angiosperms produce their gametophytes in flowers and gymnosperms produce gametes in cones.
2. Student diagrams should resemble one of the flowers in **Figure 16-11.**
3. wind, being eaten, gravity (Refer to "Seed Dispersal" in this section.)
4. **Think Critically** This arrangement prevents self-pollination of the plant. Pollen cannot fall on the female cones if they are above the male cones, but pollen will be blown to a nearby tree. The female cones can receive only windblown pollen.

Science Journal

Answers will vary depending on the species of flowers they observe.

5.  **Skill Builder**
The traits listed are all common to wind-pollinated plants. Gravity is also a factor.

Assessment

Performance Assess students' abilities to observe and infer by giving students flowers and having them infer how each flower may be pollinated. **Use Performance Assessment in the Science Classroom,** p. 17.

Activity 16•2 Design Your Own Experiment

Recognize the Problem

Purpose

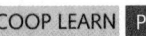

Logical-Mathematical Students will design and carry out an experiment to determine how germination rate varies with an environmental factor. L2

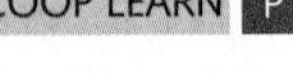
COOP LEARN P

Process Skills

designing an experiment, collecting, interpreting, and analyzing data, drawing conclusions, communicating, making and using tables and graphs, comparing and contrasting, recognizing cause and effect, forming a hypothesis, separating and controlling variables, measuring in SI

Time

one class period plus 10 minutes per day for five additional days

Materials

Alternate Materials Use any fast-germinating seeds. You may also substitute Epsom salts for table salt. Seedling warming cables.

Safety Precautions

Have students review safety symbols and precautions on the student page.

Form a Hypothesis

Possible Hypotheses

Students may test the germination rate with salt solutions. They may predict that seeds will germinate at a higher rate with water than with salt solutions. They may predict that warmer soil will increase the rate of germination. The presence and absence of light may be tested. Planting depth may also be the variable.

Design Your Own Experiment

Activity 16•2

Germination Rate of Seeds

Possible Materials

- Seeds
- Water
- Salt
- Potting soil
- Plant trays or plastic cups
  - * *seedling warming cables*
- Thermometer
- Graduated cylinder
- Beakers

* *Alternate Materials*

Many environmental factors affect the germination rate of seeds. Among these are soil temperature, air temperature, moisture content of soil, and salt content of soil. What happens to the germination rate when one of these variables is changed? Can you determine a way to predict the best conditions for seed germination?

Recognize the Problem

How does an environmental factor affect seed germination?

Form a Hypothesis

Based on your knowledge of seed germination, state a hypothesis about how environmental factors affect germination rates.

Goals

- **Design an experiment** to test the effect of an environmental factor on seed germination rate.
- **Compare** germination rates under different conditions.

Safety Precautions

Some kinds of seeds are poisonous. Do not place any seeds in your mouth. Be careful when using any electrical equipment to avoid shock hazards.

Test Your Hypothesis

Possible Procedures

Students will plant seeds in shallow trays or plastic cups. They may use one variable in their setups. Students should be encouraged to use at least two strengths of salt solution if they use salt solutions in their design. The control will be distilled water. If they use the heating cables as a variable, then seeds without heat will be the control. If planting depth is the variable, the control is the recommended depth.

Test Your Hypothesis

Plan

1. As a group, agree upon and **write** out your hypothesis statement.
2. As a group, list the steps that you need to take to test your hypothesis. Be specific, and **describe** exactly what you will do at each step. List your materials.
3. **Identify** any constants, variables, and controls of the experiment.
4. What measurements will you take? What data will you collect? How often will you collect data? If you need a data table, **design** one in your Science Journal so that it is ready to use as your group collects data. Will the data be summarized in a graph?
5. **Read** over your entire experiment to make sure that all steps are in logical order. How many tests will you run?

Do

1. Make sure your teacher approves your plan before you proceed.
2. Carry out the experiment as planned.
3. While the experiment is going on, **record** any observations that you make and complete the data table in your Science Journal.

Analyze Your Data

1. **Compare** your results with those of other groups.
2. Did changing the variable affect germination rates? Explain.
3. **Graph** your results using a bar graph, placing germination rate on the *y*-axis and the environmental variables on the *x*-axis.

Draw Conclusions

1. **Interpret** your graph to estimate the conditions that give the best germination rate.
2. What things affect the germination rate?

Teaching Strategies

Review the Problem Solving feature in this chapter to give added background for measuring germination rate.

Troubleshooting Students may confuse rate of germination (how quickly seeds germinate) with germination rate (the percent of seeds that actually germinate).

Expected Outcome

Students will observe that seeds germinate better under some environmental conditions than others.

Error Analysis

Have students try to explain differences in their results from others who tested the same variable.

Analyze Your Data

1. Group results should be similar for the same variable.
2. The rate of germination and germination rate are affected by temperature but vary with each species. Increased salt concentration should affect the germination rate more than the rate of germination. Planting depth's effect varies with species. Presence or absence of light only affects seeds that are sown on the surface of soil.
3. Graphs should accurately reflect experimental data.

Draw Conclusions

1. Student graphs will vary, but each graph should indicate a range for best germination of the variable tested.
2. Answers will vary but may include water quality, amount of water, planting depth.

GO Further

Students may test other temperatures or other chemicals if time is available.

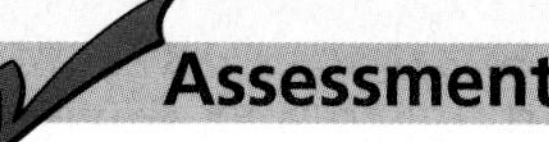

Assessment

Oral Have students explain their results to the class. **Use Performance Assessment in the Science Classroom,** p. 71.

FIELD GUIDE

Using the Field Guide

- Use this field guide with student pp. 458–459.
- This field guide applies nationally; local and regional field guides are usually available.
- Encourage students to use the field guide outside.
- Remind students that plants vary and cones may not match exactly.

Tying to Previous Knowledge

Students may have seen cones on different needled trees and referred to all them as pine cones. After using this field guide, they will be aware of the different needled plants and the uniqueness of their cones.

FIELD ACTIVITY

Student responses to this activity will vary. If students use cones from craft items, help them identify the species then have them research it to find a description of the plant.

FIELD GUIDE to Cones

When we hear the word *cone*, we may think of a holder for our favorite ice cream. Or, we may think of the orange cones that we see on highways and in public places to direct traffic. But, there's another type of cone in our environment that plays an important role for some plants. They are the reproductive organs of a large plant group called the *conifers*, or cone bearers. The seeds of pines, firs, spruces, and redwoods are formed on cones.

FIELD ACTIVITY

Find three different cones in your neighborhood, a park, around your school or as part of a craft item. Using this guide, identify the genus of each cone. In your Science Journal, make a sketch of each cone and write a description of the plant it came from.

Types of Cones

All conifers have two types of cones, male and female. The male cones produce pollen grains. They are short lived, breaking apart shortly after they release pollen. Depending on the species of conifer, the familiar female cones may stay on plants for nearly one year, two years, or three years. Female cones may be woody or berrylike. Woody cones consist of scales growing from a central stalk. Berrylike cones are round and may be either hard or soft. Each genus of conifers has a different female cone. They are so different from one another that you can use them to identify a conifer's genus.

Cone Characteristics

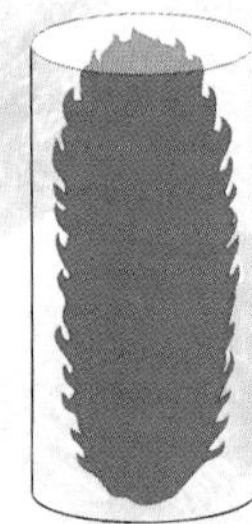

- **cylindrical**—shaped like a cylinder; nearly uniform in size from the base to the tip of the cone

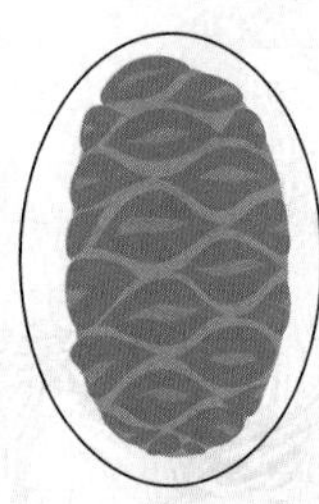

- **ovoid**—shaped like a cylinder but smaller at the ends than in the middle

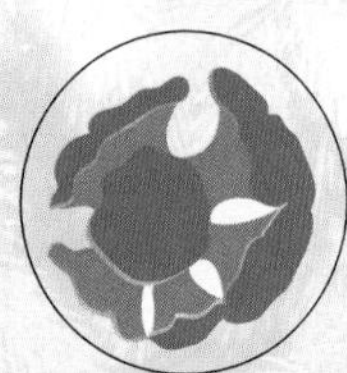

- **globose**—rounded like a globe

- **conic**—shaped like a cone; decreasing in diameter from the base to the tip of the cone

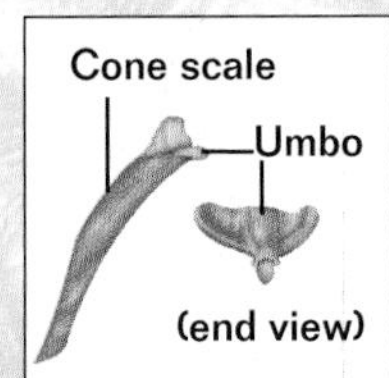

- **umbo**—a raised, triangular area at the tip of a cone scale; size and thickness of area varies

Other Field Guides to Cones

- Little, Elbert L., Jr. and Angelo Lomeo (photographer), *The Audubon Society Field Guide to North American Trees: Eastern Region.* Alfred A. Knopf Inc., 1980.
- Little, Elbert L., Jr. and Angelo Lomeo (photographer), *The Audubon Society Field Guide to North American Trees: Western Region.* Alfred A. Knopf Inc., 1980
- Zim, Herbert Spencer and Alexander Martin (contributor), *Trees: A Guide to Familiar American Trees.* Golden Books Publishing Co., 1987

Cone Identification

This field guide contains some of the conifers. ***Remember*** *that plant features may differ in appearance because of environmental conditions.*

Juniper—*Juniperus*

- Hard, berrylike structures that stay on the tree or shrub for two to three years
- About 1.3 cm in diameter
- May be bluish, pale green, reddish, or brown and covered with a whitish, waxy coating called a bloom

Douglas Fir—*Psuedotsuga*

- Three-pointed, papery structure extends from below each cone scale
- Ovoid, on short stalks
- 5 cm to 10 cm in length

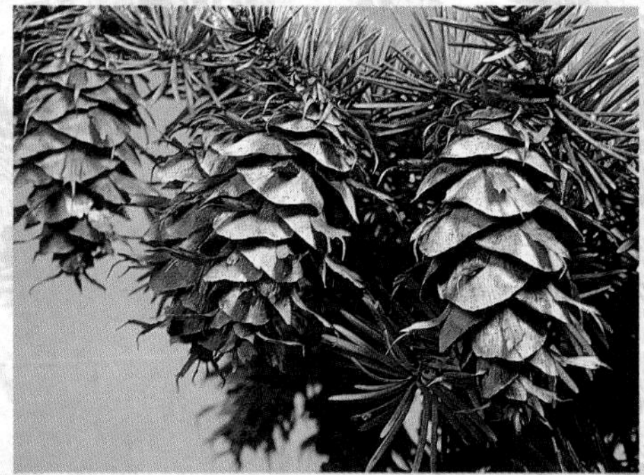

Spruce—*Picea*

- Cylindrical and brown, 6 cm to 15 cm in length
- Hang from branches on the upper third of the tree
- Thin cone scales, tips are usually pointed; brittle when mature
- Stay on the plant for two years

Redwood—*Sequoia*

- Ovoid, reddish brown, hang from the tips of neddled twigs
- Small in comparison to the size of the tree, only 1.2 cm to 3 cm
- Cone scales flattened on the end
- Mature in one year

Using Science Words

Cone is used to refer the reproductive structures on conifer plants. It also is the name of a geometric solid. Have students write a short paragraph about which object was named first. Have them explain their choice.

Quick Demo

Bring in branches from several different pines. Show students that pines have their needles in groups of two or three to five.

Teacher FYI

The seeds of nearly all pines are edible. They contain mostly oils but the protein content ranges from 15 percent to 30 percent.

Across the Curriculum

Geography Have students choose a conifer and find its place of origin. Place the different origins on a world map.

Activity

Have students bring in an item(s) made from the wood of a conifer. Make a list of the different genera.

Enrichment

Share items made from amber with students. Explain that amber is the fossilized resin of a pine found in New Zealand. Often in the amber are fossilized insects that were trapped in the resin.

FIELD•GUIDE•FIELD•GUIDE•FIELD•GUIDE•FIELD•GUIDE•FIELD•GUIDE•FIELD•GUIDE•FI

Hemlock—*Tsuga*

- Small, ovoid to cylindrical, 2 cm to 7 cm long, hang from twigs
- Cone scales are few and have rounded tips
- Mature in one year but usually stay on tree for more than one year

Douglas Fir—*Psuedotsuga*

- Three-pointed, papery structure extends from below each cone scale
- Ovoid, on short stalks
- 5 cm to 10 cm in length

Arborvitae—*Thuja*

- Egg-shaped cones, 1.2 cm to 1.5 cm long
- Paired cone scales, usually six to twelve, straplike and end in a sharp point
- Remain attached to shrub after opening and releasing seeds

Cypress—*Cupressus*

- Globose, usually 2 cm to 2.5 cm in diameter, only six to eight scales
- Cone scales have raised point in the center
- Mature in about 18 months and stay closed and attached to the tree

Integrating the Sciences

Earth Science The petrified forests of the southwestern United States contain the remains of ancient conifers. Have students explore the topic of petrifaction.

False Cypress—*Chamaecyparis*

- Small globose, only 0.5 cm to 4 cm in diameter with four to ten cone scales
- Open at maturity (unlike cones of *Cupressus* trees)

Swamp or Bald Cypress—*Taxodium*

- Globose, about 2.5 cm across
- Tips of cone scales are four sided, forming irregular pattern on the surface of cone
- Ripen in one year
- Trees in this genus recognizable by "knees" that form around the base of the tree trunk.

Fir—*Abies*

- Grow upright on branch
- Seldom used for identification because scales drop off at maturity leaving only the bare, central stalk
- 5 cm to 20 cm in length

Cedar—*Cedrus*

- Barrel-shaped cones with flattened tips grow upright on branches
- 5 cm to 10 cm in length and nearly half as wide
- Scales drop off at maturity (like firs) after two years
- Not produced until trees are 40 to 50 years old

Discussion

Have students discuss how their life would be different without conifers.

VISUAL Learning

Show students a photograph of a bald cypress tree(s). Point out the "knees" that form around the base of the trunk.

GO Further

Have students find cones that belong to genera not listed in this field guide. Use other field guides to identify the genera. Students should write descriptions of these cones and genera in their Science Journals. At the end of the school year, see how many different genera have been identified.

Inclusion Strategies

Visually Impaired Help visually impaired students to develop a key for several cones using sensory characteristics such as texture, smell, size, etc.

Reviewing Main Ideas can be used to preview, review, reteach, and condense chapter content.

Preview

Linguistic Have students try to answer the questions in their Science Journals. Use student answers as a source for discussion throughout the chapter.

Review

Interpersonal Have students answer the questions on separate pieces of paper and compare their answers with those of other students in the class. COOP LEARN

Reteach

Visual-Spatial Have students look at the illustrations on these pages. Ask them to describe details of each illustration that support the main idea of the accompanying statement.

OUT OF TIME?

Auditory-Musical If time does not permit teaching the entire chapter, use the information on these pages along with the chapter Audiocassettes to present the material in a condensed format.

Chapter 16 Reviewing Main Ideas

For a **preview** of this chapter, study this Reviewing Main Ideas before you read the chapter. After you have studied this chapter, you can use the Reviewing Main Ideas to **review** the chapter.

The Glencoe MindJogger, Audiocassettes, and CD-ROM provide additional opportunities for review.

Section

16-1 INTRODUCTION TO PLANT REPRODUCTION

Plants reproduce sexually and asexually. Sexual reproduction involves the formation of sex cells and fertilization. Asexual reproduction does not involve sex cells and produces organisms genetically identical to the parent organism. Plant life cycles include a gametophyte and a sporophyte stage. The gametophyte stage begins with meiosis. The sporophyte stage begins when the egg is fertilized by a sperm. In some plant life cycles, these stages are separate and not dependent on each other. In other plant life cycles, they are part of the same organism. For liverworts and mosses, the **gametophyte stage** is the familiar plant form. The **sporophyte stage** produces spores. In ferns, the sporophyte stage, not the gametophyte stage, is the familiar plant form. Ferns, like mosses and liverworts, produce spores. ***What does alternation of generations mean?***

Cultural Diversity

Drip Irrigation Crop production on a Navajo reservation in Arizona was once very limited because of the scarcity of water. In 1984, David Mazigh was invited to visit the reservation. Mazigh had managed an experimental farm in Israel. He shared his knowledge of drip irrigation with the Navajos. Some Israeli farmers use drip irrigation to get water to plants in their desert lands. Water is pumped from a nearby well and mixed with fertilizer. The fertilizer supplies nutrients that are necessary for plant growth and lacking in desert soils. The water travels in thick pipes to thin drip lines in a field. The drip lines lie beside the rows of planted seeds. Small drippers are inside the drip lines at two-foot intervals that allow water to drip out. Plants receive a slow and constant supply of water and fertilizer for growth.

Reading Check ✓

Find five science words in this chapter that begin with the letter *a*. Identify the words in which *a* is the prefix that means "without."

Section

16-2 SEED PLANT REPRODUCTION

Seed plants include gymnosperms and angiosperms. The male reproductive organs produce **pollen grains** that eventually contain sperm. Eggs are produced in the **ovules** of the female reproductive organs. The reproductive organs of gymnosperms are called cones. Wind usually moves pollen from the male cone to the female cone for fertilization. The reproductive organs of angiosperms are in a flower. The male reproductive organ is the **stamen,** and the female reproductive organ is the **pistil.** Gravity, wind, rain, and animals may pollinate a flower. Seeds of gymnosperms and angiosperms are dispersed in many ways. ***How are the reproductive organs of gymnosperms and angiosperms alike?***

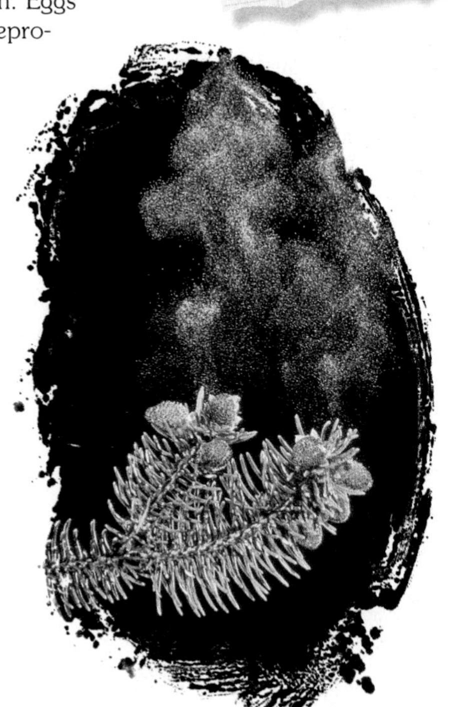

Career CONNECTION

Flora Ninomiya, Horticulturist

As a horticulturist, Flora Ninomiya is interested in the science of cultivating plants. She is responsible for 600 000 rose plants that occupy about 92 000 m^2 of greenhouse space. In addition to experimenting with new rose varieties, Flora schedules plant production, checks plants for diseases and insects, and oversees plant watering and fertilization. She uses the latest technologies, including computer-automated greenhouses and hydroponics.

Answers to Questions

Section 16-1

Introduction to Plant Reproduction The plant life cycle alternates between a sporophyte ($2n$) and gametophyte (n) generation.

Section 16-2

Seed Plant Reproduction Gymnosperms and angiosperms produce pollen grains containing sperm. They have ovaries, but the ovary tissue of gymnosperms does not surround the seed.

GLENCOE TECHNOLOGY

 **CD-ROM**

Glencoe Science Voyages Interactive CD-ROM

Chapter Summaries and Quizzes

Have students read the Chapter Summary, then take the Chapter Quiz to determine whether they have mastered chapter content.

Assessment

Portfolio Encourage students to place in their portfolios one or two items of what they consider to be their best work. Examples include:

- Activity 16-1, p. 456
- Activity, p. 460
- MiniLab, p. 465
- Activity 16-2, pp. 468–469 P

Performance Additional performance assessments may be found in the **Performance Assessment** and **Science Integration Activities.** Performance Task Assessment Lists and rubrics for evaluating these activities can be found in Glencoe's **Performance Assessment in the Science Classroom.**

Using Vocabulary

1. f, m
2. e, g
3. c, l
4. a
5. b, j, k (any two)

interNET CONNECTION To reinforce chapter vocabulary, use the **Study Guide for Content Mastery** booklet. Also available are activities for **Glencoe Science Voyages** on the Glencoe Science Web Site. **www.glencoe.com/sec/science**

Checking Concepts

6. A	11. C
7. D	12. C
8. D	13. B
9. A	14. D
10. A	15. A

Thinking Critically

16. The chances that a pollen grain will be blown to an ovule are increased.
17. Student answers will vary but should include flowers with long, tube-like forms.
18. Bryophytes and ferns require free water to transport their sperm to egg cells.
19. The sporophyte is not photosynthetic so it depends on the photosynthetic gametophyte for nutrition.
20. Brightly colored structures, scents, and flower form help to ensure pollination by specialized pollinators.

Chapter 16 Assessment

Using Vocabulary

a. alternation of generations
b. frond
c. gametophyte stage
d. ovary
e. ovule
f. pistil
g. pollen grain
h. pollination
i. prothallus
j. rhizome
k. sori
l. sporophyte stage
m. stamen

Complete the following sentences with the best choices from the Vocabulary list.

1. A(n) _______ has an ovary and a(n) _______ has an anther.
2. In seed plants, the _______ contains the egg and the _______ contains the sperm.
3. Haploid cells make up the _______ _______ and diploid cells make up the _______ _______.
4. Moss capsules and moss plants are examples of _______ ___ _______.
5. Two parts of a sporophyte fern are _______ and _______.

Checking Concepts

Choose the word or phrase that best answers the question.

6. How are colorful flowers usually pollinated?
   A) insects
   B) wind
   C) clothing
   D) gravity
7. What is part of all plant life cycles?
   A) seeds
   B) fruits
   C) flowers
   D) alternation of generations
8. What part of the flower receives the pollen grain?
   A) sepal
   B) ovary
   C) stamen
   D) stigma
9. What do ferns form when they reproduce sexually?
   A) spores
   B) vascular tissue
   C) seeds
   D) flowers
10. What contains food for the embryo?
    A) endosperm
    B) pollen grain
    C) stigma
    D) root
11. What disperses most dandelion seeds?
    A) rain
    B) animals
    C) wind
    D) insects
12. What is the series of events that results in an organism from a seed?
    A) pollination
    B) alternation of generations
    C) germination
    D) asexual reproduction
13. What is another name for seed leaves?
    A) root hairs
    B) cotyledons
    C) stigmas
    D) stomata
14. Ovules and pollen grains are involved in what process?
    A) germination
    B) asexual reproduction
    C) seed dispersal
    D) sexual reproduction
15. Which of the following terms describes the cells in the gametophyte stage?
    A) haploid
    B) prokaryotic
    C) diploid
    D) missing a nucleus

Thinking Critically

16. Explain why male cones produce so many pollen grains.
17. Describe a flower that is pollinated by a hummingbird.
18. Discuss the importance of water in the reproduction of bryophytes and ferns.
19. In mosses, why is the sporophyte stage dependent on the gametophyte stage?
20. What features of flowers ensure pollination?

Developing Skills

If you need help, refer to the Skill Handbook.

21. **Concept Mapping:** Complete this concept map of a moss life cycle.

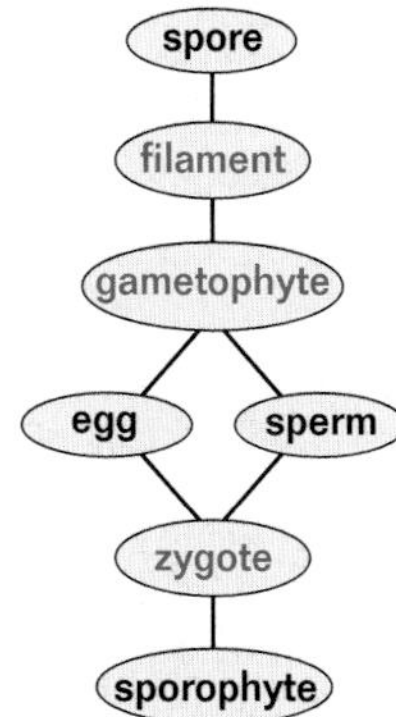

22. **Comparing and Contrasting:** Describe the differences and similarities between the fern sporophyte and gametophyte stages.
23. **Observing and Inferring:** Observe pictures of flowers or actual flowers and infer how each is pollinated. Explain your suggestion.
24. **Sequencing:** Number the following events in the correct order. *Pollen is trapped on the stigma; pollen tube reaches the ovule; fertilization; pollen released from the anther; pollen tube forms through the style; a seed forms.*
25. **Making and Using Graphs:** Make a bar graph for the following data table about onion seeds. Put the temperature on the horizontal axis and days on the vertical axis.

Onion Seed Data

Temperature (°C)	10	15	20	25	30	35
Days to germinate	13	7	5	4	4	13

Test-Taking Tip

Use as Much Time as You Can You will not get extra points for finishing early. Work slowly and carefully on any test and make sure you don't make careless errors because you are hurrying to finish.

Test Practice

Use these questions to test your Science Proficiency.

1. What does the gametophyte stage of a moss or fern life cycle produce?
   A) sex cells C) spores
   B) seeds D) fruits
2. What is the usual pollinator for gymnosperms?
   A) wind C) rain
   B) insects D) gravity
3. If a flower has a pistil but no stamen, what type of flower is it?
   A) pollinator C) infertile
   B) male D) female
4. You see a dandelion growing near a rose. Which of the following **BEST** explains how the dandelion came to be there?
   A) It grew from an underground dandelion.
   B) The seed was carried there by the wind and grew.
   C) The plant was put there by an animal.
   D) Dandelions often grow from the roots of roses.

Assessment Resources

The **Test Practice Workbook** provides students with practice in the format, concepts, and critical-thinking skills tested in standardized exams.

Reproducible Masters

Chapter Review, pp. 31–32 L2
Performance Assessment, p. 30 L2
Assessment, pp. 69–72 L2

Glencoe Technology

Chapter Review Software
Computer Test Bank
MindJogger Videoquiz

THE PRINCETON REVIEW **Test Practice**

The Test-Taking Tip was written by The Princeton Review, the nation's leader in test preparation.

1. A **3.** D
2. A **4.** B

Developing Skills

21. See student page.
22. Haploid gametophyte stage—small and inconspicuous; diploid sporophyte stage—large and conspicuous; both stages are independent and photosynthetic.
23. Answers will vary depending on flowers observed.
24. 1—pollen is released from the anther; 2—pollen is trapped on the stigma; 3—pollen tube forms through style; 4—pollen tube reaches the ovule; 5—a seed forms.
25.

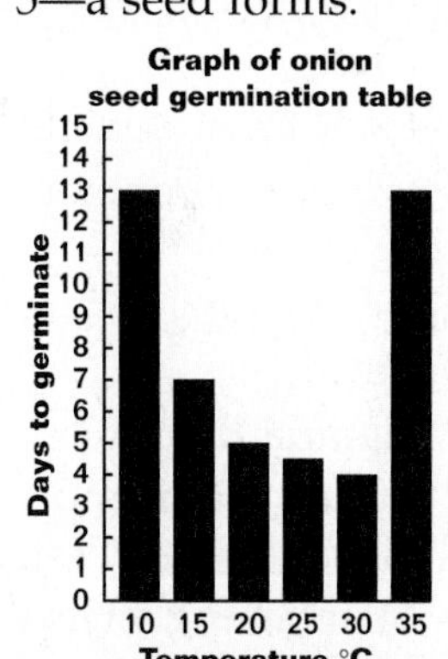

Bonus Question

The petals and sepals of tulips are alike in color and size. Why might natural selection favor this arrangement? *The flower petals appear to be six not three, which helps to attract insect pollinators and increase the chances of pollination and reproduction.*

UNIT 6

Ecology

In this unit, students are introduced to the fundamentals of ecology, including interaction of abiotic and biotic factors, characteristics of populations, the flow of energy, and the cycling of matter. Ecosystems and succession in ecosystems are explored. The unit concludes with a discussion of renewable and nonrenewable resources and how these resources are affected by human use.

Unit Overview

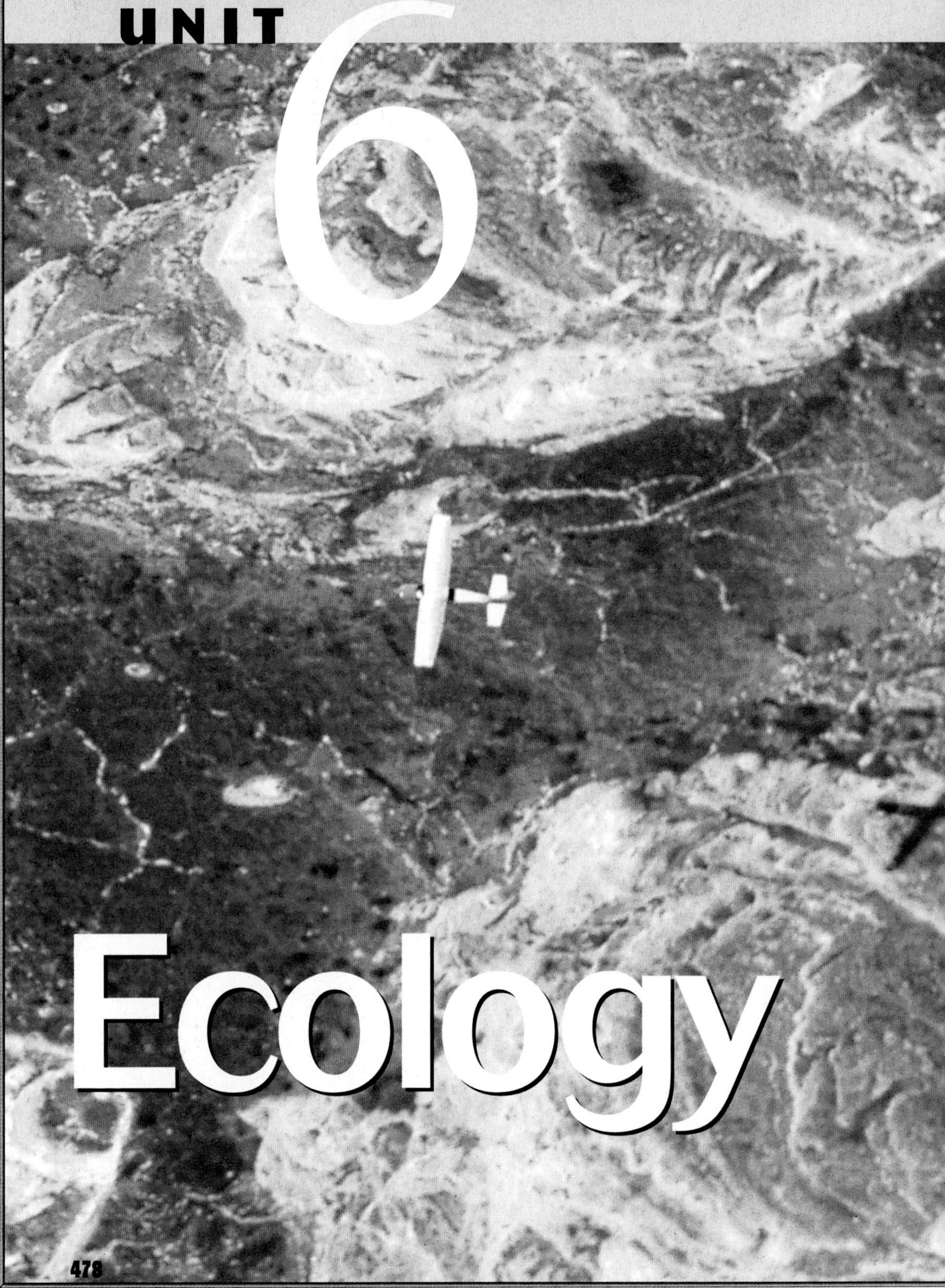

Science at Home

Interactions with the Environment Have students identify ways in which they interact with their environment and explain how the interactions help them carry out their life processes. For example, they use their senses to avoid danger.

NATIONAL GEOGRAPHIC

What's Happening Here?

A small plane flies over one of the soda lakes of eastern Africa (left). Dotted with islands of foam, where liquid and gas bubble through its salt crust, Tanzania's Lake Natron appears to be a wasteland. Yet, notice the color. Pink algae bloom everywhere. After a rain, fresh water collects on the salt flats, and there the algae survive. The algae feed the flamingos (below) that flock to the lake by the millions to breed, and the birds' droppings feed the algae. The algae also give the birds' feathers their pink hue. Moreover, the harsh salt crust keeps many predators from crossing the treacherous flats—thereby providing a safe place for the flamingos to nest. Thus, living and nonliving parts of the environment—the algae and the salt crust—work together to support life. In this unit, you will learn that complex webs connect living things and are key to supporting life, even in hostile environments.

interNET CONNECTION

Explore the Glencoe Science Web Site at **www.glencoe.com/sec/science** to find out more about topics found in this unit.

479

Introducing the Unit

What's happening here?

Have students read the text and examine the pictures. Ask them if they know other plants and animals that live together in close association. Have them name nonliving things in their own environments that help them to survive.

Content Background

Ecosystems exist at all levels. Even a square meter of garden soil may be considered a micro-ecosystem and is filled with information about the living world. Ecologists study the interactions among living and nonliving components of various ecosystems.

Previewing the Chapters

- Have students identify photos in the chapters that show interactions of living organisms with their nonliving environments.
- Have students find photographs or illustrations of plants and animals and speculate on the type of environment in which they live.
- Have students study the diagrams in the unit that show ecological principles such as the cycling of matter, flow of energy, and succession.

Tying to Previous Knowledge

Discuss ecosystems with which students may be familiar, such as water ecosystems or parks and wilderness areas. Encourage students to recognize how much they already know about ecology.

interNET CONNECTION

Internet Addresses

____

____

____

Explore the Glencoe Science Web Site at **www.glencoe.com/sec/science** to find out more about topics found in this unit.

Chapter 17 Life and the Environment

Section	Objectives	Activities/Features
Chapter Opener		**Explore Activity:** Measuring Space, p. 481
17-1 **The Living and Nonliving Environment** 2 Sessions 1 Block	1. **Identify** biotic and abiotic factors in the ecosystem. 2. **Describe** the characteristics of populations. 3. **Explain** the levels of biological organization.	**Earth Science Integration,** p. 484 **Skill Builder:** Observing and Inferring, p. 486 **Using Computers,** p. 486 **Activity 17-1:** Soil Composition, p. 487
17-2 **Interactions Among Living Organisms** 4 Sessions 2 Blocks	4. **Describe** the characteristics of populations. 5. **Identify** the types of relationships that occur among populations in a community. 6. **Compare** the habitat and niche of a species in a community.	**Using Math,** p. 491 **MiniLab:** Observing Symbiosis, p.492 **Skill Builder:** Observing and Inferring, p. 493 **Using Math,** p. 493 **Activity 17-2:** Identifying a Limiting Factor, pp. 494–495
17-3 **Matter and Energy** 2 Sessions 1 Block	7. **Explain** how energy flows through ecosystems. 8. **Describe** the cycling of matter in the biosphere.	**Chemistry Integration,** p. 497 **Problem Solving:** Changes in Antarctic Food Webs, p. 499 **MiniLab:** Modeling the Water Cycle, p. 500 **Skill Builder:** Classifying, p. 502 **Science Journal,** p. 502 **Reading and Writing in Science:** Never Cry Wolf, p. 503

The number of recommended single-period sessions — The number of recommended blocks
One session and one-half block are allowed for chapter review and assessment.

Activity Materials

Explore	Activities	MiniLabs
p. 481 meterstick	p. 487 3 small paper cups, freshly dug soil, newspaper, beaker, water, hand lens, jar with lid, scale pp. 494–495 bean seeds, small planting containers, soil, labels, trowel or spoon, aluminum foil, light source, refrigerator or oven, water	p. 492 legumes, non-legumes, prepared microscope slide of nitrogen-fixing bacteria, microscope p. 500 plastic cup, plastic wrap, rubber band

Need Materials? Contact Science Kit at 1-800-828-7777 or at www.sciencekit.com on the Internet.
For alternate materials, see the activity on the listed page.

Chapter Organizer

Standards		Reproducible Resources	Technology
National	State/Local	Test Practice Workbooks are available for use with each chapter.	English and Spanish audiocassettes are available for use with each section.
National Content Standards: UCP1, A1, A2, C4, D1		**Activity Worksheets,** pp. 93–94 **Enrichment,** p. 44 **Laboratory Manual,** pp. 99–101 **Reinforcement,** p. 44 **Study Guide,** pp. 65–66	Section Focus Transparency 44 National Geographic Society: GTV The Infinite Voyage Series
National Content Standards: UCP1, A1, A2, C4, F2		**Activity Worksheets,** pp. 95–97 **Critical Thinking/Problem Solving,** p. 17 **Enrichment,** p. 45 **Laboratory Manual,** pp. 103–106 **Multicultural Connections,** pp. 33–34 **Reinforcement,** p. 45 **Study Guide,** p. 67	Section Focus Transparency 45 National Geographic Society: STV The Infinite Voyage Series
National Content Standards: UCP2, A1, B1, B3, C4		**Activity Worksheets,** p. 98 **Enrichment,** p. 46 **Reinforcement,** p. 46 **Study Guide,** pp. 67–68	Section Focus Transparency 46 Teaching Transparency 33 Teaching Transparency 34 Science Integration Transparency 17 National Geographic Society: STV Glencoe Science Voyages Interactive CD-ROM **Internet Connection,** p. 501

Key to Teaching Strategies

The following designations will help you decide which activities are appropriate for your students.

L1 Level 1 activities should be appropriate for students with learning difficulties.

L2 Level 2 activities should be within the ability range of all students.

L3 Level 3 activities are designed for above-average students.

ELL ELL activities should be within the ability range of English Language Learners.

COOP LEARN Cooperative Learning activities are designed for small group work.

P These strategies represent student products that can be placed into a best-work portfolio.

Multiple Learning Styles logos, as described on page 61T, are used throughout to indicate strategies that address different learning styles.

Assessment Resources

Chapter Review, pp. 33–34
Assessment, pp. 75–78
Performance Assessment in the Science Classroom (PASC)
MindJogger Videoquiz
Alternate Assessment in the Science Classroom
Performance Assessment, p. 31
Chapter Review Software
Computer Test Bank

Chapter 17 Life and the Environment

This is a representation of key blackline masters available in the Teacher Classroom Resources. See Resource Manager boxes within the chapter for additional information.

Transparencies

Section Focus Transparencies

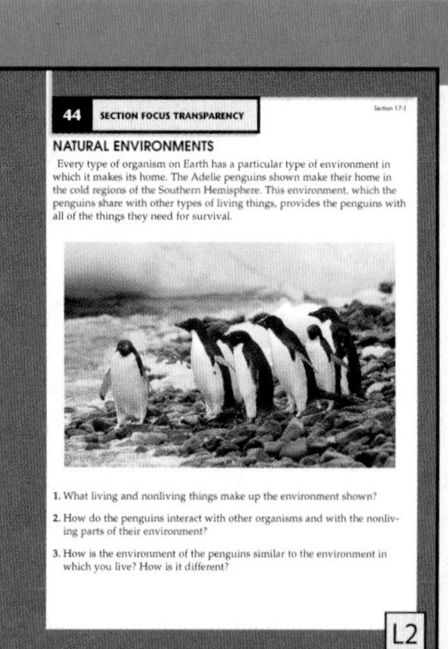

44 SECTION FOCUS TRANSPARENCY — Section 17-1

NATURAL ENVIRONMENTS

Every type of organism on Earth has a particular type of environment in which it makes its home. The Adelie penguins shown make their home in the cold regions of the Southern Hemisphere. This environment, which the penguins share with other types of living things, provides the penguins with all of the things they need for survival.

1. What living and nonliving things make up the environment shown?
2. How do the penguins interact with other organisms and with the nonliving parts of their environment?
3. How is the environment of the penguins similar to the environment in which you live? How is it different?

L2

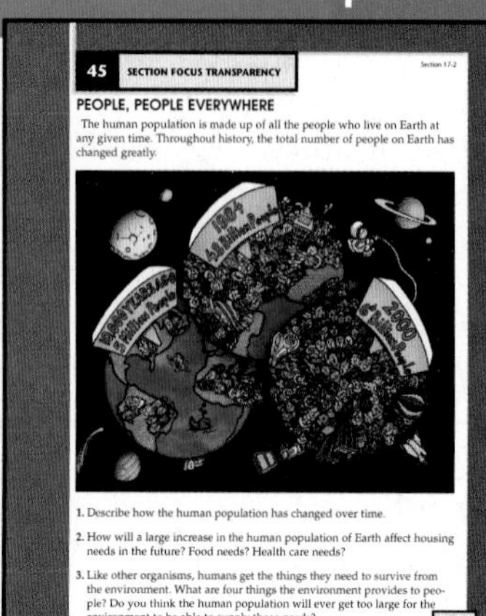

45 SECTION FOCUS TRANSPARENCY — Section 17-2

PEOPLE, PEOPLE EVERYWHERE

The human population is made up of all the people who live on Earth at any given time. Throughout history, the total number of people on Earth has changed greatly.

1. Describe how the human population has changed over time.
2. How will a large increase in the human population of Earth affect housing needs in the future? Food needs? Health care needs?
3. Like other organisms, humans get the things they need to survive from the environment. What are four things the environment provides to people? Do you think the human population will ever get too large for the environment to be able to supply those needs?

L2

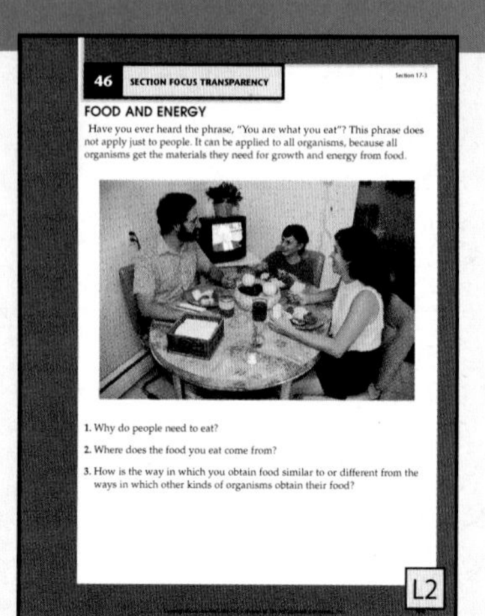

46 SECTION FOCUS TRANSPARENCY — Section 17-3

FOOD AND ENERGY

Have you ever heard the phrase, "You are what you eat"? This phrase does not apply just to people. It can be applied to all organisms, because all organisms get the materials they need for growth and energy from food.

1. Why do people need to eat?
2. Where does the food you eat come from?
3. How is the way in which you obtain food similar to or different from the ways in which other kinds of organisms obtain their food?

L2

Science Integration Transparencies

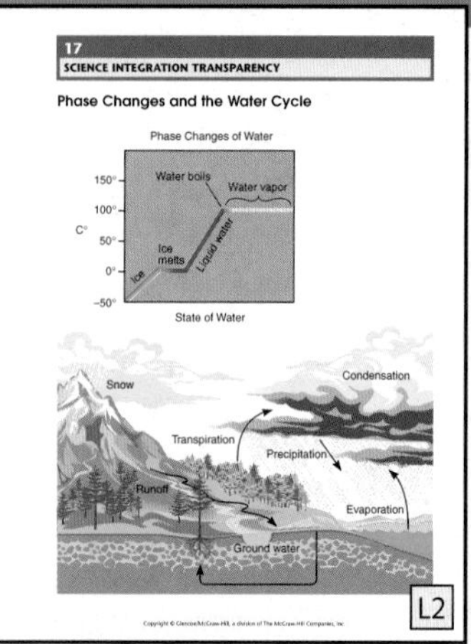

Teaching Transparencies

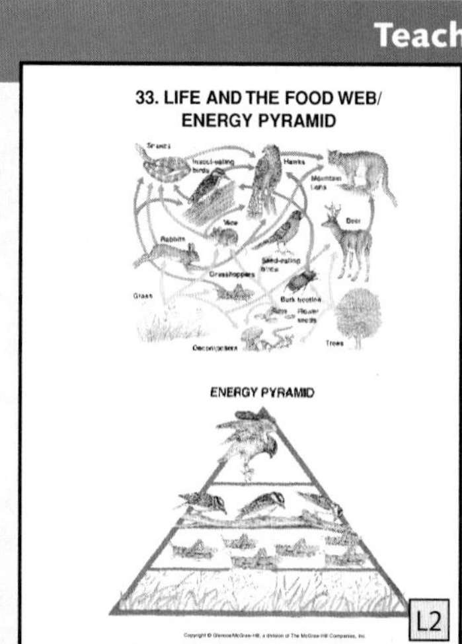

Meeting Different Ability Levels

Study Guide for Content Mastery

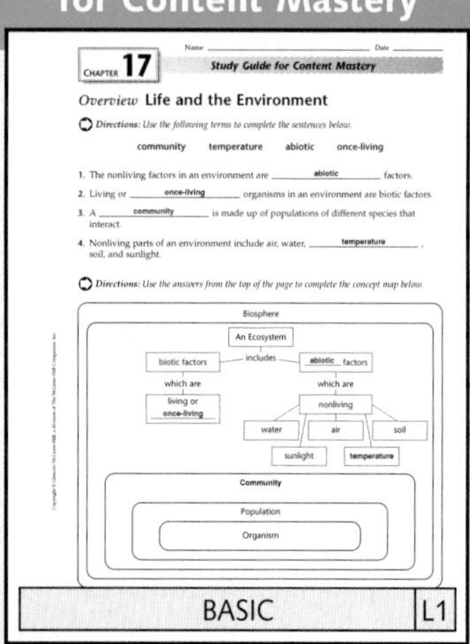

Name ______ Date ______

CHAPTER 17 — Study Guide for Content Mastery

Overview Life and the Environment

Directions: Use the following terms to complete the sentences below.

community   temperature   abiotic   once-living

1. The nonliving factors in an environment are ___abiotic___ factors.
2. Living or ___once-living___ organisms in an environment are biotic factors.
3. A ___community___ is made up of populations of different species that interact.
4. Nonliving parts of an environment include air, water, ___temperature___, soil, and sunlight.

Directions: Use the answers from the top of the page to complete the concept map below.

BASIC L1

Reinforcement

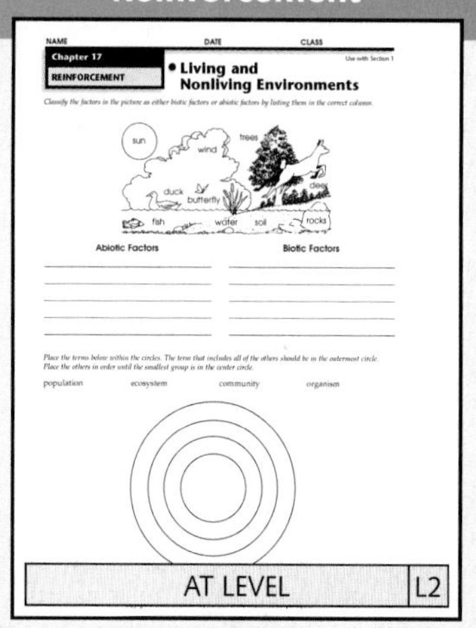

NAME DATE CLASS

Chapter 17 REINFORCEMENT — Living and Nonliving Environments — Use with Section 1

Classify the factors in the picture as either biotic factors or abiotic factors by listing them in the correct column.

Abiotic Factors	Biotic Factors

Place the terms below within the circles. The term that includes all of the others should be in the outermost circle. Place the others in order until the smallest group is in the center circle.

population   ecosystem   community   organism

AT LEVEL L2

Enrichment Worksheets

NAME DATE CLASS

Chapter 17 ENRICHMENT — Living and Nonliving Environments — Use with Section 1

Life on the Ocean Floor

In 1974, scientists exploring the floor of the Pacific Ocean in the deep-sea submersible *Alvin* made a great discovery. They were exploring west of the Galapagos Islands at a depth of about 2700 meters. The water, which is usually between 3°C and 5°C, was getting *warmer*.

Here, as in several other places, fissures or cracks open in the ocean floor. Water seeps into the rocks, becomes superheated, and picks up minerals as it rises. Finally, the water shoots up through volcanic vents in the ocean floor; and this water is *hot*, about 300°C.

An even greater surprise to the scientists: near the vents were giant tube worms, huge clams, and eyeless, colorless crabs. Immediately the question arose: What is the source of energy for these organisms?

As the water moves away from the vent, it cools. In these waters scientists found unusual chemosynthetic bacteria. Chemosynthetic bacteria are able to absorb chemicals, in this case hydrogen sulfide carried up from under the earth's crust by water flowing from the vents. The chemosynthetic bacteria use the energy in the hydrogen sulfide molecules, rather than the energy in sunlight, to build up organic molecules such as glucose. These bacteria become the food source, or source of energy, for the tube worms, clams, crabs, and other organisms.

These organisms make up an extraordinary ecosystem. The producers are not green plants, as in land and other water ecosystems, but chemosynthetic bacteria. This ecosystem depends on heat energy from deep within Earth; it does not depend on energy from sunlight.

Conclude and Apply

1. What are chemosynthetic bacteria?
2. Why is the area described here an ecosystem rather than a community?
3. Why is this ecosystem unusual?
4. What are the biotic and abiotic factors?

CHALLENGE L3

Hands-on Activities

Activity Worksheets

NAME DATE CLASS

Chapter 17 ACTIVITY 17-1 • Soil Composition

Lab Preview

1. What are abiotic factors?
2. Name at least three abiotic factors.

Soil is more than minerals mixed with the decaying bodies of dead organisms. It contains other biotic and abiotic factors.

What You'll Investigate

Goals

Materials

Procedure

Data and Observations

L2

Lab Manual

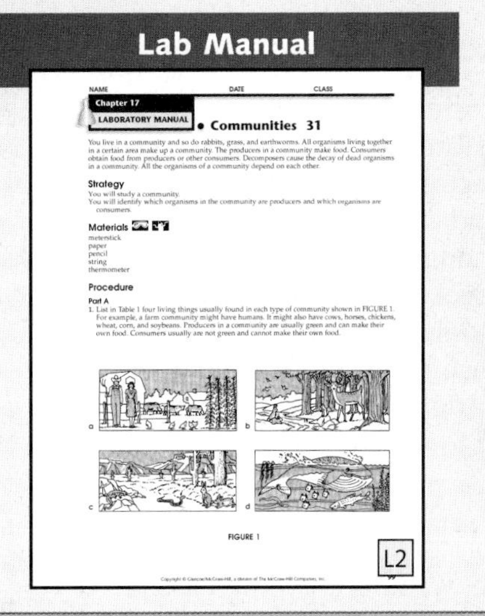
NAME DATE CLASS

Chapter 17 LABORATORY MANUAL • Communities 31

Strategy

Materials

Procedure

Part A

FIGURE 1

L2

Accessibility

Spanish Resources

Assessment

Performance Assessment

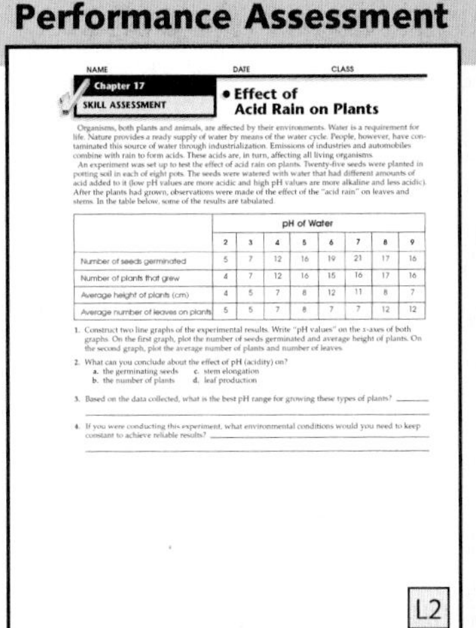
NAME DATE CLASS

Chapter 17 SKILL ASSESSMENT • Effect of Acid Rain on Plants

L2

Chapter Review

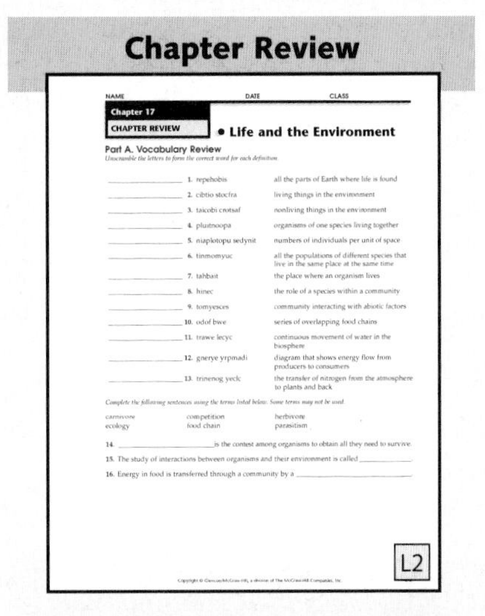
NAME DATE CLASS

Chapter 17 CHAPTER REVIEW • Life and the Environment

Part A. Vocabulary Review

L2

Assessment

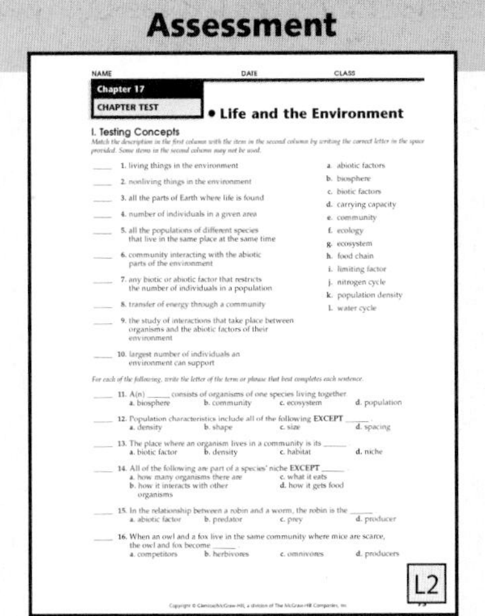
NAME DATE CLASS

Chapter 17 CHAPTER TEST • Life and the Environment

I. Testing Concepts

L2

Test Practice Workbook

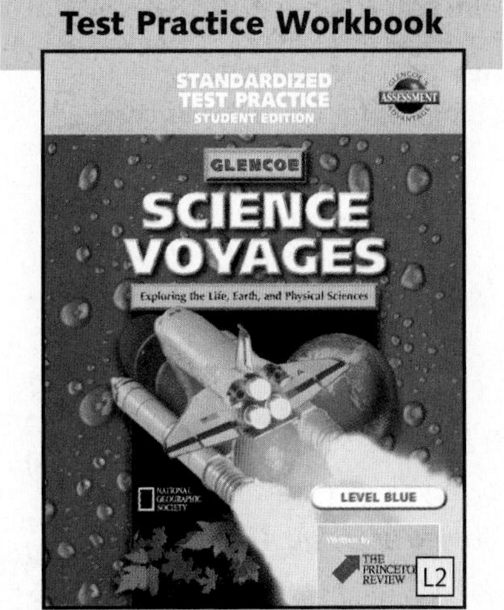

Extending Content

Critical Thinking/ Problem Solving

Multicultural Connections

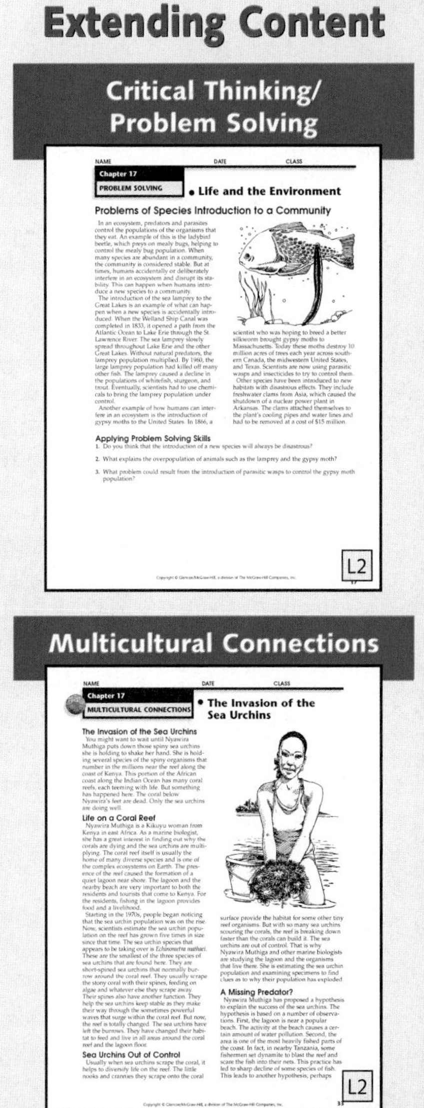
NAME DATE CLASS

Chapter 17 PROBLEM SOLVING • Life and the Environment

Problems of Species Introduction to a Community

Applying Problem Solving Skills

L2

NAME DATE CLASS

Chapter 17 MULTICULTURAL CONNECTIONS • The Invasion of the Sea Urchins

The Invasion of the Sea Urchins

Life on a Coral Reef

Sea Urchins Out of Control

A Missing Predator?

L2

Helping You Prepare

Abiotic Factors (Section 17-1)

Important abiotic factors include air currents, temperature, moisture, light, and soil. The importance of each factor varies from environment to environment and over time. Consider temperature, which changes from hour to hour, day to day, season to season, and year to year. Abiotic and biotic factors are not independent. Lack of rainfall can cause a drought in a grassland. The animals that depend on plants for food would find it hard to survive.

Soil (Section 17-1)

Soil forms by the weathering and erosion of rock. Soil is a mixture of humus, decayed organic matter, and particles of weathered rock, sand, silt, and clay. Clay is an important component of soil because it helps hold water in the soil and contains many minerals that plants need for growth. The types of minerals found in clays are largely dependent on the climate. Humus is equally important because it helps separate clay and sand particles, allowing more water and air to enter the soil. It also provides food for soil organisms as well as nutrients for plants.

Biotic Factors (Section 17-1)

All organisms depend on others for food, shelter, reproduction, or protection. Ecologists study interactions among organisms at several different levels. They study individual organisms, interactions among organisms of the same species, and interactions among organisms of different species. They also study how abiotic factors affect groups of interacting species.

GLENCOE TECHNOLOGY

Glencoe Science Voyages Interactive CD-ROM

Chapter Summaries

Use the Chapter Summary to introduce, teach, or review chapter material.

Characteristics of Populations (Section 17-2)

Population size is an important characteristic, but it can be difficult to measure. Animal population size can be influenced by the amount of food and space available. Natural populations cannot increase forever.

Population density measures how crowded a population is. It is always expressed as the number of individuals per unit area or volume.

Dispersion is the spatial distribution of indi-

NATIONAL GEOGRAPHIC — **Teacher's Corner**

Products Available from Glencoe

To order the following products for use with this chapter, call Glencoe at 1-800-334-7344:

CD-ROMs

NGS Picture Show: Looking at Ecosystems

NGS Picture Show: Looking at Living Things

Poster

Water

Transparency Sets

NGS PicturePack: Looking at Ecosystems

NGS PicturePack: Looking at Living Things

Videodiscs

STV: Habitats

STV: Water

Products Available from National Geographic Society

To order the following products for use with this chapter, call the National Geographic Society at 1-800-368-2728:

Videos

Ecosystem: A Struggle for Survival

Pond-Life: Food Web

Web of Life

viduals within a population. The three patterns of dispersion are even, clumped, and random. The dispersion pattern sometimes depends on how the population is observed. Waterbirds that live near the shore may appear evenly spaced. If the entire island is observed, the birds may appear clumped.

Carrying Capacity (Section 17-2)

When a population arrives at the point where its size is no longer increasing, it has reached the carrying capacity of the environment. The carrying capacity is the greatest number of individuals in a certain population that a given environment is capable of supporting under a specific set of conditions. The carrying capacity may vary with the time of year as conditions change. If the weather becomes colder in winter, the food supply may diminish, and the environment will not be able to support as many organisms. At carrying capacity, the number of organisms born or produced in a given period of time balances the number of organisms that die during that time. At this point, the size of the population remains fairly stable.

The Flow of Energy Through Ecosystems (Section 17-3)

The energy in an ecosystem is passed from one organism to another through a series of interactions called a food chain. Food chains, food webs, and ecological pyramids show how energy moves in only one direction through the trophic levels of an ecosystem and how energy is lost at each transition, from one trophic level to the next. The energy is lost to the environment in the form of heat generated by the body processes of organisms. Sunlight is the source of all energy, so energy is always being replaced.

Two types of food webs are grazing and detrital. Detritivores are organisms, such as crabs and earthworms, that consume dead or decomposing organic matter. The largest amount of energy passes through detrital food webs.

SCIENCE UPDATE

For current events or science in the news, access the Glencoe Science Web Site at **www.glencoe.com/sec/science**

The Cycles of Matter (Section 17-3)

Matter, in the form of nutrients, moves through the organisms at each trophic level in an ecosystem. But matter cannot be replenished like the energy from sunlight. The atoms of carbon, nitrogen, and other elements that make up the bodies of organisms alive today are the same atoms that have been on Earth since life began. Matter is constantly being recycled.

In addition to carbon, oxygen, and hydrogen, living things need phosphorus, potassium, sulfur, magnesium, calcium, sodium, iron, and cobalt. These substances are held in rocks and enter the soil after the rocks weather. Rocks and the atmosphere are reservoirs for the inorganic substances that organisms need.

Teacher to Teacher

"To evaluate student understanding of abiotic and biotic factors of the environment, I take them outside and have them make two lists of the factors and how they are interrelated to one another. I also have the students make food chains from their observations."

Steve Manns, Teacher
Derry Area Middle School
Derry, PA

CHAPTER 17
Life and the Environment

CHAPTER OVERVIEW

Section 17-1 This section examines the units that make up the biosphere and how factors within the biosphere interact.

Section 17-2 Characteristics of populations and how populations interact in communities are discussed.

Section 17-3 This section focuses on how energy flows through an ecosystem and the cycling of water, nitrogen, oxygen, and carbon.

Chapter Vocabulary

biosphere
ecology
abiotic factor
biotic factor
population
community
ecosystem
population density
limiting factor
carrying capacity
symbiosis
habitat
niche
food chain
food web
ecological pyramid
water cycle
nitrogen cycle

Theme Connection

Systems and Interactions In learning about relationships among living and nonliving things in populations, communities, and ecosystems, students will discover how all living and nonliving things on Earth are connected.

If time does not permit teaching the entire chapter, use Reviewing Main Ideas on pp. 504–505.

CHAPTER
17 Life and the Environment

Chapter Preview

Section 17-1
The Living and Nonliving Environments

Section 17-2
Interactions Among Living Organisms

Section 17-3
Matter and Energy

Skills Preview

Skill Builders
- Classify

Activities
- Graph

MiniLabs
- Infer

Reading Check ✓

Define several terms that begin with the prefix *a* (meaning "without"), such as *abiotic.*

Multiple Learning Styles

Look for the following logos for strategies that emphasize different learning modalities.

Linguistic Using Science Words, p. 483; Reteach, p. 485; Science Journal, p. 489; Preview, p. 504

Logical-Mathematical Explore Activity, p. 481; Assessment, pp. 493, 495

Visual-Spatial Integrating the Sciences, p. 483; Activity, pp. 485, 491, 492, 497, 501; Assessment, pp. 486, 502; Across the Curriculum, pp. 490, 491; MiniLab p. 492; Reteach, p. 504

Kinesthetic Integrating the Sciences, p. 484; Activity, p. 487; Inclusion Strategies, p. 499; MiniLab p. 500; Reteach, p. 501

Interpersonal Discussion, p. 537; Enrichment, p. 491; Activity, p. 494; Review, p. 504

Naturalist Science Journal, p. 489; Activity, p. 490; Multiple Learning Styles, p. 497

Explore Activity

Mountain goats rely on winter winds to uncover food plants buried beneath the snow. Surefooted and strong, they scale high cliffs to get their next meal. A mountain goat's range consists of high terrain where few other animals dare to tread. This reduces competition from different organisms for food. How does the number of related organisms in an area affect each individual? You share your science classroom with other students. How much space is available to each student?

Measure Space

1. Use a meterstick to measure the length and width of the classroom.
2. Multiply the length times the width to find the area of the room in square meters.
3. Count the number of individuals in your class. Divide the number of square meters in the classroom by the number of individuals.

Science Journal

In your Science Journal, record how much space each person has. Determine the amount of space each person would have if the number of individuals in your class doubled. Predict how having that amount of space would affect you and your classmates.

481

Explore Activity

Purpose

Logical-Mathematical Use the Explore Activity to give students firsthand experience in determining the density of a population. L2 ELL COOP LEARN

Materials

meterstick

Teaching Strategies

Have one student measure and the other student record. They can find the answers to the questions together.

Science Journal If the student population is 30 and the classroom size is 240 m^2, then each student would have 8 m^2. Explain that if the population density of the classroom doubled, each person would have only 4 m^2. However, to calculate population density, you divide the number of individuals in the population by the area to get individuals per unit area. In this case, the population density would be:

$$\frac{\text{30 students}}{\ } = \frac{\text{0.125 students}}{\ }.$$

Assessment

Performance Have students list the populations that might be in the area where they live. **Use Performance Assessment in the Science Classroom,** p. 17.

Assessment Planner

Portfolio

Refer to p. 505 for suggested items that students might select for their portfolios.

Performance Assessment

See p. 505 for additional Performance Assessment options.
Skill Builder, pp. 486, 502
MiniLab, pp. 492, 500
Activity, 17-1, pp. 487; 17-2, pp. 494–495

Content Assessment

Section Assessment, pp. 486, 493, 502
Chapter Assessment, pp. 506–507
Proficiency Prep, pp. 486, 493, 502

SECTION 17-1

Prepare

Refer to **Abiotic Factors, Soil,** and **Biotic Factors** on p. 480E

Preplanning

Refer to the **Chapter Organizer** on pp. 480A–B.

1 Motivate

Bellringer

Before presenting the lesson, display **Section Focus Transparency 44** on the overhead projector. Use the accompanying **Focus Activity** worksheet. L2 ELL

Section 17-1

44 SECTION FOCUS TRANSPARENCY

NATURAL ENVIRONMENTS

Every type of organism on Earth has a particular type of environment in which it makes its home. The Adelie penguins shown make their home in the cold regions of the Southern Hemisphere. This environment, which the penguins share with other types of living things, provides the penguins with all of the things they need for survival.

1. What living and nonliving things make up the environment shown?
2. How do the penguins interact with other organisms and with the nonliving parts of their environment?
3. How is the environment of the penguins similar to the environment in which you live? How is it different?

Tying to Previous Knowledge

Review producers, consumers, classification, and species. Students will be familiar with organisms from their own environment. Ask how these organisms interact in their environment.

17-1 The Living and Nonliving Environment

What You'll Learn

- How to identify biotic and abiotic factors in an ecosystem
- The characteristics of populations
- The levels of biological organization

Vocabulary
biosphere
ecology
abiotic factor
biotic factor
population
community
ecosystem

Why It's Important

- Abiotic and biotic factors work together to form your ecosystem.

The Biosphere

Think of all the organisms on Earth. Millions of species exist. Where do all these organisms live? Living things can be found 11 000 m below the surface of the ocean and on tops of mountains 9000 m high. The part of Earth that supports organisms is known as the **biosphere** (BI uh sfihr). The biosphere seems huge, but it is actually only a small portion of Earth. The biosphere includes the topmost portion of Earth's crust, all the waters that cover Earth's surface, and the surrounding atmosphere. Overall though, the thickness could be compared to the thickness of the skin of an apple.

Within the biosphere, many different environments can be found. For example, red-tailed hawks are found in environments where tall trees live near open grassland. The hawks nest high in the trees and soar over the land in search of rodents and rabbits to eat. In environments with plenty of moisture, such as the banks of streams, willow trees provide food and shelter for birds, mammals, and insects. All organisms interact

Figure 17-1 The biosphere is the region of Earth that contains all living organisms. An ecologist is a scientist who studies relationships among organisms and between organisms and the physical features of the biosphere.

Resource Manager

The following **Teacher Classroom Resources** can be used with Section 17-1:

 **Reproducible Masters**

Activity Worksheets, pp. 93–94 L2

Enrichment, p. 44 L3

Laboratory Manual, pp. 99–101 L2

Reinforcement, p. 44 L2

Study Guide, pp. 65–66 L1 ELL

with the environment. The science of **ecology** is the study of the interactions that take place among organisms and between organisms and the physical features of the environment. Ecologists, such as the one in **Figure 17-1,** are the scientists who study interactions between organisms and the environment.

Abiotic Factors

A forest environment is made up of trees, birds, insects, and other living things that depend on one another for food and shelter. But, these organisms also depend on factors that surround them such as soil, sunlight, water, temperature, and air. These factors—the nonliving, physical features of the environment—are called **abiotic factors.** Abiotic—*a* meaning "not" and *biotic* meaning "living"—factors have effects on living things and often determine the organisms that are able to live in a certain environment. Some abiotic factors are shown in **Figure 17-2.**

Figure 17-2 Abiotic factors help determine which species can survive in an area.

A Soil
Soil consists of minerals mixed with decaying, dead organisms. It contains both living and nonliving components.

B Light
Seasonal events, such as flowering in plants or migration of birds, are often triggered by a change in the number of hours of daylight.

C Water
Many organisms live in water, such as this lake in Pennsylvania, rather than air.

D Temperature
Temperatures change with daily and seasonal cycles. Desert-dwelling rattlesnakes, like this sidewinder in the Colorado desert, are active only in the cool, early morning hours. During the hottest part of the day, they rest in the shade.

2 Teach

Using Science Words

Linguistic Write the words *biosphere, biotic,* and *abiotic* on the chalkboard. Ask students to find the meanings of *bio, sphere,* and *tic.* (*bio*—life, *sphere*—area, *tic*—relating to). L2

Discussion

Lead students in a discussion of how abiotic and biotic factors interact in an ecosystem to support life.

Activity

Have students list the biotic and abiotic factors that would affect the population growth of frogs near a pond. L2

Videodisc

GTV: Planetary Manager
Side 1, Show 1.2
'Round and 'Round

5834–10218

Refer to the Teacher Guide for additional bar codes and teaching strategies.

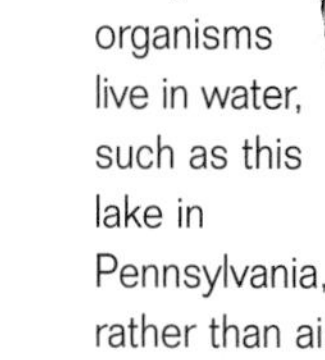

Content Background

The word *ecology* comes from the Greek work *oikos,* meaning "house" or "place to live" and *-ology,* meaning "the study of."

Integrating the Sciences

Earth Science The biosphere is made up of water, land, and air. These three parts are called the hydrosphere, the lithosphere, and the atmosphere. Have students use Earth science reference books to draw how the three spheres intersect. L3 P

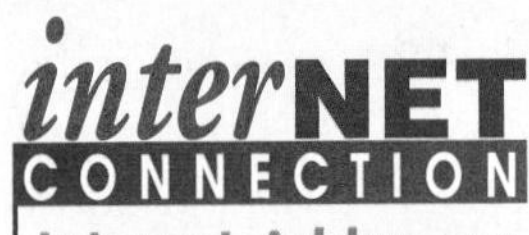

Internet Addresses

For Internet tips, see Glencoe's **Using the Internet in the Science Classroom.**

Discussion

Why is topsoil fertile? *Topsoil contains large amounts of humus, which is made up of the decayed remains of dead organisms.*

GLENCOE TECHNOLOGY

Videodisc

The Infinite Voyage: To the Edge of the Earth

Chapter 5 *The Tropical Rain Forest* 8:00

Chapter 6 *Exploring Life in the Canadian Arctic* 8:00

Refer to the Teacher Guide for bar codes and teaching strategies.

Visit the Glencoe Science Web Site at www.glencoe.com/sec/science for more information about how ecologists study the biosphere.

Water

Water is an important abiotic factor. The bodies of most organisms are 50 to 95 percent water. Water is an important part of cytoplasm and the fluid that surrounds cells. Respiration, photosynthesis, digestion, and other important life processes can take place only in the presence of water.

Soil

The type of soil in a particular location helps determine which plants and other organisms live in that location. Most soil is a combination of sand, clay, and humus. Soil type is determined by the relative amounts of sand, clay, and humus in the soil. Humus is the decayed remains of dead organisms. The greater the humus content, the more fertile the soil.

Light and Temperature

The abiotic factors of light and temperature also impact the environment. Through the process of photosynthesis, the radiant energy of sunlight is transformed into chemical energy that drives virtually all of life's processes. The availability of sunlight is a major factor in determining where green plants and other photosynthetic organisms live, as shown in **Figure 17-3.** Sunlight does not penetrate far into deep water. Most green algae benefit from living near the surface. In a similar situation, because little sunlight reaches the shady darkness of the forest floor, plant growth there is limited.

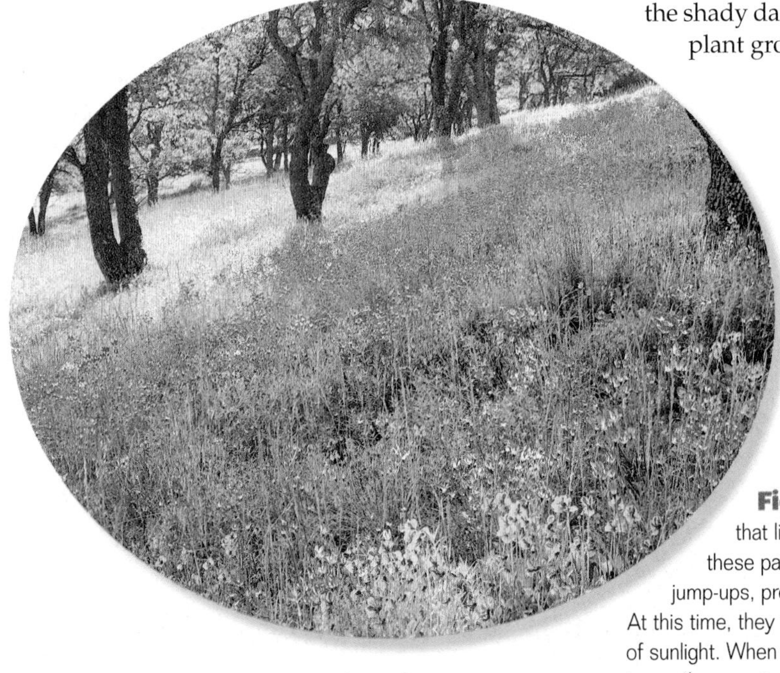

Figure 17-3 Many wildflowers that live on the forest floor, such as these padres shooting stars and Johnny jump-ups, produce seeds early in the spring. At this time, they receive the maximum amount of sunlight. When the leaves are fully out on the trees, they receive little direct sun.

Integrating the Sciences

Earth Science Clay, silt, and sand are types of soil, classified by the size of their particles. *Loam* is the most common type of soil and is a mixture of clay, silt, and sand. Provide students with samples of different kinds of soil and a hand lens to observe and compare the sizes of their particles. L2 ELL

VISUAL Learning

Figure 17-3 **Explain how the biotic and abiotic factors are interacting in the photograph.** *Plants need light and water to make food and reproduce. Decaying plants provide nutrients for new plants.*

Biotic Factors

Abiotic factors do not provide everything an organism needs for survival. Mushrooms would not be able to grow without the decaying bodies of other organisms to feed on. Honeybees could not survive without pollen from flowers. Some species of owls and woodpeckers prefer to nest in the hollow trunks of dead trees. Organisms depend on other organisms for food, shelter, protection, or reproduction. Living or once-living organisms in the environment are called **biotic factors.**

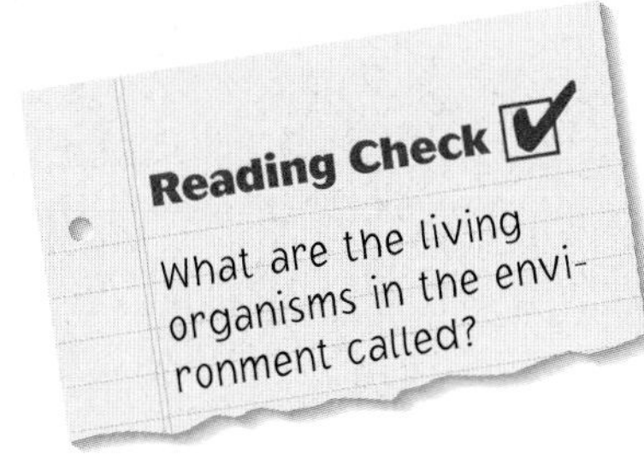

Reading Check
What are the living organisms in the environment called?

Levels of Biological Organization

The living world is highly organized. Atoms are arranged into molecules, which are in turn organized into cells. Cells form tissues, tissues form organs, and organs form systems. Similarly, the biotic and abiotic factors studied by ecologists can be arranged into layers of organization, as shown in **Figure 17-4.**

Figure 17-4 The living world is organized into several levels.

Organism
An organism is a single individual from a population.

Population
A population is all of the individuals of one species that live and reproduce in the same area at the same time.

Community
A community is made up of populations of different species that interact in some way.

Ecosystem
An ecosystem consists of communities and the abiotic factors that affect them.

Biosphere
The biosphere is the highest level of biological organization. It is made up of all the ecosystems on Earth.

Correcting Misconceptions

Students may think that communities always include people and the structures they create. Help students see that there are many nonhuman populations that are a part of their community.

3 Assess

Check for Understanding

Activity

Visual-Spatial Provide students with photographs from old magazines. Ask them to identify the biotic factors in each photograph. Ask them to explain why they identified them as biotic factors. L2

Reteach

Linguistic Have students write a paragraph in their Science Journal explaining the relationships among population, community, and ecosystem. They should include that populations interact to make a community and that communities and nonliving things make up the ecosystem. L2

Extension

For students who have mastered this section, use the **Reinforcement** and **Enrichment** masters.

Guided Reading Strategy

Reciprocal Teaching This strategy is designed to help construct meaning and apply reading skills. Have pairs of students begin by having each partner silently read a chunk of text. After several minutes of reading, one student retells the key points of what was read in his or her own words. The other student creates a question that can be answered directly from the text but could require inferences or evaluation. Continue the reading with each student alternating the questions and summaries. Consciously asking questions and summarizing content helps the reader attend deliberately to what is being read. Have students do Reciprocal Teaching with a chunk of section content. You might want to choose a section such as abiotic factors that may be more difficult to understand the first time it is read.

4 Close

Proficiency Prep

Use this quiz to check students' recall of section content.

1. **What are all parts of Earth where life is found called?** *biosphere*
2. **What are nonliving, physical features of the environment called?** *abiotic factors*
3. **What is made up of communities and the abiotic factors that affect them?** *ecosystem*

Section Assessment

1. Biotic factors are living. Abiotic factors are nonliving. Biotic factors are bacteria, protists, fungi, plants, and animals; abiotic factors include soil, temperature, light, water, and wind.
2. A population is all the organisms of one species living together in the same place at the same time. A community is made up of groups of populations. An ecosystem is made up of a community and the abiotic factors that affect it.
3. **Think Critically** Living organisms interact with oxygen and carbon dioxide, which are nonliving and considered abiotic factors.

Using Computers

Answers will vary depending on the type of ecosystem that is present.

Figure 17-5 This coral reef is an example of an ecosystem. It is made up of hundreds of populations of organisms, as well as ocean water, sunlight, and other abiotic factors.

Populations

Individual organisms of the same species that live in the same place and can produce young form a **population.** Members of several populations on a coral reef are seen in **Figure 17-5.** Members of populations of organisms compete with each other for food, water, mates, and space. The resources of the environment and how the organisms use these resources determine how large a population can be.

Communities

Most populations of organisms do not live alone. They live and interact with populations of other organisms. Groups of populations that interact with each other in a given area form a **community.** Populations of organisms in a community depend on each other for food and shelter and for other needs.

Ecosystem

An **ecosystem** is made up of a biotic community and the abiotic factors that affect it. The rest of this chapter will discuss in more detail the kinds of interactions that take place between abiotic and biotic factors in an ecosystem.

Section Assessment

1. What is the difference between an abiotic factor and a biotic factor? Give at least five examples of each.
2. What is the difference between a population and a community? A community and an ecosystem?
3. **Think Critically:** Could oxygen in the atmosphere be considered an abiotic factor? Why or why not? What about carbon dioxide?
4. **Skill Builder**
   Observing and Inferring Each person lives in a population as part of a community. Describe your population and community. If you need help, refer to Observing and Inferring in the **Skill Handbook** on page 720.

Using Computers

Spreadsheet Obtain two months of temperature and rainfall data from your local newspaper or the Internet. Enter the data in a spreadsheet and then average the totals for temperature and the totals for rainfall. What kind of climate do you think you have based on your calculations? If you need help, refer to page 738.

4.  **Skill Builder**
Students may describe themselves as humans, living in towns, inside houses, and as consumers, students, children, brothers, sisters, etc.

Assessment

Portfolio Cut out pictures from magazines that can illustrate soil formation. Make a poster using the pictures. Be sure to include all stages. Use **Performance Assessment in the Science Classroom,** p. 73. P

486 CHAPTER 17 LIFE AND THE ENVIRONMENT

Soil Composition

Soil is more than minerals mixed with the decaying bodies of dead organisms. It contains other biotic and abiotic factors.

What You'll Investigate

What are the components of soil?

Goals

- **Determine** what factors are present in soil.

Materials

- Small paper cups containing freshly dug soil (3)
- Newspaper
- Beaker of water
- Hand lens
- Jar with lid
- Scale

Procedure

1. **Obtain** 3 cups of soil from your teacher. **Record** the source of your sample in your Science Journal.
2. **Pour** one of your samples onto the newspaper. **Sort** through the objects in the soil. Try to separate abiotic and biotic items. Use a hand lens to help identify the items. **Describe** your observations in your Science Journal.
3. Carefully place the second sample in the jar, disturbing it as little as possible. Quickly fill the jar with water and screw the lid on tightly. Without moving the jar, **observe** its contents for several minutes. **Record** your observations in your Science Journal.
4. **Weigh** the third sample. **Record** the weight in your Science Journal. Leave the sample undisturbed for several days, then weigh it again. **Record** the second weight in your Science Journal.

Conclude and Apply

1. Can you **infer** the presence of any organisms? Explain.
2. **Describe** the abiotic factors in your sample. What biotic factors did you **observe?**
3. Did you **record** any change in the soil weight over time? If so, why?

Activity 17•1

Purpose

Kinesthetic Students will observe the components of soil.

Process Skills

observing, measuring in SI, comparing and contrasting, forming operational definitions

Time

45 minutes

Safety Precautions

Have students wash their hands after handling soil.

Teaching Strategies

- The soil should be from a single area such as a garden, lawn, vacant field, or pond bank. Tell students the source of the soil.
- Samples should be freshly dug soil that has been disturbed as little as possible.
- The purpose of step 3 is to observe air bubbles rising from the soil.

Troubleshooting To avoid incorporating air when filling the jar with water, have students pour water into the jar from a beaker rather than the tap.

Answers to Questions

1. Students will observe worms, fungi, and other soil organisms.
2. Abiotic factors include air, water, and minerals. Biotic factors include decaying plants and animals, and soil organisms.
3. The soil weight changed because the water contained in the sample of soil evaporated.

Assessment

Performance Have students design an experiment that will allow them to compare the growth of organisms that live in different kinds of soil. They may sprinkle soil samples on moist bread or agar plates and place these in self-sealing plastic bags. Bacterial and mold colonies should be visible after a few days. Use **Performance Assessment in the Science Classroom,** p. 23.

SECTION 17-2

Prepare

Content Background

Refer to **Characteristics of Populations** and **Carrying Capacity** on pp. 480E–F.

Preplanning

Refer to the **Chapter Organizer** on pp. 480A–B.

1 Motivate

Bellringer

Before presenting the lesson, display **Section Focus Transparency 45** on the overhead projector. Use the accompanying **Focus Activity** worksheet. L2 ELL

Section 17-2

45 SECTION FOCUS TRANSPARENCY

PEOPLE, PEOPLE EVERYWHERE

The human population is made up of all the people who live on Earth at any given time. Throughout history, the total number of people on Earth has changed greatly.

1. Describe how the human population has changed over time.
2. How will a large increase in the human population of Earth affect housing needs in the future? Food needs? Health care needs?
3. Like other organisms, humans get the things they need to survive from the environment. What are four things the environment provides to people? Do you think the human population will ever get too large for the environment to be able to supply those needs?

17-2 Interactions Among Living Organisms

What You'll Learn

- The characteristics of populations
- The types of relationships that occur among populations in a community
- The habitat and niche of a species in a community

Vocabulary
population density
limiting factor
carrying capacity
symbiosis
habitat
niche

Why It's Important

- You must directly or indirectly interact with other organisms to survive.

Characteristics of Populations

As shown in **Figure 17-6,** populations can be described by their characteristics. These include the size of the population, spacing (how the organisms are arranged in a given area), and density (how many individuals there are in a specific area). Suppose you spent several months observing a population of field mice living in a pasture. You would probably observe changes in the size of the population. Older mice die, baby mice are born, some are eaten by predators, and some mice wander away to new homes. The size of a population—the number of individual organisms it contains—is always changing, although some populations change more rapidly than others. In contrast to a mouse population, the number of pine trees in a forest changes fairly slowly, but a forest fire could quickly reduce the population of pine trees in the forest.

Figure 17-6 Populations have several characteristics that define them.

For an online update of this data, visit **www.glencoe.com/sec/science** and select the appropriate chapter.

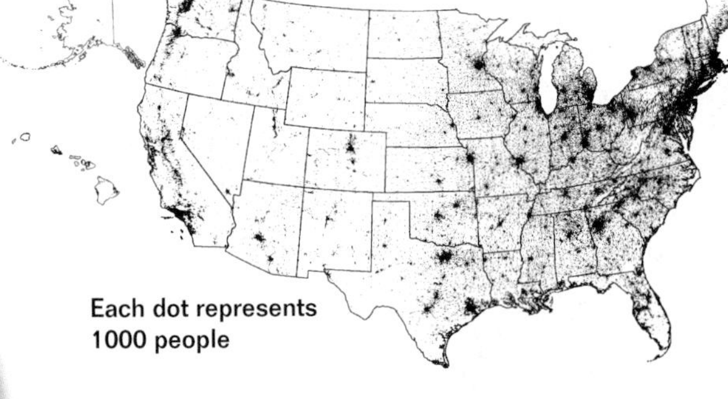

A Spacing
A characteristic of populations is spacing. In some populations, such as the oak trees of an oak-hickory forest, individuals are spaced fairly evenly throughout the area.

B Density
Human population density is higher in and around cities than in rural areas. **Which part of the United States has the highest population density?**

Caption Answer

Figure 17-6B *Population is higher along the east coast and the northeastern states.*

Resource Manager

The following **Teacher Classroom Resources** can be used with Section 17-2:

 **Reproducible Masters**

Activity Worksheets, pp. 95–97 L2

Critical Thinking/Problem Solving, p. 17 L2

Enrichment, p. 45 L3

Laboratory Manual, pp. 103–106 L2

Multicultural Connections, pp. 33–34 L2

Study Guide, p. 67

Reinforcement, p. 45 L2

Population Density

At the beginning of this chapter, when you figured out how much space is available to each student in your classroom, you were measuring another population characteristic. The size of a population that occupies an area of limited size is called **population density.** The more individuals there are in a given amount of space, as seen in **Figure 17-7,** the more dense the population. For example, if 100 mice live in an area of a square kilometer, the population density is 100 mice per km^2.

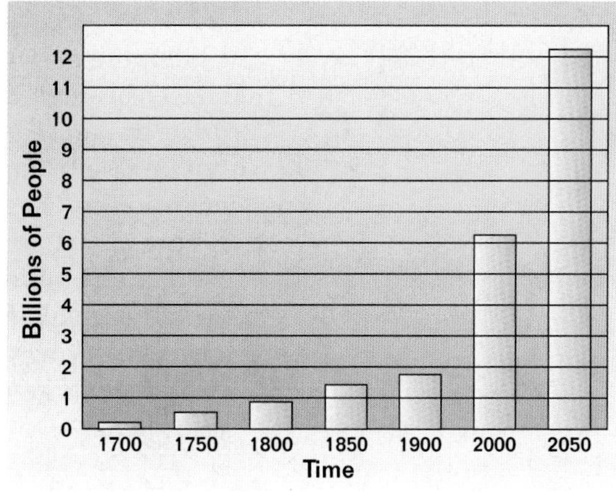

For an online update of this data, visit **www.glencoe.com/sec/science** and select the appropriate chapter.

Figure 17-7 The size of the human population is increasing at a rate of about 1.6 percent per year. At the present time, it is about 6 billion. In 2050, the population will be about 12 billion.

Limiting Factors

Populations cannot continue to grow larger and larger forever. In any ecosystem, there are limits to the amount of food, water, living space, mates, nesting sites, and other resources available. A **limiting factor** is any biotic or abiotic factor that restricts the number of individuals in a population. A limiting factor can also indirectly affect other populations in the community. For example, a drought might restrict the growth of seed-producing plants in a forest clearing. Fewer plants means that food may become a limiting factor for a mouse population that feeds on the seeds. Food also may become a limiting factor for hawks and owls that feed on the mice, as well as for the deer in **Figure 17-8.** ☑

Competition is the struggle among organisms to obtain the resources they need to survive and reproduce. As population density increases, so does competition among individuals.

Reading Check ☑

What is a limiting factor?

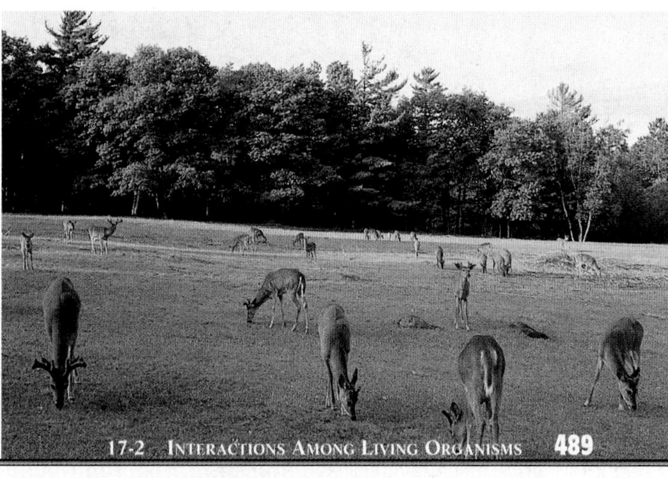

Figure 17-8 In many parts of the United States, deer populations, such as this one in northern Wisconsin, have become large enough to exceed the environment's ability to produce adequate food. Individuals starve or, weakened from lack of food, fall victim to disease.

Tying to Previous Knowledge

Have students recall the needs of living things. Knowing what living things need to grow and reproduce will be helpful in understanding limiting factors.

2 Teach

STV: Rain Forest

Unit 3 *Forest Canopy* 0:58

40695–42458

Refer to Teacher Guide for additional bar codes and teaching strategies.

Answer to Reading Check 

any biotic or abiotic factor that restricts the number of individuals in a population

Content Background

The term *population density* can refer to any kind of living population, including humans, mushrooms, bears, and bacteria. The population density of a species may vary greatly from place to place or from season to season.

Science Journal

Looking for Limiting Factors Take students on a walk around the school or an area near your school. Have them write in their journals the names of limiting factors and how they affect specific organisms in the area. L2 

Caption Answer

Figure 17-9 *Conditions are seldom ideal for a long enough period of time for a population to reach its biotic potential.*

GLENCOE TECHNOLOGY

Videodisc

The Infinite Voyage: Insects: The Ruling Class

Chapter 4 *Classifying Social Insects: Bees* 5:30

Refer to the Teacher Guide for bar codes and teaching strategies.

Activity

Naturalist Have students make lists of limiting factors for human population growth. Factors could include food, living space, pollution, and disease. L2

Discussion

What advantages does a population that feeds on several kinds of organisms have over a population that eats only one kind of plant or animal? *Feeding on several kinds of organisms ensures a food supply for the population if one food source becomes unavailable.*

Activity

Ask students to list ways cooperation is useful as it applies to success in sports. Relate their ideas to competition and cooperation in nature. L2

Teacher FYI

Reindeer and musk oxen can survive on lichens in the arctic tundra, where large plants are scarce.

Carrying Capacity

Suppose a population of robins continues to increase in size, year after year. At some point, food, nesting space, or other resources become so scarce that some individuals may not be able to survive or reproduce. When this happens, the environment has reached its carrying capacity, as seen in **Figure 17-9. Carrying capacity** is the largest number of individuals an environment can support and maintain for a long period of time. If a population begins to exceed the environment's carrying capacity, some individuals will be left without adequate resources. They may die or be forced to move elsewhere.

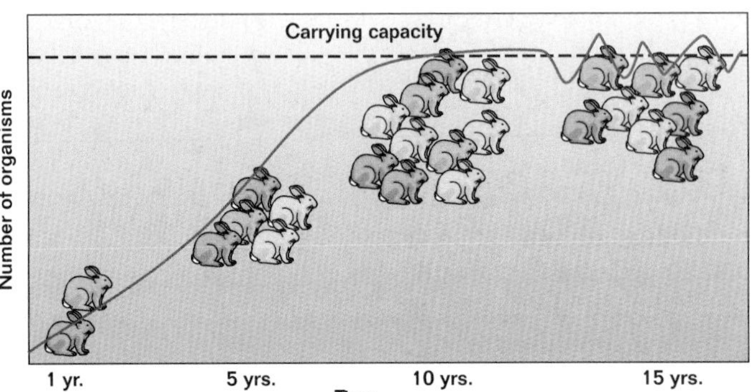

Figure 17-9 This graph shows how the size of a population increases until it reaches the carrying capacity of its environment. At first, growth is fairly slow. It speeds up as the number of adults capable of reproduction increases. Once the population reaches carrying capacity, its size remains fairly stable. **Why don't most populations achieve their biotic potential?**

Biotic Potential

What would happen if there were no limiting factors? A population living in an environment that supplies more than enough resources for survival will continue to grow. The maximum rate at which a population increases when there is plenty of food, water, ideal weather, and no disease or enemies is its biotic potential. However, most populations never reach their biotic potential, or do so for only a short period of time. Eventually, the carrying capacity of the environment is reached and the population stops increasing.

Interactions in Communities

Populations are regulated not only by the supply of food, water, and sunlight, but also by the actions of other populations. The most obvious way one population can limit another is by predation (prih DAY shun). One organism feeds on another. Owls and hawks are predators that feed on mice. Mice are their prey. Predators are biotic factors that limit the size of prey populations. Because predators are more likely to capture old, ill, or young prey, predation also helps maintain the health of a prey population. Predators leave the strongest individuals to reproduce. **Figure 17-10** shows how some predators work together to hunt their food.

Across the Curriculum

Geography Discuss and compare the habitats of different peoples on Earth. Show pictures of different cultures in distant parts of the world, such as Australia, Japan, Nigeria, the United Kingdom, India, and Turkey. Have students research the habitats of other peoples. L2 P

490 CHAPTER 17 LIFE AND THE ENVIRONMENT

Figure 17-10 Hyenas work together to hunt their food. This is called cooperation and helps all members of their population survive.

Symbiosis

Many types of relationships exist between organisms in ecosystems. Many species of organisms in nature have close, complex relationships in order to survive. When two or more species live close together, their relationship is called a symbiotic relationship. **Symbiosis** (sihm bee OH sus) is any close relationship between two or more different species.

Using Math

Calculating Population Growth

Example Problem: Estimates show the total human population will be about 6 billion in the year 2000. This number is thought to increase by 1.6 percent each year. What will the population be in the year 2005?

Problem-Solving Steps

1. What is known? Current population is 6 000 000 000. Yearly increase is 1.6%.
2. What is unknown? The population in 2001, 2002, 2003, 2004, and 2005.
3. **Solution:** Calculate the population increase for one year. Then, repeat the process four more times using the answer you came up with as a starting point.

```
 6 000 000 000             6 000 000 000
       × 0.016            + 96 000 000
36 000 000 000             6 096 000 000 people in 2001
60 000 000 000
    96 000 000 more people
```

The estimated population in the year 2005 is 6 495 607 732 people.

Practice Problem

An endangered species of fish currently has a population of 136 individuals. If the population increases by two percent every year, how many individuals will there be in three years?

Strategy Hint: When calculating percentages, remember to move your decimal two spaces to the left (0.02).

Using Math

In three years, the fish population will be 144.

On a calculator,
136 × 2 % × 2 % × 2 % =.
The answer (rounded) is 144.
Another method is:

136 × 0.02 = 2.72
2.72 + 136 = 138.72
138. 72 × 0.02 = 2.77
2.77 + 138.72 = 141.49
141.49 × 0.02 = 2.83
2.83 + 141.49 = 144

Using Science Words

Symbiosis comes from a Greek word meaning "living together." Have students find words that begin with *sym* and discuss their meanings.

Enrichment

Interpersonal Have students list as many predator-prey relationships as they can. Write all contributions on the chalkboard. Have students determine how many of the prey have more than one predator. L3

Activity

Visual-Spatial Have students look at lichens with a hand lens. Then have them prepare a wet-mount slide with lichen pieces and observe under the microscope. Ask how the algae and fungus benefit each other. *Algae make food for the fungus, and the fungus provides a habitat and moisture for the algae.* L2 COOP LEARN

Across the Curriculum

Art Have students research populations that live in areas in which limiting factors restrict the kinds of organisms that can live there. Have them create a collage that shows several different populations, such as penguins and cacti. L2 P

Using an Analogy

Use the analogy of two friends and basketball game tickets to discuss mutualism, commensalism, and parasitism. A friend offers to buy you a ticket if you will give the friend a ride to the game. (mutualism) A friend with a free ticket gives it to you. (commensalism) A friend sells you a ticket and you later find out the friend has charged you much more than the ticket was worth. (parasitism)

3 Assess

Check for Understanding Activity

Visual-Spatial Have students make a chart with the headings: Organism, Habitat, and Niche. Have them list the names, habitat, and niche for ten organisms that live in their area. L2

MiniLab

Purpose

Visual-Spatial Students will compare the roots of a legume and a non-legume plant.

Materials

legume plant (clover, alfalfa), non-legume plant (geranium, coleus), prepared slide of nitrogen-fixing bacteria, beaker of water, hand lens

Teaching Strategies

A hand lens can be used to observe the nodules on the legume plant.

Analysis

1. The legume plant has nodules that contain nitrogen-fixing bacteria.
2. The bacteria make nitrogen available to the plant roots. The plant gives bacteria food.
3. This is mutualism.

Observing Symbiosis

Procedure

1. Carefully wash then examine the roots of a legume plant and a nonlegume plant.
2. Examine a prepared microscope slide of the bacteria that live in the roots of legumes.

Analysis

1. What differences do you observe in the roots of the two plants?
2. The bacteria help legumes thrive in poor soil. What type of symbiotic relationship is this? Explain.

Not all relationships benefit one organism at the expense of another as in predation. Symbiotic relationships can be identified by the type of interaction between organisms, as shown in **Figure 17-11.** Many types of symbiotic relationships occur between organisms. These are usually described by how each organism in the relationship is affected by the relationship.

A symbiotic relationship that benefits both species is called mutualism. An example of mutualism is the lichen. Each lichen species is made up of a fungus and an alga or cyanobacterium. The fungus provides a protected living space, and the alga or bacterium provides the fungus with food.

Figure 17-11 Many examples of symbiotic relationships occur in nature.

B Tropical orchids grow on the trunks of trees. The tree provides the orchid with a sunlit living space high in the forest canopy. This relationship is an example of commensalism because the orchid benefits from the relationship without harming or helping the tree.

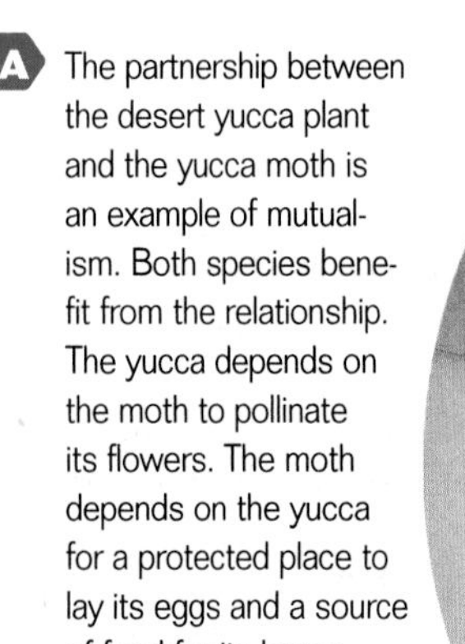

A The partnership between the desert yucca plant and the yucca moth is an example of mutualism. Both species benefit from the relationship. The yucca depends on the moth to pollinate its flowers. The moth depends on the yucca for a protected place to lay its eggs and a source of food for its larvae.

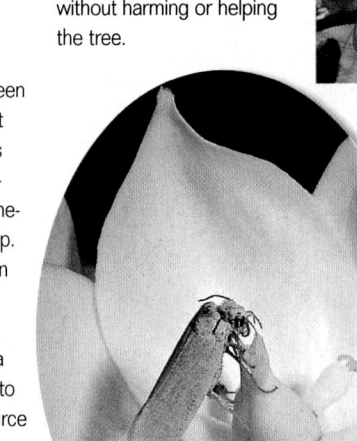

C Tapeworms are parasites that feed inside the intestines of some mammals. This one was found inside a cat.

Assessment

Performance Have students conduct research about symbiotic relationships. They should record the information they find in their Science Journals. Use **Performance Assessment in the Science Classroom,** p. 103.

In shallow tropical seas, brightly colored anemone fish find protection from predators by swimming among the stinging tentacles of sea anemones. The presence of the fish does not affect the anemone in a harmful or beneficial way. Commensalism is a symbiotic relationship that benefits one partner but does not harm or help the other.

Parasitism is a symbiotic relationship that benefits the parasite and does definite harm to the parasite's host. Many parasites live on or in the body of the host, absorbing nutrients from the host's body fluids. Tapeworms live as parasites in the intestines of mammals. Mistletoe is a parasitic plant that penetrates tree branches with its roots.

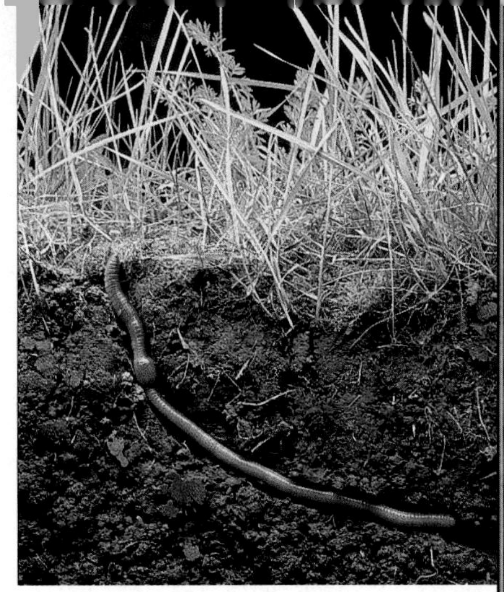

Figure 17-12 Each organism in an ecosystem uses and affects its environment in particular ways. **What role does the earthworm play in the environment?**

Habitats and Niches

In a community, every species plays a particular role. Each also has a particular place to live. The physical location where an organism lives is called its **habitat.** The habitat of an earthworm is soil. The role of an organism in the ecosystem is called its **niche**. The niche of an earthworm is shown in **Figure 17-12.** What a species eats, how it gets its food, and how it interacts with other organisms are all parts of its niche. An earthworm takes soil into its body to obtain nutrients. The soil that leaves the worm enriches the soil. The movement of the worm through soil also loosens it and aerates it, creating a better environment for plant growth.

Section Assessment

1. Describe how limiting factors can affect the organisms in a population.
2. Describe the difference between a habitat and a niche.
3. **Think Critically:** A parasite can obtain food only from its host. Most parasites weaken but do not kill their hosts. Why?
4. **Skill Builder**
   Observing and Inferring There are methods used to determine the size of a population without counting each organism. Do the **Chapter 17 Skill Activity** on page 758 to learn how to infer population size.

Using Math

In a 12 m^2 area of weeds, 46 dandelion plants, 212 grass plants, and 14 bindweed plants are growing. What is the population density per square meter of each species?

4 Close

Proficiency Prep

Use this quiz to check students' recall of section content.

1. **What is the number of individuals per unit of living space?** *population*
2. **What is the place where an organism lives?** *habitat*

Section Assessment

1. Limiting factors such as food, habitat, drought, and competition can cause a population to become smaller or limit its growth.
2. The place where an organism lives is its habitat. The way an organism interacts with its surroundings is its niche.
3. **Think Critically** If a parasite kills its host, the parasite is likely to die because its food supply will disappear.

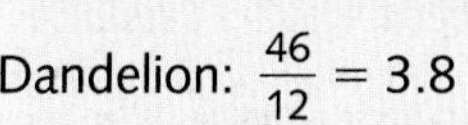

Using Math

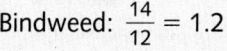

Dandelion: $\frac{46}{12} = 3.8$

Grass: $\frac{212}{12} = 17.6$

Bindweed: $\frac{14}{12} = 1.2$

Assessment

Performance Have students research data about population growth or decline of a threatened or endangered species. Have students put number of individuals on the vertical axis and year on the horizontal axis. Students should describe the growth curve. Use **Performance Assessment in the Science Classroom,** p. 39.

Reteach

Have students make a list of symbiotic relationships with which they are familiar and identify each. L2

Extension

For students who have mastered this section, use the **Reinforcement** and **Enrichment** masters.

Activity 17-2 Design Your Own Experiment

Recognize the Problem

Purpose

Interpersonal Students will determine how abiotic factors affect the germination of seeds. L2 ELL COOP LEARN

Process Skills

observing and inferring, communicating, making and using tables, comparing and contrasting, recognizing cause and effect, forming a hypothesis, designing an experiment, using numbers, separating and controlling variables, and interpreting data

Time

50 minutes for setup; 10 minutes every three to four days for data collection for a period of about two weeks

Materials

Square milk cartons may be used for planters.

Alternate Materials Other kinds of seeds such as pea seeds or flower seeds may be used.

Form a Hypothesis

Possible Hypotheses

Students may hypothesize that seeds will not germinate in the dark, in the refrigerator, or without water.

Design Your Own Experiment

Activity 17-2

Identifying a Limiting Factor

Organisms depend on many biotic and abiotic factors in their environment to survive. When these factors are limited or are not available, it can affect an organism's survival. By experimenting with some of these limiting factors, you will see how organisms depend on all parts of their environment.

Possible Materials

- Bean seeds
- Small planting containers
- Soil
- Water
- Labels
- Trowel or spoon
- Aluminum foil
- Sunny window or other light source
- Refrigerator or oven

Recognize the Problem

How do abiotic factors such as light, water, and temperature affect the germination of seeds?

Form a Hypothesis

Based on what you have learned about limiting factors, make a hypothesis about how one specific abiotic factor may affect the germination of a bean seed. Be sure to consider factors that you can change easily.

Goals

- **Observe** the effects of an abiotic factor on the germination and growth of bean seedlings.
- **Design** an experiment that demonstrates whether or not a specific abiotic factor limits the germination of bean seeds.

Safety Precautions

Wash hands after handling soil and seeds.

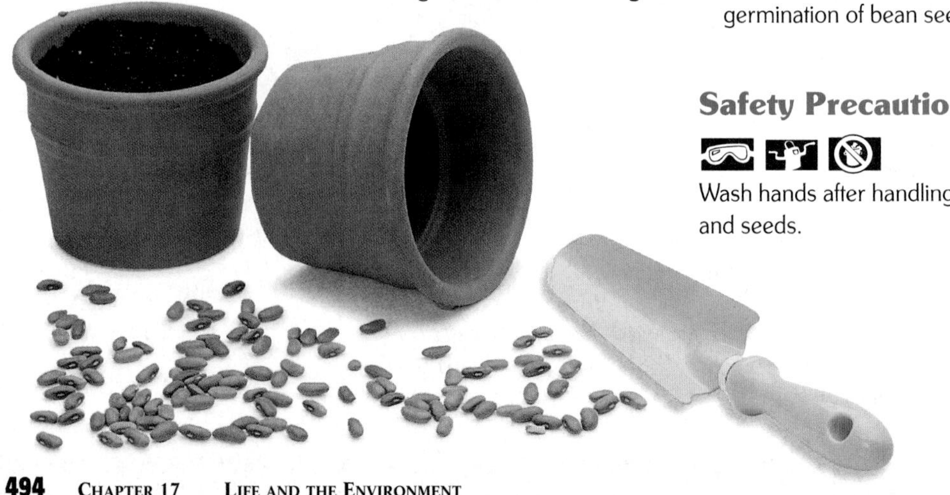

Sample Data based on planting 10 seeds						
Number of Seeds That Germinate						
Days since planting	**Sunlight**	**No sunlight**	**7.2°C**	**21.1°C**	**No water**	**20 mL water per day**
3 days	0	0	0	0	0	0
6 days	3	0	0	3	0	3
9 days	6	0	0	6	0	6
12 days	10	0	0	10	0	10
15 days	10	0	0	10	0	10

Test Your Hypothesis

Plan

1. As a group, agree upon and write out a hypothesis statement.
2. Decide on a way to test your group's hypothesis. Keep available materials in mind as you plan your procedure. **List** your materials.
3. **Prepare** a data table in your Science Journal.
4. Remember to **test** only one variable at a time and use suitable controls.
5. **Read** over your entire experiment to make sure that all steps are in logical order.
6. **Identify** any constants, variables, and controls in your experiment.
7. Be sure the factor you test is measurable.

Do

1. Make sure your teacher has approved your plan before you proceed.
2. Carry out the experiment as planned.
3. While the experiment is going on, write down any observations that you make and complete the data table in your Science Journal.

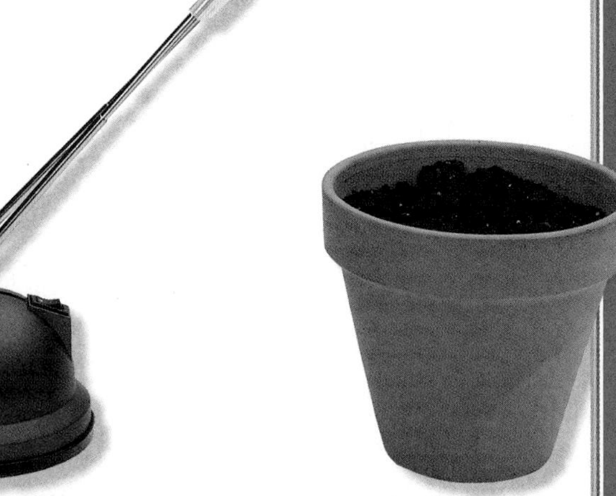

Analyze Your Data

1. **Compare** your results with those of other groups.
2. **Infer** how the abiotic factor you tested affected the germination of bean seeds.
3. **Graph** your results in a bar graph that compares the number of bean seeds that germinated in the experimental container with the number of seeds that germinated in the control container.

Draw Conclusions

1. **Identify** which factor had the greatest effect on the seeds.
2. **Determine** whether you could substitute one factor for another and still grow the seeds.

Test Your Hypothesis

Possible Procedures

Plant the same number of seeds in each of two planters and keep all conditions the same, except for the variable. For example, place one planter in a refrigerator and another in a closed cabinet at room temperature. Give each the same amount of water. Observe the results.

Teaching Strategies

Tying to Previous Knowledge Most students will have observed the germination of seeds and will be aware of the conditions that are necessary for germination. Ask students to describe it.

Troubleshooting Caution students not to plant the seeds too deep in the soil and not to overwater the planter.

Expected Outcome

Most results will reflect that seeds need water and the proper temperature to germinate.

Error Analysis

Have students compare their results and their hypotheses and explain why any differences occurred.

Analyze Your Data

1. Student results should be consistent with those of other groups using the same variable.
2. Student answers will vary based on the abiotic factor tested.
3. The graph will be determined by the number of seeds used in the experiment.

Draw Conclusions

1. Answers will vary depending on the abiotic factor tested.
2. Each different type of abiotic factor is necessary for seeds to germinate.

GO Further

Have students set up a terrarium and observe the growth and development of plants and animals. Have them record the effects of variations in biotic and abiotic factors on the organisms.

Assessment

Performance Have students design an experiment to test the effect of the same variable on another kind of seed. Use **Performance Assessment in the Science Classroom,** p. 23. 

SECTION 17-3

Prepare

Refer to **The Flow of Energy Through Ecosystems** and **The Cycles of Matter** on p. 480F.

Preplanning

Refer to the **Chapter Organizer** on pp. 480A–B.

1 Motivate

Bellringer

Before presenting the lesson, display **Section Focus Transparency 46** on the overhead projector. Use the accompanying **Focus Activity** worksheet. L2 ELL

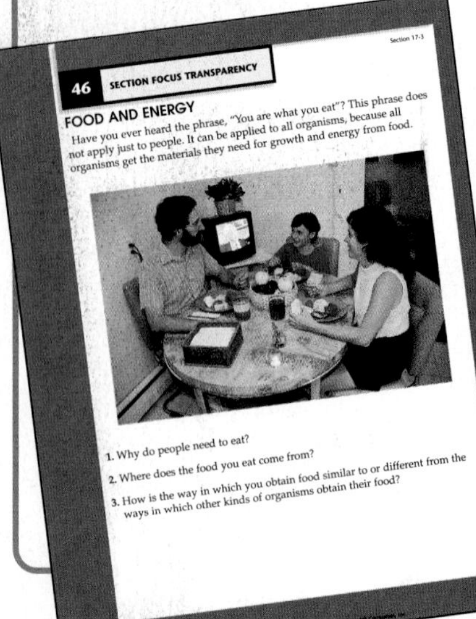

Section 17-3

46 SECTION FOCUS TRANSPARENCY

FOOD AND ENERGY

Have you ever heard the phrase, "You are what you eat"? This phrase does not apply just to people. It can be applied to all organisms, because all organisms get the materials they need for growth and energy from food.

1. Why do people need to eat?
2. Where does the food you eat come from?
3. How is the way in which you obtain food similar to or different from the ways in which other kinds of organisms obtain their food?

Tying to Previous Knowledge

Solar energy is transformed into chemical energy that is stored in food. Through chemical changes in cells, this energy is released for use by an organism.

17-3 Matter and Energy

What You'll Learn

- How energy flows through ecosystems
- The cycling of matter in the biosphere

Vocabulary
food chain
food web
ecological pyramid
water cycle
nitrogen cycle

Why It's Important

- You depend on the recycling of matter and energy to survive.

Energy Flow Through Ecosystems

As you can see, life on Earth is not simply a collection of living organisms. Even organisms that seem to spend most of their time alone interact with other members of their species. They also interact with other organisms. Most of the interactions between members of different species are feeding relationships. They involve the transfer of energy from one organism to another. Energy moves through an ecosystem in the form of food. Producers are organisms that capture energy from the sun. They use the sun's energy for photosynthesis to produce chemical bonds in carbohydrates. Consumers are organisms that

Figure 17-13 In any community, energy flows from producers to consumers. Follow several food chains in the pond ecosystem shown here.

A The first link in any food chain is a producer. In this pond ecosystem, the producers are phytoplankton, algae, and a variety of plants—both aquatic and those on the shore.

B The second link of a food chain is usually an herbivore, an organism that feeds only on producers. Here, snails and small aquatic crustaceans are feeding on the algae and pond plants.

C The third link of a food chain is a carnivore, an animal that feeds on other animals. Some of the carnivores in this pond are bluegill, turtles, and frogs.

Resource Manager

The following **Teacher Classroom Resources** can be used with Section 17-3:

Reproducible Masters

Activity Worksheets, p. 98 L2

Enrichment, p. 46 L3

Reinforcement, p. 46 L2

Study Guide, pp. 67–68 L1 ELL

Transparencies

Teaching Transparency 33 L2

Teaching Transparency 34 L2

Science Integration Transparency 17 L2

obtain energy when they feed on producers or other consumers. The transfer of energy does not end there. When organisms die, other organisms called decomposers obtain energy when they break down the bodies of the dead organisms. This movement of energy through a community can be drawn as food chains, and food webs.

Food Chains and Food Webs

A **food chain** is a simple way of showing how energy in the form of food passes from one organism to another. The pond community pictured in **Figure 17-13** shows examples of several aquatic food chains. When drawing a food chain, arrows between organisms indicate the direction of energy transfer. An example of a pond food chain would be as follows.

phytoplankton → insects → bluegill → bass

Food chains usually have three or four links. Most have no more than five links. This is due to the decrease in energy available at each link. The amount of energy left by the fifth link is only a small portion of the total amount of energy available at the first link. This is because at each transfer of energy, a portion of the energy is lost as heat due to the activities of the organisms as they search for food and mates.

CHEMISTRY INTEGRATION

Making Food
Certain bacteria obtain their energy through a process called chemosynthesis. In chemosynthesis, the bacteria produce food and oxygen using chemical compounds. Where do you think these bacteria are found?

D The fourth link of a food chain is a top carnivore, which feeds on other carnivores. Examples of these consumers in this pond are large fish such as crappies and bass.

E When an organism dies in any ecosystem, bacteria and fungi, which are decomposers, feed on the dead organism, breaking down the remains of the organism.

VISUAL Learning

Figure 17-13 Encourage students to take time to study the figure closely. Carefully explain each feeding level in the illustration.

Multiple Learning Styles

Naturalist Ask students to name foods eaten at a recent meal. Using labeled drawings, have students trace the flow of energy from sunlight to each food item. Ask students to orally describe the flow of energy from sunlight to each food item. L2

2 Teach

CHEMISTRY INTEGRATION

Chemosynthetic bacteria often live in habitats so extreme that most organisms cannot exist there. They live in hot springs, thermal pools, salt flats, and vents of superheated water on the bottom of the ocean floor.

Quick Demo

Use the microprojector to show a slide of algae from the classroom aquarium as you discuss the beginning of the food web.

Activity

Visual-Spatial Mount pictures of plants, animals, and fungi from magazines on construction paper. Give each group of four students seven to ten pictures. Have them develop a food chain using the pictures. Then have the groups use their food chains to make a food web. L2 ELL COOP LEARN

STV: Water
Unit 1 *Water Quality* 1:37

10619–13542

Refer to the Teacher Guide for additional bar codes and teaching strategies.

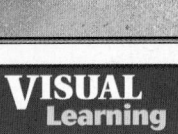

Quick Demo

Use the classroom terrarium as an ecosystem to show producers (mosses and liverworts) and consumers (salamander, turtles, and lizards). Point out that the decomposers are bacteria and fungi.

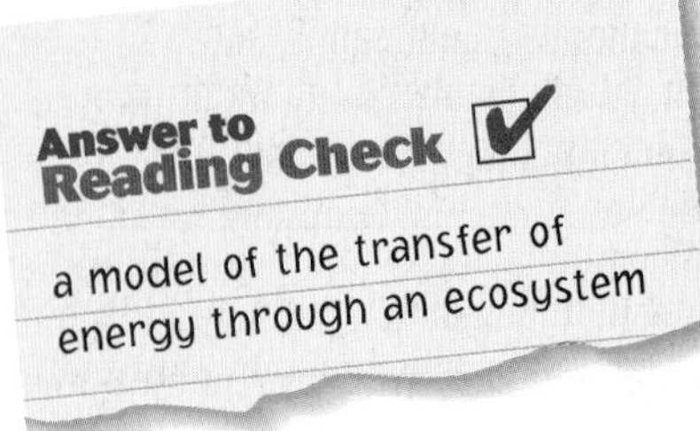

Discussion

Do all organisms remain on the same place in the food chain throughout their lives? Explain. *No. tadpoles are herbivores, and frogs and toads are carnivores. Many insect larvae are herbivores and then become carnivores as adults.*

GLENCOE TECHNOLOGY

CD-ROM

Glencoe Science Voyages Interactive CD-ROM

Explorations

Have students do the interactive exploration *How is energy transferred through a community of organisms?*

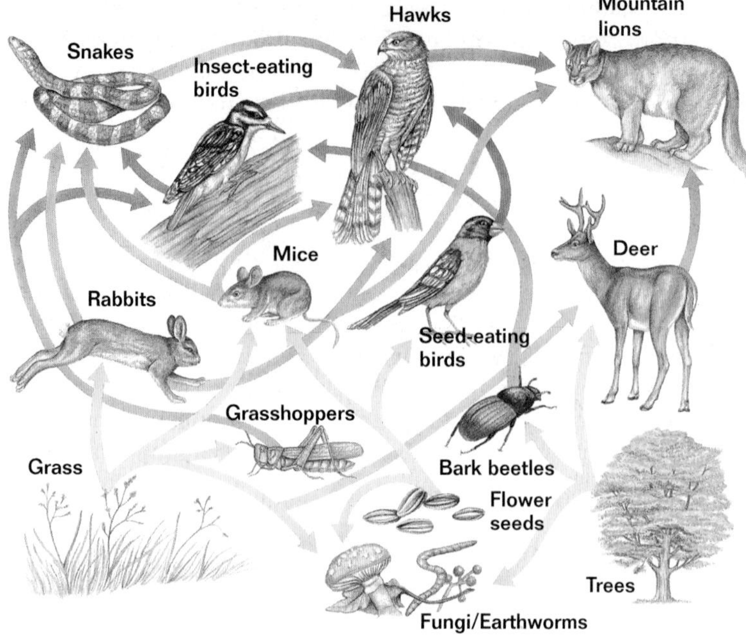

Figure 17-14 A food web includes many food chains. It provides a more accurate model of the complex feeding relationships in a community than a single food chain does.

Single food chains are too simple to describe the many interactions among organisms in an ecosystem. Many food chains exist in any ecosystem. A **food web** is a series of overlapping food chains, as seen in **Figure 17-14.** This concept provides a more complete model of the way energy moves through a community. Food webs are also more accurate models because they show the many organisms that feed on more than one level in an ecosystem.

Ecological Pyramids

Almost all the energy used in the biosphere comes from the sun. Producers capture and transform only a small part of the energy that reaches Earth's surface. When an herbivore eats a plant, some of the energy in the plant is passed on to the herbivore. However, most of it is given off into the atmosphere as heat. The same thing happens when a carnivore eats an herbivore. This transfer of energy can be modeled by an **ecological pyramid.** The bottom of an ecological pyramid represents the producers of an ecosystem. The rest of the levels represent successive organisms in the food chain. ☑

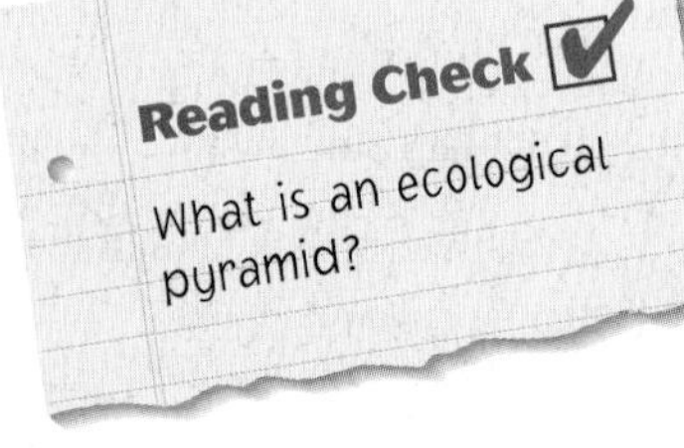

Energy Pyramid

The flow of energy from grass to the hawk in **Figure 17-15** can be illustrated by an energy pyramid. An energy pyramid compares the energy available at each level of the food chain in an ecosystem. Just as most food chains have three or four links,

Integrating the Sciences

Chemistry Have students research biological magnification. Biological magnification is the process in which hazardous wastes become increasingly concentrated in successive levels of the food chain. It can be seen in environmental levels of lead. L3

Caption Answer

Figure 17-15 *At each level only 10 percent of energy available is transferred to the next level. By the top of the energy pyramid, the available energy is greatly reduced. Organisms at the top of bigger pyramids would have little energy available to them.*

498 CHAPTER 17 LIFE AND THE ENVIRONMENT

a pyramid of energy usually has three or four levels. Only about ten percent of the energy available at each level of the pyramid is available to the next level. By the time the top level is reached, the amount of energy is greatly reduced.

Figure 17-15 An energy pyramid illustrates that energy decreases at each successive feeding step. **Why aren't there more levels in an energy pyramid?**

The Cycles of Matter

The energy available at each link in the food chain is constantly renewed by sunlight. But, what about the physical matter that makes up the bodies of living organisms? The laws of conservation of mass and energy state that matter on Earth is never lost or gained. It is used over and over again. In other words, it is recycled. The carbon atoms present in your body right now have been on Earth since the planet formed billions of years ago.

Problem Solving

Changes in Antarctic Food Webs

The food chain in the ice-cold Antarctic Ocean is based on phytoplankton—microscopic algae that float near the water's surface. The algae are eaten by tiny shrimp-like krill, which are consumed by baleen whales, squid, and fish. The fish and squid are eaten by toothed whales, seals, and penguins. In the past, humans have hunted baleen whales. Now with laws against it, there is hope that the population of baleen whales will increase. How will an increase in the whale population affect this food web? Which organisms compete for the same source of food?

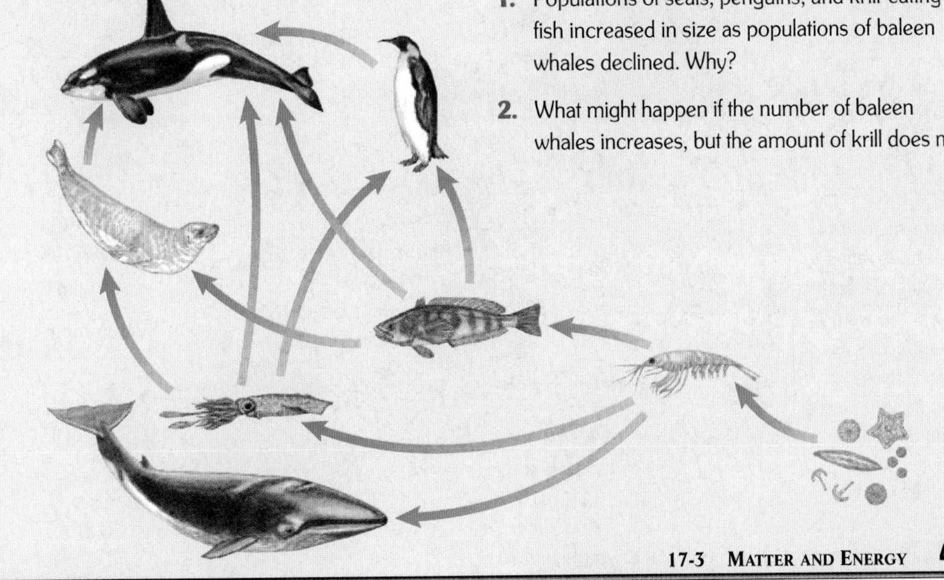

Think Critically

1. Populations of seals, penguins, and krill-eating fish increased in size as populations of baleen whales declined. Why?
2. What might happen if the number of baleen whales increases, but the amount of krill does not?

Correcting Misconceptions

Students may think that the same water falls in a given area again and again. Emphasize that water vapor moves great distances through the air all over the Earth; that water in lakes, rivers, and streams is always moving; that currents in the oceans are constantly moving; and that groundwater may move great distances.

Flex Your Brain

Use the Flex Your Brain activity to have students explore CYCLING OF MATTER.

Problem Solving

To help them solve this problem, have students draw a pyramid and write the names of the organisms in the appropriate levels.

Think Critically

1. The absence of whales made more krill available for the fish and squid. Food was no longer a limiting factor, so their numbers increased. Similarly, large numbers of fish and squid meant more food available for seals and penguins.
2. Populations of fish, squid, seals, and penguins could decrease because the whales are taking some of the food supply.

Inclusion Strategies

Visually Impaired Obtain or make a pyramid-shaped model. Allow visually impaired students to hold the model and identify its shape. Then explain that energy and the number of organisms decrease in an energy pyramid in the same manner as the model. L2

Across the Curriculum

History According to the Gaia hypothesis, Earth is a living organism capable of maintaining homeostasis. This idea was proposed by James Lovelock, a British scientist, and Lynn Marguilis, an American microbiologist. The hypothesis argues that Earth's environment co-evolved along with life and is constantly being adjusted and regulated by the interactions of all Earth's living inhabitants.

Try at Home Mini Lab

For additional help doing this activity at home, see the corresponding pages in the **Home Involvement** booklet.

Purpose

Kinesthetic Students will model what happens in the water cycle. L2 ELL COOP LEARN

Materials

marker, clear plastic cup, plastic wrap, rubber band

Teaching Strategies

Remind students that they will have to observe their water-cycle model for three days and record their observations.

Analysis

1. condensation, evaporation, and precipitation
2. It decreased.

Assessment

Performance Have students diagram the water cycle in their Science Journals. Use **Performance Assessment in the Science Classroom,** p. 55.

Modeling the Water Cycle

Procedure

1. With a marker, make a line halfway up on a plastic cup. Fill the cup to the mark with water.
2. Cover the top with plastic wrap and secure it with a rubber band or tape.
3. Put the cup in direct sunlight. Observe the cup for three days. Record your observations.
4. Remove the plastic wrap and observe it for a week.

Analysis

1. What parts of the water cycle did you observe in this activity?
2. What happened to the water level in the cup when the plastic wrap was removed?

They have been recycled untold billions of times. Many important materials that make up your body cycle through ecosystems. Some of these materials are water, carbon, and nitrogen.

The Water Cycle

Water molecules on Earth are on a constant journey, rising into the atmosphere, falling to land or the ocean as rain or snow, and flowing into rivers and oceans. The **water cycle** involves the processes of evaporation, condensation, and precipitation.

When energy, such as heat, is added to a liquid, its molecules begin to move faster. The more energy the molecules absorb, the faster they move, until they are moving so fast they break free and rise into the atmosphere. The liquid evaporates, or changes from a liquid to a gas. The heat of the sun causes water on the surface of Earth to evaporate and rise into the atmosphere as water vapor.

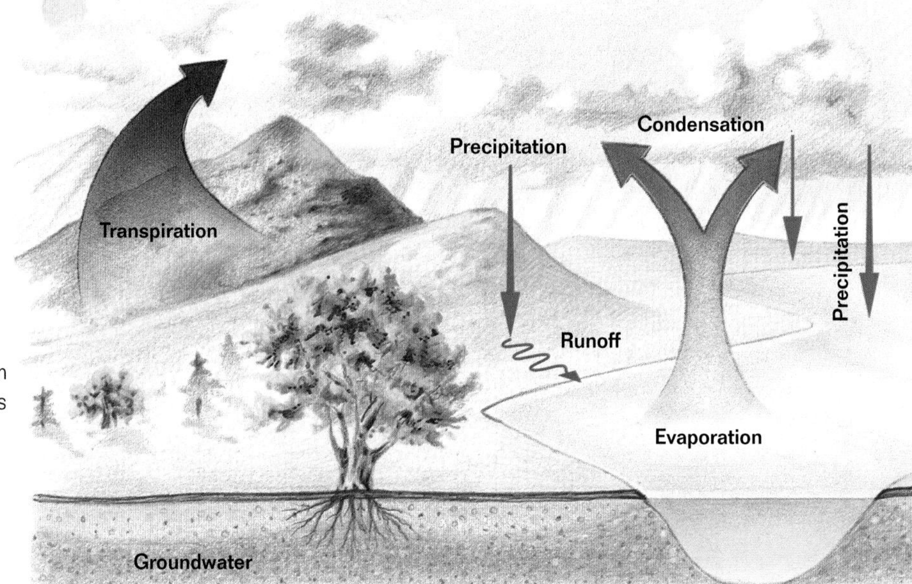

Figure 17-16 A water molecule that falls as rain can follow several paths through the water cycle. **Identify as many of these paths as you can in this diagram.**

Caption Answer

Figure 17-16 *Examples include the following: seeps into groundwater, taken up by plants, transpired into air, runs off ground into a lake, evaporates into air.*

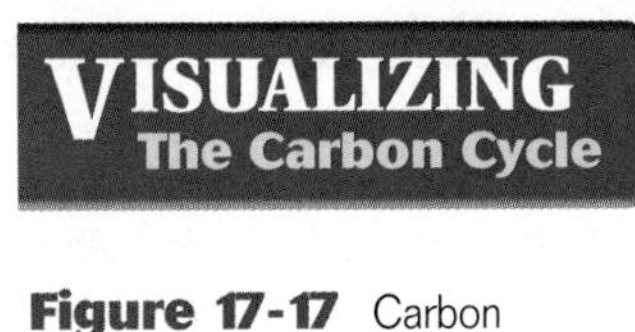

VISUALIZING
The Carbon Cycle

Figure 17-17 Carbon is cycled between the atmosphere and living organisms. **Why is the carbon cycle important?**

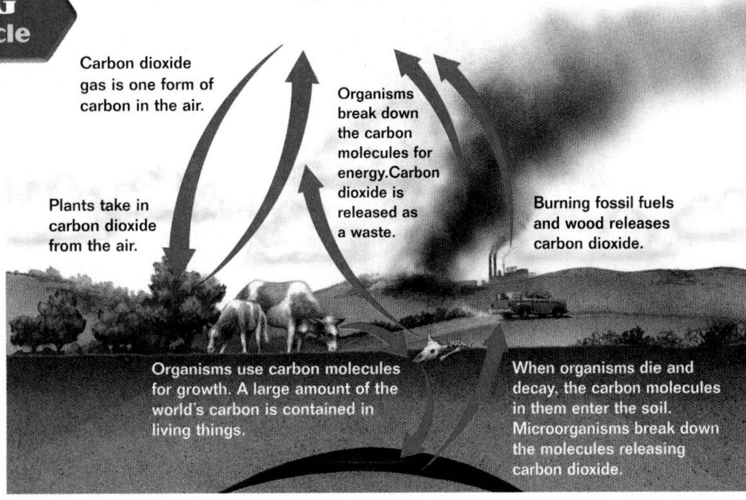

Carbon Dioxide
Carbon dioxide gas is one form of carbon in the air.
Organisms break down the carbon molecules for energy.Carbon dioxide is released as a waste.
Plants take in carbon dioxide from the air.
Burning fossil fuels and wood releases carbon dioxide.
Organisms use carbon molecules for growth. A large amount of the world's carbon is contained in living things.
When organisms die and decay, the carbon molecules in them enter the soil. Microorganisms break down the molecules releasing carbon dioxide.

As the water vapor rises, it encounters colder and colder air temperatures. As the molecules of water vapor become colder, they slow down. Eventually, the water vapor changes back into tiny droplets of water. It condenses, or changes from a gas to a liquid. These water droplets clump together to form clouds. When the droplets become large and heavy enough, they fall back to Earth as rain, or precipitation. This process is illustrated in **Figure 17-16.**

The Carbon Cycle

What do you have in common with all organisms? You all contain carbon. Earth's atmosphere contains about 0.03 percent carbon in the form of a gas called carbon dioxide. The movement of the element carbon through Earth's ecosystem is called the carbon cycle.

The carbon cycle begins with plants. During photosynthesis, plants remove carbon from the air and use it along with sunlight and water to make carbohydrates. These carbohydrates are used by other organisms and then returned to the atmosphere through cellular respiration, combustion, and erosion. See **Figure 17-17.** Once the carbon is returned to the atmosphere, the cycle begins again.

The Nitrogen Cycle

Nitrogen is an important element that is used by organisms to make proteins. Even though nitrogen gas makes up 78 percent of the atmosphere, most living organisms cannot use nitrogen in this form. It has to be combined with other elements through a process that is called nitrogen fixation.

interNET CONNECTION

Visit the Glencoe Science Web Site at **www.glencoe.com/sec/science** for more information about food chains and food webs.

3 Assess

Check for Understanding Activity

Visual-Spatial Have students research, diagram, and describe the carbon cycle. L2

Reteach

Kinesthetic Play the food web game. List producers, consumers, and decomposers in a food web on separate index cards. Give a card to each student. Give each producer a ball of colored yarn. Have producers roll the ball to their primary consumers, then each subsequent consumer, until each chain is complete to create a food web. L2 ELL COOP LEARN

Extension

For students who have mastered this section, use the **Reinforcement** and **Enrichment** masters.

Caption Answer

Figure 17-17 *Answers will vary but should include that all organisms contain carbon. It is an important part of photosynthesis.*

interNET CONNECTION

Internet Addresses

For Internet tips, see Glencoe's **Using the Internet in the Science Classroom.**

4 Close

Proficiency Prep

Use this quiz to check students' recall of section content.

1. **What is a series of overlapping food chains?** *food web*
2. **How can the transfer of energy be modeled?** *an ecological pyramid*
3. **What involves the processes of evaporation, condensation, and precipitation?** *water cycle*

Section Assessment

1. A food chain shows how energy from food passes from one organism to another. A food web is a series of overlapping food chains.
2. The matter in a food chain is used over and over again.
3. **Think Critically** There is not enough energy left at the top of an energy pyramid to support large numbers of top carnivores.

Check to make sure answers are consistent with information in text.

You can see in **Figure 17-18** how nitrogen is changed into usable compounds by bacteria associated with certain plants. A small amount is changed into nitrogen compounds by lightning. The transfer of nitrogen from the atmosphere to plants and back to the atmosphere or directly into plants again is the **nitrogen cycle.**

Phosphorus, sulfur, and other elements needed by living organisms also are used and returned to the environment. Just as we recycle aluminum, glass, and paper products, the materials that organisms need to live are recycled continuously in the biosphere.

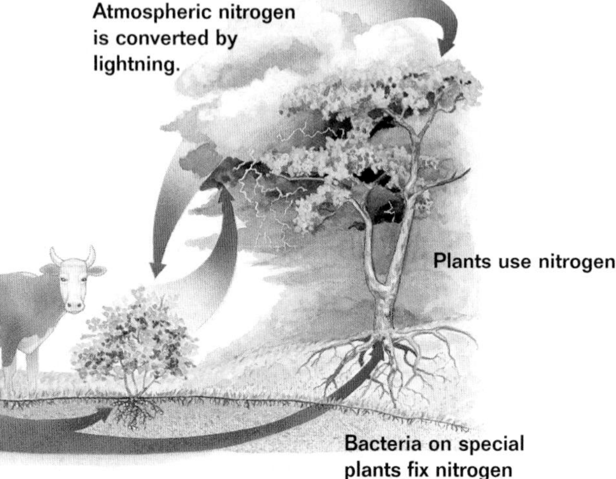

Atmospheric nitrogen is converted by lightning.
Animals eat plants.
Plants use nitrogen.
Animals and plants die and decompose.
Bacteria on special plants fix nitrogen and change it to a usable form.

Figure 17-18 Nitrogen can be cycled from bacteria on plant roots to plants, then to animals, and directly back to plants again as a result of decomposition.

Section Assessment

1. What is the difference between a food chain and a food web?
2. How does the cycling of matter affect a food chain?
3. **Think Critically:** Use your knowledge of food chains and the energy pyramid to explain why fewer lions than gazelles live on the African plains.
4. **Skill Builder**
   Classifying Look at the food web pictured in **Figure 17-14.** Classify each organism pictured as a producer, an herbivore, a carnivore, or a decomposer. If you need help, refer to Classifying in the **Skill Handbook** on page 713.

In your Science Journal, compare the water cycle, carbon cycle, and nitrogen cycle. Use this information to discuss the processes that are involved in each cycle and how each cycle is important to living organisms.

4. **Skill Builder**
carnivore: snake, insect-eating bird, hawk, mountain lion; herbivore: mouse, rabbit, seed-eating bird, deer, grasshopper, bark beetle; producer: flower seed, tree, grass; decomposer: fungus, earthworm.

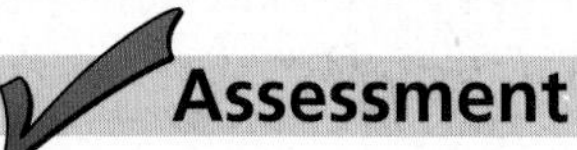

Performance Place a picture of an underwater pond scene on the overhead projector. Have students identify the producers, consumers, and decomposers. Then have students diagram a possible food chain or web in their Science Journals. Use **Performance Assessment in the Science Classroom,** p. 17.

Never Cry Wolf by Farley Mowat

In the book *Never Cry Wolf,* Canadian biologist Farley Mowat details his yearlong expedition learning about wolves and surviving on the frozen tundra of northern Canada. When Mowat set up camp in a remote wilderness area, he didn't know he would end up eating mice to prove a point. Mowat was hired by the Canadian Wildlife Service to investigate and live among the wolves to help solve the country's growing "*Canis lupus* problem." Hunters were reporting that packs of bloodthirsty wolves were slaughtering caribou by the thousands and contributing to their extinction.

Mowat's Discovery

This action-packed book is more than just an adventure story. It's also the report of a stunning scientific discovery. Instead of fierce killers, Mowat found wolves to be gentle, skillful providers and devoted protectors of their young. Mowat challenged the idea that wolves were causing the decline in the caribou population. He showed that his wolf population fed almost exclusively on mice during the warmer summer months when the mouse population skyrocketed. To prove that a large mammal could survive on mice, he ate them himself. Following the publication of *Never Cry Wolf,* Mowat's conclusions about the habits and behaviors of wolves were criticized by people clinging to the old image of wolves as vicious killers.

Filled with beautiful images of animals in their natural setting, *Never Cry Wolf* describes one person's struggle to preserve a vanishing species. Mowat's heroic efforts to document never-before-seen behaviors in wild wolves focused international attention on wolves, which are threatened with extinction in North America and elsewhere. In 1983, Mowat's groundbreaking book was made into an entertaining movie.

Science JOURNAL

Never Cry Wolf was made into a movie based on the book. In your Science Journal, explain how books and movies like *Never Cry Wolf* can be used to persuade or to change a person's attitude toward a subject.

Teaching Strategies

- **Reading** Have students read the book *Never Cry Wolf* as an assignment for your unit on ecology or animals. You may wish to have the students read the book on their own, or aloud as a class.
- **Writing** Have the students prepare a list of 10 things they currently know about wolves. Then, after they read the book, ask them to list 10 new things they have learned about wolves. They can include the information in a short book report after they complete the book.

NATIONAL GEOGRAPHIC

Reading & Writing in Science

Content Background

Farley Mowat is recognized internationally as one of Canada's most brilliant authors. For nearly half a century, Mowat has written about the land, seas, and people of the Far North. Born in Belleville, Ontario, in 1921, Mowat always had a keen interest in nature, mainly due to the influence of his uncle, a professional ornithologist. Mowat has said of himself, "I am a Northern Man. I like to think I am a reincarnation of the Norse saga men and, like them, my chief concern is with the tales of men, and other animals, living under conditions of natural adversity."

Science JOURNAL Movies and books on topics like wolves can help educate people. However, most try to persuade the audience to change their view by presenting the information in a different way than commonly viewed. This can often change a person's attitude toward a particular subject.

For Additional Information

- Mowat, Farley, *Never Cry Wolf,* Bantam Books: New York, 1963.
- His other works include: *People of the Deer, Owls in the Family, The Dog Who Wouldn't Be,* and *A Whale for the Killing.*

Reviewing Main Ideas can be used to preview, review, reteach, and condense chapter content.

Preview

Linguistic Have students try to answer the questions in their Science Journals. Use student answers as a source for discussion throughout the chapter.

Review

Interpersonal Have students answer the questions on separate pieces of paper and compare their answers with those of other students in the class.

Reteach

Visual-Spatial Have students look at the illustrations on these pages. Ask them to describe details that support the main ideas of the chapter found in the statement for each illustration.

00:00 OUT OF TIME?

Auditory-Musical If time does not permit teaching the entire chapter, use the information on these pages along with the chapter Audiocassettes to present the material in a condensed format.

Career CONNECTION

Discovering how animals adapt can provide clues to how we can adapt to our own environment.

Chapter 17 Reviewing Main Ideas

For a **preview** of this chapter, study this Reviewing Main Ideas before you read the chapter. After you have studied this chapter, you can use the Reviewing Main Ideas to **review** the chapter.

The Glencoe MindJogger, Audiocassettes, and CD-ROM provide additional opportunities for review.

Section 17-1 THE LIVING AND NONLIVING ENVIRONMENT

The region of Earth in which all organisms live is the **biosphere.** The nonliving features of the environment are **abiotic factors,** and the organisms in the environment are **biotic factors. Populations** and **communities** make up an **ecosystem. Ecology** is the study of interactions among organisms and their environment. ***How does the relationship between an organism, a population, and a community affect an ecosystem?***

Section 17-2 INTERACTIONS AMONG LIVING ORGANISMS

A **population** can be described by characteristics that include size, spacing, and density. Any biotic or abiotic factor that limits the number of individuals in a population is a **limiting factor.** A close relationship between two or more species is a symbiotic relationship. The place where an organism lives is its **habitat,** and its role in the environment is its **niche.** ***How could two similar species of birds live in the same area and nest in the same tree without occupying the same niche?***

Cultural Diversity

Environmental Impact Have students develop a list of countries from various areas of the world. Then have each student choose two countries to study: one that is highly industrialized and one that is not. Have them research to compare the environmental impact observed in highly industrialized nations with that of less industrialized nations.

What do people eat? Have students research how people in different countries meet their food needs. Suggest that students choose a country and find information about the diets of the people living there. Have them consider whether the people are mainly first-, second-, or third-level consumers.

Reading Check ✔

Translate the information in **Figure 17-14** into a diagram. Clearly show the relationships among the links in a food chain.

Section **17-3 MATTER AND ENERGY**

Food chains and **food webs** are models that describe the feeding relationships in a community. An **energy pyramid** describes the flow of energy through a community. Energy is distributed at each level of the food chain but is replenished by the sun. Matter is never lost or gained but is recycled. ***If the rabbits, birds, mice, beetles, and deer were removed from the food web shown in this figure, which organisms would be affected and how?***

Career CONNECTION **Isidro Bosh, Aquatic Biologist**

As an aquatic biologist, Isidro Bosh studies ocean invertebrates such as sea urchins, sea slugs, and sponges. He is interested in how these animals live in tough environmental conditions, such as cold polar oceans and the dark deep sea with its high pressure. He has explored the oceans in everything from huge research vessels to small, inflatable rafts. He also has explored tropical coral reefs and giant kelp forests. ***Why is it important to study how animals adapt to tough environments?***

Answers to Questions

Section 17-1

The Living and Nonliving Environment Organisms of the same species interact to make up a population. Populations interact and make up a community. Communities of organisms interact with one another and the environment and this is the ecosystem.

Section 17-2

Interactions Among Living Organisms The two species may nest at different levels on the tree and one species may feed on insects while the other feeds on seeds.

Section 17-3

Matter and Energy All of the organisms would be affected. The flow of energy would be interrupted by the removal of the herbivores. The carnivores would have to look for food in other places. The grass and trees would grow.

GLENCOE TECHNOLOGY

CD-ROM

Glencoe Science Voyages Interactive CD-ROM

Chapter Summaries and Quizzes

Have students read the Chapter Summary then take the Chapter Quiz to determine whether they have mastered chapter content.

Assessment

Portfolio Encourage students to place in their portfolios one or two items of what they consider to be their best work. Examples include:

- Skill Builder, p. 486
- Science Journal, p. 489
- Activity 17-2, pp. 494–495 P

Performance Additional performance assessments may be found in **Performance Assessment** and **Science Integration Activities.** Performance Task Assessment Lists and rubrics for evaluating these activities can be found in Glencoe's **Performance Assessment in the Science Classroom.**

Using Vocabulary

1. c
2. o
3. e
4. j
5. k

interNET CONNECTION To reinforce chapter vocabulary, use the **Study Guide for Content Mastery** booklet. Also available are activities for **Glencoe Science Voyages** on the Glencoe Science Web Site. **www.glencoe.com/sec/science**

Checking Concepts

6. A	11. D
7. D	12. B
8. C	13. B
9. D	14. C
10. D	15. C

Thinking Critically

16. More energy is available from organisms lower on the food chain.
17. The virus benefits and the host is harmed.
18. The carrying capacity of the environment limits population size. Biotic potential is the largest size the population can reach under the best possible conditions. Carrying capacity usually prevents populations from reaching biotic potential.
19. They break down dead organisms and make the nutrients contained in their bodies available for plants to use.

Chapter 17 Assessment

Using Vocabulary

a. abiotic factor	j. food web
b. biosphere	k. habitat
c. biotic factor	l. limiting factor
d. carrying capacity	m. niche
e. community	n. nitrogen cycle
f. ecological pyramid	o. population
g. ecology	p. population density
h. ecosystem	q. symbiosis
i. food chain	r. water cycle

Match each phrase with the correct term from the list of Vocabulary words.

1. any living thing in the environment
2. number of individuals of a species living in the same place at the same time
3. all the populations in an ecosystem
4. series of overlapping food chains
5. where an organism lives in an ecosystem

Checking Concepts

Choose the word or phrase that best answers the question.

6. Which of the following is a biotic factor?
   A) animals C) sunlight
   B) air D) soil
7. What are coral reefs and oak-hickory forests examples of?
   A) niches C) populations
   B) habitats D) ecosystems
8. What is made up of all populations in an area?
   A) niche C) community
   B) habitat D) ecosystem
9. What does the number of individuals in a population occupying an area of a specific size describe?
   A) clumping C) spacing
   B) size D) density
10. Which of the following is an example of an herbivore?
    A) wolf C) tree
    B) moss D) rabbit
11. Which level of the food chain has the most energy?
    A) omnivores C) decomposers
    B) herbivores D) producers
12. What is a relationship in which one organism is helped and the other is harmed?
    A) mutualism C) commensalism
    B) parasitism D) symbiosis
13. Which of the following is **NOT** cycled in the biosphere?
    A) nitrogen C) water
    B) soil D) carbon
14. Which of the following is a model that shows how energy is lost as it flows through an ecosystem?
    A) pyramid of biomass
    B) pyramid of numbers
    C) pyramid of energy
    D) niche
15. What does returning wolves to Yellowstone National Park add to the food web?
    A) producer C) top carnivore
    B) herbivore D) decomposer

Thinking Critically

16. What would be the advantage to a human or other omnivore of eating a diet of organisms that are lower rather than higher on the food chain?
17. Why are viruses considered parasites?
18. What does carrying capacity have to do with whether or not a population reaches its biotic potential?
19. Why are decomposers vital to the cycling of matter in an ecosystem?
20. Describe your own habitat and niche.

20. Answers will vary. Habitat is the student's home. Niche includes food, ways of getting food and water, relationships with other organisms, and daily activities.

506 CHAPTER 17 LIFE AND THE ENVIRONMENT

Developing Skills

If you need help, refer to the Skill Handbook.

21. **Classifying:** Classify each event in the water cycle as the result of either evaporation or condensation.
    A) A puddle disappears after a rainstorm.
    B) Rain falls.
    C) A lake becomes shallower.
    D) Clouds form.
22. **Making and Using Graphs:** Use the following data to graph the population density of a deer population over the years. Plot the number of deer on the *y*-axis and years on the *x*-axis. Propose a hypothesis to explain what might have happened to cause the changes in the size of the population.

Arizona Deer Population

Year	Deer per 400 hectares
1905	5.7
1915	35.7
1920	142.9
1925	85.7
1935	25.7

23. **Observing and Inferring:** A home aquarium contains water, an air pump, a light, algae, a goldfish, and algae-eating snails. What are the abiotic factors in this environment? Which of these items would be considered a population? A community?
24. **Concept Mapping:** Use the following information to draw a food web of organisms living in a goldenrod field. *Goldenrod sap is eaten by aphids, goldenrod nectar is eaten by bees, goldenrod pollen is eaten by beetles, goldenrod leaves are eaten by beetles, stinkbugs eat beetles, spiders eat aphids, assassin bugs eat bees.*

Test-Taking Tip

Skip Around, If You Can Just because the questions are in order doesn't mean you have to answer them that way. You may want to skip over hard questions and come back to them later. Answer all the easier questions first to guarantee you more points toward your score.

Test Practice

Use these questions to test your Science Proficiency.

1. According to the table, at which point are there more deer than available food?
   A) 1
   B) 2
   C) 3
   D) 4
2. In the water cycle, how is water returned to the atmosphere?
   A) evaporation
   B) condensation
   C) precipitation
   D) fixation
3. What are the food relationships among all organisms in the same environment called?
   A) food chain
   B) ecological pyramid
   C) food web
   D) energy pyramid
4. In an energy pyramid, which level has the most available energy?
   A) first
   B) second
   C) third
   D) fourth

Assessment Resources

The **Test Practice Workbook** provides students with practice in the format, concepts, and critical-thinking skills tested in standardized exams.

Chapter Review, pp. 33–34 L2
Performance Assessment, p. 31 L2
Assessment, pp. 75–78 L2

Glencoe Technology

Chapter Review Software
Computer Test Bank
MindJogger Videoquiz

THE PRINCETON REVIEW Test Practice

The Test-Taking Tip was written by The Princeton Review, the nation's leader in test preparation.

1. D
2. A
3. C
4. A

Developing Skills

21. (a) evaporation, (b) condensation, (c) evaporation, (d) condensation
22. The deer population built up so high that the deer consumed all the available food. The next generation lost animals to starvation.
23. Water, light, and air are all abiotic factors; algae and snails are two different populations; goldfish, algae, and plants make up a community.
24. producer—grass, green algae, oak tree; herbivore—cow, deer, rabbit; carnivore—wolf; omnivore—human

Bonus Question

Compare parasitism and predation. Compare commensalism and mutualism. *A parasite lives on or in the body of a living host. A predator kills its prey immediately. In a commensal relationship, one benefits and the other is not harmed. In a mutualistic relationship, both organisms benefit.*

Chapter 18 Ecosystems

Section	Objectives	Activities/Features
Chapter Opener		**Explore Activity:** Observe Climate, p. 509
18-1 **How Ecosystems Change** 2 Sessions 1 Block	1. **Describe** how ecosystems change over time. 2. **Explain** how new communities arise in areas that were bare of life. 3. **Compare** and **contrast** pioneer communities and climax communities.	**Chemistry Integration,** p. 511 **Skill Builder:** Sequencing, p. 513 **Science Journal,** p. 513 **On the Internet:** Endangered and Threatened Species, pp. 514–515
18-2 **Land Environments** 4 Sessions 2 Blocks	4. **Explain** how climate influences land environments. 5. **Describe** the six biomes that make up land environments on Earth. 6. **Compare** and **contrast** the adaptations of plants and animals found in each biome.	**Using Math,** p. 517 **MiniLab:** Comparing Tundra and Taiga, p. 519 **Problem Solving:** Saving the Rain Forest, p. 522 **Using Math,** p. 524 **Using Computers,** p. 525 **Skill Builder:** Observing and Inferring, p. 525 **Activity 18-2:** Studying a Land Environment, p. 526 **Science and Society:** Protecting Antarctica, p. 527
18-3 **Water Environments** 1 Session ½ Block	7. **Distinguish** between flowing-freshwater and standing-freshwater ecosystems. 8. **Describe** the important seashore and deep-ocean ecosystems.	**MiniLab:** Modeling Freshwater Environments, p. 530 **Skill Builder:** Comparing and Contrasting, p. 531 **Science Journal,** p. 531 **Field Guide to Ecosystems,** pp. 532–535

The number of recommended single-period sessions The number of recommended blocks
One session and one-half block are allowed for chapter review and assessment.

Activity Materials

Explore	Activities	MiniLabs
p. 509 globe or world map	p. 526 graph paper, thermometer, tape measure, hand lens, notebook, binoculars, field guide	p. 519 no materials needed p. 530 freezer bag, gravel and other debris from the bottom of a pond, dip net

Need Materials? Contact Science Kit at 1-800-828-7777 or at www.sciencekit.com on the Internet.
For alternate materials, see the activity on the listed page.

Standards		Reproducible Resources	Technology
National	State/Local	Test Practice Workbooks are available for use with each chapter.	English and Spanish audiocassettes are available for use with each section.
National Content Standards: UCP3, UCP4, A1, A2, B1, C4, C5		**Enrichment,** p. 47 **Reinforcement,** p. 47 **Study Guide,** pp. 69–70	Section Focus Transparency 47 National Geographic Society: GTV
National Content Standards: UCP3, A1, C4, D1		**Activity Worksheets,** pp. 99–101 **Critical Thinking/Problem Solving,** p. 18 **Enrichment,** p. 48 **Laboratory Manual,** pp. 107–108 **Laboratory Manual,** pp. 109–110 **Reinforcement,** p. 48	Section Focus Transparency 48 Teaching Transparency 35 Teaching Transparency 36 Science Integration Transparency 18 Internet Connection, p. 518 Glencoe Science Voyages Interactive CD-ROM The Infinite Voyage Series
National Content Standards: UCP1, A1, C4, D1		**Activity Worksheets,** p. 102 **Enrichment,** p. 49 **Multicultural Connections,** pp. 35–36 **Reinforcement,** p. 49 **Study Guide,** pp. 71–72	Section Focus Transparency 49 Glencoe Science Voyages Interactive Videodisc—Life The Infinite Voyage Series

Key to Teaching Strategies

The following designations will help you decide which activities are appropriate for your students.

L1 Level 1 activities should be appropriate for students with learning difficulties.

L2 Level 2 activities should be within the ability range of all students.

L3 Level 3 activities are designed for above-average students.

ELL ELL activities should be within the ability range of English Language Learners.

COOP LEARN Cooperative Learning activities are designed for small group work.

P These strategies represent student products that can be placed into a best-work portfolio.

Multiple Learning Styles logos, as described on page 61T, are used throughout to indicate strategies that address different learning styles.

Assessment Resources

Chapter Review, pp. 35–36
Assessment, pp. 79–82
Performance Assessment in the Science Classroom (PASC)
MindJogger Videoquiz
Alternate Assessment in the Science Classroom
Performance Assessment, p. 32
Chapter Review Software
Computer Test Bank

Chapter 18 Ecosystems

This is a representation of key blackline masters available in the Teacher Classroom Resources. See Resource Manager boxes within the chapter for additional information.

Section Focus Transparencies

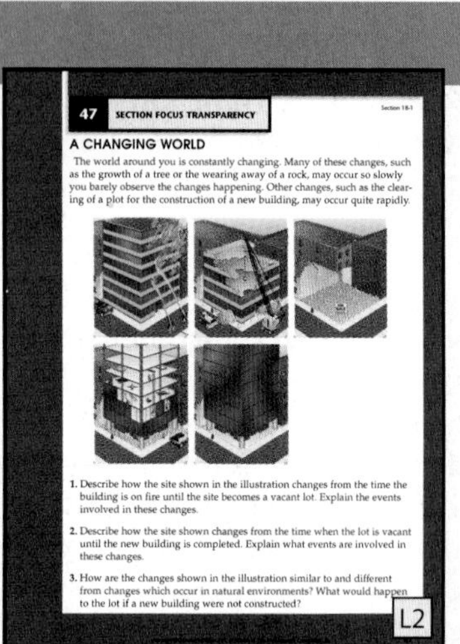

47 SECTION FOCUS TRANSPARENCY

A CHANGING WORLD

The world around you is constantly changing. Many of these changes, such as the growth of a tree or the wearing away of a rock, may occur so slowly you barely observe the changes happening. Other changes, such as the clearing of a plot for the construction of a new building, may occur quite rapidly.

1. Describe how the site shown in the illustration changes from the time the building is on fire until the site becomes a vacant lot. Explain the events involved in these changes.
2. Describe how the site shown changes from the time when the lot is vacant until the new building is completed. Explain what events are involved in these changes.
3. How are the changes shown in the illustration similar to and different from changes which occur in natural environments? What would happen to the lot if a new building were not constructed?

L2

48 SECTION FOCUS TRANSPARENCY

LIFE IN DIFFERENT CLIMATES

Climate describes the general weather pattern of an area. The factors that determine a region's climate include temperature and precipitation. These may vary from season to season. These factors are determined partly by an area's latitude, or distance north or south of the equator. Other factors that determine climate are an area's altitude, or height above sea level, how far or close an area is to an ocean, and whether an area is located near mountains.

1. How do you think the climate conditions of the two areas shown affect the daily life of people living in these areas?
2. Describe the general climate conditions of the two areas shown. Include a description of the temperature and type of precipitation you would expect to find in each area.
3. How are the climates of the areas shown different from or similar to the climate of the area in which you live? What effect does the climate in your area have on the clothes you choose to wear and the activities in which you participate?

L2

49 SECTION FOCUS TRANSPARENCY

WATER, WATER EVERYWHERE

Almost three-fourths of Earth's surface is covered by water, most of it located in Earth's oceans. The rest is located in freshwater ponds, streams, and lakes, or exists as snow or ice in the far northern and southern regions of the world. People and other organisms use this water in a variety of ways.

1. What types of recreational activities do people carry out in lakes, ponds, and streams? What type of activities do people carry out in oceans?
2. In addition to recreation, what are some other ways people use water?
3. What are some ways in which water is important to organisms other than people?

L2

Science Integration Transparencies

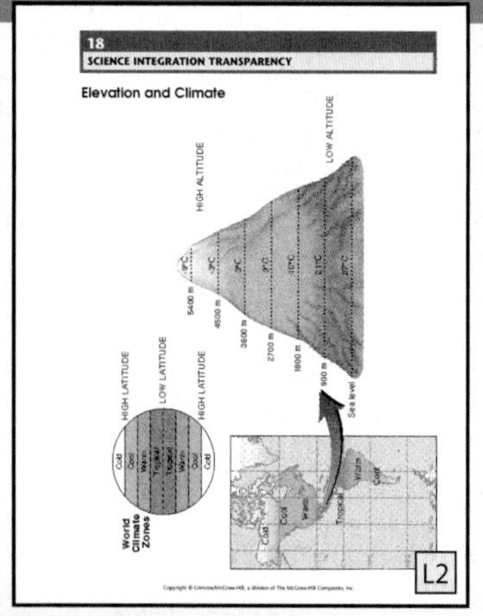

18 SCIENCE INTEGRATION TRANSPARENCY

Elevation and Climate

L2

Teaching Transparencies

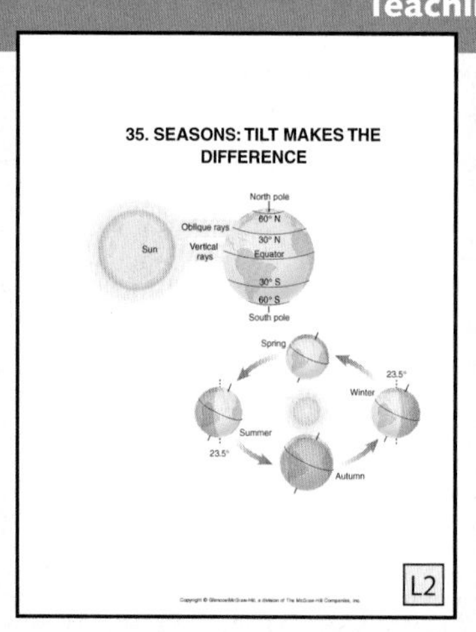

35. SEASONS: TILT MAKES THE DIFFERENCE

L2

36. BIOME MAP

L2

Meeting Different Ability Levels

Study Guide for Content Mastery

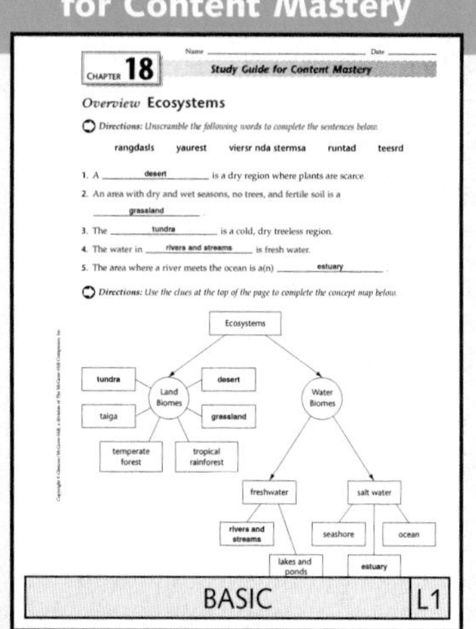

CHAPTER 18 Study Guide for Content Mastery

Overview Ecosystems

Directions: Unscramble the following words to complete the sentences below.

rangdasls yaurest viersr nda stermsa runtad teesrd

1. A desert is a dry region where plants are scarce.
2. An area with dry and wet seasons, no trees, and fertile soil is a grassland.
3. The tundra is a cold, dry treeless region.
4. The water in rivers and streams is fresh water.
5. The area where a river meets the ocean is a(n) estuary.

Directions: Use the clues at the top of the page to complete the concept map below.

BASIC L1

Reinforcement

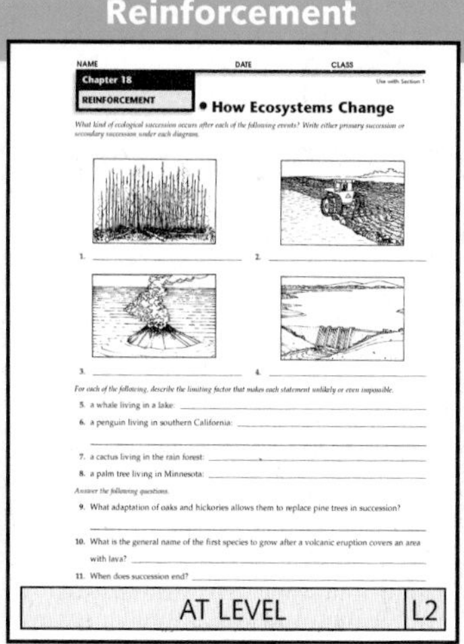

Chapter 18 REINFORCEMENT • How Ecosystems Change

What kind of ecological succession occurs after each of the following events? Write either primary succession or secondary succession under each diagram.

1. ______ 2. ______

3. ______ 4. ______

For each of the following, describe the limiting factor that makes each statement unlikely or even impossible.

5. a whale living in a lake:
6. a penguin living in southern California:
7. a cactus living in the rain forest:
8. a palm tree living in Minnesota:

Answer the following questions.

9. What adaptation of oaks and hickories allows them to replace pine trees in succession?
10. What is the general name of the first species to grow after a volcanic eruption covers an area with lava?
11. When does succession end?

AT LEVEL L2

Enrichment Worksheets

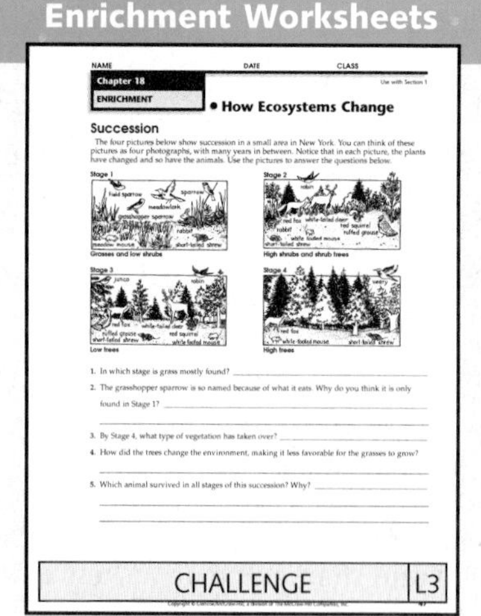

Chapter 18 ENRICHMENT • How Ecosystems Change

Succession

The four pictures below show succession in a small area in New York. You can think of these pictures as four photographs, with many years in between. Notice that in each picture, the plants have changed and so have the animals. Use the pictures to answer the questions below.

1. In which stage is grass mostly found?
2. The grasshopper sparrow is so named because of what it eats. Why do you think it is only found in Stage 1?
3. By Stage 4, what type of vegetation has taken over?
4. How did the trees change the environment, making it less favorable for the grasses to grow?
5. Which animal survived in all stages of this succession? Why?

CHALLENGE L3

Hands-on Activities

Lab Manual

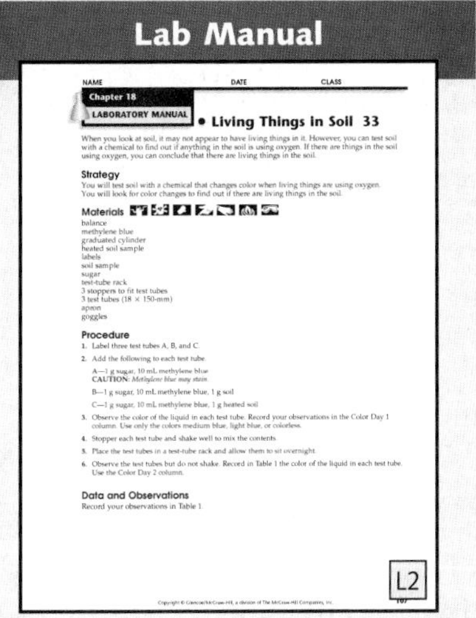

Accessibility

Spanish Resources

Assessment

Performance Assessment

Chapter Review

Assessment

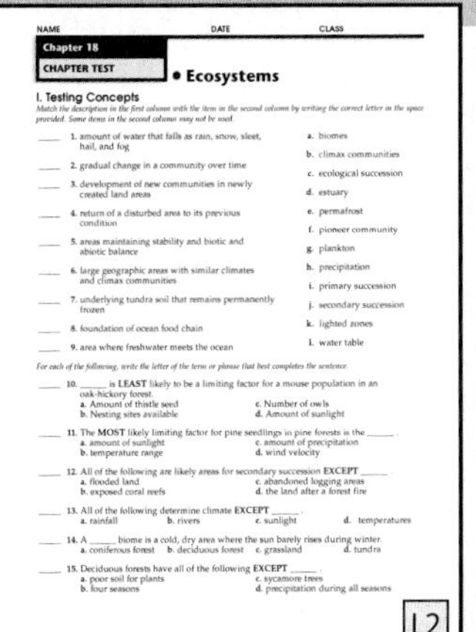

Test Practice Workbook

Extending Content

Critical Thinking/ Problem Solving

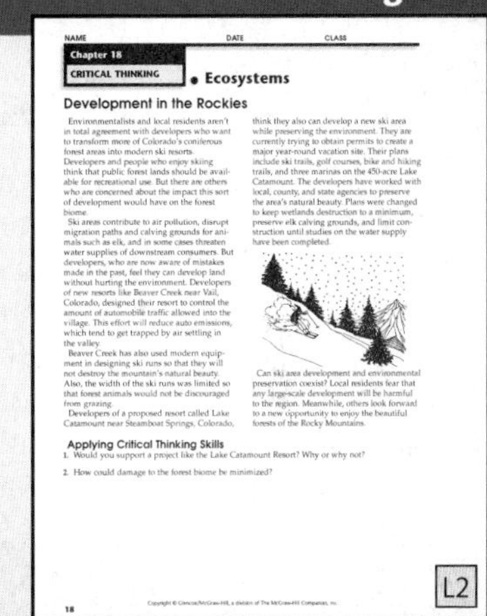

Multicultural Connections

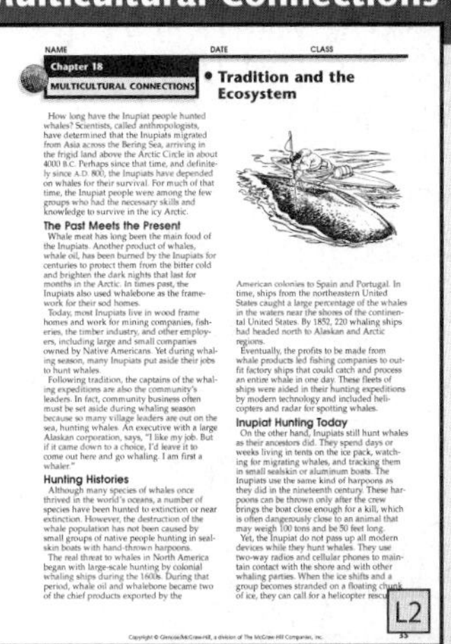

Helping You Prepare

Pioneer Species (Section 18-1)

Succession occurs in places where no living community existed before. When a new volcanic island arises from the sea, its newly cooled lava has no life. The organisms that first appear are called pioneer species. They are much like pioneers who first built farms and small towns. After the pioneers settled, different kinds of people with varied skills and living requirements were able to move into the area.

Climax Communities (Section 18-1)

Succession often leads to a stable group of organisms called a climax community. Climax communities are often described by the most obvious species they contain. An area's climax community is due partly to chance because succession can take different paths. An ecosystem may eventually return to the way it was after trees are cut down, land is dug up for mining, or any other kind of environmental damage occurs.

Succession (Section 18-1)

Many ecologists once believed that succession was an orderly and predictable process. Ecologists today realize that random, unpredictable events can influence which species succeed and which die off. They are also concluding that climax communities are often not as stable as they were once thought to be.

GLENCOE TECHNOLOGY

 **CD-ROM**

Glencoe Science Voyages Interactive CD-ROM

Chapter Summaries

Use the Chapter Summary to introduce, teach, or review chapter material.

Precipitation (Section 18-2)

The surface of Earth is about 28 percent land and 72 percent water. Precipitation falls fairly evenly across Earth's surface. About 23 percent falls on land and 77 percent falls on oceans. However, of the water that evaporates into the atmosphere, 16 percent comes from land and 84 percent comes from oceans. These percentages can be explained by the fact that some of the precipitation that falls on land runs off into streams and rivers and is carried to the ocean.

Fronts (Section 18-2)

A front is a dividing line between a warm air mass and a cold air mass. Fronts usually bring on a sharp change in weather. Typically, a cold air mass moves into an area and slides under warmer air, causing clouds and often rain or

NATIONAL GEOGRAPHIC — Teacher's Corner

Products Available from Glencoe

To order the following products for use with this chapter, call Glencoe at 1-800-334-7344:

CD-ROM

NGS PictureShow: Looking at Ecosystems

Poster

Water

Transparency Set

NGS PicturePack: Looking at Ecosystems

Videodiscs

STV: Habitats; STV: Water

Products Available from National Geographic Society

To order the following products for use with this chapter, call the National Geographic Society at 1-800-368-2728:

Videos

The Living Ocean

Water: A Celebration

Water: A Precious Resource

snow. When a warm air mass moves into a cold area, warm air rises above the cold air, causing precipitation.

Tundra (Section 18-2)

The tundra receives less energy from the sun than does any other biome. The sun's energy is dispersed over a greater area at higher latitudes. The sun's rays lose much of their energy because they must travel diagonally through the atmosphere.

Desert (Section 18-2)

Desert covers less than five percent of North America. The North American deserts are Mojave, Sonoran, Great Basin, and Chihuahuan. Temperatures in the desert undergo drastic changes over a 24-hour period. Daytime temperatures can be 30°C higher than night readings. These fluctuations occur because of the lack of heat-retaining moisture in the desert air.

Photosynthesis in the Ocean (Section 18-3)

When sunlight strikes the ocean surface, red, orange, and yellow wavelengths of light are absorbed first. Only blue and green can penetrate deeply. Below a depth of a few meters, only those photosynthetic organisms capable of using these shorter wavelengths of light can survive.

Salinity (Section 18-3)

Salinity is the amount of dissolved salts present in water. As the surface of an ocean evaporates, the salinity level rises because there is more salt left in relation to the amount of remaining water. However, water with low salt levels is constantly flowing into the ocean water from rivers and in the form of rain.

SCIENCE UPDATE

For current events or science in the news, access the Glencoe Science Web Site at **www.glencoe.com/sec/science**

Nutrients in Aquatic Ecosystems (Section 18-3)

In aquatic ecosystems, nutrients tend to sink below the light zone where organisms cannot use them. Nature has a way of bringing these nutrients back to the surface. In deep lakes, the spring thaw combines with strong winds to mix lake water. Bottom water is brought to the surface, and all nutrients and sunlight are present in abundance. This results in a bloom of phytoplankton. Some lakes also have a fall plankton bloom as well.

In the ocean, the process that moves the bottom water with its valuable nutrients up to the surface is called an upwelling. In an upwelling, winds and currents work together near the continental shelf. The winds carry water away from land. Water must come from somewhere to replace it, and so it comes from the bottom of the ocean. Bottom water with its nutrients is pulled up into the photic zone to replace water that has moved out to sea. Upwellings occur in only a few places.

Teacher to Teacher

"At the beginning of our ecosystems unit, I assign each biome to a group of students. On bulletin boards, they create a 3-D mural of their biome, complete with cutouts and pictures of appropriate plants, animals, land features, climate, and so forth. The murals grow as their understanding increases."

Maureen E. Allen

Maureen E. Allen, Science Resource Specialist
Brywood Elementary School
Irvine, CA

CHAPTER 18 Ecosystems

CHAPTER OVERVIEW

Section 18-1 Primary succession and secondary succession are differentiated in this section.

Section 18-2 This section discusses the factors that determine climate, identifies the location of six major land biomes, and describes the characteristics of each one.

Section 18-3 Characteristics of freshwater and saltwater environments are described in this section.

Chapter Vocabulary

ecological succession
primary succession
pioneer community
secondary succession
climax community
biome
tundra
taiga
temperate deciduous forest
tropical rain forest
grassland
desert
plankton
estuary
intertidal zone

Theme Connection

Systems and Interactions Organisms interact with their environment. Where an organism can live depends on the abiotic and biotic factors in the environment.

If time does not permit teaching the entire chapter, use Reviewing Main Ideas on pp. 536–537.

CHAPTER 18 Ecosystems

Chapter Preview

Skills Preview

Skill Builders
- Map Concepts
- Compare and Contrast

Activities
- Observe

MiniLabs
- Observe
- Infer

Reading Check

As you read about succession, record words and phrases that indicate a time sequence, such as *long ago, gradually,* and *as time passed.*

508

Multiple Learning Styles

Look for the following logos for strategies that emphasize different learning modalities.

Linguistic Enrichment, pp. 523, 524; Assessment, p. 525; Preview, p. 536

Logical-Mathematical Activity, p. 512; Using Math, pp. 517, 524; MiniLab, p. 519; Enrichment, p. 520

Visual-Spatial Explore Activity, p. 509; Making a Model, p. 512; Activity, p. 517; Enrichment, pp. 517, 518; Inclusion Strategies, pp. 521, 522; Reteach, p. 536

Kinesthetic MiniLab, p. 530

Interpersonal Discussion, p. 520; Multiple Learning Styles, p. 524; Review, p. 536

Intrapersonal Activity, pp. 523, 526

Naturalist Science Journal, p. 511; Skill Builder, p. 513; Activity, p. 521

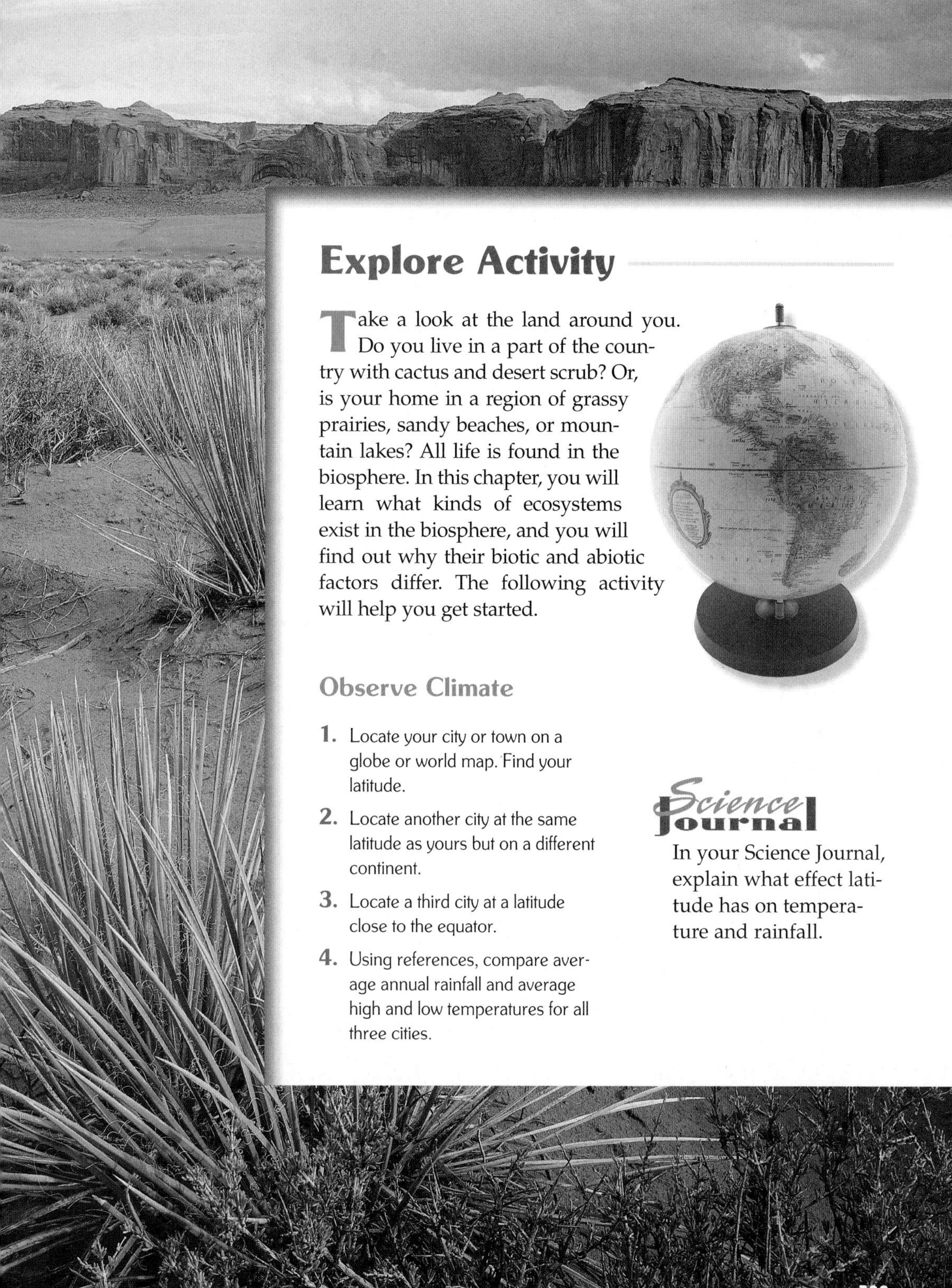

Explore Activity

Take a look at the land around you. Do you live in a part of the country with cactus and desert scrub? Or, is your home in a region of grassy prairies, sandy beaches, or mountain lakes? All life is found in the biosphere. In this chapter, you will learn what kinds of ecosystems exist in the biosphere, and you will find out why their biotic and abiotic factors differ. The following activity will help you get started.

Observe Climate

1. Locate your city or town on a globe or world map. Find your latitude.
2. Locate another city at the same latitude as yours but on a different continent.
3. Locate a third city at a latitude close to the equator.
4. Using references, compare average annual rainfall and average high and low temperatures for all three cities.

Science Journal

In your Science Journal, explain what effect latitude has on temperature and rainfall.

509

Explore Activity

Purpose

Visual-Spatial Use the Explore Activity to introduce students to biomes. They will learn how climate, soil, and other abiotic factors determine where living organisms are found. L2

Materials

one globe or world map for every four students

Teaching Strategies

- You may need to explain that latitude is the distance north or south of the equator and is measured in degrees.
- Climate data for larger cities will be easier to obtain. Travel guides and almanacs contain this information. Newspapers usually can supply local data. Other sources include the National Weather Service or a regional office of the U.S. Geological Survey (ask for hydrological data).

Science Journal Students will probably find that average rainfall and temperature are higher near the equator than at higher latitudes. Depending on the cities chosen, they may also notice that localities at similar latitude (and altitude) tend to have similar temperatures.

Assessment

Process Make a table of average temperatures in 20 cities around the world. Note the locations (longitude and latitude). What correlation is there? Use **Performance Assessment in the Science Classroom,** p. 37.

Assessment Planner

Portfolio
Refer to p. 533 for suggested items that students might select for their portfolios.

Performance Assessment
See p. 533 for additional Performance Assessment options.
Skill Builder, pp. 513, 531
MiniLab, pp. 519, 525, 530
Activity 18-1, pp. 514–515; 18-2, p. 526

Content Assessment
Section Assessment, pp. 513, 525, 531
Chapter Assessment, pp. 534–535
Proficiency Prep, pp. 513, 525, 531

SECTION 18·1

Prepare

Content Background

Refer to **Pioneer Species, Climax Communities,** and **Succession** on p. 508E.

Preplanning

Refer to the **Chapter Organizer** on pp. 508A–B.

1 Motivate

Bellringer

Before presenting the lesson, display **Section Focus Transparency 47** on the overhead projector. Use the accompanying **Focus Activity** worksheet. L2 ELL

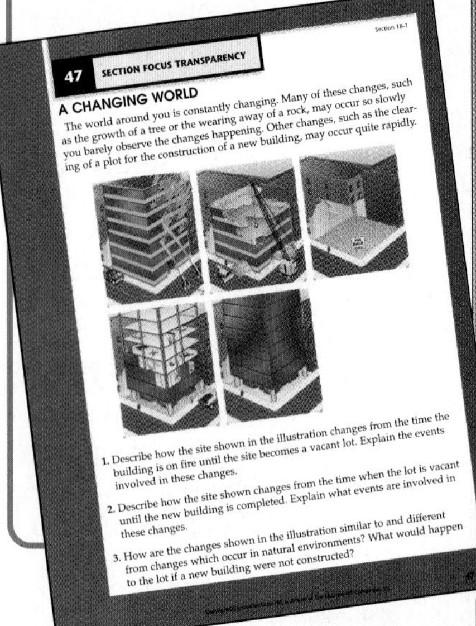

Section 18-1

47 SECTION FOCUS TRANSPARENCY

A CHANGING WORLD

The world around you is constantly changing. Many of these changes, such as the growth of a tree or the wearing away of a rock, may occur so slowly you barely observe the changes happening. Other changes, such as the clearing of a plot for the construction of a new building, may occur quite rapidly.

1. Describe how the site shown in the illustration changes from the time the building is on fire until the site becomes a vacant lot. Explain the events involved in these changes.
2. Describe how the site shown changes from the time when the lot is vacant until the new building is completed. Explain what events are involved in these changes.
3. How are the changes shown in the illustration similar to and different from changes which occur in natural environments? What would happen to the lot if a new building were not constructed?

47

Tying to Previous Knowledge

Find a decaying log with fungi, slime molds, lichens, mosses, ferns, and plant seedlings on it. Display the log and ask students how it illustrates succession.

18·1 How Ecosystems Change

What You'll Learn

- How ecosystems change over time
- How new communities arise in areas that were bare of life
- How to compare and contrast pioneer communities and climax communities

Vocabulary

ecological succession
primary succession
pioneer community
secondary succession
climax community

Why It's Important

- Your ecosystem is changing right now.

Ecological Succession

Imagine hiking through a forest. Huge trees tower over the trail. You know it can take many years for trees to grow this large, so it's easy to think of the forest as something that has always been here. But, this area has not always been covered with trees. Long ago, it may have been a pond full of fish and frogs surrounded by water-loving plants. As time passed, the decomposed bodies of plants and animals slowly filled in the pond until it eventually became a lush, green meadow full of grass and wildflowers. Gradually, over many more years, seeds blew in, trees began to grow, and a forest developed. The process of gradual change from one community of organisms to another is called **ecological succession.** The changes associated with succession usually take place in a fairly predictable order and involve animals, plants, and other organisms.

VISUALIZING Succession

Figure 18-1 The following are the stages in primary succession.

A Life on this bare rock begins with a pioneer community of lichens. These hardy organisms produce acids that help to break down the rock. The acids release chemicals and nutrients from the rock that can then be absorbed by the lichens. The decaying bodies of dead lichens contribute to soil formation.

B Mosses and ferns gradually replace the lichens. These plants can grow even in extremely poor, thin soil. As they die, their decomposed bodies add humus to the soil. Insects and other small animals appear.

Resource Manager

The following **Teacher Classroom Resources** can be used with Section 18-1:

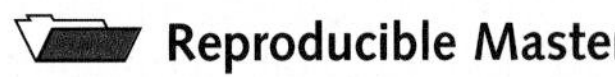

Reproducible Masters

Study Guide, pp. 69–70 L1
Enrichment, p. 47 L3
Reinforcement, p. 47 L2

Primary Succession

Think about conditions around an erupting volcano. Incredibly hot, molten lava flows along the ground, destroying everything in its path. As the lava cools, it forms new land. Soil is formed from bare rock. Similar events happen to this newly formed land. Particles of dust and ash fall to the ground. The forces of weather and erosion break up the lava rock. A thin layer of soil begins to form. Birds, wind, and rain deposit more dust, along with bacteria, seeds, and fungal spores. Plants start to grow and decay. A living community has begun to develop.

Ecological succession that begins in a place that does not have soil is called **primary succession.** The first community of organisms to move into a new environment is called the **pioneer community,** as shown in **Figure 18-1.** Members of pioneer communities are usually hardy organisms that can survive drought, extreme heat and cold, and other harsh conditions. Pioneer communities change the conditions in their environments. These new conditions support the growth of other types of organisms that gradually take over.

CHEMISTRY INTEGRATION

Freezing Water

Freezing temperatures are harmful to living organisms because water is the main component of cells. As water freezes, it expands. Infer what happens to cells if ice crystals form inside them.

C As the soil layer thickens, its ability to absorb and hold water improves. Grasses, wildflowers, and other plants that require richer, more moist soil begin to take over. Butterflies, bees, and caterpillars come to feed on the leaves and flowers. When these plants die, they also enrich the soil, which will become home to earthworms and other large soil organisms.

D Thicker, richer soil supports the growth of shrubs and trees. More insects, birds, mammals, and reptiles move into the area. After hundreds or thousands of years of gradual change, what was once bare rock has become a forest.

2 Teach

CHEMISTRY INTEGRATION

The ice crystals take up extra room, piercing cell membranes and destroying the cells.

Discussion

What happens to a community after a natural disaster such as a fire? *The land goes through the process of succession.*

Videodisc

GTV: Planetary Manager

Side 1, Show 1.3

Ecosystems International

10220

Side 1, Show 1.7

Vanishing Act

32716

The Planetary Manager Directory contains synopses of all the shows.

Content Background

The most important cause of succession is the altering of the physical environment by the community itself. Communities tend to alter the area in which they live in such a way as to make it less favorable for themselves and more favorable for other communities.

Science Journal

Your Biome In your Science Journal, describe the area where you live. Write about soil, rainfall, temperature, and kinds of plants and animals. Infer what kind of biome you think you live in. L1

P 

Answer to Reading Check

Secondary succession begins in a place that already has soil and was once the home of organisms.

Making a Model

Visual-Spatial Draw a model of succession on abandoned farmland.

Using an Analogy

Use a flower garden as an analogy to what happens in succession. Ask what would happen if gardeners did not remove weeds from their gardens. Explain that the garden would soon have a community of new plants. Weeding a garden disrupts succession.

3 Assess

Check for Understanding Activity

Logical-Mathematical Use the overhead projector to show transparencies of farmland succession and pond succession. Ask students to compare the two types of succession. L2

Reteach

Arrange the stages of succession in a pond community or a forest community out of sequence in a diagram. Photocopy the diagram and have students use numbers to reorder the pictures in the proper sequence. L1 ELL

Figure 18-2 The tangled growth of weeds and grasses in untended yards and vacant lots, on abandoned farms, and along country roadsides is the beginning stage of secondary succession.

Secondary Succession

What happens when a forest is destroyed by a fire or a city building is torn down? After a forest fire, nothing is left except dead trees and ash-covered soil. Once the rubble of a demolished building has been taken away, all that remains is bare soil. But, these places do not remain lifeless for long. The soil may already contain the seeds of weeds, grasses, and trees. More seeds are carried to the area by wind and birds. As the seeds germinate and plants begin to grow, insects, birds, and other wildlife move in. Ecological succession has begun again. Succession that begins in a place that already has soil and was once the home of living organisms is called **secondary succession,** shown in **Figure 18-2.**

Reading Check

What is secondary succession?

Climax Communities

Succession involves changes in abiotic factors as well as biotic factors. You have already seen how lichens, mosses, and ferns change the environment by helping to form the rich, thick soil needed for the growth of shrubs and trees. Shrubs and trees also cause changes in abiotic factors. Their branches shade the ground beneath them, reducing the temperature. Shade also reduces the rate of evaporation, increasing the moisture content of the soil. Amount of sunlight, temperature, and moisture level determine which species will grow in soil.

The redwood forest shown in **Figure 18-3** is an example of a community that has reached the end of succession. As long as the trees are not cut down or destroyed by fire or widespread disease, the species that make up the redwood community tend to remain the same. When a community has

interNET CONNECTION

Visit the Glencoe Science Web Site at **www.glencoe.com/sec/science** for more information about the Yellowstone fires and how they contributed to succession.

Extension

For students who have mastered this section, use the **Reinforcement** and **Enrichment** masters.

Integrating the Sciences

Earth Science The eruption of Mount St. Helens killed practically all the local plant and animal life. Have students find out what plants and animals have returned to the area. *Pioneer plants began to grow and some deer began to graze six months after the eruption.* L3

reached the final stage of ecological succession, it is called a **climax community.** Because primary succession begins in areas with no life at all, it can take hundreds or even thousands of years for a pioneer community to develop into a climax community. Secondary succession is a shorter process, but it still may take a century or more.

Comparing Communities

As you have seen, pioneer communities are simple. They contain only a few species, and feeding relationships usually can be described with simple food chains. Climax communities are much more complex. They may contain hundreds of thousands of species, and feeding relationships usually involve complex food webs. Interactions among the many biotic and abiotic factors in a climax community create a more stable environment that does not change much over time. Climax communities are the end product of ecological succession. A climax community that has been disturbed in some way will eventually return to the same type of community, as long as all other factors remain the same. However, it may take a century or more for the community to return to its former state.

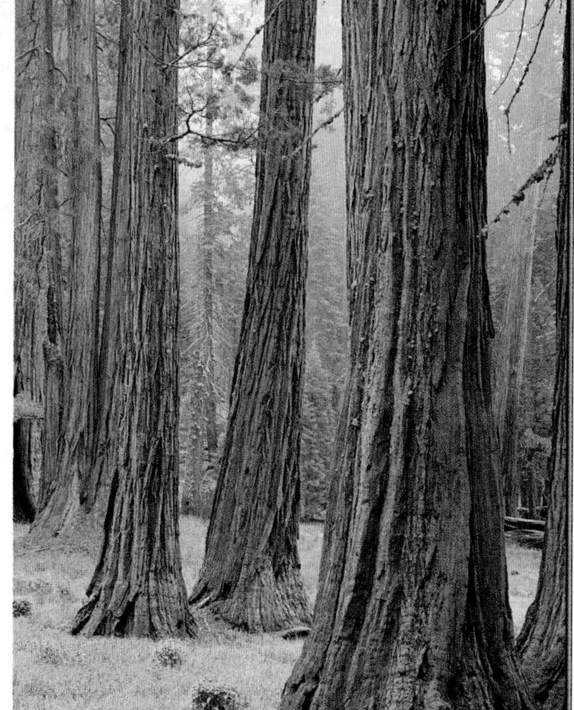

Figure 18-3 This forest of redwood trees in California is an example of a climax community. Redwoods live for hundreds of years. They create shade on the ground beneath them. Needles constantly fall from their branches. Eventually, they form an acidic soil that allows the growth of young redwoods but prevents the growth of many other types of plants.

Section Assessment

1. What is ecological succession?
2. What is the difference between primary and secondary succession?
3. What is the difference between pioneer and climax communities?
4. **Think Critically:** What kind of succession will take place on an abandoned, unpaved country road? Why?
5. **Skill Builder**
Sequencing Describe the sequence of events in primary succession. Include the term *climax community*. If you need help, refer to Sequencing on page 714.

Science Journal
In your Science Journal, draw a food chain for a pioneer community of lichens and a food web for the climax community of an oak-maple forest. Write a short paragraph comparing the two communities.

4 Close

Proficiency Prep

Use the quiz to check students' recall of section content.

1. **What is succession that begins where organisms once lived?** *secondary succession*
2. **What is the process of gradual change from one community of organisms to another?** *ecological succession*

Section Assessment

1. a gradual change from one community of organisms to another
2. Primary succession begins in a place that has never supported living organisms. Secondary succession begins in a place that was once the home of living organisms.
3. Pioneer communities begin in an area that has no life. Climax communities develop from other life.
4. **Think Critically** secondary succession because the area has some soil and once supported a living community

5. **Skill Builder**
Primary succession: lichens-mosses-ferns-insects and tiny animals; larger plants; insects and larger animals, soil organisms-shrubs and trees; insects, birds, mammals, reptiles
Secondary succession: grasses and weeds-insects, birds, and wildlife; shrubs and trees; climax community P

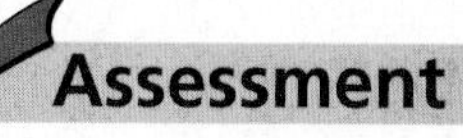

Assessment

Process Have students identify how each of the following is undergoing succession: a cornfield after a flood, a volcanic eruption, and a newly formed sandbar in a river. Use **Performance Assessment in the Science Classroom,** p. 89. L2

The pioneer community can be described with a simple food chain. Within the lichens, algae are producers, fungi are consumers, and bacteria are decomposers. Climax community answers may be: trees are producers; caterpillars, squirrels, mice, and seed-eating birds eat leaves, bark, and seeds; raccoons eat seeds, insects, and birds; hawks, foxes, and snakes eat mice.

Activity 18•1 On the Internet

Recognize the Problem

Students will locate information on endangered or threatened species in their region of the country. Students will determine the factors that are harming the organism and the steps that are being taken to protect the organism. At the conclusion of their analysis, students can post their data and results on the Glencoe Science Web Site.

Form a Hypothesis

Internet Students will gather data from the internet sites that can be accessed through the Glencoe Science Web Site at **www.glencoe.com/sec/science.** Students can post their findings on the site and get information from other schools around the country.

Non-Internet Sources Information about endangered plants and animals can be found at the school and local libraries. A botanical garden, zoo, or preserve will also have information about the state of the flora and fauna.

Time Required

one week

Preparation

Internet Access the Glencoe Science Web Site at **www.glencoe.com/sec/science** to run through the steps that the students will follow.

Non-Internet Sources Scan the local newspaper for articles concerning the health of local plant or animal species.

Activity 18•1

Endangered and Threatened Species

A species becomes endangered when its numbers are so low that it is in danger of extinction in the near future. The list of threatened and endangered species in the United States and around the world is constantly growing due to a variety of reasons. In 1998, about 965 species in the United States were listed as endangered or threatened.

Recognize the Problem

What endangered or threatened species have been identified for your region of the country?

Form a Hypothesis

Form a hypothesis to explain some of the reasons why the organisms identified as threatened or endangered in your region are on the list.

Goals

- **Obtain** and **organize** data.
- **Infer** relationships between the plant or animal and its environment.
- **Use the Internet** to collect and compare data from other students.

Data Sources

Go to the Glencoe Science Web Site at **www.glencoe.com/sec/science** to find links to information about endangered plants and animals around the country. You also will find information posted by other students from around the country.

Species Data

Organism Genus species	Threatened or Endangered	Length of Time on List	Recovery Plan	General Information

interNET CONNECTION

Internet Addresses

____

____

____

____

For Internet tips, see Glencoe's **Using the Internet in the Science Classroom.**

Test Your Hypothesis

Plan

1. Find links to information on the Glencoe Science Web Site. You can also find information on endangered species at the local library or a local zoo.
2. Prepare a data table similar to the one below to record your findings.
3. If possible, observe one of the endangered or threatened species you've identified either in a zoo or in the wild.

Do

1. **Describe** the habitat and range of the organism you chose to study.
2. **Identify** any steps being taken to protect the organism. Outline the recovery plan written for one of the organisms in your region.
3. **Post** the information you collected in the table provided for this activity on the Glencoe Science Web Site.
4. **Check** the postings by other students for more information on your organism and on other organisms.

Analyze Your Data

1. Brainstorm possible reasons why your organism is threatened or endangered.
2. What factors were you able to identify as reasons for the organism becoming endangered?
3. Was your hypothesis supported by the information you collected? **Explain** your answer.

Draw Conclusions

1. What might help the organism you are studying survive the changes in conditions or other changes that have occurred in its range that caused its numbers to decrease.
2. How successful have any techniques established to protect the organism been?
3. Did you find more threatened or endangered species of plants or animals in your region? What explanation might there be for your findings?
4. What steps do you think should be taken, if any, to protect endangered or threatened species in your region? What objections might be raised for the steps taken to protect a species?

Teaching Strategies

- If students do not have access to the Internet, then encourage them to go to the local library and access the Internet there. The links that can be accessed through the Glencoe Science Web Site quickly provide a wealth of information on endangered species.
- To give students a sense of immediacy, have them record direct evidence of habitat destruction in their local area. Have them find out which organisms are most affected by the loss of habitat.
- **Troubleshoot** Students may come across the argument that extinction is a natural process and we should not worry about it. Extinction is normal, but the current rate of extinction is not. Scientist estimate that natural extinction rates are one species lost every 100 years.

GO Further

Adopt an endangered species in your region and find out how you can help preserve it. Conduct a community awareness survey to determine what people know about your species. Design a plan of action to inform the citizens of your community about your adopted plant or animal. As part of the project, prepare flyers, newspaper articles, brochures, buttons, videos, and so on. P

References

- *Endangered Species*, Rob Nagel (Editor), The Gale Group, 1998.
- *Our Endangered Planet: Life on Land*, Mary King Hoff, and Mary M. Rodgers, Lerner Publications Company, 1992.

Assessment

Performance Have students develop a concept map of the endangered species situation of their region. Have them diagram the cause and effect relationships as well as highlight how the current conservation efforts fit in. Have them briefly explain their maps to the rest of the class. Use **Performance Assessment in the Science Classroom,** p. 89.

SECTION 18 2

Prepare

Refer to **Precipitation, Fronts, Tundra,** and **Desert** on pp. 508E–F.

Preplanning

Refer to **Chapter Organizer** on pp. 508A–B.

1 Motivate

Bellringer

Before presenting the lesson, display **Section Focus Transparency 48** on the overhead projector. Use the accompanying **Focus Activity** worksheet. L2 ELL

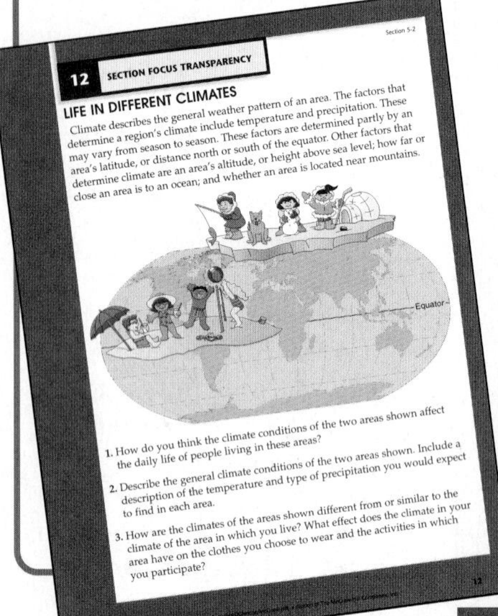

Section 5-2

12 SECTION FOCUS TRANSPARENCY

LIFE IN DIFFERENT CLIMATES

Climate describes the general weather pattern of an area. The factors that determine a region's climate include temperature and precipitation. These may vary from season to season. These factors are determined partly by an area's latitude, or distance north or south of the equator. Other factors that determine climate are an area's altitude, or height above sea level; how far or close an area is to an ocean; and whether an area is located near mountains.

1. How do you think the climate conditions of the two areas shown affect the daily life of people living in these areas?
2. Describe the general climate conditions of the two areas shown. Include a description of the temperature and type of precipitation you would expect to find in each area.
3. How are the climates of the areas shown different from or similar to the climate of the area in which you live? What effect does the climate in your area have on the clothes you choose to wear and the activities in which you participate?

12

Tying to Previous Knowledge

Review the concepts of adaptation and the conditions necessary for life.

18•2 Land Environments

What You'll Learn

- How climate influences land environments
- The six biomes that make up land environments on Earth
- The adaptations of plants and animals found in each biome

Vocabulary
biome
tundra
taiga
temperate deciduous forest
tropical rain forest
grassland
desert

Why It's Important

- Resources that you need to survive are found in a variety of biomes.

Factors That Determine Climate

What does a desert in Arizona have in common with a desert in Africa? They both have water-conserving plants with thorns, lizards, heat, little rain, and poor soil. How are the plains of the American West like the veldt of central Africa? Both regions have dry summers, wet winters, and huge expanses of grassland that support grazing animals such as elk and antelope. Many widely separated regions of the world have similar ecosystems. Why? Because they have similar climates. Climate is the general weather pattern in an area. The factors that determine a region's climate include temperature and precipitation.

Temperature

The sun supplies life on Earth not only with light energy for photosynthesis, but also with heat energy for warmth. The temperature of a region is regulated primarily by the amount of sunlight that reaches it. In turn, the amount of sunlight is determined by an area's latitude and elevation.

Latitude

As **Figure 18-4** shows, not all parts of Earth receive the same amount of energy from the sun. When you conducted the Explore Activity at the beginning of this chapter, you probably concluded that temperature is affected by latitude.

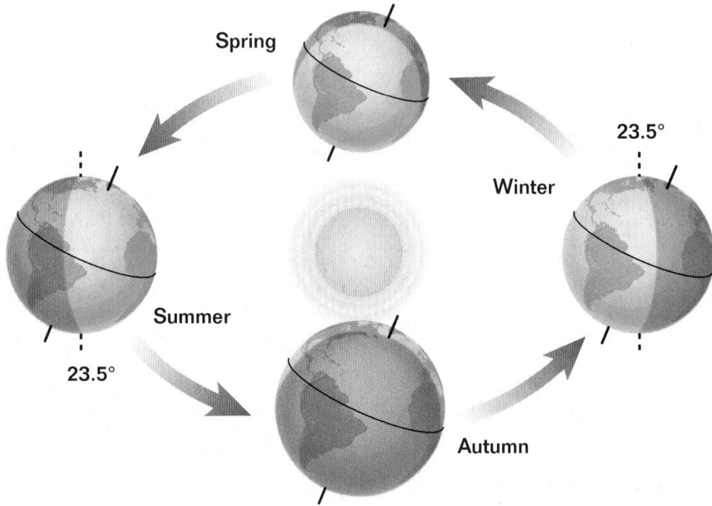

Figure 18-4 Because Earth is tilted on its axis, the angle of the sun's rays changes during the year. These changes create the seasons. The tilt of Earth's axis does not have as much of an effect on regions near the equator.

Resource Manager

The following **Teacher Classroom Resources** can be used with Section 18-2:

 **Reproducible Masters**

Activity Worksheets, pp. 99-101
Critical Thinking/Problem Solving, p. 18 L2
Enrichment, p. 48 L3
Laboratory Manual, pp. 107–110 L2
Reinforcement, p. 48 L2

 **Transparencies**

Teaching Transparency 35 L2
Teaching Transparency 36 L2
Science Integration Transparency 18 L2

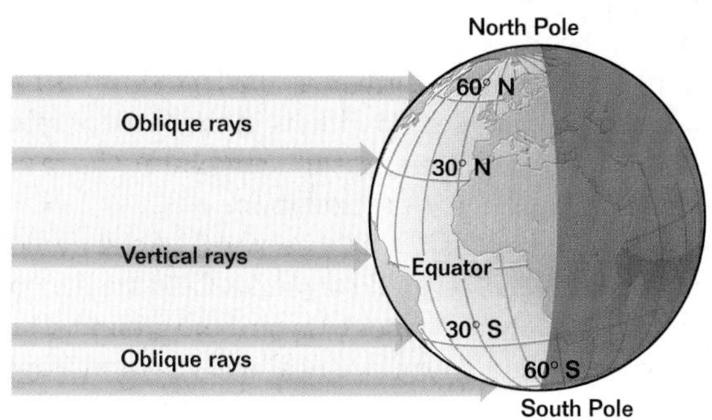

Figure 18-5 Because Earth is curved, oblique rays of sunlight reaching higher latitudes near the poles are more spread out. These rays are therefore weaker than the sunlight reaching lower latitudes near the equator. Climates near the equator are warmer, and those near the poles are colder.

The nearer a region is to the north or south pole, the higher its latitude, the smaller the amount of energy it receives from the sun, as seen in **Figure 18-5,** and the colder its climate.

EARTH SCIENCE INTEGRATION

Seasonal changes in sunlight also have an effect on the temperature of a climate. Because Earth is tilted on its axis, the angle of the sun's rays changes as Earth moves through its yearly orbit. During winter in the northern hemisphere, regions north of the equator are tilted away from the sun. Rays of sunlight are spread over a larger area, reducing their warming effect. As a result, winter temperatures are colder than summer temperatures.

Using Math

Earth is tilted at an angle of 23.5°. Without using a protractor, sketch an angle that measures about 23.5°. Then, check your angle by measuring it with a protractor.

Elevation

A region's elevation, or distance above sea level, also has an influence on temperature. Earth's atmosphere acts as insulation that traps some of the heat that reaches Earth's surface. At higher elevations, the atmosphere is thinner, so more heat escapes back into space. As a result, the higher the elevation, the colder the climate. The climate on a mountain will be cooler than the climate at sea level at the same latitude. Higher elevations affect plant growth, as seen in **Figure 18-6.**

Figure 18-6 These Rocky Mountain bristlecone pines show the effects of higher elevations on plants. These trees are shaped by the wind and stunted by the cold, harsh conditions.

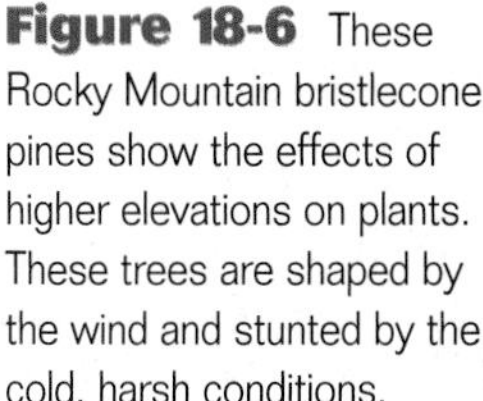

Activity

Visual-Spatial Pass out photographs of plants and animals from magazines. Ask students to predict where the organism lives and give a reason for the prediction. L1

Flex Your Brain

Use the Flex Your Brain activity to have students explore DESERTIFICATION.

EARTH SCIENCE INTEGRATION

Climatic changes on Earth depend on how directly sunlight falls on the hemispheres as Earth revolves around the sun. The amount of sunlight falling on the hemispheres changes as Earth orbits the sun because of the tilt of Earth's axis (23.5°).

Enrichment

Visual-Spatial Have students examine a globe to understand the difference between latitude and longitude. Ask them to find the latitude and longitude for their location. L2

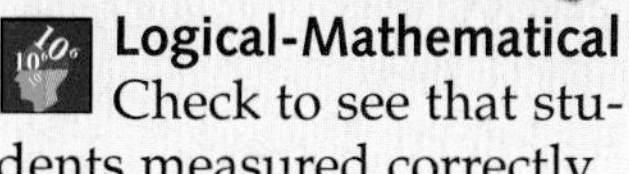

Using Math

Logical-Mathematical Check to see that students measured correctly.

VISUAL Learning

Figure 18-5 Shine a flashlight on a globe, directing the light on the equator. Compare the intensity of the light at different latitudes. *The light's intensity is greatest at the equator and decreases with increasing latitude.* Help students understand that as the intensity of sunlight decreases the average temperature also decreases.

Integrating the Sciences

Earth Science Climate is the average temperature and precipitation over a period of time. Weather involves atmospheric changes on a daily basis. Have students record temperature and precipitation for a week and average the figures. Ask what kind of climate this represents. L2

Quick Demo

To demonstrate that warm air holds more moisture than cold air, place a jar in the refrigerator overnight. The next day, take the jar out and have students observe water droplets forming on the jar. Explain that the cold jar cooled the air next to the glass, causing water vapor in the air to condense and form tiny droplets on the glass.

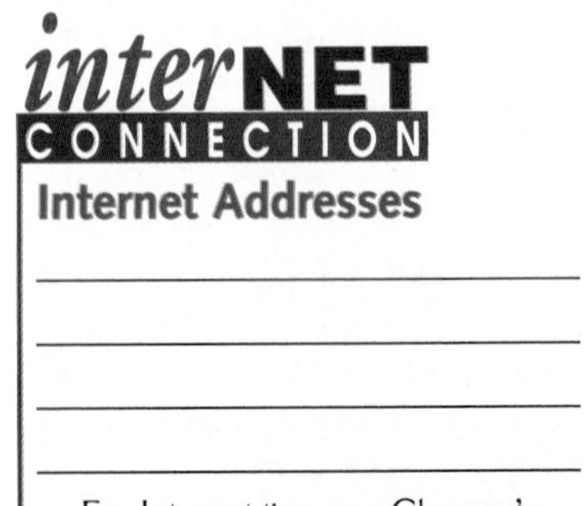

interNET CONNECTION

Internet Addresses

For Internet tips, see Glencoe's **Using the Internet in the Science Classroom.**

GLENCOE TECHNOLOGY

CD-ROM

Glencoe Science Voyages Interactive CD-ROM

Explorations

Have students do the interactive exploration, What are the different types of land environments?

Videodisc

The Infinite Voyage: Life in the Balance

Chapter 5 *BioLab II Classifying the Community of Insects* 6:00

The Infinite Voyage: To the Edge of the Earth

Chapter 6 *Exploring Life in the Canadian Arctic* 8:00

Refer to the Teacher Guide for bar codes and teaching strategies.

interNET CONNECTION

Little precipitation falls in the desert. Visit the Glencoe Science Web Site at **www.glencoe.com/sec/science** for more information about how cacti thrive.

Precipitation

Water is one of the most important factors affecting the climate of an area. Precipitation (prih sihp uh TAY shun) is the amount of water that condenses and falls in the form of rain, snow, sleet, hail, and fog. Differences in temperature have an important effect on patterns of precipitation.

Have you heard the expression "Hot air rises"? Actually, hot air is pushed upward whenever cold air sinks. Cold air is more dense than hot air, so it tends to move toward the ground. This pushes warm air near Earth's surface upward. In warm tropical regions near the equator, the air, land, and oceans are constantly being heated by the direct rays of the sun. As the cooler air sinks, the warm air is pushed upward into the atmosphere. This warm air carries large amounts of water vapor from the oceans. When the air reaches a high enough altitude in the atmosphere, the water vapor it contains cools and condenses as rain. While the air rises, it also moves slowly toward either the north or south pole. The air loses virtually all of its moisture by the time it reaches a latitude of about 30°. Because of this pattern, deserts are common at latitudes near 30° in both the northern and southern hemispheres. Latitudes between 0° and 22° receive much larger amounts of rain.

The Rain Shadow Effect

The presence of mountain ranges also has an effect on rainfall patterns. As **Figure 18-7** shows, air that is moving toward a mountain range is forced upward by the shape of the land. As warm air is forced upward, it cools, condensing the water vapor it contains and creating rain or snow. By the time the air has passed over the mountains, it has lost its moisture. The region on the opposite side of the mountain range receives very little rain because it is in a "rain shadow" created by the mountains.

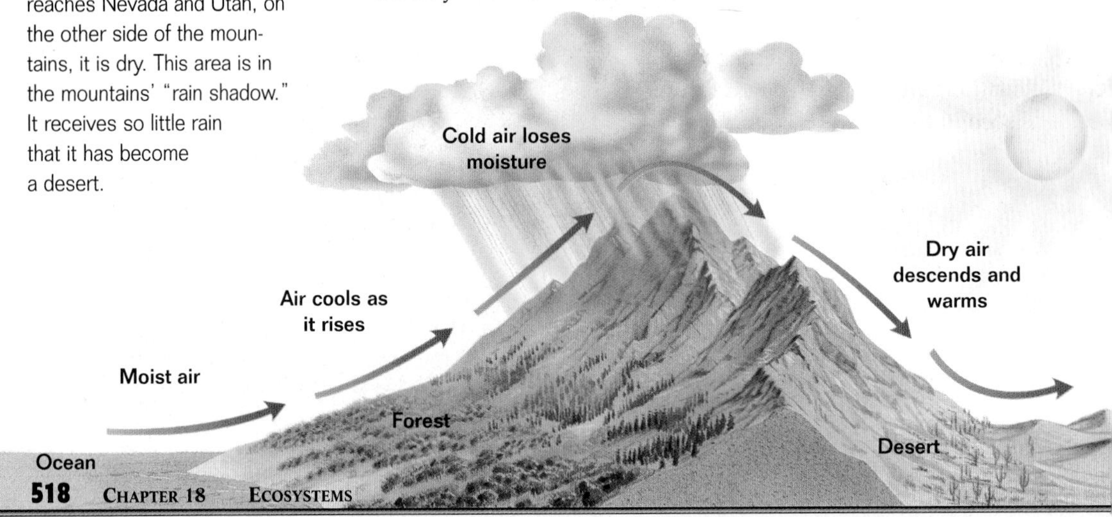

Figure 18-7 Moist air moving into California from the Pacific Ocean is forced upward when it reaches the Sierra Nevada Mountains. As air rises, it cools and loses its moisture in the form of rain or snow. By the time the air reaches Nevada and Utah, on the other side of the mountains, it is dry. This area is in the mountains' "rain shadow." It receives so little rain that it has become a desert.

Guided Reading Strategy

News Summary This strategy helps students explain and make connections to their study of science. Students are assigned the job of being television reporters. They are given several minutes to summarize, retell, or analyze their investigation for their "television" audience. Have students do a News Summary for an application of a concept from this chapter.

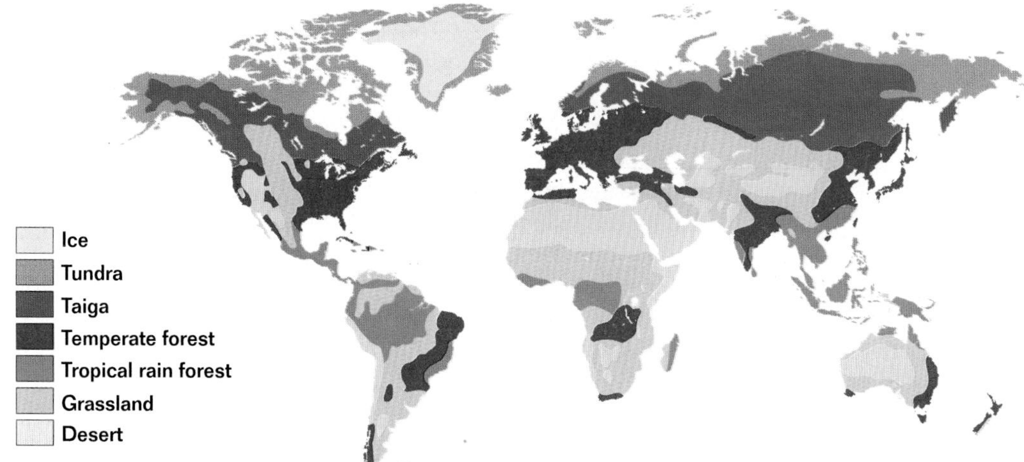

Figure 18-8 The land portion of the biosphere can be divided into several biomes. Tundra, taiga, temperate forest, tropical rain forest, grassland, and desert are the most commonly known. **Which biome is most common in the United States?**

Land Biomes

As you will see in the **Field Guide to Biomes** at the end of this chapter, regions with similar climates tend to have ecosystems with climax communities of similar structure. Tropical rain forests are climax communities found near the equator, where temperatures are warm and rainfall is plentiful. Coniferous forests grow where winter temperatures are cold and rainfall is moderate. Large geographic areas that have similar climates and ecosystems are called **biomes** (BI ohmz). The six most common biomes are mapped in **Figure 18-8.**

Tundra

At latitudes surrounding the north pole lies a biome that receives little precipitation but is covered with ice most of the year. The **tundra** (TUN dra) is a cold, dry, treeless region, sometimes called a cold desert, where winters are six to nine months long. For some of those months, the land remains dark because the sun never rises above the horizon. For a few days during the short, cold summer, the sun never sets. Precipitation averages less than 25 cm per year, and winter temperatures drop to −40°C, so water in the tundra soil remains frozen solid during the winter. During the summer, only the top few inches thaw.

Comparing Tundra and Taiga

Procedure

1. Compare the latitudes where tundra is found in the northern hemisphere with the same latitudes in South America.
2. Compare the latitudes where taiga is found in the northern hemisphere with the same latitudes in South America.

Analysis

Are either of these biomes found in South America? Explain why or why not.

Try at Home MiniLab

For additional help doing this activity at home, see the corresponding pages in the **Home Involvement** booklet.

Purpose

Logical-Mathematical Students will use latitude information from a world map to find out whether the tundra or taiga biomes exist on the South American continent. L2

Materials

a world map

Teaching Strategies

- Make sure students trace latitudes 60° and 75° on both northern and southern halves of the globe to see which land areas fall between those latitudes.
- Point out which land areas correspond to 30° south in the northern hemisphere.

Analysis

1. There are no landmasses in the southern hemisphere at the latitudes where these biomes are found in the northern hemisphere.

Assessment

Performance To further assess students' understanding of biomes, have them use the biome map to infer why no coniferous forests exist in the southern hemisphere. Use **Performance Assessment in the Science Classroom,** p. 17.

Caption Answer

Figure 18-8 *The United States is primarily made up of temperate forests.*

VISUAL Learning

Figure 18-8 Have students look at the biome map and locate the biome in which they live. L1

Using Science Words

Taiga comes from the Russian word *tajga,* which means "swampy forest."

Discussion

Interpersonal Have students discuss whether they think the taiga is an inviting home for humans. Ask students to cite reasons for their answers.

Correcting Misconceptions

Students may think that the location of a particular biome on Earth is permanent. They may not realize that a change in climate would cause a biome to change. Discuss extinction of dinosaurs and global warming.

Enrichment

Logical-Mathematical Give students a copy of a world map with the biomes drawn on it. Have students use their own methods to calculate and compare the area of each biome. Ask them to explain how much larger the taiga is than the other biomes.

Below the thawed surface is a layer of permanently frozen soil called permafrost. The cold temperatures slow down the process of decomposition, so the soil is also poor in nutrients.

Tundra plants are resistant to drought and cold. They include species of lichens known as reindeer moss, true mosses, grasses, and small shrubs, as seen in **Figure 18-9.** During the summer, mosquitoes, blackflies, and other biting insects are abundant. Many birds, including ducks, geese, various shorebirds, and songbirds, migrate to the tundra to nest during the summer. Hawks, snowy owls, mice, voles, lemmings, arctic hares, caribou, and musk oxen are also found there.

Figure 18-9 Land is so flat in the tundra that water does not drain away. Because the frozen soil also prevents water from soaking into the soil, part of the tundra becomes wet and marshy during the summer. Frozen soil also prevents trees and other deep-rooted plants from growing in the tundra biome.

Taiga

Just below the tundra, at latitudes between about 50°N and 60°N, and stretching across Canada, northern Europe, and Asia, lies the world's largest biome. The **taiga** (TI guh), as shown in **Figure 18-10,** is a cold region of cone-bearing evergreen trees. This biome is also called the northern coniferous forest. Although the winter is long and cold, the taiga is warmer and wetter than the tundra. Precipitation is mostly snow and averages 35 cm to 100 cm each year.

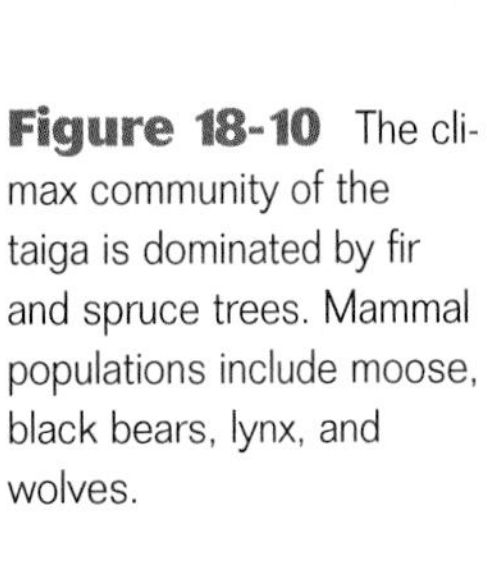

Figure 18-10 The climax community of the taiga is dominated by fir and spruce trees. Mammal populations include moose, black bears, lynx, and wolves.

Across the Curriculum

Geography Have students research the Inuit people who live in the Arctic tundra and report on how they have adapted to the harsh climate. L2

Visual Learning

Figure 18-8 Make sure that students understand that a biome is a category and not a place. A tropical rain forest does not refer to any specific geographical location on Earth. It refers to all regions on Earth where such a biome is found. Emphasize that the boundaries of biomes are not as well defined as shown in the figure.

No permafrost is found in a taiga. The ground thaws completely during the summer, making it possible for trees to grow. There are few shrubs and grasses, primarily because the forests of the taiga are so dense that little sunlight penetrates through the trees. Lichens and mosses grow on the forest floor.

Temperate Deciduous Forest

Temperate forests are found in both the northern and southern hemispheres, at latitudes below about 50°. Temperate regions usually have four distinct seasons each year. Precipitation ranges from about 75 cm to 150 cm and is distributed evenly throughout the year. Temperatures range from below freezing during the winter to 30°C or more during the warmest days of summer.

Many coniferous forests exist in the temperate regions of the world, particularly in mountainous areas. However, most of the temperate forests in Europe and North America are dominated by climax communities of deciduous trees, which lose their leaves every autumn. These forests, like the one in **Figure 18-11,** are called **temperate deciduous forests.** In the United States, they are found primarily east of the Mississippi River.

Reading Check
Where are temperate deciduous forests found?

The loss of leaves in the fall signals a dramatic change in the life of the deciduous forest. Food becomes less abundant, and the leafless trees no longer provide adequate shelter for many organisms. Some animals, particularly birds, migrate to warmer regions during the winter. Other organisms reduce their activities and their need for food by going into hibernation until spring.

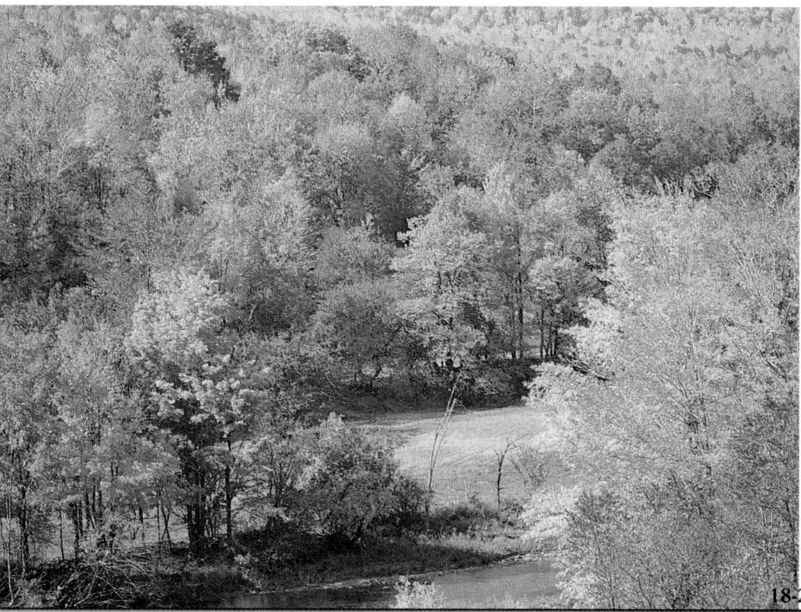

Figure 18-11 The mild climate and rich soil of the temperate deciduous forest support a wide variety of organisms. Animal life includes deer, foxes, squirrels, mice, snakes, and a huge number of bird and insect species. **Why do you think the temperate forests support a wide variety of organisms?**

Content Background

Many students in the United States live in or near the temperate forest biome, the largest biome of the United States. However, if students live in the inner city, they may be unaware of the forest biome. Relate factors outside the city that are examples of the biome to students.

Activity

Naturalist Have students describe food chains that exist within the temperate forest biome. Remind students always to begin a food chain with a plant. L2

Visual Learning

Figure 18-11 How does the soil in temperate deciduous forests help support a large and diverse wildlife community? *It is fertile and moist. Many layers of vegetation can grow there and support a wide variety of animals on the forest floor, in the treetops, and in the soil.* **How do the fungi and bacteria of the forest floor contribute to the health of the entire biome?** *They decompose and recycle materials that keep the soil fertile.*

Inclusion Strategies

Hearing Impaired Bring examples of both evergreen and deciduous leaves to class. Have students describe similarities and differences between the two leaf types. Have students collect pictures of fall foliage from areas that have temperate deciduous forests and bring them to class. L2 ELL

Caption Answer

Figure 18-11 *Answers will vary but should include mild climate, rich soil, and a variety of habitats.*

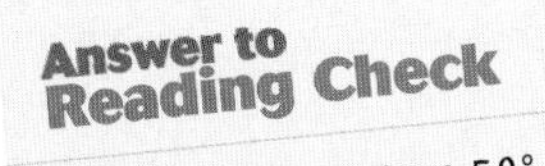

Teacher FYI

Deciduous forest biomes were among the first biomes to be converted to agricultural use. In many parts of the world, soils that originally supported deciduous forests have been cultivated by traditional agricultural methods for thousands of years without a substantial loss in fertility. American farmers saw the land as a limitless resource and abandoned the wise soil conservation practices of their ancestors. This has resulted in erosion and other forms of soil depletion.

Problem Solving

Humans are competing with rain forest species for living space and for resources.

Think Critically

Possible reasons for recommending the continuous harvest include these. At the end of four years, the source of income is still there; it has not been destroyed. The diversity of species in the rain forest has also been preserved. Possible reasons for choosing the one-time timber harvest might include that more money comes in all at once.

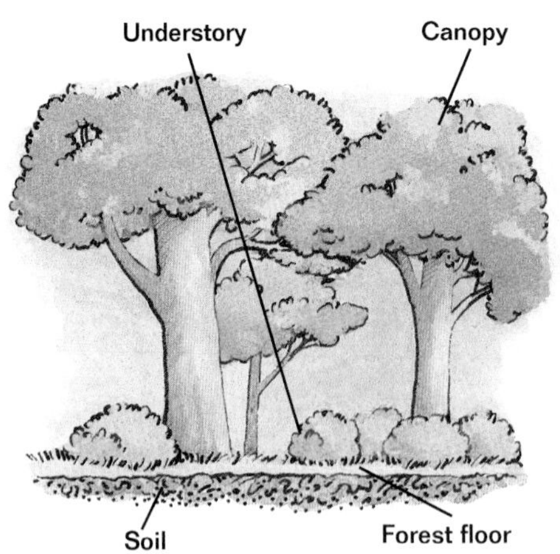

Figure 18-12 All forests are made up of layers with distinctly different biotic and abiotic factors.

Layers of Vegetation

Forests form layers of vegetation, as illustrated in **Figure 18-12.** At the top of the forest is the canopy, which consists of the leafy branches of trees. The *canopy* shades the ground below and provides homes for birds, insects, mammals, and many other organisms.

Beneath the canopy and above the forest floor is the shrub layer, or *understory*. The understory is made up of shorter plants that tolerate shade, along with organisms that depend on these plants for food and shelter.

The forest floor is dark and moist. It is home to many insects, worms, and fungi, as well as plants that can survive in dim light. Leaves, twigs, seeds, and the bodies of dead animals that fall to the forest floor either decompose or are eaten.

Problem Solving

Saving the Rain Forests

Many of the world's rain forests are being destroyed for economic reasons. Logging and farming provide income for people living in these areas. When a section of rain forest is cleared, trees that can be used as lumber are removed and sold. The remaining plants are cut down and burned, the ash is used to fertilize the soil, and food crops are planted. After a couple of years, the soil becomes too poor to produce a harvest, so the land is abandoned and another patch of forest is cleared.

People can make a living from the rain forest in other ways. Latex, a material used in surgical gloves, rubber bands, tires, and shoes, is the sap of rubber trees. Carefully tapping the trees provides a continual harvest without harming the forest. Many rain forest plants produce edible fruits, nuts, and oils that can be harvested year after year, without the need for clearing land. Harvesting these plants, rather than clearing land on which other crops can be grown for only a short time, could provide people with a sustainable income.

Think Critically: Suppose a family could earn the same amount of money in two different ways. One is to clear several hectares of rain forest, sell the timber, and grow food crops for two years. The other is to harvest latex and edible fruits and nuts from a larger area of rain forest for four years. Which course of action would you recommend? Why? Give reasons why the family might choose the other method.

Inclusion Strategies

Learning Disabled Students with poorly developed geography skills may have difficulty understanding where biomes are located and why. Use globes to give these students a three-dimensional perspective and maps to compare biomes and latitudes. L1

ELL 

Across the Curriculum

History Compare maps that show the amount of forested area in the United States 100 years ago with current maps. Have students research the reasons for the disappearance of the forests during this time. *Most of the changes are human induced and result from building and farming activities.* L2

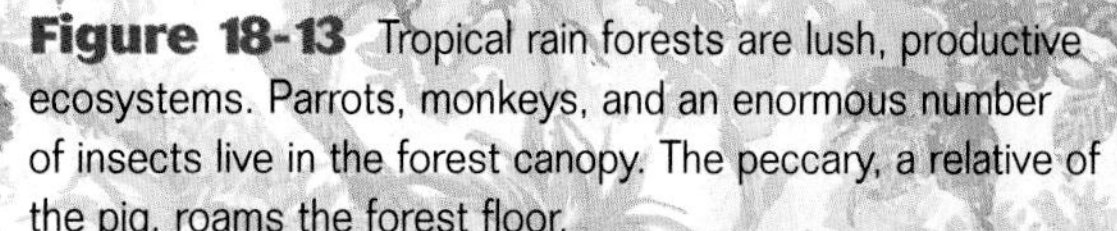

Figure 18-13 Tropical rain forests are lush, productive ecosystems. Parrots, monkeys, and an enormous number of insects live in the forest canopy. The peccary, a relative of the pig, roams the forest floor.

Tropical Rain Forest

The most important climax community in the equatorial regions of the world is the lush, green plant growth of the **tropical rain forest.** Rainfall averages 200 cm to 225 cm each year, and some areas receive as much as 400 cm of rain annually. Temperatures are warm and stable, never varying much above or below about 25°C. The abundant rainfall and high temperatures combine to create a hot, humid environment that can be compared to the atmosphere inside a greenhouse.

Plants

The highest part of the rain forest canopy is formed by the leaves and branches of trees that may reach 30 m to 40 m in height. A rain forest may contain more than 700 species of trees and more than 1000 species of flowering plants. The canopy is so dense that it prevents much sunlight from filtering through to the regions below. Vines that are rooted in the soil grow up along tree trunks to reach the sun. Some types of plants such as orchids reach the light by anchoring themselves on tree trunks instead of in the soil. The understory is only dimly lit. Many of the plants growing here have huge leaves that catch what little sunlight is available. The forest floor is almost completely dark, with few plants other than ferns and mosses. Many of the tallest trees have support roots that rise above the ground. Most plants have shallow roots that form a tangled mat at the soil surface.

Animals

The rain forest is home to a huge number of animals. It is estimated that 1000 hectares (about 2500 acres) of rain forest in South America contain thousands of insect species, including 150 different

Enrichment

Linguistic Have students research rain forest use and write a report on what steps people can take now to save the rain forest. L2

Correcting Misconceptions

Some students may think that brightly colored insects, such as butterflies living in the rain forest, would be easy prey for insect-eating birds. In this environment, where the background consists of brightly colored flowers, the brightly colored insects are almost invisible.

Discussion

How do plants in a tropical rain forest change from the topmost layer to the bottom layer? *The plants decrease in size from top to bottom.* **What causes this change?** *a decrease in the amount of sunlight available to the plants*

Activity

Intrapersonal Have students prepare a chart of the major features of the three zones of the tropical rain forest: the canopy, understory, and forest floor. L2

Discussion

Infer why most rain forest animals live in trees. *More food is available in the trees than on the ground.* **Why do few plants grow on the forest floor in the tropical rain forest?** *The broad leaves of the tall trees shade the forest floor, making it difficult for low-growing plants to receive enough sunlight to grow.*

Across the Curriculum

History Certain human diseases, such as malaria and yellow fever, are common among populations living in tropical rain forests. Have students research tropical diseases and identify the microorganism that causes each disease. Have students identify the abiotic factors that might encourage the development of yellow fever and malaria. L3

Teacher FYI

At one time, the grassland biome covered nearly half of the land on Earth. Today, most of the grassland is used by humans for growing crops, raising animals, and housing.

Quick Demo

Show the class a picture of a Joshua tree—a North American desert plant. This tree was named by early Mormon colonists who thought it resembled a bearded elder bowed in prayer.

3 Assess

Check for Understanding

Enrichment

Linguistic Research and report on the adaptations of a desert animal or plant that enable it to live and reproduce in the desert. L2

Reteach

Make a table showing precipitation, temperature, common plants, and common animals for each biome. Have students identify the name of each biome described. L1

Extension

For students who have mastered this section, use the **Reinforcement** and **Enrichment** masters.

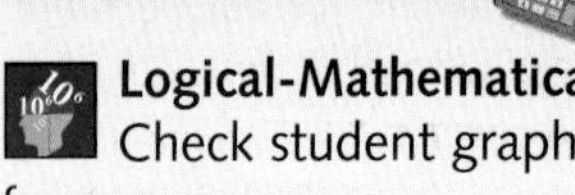

Using Math

Logical-Mathematical Check student graphs for accuracy.

Using Math

Make a bar graph that shows the average yearly precipitation in each of the land biomes.

kinds of butterflies. The same patch of forest also contains dozens of species of snakes, lizards, frogs, and salamanders, and hundreds of varieties of brightly colored birds, including parrots, toucans, cockatoos, and hummingbirds. Tree-dwelling mammals include monkeys, sloths, and bats. Ocelots and jaguars are tropical cats that prowl the forest floor in search of small mammals such as pacas and agoutis, or piglike peccaries, shown in **Figure 18-13.**

Grassland

Temperate and tropical regions that receive between 25 cm and 75 cm of precipitation each year and are dominated by climax communities of grasses are known as **grasslands.** Most grasslands have a dry season, when little or no rain falls, which prevents the development of forests. Virtually every continent has grasslands, like the one in **Figure 18-14,** and they are known by a variety of names. The prairie and plains of North America, the steppes of Asia, the veldts of Africa, and the pampas of South America are all grasslands.

Figure 18-14 Grasslands, like this one in South Dakota, are hot and dry during the summer and cold and wet during the winter. They once supported huge herds of bison. Today, they are inhabited by pronghorn, gophers, ground squirrels, prairie chickens, and meadowlarks.

Grass plants have extensive root systems, called sod, that absorb water when it rains and can withstand drought during long dry spells. The roots remain dormant during winter and sprout new stems and leaves when the weather warms in the spring. The soil is rich and fertile, and many grassland regions of the world are now important farming areas. Cereal grains such as wheat, rye, oats, barley, and corn, which serve as staple foods for humans, are types of grasses.

The most noticeable animals in grassland ecosystems are usually mammals that graze on the stems, leaves, and seeds of grass plants. Kangaroos graze in the grasslands of Australia. In Africa, common grassland inhabitants include wildebeests and zebras.

Desert

The **desert,** the driest biome on Earth, receives less than 25 cm of rain each year and supports little plant life. Some desert areas may receive no rain for years. When rain does come, it quickly drains away due to the sandy soil. Any water that remains on the ground evaporates rapidly, so the soil retains almost no moisture.

Multiple Learning Styles

Interpersonal Have students form groups to find information about the tropical rain forests of different continents. Assign a continent to each group. Each group member should research one aspect of the tropical rain forest, such as geography, plant life, animal life, or products obtained from the forest of that continent. The information should be combined in the form of a booklet. Have groups exchange booklets to increase their knowledge of tropical rain forests. L2 COOP LEARN

Because of the lack of water, desert plants are spaced widely apart, and much of the ground is bare. Some areas receive enough rainfall to support the growth of a few shrubs and small trees. Barren, windblown sand dunes are characteristic of the driest deserts, where rain rarely falls. Most deserts are covered with a thin, sandy or gravelly soil that contains little humus.

Adaptations of Desert Plants and Animals

Desert plants have developed a variety of adaptations for survival in the extreme dryness and hot and cold temperatures of this biome. Cactus plants, like the one in **Figure 18-15A,** with their reduced, spiny leaves, are probably the most familiar desert plants. Cacti have large, shallow roots that quickly absorb any water that becomes available.

Water conservation is important to all desert animals. Some, like the kangaroo rat, never need to drink water. They get all the moisture they need from the breakdown of food during digestion. Other adaptations involve behavior. Most animals are active only during the early morning or late afternoon, when temperatures are less extreme. Few large animals are found in the desert because there is not enough water or food to support them.

Figure 18-15 Desert organisms are adapted to hot, dry conditions.

A Giant saguaro cacti expand to store water after it rains.

B Desert iguanas, common in deserts of the southwestern United States and Mexico, prefer temperatures above 100°F.

Section Assessment

1. Name two biomes that receive less than 25 cm of rain each year.
2. Compare the adaptations of tundra organisms to their environment with those of a desert organism to its environment.
3. **Think Critically:** Compare and contrast the canopies of temperate deciduous forests and tropical rain forests.
4. **Skill Builder**
Observing and Inferring Animals adapt to their environments in order to survive. Do the **Chapter 18 Skill Activity** on page 759 to infer how some organisms adapt.

Using Computers

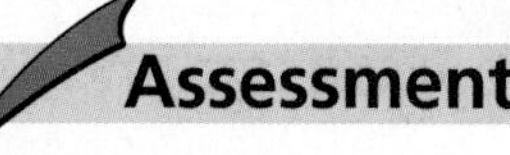

Database Create a database of information on Earth's land biomes. Include data on temperature range, precipitation, limiting factors, and descriptions of climax communities. If you need help, refer to page 733.

Assessment

Portfolio Have students write a story with the setting being one of the biomes and the plot revolving around characteristics of that biome. Students can take turns reading stories to the class. Use **Performance Assessment in the Science Classroom,** p. 83. P

4 Close

Proficiency Prep

Use the quiz to check students' recall of section content.

1. **What are large geographic areas with similar climates and climax communities?** *biomes*
2. **What are six major land biomes on Earth?** *tundra, taiga, temperate deciduous forest, tropical rain forest, grassland, desert*

Section Assessment

1. tundra and desert
2. Tundra plants are resistant to cold and drought. Desert plants are resistant to heat and drought. Many tundra organisms migrate during the coldest months. Desert animals have adaptations for water conservation.
3. **Think Critically** Tropical rain forest trees retain their leaves all year long, so the forest floor is always dark. Temperate deciduous trees lose their leaves during winter. Some plants have a chance to begin growing on the forest floor in early spring before the trees grow new leaves. Both canopies limit growth on the forest floor.

Using Computers

Students can take data from the text. Each biome discussion includes data on temperature and precipitation ranges, climax communities, and so on.

Activity 18•1

Purpose

Intrapersonal Students will conduct a study of an ecosystem, determine how the living and nonliving things interact, and determine the relationships that exist among the organisms that live there. L2 COOP LEARN

Process Skills

observing, classifying, communicating, defining operationally, recognizing cause and effect, predicting

Time

50 minutes for setup, four weeks to make observations

Teaching Strategies

- Arrange for students to check out binoculars, field guides, and other useful materials from the science classroom and library. Approve the ecosystems chosen by the students before they begin their observations.
- This may be the first independent study that students have undertaken at great depth and for such a long length of time. Offer encouragement to students at regular intervals during this investigation.
- Offer students a set time each day to discuss any problems they may have concerning their method of study.

Answers to Questions

1. Answers will vary depending on the ecosystem chosen by each group.
2. Answers will vary with the ecosystems.
3. Populations would be affected by changes in temperature, water, or other abiotic factors. The entire ecosystem could be disrupted.
4. Other populations could be affected.

Activity 18•2

Using Scientific Methods

Studying a Land Environment

Materials

- Graph paper
- Thermometer
- Tape measure
- Hand lens
- Notebook
- Binoculars
- Pencil
- Field guides

An ecological study includes observation and analysis of living organisms and the physical features of the environment.

What You'll Investigate

How do you study an ecosystem?

Goals

- **Observe** biotic and abiotic factors of an ecosystem.
- **Analyze** the relationships among organisms and their environment.

Procedure

1. **Choose** a portion of an ecosystem near your school or home as your area of study. You might choose to study a pond, a forest area in a park, a garden, or another area.
2. **Decide** the boundaries of your study area.
3. Using a tape measure and graph paper, **make a map** of your study area.
4. Using a thermometer, **measure and record** the air temperature in your study area.
5. **Observe** the organisms in your study area. Use field guides to identify them. Use a hand lens to study small organisms. Use binoculars to study animals you cannot get near. Also, look for evidence (such as tracks or feathers) of organisms you do not see.
6. Record your observations in a table like the one shown. Make drawings to help you remember what you see.
7. Visit your study area as many times as you can and at different times of the day for four weeks. At each visit, be sure to make the same measurements and record all observations. Note how biotic and abiotic factors interact.

Conclude and Apply

1. **Identify** relationships among the organisms in your study area, such as predator-prey or symbiosis.
2. **Diagram** a food chain or food web for your ecosystem.
3. **Predict** what might happen if one or more abiotic factors were changed suddenly.
4. **Predict** what might happen if one or more populations were removed from the area.

Environmental Data

Date	Time of Day	Temperature	Organisms Observed	Observations and Comments

Assessment

Performance Have students alter the ecosystem in a way that is not harmful. Have them observe how foreign materials affect the behavior of living things in the ecosystem. Use **Performance Assessment in the Science Classroom,** p. 23.

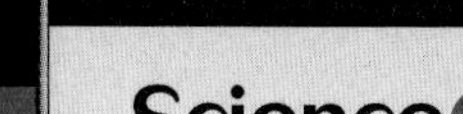

Protecting Antarctica

The Coldest Place on Earth

Antarctica is a vast continent of rock covered with ice and surrounded by ocean. It is the least changed landmass in the world, in part because it is an environment hostile to humans. Winters are dark and long, with temperatures dipping to –90°C. During winter, shelves of ice extend from the land out over the ocean, essentially doubling the size of the continent. The yearly freezing and thawing of this ice has important effects on worldwide weather patterns and is a force that drives ocean currents.

Antarctica's Resources

Although the land is barren, seals and penguins, like the ones at left, use the shores as breeding grounds, and the waters of the Antarctic Ocean teem with life. Under the surface of Antarctica lie untouched mineral resources. Coal and oil probably exist in enormous quantities, as do other minerals that have already been discovered.

Antarctica and its remarkable natural resources are fully protected by a treaty that was drawn up in 1959 and signed by 12 nations—the United States, Great Britain, Argentina, Chile, France, Belgium, Norway, Australia, New Zealand, Japan, South Africa, and what was then the USSR. The Antarctic Treaty made the entire continent "a natural reserve, devoted to peace and science." Military activities, hunting, mining, and other actions that might harm the environment and its wild inhabitants are banned.

Since 1959, the Antarctic Treaty has been expanded to promote even greater environmental protection, international cooperation, and freedom for scientific research. Thanks to this agreement, Antarctica will remain an essentially undisturbed wilderness far into the future.

interNET CONNECTION

- Visit the Glencoe Science Web Site at **www.glencoe.com/sec/science** to find out more about research in Antarctica.

NATIONAL GEOGRAPHIC

Science & Society

Teaching Strategies

Have students investigate Antarctica's resources and how world leaders would like to see the resources managed.

Using a globe, review the location of Antarctica with students. Review with students the reasons scientists are interested in Antarctica.

interNET CONNECTION

Internet Addresses

For Internet tips, see Glencoe's **Using the Internet in the Science Classroom.**

For More Information

Winckler, Suzanne, and Rodgers, Mary M. *Antarctica (Our Endangered Planet). Lerner Publications Company,* 1992.

Content Background

- Only two percent of the Antarctica landmass is free of ice. Portions of this area receive no precipitation at all. Hundreds of species of lichens, along with mosses and two species of tiny flowering plants, are found in Antarctica. The largest coal field in the world may lie beneath its mountains. Gold and platinum have been found. It is believed the continent contains rich deposits of iron, lead, copper, and uranium.

SECTION 18-3

Prepare

Refer to **Photosynthesis in the Ocean, Salinity,** and **Nutrients in Aquatic Ecosystems** on p. 508F.

Preplanning

Refer to **Chapter Organizer** on pp. 508A–B.

1 Motivate

Bellringer

Before presenting the lesson, display **Section Focus Transparency 49** on the overhead projector. Use the accompanying **Focus Activity** worksheet. L2 ELL

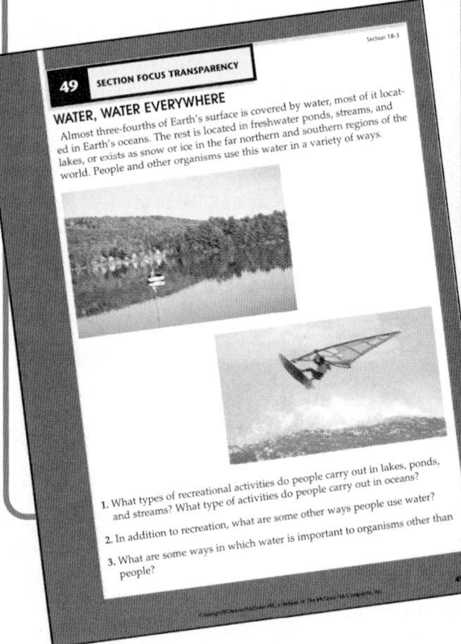

Section 18-3

49 SECTION FOCUS TRANSPARENCY

WATER, WATER EVERYWHERE

Almost three-fourths of Earth's surface is covered by water, most of it located in Earth's oceans. The rest is located in freshwater ponds, streams, and lakes, or exists as snow or ice in the far northern and southern regions of the world. People and other organisms use this water in a variety of ways.

1. What types of recreational activities do people carry out in lakes, ponds, and streams? What type of activities do people carry out in oceans?
2. In addition to recreation, what are some other ways people use water?
3. What are some ways in which water is important to organisms other than people?

49

Tying to Previous Knowledge

Review cyanobacteria, protists, and green algae and their importance in the food chains of marine and freshwater ecosystems.

18-3 Water Environments

What You'll Learn

- The difference between flowing freshwater and standing freshwater ecosystems
- Important seashore and deep-ocean ecosystems

Vocabulary
plankton
estuary
intertidal zone

Why It's Important

- You depend on water for your life processes.

Freshwater Biomes

You've learned that temperature and precipitation are the most important factors determining which species can survive in a land environment. The limiting factors in water environments are the amount of salt in the water, dissolved oxygen, water temperature, and sunlight. The amount of salts dissolved in the water is called salinity. Freshwater contains little or no dissolved salts, and so has a low salinity. Earth's freshwater biomes include flowing water like these rivers and streams, as well as still or standing water, such as lakes and ponds.

Rivers and Streams

Flowing freshwater environments range from small, swiftly flowing streams, like the one in **Figure 18-16A,** to large, slow rivers. The faster a stream flows, the clearer its water tends to be and the higher its oxygen content. Swift currents quickly wash loose particles downstream, leaving a rocky or gravelly bottom. The tumbling and splashing of swiftly flowing water mixes in air from the atmosphere, increasing the oxygen content of the water.

Most of the nutrients that support life in flowing-water ecosystems are washed into the water from land. In areas where the water movement slows down, such as wide pools in streams or large rivers, debris settles to the bot-

Figure 18-16

A Freshwater streams are important in the ecosystem.

B The cold water, rapid current, and high oxygen content of this stream provide the kind of habitat required for fish like this rainbow trout.

Resource Manager

The following **Teacher Classroom Resources** can be used with Section 18-3:

 **Reproducible Masters**

Activity Worksheets, p. 102 L2

Enrichment, p. 49 L3

Multicultural Connections, pp. 35–36 L2

Reinforcement, p. 49 L2

Study Guide, pp. 71–72 L1 ELL

Figure 18-17 Ponds and lakes differ in the types of communities inhabiting them. **What are some other differences between ponds and lakes?**

A The warm, sunlit waters of this pond are home to a large variety of organisms. Plants and algae form the basis of a food web that includes snails, insects, frogs, snakes, turtles, and fish.

B The population density of the warm, shallow water of the lakeshore is high. Fewer types of organisms live in the deeper water.

tom. These environments tend to have higher nutrient levels and lower dissolved oxygen levels. They contain organisms such as freshwater mussels, minnows, and leeches that are not so well adapted for swiftly flowing water. They also tend to have more plant growth.

Lakes and Ponds

A lake or pond forms when a low place in the land fills with rainwater, snowmelt, or water from a stream. The waters of lakes and ponds hardly move at all. They contain more plant growth than flowing-water environments contain.

Ponds, like the one in **Figure 18-17A,** are smaller, shallow bodies of water. Because they are shallow, sunlight can usually penetrate all the way to the bottom, making the water warmer and promoting the growth of plants and algae. In fact, many ponds are almost completely filled with plant material, so the only clear, open water is at the center. Because of the lush growth in pond environments, they tend to be high in nutrients.

Lakes are larger and deeper than ponds. They tend to have more open water because most plant growth is limited to shallow areas along the shoreline. In fact, organisms found in the warm, sunlit waters of the lakeshore are often similar to those found in ponds.

Floating in the warm, sunlit waters near the surface of freshwater lakes and ponds are microscopic organisms known as plankton. **Plankton** includes algae, plants, and other organisms. If you were to dive all the way to the bottom, you would discover few, if any, plants or algae growing. Colder temperatures and lower light levels limit the types of organisms that can live in deep lake waters. Most lake organisms are found along the shoreline and in the warm water near the surface. ☑

Reading Check
What is plankton?

2 Teach

Caption Answer

Figure 18-17 *Students may discuss the size and depth differences. Ponds are smaller and lakes are deeper.*

Answer to Reading Check ☑

Plankton is the microscopic algae, plants, and other organisms found floating near the surface of freshwater lakes and ponds.

GLENCOE TECHNOLOGY

Videodisc

Glencoe Science Voyages Interactive Videodisc—Life

Lesson 9

Ecosystems: Wetlands

38845

38847

Refer to Videodisc Teacher Guide for additional bar codes.

The Infinite Voyage: Secrets from a Frozen World

Chapter 1 *The Southern Ocean —A Rich Marine Ecosystem*

5:30

Refer to the Teacher Guide for bar codes and teaching strategies

Enrichment

Have students describe the adaptations of animals that live in fast-moving waters. Some animals have adapted to life attached to rocks in these areas. Mussels attach themselves to rocks with strong threads, and barnacles use a gluelike cement for attachment. Some insect larvae and plants also have adaptations for these environments.

Across the Curriculum

Language Arts Have students use the library to research the cleanup of Lake Erie. Make sure they include the types of cleanup strategies that have been used. Ask them to find out the current status of the lake. L2

Purpose

Kinesthetic Students will observe a sampling from a freshwater ecosystem.

Materials

2-L bottle, gravel or other debris from the bottom of a pond, pond plants, small animals

Teaching Strategies

Make sure students don't disturb the bottle excessively while observing.

Analysis

1. Student records will depend on organisms observed.
2. Answers will depend on which organisms students observe.

Oral Have students use their observations from the MiniLab to identify adaptations of the organisms. Use **Performance Assessment in the Science Classroom,** p. 27.

3 Assess

Check for Understanding

Reteach

Write on the chalkboard a description of the three major ocean zones. Have students identify each one. L1

Saltwater Biomes

About 95 percent of the water on the surface on Earth contains high concentrations of salts. The saltwater biomes include the oceans, seas, and a few inland lakes, such as the Great Salt Lake in Utah.

Figure 18-18 These Canada geese are swimming in an estuary of the Chesapeake Bay.

Estuaries

Virtually every river on Earth eventually flows into the ocean. The area where a river meets the ocean and contains a mixture of freshwater and salt water is called an **estuary.** Estuaries are located near coastlines and border the land. Salinity changes with the amount of freshwater brought in by rivers and streams, and with the amount of salt water pushed inland by the tides.

Estuaries like the one in **Figure 18-18** are extremely fertile, productive environments because freshwater streams bring in tons of nutrients from inland soils. Nutrient levels in estuaries are higher than those in freshwater or other saltwater ecosystems. Estuarine organisms include many species of algae, a few salt-tolerant grasses, shrimp, crabs, clams, oysters, snails, worms, and fish. Estuaries serve as important nursery grounds for many species of ocean fish.

Modeling Freshwater Environments

Procedure

1. Cover the bottom of a 2-L bottle with about 2 cm of gravel, muck, and other debris from the bottom of a pond. If plants are present, add one or two to the bottle. Use a dip net to capture small fish, insects, or tadpoles.
2. Carefully pour pond water into the bottle until it is about two-thirds full. Seal the bottle.
3. Keep the bottle indoors at room temperature and out of direct sunlight.

Analysis

1. Using a hand lens, observe as many organisms as possible. Record your observations. After two or three days, return your sample to the original habitat.
2. Write a short paper describing the organisms in your sample ecosystem and explaining their interactions.

Seashores

All of Earth's landmasses are bordered by ocean water. The fairly shallow waters along the world's coastlines contain a variety of saltwater ecosystems, all of which are influenced by the tides and by the action of waves. The gravitational pull of the sun and moon causes the tides to rise and fall twice each day in most parts of the world. The **intertidal zone** is the portion of the shoreline that is covered with water at high tide and exposed to the air during low tide. Organisms living in the intertidal zone must not only be adapted to dramatic changes in temperature, moisture, and salinity, but also be able to withstand the force of wave action. Two kinds of intertidal zones are shown in **Figure 18-19.**

Content Background

More than 95 percent of Earth's water is found in oceans. The remaining percentage is freshwater.

Rivers, lakes, and ponds are easily polluted because less dissolved oxygen is in the water to break down the pollutants, and no currents wash away the pollutants.

Extension

For students who have mastered this section, use the **Reinforcement** and **Enrichment** masters.

Figure 18-19 Organisms living in intertidal zones have adaptations to survive in these changing environments.

A Wave action keeps the sandy bottom in constant motion, and organisms that live on sandy shores, such as clams, crabs, and worms, burrow into the sand to avoid being washed away.

B Algae, mussels, barnacles, snails, and other organisms adapted for clinging to the rocks are typically found on rocky shores. These organisms must be able to tolerate the heavy force of breaking waves.

Open Ocean

Life abounds in the open ocean, where there is no land. The ocean can be divided into life zones based on the depth to which sunlight can penetrate the water. The lighted zone of the ocean is the upper 200 m or so. It is the home of the plankton that make up the foundation of the food chain in the open ocean. Below about 200 m, where sunlight cannot reach, is the dark zone of the ocean. Animals living in this region feed on material that floats down from the lighted zone, or they feed on each other.

Section Assessment

1. What are the similarities and differences between a lake and a stream?
2. What biotic or abiotic factor limits life on the floor of a tropical rain forest and the bottom of the deep ocean? Why?
3. **Think Critically:** Why do few plants grow in the waters of a swift-flowing mountain stream?
4. **Skill Builder**
   Comparing and Contrasting Compare and contrast the effects of (1) temperature in the tundra and desert and (2) sunlight in deep-lake and deep-ocean waters. If you need help, refer to Comparing and Contrasting in the **Skill Handbook** on page720.

Science Journal

Write a paragraph in your Science Journal explaining how starting from the equator and moving toward the north pole is like climbing a mountain. Refer to abiotic factors in your explanation.

4 Close

Proficiency Prep

Use this quiz to check students' recall of section content.

1. **During low tide, which zone is exposed to the air?** *intertidal*
2. **What is formed where a river meets the ocean?** *estuary*
3. **In what ecosystems do organisms adapt to a narrow range of water temperature?** *freshwater ecosystems*

Section Assessment

1. lake: standing water, low oxygen concentration, rich plant growth in shallow water; stream: swift water currents, high oxygen concentration, rock or gravel bottom
2. Light is a limiting factor. The dense growth of rain forest trees prevents sunlight from reaching the forest floor. Sunlight cannot penetrate seawater more than 200 m deep.
3. **Think Critically** Possible answers: The water washes away the soil, and plants would be washed downstream.
4. **Skill Builder**
   Low temperatures in the tundra cause permafrost, which reduces available soil and limits plant life. High temperatures in the desert increase evaporation and decrease water availability, limiting plant life. Sunlight penetrates only a certain distance into surface waters. Deeper waters are cold and dark and cannot support organisms that need light.

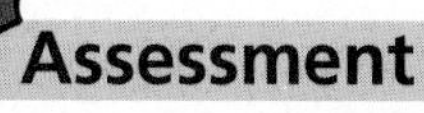

Assessment

Performance Assess students' abilities to compare and contrast by having them compare the salinity of estuaries and the open ocean. *In estuaries, salinity changes freshwater's brought in by rivers and streams and salt water pushed in by the tides. The salinity of the ocean is more constant.* Use **Performance Assessment in the Science Classroom,** p. 17.

Science Journal

Temperatures decrease as one moves toward the poles because fewer direct rays of sunlight reach these regions. Temperatures also decrease as one moves to higher altitudes because there is less atmosphere to prevent heat from the sun from radiating back into space.

18-3 Water Environments 531

Using the Field Guide

- Use this field guide with student pp. 519 to 525.
- A field guide contains a key that enables the user to classify or identify an item or concept.
- This field guide applies globally; local and regional resources are available for more specific local use. One source of information is listed below.
- In using a field guide, students will apply steps of a scientific method as they observe, investigate, and draw conclusions.
- Encourage students to use this field guide outside.

FIELD ACTIVITY

Student answers should be based on information obtained from a local weather station or publication. Student graphs will not be identical to the graphs in the field guide, but should resemble one close enough to draw conclusions. The types of organisms found will vary depending on which biome you live in.

Tying to Previous Knowledge

Students should be familiar with the biome that they live in. However, they may not be aware of the diversity of organisms in their biome. Have students list as many plants and animals they can think of that they have seen in their biome.

FIELD GUIDE to BIOMES

FIELD ACTIVITY

Research the average monthly rainfall, high temperature, and low temperature for each month of the past year for the area where you live. Prepare a graph of data using the example below. Based on your findings, which biome graph most closely matches your data? What biome do you live in? What type of plant and animal life do you expect to find in your biome?

Have you ever wondered why you do not find polar bears in Florida or palm trees in Alaska? Organisms are limited to where they can live and survive due to temperature, amount of rainfall, and type of soil found in a region. A biome's boundaries are determined by climate more than anything else. Climate is a way of categorizing temperature extremes and yearly precipitation patterns. Use this field guide to identify some of the world's biomes and to determine which biome you live in.

Interpreting Land Biome Climates

The following graphs represent the climates of six different biomes. To read each biome graph, use the following information. Axis *A* shows the months of the year. Axis *B* shows the average amount of precipitation for each month. Axis *C* shows the average high and low temperature for each month.

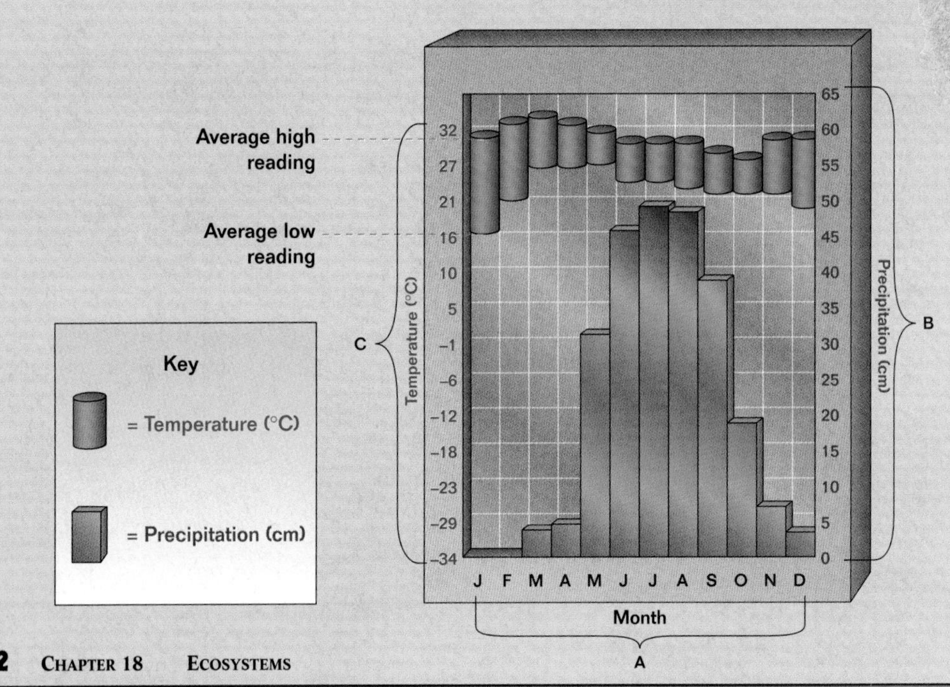

Other References to Biomes

- Ricciuti, Edward. *The Natural History of North America*, Random House. Crescent, 1995.

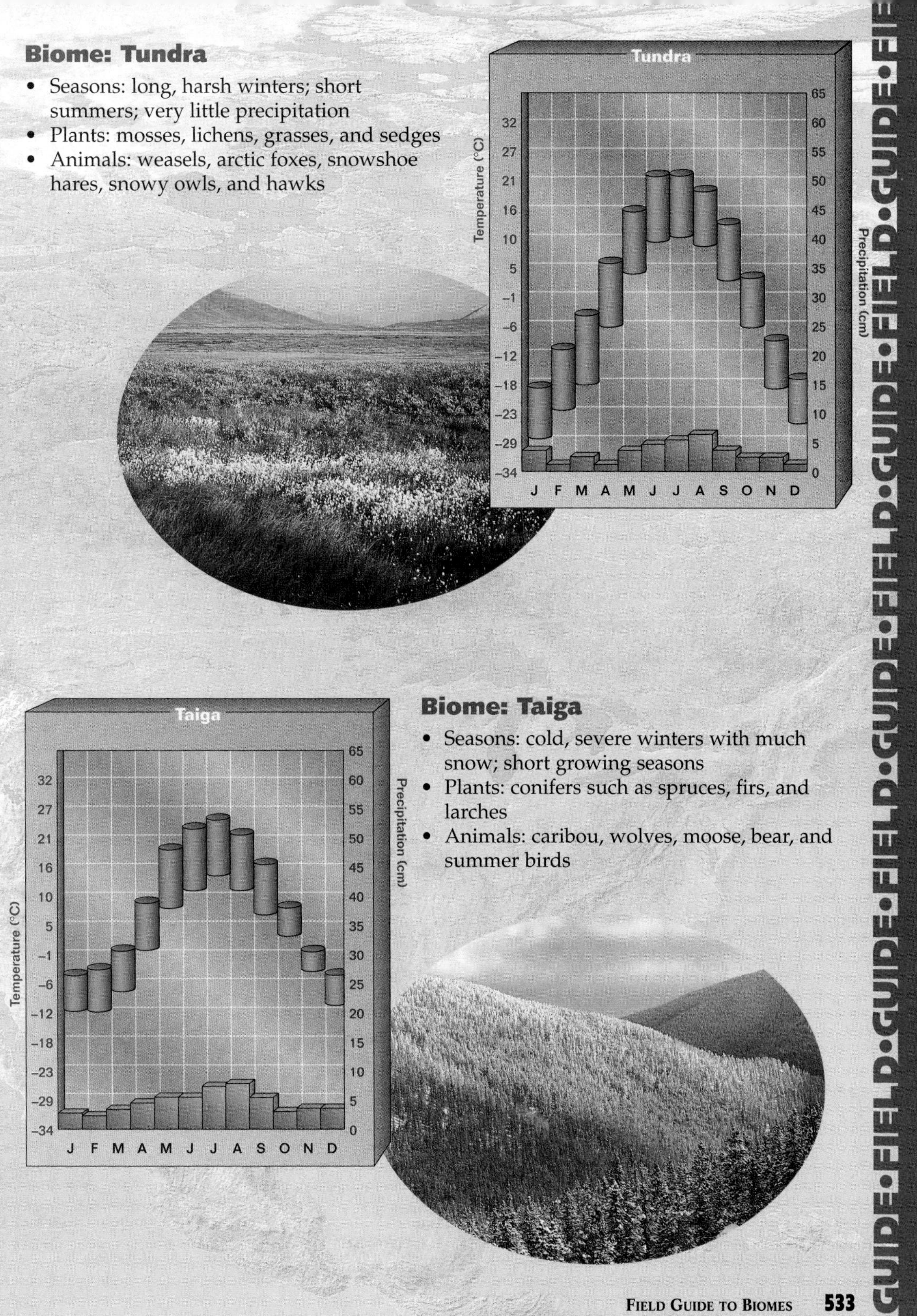

Biome: Tundra

- Seasons: long, harsh winters; short summers; very little precipitation
- Plants: mosses, lichens, grasses, and sedges
- Animals: weasels, arctic foxes, snowshoe hares, snowy owls, and hawks

Biome: Taiga

- Seasons: cold, severe winters with much snow; short growing seasons
- Plants: conifers such as spruces, firs, and larches
- Animals: caribou, wolves, moose, bear, and summer birds

Content Background

Permanently frozen soil called permafrost underlies much of the tundra. Permafrost occurs when the ground temperature is below freezing for two or more years. It is covered with a thin sheet of soil that freezes in the winter and thaws in the summer.

Discussion

Lead students in a discussion about why they may not be able to observe the expected types of plants and animals in their biome. *Many plants and animals only live in certain areas of a given biome. For example, Pink Ladies Slipper orchids are found in temperate forests but only in certain soils. Therefore, you could live in a temperate region and possibly never see a Pink Ladies Slipper.*

Across the Curriculum

Geography The Grand Canyon has starkly different climates that occur vertically instead of horizontally. The floor of the Grand Canyon has a hot, dry climate, and vegetation similar to the Sonoran Desert. The rim of the canyon has pinyon pines that are typical of mid-altitude mountain slopes. Explain to students that the rim of the canyon is far above its floor, accounting for its major climatic differences.

Activity

Obtain a map of the U.S. Have the students use the information from the text and field guide to divide the map into biomes.

Using Science Words

Have students investigate the meaning of the word deciduous, which is derived from Latin.

The word deciduous means, "to fall off" and describes the seasonal shedding of leaves by trees. Trees that shed their leaves each year are called deciduous trees. Some examples are Oak, Maple, and Hickory.

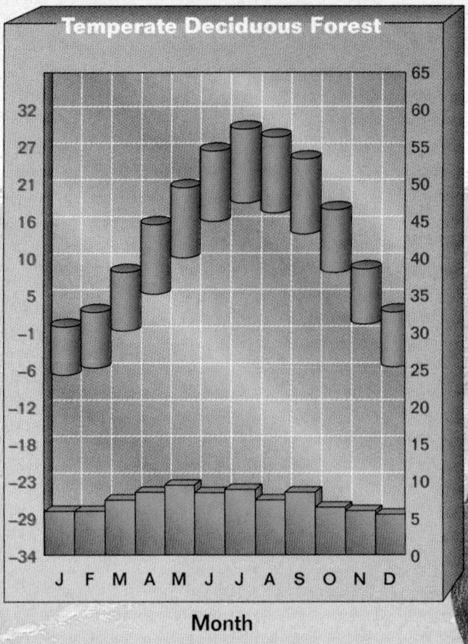

Temperate Deciduous Forest

Temperature (°C): 32, 27, 21, 16, 10, 5, –1, –6, –12, –18, –23, –29, –34

Precipitation (cm): 65, 60, 55, 50, 45, 40, 35, 30, 25, 20, 15, 10, 5, 0

Month: J F M A M J J A S O N D

Biome: Temperate Deciduous Forest

- Seasons: cold winters, hot summers, and moderate precipitation
- Plants: deciduous trees such as oak, hickory, and beech, which lose their leaves every autumn
- Animals: wolves, deer, bears, small mammals, and birds

Biome: Grassland

- Seasons: cold winters, hot summers with little precipitation
- Plants: grasses and a few trees
- Animals: grazing animals, wolves, prairie dogs, foxes, ferrets, snakes, lizards, and insects

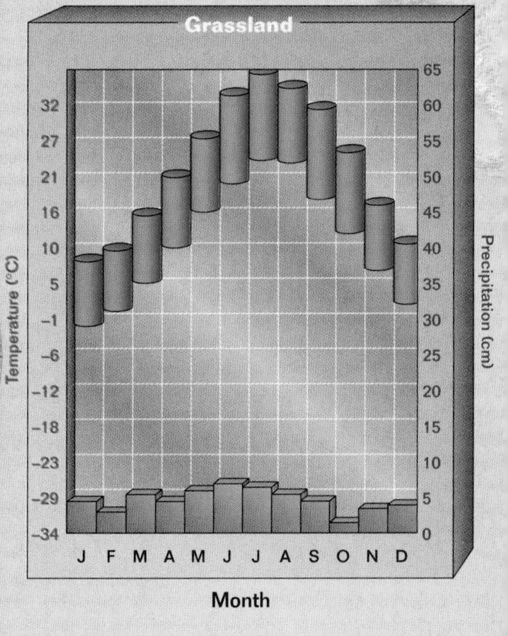

Grassland

Temperature (°C): 32, 27, 21, 16, 10, 5, –1, –6, –12, –18, –23, –29, –34

Precipitation (cm): 65, 60, 55, 50, 45, 40, 35, 30, 25, 20, 15, 10, 5, 0

Month: J F M A M J J A S O N D

interNET CONNECTION

Internet Addresses

Explore the Glencoe Science Web Site at **www.glencoe.com/sec/science** to find out more about topics found in this unit.

534 CHAPTER 18 ECOSYSTEMS

Biome: Desert

- Seasons: warm to hot in daytime, cool in the evening, little precipitation
- Plants: cacti, yuccas, Joshua trees, and bunchgrasses
- Animals: small rodents, jackrabbits, birds of prey, and snakes

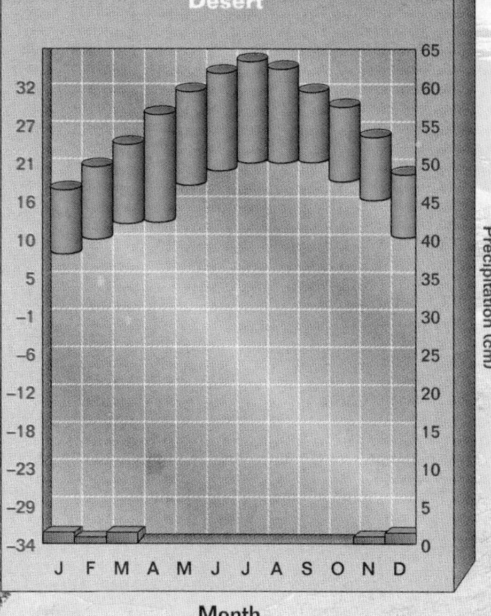

Biome: Tropical Rain Forest

- Seasons: hot all year with precipitation almost every day
- Plants: trees and orchids
- Animals: birds, reptiles, insects, monkeys, and sloths

Tropical Rain Forest

Temperature (°C): 32, 27, 21, 16, 10, 5, –1, –6, –12, –18, –23, –29, –34

Precipitation (cm): 65, 60, 55, 50, 45, 40, 35, 30, 25, 20, 15, 10, 5, 0

J F M A M J J A S O N D

Month

Correcting Misconceptions

Many students think deserts are large expanses of sand that have little or no life. In fact, most deserts actually contain a large variety of plants and animal that are specially adapted to living in arid environments.

Deserts are known for venomous species of spiders and scorpions. However, of the many desert species of spiders and scorpions, only a few are venomous enough to endanger humans. For example, the tarantula and giant hairy scorpion are not deadly but they look fierce.

VISUAL Learning

Obtain a map showing the tropical rain forests of the world. Have students locate the country that has the largest concentration of tropical rain forest land.

GO Further

To further students' understanding of biomes, have them use the information in this field guide to write a summary of how temperature and precipitation serve as important abiotic factors in determining biome type.

FIELD GUIDE TO BIOMES 535

Chapter 18 Reviewing Main Ideas

Reviewing Main Ideas can be used to preview, review, reteach, and condense chapter content.

Preview

Linguistic Have students try to answer the questions in their Science Journals. Use student answers as a source of discussion throughout the chapter.

Review

Interpersonal Have students answer the questions on separate pieces of paper and compare their answers with those of other students in the class.

Reteach

Visual-Spatial Have students look at the illustrations on these pages. Ask them to describe details that support the main ideas of the chapter found in the statement for each illustration.

00:00 OUT OF TIME?

Auditory-Musical If time does not permit teaching the entire chapter, use the information on these pages along with the chapter Audiocassettes to present the material in a condensed format.

Chapter 18 Reviewing Main Ideas

For a **preview** of this chapter, study this Reviewing Main Ideas before you read the chapter. After you have studied this chapter, you can use the Reviewing Main Ideas to **review** the chapter.

The Glencoe MindJogger, Audiocassettes, and CD-ROM provide additional opportunities for review.

Section 18-1 HOW ECOSYSTEMS CHANGE

The process of gradual change from one community of organisms to another is **ecological succession.** It involves changes in both abiotic and biotic factors. Succession can be divided into **primary** and **secondary succession. Pioneer communities** are the first to move into an environment, and **climax communities** are the final organisms to move in. ***How can you explain that lawns usually do not go through succession?***

Section 18-2 LAND ENVIRONMENTS

Climate is the general weather pattern in an area. The factors that determine a region's climate are temperature and precipitation. Large geographic areas with similar climates and climax communities are biomes. The six major biomes are the **tundra, taiga, temperate deciduous forests, tropical rain forests, grasslands,** and **deserts.** ***How does climate influence the type of biomes?***

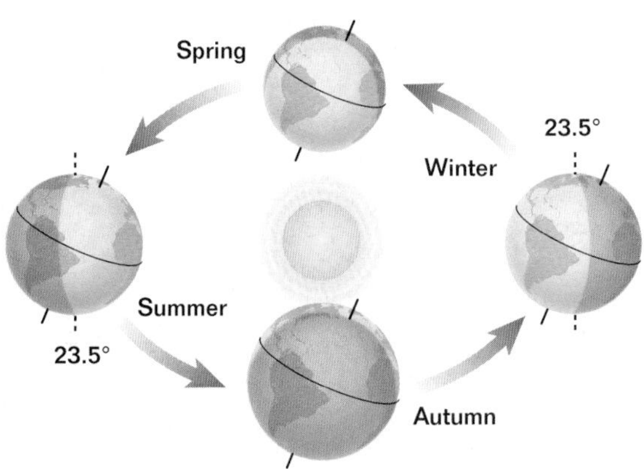

Cultural Diversity

Lost Cities Abandoned cities and other cultural sites may become overgrown when the cultures that built them decline or are conquered, or when the people leave the area. Then, the natural processes of succession take over, and the cultural site may disappear in undergrowth. Have students research what happened in the Maya and Inca sites in the rain forests of Central and South America. L2

Present-Day Near Extinction Have students research why buffalo almost became extinct when the western United States was settled by pioneers. Native Americans harvested the buffalo at a rate that allowed the population to replenish itself. How did the two cultures differ? How might this difference have led to the near extinction of the buffalo? L3

Reading Check

Diagram changes in an ecosystem as a series of causes and effects. You might start with this cause: an ecosystem's soil is thin and poor. What is a possible effect?

Section **18-3 WATER ENVIRONMENTS**

The limiting factors in water environments include the amount of salt in the water, dissolved oxygen, water temperature, and sunlight. Freshwater ecosystems include rivers, streams, lakes, and ponds. Saltwater ecosystems include the oceans, seas, and a few inland lakes. An area where a river meets the ocean is called an **estuary.** All land on Earth is surrounded by ocean water. The **intertidal zone** is the portion of the shoreline that is covered with water at high tide and exposed to the air during low tide. The open ocean is divided into life zones based on the depth to which sunlight can penetrate the water. ***Describe where estuaries form. How are they important?***

Answers to Questions

Section 18-1

How Ecosystems Change Lawns are usually mowed during growing seasons, and this prevents the growth of species that would gradually replace grass.

Section 18-2

Land Environments Climate, temperature, and precipitation influence the plant life that can live in an area. The plant life supports the animal life.

Section 18-3

Water Environments Estuaries form in areas near coastlines where a river meets the ocean. Estuaries serve as nursery grounds for many species of fish and provide much of the seafood consumed by humans.

GLENCOE TECHNOLOGY

CD-ROM

Glencoe Science Voyages Interactive CD-ROM

Chapter Summaries and Quizzes

Have students read the Chapter Summary then take the Chapter Quiz to determine whether they have mastered chapter content.

Assessment

Portfolio Encourage students to place in their portfolios one or two items of what they consider to be their best work. Examples include:

- Science Journal, p. 511
- Skill Builder, p. 513
- Go Further, p. 515 P

Performance Additional performance assessments may be found in **Performance Assessment** and **Science Integration Activities.** Performance Task Assessment Lists and rubrics for evaluating these activities can be found in Glencoe's **Performance Assessment in the Science Classroom.**

Chapter 18 Assessment

Using Vocabulary

1. d
2. h
3. a
4. n
5. e

interNET CONNECTION To reinforce chapter vocabulary, use the **Study Guide for Content Mastery** booklet. Also available are activities for **Glencoe Science Voyages** on the Glencoe Science Web Site. **www.glencoe.com/sec/science**

Checking Concepts

6. D	11. C
7. B	12. C
8. B	13. A
9. D	14. D
10. B	15. A

Thinking Critically

16. The temperate forest soil contains more humus because the plants of the tropical forest absorb decayed material before it can become part of the soil.
17. The meadow is undergoing succession. Because a forest is already growing there, the climate must be appropriate for development of a forest.

Chapter 18 Assessment

Using Vocabulary

a. biome
b. climax community
c. desert
d. ecological succession
e. estuary
f. grassland
g. intertidal zone
h. pioneer community
i. plankton
j. primary succession
k. secondary succession
l. taiga
m. temperate deciduous forest
n. tropical rain forest
o. tundra

Each of the following sentences is false. Make the sentence true by replacing the italicized word with a word from the list above.

1. *Primary succession* has occurred when one community of organisms replaces another.
2. *Plankton* are the first organisms to inhabit an area.
3. An *estuary* is a region with similar climate and climax communities.
4. A *biome* is an equatorial region that receives large amounts of rainfall.
5. A *tropical rain forest* is where freshwater mixes with salt water.

Checking Concepts

Choose the word or phrase that best answers the question.

6. What determines the climate of an area?
   A) plankton C) limiting factors
   B) succession D) abiotic factors
7. What are tundra and desert examples of?
   A) ecosystems C) habitats
   B) biomes D) communities
8. What is a treeless, cold, and dry biome called?
   A) taiga C) desert
   B) tundra D) grassland
9. Which is **NOT** a grassland?
   A) pampas C) steppes
   B) veldts D) estuaries
10. Mussels and barnacles have adapted to the wave action of what?
   A) sandy beach C) open ocean
   B) rocky shore D) estuary
11. Which biome contains the largest number of species?
   A) taiga
   B) temperate deciduous forest
   C) tropical rain forest
   D) grassland
12. What is the end result of succession?
   A) pioneer community
   B) limiting factor
   C) climax community
   D) permafrost
13. Which biome does **NOT** have trees as a climax community?
   A) tundra C) tropical rain forest
   B) taiga D) grassland
14. Which does **NOT** contain freshwater?
   A) lakes C) rivers
   B) ponds D) oceans
15. Which does **NOT** have flowing water?
   A) ponds C) seashores
   B) rivers D) streams

Thinking Critically

16. Would a soil sample from a temperate deciduous forest contain more or less humus than soil from a tropical rain forest? Explain.
17. A grassy meadow borders an oak-maple forest. Is one of these ecosystems undergoing succession? Why?
18. Describe how ecological succession eventually results in the layers of vegetation found in forests.
19. Why do many tropical rain forest plants make good houseplants?

18. Succession begins with small plants that grow low to the ground. As soil develops, it supports the growth of increasingly larger plants.
19. The environment indoors is about the same temperature as the tropics.

Developing Skills

If you need help, refer to the Skill Handbook.

20. **Concept Mapping:** Make a concept map for water environments. Include these terms: *saltwater ecosystems, freshwater ecosystems, intertidal zone, lighted zone, dark zone, lake, pond, river, stream, flowing water,* and *standing water.*
21. **Making and Using Graphs:** Make a bar graph of the amount of rainfall per year in each biome.

Rainfall Amounts

Biome	Rainfall/Year
Deciduous forests	100 cm
Tropical rain forests	225 cm
Grasslands	50 cm
Deserts	20 cm

22. **Hypothesizing:** Make a hypothesis as to what would happen to succession in a pond if the pond owner removed all the cattails and reeds from around the pond edges every summer.
23. **Comparing and Contrasting:** Compare and contrast the adaptations of organisms living in swiftly flowing streams and organisms living in the rocky intertidal zones.
24. **Recognizing Cause and Effect:** Devastating fires, like the one in Yellowstone National Park in 1988, cause many changes to the land. Determine the effect of a fire to an area that has reached its climax community.

Test-Taking Tip

Where's the fire? Slow down! Go back over reading passages and double check your math. Remember that doing most of the questions and getting them right is always better than doing all the questions and getting lots of them wrong.

Test Practice

Use these questions to test your Science Proficiency.

1. What determines whether a land supports a deciduous forest or a grassland?
   A) temperature
   B) latitude
   C) precipitation
   D) length of growing season
2. What causes the vertical distribution of plants in a deep lake?
   A) color of the water
   B) depth that light can penetrate
   C) kind of plants in the lake
   D) kind of animals in the lake
3. How are primary succession and secondary succession similar?
   A) both begin where no soil is present
   B) both end in climax communities
   C) both begin with a pioneer community
   D) both develop where lava has cooled
4. What is the layer of vegetation that shades the ground below and provides homes for birds, insects, and mammals called?
   A) soil
   B) understory
   C) canopy
   D) forest floor

Assessment Resources

The **Test Practice Workbook** provides students with practice in the format, concepts, and critical-thinking skills tested in standardized exams.

Chapter Review, pp. 35–36 L2
Performance Assessment, p. 32 L2
Assessment, pp. 79–82 L2

Glencoe Technology

- **Chapter Review Software**
- **Computer Test Bank**
- **MindJogger Videoquiz**

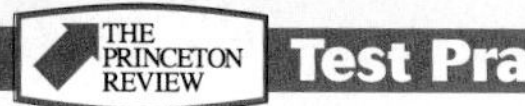

The Test-Taking Tip was written by The Princeton Review, the nation's leader in test preparation.

1. C
2. B
3. C
4. C

Developing Skills

20. Students should separate water ecosystems into saltwater and freshwater ecosystems. Saltwater ecosystems include the intertidal zone and the lighted zone and the dark zone of the open ocean. Freshwater ecosystems include lakes and ponds, which contain standing water, and rivers and streams, which contain flowing water.
21. Student graphs should show the biomes across the bottom and the rainfall up the side.
22. Succession might slow down or stop altogether.
23. Both types are adapted to avoid being washed away by the force of flowing water or waves. Their adaptations allow them to cling to hard surfaces or hide under rocks in crevices.

Bonus Question

Explain how a mountain range affects precipitation in nearby regions. *As air moves up the mountains, it cools, and the moisture in it condenses as rain or snow. When air reaches the other side of the mountains, it no longer contains moisture, so the region on the other side of the mountain range gets much less precipitation.*

Chapter 19 Resources and the Environment

Section	Objectives	Activities/Features
Chapter Opener		**Explore Activity:** Model Topsoil Loss, p. 541
19-1 **Natural Resources** 1 Session ½ Block	1. **Identify** natural resources and **explain** why they are important to living organisms. 2. **Distinguish** between renewable and nonrenewable resources. 3. **Distinguish** between renewable and nonrenewable energy sources.	**MiniLab:** Observing Mineral Mining Effects, p. 543 **Physics Integration,** p. 547 **Skill Builder:** Comparing and Contrasting, p. 547 **Science Journal,** p. 547
19-2 **Conservation and Wildlife Protection** 4 Sessions 2 Blocks	4. **Define** *conservation* and **describe** how it relates to natural resources. 5. **Describe** how renewable resources can be conserved and protected.	**Using Math,** p. 550 **Skill Builder:** Comparing and Contrasting, p. 554 **Using Computers,** p. 554 **Reading and Writing in Science:** What did Chief Seattle really say? p. 555 **Activity 19-1:** Is it biodegradable?, pp. 556–557
19-3 **Maintaining a Healthy Environment** 4 Sessions 2 Blocks	6. **Describe** the origins and effects of pollutants that contaminate air, land, and water. 7. **Explain** the causes of acid rain, ozone depletion, and the greenhouse effect.	**Earth Science Integration,** p. 559 **Problem Solving:** Why should you repair a leaky faucet? p. 559 **MiniLab:** Measuring Acid Rain, p. 560 **Chemistry Integration,** p. 561 **Skill Builder:** Comparing and Contrasting, p. 564 **Using Math,** p. 564 **Activity 19-2:** Modeling Greenhouse Effect, p. 565

The number of recommended single-period sessions — The number of recommended blocks
One session and one-half block are allowed for chapter review and assessment.

Activity Materials

Explore	Activities	MiniLabs
p. 541 moist sand, potting soil, plastic basin or aluminum foil baking pan, dropper or spray bottle	pp. 556–557 2 2-L plastic bottles, plastic wrap, potting soil, gravel or sand, labels, biodegradable and nonbiodegradable waste materials, hand lens, plastic teaspoon, transparent tape, scissors p. 565 2 2-L plastic bottles, 2 thermometers, potting soil, masking tape, plastic wrap, rubber band, lamp with a 100-W lightbulb, timer	p. 543 chocolate chip cookie, paper plate, toothpick p. 560 pH indicator paper, rain water, tap water, and distilled water

Need Materials? Contact Science Kit at 1-800-828-7777 or at www.sciencekit.com on the Internet.
For alternate materials, see the activity on the listed page.

Standards: National	Standards: State/Local	Reproducible Resources Test Practice Workbooks are available for use with each chapter.	Technology English and Spanish audiocassettes are available for use with each section.
National Content Standards: UCP3, A1, B1, B3, D1		**Activity Worksheets,** p. 107 **Enrichment,** p. 50 **Home Involvement,** p. 28 **Laboratory Manual,** pp. 111–112 **Reinforcement,** p. 50 **Study Guide,** pp. 73–74	**Section Focus Transparency 50** **Glencoe Science Voyages Interactive Videodisc—Physical**
National Content Standards: A1, A2, C4, F2		**Activity Worksheets,** pp. 103–104 **Enrichment,** p. 51 **Reinforcement,** p. 51	**Section Focus Transparency 51** **The Infinite Voyage Series** **Glencoe Science Voyages Interactive Videodisc—Life** **Internet Connection,** p. 553
National Content Standards: A1, A2, B1, D1, F2		**Activity Worksheets,** pp. 105–106, 108 **Critical Thinking/Problem Solving,** p. 19 **Enrichment,** p. 52 **Laboratory Manual,** pp. 113–116 **Multicultural Connections,** pp. 37–38 **Reinforcement,** p. 52 **Study Guide,** pp. 75–76	**Section Focus Transparency 52** **Teaching Transparency 37** **Teaching Transparency 38** **Science Integration Transparency 19** **Glencoe Science Voyages Interactive CD-ROM** **The Infinite Voyage Series** **Internet Connection,** p. 563

Key to Teaching Strategies

The following designations will help you decide which activities are appropriate for your students.

L1 Level 1 activities should be appropriate for students with learning difficulties.

L2 Level 2 activities should be within the ability range of all students.

L3 Level 3 activities are designed for above-average students.

ELL ELL activities should be within the ability range of English Language Learners.

COOP LEARN Cooperative Learning activities are designed for small group work.

P These strategies represent student products that can be placed into a best-work portfolio.

Multiple Learning Styles logos, as described on page 61T, are used throughout to indicate strategies that address different learning styles.

Assessment Resources

Chapter Review, pp. 37–38
Assessment, pp. 83–86
Performance Assessment in the Science Classroom (PASC)
MindJogger Videoquiz
Alternate Assessment in the Science Classroom
Performance Assessment, p. 33
Chapter Review Software
Computer Test Bank

Chapter 19 Resources and the Environment

This is a representation of key blackline masters available in the Teacher Classroom Resources. See Resource Manager boxes within the chapter for additional information.

Transparencies

Section Focus Transparencies

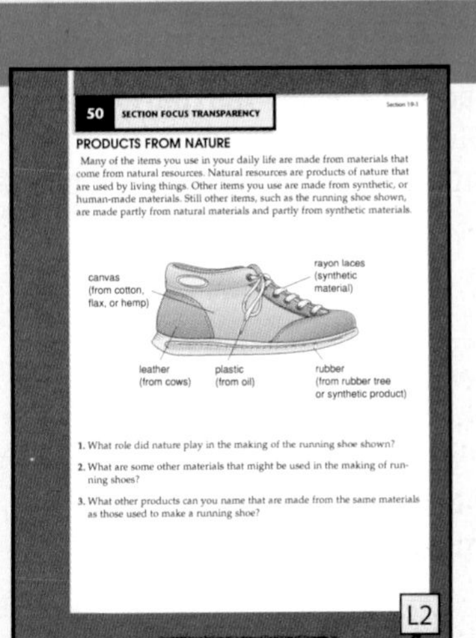

50 SECTION FOCUS TRANSPARENCY

PRODUCTS FROM NATURE

Many of the items you use in your daily life are made from materials that come from natural resources. Natural resources are products of nature that are used by living things. Other items you use are made from synthetic, or human-made materials. Still other items, such as the running shoe shown, are made partly from natural materials and partly from synthetic materials.

1. What role did nature play in the making of the running shoe shown?
2. What are some other materials that might be used in the making of running shoes?
3. What other products can you name that are made from the same materials as those used to make a running shoe?

L2

51 SECTION FOCUS TRANSPARENCY

IN THE NAME OF PROGRESS

Each year, people in many parts of the world clear land for use in the building of communities, shopping malls, roads, industrial centers, and for farms, mines, and timber.

1. What are some ways the activities of people change the natural environment?
2. How does changing the natural environment of an area affect the organisms that live in the area?
3. How might changing the natural environment of an area affect the quality of abiotic factors such as soil, air, and water?

L2

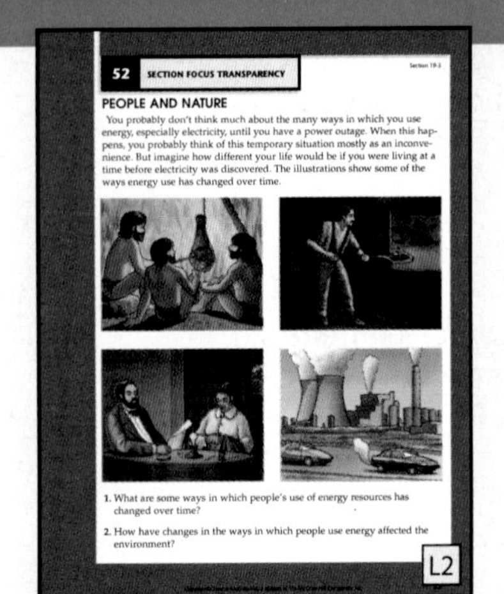

52 SECTION FOCUS TRANSPARENCY

PEOPLE AND NATURE

You probably don't think much about the many ways in which you use energy, especially electricity, until you have a power outage. When this happens, you probably think of this temporary situation mostly as an inconvenience. But imagine how different your life would be if you were living at a time before electricity was discovered. The illustrations show some of the ways energy use has changed over time.

1. What are some ways in which people's use of energy resources has changed over time?
2. How have changes in the ways in which people use energy affected the environment?

L2

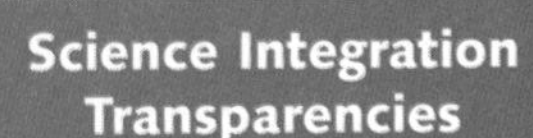

Science Integration Transparencies

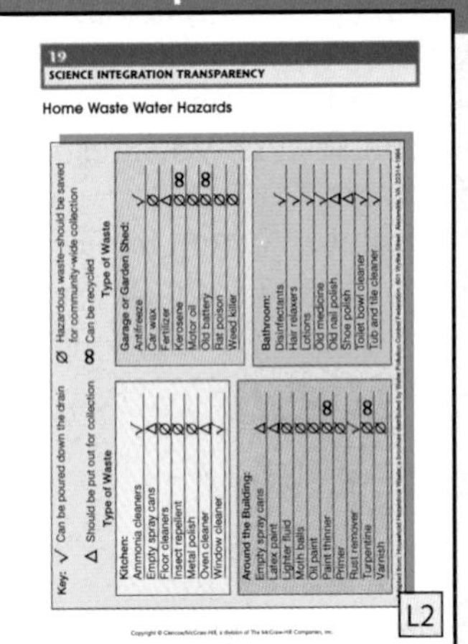

19 SCIENCE INTEGRATION TRANSPARENCY

Home Waste Water Hazards

L2

Teaching Transparencies

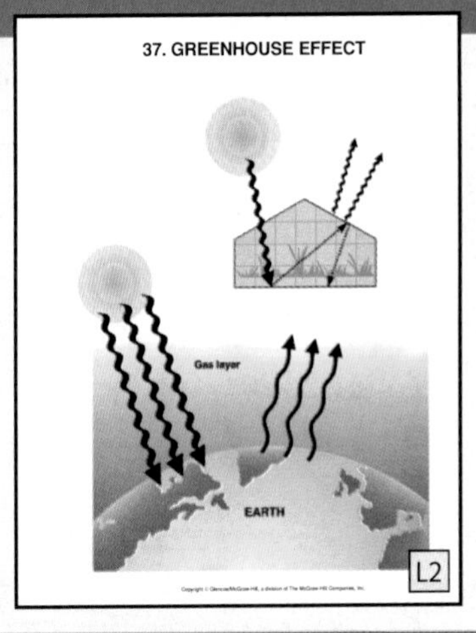

37. GREENHOUSE EFFECT

L2

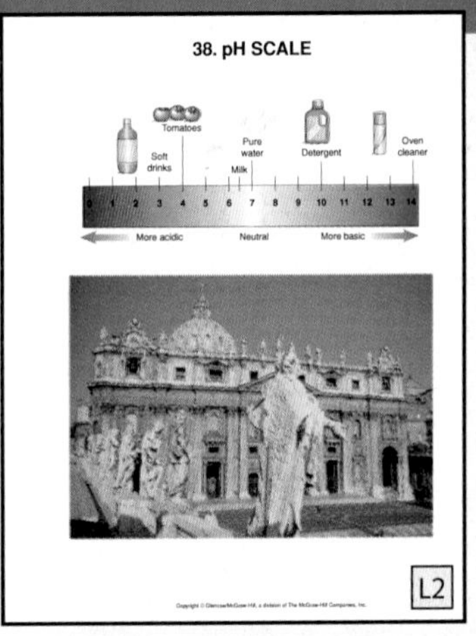

38. pH SCALE

L2

Meeting Different Ability Levels

Study Guide for Content Mastery

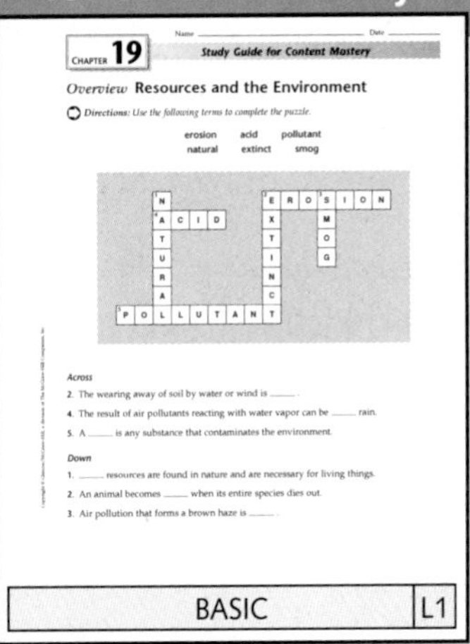

CHAPTER 19 Study Guide for Content Mastery

Overview Resources and the Environment

Directions: Use the following terms to complete the puzzle.

erosion acid pollutant natural extinct smog

Across

2. The wearing away of soil by water or wind is ______.
4. The result of air pollutants reacting with water vapor can be ______ rain.
5. A ______ is any substance that contaminates the environment.

Down

1. ______ resources are found in nature and are necessary for living things.
2. An animal becomes ______ when its entire species dies out.
3. Air pollution that forms a brown haze is ______.

BASIC L1

Reinforcement

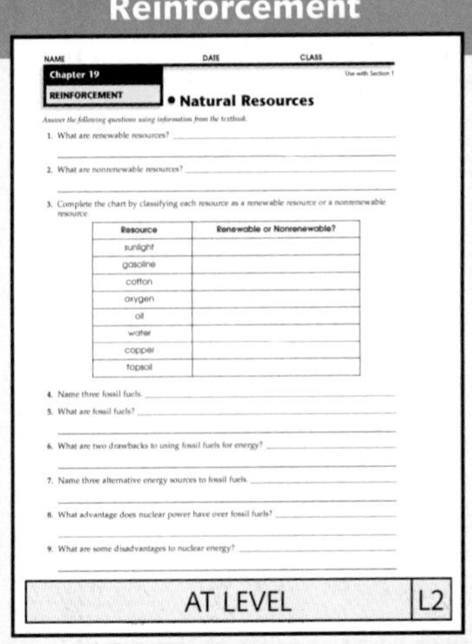

Chapter 19 REINFORCEMENT • Natural Resources

1. What are renewable resources?
2. What are nonrenewable resources?
3. Complete the chart by classifying each resource as a renewable resource or a nonrenewable resource.

Resource	Renewable or Nonrenewable?
sunlight	
gasoline	
cotton	
oxygen	
oil	
water	
copper	
topsoil	

4. Name three fossil fuels.
5. What are fossil fuels?
6. What are two drawbacks to using fossil fuels for energy?
7. Name three alternative energy sources to fossil fuels.
8. What advantage does nuclear power have over fossil fuels?
9. What are some disadvantages to nuclear energy?

AT LEVEL L2

Enrichment Worksheets

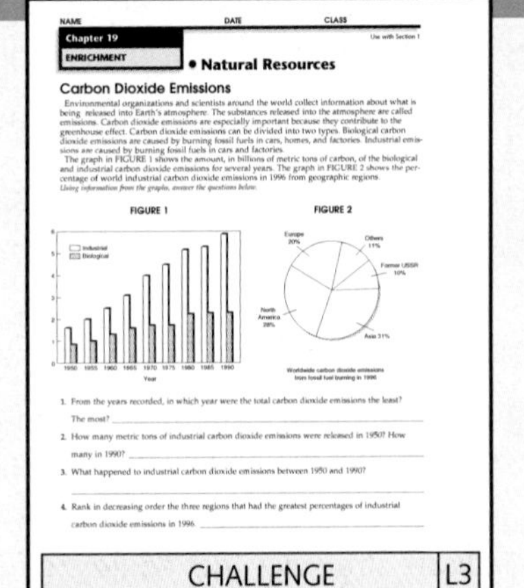

Chapter 19 ENRICHMENT • Natural Resources

Carbon Dioxide Emissions

FIGURE 1 FIGURE 2

CHALLENGE L3

Hands-on Activities

Activity Worksheets

Chapter 19 ACTIVITY 19-1 • Is it biodegradable?

Lab Preview

As you probably know, all trash is not the same. One important way in which one waste material may differ from another is whether or not the material is biodegradable. A biodegradable substance is anything that can be broken down by organisms in the environment. After it is broken down, the substance can become part of the environment. Whether a material is biodegradable or not can make a big difference in how it affects the environment.

What You'll Investigate · Goals · Materials · Safety Precautions · Procedure

L2

Lab Manual

Chapter 19 LABORATORY MANUAL • Home Energy Needs 35

Strategy · Materials · Procedure/Data and Observations · Questions and Conclusions

L2

Accessibility

Spanish Resources

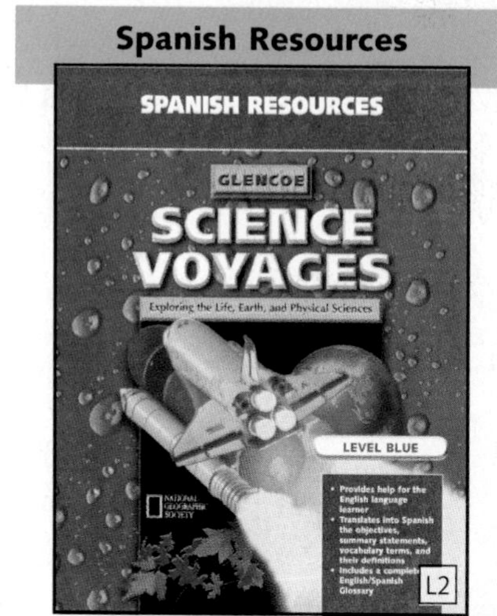

Assessment

Performance Assessment

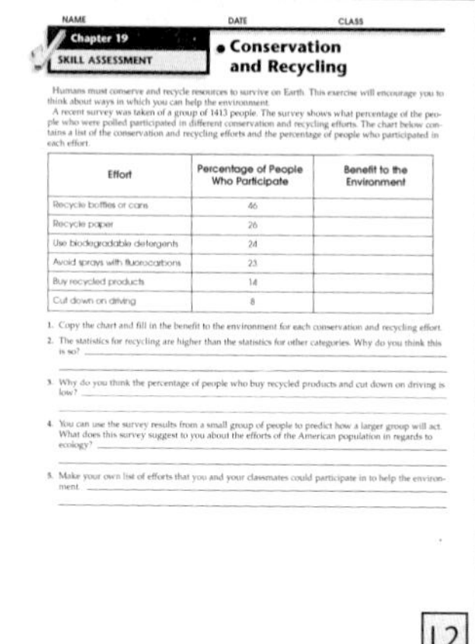

Chapter Review

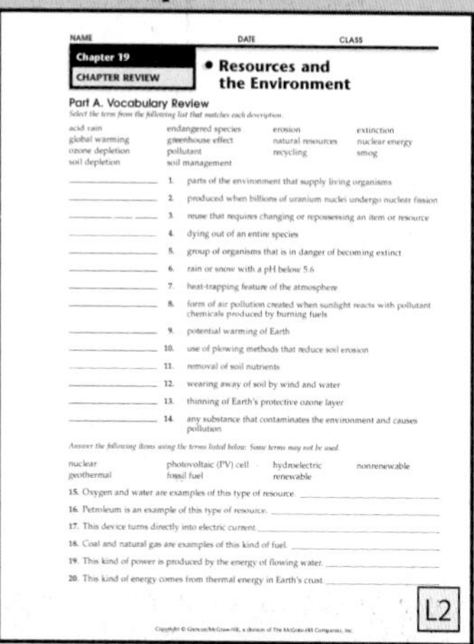

Assessment

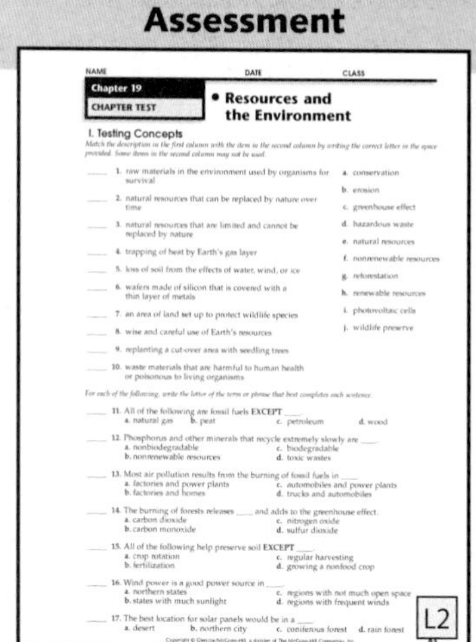

Test Practice Workbook

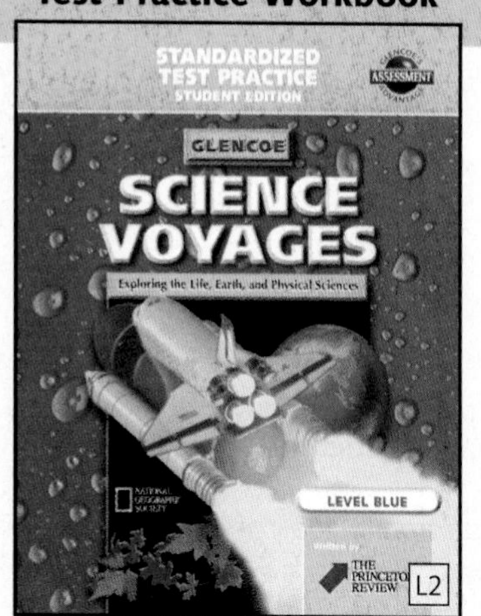

Extending Content

Critical Thinking/ Problem Solving

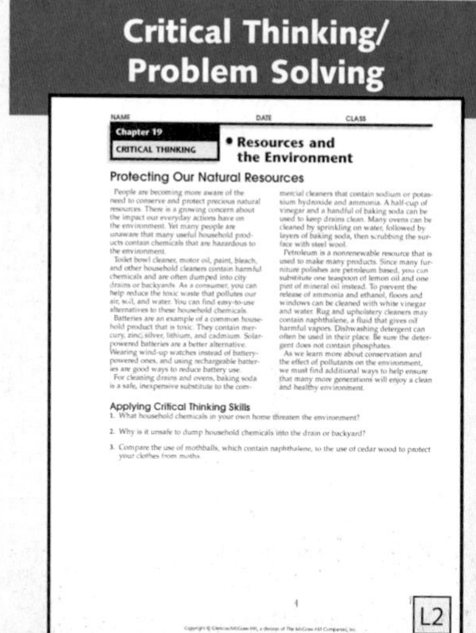

Multicultural Connections

Helping You Prepare

Renewable Resources (Section 19-1)

Renewable resources include trees in forests; fish in lakes, rivers, and oceans; fertile agricultural soil; and freshwater in lakes and rivers. Nature replaces these resources, and they can be used forever as long as they are not overexploited in the short term. Some resources, like agricultural soil, can be considered renewable or nonrenewable. Soil is constantly replaced but at a very slow rate.

Nonrenewable Resources (Section 19-1)

Nonrenewable resources, which include minerals and fossil fuels, are present in limited supplies and are depleted by use. They are not replenished by natural processes within a reasonable period of time. Fossil fuels, for example, take millions of years to form. Recycling nonrenewable resources can help sustain the supply of certain substances. In the future, most products will contain some recycled material.

Energy and Economics (Section 19-1)

Most industrial countries want to ensure a continuous supply of inexpensive energy. The higher the price of energy, the more expensive goods and services become. To keep costs down, many countries subsidize their energy industries and maintain artificially low energy prices. The subsidizing of fuels encourages high rates of consumption.

GLENCOE TECHNOLOGY

CD-ROM

Glencoe Science Voyages Interactive CD-ROM

Chapter Summaries

Use the Chapter Summary to introduce, teach, or review chapter material.

Forest Management (Section 19-2)

Forests can be managed to meet different needs. The forest products industry prefers even-aged stands of a single species of tree for the most efficient harvest. Wildlife managers prefer to see a variety of trees at different stages of maturity to encourage many species of wildlife. A single-species, even-aged forest does not support as wide a variety of wildlife as does a mixed-age forest. Some species even require diseased trees. For example, in the southern pine forests of the United States, the red-cockaded woodpecker requires old, diseased pine trees in which to build its nest. A well-managed forest does not provide these sites. Forest management and wildlife conservation are connected. You can't have one without the other.

NATIONAL GEOGRAPHIC Teacher's Corner

Products Available from Glencoe

To order the following products for use with this chapter, call Glencoe at 1-800-334-7344:

Posters: *Energy, Ozone, Pollution, Vanishing Wildlife*

Products Available from National Geographic Society

To order the following products for use with this chapter, call National Geographic Society at 1-800-368-2728:

Books: *National Geographic Book of Mammals; The Company We Keep: America's Endangered Species; There's Still Time: The Success of the Endangered Species Act;*

Videos: *America's Endangered Species: Don't Say Goodbye; Endangered Animals: Survivors on the Brink; Energy: The Fuels and Man; Energy: The Problems and the Future; Investigating Global Warming; Ozone: Protecting the Invisible Shield; Pollution: World at Risk; Power of Water; Recycling: The Endless Cycle*

Erosion (Section 19-2)

Erosion is a natural process that has occurred since Earth was formed. Humans have little control over the erosion caused by glaciers, rivers, and oceans. A number of human activities, mainly farming and logging, have increased erosion. Scientists estimate that between 2 and 3 billion metric tons of soil are lost from farmlands in the United States each year.

Mineral Resources (Section 19-2)

Because no country has within its territorial limits all of the mineral resources it needs, an international exchange has developed. The industrially developed countries import many of the minerals they need from countries that have the resources but no economic ability to develop them. North America lacks a large number of materials and must import them from other countries, often in less-developed areas of the world.

Ozone (Section 19-3)

Ozone, a molecule made up of three oxygen atoms, traps excess ultraviolet radiation and prevents it from reaching Earth. In 1985, it was discovered that a significant thinning of the ozone layer over the Antarctic occurred during the southern hemisphere spring. Some regions of the ozone layer showed 95 percent depletion. Ozone depletion is also occurring farther north. Measurements in arctic regions suggest a thinning of the ozone layer there. These findings have caused several countries to become involved in efforts to protect the ozone layer.

Global Warming (Section 19-3)

Carbon dioxide is the most abundant of the greenhouse gases. It occurs as a natural consequence of respiration. However, much larger quantities are put into the atmosphere as a waste product of energy production. Coal, oil, natural gas, and biomass are all burned to provide heat and electricity for industrial processes, home heating, and cooking. These sources are increasing the amount of carbon dioxide in the atmosphere. A major step toward slowing global warming is to increase the efficiency of energy utilization.

Acid Rain (Section 19-3)

Acid rain is a worldwide problem. Reports of highly acidic rain have come from Canada, England, Germany, France, Scandinavia, and the United States. Rain is normally slightly acidic, with a pH between 5.6 and 5.7 due to atmospheric carbon dioxide that dissolves to produce carbonic acid. But acid rains sometimes have a concentration of acid 1000 times higher than normal. The average rain in much of the northeastern part of the United States and adjoining parts of Ontario has a pH between 4.0 and 4.5.

SCIENCE UPDATE

For current events or science in the news, access the Glencoe Science Web Site at **www.glencoe.com/sec/science**

Teacher to Teacher

"To improve content comprehension, I have pairs of students sit next to each other facing in opposite directions. One student reads a paragraph aloud as the other follows along. With book closed, the "follower" restates as much information as possible. The reader fills in any missing content. Then, they switch roles."

Steve Manns, Teacher
Derry Area Middle School
Derry, PA

CHAPTER 19 Resources and the Environment

CHAPTER OVERVIEW

Section 19-1 This section defines natural resources and explains how renewable and nonrenewable resources are different. It then identifies energy sources for use now and in the future.

Section 19-2 This section describes conservation of energy, soil, wildlife, land, and minerals.

Section 19-3 Problems resulting from air, land, and water pollution are discussed.

Chapter Vocabulary

natural resource
renewable resource
nonrenewable resource
fossil fuel
photovoltaic (PV) cell
hydroelectric power
geothermal energy
nuclear energy
soil depletion
erosion
soil management
extinction
endangered species
recycling
pollutant
smog
acid rain
ozone depletion
greenhouse effect
global warming
hazardous waste
groundwater

Theme Connection

Energy Even though the total amount of energy on Earth remains constant, the sources of usable energy are limited. Energy is often transformed from one form to another, such as fossil fuel energy into electricity and then into light energy.

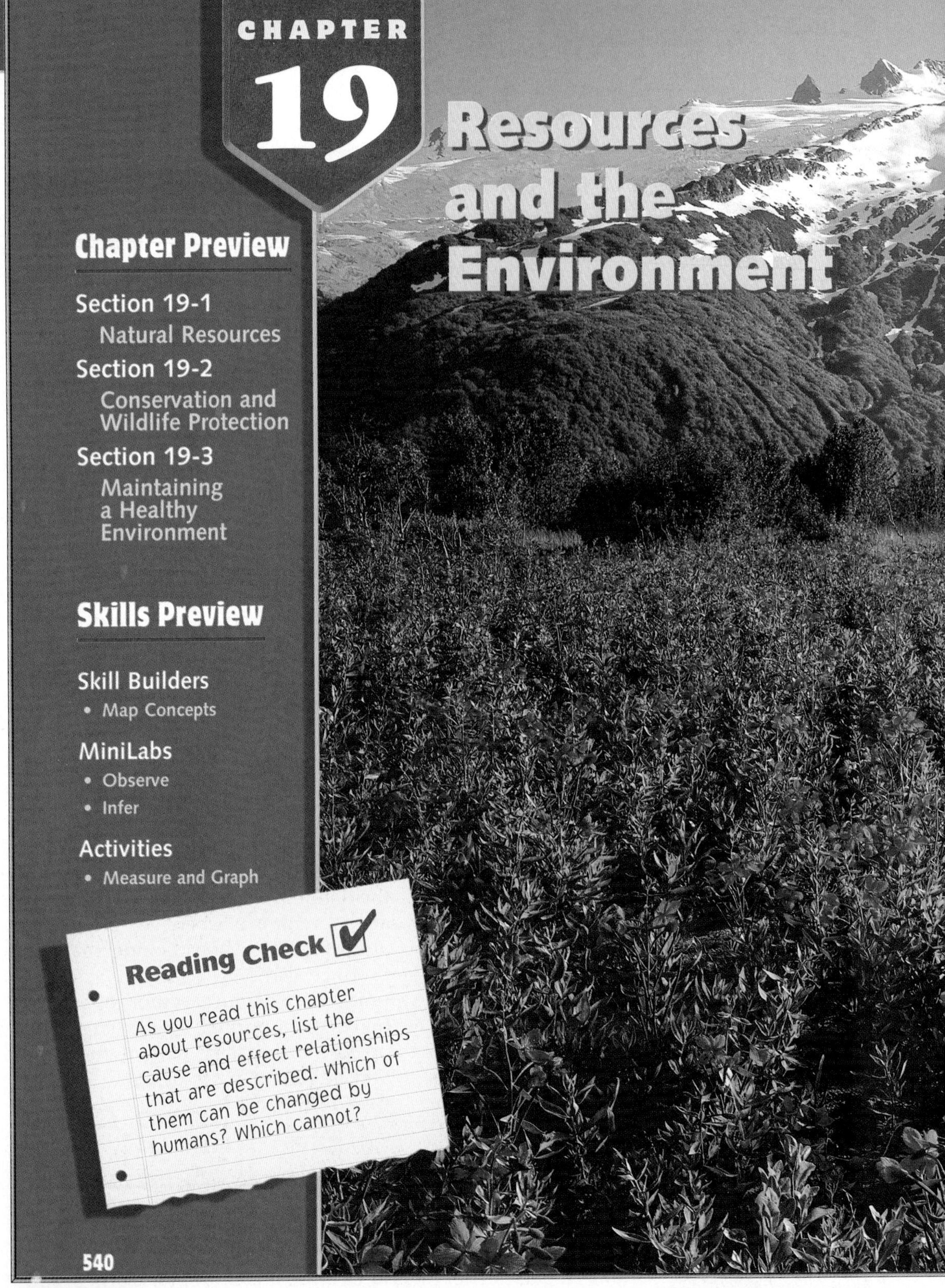

CHAPTER 19 Resources and the Environment

Chapter Preview

Skills Preview

Skill Builders
- Map Concepts

MiniLabs
- Observe
- Infer

Activities
- Measure and Graph

Reading Check

As you read this chapter about resources, list the cause and effect relationships that are described. Which of them can be changed by humans? Which cannot?

540

Multiple Learning Styles

Look for the following logos for strategies that emphasize different learning modalities.

Linguistic Across the Curriculum, p. 549; Using Science Words, p. 562; Multiple Learning Styles, p. 562; Science Journal, p. 563, Preview, p. 566

Logical-Mathematical Integrating the Sciences, p. 546

Visual-Spatial Making a Model, p. 545; Assessment, p. 554; Activity, pp. 556–557; Reteach, p. 566

Kinesthetic Explore Activity, p. 541; MiniLab, p. 543, 560; Inclusion Strategies, p. 549

Interpersonal Activity, pp. 544, 565; Enrichment, p. 546, 549; Discussion, p. 549; Review, p. 566

Intrapersonal Enrichment, p. 546; Assessment, p. 567

Naturalist Activity, p. 550, 562; Science Journal, p. 551

Explore Activity

Nothing is so reliable as the ground beneath our feet. We walk on it, plant lawns and flowers in it, and pave it over to drive cars on it. But, topsoil is something we shouldn't take for granted. Topsoil is the loose, nutrient-rich, top layer of soil that is vital to the growth of everything. Layers of plants, like these wildflowers in Glacier Bay National Park in Alaska, help protect topsoil and keep it in place. What happens when topsoil is left unprotected? Do the activity below to find out.

Model Topsoil Loss

1. Use a mixture of moist sand and potting soil to create a miniature landscape in a plastic basin or aluminum-foil baking pan. Include hills and valleys in your landscape.
2. Cover portions of your landscape with clumps of moss as a plant cover. Leave some sloping portions of your landscape without plant cover.
3. Simulate a rainstorm by pouring water from a dropper or spraying water from a spray bottle over your landscape.

Science Journal

In your Science Journal, record what happens to the land that is not protected by plant cover.

Assessment Planner

Portfolio

Refer to p. 567 for suggested items that students might select for their portfolios.

Performance Assessment

See p. 567 for additional Performance Assessment options.
Skill Builder, pp. 554, 564
MiniLab, pp. 543, 560
Activity 19-1, pp. 556–557; 19-2, 565

Content Assessment

Section Assessment, pp. 547, 554, 564
Chapter Assessment, pp. 568–569
Proficiency Prep, pp. 547, 554, 564

Explore Activity

Purpose

Kinesthetic Use the Explore Activity to show students how plant cover protects topsoil. L2

ELL COOP LEARN

Preparation

Before doing the activity, mix one part sand and two parts topsoil for the landscapes.

Materials

sand and topsoil, containers, clumps of moss, spray bottles, droppers

Teaching Strategies

- Have students make hills and valleys in their landscapes and leave some sloping portions without plant cover.
- Clumps of grass may be used in place of mosses.
- Caution students to spray with care. Have paper towels available for spills.

Water washes the uncovered soil down slopes, forming gullies.

Assessment

Performance Have students use the same landscapes to demonstrate the principle of terracing. Remove the plants and form two small hills, one with a flat incline and one with a series of ridges (terraces) cut into the incline. Use the spray bottle to simulate rain falling. Observe what happens. *Soil does not wash away on the incline with the ridges.* **Use Performance Assessment in the Science Classroom,** p. 33.

SECTION 19-1

Prepare

Content Background

Refer to **Renewable Resources, Nonrenewable Resources,** and **Energy and Economics** on p. 540E.

Preplanning

Refer to the **Chapter Organizer** on pp. 540A–B.

1 Motivate

Bellringer

Before presenting the lesson, display **Section Focus Transparency 50** on the overhead projector. Use the accompanying **Focus Activity** worksheet. L2 ELL

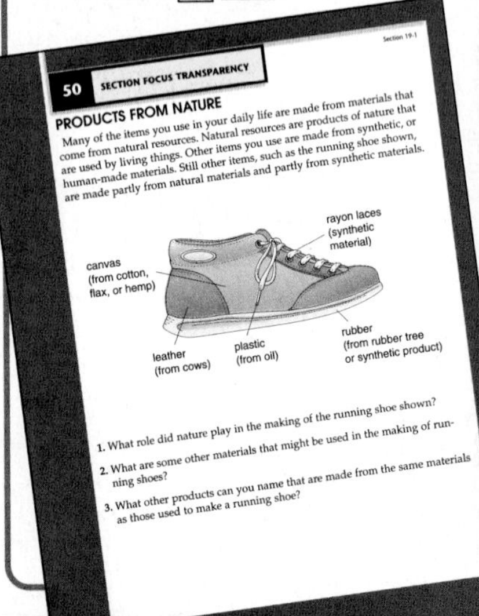

Section 19-1

50 SECTION FOCUS TRANSPARENCY

PRODUCTS FROM NATURE

Many of the items you use in your daily life are made from materials that come from natural resources. Natural resources are products of nature that are used by living things. Other items you use are made from synthetic, or human-made materials. Still other items, such as the running shoe shown, are made partly from natural materials and partly from synthetic materials.

1. What role did nature play in the making of the running shoe shown?
2. What are some other materials that might be used in the making of running shoes?
3. What other products can you name that are made from the same materials as those used to make a running shoe?

Tying to Previous Knowledge

Review with the students the definitions of *habitat, water cycle, carbon cycle,* and the other cycles of matter.

19-1 Natural Resources

What You'll Learn

- How to identify natural resources and explain why they are important to living organisms
- Renewable and nonrenewable resources
- Which energy sources are renewable and nonrenewable

Vocabulary
natural resource
renewable resource
nonrenewable resource
fossil fuel
photovoltaic (PV) cell
hydroelectric power
geothermal energy
nuclear energy

Why It's Important

- You can help conserve Earth's nonrenewable resources by using alternative energy sources.

Earth's Resources

A robin eats an earthworm, then collects twigs for a nest. A fox burrows underground, preparing a den for pups that will soon be born. The leaves of a tree absorb carbon dioxide from the air. A sea otter stays afloat by wrapping itself in a strand of giant kelp, while it uses a stone to hammer open the shell of a sea urchin. A group of young humans climbs aboard a bus for the ride to school.

What do these organisms have in common? They rely on Earth's natural resources for their survival. **Natural resources** are materials found in nature that are useful or necessary for living things. The natural resources people use include food, air, water, and the materials and energy needed to make everything from clothes and buildings to automobiles, books, computers, gasoline, and electricity.

Renewable Resources

Water moves from the surface of Earth to the atmosphere and back again via the water cycle. Oxygen is produced by plants during photosynthesis. Oxygen and water are examples of renewable resources. A **renewable resource** is a natural resource that is recycled or replaced by ongoing natural processes. Cotton used to make a pair of blue jeans is renewable because a new crop of cotton plants can be grown every year. Plants such as those in **Figure 19-1,** animals, water, and air are all renewable resources.

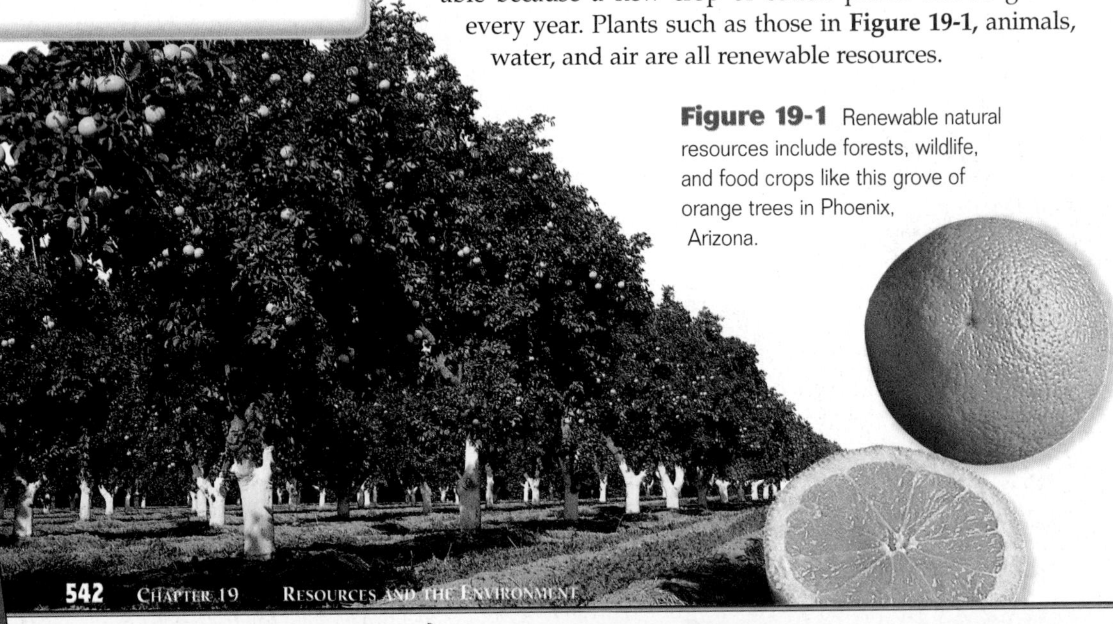

Figure 19-1 Renewable natural resources include forests, wildlife, and food crops like this grove of orange trees in Phoenix, Arizona.

542 CHAPTER 19 RESOURCES AND THE ENVIRONMENT

Resource Manager

The following **Teacher Classroom Resources** can be used with Section 19-1:

Reproducible Masters

Activity Worksheets, p. 107 L2

Enrichment, p. 50 L3

Home Involvement, p. 28 L2

Laboratory Manual, pp. 111–112 L2

Reinforcement, p. 50 L2

Study Guide, pp. 73–74 L1 ELL

Figure 19-2 Nonrenewable resources include many metals and minerals, as well as fossil fuels such as coal and oil.

A Oil wells, like this one in the North Sea, provide oil that is used to heat homes and fuel cars.

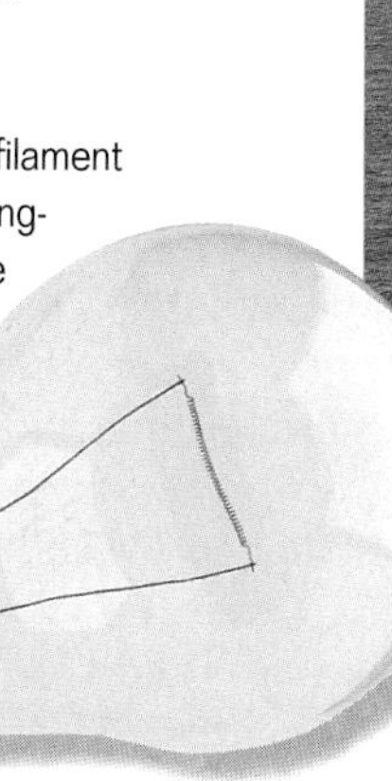

B Lightbulbs contain a filament made of the metal tungsten, a nonrenewable substance.

Nonrenewable Resources

Although some resources will never run out, we do have to worry about running out of some natural resources. Whenever you take home a plastic grocery bag; drink from a plastic cup; paint a wall; or travel by car, bus, or airplane, you are using products made from a natural resource called petroleum. Petroleum, also known as crude oil, is a thick, greasy liquid formed from the bodies of organisms that died hundreds of millions of years ago. It is the raw material used to make fuel oil, gasoline, plastics, paints, chemicals, fertilizers, pesticides, and a huge number of other products that have become essential to modern life. Petroleum is an example of a nonrenewable resource. A **nonrenewable resource** is a natural resource that is available only in limited amounts and is not quickly replaced by natural processes. A lightbulb made from nonrenewable resources is shown in **Figure 19-2.**

Try at Home MiniLab

Observing Mineral Mining Effects

Procedure

1. Place a chocolate-chip cookie or nut-filled brownie on a paper plate. Pretend the cookie is Earth's crust and the nuts or chips are mineral deposits. **CAUTION:** *Never eat food or put anything in your mouth from an experiment.*
2. Use a toothpick to locate and dig up mineral deposits. Try to disturb the "land" as little as possible.
3. When mining is completed, do your best to restore the land to its original condition.

Analysis

1. Were you able to restore the land to its original condition? Describe the kinds of changes in an ecosystem that might result from a mining operation.
2. How do mining deposits found close to the surface compare with mining deposits found deeper within Earth's crust?

2 Teach

Try at Home MiniLab

For additional help doing this activity at home, see the corresponding pages in the **Home Involvement** booklet.

Purpose

Kinesthetic Students will "mine" a model mineral deposit and attempt to restore it to its original condition. L2 ELL COOP LEARN

Materials

chocolate-chip cookie or nut-filled brownie, paper plate, toothpick

Teaching Strategies

Oatmeal-raisin cookies also may be used.

Analysis

1. Students will experience difficulty in the restoration process. This compares with how some forms of mining disrupt Earth's surface. An ecosystem could be permanently damaged from mining.
2. The ones closer to the surface are easier to remove than those found deeper within Earth's crust.

Assessment

Oral Which do you think is more expensive: mining at the surface or deep within Earth's crust? Explain. *In general, surface mining is less expensive. It doesn't require as much machinery or time.* Use **Performance Assessment in the Science Classroom,** p. 71.

Integrating the Sciences

Earth Science It will take millions of years for today's plants to become coal. A large supply of coal is in the ground. Even though the United States burns more than 900 million metric tons of coal each year, coal supplies are plentiful enough to last hundreds of years.

Visual Learning

Figure 19-2 **What is one way to preserve metal and mineral resources?** *Recycling and restricting mining are examples.*

Using an Analogy

Compare nonrenewable resources to a savings account to which nothing is added. The depletion of the savings account depends on how fast withdrawals are made and how large they are.

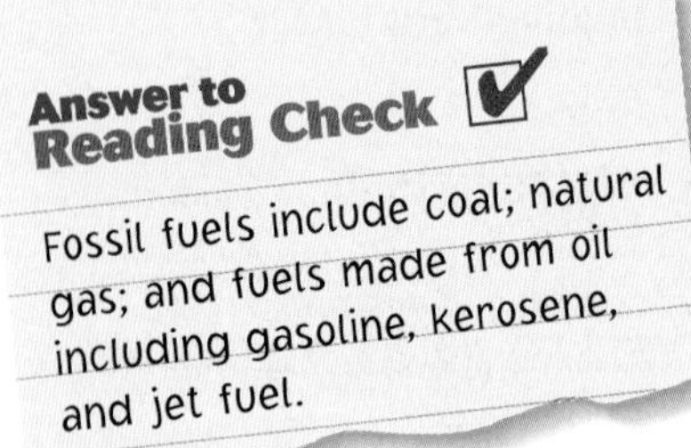

Activity

Interpersonal Have students make a list of all the things they have used or relied upon today. Then place the items on the list into the categories of Food, Transportation, Clothing, and Household Items and make a check mark by the items they believe are renewable. Compare and discuss their answers. L2

Correcting Misconceptions

Some students may not realize that the fossil fuels and other mineral resources being used today are nonrenewable. To help clarify this misconception, point out that much of the coal being mined today was formed from plants that grew during the Carboniferous period. Have students research how long ago that was. *It was about 345 to 280 million years ago.* L2

Caption Answer

Figure 19-3 *Students should mention that it takes many hundreds of years to replace fossil fuels.*

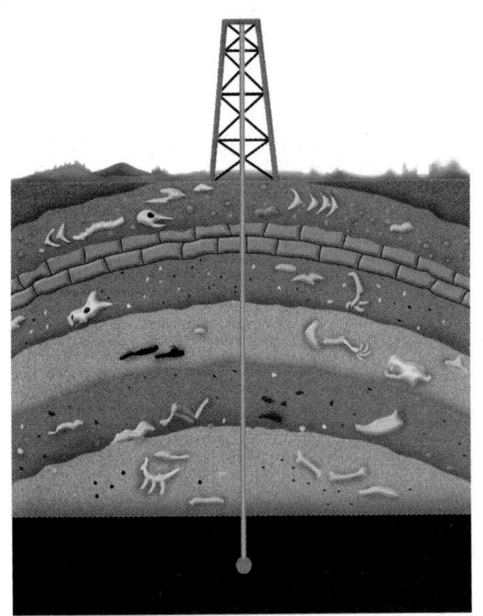

Figure 19-3 Fossil fuels—coal, oil, and natural gas—are formed when organisms die and are buried by layers of rock and sediment. **Why are fossil fuels considered non-renewable?**

Minerals are also nonrenewable. Minerals are formed in Earth's crust. They include diamonds, and the graphite used in pencil leads. They also include elements such as aluminum, copper, tin, iron, gold, silver, tungsten, and uranium. Phosphorus, an element important to the growth of plants and animals, is recycled so slowly in nature that it is considered nonrenewable. Topsoil is also considered nonrenewable because it takes hundreds of years to replace.

Meeting Energy Needs

Imagine what life was like before the invention of the electric lightbulb or the internal combustion engine. Candles were used for light at night, wood for cooking and heating, and horse-drawn wagons or walking for getting from one place to another. Today, we have electric lights, TV and radio, electric ranges, gas stoves, gasoline-powered vehicles, and jet-fueled airplanes. However, it takes energy to operate and manufacture all these modern conveniences. Where does all this energy come from?

Fossil Fuels

Right now, much of this energy comes from fossil fuels. **Fossil fuels** include coal; natural gas; and fuels made from oil including gasoline, diesel fuel, jet fuel, heating oil, and kerosene. **Figure 19-3** describes how fossil fuels form. Fossil fuels power everything from automobiles and lawn mowers to factories. They provide us with many of the conveniences we consider essential to modern life. However, burning fossil fuels contaminates air and water. Other forms of energy can provide some or all of the power we need without polluting the environment the way fossil fuels do. These alternatives include solar power and geothermal energy. Nuclear energy is another energy source, but it has its own pollution problems. ☑

Solar Energy

You've probably heard many times that you should never leave a pet or a child in a parked car with the windows closed when it's hot. Sunlight entering through the windows heats the interior of the car. This heat cannot escape through the closed windows, and the temperature inside can rise rapidly to dangerous levels. Ways in which solar energy can be trapped and used are seen in **Figure 19-4.**

Across the Curriculum

Social Studies Ancient Egyptians used petroleum to help preserve mummies. The ancient Chinese used petroleum to heat and light their homes and to cook. Tar pits supplied crude oil that was used for fuel, cooking, and lighting in ancient Latin America. At the same time, petroleum was used in Europe for lubricating wagon wheels and to make ointments that stopped swelling and helped heal cuts.

544 CHAPTER 19 RESOURCES AND THE ENVIRONMENT

Solar Cells

Do you know how a solar-powered calculator works or how the solar-powered satellites that orbit Earth generate their electricity? These devices use photovoltaic (foh toh vohl TAY ihk) solar cells to turn sunlight directly into electric current. **Photovoltaic (PV)** cells are wafers made of the element silicon that is covered with thin layers of metals. When the sun's light hits these layers, a stream of electrons, called electricity, is created. PV cells are small, and they are easy to use because they don't have any moving parts. However, at the present time, they are too expensive to use for generating large amounts of electricity. But, improvements in the materials used to make them could bring prices down in the future. In the meantime, PV cells are being used to power a variety of small items, including flashlights, radios, watches, and toys.

Figure 19-4 Solar energy can be captured in a number of ways and used instead of fossil fuels to heat homes and water, generate electricity, and even cook food.

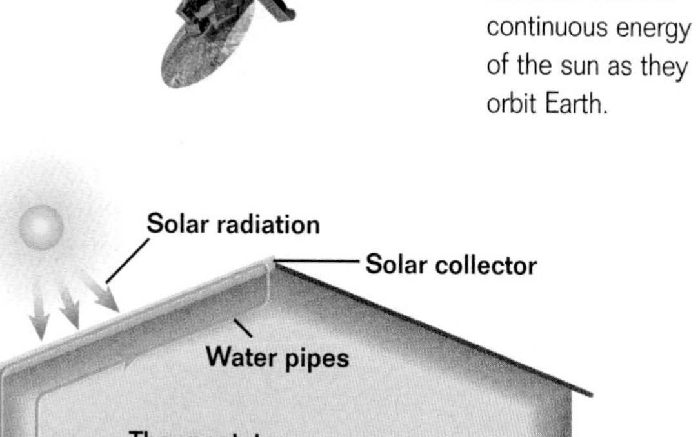

A Solar-powered satellites use the continuous energy of the sun as they orbit Earth.

B This home has been designed to use solar heating. The floors and walls are made of heat-absorbing stone, tile, or brick. At night, the heat stored in the walls and floors keeps the building warm.

Solar radiation
Solar collector
Water pipes
Thermostat
Heat
Hot-water radiator
Pump
Water-storage tank

C Active solar designs use a combination of solar collectors, pumps, and fans to heat indoor air and to heat water for household use.

D In the Mojave Desert in southern California, an electric utility company constructed a huge array of mirrors to focus sunlight on a water-filled tower. The steam produced by this system was used to generate electricity.

Content Background

One of the disadvantages of solar energy is that it is not constant. Solar cells absorb little energy on cloudy days. Seasonal weather changes often cause uneven heating. A solar house is dependent on warm, sunny days in order to remain consistently warm at night.

Integrating the Sciences

Physics Solar cells produce a voltage that causes a small electric current. Many solar cells are required for a larger current. Solar cells have been installed in some power plants. Mirrors in the plants focus sunlight onto the cells and directly generate electricity. Solar electric plants cost less to build than plants that use fossil fuels, but they require large amounts of land.

Quick Demo

Demonstrate how a radiometer or a solar cell works.

Enrichment

Have students research energy sources used in other parts of the world and compare them with energy sources used in the United States. In many countries, wood and other biomass fuels provide 95 percent of all the energy they use. If there is a shortage of biomass fuels, animal feces is dried and burned. L3

GLENCOE TECHNOLOGY

Videodisc

Glencoe Science Voyages Interactive Videodisc—Physical

Side 2, Lesson 8 *Electricity and Magnetism*

40804

Refer to Videodisc Teacher Guide for additional bar codes.

Making a Model

Visual-Spatial Have students draw a model of an energy-efficient house that uses energy from the sun for heat and light. L2 ELL P

Flex Your Brain

Use the Flex Your Brain activity to have students explore ENERGY SOURCES.

Teacher FYI

Geothermal power plants are not completely environmentally friendly. Minerals brought up with underground steam include sulfur, salts, and some toxic elements. Precautions must be taken to make sure that workers are not exposed to toxic levels of these minerals and that water released into the environment is not so hot or mineral laden that it damages plant and animal life.

3 Assess

Check for Understanding

Enrichment

Intrapersonal Some have proposed the creation of giant windmills in the Arctic. Have students investigate the advantages of this and report to the class. L2

Reteach

Have students list reasons renewable resources must be used wisely and nonrenewable resources must be conserved. L1

Extension

For students who have mastered this section, use the **Reinforcement** and **Enrichment** masters.

Caption Answers

Figure 19-5 *Students may indicate that the sun is an important factor in the cycling of Earth's matter and climate.*

Figure 19-6 *Answers should include that radioactive wastes are hard to dispose of safely and mining uranium disrupts land ecosystems.*

Wind and Water Power

Wind can be used to generate electricity. In regions with frequent winds, electricity is produced on wind farms, on which large numbers of windmills are placed. A windmill like the one in **Figure 19-5A** is a turbine that is rotated by the wind instead of by steam or water. Wind power is a nonpolluting, renewable energy source. However, much open space is needed for a wind farm so use of this resource is limited.

Electricity also can be created by water. Water that is prevented from flowing downstream by a dam contains a tremendous amount of stored, or potential, energy. When the water flows through openings in the dam, that stored energy is released. Hydroelectric power plants, located inside dams, use the energy of flowing water to turn gigantic turbines that generate enormous amounts of electricity. **Hydroelectric power,** or hydropower, is electricity produced by the energy of flowing water. Hydroelectric power plants like the one in **Figure 19-5B** are a renewable energy resource because the water in the reservoir behind the dam is continually replaced by Earth's water cycle. They are also efficient and produce little pollution.

Figure 19-5
Water power and wind power are actually indirect forms of solar power. **Describe why.**

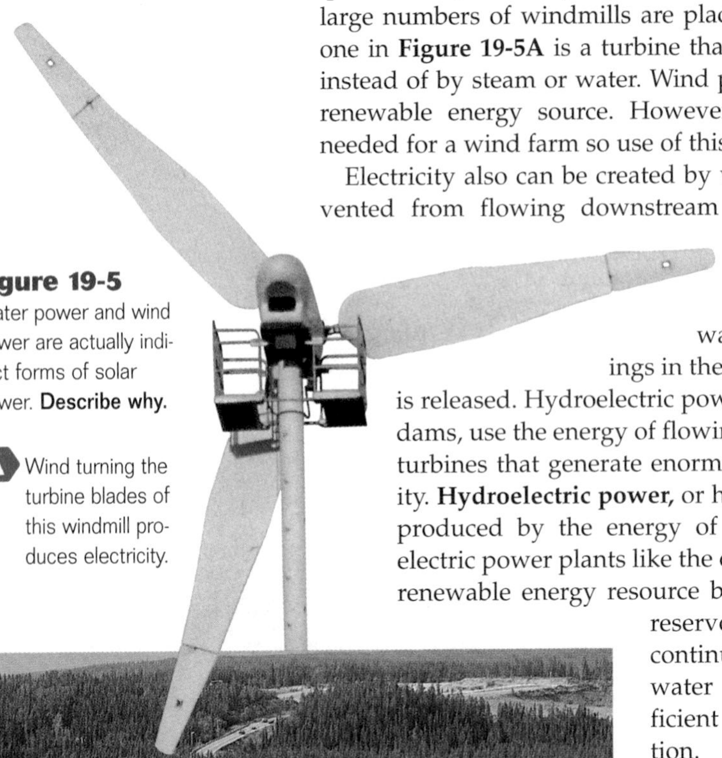

A Wind turning the turbine blades of this windmill produces electricity.

B When the water in this reservoir flows through narrow channels inside the dam, it turns the blades of turbines to generate electricity.

Geothermal Energy

When a volcano erupts, lava and hot gases pour out of the ground. When a geyser erupts, steam and hot water spew out of the ground. Where does the energy for these eruptions come from? It comes from hot, molten rock that lies deep underground. Volcanoes erupt when molten rock is forced to the surface. Geysers develop when underground water that has been trapped in hot rock is heated to the boiling point and forced up through cracks and openings in the ground. The thermal energy contained in Earth's crust is called **geothermal energy.** Geothermal power plants use the thermal energy that lies in Earth's crust to generate electricity.

Integrating the Sciences

Physics The molecules that make up liquid water are closely packed and held together by weak chemical bonds. When water evaporates and turns into steam, the chemical bonds are broken, and the molecules spread farther apart. So, when liquid water turns to steam, it expands and its volume increases. If the expanding steam is forced through a narrow opening, its energy can be used to move physical objects, including the turbine blades of an electric generator. Ask students to use this information to describe how a whistling teakettle works.

Nuclear Energy

Another form of energy that does not require burning fossil fuels takes advantage of the huge amounts of energy bound up in the nuclei of atoms. **Nuclear energy** is produced when billions of nuclei from uranium, a radioactive element, split apart in a nuclear fission reaction. This energy can be used to heat water to produce steam, which turns turbines that produce electricity. A primary advantage of nuclear power is that it does not contribute to air pollution. However, mining uranium does disrupt land ecosystems, and nuclear power plants, such as the one shown in **Figure 19-6,** produce radioactive waste materials. These materials remain radioactive for thousands of years. Safe disposal of nuclear wastes is a problem that has not yet been solved. Therefore, nuclear energy is not widely used.

Figure 19-6 Nuclear energy is an alternative energy source that can be produced cleanly and cheaply. **Why isn't nuclear energy more widely used?**

PHYSICS INTEGRATION

Nuclear Power
Use references to determine the advantages and disadvantages of nuclear power.

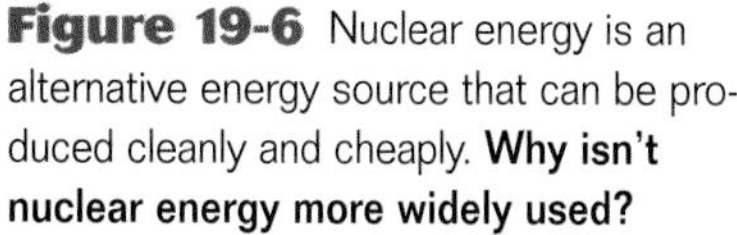

Section Assessment

1. What are natural resources?
2. Compare and contrast renewable and nonrenewable resources, and give five examples of each.
3. Name five alternative energy sources.
4. **Think Critically:** Explain how fossil fuels could be considered a form of solar energy.
5. **Skill Builder**
Comparing and Contrasting Deciding which energy source to use is easier when you compare and contrast all the alternative sources. Do the **Chapter 19 Skill Activity** on page 720 to learn how to decide which energy source is best for you.

Science Journal

In your Science Journal, invent a new alternative energy source. The source should be available in your community.

PHYSICS INTEGRATION

Nuclear power can provide plentiful, cheap energy. Power plants must be designed to be fail-safe and located away from densely populated areas. No safe way has been devised to dispose of highly radioactive wastes. Some of the uranium in nuclear fuel is converted to plutonium, which could be recovered from spent fuel to make nuclear weapons.

4 Close

Proficiency Prep

Use this quiz to check students' recall of section content.

1. **What are coal, natural gas, and oil?** *fossil fuels*
2. **What is the thermal energy contained in Earth's crust?** *geothermal energy*

Section Assessment

1. the raw materials that organisms use for survival
2. Renewable resources can be replaced by nature. Examples are water, plants, animals, sunlight, and air. Nonrenewable resources cannot be replaced by nature. Examples are petroleum, diamonds, metals, phosphorus, and topsoil.
3. nuclear, solar, geothermal, wind, and water power
4. **Think Critically** Fossil fuels come from plants that fix energy from the sun.

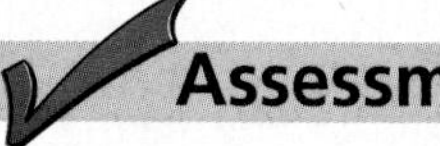

Assessment

Oral Have students explain the energy source they chose in the Skill Activity. **Use Performance Assessment in the Science Classroom,** p. 71.

Science Journal

Answers will vary but should include advantages and disadvantages.

SECTION 19•2

Prepare

Refer to **Forest Management, Erosion,** and **Mineral Resources** on pp. 540E–F.

Preplanning

Refer to the **Chapter Organizer** on pp. 540A–B.

1 Motivate

Bellringer

Before presenting the lesson, display **Section Focus Transparency 51** on the overhead projector. Use the accompanying **Focus Activity** worksheet. L2 ELL

Section 19-2

51 SECTION FOCUS TRANSPARENCY

IN THE NAME OF PROGRESS

Each year, people in many parts of the world clear land for use in the building of communities, shopping malls, roads, industrial centers, and for farms, mines, and timber.

1. What are some ways the activities of people change the natural environment?
2. How does changing the natural environment of an area affect the organisms that live in the area?
3. How might changing the natural environment of an area affect the quality of abiotic factors such as soil, air, and water?

Tying to Previous Knowledge

Ask students to list how they affect the environment each day. *They should think of transportation, waste, and water.* L2

19•2 Conservation and Wildlife Protection

What You'll Learn

- What conservation is and how it relates to natural resources
- How renewable resources can be conserved and protected

Vocabulary
soil depletion
erosion
soil management
extinction
endangered species
recycling

Why It's Important

- As the human population grows, you will have to learn to conserve natural resources.

What We Can Do

Many Native American traditions teach people to think about their actions and how they will affect the next seven generations of their descendants. That means thinking of your children, grandchildren, and great-grandchildren. It means thinking about what Earth will be like 200 years from now. We can take actions to make sure we leave Earth's land, soil, minerals, wildlife, and other resources in good condition for the generations who will live on this planet after us.

Energy Conservation

Nonrenewable resources can be conserved by using less, using a renewable resource, or recycling. You already know about some of the alternatives to nonrenewable fossil fuels. More and more home builders are designing houses that take advantage of sunlight, not only for warmth but also for lighting. Well-placed windows and skylights can reduce the need for electric lights during the day. The amount of electricity produced by solar, wind, and geothermal power plants also will increase. But, the fact remains that most of the energy we

VISUALIZING Energy Conservation

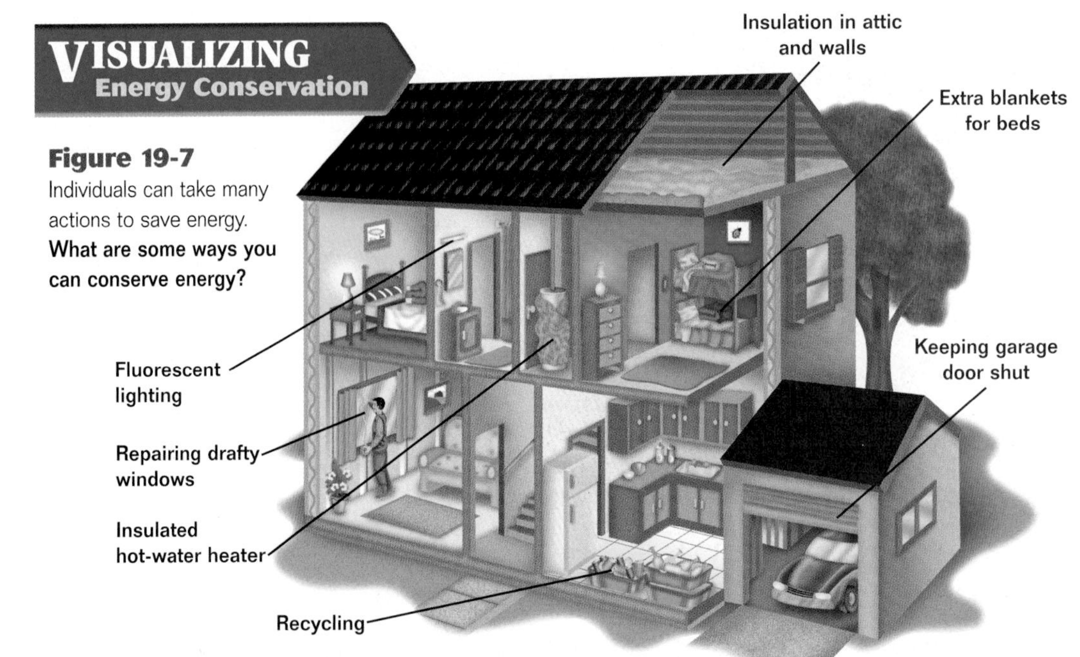

Figure 19-7
Individuals can take many actions to save energy. **What are some ways you can conserve energy?**

Caption Answer

Figure 19-7 *Students may mention turning out lights and turning off televisions and radios when they are not being used. Lowering the household thermostat in the winter and raising it in the summer are also examples.*

Resource Manager

The following **Teacher Classroom Resources** can be used with Section 19-2:

 **Reproducible Masters**

Enrichment, p. 51 L3

Reinforcement, p. 51 L2

Activity Worksheets, pp. 103–104 L2

use today still is produced by fossil fuels. In order to conserve those resources, we need to reduce our energy use. Recycling is one way to do that, as well as reducing energy use as shown in **Figure 19-7.** Using recycled aluminum cans to make new cans uses only about ten percent of the energy required to make new cans from aluminum ore. Recycling glass also saves energy.

Soil Conservation

When soil is used for agriculture, native plants are replaced with crops. The crops use the nutrients in the soil to grow. When the crops are harvested, little material is left to decay and replenish the nutrients in the soil. This removal of soil nutrients is called **soil depletion.** Over a period of time, if the nutrients are not replaced, the soil may become too poor to grow crops.

Farmers replenish the soil in several ways, including crop rotation and the addition of fertilizers. Crop rotation is the process of changing the crops that are grown in a field from one season to the next. Every few seasons, a nonfood crop is grown and tilled back into the soil to help replenish nutrients. Fertilizers include materials such as compost and chemicals made from petroleum. Other methods of soil conservation are shown in **Figure 19-8.**

Figure 19-8 Soil management helps reduce the erosion of farmland. **Why is erosion a concern for farmers?**

A By plowing at right angles to the slope of the land, contour farming reduces erosion from the downhill flow of water.

B In areas with steep hillsides, the downhill flow of water is reduced by creating flat areas, called terraces.

C Strip-cropping involves alternating rows of plant crops, such as corn, with a cover crop such as wheat or hay.

D No-till farming is a soil-management method that involves planting crops in untilled, undisturbed soil.

2 Teach

Discussion

Interpersonal Ask students to discuss a list of things that are being done today to protect the environment. They can name people or organizations that are involved in each example.

Enrichment

Interpersonal Have students list all the types of energy they use in their home. Then, ask them to discuss the alternative forms of energy they could use instead of their current sources. L2

Caption Answer

Figure 19-8 *Answers will vary but should include that erosion depletes the available topsoil. It also washes away nutrients needed to grow healthy crops.*

Inclusion Strategies

Gifted Have students make a game that promotes wise use of resources or that raises other environmental issues. Game cards can give bonus moves or points for environmentally wise activities. L3

Across the Curriculum

Social Studies Drought and unsound agricultural practices contributed to the formation of the Dust Bowl in the United States. Have students research the Dust Bowl period in history and write a report on what the Dust Bowl was, where it occurred, its causes, and its effect on people. L3 P

Using Math

2.4 m × 100 cm/m ÷ 180 cm = 1.3 times

Correcting Misconceptions

Many students may not understand that humans are responsible for only a part of the many plant and animal extinctions that have occurred over the years. Explain that thousands of species of organisms became extinct long before humans existed.

Activity

Naturalist Have students choose an animal and assume it has become endangered. Then, make an outline showing what they would do to protect the species. Students should consider the needs of the animal. L2 COOP LEARN

Teacher FYI

The Endangered Species Act, designed to stop human-caused extinction, was passed in the United States in 1973. A species listed as endangered is given protection under the act, and efforts are made to restore its population. Recovery steps may include restoring habitats, cleaning up pollution, providing protection from hunters, and breeding the species in captivity.

Caption Answer

Figure 19-9B *Plants introduced from other parts of the world compete with native plants for space.*

Using Math

Most eagles have a wingspan of about 180 cm. However, one of the largest eagles, the harpy eagle, has a wingspan of 2.4 m. How many times greater is the harpy eagle's wingspan than the average eagle's wingspan?

Erosion

Another process that destroys soil fertility is erosion. **Erosion** is the wearing away of soil by wind and water. If you conducted the Explore Activity at the beginning of the chapter, you noticed that flowing water can pick up loose topsoil and wash it away. An important part of farming is soil management. As shown in **Figure 19-8** on the previous page, **soil management** is the use of plowing methods that reduce soil erosion. These methods include contour plowing, strip-cropping, terracing, and no-till farming. Plowing loosens the soil, making it easier for seedlings to take root, but also making it easier for water and wind to carry away the soil.

Wildlife Conservation

A hundred years ago, up to a million passenger pigeons would darken the skies above North America. Today, there are none. The last member of the species died in a New York zoo in 1914. Human hunters killed them by the thousands until the species became extinct. **Extinction** is the dying out of an entire species. Extinction does occur naturally. Over time, many species that once lived on Earth have become extinct. But, changes in the environment due to competition among organisms have increased the rate of extinction.

Figure 19-9 Species can become endangered because of pollution, habitat destruction, illegal hunting, or competition with introduced species.

A The destruction of habitat and breeding ground is the reason many species have become endangered, including the sea turtle in the United States.

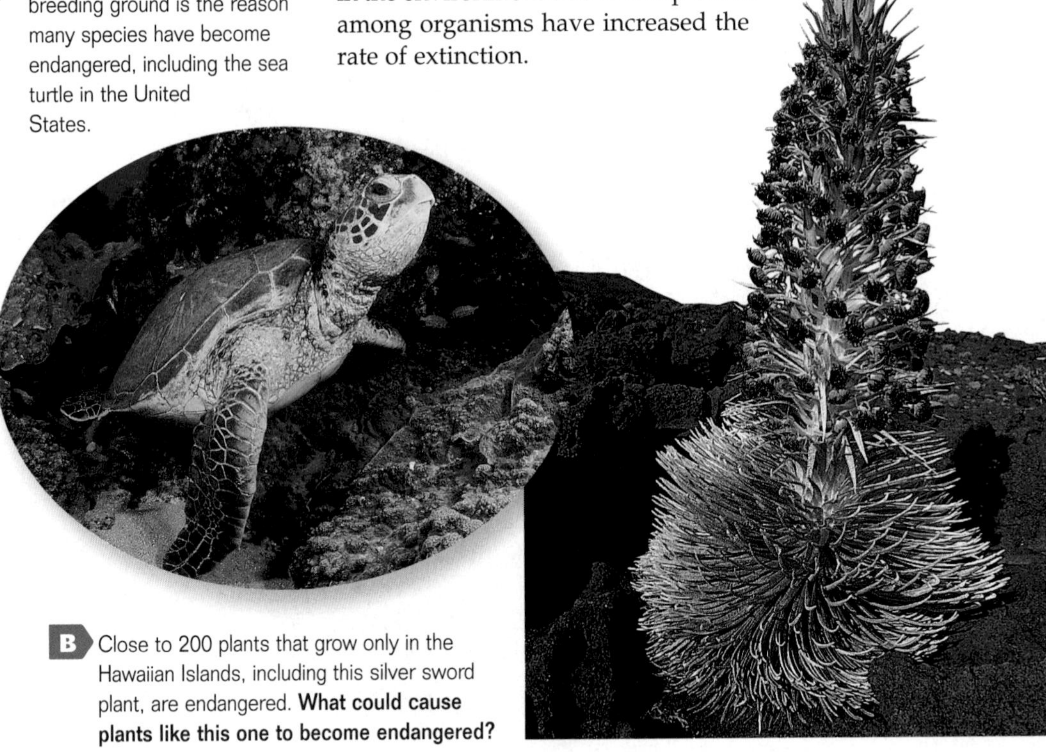

B Close to 200 plants that grow only in the Hawaiian Islands, including this silver sword plant, are endangered. **What could cause plants like this one to become endangered?**

Content Background

Deforestation is occurring worldwide. It is becoming a serious problem in South America. In the rain forest, many animals live in trees and do not move down to the ground. Discuss with students what happens to plants and animals as the forests are cleared for farms and ranches.

Figure 19-10 When the pesticide DDT was sprayed on farmland, runoff from rainwater carried it into nearby streams, where it entered the food chain. DDT built up in the tissues of fish, which were eaten by ospreys. DDT buildup in the bodies of the ospreys caused them to produce eggs with shells so thin that the eggs broke open before the young could develop. This resulted in a decline of the osprey population.

An **endangered species** is a species that is in danger of becoming extinct unless action is taken to protect it. The bald eagle, the national bird of the United States, is an example of a species that was endangered for a time. In the early 1960s, only about 400 bald eagles were left in the 48 lower states. By 1999, because of preservation efforts, the population had increased to approximately 5000 and is still rising.

Most species become endangered because of damage to their habitat such as that caused by building roads, clearing forest, or draining marshes to provide dry land for buildings. In other cases, pollution is to blame. The pesticide DDT was used in the United States from the 1940s to the 1970s. This chemical provided farmers with relief from large populations of insect pests that were damaging crops. But, as **Figure 19-10** describes, DDT remains in the environment for many years after it is used and is passed along the food chain from one organism to another. When it entered the bodies of large predatory birds, such as eagles, ospreys, falcons, and pelicans, the birds began to have difficulty reproducing. After DDT use was stopped, the bird populations began to recover. Bald eagles had recovered enough by 1995 to be removed from the list of endangered species. As **Figure 19-9** shows, a species also may become endangered because it is overhunted by predators or it is crowded out by a species that has been introduced to the area from another part of the world.

Wildlife conservation involves determining what species are endangered and why, and devises methods to help the species recover. Recovery may involve ridding the environment of a harmful pollutant, as was the case with DDT, preserving the habitat of a species, or even breeding a disappearing species in captivity and then restoring it to the wild as with the California condor. ☑

Reading Check
What does wildlife conservation involve?

Discussion

Display a state map on the bulletin board and highlight state park and wildlife preserves. Ask how many students have visited these areas. Discuss with students how these areas are beneficial to humans. L2

Answer to Reading Check

Wildlife conservation involves determining what species are endangered and why, and devising methods of helping the species recover.

GLENCOE TECHNOLOGY

Videodisc

The Infinite Voyage: The Keepers of Eden

Chapter 8 *Preserves of Endangered Species: San Diego and Kenya* 8:30

The Great Dinosaur Hunt

Chapter 11 *Theories of Extinction* 3:30

Refer to Teacher Guide for bar codes and teaching strategies.

Science Journal

Resource Conservation Have students make a list of the things each of them can do to help conserve natural resources. They should include suggestions for energy, soil, wildlife, forests, and minerals.

VISUAL Learning

Figure 19-11 What other ways can humans protect the land? *Answers may include minimizing pollution and extracting a mineral and fossil fuel resources wisely.*

Caption Answer

Figure 19-12 *According to the map, Alaska has the most land set aside as National parks.*

GLENCOE TECHNOLOGY

Videodisc

Glencoe Science Voyages Interactive Videodisc—Life

Side 2, Lesson 9

Ecoystems: Wetlands

40199

40707

Refer to Videodisc Teacher Guide for bar codes and teaching strategies.

The Infinite Voyage: Miracles by Design

Chapter 4 *Biodegradable Plastic: The Miracle Material?* 7:00

Refer to Teacher Guide for bar codes and teaching strategies.

Figure 19-11 From the human perspective, wetlands may look like nothing more than a swamp. In the past, wetlands have been destroyed by filling them in with soil and using the land for roads and buildings. Today, many remaining wetlands have been set aside as protected areas.

Land Conservation

When European settlers first came to North America, much of the continent was covered with forests. Settlers cut down many of these forests to farm and to obtain fuel and lumber for building. About 100 years ago, people began to realize that if this kept up, we eventually would lose all of our forests. The U.S. government began a conservation program that involved setting aside wilderness areas, including forests, to protect them from development.

Many other countries also have made efforts to protect forests and wildlife habitat. **Figure 19-12** shows a map of U.S. national parks. Worldwide, more than 4000 national parks

Figure 19-12 The United States has set aside land as national parks. **Which state has the most land set aside as national parks?**

552 CHAPTER 19 RESOURCES AND THE ENVIRONMENT

A Plastic can be recycled into items like this picnic table.

B This jacket is actually made from soda-pop bottles.

C This mountain lion sculpture is made from discarded bumpers. This is an example of reuse.

Figure 19-13 Many products can be made from recycled or reused materials. **What are some other products you can think of that are made from recycled materials?**

and other protected areas, covering about 8.5 million km^2 (an area slightly larger than the country of Brazil), have now been set aside. In many areas, including the United States, land that was once forested is being replanted. The replanting of a forest is called reforestation. Reforestation not only restores forest ecosystems, it also helps preserve topsoil because the roots of young trees help hold the soil in place.

Recycling

How many garbage bins do you set beside the curb for pickup every week? As the world population grows, more and more garbage is produced. As a result, landfills are slowly taking up valuable land space. They often disrupt the local ecosystem, smell bad, and contain toxic materials that can pollute air and water.

One way to prevent this waste is to reuse items or purchase items that have little packaging. For example, you can reuse old clothes by giving them to someone else or cutting them up into rags. **Recycling** is a process that changes or reprocesses an item or resource. Not only does it conserve the resource being recycled, it conserves land space that would normally become the next landfill. **Figure 19-13** shows some products made from recycled and reused materials.

interNET CONNECTION

Paper accounts for more than 30 percent of discarded waste. Visit the Glencoe Science Web Site at **www.glencoe.com/sec/science** for more information about how to recycle your own paper by making handmade paper from scraps.

interNET CONNECTION

Internet Addresses

For Internet tips, see Glencoe's **Using the Internet in the Science Classroom.**

3 Assess

Check for Understanding Activity

Have students create posters illustrating ways that soil, wildlife, land, and minerals can be conserved.

Reteach

Have students choose one of the following and write an essay based on what they have studied in this section: energy conservation, land conservation, and mineral conservation.

Extension

For students who have mastered this section, use the **Reinforcement** and **Enrichment** masters.

Caption Answer

Figure 19-13 *Answers will vary but can include plastic and glass materials.*

Guided Reading Strategy

Reciprocal Teaching This strategy is designed to help construct meaning and apply reading skills. Have pairs of students begin by each partner silently reading a chunk of text. After several minutes of reading, one student retells the key points of what was read in his or her own words. The other student creates a question that can be answered directly from the text but could require inferences or evaluation. Continue the reading with each student alternating the questions and summaries. Consciously asking questions and summarizing content helps the reader attend deliberately to what is being read. Have students do Reciprocal Teaching with a chunk of section content.

Mineral Conservation

Minerals are nonrenewable resources. Because we can't replace them, the way to conserve them is to use less and to recycle whenever we can. Not only does this save them for future generations, but it also helps avoid the need for mining. Most minerals—and fossil fuels—are obtained by digging mines into the earth. Mining disrupts ecosystems, destroys topsoil, and sometimes releases toxic substances into air and water, as you can see in **Figure 19-14.** Recycling aluminum, steel, silver, and other minerals reduces the need for mining operations.

Figure 19-14 This open-pit copper mine cuts into the Arizona landscape.

Section Assessment

1. Compare and contrast soil depletion and erosion.
2. Describe four ways in which a species can become endangered.
3. Name three ways to conserve nonrenewable resources.
4. **Think Critically:** What might happen to topsoil during the first rain after a forest fire? Why?
5. **Skill Builder**
   Comparing and Contrasting
   Compare and contrast biodegradable and nonbiodegradable materials and give five examples of each. If you need help, refer to Comparing and Contrasting in the **Skill Handbook** on page 720.

Using Computers

Database Use references to create an endangered species database. Include each organism's common and scientific names, biome in which it's found, habitat description, and reasons why it is threatened. Sort the database by biome to obtain a list of endangered species from each of the world's biomes. If you need help, refer to page 733.

4 Close

Proficiency Prep

Use this quiz to check students' recall of section content.

1. **What are species that are in danger of becoming extinct unless action is taken to protect them?** *endangered species*
2. **What is the wearing away of soil by wind and water?** *erosion*
3. **What is the use of plowing methods to reduce erosion?** *soil management*
4. **What is the removal of soil nutrients?** *soil depletion*

Section Assessment

1. Soil depletion is the removal of soil nutrients. Crops are not left to decay and replenish the nutrients. Erosion is the wearing away of the soil by wind and water.
2. pollution, habitat destruction, overhunting, competition
3. recycling, using less, and reusing
4. **Think Critically** If there has not been enough time for new plant cover to grow, topsoil on slopes could be washed away.
5. **Skill Builder** Biodegradable materials are broken down by natural processes; nonbiodegradable materials are not. Paper, wood, dead organisms, food scraps, and cotton cloth are biodegradable. Plastic bags, motor oil, aluminum cans, plastic containers, and plastic toys are not.

Using Computers

Example entry: Organism: Manatee; Scientific name: *Trichechus mammatus;* Habitat: shallow, brackish water; Niche: first-order consumers of aquatic vegetation

Assessment

Performance Have students make a concept map that compares biodegradable and nonbiodegradable materials. Use **Performance Assessment in the Science Classroom,** p. 89.

What did Chief Seattle really say?

Before tape recorders and video cameras, the record of what someone said depended on a quick pencil or the good memory of a listener. In 1854, Chief Seattle (left), a leader of the Suquamish, an indigenous people of Puget Sound, gave a speech in response to an offer to move his people to a reservation.

Dr. Henry Smith witnessed Chief Seattle's original speech and took notes. More than 30 years later, he published a translation of the speech in the newspaper *Seattle Sunday Star.* In Smith's version of the speech, Chief Seattle was concerned with his people being able to visit their ancient burial grounds.

> *Every part of this country is sacred to my people. Every hillside, every valley, every plain and grove has been hallowed by some fond memory or some sad experience of my tribe. Even the rocks that seem to lie dumb as they swelter in the sun ... thrill with memories of past events connected with the fate of my people, and the very dust under your feet responds more lovingly to our footsteps than to yours, because it is the ashes of our ancestors, and our bare feet are conscious of the sympathetic touch, for the soil is rich with the life of our kindred.*

In 1972, another version of the speech was written by Ted Perry for a film about ecology. This version has been widely quoted in newspapers, books, and speeches by environmentalists, politicians, and religious leaders. The following is a quote from Perry's version:

> *How can you buy or sell the sky, the warmth of the land? The idea is strange to us. If we do not own the freshness of the air and the sparkle of the water, how can you buy them? Every part of the Earth is sacred to my people.*

Science JOURNAL

Write an essay that compares and contrasts Dr. Smith's version with that of Ted Perry's. Use the library to locate both versions of the speech and read about the controversy surrounding them.

NATIONAL GEOGRAPHIC

Reading & Writing in Science

Content Background

- People have disagreed over the exact words spoken by Chief Seattle in his 1854 speech. In 1992, several magazines including *Newsweek* and *Readers' Digest* published articles about controversies surrounding the various interpretations of Chief Seattle's speech.
- While it may never be certain which version is correct, both are worth consideration. Both convey a powerful message about the environment, culture, and the future of humanity.

Science JOURNAL Have students use their essay to have a class debate about which version is the real one.

For Additional Information

- Frederick, Heather. "Authenticity of Chief's Speech Questioned." *Publishers Weekly*. June 1, 1992, p. 22.
- Murray, Mary. "The Little Green Lie." *Readers' Digest*. July 1993. pp. 100–104.

Teaching Strategies

- **Writing** Have the students listen to a speech and take notes. Then, have them attempt to write that speech using only their notes.
- **Reading** Have the students pretend they are Abraham Lincoln and read the Gettysburg Address out loud for the class. Emphasize that each student will read it a little differently and that could change the interpretation of the speech.

Activity 19•1

What You'll Investigate

Purpose

Visual-Spatial Observe decomposition in nature using substances found in garbage and determine which materials are biodegradable and which are nonbiodegradable. L2 ELL COOP LEARN

Process Skills

observing and inferring, interpreting data, communicating, classifying, making and using tables, comparing and contrasting, forming operational definitions, forming a hypothesis

Procedure

Time

50 minutes plus 10 minutes two times per week for 4 weeks

Materials

- Divide the biodegradable and nonbiodegradable materials into chunks approximately 2 cm in size for students to use.
- Biodegradable substances may include fruits and vegetables, eggshells, bread, packaging materials, coffee grounds, leaves, nuts, water-soluble plastics, and newspapers. Nonbiodegradable substances may include glass, aluminum, tin, and plastic.

Safety Precautions

Caution students to wash their hands after handling soil and waste materials.

Activity 19•1

Is it biodegradable?

Materials

- Soft-drink bottles (2 L) (2)
- Plastic wrap
- Potting soil
- Gravel or sand
- Labels
- Biodegradable and nonbiodegradable waste materials
- Hand lens
- Plastic teaspoon
- Transparent tape
- Scissors

As you probably know, all trash is not the same. One important way in which one waste material may differ from another is whether or not the material is biodegradable. A biodegradable substance is anything that can be broken down by organisms in the environment. After it is broken down, the substance can become part of the environment. Whether a material is biodegradable or not can make a big difference in how it affects the environment.

What You'll Investigate

What kinds of materials are biodegradable?

Goals

- **Distinguish** between biodegradable and nonbiodegradable substances.
- **Observe** the decomposition of biodegradable materials.

Safety Precautions

Wash hands after handling soil or waste materials.

Procedure

1. **Cut** a square in the side of the soft-drink bottles as shown.
2. **Label** the bottles 1 and 2.
3. **Add** 1 cm of sand or gravel to each bottle and then fill with 4 cm of potting soil.
4. Your teacher will give you ten substances. **Hypothesize** which substances are biodegradable and which ones are not. **Record** your hypotheses in your Science Journal. **Make a table** in your Science Journal to record your observations.

556 CHAPTER 19 RESOURCES AND THE ENVIRONMENT

Sample Data Table

Time	Biodegradable Substances					Nonbiodegradable Substances				
	1	2	3	4	5	1	2	3	4	5
5 days	Substances begin to decompose. (Specific observations will vary.)					Substances have not changed.				
10 days	Most substances are highly decomposed. (Specific observations will vary.)					Substances have not changed.				

5. **Place** the substances you think are biodegradable in bottle 1 and the others in bottle 2.
6. **Cover** the substances with 1 cm to 2 cm of potting soil.
7. **Sprinkle water** on the top of the soil. Cover the hole in the bottle with plastic wrap and secure it with transparent tape.
8. **Observe** each bottle at the end of five days. Note any change in the level of the layers. Use the teaspoon to carefully remove the soil from each substance. Use your hand lens to observe the substance and record your observations. Carefully replace each substance and cover with soil.
9. **Observe** the contents of the bottles after five more days and record your results.

Conclude and Apply

1. Which substances decomposed?
2. Which substances decomposed partially?
3. Was your hypothesis supported? Why or why not?
4. Describe any organisms you observed.
5. Explain how substances that are biodegradable affect the environment.
6. Explain how substances that are not biodegradable affect the environment.

Teaching Strategies

- Discuss differences between organic and inorganic materials and the role of bacteria and fungi in decomposition.
- Have students stir the soil to look at the items once or twice each week.

Expected Outcome

The organic materials will decompose; the inorganic materials will not.

Error Analysis

Have students compare their results and their hypothesis and explain why any differences occurred.

Conclude and Apply

1. leaves, vegetables, fruit peelings, newspaper (organic substances)
2. Answers will vary depending on the amount of time the experiment is observed.
3. Answers will vary.
4. fungi (molds) and the action of bacteria
5. Biodegradable substances are recycled and used again by organisms that make food.
6. Substances that are not biodegradable remain in the environment and cause pollution.

Assessment

Performance Design an experiment to compare different plastic bags and packaging materials that are supposed to be biodegradable. Some plastic bags break down when exposed to sunlight. Use **Performance Assessment in the Science Classroom,** p. 23.

GO Further

Ask students to develop a plan to minimize the amount of landfill space needed by your community.

People can avoid using materials that are not recyclable and dispose of nonbiodegradable materials in ways provided by the community. They can recycle materials and use biodegradable materials. Plans may include using the food wastes for feeding farm animals.

SECTION 19-3

Prepare

Refer to **Ozone, Water, Global Warming,** and **Acid Rain** on p. 540F.

Preplanning

Refer to the **Chapter Organizer** on pp. 540A–B.

1 Motivate

Bellringer

Before presenting the lesson, display **Section Focus Transparency 52** on the overhead projector. Use the accompanying **Focus Activity** worksheet. L2 ELL

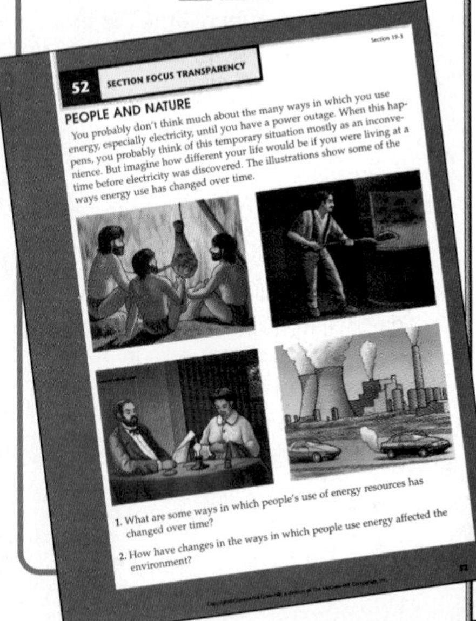

Section 19-3

52 SECTION FOCUS TRANSPARENCY

PEOPLE AND NATURE

You probably don't think much about the many ways in which you use energy, especially electricity, until you have a power outage. When this happens, you probably think of this temporary situation mostly as an inconvenience. But imagine how different your life would be if you were living at a time before electricity was discovered. The illustrations show some of the ways energy use has changed over time.

1. What are some ways in which people's use of energy resources has changed over time?
2. How have changes in the ways in which people use energy affected the environment?

52

Tying to Previous Knowledge

Relate examples of humans' effects on the environment to each of the topics in this section.

19-3 Maintaining a Healthy Environment

What You'll Learn

- The origins and effects of pollutants that contaminate air, land, and water
- The causes of acid rain, ozone depletion, and the greenhouse effect

Vocabulary
pollutant
smog
acid rain
ozone depletion
greenhouse effect
global warming
hazardous waste
groundwater

Why It's Important

- Clean air and water promote good health.

How We Affect the Environment

Safeguarding our air, land, and water requires more than conserving resources. It also means paying attention to how our use of those resources affects the health of the environment. Every action we take—from starting the car or revving up the lawn mower to painting a building, using bug spray, cutting down a tree, turning on a light, and even recycling—has an effect on the environment.

Air Pollution

On almost any warm, sunny, windless day in any populated area in the world, you can see a distinct layer of brown haze hanging in the air. The brown color comes from smoke, dust, and exhaust fumes that pollute the air. Wherever there are cars, trucks, airplanes, factories, furnaces, fireplaces, cookstoves, or power plants, there is air pollution. Although it also is caused by volcanic eruptions, forest fires, and the evaporation of chemicals such as paints and dry-cleaning fluid, most air pollution results from the burning of fossil fuels.

Figure 19-15 Some components of smog are nitrogen oxide, nitrogen dioxide, ozone, and soot particles. Tiny particles of soot suspended in the air make visibility difficult in Los Angeles. These particles irritate the eyes and respiratory system.

Resource Manager

The following **Teacher Classroom Resources** can be used with Section 19-3:

Reproducible Masters

Activity Worksheets, pp. 105–106, 108 L2
Critical Thinking/Problem Solving, p. 19 L2
Enrichment, p. 52 L3
Laboratory Manual, pp. 113–116 L2
Multicultural Connections, pp. 37–38 L2
Reinforcement, p. 52 L2
Study Guide, pp. 75–76 L1 ELL

Transparencies

Teaching Transparency 37 L2
Teaching Transparency 38 L2
Science Integration Transparency 19 L2

Smog

Burning wood or coal in a fireplace produces smoke and ash as well as heat. Burning gasoline not only provides the energy to run a car engine, but also creates a number of unwanted chemicals, including tiny particles of soot and a number of gases, such as carbon monoxide, carbon dioxide, and oxides of nitrogen and sulfur. The unwanted by-products created when wood and fossil fuels are burned are examples of pollutants. Any substance that contaminates the environment and causes pollution is a **pollutant.** The brown haze as shown in **Figure 19-15** that hangs over cities and other heavily populated areas is **smog,** a form of air pollution that is created when sunlight reacts with pollutant chemicals produced by burning fuels.

Figure 19-16 Acid rain is formed when pollutants mix with water vapor to create acidic solutions. **What activities in this picture could cause acid rain?**

Acid Rain

When you studied the water cycle, you learned that water evaporates from Earth's surface and rises into the air as water vapor. While in the atmosphere, it comes into contact with air pollutants. When it condenses and falls to the ground, it may bring pollutants with it.

Problem Solving

Why should you repair a leaky faucet?

Have you ever heard a faucet dripping in your home? Perhaps you tried to turn it off but it still leaked. Not only can a leaky faucet be annoying, but it can also be expensive if it is not repaired.

There are 20 drops of water in 1 cm^3 of water. If a faucet drips 20 times per minute, how much water would be lost in one hour? How much water would be lost in one day?

Think Critically

1. Name three reasons why it is important to fix leaky faucets.
2. Why is cost an important factor in water usage?
3. What are some other things you can do to conserve water in your home?

Caption Answer

Figure 19-16 *burning fossil fuels*

Across the Curriculum

Health Have students research sources of indoor air pollution. Have them study the effects of asbestos, formaldehyde, radon, cigarette smoke, and other substances found in houses. L3

2 Teach

Problem Solving

The average person in the United States consumes about 200 gallons of water daily. Agriculture and industry use at least ten times this much. Such high rates of consumption can tax available supply, particularly in arid regions, and have negative effects on the environment.

Think Critically

1. Cost, it's annoying, and you waste water.
2. A leaky faucet can add extra cost to your water bill.
3. Answers will vary.

CHEMISTRY INTEGRATION

Some of the most harmful pollutants produced by burning fossil fuels include carbon monoxide, nitrogen oxides, and sulfur oxides. Carbon monoxide forms as a result of incomplete burning of fuels. Nitrogen oxides form when atmospheric nitrogen reacts with oxygen at high temperatures. Sulfur-containing fossil fuels produce sulfur oxides when burned.

EARTH SCIENCE INTEGRATION

Most sulfur oxide pollution comes from the burning of high-sulfur coal, which is common in the eastern United States. These emissions can be reduced, however, by allowing smokestack gases to react with limestone.

Purpose

Kinesthetic Students will collect samples of rain and determine the pH of each sample. L2 ELL COOP LEARN

Materials

small containers; pH paper

Teaching Strategies

- Have students collect their samples from the same sources of precipitation.
- Have students use the same chart to determine the pH level of the samples.
- Have students test the pH of rain on different days throughout the school year to detect variations.

Analysis

1. pH will be either acidic or neutral. The pH of normal rain is 5.6. Students' results may range from pH 4 to pH 7.
2. Tap water is about pH 6; distilled water is pH 7.

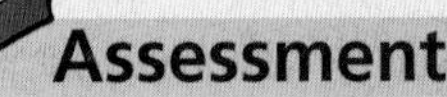

Assessment

Performance Set up several liquids of unknown pH. Have students test each with pH paper to determine whether they are acids or bases. Have them make a table that shows the pH of unknown liquids and compares them with substances of known pHs. Use **Performance Assessment in the Science Classroom,** p. 27. P

Figure 19-17 The pH scale shows whether a solution is acidic or basic. Acid rain can have damaging effects.

Soft drinks
Tomatoes
Milk
Pure water
Detergent
Oven cleaner
0 1 2 3 4 5 6 7 8 9 10 11 12 13 14
More acidic
Neutral
More basic

Acidic solutions have a pH below 7.0. Basic solutions have a pH greater than 7.0. Neutral solutions have a pH of 7.0.

MiniLab

Measuring Acid Rain

Use a container to collect samples of rain.

Procedure

1. Dip a piece of pH indicator paper into the sample.
2. Compare the color of the paper with the pH chart provided. Record the pH of the rainwater.
3. Use separate pieces of pH paper to test the pH of tap water and distilled water. Record these values.

Analysis

1. Is the rainwater acidic, basic, or neutral?
2. How does the pH of the rainwater compare with the pH of tap water? Distilled water?

Air pollutants can increase the acidity of rain. As shown in **Figure 19-16,** the pollutants released by the burning of fossil fuels can react with water vapor in the atmosphere to form strong acids, including sulfuric acid and nitric acid. Acids are measured by a value called pH. **Acid rain** is rain or snow with a pH below 5.6. It washes valuable nutrients from the soil, which can lead to the death of trees and other plants. When the runoff from acid rain flows into a lake or pond, it changes the pH of the water. Algae and microscopic plankton cannot survive, so fish and other organisms that depend on them for food also die. A lake damaged by acid rain may look clear. But, the water is clear because few organisms can survive in it.

Ozone Depletion

When ozone forms in the lower atmosphere, it is considered an air pollutant. But, ozone also forms in the upper atmosphere. This upper ozone layer acts as a sunscreen that helps protect living organisms from exposure to harmful ultraviolet (UV) radiation that comes from the sun. When ultraviolet rays from the sun strike molecules of oxygen in the upper atmosphere, ozone is formed. Ozone absorbs UV rays, preventing some of the rays from reaching Earth's surface.

Correcting Misconceptions

Students may think that only water is affected by acid rain. Explain that acid rain can affect air, water, and land. Any precipitation can be acidic. Fog, snow, and sleet also can have an acidic pH level.

Integrating the Sciences

Chemistry When ultraviolet light from the sun strikes ozone molecules, they are split apart. The ozone quickly re-forms, releasing heat that escapes into space. The ozone layer protects living organisms from harmful radiation. Some substances such as chlorofluorocarbons destroy the ozone layer.

Scientists have discovered that Earth's protective ozone layer is becoming thinner. The thinning of the ozone layer is called **ozone depletion.** It is being caused by air pollutants, but not pollutants that are created by the burning of fossil fuels. Chemicals known as chlorofluorocarbons (CFCs), used in the cooling systems of refrigerators, freezers, and air conditioners, are the primary cause of ozone depletion. These chemicals contain chlorine and fluorine molecules. When these molecules escape into the air, they rise in the atmosphere until they reach the level of the protective ozone layer. Once there, they react with and destroy ozone molecules. The ozone layer is so important to the survival of life on Earth that world governments have agreed to stop producing CFCs by the year 2000. ☑

Greenhouse Effect

Earth's atmosphere allows sunlight to penetrate the surface but prevents much of the resulting heat from radiating back into space. This heat-trapping feature of the atmosphere shown in **Figure 19-18** is known as the **greenhouse effect.** Without it, temperatures would be too cold to support life as we know it.

The heat-reflecting atmospheric gases responsible for the greenhouse effect are called greenhouse gases. The most important is carbon dioxide. Although carbon dioxide is a normal part of the atmosphere, it is also a by-product when fossil fuels are burned. Over the past hundred years or so, larger and larger quantities of fossil fuels have been burned and more and more carbon dioxide and other greenhouse gases have been released into the atmosphere. These extra greenhouse gases could cause Earth to get warmer. **Global warming** is an increase in the average yearly temperature.

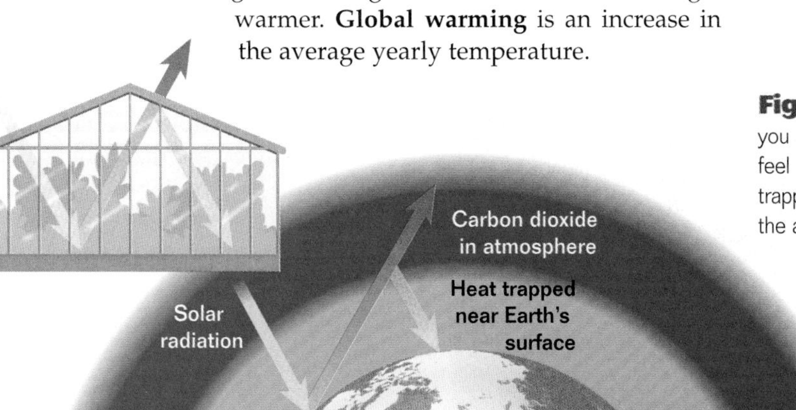

Figure 19-18 The moment you step inside a greenhouse, you feel the greenhouse effect. Heat trapped by the glass walls warms the air inside. Similarly, atmospheric greenhouse gases, particularly carbon dioxide, trap heat close to Earth's surface.

CHEMISTRY INTEGRATION

CFCs

Chlorofluorocarbon, or CFC, molecules found in certain cooling systems contain atoms of chlorine, fluorine, and carbon. When they reach the ozone layer in the upper atmosphere, they are broken apart. The breakdown of CFCs releases chlorine atoms that destroy ozone. Explain how this information persuaded world leaders to agree that CFC use should be stopped.

CHEMISTRY INTEGRATION

It became obvious to the world leaders that each CFC molecule released into the atmosphere could destroy many molecules of the protective ozone layer. If CFCs continued to be released, total destruction of protective ozone would be unavoidable.

Answer to Reading Check ☑

CFCs are the primary cause of ozone depletion.

GLENCOE TECHNOLOGY

CD-ROM

Glencoe Science Voyages Interactive CD-ROM

Explorations

Have students do the interactive exploration *Which countries contribute the most global air pollution.*

Videodisc

The Infinite Voyage: Crisis in the Atmosphere

Chapter 1 *Historical Aspects of the Greenhouse Effect and Fossil Air* 5:30

Refer to the Teacher Guide for bar codes and teaching strategies.

Integrating the Sciences

Physical Science About 45 percent of the sunlight reaching Earth is absorbed by Earth's surface. This energy rises from the surface of infrared radiation. Most infrared radiation cannot escape through the atmosphere. It is absorbed by gas molecules in the atmosphere such as carbon dioxide, water vapor, and ozone.

Quick Demo

Bring a container of trash to class. Include a glass bottle, an aluminum can, a twist tie, plastic wrappers, paper, a coffee filter with grounds, vegetable peelings, eggshells, and other household items. Wear plastic gloves and remove each piece from the container. Discuss which items are biodegradable and which items are not.

Caption Answer

Figure 19-19 *The waste has been stored in a sealed barrel, labeled as poison, and labeled as a hazardous waste.*

Activity

Naturalist Many household cleaners contain toxic chemicals. Many new products are on the market that are just as effective but do not contain harmful chemicals. Under adult supervision, have students investigate cleaning products in their homes to see what kinds of ingredients they contain. Be sure to warn students to take care when handling cleaning products or other chemicals. They should read labels only and not open the products. L2

Using Science Words

Linguistic Ask students how the word *biodegradable* is related to living things. *Biodegradable means capable of being broken down by living things.*

interNET CONNECTION

Hazardous waste can be found in many homes. Visit the Glencoe Science Web Site at **www.glencoe.com/sec/science** for more information about household hazardous waste and what you can do to eliminate it.

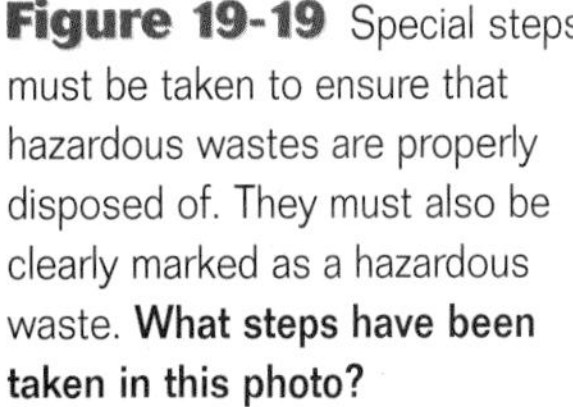

Effects of Global Warming

Scientists disagree about whether or not the increase in atmospheric carbon dioxide and other greenhouse gases is actually warming up Earth. What might happen if the temperature of Earth did increase? Rainfall amounts could decrease, which could affect the production of food, as well as affect the health of wildlife. A rise in temperature of just 5°C would begin to melt the polar ice caps, which would raise sea levels and flood coastal communities. There also could be an increase in the number and severity of storms and hurricanes. Many people feel that the possibility of global warming is a good reason to slow our consumption of fossil fuels.

Land Pollution

As you learned earlier in this chapter, the human population is running out of land space for burying solid waste. For a long time, most people expected that biodegradable items in landfills would eventually decompose. But, it turns out that they decompose quite slowly. A newspaper thrown away in the 1950s was still readable when scientists dug it out of a landfill almost 40 years later. What about the nonbiodegradable substances we put in landfills? They won't break down at all. Any toxic materials that are disposed of in landfills can pollute the soil and surrounding waterways.

Waste materials that are harmful to human health or poisonous to living organisms in general are known as **hazardous wastes.** Pesticides, medical wastes that may contain disease organisms, nuclear waste, chemicals used in industry, and even items you might have around the house such as dead batteries, paints, and household cleaning products are all examples of hazardous waste. If hazardous wastes are not properly contained, as in **Figure 19-19,** they may leak out of the landfill and into the surrounding soil and waterways.

Figure 19-19 Special steps must be taken to ensure that hazardous wastes are properly disposed of. They must also be clearly marked as a hazardous waste. **What steps have been taken in this photo?**

562 CHAPTER 19 RESOURCES AND THE ENVIRONMENT

Integrating the Sciences

Earth Science The reason to recycle materials for human use is that many resources are nonrenewable. In many cases, recycling is not the cheapest alternative. A throwaway is often less expensive in the long run, but recycling is the wiser alternative.

Multiple Learning Styles

Gifted Have students use recycled paper to write a letter to the nearest recycling agency requesting information on how the students can implement a recycling program. L3

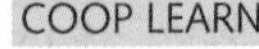
COOP LEARN

Water Pollution

Many pollutants released into the air may pollute water, as well. Acid rain starts as an air pollution problem but ends up affecting waterways because rain eventually flows into rivers and lakes. Water flowing over or through soil that contains hazardous wastes can pick up and carry some of those wastes along with it, as shown in **Figure 19-20.**

Water pollution can have more direct sources. Wastewater from factories and sewage-treatment plants is released into streams, rivers, or sometimes directly into the ocean. In the United States and many other countries, this wastewater is treated to remove some or all pollutants before it is released into the environment. But, in many parts of the world, wastewater treatment is not always possible.

Figure 19-20 When rain falls on roads and parking lots, it can wash oil and grease into nearby waterways. When rain falls on agricultural land that has been sprayed with pesticides, chemical residues may be washed into neighboring streams.

Groundwater Pollution

Water pollution can also affect **groundwater.** Groundwater comes from rainfall and runoff that gets trapped in underground pockets. The water in these underground pools, or aquifers, comes from rainfall and runoff that soaks down through the soil. If the water contacts waste materials as it makes its way underground, the aquifer may become contaminated. Groundwater contamination has already become a problem for rural residents and communities that draw their water supply from wells that tap into underground aquifers, as shown in **Figure 19-21.** ☑

How can groundwater become polluted?

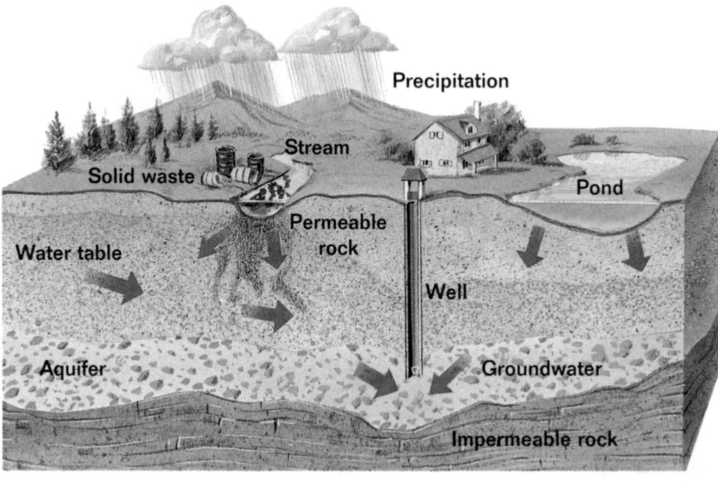

Figure 19-21 Pollutants leaking from storage containers can eventually reach and contaminate groundwater.

Discussion

With the world's population increasing at its current rate, what are some possible problems you will have with renewable and nonrenewable resources during your lifetime? *Answers will vary but may include living with a shortage of resources, mandatory recycling, and rationing of resources.*

Answer to Reading Check
Groundwater is polluted when it comes in contact with waste materials as it makes its way underground.

3 Assess

Check for Understanding

Science Journal

Linguistic Have students make a list of environmental concerns in their area along with suggestions as to what can be done about each problem. L2

Reteach

Review the causes and effects of air pollution, land pollution, and water pollution.

Extension

For students who have mastered this section, use the **Reinforcement** and **Enrichment** masters.

interNET CONNECTION

Internet Addresses

____

____

____

____

For Internet tips, see Glencoe's **Using the Internet in the Science Classroom.**

Using Water Water usage is a growing concern in the world. By the year 2000, world demand for freshwater may be double what it was in the 1980s. Ask students to research the demand for freshwater and write their suggestions for dealing with the problem in their journals. L3

4 Close

Proficiency Prep

Use this quiz to check students' recall of section content.

1. **What is the thinning of the ozone layer?** *ozone depletion*
2. **What is water contained in soil or porous rock?** *groundwater*
3. **What is the potential warming of Earth?** *global warming*
4. **What is any substance that contaminates the environment?** *pollutant*

Section Assessment

1. smog, acid rain, greenhouse effect, ozone depletion
2. the potential increase in the temperature of Earth's atmosphere due to the greenhouse effect
3. Acid rain lowers the pH of lakes, kills microscopic algae and plankton, and washes nutrients from the soil.
4. CFCs that escape into the air
5. **Think Critically** Runoff from rainfall can carry these chemicals over the ground into streams or into the ground to underground aquifers.

Using Math

A solution with a pH of 4 is 100 times more acidic than a solution with a pH of 6.

Caption Answer

Figure 19-22 *Students' answers will vary but should include damages.*

Figure 19-22 Oil spill cleanup, like this one in Wales, is a messy task. Oil-soaked sand has to be shoveled into bags by hand. If the water is contaminated, it must be skimmed from the surface. **What would happen if the beach wasn't cleaned up?**

Ocean Pollution

Rivers eventually flow into the ocean, bringing their pollutants along. The areas of the ocean most seriously affected by pollution are those near the coastlines, where freshwater enters the sea or where factories, sewage-treatment plants, and shipping activities are concentrated. As is the case with freshwater pollution, the discharge of raw sewage into coastal waters can encourage the overgrowth of algae and plankton. Wastes produced by many of these species are poisonous to fish and wildlife.

Another well-known ocean pollution problem involves oil spills. About 4 million metric tons of oil are released into ocean waters every year. Some of that total comes from freshwater runoff and some comes from ships, including oil tankers that use ocean water to wash out empty tanks before refilling them. Some also is spilled by accident. One of the worst oil spills ever seen occurred during the Persian Gulf War, when a huge amount of crude oil was released into the water on purpose. Tens of thousands of seabirds died, and salt marshes and other estuarine ecosystems were destroyed.

Section Assessment

1. List four ways in which air pollution affects the atmosphere.
2. Describe global warming.
3. How does acid rain affect the environment?
4. What causes ozone depletion?
5. **Think Critically:** How can hazardous chemicals deposited in landfills affect groundwater? Surface streams?
6. **Skill Builder**
   Comparing and Contrasting
   Compare and contrast the causes and effects of air and water pollution. If you need help, refer to Comparing and Contrasting in the **Skill Handbook** on page 720.

Using Math

The pH scale is based on the powers of 10. For example, a solution with a pH of 4 is ten times more acidic than a solution with a pH of 5. Similarly, a pH of 5 is ten times more acidic than a pH of 6. How many times more acidic is a solution with a pH of 4 than a solution with a pH of 6?

6. **Skill Builder**
Most air pollution is caused by the burning of fossil fuels. Water pollution occurs when runoff carries pollutants from dumps and landfills into streams and by direct release of pollutants into waterways. Air pollution causes smog, acid rain, the greenhouse effect, and ozone depletion. Water pollution causes overgrowth of plants, and endangers people's drinking-water supplies.

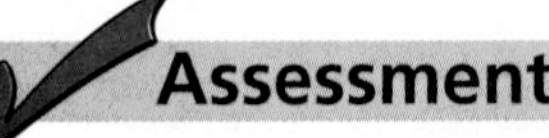

Assessment

Content Have students work in groups of two or three to write a song or poem about the dangers of pollution to the environment. Use **Performance Assessment in the Science Classroom,** p. 79.

Activity 19•2

Modeling the Greenhouse Effect

You can create models of Earth with and without heat-reflecting greenhouse gases. Then, experiment with the models to observe the greenhouse effect.

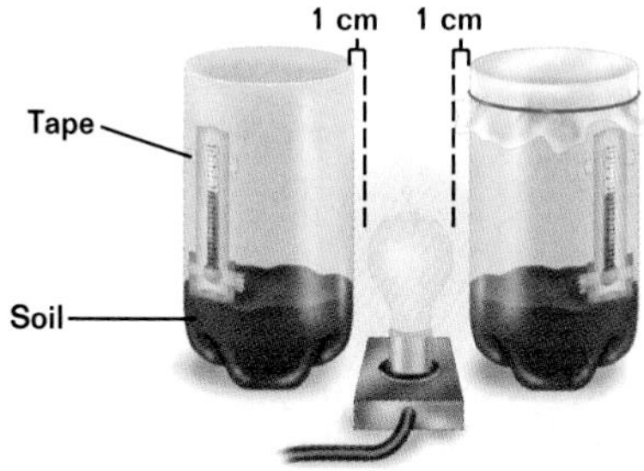

What You'll Investigate

How does the greenhouse effect influence temperatures on Earth?

Goals

- **Observe** the greenhouse effect.
- **Describe** the effect that a heat source has on an environment.

Materials

- Clear, plastic, 2-L soft-drink bottles with tops cut off and labels removed (2)
- Thermometers (2)
- Cups of potting soil (4)
- Masking tape
- Plastic wrap
- Rubber band
- Lamp with 100-watt lightbulb
- Watch or clock

Procedure

1. Copy the data table and use it to record your temperature measurements.
2. Put an equal volume of potting soil in the bottom of each container.
3. Use masking tape to affix a thermometer to the inside of each container. Place the thermometers at the same height relative to the soil. Shield each thermometer bulb by putting a double layer of masking tape over it.
4. Seal the top of one container with plastic wrap held in place with the rubber band.
5. Place the lamp with the exposed 100-watt bulb between the two containers, exactly 1 cm from each, as shown in the diagram. Do not turn on the light.
6. Let the apparatus sit undisturbed for five minutes, then record the temperature in each container.
7. Turn on the light. Record the temperature in each container every two minutes for the next 15 to 20 minutes.
8. **Record** the results on a graph.

Changes in Temperature

Time	Open Container Temperature (°C)	Sealed Container Temperature (°C)
0 minutes		
2 minutes		
4 minutes		
6 minutes		

Conclude and Apply

1. How did the temperature of each container change during the experiment?
2. **Compare and contrast** the temperature of the two containers at the end of the experiment.
3. What does the lightbulb represent in this experimental model? What does the plastic wrap represent?

Activity 19•2

Purpose

Interpersonal Students will make a model of the atmosphere and determine what happens when light shines on it.

L2 ELL COOP LEARN

Process Skills

modeling, observing and inferring, interpreting data, communicating, comparing and contrasting, recognizing cause and effect, measuring in SI, making and using tables, making and using graphs

Time

50 minutes

Safety Precautions

Caution students to use extreme care in working with thermometers and 100-W lightbulbs. Use only alcohol thermometers.

Teaching Strategies

- Drafts in the room could affect experimental results. Close doors and windows if necessary.
- Have students work in teams of three to four.
- Make sure the containers are set up so that the thermometers face outward. This will make it easier for students to read the temperatures.

Troubleshooting If the two thermometers did not read the same temperature when the experiment began, readings will need to be adjusted so both sets of data can be plotted on the same graph.

Answers to Questions

1. In most cases, students observe that the temperature increased, then leveled off; at the end of the experiment, the open bottle was cooler than the closed bottle.
2. Answers will vary.
3. sunlight, greenhouse gases
4. The sun and the lightbulb represent a constant source of light and heat. The open container is unlike Earth because there is nothing to model heat-absorbing gases.

Assessment

Oral Have students summarize the information in their graphs in writing. Make sure the summaries are clear and concise. Use **Performance Assessment in the Science Classroom,** p. 41. 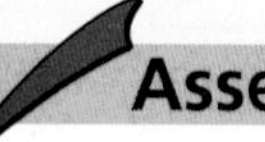

Chapter 19 Reviewing Main Ideas

Reviewing Main Ideas can be used to preview, review, reteach, and condense chapter content.

Preview

Linguistic Have students try to answer the questions in their Science Journals. Use student answers as a source for discussion throughout the chapter.

Review

Interpersonal Have students answer the questions on separate pieces of paper and compare their answers with those of other students in the class.

Reteach

Visual-Spatial Have students look at the illustrations on these pages. Ask them to describe details that support the main ideas of the chapter found in the statement for each illustration.

00:00 OUT OF TIME?

If time does not permit teaching the entire chapter, use the information on these pages along with the chapter Audiocassettes to present the material in a condensed format.

Chapter 19 Reviewing Main Ideas

For a **preview** of this chapter, study this Reviewing Main Ideas before you read the chapter. After you have studied this chapter, you can use the Reviewing Main Ideas to **review** the chapter.

The Glencoe MindJogger, Audiocassettes, and CD-ROM provide additional opportunities for review.

Section 19-1 NATURAL RESOURCES

Natural resources are materials in the environment that are useful for living things. Some of these resources are **renewable** and replenished by the environment, but **nonrenewable resources** cannot be replaced or are only replaced slowly. **Fossil fuels,** solar energy, water and wind power, **geothermal energy,** and **nuclear energy** are energy sources used today. *How are renewable and nonrenewable resources different? Give examples of each.*

Section 19-2 CONSERVATION AND WILDLIFE PROTECTION

Conservation is the process of saving resources. A nonrenewable resource can be conserved by using less of that resource or using a renewable resource instead. **Recycling,** the process of changing a used item into a new item for a different use, is one method used to reduce energy use. Wildlife, land, and mineral conservation are methods used to preserve natural resources. *What methods are used to preserve our natural resources?*

Cultural Diversity

Reforestation Recently, countries as diverse as India, Haiti, and Hungary have started reforestation programs to correct environmental problems. Deforestation around the world has created severe problems. An example: as the population in Rio de Janiero, Brazil increases, luxury homes and shantytowns move up the mountains. People cut down more trees. Every rain washes tons of topsoil from the mountain slopes and fills the rivers with silt. Water floods the streets and mud slides bury shantytowns and their occupants. In Borneo, the most intensive logging in the world has caused soil erosion and muddied rain forest rivers and streams, blinding fish and releasing toxins from trees and plants into the water.

Reading Check ✓

You can better understand new words if you analyze their parts. What do the parts of these words mean: *non-renewable, photovoltaic, geothermal?*

Section **19-3 MAINTAINING A HEALTHY ENVIRONMENT**

Any substance that contaminates the environment and causes pollution is a **pollutant.** There are three types of pollution: air pollution, water pollution, and land pollution. **Smog** is air pollution created when sunlight reacts with the by-products of fossil fuels. **Acid rain** results from the mixture of water vapor and air pollutants in the atmosphere.

THE GREENHOUSE EFFECT

The **greenhouse effect** is the warming of Earth due to a blanket of gases in the atmosphere. It is essential to life on Earth. Without it, temperatures would be too cold to support life as we know it. However, the burning of fossil fuels has added to the amount of greenhouse gases in the atmosphere. These gases are responsible for **global warming.** *What could happen if Earth temperatures rise by 5°C?*

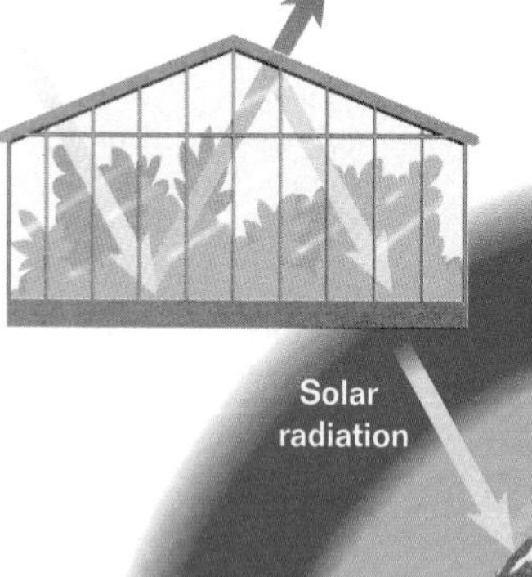

Career CONNECTION

Alice Derby Erickson, Pipestone Carver

Alice Derby Erickson works as a park ranger at the Pipestone National Monument in southwestern Minnesota. She is a full-blooded Dakota Sioux and a pipestone carver. Carrying on a longtime family tradition, Alice started carving pipestone at the age of ten. She starts with a piece of carefully quarried pipestone and shapes it using various files and sandpaper. Heating the stone and applying beeswax produces a rich, red color. *What are the physical properties that make a rock desirable for carving?*

Answers to Questions

Section 19-1

Natural Resources Renewable resources are replaced by natural processes. Examples are: oxygen, water, plants, and animals. Nonrenewable resources cannot be replaced or are replaced slowly. Examples are: petroleum, minerals, and topsoil.

Section 19-2

Conservation and Wildlife Protection Our natural resources can be preserved by using less or using a renewable resource instead.

Section 19-3

The Greenhouse Effect A slight rise in temperature could cause significant climate and weather change. A 5° rise could melt the polar ice caps.

GLENCOE TECHNOLOGY

 **CD-ROM**

Glencoe Science Voyages Interactive CD-ROM

Chapter Summaries and Quizzes

Have students read the Chapter Summary, then take the Chapter Quiz to determine whether they have mastered chapter content.

Assessment

Portfolio Encourage students to place in their portfolios one or two items of what they consider to be their best work. Examples include:

- Across the Curriculum, p. 549
- Assessment, p. 560
- Assessment, p. 565 P

Performance Additional performance assessments may be found in **Performance Assessment** and **Science Integration Activities.** Performance Task Assessment Lists and rubrics for evaluating these activities can be found in Glencoe's **Performance Assessment in the Science Classroom.**

Career CONNECTION

A rock should be soft so it can be easily carved and it should be colorful.

Using Vocabulary

1. m
2. f
3. r
4. t
5. g

interNET CONNECTION To reinforce chapter vocabulary, use the **Study Guide for Content Mastery** booklet. Also available are the activities in the Interactive Tutor for **Glencoe Science Voyages** on the Glencoe Science Web Site. **www.glencoe.com/sec/science**

Checking Concepts

6. D
7. A
8. D
9. B
10. C
11. B
12. C
13. D
14. B

Thinking Critically

15. Fossil fuels were formed from plants and animals. Wood is from a plant.
16. the desert region because sunshine is more constant there than at the poles
17. If on a slope, it might be eroded away because there are no longer any plant roots to secure it.

Chapter 19 Assessment

Using Vocabulary

a. acid rain
b. endangered species
c. erosion
d. extinction
e. fossil fuel
f. geothermal energy
g. global warming
h. greenhouse effect
i. groundwater
j. hazardous waste
k. hydroelectric power
l. natural resource
m. nonrenewable resource
n. nuclear energy
o. ozone depletion
p. photovoltaic (PV) cell
q. pollutant
r. recycling
s. renewable resource
t. smog
u. soil depletion
v. soil management

The sentences below include terms that have been used incorrectly. Change the italicized terms so that the sentence reads correctly. Underline your change.

1. *Geothermal energy* is a natural resource that is not replaceable.
2. *Hydroelectric power* is heat energy from below the surface of Earth.
3. Reducing the use of natural resources by reusing an item after it has been reprocessed is called *soil depletion.*
4. *Erosion* is a combination of smoke, dust, and oxides of nitrogen and sulfur.
5. The *greenhouse effect* is an increase in the temperature of Earth due to an increase in the levels of certain gases in the atmosphere.

Checking Concepts

Choose the word or phrase that best answers the question.

6. What does smog **NOT** include?
A) ozone
B) nitrogen oxides
C) soot
D) acid rain

7. Which of the following is **NOT** a fossil fuel?
A) wood
B) oil
C) natural gas
D) coal

8. Which of the following is **NOT** a renewable resource?
A) wood
B) water
C) sunlight
D) aluminum

9. Which of the following is **NOT** either directly or indirectly caused by the sun?
A) hydroelectric power
B) nuclear energy
C) photosynthesis
D) wind power

10. What kind of renewable energy source is found deep in the crust of Earth?
A) groundwater
B) solid waste
C) geothermal energy
D) nuclear power

11. What are methods used to prevent or reduce soil depletion and erosion forms of?
A) crop rotation
B) soil management
C) fertilizers
D) terracing

12. Which of the following is **NOT** a description of carbon dioxide?
A) component of acid rain
B) greenhouse gas
C) ozone-depleting gas
D) waste product from the burning of fossil fuels

13. What is ozone depletion caused by?
A) acid rain
B) oxygen
C) carbon dioxide
D) chlorine molecules

14. Which of the following does **NOT** cause water pollution?
A) air pollution
C) solid-waste disposal
B) ozone depletion
D) runoff from rainfall

Thinking Critically

15. Why does the burning of wood produce similar pollutants to the burning of fossil fuels?
16. What would make a better location for a solar power plant—a polar region or a desert region? Why?
17. Why is it beneficial to grow another crop in soil after the major crop has been harvested?

Developing Skills

If you need help, refer to the **Skill Handbook.**

18. **Comparing and Contrasting:** Compare and contrast the reasons for using crop rotation, strip-cropping, contour plowing, terracing, and no-till farming.
19. **Making and Using a Concept Map:** Complete the concept map describing how air can be polluted. Use the following terms and events: *nitrogen oxides, sulfur dioxides, acid rain,* and *smog.*

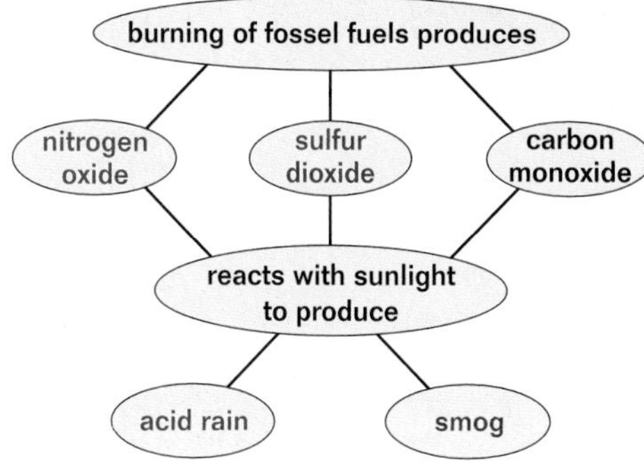

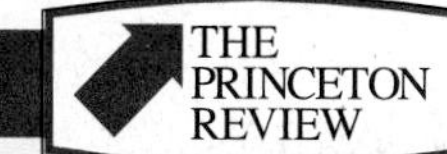

Test-Taking Tip

Stock Up on Supplies Be sure to supply yourself with the test-taking essentials: number two pencils, pens, erasers, a ruler, and a pencil sharpener. If the room doesn't have a pencil sharpener, a broken pencil can be a problem.

Test Practice

Use these questions to test your Science Proficiency.

1. What are renewable resources?
   A) minerals such as phosphorus
   B) fuel oil, gasoline, plastics, and paint
   C) oxygen, water, plants, and animals
   D) petroleum products
2. Where does most of the energy we use today come from?
   A) solar cells
   B) fossil fuels
   C) geothermal energy
   D) wind farms
3. Why must topsoil be conserved?
   A) It is fertile soil that has accumulated over thousands of years.
   B) Its underground reservoir is being used up at a fast rate.
   C) Terracing has caused the loss of several centimeters of topsoil each decade.
   D) No-till farming has caused topsoil to be used up.
4. What causes water pollution?
   A) solid-waste disposal
   B) runoff from rainfall
   C) air pollution
   D) all of the above

THE PRINCETON REVIEW **Test Practice**

The Test-Taking Tip was written by The Princeton Review, the nation's leader in test preparation.

1. C
2. B
3. A
4. D

Developing Skills

18. Strip-cropping helps reduce erosion caused by wind and water. Contour plowing and terracing reduces the downhill flow of water. No-till farming does not disturb the soil.
19. Nitrogen oxides and sulfur dioxides are produced by burning fossil fuels, and acid rain and smog are the end result.

Bonus Question

Why are fossil fuels considered nonrenewable? *It takes millions of years to produce what humans can use in one century.*

Assessment Resources

The **Test Practice Workbook** provides students with practice in the format, concepts, and critical-thinking skills tested in standardized exams.

 Reproducible Masters

Chapter Review, pp. 37–38 L2
Performance Assessment, p. 33 L2
Assessment, pp. 83–86 L2

Glencoe Technology

- Chapter Review Software
- Computer Test Bank
- MindJogger Videoquiz

UNIT 7

Astronomy

In this unit, students are introduced to the size, structure, and evolution of the universe. The unit is organized as an exploration outward from Earth, with chapters on exploring space, the sun-moon-Earth system, the solar system, stars, and galaxies. Students will learn about the energy that provides the intense heat inside stars and about interactions of objects orbiting stars. Students also will explore the immense nature of the universe and develop an understanding of Earth's place in it.

Unit Overview

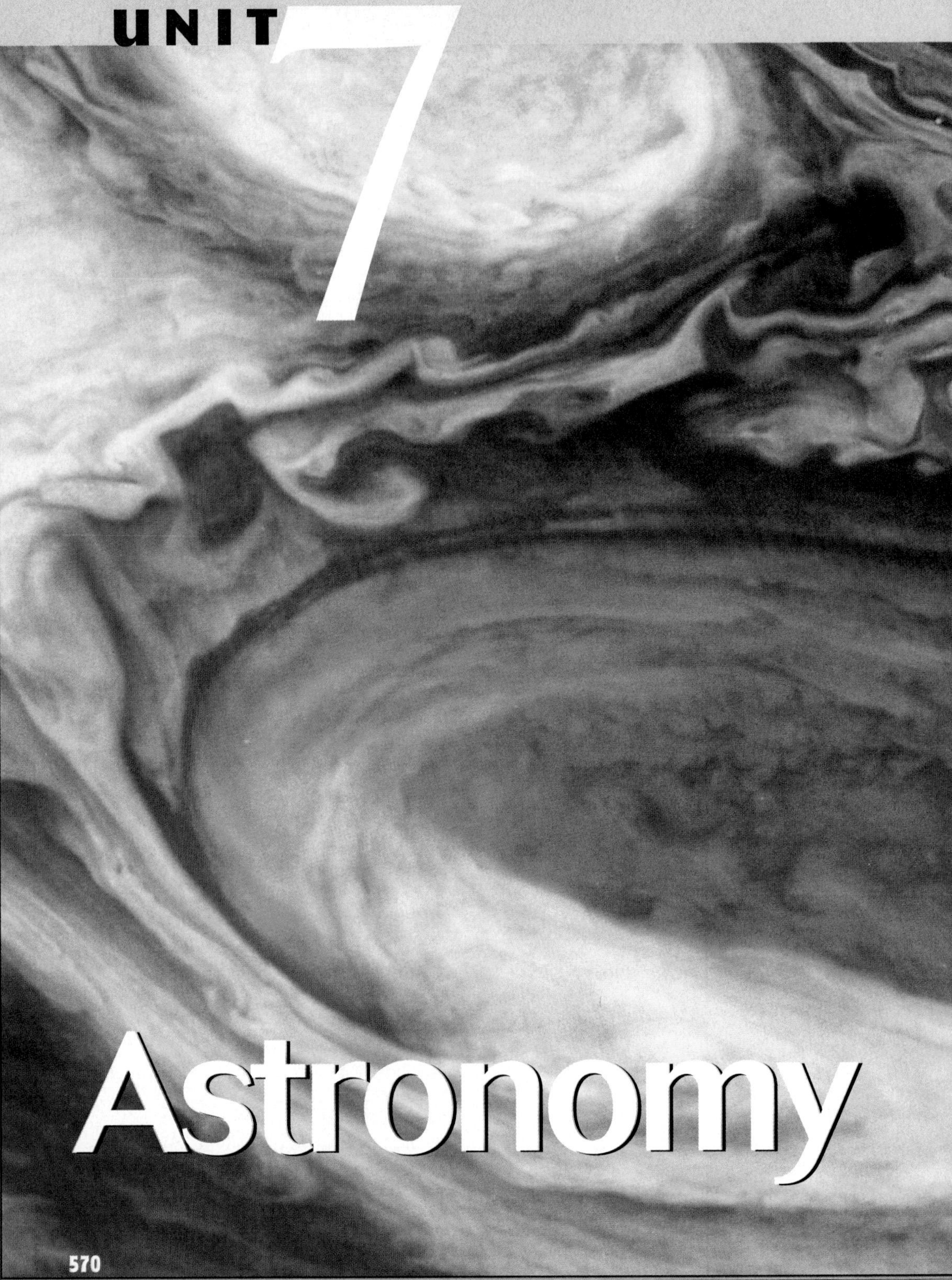

Science at Home

Patterns in the Sky Draw the Big Dipper and the Little Dipper on the chalkboard. Have students copy the pattern and try to locate it in the night sky. Ask them to note bright stars and any other unusual sights. For example, the faint blurred outline of a nova that exploded many years ago sometimes can be seen.

NATIONAL GEOGRAPHIC

What's Happening Here?

Much of the light you see twinkling in the night sky bears witness to a distant past. How so? If you peered at one of those stars through a powerful telescope, you would discover not how the star appears today but how it appeared millions of years ago. Likewise, if people on a distant planet were to aim a telescope at you, they would see Earth as it existed in the age of the dinosaurs! Outer space is so vast that light traveling at 300 000 kilometers a second takes millions of years to span the distance from a distant star to Earth. To grasp the subject of astronomy, you must expand your notion of distance to the unfathomable. In this unit, you will learn how the lure of this vastness has triggered a new age of exploration. En route into deep space, the *Voyager* probes launched in 1977 photographed Jupiter's Great Red Spot (left), a massive storm in the planet's outer gases. In 1996, this astronaut (inset) tested a minirocket backpack by flying solo above the space shuttle *Discovery*.

interNET CONNECTION

Explore the Glencoe Science Web Site at **www.glencoe.com/sec/science** to find out more about topics found in this unit.

571

Introducing the Unit

What's happening here?

Have students read the text and examine the pictures. Ask students how many of them have seen photos of the surface of other planets taken by space probes. Point out that it takes years for these probes to reach other planets in our solar system, even though these other planets are relatively close to Earth.

Content Background

One project currently planned is Mars Surveyor 2001, scheduled for launch in April 2001. The first phase will use the atmosphere of Mars to slow down an orbiter and establish an orbit around the planet. This orbiter will use a spectrophotometer to determine the composition of the Martian surface. The lander will arrive soon after the orbiter and will perform actual tests on the Martian surface.

Previewing the Chapters

- Have students search for a figure that shows the relative sizes of all the planets in our solar system.
- Have students look for the names of space missions and tell whether they have heard about them in the news.

Tying to Previous Knowledge

- Ask students to speculate on how the collision of a large meteorite with Earth might have caused the extinction of ancient lifeforms. Many fires could be started by such a collision. Also, large amounts of dust could be thrown into the atmosphere, blocking light from the sun.
- Have students name as many objects and phenomena as they can that are found in outer space, such as galaxies, black holes, moons, and asteroids.

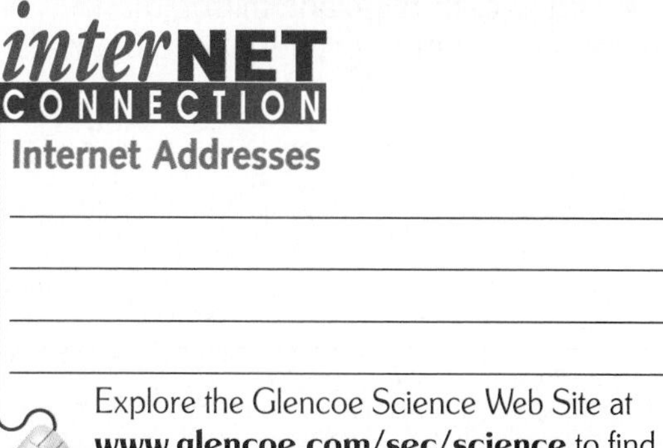

Internet Addresses

Explore the Glencoe Science Web Site at **www.glencoe.com/sec/science** to find out more about topics found in this unit.

Chapter 20 Exploring Space

Section	Objectives	Activities/Features
Chapter Opener		**Explore Activity:** Observe White Light, p. 573
20-1 **Radiation from Space** 3½ Sessions 1½ Blocks	1. **Describe** the electromagnetic spectrum. 2. **Compare** and **contrast** refracting and reflecting telescopes. 3. **Compare** and **contrast** optical and radio telescopes.	**Physics Integration,** p. 575 **Problem Solving:** Interpreting Telescope Data, p. 577 **Skill Builder:** Sequencing, p. 579 **Using Math,** p. 579 **Activity 20-1:** Telescopes, p. 580 **How It Works:** Seeing in 3-D, p. 581
20-2 **Early Space Missions** 2 Sessions 1 Block	4. **Compare** and **contrast** natural and artificial satellites. 5. **Differentiate** between an artificial satellite and a space probe. 6. **Trace** the history of the race to the moon.	**Using Math,** p. 583 **Life Science Integration,** p. 585 **MiniLab:** Comparing the Effects of Light Pollution, p. 586 **Skill Builder:** Concept Mapping, p. 587 **Using Computers,** p. 587 **On the Internet:** Star Sightings, pp. 588–589
20-3 **Recent and Future Space Missions** 1 Session ½ Block	7. **Describe** the benefits of the space shuttle. 8. **Evaluate** the usefulness of orbital space stations. 9. **List** recent and future space missions.	**MiniLab:** Modeling Gravity, p. 592 **Skill Builder:** Making and Using Graphs, p. 595 **Science Journal,** p. 595

The number of recommended single-period sessions   The number of recommended blocks
One session and one-half block are allowed for chapter review and assessment.

Activity Materials

Explore	Activities	MiniLabs
p. 573 3 flashlights; white paper; colorless, green, blue, red cellophane paper	p. 580 candle, white cardboard, flashlight, hand lens, large glass, concave mirror, plane mirror, masking tape, convex mirror, empty paper towel tube, water	p. 586 empty paper towel tube, clear night sky p. 592 stereo record album, turntable, construction paper, masking tape, 3 marbles, scissors

Need Materials? Contact Science Kit at 1-800-828-7777 or at www.sciencekit.com on the Internet.
For alternate materials, see the activity on the listed page.

Chapter Organizer

Standards		Reproducible Resources	Technology
National	**State/Local**	Test Practice Workbooks are available for use with each chapter.	English and Spanish audiocassettes are available for use with each section.
National Content Standards: UCP3, UCP5, A1, B2, B3, D1, D3, E2, G1, G3		**Activity Worksheets,** pp. 109–110 **Enrichment,** p. 53 **Laboratory Manual,** pp. 117–118 **Laboratory Manual,** pp. 119–120 **Reinforcement,** p. 53 **Study Guide,** pp. 77–78	**Section Focus Transparency 53** **Teaching Transparency 39** **Teaching Transparency 40** **Glencoe Science Voyages Interactive Videodisc—Earth** **The Infinite Voyage Series**
National Content Standards: UCP5, A1, A2, D1, D3, E2, G1, G2, G3		**Activity Worksheets,** p. 111 **Enrichment,** p. 54 **Home Involvement,** p. 29 **Reinforcement,** p. 54	**Section Focus Transparency 54** **Science Integration Transparency 20** **Glencoe Science Voyages Interactive CD-ROM**
National Content Standards: A2, D3, E2, F2, G1, G2, G3		**Activity Worksheets,** p. 112 **Critical Thinking/Problem Solving,** p. 20 **Enrichment,** p. 55 **Multicultural Connections,** pp. 39–40 **Reinforcement,** p. 55 **Study Guide,** pp. 79–80	**Section Focus Transparency 55** **Glencoe Science Voyages Interactive Videodisc—Earth** **Internet Connection,** p. 591

Key to Teaching Strategies

The following designations will help you decide which activities are appropriate for your students.

L1 Level 1 activities should be appropriate for students with learning difficulties.

L2 Level 2 activities should be within the ability range of all students.

L3 Level 3 activities are designed for above-average students.

ELL ELL activities should be within the ability range of English Language Learners.

COOP LEARN Cooperative Learning activities are designed for small group work.

P These strategies represent student products that can be placed into a best-work portfolio.

Multiple Learning Styles logos, as described on page 61T, are used throughout to indicate strategies that address different learning styles.

Assessment Resources

Chapter Review, pp. 39–40
Assessment, pp. 89–92
Performance Assessment in the Science Classroom (PASC)
MindJogger Videoquiz
Alternate Assessment in the Science Classroom
Performance Assessment, p. 34
Chapter Review Software
Computer Test Bank

Chapter 20 Exploring Space

This is a representation of key blackline masters available in the Teacher Classroom Resources. See Resource Manager boxes within the chapter for additional information.

Transparencies

Section Focus Transparencies

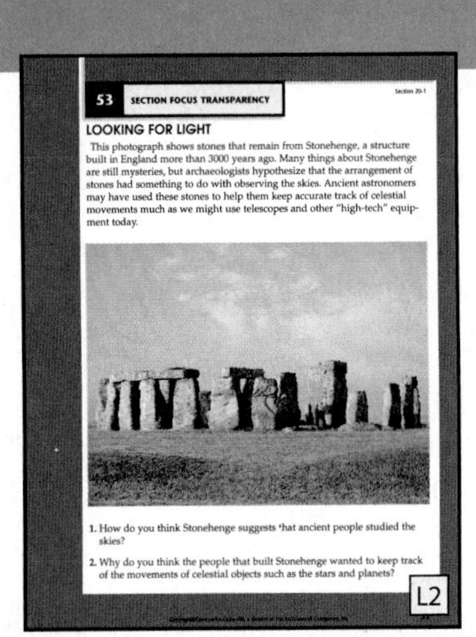

53 SECTION FOCUS TRANSPARENCY Section 20-1

LOOKING FOR LIGHT

This photograph shows stones that remain from Stonehenge, a structure built in England more than 3000 years ago. Many things about Stonehenge are still mysteries, but archaeologists hypothesize that the arrangement of stones had something to do with observing the skies. Ancient astronomers may have used these stones to help them keep accurate track of celestial movements much as we might use telescopes and other "high-tech" equipment today.

1. How do you think Stonehenge suggests that ancient people studied the skies?
2. Why do you think the people that built Stonehenge wanted to keep track of the movements of celestial objects such as the stars and planets?

L2

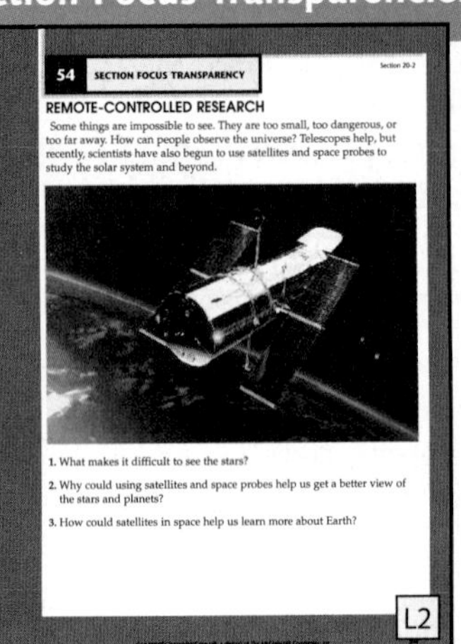

54 SECTION FOCUS TRANSPARENCY Section 20-2

REMOTE-CONTROLLED RESEARCH

Some things are impossible to see. They are too small, too dangerous, or too far away. How can people observe the universe? Telescopes help, but recently, scientists have also begun to use satellites and space probes to study the solar system and beyond.

1. What makes it difficult to see the stars?
2. Why could using satellites and space probes help us get a better view of the stars and planets?
3. How could satellites in space help us learn more about Earth?

L2

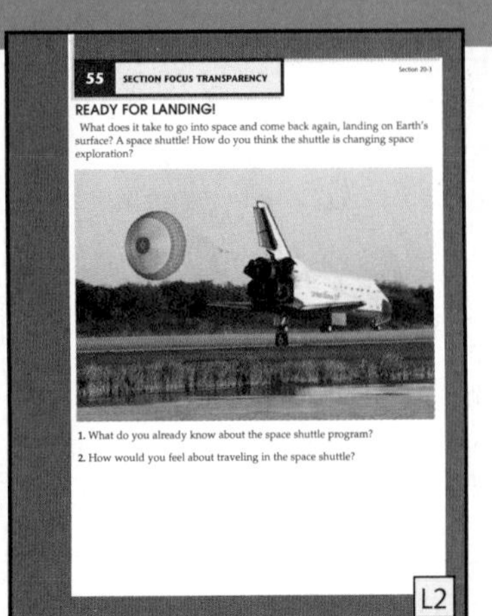

55 SECTION FOCUS TRANSPARENCY Section 20-3

READY FOR LANDING!

What does it take to go into space and come back again, landing on Earth's surface? A space shuttle! How do you think the shuttle is changing space exploration?

1. What do you already know about the space shuttle program?
2. How would you feel about traveling in the space shuttle?

L2

Science Integration Transparencies

20 SCIENCE INTEGRATION TRANSPARENCY

Leaving Earth

L2

Teaching Transparencies

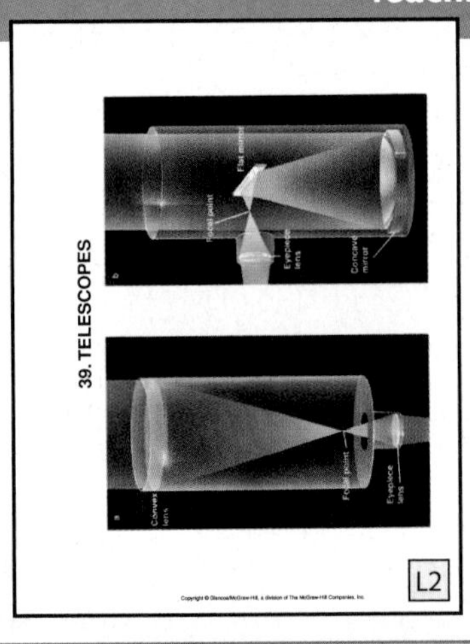

L2

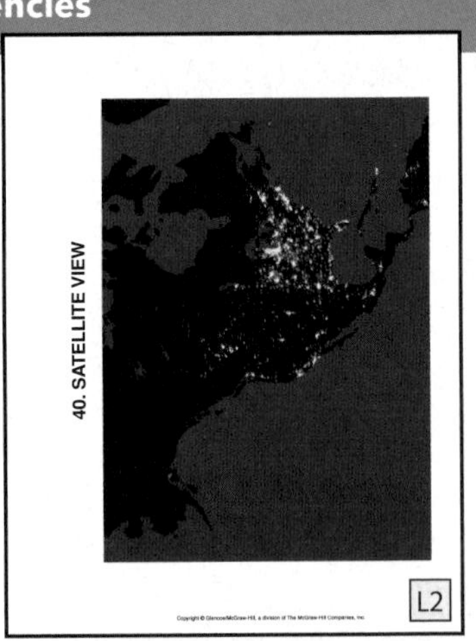

L2

Meeting Different Ability Levels

Study Guide for Content Mastery

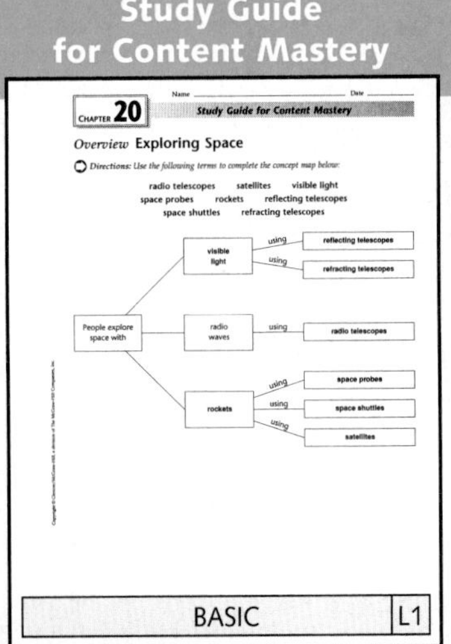

Name ______ Date ______

CHAPTER 20 Study Guide for Content Mastery

Overview Exploring Space

Directions: Use the following terms to complete the concept map below:

radio telescopes, satellites, visible light, space probes, rockets, reflecting telescopes, space shuttles, refracting telescopes

BASIC L1

Reinforcement

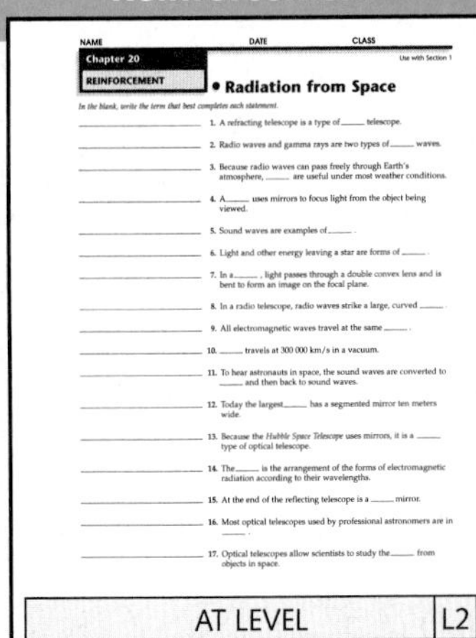

NAME ______ DATE ______ CLASS ______

Chapter 20 REINFORCEMENT Use with Section 1

• Radiation from Space

In the blank, write the term that best completes each statement.

1. A refracting telescope is a type of ______ telescope.
2. Radio waves and gamma rays are two types of ______ waves.
3. Because radio waves can pass freely through Earth's atmosphere, ______ are useful under most weather conditions.
4. A ______ uses mirrors to focus light from the object being viewed.
5. Sound waves are examples of ______.
6. Light and other energy leaving a star are forms of ______.
7. In a ______, light passes through a double convex lens and is bent to form an image on the focal plane.
8. In a radio telescope, radio waves strike a large, curved ______.
9. All electromagnetic waves travel at the same ______.
10. ______ travels at 300 000 km/s in a vacuum.
11. To hear astronauts in space, the sound waves are converted to ______ and then back to sound waves.
12. Today the largest ______ has a segmented mirror ten meters wide.
13. Because the *Hubble Space Telescope* uses mirrors, it is a ______ type of optical telescope.
14. The ______ is the arrangement of the forms of electromagnetic radiation according to their wavelengths.
15. At the end of the reflecting telescope is a ______ mirror.
16. Most optical telescopes used by professional astronomers are in ______.
17. Optical telescopes allow scientists to study the ______ from objects in space.

AT LEVEL L2

Enrichment Worksheets

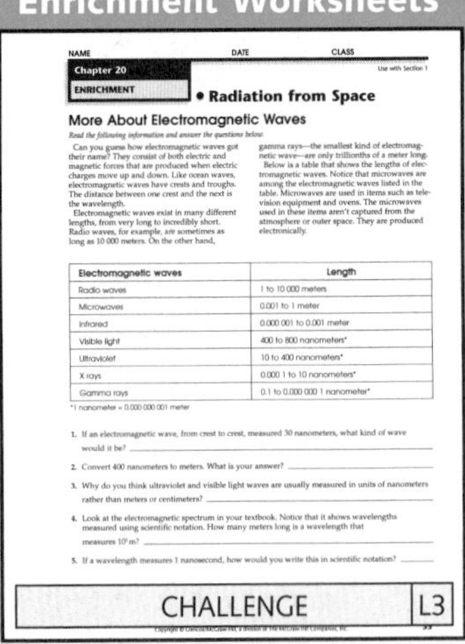

NAME ______ DATE ______ CLASS ______

Chapter 20 ENRICHMENT Use with Section 1

• Radiation from Space

More About Electromagnetic Waves

Electromagnetic waves	Length
Radio waves	1 to 10 000 meters
Microwaves	0.001 to 1 meter
Infrared	0.000 001 to 0.001 meter
Visible light	400 to 800 nanometers*
Ultraviolet	10 to 400 nanometers*
X rays	0.000 1 to 10 nanometers*
Gamma rays	0.1 to 0.000 000 1 nanometer*

*1 nanometer = 0.000 000 001 meter

1. If an electromagnetic wave, from crest to crest, measured 30 nanometers, what kind of wave would it be?
2. Convert 400 nanometers to meters. What is your answer?
3. Why do you think ultraviolet and visible light waves are usually measured in units of nanometers rather than meters or centimeters?
4. Look at the electromagnetic spectrum in your textbook. Notice that it shows wavelengths measured using scientific notation. How many meters long is a wavelength that measures 10^3 m?
5. If a wavelength measures 1 nanometer, how would you write this in scientific notation?

CHALLENGE L3

Resource Manager

Hands-on Activities

Activity Worksheets

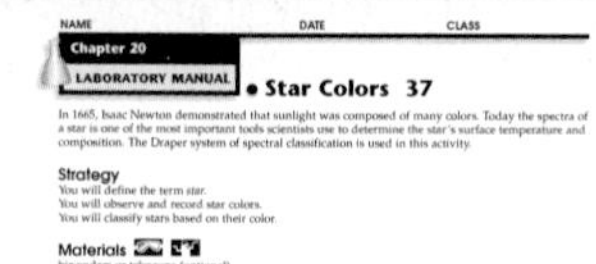
NAME DATE CLASS

Chapter 20

LABORATORY MANUAL

Star Colors 37

Strategy

Materials

Table 1—Star Classification Chart

Star spectral type	Color	Surface temperature (K)
M	red	2000–4000
K	red to orange	3500–5000
G	yellow	5000–6000
F	yellow-white	6000–7500
A	white	9000
B	bluish-white	11 000–25 000
O	bluish-white	60 000

Procedure

L2

Lab Manual

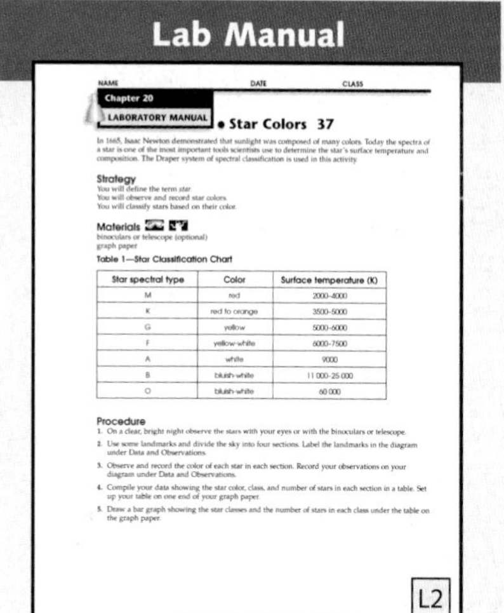
NAME DATE CLASS

Chapter 20

LABORATORY MANUAL

Star Colors 37

Strategy

Materials

Table 1—Star Classification Chart

Star spectral type	Color	Surface temperature (K)
M	red	2000–4000
K	red to orange	3500–5000
G	yellow	5000–6000
F	yellow-white	6000–7500
A	white	9000
B	bluish-white	11 000–25 000
O	bluish-white	60 000

Procedure

L2

Accessibility

Spanish Resources

Assessment

Performance Assessment

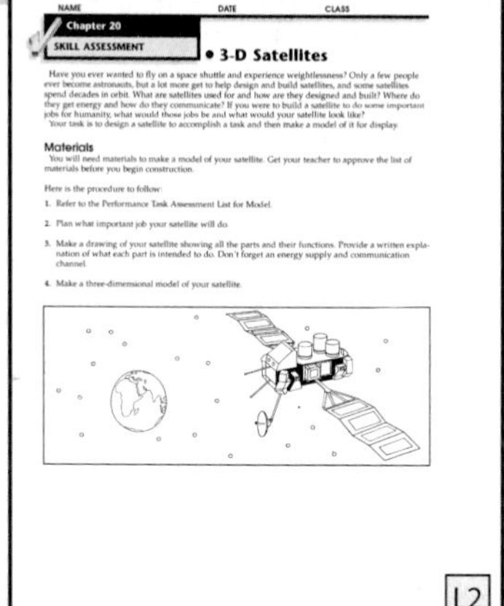
NAME DATE CLASS

Chapter 20

SKILL ASSESSMENT

3-D Satellites

Materials

L2

Chapter Review

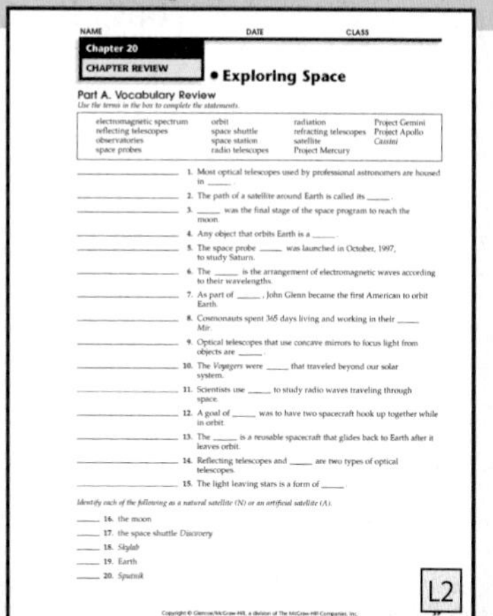
NAME DATE CLASS

Chapter 20

CHAPTER REVIEW

Exploring Space

Part A. Vocabulary Review

L2

Assessment

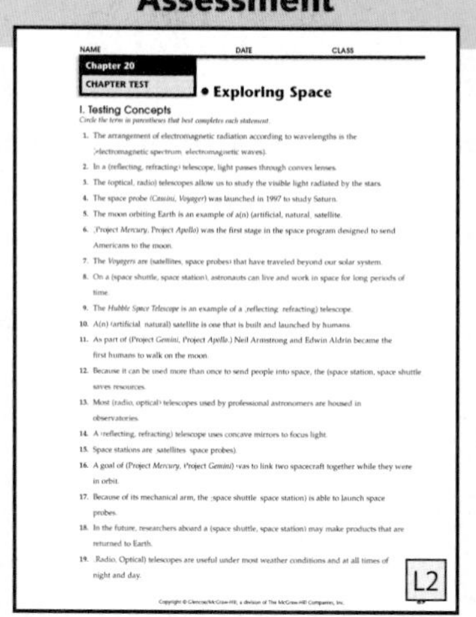
NAME DATE CLASS

Chapter 20

CHAPTER TEST

Exploring Space

I. Testing Concepts

L2

Test Practice Workbook

Extending Content

Critical Thinking/ Problem Solving

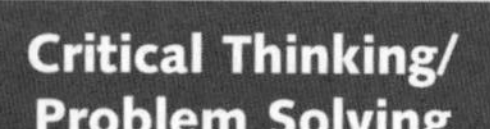

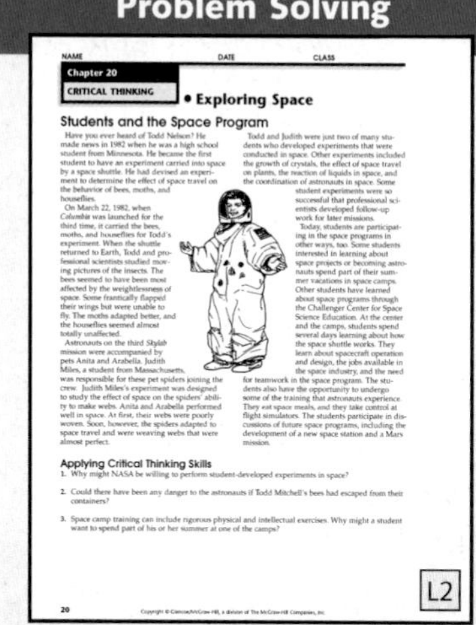
NAME DATE CLASS

Chapter 20

CRITICAL THINKING

Exploring Space

Students and the Space Program

Applying Critical Thinking Skills

L2

Multicultural Connections

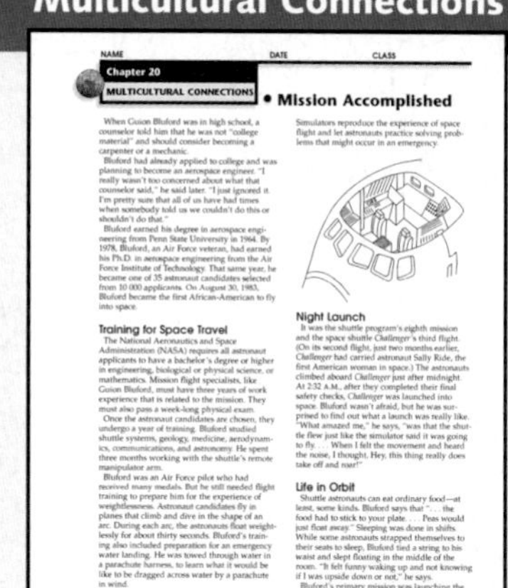
NAME DATE CLASS

Chapter 20

MULTICULTURAL CONNECTIONS

Mission Accomplished

Training for Space Travel

Night Launch

Life in Orbit

L2

Helping You Prepare

Large Telescopes (Section 20-1)

On April 21, 1998, the largest telescope on Earth captured light from its first star. The European Southern Observatory's Very Large Telescope (VLT) is located in Cerro Paranal, a mountaintop in the Chilean Andes. The VLT is composed of four identical 8.2-m individual telescopes and several movable 1.8-m telescopes.

Other large telescopes include the twin 10-m Keck reflecting telescopes on Mauna Kea in Hawaii. The primary mirror of each telescope has been constructed from 36 hexagonal glass segments, each 1.8 m in diameter.

The NASA Orbital Debris Observatory (NODO) uses a liquid mirror telescope. The objective mirror is made of a shallow container of the liquid element mercury. It is 3 m in diameter and is constantly spinning at one revolution every 6.02315 seconds. This spinning forces the liquid mercury to form a parabolic reflector. The telescope is kept level; thus, it only observes the sky's zenith. Its main mission is to locate and count orbital debris (space junk) as small as 1 cm in diameter.

The Very Large Array (VLA) of telescopes near Socorro, New Mexico, is composed of 27 radio telescopes. All 27 telescopes can be used at once to operate as one large telescope.

GLENCOE TECHNOLOGY

CD-ROM

Glencoe Science Voyages Interactive CD-ROM

Chapter Summaries

Use the Chapter Summary to introduce, teach, or review chapter material.

Light Pollution (Section 20-1)

Light pollution is a glow in the sky caused by city lights. The glow makes it difficult to see dim stars.

In several U.S. cities, work has begun to reduce light pollution. Tucson, Arizona, located only 80 km from the Kitt Peak National Observatory, has replaced its streetlights with low-pressure sodium lamps. These lights shine at wavelengths that can be filtered out by astronomers.

Other cities have put hoods on billboards, parking-lot lights, and floodlights so they illuminate the object or the ground rather than the sky.

NATIONAL GEOGRAPHIC — **Teacher's Corner**

Products Available from National Geographic Society

To order the following products for use with this chapter, call National Geographic Society at 1-800-368-2728:

Books

Discover Mars

Mars: Uncovering the Secrets of the Red Planet

National Geographic Satellite Atlas of the World

Waves: The Electromagnetic Universe

Video

What We Learn About Earth from Space

Index to National Geographic Magazine

The following articles may be used for research relating to this chapter:

"Return to Mars," by William R. Newcott, August 1998.

"New Eyes on the Universe," by Bradford A. Smith, January 1994.

"Satellite Rescue," by Thomas Y. Canby, November 1991.

"Mission to Mars," by Michael Collins, November 1988.

Satellites and Space Probes
(Section 20-2)

The first U.S. weather satellite, *Vanguard 2,* was launched in February 1959. Its mission was to take photographs of Earth's cloud patterns.

Evidence of possible water on the moon was first discovered by the *Clementine* space probe in 1994. Radio signals beamed from *Clementine* bounced off the moon and were received on Earth. Initial readings were similar to those produced by ice on Earth. In 1998, using data gathered by the *Lunar Prospector*, NASA mission scientists estimated that 6 billion tons of water are hidden in permanently shadowed regions of the moon's north and south poles.

Jupiter's moon, Europa, may contain water, too. Recent preliminary studies of Europa by the *Galileo* spacecraft indicate an ocean of water or ice under the moon's crustal layer of ice.

Space Spin-offs **(Section 20-2)**

Much of the technology developed by NASA to achieve its goals in space is now being used by people throughout the world. Technologies developed by NASA that are later used by the general public are called spin-offs.

NASA developed lightweight, compact breathing systems for astronauts to carry as they ventured out of their spacecraft and onto the moon. Today, firefighters use these breathing systems as well as fire-resistant uniforms originally designed as flight suits for NASA pilots. The lightweight material in the suits won't burn or crack.

A material designed for boots worn by astronauts on the moon is now found in some athletic shoes. Other materials have been incorporated into ski goggles, blankets, and bicycle seats.

People who are visually impaired also have benefited from spin-offs. One device vibrates ink on a printed page, enabling them to read materials that are not printed in Braille. Another device determines the denomination of currency and generates an audible signal.

Other spin-offs include pens that write without the help of gravity and sunglasses that adjust to various light levels.

SCIENCE UPDATE

For current events or science in the news, access the Glencoe Science Web Site at **www.glencoe.com/sec/science**

International Space Station
(Section 20-3)

The International Space Station will be a permanently crewed satellite in which teams of astronauts from many nations will work cooperatively in space. Launch of materials and modules that are part of the International Space Station assembly began with the launch of the space shuttle *Endeavor.* It is believed that humans will find thousands of ways to use the space station that no one has even thought of yet.

Teacher to Teacher

"I encourage students to visit the media center to investigate how we continue to explore space. Ask students to use periodicals to investigate current NASA projects, or visit the NASA Web Site to gather and share information about current events."

Tracey L. Smeltzer, Library Media Specialist
Derry Area High School
Derry, PA

CHAPTER 20
Exploring Space

CHAPTER OVERVIEW

Section 20-1 This section discusses electromagnetic radiation and telescopes.

Section 20-2 Early artificial satellites and space probes are described.

Section 20-3 This section discusses recent and future space missions.

Chapter Vocabulary

electromagnetic spectrum
refracting telescope
reflecting telescope
observatory
radio telescope
satellite
orbit
space probe
Project Mercury
Project Gemini
Project Apollo
space shuttle
space station

Theme Connection

Energy/Scale and Structure The properties of electromagnetic radiation have enabled scientists to describe the scale and structure of our solar system and beyond.

00:00 OUT OF TIME?

If time does not permit teaching the entire chapter, use Reviewing Main Ideas on pp. 596–597.

CHAPTER 20
Exploring Space

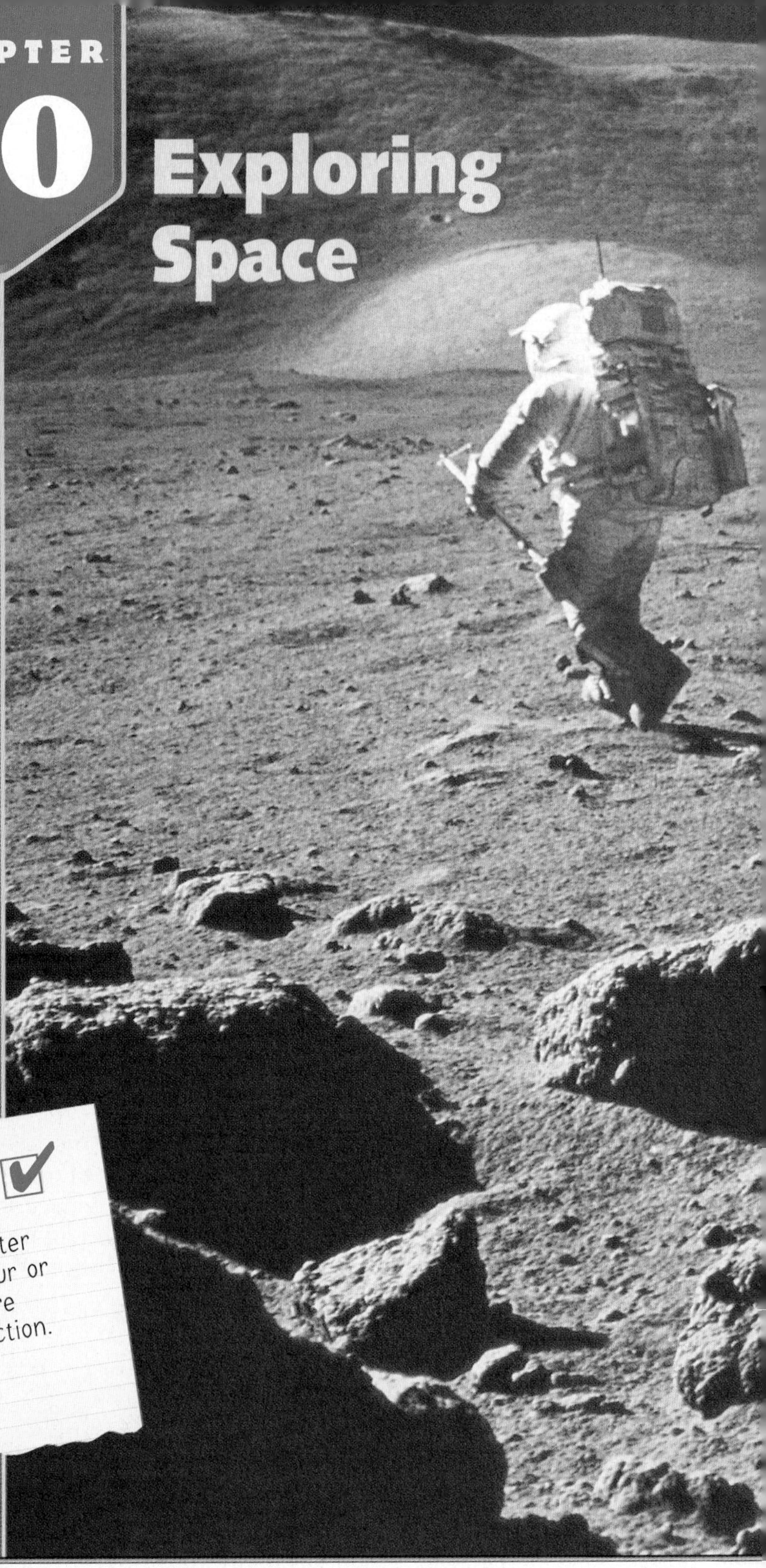

Chapter Preview

Skills Preview

Skill Builders
- Sequence
- Map Concepts

MiniLabs
- Analyze Data
- Infer

Activities
- Draw Conclusions

Reading Check ✓

As you read this chapter about space, write four or five questions that are answered in each section.

572

Multiple Learning Styles

Look for the following logos for strategies that emphasize different learning modalities.

Linguistic Science Journal, pp. 576, 577, 586; Using Science Words, p. 584; Activity, p. 585; Across the Curriculum, p. 593; Preview, p. 596

Visual-Spatial Explore Activity, p. 573; Reteach, pp. 578, 596; Multiple Learning Styles, p. 578; Activity, p. 580; MiniLab, p. 586; Quick Demo, p. 591; Inclusion Strategies, p. 591; Making a Model, p. 593

Auditory-Musical Out of Time, p. 596

Kinesthetic MiniLab, p. 592

Interpersonal Discussion, p. 583; Reteach, p. 587; Review, p. 596

Intrapersonal Visual Learning, p. 581

Explore Activity

The first space exploration didn't occur in a spaceship or a satellite. Instead, it was done by a person simply looking upward, studying countless points of shimmering light. Over time, people devised more and more accurate ways to study the moon, the planets, and the stars. We can learn a lot about a star's temperature, size, and composition, for instance, by studying its light. In this activity, you'll observe some of the colors that make up visible light, which is one form of radiation emitted by stars.

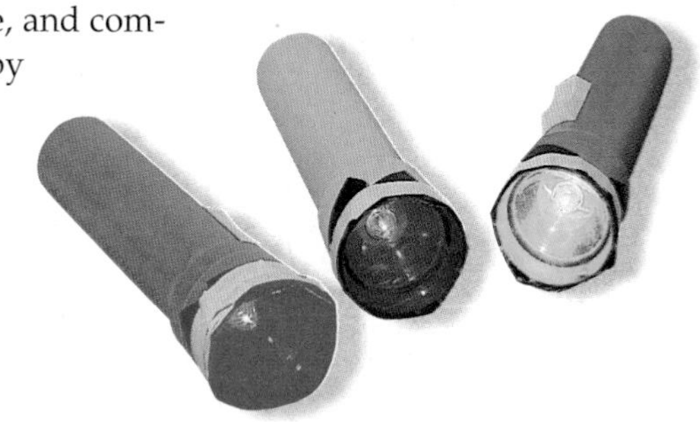

Observe White Light

1. Cover the end of a flashlight with green cellophane paper.
2. Cover another flashlight with blue cellophane and a third with red cellophane.
3. In a darkened room, experiment with the three lights by shining different combinations of two lights on the same spot on a sheet of white paper.

Science Journal

Observe all colors shining on the same spot on the paper and infer what is happening. Record your observations and inferences in your Science Journal.

573

Assessment Planner

Portfolio
Refer to p. 597 for suggested items that students might select for their portfolios.

Performance Assessment
See p. 597 for additional Performance Assessment options.
Skill Builder, pp. 579, 587, 595
MiniLab, pp. 586, 592
Activity 20-1, p. 580; 20-2, pp. 588–589

Content Assessment
Section Assessment, pp. 579, 587, 595
Chapter Assessment, pp. 598–599
Proficiency Prep, pp. 579, 587, 594

Explore Activity

Purpose

Visual-Spatial Use the Explore Activity to introduce students to the composition of white light. Inform students that they will be learning about electromagnetic radiation and how it can be used to study objects in space. L2 ELL COOP LEARN

Preparation

Have students bring in flashlights.

Materials

sheet of white paper; 3 flashlights; colorless, green, blue, and red cellophane sheets

Teaching Strategies

Troubleshooting The flashlights used by each group should be as close to identical as possible. Have students attach the cellophane to the flashlights with transparent tape. Make the room as dark as possible.

The red and blue light created a new color when added together. As different-colored lights were combined, different colors were produced. When all colors were combined, white light was seen on the white paper.

Assessment

Oral As lights of different colors are added together on the white paper, ask students to explain what is happening. Use **Performance Assessment in the Science Classroom**, p. 71. P

SECTION 20•1

Prepare

Refer to **Large Telescopes and Light Pollution** on p. 572E.

Preplanning

Refer to the **Chapter Organizer** on pp. 572A–B.

1 Motivate

Bellringer

Before presenting the lesson, display **Section Focus Transparency 53** on the overhead projector. Use the accompanying **Focus Activity** worksheet. L2 ELL

Section 20-1

53 SECTION FOCUS TRANSPARENCY

LOOKING FOR LIGHT

This photograph shows stones that remain from Stonehenge, a structure built in England more than 3000 years ago. Many things about Stonehenge are still mysteries, but archaeologists hypothesize that the arrangement of stones had something to do with observing the skies. Ancient astronomers may have used these stones to help them keep accurate track of celestial movements much as we might use telescopes and other "high-tech" equipment today.

1. How do you think Stonehenge suggests that ancient people studied the skies?
2. Why do you think the people that built Stonehenge wanted to keep track of the movements of celestial objects such as the stars and planets?

Tying to Previous Knowledge

Inform students that binoculars can be used to view large areas of the sky. Binoculars are actually two refracting telescopes side by side.

20 Radiation from Space

What You'll Learn

- The electromagnetic spectrum
- The differences between refracting and reflecting telescopes
- The differences between optical and radio telescopes

Vocabulary

electromagnetic spectrum
refracting telescope
reflecting telescope
observatory
radio telescope

Why It's Important

- You'll learn about the tools and methods used to study space.

Electromagnetic Waves

On a crisp, autumn evening, you take a break from your homework to gaze out the window at the many stars that fill the night sky. Looking up at the stars, it's easy to imagine future spaceships venturing through space and large space stations circling above Earth, where people work and live. But, when you look into the night sky, what you're really seeing is the distant past, not the future.

Light from the Past

When you look at a star, you see light that left the star many years ago. The light that you see travels fast. Still, the distances across space are so great that it takes years for the light to reach Earth—sometimes millions of years.

The light and other energy leaving a star are forms of radiation. Recall that radiation is energy that's transmitted from one place to another by electromagnetic waves. Because of the electric and magnetic properties of this radiation, it's called electromagnetic radiation. Electromagnetic waves carry energy through empty space as well as through matter.

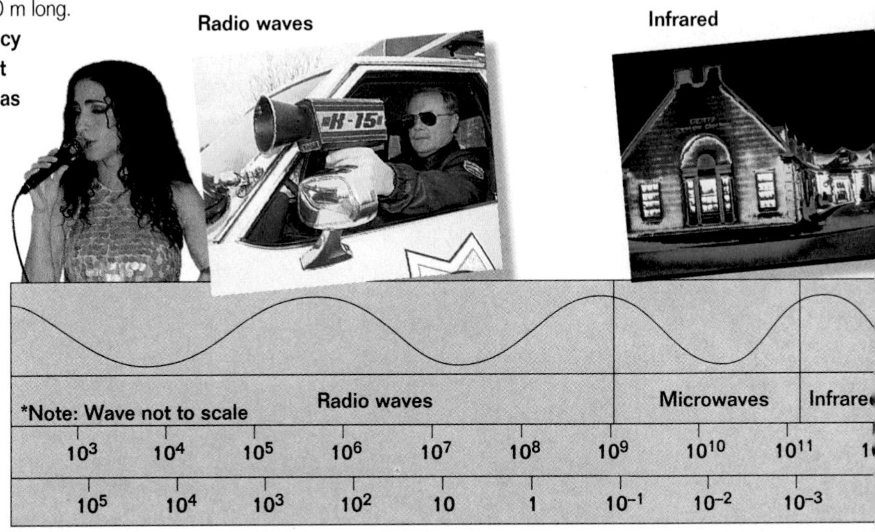

Figure 20-1 The electromagnetic spectrum ranges from gamma rays with wavelengths of less than 0.000 000 000 01 m to radio waves more than 100 000 m long. **What happens to frequency (the number of waves that pass a point per second) as wavelength shortens?**

Resource Manager

The following **Teacher Classroom Resources** can be used with Section 20-1:

Reproducible Masters

Activity Worksheets, pp. 109–110 L2
Enrichment, p. 53 L3
Laboratory Manual, pp. 117–118 L2
Laboratory Manual, pp. 119–120 L2
Reinforcement, p. 53 L2
Study Guide, pp. 77–78 L1 ELL 

Transparencies

Teaching Transparency 39 L2
Teaching Transparency 40 L2

Electromagnetic Radiation

Sound waves, a type of mechanical wave, can't travel through empty space. How do we hear the voices of the astronauts while they're in space? When they speak into a microphone, the sound is converted into electromagnetic waves called radio waves. The radio waves travel through space and through our atmosphere. They are then converted back into sound by electronic equipment and audio speakers.

Radio waves and visible light from the sun are just two types of electromagnetic radiation. The other types include gamma rays, X rays, ultraviolet waves, infrared waves, and microwaves. **Figure 20-1** shows these forms of electromagnetic radiation arranged according to their wavelengths. This arrangement of electromagnetic radiation is called the **electromagnetic spectrum.**

Although the various electromagnetic waves differ in their wavelengths, they all travel at the speed of 300 000 km/s in a vacuum. You're probably more familiar with this speed as the "speed of light." Visible light and other forms of electromagnetic radiation travel at this incredible speed, but the universe is so large that it takes millions of years for the light from some stars to reach Earth.

Once electromagnetic radiation from stars and other objects reaches Earth, we can use it to learn about the source of the electromagnetic radiation. What tools and methods do scientists use to discover what lies beyond our planet? One tool for observing electromagnetic radiation from distant sources is a telescope.

Bending Light
Pass a beam of white light through a prism. Note that different colors of light are bent, forming a spectrum. Infer how the white light and prism form a spectrum with violet on one end and red on the other.

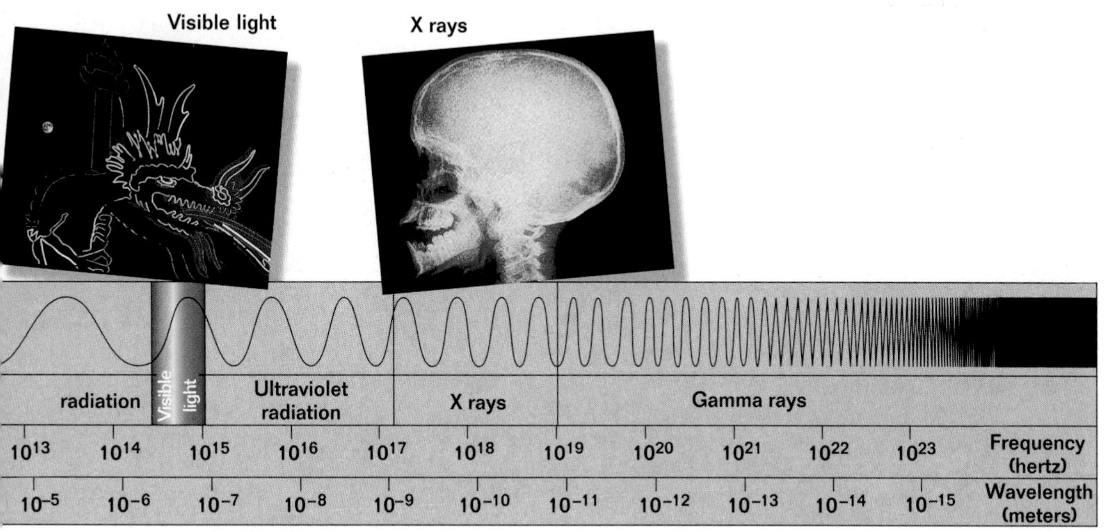

2 Teach

All colors in the visible spectrum, which have varying wavelengths, are bent through different angles, thus dispersing. Violet light, which has the shortest wavelength of light in the visible spectrum, is bent the most, whereas red light, which has the longest wavelength of light in the visible spectrum, is bent the least.

Caption Answer

Figure 20-1 *Because light of all wavelengths travels at the same speed, 300 000 km/s, shorter wavelengths have higher frequencies (more of the waves pass a particular point each second).*

Discussion

Which form of electromagnetic radiation has the highest frequency? *gamma rays*

GLENCOE TECHNOLOGY

Videodisc

Glencoe Science Voyages Interactive Videodisc—Earth

Side 2, Lesson 8 *Space Exploration*

36541

Refer to Videodisc Teacher Guide for additional bar codes.

Inclusion Strategies

Gifted Have students research the index of refraction. Have them relate what they learn to the use of lenses in a telescope. *The index of refraction of a substance is equal to the sine of the angle of incidence of light from a vacuum divided by the sine of the angle of refraction. The index of refraction of glass is used when determining how to shape the objective lens of a telescope.* L3

Integrating the Sciences

Physics Have students find out how concave and convex lenses affect the path of light that passes through them. Some students may wish to demonstrate the difference by using both types of lenses. L2

Teacher FYI

Hubble is so powerful that if you were in Washington, D.C., you could use it to read a newspaper headline in Missouri.

VISUAL Learning

Figure 20-2 Ask students to make a rough copy of each telescope design in their Science Journals. On the copy of each type of telescope, ask students to identify where the eyepiece, objective, focus (focal point or focal plane), and focal length would be. Then have students explain the difference in these two telescopes using the above-listed telescope parts. L2 ELL

Caption Answer

Figure 20-2 *reflecting*

GLENCOE TECHNOLOGY

Videodisc

The Infinite Voyage: Unseen Worlds

Chapter 2 *The Very Large Array: Monitoring Radio Waves* 3:30

Secrets from a Frozen World

Chapter 7 *Solar Ultraviolet Light and the Diminishing Ozone Layer* 3:00

Refer to the Teacher Guide for bar codes and teaching strategies.

Optical Telescopes

Optical telescopes produce magnified images of objects. Light is collected by an objective lens or mirror, which then forms an image at the focal point of the telescope. The eyepiece lens then magnifies the image. The two types of optical telescopes are shown in **Figure 20-2.**

In a **refracting telescope,** the light from an object passes through a double convex objective lens and is bent to form an image on the focal point. The image is then magnified by the eyepiece.

A **reflecting telescope** uses a mirror as an objective to focus light from the object being viewed. Light passes through the open end of a reflecting telescope and strikes a concave mirror at its base. The light is then reflected to the focal point to form an image. A smaller mirror is often used to reflect the light into the eyepiece lens so the magnified image can be viewed.

Figure 20-2 These diagrams show how each type of optical telescope collects light and forms an image.

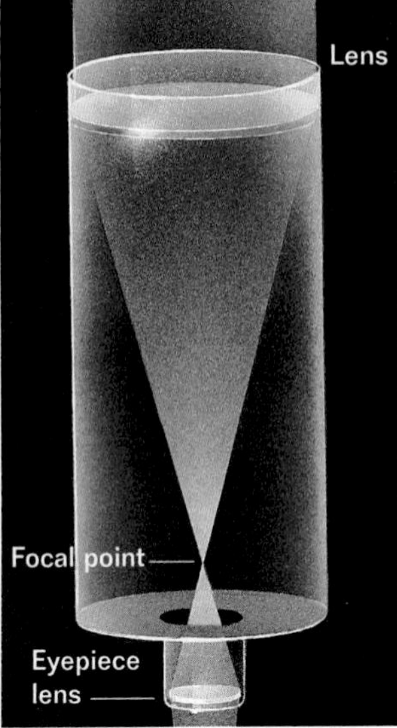

A In a refracting telescope, a double convex lens focuses light to form an image at the focal point.

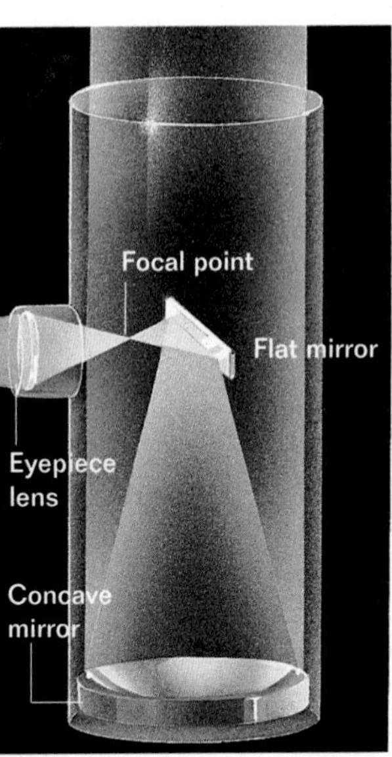

B In a reflecting telescope, a concave mirror focuses light to form an image at the focal point.

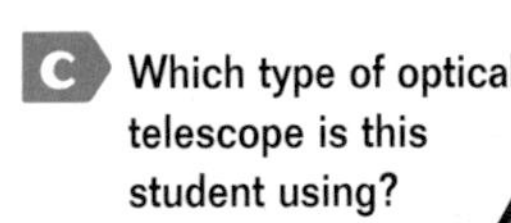

C Which type of optical telescope is this student using?

Using Optical Telescopes

Most optical telescopes used by professional astronomers are housed in buildings called **observatories.** Observatories often have a dome-shaped roof that opens up to let in light. However, not all telescopes are in observatories.

Telescopes Ask students to select one of the following questions and to write a brief paragraph in their Science Journals that answers the question selected.

- **How do reflecting and refracting telescopes differ in the way they form images?** *A reflecting telescope uses a concave mirror to reflect light to the focal plane, while a refracting telescope uses a convex lens to bend light to the focal plane.*
- **What advantage does a radio telescope have over optical telescopes?** *Radio telescopes can be used in almost all kinds of weather and at all times of the day and night. Radio telescopes can receive energy from objects that cannot be observed with optical telescopes.*

The *Hubble Space Telescope,* shown in **Figure 20-3,** was launched in 1990 by the space shuttle *Discovery.* Earth's atmosphere absorbs and distorts some of the energy received from space. Because *Hubble* didn't have to view space through our atmosphere, it should have produced clear images. However, when the largest mirror of this reflecting telescope was shaped, there was a mistake. Images obtained by the telescope were not as clear as expected. In December 1993, a team of astronauts repaired *Hubble's* telescope mirror and other equipment. Now, the clear images obtained by *Hubble Space Telescope* are changing scientists' ideas about space.

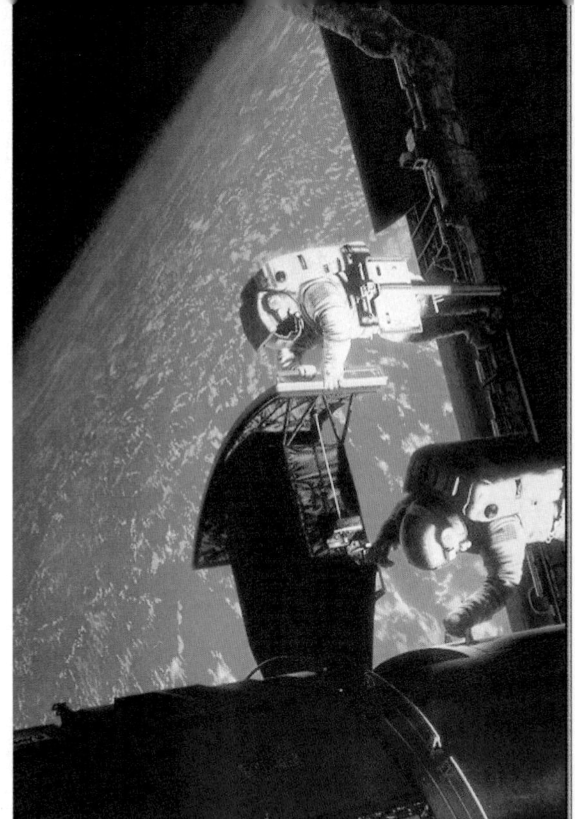

Figure 20-3 The *Hubble Space Telescope* was released from the cargo bay of the space shuttle *Discovery* on April 25, 1990. It's now orbiting Earth, sending back images and data about distant space objects.

Problem Solving

Interpreting Telescope Data

The magnifying power *(Mp)* of a telescope is determined by the focal lengths of the telescope's objective lens and eyepiece. Once built, you cannot easily change the objective lens, but you can easily change the eyepiece. That's why telescopes are often sold with three or four eyepieces—each with a different focal length. The magnifying power of a telescope is equal to the focal length of its objective lens divided by the focal length of its eyepiece.

Telescopes also have light-gathering power (LGP). Generally, the larger the diameter (aperture) of a telescope's objective, the more light the telescope can gather. Therefore, a telescope with an objective aperture of 125 mm will gather more light than a telescope with an objective aperture of 75 mm.

The following table lists the characteristics of two telescopes. Study the data about each telescope and interpret which has the greater magnifying power and which has the greater light-gathering power.

Telescope Data

Telescope	Aperture	Objective Focal Length	Eyepiece Focal Length
1	75 mm	1200 mm	9 mm, 12 mm
2	125 mm	900 mm	9 mm, 12 mm

Think Critically: Which telescope would you want to use to observe stars? Which telescope would you want to use to observe craters on the moon? Explain your selections.

Content Background

The largest radio telescope in the world is located near Arecibo, Puerto Rico. The curved dish, made of more than 38 400 aluminum panels, is 305 m in diameter.

Problem Solving

Review the equation for finding magnifying power (Mp). *Mp = focal length of the objective/focal length of the eyepiece* Make certain students understand that a telescope's magnifying power can vary, depending on the eyepiece used. For instance, using the 9-mm eyepiece, Telescope 1 has an Mp of 133. With the 12-mm eyepiece, Telescope 1 has an Mp of 100. By the same token, Telescope 2 has an Mp of 100 when equipped with the 9-mm eyepiece. With the 12-mm eyepiece, Telescope 2 has an Mp of 75.

Think Critically

Telescope 2, with an aperture of 125 mm, would be best for viewing stars—the larger the aperture, the more light the telescope can gather. Telescope 1 equipped with the 9-mm eyepiece would be best for viewing moon craters—it has the highest magnifying power.

Hubble Space Telescope Have students write about the space shuttle missions to repair the *Hubble Space Telescope. Aviation Week & Space Technology* (May 24, 1993) reports on one of the repair missions. One of its goals was to demonstrate the feasibility of in-orbit servicing of a complex satellite. L2

Caption Answer

Figure 20-4 *Being in space, it doesn't have the distorting effects of Earth's atmosphere.*

3 Assess

Check for Understanding

Enrichment

Have students research the issue of light pollution, which is a glow in the sky caused by city lights. Light pollution affects astronomers' abilities to view stars. Have students brainstorm possible solutions to light pollution.

Reteach

Visual-Spatial Show students labeled cross sections of refracting, reflecting, and radio telescopes. The cross sections should show the path of electromagnetic energy through the telescopes. Have students study the diagrams, then ask the class: **What is the function of the objective of each telescope?** *The objective is the lens, mirror, or dish antenna that collects visible light or radio waves and focuses them onto the focal plane.*

Extension

For students who have mastered this section, use the **Reinforcement** and **Enrichment** masters.

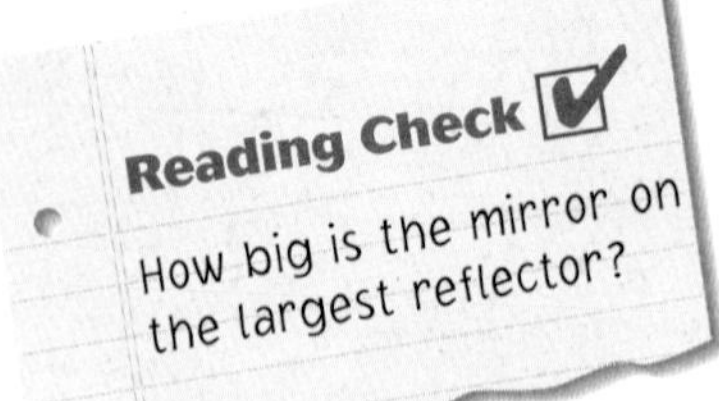

Reading Check
How big is the mirror on the largest reflector?

Active Optics

Since the early 1600s, when the Italian scientist Galileo Galilei first turned a telescope toward the stars, people have been searching for better ways to study what lies beyond our atmosphere, such as the twin Keck telescopes shown in **Figure 20-4.** Today, the largest reflector has a segmented mirror 10 m wide. The most recent innovations in optical telescopes involve active and adaptive optics. With active optics, a computer is used to compensate for changes in temperature, mirror distortions, and bad viewing conditions. Even more ambitious is adaptive optics, which uses a laser to probe the atmosphere and relay information to a computer about air turbulence. The computer then adjusts the telescope's mirror thousands of times per second, thus reducing the effects of atmospheric turbulence.

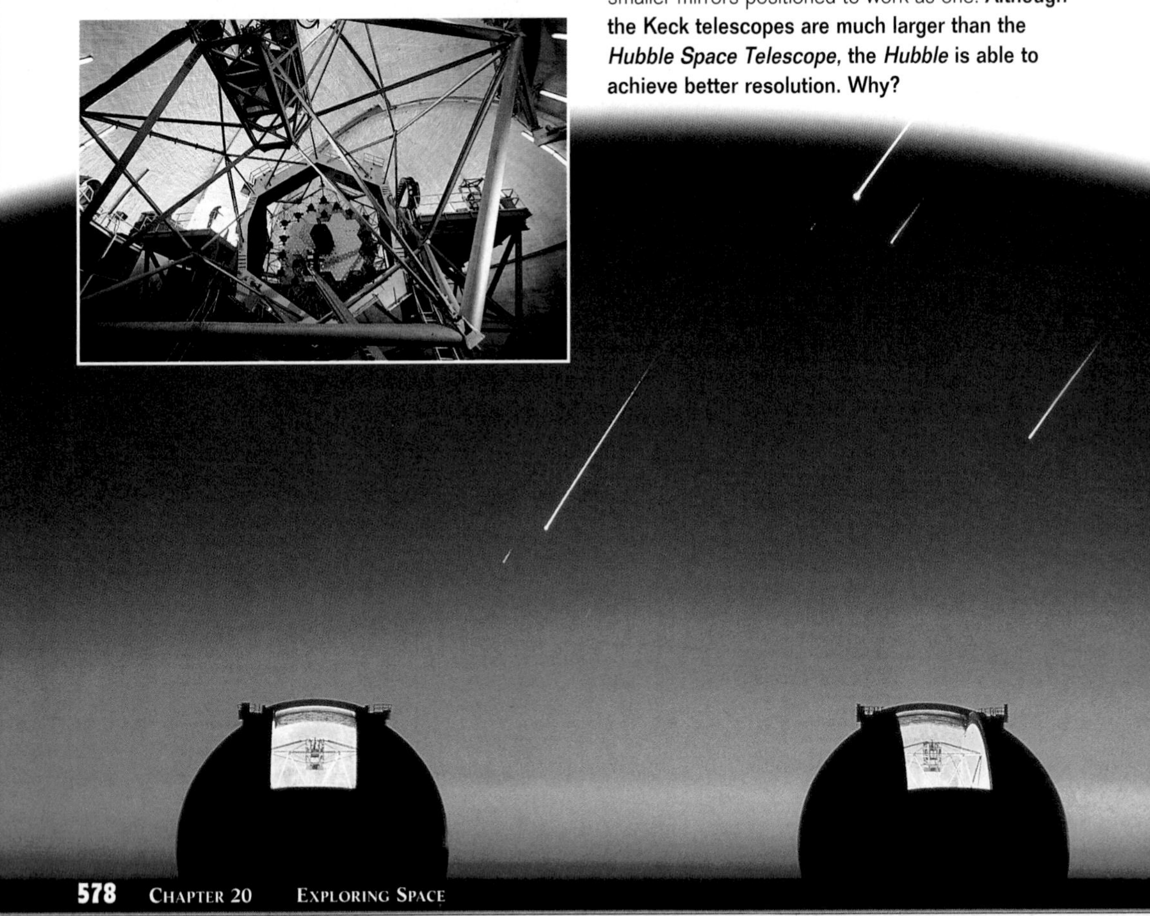

Figure 20-4 The twin Keck telescopes on Mauna Kea in Hawaii can be used together, more than doubling the resolving power. Each individual telescope has an objective mirror 10 m in diameter. To cope with the difficulty of building such a large mirror, this telescope design used several smaller mirrors positioned to work as one. **Although the Keck telescopes are much larger than the *Hubble Space Telescope*, the *Hubble* is able to achieve better resolution. Why?**

Multiple Learning Styles

Visual-Spatial Invite to class a person who rents or sells dish antennas for televisions. Ask him or her to explain how the dish antenna works and to show students a model of one. After students examine the model, ask them to compare and contrast dish antennas to radio telescopes. Explain to students that dish antennas and radio telescopes operate in the same basic way. Electromagnetic energy is collected by the dish and reflected to the receiver.

Radio Telescopes

As you know, stars and other objects radiate energy throughout the electromagnetic spectrum. A **radio telescope,** such as the one shown in **Figure 20-5,** is used to study radio waves traveling through space. Unlike visible light, radio waves pass freely through Earth's atmosphere. Because of this, radio telescopes are useful 24 hours a day under most weather conditions.

Radio waves reaching Earth's surface strike the large, curved dish of a radio telescope. This dish reflects the waves to a focal point where a receiver is located. The information allows scientists to detect objects in space, to map the universe, and to search for intelligent life on other planets.

In the remainder of this chapter, you'll learn about the instruments that travel into space and send back information that telescopes on Earth's surface cannot obtain.

Figure 20-5 This radio telescope is used to study radio waves traveling through space.

Section Assessment

1. What is the difference between radio telescopes and optical telescopes?
2. The frequency of electromagnetic radiation is the number of waves that pass a point in a specific amount of time. If red light has a longer wavelength than blue light, which would have a greater frequency?
3. **Think Critically:** It takes light from the closest star to Earth (other than the sun) about four years to reach us. If there were intelligent life on a planet circling that star, how long would it take for us to send them a radio transmission and for us to receive their reply?
4. **Skill Builder**
   Sequencing Sequence these electromagnetic waves from longest wavelength to shortest wavelength: *gamma rays, visible light, X rays, radio waves, infrared waves, ultraviolet waves,* and *microwaves.* If you need help, refer to Sequencing in the **Skill Handbook** on page 714.

Using Math

The magnifying power (Mp) of a telescope is determined by dividing the focal length of the objective lens (FL_{obj}) by the focal length of the eyepiece (FL_{eye}) using the following equation.

$$Mp = \frac{FL_{obj}}{FL_{eye}}$$

If $FL_{obj} = 1200$ mm and $FL_{eye} = 6$ mm, what is the telescope's magnifying power?

4. **Skill Builder**
radio waves, microwaves, infrared waves, visible light, ultraviolet waves, X rays, gamma rays

Assessment

Content Assess students' abilities to sequence events by having them compare and contrast their sequences with those of other students. Use **Performance Assessment in the Science Classroom,** p. 97.

4 Close

Proficiency Prep

Use this quiz to check students' recall of section content.

1. **What type of telescope bends light to produce an image?** *refracting telescope*
2. **What type of telescope uses a mirror to focus light from the object being viewed?** *reflecting telescope*

Section Assessment

1. A radio telescope uses a curved dish antenna to collect and focus radio waves, whereas an optical telescope uses lenses or mirrors to collect and focus visible light.
2. More waves of light with a shorter wavelength would pass a point in a specific time period. Blue light would have a greater frequency.
3. **Think Critically** Assuming the message is understood and the intelligent life could send radio transmissions, it would take about eight years to receive the reply—four years for the message to reach them and four years for their reply to travel back to Earth.

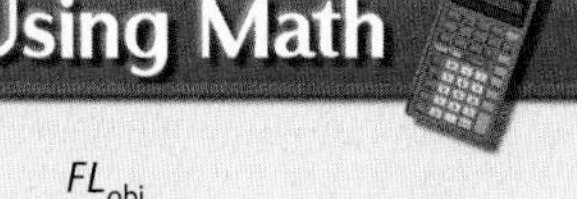

Using Math

$$Mp = \frac{FL_{obj}}{FL_{eye}} =$$

1200 mm/6 mm = 200

Activity 20•1

Purpose

Visual-Spatial Students will compare and contrast the paths taken by light in reflecting and refracting telescopes. L2

ELL COOP LEARN P

Process Skills

observing and inferring, communicating, comparing and contrasting, recognizing cause and effect, interpreting data, experimenting, defining operationally, separating and controlling variables

Time

50 to 60 minutes

Safety Precautions

Caution students to handle the hand lenses and mirrors with care. Caution them to keep hair and clothes away from the candle flame.

Answers to Questions

1. The focus of the lens is where the light from the candle is concentrated almost to a single point. The rays must have been bent to be concentrated to one point.
2. A concave mirror enlarges an image. The image in the convex mirror is smaller and farther away than the object. The image in a plane mirror is the same size and at the same distance as the object.
3. In both types of telescopes, light is directed to a focus. In refracting telescopes, light is bent to focus as it passes through a lens. Reflecting telescopes use a mirror to reflect light rays to a focus.
4. It collects incoming light and produces a small image at the focal point.

Activity 20•1 Using Scientific Methods

Telescopes

You have learned that optical telescopes use lenses and mirrors as objectives to collect light from an object. They use eyepiece lenses to magnify images of that object. Try this activity to see how the paths of light differ in reflecting and refracting telescopes.

Materials

- Candle
- White cardboard (50 cm × 60 cm)
- Flashlight
- Hand lens
- Large glass of water
- Concave mirror
- Plane mirror
- Masking tape
- Convex mirror
- Empty paper-towel tube

What You'll Investigate

In what way are paths of light affected by the lenses and mirrors in refracting and reflecting telescopes?

Goals

- **Observe** how different mirrors and lenses affect light and the appearance of objects.

Procedure

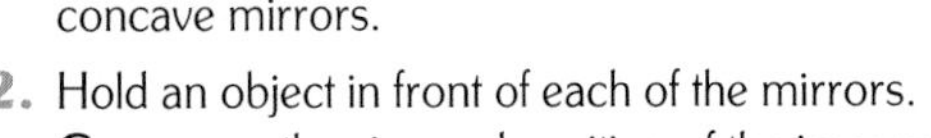

1. **Observe** your reflection in plane, convex, and concave mirrors.
2. Hold an object in front of each of the mirrors. **Compare** the size and position of the images.
3. **Darken** the room and hold the convex mirror in front of you at a 45° angle, slanting downward. Direct the flashlight toward the mirror. **Note** the size and position of the reflected light.
4. Repeat step 3 using a plane mirror. **Draw** a diagram to show what happens to the beam of light.
5. **Tape** the paper-towel tube to the flashlight so that the beam of light will pass through the tube. Direct the light into a glass of water, first directly from above, then from an angle 45° to the water's surface. **Observe** the direction of the light rays when viewed from the side of the glass.
6. **Light** a candle and set it some distance from the vertically held cardboard screen. **CAUTION:** *Keep hair and clothing away from the flame.* Using the hand lens as a convex lens, move it between the candle and the screen until you have the best possible image.
7. **Move** the lens closer to the candle. Note what happens to the size of the image. Move the cardboard until the image is in focus.

Conclude and Apply

1. How did you **determine** the position of the focal point of the hand lens in step 6? What does this tell you about the position of the light rays?
2. **Compare and contrast** the effect the three types of mirrors had on your reflection.
3. **Compare and contrast** the path of light in refracting and reflecting telescopes.
4. What is the purpose of the concave mirror in a reflecting telescope?

Assessment

Performance Provide each group of students with two lenses of different focal lengths. Ask students to design a working telescope using only the two lenses. Students should realize that if the lenses are lined up and held up to the eye with the lens of shortest focal length near the eye, a working telescope is built. Use **Performance Assessment in the Science Classroom,** p. 23.

How it Works

Seeing in 3-D

Why do humans have two eyes? One reason is that the second eye lets us see more of the world. It increases our field of view. Many animals have eyes set on opposite sides of their heads, so each eye sees a separate half of the world. But, human eyes are set closer together. They see almost the same scene but from a slightly different angle. Look at the student in front of you, first through only your right eye then only your left eye. You'll notice that each eye sees a slightly different view. But, your brain puts the two different views together, giving you the ability to figure out which object is closer to you and which is farther away. You see in three dimensions (3-D).

In the figure on the left, notice how the green block appears to the left of the yellow cylinder when seen by the left eye but to the right when seen by the right eye. Your brain interprets these two images, and you know that the yellow cylinder is in front of the green block.

Left eye | Right eye | View from left eye | View from right eye

Left eye | Right eye | View from left eye | View from right eye

Movies and Television

How can you have a 3-D experience at the movies or on a TV? A camera with two lenses a few inches apart records the images on film or videotape. But, one lens has a red filter in front of it and the other a blue, as shown in the figure on the right. So, the image recorded by one lens is in shades of red, while the one recorded by the other lens is in shades of blue. The viewer watches the film through 3-D glasses that have the same color filters. Because the red filter allows only red light through it, only the image meant for that eye passes through that filter. The filters send the images meant for the right eye only to the right eye and the images meant for the left only to the left. The brain does the rest of the work. It combines the two colors, giving different shades of gray and interprets the slightly different images so that you can tell which object is in front and which is behind.

Career CONNECTION

Research how 3-D technology is being used in the latest computer animation software. Find out how the 3-D images used in computer animations are made.

NATIONAL GEOGRAPHIC

How it Works

Purpose

Students will gain an understanding of three-dimensional vision.

Content Background

The ability to judge distance and shape using two side-by-side eyes is called stereoscopic vision. Stereoscopic vision gives humans and many other animals depth perception. Predators in particular need this skill to hunt. However, the brain does not rely on stereoscopic vision alone to judge distance. It uses other learned techniques as well, such as perspective and parallax. Perspective causes an object to look big when it is close and small when it is far. Parallax makes close objects appear to move while more distant objects stay in place.

VISUAL Learning

Intrapersonal Have students test their 3-D vision by observing objects with one eye closed, then the other. Students should observe objects that are both near and far away.

Teaching Strategies

- If possible, obtain a model of a human eye and allow students to examine its parts.
- Help students make 3-D glasses. Obtain sheets of red and blue cellophane. Cut out small squares (approximately 6 cm by 6 cm) of each color. Cut eye holes in a rectangular piece of cardboard (roughly 8 cm by 16 cm), and paste the squares of red and blue cellophane over the holes.

Career CONNECTION

Computer graphic artists usually obtain at least a two-year degree, although many opt for four-year bachelor's degrees. Computer graphic artists work in a wide variety of fields ranging from film animation to newspaper design. Invite a computer graphic artist to speak to the class about training and job opportunities in his or her field.

SECTION 20-2

Prepare

Refer to **Satellites and Space Probes** and **Space Spin-offs** on p. 572F.

Preplanning

Refer to the **Chapter Organizer** on pp. 572A–B.

1 Motivate

Bellringer

Before presenting the lesson, display **Section Focus Transparency 54** on the overhead projector. Use the accompanying **Focus Activity** worksheet. L2 ELL

Section 20-2

54 SECTION FOCUS TRANSPARENCY

REMOTE-CONTROLLED RESEARCH

Some things are impossible to see. They are too small, too dangerous, or too far away. How can people observe the universe? Telescopes help, but recently, scientists have also begun to use satellites and space probes to study the solar system and beyond.

1. What makes it difficult to see the stars?
2. Why could using satellites and space probes help us get a better view of the stars and planets?
3. How could satellites in space help us learn more about Earth?

54

Tying to Previous Knowledge

Blow up a balloon and release it. The balloon travels in the direction opposite from where the air is escaping. Rockets are propelled forward as gases escape from the nozzle at the back of the rocket.

20-2 Early Space Missions

What You'll Learn

- How to compare and contrast natural and artificial satellites
- The differences between artificial satellites and space probes
- The history of the race to the moon

Vocabulary

satellite
orbit
space probe
Project Mercury
Project Gemini
Project Apollo

Why It's Important

- Learning about space exploration will help you better understand the vastness of space.

The First Steps into Space

If you had your choice of watching your favorite sports team on television or from the stadium, which would you prefer? You would probably want to be as close as possible to the game so you wouldn't miss any of the action. Scientists feel the same way about space. Even though telescopes have taught them a great deal about the moon and planets, they want to learn more by actually going to those places or by sending spacecraft where they can't go.

Satellites

Space exploration began in 1957 when the former Soviet Union used a rocket to send *Sputnik I* into space. It was the first artificial satellite. A **satellite** is any object that revolves around another object. When an object enters space, it travels in a straight line unless a force such as gravity deflects it. When Earth's gravity pulls on a satellite, it falls toward Earth. The result of the satellite traveling forward while at the same time falling toward Earth is a curved path, called an **orbit,** around Earth. This is shown in **Figure 20-6.**

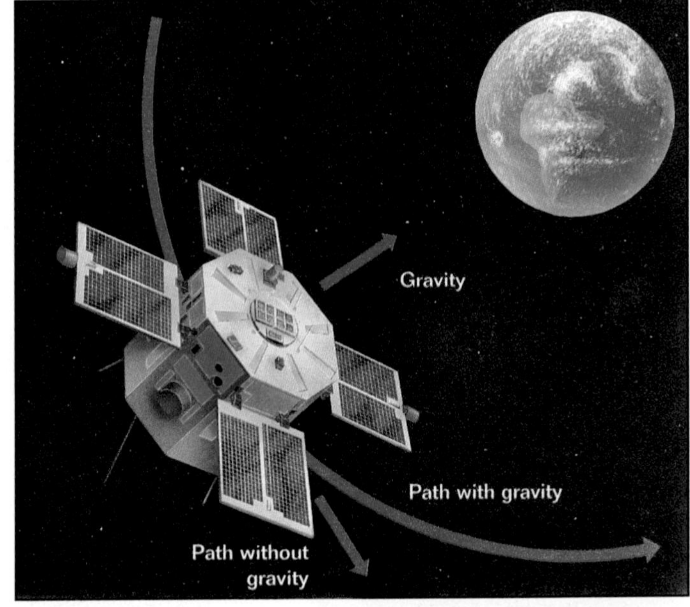

Figure 20-6 The combination of the satellite's forward movement and the gravitational attraction of Earth causes the satellite to travel in a curved path, called an orbit. **What would happen if the forward speed of the satellite decreased?**

Resource Manager

The following **Teacher Classroom Resources** can be used with Section 20-2:

Reproducible Masters

Activity Worksheets, p. 111 L2
Enrichment, p. 54 L3
Home Involvement, p. 29 L2
Reinforcement, p. 54 L2

Transparencies

Science Integration Transparency 20 L2

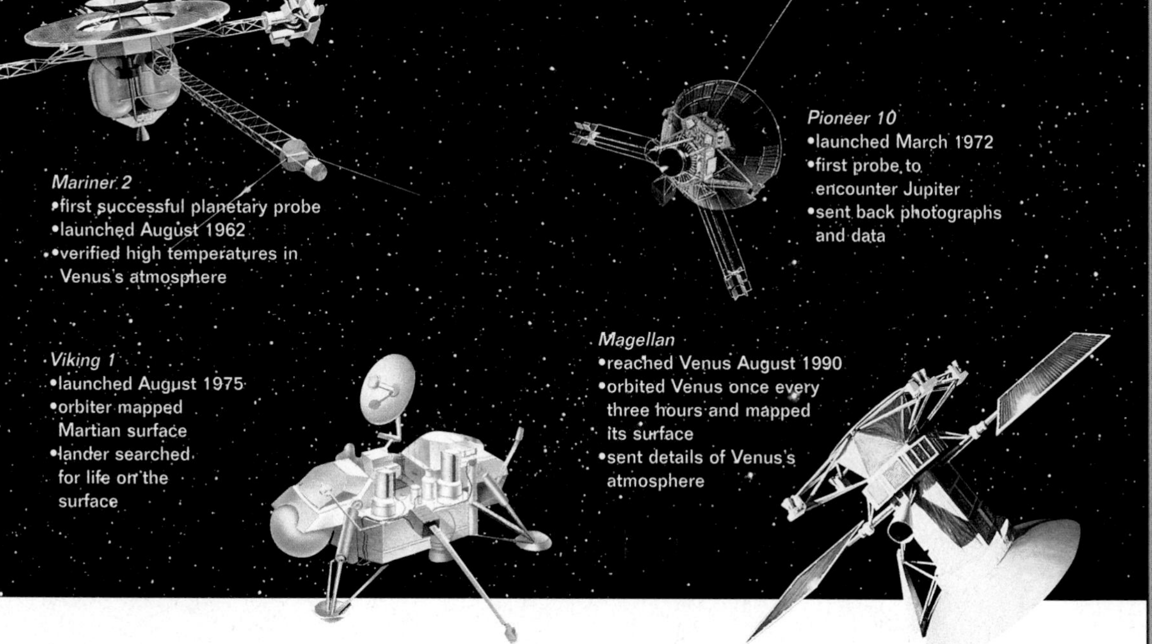

Mariner 2
•first successful planetary probe
•launched August 1962
•verified high temperatures in Venus's atmosphere
Pioneer 10
•launched March 1972
•first probe to encounter Jupiter
•sent back photographs and data
Viking 1
•launched August 1975
•orbiter mapped Martian surface
•lander searched for life on the surface
Magellan
•reached Venus August 1990
•orbited Venus once every three hours and mapped its surface
•sent details of Venus's atmosphere

Figure 20-7 Some early U.S. space probes and their missions provided much useful data.

Satellite Uses

The moon is a natural satellite of Earth. It completes one orbit every month. *Sputnik I* orbited Earth for 57 days before gravity pulled it back into the atmosphere, where it burned up. *Sputnik I* was an experiment to show that artificial satellites could be made. Today, thousands of artificial satellites orbit Earth.

Present-day communication satellites transmit radio and television programs to locations around the world. Other satellites gather scientific data that can't be obtained from Earth, and weather satellites constantly monitor Earth's global weather patterns.

Space Probes

Not all objects carried into space by rockets become satellites. Rockets also can be used to send instruments into space. A **space probe** is an instrument that gathers information and sends it back to Earth. Unlike satellites that orbit Earth, space probes travel far into the solar system. Some have even traveled out of the solar system. Space probes, like many satellites, carry cameras and other data-gathering equipment, as well as radio transmitters and receivers that allow them to communicate with scientists on Earth. **Figure 20-7** shows some of the early space probes launched by NASA (National Aeronautics and Space Administration).

Using Math

Suppose a spacecraft is launched at a speed of 40 200 km per hour. Express this speed in kilometers per second.

2 Teach

Discussion

Interpersonal Have pairs of students collaborate on a written report about information that could be obtained by artificial satellites in orbit around Earth. Then have the class discuss how this information could be used by humans on Earth's surface. To help students get started, list various types of artificial satellites: weather, communications, military, and astronomical. L2 COOP LEARN

Correcting Misconceptions

Many people think artificial satellites and space probes are identical. Explain that artificial satellites orbit other objects. Probes are spacecraft sent far into space by rockets. They don't orbit other objects. Both satellites and probes send information back to Earth.

40 200 km/hr ÷ 3600 s/hr = 11.2 km/s

Using an Analogy

To help students understand the vast distances space probes travel, tell them that the *Cassini* probe, headed toward Saturn, must travel roughly 1.3 billion km, one way. That's nearly equivalent to walking around Earth along the equator more than 100 000 times.

Caption Answer

Figure 20-6 *The lower momentum would no longer balance the force of gravity, and the satellite would fall toward Earth.*

Guided Reading Strategy

Buddy Interviews This strategy helps students understand and clarify the reading. Have students interview one another to find out what helps them understand what they are reading, how they find answers, and how they figure out new vocabulary terms. Have students use Buddy Interviews to help them master section concept.

Using Science Words

Linguistic To help students better understand science words, ask them to list artificial objects and natural objects. Cars, for instance, are artificial objects, while trees are natural objects. Ask: **What is the difference between an artificial satellite and a natural satellite?** *Artificial satellites are made by humans. Natural satellites are made by natural processes.*

Enrichment

Help students understand why communication satellites should have a geostationary or synchronous orbit. Satellites that are not placed in a geostationary orbit pass over a particular location only once per orbit and for only a brief time. This limits their usefulness for communication purposes. A satellite that has a geostationary orbit circles Earth at a speed that matches Earth's rotational speed; thus, it appears to an Earth-based observer to be stationary. This keeps the satellite in the same location relative to Earth's surface.

GLENCOE TECHNOLOGY

CD-ROM

Glencoe Science Voyages Interactive CD-ROM

Explorations

Have students do the interactive exploration *How does an artificial satellite stay in orbit?*

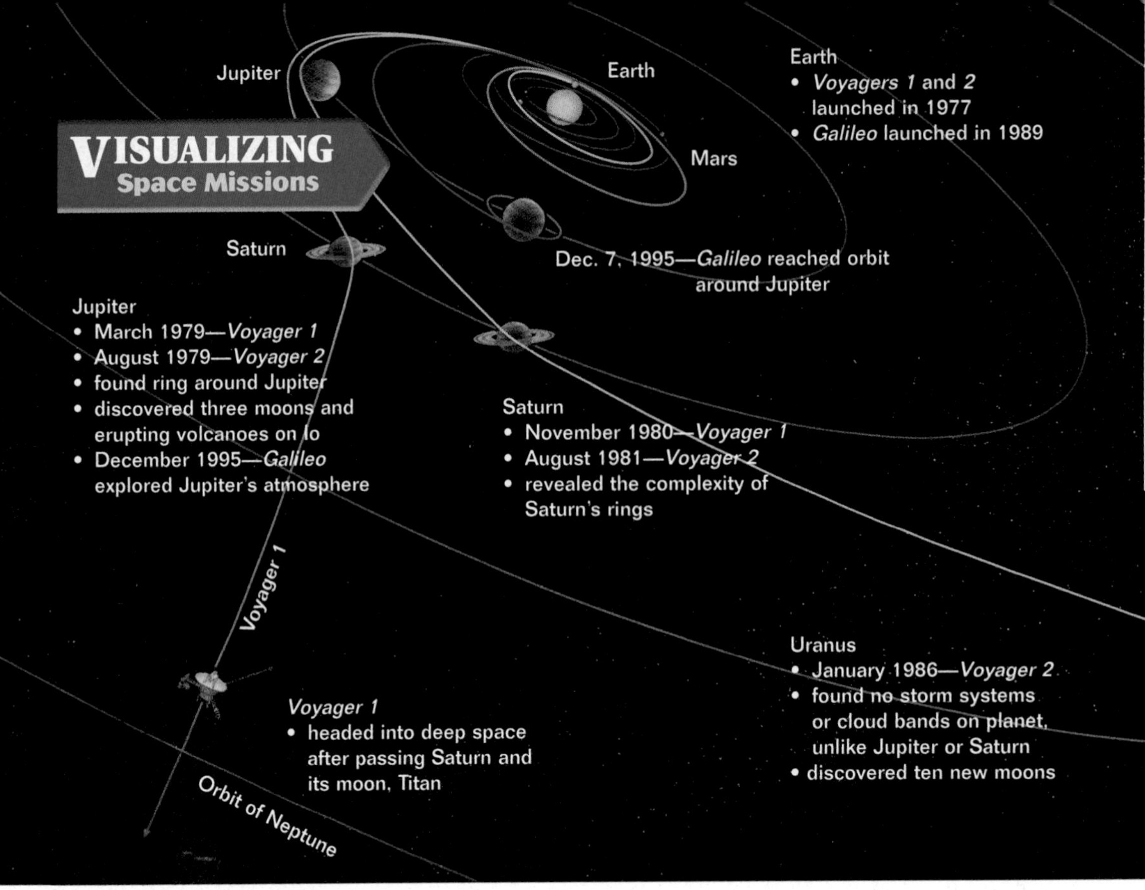

VISUALIZING Space Missions
Jupiter
Earth
Mars
Saturn
Earth
• Voyagers 1 and 2 launched in 1977
• Galileo launched in 1989
Dec. 7, 1995—Galileo reached orbit around Jupiter
Jupiter
• March 1979—Voyager 1
• August 1979—Voyager 2
• found ring around Jupiter
• discovered three moons and erupting volcanoes on Io
• December 1995—Galileo explored Jupiter's atmosphere
Saturn
• November 1980—Voyager 1
• August 1981—Voyager 2
• revealed the complexity of Saturn's rings
Voyager 1
Uranus
• January 1986—Voyager 2
• found no storm systems or cloud bands on planet, unlike Jupiter or Saturn
• discovered ten new moons
Voyager 1
• headed into deep space after passing Saturn and its moon, Titan
Orbit of Neptune

Figure 20-8 The *Voyager* and *Galileo* spacecraft helped make many major discoveries.

You've probably heard of the space probes *Voyager 1* and *Voyager 2*. These two probes were launched in 1977 and are now heading toward deep space. *Voyager 1* flew past Jupiter and Saturn. *Voyager 2* flew past Jupiter, Saturn, Uranus, and Neptune. **Figure 20-8** describes some of what we've learned from the *Voyager* probes. Now, these probes are exploring beyond our solar system as part of the Voyager Interstellar Mission. Scientists expect these probes to continue to transmit data to Earth for at least 20 more years.

The fate of a probe is never certain, and not all probes are successful. In 1993, *Mars Observer* was only days away from entering orbit around Mars when it was lost. The problem was most likely a critical failure in the propulsion system.

Galileo, launched in 1989, reached Jupiter in 1995. In July 1995, *Galileo* released a smaller probe that began a five-month approach to Jupiter. The small probe took a parachute ride through Jupiter's violent atmosphere in December 1995.

Across the Curriculum

Social Studies Have students speculate on why so many developments occurred in the space program during the 1960s. Students should realize that the United States and the former Soviet Union were participating in a "race for space."

VISUAL Learning

Figure 20-8 Ask students to review the flights of *Voyager 1* and *Voyager 2*. Then ask students: **What was different about the flight paths of the two probes?** Voyager 2 *used the gravity of Saturn to give it the speed necessary to arrive at Uranus. It then used the gravity of Uranus to send it on to Neptune.*

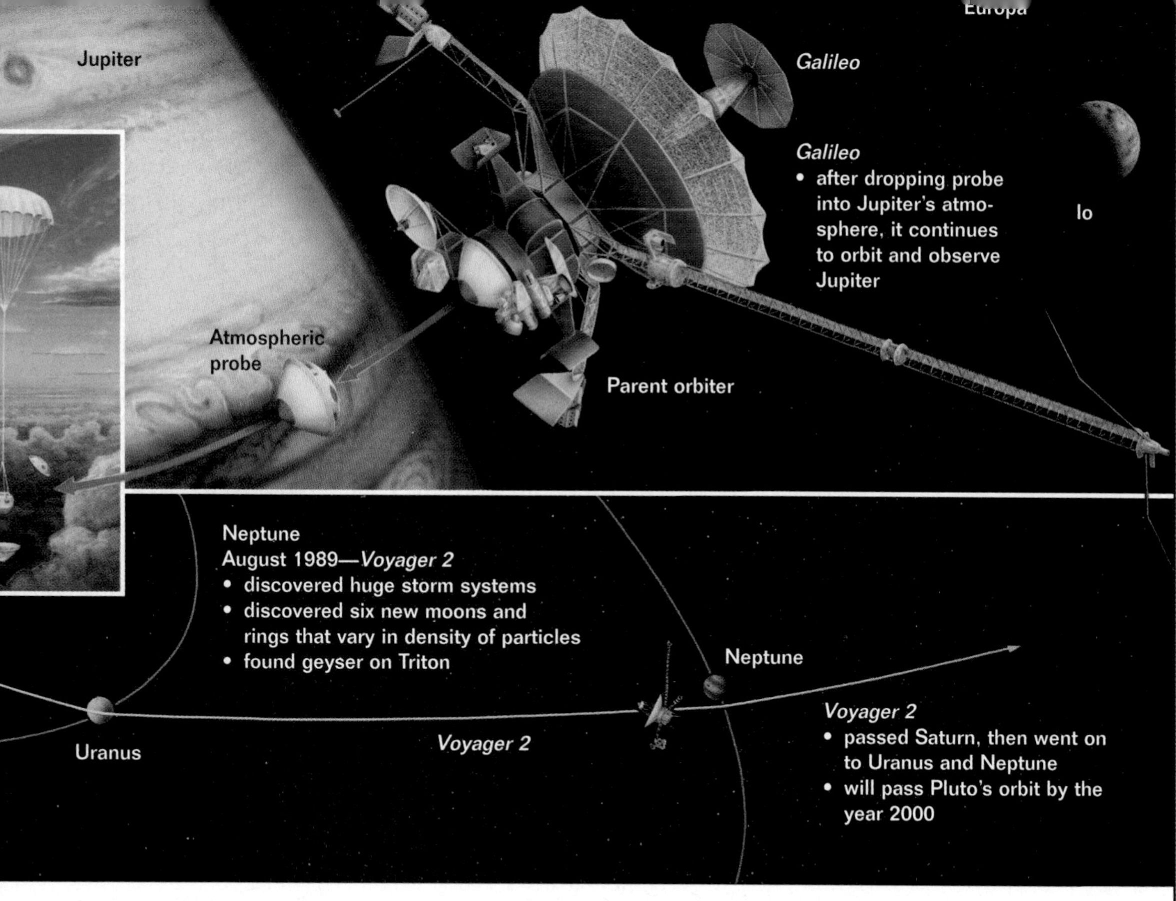

• discovered six new moons and rings that vary in density of particles
• found geyser on Triton

• will pass Pluto's orbit by the year 2000

Before being crushed by the atmospheric pressure, it transmitted information about Jupiter's composition, temperature, and pressure to the ship orbiting above. *Galileo* studied Jupiter's moons, rings, and magnetic fields and then relayed this information back to scientists who were eagerly waiting for it on Earth.

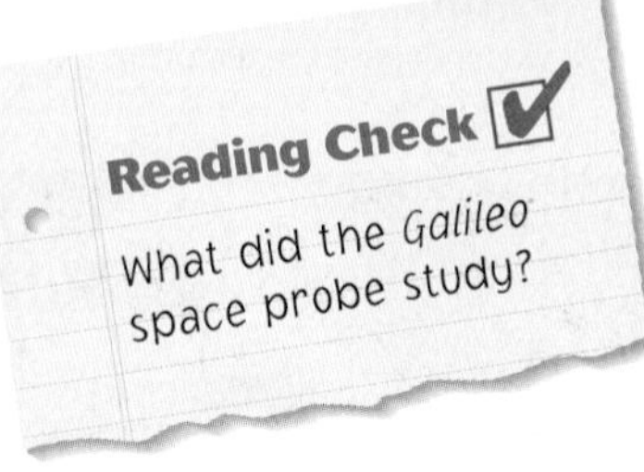

Reading Check
What did the Galileo space probe study?

Galileo
• after dropping probe into Jupiter's atmosphere, it continues to orbit and observe Jupiter
Parent orbiter

Recent studies of Jupiter's moon Europa by *Galileo* indicate that an ocean of water or ice may exist under the outer layer of ice that covers Europa's cracked surface. The cracks in the surface may be caused by geologic activity that heats the ocean underneath the surface. Sunlight penetrates these cracks, further heating the ocean and setting the stage for the possible existence of life on Europa. *Galileo* studied Europa through 1999. More advanced probes will be needed to determine whether molecular life actually does exist on this icy moon.

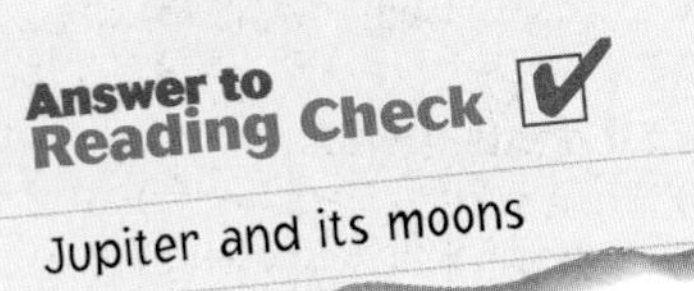

LIFE SCIENCE INTEGRATION

When searching for life elsewhere in space, scientists look for the presence of organic molecules—life as we know it is made up of these molecules. Titan, one of the satellites of Saturn, contains organic molecules. The molecules themselves aren't considered to be life, but they are thought to resemble the molecules from which life evolved on Earth. Given enough time—millions or billions of years—it's possible that the molecules on Titan may evolve into life as they did on Earth.

Activity

Linguistic Have pairs of students use the school library to research the original seven Project Mercury astronauts. Students should collaborate on a written report about the missions each astronaut performed in the Mercury and other space missions, and what these astronauts are doing now. L2 COOP LEARN

3 Assess

Check for Understanding

Enrichment

Have students research geostationary satellites to find out what these satellites are used for and how the term describes the type of orbit of such a satellite.

Inclusion Strategies

Gifted Have students research space junk. Space junk includes unused and nonfunctioning materials in orbit around Earth. It ranges from sand-grain-sized paint chips to large communication satellites. Students can write to NASA for more information. Students should discuss the growing threat space junk may pose to the safety of future crewed spaceflights. L3

Content Background

The most distant human-made object as of 1998 is the *Voyager 1* space probe. At that time, it was 10.4 billion km (70 AU) from Earth. *Voyager 1* is expected to continue to send information back to Earth until it runs out of electrical power, around 2020.

Try at Home Mini Lab

For additional help doing this activity at home, see the corresponding pages in the **Home Involvement** booklet.

Purpose

Visual-Spatial Students will observe that light pollution affects the number of objects visible in the night sky. L2 ELL

Materials

cardboard tube from empty roll of paper towels

Teaching Strategies

Troubleshooting If all students live in the same area, have them call friends or relatives for additional star data.

Analysis

1. More stars should be visible in suburban than urban areas; even more stars should be visible in rural areas.
2. Because suburban and rural areas have less light pollution, more objects are visible in the sky.

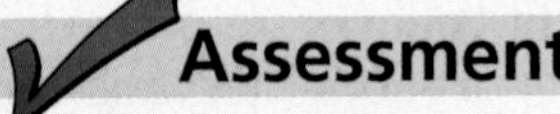

Process Have students list common sources of light pollution that they've probably taken for granted, such as lights at car dealerships and shopping centers, and streetlights. Use **Performance Assessment in the Science Classroom,** p. 17.

Comparing the Effects of Light Pollution

Procedure

1. Obtain a cardboard tube from an empty roll of paper towels.
2. Select a night when clear skies are predicted. Go outside about two hours after sunset and look through the cardboard tube at a specific constellation decided upon ahead of time.
3. Count the number of stars you are able to see without moving the observing tube. Repeat this three times.
4. Determine the average number of observable stars at your location.

Analysis

1. Compare and contrast the number of stars visible from other students' homes.
2. Explain the cause and effect of differences in your observations.

The Race to the Moon

Throughout the world, people were shocked when they turned on their radios and television sets in 1957 and heard the radio transmissions from *Sputnik I* as it orbited over their heads. All that *Sputnik I* transmitted was a sort of beeping sound, but people quickly realized that putting a human into space wasn't far off.

In 1961, the Soviet cosmonaut Yuri A. Gagarin became the first human in space. He orbited Earth and then returned safely. Soon, President John F. Kennedy called for the United States to place people on the moon and return them to Earth by the end of that decade. The "race for space" had begun.

The U.S. program to reach the moon began with **Project Mercury.** The goals of Project Mercury were to orbit a piloted spacecraft around Earth and to bring it safely back. The program provided data and experience in the basics of space flight. On May 5, 1961, Alan B. Shepard became the first U.S. citizen in space. In 1962, *Mercury* astronaut John Glenn became the first U.S. citizen to orbit Earth. **Figure 20-9** shows Glenn preparing for liftoff. In 1998, Glenn returned to space aboard the space shuttle *Discovery.* You'll learn more about space shuttles in the next section.

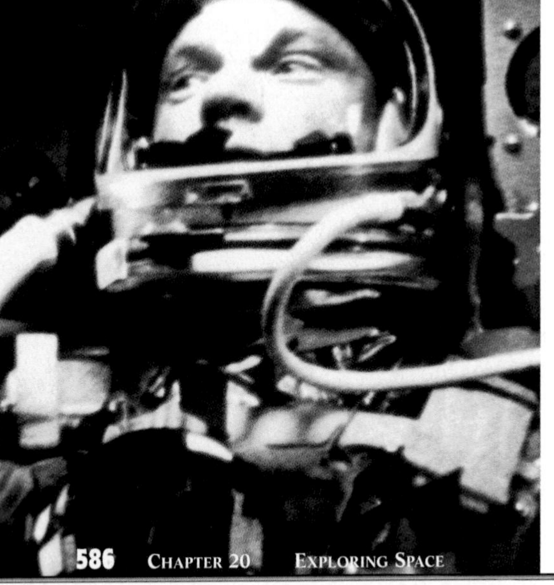

Figure 20-9 John Glenn was the first U.S. astronaut to orbit Earth.

Project Gemini

Project Gemini was the next step in reaching the moon. Teams of two astronauts in the same *Gemini* spacecraft orbited Earth. One *Gemini* team met and connected with another spacecraft in orbit—a skill that would be needed on a voyage to the moon.

Along with the *Mercury* and *Gemini* programs, a series of robotic probes was sent to the moon. *Ranger* proved we could get spacecraft to the moon. *Surveyor* landed gently on the moon's surface, indicating that the moon's surface could support spacecraft and humans. The mission of *Lunar Orbiter* was to take pictures of the moon's surface to help determine the best landing sites on the moon.

Science Journal

Project Apollo Use these questions as a starting point for student reports about Project Apollo: **How did the information gained in Project Gemini lead to success in the Apollo mission?** *Project Gemini provided the opportunity for astronauts to work in space. It also showed that two spacecraft could meet and rendezvous while in orbit.* **Why do you think Michael Collins remained in the command module while Neil Armstrong and Edwin Aldrin landed on the moon?** *It was considered safer to have a person in the command module in case of problems during the connection of the spacecraft.* L2

Project Apollo

The final stage of the U.S. program to reach the moon was **Project Apollo.** On July 20, 1969, *Apollo* 11 landed on the lunar surface. Neil Armstrong was the first human to set foot on the moon. His first words as he stepped onto its surface were, "That's one small step for man, one giant leap for mankind." Edwin Aldrin, the second of the three *Apollo* 11 astronauts, joined Armstrong on the moon, and they explored its surface for two hours. Michael Collins remained in the Command Module orbiting the moon, where Armstrong and Aldrin returned before beginning the journey home. A total of six lunar landings brought back more than 2000 samples of moon rock and soil for study before the program ended in 1972. **Figure 20-10** shows astronauts on the moon.

During the past three decades, most missions in space have been carried out by individual countries, often competing to be the first or the best. Today, there is much more cooperation among countries of the world to work together and share what each has learned. Projects are now being planned for cooperative missions to Mars and elsewhere. As you read the next section, you'll see how the U.S. program has progressed since the days of Project Apollo, and where it may be going in the future.

Figure 20-10 The Lunar Rover Vehicle was first used during the *Apollo 15* mission. Riding in the moon buggy, *Apollo 15, 16,* and *17* astronauts explored large areas of the lunar surface.

Section Assessment

1. Currently, no human-made objects are orbiting Neptune, yet Neptune has eight satellites. Explain.
2. *Galileo* was considered a space probe as it traveled to Jupiter. Once there, however, it became an artificial satellite. Explain.
3. **Think Critically:** Is Earth a satellite of any other body in space? Explain your answer.
4. **Skill Builder**
   Concept Mapping Make an events-chain concept map that lists the events in the U.S. space program to place people on the moon. If you need help, refer to Concept Mapping in the **Skill Handbook** on page 714.

Using Computers

Spreadsheet Use the spreadsheet feature on your computer to generate a table of recent successful satellites and space probes launched by the United States. Include a description of the craft, the date launched, and the mission. If you need help, refer to page 738.

Reteach

Interpersonal Have pairs of students make outlines of the material presented in this section. Have partners quiz each other to review the material. L1 COOP LEARN

Extension

For students who have mastered this section, use the **Reinforcement** and **Enrichment** masters.

4 Close

Proficiency Prep

Use this quiz to check students' recall of section content.

1. **What object in space revolves around another object?** *satellite*
2. **Which space probe flew past Jupiter, Saturn, Uranus, and Neptune?** Voyager 2

Section Assessment

1. These eight satellites are natural satellites of the planet.
2. Once the probe arrived at Jupiter, it went into orbit around that planet and became an artificial satellite.
3. **Think Critically** Yes, Earth is a natural satellite of the sun.

Using Computers

NASA has information students can use to produce their spreadsheets. Also, several magazines—*Astronomy, Final Frontier,* and *Sky and Telescope*—provide information about recent satellites and space probes.

4. **Skill Builder**
   Students' concept maps may include the following events: President Kennedy calls for placing people on the moon; Project Mercury places people in orbit; Project Gemini has spacecraft meet and connect in space; probes are sent to the moon; Project Apollo places astronauts on the moon.

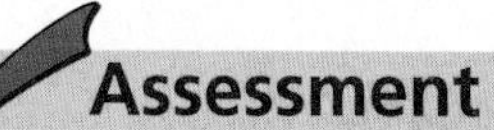

Assessment

Oral Use this Skill Builder to assess students' abilities to make concept maps. Have students make concept maps on the *Voyager 1* mission. Use **Performance Assessment in the Science Classroom,** p. 89.

Recognize the Problem

Students will use an astrolabe to make star sightings of Polaris. From their observations and data gathered off the Glencoe Science Web Site, students will determine the circumference of Earth. P

Form a Hypothesis

Internet

Students will use the Internet to learn more about stars and about astronomical instruments such as the astrolabe or sextant. Students will also post their data on the Internet as well as collect star-sighting information from other parts of the country.

Non-Internet Sources

Students should research the historical use of the astrolabe. Students can make repeated measurements of Polaris over time. If any class members are traveling north or south of your location, have them make star sightings while they are away and share their data with the class.

Time Required

one week

Activity 20•2

Star Sightings

For thousands of years, humans have used the stars to learn about the planet we live on. From star sightings, you can map the change of seasons, navigate the oceans, and even determine the size of Earth.

Polaris, or the North Star, has occupied an important place in human history. The location of Polaris is not affected by Earth's rotation. At any given observation point, it always appears at the same angle above the horizon. At Earth's north pole, Polaris appears directly overhead. At the equator, it is just above the northern horizon. Polaris provides a standard from which other locations can be measured. Such star sightings can be made using the astrolabe, an instrument used to measure the height of a star above the horizon.

Recognize the Problem

How can you determine the size of Earth?

Form a Hypothesis

Think about what you have learned about sightings of Polaris. How does this tell you that Earth is round? Knowing that Earth is round, **form a hypothesis** about whether you can estimate the circumference of Earth based on star sightings.

Goals

- **Record** your sightings of Polaris.
- **Share** the data with other students to **calculate** the circumference of Earth.

Safety Precautions

Do not use the astrolabe during the daytime to observe the sun.

Data Sources

Go to the Glencoe Science Web Site at *www.glencoe.com/sec/science* to obtain instructions on how to make an astrolabe, for more information about the location of Polaris, and for data from other students.

588 CHAPTER 20 EXPLORING SPACE

Preparation

Internet Access the Glencoe Science Web Site at **www.glencoe.com/sec/science** to run through the steps the students will follow.

Non-Internet Sources Find books concerning the history of astronomy. Bring them to class for students to use as references.

interNET CONNECTION

Internet Addresses

____

____

____

____

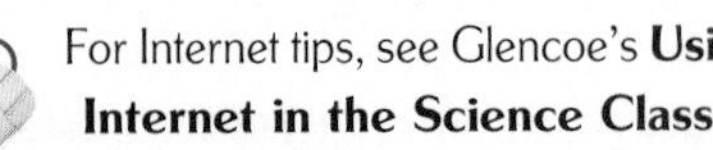
For Internet tips, see Glencoe's **Using the Internet in the Science Classroom.**

Test Your Hypothesis

Plan

1. Obtain an astrolabe or **construct** one using the instructions posted on the Glencoe Science Web Site.
2. **Design** a data table in your Science Journal similar to the one below.
3. Decide as a group how you will make your observations. Does it take more than one person to make each observation? When will it be easiest to see Polaris?

Do

1. Make sure your teacher approves your plan before you proceed.
2. Carry out your observations.
3. **Record** your observations in your data table.
4. **Average** your readings and post them in the table provided on the Glencoe Science Web Site.

Analyze Your Data

1. **Research** the names of cities that are at approximately the same longitude as your hometown. **Gather** astrolabe readings at the Glencoe Science Web Site from students in one of those cities.
2. **Compare** your astrolabe readings. **Subtract** the smaller reading from the larger one.
3. Determine the distance between your star sighting location and the other city.
4. To calculate the circumference of Earth, use the following relationship.

$$\text{Circumference} = \frac{(360°)(\text{distance between locations})}{\text{difference between readings}}$$

Draw Conclusions

1. How does the circumference of Earth that you calculated compare with the accepted value of 40 079 km?
2. What are some possible sources of error in this method of determining the size of Earth? What improvements would you suggest?

Polaris Observations

Your location:		
Date	Time	Astrolabe Reading
Average astrolabe reading:		

Test Your Hypothesis

Teaching Strategies

- Have students make repeated star sightings of Polaris and other stars over a few nights and at different times. By doing repeated sightings of different stars, students will discover the unique nature of Polaris.
- After students have made a few observations, explain the circumference equation. Have them practice explaining the logic behind the circumference equation to a partner.

Troubleshooting Ask students why it is important that they obtain astrolabe readings from a town on the same longitude as they are. Use a globe to facilitate understanding.

Have students think about the fact that Earth is spinning on an axis. Have them consider how they might go about determining the speed at which they are spinning at their particular location on Earth. How might an astrolabe help in determining this speed?

References

- Turner, A.J., ed. *Time-Measuring Instruments, Part 1: Astrolabes, Astrolabe-Related Instruments.* Time Museum, 1986.
- Dickinson, Terence. *The Backyard Astronomer's Guide.* Camden House.

Assessment

Oral Have students work in groups to devise a method of determining the circumference of Earth if they lived in Australia, where Polaris is not visible. Have groups present their plans to the class.

SECTION 20-3

Prepare

Content Background

Refer to **International Space Station** on p. 572F.

Preplanning

Refer to the **Chapter Organizer** on pp. 572A–B.

1 Motivate

Bellringer

Before presenting the lesson, display **Section Focus Transparency 55** on the overhead projector. Use the accompanying **Focus Activity** worksheet. L2 ELL

Section 20-3

55 SECTION FOCUS TRANSPARENCY

READY FOR LANDING!

What does it take to go into space and come back again, landing on Earth's surface? A space shuttle! How do you think the shuttle is changing space exploration?

1. What do you already know about the space shuttle program?
2. How would you feel about traveling in the space shuttle?

Tying to Previous Knowledge

Ask students if they have watched the preparation, launch, and landing of a space shuttle. Show a film of a recent launch.

20-3 Recent and Future Space Missions

What You'll Learn

- The benefits of the space shuttle
- The usefulness of orbital space stations
- Future space missions

Vocabulary

space shuttle
space station

Why It's Important

- Many exciting things are planned for the future of space exploration.

The Space Shuttle

Imagine spending millions of dollars to build a machine, sending it off into space, and watching its 3000 metric tons of metal and other materials burn up after only a few minutes of work. That's exactly what NASA did for many years. The early rockets lifted a small capsule holding the astronauts into orbit. Sections of the rocket separated from the rest of the rocket body and burned as they reentered the atmosphere.

A Reusable Spacecraft

NASA administrators, like many others, realized that it would be less expensive and less wasteful to reuse resources. The reusable spacecraft that transports astronauts, satellites, and other materials to and from space is the **space shuttle.** The space shuttle is shown in **Figure 20-11.**

At launch, the space shuttle stands on end and is connected to an external liquid-fuel tank and two solid-fuel booster rockets. When the shuttle reaches an altitude of about 45 km, the emptied solid-fuel booster rockets drop off and parachute back to Earth. They are recovered and used again. The larger, external liquid-fuel tank eventually separates and falls back to Earth, but it isn't recovered.

Once the space shuttle reaches space, it begins to orbit Earth. There, astronauts perform many different tasks. The cargo bay can carry a self-contained laboratory, where astronauts conduct scientific experiments and determine the effects of space flight on the human body. On missions in which the cargo bay isn't used as a laboratory, the shuttle can launch, repair, and retrieve satellites.

To retrieve a satellite, a large mechanical arm in the cargo bay is extended. An astronaut inside the shuttle moves the arm by remote control. The arm grabs the satellite and pulls it back into the cargo bay. The doors are closed, and it is then returned to Earth.

Figure 20-11 The space shuttle is designed to make many trips into space.

Resource Manager

The following **Teacher Classroom Resources** can be used with Section 20-3:

Reproducible Masters

Activity Worksheets, p. 112 L2

Critical Thinking/Problem Solving, p. 20 L2

Enrichment, p. 55 L3

Multicultural Connections, pp. 39–40 L2

Reinforcement, p. 55 L2

Study Guide, pp. 79–80 L1 ELL

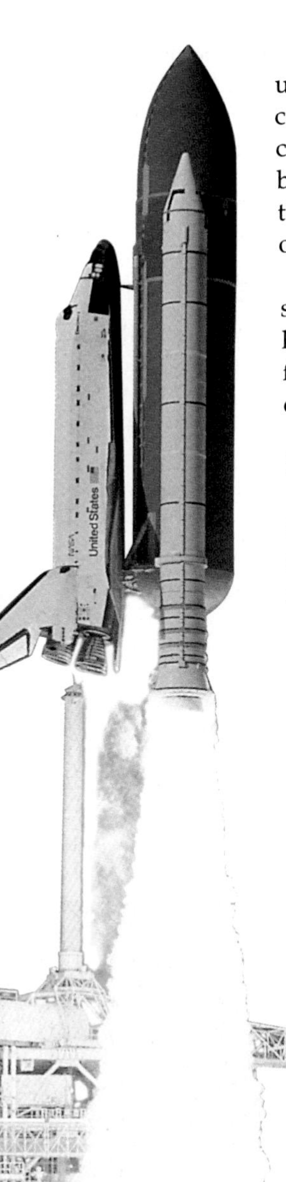

Similarly, the mechanical arm can be used to lift a satellite or probe out of the cargo bay and place it into space. In some cases, a defective satellite can be pulled in by the mechanical arm, repaired while in the cargo bay, and then placed into space once more.

After each mission is completed, the space shuttle glides back to Earth and lands like an airplane. A large landing field is needed because the gliding speed of the shuttle is 335 km/hr.

Space Stations

Astronauts can spend only a short time in space in the space shuttle. Its living area is small, and the crew needs more room to live, exercise, and work. A **space station** has living quarters, work and exercise areas, and all the equipment and support systems needed for humans to live and work in space.

The United States had such a station in the past. The space station *Skylab* was launched in 1973. Crews of astronauts spent up to 84 days in it performing experiments and collecting data on the effects that living in space had on humans. In 1979, the abandoned *Skylab* fell out of orbit and burned up as it entered Earth's atmosphere.

interNET CONNECTION

In 1962, John Glenn became the first U.S. citizen to orbit Earth. In 1998, Glenn returned to space aboard the space shuttle *Discovery*. Visit the Glencoe Science Web Site at **www.glencoe.com/sec/science** for more information about the historical significance of Glenn's *Discovery* flight.

2 Teach

Quick Demo

Visual-Spatial If possible, obtain a working model of a space shuttle. Use the model to demonstrate how the cargo bay is used to carry satellites to and from Earth and how the mobile arm is used to place satellites into orbit and to bring them back into the cargo bay for repairs.

Flex Your Brain

Use the Flex Your Brain activity to have students explore THE INTERNATIONAL SPACE STATION.

GLENCOE TECHNOLOGY

Videodisc

Glencoe Science Voyages Inteactive Videodisc—Earth

Side 2, Lesson 8 *Space Exploration*

32923

Refer to Videodisc Teacher Guide for additional bar codes.

interNET CONNECTION

Internet Addresses

For Internet tips, see Glencoe's **Using the Internet in the Science Classroom.**

Inclusion Strategies

Hearing Impaired Assist students as they make models of space probes, space capsules, or space shuttles. Have them discuss some of the proposed future spacecraft and space stations. Students can draw or make models of their own ideas about future spacecraft. L2 ELL

MiniLab

Purpose

Kinesthetic Students will simulate artificial gravity. L2 ELL COOP LEARN

Materials

turntable, LP record, scissors, construction paper, masking tape, marbles

Teaching Strategies

Troubleshooting Inform students that only the slowest speed of the turntable should be used.

Safety Precautions Caution students to wear safety goggles in case marbles fly off the turntable.

Analysis

1. The marbles are accelerated outward from the center by forces generated by the rotation of the turntable. The inertia of the marbles causes them to continue to move outward. The surface of the paper exerts a force on the marbles and stops them from continuing their outward motion.
2. A space station could simulate artificial gravity by spinning slowly around a central axis of rotation.

Assessment

Oral Ask students: **What might happen if you partially filled a bucket with water and then swung it quickly over your head?** *No water would be spilled.* Have students relate their answers to their observations in the MiniLab. Use **Performance Assessment in the Science Classroom,** p. 71.

MiniLab

Modeling Gravity

Procedure

1. Locate a stereo record album and turntable you can use for this activity.
2. Fold 8-cm-wide strips of construction paper in half, then unfold them.
3. Wrap the strips along the fold around the circumference of the record so there is a 4-cm wall around the outside edge of the disc.
4. Securely tape the rest underneath the record.
5. Place the record on a turntable and place three marbles at its center.
6. Switch on the turntable.

Analysis

1. What did you observe about the movements of the marbles?
2. Hypothesize how what you've observed could be useful for simulating the effects of gravity on a space station.

Crews from the former Soviet Union have spent the most time in space aboard the space station *Mir.* Cosmonaut Dr. Valery Polyakov returned to Earth after 438 days in space studying the long-term effects of weightlessness.

Cooperation in Space

In 1995, the United States and Russia began an era of cooperation and trust in exploring space. Early in the year, Dr. Norman Thagard was launched into orbit aboard the Russian *Soyuz* spacecraft, along with two Russian cosmonaut crewmates. Dr. Thagard was the first U.S. astronaut launched into space by a Russian booster and the first American resident of the Russian space station *Mir.*

In June 1995, Russian cosmonauts rode into orbit aboard the space shuttle *Atlantis,* America's 100th crewed launch. The mission of *Atlantis* involved, among other studies, a rendezvous and docking with space station *Mir.* The cooperation that existed on this mission continued through

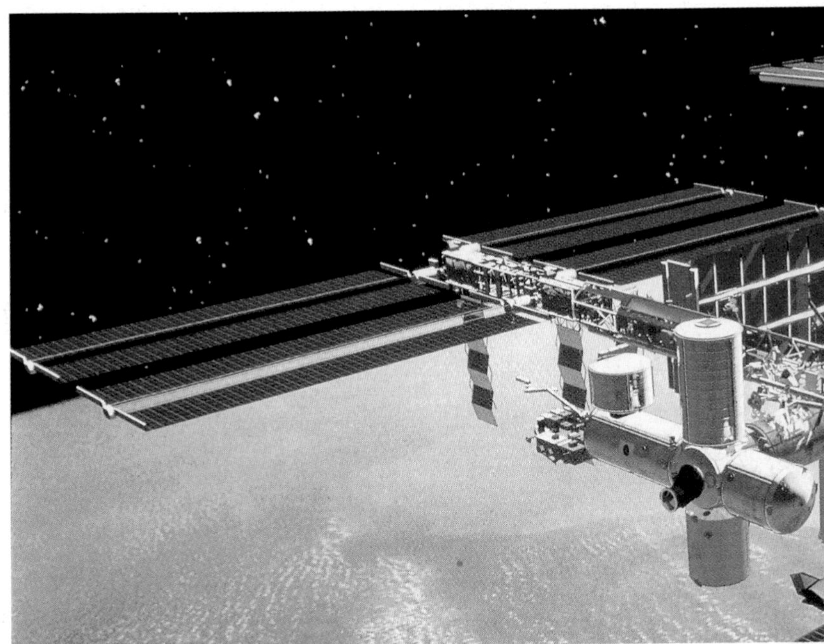

Figure 20-12 The proposed International Space Station is scheduled for completion in 2003.

Integrating the Sciences

Life Science When the United States and the former Soviet Union began their piloted space programs, humans were not the first to go into space. Ask students to find out what animals were used by each country and why these animals were used. Also ask students to describe how Project Mercury helped prepare the United States for future moon exploration. L2

Content Background

Space exploration is becoming a global endeavor. The International Space Station will draw on the resources of more than 16 nations. In addition, research and tracking facilities for the station are located in many countries around the globe.

eight more space shuttle-*Mir* docking missions. Each was an important step toward building and operating the International Space Station.

The International Space Station

The International Space Station (ISS) will be a permanent laboratory designed to use in long-term research. Diverse topics will be studied, such as researching the growth of protein crystals. This project will help scientists determine protein structure and function. This could enhance work on drug design and the treatment of diseases.

The space station will draw on the resources of more than 16 nations. Various nations will build units for the space station, which will then be transported into space aboard the space shuttle and Russian launch rockets. The station will be constructed in space. **Figure 20-12** shows what the completed station will look like.

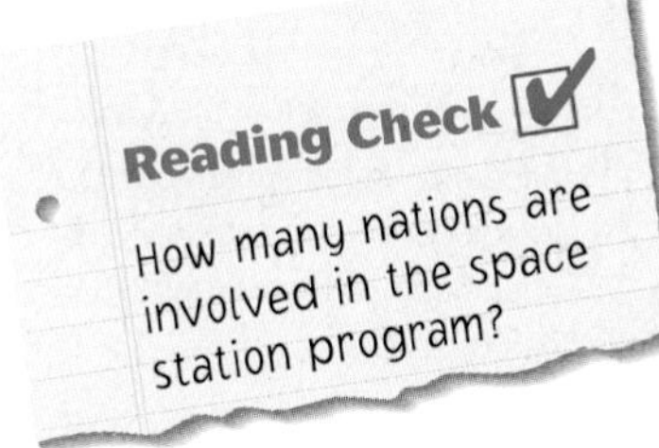
Reading Check
How many nations are involved in the space station program?

NASA is planning the space station program in three phases. Phase One, now concluded, involved the space shuttle-*Mir* docking missions. Phase Two began in 1998 with the launch of the Russian-built Functional Cargo Block, and will end with the delivery of a U.S. laboratory aboard the space shuttle. During Phase Two, a crew of three people will be delivered to the space station. This is expected to occur by January 2000.

Making a Model

Visual-Spatial Use the following model to help students understand how solid-fuel booster rockets help space shuttles go into space. Obtain a cardboard tube from an empty roll of paper towels. Attach two inflated balloons on either side of the tube. Attach a string to the ceiling, pull it tight, and place it through the tube. Have students help you open the closed nozzles of the balloons. Show students how the balloons act like the solid-fuel booster rockets attached to a space shuttle. The balloons will lift the cardboard tube like the solid-fuel rockets help to lift a space shuttle.

Answer to Reading Check
16 nations

GLENCOE TECHNOLOGY

Videodisc

Glencoe Science Voyages Interactive Videodisc—Earth

Side 2, Lesson 8 *Space Exploration*

33168

Side 2, Lesson 8 *Space Exploration*

33975

Refer to Videodisc Teacher Guide for additional bar codes.

Across the Curriculum

Agriculture, Geography, Meteorology, and Medicine The space program has been used to benefit humans in many scientific fields. Ask interested students to pick a field of their choice and write a report in their Science Journals about what advancement has occurred in that particular field as a direct result of the space program. L2

3 Assess

Check for Understanding

Enrichment

Have students research the space shuttle *Challenger*, which exploded 75 seconds after its launch on Jan. 28, 1986. The explosion occurred when one of two solid-fuel booster rockets developed a leak. The hot gases burned through the main fuel tank, causing it to explode. All people on board were killed.

Reteach

Ask students to list some of the advantages of sharing space missions with other countries. *The cost of the space missions can be shared. Also, when data are shared by all nations, the number of repetitive missions can be reduced. This could provide funds for other space missions and research.* L2

Extension

For students who have mastered this section, use the **Reinforcement** and **Enrichment** masters.

4 Close

Proficiency Prep

Use this quiz to check students' recall of section content.

1. **What is a usable spacecraft that transports astronauts, satellites, and other materials to and from space?** *space shuttle*
2. **What is a space station?** *a spacecraft that has everything needed to live and work in space*

Figure 20-13 Using the space shuttle, scientists have already performed extensive experiments in the weightlessness of space.

Living in Space

The project will continue with Phase Three when the Japanese Experiment Module, the European Columbus Orbiting Facility, and another Russian lab will be delivered.

The U.S. hopes to deliver its Habitation module in 2003, although this date may be delayed. This will end Phase Three and make the International Space Station fully operational and ready for its permanent six- or seven-person crew. A total of 45 separate launches are required to take all components of ISS into space. NASA plans for crews of astronauts to stay on board the station for several months at a time. As shown in **Figure 20-13,** NASA has already conducted numerous tests to prepare astronauts for extended space missions. One day, the station could be a construction site for ships that will go to the moon and Mars.

Exploring Mars

Two of the most successful missions in recent years were the 1996 launchings of the Mars *Global Surveyor* and Mars *Pathfinder*. *Surveyor* orbited Mars, taking high-quality photos of the planet's surface. *Pathfinder* descended to the Martian surface, using rockets and a parachute system to slow its descent. Large balloons were used to absorb the shock of landing. *Pathfinder* carried technology to study the surface of the planet, including a remote-controlled robot rover called *Sojourner*. Using information gathered by the rover and photographs taken by *Surveyor*, scientists determined that areas of the planet's surface were once covered with water during Mars's distant past.

Content Background

The first space station placed into orbit by the United States was *Skylab*. When *Skylab* was launched in 1973, several problems occurred. It lost part of its outer protective covering and one of its solar panels. The other solar panel was not fully deployed and did not work. Temperatures inside the station were increasing and limited electrical power was being supplied from the solar panels. Astronauts first had to repair the station before they could occupy it. Once repairs were made, *Skylab* went on to complete a successful mission.

Exploring the Moon

Does water exist in the craters of the moon's poles? This is one question NASA intends to explore with data gathered from the *Lunar Prospector* spacecraft. Launched in 1998, the *Lunar Prospector's* one-year mission was to orbit the moon, taking photographs of the moon's surface for mapping purposes. Early data obtained from the spacecraft indicate that hydrogen is present in the rocks of the moon's poles. Hydrogen is one of the elements found in water. Scientists now theorize that ice on the floors of the moon's polar craters may be the source of this hydrogen.

Cassini

In October 1997, NASA launched the space probe *Cassini.* Destination: Saturn. *Cassini* will not reach its goal until 2004. At that time, the space probe will explore Saturn and surrounding areas for four years. One part of its mission is to deliver the European Space Agency's *Huygens* probe to Saturn's largest moon, Titan, as shown in **Figure 20-14.** Some scientists theorize that Titan's atmosphere may be similar to the atmosphere of early Earth.

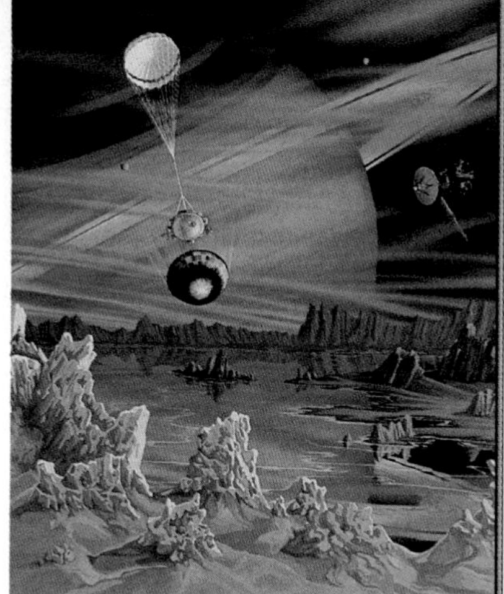

Figure 20-14 *Cassini* will reach Saturn in 2004.

Section Assessment

1. What is the main advantage of the space shuttle?
2. Why were the space shuttle-*Mir* docking missions so important?
3. Describe Phase Three of the International Space Station program.
4. Recent space missions have been characterized by a spirit of cooperation. How does this compare and contrast with early space missions?
5. **Think Critically:** Why is the space shuttle more versatile than earlier spacecraft?
6.  **Skill Builder**
   Making and Using Graphs *Lunar Prospector* was placed in lunar orbit to photograph the moon's surface. Do the **Chapter 20 Skill Activity** on page 761 to learn more about satellites placed in orbit around Earth.

Science Journal

Suppose you're in charge of assembling a crew for a new space station. Select 50 people you want for the station. Remember, you will need people to do a variety of jobs, such as farming, maintenance, scientific experimentation, and so on. In your Science Journal, explain whom you would select and why.

Section Assessment

1. It is a reusable spacecraft.
2. The space shuttle-*Mir* docking missions were a key initial step in the successful completion of the International Space Station. These missions also provided experience for sharing space technology among nations and worked to advance cooperation in space.
3. During Phase Three, the Japanese Experiment Module, the European Columbus Orbiting Facility, and another Russian lab will be delivered. Phase Three is currently scheduled to end with the delivery of the U.S. Habitation Module early in 2003.
4. Answers will vary, but students should realize that early space missions were marked by competition rather than cooperation.
5. **Think Critically** In addition to being reusable, it has a large cargo bay that enables it to carry satellites to and from Earth, it can be used to repair defective satellites, and it can land like an airplane.

Science Journal

Make sure students realize that the 50 people don't have to be known to them personally. Students' lists should include farmers, mechanics, writers, and so on.

Assessment

Process Use the Skill Builder to assess students' abilities to make graphs. Ask students to explain the benefits of creating a graph. Use **Performance Assessment in the Science Classroom,** p. 41.

Chapter 20 Reviewing Main Ideas

Reviewing Main Ideas can be used to preview, review, reteach, and condense chapter content.

Preview

Linguistic Have students try to answer the questions in their Science Journal. Use student answers as a source for discussion throughout the chapter.

Review

Interpersonal Have students answer the questions on separate pieces of paper and compare their answers with those of other students in the class.

Reteach

Visual-Spatial Have students look at the illustrations on these pages. Ask them to describe details that support the main ideas of the chapter found in the statement for each illustration.

00:00 OUT OF TIME?

Auditory-Musical If time does not permit teaching the entire chapter, use the information on these pages along with the chapter Audiocassettes to present the material in a condensed format.

Chapter 20 Reviewing Main Ideas

For a **preview** of this chapter, study this Reviewing Main Ideas before you read the chapter. After you have studied this chapter, you can use the Reviewing Main Ideas to **review** the chapter.

The Glencoe MindJogger, Audiocassettes, and CD-ROM provide additional opportunities for review.

Section 20-1 RADIATION FROM SPACE

Electromagnetic waves are arranged in the electromagnetic spectrum according to their wavelengths. Optical telescopes produce magnified images of objects. A **refracting telescope** bends light to form an image. A **reflecting telescope** uses mirrors to focus light to produce an image. **Radio telescopes** collect and record radio waves given off by some space objects. ***Why can radio telescopes be used during the day or night and in all types of weather?***

Section 20-2 EARLY SPACE MISSIONS

A **satellite** is an object that revolves around another object. The moons of planets are natural satellites. Artificial satellites are those made by people. An artificial satellite collects data as it **orbits** a planet. A **space probe** travels into the solar system, gathers data, and sends the information back to Earth. Some space probes become artificial satellites of the planet or other object they are sent to study. ***Why can the Galileo spacecraft be referred to both as a probe and as an artificial satellite of Jupiter?***

Cultural Diversity

History Early standards for U.S. astronauts severely limited which Americans could participate in the program. For example, the earliest criteria required astronaut candidates (ASCANs) to be test pilots, but women were not allowed to train as test pilots until 1970. After a nine-year hiatus, ASCAN selection broadened in the late 1970s. The 1978 ASCAN group included six women, three African-American men, and an Asian-American. Three members of this group—Judith Resnick, Ronald McNair, and Ellison Onizuka—were killed in the 1986 *Challenger* explosion.

Reading Check

Review the space missions discussed in the chapter. Then, create a timeline that shows these discoveries in chronological order.

Section

20-3 RECENT AND FUTURE SPACE MISSIONS

The **space shuttle** is a reusable spacecraft that carries astronauts, satellites, and other equipment to and from space. **Space stations,** such as *Mir* and *Skylab,* provide the opportunity to conduct research not possible on Earth. The International Space Station will be constructed in Earth orbit with the cooperation of 16 different nations. Completion of the ISS should occur in the year 2003, if all goes as planned. ***What advantage does the space shuttle have over other launch vehicles?***

Answers to Questions

Section 20-1

Radiation from Space Radio waves pass freely through Earth's atmosphere. They are not affected by most weather conditions and do not scatter during daylight hours.

Section 20-2

Early Space Missions The *Galileo* spacecraft was a space probe while traveling toward Jupiter. Once there and in orbit around Jupiter, it became a satellite of Jupiter.

Section 20-3

Recent and Future Space Missions The space shuttle is a reusable spacecraft that can carry astronauts, satellites, and other payloads to and from space. It can return damaged satellites, or astronauts can repair satellites from the cargo bay.

GLENCOE TECHNOLOGY

CD-ROM

Glencoe Science Voyages Interactive CD-ROM

Chapter Summaries and Quizzes

Have students read the Chapter Summary then take the Chapter Quiz to determine whether they have mastered chapter content.

Assessment

Portfolio Encourage students to place in their portfolios one or two items of what they consider to be their best work. Examples include:

- Explore Activity, p. 573
- Activity 20-1, p. 580
- Activity 20-2, pp. 588–589 P

Performance Additional performance assessments may be found in **Performance Assessment** and **Science Integration Activities.** Performance Task Assessment Lists and rubrics for evaluating these activities can be found in Glencoe's **Performance Assessment in the Science Classroom.**

Using Vocabulary

1. h
2. j
3. f
4. l
5. a

interNET CONNECTION To reinforce chapter vocabulary, use the **Study Guide for Content Mastery** booklet. Also available are activities for **Glencoe Science Voyages** on the Glencoe Science Web Site. **www.glencoe.com/sec/science**

Checking Concepts

6. D
7. D
8. B
9. A
10. B
11. A
12. C
13. C
14. B
15. D

Thinking Critically

16. Earth-based observations are obscured by the atmosphere. The atmosphere absorbs and distorts incoming radiation. Because the moon has no atmosphere, light and other forms of energy can reach its surface without distortion.
17. Most students should realize that the surface temperature of the sun and the immense heat that is radiated from it would make a space-probe encounter useless because the probe would burn up before getting close enough to gather data.

Chapter 20 Assessment

Using Vocabulary

a. electromagnetic spectrum
b. observatory
c. orbit
d. Project Apollo
e. Project Gemini
f. Project Mercury
g. radio telescope
h. reflecting telescope
i. refracting telescope
j. satellite
k. space probe
l. space shuttle
m. space station

The sentences below include italicized terms that have been used incorrectly. Change the incorrect terms so that the sentences read correctly. Underline your change.

1. A *reflecting telescope* uses lenses to bend light toward a focal point.
2. A *space probe* is an object that revolves around another object.
3. *Project Apollo* was the first piloted U.S. space program.
4. A *space station* carries people and tools to and from space.
5. In an *observatory,* electromagnetic waves are arranged according to their wavelengths.

Checking Concepts

Choose the word or phrase that best answers the question.

6. Which spacecraft has sent back images of Venus?
A) *Voyager* C) *Apollo 11*
B) *Viking* D) *Magellan*
7. Which telescope uses mirrors to collect light?
A) radio C) refracting
B) electromagnetic D) reflecting
8. *Sputnik I* was the first what?
A) telescope C) observatory
B) artificial satellite D) U.S. space probe
9. Which telescope can be used during day or night and during bad weather?
A) radio C) refracting
B) electromagnetic D) reflecting
10. When fully operational, the International Space Station will be crewed by up to how many people?
A) 3 C) 15
B) 7 D) 50
11. Which space mission had the goal to put a spacecraft in orbit and bring it back safely?
A) Project Mercury C) Project Gemini
B) Project Apollo D) *Viking I*
12. The space shuttle reuses which of the following?
A) liquid-fuel tanks C) booster engines
B) *Gemini* rockets D) *Saturn* rockets
13. What does the space shuttle use to place a satellite into space?
A) liquid-fuel tank C) mechanical arm
B) booster rocket D) cargo bay
14. What was *Skylab?*
A) space probe C) space shuttle
B) space station D) optical telescope
15. Which of the following is a natural satellite of Earth?
A) *Skylab* C) the sun
B) the space shuttle D) the moon

Thinking Critically

16. How would a moon-based telescope have advantages over the Earth-based telescopes being used today?
17. Would a space probe to the sun's surface be useful? Explain.
18. Which would you choose—space missions with people aboard or robotic space probes? Why?

18. Answers will vary. Robotic space probes need fewer resources and can provide more data about the outer solar system and deep space. Spaceflights with people aboard provide information about living in space and also valuable technological data.
19. No, sound requires matter through which to travel. Space is a virtual vacuum.
20. When the probes crossed Pluto's orbit, Pluto was at another point in its orbit.

19. Suppose two astronauts were outside the space shuttle, orbiting Earth. The audio speaker in the helmet of one astronaut quits working. The other astronaut is 1 m away, so she shouts a message to him. Can he hear her? Explain.

20. No space probes have visited the planet Pluto. Nevertheless, probes have crossed Pluto's orbit. How?

Developing Skills

If you need help, refer to the Skill Handbook.

21. **Measuring in SI:** Explain whether or not the following pieces of equipment could be used aboard the space shuttle as it orbits Earth: a balance, a meterstick, and a thermometer.

22. **Making and Using Tables:** Copy the table below. Use information in the chapter as well as news articles and other resources to complete your table.

U.S. Space Probes

Probe	Launch Date	Destinations	Planets or Objects Visited
Vikings 1 & 2	1975	Mars	Mars
Galileo	1989	Jupiter	Venus, Europa, Jupiter
Lunar Prospector	1998	Earth's moon	Earth's moon
Mars Pathfinder & Sojourner	1996	Mars	Mars

23. **Classifying:** Classify the following as a satellite or a space probe: *Cassini, Sputnik I, Hubble Space Telescope, space shuttle,* and *Voyager 2.*

Test-Taking Tip

Best Times If your test is going to be timed, then practice under timed conditions. Try timing yourself on specific sections to see if you can improve your overall speed while maintaining accuracy.

Test Practice

Use these questions to test your Science Proficiency.

1. Large telescopes are usually reflectors. Which of the following statements **BEST** explains why this is true?
   A) Reflecting telescopes are easier to use and carry around.
   B) Reflecting telescopes have greater magnifying power.
   C) Reflecting telescopes are less expensive to build and maintain.
   D) In reflecting telescopes, the objective mirror can be supported from beneath and, therefore, can be made larger.

2. The *Lunar Prospector* was classified as a space probe when launched but is now classified as a satellite. What does this illustrate about this spacecraft's flight?
   A) The *Lunar Prospector* is in orbit around Earth.
   B) The *Lunar Prospector* was a space probe on its flight to the moon and became a satellite when it went into orbit around the moon.
   C) The *Lunar Prospector* is moving out of our solar system.
   D) The *Lunar Prospector* was launched from Earth, went into orbit around the moon, and landed on the moon.

THE PRINCETON REVIEW **Test Practice**

The Test-Taking Tip was written by The Princeton Review, the nation's leader in test preparation.

1. D
2. B

Developing Skills

21. The balance couldn't be used because the objects and fluids to be measured wouldn't stay on the balance pans. However, distances and temperatures are not affected by the microgravity environment of space, so a meterstick and thermometer could be used.
22. See student page.
23. All are satellites except *Voyager 2,* which did not orbit any object and is therefore a probe.

Bonus Question

The *Cassini* spacecraft is presently traveling through space. Ask students to find out when it was launched, where it is heading, and when it is expected to arrive. Cassini *was launched in 1997, is heading for Saturn, and is expected to arrive in 2004.*

Assessment Resources

The **Test Practice Workbook** provides students with practice in the format, concepts, and critical-thinking skills tested in standardized exams.

Reproducible Masters

Chapter Review, pp. 39–40 L2

Performance Assessment, p. 34 L2

Assessment, pp. 89–92 L2

Glencoe Technology

Chapter Review Software

Computer Test Bank

MindJogger Videoquiz

Chapter 21 The Sun-Earth-Moon System

Section	Objectives	Activities/Features
Chapter Opener		**Explore Activity:** Model Seasons, p. 601
21-1 **Planet Earth** 3 Sessions 1½ Blocks	1. **Describe** Earth's shape and list physical data about Earth. 2. **Compare** and **contrast** the rotation and revolution of Earth. 3. **Demonstrate** how Earth's revolution and tilt causes seasons to change on Earth.	**MiniLab:** Comparing Spheres, p. 603 **Physics Integration,** p. 604 **Skill Builder:** Recognizing Cause and Effect, p. 608 **Using Computers,** p. 608 **Reading and Writing in Science:** A Brave and Startling Truth, p. 609 **Activity 21-1:** Tilt and Temperature, pp. 610–611
21-2 **Earth's Moon** 1 Session ½ Block	4. **Explain** how the moon's phases depend on the relative positions of the sun, the moon, and Earth. 5. **Describe** why eclipses occur, and compare solar and lunar eclipses. 6. **Hypothesize** what surface features of the moon tell us about its history.	**Using Math,** p. 613 **MiniLab:** Comparing the Sun and Moon, p. 614 **Life Science Integration,** p. 615 **Problem Solving:** Survival on the Moon, p. 617 **Skill Builder:** Interpreting Scientific Illustrations, p. 619 **Science Journal,** p. 619
21-3 **Exploration of the Moon** 2 Sessions 1 Block	7. **List** and **discuss** new information about the moon discovered by spacecraft. 8. **List** facts about the moon's poles that may be important to future space travel.	**Skill Builder:** Sequencing, p. 622 **Using Math,** p. 622 **Activity 21-2:** Moon Phases and Eclipses, p. 623

The number of recommended single-period sessions The number of recommended blocks
One session and one-half block are allowed for chapter review and assessment.

Activity Materials

Explore	Activities	MiniLabs
p. 601 unshaded lamp, globe	pp. 610–611 tape, black construction paper, gooseneck lamp with 75-W bulb, thermometer, watch, protractor p. 623 unshaded light source, polystyrene ball, pencil, globe	p. 603 string, basketball or volleyball, ruler, protractor, calculator p. 614 chalk, string, meterstick

Need Materials? Contact Science Kit at 1-800-828-7777 or at www.sciencekit.com on the Internet.
For alternate materials, see the activity on the listed page.

Standards		Reproducible Resources	Technology
National	State/Local	Test Practice Workbooks are available for use with each chapter.	English and Spanish audiocassettes are available for use with each section.
National Content Standards: A1, A2, B3, D1, D3, F1, G3		**Activity Worksheets,** pp. 113–114, 117 **Critical Thinking/Problem Solving,** p. 21 **Enrichment,** p. 56 **Home Involvement,** p. 29 **Laboratory Manual,** pp. 121–122 **Laboratory Manual,** pp. 123–124 **Reinforcement,** p. 56 **Study Guide,** pp. 81–82	**Section Focus Transparency 56** **Teaching Transparency 41** **Glencoe Science Voyages Interactive Videodisc—Earth** **National Geographic Society: STV** **Internet Connection,** p. 551 **Internet Connection,** p. 553 **The Infinite Voyage Series**
National Content Standards: UCP5, A2, C3, D2, D3, E2, F1, G1, G3		**Activity Worksheets,** p. 118 **Enrichment,** p. 57 **Multicultural Connections,** pp. 41–42 **Reinforcement,** p. 57	**Section Focus Transparency 57** **Science Integration Transparency 21** **Teaching Transparency 42** **National Geographic Society: STV** **Internet Connection,** p. 561 **Glencoe Science Voyages Interactive CD-ROM**
National Content Standards: UCP5, A2, D3, E2		**Activity Worksheets,** pp. 115–116 **Enrichment,** p. 58 **Reinforcement,** p. 58 **Study Guide,** pp. 82–84	**Section Focus Transparency 58**

Key to Teaching Strategies

The following designations will help you decide which activities are appropriate for your students.

L1 Level 1 activities should be appropriate for students with learning difficulties.

L2 Level 2 activities should be within the ability range of all students.

L3 Level 3 activities are designed for above-average students.

ELL ELL activities should be within the ability range of English Language Learners.

COOP LEARN Cooperative Learning activities are designed for small group work.

P These strategies represent student products that can be placed into a best-work portfolio.

Multiple Learning Styles logos, as described on page 61T, are used throughout to indicate strategies that address different learning styles.

Assessment Resources

Chapter Review, pp. 41–42
Assessment, pp. 93–96
Performance Assessment in the Science Classroom (PASC)
MindJogger Videoquiz
Alternate Assessment in the Science Classroom
Performance Assessment, p. 35
Chapter Review Software
Computer Test Bank

Chapter 21 The Sun-Earth-Moon System

This is a representation of key blackline masters available in the Teacher Classroom Resources.
See Resource Manager boxes within the chapter for additional information.

Section Focus Transparencies

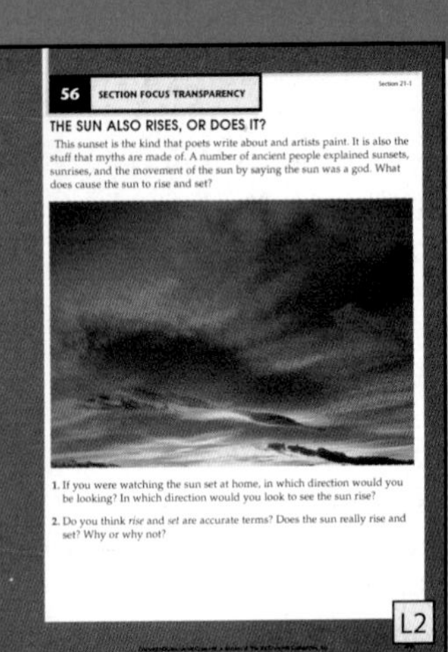

56 SECTION FOCUS TRANSPARENCY

Section 21-1

THE SUN ALSO RISES, OR DOES IT?

This sunset is the kind that poets write about and artists paint. It is also the stuff that myths are made of. A number of ancient people explained sunsets, sunrises, and the movement of the sun by saying the sun was a god. What does cause the sun to rise and set?

1. If you were watching the sun set at home, in which direction would you be looking? In which direction would you look to see the sun rise?
2. Do you think *rise* and *set* are accurate terms? Does the sun really rise and set? Why or why not?

L2

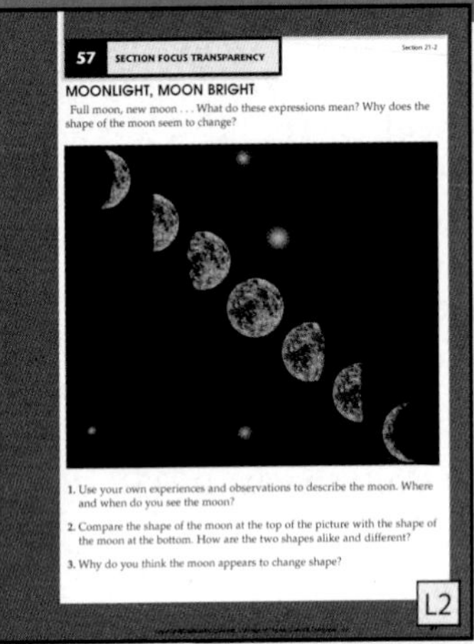

57 SECTION FOCUS TRANSPARENCY

Section 21-2

MOONLIGHT, MOON BRIGHT

Full moon, new moon . . . What do these expressions mean? Why does the shape of the moon seem to change?

1. Use your own experiences and observations to describe the moon. Where and when do you see the moon?
2. Compare the shape of the moon at the top of the picture with the shape of the moon at the bottom. How are the two shapes alike and different?
3. Why do you think the moon appears to change shape?

L2

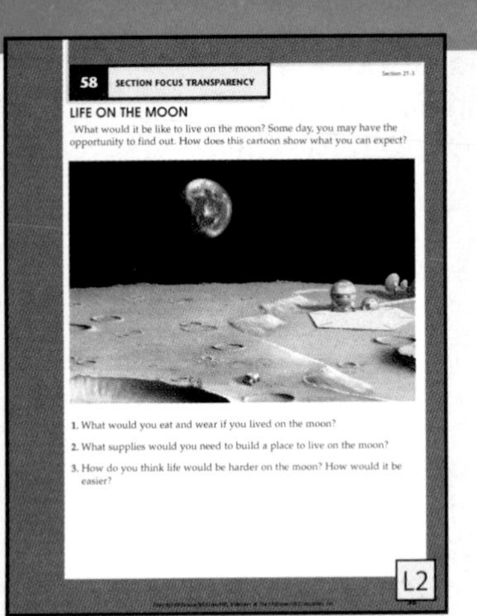

58 SECTION FOCUS TRANSPARENCY

Section 21-3

LIFE ON THE MOON

What would it be like to live on the moon? Some day, you may have the opportunity to find out. How does this cartoon show what you can expect?

1. What would you eat and wear if you lived on the moon?
2. What supplies would you need to build a place to live on the moon?
3. How do you think life would be harder on the moon? How would it be easier?

L2

Science Integration Transparencies

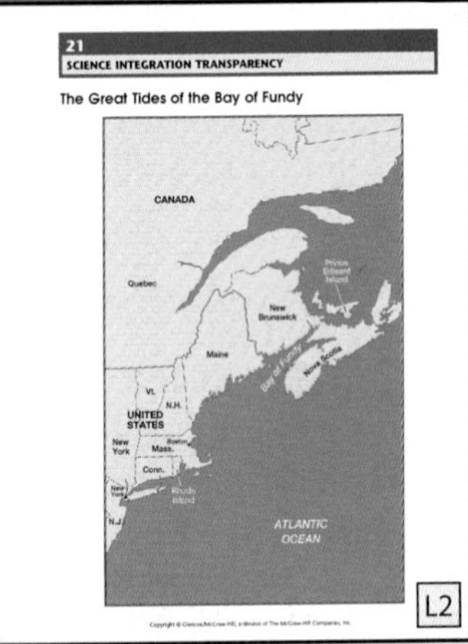

21 SCIENCE INTEGRATION TRANSPARENCY

The Great Tides of the Bay of Fundy

L2

Teaching Transparencies

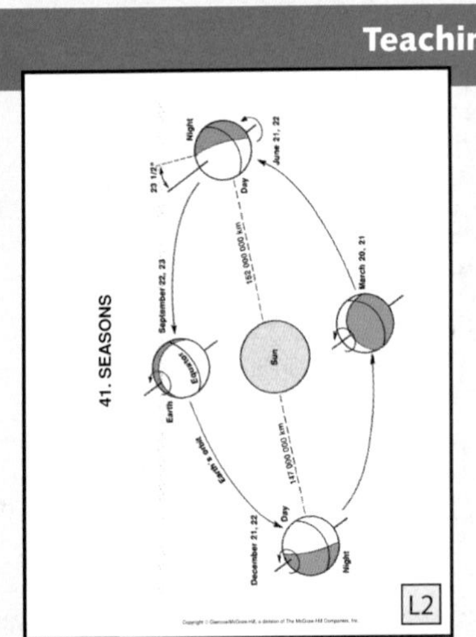

41. SEASONS

L2

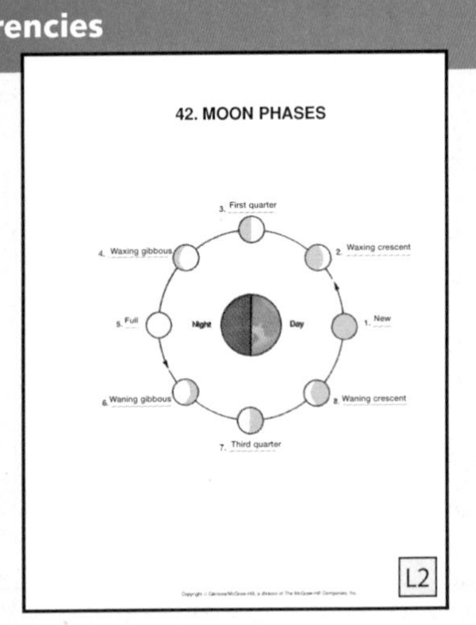

42. MOON PHASES

L2

Meeting Different Ability Levels

Study Guide for Content Mastery

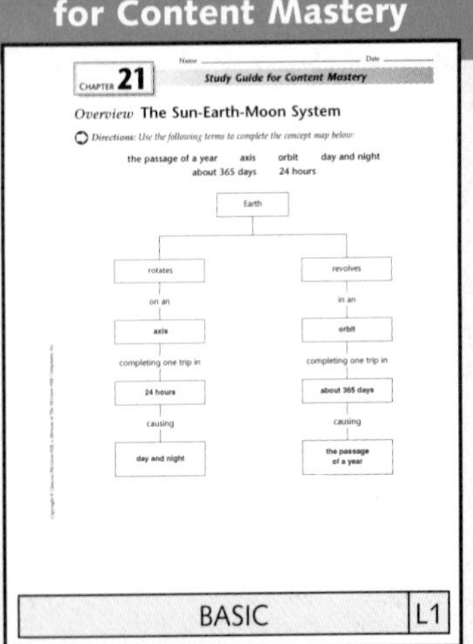

Chapter 21 Study Guide for Content Mastery

Overview The Sun-Earth-Moon System

Directions: Use the following terms to complete the concept map below:

the passage of a year · axis · orbit · day and night · about 365 days · 24 hours

BASIC L1

Reinforcement

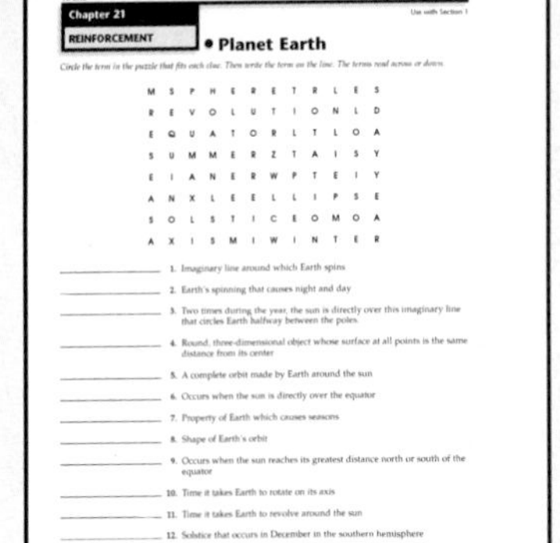

NAME DATE CLASS

Chapter 21 REINFORCEMENT • Planet Earth

Use with Section 1

Circle the term in the puzzle that fits each clue. Then write the term on the line. The terms read across or down.

M	S	P	H	E	R	E	T	R	L	E	S
R	E	V	O	L	U	T	I	O	N	L	D
E	Q	U	A	T	O	R	L	T	L	O	A
S	U	M	M	E	R	Z	T	A	I	S	Y
E	I	A	N	E	R	W	P	T	E	I	Y
A	N	X	L	E	E	L	L	I	P	S	E
S	O	L	S	T	I	C	E	O	M	O	A
A	X	I	S	M	I	W	I	N	T	E	R

______ 1. Imaginary line around which Earth spins
______ 2. Earth's spinning that causes night and day
______ 3. Two times during the year, the sun is directly over this imaginary line that circles Earth halfway between the poles
______ 4. Round, three-dimensional object whose surface at all points is the same distance from its center
______ 5. A complete orbit made by Earth around the sun
______ 6. Occurs when the sun is directly over the equator
______ 7. Property of Earth which causes seasons
______ 8. Shape of Earth's orbit
______ 9. Occurs when the sun reaches its greatest distance north or south of the equator
______ 10. Time it takes Earth to rotate on its axis
______ 11. Time it takes Earth to revolve around the sun
______ 12. Solstice that occurs in December in the southern hemisphere
______ 13. Solstice that occurs in December in the northern hemisphere

AT LEVEL L2

Enrichment Worksheets

NAME DATE CLASS

Chapter 21 ENRICHMENT • Planet Earth

Use with Section 1

Determining Hours of Daylight

The illustrations show the length of day at every 10° of latitude for the winter and summer solstices in the northern hemisphere. On each figure, begin at the equator, which has daylight hours of 12 hours and 0 minutes, and label every 10 degrees north and south of the equator to the 60° latitude north and south. Mark the final north and south latitude shown 66.5°. From this latitude to the poles, the daylight hours remain the same. Use the figures to help you answer the questions.

FIGURE 1 FIGURE 2

1. Which figure shows the summer solstice for the northern hemisphere? How do you know?
2. If you lived at 50° north latitude, how many hours of daylight would you have during the summer solstice? During the winter solstice?
3. If the figures were used to show the summer and winter solstices in the southern hemisphere, which figure would show the summer solstice in the southern hemisphere? How do you know?
4. If you lived at the north pole, how many daylight hours would you have at the summer solstice? At the winter solstice?

CHALLENGE L3

Hands-on Activities

Activity Worksheets

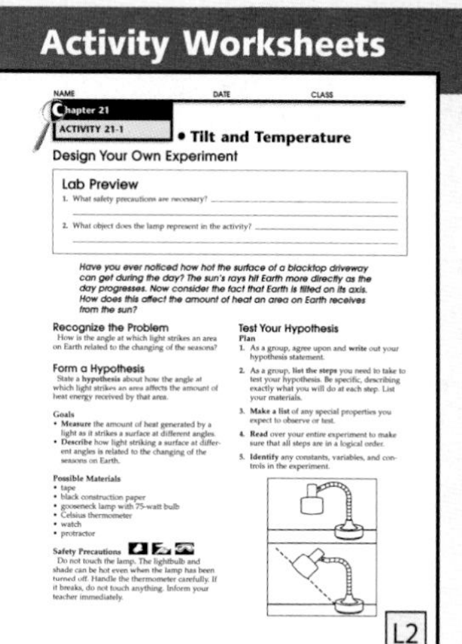

Lab Manual

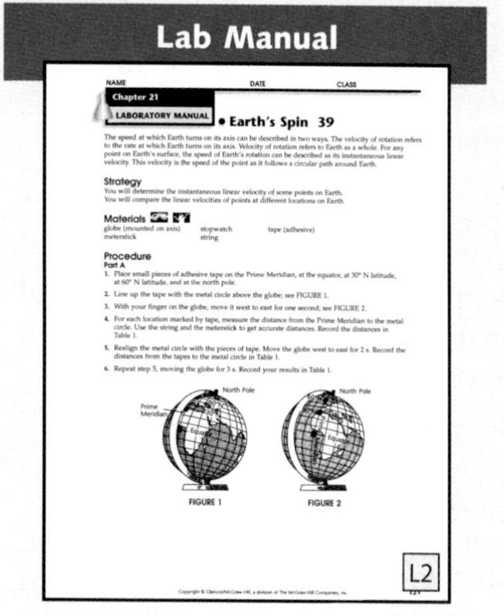

Accessibility

Spanish Resources

Assessment

Performance Assessment

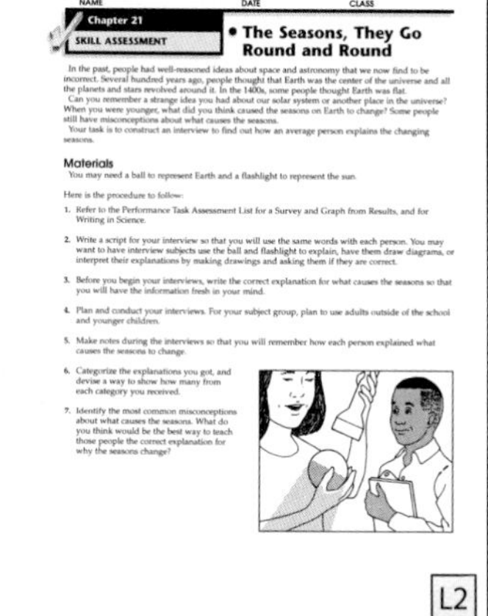

Chapter Review

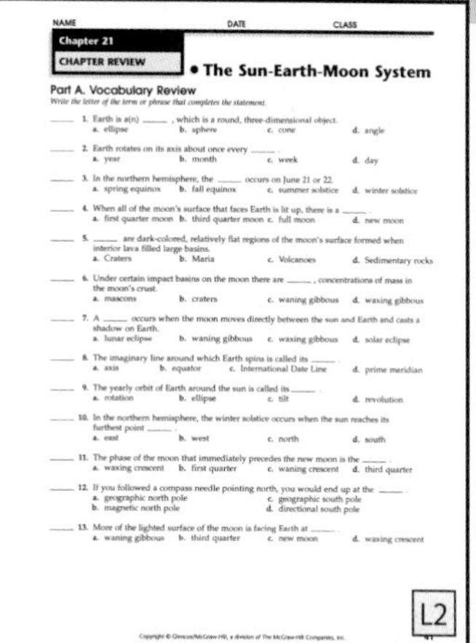

Assessment

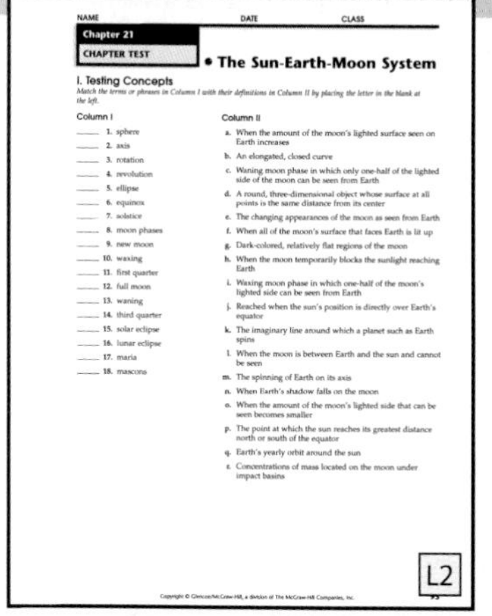

Test Practice Workbook

Extending Content

Critical Thinking/ Problem Solving

Multicultural Connections

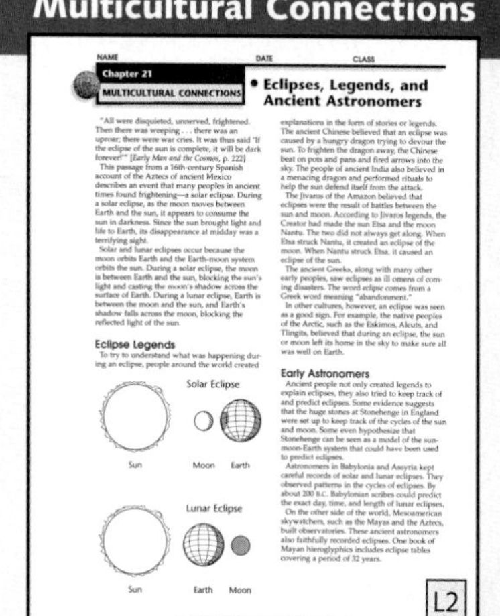

Helping You Prepare

Earth's Rotation (Section 21-1)

Atomic clocks measure time by recording the frequency of electromagnetic waves given off by atoms. Unlike conventional clocks, atomic clocks are not affected by changes in temperature or the wearing of their parts. They gain or lose less than one second in 200 000 years. Using these clocks, scientists have found that each successive day on Earth is getting longer.

Apparently, Earth's rotation has been slowing down for millions of years. By studying the growth lines on 375-million-year-old corals, scientists have determined that a year had 440 days at the time these corals were growing. Corals deposit monthly growth lines on their shells in much the same way trees develop yearly growth rings.

Atomic clocks and ancient corals indicate that Earth's rotation is slowing down. Scientists hypothesize that the gravitational attraction of the moon is dragging on Earth.

As this drag continues, the length of a day will increase. The length of a year will not be affected. Earth's period of revolution is not dependent on its period of rotation. This means that the number of days in a year will decrease, but the length of a year will not change.

GLENCOE TECHNOLOGY

CD-ROM

Glencoe Science Voyages Interactive CD-ROM

Chapter Summaries

Use the Chapter Summary to introduce, teach, or review chapter material.

Earth's Magnetic Field (Section 21-1)

Convection currents of molten iron deep in Earth's core produce huge electrical currents. These electrical currents, in turn, cause Earth's magnetic field. The orientation of the direction of Earth's magnetic field changes periodically over time. This is one of the bits of evidence that has been used to support the theories of seafloor spreading and plate tectonics. Scientists examine iron minerals in rocks such as basalt, which align themselves according to the magnetic field orientation at the time they form. When Earth's magnetic field is reversed, new iron minerals being formed reflect that magnetic reversal.

NATIONAL GEOGRAPHIC — **Teacher's Corner**

Products Available from National Geographic Society

To order the following products for use with this chapter, call National Geographic Society at 1-800-368-2728:

Poster

The Earth's Moon

Video

Sun, Earth, Moon

Index to National Geographic Magazine

"Physical World," by Joel L. Swerdlow, May 1998.

"Orbit: The Astronauts' View of Home," by Jay Apt, November 1996.

"The Darkness That Enlightens," by Jay M. Pasachoff, May 1992.

"The Moon's Racing Shadow," by Roger H. Ressmeyer, May 1992.

"Our Restless Planet Earth," by Rick Gore, August 1985.

Moon Craters (Section 21-2)

About 4 billion years ago, large meteorites created huge impact basins on the moon's surface. By 3.3 billion years ago, lava flows had filled in these impact basins, forming the large, relatively flat maria seen today. Although craters have formed on the maria and other areas of the moon since that time, its surface looks much as it did 3.3 billion years ago. It appears that meteorite impacts were much more frequent prior to the formation of maria.

Crater density is found by calculating the number of craters of different sizes found on an area of the moon's surface. Astronomers use crater density to determine the age of an area of the moon's surface. From this, they have been able to learn more about the history of the moon.

Origin of the Moon (Section 21-2)

Three early theories of the moon's origin were the capture, the condensation, and the fission theories.

The capture theory states that the moon formed in some other area of the solar system and was later captured by Earth as it passed by. In this theory, the compositions of Earth and the moon were different because they formed at different locations in the solar system. Although the compositions of the two objects are not the same, there are too many similarities in the makeup of their mantles for them to have formed totally apart. Also, it's highly unlikely that Earth's gravity could capture an object the size of the moon.

The condensation theory states that the moon and Earth formed at the same time from the same preformation materials. In this theory, Earth and the moon should have the same density and be made of similar materials. Because Earth and the moon do not have the same density and are composed of different materials, this theory has been largely discarded.

The fission theory states that the moon formed by splitting off of Earth. The Pacific Ocean is often mentioned as the area from which the moon split off. The problem with this theory is that it cannot explain how Earth could have thrown such a large portion of itself into a stable orbit.

The most recent theory of the moon's origin, the impact theory, was developed in part from data gathered by the *Apollo* space missions. The impact theory, which is described in detail in the student text, can be considered a hybrid of the capture and the fission theories.

SCIENCE UPDATE

For current events or science in the news, access the Glencoe Science Web Site at **www.glencoe.com/sec/science**

Exploration of the Moon (Section 21-3)

Deviations in the lunar orbits of spacecraft led to the discovery of mascons, which are areas of high concentrations of mass. The presence of mascons indicates that the entire interior of the moon cannot be liquid. Enough crust must be present to support mascons.

Teacher to Teacher

"To help my students understand that the moon's phases are caused by the position of the moon in relation to Earth and the sun, I have them make observations of the moon at approximately the same time each day for three to four days."

Ralph M. Feather, Jr., Teacher
Derry Area High School
Derry, PA

CHAPTER 21
The Sun-Earth-Moon System

CHAPTER OVERVIEW

Section 21-1 Physical data about Earth are presented. Seasons are explained in terms of Earth's position in space with respect to the sun and the tilt of Earth's axis.

Section 21-2 This section explains moon phases and eclipses. The structure and origin of the moon also are explored.

Section 21-3 Early and recent moon missions are described.

Chapter Vocabulary

sphere	waxing
axis	first quarter
rotation	full moon
revolution	waning
ellipse	third quarter
equinox	solar eclipse
solstice	lunar eclipse
moon phase	maria
new moon	mascon

Theme Connection

Systems and Interactions Earth's rotation and revolution cause daily and seasonal changes due to the interaction of the sun, the moon, and Earth. Phases of the moon occur monthly and also rely on the interaction among the sun, the moon, and Earth.

00:00 OUT OF TIME?

If time does not permit teaching the entire chapter, use Reviewing Main Ideas on pp. 624–625.

CHAPTER 21
The Sun-Earth-Moon System

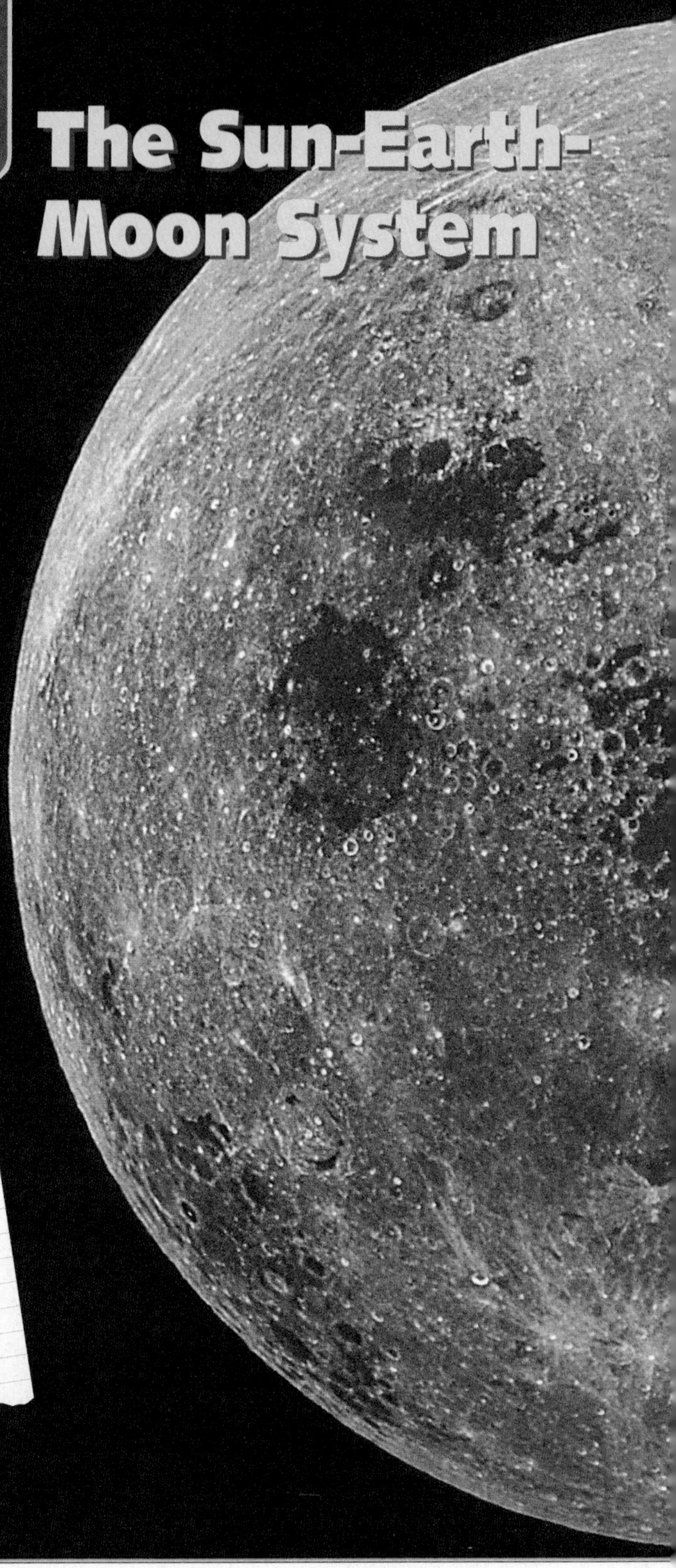

Chapter Preview

Skills Preview

Skill Builders
- Sequence

Activities
- Make a Model
- Interpret Data

MiniLabs
- Compare and Contrast
- Use Numbers

Reading Check ✓

As you read about the phases of the moon and other topics in this chapter, write down the signal words that indicate a sequence, such as *shortly after* and *just before.*

600

Multiple Learning Styles

Look for the following logos for strategies that emphasize different learning modalities.

Linguistic Science Journal, pp. 614, 618, 621; Integrating the Sciences, p. 618; Using Science Words, p. 621; Preview, p. 624

Logical-Mathematical MiniLab, p. 603; Activity, pp. 610–611

Visual-Spatial Explore Activity, p. 601; Reteach, pp. 607, 621, 624; Quick Demo, p. 616

Auditory-Musical Out of Time, p. 624

Kinesthetic Activity, p. 623

Interpersonal Activity, pp. 604, 618; Enrichment, p. 605; Multiple Learning Styles, p. 605; Discussion, p. 607; Review, p. 624

Explore Activity

Earth, the moon, and the sun are constantly moving through space. That's why one night you may see a shining full moon and weeks later see no moon at all. Is the appearance of the moon the only thing that changes because of these movements? No, seasons change, too, because of Earth's tilted axis as it moves around the sun. Let's explore how this happens.

Model Seasons

1. Use a lamp without a shade to represent the sun.
2. Turn on the lamp and hold a globe of Earth about 2 m from the lamp.
3. Tilt the globe slightly so the northern half points toward the sun.
4. Keeping the globe tilted in the same direction, walk halfway around the sun. Be careful not to turn or twist the globe as you walk.

Science Journal

In which direction is the northern hemisphere pointing relative to the sun in step 3? In step 4? In your Science Journal, describe which seasons these positions represent for the northern hemisphere.

601

Purpose

Visual-Spatial Use the Explore Activity to introduce students to the causes of seasons. L2 ELL COOP LEARN

Preparation

Have students bring in small lamps from home. Also obtain several globes of Earth.

Materials

lamp without a shade, globe

Teaching Strategies

Put students into groups of three. As two students perform the activity, the third should record observations.

Safety Precautions Caution students to handle the lamp with care. The bulb will be hot.

Troubleshooting Be sure students understand that the orientation or "tilt" of the globe must remain constant.

Science Journal In step 3, the northern hemisphere is pointing toward the sun. This represents summer in that hemisphere. In step 4, the northern hemisphere is pointing away from the sun. This represents winter in that hemisphere.

Assessment

Performance Ask students to determine the seasons for the southern hemisphere in steps 3 and 4. Use **Performance Assessment in the Science Classroom,** p. 17.

Assessment Planner

Portfolio
Refer to p. 625 for suggested items that students might select for their portfolios.

Performance Assessment
See p. 625 for additional Performance Assessment options.
Skill Builder, pp. 608, 619, 622
MiniLab, pp. 603, 614
Activity 21-1, pp. 610–611; 21-2, p. 623

Content Assessment
Section Assessment, pp. 608, 619, 622
Chapter Assessment, pp. 626–627
Proficiency Prep, pp. 608, 619, 622

SECTION 21•1

Prepare

Content Background

Refer to **Earth's Rotation** and **Earth's Magnetic Field** on p. 600E.

Preplanning

Refer to the **Chapter Organizer** on pp. 600A–B.

1 Motivate

Bellringer

Before presenting the lesson, display **Section Focus Transparency 56** on the overhead projector. Use the accompanying **Focus Activity** worksheet. L2 ELL

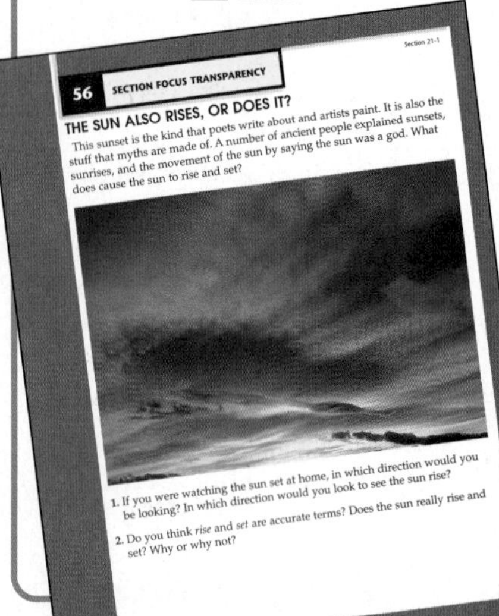

Section 21-1

56 SECTION FOCUS TRANSPARENCY

THE SUN ALSO RISES, OR DOES IT?

This sunset is the kind that poets write about and artists paint. It is also the stuff that myths are made of. A number of ancient people explained sunsets, sunrises, and the movement of the sun by saying the sun was a god. What does cause the sun to rise and set?

1. If you were watching the sun set at home, in which direction would you be looking? In which direction would you look to see the sun rise?
2. Do you think *rise* and *set* are accurate terms? Does the sun really rise and set? Why or why not?

56

Tying to Previous Knowledge

Have students recall that physical properties of matter can be measured without changing a substance into a new substance. Have students list some physical properties of Earth.

21•1 Planet Earth

***What* You'll Learn**

- Physical data about Earth
- The difference between the rotation and revolution of Earth
- How Earth's revolution and tilt cause seasons to change on Earth

Vocabulary

sphere, axis, rotation, revolution, ellipse, equinox, solstice

***Why* It's Important**

- The movements of Earth cause night and day.

Planet Earth Data

You rise early in the morning, while it's still dark outside. You sit by the window and watch the sun come up. Finally, day breaks, and the sun begins its journey across the sky. But, is the sun moving, or are you?

Today, we know that the sun appears to move across the sky because Earth is spinning as it travels around the sun. But, it wasn't long ago that people believed Earth was the center of the universe. They believed Earth stood still and the sun traveled around it.

As recently as the days of Christopher Columbus, some people also believed Earth was flat. They thought that if you sailed far out to sea, you eventually would fall off the edge of the world. How do you know this isn't true? How have scientists determined Earth's shape?

Earth's Shape

Space probes and artificial satellites have sent back images that show Earth is sphere-shaped. A **sphere** (SFIHR) is a round, three-dimensional object. Its surface at all points is the same distance from its center. Tennis balls and basketballs are examples of spheres. But, people had evidence of Earth's true shape long before cameras were sent into space.

Around 350 B.C., the Greek astronomer and philosopher Aristotle reasoned that Earth was spherical because it always casts a round shadow on the moon during an eclipse, as shown in **Figure 21-1.** Only a spherical object always produces a round shadow. If Earth were flat, it would cast a straight shadow.

Other evidence of Earth's shape was observed by early sailors. They watched as ships approached from across the ocean and saw that the top of the ship would come into view first. As they continued to watch the ship, more and more of it

Figure 21-1 If Earth were flat, its shadow during an eclipse would be straight on the moon, not curved, as shown.

Resource Manager

The following **Teacher Classroom Resources** can be used with Section 21-1:

 **Reproducible Masters**

Activity Worksheets, pp. 113–114, 117 L2
Critical Thinking/Problem Solving, p. 21 L2
Enrichment, p. 56 L3
Home Involvement, p. 29 L2
Laboratory Manual, pp. 121–124 L2
Reinforcement, p. 56 L2
Study Guide, pp. 81–82 L1 ELL

 **Transparencies**

Teaching Transparency 41 L2

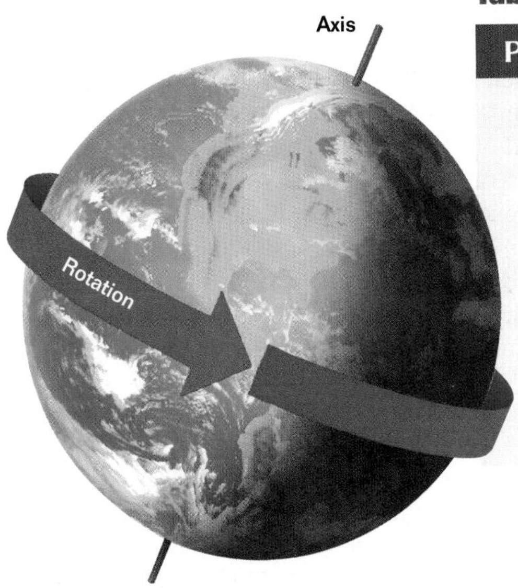

Table 21-1

Physical Properties of Earth	
Diameter (pole to pole)	12 714 km
Diameter (equator)	12 756 km
Circumference (poles)	40 008 km
Circumference (equator)	40 075 km
Mass	5.98×10^{27} g
Density	5.52 g/cm^3
Average distance to the sun	149 600 000 km
Period of rotation (1 day)	23 hr, 56 min
Period of revolution (1 year)	365 days, 6 hr, 9 min

would appear until they could see all of it. This was possible only if Earth was a sphere.

Today, we know that Earth is sphere-shaped, but it is not a perfect sphere. It bulges slightly at the equator and is somewhat flattened at the poles. The poles are located at the north and south ends of Earth's axis. Earth's **axis** is the imaginary line around which Earth spins. The spinning of Earth on its axis, called **rotation,** causes day and night to occur.

Earth's Rotation

As Earth rotates, the sun comes into view at daybreak. Earth continues to spin, making it seem as if the sun moves across the sky until it sets at night. During night, your area of Earth has spun away from the sun. Because of this, the sun is no longer visible. Earth continues to rotate steadily, and the sun eventually comes into view the next morning. One complete rotation takes about 24 hours, or one day. How many rotations does Earth complete during one year? As you can see in **Table 21-1,** it completes about 365 rotations during its journey around the sun.

Try at Home MiniLab

Comparing Spheres

Procedure 

1. Use a long piece of string to measure the circumference of a basketball or volleyball.
2. Measure the circumference of the ball at a right angle to your first measurement.
3. Determine the roundness ratio by dividing the larger measurement by the smaller one.
4. Compare these data with the roundness ratio data about Earth's circumference provided in **Table 21-1.**

Analysis

1. How round is Earth compared with the ball?
2. Is Earth larger through the equator or through the poles?
3. Explain how your observations support your answer.

2 Teach

Try at Home MiniLab

For additional help doing this activity at home, see the corresponding pages in the **Home Involvement** booklet.

Purpose

 **Logical-Mathematical** Students will compare spheres. L2 ELL COOP LEARN 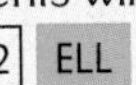

Materials

string, ruler, basketball or volleyball, **Table 21-1**

Teaching Strategies

Troubleshooting Stress that precise measurements must be made because approximations will not produce accurate results.

Analysis

1. Measurements should confirm that the balls are actually less of a sphere than Earth is.
2. Earth is larger through the equator.
3. Measurements taken at right angles to other measurements will not be exactly equal, indicating that the balls are not perfect spheres.

Assessment

Performance Have students measure other kinds of balls. Have them arrange their data in a table and graph the results. Use **Performance Assessment in the Science Classroom,** p. 39

Across the Curriculum

Geography Help students recall how the length of day changes from winter to summer for the area in which they live. Encourage them to write letters to city or other government officials in other parts of the world (friends or relatives would work as well) to find out how much the number of daylight hours changes from winter to summer in those areas. Once the students collect data on the number of daylight hours in other parts of the world, have them produce a bar graph showing these data. Ask volunteers to select areas from the graph and discuss how living conditions might be affected by differences in the number of daylight and nighttime hours. L2

PHYSICS INTEGRATION

The movement of convection currents inside Earth's mantle generates an electromagnet similar to one created when an electrical current is passed through a coil of wire. Turns in the coil of wire (similar to convection currents inside Earth) cause increased overlapping of the magnetic field lines, intensifying the magnetic field.

Activity

Interpersonal Have students demonstrate evidence of Earth's shape. First, put students into groups of two. Have one student in each pair hold a basketball at eye level, about 33 cm from his or her face. Have the second student slowly move a small object up and over the basketball from the opposite side. The first student should see the top of the object first, then the bottom. Have students reverse roles. Relate this to how the top of a ship is seen first when a ship at sea approaches shore. Then have students use a flashlight to cast shadows of a book and a ball against a wall. Have students relate this to the fact that Earth casts a curved shadow on the moon during a lunar eclipse. L2 ELL COOP LEARN

GLENCOE TECHNOLOGY

Videodisc

Glencoe Science Voyages Interactive Videodisc—Earth

Side 2, Lesson 8 *Space Exploration*

31965

Refer to Videodisc Teacher Guide for additional bar codes.

Earth's Magnetic Field

Convection currents inside Earth's mantle power the movement of tectonic plates. Scientists hypothesize that movement of material inside Earth along with Earth's rotation generates a magnetic field, as shown in **Figure 21-2.**

The magnetic field of Earth is much like that of a bar magnet. Earth has a north and a south magnetic pole, just as a bar magnet has opposite magnetic poles at its ends. **Figure 21-3** illustrates the effects of sprinkling iron shavings over a bar magnet. The shavings align with the magnetic field of the magnet. Earth's magnetic field is similar, almost as if Earth had a giant bar magnet in its core.

Magnetic North

When you observe a compass needle pointing toward the north, you are seeing evidence of Earth's magnetic field. Earth's magnetic axis, the line joining its north and south magnetic poles, does not align with its rotational axis. The magnetic axis is inclined at an angle of 11.5° to the rotational axis. If you followed a compass needle pointing north, you would end up at the magnetic north pole rather than the geographic (rotational) north pole.

Earth's magnetic field and other physical properties affect us every day. What occurrences can you explain in terms of Earth's physical properties and movement in space?

Figure 21-2 Heat and pressure within Earth cause the liquid outer core to move continuously. Driven by Earth's rotation and convection currents deep within Earth, the molten liquid forms spiraling columns. These spirals generate mechanical energy, which in turn generates electricity that creates the magnetic field.

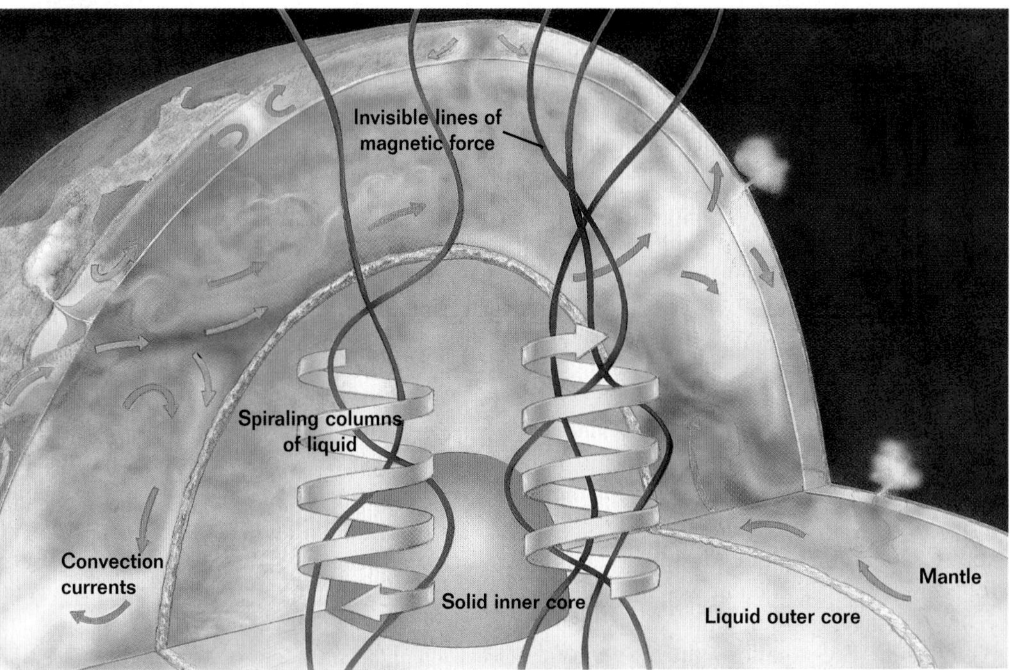

Integrating the Sciences

Physics Make a sketch of Earth on an overhead transparency. Label the geographic poles. Place the transparency over a bar magnet on an overhead projector. Rotate the figure so that the magnet makes an 11.5° angle with the rotational axis of Earth. Sprinkle iron shavings over the transparency and tap it lightly. Have a volunteer relate this demonstration to Earth's magnetic field.

Figure 21-3 Particles in the solar wind streaming through space from the sun distort Earth's magnetic field. As a result, Earth's magnetic field isn't symmetrical. It doesn't have the same shape as a magnetic field surrounding a bar magnet, which is symmetrical.

Seasons

Autumn is coming, and each day it gets colder outside. Dawn comes later each morning, and the sun appears lower in the sky. A month ago, it was light enough to ride your bike at 8:00 P.M. Now, it's dark at 8:00 P.M. What is causing this change?

Earth's Revolution

You learned earlier that Earth's rotation causes day and night. Another important motion of Earth is its **revolution,** or yearly orbit around the sun. Just as the moon is a satellite of Earth, Earth is a satellite of the sun. If Earth's orbit were a circle and the sun were at the center of the circle, Earth would maintain a constant distance from the sun. However, this is not the case. Earth's orbit is an **ellipse** (ee LIHPS), which is an elongated, closed curve. As **Figure 21-4** shows, the sun is offset from the center of the ellipse. Because of this, the distance between Earth and the sun changes during Earth's yearlong orbit. Earth gets closest to the sun—about 147 million km away—around January 3. The farthest point in Earth's orbit is about 152 million km away from the sun and is reached around July 4.

Does this elliptical orbit cause seasonal temperatures on Earth? If it did, you would expect the warmest days in January. You know this isn't the case in the northern hemisphere. Something else causes the change.

Even though Earth is closest to the sun in January, the overall amount of energy Earth receives from the sun changes little throughout the year. However, the amount of energy any one place on Earth receives can vary greatly.

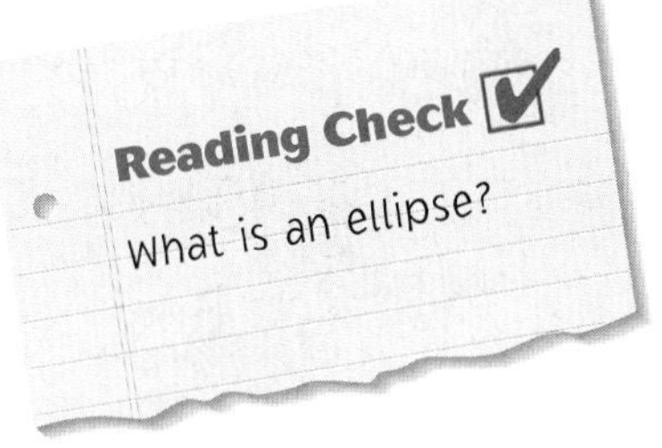

Enrichment

Interpersonal Separate students into groups of four. Ask each group to devise a method to demonstrate the difference between Earth's rotation and revolution. Once finished, groups can demonstrate their ideas to other groups. L2 ELL COOP LEARN

Answer to Reading Check

An ellipse is an elongated, closed curve.

Flex Your Brain

Use the Flex Your Brain activity to have students explore SEASONS.

GLENCOE TECHNOLOGY

Videodisc

The Infinite Voyage: The Living Clock

Chapter 5 *How Living Things Convert Light into Time* 5:30

Chapter 14 *Mental Health and the Biological Clock* 5:30

Refer to the Teacher Guide for bar codes and teaching strategies.

Multiple Learning Styles

Interpersonal Celebrate the seasons by having students work with elementary students to select a special day for each season. On this day, students can decorate the school halls, library, cafeteria, and other areas where the younger students congregate. Invite administrative personnel to planning sessions. L2

Caption Answers

Figure 21-4 *No, if it were, we would have the warmest temperatures in January when Earth is closest to the sun.*

Figure 21-5 *During summer in either hemisphere, Earth's axis is tilted toward the sun. The hemisphere tilted toward the sun receives more energy.*

Teacher FYI

Earth's orientation in space gradually changes with time. Presently, Earth's axis points toward Polaris, the North Star. In about 12 000 years, Earth's axis will point toward the star Vega in the constellation Lyra. This change is the result of Earth's "wobbling" on its axis.

Videodisc

STV: Solar System

Unit 1 *The Big Picture, Rotation and Revolution* 0:33

05295-06309

Refer to the Teacher Guide for additional bar codes and teaching strategies.

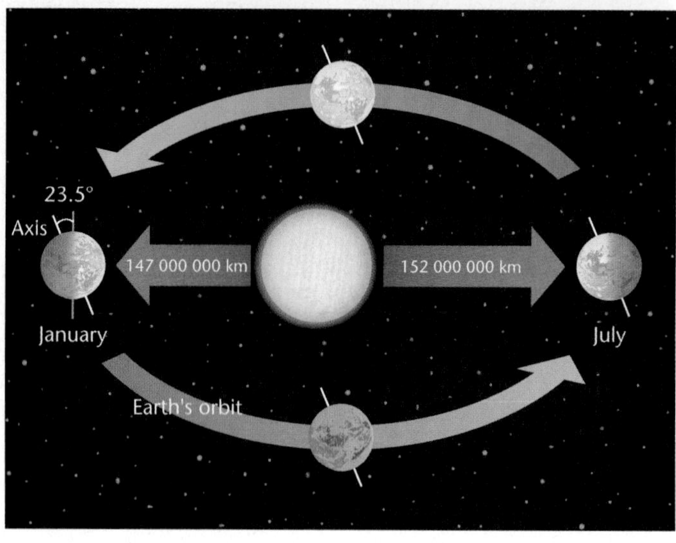

Figure 21-4 The northern hemisphere experiences summer when Earth is farthest from the sun. It experiences winter when Earth is closest to the sun. **Is the change of seasons caused by Earth's elliptical orbit? Explain your answer.**

Earth's Tilted Axis

Earth's axis is tilted 23.5° from a line perpendicular to its orbit. This tilt causes the seasons. Daylight hours are longer for the hemisphere tilted toward the sun. Think of how early it gets dark in the winter compared to the summer. As shown in **Figure 21-4,** the hemisphere tilted toward the sun receives more hours of sunlight than the hemisphere tilted away from the sun.

Earth's tilt also causes the sun's radiation to strike the hemisphere tilted toward it at a higher angle than it does the other hemisphere. Because of this, the hemisphere tilted toward the sun receives more electromagnetic radiation per unit area than the hemisphere tilted away. In other words, if you measured the amount of radiation received in a 1-km^2 area in the northern hemisphere and, at the same time, measured it for 1 km^2 in the southern hemisphere, you would find a difference. The hemisphere tilted toward the sun would be receiving more energy.

A summer season results when the sun's electromagnetic radiation strikes Earth at a higher angle. Just the opposite occurs during winter. **Figure 21-5** shows scenes from winter and summer.

Figure 21-5 Temperatures during summer are warmer than those during winter. **Why?**

Across the Curriculum

Geography Arrange students into groups of four. Supply each group with a globe of Earth and a flashlight. Instruct them to shine the flashlight directly on the Tropics of Cancer and Capricorn to illustrate why the areas within the Arctic and Antarctic Circles are called the lands of the midnight sun during summer solstice. L2 COOP LEARN

The slowing of Earth's rotation has been documented by Babylonian records of solar eclipses. The recorded dates of the eclipses could have occurred only if Earth were rotating slightly faster in the past.

Equinoxes and Solstices

Because of the tilt of Earth's axis, the sun's position relative to Earth's equator constantly changes. Most of the time, the sun is north or south of the equator. Two times during the year, however, the sun is directly over the equator.

Equinox

Look at **Figure 21-6.** When the sun reaches an **equinox** (EE kwuh nahks), it is directly above Earth's equator, and the number of daylight hours equals the number of nighttime hours all over the world. At that time, neither the northern nor the southern hemisphere is tilted toward the sun. In the northern hemisphere, the sun reaches the spring equinox on March 20 or 21 and the fall equinox on September 22 or 23. In the southern hemisphere, the equinoxes are reversed. Spring occurs in September and fall occurs in March.

Solstice

The **solstice** is the point at which the sun reaches its greatest distance north or south of the equator. In the northern hemisphere, the sun reaches the summer solstice on June 21 or 22, and the winter solstice occurs on December 21 or 22. Just the opposite is true for the southern hemisphere. When the sun is at the summer solstice, there are more daylight

Visit the Glencoe Science Web Site at **www.glencoe.com/sec/science** for more information about seasons.

Figure 21-6 At summer solstice in the northern hemisphere, the sun is directly over the Tropic of Cancer, 23.5° north latitude at noon. At winter solstice, the sun is directly over the Tropic of Capricorn, 23.5° south latitude at noon. At both fall and spring equinoxes, the sun is directly over the equator at noon.

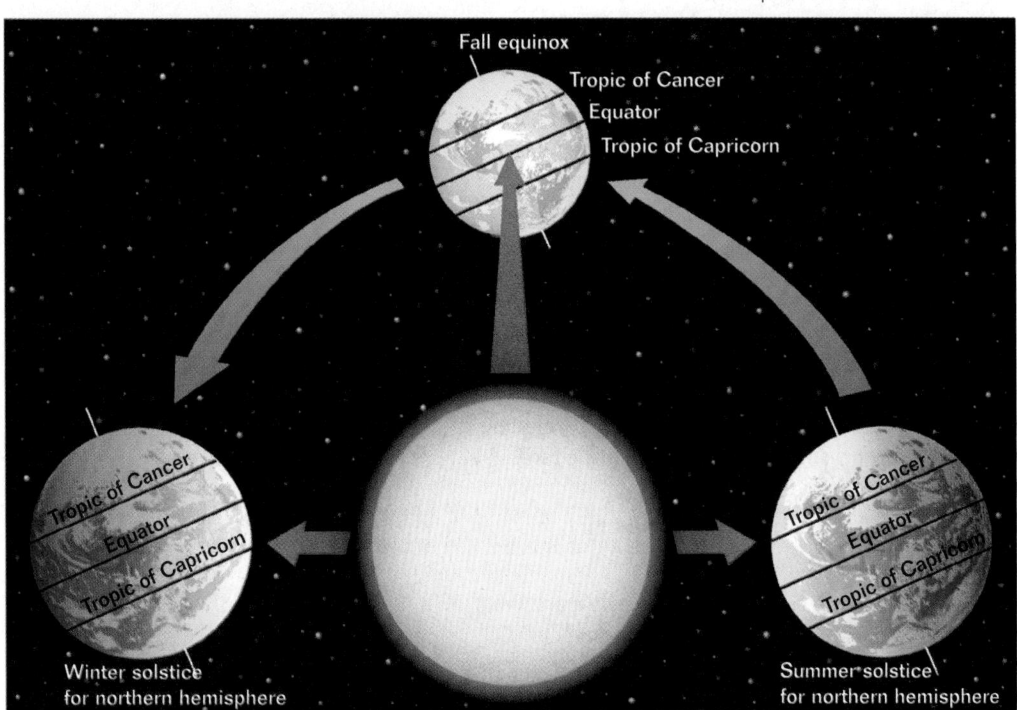

Content Background

Earth's magnetic poles are not located in the same location as Earth's geographic poles. The difference in location between the two different poles, measured in degrees, is declination. Magnetic compass directions can be corrected to true geographic directions by either adding or subtracting the declination value listed on a map. If the declination is east, the value is subtracted from the compass reading. If the declination is west, the value is added. Many cars today are built with electronic compasses. The compasses must be adjusted for the local declination before they will show a correct reading.

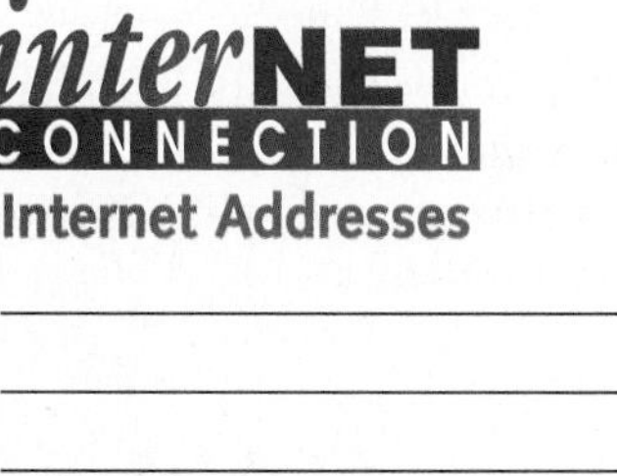

Internet Addresses

____

____

____

____

For Internet tips, see Glencoe's **Using the Internet in the Science Classroom.**

3 Assess

Check for Understanding

Discussion

Interpersonal Arrange students into groups of four. Have each group discuss what they like best about each season. When finished, conduct a class discussion about the pros and cons of each season. Encourage students to be creative and to describe specific characteristics about their favorite seasons. L1 COOP LEARN

Reteach

Visual-Spatial Darken the room and place a globe of Earth next to a light source. Tilt the globe 23.5°. Hold the globe so that its axis points toward and then away from the light. Slowly spin the globe to demonstrate how the amount of light striking each hemisphere of the globe changes. Help students conclude that days are shorter in the northern hemisphere when Earth's axis is tilted away from the sun, and longer when Earth's axis is tilted toward the sun.

Extension

For students who have mastered this section, use the **Reinforcement** and **Enrichment** masters.

4 Close

Proficiency Prep

Use this quiz to check students' recall of section content.

1. **What is the imaginary line around which Earth spins?** *axis*
2. **What is Earth's rotation?** *the spinning of Earth on its axis*
3. **What type of currents deep inside Earth are thought to generate its magnetic field?** *convection currents*
4. **What is the yearly orbit of Earth around the sun called?** *revolution*

Section Assessment

1. rotation
2. Light from the sun strikes Earth's surface at a higher angle, and the days are longer.
3. **Think Critically** Earth's orbit around the sun is an ellipse. Thus, its distance from the sun varies.

Using Computers

Student tables of Earth's physical data should include the information listed in **Table 21-1**.

hours than during any other day of the year. When it's at the winter solstice, on the shortest day of the year, the most nighttime hours occur.

Earth Data Review

Earth, shown in **Figure 21-7,** is an imperfect sphere that bulges very slightly at the equator and is somewhat flattened at the poles. The rotation of Earth causes day and night. Earth's tilted axis is responsible for the seasons you experience, and our revolution around the sun marks the passing of a year. In the next section, you will read how Earth's nearest neighbor, the moon, is also in constant motion and how you observe this motion each day.

Figure 21-7 In this photo, Earth appears to be nearly a perfect sphere. In reality, its diameter is 42 km larger at the equator than at the poles.

Section Assessment

1. Which Earth motion causes night and day?
2. Why does summer occur in Earth's northern hemisphere when Earth's north pole is tilted toward the sun?
3. **Think Critically:** Table 21-1 lists Earth's distance from the sun as an average. Why isn't there one exact measurement of this distance?
4. **Skill Builder**
   Recognizing Cause and Effect
   Answer these questions about the sun-Earth-moon relationship. If you need help, refer to Recognizing Cause and Effect in the **Skill Handbook** on page 721.
   a. What causes seasons on Earth?
   b. What causes winter?
   c. Earth is closest to the sun in January. What effect does this have on seasons?

Using Computers

Spreadsheet Using the table or spreadsheet capabilities of a computer program, generate a table of Earth's physical data showing its diameter, mass, period of rotation, and other data. Then, write a description of the planet based on the table you have created. If you need help, refer to page 738.

4. 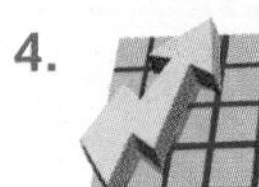 **Skill Builder**
   a. the tilt of Earth's axis
   b. The sun's radiation strikes Earth at a low angle.
   c. It has little effect. The seasons are primarily due to the tilt of Earth on its axis, not its distance from the sun.

Assessment

Oral Use this Skill Builder to assess students' abilities to recognize cause and effect. Ask students to identify the cause of Earth's magnetic field and the effect this field has on a compass needle. Use **Performance Assessment in the Science Classroom,** p. 71.

A Brave and Startling Truth
by Maya Angelou

In this chapter, you have learned some of the physical characteristics of our planet. Now, find out how one poet, Maya Angelou, uses Earth-science imagery to describe the human race and the quest for world peace. Below are several excerpts, or parts, from her poem "A Brave and Startling Truth."

We, this people, on a small and lonely planet
Traveling through casual space
Past aloof stars, across the way of indifferent suns
To a destination where all signs tell us
It is possible and imperative that we learn
A brave and startling truth...

When we come to it
Then we will confess that not the Pyramids
With their stones set in mysterious perfection
Nor the Gardens of Babylon
Hanging as eternal beauty
In our collective memory
Not the Grand Canyon
Kindled into delicious color
By Western sunsets
These are not the only wonders of the world...

When we come to it
We, this people, on this wayward, floating body
Created on this earth, of this earth
Have the power to fashion for this earth
A climate where every man and every woman
Can live freely without sanctimonious piety
And without crippling fear

When we come to it
We must confess that we are the possible
We are the miraculous, the true wonder of this world
That is when, and only when
We come to it.

interNET CONNECTION

Visit the Glencoe Science Web Site at www.glencoe.com/sec/science to learn more about Maya Angelou and her works. Do her other books and poems also contain Earth-science imagery? Using your knowledge of Earth science, write a short poem that uses Earth-science imagery to describe a social issue important to you.

Reading & Writing in Science

Maya Angelou is probably best known as a poet. This Pulitzer prize winner, however, is also a playwright, director, actor, and producer, and is recognized as an important social voice in America. In the 1960s, Dr. Martin Luther King, Jr. made her the northern coordinator of the Southern Christian Leadership Conference. Gerald Ford chose her to be on the American Revolution Advisory Bicentennial Council. She was appointed to the National Commission on the Observance of International Women's Year by Jimmy Carter. President Bill Clinton requested that she write and deliver a poem at his 1993 presidential inauguration. Ms. Angelou is currently Reynolds professor of American Studies at Wake Forest University in North Carolina. She holds positions in many professional organizations including the board of trustees of the American Film Institute and the Director's Guild.

Teaching Strategies

Have a volunteer state some of the physical characteristics of Earth—its diameter, mass, volume, and so on. Lead a discussion that contrasts these measurements with Angelou's descriptions of the planet (small, miniscule, mote of matter). Make sure students realize that our planet is in fact but a speck in the universe.

For Additional Information

Angelou, Maya. *A Brave and Startling Truth.* New York: Random House, 1995.

interNET CONNECTION

Internet Addresses

____

____

____

____

For Internet tips, see Glencoe's **Using the Internet in the Science Classroom.**

Activity 21·1 Design Your Own Experiment

Recognize the Problem

Purpose

Logical-Mathematical To design and carry out an experiment to show how the angle at which sunlight strikes an area of Earth's surface determines the amount of heat received by that area. L2 ELL COOP LEARN P

Process Skills

communicating, making and using tables, observing and inferring, comparing and contrasting, recognizing cause and effect, designing an experiment, measuring in SI, hypothesizing, separating and controlling variables, interpreting data, formulating models

Time

one class period

Alternate Materials A desk lamp held at the proper angle can be used instead of a gooseneck lamp.

Safety Precautions

The lightbulb and shade may be hot for some time after the lamp is turned off.

Form a Hypothesis

Possible Hypotheses

When light strikes a surface area from directly above, the area will receive more heat per unit area than when the light strikes the same surface area at a glancing angle.

Design Your Own Experiment

Activity 21·1

Tilt and Temperature

Possible Materials

- Tape
- Black construction paper (one sheet)
- Gooseneck lamp with 75-watt bulb
- Celsius thermometer
- Watch
- Protractor

Have you ever noticed how hot the surface of a blacktop driveway can get during the day? The sun's rays hit Earth more directly as the day progresses. Now, consider the fact that Earth is tilted on its axis. How does this affect the amount of heat an area on Earth receives from the sun?

Recognize the Problem

How is the angle at which light strikes an area on Earth related to the changing of the seasons?

Form a Hypothesis

State a hypothesis about how the angle at which light strikes an area affects the amount of heat energy received by that area.

Goals

- **Measure** the amount of heat generated by a light as it strikes a surface at different angles.
- **Describe** how light striking a surface at different angles is related to the changing of the seasons on Earth.

Safety Precautions

Do not touch the lamp without safety gloves. The lightbulb and shade can be hot even when the lamp has been turned off. Handle the thermometer carefully. If it breaks, do not touch anything. Inform your teacher immediately.

Test Your Hypothesis

Possible Procedures

Fold the black construction paper in half lengthwise. Tape the short edges together to form an envelope. Use this envelope to hold the thermometer. As an independent variable, set the lamp so that light shines directly down on the envelope containing the thermometer, and then change the angle to 45°. Select a specific time period for recording the temperature (for example, every three to nine minutes).

Test Your Hypothesis

Plan

1. As a group, agree upon and write out your hypothesis statement.
2. As a group, **list the steps** you need to take to test your hypothesis. Be specific, describing exactly what you will do at each step. List your materials.
3. **Make a list** of any special properties you expect to observe or test.
4. Read over your entire experiment to make sure that all steps are in a logical order.
5. **Identify** any constants, variables, and controls in the experiment.
6. Will you **summarize** data in a graph, table, or some other format?
7. How will you **determine** whether the length of time the light is turned on affects heat energy?
8. How will you **determine** whether the angle at which light strikes an area causes changes in heat and energy?

Do

1. Make sure your teacher approves your plan before you proceed.
2. **Carry out** the experiment as planned.
3. **Complete** the data table in your Science Journal.

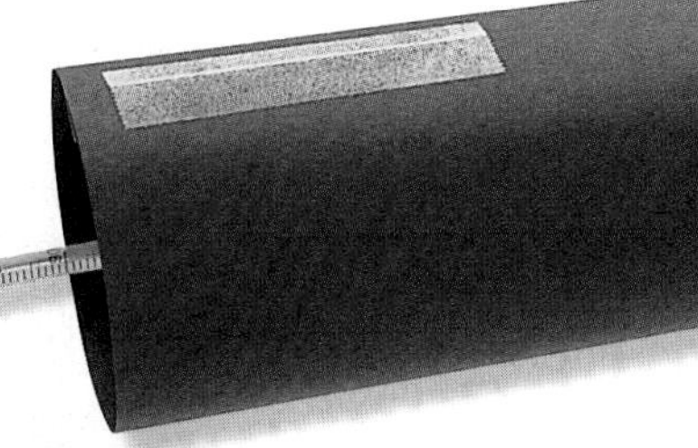

Analyze Your Data

1. **Describe** your experiment, including how you used independent variables to test your hypothesis.
2. What happened to the temperature of the area being measured as you modified your variables?
3. **Identify** the dependent variable in your experiment.

Draw Conclusions

1. Did your experiment support your hypothesis? **Explain.**
2. If not, **determine** how you might change the experiment in order to retest your hypothesis. How might you change your hypothesis?

Teaching Strategies

Troubleshooting Remind students to allow the thermometer to return to room temperature before each use.

Expected Outcome

Students should realize that the surface area heats up more quickly when light hits it from a more direct angle. They should also realize that this causes the warmer temperatures of summer.

Error Analysis

Ask students if they believe they would receive more energy from the sun when it is high in the sky or when it is low in the sky. Ask students to compare air temperatures at noon and at dusk.

Analyze Your Data

1. Descriptions will vary, but students should mention that they varied the angle at which light struck the thermometer.
2. Answers will vary, but students should note that when light strikes a surface at an angle, temperature increases more slowly.
3. Temperature is the dependent variable.

Draw Conclusions

1. Answers will vary depending on student hypotheses.
2. Answers will vary. Students may say that they need to change the angles of the light source or record temperatures at a different rate.

GO Further

Predict how the absorption of heat would be affected by changing your independent variable. Try your experiment with different values for your independent variable. Students should realize that lowering the angle should cause less of a temperature rise, and increasing the angle to a greater amount should cause the temperature to rise more quickly.

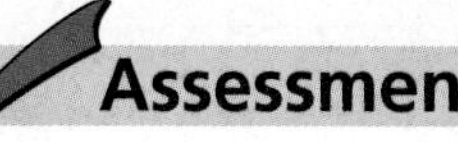

Assessment

Process Ask students to explain in writing why temperatures rise faster when light hits a surface area at a more direct angle. Use **Performance Assessment in the Science Classroom,** p. 87.

Prepare

Content Background Refer to **Moon Craters** and **Origin of the Moon** on p. 600F.

Preplanning

Refer to the **Chapter Organizer** on pp. 600A–B.

1 Motivate

Bellringer

Before presenting the lesson, display **Section Focus Transparency 57** on the overhead projector. Use the accompanying **Focus Activity** worksheet. L2 ELL

57 SECTION FOCUS TRANSPARENCY

MOONLIGHT, MOON BRIGHT

Full moon, new moon . . . What do these expressions mean? Why does the shape of the moon seem to change?

1. Use your own experiences and observations to describe the moon. Where and when do you see the moon?
2. Compare the shape of the moon at the top of the picture with the shape of the moon at the bottom. How are the two shapes alike and different?
3. Why do you think the moon appears to change shape?

Tying to Previous Knowledge

Help students recall the cause of tides from their earlier studies. Also, help students recall that large tidal ranges occur when Earth, the sun, and the moon are lined up.

21•2 Earth's Moon

What You'll Learn

- How the moon's phases depend on the relative positions of the sun, the moon, and Earth
- Why eclipses occur and how solar and lunar eclipses compare
- What the surface features of the moon may tell us about its history

Vocabulary
moon phase, new moon, waxing, first quarter, full moon, waning, third quarter, solar eclipse, lunar eclipse, maria

Why It's Important

- The moon is our closest neighbor in space.

Motions of the Moon

You have probably noticed how the moon's apparent shape changes from day to day. Sometimes, just after sunset, you can see a full, round moon low in the sky. Other times, only half of the moon is visible, and it's high in the sky at sunset. Sometimes, the moon is visible during the day. Why does the moon look the way it does? What causes it to change its appearance and position in the sky?

The Moon's Rotation and Revolution

Just as Earth rotates on its axis and revolves around the sun, the moon rotates on its axis and revolves around Earth. The moon's revolution causes changes in its appearance. If the moon rotates on its axis, why don't we see it spin around in space? The moon rotates on its axis once every 27.3 days. It takes the same amount of time to revolve once around Earth. As **Figure 21-8** shows, because these two motions take the same amount of time, the same side of the moon always faces Earth.

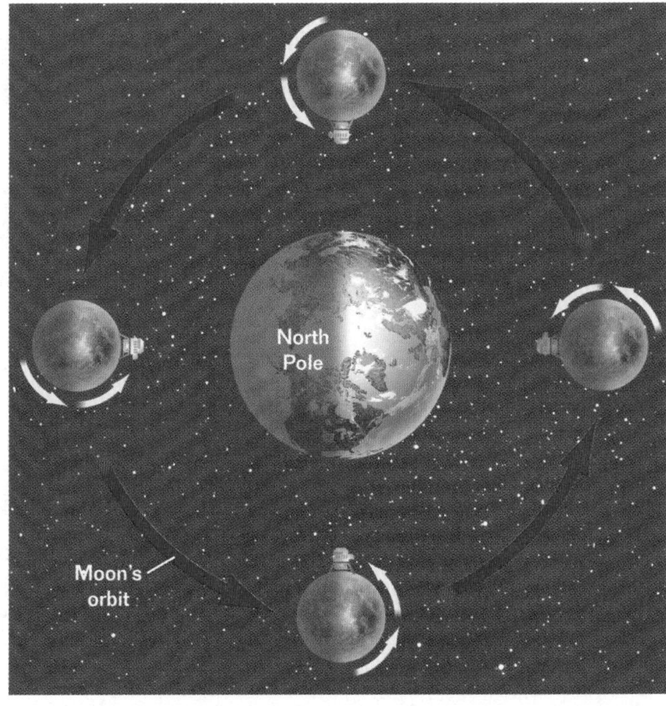

Figure 21-8 In about one month, the moon orbits Earth. It also completes one rotation on its axis during the same period. **Does this affect which side of the moon faces Earth? Explain.**

Resource Manager

The following **Teacher Classroom Resources** can be used with Section 21-2:

 **Reproducible Masters**

Activity Worksheets, p. 118 L2

Enrichment, p. 57 L3

Multicultural Connections, pp. 41-42 L2

Reinforcement, p. 57 L2

 **Transparencies**

Science Integration Transparency 21 L2

Teaching Transparency 42 L2

Figure 21-9 The phases of the moon are: (A) new moon, (B) waxing crescent, (C) first quarter, (D) waxing gibbous, (E) full moon, (F) waning gibbous, (G) third quarter, and (H) waning crescent.

You can show this by having a friend hold a ball in front of you. Instruct your friend to move the ball around you while keeping the same side of it facing you. Everyone else in the room will see all sides of the ball. You will see only one side.

Why the Moon Shines

The moon shines because it reflects sunlight from its surface. Just as half of Earth experiences day as the other half experiences night, half of the moon is lighted while the other half is dark. As the moon revolves around Earth, you see different portions of its lighted side, causing the moon's appearance to change. **Moon phases,** as shown in **Figure 21-9,** are the changing appearances of the moon as seen from Earth. The phase you see depends on the relative positions of the moon, Earth, and the sun.

Phases of the Moon

A new moon occurs when the moon is between Earth and the sun. During a **new moon,** the lighted half of the moon is facing the sun and the dark side faces Earth. The moon is in the sky, but it cannot be seen.

Waxing Phases

Shortly after a new moon, more and more of the moon's lighted side becomes visible—the phases are **waxing.** About 24 hours after a new moon, you can see a thin slice of the side of the moon that is lighted by the sun. This phase is called the waxing crescent. About a week after a new moon, you can see half of the lighted side, or one-quarter of the moon's surface. This phase is **first quarter.**

The phases continue to wax. When more than one-quarter is visible, it is called waxing gibbous. A **full moon** occurs when all of the moon's surface that faces Earth is lit up.

Using Math

Earth rotates through an angle of 360° in one day. How many degrees does Earth rotate in one hour?

2 Teach

Caption Answer

Figure 21-8 *Yes, because the moon's rotation and revolution take the same amount of time, the same side of the moon always faces Earth.*

Correcting Misconceptions

Some students may think that the far side of the moon is not seen because it is dark. Explain that this side of the moon receives as much light as the side that faces Earth. The far side is not seen because it always faces away from Earth.

Using Math

360°/24 hrs = 15°/hr

GLENCOE TECHNOLOGY

CD-ROM

Glencoe Science Voyages Interactive CD-ROM

Explorations

Have students do the interactive exploration *How do Earth and the moon interact to cause the moon's phases?*

Inclusion Strategies

Gifted Have students work in pairs to make time-lapse videos of the phases of the moon. Every night, the partners should videotape the moon for a few seconds. They should do this for one month. A regular 35-mm camera can be used if a video camera is not available. L2 COOP LEARN

Behaviorally Disordered Have students research myths about the full moon. After gathering the information, encourage students who have difficulty working within normal classroom constraints to perform skits that illustrate some of the myths. L2 COOP LEARN

Purpose

Students will compare the sizes of the sun, the moon, and Earth.

Materials

chalk, string, meterstick

Teaching Strategies

This activity works best in a large, open, paved area. Make sure students have at least 4 m of string with which to draw their circles.

Analysis

1. The sun is more than 400 times the size of the moon.
2. & 3. The sun's diameter is approximately 109 times greater than Earth's. The diameters of new circles representing the sun and Earth would be 109 cm and 1 cm, respectively.

Assessment

Performance Tell students that the moon's diameter is 3476 km. Have them draw two new circles representing the relative sizes of Earth and the moon. Use **Performance Assessment in the Science Classroom,** p. 29.

Videodisc

STV: Solar System

Unit 1 *The Big Picture, Landing on the Moon* 1:41

08780-11815

Refer to the Teacher Guide for additional bar codes and teaching strategies.

Comparing the Sun and Moon

Procedure

1. Find an area where you can make a chalk mark on pavement or another surface.
2. Tie a piece of chalk to one end of a string that's 400 cm long.
3. Hold the other end of the string to the pavement.
4. Have a friend pull the string tight and walk around you, leaving a mark on the pavement as he or she circles you.
5. Draw a circle with a 1-cm diameter in the middle of the large circle.

Analysis

1. The small circle represents the moon, and the larger circle represents the sun. How big is the sun compared to the moon?
2. The diameter of the sun is 1.39 million km. The diameter of the Earth is 12 756 km. Draw two new circles modeling the sizes of the sun and Earth.
3. What are the diameters of your two new circles?

Figure 21-10 The orbit of the moon is not in the same plane as Earth's orbit around the sun. If it were, we would experience a solar eclipse each month during the new moon. The plane of the moon's orbit is tilted about 5° to the plane of Earth's orbit.

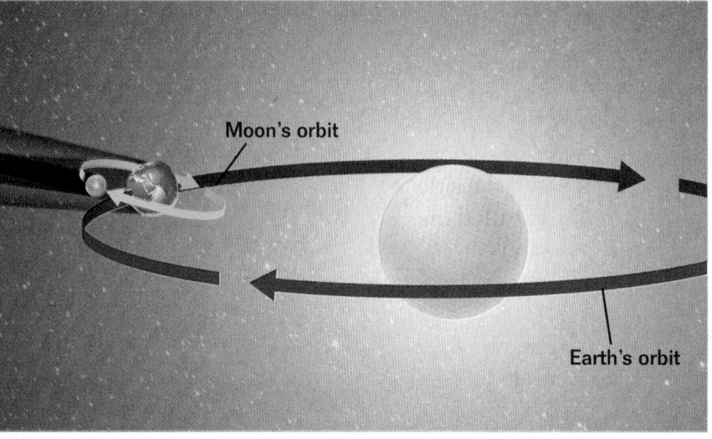

Waning Phases

After a full moon, the amount of the moon's lighted side that can be seen becomes smaller. The phases are said to be **waning.** Waning gibbous begins just after a full moon. When you can see only half of the lighted side, the **third-quarter** phase occurs. The amount of the moon that can be seen continues to become smaller. Waning crescent occurs just before another new moon. Once again, you can see a small slice of the lighted side of the moon.

The complete cycle of the moon's phases takes about 29.5 days. Recall that it takes about 27.3 days for the moon to revolve around Earth. The discrepancy between these two numbers is due to Earth's revolution. It takes the moon about two days to "catch up" with Earth's advancement around the sun.

Eclipses

Imagine yourself as one of your ancient ancestors, living 10 000 years ago. You are out foraging for nuts and other fruit in the bright afternoon sun. Gradually, the sun disappears from the sky, as if being swallowed by a giant creature. The darkness lasts only a short time, and the sun soon returns to full brightness. You realize something unusual has happened, but you don't know what caused it. It will be almost 8000 years before anyone can explain the event that you just experienced.

The event just described was a total solar eclipse (ih KLIPS). Today, we know what causes such eclipses, but for our early ancestors, they must have been terrifying events. Many animals act as if night has come. Cows return to their barns, and chickens go to sleep. What causes the day to suddenly change into night and then back into day?

Phases of the Moon Ask students to spend five to ten minutes writing freely in their Science Journals about everything they now know about the moon's phases. Have them use their free-writing exercise to formulate questions that will teach them information they still need or want to know. L2

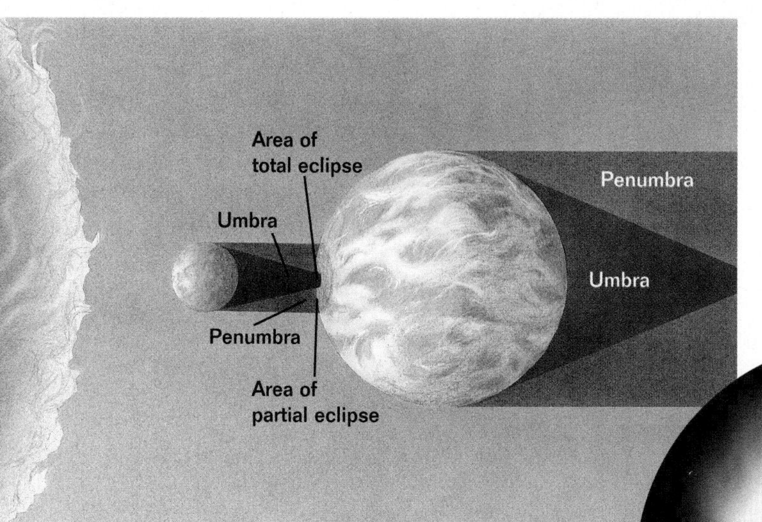

Figure 21-11 Only a small area of Earth experiences a total solar eclipse during the eclipse event. Only the outer portion of the sun's atmosphere is visible during a total solar eclipse. Distances are not drawn to scale.

The Cause of Eclipses

Revolution of the moon causes eclipses. Eclipses occur when Earth or the moon temporarily blocks the sunlight reaching the other. Sometimes, during a new moon, a shadow cast by the moon falls on Earth and causes a solar eclipse. During a full moon, a shadow of Earth can be cast on the moon, resulting in a lunar eclipse.

Eclipses can occur only when the sun, the moon, and Earth are lined up perfectly. Look at **Figure 21-10.** Because the moon's orbit is not in the same plane as Earth's orbit around the sun, eclipses happen only a few times each year.

Solar Eclipses

A **solar eclipse,** such as the one in **Figure 21-11,** occurs when the moon moves directly between the sun and Earth and casts a shadow on part of Earth. The darkest portion of the moon's shadow is called the umbra (UM bruh). A person standing within the umbra experiences a total solar eclipse. The only portion of the sun that is visible is part of its atmosphere, which appears as a pearly white glow around the edge of the eclipsing moon.

Surrounding the umbra is a lighter shadow on Earth's surface called the penumbra (puh NUM bruh). Persons standing in the penumbra experience a partial solar eclipse. **CAUTION:** *Regardless of where you are standing, never look directly at a solar eclipse. The light can permanently damage your eyes.*

Changing Seasons
Suppose that Earth's rotation took twice the time that it presently does. Write a report on how conditions such as global temperatures, work schedules, plant growth, and other factors might be different.

Guided Reading Strategy

Reciprocal Teaching This strategy is designed to help construct meaning and apply reading skills. Have pairs of students begin by each partner silently reading a chunk of text. After several minutes of reading, one student retells the key points of what was read in his or her own words. The other student creates a question that can be answered directly from the text but could require inferences or evaluation. Continue the reading with each student alternating questions and summaries. Consciously asking questions and summarizing content helps the reader focus on what is being read. Have students do Reciprocal Teaching with a chunk of section content.

Answers will vary but may include the fact that daytime temperatures would be higher, whereas nighttime temperatures would be lower. With longer daytime hours, work schedules might be more flexible. Plants would adapt to a longer cycle of food production based on photosynthesis.

Content Background

Eclipses can occur only if the moon, the sun, and Earth are in a straight line, which is a state known as *syzygy.* Also, eclipses occur only when the moon is at new-moon or full-moon stage and is located near a node (a point where the moon's path crosses the ecliptic). In the case of solar eclipses, the moon needs to be close to perigee (its closest approach to Earth). The closer the moon is to perigee (and the closer Earth is to aphelion), the more likely it is that a total solar eclipse will occur and the longer it will last.

Using an Analogy

Tell students to imagine they are sitting on the couch, watching television. Ask them how their view of the television screen would change if someone stood between the television and the couch. Compare this analogy to the positions of the moon or Earth during eclipses.

Enrichment

Help students realize that the word *month* comes from the same root as the word *moon*. Month describes the period of time that can be measured by the movement of the moon. A sidereal month is 27.3 days long, which is the actual period of the moon's revolution around Earth. A synodic month, the time between successive phases, is 29.5 days long. The discrepancy is due to Earth's revolution. It takes the moon about two days to catch up with Earth's advancement around the sun.

Quick Demo

Visual-Spatial Obtain a globe of the moon, or use a volleyball to represent the moon. Darken the room, and place three overhead projectors across the front of the room with their lights aimed toward the back of the room at an angle above students' heads. Have students cluster near the center of the room. Inform students that the projectors represent the sun, and the globe or ball represents the moon. The students represent observers on Earth. Keep the same side of the moon facing the students as you revolve the moon around them. Students should be able to see the moon go through phases beginning with new moon. Point out that the side of the moon that we aren't able to see is lighted during new moon. After the demonstration of lunar phases, position the moon properly during new and full moon to demonstrate how light is blocked out during solar and lunar eclipses. ELL COOP LEARN

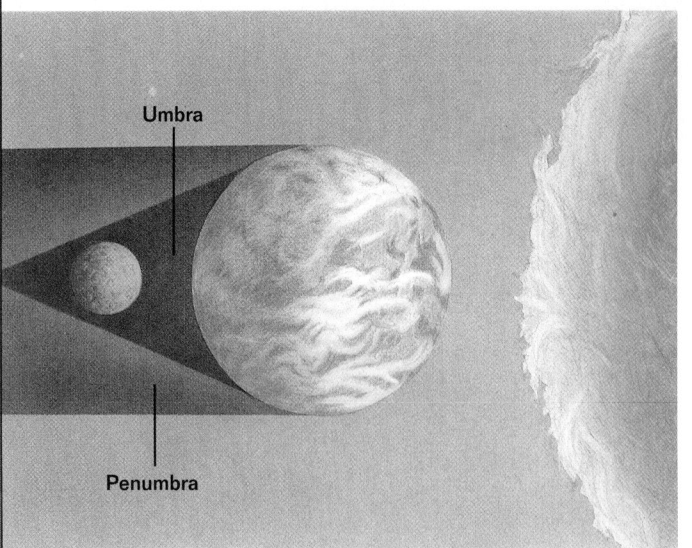

Figure 21-12 During a total lunar eclipse, Earth's shadow blocks light coming from the sun.

Lunar Eclipses

When Earth's shadow falls on the moon, a **lunar eclipse** like the one shown in **Figures 21-12** and **21-13** occurs. A lunar eclipse begins when the moon moves into Earth's penumbra. As the moon continues to move, it enters Earth's umbra and you see a curved shadow on the moon's surface. It was from this shadow that Aristotle concluded that Earth's shape was spherical. When the moon moves completely into Earth's umbra, the moon becomes dark red because light from the sun is refracted by Earth's atmosphere onto the moon. A total lunar eclipse has occurred.

A partial lunar eclipse occurs when only a portion of the moon moves into Earth's umbra. The remainder of the moon is in Earth's penumbra and, therefore, receives some direct sunlight.

A total solar eclipse occurs up to two times every year, yet most people live their entire lives without witnessing one. You may not be lucky enough to see a total solar eclipse, but it is almost certain you will have a chance to see a total lunar eclipse in your lifetime. The reason it is so difficult to view a total solar eclipse is that only those people in the small region where the moon's umbra strikes Earth can witness one. In contrast, anyone on the nighttime side of Earth can see a total lunar eclipse.

Figure 21-13 These photographs show the moon moving from right to left into Earth's umbra, then out again.

Cloudless Moon Have students research and write a one-page report in their Science Journals about why the moon does not have an atmosphere and whether it ever did have one. *The moon's gravitational force is not strong enough to hold gases at its surface. When sunlight falls on the moon, the moon's surface becomes intensely hot. Thus, the molecules that make up air travel fast enough to escape the moon's force of gravity. Atmospheric gases have probably been released by volcanic activity on the moon's surface in the past, but they have escaped into space.* L3

Structure of the Moon

When you look at the moon, you can see many of its larger surface features. The dark-colored, relatively flat regions are called **maria.** Maria formed when ancient lava flows from the moon's interior filled large basins on the moon's surface. The basins formed early in the moon's history.

Craters

Many depressions on the moon were formed by meteorites, asteroids, and comets, which strike the surfaces of planets and their satellites. These depressions are called craters. During impact, cracks may have formed in the moon's crust, allowing lava to reach the surface and fill in the large craters, forming maria. The igneous rocks of the maria are 3 to 4 billion years old. They are the youngest rocks found on the moon thus far.

The Moon's Interior

Seismographs left on the moon by *Apollo* astronauts have enabled scientists to study moonquakes. The study of earthquakes allows scientists to map Earth's interior. Likewise, the study of moonquakes has led to a model of the moon's interior. One model of the moon shows that its crust is about 60 km thick on the side facing Earth and about 150 km thick on the far side. Below the crust, a solid mantle may extend to a depth of 1000 km. A partly molten zone of the mantle extends farther down. Below this may be an iron-rich, solid core.

interNET CONNECTION

Visit the Glencoe Science Web Site at **www.glencoe.com/sec/science** to learn more about the *Apollo* space missions.

Problem Solving

Survival on the Moon

You and your crew have crash-landed on the moon, far from your intended landing site at the moon colony. It will take one day to reach the colony on foot. The side of the moon that you are on will be facing away from the sun during your entire trip back. You manage to salvage the following items from your wrecked ship: food, rope, solar-powered heating unit, battery-operated heating unit, three 70-kg oxygen tanks, map of the constellations, magnetic compass, oxygen-burning signal flares, matches, 8 L of water, solar-powered radio receiver and transmitter, three flashlights and extra batteries, signal mirror, and binoculars. Keep in mind that the moon's gravity is about one-sixth that of Earth's, and it lacks a magnetic field. Determine which items will be of no use to you. Determine which items to take with you on your journey to the colony.

Think Critically: Based on what you have learned about the moon, describe why each of the salvaged items is useful or not useful.

1. How did the moon's physical properties affect your decisions?
2. How did the lack of sunlight affect your decisions?

Problem Solving

Help students understand that items necessary for survival on Earth may not be important for survival on the moon.

Think Critically

Food and water will be needed. A battery-operated heating unit is also necessary because of the low temperatures on the moon's nightside. Oxygen tanks are the most important items to bring. A map of the constellations may help if the crew becomes lost. A flashlight is absolutely necessary. Binoculars will be useless unless you transverse into the daytime side. Rope may be needed to cross rough terrain. The solar-powered heating unit and radio and the signal mirror are useless without sunlight. Signal flares and matches cannot be used in the oxygen-free environment.

1. The moon's rough terrain, lack of oxygen, and low temperatures determine many of the objects selected.
2. The signal mirror, solar-powered heating unit, radio, and binoculars are left behind because they are useless without sunlight. By the same token, the flashlight is essential.

interNET CONNECTION

Internet Addresses

For Internet tips, see Glencoe's **Using the Internet in the Science Classroom.**

VISUAL Learning

Figure 21-14 Have students research the moons of other planets such as Jupiter or Mars. Have them compare and contrast the various moons.

Answer to Reading Check

The impact theory states that the moon was formed about 4.6 billion years ago when a Mars-sized object collided with Earth, throwing gas and debris into orbit, some of which later formed the moon.

3 Assess

Check for Understanding Activity

Interpersonal Put students into groups of four. Provide each group with a map of the moon's surface which can be found in astronomy field guides and reference books. Have students find and describe key surface features and explain how each feature might have formed. L2 COOP LEARN

Reteach

Using a globe of Earth, a tennis ball, and a large beach ball, simulate solar and lunar eclipses with the help of volunteers.

Extension

For students who have mastered this section, use the **Reinforcement** and **Enrichment** masters.

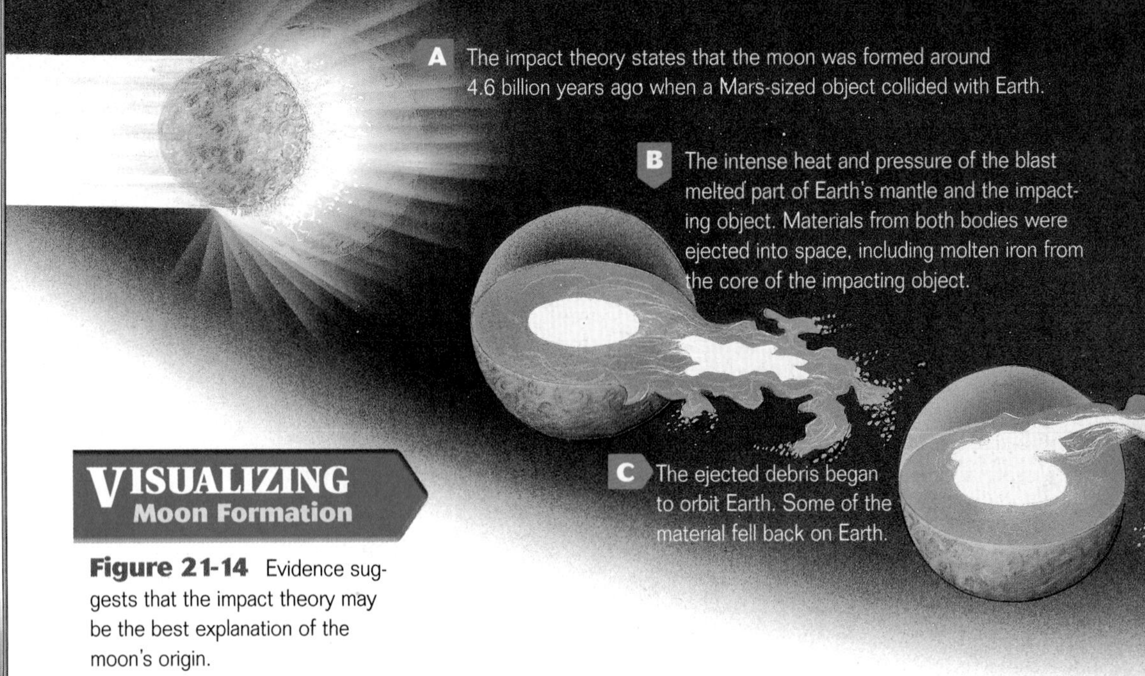

A The impact theory states that the moon was formed around 4.6 billion years ago when a Mars-sized object collided with Earth.
B The intense heat and pressure of the blast melted part of Earth's mantle and the impacting object. Materials from both bodies were ejected into space, including molten iron from the core of the impacting object.
C The ejected debris began to orbit Earth. Some of the material fell back on Earth.

VISUALIZING Moon Formation

Figure 21-14 Evidence suggests that the impact theory may be the best explanation of the moon's origin.

Origin of the Moon

Prior to the data obtained from the *Apollo* space missions, there were three theories about the moon's origin. The first was that the moon was captured by Earth's gravity. It had formed elsewhere and wandered into Earth's vicinity. The second theory was that the moon condensed from loose material surrounding Earth during the early formation of the solar system. The last theory was that a blob of molten material was ejected from Earth while Earth was still in its early molten stage.

Impact Theory

The data gathered by the *Apollo* missions have led many scientists to support a new impact theory. According to the impact theory, the moon was formed about 4.6 billion years ago when a Mars-sized object collided with Earth, throwing gas and debris into orbit. The gas and debris then condensed into one large mass, forming the moon. **Figure 21-14** illustrates the impact theory.

Reading Check

What is the impact theory of the moon's origin?

Regardless of the moon's true origin, it has played an important role in our history. It was a source of curiosity for many early astronomers. Studying the phases of the moon and eclipses led people to conclude that Earth and the moon were in motion around the sun. Earth's shadow on the moon proved that Earth's shape was spherical. When Galileo first turned his telescope to the moon, he found a surface scarred by craters

Science Journal

Moon Observations Have students keep a two-week log of moon observations, including the moon phase, the time it was observed, the moon's altitude above the horizon, and a brief description of sky conditions. The width of a fist when held at arm's length is approximately equal to 10° of altitude. L2

Integrating the Sciences

Seismology Have students write a report in their Science Journals about the kinds of equipment left behind on the moon and how these instruments have given scientists a better understanding of the moon's structure and history. L3

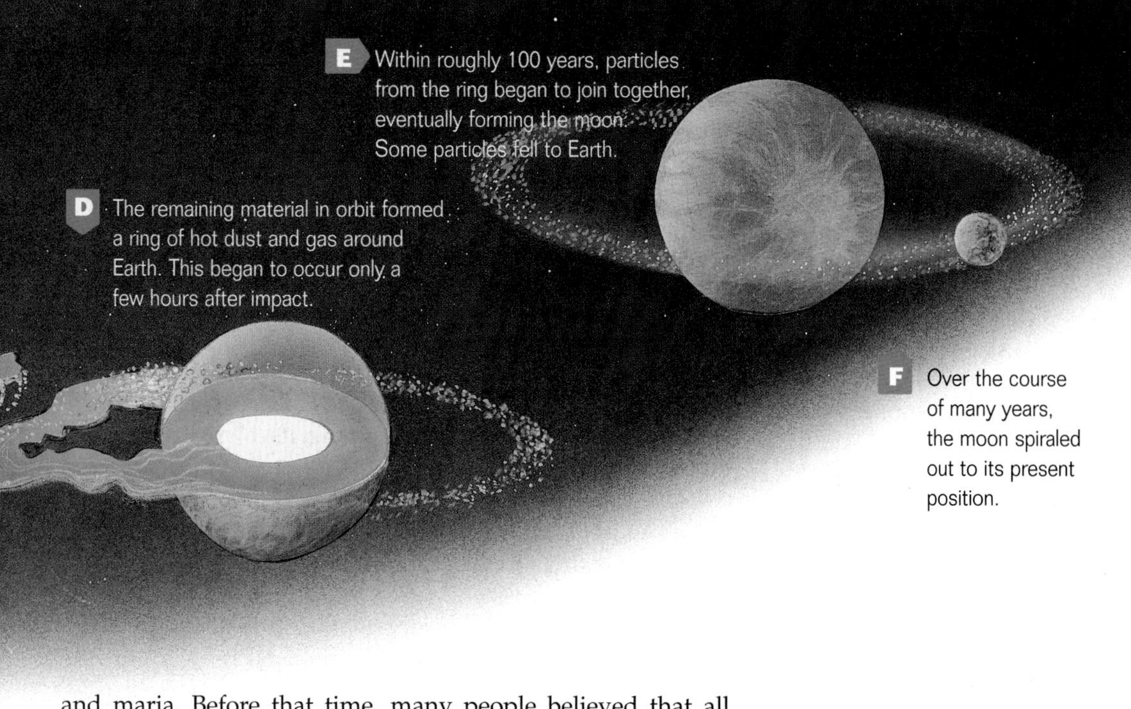

and maria. Before that time, many people believed that all planetary bodies were perfect, without surface features.

E Within roughly 100 years, particles from the ring began to join together, eventually forming the moon. Some particles fell to Earth.
D The remaining material in orbit formed a ring of hot dust and gas around Earth. This began to occur only a few hours after impact.
F Over the course of many years, the moon spiraled out to its present position.

By studying the moon, we can learn about ourselves and the planet we live on. As you will read in the next section, not only is the moon important as an object from our past, but it is important to our future, as well.

Section Assessment

1. What are the relative positions of the sun, the moon, and Earth during a full moon?
2. Why does a lunar eclipse occur only during a full moon?
3. Compare and contrast umbra and penumbra.
4. **Think Critically:** What provides the force necessary to form craters on the moon?
5. **Skill Builder**
   Interpreting Scientific Illustrations By tracking the changing positions of the sun, Earth, and the moon, scientists can predict solar eclipses. Do the **Chapter 21 Skill Activity** on page 762 to see when and where future solar eclipses will occur.

Research the moon's origin in astronomy books and magazines. In your Science Journal, write a report about the various theories, including the theory about a Mars-sized object colliding with Earth. Make a drawing of each theory.

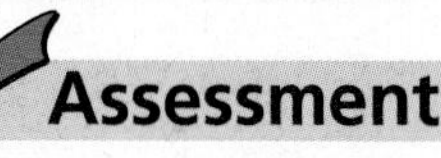

Performance Assess students' abilities to interpret scientific illustrations by having them draw the impact theory of the moon's formation. Use **Performance Assessment in the Science Classroom,** p. 55.

4 Close

Proficiency Prep

Use this quiz to check students' recall of section content.

1. **Which type of eclipse occurs when the moon moves directly between Earth and the sun?** *solar eclipse*
2. **Which type of eclipse occurs when Earth's shadow falls on the moon?** *lunar eclipse*
3. **What are maria and how did they form?** *Maria are dark-colored, relatively flat areas on the moon that formed when lava filled large basins on the surface of the moon.*

Section Assessment

1. Earth is between the sun and the moon.
2. In order for a lunar eclipse to occur, the moon must be within Earth's shadow. This happens only during full moon.
3. The darkest part of the moon's or Earth's shadow during an eclipse is the umbra. The lighter, broader shadow is the penumbra.
4. **Think Critically** the collision of meteorites into the moon's surface

Answers should relate to the theories of capture, condensation, fission, and impact.

SECTION 21-3

Prepare

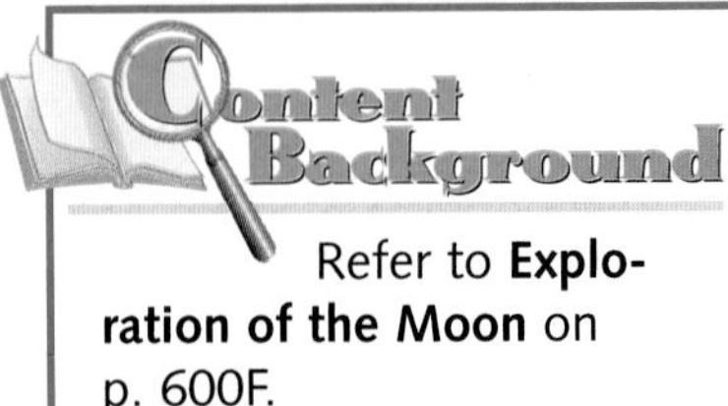

Refer to **Exploration of the Moon** on p. 600F.

Preplanning

Refer to the **Chapter Organizer** on p. 600A–B.

1 Motivate

Bellringer

Before presenting the lesson, display **Section Focus Transparency 58** on the overhead projector. Use the accompanying **Focus Activity** worksheet. L2 ELL

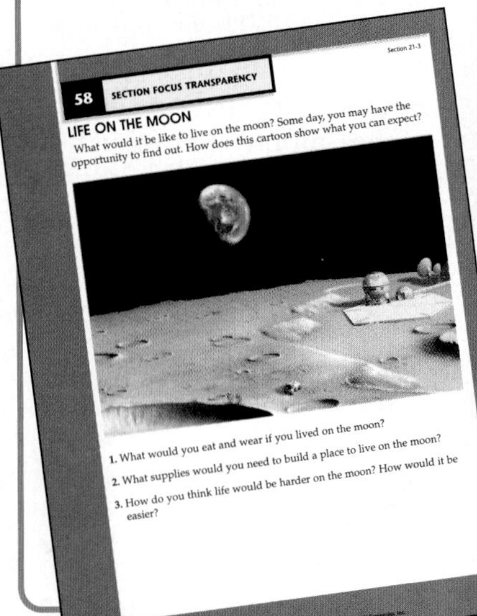

Section 21-3

58 SECTION FOCUS TRANSPARENCY

LIFE ON THE MOON

What would it be like to live on the moon? Some day, you may have the opportunity to find out. How does this cartoon show what you can expect?

1. What would you eat and wear if you lived on the moon?
2. What supplies would you need to build a place to live on the moon?
3. How do you think life would be harder on the moon? How would it be easier?

58

Tying to Previous Knowledge

Help students recall that humans first landed on the moon in 1969 and that a total of six *Apollo* missions have explored the moon with crews on its surface.

21-3 Exploration of the Moon

What You'll Learn

- Recent information about the moon discovered by spacecraft
- Facts about the moon's poles that may be important to future space travel

Vocabulary

mascon

Why It's Important

- Future missions to the moon may lead to important discoveries about Earth's origin.

Early Moon Missions

For centuries, astronomers have studied the moon for clues to its makeup and origin. In 1958, the former Soviet Union took studies of the moon into space with the launching of the *Luna* spacecraft. Three years later, the United States launched the first *Ranger* spacecraft, beginning its own lunar space exploration program.

Early U.S. moon missions, such as those involving the uncrewed *Ranger* and later the *Lunar Orbiter* spacecraft, focused on taking detailed photographs of the moon's surface. The *Lunar Orbiter* missions were followed by the *Surveyor* missions, wherein seven *Surveyor* spacecraft landed on the moon in preparation for the ultimate goal: to land astronauts on the moon. In 1969, this goal was realized with the launching of *Apollo 11*. By 1972 when the *Apollo* missions ended, 12 U.S. astronauts had walked on the moon.

Return to the Moon

More than 20 years passed before the United States resumed its studies of the moon from space. In 1994, the *Clementine* spacecraft was placed into lunar orbit to conduct a two-month survey of the moon's surface. *Clementine's* mission was to test new sensors for tracking cold objects, such as satellites, in space.

Figure 21-15 This false-color photograph, taken by cameras on the *Clementine* spacecraft, shows the moon, the sun, and the planet Venus.

Resource Manager

The following **Teacher Classroom Resources** can be used with Section 21-3:

Reproducible Masters

Activity Worksheets, pp. 115–116 L2

Enrichment, p. 58 L3

Reinforcement, p. 58 L2

Study Guide, pp. 82–84 L1 ELL

In addition, *Clementine* was placed in lunar orbit to take high-resolution photographs in order to compile a detailed map of the moon's surface. **Figure 21-15** shows a photograph taken by *Clementine. Clementine's* four cameras were able to resolve features as small as 200 m across, enhancing our knowledge of the moon's surface.

Reading Check
Why was Clementine placed in lunar orbit?

The Moon's South Pole

The South Pole-Aitken Basin is the oldest identifiable impact feature on the moon's surface. It is also the largest and deepest impact basin or depression found thus far anywhere in the solar system, measuring 12 km in depth and 2500 km in diameter. Data returned by *Clementine* gave scientists the first set of high-resolution photographs of this area of the moon. Much of this depression stays in shadow throughout the moon's rotation, forming a cold area where ice deposits from impacting comets may have collected. Radio signals reflected from *Clementine* to Earth indicated the presence of ice at the moon's south pole. Also, a large plateau that is always in sunlight was discovered in this area. If there truly is ice near the plateau, this would be an ideal location for a moon colony powered by solar energy.

Figure 21-16 is a global map showing the moon's crustal thickness based on *Clementine* data. According to the data, the moon's crust thins under impact basins. Also, the moon's crust on the side facing Earth is much thinner than on the far side. Such maps show the location of **mascons,** which are concentrations of mass. Mascons are located under impact basins. Data collected by *Clementine* also provided information on the mineral content of moon rocks. In fact, this part of its mission was instrumental in naming the spacecraft. Clementine was the daughter of a miner in the ballad "My Darlin' Clementine."

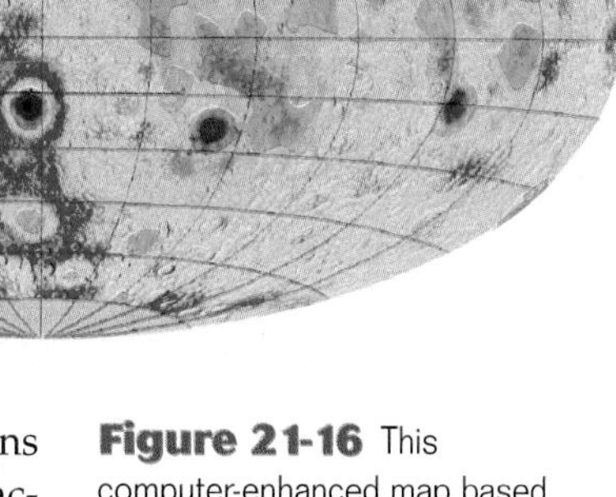

Figure 21-16 This computer-enhanced map based on *Clementine* data indicates the thickness of the moon's crust. The crust of the side of the moon facing Earth, shown mostly in red, is thinner than the crust on the far side of the moon.

The Lunar Prospector

The success of *Clementine* at a relatively low cost opened the door for further moon missions. In 1998, NASA launched the *Lunar Prospector* spacecraft. Its mission was to orbit the moon, taking photographs of the lunar surface for mapping purposes. These maps confirmed the *Clementine* data. The

2 Teach

Answer to Reading Check

to take photographs to compile a detailed map of the moon's surface

3 Assess

Check for Understanding

Using Science Words

Linguistic Ask students to research and write about cold objects in space. Student reports should explain why objects such as satellites, warheads, and near-Earth asteroids are referred to as cold objects, and why scientists need to track such objects. L3

Reteach

Visual-Spatial Obtain photographs of the moon from early crewed and uncrewed missions to the moon and from the recent *Clementine* and *Lunar Prospector* spacecraft. Help students decide which photographs show more detail and would best be used for mapmaking. Contact NASA for photographs. L2 ELL COOP LEARN

Extension

For students who have mastered this section, use the **Reinforcement** and **Enrichment** masters.

Content Background

One of the first scientists to recognize possible causes of craters on the moon and Earth was Grove K. Gilbert (1843–1918). His explanation of impact cratering on the moon led to our current understanding of the evolution of terrestrial planets.

Science Journal

The Back of the Moon Show students maps of the back of the moon and have them list the names of some of the larger features found there. Ask them to also write a report on which lunar missions were responsible for providing the first photographs of these features. L2

4 Close

Proficiency Prep

Use this quiz to check students' recall of section content.

1. **The former Soviet Union launched the study of the moon with which spacecraft?** *Luna 1*
2. **Which U.S. spacecraft soft-landed on the moon in preparation for landing astronauts on the moon?** *Surveyor*

Section Assessment

1. the presence of ice at the moon's poles, a sunlit plateau near the moon's south pole, thinning of the moon's crust under impact basins, location of mascons, information on mineral content of moon rocks
2. to orbit the moon, take photos of its surface, and search for clues to its origin and makeup
3. Countries began to study the moon from space.
4. **Think Critically** With the possibility of water from the ice, the large plateau near the moon's south pole would be an ideal location for a moon colony. Also, oxygen and hydrogen from the water could be used to produce fuel for future space flights.

Using Math

Lunar Prospector also was scheduled to conduct a detailed study of the moon's surface, searching for clues as to the origin and makeup of the moon.

Icy Poles

Early data obtained from the *Lunar Prospector* indicate that hydrogen is present in the rocks found in the craters at the moon's poles, as shown in **Figure 21-17.** Hydrogen is one of the elements that make up water. These data, combined with data from *Clementine,* have led scientists to theorize that ice may exist in the floors of the craters at both of the moon's poles. These craters are deep and cold. Sunlight never reaches their floors, where temperatures are as low as –233°C—definitely cold enough to have preserved any ice that may have collected in the craters from colliding comets or meteorites.

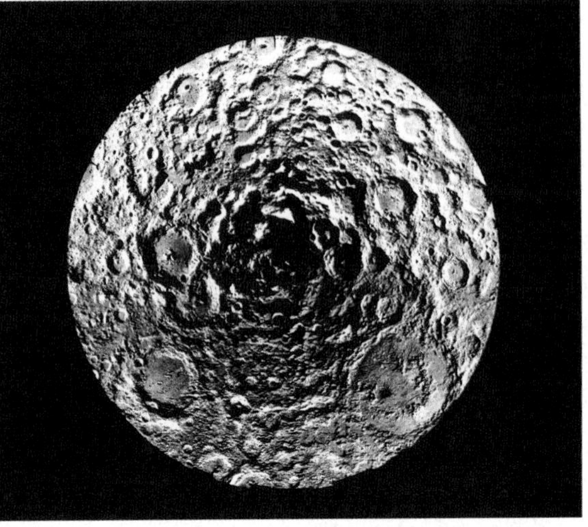

Figure 21-17 Data from *Lunar Prospector* indicate the presence of twice as much ice at the moon's north pole as at its south pole.

Based on the *Lunar Prospector* data, scientists estimate that 6 billion tons of ice lie under the surface of the moon's poles. The ice may be buried under about 40 cm of crushed rock. Data from *Lunar Prospector* also have enabled scientists to conclude that the moon has a small, iron-rich core about 600 km across.

Section Assessment

1. List two discoveries about the moon made by the *Clementine* spacecraft.
2. What was the main mission of the *Lunar Prospector?*
3. How did studies of the moon change after the 1950s?
4. **Think Critically:** Why would the discovery of ice at the moon's poles be important to future space flights?
5. **Skill Builder**
   Sequencing Sequence the following moon missions in the order in which they occurred: *Surveyor, Lunar Prospector, Apollo, Lunar Orbiter, Ranger,* and *Clementine.* If you need help, refer to Sequencing in the **Skill Handbook** on page 714.

Using Math

The moon's orbit is tilted at an angle of about 5° to Earth's orbit around the sun. Using a protractor, draw an angle of 5°. Draw a model of the moon's orbit around Earth.

5. **Skill Builder**
   Ranger, Lunar Orbiter, Surveyor, Apollo, Clementine, and *Lunar Prospector*

Assessment

Performance Assess student understanding of moon studies by asking them which missions landed on the moon and which orbited the moon. *Surveyor and Apollo landed on the moon; and Lunar Orbiter, Clementine, and Lunar Prospector orbited the moon.* Use **Performance Assessment in the Science Classroom,** p. 103.

Using Scientific Methods

Activity 21-2

Moon Phases and Eclipses

Materials
- Light source (unshaded)
- Polystyrene ball on pencil
- Globe

You know that moon phases and eclipses result from the relative positions of the sun, the moon, and Earth. In this activity, you will demonstrate the positions of these bodies during certain phases and eclipses. You also will see why only people on a small portion of Earth's surface see a total solar eclipse.

What You'll Investigate
Can a model be devised to show the positions of the sun, the moon, and Earth during various phases and eclipses?

Goals
- **Model** moon phases.
- **Model** solar and lunar eclipses.

Procedure
1. Review the illustrations of moon phases and eclipses shown in Section 21-2.
2. **Use** the light source as a model sun and a polystyrene ball on a pencil as a model moon. **Move** the model moon around the globe to duplicate the exact position that would have to occur for a lunar eclipse to take place.
3. **Move** the model moon to the position that would cause a solar eclipse.
4. **Place** the model moon at each of the following phases: first quarter, full moon, third quarter, and new moon. **Identify** which, if any, type of eclipse could occur during each phase. Record your data.
5. **Place** the model moon at the location where a lunar eclipse could occur. **Move** it slightly toward Earth, then away from Earth. Note the amount of change in the size of the shadow causing the eclipse. Record this information.
6. **Repeat** step 5 with the model moon in a position where a solar eclipse could occur.

Conclude and Apply
1. During which phase(s) of the moon is it possible for an eclipse to occur?
2. **Describe** the effect that a small change in the distance between Earth and the moon has on the size of the shadow causing the eclipse.
3. As seen from Earth, how does the apparent size of the moon **compare** with the apparent size of the sun? How can an eclipse be used to confirm this?
4. **Infer** why a lunar and solar eclipse do not occur every month.
5. Suppose you wanted to more accurately model the movement of the moon around Earth. **Explain** how your model moon moves around the globe. Would it always be in the same plane as the light source and the globe?
6. Why have only a few people seen a total solar eclipse?

Sample Data

Moon Phase Observations

Moon Phase	Observations
first quarter	no eclipse
full	lunar eclipse
third quarter	no eclipse
new	solar eclipse

5. In order to model lunar motions around Earth, the moon must be located either above or below Earth's orbital plane. It will move slightly away from and closer to Earth during its elliptical orbit.
6. If the sun, the moon, and Earth are not lined up perfectly, the umbra of the moon's shadow will not fall on Earth. When the umbra does fall on Earth, it covers only a small band across Earth's surface.

Assessment
Performance To further assess students' understanding of moon phases and eclipses, have students repeat the activity using themselves as the model of Earth. Have one student move the moon model around another student so that the class can observe all phases and eclipses. Use **Performance Assessment in the Science Classroom,** p. 25.

Activity 21-2

Purpose
Kinesthetic Students will formulate a model and demonstrate the relative positions of Earth and the moon during lunar phases. L2 ELL COOP LEARN P

Process Skills
communicating, sequencing, observing and inferring, recognizing and using spatial relationships, comparing and contrasting, recognizing cause and effect

Time
30 to 40 minutes

Safety Precautions
Caution students to handle the light source with care.

Teaching Strategies
Troubleshooting Point out that the distance between the moon and Earth is not constant.

Answers to Questions
1. Lunar eclipses occur at full moon. Solar eclipses occur during new moon.
2. It has little effect. During solar eclipses, the closer the two bodies, the larger the moon's shadow on Earth and the longer the duration of the eclipse.
3. The moon and sun appear similar in size. During a solar eclipse, the moon seems to exactly fit the solar disk being eclipsed.
4. Eclipses are possible only when the moon is crossing Earth's orbital plane around the sun. Except for a few minutes each month, the moon is always located either above or below Earth's orbital plane.

Chapter 21 Reviewing Main Ideas

Reviewing Main Ideas can be used to preview, review, reteach, and condense chapter content.

Preview

Linguistic Have students try to answer the questions in their Science Journals. Use student answers as a source for discussion throughout the chapter.

Review

Interpersonal Have students answer the questions on separate pieces of paper and compare their answers with those of other students in the class.

Reteach

Visual-Spatial Have students look at the illustrations on these pages. Ask them to describe details that support the main ideas of the chapter found in the statement for each illustration.

00:00 OUT OF TIME?

Auditory-Musical If time does not permit teaching the entire chapter, use the information on these pages along with the chapter Audiocassettes to present the material in a condensed format.

Chapter 21 Reviewing Main Ideas

For a **preview** of this chapter, study this Reviewing Main Ideas before you read the chapter. After you have studied this chapter, you can use the Reviewing Main Ideas to **review** the chapter.

The Glencoe MindJogger, Audiocassettes, and CD-ROM provide additional opportunities for review.

Section 21-1 PLANET EARTH

Earth is a **sphere** that is slightly flattened at its poles. Earth **rotates** once each day and **revolves** around the sun in a little more than 365 days. Seasons on Earth are due to the amount of solar radiation received by a hemisphere at a given time. The tilt of Earth on its **axis** causes the amount of solar energy to vary. ***How does Earth's interior act like an electromagnet?***

Section 21-2 EARTH'S MOON

Earth's moon goes through **phases** that depend on the relative positions of the sun, the moon, and Earth. Eclipses occur when Earth or the moon temporarily blocks sunlight from the other. A **solar eclipse** occurs when the moon moves directly between the sun and Earth. A **lunar eclipse** occurs when Earth's shadow falls on the moon. The moon's **maria** are the result of ancient volcanism. Craters on the moon's surface formed from impacts with meteorites, asteroids, and comets. ***If the moon is between Earth and the sun for each new moon, why are there only one or two solar eclipses each year?***

Cultural Diversity

Social Studies For some groups, time defines activities. For others, activities define time. Many Americans do certain activities on certain months of the year—we celebrate Independence Day because it is July 4. But for the Nuer, a group of seminomadic pastoralists living in East Africa, months are defined by activities. The Nuer base their yearly cycle on a system of full moons. Each moon is named after the activities associated with it. *Kur*, for example, is a time to make the first fishing dams and build the first cattle camps. It is part of *mai* (the dry season). *Dwat* is the month when they break camp and return to their village. It is part of *tot* (the wet season). Two transitional seasons, *rwil* and *jiom* (meaning "wind"), are recognized as seasons of rapid change.

Reading Check

Use these words in sentences that do not relate to the sun, Earth, or moon: *sphere, axis, rotation, revolution, ellipse, waxing,* and *waning.*

Section

21-3 EXPLORATION OF THE MOON

The *Clementine* spacecraft took detailed, high-resolution photographs of the moon's surface. Data from *Clementine* indicate that the moon's South Pole-Aitken Basin may contain ice deposits that could supply water for a moon colony. The *Clementine* spacecraft also noted that **mascons** occur beneath impact basins on the moon. NASA has returned to exploring the moon with its latest spacecraft, the *Lunar Prospector.* Data from *Lunar Prospector* seem to support the ice theory and also indicate that the moon's north pole may contain twice as much ice as the south pole. ***How did the* Clementine *spacecraft get its name?***

Career CONNECTION

Gibor Barsi, Astronomer

Gibor Barsi is an astronomer who works with the Keck Telescopes on Mauna Kea, Hawaii. The summit of Mauna Kea is considered the world's premier site for astronomical observation. Gibor is interested in answering the questions, "How many planets are there around other stars, what are they like, and how do they form?" He feels that the next generation of astronomers and technology will answer these questions. ***Why do you suppose astronomers are interested in finding new planets?***

Answers to Questions

Section 21-1

Planet Earth Convection currents of molten iron in Earth's core produce electrical currents, which cause Earth's magnetic field.

Section 21-2

Earth's Moon The moon is not always on the ecliptic during new-moon phase. Usually, the moon is above or below the plane of Earth's orbit around the sun.

Section 21-3

Exploration of the Moon Part of the mission of the *Clementine* spacecraft was to provide information on the mineral content of moon rocks. This was instrumental in naming the spacecraft *Clementine.* Clementine was the daughter of a miner in the ballad, "My Darlin' Clementine."

Career CONNECTION

to explore the possibility of life on other planets and to learn more about how planets form

Assessment

Portfolio Encourage students to place in their portfolios one or two items of what they consider to be their best work. Examples include:

- MiniLab, p. 603
- Activity 21-1, pp. 610–611
- Activity 21-2, p. 623 

Performance Additional performance assessments may be found in **Performance Assessment** and **Science Integration Activities.** Performance Task Assessment Lists and rubrics for evaluating these activities can be found in Glencoe's **Performance Assessment in the Science Classroom.**

GLENCOE TECHNOLOGY

 **CD-ROM**

Glencoe Science Voyages Interactive CD-ROM

Chapter Summaries and Quizzes

Have students read the Chapter Summary then take the Chapter Quiz to determine whether they have mastered chapter content.

Using Vocabulary

1. rotation
2. equinox
3. full moon
4. solar eclipse
5. mascon

interNET CONNECTION To reinforce chapter vocabulary, use the **Study Guide for Content Mastery** booklet. Also available are activities for **Glencoe Science Voyages** on the Glencoe Science Web Site. **www.glencoe.com/sec/science**

Checking Concepts

6. C	11. B
7. A	12. A
8. C	13. B
9. C	14. D
10. D	15. B

Thinking Critically

16. If the moon moved between the observer and the sun, phases would be observed. The specific phases would depend on the relative positions of the observer, the moon, and the sun.
17. Earth bulges at the equator. The gravitational attraction there is less than that at the poles. Thus, a person weighs less at the equator.
18. During full and new moons, Earth, the sun, and the moon align; thus, the gravitational attraction is greatest then. High tides are the highest and low tides are the lowest during these two phases.

Chapter 21 Assessment

Using Vocabulary

a. axis	j. new moon
b. ellipse	k. revolution
c. equinox	l. rotation
d. first quarter	m. solar eclipse
e. full moon	n. solstice
f. lunar eclipse	o. sphere
g. maria	p. third quarter
h. mascon	q. waning
i. moon phase	r. waxing

Each phrase below describes a science term from the list. Write the term that matches the phrase describing it.

1. causes day and night to occur on Earth
2. occurs when the sun's position is directly above the equator
3. moon phase in which all of the lighted side of the moon is seen
4. eclipse that occurs when the moon is between Earth and the sun
5. concentration of mass on the moon located under an impact basin

Checking Concepts

Choose the word or phrase that completes the sentence.

6. How long does it take for the moon to rotate?
A) 24 hours C) 27.3 hours
B) 365 days D) 27.3 days
7. Where is Earth's circumference greatest?
A) equator C) poles
B) mantle D) axis
8. During an equinox, the sun is directly over what part of Earth?
A) southern hemisphere
B) northern hemisphere
C) equator
D) pole
9. Why does the sun appear to rise and set?
A) Earth revolves.
B) The sun moves around Earth.
C) Earth rotates.
D) Earth orbits the sun.
10. How long does it take for the moon to revolve?
A) 24 hours C) 27.3 hours
B) 365 days D) 27.3 days
11. As the lighted portion of the moon appears to get larger, what is it said to be?
A) waning C) rotating
B) waxing D) crescent shaped
12. During what kind of eclipse is the moon directly between the sun and Earth?
A) solar C) full
B) new D) lunar
13. What is the darkest part of the shadow during an eclipse?
A) waxing gibbous C) waning gibbous
B) umbra D) penumbra
14. What are depressions on the moon called?
A) eclipses C) phases
B) moonquakes D) craters
15. What fact do data gathered from the *Clementine* spacecraft support?
A) The moon rotates once in 29.5 days.
B) The moon has a thinner crust on the side facing Earth.
C) The moon revolves once in 29.5 days.
D) The moon has a thicker crust on the side facing Earth.

Thinking Critically

16. How would the moon appear to an observer in space during its revolution? Would phases be observable? Explain.
17. Would you weigh more at Earth's equator or at the north pole? Explain.

19. The moon does not have a magnetic field. Star charts could be used to navigate, but a compass could not.
20. The changing position of the moon from night to night is a real motion because the moon is orbiting Earth. The moon appears to move westward across the sky due to Earth's rapid rotation. Although the moon is progressing eastward in its revolution around Earth, its trip across the sky in a single night is due to Earth's rotation. Seeing the same side of the moon seems to indicate a lack of rotation. This is an apparent motion because the moon's period of rotation equals its period of revolution.

18. Tides occur due to the gravitational attraction among the sun, the moon, and Earth. During which phases of the moon are tides the highest? Explain.
19. If you were lost on the moon's surface, why would it be more beneficial to have a star chart rather than a compass?
20. Which of the moon's motions are real? Which are apparent? Explain.

Developing Skills

If you need help, refer to the **Skill Handbook.**

21. **Hypothesizing:** Why do locations near Earth's equator travel faster during one rotation than places near the poles?
22. **Using Variables, Constants, and Controls:** Describe a simple activity to show how the moon's rotation and revolution work to keep one side facing Earth at all times.
23. **Comparing and Contrasting:** Compare and contrast a waning moon with a waxing moon.
24. **Concept Mapping:** Copy and complete the cycle map shown on this page. Show the sequences of the moon's phases.

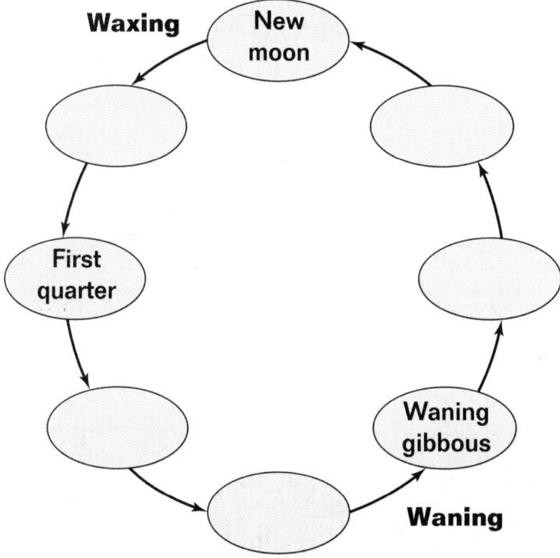

Test-Taking Tip

Practice, Practice, Practice Practice to improve *your* performance. Don't compare yourself with anyone else.

Test Practice

Use these questions to test your Science Proficiency.

1. As the moon revolves around Earth, it keeps the same side facing Earth. Which of the following statements **BEST** explains why this is so?
   - A) The moon rotates once on its axis as it makes one complete revolution around Earth.
   - B) The moon does not rotate as it revolves.
   - C) The speed of rotation for the moon exactly equals its speed of revolution.
   - D) The speed of revolution for the moon is constant and therefore keeps one side facing Earth at all times.
2. More craters are on the far side of the moon than on the side facing Earth. Which of the following statements would **BEST** explain this fact?
   - A) A greater number of volcanoes occur on the far side of the moon.
   - B) Earth's gravity attracts more of the objects that would produce craters on the side of the moon facing Earth.
   - C) Earth blocks the paths of any objects that would collide with the side of the moon facing Earth.
   - D) The far side of the moon is always facing away from the sun.

THE PRINCETON REVIEW Test Practice

The Test-Taking Tip was written by The Princeton Review, the nation's leader in test preparation.

1. A
2. B

Developing Skills

21. The circumference of Earth is greater at low latitudes than at high latitudes. Thus, locations near the equator have a greater distance to travel to complete one rotation than do locations near the poles.
22. Place an X on a basketball. As you walk around a classmate, keep the X pointed toward him or her. You must turn the ball to keep the X facing him or her as you walk. As the ball revolves once, it rotates once.
23. At both times, the moon's apparent size is changing. A waxing moon is one that appears to get larger each night. A waning moon appears to get smaller each night.
24. See student page.

Bonus Question

How might your life be different if you lived in the southern hemisphere? Mention the seasons and how they compare with those in the northern hemisphere. *Answers will vary but should reference the fact that summer would begin in December and winter would begin in June. Also, the seasons of spring and fall would begin in September and March, respectively.*

Assessment Resources

The **Test Practice Workbook** provides students with practice in the format, concepts, and critical-thinking skills tested in standardized exams.

Reproducible Masters

Chapter Review, pp. 41–42 L2
Performance Assessment, p. 35 L2
Assessment, pp. 93–96 L2

Glencoe Technology

Chapter Review Software
Computer Test Bank
MindJogger Videoquiz

Chapter 22 The Solar System

Section	Objectives	Activities/Features
Chapter Opener		**Explore Activity:** Model Comet Collisions, p. 629
22-1 **The Solar System** 2½ Sessions 1 Block	1. **Compare** and **contrast** the sun-centered and Earth-centered models of the solar system. 2. **Describe** current models of the formation of the solar system.	**Physics Integration,** p. 634 **Skill Builder:** Concept Mapping, p. 634 **Using Math,** p. 634 **Activity 22-1:** Planetary Orbits, p. 635
22-2 **The Inner Planets** 1 Session ½ Block	3. **List** the inner planets in their relative order from the sun. 4. **Identify** important characteristics of each inner planet. 5. **Compare** and **contrast** Venus and Earth.	**Using Math,** p. 637 **Problem Solving:** Interpret Planetary Data, p. 638 **MiniLab: Inferring Effects of Gravity,** p. 639 **Life Science Integration,** p. 640 **Skill Builder:** Interpreting Data, p. 641 **Science Journal,** p. 641
22-3 **The Outer Planets** 3 Sessions 1½ Blocks	6. **List** the major characteristics of Jupiter, Saturn, Uranus, and Neptune. 7. **Recognize** how Pluto differs from the other outer planets.	**MiniLab:** Modeling Planets, p. 644 **Skill Builder:** Recognizing Cause and Effect, p. 647 **Using Computers,** p. 647 **Activity 22-2:** Solar System Distance Model, pp. 648–649
22-4 **Other Objects in the Solar System** 1 Session ½ Block	8. **Explain** where a comet comes from and describe how a comet develops as it approaches the sun. 9. **Differentiate** among comets, meteoroids, and asteroids.	**Skill Builder:** Inferring, p. 654 **Science Journal,** p. 654 **Science and Society:** Mission to Mars, p. 655

The number of recommended single-period sessions — The number of recommended blocks
One session and one-half block are allowed for chapter review and assessment.

Activity Materials

Explore	Activities	MiniLabs
p. 629 flour, cake pan, cement mix, various-sized objects, metric ruler	p. 635 thumbtacks, metric ruler, string, cardboard, paper pp. 648–649 meterstick, scissors, string	p. 639 Appendix A p. 644 drawing compass, metric ruler, paper, pencil

Need Materials? Contact Science Kit at 1-800-828-7777 or at www.sciencekit.com on the Internet.
For alternate materials, see the activity on the listed page.

Standards		Reproducible Resources	Technology
National	State/Local	Test Practice Workbooks are available for use with each chapter.	English and Spanish audiocassettes are available for use with each section.
National Content Standards: UCP5, A2, B1, B3, D3, G1, G2, G3		**Activity Worksheets,** pp. 119–120 **Enrichment,** p. 59 **Multicultural Connections,** pp. 43–44 **Reinforcement,** p. 59 **Study Guide,** pp. 85–86	Section Focus Transparency 59 Teaching Transparency 43 Teaching Transparency 44 Science Integration Transparency 22
National Content Standards: A2, D3, E2		**Activity Worksheets,** p. 123 **Enrichment,** p. 60 **Home Involvement,** p. 28 **Laboratory Manual,** pp. 125–128 **Reinforcement,** p. 60 **Study Guide,** p. 86	Section Focus Transparency 60 National Geographic Society: STV Glencoe Science Voyages Interactive CD-ROM
National Content Standards: UCP2, A2, B1, D3, E2, G3		**Activity Worksheets,** pp. 121–122, 124 **Enrichment,** p. 61 **Home Involvement,** p. 37 **Laboratory Manual,** pp. 129–130 **Reinforcement,** p. 61 **Study Guide,** p. 87	Section Focus Transparency 61 National Geographic Society: STV **Internet Connection,** p. 645 The Infinite Voyage Series
National Content Standards: A2, B2, D2, D3, G1, G3		**Critical Thinking/Problem Solving,** p. 22 **Enrichment,** p. 62 **Reinforcement,** p. 62 **Study Guide,** p. 88	Section Focus Transparency 62 National Geographic Society: STV **Internet Connection,** p. 651 **Internet Connection,** p. 652

Key to Teaching Strategies

The following designations will help you decide which activities are appropriate for your students.

L1 Level 1 activities should be appropriate for students with learning difficulties.

L2 Level 2 activities should be within the ability range of all students.

L3 Level 3 activities are designed for above-average students.

ELL ELL activities should be within the ability range of English Language Learners.

COOP LEARN Cooperative Learning activities are designed for small group work.

P These strategies represent student products that can be placed into a best-work portfolio.

Multiple Learning Styles logos, as described on page 61T, are used throughout to indicate strategies that address different learning styles.

Assessment Resources

Chapter Review, pp. 43–44
Assessment, pp. 97–100
Performance Assessment in the Science Classroom (PASC)
MindJogger Videoquiz
Alternate Assessment in the Science Classroom
Performance Assessment, p. 36
Chapter Review Software
Computer Test Bank

Chapter 22 The Solar System

This is a representation of key blackline masters available in the Teacher Classroom Resources.
See Resource Manager boxes within the chapter for additional information.

Transparencies

Section Focus Transparencies

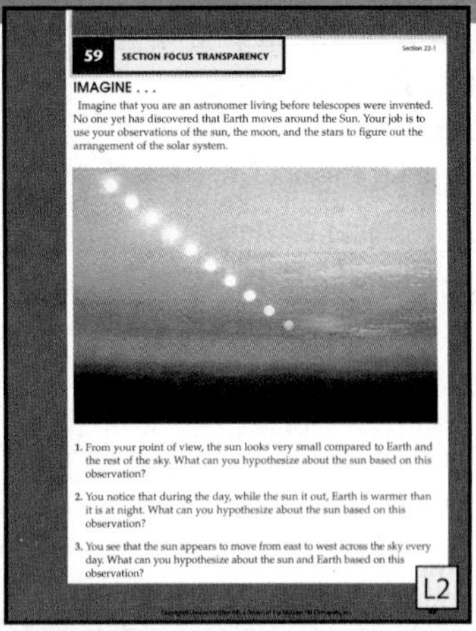

59 SECTION FOCUS TRANSPARENCY Section 22-1

IMAGINE . . .

Imagine that you are an astronomer living before telescopes were invented. No one yet has discovered that Earth moves around the Sun. Your job is to use your observations of the sun, the moon, and the stars to figure out the arrangement of the solar system.

1. From your point of view, the sun looks very small compared to Earth and the rest of the sky. What can you hypothesize about the sun based on this observation?
2. You notice that during the day, while the sun it out, Earth is warmer than it is at night. What can you hypothesize about the sun based on this observation?
3. You see that the sun appears to move from east to west across the sky every day. What can you hypothesize about the sun and Earth based on this observation?

L2

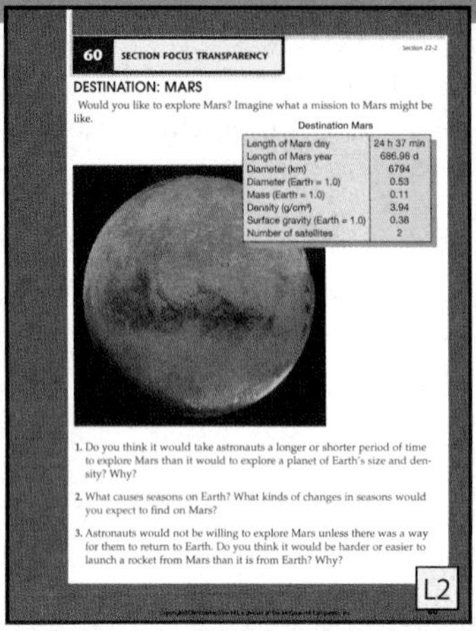

60 SECTION FOCUS TRANSPARENCY Section 22-2

DESTINATION: MARS

Would you like to explore Mars? Imagine what a mission to Mars might be like.

Destination Mars

Length of Mars day	24 h 37 min
Length of Mars year	686.98 d
Diameter (km)	6794
Diameter (Earth = 1.0)	0.53
Mass (Earth = 1.0)	0.11
Density (g/cm³)	3.94
Surface gravity (Earth = 1.0)	0.38
Number of satellites	2

1. Do you think it would take astronauts a longer or shorter period of time to explore Mars than it would to explore a planet of Earth's size and density? Why?
2. What causes seasons on Earth? What kinds of changes in seasons would you expect to find on Mars?
3. Astronauts would not be willing to explore Mars unless there was a way for them to return to Earth. Do you think it would be harder or easier to launch a rocket from Mars than it is from Earth? Why?

L2

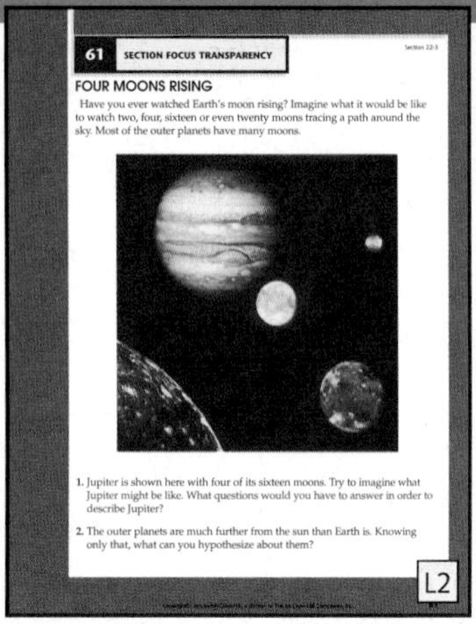

61 SECTION FOCUS TRANSPARENCY Section 22-3

FOUR MOONS RISING

Have you ever watched Earth's moon rising? Imagine what it would be like to watch two, four, sixteen or even twenty moons tracing a path around the sky. Most of the outer planets have many moons.

1. Jupiter is shown here with four of its sixteen moons. Try to imagine what Jupiter might be like. What questions would you have to answer in order to describe Jupiter?
2. The outer planets are much further from the sun than Earth is. Knowing only that, what can you hypothesize about them?

L2

Science Integration Transparencies

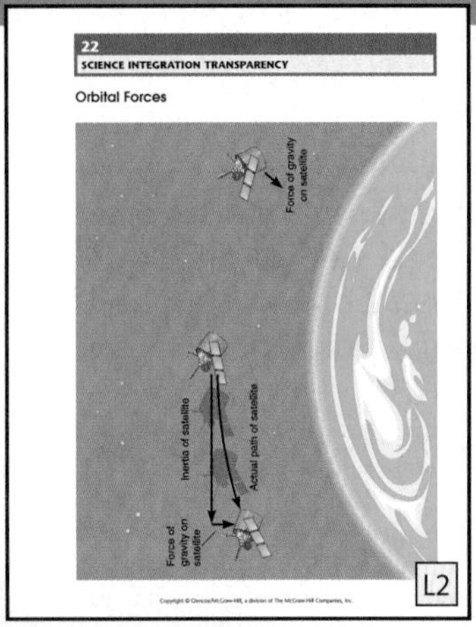

22 SCIENCE INTEGRATION TRANSPARENCY

Orbital Forces

Force of gravity on satellite

Inertia of satellite

Actual path of satellite

Force of gravity on satellite

L2

Teaching Transparencies

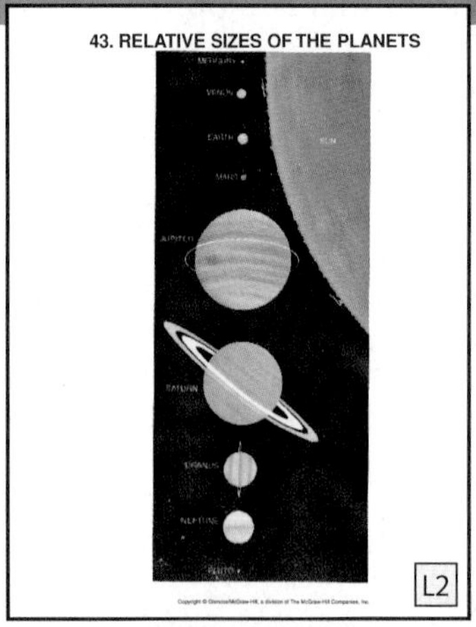

43. RELATIVE SIZES OF THE PLANETS

L2

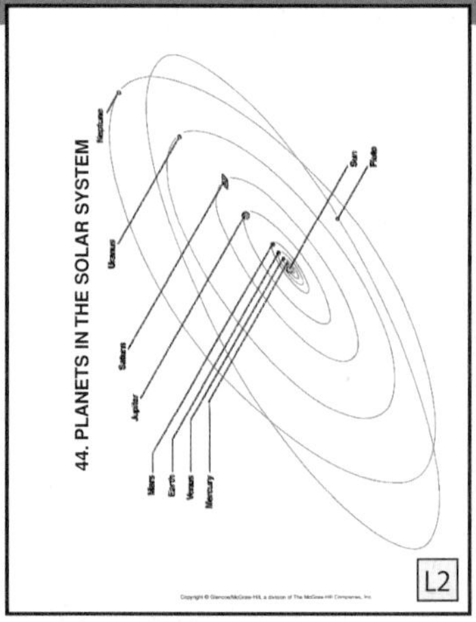

44. PLANETS IN THE SOLAR SYSTEM

L2

Meeting Different Ability Levels

Study Guide for Content Mastery

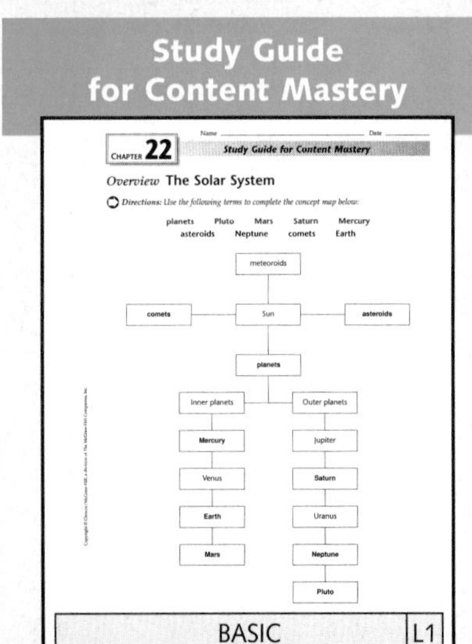

Name ____ Date ____

CHAPTER 22 Study Guide for Content Mastery

Overview The Solar System

Directions: Use the following terms to complete the concept map below:

planets Pluto Mars Saturn Mercury
asteroids Neptune comets Earth

BASIC L1

Reinforcement

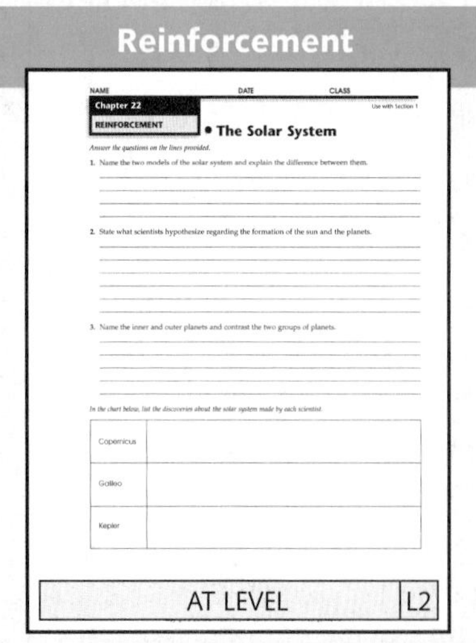

NAME DATE CLASS

Chapter 22 REINFORCEMENT • The Solar System

Use with Section 1

Answer the questions on the lines provided.

1. Name the two models of the solar system and explain the difference between them.
2. State what scientists hypothesize regarding the formation of the sun and the planets.
3. Name the inner and outer planets and contrast the two groups of planets.

In the chart below, list the discoveries about the solar system made by each scientist.

Copernicus	
Galileo	
Kepler	

AT LEVEL L2

Enrichment Worksheets

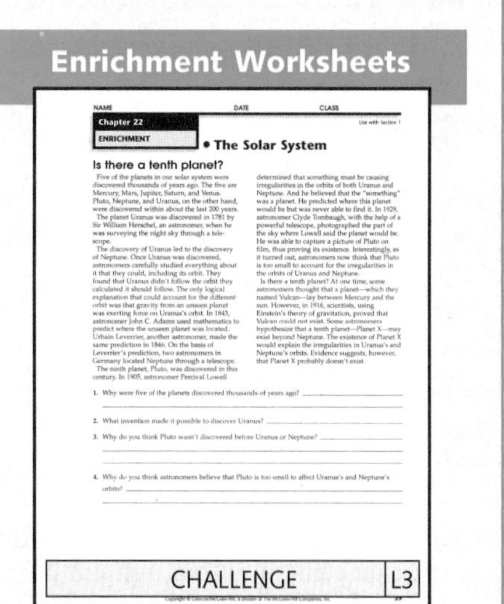

NAME DATE CLASS

Chapter 22 ENRICHMENT • The Solar System

Use with Section 1

Is there a tenth planet?

Five of the planets in our solar system were discovered thousands of years ago. The five are Mercury, Mars, Jupiter, Saturn, and Venus. Pluto, Neptune, and Uranus, on the other hand, were discovered within about the last 200 years.

The planet Uranus was discovered in 1781 by Sir William Herschel, an astronomer, when he was surveying the night sky through a telescope.

The discovery of Uranus led to the discovery of Neptune. Once Uranus was discovered, astronomers carefully studied everything about it that they could, including its orbit. They found that Uranus didn't follow the orbit they calculated it should follow. The only logical explanation that could account for the different orbit was that gravity from an unseen planet was exerting force on Uranus's orbit. In 1843, astronomer John C. Adams used mathematics to predict where the unseen planet was located. Urbain Leverrier, another astronomer, made the same prediction in 1846. On the basis of Leverrier's prediction, two astronomers in Germany located Neptune through a telescope.

The ninth planet, Pluto, was discovered in this century. In 1905, astronomer Percival Lowell determined that something must be causing irregularities in the orbits of both Uranus and Neptune. And he believed that the "something" was a planet. He predicted where this planet would be but was never able to find it. In 1929, astronomer Clyde Tombaugh, with the help of a powerful telescope, photographed the part of the sky where Lowell said the planet would be. He was able to capture a picture of Pluto on film, thus proving its existence. Interestingly, as it turned out, astronomers now think that Pluto is too small to account for the irregularities in the orbits of Uranus and Neptune.

Is there a tenth planet? At one time, some astronomers thought that a planet—which they named Vulcan—lay between Mercury and the sun. However, in 1916, scientists, using Einstein's theory of gravitation, proved that Vulcan could not exist. Some astronomers hypothesize that a tenth planet—Planet X—may exist beyond Neptune. The existence of Planet X would explain the irregularities in Uranus's and Neptune's orbits. Evidence suggests, however, that Planet X probably doesn't exist.

1. Why were five of the planets discovered thousands of years ago?
2. What invention made it possible to discover Uranus?
3. Why do you think Pluto wasn't discovered before Uranus or Neptune?
4. Why do you think astronomers believe that Pluto is too small to affect Uranus's and Neptune's orbits?

CHALLENGE L3

Hands-on Activities

Activity Worksheets

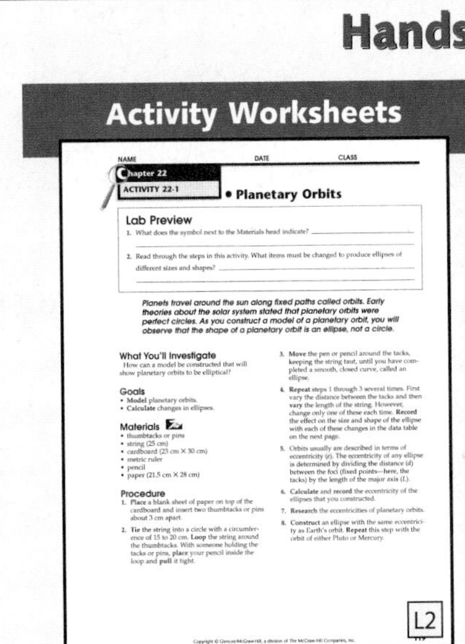
NAME DATE CLASS

Chapter 22
ACTIVITY 22-1
• Planetary Orbits

Lab Preview

What You'll Investigate

Goals

Materials

Procedure

L2

Lab Manual

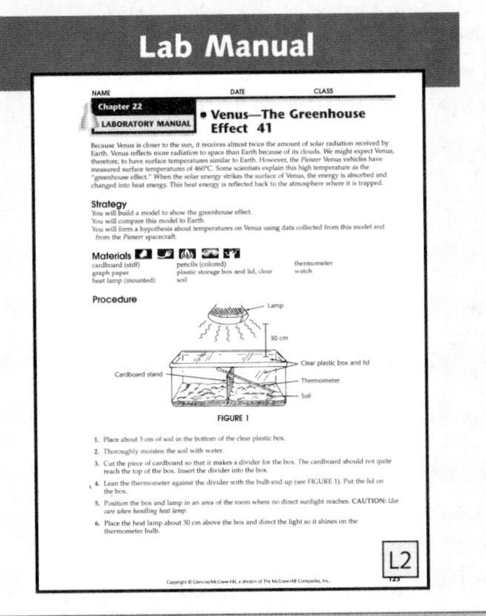
NAME DATE CLASS

Chapter 22
LABORATORY MANUAL
• Venus—The Greenhouse Effect 41

Strategy

Materials

Procedure

FIGURE 1

L2

Accessibility

Spanish Resources

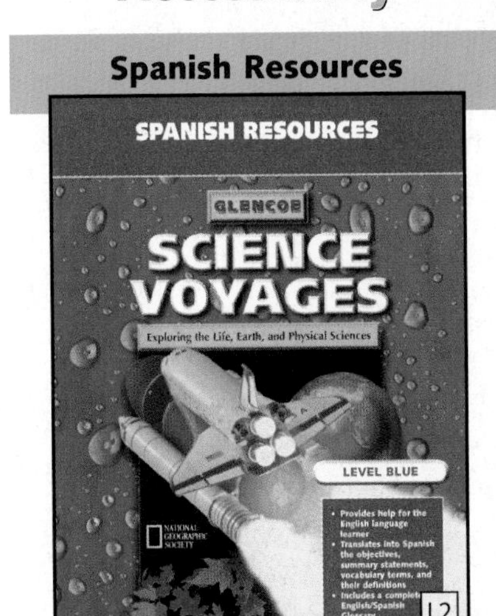
SPANISH RESOURCES

GLENCOE

SCIENCE VOYAGES

Exploring the Life, Earth, and Physical Sciences

LEVEL BLUE

L2

Assessment

Performance Assessment

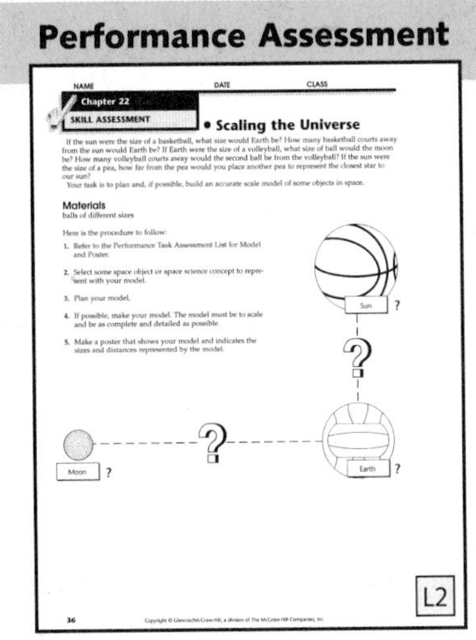
NAME DATE CLASS

Chapter 22
SKILL ASSESSMENT
• Scaling the Universe

Materials

L2

Chapter Review

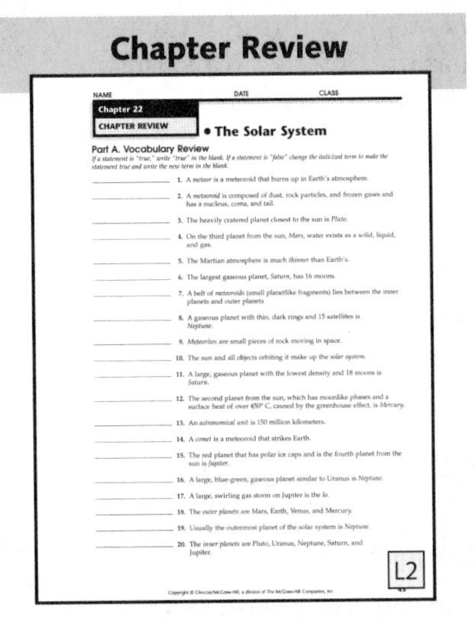
NAME DATE CLASS

Chapter 22
CHAPTER REVIEW
• The Solar System

Part A. Vocabulary Review

L2

Assessment

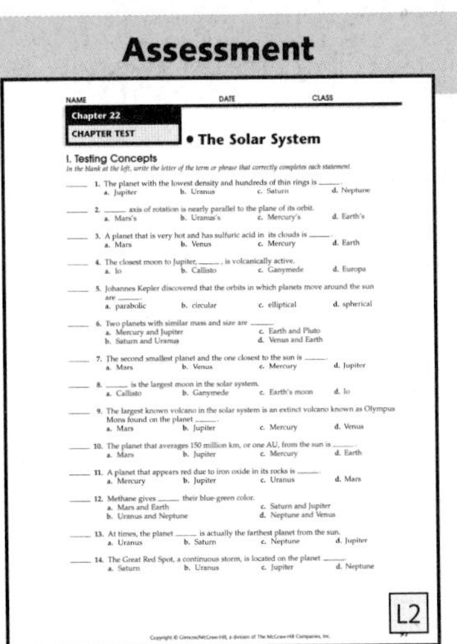
NAME DATE CLASS

Chapter 22
CHAPTER TEST
• The Solar System

I. Testing Concepts

L2

Test Practice Workbook

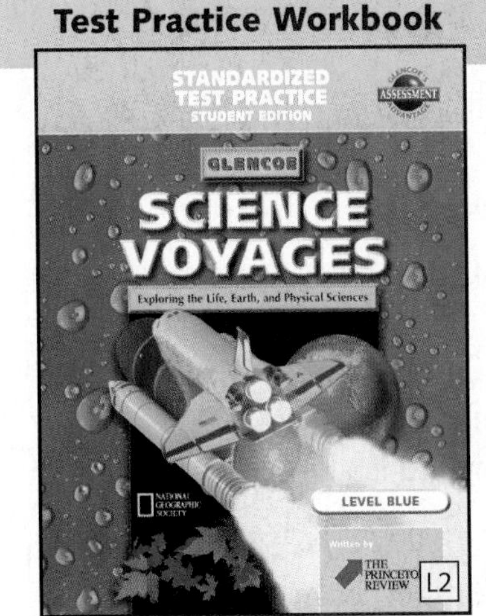
STANDARDIZED TEST PRACTICE
STUDENT EDITION

GLENCOE

SCIENCE VOYAGES

Exploring the Life, Earth, and Physical Sciences

LEVEL BLUE

L2

Extending Content

Critical Thinking/ Problem Solving

Multicultural Connections

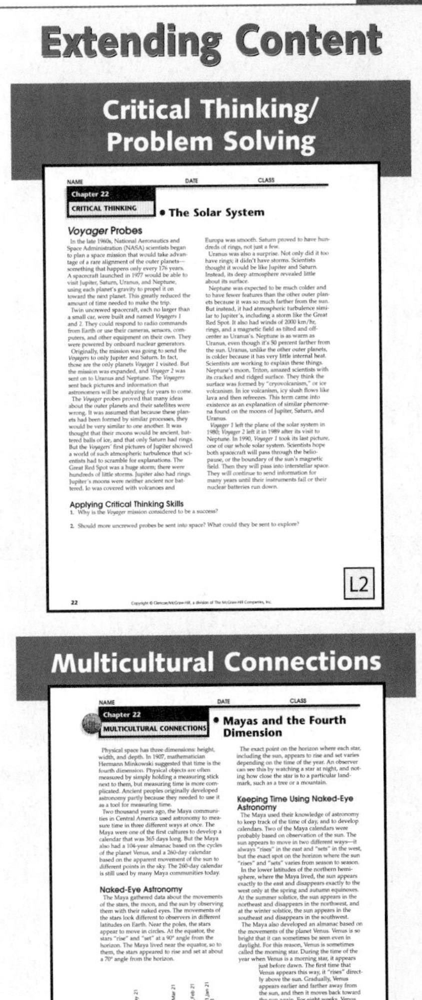
NAME DATE CLASS

Chapter 22
CRITICAL THINKING
• The Solar System

Voyager Probes

Applying Critical Thinking Skills

L2

NAME DATE CLASS

Chapter 22
MULTICULTURAL CONNECTIONS
• Mayas and the Fourth Dimension

Keeping Time Using Naked-Eye Astronomy

Naked-Eye Astronomy

L2

Helping You Prepare

Sun-Centered Model (Section 22-1)

Most objects in the solar system rotate and revolve toward the east. Any motion different from this eastward motion is called retrograde motion. The retrograde motion of Mars was one piece of evidence used by Copernicus to support his sun-centered model of the solar system.

Solar System Formation (Section 22-1)

Several modern theories attempt to explain the formation of our solar system. One hypothesis suggests that a nearby star may have exploded, sending shock waves through the resulting cloud, or nebula. The shock waves caused the particles in the cloud to condense, leading to the formation of the solar system. Other scientists propose that the movement of one of the arms of the Milky Way Galaxy through the nebula started the formation process. Most scientists agree that something provided the shock that started the motions within the nebula that eventually formed the solar system.

Earth's Atmosphere (Section 22-2)

Carbon dioxide dissolves in water; therefore, much of the carbon dioxide in Earth's atmosphere has been removed by rain. If it weren't for the presence of liquid water on Earth, the amount of carbon dioxide in the air would probably be similar to that in Venus's atmosphere, causing a tremendous increase in the greenhouse effect on Earth.

Planet Classification (Section 22-2)

All planets except Earth can be classified as inferior or superior. Inferior planets—Mercury and Venus—have orbits that are inside Earth's orbit. Superior planets have orbits that lie outside Earth's orbit. These include Mars, Jupiter, Saturn, Uranus, Neptune, and Pluto.

GLENCOE TECHNOLOGY

Glencoe Science Voyages Interactive CD-ROM

Chapter Summaries

Use the Chapter Summary to introduce, teach, or review chapter material.

NATIONAL GEOGRAPHIC Teacher's Corner

Products Available from Glencoe

To order the following products for use with this chapter, call Glencoe at 1-800-334-7344:

CD-ROM

NGS PictureShow: Solar System

Transparency Set

NGS PicturePack: Solar System

Videodisc

STV: Solar System

Products Available from National Geographic Society

To order the following products for use with this chapter, call National Geographic Society at 1-800-368-2728:

Poster

Solar System/Celestial Family

Video

Comets and Asteroids

Index to National Geographic Magazine

The following articles may be used for research relating to this chapter:

"The Age of Comets," by William R. Newcott, December 1997.

"Venus Revealed," by William R. Newcott, February 1993.

"Neptune: Voyager's Last Picture Show," by Rick Gore, August 1990.

"Halley's Comet 1986," by Rick Gore, December 1986.

Outer Planets (Section 22-3)

The atmospheres of Jupiter and Saturn contain three distinct layers. The upper layer is composed of ammonia ice, the second layer is composed of ammonium hydrosulfide ice, and the lowest layer is composed mostly of water ice.

Most of the material in Saturn's rings lies below the Roche distance for that planet. The Roche distance is the distance from an object below which other objects would be torn apart by gravitational forces.

Uranus doesn't appear to have an internal heat source. Some scientists believe a collision with another object may have turned Uranus on its side and destroyed its heat source.

Pluto (Section 22-3)

Pluto is very different from the other outer planets. Hypotheses suggest it may not have formed in the orbit it now occupies, or that Pluto and its moon Charon are large cometary members of the Kuiper belt.

In 1996, the *Hubble Space Telescope* sent back new images of Pluto showing 12 distinct areas on the planet's surface. Some of these areas are more than 1000 km across—some are bright; others are dark.

Based on current knowledge of the outer solar system, it appears that Pluto and Neptune's moon Triton are more similar to each other than any other two objects in the solar system. Some scientists believe the retrograde (backward) revolution of Triton indicates it was captured by the gravity of Neptune and could once have been a planet of the sun, just like Pluto. This line of thinking supports the idea that Pluto, and perhaps Triton, are two of many icy, dwarf planets that may have formed far from the sun.

Discovery of the Kuiper belt further supports this idea. This area, which begins about 30 to 50 AU from the sun, is littered with icy, dwarf planets; comets; and other debris.

SCIENCE UPDATE

For current events or science in the news, access the Glencoe Science Web Site at **www.glencoe.com/sec/science**

Comets (Section 22-4)

Comets appear to orbit the sun in the Oort Cloud some 50 000 AU from the sun. Some comets take more than a million years to complete one orbit.

Another area of comets, the Kuiper belt, is thought to extend outward from the orbit of Neptune to a distance of 100 AU from the sun. Formerly, it was probably much larger than it is today, but it was cleared out by the large gravitational field of Neptune. The Kuiper belt may represent an area of the solar system where the formation of a large planet failed.

Teacher to Teacher

"When studying our solar system's planets, I give students the assignment of developing an ad campaign for selling one of the planets. They develop and present to the class a bumper sticker, a poster, and an ad that contains ten facts and the historical significance of the planet's name."

John E. Burns

John E. Burns, Teacher
Ramona Junior High School
Chino, CA

CHAPTER 22 The Solar System

CHAPTER OVERVIEW

Section 22-1 This section describes the sun-centered model of the solar system and the formation of the solar system.

Section 22-2 Characteristics of the inner planets are described. Information about Mars gathered from recent space missions is presented.

Section 22-3 This section describes the outer planets. Information gathered from the *Voyager* space probes is presented.

Section 22-4 Comets, meteoroids, asteroids, meteors, and meteorites are compared and contrasted.

Chapter Vocabulary

solar system	Great Red Spot
inner planet	Saturn
outer planet	Uranus
Mercury	Neptune
Venus	Pluto
Earth	comet
astronomical unit	Oort Cloud
	meteor
Mars	meteorite
Jupiter	asteroid

Theme Connection

Scale and Structure The theme of this chapter is the scale and structure of the solar system. All objects in this system are compared and contrasted according to size and composition.

OUT OF TIME?

If time does not permit teaching the entire chapter, use Reviewing Main Ideas on pp. 656–657.

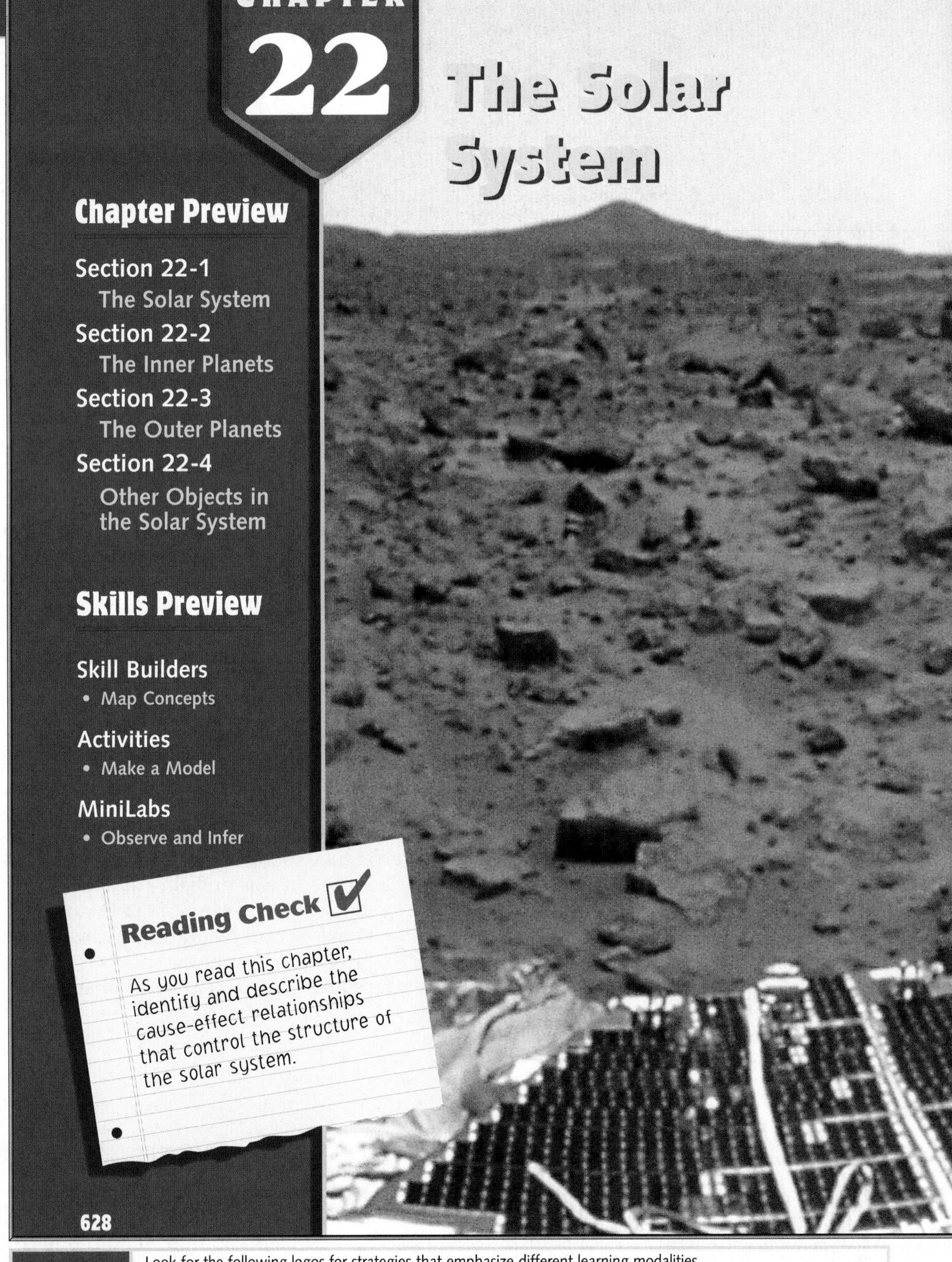

Multiple Learning Styles

Look for the following logos for strategies that emphasize different learning modalities.

Linguistic Science Journal, pp. 631, 640, 646; Using an Analogy, p. 632; Enrichment, p. 637; Preview, p. 656

Logical-Mathematical Activity pp. 635, 648–649; Across the Curriculum, pp. 637, 639; MiniLab, p. 639; Reteach, p. 653

Visual-Spatial Making a Model, p. 631; Reteach, pp. 633, 656; Activity, p. 638; Multiple Learning Styles, p. 643; Across the Curriculum, p. 644

Auditory-Musical Out of Time, p. 656

Kinesthetic Explore Activity, p. 629; MiniLab, p. 644

Interpersonal Activity, pp. 631, 643; Inclusion Strategies, p. 632; Reteach, pp. 640, 646; Review, p. 656

Intrapersonal Enrichment, p. 646

Explore Activity

The planets of our solar system are our neighbors in space. But to us on Earth, they look like tiny points of light among the thousands of others visible on a clear night. With the help of telescopes and space probes, the points of light become giant colorful spheres, some with rings, others pitted with countless craters. This false-color image of Mars shows the space rover *Sojourner* exploring the planet's surface. Mars has two heavily cratered moons. In this activity, you'll explore how craters are made on the surfaces of planets and moons.

Model Comet Collisions

1. Place fine white flour into a cake pan to a depth of 3 cm, completely covering the bottom of the pan.
2. Cover the flour with 1 cm of fine, gray, dry cement mix, or try different colors of gelatin powder.
3. From different heights ranging from 10 cm to 25 cm, drop various-sized objects into the pan. Use marbles, lead weights, bolts, and nuts.

Science Journal

In your Science Journal, draw what happened to the surface of the powder in the pan when each object was dropped from different heights.

Assessment Planner

Portfolio
Refer to p. 657 for suggested items that students might select for their portfolios.

Performance Assessment
See p. 657 for additional Performance Assessment options.
Skill Builder, pp. 634, 641, 647, 654
MiniLab, pp. 639, 644
Activity 22-1, p. 635; 22-2, pp. 648–649

Content Assessment
Section Assessment, pp. 634, 641, 647, 654
Chapter Assessment, pp. 658–659
Proficiency Prep, pp. 634, 641, 647, 654

Explore Activity

Purpose

Kinesthetic Use the Explore Activity to introduce students to the cause and effect of comet impacts on planetary surfaces. L2 ELL COOP LEARN

Preparation

Prior to beginning this chapter, obtain flat pans or ask students to bring in flat pans from home.

Materials

flat pans; metric ruler; white flour; gray, dry cement mix (or colored, powdered gelatin); and objects such as marbles, lead weights, bolts, and nuts

Teaching Strategies

Troubleshooting Have students place the pans on large sheets of newspaper.

Safety Precautions Caution students to wear safety goggles while dropping objects.

Science Journal The white powder splashes out over the darker powdered surface. A crater forms as the object is buried in the powder. Craters are deeper when the objects are dropped from greater distances. Craters on Mars and the moon probably formed in the same way.

Assessment

Performance Let groups examine each other's pans. Have students determine which craters were caused by big objects. Ask them to determine which craters formed first. Use **Performance Assessment in the Science Classroom,** p. 17.

SECTION 22-1

Prepare

Refer to **Sun-Centered Model** and **Solar System Formation** on p. 628E.

Preplanning

Refer to the **Chapter Organizer** on pp. 628A–B.

1 Motivate

Bellringer

Before presenting the lesson, display **Section Focus Transparency 59** on the overhead projector. Use the accompanying **Focus Activity** worksheet. L2 ELL

Section 22-1

59 SECTION FOCUS TRANSPARENCY

IMAGINE . . .

Imagine that you are an astronomer living before telescopes were invented. No one yet has discovered that Earth moves around the Sun. Your job is to use your observations of the sun, the moon, and the stars to figure out the arrangement of the solar system.

1. From your point of view, the sun looks very small compared to Earth and the rest of the sky. What can you hypothesize about the sun based on this observation?
2. You notice that during the day, while the sun it out, Earth is warmer than it is at night. What can you hypothesize about the sun based on this observation?
3. You see that the sun appears to move from east to west across the sky every day. What can you hypothesize about the sun and Earth based on this observation?

59

Tying to Previous Knowledge

Remind students that the "rising" and "setting" of the sun are caused by Earth's rotation. Ask students why people once thought that Earth was the center of the solar system. L2

22-1 The Solar System

What You'll Learn

- The sun-centered and Earth-centered models of the solar system
- Current models of the formation of the solar system

Vocabulary

solar system
inner planet
outer planet

Why It's Important

- You'll learn how views of the solar system have changed over time.

Early Ideas About the Solar System

Imagine yourself on a warm, clear summer night lying in the grass and gazing at the stars and the moon. The stars and the moon seem so still and beautiful. You may even see other planets in the solar system, thinking they are stars. Although the planets are different from the stars, they blend in with the stars and are usually hard to pick out.

Earth-Centered Model

It is generally known today that the sun and the stars appear to move through the sky because Earth is moving. This wasn't always an accepted fact. Many early Greek scientists thought the planets, the sun, and the moon were embedded in separate spheres that rotated around Earth. The stars were thought to be embedded in another sphere that also rotated around Earth. Early observers described moving objects in the night sky using the term *planasthai,* which means "to wander." The word *planet* comes from this term.

This model is called the Earth-centered model of the solar system. It included Earth, the moon, the sun, five planets—Mercury, Venus, Mars, Jupiter, and Saturn—and the sphere of stars.

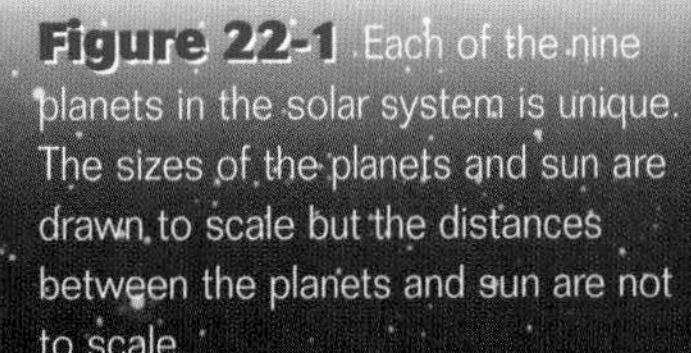

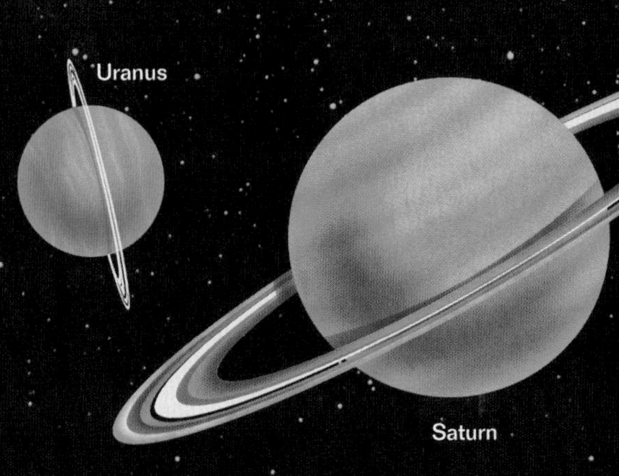

Figure 22-1 Each of the nine planets in the solar system is unique. The sizes of the planets and sun are drawn to scale but the distances between the planets and sun are not to scale.

Resource Manager

The following **Teacher Classroom Resources** can be used with Section 22-1:

Reproducible Masters

Activity Worksheets, pp. 119–120 L2
Enrichment, p. 59 L3
Multicultural Connections, pp. 43–44 L2
Reinforcement, p. 59 L2
Study Guide, pp. 85–86 L1 ELL

Transparencies

Teaching Transparency 43 L2
Teaching Transparency 44 L2
Science Integration Transparency 22 L2

Sun-Centered Model

The idea of an Earth-centered solar system was held for centuries until the Polish astronomer Nicholas Copernicus published a different view in 1543. Using an idea proposed by an early Greek scholar, Copernicus stated that the moon revolved around Earth, which was a planet. Earth, along with the other planets, revolved around the sun. He also stated that the daily movement of the planets and the stars was due to Earth's rotation. This is the sun-centered model of the solar system.

Using his telescope, the Italian astronomer Galileo Galilei found evidence that supported the ideas of Copernicus. He discovered that Venus went through phases like the moon's. These phases could be explained only if Venus were orbiting the sun. From this, he concluded that Venus revolves around the sun and that the sun is the center of the solar system.

Modern View of the Solar System

We now know that the **solar system** is made up of the nine planets, including Earth, and many smaller objects that orbit the sun. The sizes of the nine planets and the sun are shown to scale in **Figure 22-1.** However, the distances between the planets are not to scale. The dark areas on the sun are sunspots, which you will learn about later. Notice how small Earth is compared with some of the other planets and the sun, which is much larger than any of the planets.

The solar system includes a vast territory extending billions of kilometers in all directions from the sun. The sun contains 99.86 percent of the mass of the whole solar system. Because of its gravitational pull, the sun is the central object around which other objects of the solar system revolve.

2 Teach

Activity

Interpersonal Have pairs of students make flash cards of the planets in the solar system. They can draw the planet on one side of the card and write anything they know about it on the other side. Students should keep their flash cards handy so they can correct or update their information as they read this chapter. L2

Making a Model

Visual-Spatial Have volunteers compare and contrast the sun-centered model of the solar system with the Earth-centered model by making sketches on the chalkboard. As one student draws the models, have a partner point out how the two models are similar and how they are different. L2 COOP LEARN

Content Background

The Earth-centered model of the solar system is known as the geocentric model and the sun-centered model is known as the heliocentric model. A combination of the two, called the hybrid model, was proposed by Tycho Brahe (1546–1601). In this model, the sun and moon went around Earth and everything else went around the sun.

Science Journal

Solar System Models Have students write a report that describes what evidence led Copernicus to propose the sun-centered model of the solar system. Ask students to explain how this evidence refuted the Earth-centered model. They should list which scientists discovered the evidence used by Copernicus. L3

Using Science Words

Assess students' understanding of astronomical terms by asking the following questions. **What was Johannes Kepler's contribution to the sun-centered solar system model?** *He used mathematics to determine the shapes of the orbits and to calculate that the sun was not at the center of the elliptical paths.* **How do the planets' revolutions support the idea that the cloud that formed the solar system spun faster as it contracted?** *The inner planets revolve faster than the outer planets.*

Using an Analogy

Linguistic Ask students why ice skaters pull their arms toward their bodies as they spin. *to increase their rotational speed* Compare this analogy to the rotational speed of the cloud from which the solar system formed, which spun faster as more material was pulled toward its center.

VISUAL Learning

Figure 22-2 Scientists have recently discovered planetary systems in orbit around stars other than the sun. Have students research the planetary systems of the stars 51 Pegasi, 47 Ursae Majoris, and 16 Cygni B. Using **Figure 22-2,** have them compare and contrast these systems to our solar system.

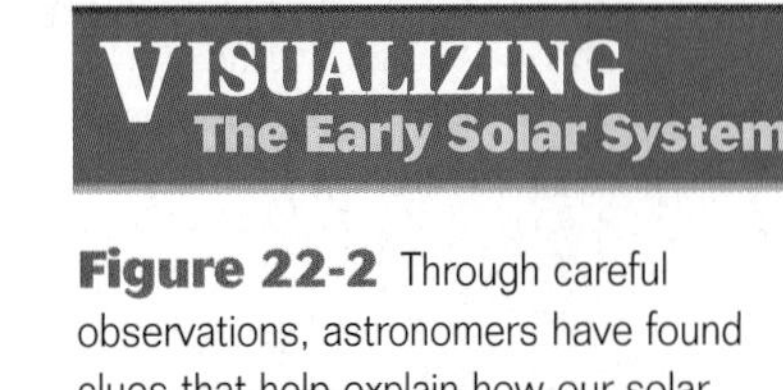

Figure 22-2 Through careful observations, astronomers have found clues that help explain how our solar system may have formed.

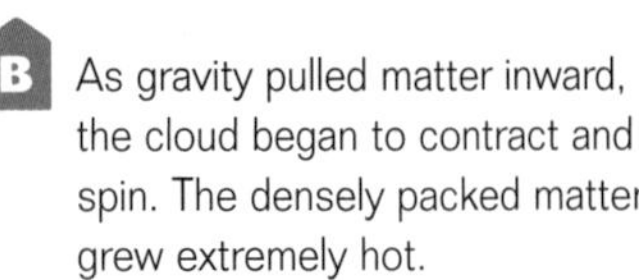

B As gravity pulled matter inward, the cloud began to contract and spin. The densely packed matter grew extremely hot.

A About 4.6 billion years ago, a large cloud of gas, ice, and dust occupied our place in space.

How the Solar System Formed

Scientists hypothesize that the sun and the solar system formed from a cloud of gas, ice, and dust about 4.6 billion years ago. **Figure 22-2** illustrates how this may have happened. This cloud was slowly rotating in space. A nearby star may have exploded, and the shock waves from this event may have caused the cloud to start contracting. At first, the cloud was rotating slowly. As it contracted, the matter in the cloud was squeezed into less space. The cloud's density became greater and the increased attraction of gravity pulled more gas and dust toward the cloud center. This caused the cloud to rotate faster, which in turn caused it to flatten into a disk with a dense center. ✔

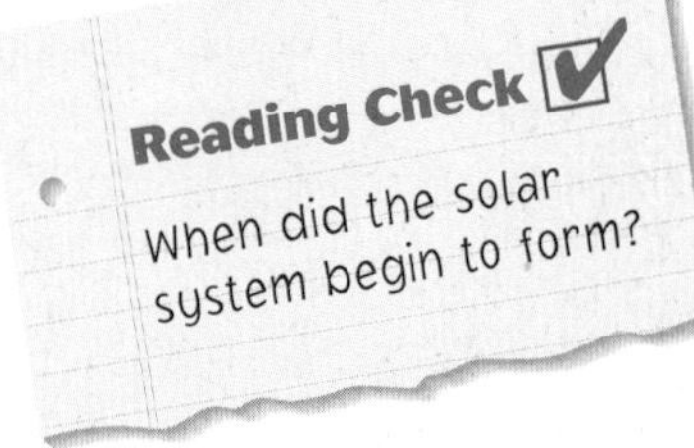

Reading Check
When did the solar system begin to form?

As the cloud contracted, the temperature began to increase. Eventually, the temperature in the core of the cloud reached about 10 million °C and nuclear fusion began. A star was born—this was the beginning of our sun. Nuclear fusion occurs when atoms with low mass, such as hydrogen, combine to form heavier elements, such as helium. The new, heavy element contains slightly less mass than the sum of the light atoms that formed it. The lost mass is converted into energy.

Not all of the nearby gas, ice, and dust were drawn into the core of the cloud. Remaining gas, ice, and dust particles

Inclusion Strategies

Gifted Have students research famous astronomers. Students can work in groups of five or six to write plays in which these astronomers are brought together in time to discuss their ideas. Students can perform the plays for the class. L3 COOP LEARN

Physically Challenged Have students work in small groups to make mobiles of the solar system to display in class. Place physically challenged students in groups where they can contribute their knowledge and ideas. On the back side of each model planet, students should include pertinent facts, such as temperature extremes, atmospheric conditions (or lack of atmosphere), length of orbit, number of moons, and so on. L2 COOP LEARN

C The center of the rotating disk continued to heat. Meanwhile, gas and dust particles in the outer rim clumped together, forming larger objects.

D The larger clumps continued to grow as more objects collided.

collided and stuck together, forming larger objects that in turn attracted more particles because of the stronger pull of gravity. Close to the sun, the temperature was hot, and the easily vaporized elements could not condense into solids. This is why light elements are more scarce in the planets closer to the sun than in planets farther out in the solar system. Instead, the inner solar system is dominated by small, rocky planets with iron cores.

The **inner planets**—Mercury, Venus, Earth, and Mars—are the solid, rocky planets closest to the sun. The **outer planets**—Jupiter, Saturn, Uranus, Neptune, and Pluto—are those farthest from the sun. Except for Pluto, which is made of rock and ice, the outer planets are made mostly of lighter elements such as hydrogen, helium, methane, and ammonia.

E Eventually, the larger clumps gathered enough matter to become planets. The core of the disk grew even denser and hotter.

F Nuclear fusion began in the core, and the sun became a star. Some of the smaller objects became moons and rings around the planets.

PHYSICS INTEGRATION

Planetary motion is discussed on the following page. Have students research and write about Kepler's three laws of planetary motion. Students should describe the steps that led Kepler to devise the laws. L3

Flex Your Brain

Use the Flex Your Brain activity to have students explore FORMATION OF THE SOLAR SYSTEM.

Teacher FYI

Clouds of gas, ice, and dust in space that form into planetary systems such as our solar system are called nebulae.

3 Assess

Check for Understanding

Reteach

Visual-Spatial Have students compare and contrast labeled photographs or illustrations of the planets. Have students divide the planets into two groups based on size alone. Discuss where Pluto fits in this classification. L2

Extension

For students who have mastered this section, use the **Reinforcement** and **Enrichment** masters.

Guided Reading Strategy

News Summary This strategy helps students explain and make connections to their study of science. Students are assigned the job of being television reporters. They are given several minutes to summarize, retell, or analyze their investigation for their "television" audience. Have students do a News Summary for an application of a concept from this chapter.

4 Close

Proficiency Prep

Use this quiz to check students' recall of section content.

1. **What model of the solar system did Copernicus propose in 1543?** *sun-centered*
2. **What do the sun, nine planets, their moons, and many smaller objects make up?** *solar system*
3. **Which planets are small and rocky and have iron cores?** *inner*
4. **Which planets, except for Pluto, are composed mostly of lighter elements?** *outer*

Section Assessment

1. In the sun-centered model, all objects orbit the sun. In the Earth-centered model, the sun, planets, and other objects moved around Earth.
2. About 4.6 billion years ago, a large cloud of gas, ice, and dust began to condense. The center of the cloud formed the sun. The planets and other objects in the solar system formed from outer portions of the cloud.
3. Temperatures are too low for water to exist as a liquid.
4. **Think Critically** It would be longer because Uranus's orbit is much longer than Earth's. One year on Uranus equals 84 years on Earth.

Using Math

Mercury orbits at a speed of 47.89 km/s and Earth orbits at a speed of 29.79 km/s. 47.89 km/s divided by 29.79 km/s = 1.6 times faster.

PHYSICS INTEGRATION

Motions of the Planets

When Nicholas Copernicus developed his sun-centered model of the solar system, he thought that the planets orbited the sun in circles. In the early 1600s, the German mathematician Johannes Kepler began studying the orbits of the planets. He discovered that the shapes of the orbits are not circular, but elliptical. He also calculated that the sun is not at the center of the ellipse but is offset from the center.

Kepler also discovered that the planets travel at different speeds in their orbits around the sun. By studying these speeds, you can see that the planets closer to the sun travel faster than planets farther away from the sun. As a result, the outer planets take much longer to orbit the sun than the inner planets do.

Copernicus's ideas, considered radical at the time, led to the birth of modern astronomy. Early scientists didn't have technology such as space probes to learn about the planets. They used instruments such as the one shown in **Figure 22-3.** Nevertheless, they developed theories about the solar system that we still use today. In the next section, you'll learn about the inner planets—our nearest neighbors in space.

Figure 22-3 This instrument, called an astrolabe, was used for a variety of astronomical calculations.

Section Assessment

1. What is the difference between the sun-centered and the Earth-centered models of the solar system?
2. How do scientists hypothesize the solar system formed?
3. The outer planets are rich in water, methane, and ammonia—the materials needed for life. Yet life is unlikely on these planets. Explain.
4. **Think Critically:** Would a year on the planet Uranus be longer or shorter than an Earth year? Explain.
5. **Skill Builder**
   Concept Mapping Make a concept map that compares and contrasts the Earth-centered model with the sun-centered model of the solar system. If you need help, refer to Concept Mapping in the **Skill Handbook** on page 714.

Using Math

Assuming that the planets travel in nearly circular orbits, research their value of average orbital speeds to determine how much faster (in km/s) Mercury travels in its orbit than Earth travels in its orbit.

5. **Skill Builder**

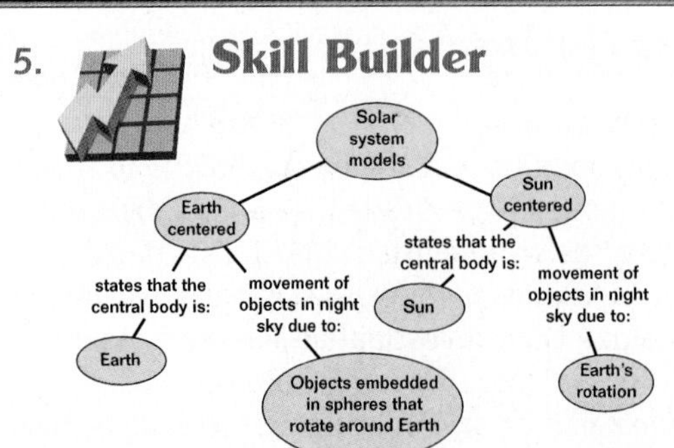

Assessment

Content Use this Skill Builder to assess students' understanding of concept maps. Ask students to compare how the sun is handled in the two models shown in their concept maps. Use **Performance Assessment in the Science Classroom,** p. 89.

Planetary Orbits

Planets travel around the sun along fixed paths called orbits. Early theories about the solar system stated that planetary orbits were perfect circles. As you construct a model of a planetary orbit, you will observe that the shape of planetary orbits is an ellipse, not a circle.

Materials

- Thumbtacks or pins
- Metric ruler
- String (25 cm)
- Pencil
- Cardboard (23 cm × 30 cm)
- Paper (21.5 cm × 28 cm)

What You'll Investigate

How can a model be constructed that will show planetary orbits to be elliptical?

Goals

- **Model** planetary orbits.
- **Calculate** changes in ellipses.

Procedure

1. **Place** a blank sheet of paper on top of the cardboard and insert two thumbtacks or pins about 3 cm apart.
2. **Tie** the string into a circle with a circumference of 15 to 20 cm. **Loop** the string around the thumbtacks. With someone holding the tacks or pins, **place** your pencil inside the loop and **pull** it tight.

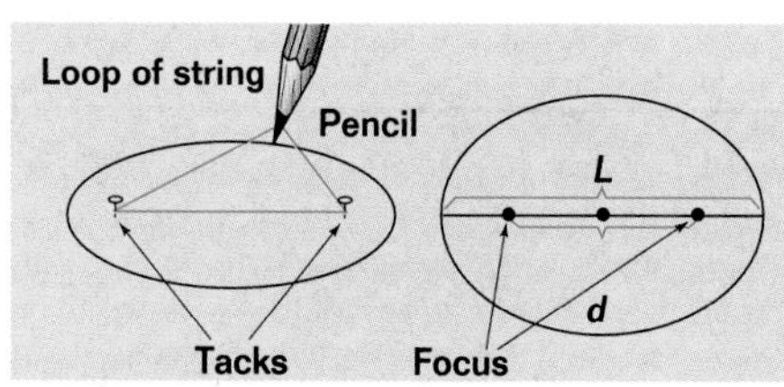

3. **Move** the pencil around the tacks, keeping the string tight, until you have completed a smooth, closed curve, called an ellipse.
4. **Repeat** steps 1 through 3 several times. First, **vary** the distance between the tacks, then **vary** the length of the string. However, change only one of these each time. Make a data table to record the changes in the sizes and shapes of the ellipses.
5. Orbits usually are described in terms of eccentricity (e). The eccentricity of any ellipse is determined by dividing the distance (d) between the foci (fixed points—here, the tacks) by the length of the major axis (L). See the diagram at left.
6. **Calculate** and **record** the eccentricity of the ellipses that you constructed.
7. **Research** the eccentricities of planetary orbits.
8. **Construct** an ellipse with the same eccentricity as Earth's orbit. **Repeat** this step with the orbit of either Pluto or Mercury.

Conclude and Apply

1. **Analyze** the effect a change in the length of the string or the distance between the tacks has on the shape of the ellipse.
2. **Hypothesize** what must be done to the string or placement of tacks to decrease the eccentricity of a constructed ellipse.
3. **Describe** the shape of Earth's orbit. Where is the sun located within the orbit?
4. **Identify** the planets that have the most eccentric orbits.
5. **Describe** the path of an orbit with an eccentricity of zero.

Data and Observations

Eccentricity of Ellipses	d (cm)	L (cm)	e (d/L)
# 1	3	15.6	0.19
# 2	5	13.5	0.37
# 3	5	8.7	0.57
Earth's orbit	0.48	28	0.017
Mercury's orbit			0.206
Pluto's orbit			0.248

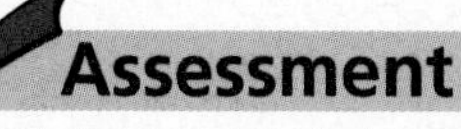

Assessment

Oral Based on this activity, ask students to describe what must be true to obtain a circular orbit. What conditions would provide a more elliptical orbit? Use **Performance Assessment in the Science Classroom,** p. 71.

Activity 22•1

Purpose

Logical-Mathematical Students will describe a model that best represents the shape of planetary orbits. L2 ELL COOP LEARN

Process Skills

measuring in SI, observing, inferring, using numbers, comparing and contrasting, forming operational definitions, and making and using tables

Time

40 minutes

Safety Precautions

Caution students to handle thumbtacks or pins with care.

Teaching Strategies

Provide students with several values for d and L for imaginary ellipses and allow them to solve for e.

Troubleshooting If students have a problem with the equation $e = d/L$, relate the equation to known numbers such as $3 = 6/2$ or $3 = 12/4$.

Answers to Questions

1. Increasing the length of the string or decreasing the distance between the tacks makes the ellipse more circular. Decreasing the string's length or increasing the distance between foci makes the shape more elliptical.
2. lengthen the string or move the tacks closer to each other
3. Although it appears to be circular, Earth's orbit is an ellipse with the sun at one of the foci.
4. Pluto (0.248), Mercury (0.206), and Mars (0.093)
5. circular

SECTION 22-2

Prepare

Content Background

Refer to **Earth's Atmosphere** and **Planet Classification** on p. 628E.

Preplanning

Refer to the **Chapter Organizer** on pp. 628A–B.

1 Motivate

Bellringer

Before presenting the lesson, display **Section Focus Transparency 60** on the overhead projector. Use the accompanying **Focus Activity** worksheet. L2 ELL

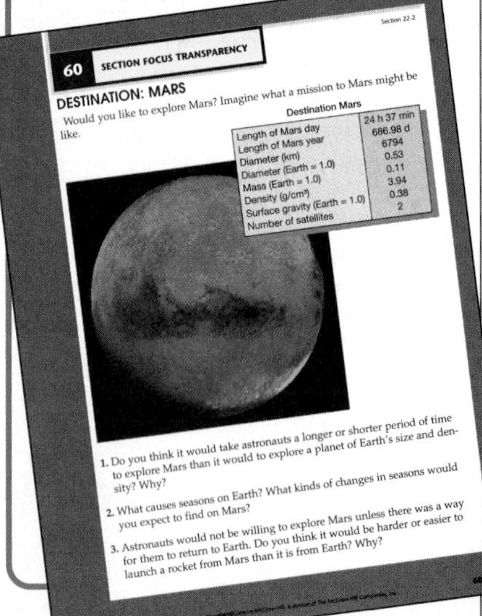

Section 22-2

60 SECTION FOCUS TRANSPARENCY

DESTINATION: MARS

Would you like to explore Mars? Imagine what a mission to Mars might be like.

Destination Mars	
Length of Mars day	24 h 37 min
Length of Mars year	686.98 d
Diameter (km)	6794
Diameter (Earth = 1.0)	0.53
Mass (Earth = 1.0)	0.11
Density (g/cm³)	3.94
Surface gravity (Earth = 1.0)	0.38
Number of satellites	2

1. Do you think it would take astronauts a longer or shorter period of time to explore Mars than it would to explore a planet of Earth's size and density? Why?
2. What causes seasons on Earth? What kinds of changes in seasons would you expect to find on Mars?
3. Astronauts would not be willing to explore Mars unless there was a way for them to return to Earth. Do you think it would be harder or easier to launch a rocket from Mars than it is from Earth? Why?

60

Tying to Previous Knowledge

Remind students that much of what we know about the solar system has been sent back to Earth by space probes.

22-2 The Inner Planets

What You'll Learn

- The inner planets in their relative order from the sun
- Important characteristics of each inner planet
- How Venus and Earth compare and contrast

Vocabulary

Mercury
Venus
Earth
astronomical unit
Mars

Why It's Important

- Other planets have characteristics that are different from those of Earth.

Inner Planets

We have learned much about the solar system since the days of Copernicus and Galileo. Advancements in telescopes allow astronomers to observe the planets from Earth. In addition, space probes have explored much of our solar system, adding greatly to the knowledge we have about the planets. Let's take a tour of the solar system through the "eyes" of the space probes.

Mercury

The closest planet to the sun is **Mercury.** It is also the second-smallest planet. The first and only American spacecraft mission to Mercury was in 1974-1975 by *Mariner 10,* which flew by the planet and sent pictures back to Earth. *Mariner 10* photographed only 45 percent of Mercury's surface—we do not know what the other 55 percent looks like. What we do know is that the surface of Mercury has many craters and looks much like our moon. It also has cliffs as high as 3 km on its surface, as seen in **Figure 22-4.** These cliffs may have formed when Mercury apparently shrank about 2 km in diameter.

Why did Mercury apparently shrink? Scientists think the answer may lie inside the planet. *Mariner 10* detected a weak magnetic field around Mercury, indicating that the planet has a large iron core. Some scientists hypothesize that the crust of Mercury solidified while the iron core was still hot and

Figure 22-4 Giant cliffs on Mercury, like the one marked by the arrow, suggest that the planet might have shrunk.

Resource Manager

The following **Teacher Classroom Resources** can be used with Section 22-2:

 **Reproducible Masters**

Activity Worksheets, p. 123 L2

Enrichment, p. 60 L3

Home Involvement, p. 28 L2

Laboratory Manual, pp. 125–128 L2

Reinforcement, p. 60 L2

636 CHAPTER 22 THE SOLAR SYSTEM

molten. Then, as the core cooled and solidified, it contracted, causing the planet to shrink. The large cliffs may have resulted from breaks in the crust caused by this contraction, similar to what happens when an apple dries out and shrivels up.

Because of Mercury's small size and low gravitational pull, most gases that could form an atmosphere escape into space. Mercury's thin atmosphere is composed of hydrogen, helium, sodium, and potassium. The sodium and potassium may diffuse upward through the crust. The thin atmosphere and the nearness of Mercury to the sun cause this planet to have large extremes in temperature. Mercury's surface temperature can reach 450°C during the day and drop to –170°C at night.

Using Math

The average distance from the sun to Earth is 150 million km. How many minutes does it take light traveling at 300 000 km/s to reach Earth? Use the equation

$$\text{Time} = \frac{\text{distance}}{\text{speed}}$$

Venus

The second planet outward from the sun is **Venus.** Venus is sometimes called Earth's twin because its size and mass are similar to Earth's. One major difference is that the entire surface of Venus is blanketed by a dense atmosphere. The atmosphere of Venus, which has 96 times the surface pressure of Earth's at sea level, is mostly carbon dioxide. The clouds in the atmosphere contain droplets of sulfuric acid, which gives them a slightly yellow color.

Clouds on Venus are so dense that only two percent of the sunlight that strikes the top of the clouds reaches the planet's surface. The solar energy that reaches the surface is trapped by the carbon dioxide gas and causes a greenhouse effect similar to but more intense than Earth's greenhouse effect. Due to this intense greenhouse effect, the temperature on the surface of Venus is 470°C.

The former Soviet Union led the exploration of Venus. Beginning in 1970 with the first *Venera* probe, the Russians have photographed and mapped the surface of Venus using radar and surface probes. Between 1990 and 1994, the *U.S. Magellan* probe used its radar to make the most detailed maps yet of Venus's surface. *Magellan* revealed huge craters, faultlike cracks, and volcanoes with visible lava flows, as seen in **Figure 22-5.**

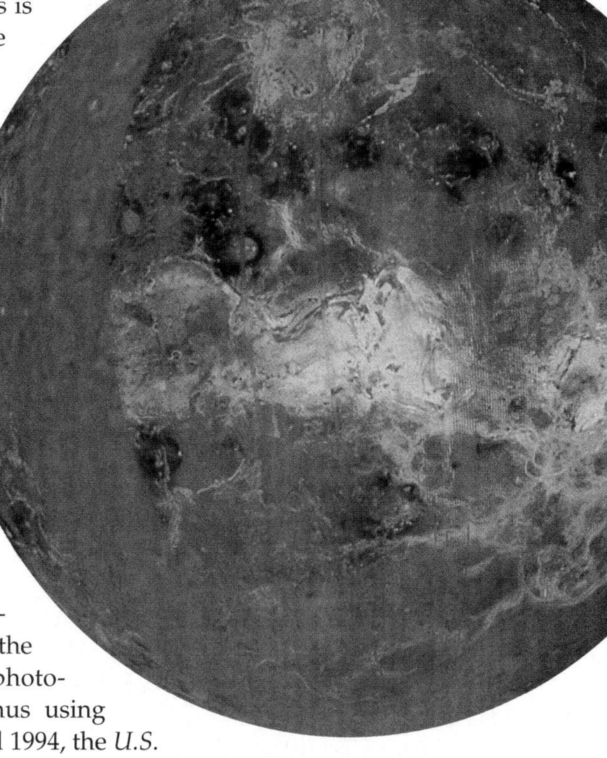

Figure 22-5 Although Venus is similar to Earth, there are important differences. **How could studying Venus help us learn more about Earth?**

2 Teach

Enrichment

Linguistic Encourage students to make up sentences that help them to remember the planets in order from the sun. For example, My Very Exceptional Mother Just Served Us Nutritious Pizza. L2

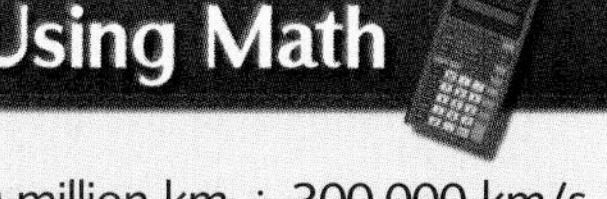

Using Math

150 million km ÷ 300 000 km/s = 500 s; 500 s ÷ 60 s = 8.3 minutes

Caption Answer

Figure 22-5 *Studying processes that occur on Venus allows us to learn about similar processes that may have occurred on Earth during our planet's early history.*

Videodisc

STV: Solar System

Unit 1 *The Big Picture, The Nine Planets* 0:56

03600-05294

Refer to the Teacher Guide for additional bar codes and teaching strategies.

Content Background

Venus's yellow color is due to the sulfuric acid in its clouds. Earth's oceans of liquid water give it a distinctive blue color. Mars, the red planet, gets its color from iron oxide in weathered rocks on its surface. The composition of particular parts of each planet produces each planet's unique color.

Across the Curriculum

Mathematics Have students compute the volumes of the inner planets using the equation $V = 0.166\pi d^3$, where V is the volume and d is the diameter of each planet. Students can use astronomical books to research the volumes of the inner planets. L3

Activity

Visual-Spatial Have students research and list sizes of the inner planets and surface conditions. Have student volunteers draw each planet to scale on the chalkboard. Using colored chalk, have the volunteers illustrate at least one important characteristic of each planet's surface. Encourage all students to do the same in their Science Journals. L2 ELL COOP LEARN

Problem Solving

Normally, one would expect planets closer to the sun to be hotter than those farther away. However, if the more distant planet has an atmosphere that can trap heat, conditions on that planet's surface can be quite different from what is expected. The atmosphere of a planet can trap heat on the planet's surface just as the glass of a greenhouse traps heat inside the greenhouse.

Think Critically

The thick atmosphere of Venus absorbs solar energy and prevents it from rapidly radiating back into space. Mercury, which has little atmospheric gas, loses energy rapidly from its surface. Even though Venus is farther from the sun than Mercury, its atmosphere holds and circulates solar energy to a much greater extent. P

GLENCOE TECHNOLOGY

CD-ROM

Glencoe Science Voyages Interactive CD-ROM

Explorations

Have students do the interactive exploration *How do planets in our solar system differ?*

Earth

Earth, shown in **Figure 22-6,** is the third planet from the sun. The average distance from Earth to the sun is 150 million km, or one astronomical unit (AU). **Astronomical units** are used to measure distances to objects in the solar system.

Unlike other planets, surface temperatures on Earth allow water to exist as a solid, liquid, and gas. Earth's atmosphere causes most meteors to burn up before they reach the surface. The atmosphere also protects life from the sun's intense radiation.

Figure 22-6 More than 70 percent of Earth's surface is covered by liquid water. **What is unique about surface temperatures on Earth?**

Mars

Mars, the fourth planet from the sun, is called the red planet because iron oxide in the weathered rocks on its surface gives it a reddish color, as seen in **Figure 22-7.** Other features of Mars visible from Earth are its polar ice caps, which get larger during the Martian winter and shrink during the summer. The ice caps are made mostly of frozen carbon dioxide and frozen water.

Most of the information we have about Mars came from the *Mariner 9, Viking* probes, *Mars Global Surveyor,* and *Mars Pathfinder. Mariner 9* orbited Mars in 1971–1972. It revealed long channels on the planet that may have been carved by

Problem Solving

Interpret Planetary Data

Your teacher asks you to determine which planet's surface is hotter, Mercury or Venus. You must also explain the temperature difference. You decide that this assignment is going to be easy. Of course, Mercury has to be hotter than Venus because it is much closer to the sun. Venus is almost twice as far away as Mercury. You write your answer and turn in your paper. Later, when you receive your paper back, you find out that your assumptions were evidently wrong. Your teacher suggests that you research the question further, using the table on this page as a guide. As a further hint, your teacher tells you to consider how a greenhouse works to keep it warmer inside than outside and to relate this to what might happen to a planet with a thick atmosphere.

Data for Mercury and Venus

	Mercury 0.39 AU from sun	Venus 0.72 AU from sun
Surface Temperature (High)	450°	470°
Atmosphere Density	very thin	very dense
Atmosphere Compostion	potassium, sodium, hydrogen, helium	carbon dioxide sulfuric acid

Think Critically: What causes Venus to have a higher surface temperature than Mercury? Explain.

Caption Answer

Figure 22-6 *They allow water to exist as a solid, liquid, and gas.*

Integrating the Sciences

Chemistry Mars is commonly known as the red planet. Ask students to research the composition of surface rocks on Mars. Based on their research, have them explain the chemical reaction in the Martian soil responsible for the planet's red color. *Iron in the Martian soil may have reacted with oxygen in the ancient Martian atmosphere, forming iron oxide.* L3

flowing water. *Mariner 9* also discovered the largest volcano in the solar system, Olympus Mons. Like all Mars's volcanoes, Olympus Mons is extinct. Large rift zones that formed in the Martian crust were also discovered. One such rift, Valles Marineris, is shown in **Figure 22-7.**

The Viking probes

In 1976, the *Viking 1* and *2* probes arrived at Mars. Each spacecraft consisted of an orbiter and a lander. The *Viking 1* and *2* orbiters photographed the entire surface of Mars from orbit, while the *Viking 1* and *2* landers touched down on the planet's surface to conduct meteorological, chemical, and biological experiments. The biological experiments found no evidence of life in the soil. The *Viking* landers also sent back pictures of a reddish-colored, barren, rocky, and windswept surface.

Try at Home

MiniLab

Inferring Effects of Gravity

Procedure

1. Suppose you are a crane operator who is sent to Mars to help build a Mars colony.
2. You know that your crane can lift 44 500 N on Earth, but the gravity on Mars is only 40 percent of Earth's gravity.
3. Using Appendix A, determine how much mass your crane could lift on Mars.

Analysis

1. How can what you have discovered be an advantage over construction on Earth?
2. In what ways might construction advantages change the overall design of the Mars colony?

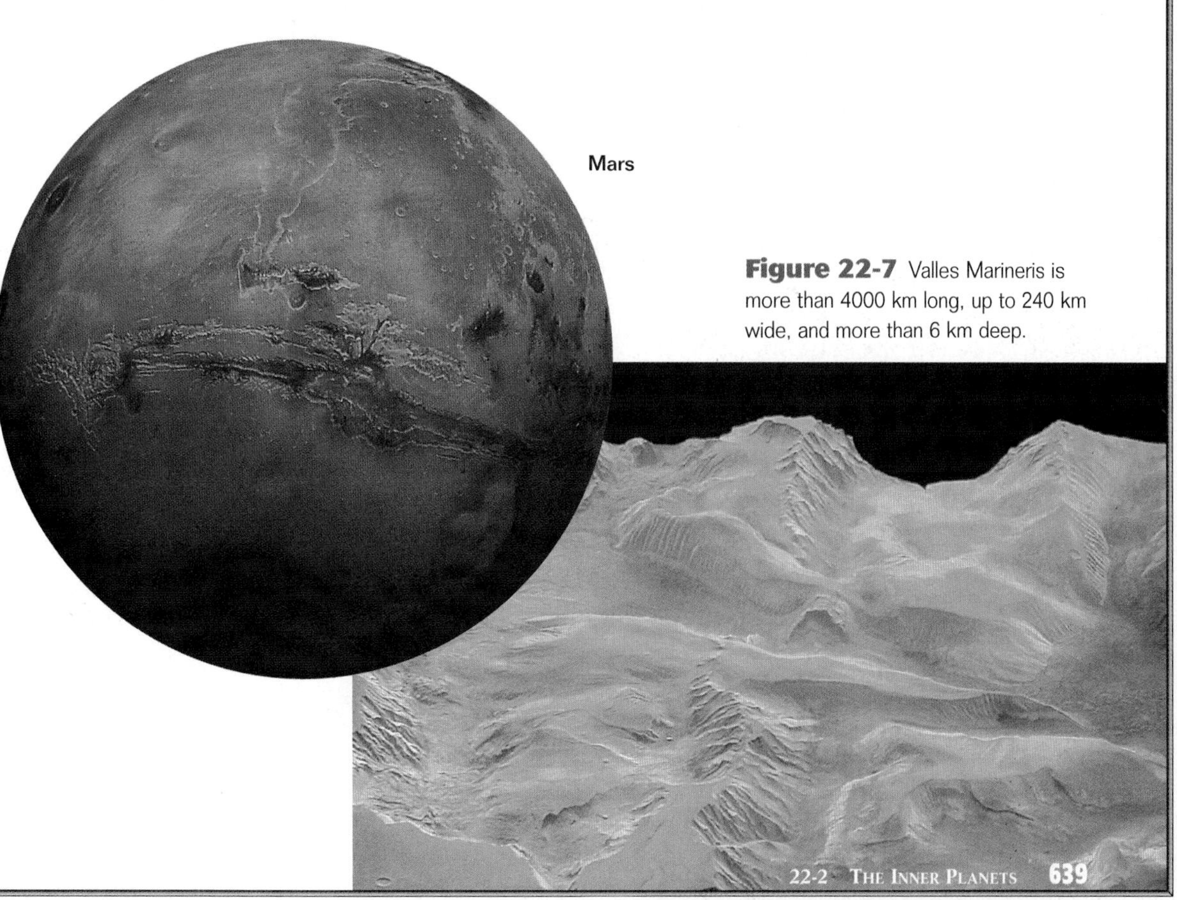

Mars

Figure 22-7 Valles Marineris is more than 4000 km long, up to 240 km wide, and more than 6 km deep.

Try at Home

MiniLab

For additional help doing this activity at home, see the corresponding pages in the **Home Involvement** booklet.

Purpose

Logical-Mathematical Students will study gravity and mass on Mars. L2

Teaching Strategies

- Remind students that force equals mass times acceleration due to gravity: $F = ma$.
- Mars's gravity is 40 percent that of Earth's. To determine the acceleration due to gravity on Mars, multiply Earth's acceleration due to gravity by 0.4. Earth's acceleration due to gravity, a, is 9.8 m/s^2. Acceleration due to gravity on Mars is 0.4×9.8 m/s^2, or 3.92 m/s^2.
- $F_e = ma_e$; $m = F_e/a_e$
  $m = 44\ 500$ N/9.8 m/s^2
  $= 4541$ kg on Earth
  $F_m = ma_m$; $m = F_m/a_m$
  $m = 44\ 500$ N/3.92 m/s^2
  $= 11\ 352$ kg on Mars

Analysis

1. The crane could lift more material on Mars and thus speed up construction.
2. The structure could be made of larger sections. Massive objects could be lifted higher.

Assessment

Performance To further assess students' understanding of conditions on Mars, have them calculate how much mass they could lift on the planet. Use **Performance Assessment in the Science Classroom,** p. 29.

Across the Curriculum

Mathematics Tell students that the average distance between the orbits of Earth and Mars is 78 million km. Have them calculate how many years it would take to travel from Earth's orbit to Mars's orbit, if they were traveling at 88 km/hr, the average highway speed of a car. *The trip would take about 100 years.* L2

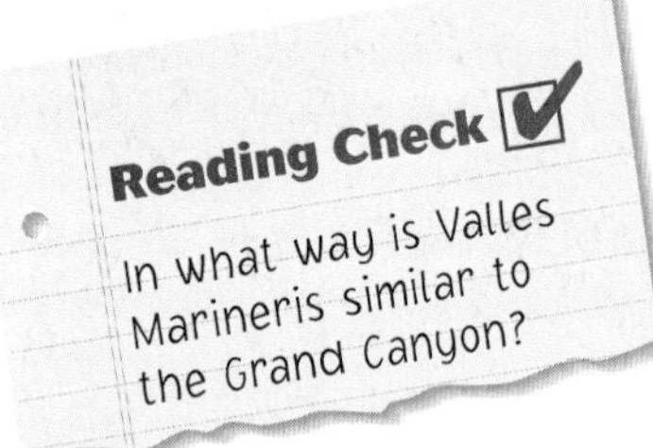

Reading Check
In what way is Valles Marineris similar to the Grand Canyon?

CHEMISTRY INTEGRATION

Mars has always been known as the red planet. Research the composition of surface rocks on Mars. Describe the chemical reaction in the Martian soil responsible for the planet's red color.

Global Surveyor and Pathfinder

The *Mars Pathfinder,* shown in **Figure 22-8,** gathered data that indicated that iron in Mars's crust may have been leached out by groundwater. In addition, high-quality cameras on board *Global Surveyor* showed that the walls of Valles Marineris have distinct layers similar to the Grand Canyon on Earth. *Global Surveyor* also noticed that a vast flat region, similar to a dried-up seabed or mudflat, covers a large area of Mars's northern hemisphere. This evidence, combined with evidence gathered from *Mariner 9,* indicates that large amounts of water were once present on the planet. Where has all the water gone? Many believe it is frozen into Mars's crust at the poles, shown in **Figure 22-9,** or has soaked into the ground. ✓

The Martian atmosphere is much thinner than Earth's and is composed mostly of carbon dioxide, with some nitrogen and argon. The thin atmosphere does not filter out harmful rays from the sun as Earth's atmosphere does. Surface temperatures range from 35°C to –170°C. The temperature difference between day and night sets up strong winds on the planet, which can cause global dust storms during certain seasons.

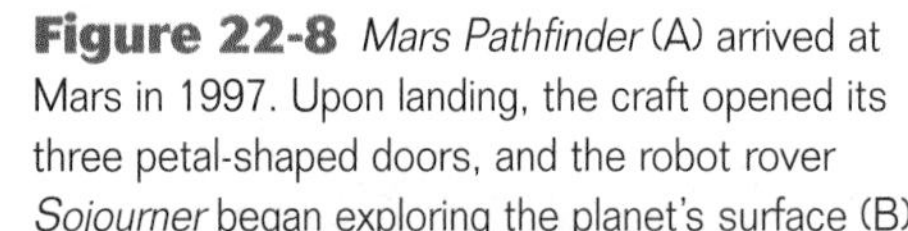

Figure 22-8 *Mars Pathfinder* (A) arrived at Mars in 1997. Upon landing, the craft opened its three petal-shaped doors, and the robot rover *Sojourner* began exploring the planet's surface (B).

Answer to Reading Check
It has distinct layers similar to the Grand Canyon.

Iron oxide in the weathered rocks gives Mars its reddish color.

3 Assess

Check for Understanding

Teacher FYI

Biological tests conducted on Mars by *Viking 1* and *2* were inconclusive as to whether any life is present in the Martian soil. One test gave a reading that could have indicated a biological reaction, but the same readings can be achieved by chemical reactions. Current theory leans toward the chemical rather than the biological reaction.

Reteach

Interpersonal Use the following question to reinforce data on the inner planets. **Why isn't Earth's surface marked by many craters like Mercury and the moon?** *Earth's atmosphere causes most meteors to burn up before they reach the surface.*

Science Journal

Water on Mars Have students research the recent *Mars Global Surveyor* and *Pathfinder* missions for information on whether Mars may once have had liquid water on its surface. Have students write a one-page summary in their Science Journals about the data they discover. L2

Extension

For students who have mastered this section, use the **Reinforcement** and **Enrichment** masters.

Figure 22-9 These photos show two features of Mars.

A Olympus Mons is the largest volcano in the solar system.

B Water that flowed on Mars long ago may now be frozen in polar ice caps.

Martian Moons

Mars has two small, heavily cratered moons. Phobos is 25 km in diameter, and Deimos is 13 km in diameter. Phobos's orbit is slowly spiraling inward toward Mars. Phobos is expected to impact the Martian surface in about 50 million years.

As you toured the inner planets using the "eyes" of the space probes, you saw how each planet is unique. Mercury, Venus, Earth, and Mars are different from the outer planets, which you'll explore in the next section.

Section Assessment

1. How are Mercury and Earth's moon similar?
2. List one important characteristic of each inner planet.
3. Although Venus is often called Earth's twin, why would life as we know it be unlikely on Venus?
4. Name the inner planets in order from the sun.
5. **Think Critically:** Do the closest planets to the sun always have the hottest surface temperatures? Explain your answer.
6. **Skill Builder**
   Interpreting Data Using the information in this section, explain how Mars is like Earth. How are they different? If you need help, refer to Interpreting Data in the **Skill Handbook** on page 724.

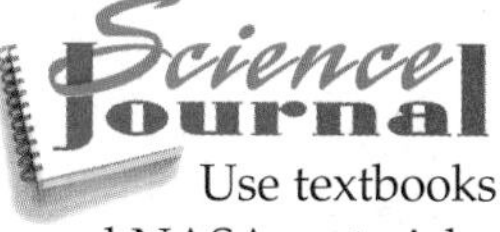

Use textbooks and NASA materials to investigate NASA's missions to Mars. In your Science Journal, report on the possibility of life on Mars and the tests that have been conducted to see whether life is there.

6. **Skill Builder**
Answers should include that both are inner planets. The processes of volcanism and weathering helped to form each planet. Both have polar ice caps. Liquid water is common on Earth's surface now, and may once have been present on Mars.

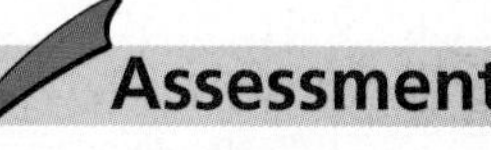

Assessment

Performance Use this Skill Builder to assess students' abilities to interpret data. Ask students to explain what equipment they would need in order to live on Mars's surface. Use **Performance Assessment in the Science Classroom,** p. 27.

4 Close

Proficiency Prep

Use this quiz to check students' recall of section content.

1. **Which planet is closest to the sun?** *Mercury*
2. **Which planet is considered to be Earth's twin?** *Venus*

Section Assessment

1. The surfaces of both are heavily cratered. The amount of light reflected from both objects is low because of the dark-colored surfaces.
2. Answers might include: Mercury is heavily cratered; Venus has a dense cloud cover; water on Earth exists in three states; and Mars appears red due to iron oxide.
3. The greenhouse effect raises surface temperatures on Venus to 470°C.
4. Mercury, Venus, Earth, Mars
5. **Think Critically** No, because of its intense greenhouse effect, Venus has a hotter surface temperature than Mercury, which is closer to the sun.

Viking landers: Gas Exchange Experiment, Pyrolytic Release Experiment, and Labeled Release Experiment; *Pathfinder* and *Sojourner:* geologic studies of the Martian surface and meteorological studies. Several spacecraft have studied the planet from orbit.

22-2 The Inner Planets 641

SECTION 22-3

Prepare

Refer to **Outer Planets** and **Pluto** on p. 628F.

Preplanning

Refer to the **Chapter Organizer** on pp. 628A–B.

1 Motivate

Bellringer

Before presenting the lesson, display **Section Focus Transparency 61** on the overhead projector. Use the accompanying **Focus Activity** worksheet. L2 ELL

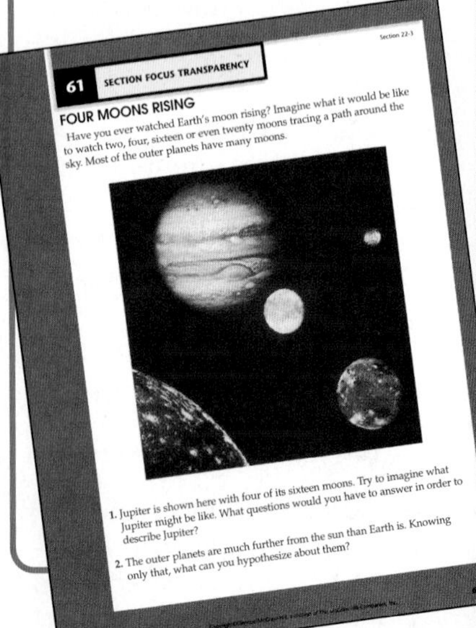

Section 22-3

61 SECTION FOCUS TRANSPARENCY

FOUR MOONS RISING

Have you ever watched Earth's moon rising? Imagine what it would be like to watch two, four, sixteen or even twenty moons tracing a path around the sky. Most of the outer planets have many moons.

1. Jupiter is shown here with four of its sixteen moons. Try to imagine what Jupiter might be like. What questions would you have to answer in order to describe Jupiter?
2. The outer planets are much further from the sun than Earth is. Knowing only that, what can you hypothesize about them?

61

Tying to Previous Knowledge

Voyager 1 and 2 have sent back information about the outer planets. *Galileo* has sent back information about Jupiter and its moons.

22-3 The Outer Planets

What You'll Learn

- The major characteristics of Jupiter, Saturn, Uranus, and Neptune
- How Pluto differs from the other outer planets

Vocabulary

Jupiter, Great Red Spot, Saturn, Uranus, Neptune, Pluto

Why It's Important

- You'll learn about the planets in our solar system that differ most from Earth.

Outer Planets

You have learned that the inner planets are small, solid, rocky bodies in space. By contrast, the outer planets, except for Pluto, are large, gaseous objects.

You may have heard or read about the *Voyager* and *Galileo* spacecraft. Although they were not the first probes to the outer planets, they have uncovered a wealth of new information about Jupiter, Saturn, Uranus, and Neptune. Let's follow the spacecraft on their journeys to the outer planets of the solar system.

Jupiter

In 1979, *Voyager 1* and *Voyager 2* flew past **Jupiter,** the largest planet and the fifth planet from the sun. *Galileo* reached Jupiter in 1995. The major discoveries of the probes include new information about the composition and motion of Jupiter's atmosphere and the discovery of three new moons. *Voyager* probes also discovered that Jupiter has faint dust rings around it and that one of its moons has volcanoes on it.

Jupiter is composed mostly of hydrogen and helium, with some ammonia, methane, and water vapor as well. Scientists theorize that the atmosphere of hydrogen and helium gradually changes to a planetwide ocean of liquid hydrogen and helium toward the middle of the planet. Below this liquid layer may be a solid rocky core. The extreme pressure and temperature, however, make the core different from any rock on Earth.

You've probably seen pictures from the probes of Jupiter's colorful clouds. Its atmosphere has bands of white, red, tan, and brown clouds, as shown in **Figure 22-10.** Continuous storms of swirling, high-pressure gas have been observed on Jupiter. The **Great Red Spot** is the most spectacular of these storms. Lightning also has been observed within Jupiter's clouds.

Figure 22-10 Jupiter (A) is the largest planet in our solar system, containing more mass than all of the other planets combined. The Great Red Spot (B) is a giant storm about 12 000 km from top to bottom.

Resource Manager

The following **Teacher Classroom Resources** can be used with Section 22-3:

Reproducible Masters

Activity Worksheets, pp. 121–122, 124 L2

Enrichment, p. 61 L3

Home Involvement, p. 37 L2

Laboratory Manual, pp. 129–130 L2

Reinforcement, p. 61 L2

Study Guide, p. 87

Moons of Jupiter

Sixteen moons orbit Jupiter. The four largest, shown in **Table 22-1,** were discovered by Galileo in 1610. Io is the closest large moon to Jupiter. Jupiter's tremendous gravitational force and the gravity of Europa pull on Io. This force heats up Io, causing it to be the most volcanically active object in the solar system. The next large moon is Europa. It is composed mostly of rock with a thick, smooth crust of ice, which may indicate the presence of an ocean under the ice. Next is Ganymede, which is the largest moon in the solar system. It's larger than the planet Mercury. Callisto, the last of the large moons, is composed of ice and rock. Studying these moons and events such as the comet collision shown in **Figure 22-11** further our knowledge of the solar system.

Saturn

The next planet surveyed by the *Voyager* probes was Saturn, in 1980 and 1981. **Saturn** is the sixth planet from the sun and is also known as the ringed planet. Saturn is the second-largest planet in the solar system but has the lowest density. Its density is so low that the planet would float on water.

Table 22-1

Large Moons of Jupiter	
Io The most volcanically active object in the solar system; sulfur lava gives it its distinctive red and orange color; has a thin oxygen, sulfur, and sulfur dioxide atmosphere.	
Europa Rocky interior is covered by a 100-km-thick ice crust, which has a network of cracks, indicating tectonic activity; has a thin oxygen atmosphere.	
Ganymede Has an ice crust about 100 km thick, covered with grooves; crust may surround a mantle of water or slushy ice; has a rocky core and a thin hydrogen atmosphere.	
Callisto Has a heavily cratered, ice-rock crust several hundred kilometers thick; crust may surround a salty ocean around a rock core; has a thin atmosphere of hydrogen, oxygen, and carbon dioxide.	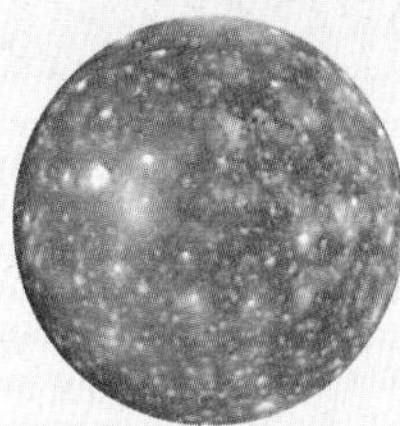

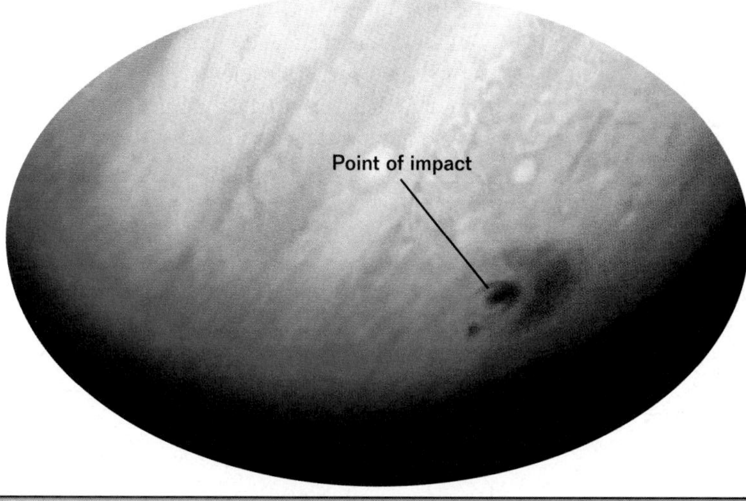

Figure 22-11 In 1994, comet Shoemaker-Levy 9 collided into Jupiter causing a series of spectacular explosions. Information from this impact gives us clues about what might happen if such an impact occurred on Earth.

2 Teach

Activity

Interpersonal Form groups of four students. Have students play "Planet Jeopardy" by reading statements from this section and the previous section and calling on a student to form an appropriate question. Award points for every correct question by a group. L2 COOP LEARN

VISUAL Learning

Table 22-1 Ask students why the four moons shown in the table are called the Galilean satellites of Jupiter. *They were discovered by Galileo.* Ask them also to list the moons in their Science Journals and to write a brief description of the characteristics of each moon. L2

GLENCOE TECHNOLOGY

Videodisc

The Infinite Voyage: Sail On, Voyager

Chapter 3 *Jupiter's Atmosphere* 1:30

Chapter 4 *Jupiter's Moons and Unexpected Volcanoes* 6:00

Chapter 7 *The Rings of Saturn* 3:30

Refer to the Teacher Guide for bar codes and teaching strategies.

Multiple Learning Styles

Visual-Spatial If a local organization of sky observers exists in your area, invite one of its members to talk to the class about nighttime observations. Perhaps one of the members has searched for and found a comet at some time. If no organization exists locally, organize a nighttime observation with students. Students may wish to invite their parents or guardians to participate in a session to observe Jupiter or Saturn. Use planet observations to support in-class discussions on the solar system.

Try at Home MiniLab

For additional help doing this activity at home, see the corresponding pages in the **Home Involvement** booklet.

Purpose

Kinesthetic Students will formulate models of the solar system. L2 ELL P

Materials

metric rulers, drawing compass, pencil, paper

Teaching Strategies

Safety Precautions Caution students to handle drawing compasses carefully.

Troubleshooting Have students determine a scale for Earth first. The scale for each planet will be the product of the scale for Earth times the other planet's multiple of true Earth size. For example, Jupiter is 11.19 times larger than Earth. If model Earth were 2 cm in diameter, model Jupiter would be 2 cm × 11.19 or 22.38 cm in scale diameter.

Analysis

1. & 2. Answers will vary depending on the scale used. Have students compute their answers by multiplying Earth's scale diameter by 11 728, which is the number of Earth diameters in 1 AU.
3. At 1 AU = 2 m, the sun would be 19 mm in diameter. Model Earth would be considerably smaller—0.18 mm or 0.018 cm.

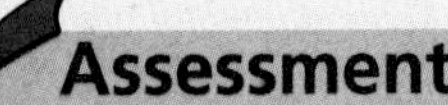

Assessment

Performance To further assess students' understanding of scale models, have them formulate models of each planet out of balls of crumpled newspaper. Use **Performance Assessment in the Science Classroom,** p. 51.

Figure 22-12 Saturn's rings are composed of pieces of rock and ice.

Try at Home MiniLab

Modeling Planets

Procedure

1. Research the planets to determine how the sizes of the planets in the solar system compare with each other.
2. Select a scale for the diameter of Earth based on the size of your paper.
3. Make a model by drawing a circle with this diameter on paper.
4. Using Earth's diameter as 1.0, draw each of the other planets to scale.

Analysis

1. At this scale, how far would your model Earth need to be located from the sun?
2. What would 1 AU be equal to in this model?
3. Using a scale of 1 AU = 2 m, how large would the sun and Earth models have to be to remain in scale?

Similar to Jupiter, Saturn is a large, gaseous planet with a thick outer atmosphere composed mostly of hydrogen and helium. Saturn's atmosphere also contains ammonia, methane, and water vapor. As you go deeper into Saturn's atmosphere, the gases gradually change to liquid hydrogen and helium. Below its atmosphere and liquid ocean, Saturn may have a small rocky core.

The *Voyager* probes gathered new information about Saturn's ring system and its moons. The *Voyager* probes showed that Saturn has several broad rings, each of which is composed of thousands of thin ringlets. Each ring is composed of countless ice and rock particles ranging in size from a speck of dust to tens of meters across, as shown in **Figure 22-12.** This makes Saturn's ring system the most complex of all the outer gaseous planets.

At least 20 moons orbit Saturn. That's more than any other planet in our solar system. The largest of these, Titan, is larger than Mercury. It has an atmosphere of nitrogen, argon, and methane. Thick clouds prevent us from seeing the surface of Titan.

Across the Curriculum

Mathematics Supply students with the following diameters of the larger moons in the solar system: Earth's moon (3476 km), Io (3630 km), Europa (3138 km), Ganymede (5262 km), Callisto (4800 km), Titan (5150 km), and Triton (2720 km). Have students compare and contrast the sizes of these moons with the sizes of the inner planets. Using a scale of 1 mm = 100 km, have students draw to scale the inner planets and moons listed above. Students should note that some of the moons are larger than Mercury.  L2

644 CHAPTER 22 THE SOLAR SYSTEM

Uranus

After touring Saturn, *Voyager 2* flew by Uranus in 1986. **Uranus,** shown in **Figure 22-13,** is the seventh planet from the sun and wasn't discovered until 1781. It is a large, gaseous planet with 17 satellites and a system of thin, dark rings.

Voyager revealed numerous thin rings and ten moons that had not been seen earlier. *Voyager* also detected that the planet's magnetic field is tilted 55 degrees from its rotational poles.

The atmosphere of Uranus is composed of hydrogen, helium, and some methane. The methane gives the planet its blue-green color. Methane absorbs the red and yellow light, and the clouds reflect the green and blue. No cloud bands and few storm systems are seen on Uranus. Evidence suggests that under its atmosphere, Uranus has a mantle of liquid water, methane, and ammonia surrounding a rocky core.

One of the most unique features of Uranus is that its axis of rotation is tilted on its side compared with the other planets. The axes of rotation of the other planets, except Pluto, are nearly perpendicular to the planes of their orbits. Uranus, however, has a rotational axis nearly parallel to the plane of its orbit, as shown in **Figure 22-14.** Some scientists believe a collision with another object turned Uranus on its side.

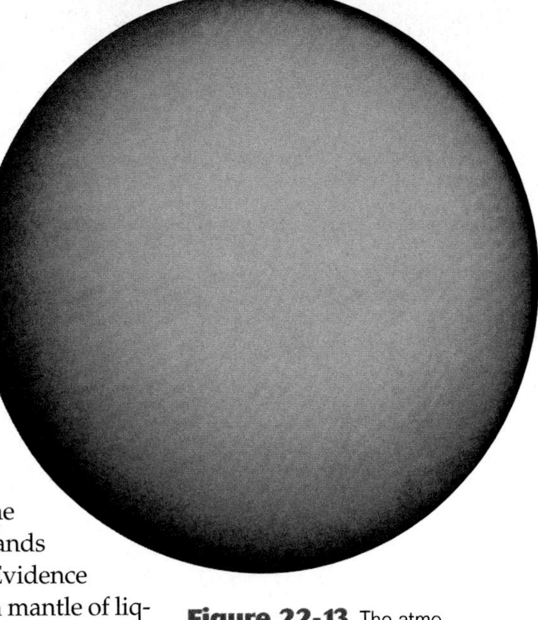

Figure 22-13 The atmosphere of Uranus gives the planet its distinct blue-green color.

interNET CONNECTION

Visit the Glencoe Science Web Site at **www.glencoe.com/sec/science** for more information about the *Voyager* space probes.

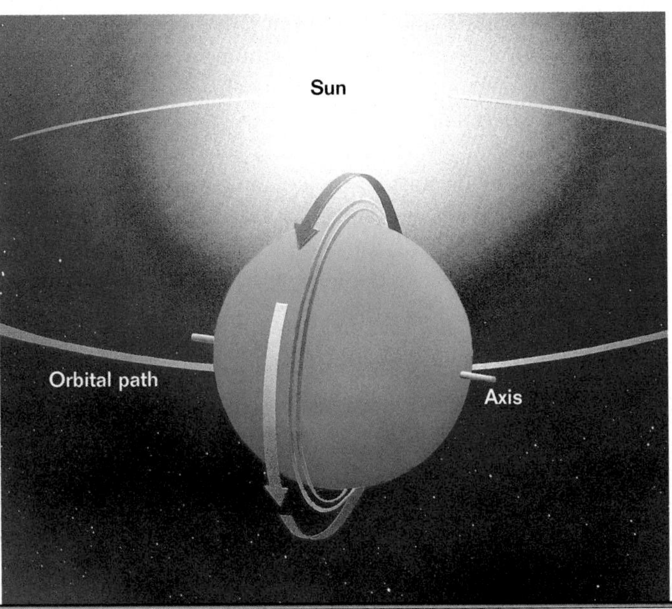

Figure 22-14 Uranus rotates on an axis nearly parallel to the plane of its orbit. During its revolution around the sun, one of the poles, at times, points almost directly at the sun.

interNET CONNECTION

Internet Addresses

For Internet tips, see Glencoe's **Using the Internet in the Science Classroom.**

NATIONAL GEOGRAPHIC

Videodisc

STV: Solar System

Unit 3 *Outer Planets* 6:33

24512-36610

Refer to the Teacher Guide for additional bar codes and teaching strategies.

GLENCOE TECHNOLOGY

Videodisc

The Infinite Voyage: Sail On, Voyager

Chapter 7 *Voyager 2: Uranus* 7:00

Refer to the Teacher Guide for bar codes and teaching strategies.

Content Background

Voyager 2 has provided astronomers with data about the composition of the atmospheres of the gaseous giant planets. Also, using data from the *Hubble Space Telescope*, the sizes of the gaseous giants, their moons, Pluto, and Charon have been determined to a much better degree. These data have enabled scientists to produce more detailed models of the solar system's scale and structure.

GLENCOE TECHNOLOGY

 **Videodisc**

The Infinite Voyage: Sail On, Voyager

Chapter 11 *Voyager 2: Neptune* 8:00

Refer to the Teacher Guide for bar codes and teaching strategies.

3 Assess

Check for Understanding

Enrichment

Intrapersonal Have each student compile a list of the physical properties of all known moons orbiting the outer planets. Suggest students use data available from the *Voyager* and *Galileo* missions. L3

Reteach

Interpersonal Have pairs of students sketch each outer planet on a separate flash card. On the reverse side of the card, instruct students to write down the characteristics of each planet. Partners can then test each other using the flash cards. L1 COOP LEARN

Extension

For students who have mastered this section, use the **Reinforcement** and **Enrichment** masters.

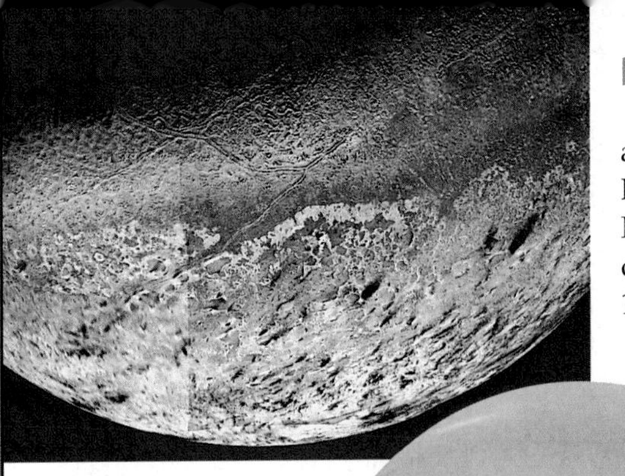

Figure 22-15
Triton, above, is Neptune's largest moon.

Neptune

Neptune

From Uranus, *Voyager 2* traveled on to Neptune, a large, gaseous planet. Discovered in 1846, **Neptune** is usually the eighth planet from the sun. However, Pluto's orbit crosses inside Neptune's during part of its voyage around the sun. Between 1979 and 1998, Pluto was closer to the sun than Neptune. In 1999, Pluto once again became the farthest planet from the sun.

Neptune's atmosphere is similar to that of Uranus. The methane content gives Neptune, shown in **Figure 22-15,** its distinctive blue-green color, just as it does for Uranus.

Neptune has dark-colored, stormlike features in its atmosphere that are similar to the Great Red Spot on Jupiter. One discovered by *Voyager* is called the Great Dark Spot.

Under its atmosphere, Neptune is thought to have liquid water, methane, and ammonia. Neptune probably has a rocky core.

Voyager 2 detected six new moons, so the total number of Neptune's known moons is now eight. Of these, Triton is the largest. Triton, shown in **Figure 22-15,** has a diameter of 2700 km and a thin atmosphere composed mostly of nitrogen. *Voyager* detected methane geysers erupting on Triton. *Voyager* also detected that Neptune has rings that are thin in some places and thick in other places. Neptune's magnetic field is tilted 47 degrees from its rotational axis. In comparison, Earth's magnetic field is tilted only 11.5 degrees from its rotational axis.

Voyager ended its tour of the solar system with Neptune. Both *Voyager* probes are now beyond the orbits of Pluto and Neptune. They will continue into space, studying how far the sun's power reaches into the outer limits of our solar system.

Reading Check
Voyager's tour ended with what planet?

Pluto

The smallest planet in our solar system, and the one we know the least about, is Pluto. Because **Pluto** is farther from the sun than Neptune during most of its orbit around the sun, it is considered the ninth planet from the sun. Pluto is not like the other outer planets. It's surrounded by only a

Galileo Have students write a report about new information gathered by *Galileo* about Jupiter, its moons, and its rings. Ask students to discuss how NASA used gravity assists to power the space probe during its long flight to Jupiter. L2

thin atmosphere, and it's the only outer planet with a solid, icy-rock surface.

Pluto's only moon, Charon, has a diameter about half the size of Pluto's. Charon orbits close to Pluto. Pluto and Charon are shown in **Figure 22-16.** Because of their close size and orbit, they are sometimes considered to be a double planet.

Recent data from the *Hubble Space Telescope* indicate the presence of a vast disk of icy comets near Neptune's orbit, called the Kuiper belt. Some of the ice comets are hundreds of kilometers in diameter. Are Pluto and Charon members of this belt? Are they escaped moons of one of the larger gaseous giants, or did they simply form at the distance they are? Maybe planets at that distance from the sun should be small and composed of icy rock. We may not find out until we send a probe to Pluto.

With the *Voyager* probes, we entered a new age of knowledge about the solar system. The space probe *Galileo*, which arrived at Jupiter in 1995, and the *Cassini* probe, which will arrive at Saturn in 2004, will continue to extend our understanding of the solar system.

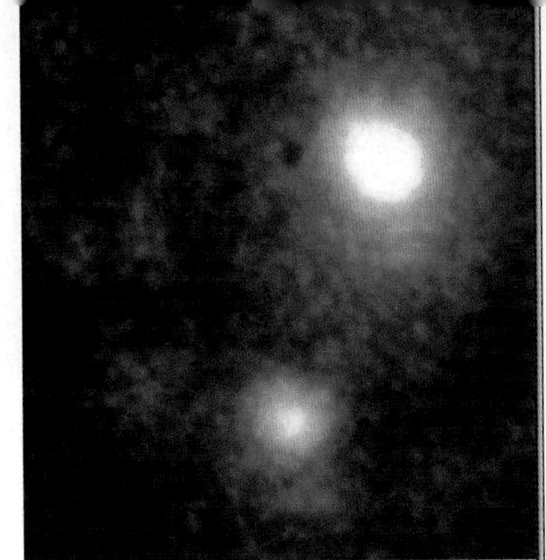

Figure 22-16 The *Hubble Space Telescope* gave astronomers their first clear view of Pluto and Charon as distinct objects.

Section Assessment

1. What are the differences between the outer planets and the inner planets?
2. Are any moons in the solar system larger than planets? If so, which ones?
3. How does Pluto differ from the other outer planets?
4. **Think Critically:** Why is Neptune sometimes the farthest planet from the sun?
5. **Skill Builder**
   Recognizing Cause and Effect
   Answer the following questions about Jupiter. If you need help, refer to Recognizing Cause and Effect in the **Skill Handbook** on page 721.
   a. What causes Jupiter's surface color?
   b. How is the Great Red Spot affected by Jupiter's atmosphere?
   c. How does Jupiter's mass affect its gravitational force?

Using Computers

Spreadsheet Design a table using spreadsheet software of the nine planets. Compare their characteristics, such as size, distance from the sun, orbital speed, and number of satellites. If you need help, refer to page 738.

4 Close

Proficiency Prep

Use this quiz to check students' recall of section content.

1. **Which planet is the largest?** *Jupiter*
2. **Which planet has the most complex ring system?** *Saturn*

Section Assessment

1. The outer planets are large, gaseous objects, except for Pluto. The inner planets are small, solid, rocklike bodies in space.
2. Yes, Ganymede and Titan are larger than Mercury. Several moons are larger than Pluto: Earth's moon, Io, Europa, Ganymede, Callisto, Titan, and Triton.
3. Pluto is small and rocky; the other outer planets are large gaseous giants.
4. **Think Critically** Pluto's orbit is more elliptical than the orbits of other planets. This causes Pluto to come closer to the sun than Neptune for about 20 years of its orbit. This most recently occurred between 1979 and 1999.

Using Computers

Student spreadsheets will vary, but should include size, distance from the sun, orbital speed, and number of satellites.

5. **Skill Builder**
   a. bands of red, tan, and brown clouds
   b. High pressure causes the gases in the storm to flow inward toward its center.
   c. Jupiter is the most massive planet and thus has the greatest gravitational force of the nine planets.

Assessment

Oral Assess students' abilities to recognize cause and effect by asking the following question: **What causes Io to be so volcanically active?** Use **Performance Assessment in the Science Classroom,** p. 17.

Activity 22•2 Design Your Own Experiment

Recognize the Problem

Purpose

Logical-Mathematical Students will model distances between the sun and the planets. L2 ELL COOP LEARN P

Process Skills

measuring in SI, using numbers, sequencing, formulating a hypothesis, separating and controlling variables, interpreting data, and making models

Time

one class period

Safety Precautions

Caution students to handle scissors with care.

Form a Hypothesis

Possible Hypotheses

Students will select a scale to represent distances in AU. The mean distances to planets in AU will be obtained and adjusted by the selected scale. The scale distances will be placed on a data chart, and a scale model of planet distances will be constructed from string.

Test Your Hypothesis

Possible Procedures

Use research materials to obtain the mean distance from the sun to each planet in AU. Record these values in a data table. Determine a scale for making a model of the solar system from string. Use paper to make planets. Design a method for placing the planets in proper positions on the solar system model.

Design Your Own Experiment

Activity 22•2

Solar System Distance Model

Distances between the planets of the solar system are large. Can you design a model that will demonstrate the large distances between and among the sun and planets in the solar system?

Possible Materials

- Meterstick
- Scissors
- Pencil
- String (several meters)
- Paper (several sheets of notebook paper)

Recognize the Problem

How can a model be designed that will show the relative distances between and among the sun and planets of the solar system?

Form a Hypothesis

State a hypothesis about how a model with scale dimensions of the solar system can be constructed.

Goals

- **Make a table** of scale distances that will represent planetary distances to be used in a model of the solar system.
- **Research** planetary distances.
- **Make a model** of the distances between the sun and planets of the solar system.

Safety Precautions

 Take care when handling scissors.

Planetary Distances

Planet	Distance to Sun (km)	Distance to Sun (AU)	Scale Distance (1 AU = 10 cm)	Scale Distance (1 AU = 2 m)
Mercury	5.8×10^7	0.39	3.9 cm	78.0 cm
Venus	1.08×10^8	0.72	7.2 cm	1.44 m
Earth	1.50×10^8	1.00	10.0 cm	2.00 m
Mars	2.28×10^8	1.52	15.2 cm	3.04 m
Jupiter	7.80×10^8	5.20	52.0 cm	10.40 m
Saturn	1.43×10^9	9.53	95.3 cm	19.06 m
Uranus	2.88×10^9	19.20	192.0 cm	38.40 m
Neptune	4.51×10^9	30.07	300.7 cm	60.14 m
Pluto	5.92×10^9	39.47	394.7 cm	78.94 m

Teaching Strategies

Tying to Previous Knowledge Remind students of the dimensions of distances between inner planets. Tell them that distances between outer planets are much larger.

Troubleshooting Some students will need help in choosing a scale to use for their models. If necessary, suggest that they use a scale of 1 AU = 10 cm. Sample data have been provided for this scale. Some students may also need help with the math.

Test Your Hypothesis

Plan

1. As a group, **agree** upon and write out your hypothesis statement.
2. **List** the steps that you need to take in making your model to **test** your hypothesis. Be specific, describing exactly what you will do at each step.
3. **Make** a list of the materials that you will need to complete your model.
4. **Make a table** of scale distances you will use in your model.
5. **Write** a description of how you will **build** your model, **explaining** how it will demonstrate relative distances between and among the sun and planets of the solar system.

Do

1. Make sure your teacher approves your plan before you proceed.
2. **Construct the model** as planned using your scale distances.
3. While constructing the model, **write** down any observations that you or other members of your group make and complete the data table in your Science Journal.
4. **Calculate** the scale distance that would be used in your model if 1 AU = 2 m.

Analyze Your Data

1. **Explain** how a scale distance is determined.
2. How much string would be required to construct a model with a scale distance 1 AU = 2 m?

Draw Conclusions

1. Was it possible to work with your scale? **Explain** why or why not.
2. Proxima Centauri, the closest star to our sun, is about 270 000 AU from the sun. Based on your scale, how much string would you need to place this star on your model?

Expected Outcome

Some students will begin with a scale that is too large. They should realize that their scale will require great lengths of string. Other scales will not be large enough to show individual planet orbits. Students should realize that a scale that allows Pluto to be placed on the string will work for all planets.

Error Analysis

If students' models are not working, review their scale. Using their scale, have them compute the distance to Pluto. This will indicate if their scale is too large.

Analyze Your Data

1. Scale distance is determined by multiplying the AU-distance of each planet by the scale selected.
2. 78.94 m or any answer near 80 m

Draw Conclusions

1. Answers will vary depending upon the scale chosen. Students may say that their scale was too large to include all planets or too small to show individual planet orbits.
2. Answers will vary, but for a scale of 1 AU = 10 cm, Proxima Centauri would be about 27 km away from the model sun.

GO Further

Have students summarize distances between and among inner and outer planets. Inner planets are closer to the sun and closer to one another. Outer planets are farther from the sun and farther apart from one another.

Assessment

Performance Using the same scale selected for their solar system models, have students place the asteroid Ceres in their models. The orbit of Ceres lies 2.77 AU from the sun. Use **Performance Assessment in the Science Classroom,** p. 29.

SECTION 22-4

Prepare

Refer to **Comets** on p. 628F.

Preplanning

Refer to the **Chapter Organizer** on pp. 628A–B.

1 Motivate

Bellringer

Before presenting the lesson, display **Section Focus Transparency 62** on the overhead projector. Use the accompanying **Focus Activity** worksheet. L2 ELL

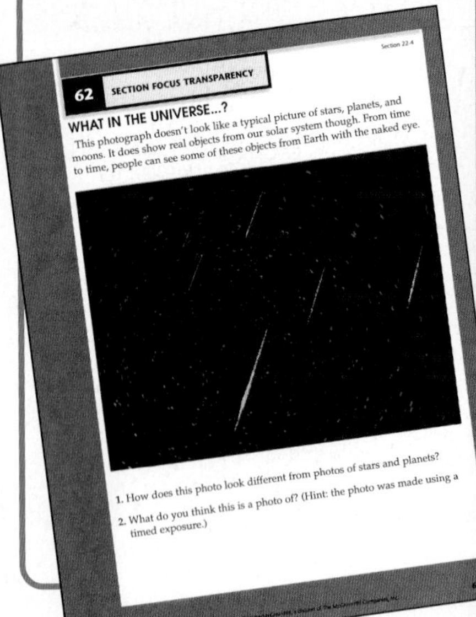

Section 22-4

62 SECTION FOCUS TRANSPARENCY

WHAT IN THE UNIVERSE...?

This photograph doesn't look like a typical picture of stars, planets, and moons. It does show real objects from our solar system though. From time to time, people can see some of these objects from Earth with the naked eye.

1. How does this photo look different from photos of stars and planets?
2. What do you think this is a photo of? (Hint: the photo was made using a timed exposure.)

62

Tying to Previous Knowledge

Remind students that the moon's surface is heavily cratered. Tell them that most craters on the moon probably formed from meteorite impacts.

Other Objects in the Solar System

What **You'll Learn**

- Where a comet comes from and how a comet develops as it approaches the sun
- Comets, meteoroids, and asteroids

Vocabulary

comet
Oort Cloud
meteor
meteorite
asteroid

Why **It's Important**

- Comets, meteoroids, and asteroids may be composed of material that formed early in the history of the solar system.

Comets

Although the planets and their moons are the most noticeable members of the sun's family, many other objects orbit the sun. Comets, meteoroids, and asteroids are other objects in the solar system.

You've probably heard of Halley's comet. A **comet** is composed of dust and rock particles mixed in with frozen water, methane, and ammonia. Halley's comet was last seen from Earth in 1986. English astronomer Edmund Halley realized that comet sightings that had taken place about every 76 years were really sightings of the same comet. This comet, which takes about 76 years to orbit the sun, was named after him. Halley's comet is just one example of the many other objects in the solar system besides the planets. The Dutch astronomer Jan Oort proposed the idea that a large collection of comets lies in a cloud that completely surrounds the solar

Figure 22-17 Comet Hale-Bopp was visible in March and April 1997.

Resource Manager

The following **Teacher Classroom Resources** can be used with Section 22-4:

Reproducible Masters

Critical Thinking/Problem Solving, p. 22 L2

Enrichment, p. 62 L3

Reinforcement, p. 62 L2

Study Guide, p. 88 L1 ELL

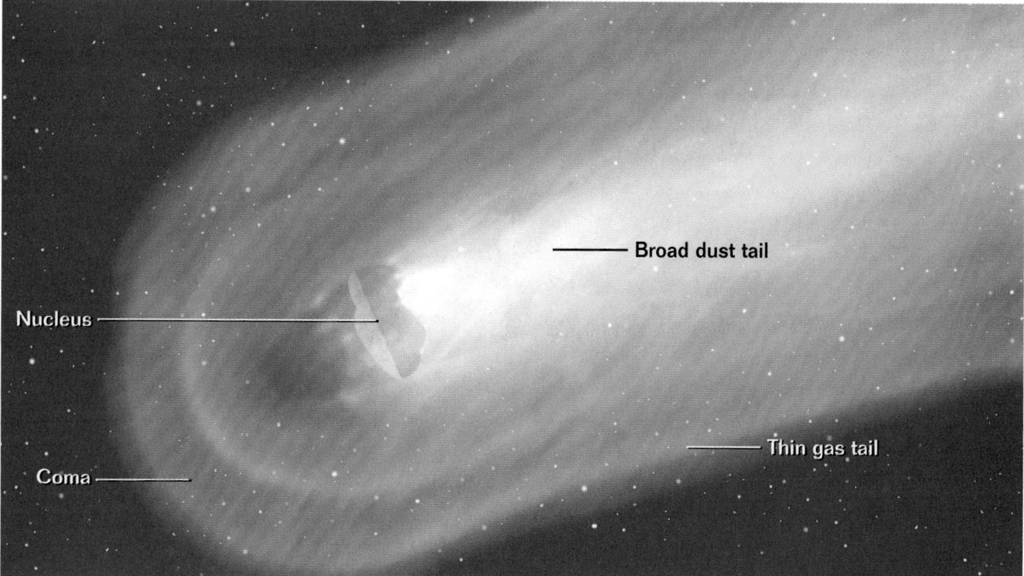

Figure 22-18 A comet consists of a nucleus, a coma, and a tail.

system. This cloud is located beyond the orbit of Pluto and is called the **Oort Cloud.** Evidence suggests that the gravity of the sun and nearby stars interacts with comets in the Oort Cloud. Comets either escape from the solar system or get captured into much smaller orbits. As mentioned earlier, another belt of comets, called the Kuiper belt, may exist near the orbit of Neptune.

On July 23, 1995, two backyard astronomers made an exciting discovery—a new comet was headed toward the sun. This comet, Comet Hale-Bopp, is larger than most that approach the sun and was the brightest comet visible from Earth in 20 years. Shown in **Figure 22-17,** it was at its brightest in March and April 1997.

Structure of Comets

The structure of a comet, shown in **Figure 22-18,** is like a large, dirty snowball or a mass of frozen ice and rock. But as the comet approaches the sun, it develops a distinctive structure. Ices of water, methane, and ammonia begin to vaporize because of the heat from the sun. Dust and bits of rock are released. The vaporized gases and released dust form a bright cloud called a coma around the nucleus, or solid part, of the comet. The solar wind pushes on the gases and released dust in the coma. These particles form a tail that always points away from the sun.

After many trips around the sun, most of the frozen ice in a comet has vaporized. All that is left are small particles that spread throughout the orbit of the original comet.

interNET CONNECTION

Visit the Glencoe Science Web Site at **www.glencoe.com/sec/science** for more information about comets.

2 Teach

interNET CONNECTION

Internet Addresses

For Internet tips, see Glencoe's **Using the Internet in the Science Classroom.**

Discussion

When students have read about comets in the text, use the following questions to guide a class discussion on comets. **What is a comet?** *an object made of dust; rocks; and frozen water, methane, and ammonia* **What is the Oort Cloud and where is it located?** *The Oort Cloud is a large collection of comets that orbits beyond Pluto.* **What is the Kuiper belt?** *a belt of comets that may exist near the orbit of Neptune*

Videodisc

STV: Solar System

Unit 4 *Smaller Objects* 3:17

21955-24475

Refer to the Teacher Guide for additional bar codes and teaching strategies.

Comet Studies Have students research the last approach of Halley's comet to Earth in 1986. Ask them to write about the five space probes sent to study the comet up close. What did these probes learn? *Five space probes were launched to study Halley's comet: the Soviet* Vega 1 *and* Vega 2; *the Japanese* Suisei *and* Sakigake; *and the European Space Agency's* Giotto. Giotto *traveled closest to the comet's nucleus. Data sent back by the probes indicate that the nucleus is black, about 15 km in length and 8 km in width, and rotates once every two days. The coma contains boulder-size rocks as well as fine dust particles.* L2

VISUAL Learning

Figure 22-19 Have students draw pictures of a meteoroid traveling through space, a meteor entering Earth's atmosphere, and a meteorite striking Earth's surface. Student drawings should be labeled.

Flex Your Brain

Use the Flex Your Brain activity to have students explore COMETS.

Answer to Reading Check

A meteorite is a meteoroid (a small, rocklike body) that strikes Earth's surface.

Using Science Words

Help students practice using science words by asking them the following questions. **What causes a meteor shower?** *A meteor shower occurs when Earth passes within the orbit of a comet that has broken apart or has left material in its orbit from passing close to the sun.* **What do meteorites tell us about the solar system?** *Meteorites come from comets or asteroids; thus, they provide data about the material that formed the solar system.* **Where else in the solar system besides the asteroid belt can asteroids be found?** *Some of the larger asteroids may have been thrown out of the belt and are scattered throughout the solar system. Some may have been captured by planets as moons.*

VISUALIZING Meteorites

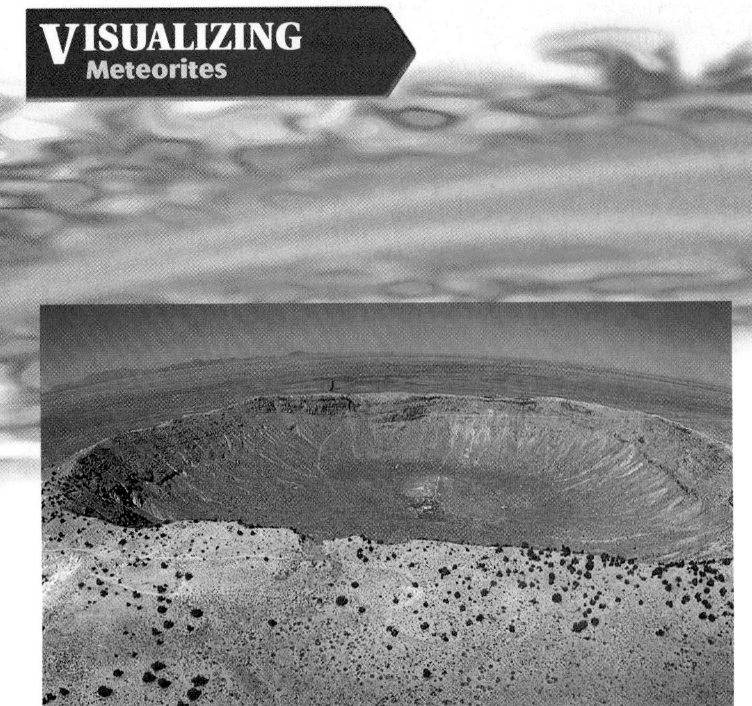

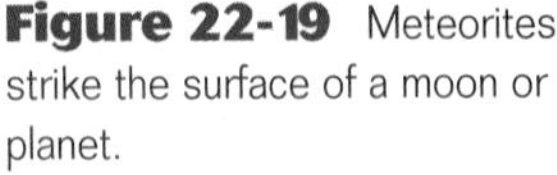

Figure 22-19 Meteorites strike the surface of a moon or planet.

A A large meteorite struck Arizona 50 000 years ago.

interNET CONNECTION

Visit the Glencoe Science Web Site at **www.glencoe.com/sec/science** for more information about meteor craters.

Meteoroids, Meteors, and Meteorites

You learned that comets tend to break up after they have passed close to the sun several times. The small pieces of the comet nucleus spread out into a loose group within the original orbit of the broken comet. These small pieces of rock moving through space are then called meteoroids.

When the path of a meteoroid crosses the position of Earth, it enters our atmosphere at between 15 and 70 km/s. Most meteoroids are so small that they are completely vaporized in Earth's atmosphere. A meteoroid that burns up in Earth's atmosphere is called a **meteor.** People often see these and call them shooting stars.

Each time Earth passes through the loose group of particles within the old orbit of a comet, many small particles of rock and dust enter the atmosphere. Because more meteors than usual are seen, this is called a meteor shower.

If the meteoroid is large enough, it may not completely burn up in Earth's atmosphere. When it strikes Earth, it is called a **meteorite.** Meteor Crater in Arizona, shown in **Figure 22-19A,** was formed when a large meteorite struck Earth about 50 000 years ago. Most meteorites are probably debris from asteroid collisions or broken-up comets, but some are from the moon and Mars. ☑

Reading Check
What is a meteorite?

Content Background

Evidence indicates that a large meteorite or asteroid collided with Earth about 66 million years ago. The collision, which occurred on what is now the Yucatan Peninsula in Mexico near the town of Chicxulub, caused tremendous destruction on a global scale. Dust, water vapor, and carbon dioxide would have been released into the air worldwide. This may have blocked the sun's rays for an extended period of time, which in turn may have caused the extinction of many organisms, including dinosaurs.

B This crater made by a meteorite is on the moon.

C A meteoroid that burns up in Earth's atmosphere is called a meteor.

Asteroids

An **asteroid** is a piece of rock similar to the material that formed into the planets. Most asteroids are located in an area between the orbits of Mars and Jupiter called the asteroid belt, shown in **Figure 22-20.** Why are they located there? The gravity of Jupiter may have kept a planet from forming in the area where the asteroid belt is now located.

Other asteroids are scattered throughout the solar system—they may have been thrown out of the belt by gravity. Some may have since been captured as moons around other planets.

Figure 22-20 The asteroid belt lies between the orbits of Mars and Jupiter.

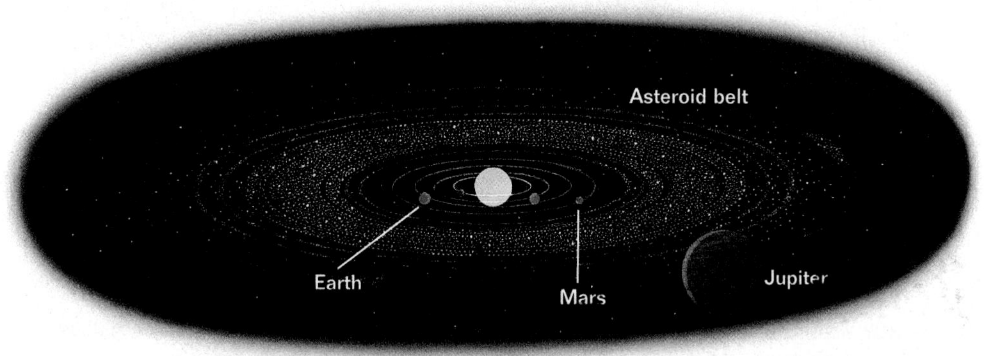

Quick Demo

Use a small fan and strips of paper fastened to a rubber ball to demonstrate why a comet's tail always points away from the sun. The wind generated by the fan is analogous to the solar wind.

3 Assess

Check for Understanding

Correcting Misconceptions

Many people incorrectly refer to meteors as shooting stars. Explain that meteors are relatively small, rocklike bodies that enter Earth's atmosphere. Stars, however, are enormous balls of gas that tend to remain in their places in space.

Reteach

Logical-Mathematical Provide students with metric rulers. Have student pairs contrast the sizes of the larger asteroids, Earth, and the moon, using a scale of 1 mm = 100 km. Have students use these data: Earth (12 756 km), the moon (3476 km), Ceres (940 km), Pallas (540 km), Vesta (510 km), and Hygeia (410 km). L2

Extension

For students who have mastered this section, use the **Reinforcement** and **Enrichment** masters.

interNET CONNECTION

Internet Addresses

For Internet tips, see Glencoe's **Using the Internet in the Science Classroom.**

Across the Curriculum

Economics Have students research the nickel mines of Sudbury Basin in Ontario, Canada. About 2 billion years ago, an asteroid 6 km in diameter collided with Earth at this location. The collision caused the formation of rich deposits of nickel, cobalt, and platinum. L2

4 Close

Proficiency Prep

Use this quiz to check students' recall of section content.

1. **What is a comet?** *an object in space composed of dust and rock particles mixed with frozen water, methane, and ammonia*
2. **What do we call the large collection of comets beyond Pluto's orbit?** *Oort Cloud*
3. **What does a meteoroid become when it burns up in Earth's atmosphere?** *meteor*

Section Assessment

1. As a comet approaches the sun, thermal energy causes some of the comet to vaporize. Solar wind pushes on these gases to form a tail on the comet.
2. a crater
3. Comets are collections of frozen gas and rocky particles that generally travel in elliptical orbits around the sun. Meteoroids are usually small fragments of rock that move independently through space. Asteroids generally orbit the sun between Mars and Jupiter. Their sizes can range from small particles to objects as large as 1000 km in diameter.
4. **Think Critically** dust and rock particles mixed with ice, methane, and ammonia; outer planets

Asteroid Size

The sizes of the asteroids in the asteroid belt range from tiny particles to 940 km. Ceres is the largest and the first one discovered. The next three in size are Pallas (523 km), Vesta (501 km), and Juno (244 km). Two asteroids, Gaspra and Ida, were photographed by *Galileo* on its way to Jupiter, as shown in **Figure 22-21.**

Comets, meteoroids, and asteroids are probably composed of material that formed early in the history of the solar system. Scientists study the structure and composition of these space objects in order to better understand what the solar system may have been like long ago. Understanding what the early solar system was like could help scientists to better understand the formation of Earth and its relationship to other objects in the solar system.

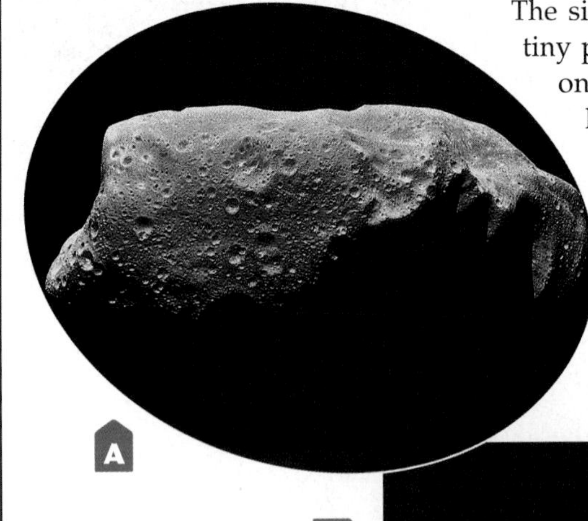

A

B

Figure 22-21 The asteroid Ida (A) is about 56 km long. Gaspra (B) is about 20 km long.

Section Assessment

1. How does a comet's tail form as it approaches the sun?
2. What type of feature might be formed on Earth if a large meteorite reached its surface?
3. Describe differences among comets, meteoroids, and asteroids.
4. **Think Critically:** What is the chemical composition of comets? Are comets more similar to the inner or the outer planets?
5. **Skill Builder**
   Inferring Scientists can learn a lot about a planet's history by studying its impact craters. Do the **Chapter 22 Skill Activity** on page 720 to infer how scientific illustrations can be used to determine the ages of impact craters.

The asteroid belt contains many objects—from tiny particles to objects 940 km in diameter. In your Science Journal, describe how mining the asteroids for valuable minerals might be accomplished.

Encourage students to be as creative as possible but to include ideas that are scientifically reasonable and possible to accomplish.

Assessment

Oral Assess students' abilities to infer. Ask students to explain why a comet tail points away from the sun. Use **Performance Assessment in the Science Classroom,** p. 17.

Science & Society 

Mission to Mars

Scientists are currently developing plans for further exploration of Mars. But even at its closest, Mars is 55 million km away from Earth, a distance that would take astronauts three years to travel round-trip. Given the long flight, not to mention conditions astronauts would face living on Mars, a journey to the Red Planet would be full of risks. This raises a question: Should humans or robots be sent to explore Mars?

Risks to Humans

Getting to and from Mars would take a toll on the human body. In the near-zero gravity of outer space, bones lose calcium and gradually become weaker. Muscles lose their strength as well, because they don't have to work against gravity to support and move body parts. Furthermore, in a weightless environment, body fluids don't flow downward as they do on Earth. Unusual circulation of body fluids can interfere with kidney function and lead to dehydration.

Assuming humans survived the long flight to Mars in good health, they would face other challenges upon arrival. To explore Mars properly, a team of astronauts would probably have to live on the planet for months, even years. The NASA painting, left, shows a module that could house explorers. Such a structure would have to withstand the Martian environment and protect astronauts from high levels of solar radiation.

The Case for Robots

Because of the many risks a Mars mission would pose for humans, some scientists suggest sending specialized robots that could operate equipment and carry out scientific experiments. These robots would be equipped with artificial senses that would allow researchers on Earth to experience the planet's surface in a way second only to being there in person. However, radio signals sent back and forth between robots on Mars and operators on Earth would take up to 20 minutes to travel each way. Scientists are working to solve this problem in the hope that extensive exploration of Mars will soon be a reality—by people or by machines.

Science JOURNAL

How do you think Mars should be further explored? Write a proposal to your class explaining how you would explore Mars.

Science & Society

Teaching Strategies

Have students research the achievements and problems experienced by former Soviet cosmonauts, current Russian cosmonauts, and American astronauts aboard the *Mir* space station.

Science JOURNAL Answers will vary. Students may note that if humans travel to Mars, they could be protected from radiation with extra shielding on the spacecraft. Also, one large shield could be deployed in space to protect astronauts from solar radiation. Bone and muscle weakening could be reduced by producing an artificial gravity field in the spacecraft.

If robots are sent, they could continually search the surface of Mars for signs of life or past life and send information to the orbiting mother ship. If certain rocks appear to contain evidence of current or past life, samples could be loaded on a robotic ship and sent back to Earth orbit, where they could be retrieved by the space shuttle.

For More Information

Refer to *The Case for Mars* by Robert Zubrin (1996), Touchstone (Simon & Schuster).

Content Background

If implemented, the Mars Direct plan for a crewed mission to Mars will begin with the launch of an uncrewed Earth return vehicle (ERV) to Mars. Once there, the ERV would produce fuel (methane and oxygen) from the Martian atmosphere for the return trip. Next a piloted habitation module would be sent to Mars. Once there, astronauts would live and work in the habitation module, and return to Earth in the ERV. When the first humans arrive on Mars, a new ERV would be sent along to start producing fuel for the next piloted landing.

Chapter 22 Reviewing Main Ideas

Reviewing Main Ideas can be used to preview, review, reteach, and condense chapter content.

Preview

Linguistic Have students try to answer the questions in their Science Journals. Use student answers as a source for discussion throughout the chapter.

Review

Interpersonal Have students answer the questions on separate pieces of paper and compare their answers with those of other students in the class.

Reteach

Visual-Spatial Have students look at the illustrations on these pages. Ask them to describe details that support the main ideas of the chapter found in the statement for each illustration.

00:00 OUT OF TIME?

Auditory-Musical If time does not permit teaching the entire chapter, use the information on these pages along with the chapter Audiocassettes to present the material in a condensed format.

Chapter 22 Reviewing Main Ideas

For a **preview** of this chapter, study this Reviewing Main Ideas before you read the chapter. After you have studied this chapter, you can use the Reviewing Main Ideas to **review** the chapter.

The Glencoe MindJogger, Audiocassettes, and CD-ROM provide additional opportunities for review.

Section 22-1 THE SOLAR SYSTEM

Early astronomers thought that the planets, the moon, the sun, and the stars were embedded in separate spheres that rotated around Earth. The sun-centered model of the **solar system** states that the sun is the center of the solar system. Using a telescope, Galileo discovered evidence that supported the sun-centered model. Later, Kepler discovered that the planets orbit the sun in elliptical orbits, not circles. ***What type of evidence did Galileo discover that indicated the sun-centered model was correct?***

Section 22-2 THE INNER PLANETS

The **inner planets,** in increasing distance from the sun are Mercury, Venus, Earth, and Mars. The moonlike **Mercury** has craters and cliffs on its surface. **Venus** has a dense atmosphere of carbon dioxide and sulfuric acid. On **Earth,** water exists in three states. **Mars** appears red due to the iron oxide content of its weathered rocks. Recent studies by *Pathfinder* indicate that Mars's surface once had large amounts of water flowing over it. ***Venus and Earth are similar in size and mass. Why, then, are their surface characteristics so different?***

Cultural Diversity

Planetary Wisdom Some of the planets are visible in Earth's night sky and have been used to explain or chart the course of life on Earth. Many early sky watchers interpreted planets appearing in conjunction (appearing to move close to each other) as an important sign. In ancient India, periodic destruction of the universe by flooding or conflagration was marked by the conjunction of Jupiter and Saturn. Jupiter passes Saturn in the night sky every 20 years. The Chaldeans believed that if all seven planets were in conjunction in Cancer, the universe would end in deluge. If all seven conjoined in Capricorn, the universe would end in fire.

Reading Check ✓

Locate a legend, myth, or folktale from another culture that explains the origin of all or part of the solar system. Share it with the class.

Section 22-3 THE OUTER PLANETS

Faint rings and 16 moons orbit the gaseous **Jupiter.** Jupiter's Great Red Spot is a high-pressure storm generated by huge thunderstorms in Jupiter's atmosphere. **Saturn** is made mostly of gas and has pronounced rings. **Uranus** is a large, gaseous planet with many moons and several rings. **Neptune** is similar to Uranus in size, composition, and stormlike features. **Pluto** has a thin, changing atmosphere, and its surface is icy rock. ***Why would the average densities of the four large, outer planets be so low when compared with the average densities of the inner planets?***

Section 22-4 OTHER OBJECTS IN THE SOLAR SYSTEM

As a **comet** approaches the sun, vaporized gases form a bright coma around the comet's nucleus and solar wind forms a tail that points away from the sun. Meteoroids form when asteroids collide, when comets break up, or when **meteorites** collide with the moon or other planets. An **asteroid** is a piece of rock usually found in the asteroid belt. ***Why does the tail of a comet always point away from the sun?***

Answers to Questions

Section 22-1

The Solar System Using a telescope, Galileo discovered that Venus goes through phases indicating that it orbits the sun.

Section 22-2

The Inner Planets Venus's entire surface is blanketed by dense clouds made up mostly of CO_2. This and other gases led Venus to develop a "runaway" greenhouse effect, raising its surface temperature to 470°C.

Section 22-3

The Outer Planets The four large, outer planets are composed mainly of gases. Even though these planets have solid rocky cores, most of their size is composed of gas. This produces a low average density.

Section 22-4

Other Objects in the Solar System The tail of a comet is made of gas and dust from the comet's coma which has been pushed outward away from the sun by solar wind.

GLENCOE TECHNOLOGY

CD-ROM

Glencoe Science Voyages Interactive CD-ROM

Chapter Summaries and Quizzes

Have students read the Chapter Summary then take the Chapter Quiz to determine whether they have mastered chapter content.

Assessment

Portfolio Encourage students to place in their portfolios one or two items of what they consider to be their best work. Examples include:

- Problem Solving, p. 638
- MiniLab, p. 644
- Activity 22-2, pp. 648–649 P

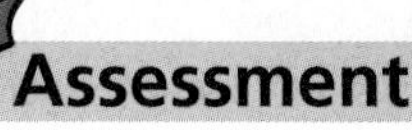

Performance Additional performance assessments may be found in **Performance Assessment** and **Science Integration Activities.** Performance Task Assessment Lists and rubrics for evaluating these activities can be found in Glencoe's **Performance Assessment in the Science Classroom.**

Chapter 22 Assessment

Using Vocabulary

1. An asteroid is a rock similar to the material that formed the planets. A comet is composed of dust and rock particles mixed with ice, methane, and ammonia.
2. The inner planets—Mercury, Venus, Earth, and Mars—are closest to the sun. The outer planets—Jupiter, Saturn, Uranus, Neptune, and Pluto—are farthest from the sun.
3. Meteors are meteoroids—small pieces of rock—that burn up in Earth's atmosphere. Meteorites are meteoroids that strike Earth's surface.
4. The Great Red Spot is a storm in Jupiter's atmosphere. The Oort Cloud is a collection of comets located beyond the orbit of Pluto.
5. Neptune is usually the eighth planet from the sun. Uranus is the seventh planet.

interNET CONNECTION To reinforce chapter vocabulary, use the **Study Guide for Content Mastery** booklet. Also available are activities for **Glencoe Science Voyages** on the Glencoe Science Web Site. **www.glencoe.com/sec/science**

Checking Concepts

6. B	11. C
7. C	12. C
8. B	13. B
9. D	14. A
10. D	15. B

Thinking Critically

16. The greenhouse effect on Venus is much greater than that on Earth because the clouds on Venus are very dense and the amount of carbon dioxide in the air is greater. The CO_2 retains the heat.
17. In general, more massive planets have more satellites.
18. The extreme heat and the dense, gaseous atmospheres would probably destroy any space probe before it could reach either of the planets' surfaces.
19. Iron contained in the weathered rocks combines with oxygen in the presence of water to produce iron oxide. Channels appear to have been carved by flowing water. Cavern walls show layering of rock. The northern ice cap is composed partly of ice.
20. Any planet orbiting the sun inside the orbit of the planet you are observing from appears to go through phases. The orbit of Venus is inside the orbit of Earth.

Chapter 22 Assessment

Using Vocabulary

a. asteroid	k. meteorite
b. astronomical unit	l. Neptune
c. comet	m. Oort Cloud
d. Earth	n. outer planet
e. Great Red Spot	o. Pluto
f. inner planet	p. Saturn
g. Jupiter	q. solar system
h. Mars	r. Uranus
i. Mercury	s. Venus
j. meteor	

Distinguish between the terms in each of the following pairs.

1. asteroid, comet
2. inner planet, outer planet
3. meteor, meteorite
4. Great Red Spot, Oort Cloud
5. Neptune, Uranus

Checking Concepts

Choose the word or phrase that best answers the question.

6. Who proposed a sun-centered solar system?
   A) Ptolemy C) Galileo
   B) Copernicus D) Oort
7. How does the sun produce energy?
   A) magnetism C) nuclear fusion
   B) nuclear fission D) the greenhouse effect
8. What is the shape of planetary orbits?
   A) circles C) squares
   B) ellipses D) rectangles
9. Which planet has extreme temperatures because it has essentially no atmosphere?
   A) Earth C) Mars
   B) Jupiter D) Mercury
10. Water is a solid, liquid, and gas on which planet?
   A) Pluto C) Saturn
   B) Uranus D) Earth
11. Where is the largest known volcano in the solar system?
   A) Earth C) Mars
   B) Jupiter D) Uranus
12. What do scientists call a rock that strikes Earth's surface?
   A) asteroid C) meteorite
   B) comet D) meteoroid
13. Which planet has a complex ring system made of hundreds of ringlets?
   A) Pluto C) Uranus
   B) Saturn D) Mars
14. Which planet has a magnetic pole tilted 60 degrees?
   A) Uranus C) Jupiter
   B) Earth D) Pluto
15. How does the tail of a comet always point?
   A) toward the sun C) toward Earth
   B) away from the sun D) away from the Oort Cloud

Thinking Critically

16. Why is the surface temperature on Venus so much higher than that on Earth?
17. Describe the relationship between the mass of a planet and the number of satellites it has.
18. Why are probe landings on Jupiter or Saturn unlikely events?
19. What evidence suggests that water is or once was present on Mars?
20. An observer on Earth can watch Venus go through phases much like Earth's moon does. Explain why this is so.

Assessment

Developing Skills

If you need help, refer to the Skill Handbook.

21. Concept Mapping: Complete the concept map on this page to show how a comet changes as it travels through space.

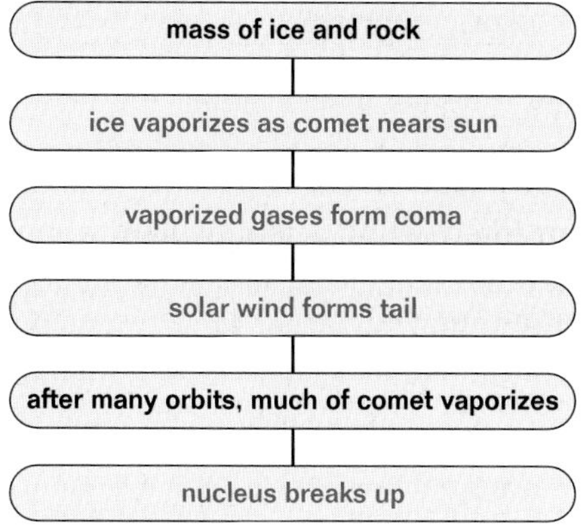

mass of ice and rock
ice vaporizes as comet nears sun
vaporized gases form coma
solar wind forms tail
after many orbits, much of comet vaporizes
nucleus breaks up

22. Hypothesizing: Mercury is the closest planet to the sun, yet it does not reflect much of the sun's light. What can you say about Mercury's color?

23. Sequencing: Arrange the following planets in order from the planet with the most natural satellites to the one with the fewest: Earth, Jupiter, Saturn, Neptune, Uranus, and Mars.

24. Making and Using Tables: Make a table that summarizes the main characteristics of each planet in the solar system.

25. Measuring in SI: The Great Red Spot of Jupiter is about 40 000 km long and about 12 000 km wide. What is its approximate area in km^2?

THE PRINCETON REVIEW

Test-Taking Tip

Get to the Root of Things If you don't know a word's meaning, you can still get an idea of its meaning if you focus on its roots, prefixes, and suffixes. For instance, words that start with *non-, un-, a-, dis-,* and *in-* generally reverse what the rest of the word means.

Test Practice

Use these questions to test your Science Proficiency.

1. Earth is probably the only planet in our solar system on which life exists. Which of the following statements **BEST** explains why this is true?
   A) Earth is the only planet on which water exists in all three states.
   B) Earth has frozen ice caps at its poles.
   C) Earth has carbon dioxide in its atmosphere.
   D) Earth has an atmosphere.
2. Both Copernicus and Kepler proposed a model of the solar system. What was the major difference between the two models?
   A) Copernicus's model had the sun in the center. Kepler's model had Earth in the center.
   B) Copernicus's model included Saturn. Kepler's model did not.
   C) Copernicus's model included circular orbits for the planets. Kepler's model included elliptical orbits for the planets.
   D) Copernicus's model showed the moon as a planet. Kepler's model showed the moon as a satellite of Earth.

THE PRINCETON REVIEW

Test Practice

The Test-Taking Tip was written by The Princeton Review, the nation's leader in test preparation.

1. A
2. C

Developing Skills

21. See student page.
22. Mercury is dark in color, and it doesn't reflect much of the light that reaches its surface.
23. Saturn, Uranus, Jupiter, Neptune, Mars, Earth
24. Student tables should include number of satellites, type of atmospheres, and other planetary characteristics.
25. area = length × width = 40 000 km × 12 000 km = 480 000 000 km^2

Bonus Question

Planetary orbits are ellipses, not circles. Based on the models of planetary orbits developed in Activity 22-1, how would you draw an orbit that is extremely elliptical? *Using one nail, stretch the string to a distance equal to the radius of the circular orbit. To draw an extremely elliptical orbit, place two nails far apart.*

Assessment Resources

The **Test Practice Workbook** provides students with practice in the format, concepts, and critical-thinking skills tested in standardized exams.

Reproducible Masters

Chapter Review, pp. 43–44 L2
Performance Assessment, p. 36 L2
Assessment, pp. 97–100 L2

Glencoe Technology

Chapter Review Software
Computer Test Bank
MindJogger Videoquiz

Chapter 23 Stars and Galaxies

Section	Objectives	Activities/Features
Chapter Opener		**Explore Activity:** Model the Universe, p. 661
23-1 Stars 1 Session ½ Block	1. **Explain** why the positions of the constellations change throughout the year. 2. **Compare** and **contrast** absolute magnitude and apparent magnitude. 3. **Describe** how parallax is used to determine distance.	**Problem Solving:** Star Light, Star Bright, p. 664 **MiniLab:** Observing Star Patterns, p. 665 **Skill Builder:** Recognizing Cause and Effect, p. 666 **Using Computers,** p. 666
23-2 The Sun 3½ Sessions 1½ Blocks	4. **Describe** how energy is produced in the sun. 5. **Recognize** that sunspots, prominences, and solar flares are related. 6. **Explain** why our sun is considered an average star and how it differs from stars in binary systems.	**Skill Builder:** Interpreting Scientific Illustrations, p. 670 **Science Journal,** p. 670 **Activity 23-1:** Sunspots, p. 671
23-3 Evolution of Stars 1 Session ½ Block	7. **Diagram** how stars are classified. 8. **Relate** the temperature of a star to its color. 9. **Outline** the evolution of a star.	**Physics Integration,** p. 674 **Chemistry Integration,** p. 675 **Skill Builder:** Sequencing, p. 677 **Using Math,** p. 677 **Reading and Writing in Science:** Dreamtime Down Under, p. 678
23-4 Galaxies and the Universe 3½ Sessions 1½ Blocks	10. **List** the three main types of galaxies. 11. **Identify** several characteristics of the Milky Way Galaxy. 12. **Relate** how the big bang theory explains the observed Doppler shifts of galaxies.	**MiniLab:** Measuring Distance in Space, p. 682 **Skill Builder:** Predicting, p. 685 **Science Journal,** p. 685 **Activity 23-2:** Measuring Parallax, pp. 686–687 **Field Guide to Astronomy,** pp. 688–691

The number of recommended single-period sessions — The number of recommended blocks
One session and one-half block are allowed for chapter review and assessment.

Activity Materials

Explore	Activities	MiniLabs
p. 661 balloon, clothespin, felt-tip marker, string, ruler,	p. 671 books, cardboard, clipboard, drawing paper, small refracting telescope, small tripod, scissors pp. 686–687 meterstick, metric ruler, masking tape, pencil	p. 665 no materials needed p. 682 metric ruler, drawing compass, paper, pencil

Need Materials? Contact Science Kit at 1-800-828-7777 or at www.sciencekit.com on the Internet.
For alternate materials, see the activity on the listed page.

Standards		Reproducible Resources	Technology
National	State/Local	Test Practice Workbooks are available for use with each chapter.	English and Spanish audiocassettes are available for use with each section.
National Content Standards: UCP3, B1, B3, D3		**Activity Worksheets,** p. 129 **Enrichment,** p. 63 **Home Involvement,** p. 28 **Laboratory Manual,** pp. 131–132 **Laboratory Manual,** pp. 133–135 **Reinforcement,** p. 63 **Study Guide,** p. 89	**Section Focus Transparency 63** **Glencoe Science Voyages Interactive CD-ROM**
National Content Standards: A2, B3, D1, D3, F1, G3		**Activity Worksheets,** pp. 125–126 **Enrichment,** p. 64 **Multicultural Connections,** pp. 45–46 **Reinforcement,** p. 64	**Section Focus Transparency 64** **Science Integration Transparency 23** **Internet Connection,** p. 669
National Content Standards: UCP3, A2, B1, B3, C1, E2, G1, G3		**Critical Thinking/Problem Solving,** p. 23 **Enrichment,** p. 65 **Reinforcement,** p. 65	**Section Focus Transparency 65** **Teaching Transparency 45** **Teaching Transparency 46**
National Content Standards: UCP2, UCP3, A1, B1, B2, D3, G1, G2		**Activity Worksheets,** pp. 127–128, 130 **Enrichment,** p. 66 **Reinforcement,** p. 66 **Study Guide,** pp. 90–92	**Section Focus Transparency 66** **National Geographic Society: STV** **Internet Connection,** p. 683 **Internet Connection,** p. 689 **The Infinite Voyage Series**

Key to Teaching Strategies

The following designations will help you decide which activities are appropriate for your students.

L1 Level 1 activities should be appropriate for students with learning difficulties.

L2 Level 2 activities should be within the ability range of all students.

L3 Level 3 activities are designed for above-average students.

ELL ELL activities should be within the ability range of English Language Learners.

COOP LEARN Cooperative Learning activities are designed for small group work.

P These strategies represent student products that can be placed into a best-work portfolio.

Multiple Learning Styles logos, as described on page 61T, are used throughout to indicate strategies that address different learning styles.

Assessment Resources

Chapter Review, pp. 45–46
Assessment, pp. 101–104
Performance Assessment in the Science Classroom (PASC)
MindJogger Videoquiz
Alternate Assessment in the Science Classroom
Performance Assessment, p. 37
Chapter Review Software
Computer Test Bank

Chapter 23 Stars and Galaxies

This is a representation of key blackline masters available in the Teacher Classroom Resources. See Resource Manager boxes within the chapter for additional information.

Transparencies

Section Focus Transparencies

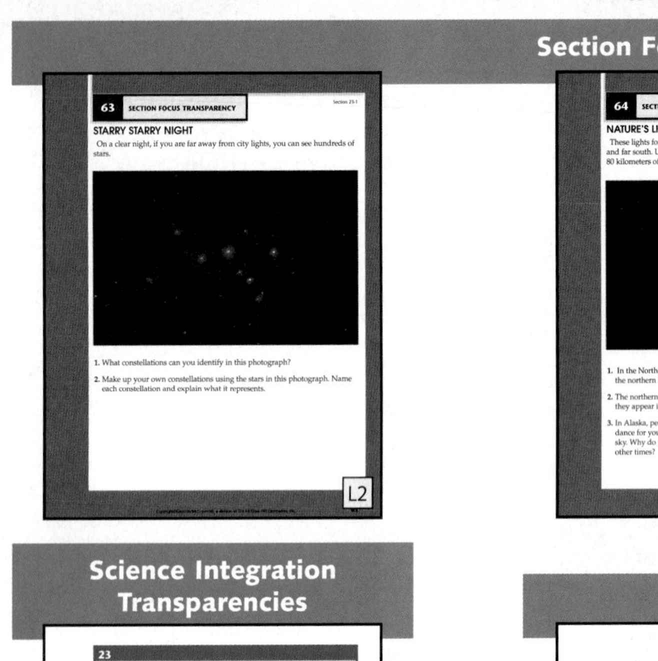

63 SECTION FOCUS TRANSPARENCY

STARRY STARRY NIGHT

On a clear night, if you are far away from city lights, you can see hundreds of stars.

1. What constellations can you identify in this photograph?
2. Make up your own constellations using the stars in this photograph. Name each constellation and explain what it represents.

L2

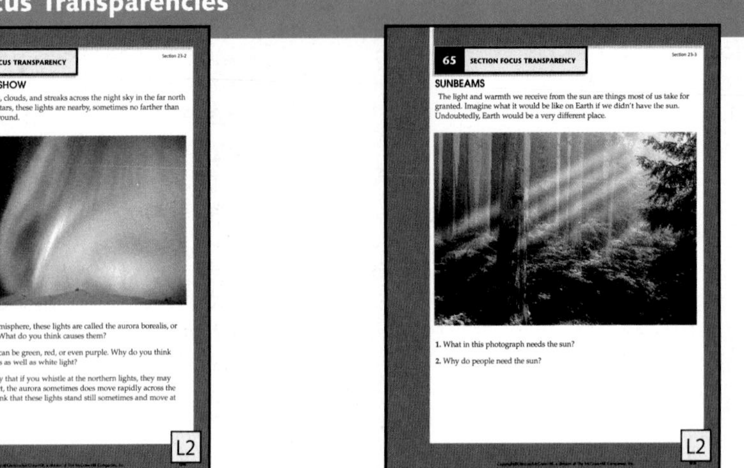

64 SECTION FOCUS TRANSPARENCY

NATURE'S LIGHT SHOW

These lights form arcs, clouds, and streaks across the night sky in the far north and far south. Unlike stars, these lights are nearby, sometimes no farther than 80 kilometers off the ground.

1. In the Northern Hemisphere, these lights are called the aurora borealis, or the northern lights. What do you think causes them?
2. The northern lights can be green, red, or even purple. Why do you think they appear in colors as well as white light?
3. In Alaska, people say that if you whistle at the northern lights, they may dance for you. In fact, the aurora sometimes does move rapidly across the sky. Why do you think that these lights stand still sometimes and move at other times?

L2

65 SECTION FOCUS TRANSPARENCY

SUNBEAMS

The light and warmth we receive from the sun are things most of us take for granted. Imagine what it would be like on Earth if we didn't have the sun. Undoubtedly, Earth would be a very different place.

1. What in this photograph needs the sun?
2. Why do people need the sun?

L2

Science Integration Transparencies

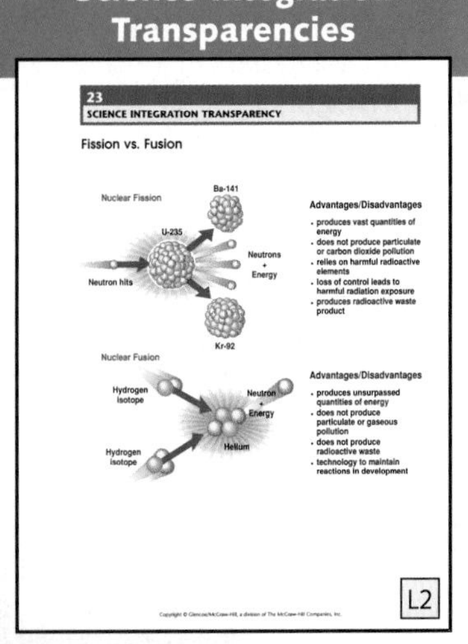

23 SCIENCE INTEGRATION TRANSPARENCY

Fission vs. Fusion

L2

Teaching Transparencies

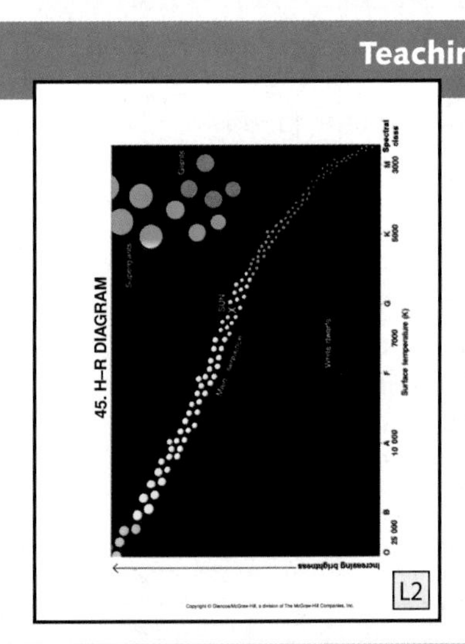

L2

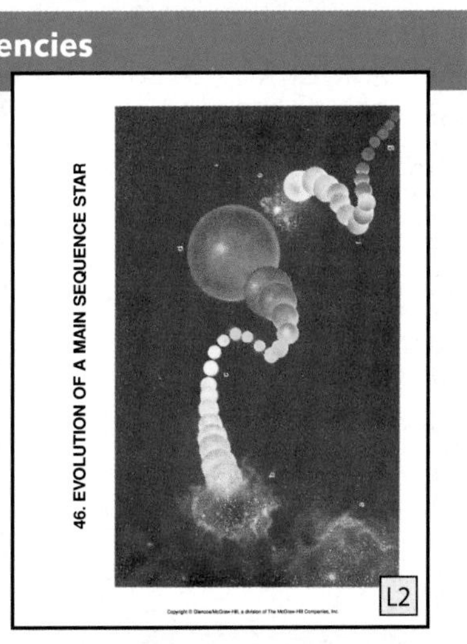

L2

Meeting Different Ability Levels

Study Guide for Content Mastery

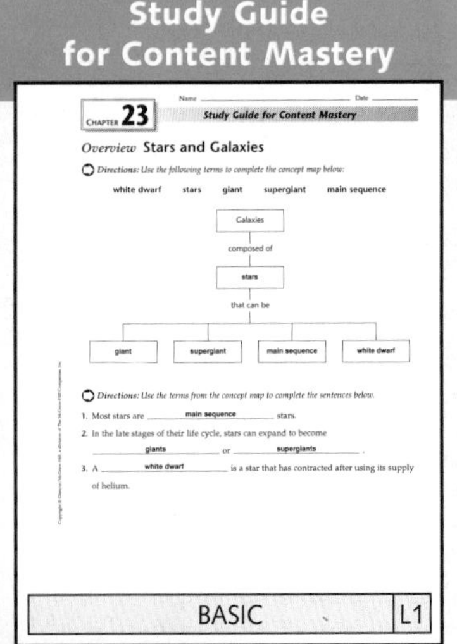

CHAPTER 23 Study Guide for Content Mastery

Overview Stars and Galaxies

Directions: Use the following terms to complete the concept map below:

white dwarf stars giant supergiant main sequence

Directions: Use the terms from the concept map to complete the sentences below.

1. Most stars are main sequence stars.
2. In the late stages of their life cycle, stars can expand to become giants or supergiants.
3. A white dwarf is a star that has contracted after using its supply of helium.

BASIC L1

Reinforcement

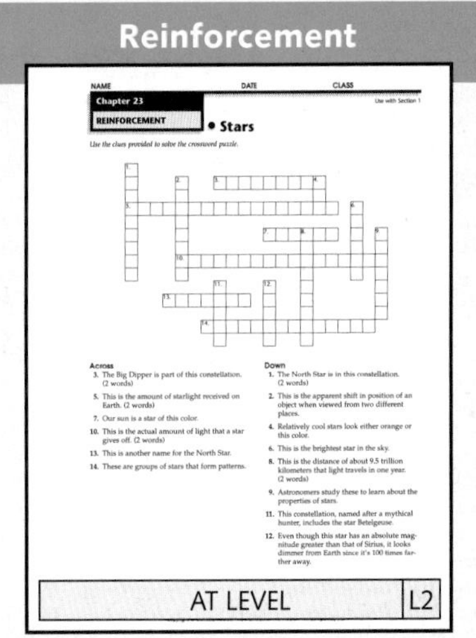

Chapter 23 REINFORCEMENT • Stars

Across
3. The Big Dipper is part of this constellation. (2 words)
5. This is the amount of starlight received on Earth. (2 words)
7. Our sun is a star of this color.
10. This is the actual amount of light that a star gives off. (2 words)
13. This is another name for the North Star.
14. These are groups of stars that form patterns.

Down
1. The North Star is in this constellation. (2 words)
2. This is the apparent shift in position of an object when viewed from two different places.
4. Relatively cool stars look either orange or this color.
6. This is the brightest star in the sky.
8. This is the distance of about 9.5 trillion kilometers that light travels in one year. (2 words)
9. Astronomers study these to learn about the properties of stars.
11. This constellation, named after a mythical hunter, includes the star Betelgeuse.
12. Even though this star has an absolute magnitude greater than that of Sirius, it looks dimmer from Earth since it's 100 times farther away.

AT LEVEL L2

Enrichment Worksheets

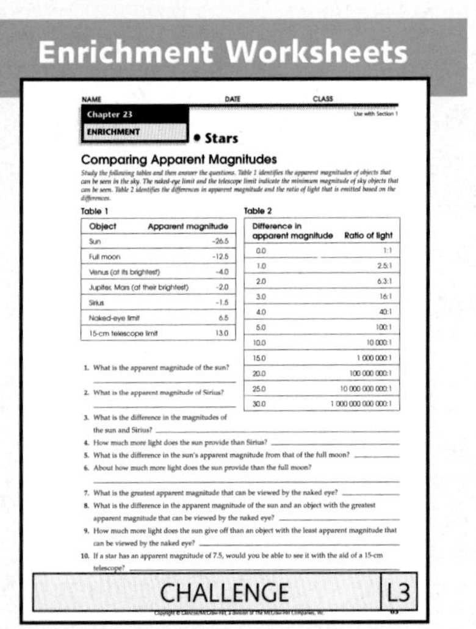

Chapter 23 ENRICHMENT • Stars

Comparing Apparent Magnitudes

Table 1

Object	Apparent magnitude
Sun	-26.5
Full moon	-12.5
Venus (at its brightest)	-4.0
Jupiter, Mars (at their brightest)	-2.0
Sirius	-1.5
Naked-eye limit	6.5
15-cm telescope limit	13.0

Table 2

Difference in apparent magnitude	Ratio of light
0.0	1:1
1.0	2.5:1
2.0	6.3:1
3.0	16:1
4.0	40:1
5.0	100:1
10.0	10 000:1
15.0	1 000 000:1
20.0	100 000 000:1
25.0	10 000 000 000:1
30.0	1 000 000 000 000:1

1. What is the apparent magnitude of the sun?
2. What is the apparent magnitude of Sirius?
3. What is the difference in the magnitudes of the sun and Sirius?
4. How much more light does the sun provide than Sirius?
5. What is the difference in the sun's apparent magnitude from that of the full moon?
6. About how much more light does the sun provide than the full moon?
7. What is the greatest apparent magnitude that can be viewed by the naked eye?
8. What is the difference in the apparent magnitude of the sun and an object with the greatest apparent magnitude that can be viewed by the naked eye?
9. How much more light does the sun give off than an object with the least apparent magnitude that can be viewed by the naked eye?
10. If a star has an apparent magnitude of 7.5, would you be able to see it with the aid of a 15-cm telescope?

CHALLENGE L3

Hands-on Activities

Activity Worksheets

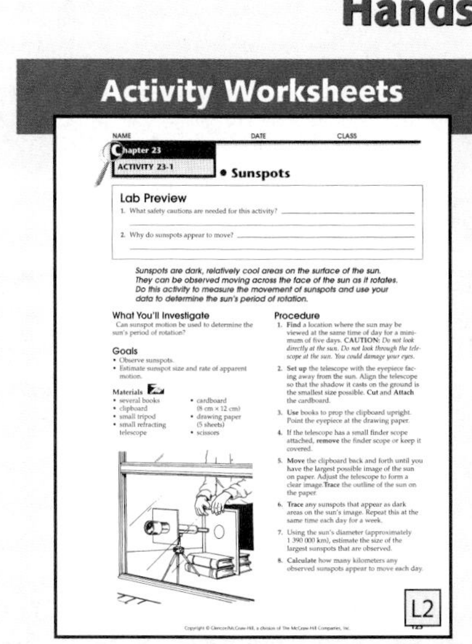

Lab Manual

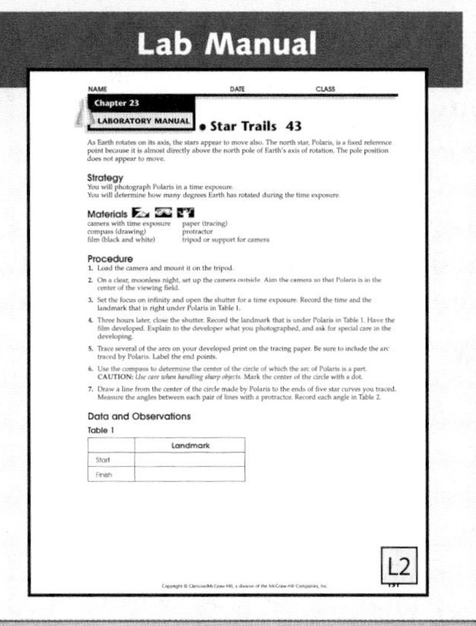

Accessibility

Spanish Resources

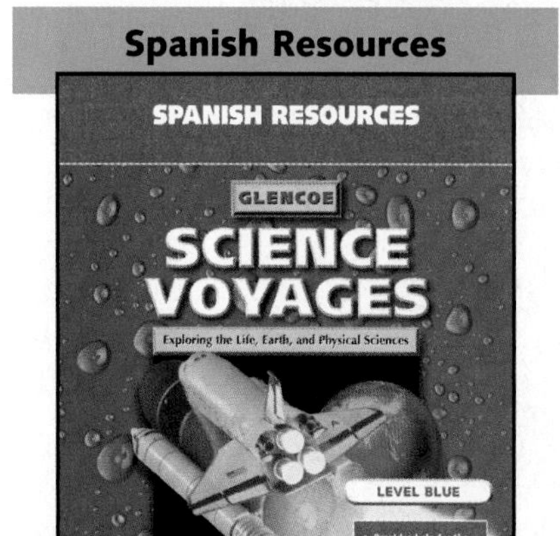

Assessment

Performance Assessment

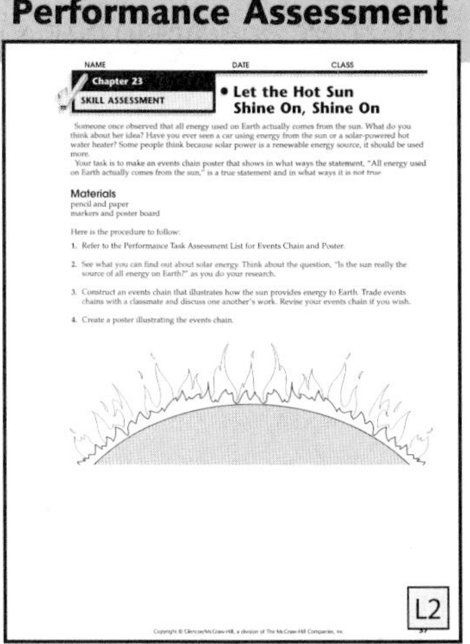

Chapter Review

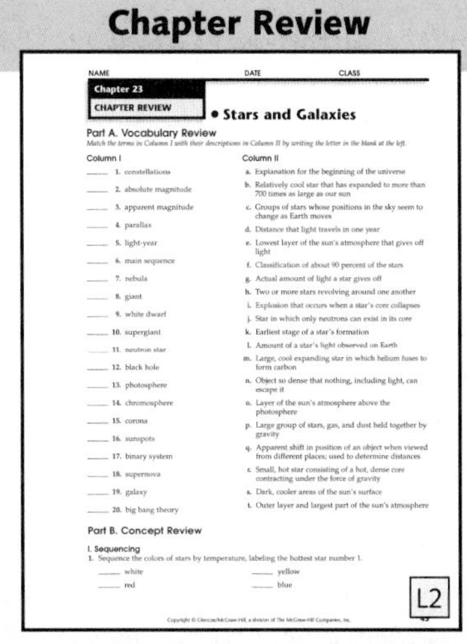

Assessment

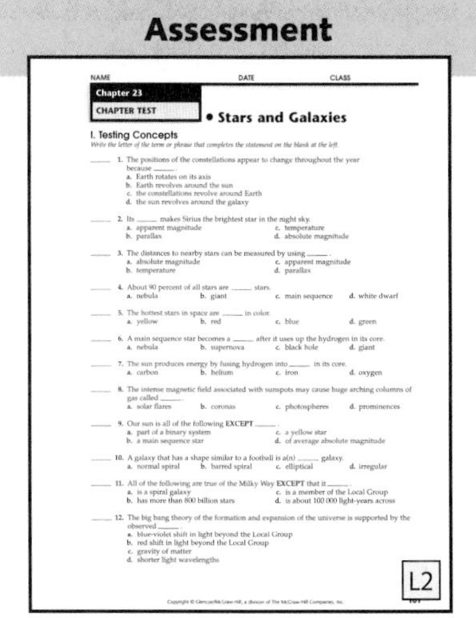

Test Practice Workbook

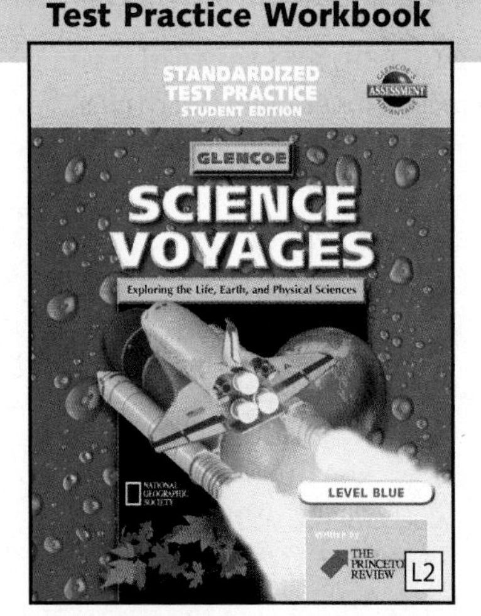

Extending Content

Critical Thinking/ Problem Solving

Multicultural Connections

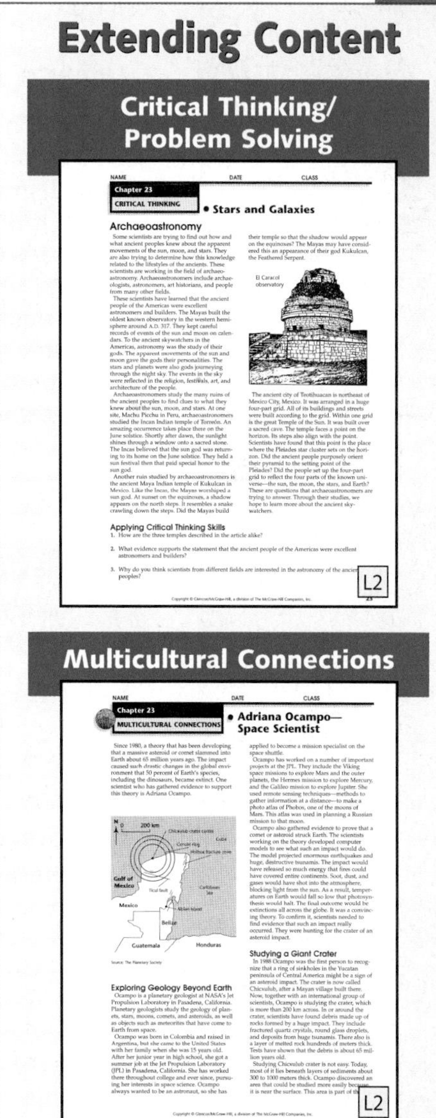

Helping You Prepare

Stars (Section 23-1)

The absolute magnitude of a star is affected by its size and its temperature. The apparent magnitude of a star is affected by its size, its temperature, and its distance. If the absolute and apparent magnitudes of a star are known, its distance from Earth can be determined.

Clouds of gas and dust in space, called nebulas, can obscure starlight, reducing a star's apparent magnitude. Interstellar nebulas make stars in large sections of our galaxy, the Milky Way, so low in apparent magnitude that they cannot be seen. The gas and dust also make stars appear more reddish. The interstellar material tends to be opaque to light of shorter wavelengths, allowing longer wavelengths of red light to pass through.

Surface of the Sun (Section 23-2)

Granulation on the surface of the sun was first seen by Galileo. He thought the phenomena resembled grains of wheat and thus called the features granules. Granules on the sun's surface are the tops of large convection cells that extend deep into the sun. The presence of these granules is evidence that convection currents do exist inside the sun, just under the photosphere. Each granule measures about 1000 km across. They form as hot gases are forced upward by surrounding denser gases. The hot gases flow toward the surface, emit energy, cool, and sink back toward the sun's interior.

GLENCOE TECHNOLOGY

Glencoe Science Voyages Interactive CD-ROM

Chapter Summaries

Use the Chapter Summary to introduce, teach, or review chapter material.

Solar Activity (Section 23-2)

Solar activity affects the circulation of Earth's atmosphere. Thus, there appears to be a correlation between the sun's 22-year activity cycle (magnetic reversals occur with each 11-year activity cycle; thus, the total cycle is 22 years) and droughts on Earth. Solar activity can affect Earth's climate over a long period of time. The Little Ice Age that occurred in northern Europe during the late 1600s occurred during the Maunder minimum, a time when the sun had very few sunspots.

NATIONAL GEOGRAPHIC — Teacher's Corner

Products Available from Glencoe

To order the following products for use with this chapter, call Glencoe at 1-800-334-7344:

CD-ROM

NGS PictureShow: Stars and Galaxies

Transparency Set

NGS PicturePack: Stars and Galaxies

Products Available from National Geographic Society

To order the following products for use with this chapter, call National Geographic Society at 1-800-368-2728:

Videos

Stars and Constellations

Sun: Earth's Star

Index to National Geographic Magazine

The following articles may be used for research relating to this chapter:

"New Eyes on the Universe," by Bradford A. Smith, January 1994.

"Orion: Where Stars Are Born," by James Reston, Jr., December 1995.

Evolution of Stars (Section 23-3)

Not all stars shine with a steady light. Stars that change in brightness are called variable stars. Stars may vary because the outer layers of the star expand and contract, causing a change in the temperature and the absolute magnitude of the star.

One class of variable star, called a Cepheid variable, is important to the study of the universe. These stars vary regularly, and their period of variation is an indication of their absolute magnitudes. Because of this, they can be used to determine distances to faraway clusters and galaxies. If two Cepheid variables have the same period of pulsation, they are the same average size and have the same average absolute magnitude. Any difference noted in the apparent magnitudes of the two stars is caused by a difference in the distances to the stars. Polaris is a Cepheid variable.

Exoplanets (Section 23-3)

Scientists are closely studying Fomalhaut, Beta Pictoris, HR 4796A, and Vega—four stars with dust rings. The dust may possibly form into planets, allowing scientists to observe the formation of new solar systems.

Exoplanets—planets outside our solar system—recently have been discovered orbiting at least nine stars other than the sun. What astronomers have found has surprised them. The exoplanets show diverse orbital characteristics when compared to those in our solar system. The star 51 Pegasi has at least one planet with a mass that may exceed 50 percent of Jupiter's.

Black Holes (Section 23-4)

New infrared studies of the center of our galaxy, the Milky Way, provide more evidence for a supermassive black hole at the core of the Milky Way. The total output of energy from the object at the Milky Way's core is more than 1 million times that of the sun. This object, called Sgr A*, appears to contain between 1 and 2 million solar masses.

New Galaxies (Section 23-4)

A new galaxy of the dwarf spheroidal type has been found just 50 000 light-years from the Milky Way's nucleus. It lies on the opposite side of the Milky Way from Earth. Researchers hypothesize that within another 100 million years, the stars from this small galaxy will be incorporated into our own Milky Way. This corresponds to a theory that states that large galaxies, such as the Milky Way, are formed, in part, by incorporating smaller galaxies. Larger galaxies are built up from smaller galaxies.

SCIENCE UPDATE

For current events or science in the news, access the Glencoe Science Web Site at **www.glencoe.com/sec/science**

Teacher to Teacher

"While studying the stars, my students build a planetarium from a 50-foot square of plastic film. The final product will be 30 feet in diameter and 16 feet tall. Plans are available in *The Science Teacher*, vol. 64, no. 7, October 1997."

Dennis L. Stockdale

Dennis L. Stockdale, Teacher
Asheville High School
Asheville, NC

CHAPTER 23
Stars and Galaxies

CHAPTER OVERVIEW

Section 23-1 This section discusses constellations and compares the absolute and apparent brightnesses of stars. Other properties of stars also are presented.

Section 23-2 The structure and surface features of the sun are discussed in this section.

Section 23-3 The evolution of stars is presented. Energy production in stars is also discussed.

Section 23-4 This section illustrates different types of galaxies. The big bang theory of the evolution of the universe is also presented.

Chapter Vocabulary

constellation
absolute magnitude
apparent magnitude
parallax
light-year
photosphere
chromosphere
corona
sunspot
binary system
main sequence
nebula
giant
white dwarf
supergiant
neutron star
black hole
galaxy
big bang theory

Theme Connection

Scale and Structure/Stability and Change The major themes of this chapter deal with the vast scale and structure of the universe and how the universe and the matter that makes up the universe change.

If time does not permit teaching the entire chapter, use Reviewing Main Ideas on pp. 692–693.

CHAPTER

23 Stars and Galaxies

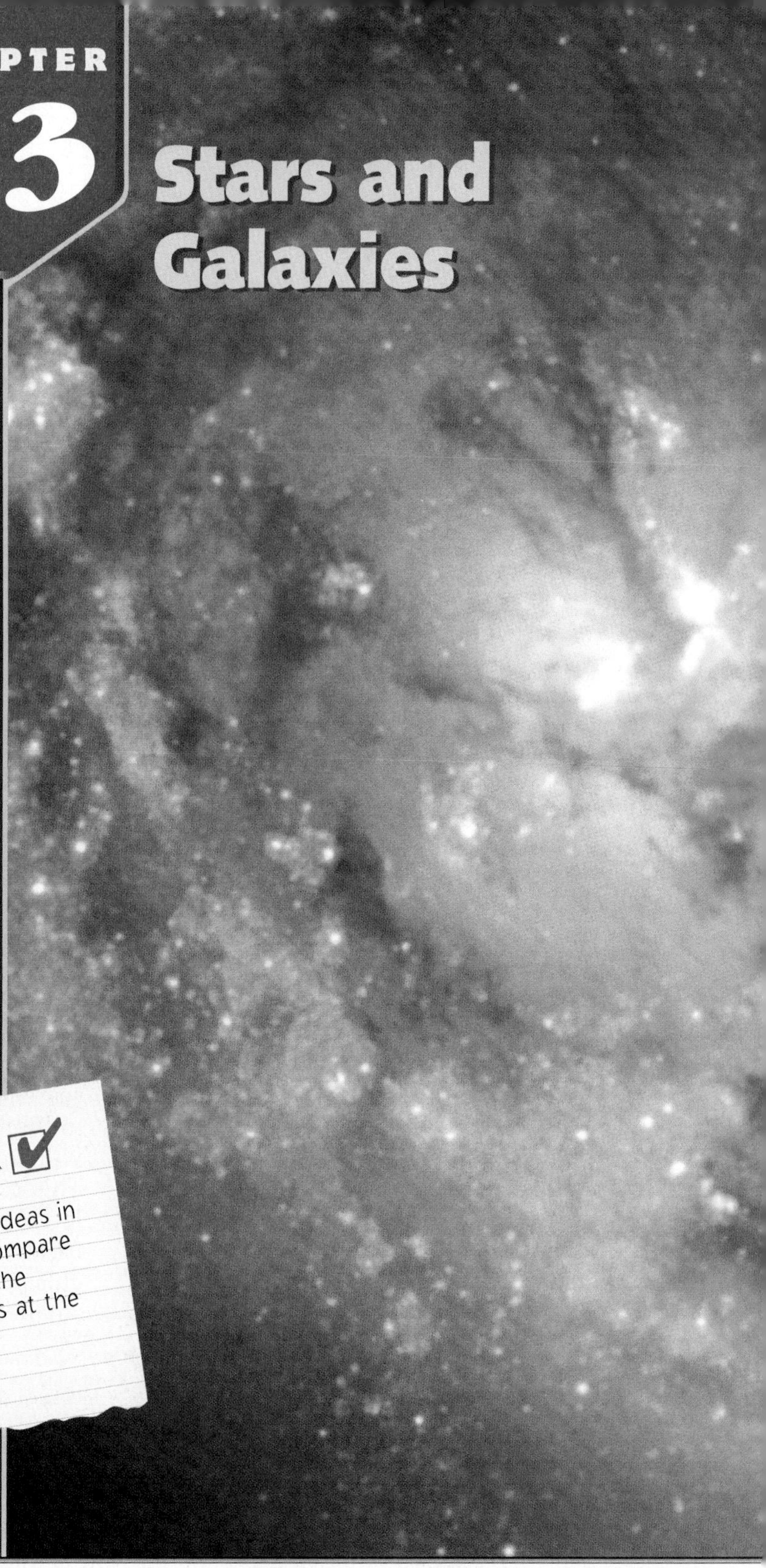

Chapter Preview

Skills Preview

Skill Builders
- Predict

Activities
- Measure in SI

MiniLabs
- Make a Model

Reading Check

Summarize the main ideas in Section 23-1. Then, compare your summary with the Reviewing Main Ideas at the end of the chapter.

660

Multiple Learning Styles

Look for the following logos for strategies that emphasize different learning modalities.

Linguistic Using Science Words, p. 673; Enrichment, p. 675; Science Journal, pp. 681, 683; Preview, p. 692

Logical-Mathematical Activity, pp. 686–687

Visual-Spatial Multiple Learning Styles, p. 663; Activity, pp. 664, 671; MiniLab, pp. 665, 682; Using an Analogy, p. 668; Reteach, pp. 669, 684, 692; Quick Demo, p. 674

Auditory-Musical Quick Demo, p. 683; Out of Time, p. 692

Kinesthetic Explore Activity, p. 661; Reteach, p. 664

Interpersonal Enrichment, p. 673; Discussion, p. 676; Activity, p. 680; Inclusion Strategies, p. 684; Review, p. 692

Intrapersonal Assessment, p. 677

Explore Activity

This photo may look like science fiction, but it shows a real event. It is a photo of two galaxies colliding. Other galaxies are moving away from each other. The universe is full of billions of galaxies, each containing billions of stars. By studying deep space, astronomers have observed that the universe is expanding in all directions. In the following activity, you can model how the universe might be expanding.

Model the Universe 

1. Partially inflate a balloon. Clip the neck shut with a clothespin.
2. Draw six evenly spaced dots on the balloon with a felt-tip marker. Label the dots A through F.
3. Use a string and ruler to measure the distance, in millimeters, from dot A to each of the other dots.
4. Remove the clothespin and inflate the balloon some more.
5. Measure the distance of each dot from A again.
6. Inflate the balloon again, tie the neck shut, and take new measurements.

Science Journal

If each dot represents a galaxy and the balloon represents the universe, describe the motion of the galaxies relative to one another. Is the universe expanding? Explain.

Assessment Planner

Portfolio
Refer to p. 693 for suggested items that students might select for their portfolios.

Peformance Assessment
See p. 693 for additional Performance Assessment options.
Skill Builder, pp. 666, 670, 677, 685
MiniLab, pp. 665, 682
Activity 23-1, p. 671; 21-2, pp. 686–687

Content Assessment
Section Assessment, pp. 666, 670, 677, 685
Chapter Assessment, pp. 694–695
Proficiency Prep, pp. 666, 670, 676, 685

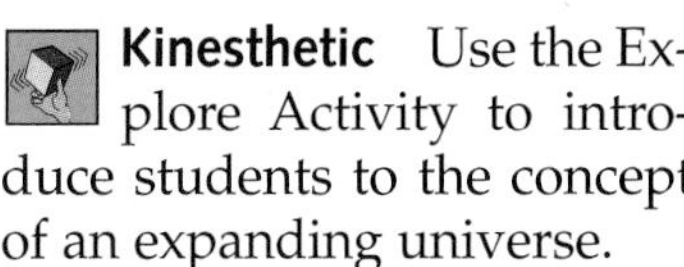

Explore Activity

Purpose

Kinesthetic Use the Explore Activity to introduce students to the concept of an expanding universe.

Preparation

Several days before you begin this chapter, have students bring in large, round balloons and clothespins.

Materials

one balloon, one clothespin, one felt-tip marker, string, and a metric ruler for each group

Teaching Strategies

Form students into groups of four. Assign appropriate student roles. One student should blow up the balloon and clip it shut. Another should draw the dots on the balloon. The other two students should measure the distance between the dots.

Safety Precautions Caution students not to blow up the balloons to the breaking point.

Science Journal The galaxy clusters are moving away from each other. This type of motion implies that the universe is expanding.

Assessment

Process Have students illustrate the motion of the galaxy clusters. Their drawings should indicate that the universe is expanding. Use **Performance Assessment in the Science Classroom,** p. 55.

SECTION 23-1

Prepare

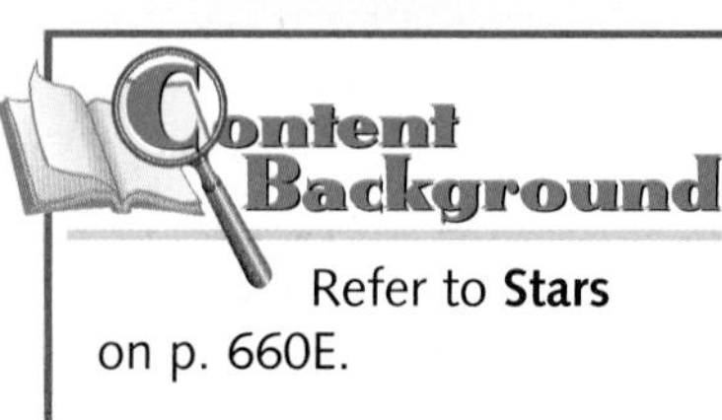

Refer to **Stars** on p. 660E.

Preplanning

Refer to the **Chapter Organizer** on pp. 660A–B.

1 Motivate

Bellringer

Before presenting the lesson, display **Section Focus Transparency 63** on the overhead projector. Use the accompanying **Focus Activity** worksheet. L2 ELL

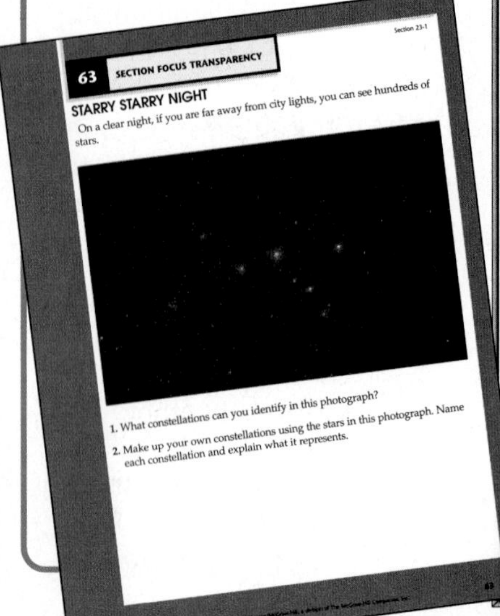

Section 23-1

63 SECTION FOCUS TRANSPARENCY

STARRY STARRY NIGHT

On a clear night, if you are far away from city lights, you can see hundreds of stars.

1. What constellations can you identify in this photograph?
2. Make up your own constellations using the stars in this photograph. Name each constellation and explain what it represents.

Tying to Previous Knowledge

Ask students if they have seen the Big Dipper. Draw the stars of the Big Dipper on the chalkboard and show why it's called a dipper.

23-1 Stars

What You'll Learn

- Why the positions of the constellations change throughout the year
- Absolute magnitude and apparent magnitude
- How parallax is used to determine distance

Vocabulary
constellation
absolute magnitude
apparent magnitude
parallax
light-year

Why It's Important

- You'll learn to recognize groups of stars found in the night sky.

Constellations

Have you ever watched clouds drift by on a summer day? It's fun to look at the clouds and imagine they have shapes familiar to you. One may look like a face. Another might resemble a rabbit or a bear. People long ago did much the same thing with patterns of stars in the sky. They named certain groups of stars, called **constellations,** after animals, characters in mythology, or familiar objects.

From Earth, a constellation looks like a group of stars that are relatively close to one another. In most cases, the stars in a constellation have no relationship to each other in space.

The position of a star in the sky can be given as a specific location within a constellation. For example, you can say that the star Betelgeuse (BEE tul jooz) is in the shoulder of the mighty hunter Orion. Orion's faithful companion is his dog, Canis Major. The brightest star in the sky, Sirius, is in the constellation Canis Major. Orion and Canis Major are shown in **Figure 23-1.**

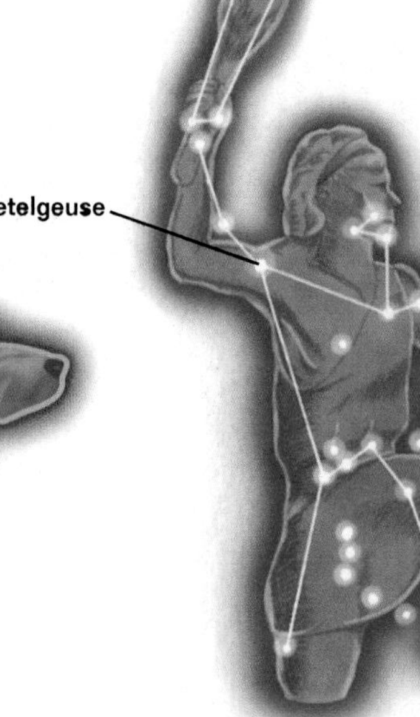

Figure 23-1 Groups of stars can form patterns that look like familiar objects or characters.

Resource Manager

The following **Teacher Classroom Resources** can be used with Section 23-1:

 **Reproducible Masters**

Activity Worksheets, p. 129 L2
Enrichment, p. 63 L3
Home Involvement, p. 28 L2
Laboratory Manual, pp. 131–132 L2
Laboratory Manual, pp. 133–135 L2
Reinforcement, p. 63 L2
Study Guide, p. 89 L1 ELL

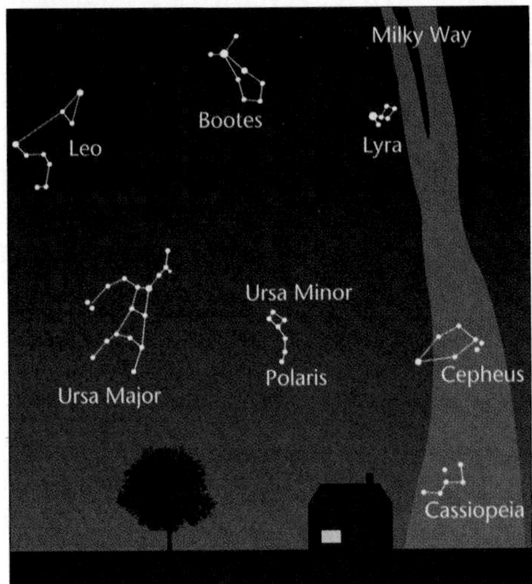

Summer

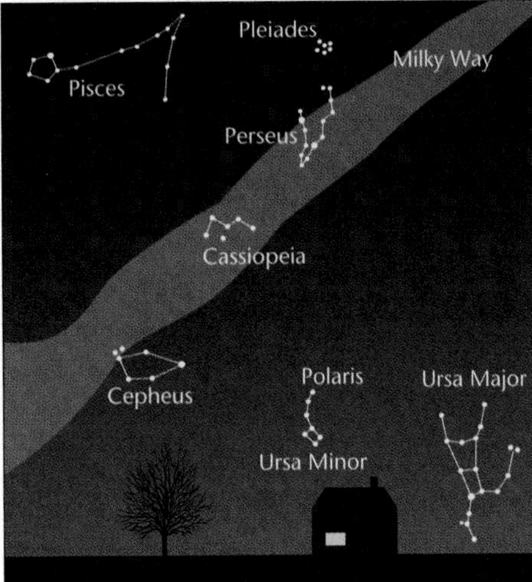

Winter

Figure 23-2 Some constellations are visible only during certain seasons of the year. Others,.such as those close to Polaris, are visible year-round.

Early Greek astronomers named many constellations. Modern astronomers used many of these names to divide the sky into 88 constellations. You may already know some of them. Have you ever tried to find the Big Dipper? It's part of the constellation Ursa Major, shown in **Figure 23-2.** Notice how the front two stars of the Big Dipper point directly at the star Polaris. Polaris, also known as the North Star, is located at the end of the Little Dipper in the constellation Ursa Minor. Polaris is almost directly over Earth's north pole. You'll learn how to locate Polaris and constellations in the **Field Guide to Backyard Astronomy** at the end of this chapter.

Circumpolar Constellations

As Earth rotates, you can watch Ursa Major, Ursa Minor, and other constellations in the northern sky circle around Polaris. Because these constellations circle Polaris, they are called circumpolar constellations.

All of the constellations appear to move because Earth is moving. Look at **Figure 23-3.** The stars appear to complete one full circle in the sky in just under 24 hours as Earth rotates on its axis. The stars also appear to change positions in the sky throughout the year as Earth revolves around the sun.

Figure 23-3 This photograph shows the path of circumpolar stars over several hours. Polaris is almost directly over the north pole. **Does Polaris appear to move as Earth rotates? Explain.**

Circumpolar constellations are visible all year long, but other constellations are not. As Earth orbits the sun, different constellations come into view while others disappear. Orion, which is visible in the winter in the northern hemisphere, can't be seen in the summer because the daytime side of Earth is facing it.

2 Teach

Correcting Misconceptions

Many students may think that stars within one constellation are close to one another in space. Explain that two stars that appear side by side may be separated by hundreds of light-years.

Caption Answer

Figure 23-3 *Because Polaris is almost directly over the north pole, it does not appear to move as Earth rotates.*

Content Background

The magnitude scale was first defined and used by Hipparchus, and later refined by Ptolemy. In the 1850s Pogson and Herschel discovered that a first magnitude star is 100 times brighter than a sixth magnitude star. (The brighter the star, the smaller the value of the magnitude.) In turn, a one magnitude difference corresponds to a factor of 2.512 in brightness ($100^{1/5} = 2.512$). Apparent magnitude is the brightness of a star as seen from Earth. But since distance affects this measurement, absolute magnitude is defined as the brightness of a star if it was located 10 parsecs (32.6 light-years) away from Earth.

Multiple Learning Styles

Visual-Spatial Have students cut black construction paper into 4-cm squares. On each square, put pinholes to form major constellations. Place a constellation square at one end of a cardboard tube. Point the tube toward a light source to view the constellations. L2

Constellations from Mythology Have students research and write a report in their Science Journals about a well-known constellation of their choice. Students should name the stars in the constellation and describe the mythological character or story that gave the constellation its name.

Absolute magnitude is a measure of the amount of light a star actually gives off.

Problem Solving

Apparent brightness is the amount of light received from an object. Because a light meter measures the light received from a light source, it measures apparent brightness. As distance from a light meter is doubled, the light intensity is cut to $\frac{1}{4}$ of what it had been. As distance is tripled, the light intensity is cut to $\frac{1}{9}$ of what it had been.

Think Critically

The relationship between light intensity and distance can be expressed as 1 divided by the square of how many times distance is increased. At 100 cm, the light intensity will be decreased to $\frac{1}{25}$ of its original intensity.

3 Assess

Check for Understanding Activity

Visual-Spatial Supply students with unlabeled star charts. Ask students to make up their own constellations using the charts. Have students explain their star patterns. L2 ELL

Absolute and Apparent Magnitudes

When you look at constellations, you'll notice that some stars are brighter than others. Sirius looks much brighter than Rigel. But is Sirius actually a brighter star, or is it just closer to Earth, which makes it appear to be brighter? As it turns out, Sirius is 100 times closer to Earth than Rigel. If Sirius and Rigel were the same distance from Earth, Rigel would appear much brighter in the night sky than would Sirius.

When you refer to the brightness of a star, you can refer to either its absolute magnitude or its apparent magnitude. The **absolute magnitude** of a star is a measure of the amount of light it actually gives off. A measure of the amount of light received on Earth is called the **apparent magnitude.** A star that's actually rather dim can appear bright in the sky if it's close to Earth. A star that's actually bright can appear dim if it's far away. If two stars are the same distance away, what factors might cause one of them to be brighter than the other?

You can experience the effect of distance on apparent magnitude when driving in a car at night. Observe the other cars' headlights as they approach. Which cars' headlights are brighter—those that are closer to you or those that are farther away?

Problem Solving

Star Light, Star Bright

Mary conducted an experiment to determine the relationship between distance and the brightness of stars. She used a meterstick, a light meter, and a lightbulb. The bulb was mounted at the zero end of the meterstick. Mary placed the light meter at the 20-cm mark on the meterstick and recorded the distance and the light-meter reading in the data table below. Readings are in luxes, which are units for measuring light intensity. Mary doubled and tripled the distance and took more readings.

Think Critically: What happened to the amount of light recorded when the distance was increased from 20 cm to 40 cm? From 20 cm to 60 cm? What does this indicate about the relationship between light intensity and distance? What would the light intensity be at 100 cm?

Effect of Distance on Light

Distance (cm)	Meter Reading (luxes)
20	4150.0
40	1037.5
60	461.1
80	259.4

Reteach

Kinesthetic Take students to an open field to demonstrate parallax. Give one student a compass with a sighting mirror. Have this student stand 50 m from another student and determine the exact compass heading to the other student. Repeat this activity, varying the distances between students. L2 ELL COOP LEARN

How far are stars?

How do we know when a star is close to our solar system? One way is to measure its parallax. **Parallax** is the apparent shift in the position of an object when viewed from two different positions. You are already familiar with parallax. Hold your hand at arm's length and look at one finger first with your left eye closed and then with your right eye closed. Your finger appears to change position with respect to the background. Now, try the same experiment with your finger closer to your face. What do you observe? The nearer an object is to the observer, the greater its parallax.

We can measure the parallax of relatively close stars to determine their distances from Earth, as shown in **Figure 23-4.** When astronomers first realized how far away stars actually are, it became apparent that a new unit of measure would be needed to record their distances. Measuring star distances in kilometers would be like measuring the distance between cities in millimeters.

Distances in space are measured in light-years. A **light-year** is the distance that light travels in one year. Light travels at 300 000 km/s, or about 9.5 trillion km in one year. The nearest star to Earth, other than the sun, is Proxima Centauri. Proxima Centauri is 4.2 light-years away, or about 40 trillion km.

Observing Star Patterns

Procedure

1. On a clear night, go outside after dark and study the stars. Take an adult with you and see if you can help each other find constellations.
2. Let your imagination go to work and try to see any patterns of stars in the sky that look like something with which you are familiar.
3. Draw the stars you see, where they are in the sky, and include a drawing of what you think the star pattern resembles.

Analysis

1. How do your constellations compare with those observed by your classmates?
2. How do you think recognizing star patterns could be useful?

Figure 23-4 Parallax can be seen if you observe the same star while Earth is at two different points during its orbit around the sun (A). The star's position relative to more-distant background stars will appear to change (B and C).

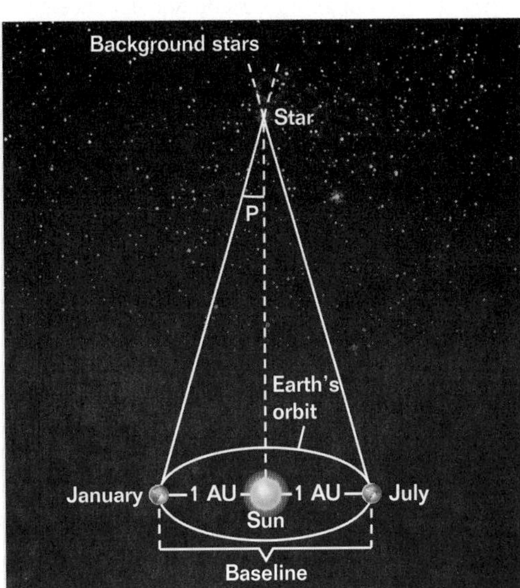

B

As seen in January

C

As seen in July

Inclusion Strategies

Gifted Students should perform this activity away from city lights. Place a single lens reflex camera on a tripod. Aim the camera so that the North Star is in the center of the viewfinder. Use fast film, such as ASA 1000. Open the shutter for 30 minutes and have the aperture wide open. As Earth rotates, the starlight will expose the film and appear as circular streaks.

Extension

For students who have mastered this section, use the **Reinforcement** and **Enrichment** masters.

For additional help doing this activity at home, see the corresponding pages in the **Home Involvement** booklet.

Purpose

Visual-Spatial Students will place stars in patterns.

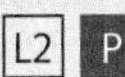

L2 P

Teaching Strategies

Troubleshooting As preparation for this MiniLab, first perform the activity on p. 664 in the teacher's edition.

Analysis

1. Answers will vary depending on student drawings.
2. Answers will vary. Students may say that constellations can be used to find direction.

Assessment

Performance Have students write a mythological story describing one of the star drawings they made while studying the night sky. Use **Performance Assessment in the Science Classroom,** p. 83.

GLENCOE TECHNOLOGY

CD-ROM

Glencoe Science Voyages Interactive CD-ROM

Explorations

Have students do the interactive exploration *How does the composition of stars determine their classification?*

Caption Answer

Figure 23-5 *elements in a star's atmosphere*

4 Close

Proficiency Prep

Use this quiz to check students' recall of section content.

1. **What term describes the distance light travels during one year?** *light-year*
2. **What does the color of a star indicate?** *temperature*

Section Assessment

1. As Earth revolves around the sun, the nighttime side of Earth faces different directions in space. As a result, different constellations are visible.
2. Because both stars give off the same amount of light, they have the same absolute magnitude. If one star looks brighter than the other, it's probably closer to Earth.
3. Its atmosphere is similar to the sun's.
4. **Think Critically** Because the nearest stars are mostly invisible when viewed from Earth, their absolute magnitudes aren't very bright.

Using Computers

Charts will vary depending on the season chosen. Reference points should be included in all charts. P

Figure 23-5
These star spectra were made by placing a prism over a telescope's objective lens. **What causes the lines in spectra?**

How hot are stars?

The color of a star indicates its temperature. For example, hot stars are a blue-white color. A relatively cool star looks orange or red. Stars the temperature of our sun have a yellow color.

Astronomers learn about other properties of stars by studying their spectra. They use spectrographs to break visible light from a star into its component colors. If you look closely at the spectrum of a star, such as the ones shown in **Figure 23-5,** you will see dark lines in it. The lines are caused by elements in the star's atmosphere.

As light radiated from a star passes through the star's atmosphere, some of it is absorbed by elements in the atmosphere. The wavelengths of visible light that are absorbed appear as dark lines in the spectrum. Each element absorbs certain wavelengths, producing a certain pattern of dark lines. The patterns of lines can be used to identify which elements are in a star's atmosphere.

Section Assessment

1. Explain how Earth's revolution affects constellations that are visible throughout the year.
2. If two stars give off the same amount of light, what might cause one to look brighter than the other?
3. If the spectrum of another star shows the same absorption lines as the sun, what can be said about its composition?
4. **Think Critically:** Only about 700 stars can be studied using parallax. Most stars are invisible to the naked eye. What does this indicate about their apparent magnitudes?
5. **Skill Builder**
   Recognizing Cause and Effect
   Suppose you viewed Proxima Centauri through a telescope. How old were you when the light that you see left Proxima Centauri? Why might Proxima Centauri look dimmer than the star Betelgeuse, a large star 310 light-years away? If you need help, refer to Recognizing Cause and Effect in the **Skill Handbook** on page 721.

Using Computers

Graphics Use drawing software on a computer to make a star chart of major constellations visible from your home during the current season. Include reference points to help others find the charted constellations. If you need help, refer to page 734.

5. **Skill Builder**
Proxima Centauri is 4.2 light-years away. Ages will vary but should equal the students' ages minus 4.2 years. Proxima Centauri is close, but it doesn't give off much light. Both the absolute and apparent magnitudes of Betelgeuse are brighter than Proxima Centauri's.

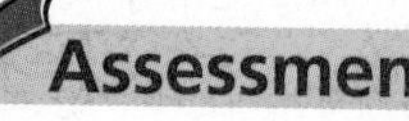

Assessment

Performance To further assess students' abilities to recognize cause and effect, ask them to explain in writing why Deneb appears so bright and yet is more than 1400 light-years away. Use **Performance Assessment in the Science Classroom,** p. 17.

666 CHAPTER 23 STARS AND GALAXIES

The Sun

23-2

Layers of the Sun

More than 99 percent of all of the matter in our solar system is in the sun. The sun is the center of our solar system, and it makes life possible on Earth. But in the grand scheme of the universe, our sun is just another star in the sky.

The sun is an average, middle-aged star. Its absolute magnitude is about average and it shines with a yellow light. Like other stars, the sun is an enormous ball of gas, producing energy by fusing hydrogen into helium in its core. **Figure 23-6** is a model of the sun's interior and atmosphere.

The Sun's Atmosphere

The lowest layer of the sun's atmosphere and the layer from which light is given off is the **photosphere.** The photosphere is often called the surface of the sun. Temperatures there are around 6000 K. Above the photosphere is the **chromosphere.** This layer extends upward about 2000 km above the photosphere. A transition zone occurs between 2000 and 10 000 km above the photosphere. Above the transition zone is the **corona.** This is the largest layer of the sun's atmosphere and extends millions of kilometers into space. Temperatures in the corona are as high as 2 million K. Charged particles continually escape from the corona and move through space as solar wind.

What You'll Learn

- How energy is produced in the sun
- That sunspots, prominences, and solar flares are related
- Why our sun is considered an average star and how it differs from stars in binary systems

Vocabulary
photosphere
chromosphere
corona
sunspot
binary system

Why It's Important

- The sun is the source of most energy on Earth.

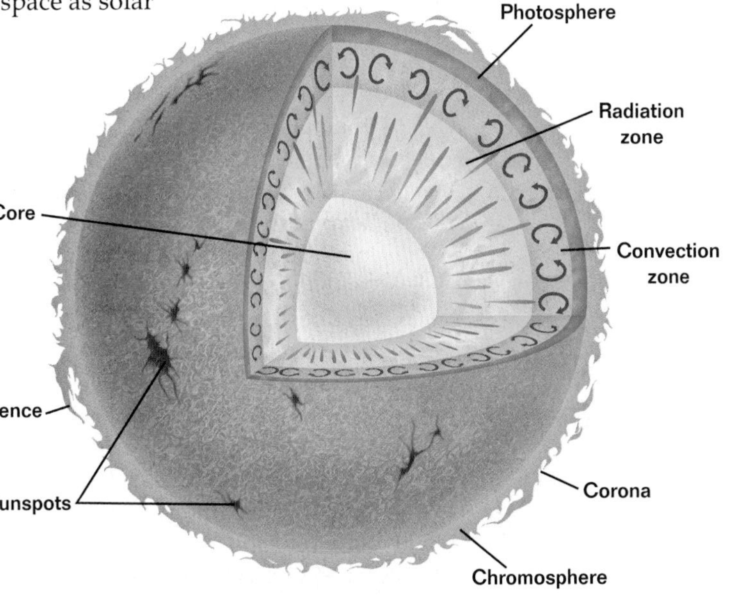

Figure 23-6 Energy produced by fusion in the sun's core travels outward by radiation and convection. The sun's atmosphere, composed of the photosphere, the chromosphere, and the corona, is illuminated by the energy produced in the core.

SECTION 23-2

Prepare

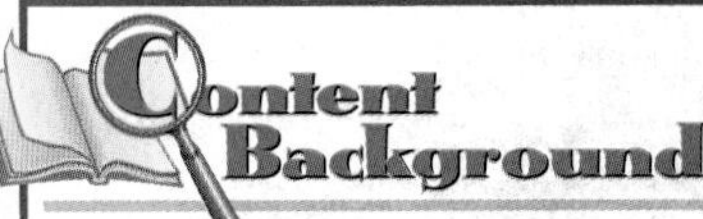

Refer to **Surface of the Sun** and **Solar Activity** on p. 660E.

Preplanning

Refer to the **Chapter Organizer** on pp. 660A–B.

1 Motivate

Bellringer

Before presenting the lesson, display **Section Focus Transparency 64** on the overhead projector. Use the accompanying **Focus Activity** worksheet. L2 ELL

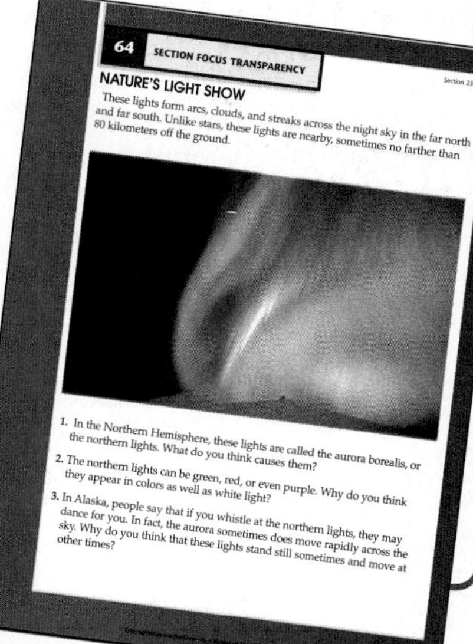

64 SECTION FOCUS TRANSPARENCY

Section 23-2

NATURE'S LIGHT SHOW

These lights form arcs, clouds, and streaks across the night sky in the far north and far south. Unlike stars, these lights are nearby, sometimes no farther than 80 kilometers off the ground.

1. In the Northern Hemisphere, these lights are called the aurora borealis, or the northern lights. What do you think causes them?
2. The northern lights can be green, red, or even purple. Why do you think they appear in colors as well as white light?
3. In Alaska, people say that if you whistle at the northern lights, they may dance for you. In fact, the aurora sometimes does move rapidly across the sky. Why do you think that these lights stand still sometimes and move at other times?

Tying to Previous Knowledge

Remind students that interactions of air, water, and energy from the sun cause Earth's weather.

Resource Manager

The following **Teacher Classroom Resources** can be used with Section 23-2:

 **Reproducible Masters**

Activity Worksheets, pp. 125–126 L2

Enrichment, p. 64 L3

Multicultural Connections, pp. 45–46

Reinforcement, p. 64 L2

 **Transparencies**

Science Integration Transparency 23 L2

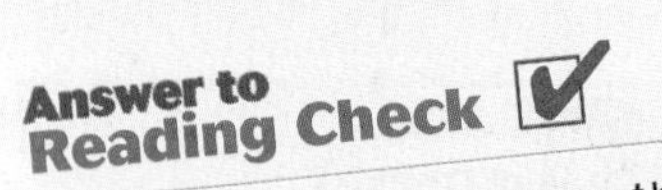

2 Teach

Answer to Reading Check

areas of the sun's surface that appear to be dark because they are cooler than surrounding areas

Using an Analogy

Visual-Spatial To help students understand why sunspots look dark even though they are quite bright, use the following analogy. Show students an overhead projector screen without the projector on. Ask them what color it is. Students will note that it is white. Now, place a transparency with white printing on the projector and turn on the projector. Students will now see that black lines appear to have been drawn on the screen. The lines are white, but next to the brighter white of the screen, they look black. A similar phenomena occurs on the sun—next to the brighter surrounding areas of the sun's surface, sunspots look dark.

Content Background

Sunspots are caused by intense magnetic storms on the sun. As the sun rotates, magnetic field lines wrap around it. These lines dip into the sun's interior and then out, forming sunspots. This explains why many sunspots occur in pairs and why each one of the pair has a magnetic sign opposite that of its partner.

Figure 23-7 Sunspots are bright, but when viewed against the rest of the photosphere, they appear dark. The small photo is a close-up of a sunspot.

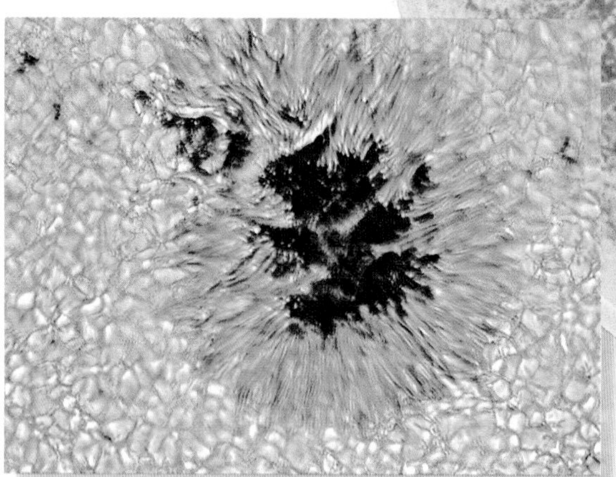

Surface Features of the Sun

Because the sun is a ball of hot gas, it's hard to imagine its surface as anything but a smooth layer. In reality, the sun's surface has many features, including sunspots, prominences, and flares.

Sunspots

Areas of the sun's surface that appear to be dark because they are cooler than surrounding areas are called **sunspots.** Ever since Galileo identified sunspots like those in **Figure 23-7,** scientists have been studying them. One thing we've learned by studying sunspots is that the sun rotates. We can observe the movement of individual sunspots as they move with the sun's rotation. The sun doesn't rotate as a solid body, as does Earth. It rotates faster at its equator than at its poles. Sunspots near the equator take about 27 days to go around the sun. At higher latitudes, they take 31 days.

Reading Check What are sunspots?

Sunspots aren't permanent features on the sun. They appear and disappear over a period of several days, weeks, or months. Also, there are times when there are many large sunspots—a sunspot maximum—and times when there are only a few small sunspots or none at all—a sunspot minimum. Periods of sunspot maximum occur about every 11 years.

Across the Curriculum

Math Using the table below, have student groups plot a graph of sunspot activity. Have each group describe any trend the group observes. L2 COOP LEARN

Year	Sunspots
1969	105
1970	104
1971	67
1972	69
1973	38
1974	35
1975	16
1976	13
1977	28
1978	93
1979	155
1980	155
1981	140
1982	116
1983	67
1984	46
1985	18
1986	14
1987	29
1988	100
1989	159
1990	147
1991	145
1992	94
1993	54
1994	31
1995	18

Prominences and Flares

Sunspots are related to several features on the sun's surface. The intense magnetic field associated with sunspots may cause prominences, which are huge arching columns of gas. Some prominences blast material from the sun into space at speeds ranging from 600 km/s to more than 1000 km/s.

Gases near a sunspot sometimes brighten up suddenly, shooting gas outward at high speed. These violent eruptions from the sun, shown in **Figure 23-8,** are called solar flares.

Ultraviolet light and X rays from solar flares can reach Earth and cause disruption of radio signals. Solar flares make communication by radio and telephone difficult at times. High-energy particles emitted by solar flares are captured by Earth's magnetic field, disrupting communication equipment. These particles also interact with Earth's atmosphere near the polar regions and create light. This light is called the aurora borealis, or northern lights, when it occurs in the northern hemisphere. In the southern hemisphere, it is called the aurora australis.

interNET CONNECTION

Visit the Glencoe Science Web Site at **www.glencoe.com/sec/science** for more information about sunspots, solar flares, and prominences.

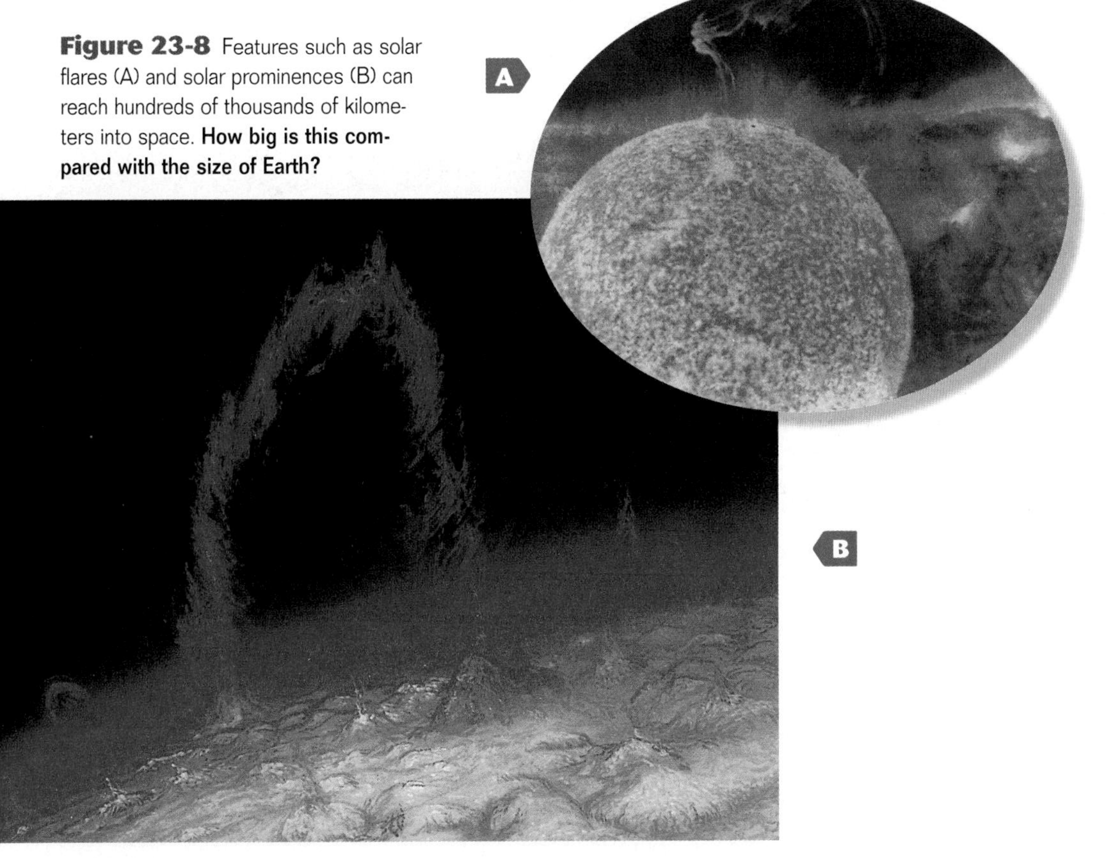

Figure 23-8 Features such as solar flares (A) and solar prominences (B) can reach hundreds of thousands of kilometers into space. **How big is this compared with the size of Earth?**

Guided Reading Strategy

Supporting Idea Chart This strategy examines the relationship between a whole and its parts. Write the name of the whole object on the single line at the left. On the next set of lines to the right, write in major parts of the object. Finally, write in the subparts of each major part. Have students design a Supporting Idea Chart for a concept in this section.

Sample Chart:

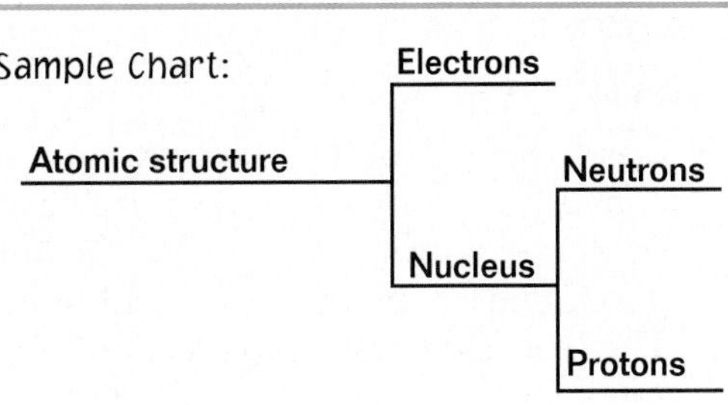

interNET CONNECTION

Internet Addresses

For Internet tips, see Glencoe's **Using the Internet in the Science Classroom.**

Caption Answer

Figure 23-8 *The flares can extend to a distance equal to several tens of Earth diameters.*

3 Assess

Check for Understanding Activity

Have students research the relationship between sunspot activity and Earth's weather and climate. Have interested students research the Maunder minimum, a period from 1645 through 1715 when few sunspots were observed. During this time, Europe experienced record low temperatures, and severe droughts occurred in the western United States. L3

Reteach

Visual-Spatial Have students illustrate how the light and heat from the sun are produced. L2 ELL

Extension

For students who have mastered this section, use the **Reinforcement** and **Enrichment** masters.

4 Close

Proficiency Prep

Use this quiz to check students' recall of section content.

1. **Which layer of the sun's atmosphere gives off light?** *photosphere*
2. **What are cooler, dark areas on the sun's surface called?** *sunspots*

Section Assessment

1. Magnetic fields near a sunspot can cause huge arching columns of gas called prominences. Gases near sunspots can become concentrated and shoot outward from the sun as a solar flare.
2. The sun's size, temperature, and absolute magnitude are similar to other yellow stars' on the main sequence. The sun is unlike many stars because it's not part of a binary system.
3. **Think Critically** Answers will vary. Students may say that our sun could have been a member of a cluster or multiple-star system that spread out across the galaxy or that the cloud from which our sun formed may not have contained enough matter for more than one star.

Science Journal

Fusion reactions in the sun's core change hydrogen into helium. Student hypotheses will vary. Some may know that when the sun exhausts its hydrogen supply, it will begin to fuse helium in its core.

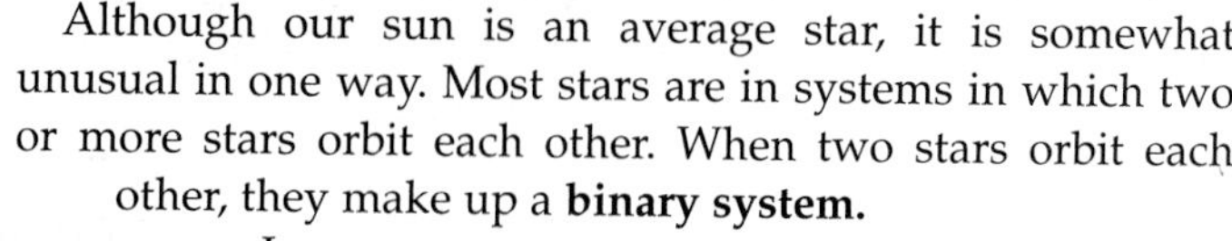

Our Sun—A Typical Star?

Although our sun is an average star, it is somewhat unusual in one way. Most stars are in systems in which two or more stars orbit each other. When two stars orbit each other, they make up a **binary system.**

In some cases, astronomers can detect binary systems because one star occasionally eclipses the other. The total amount of light from the star system becomes dim and then bright again on a regular cycle. Algol in Perseus is an example of this.

In many cases, stars move through space together as a cluster. In a star cluster, many stars are relatively close to one another and are gravitationally attracted to each other. The Pleiades star cluster, shown in **Figure 23-9,** can be seen in the constellation of Taurus in the winter sky. On a clear, dark night, you may be able to see seven of the stars of this cluster. Most star clusters are far from our solar system and appear as a fuzzy patch in the night sky.

Figure 23-9 Pleiades is a cluster of stars that are gravitationally bound to each other.

Section Assessment

1. How are sunspots, prominences, and solar flares related?
2. What properties does the sun have in common with other stars? What property makes it different from most other stars?
3. **Think Critically:** Because most stars are found in multiple-star systems, what might explain why the sun is a single star?
4. **Skill Builder**
   Interpreting Scientific Illustrations Use **Figure 23-6** to answer the questions below. If you need help, refer to Interpreting Scientific Illustrations in the **Skill Handbook** on page 726.
   a. Which layers make up the sun's atmosphere?
   b. What process occurs in the sun's convection zone that enables energy produced in the core to reach the surface?

Science Journal

Write a brief description in your Science Journal that explains how the sun generates energy. Hypothesize what might happen to the sun when it exhausts the supply of hydrogen in its core.

4. **Skill Builder**
   a. photosphere, chromosphere, corona
   b. Gases heated at the bottom of the convection zone are forced upward by denser surrounding gases. The hot gases release energy, cool, and sink. This process creates convection currents.

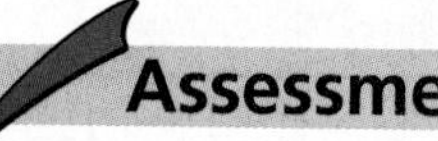

Assessment

Oral To further assess students' abilities to interpret scientific illustrations, have them hypothesize what is causing the glow around the stars in **Figure 23-9.** Use **Performance Assessment in the Science Classroom,** p. 17.

Sunspots

Sunspots are dark, relatively cool areas on the surface of the sun. They can be observed moving across the face of the sun as it rotates. Do this activity to measure the movement of sunspots, and use your data to determine the sun's period of rotation.

Materials

- Several books
- Cardboard (about 8 cm × 12 cm)
- Clipboard
- Drawing paper (5 sheets)
- Small refracting telescope
- Small tripod
- Scissors

What You'll Investigate

Can sunspot motion be used to determine the sun's period of rotation?

Goals

- **Observe** sunspots.
- **Estimate** sunspot size and rate of apparent motion.

Procedure

1. **Find** a location where the sun may be viewed at the same time of day for a minimum of five days. **CAUTION:** *Do not look directly at the sun. Do not look through the telescope at the sun. You could damage your eyes.*
2. **Set up** the telescope with the eyepiece facing away from the sun, as shown below. Align the telescope so that the shadow it casts on the ground is the smallest size possible. **Cut** and **attach** the cardboard as shown in the photo.
3. **Use** books to prop the clipboard upright. Point the eyepiece at the drawing paper.
4. If the telescope has a small finder scope attached, **remove** the finder scope or keep it covered.
5. **Move** the clipboard back and forth until you have the largest possible image of the sun on the paper. Adjust the telescope to form a clear image. **Trace** the outline of the sun on the paper.
6. **Trace** any sunspots that appear as dark areas on the sun's image. Repeat this step at the same time each day for a week.
7. Using the sun's diameter (approximately 1 390 000 km), **estimate** the size of the largest sunspots that you observed.
8. **Calculate** how many kilometers any observed sunspots appear to move each day.
9. At the rate determined in step 8, **predict** how many days it will take for the same group of sunspots to return to about the same position in which you first observed them.

Conclude and Apply

1. What was the average number of sunspots observed each day?
2. What was the estimated size and rate of apparent motion of the largest sunspots?
3. **Infer** how sunspots can be used to determine that the sun's surface is not solid like Earth's.

Purpose

Visual-Spatial Students will observe sunspots and estimate their size and rate of motion across the sun's photosphere.

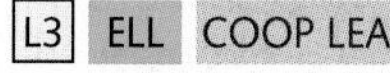

L3 ELL COOP LEARN

Process Skills

observing and inferring, interpreting data, using numbers

Time

10 minutes each day for five days

Safety Precautions

Caution students not to look directly at the sun. Do not allow them to look through the telescope at the sun.

Alternate Materials If a telescope isn't available, use binoculars with one eyepiece covered. Set the binoculars on a stack of books on the window ledge.

Teaching Strategies

Troubleshooting

- If the apparatus must be taken down or moved, ensure correct alignment by marking the exact position of the telescope, books, and clipboard.
- If no sunspots are visible, keep the setup in place until some are sighted. Check to see if you are observing the sun during a sunspot minimum.

Answers to Questions

1. & 2. Answers will vary depending on solar activity. However, the answers of each group should be approximately the same.
3. Sunspots near the sun's equator move at different rates than those near the poles.

Assessment

Content To further assess students' understanding of sunspots, ask them to hypothesize about sunspot movement on the hemisphere they did not observe. How might sunspots on the opposite hemisphere (north or south) move compared to those plotted in this activity? Use **Performance Assessment in the Science Classroom,** p. 21.

SECTION 23-3

Prepare

Refer to **Evolution of Stars** and **Exoplanets** on p. 660F.

Preplanning

Refer to the **Chapter Organizer** on pp. 660A–B.

1 Motivate

Bellringer

Before presenting the lesson, display **Section Focus Transparency 65** on the overhead projector. Use the accompanying **Focus Activity** worksheet. L2 ELL

Section 23-3

65 SECTION FOCUS TRANSPARENCY

SUNBEAMS

The light and warmth we receive from the sun are things most of us take for granted. Imagine what it would be like on Earth if we didn't have the sun. Undoubtedly, Earth would be a very different place.

1. What in this photograph needs the sun?
2. Why do people need the sun?

Tying to Previous Knowledge

Tell students that stars are composed of matter in the plasma state. Have them describe what happens to matter in the plasma state.

23-3 Evolution of Stars

What You'll Learn

- How stars are classified
- How the temperature of a star relates to its color
- How a star evolves

Vocabulary

main sequence, nebula, giant, white dwarf, supergiant, neutron star, black hole

Why It's Important

- The evolution of stars helps explain the theory for the evolution of the universe.

The H-R Diagram

In the early 1900s, Ejnar Hertzsprung and Henry Russell noticed that for most stars, the higher their temperatures, the brighter their absolute magnitudes. They developed a graph to show this relationship.

Hertzsprung and Russell placed the temperatures of stars across the bottom of the graph and the absolute magnitudes of stars up one side. A graph that shows the relationship of a star's temperature to its absolute magnitude is called a Hertzsprung-Russell (H-R) diagram. **Figure 23-10** shows a variation of an H-R diagram.

The Main Sequence

As you can see, stars seem to fit into specific areas of the chart. Most stars fit into a diagonal band that runs from the upper left to the lower right of the chart. This band, called the **main sequence,** contains hot, blue, bright stars in the upper left and cool, red, dim stars in the lower right. Yellow, medium-temperature, medium-brightness stars fall in between. The sun is a yellow main sequence star.

About 90 percent of all stars are main sequence stars, most of which are small, red stars found in the lower right of the H-R diagram. Among main sequence stars, the hottest stars generate the most light and the coolest generate the least. But,

Supergiant
Giants
Main sequence
Sun
White dwarfs
Increasing brightness
20 000 15 000 10 000 6000 3000 2000
Temperature (K)
Spectral Class O B A F G K M

Figure 23-10 This variation of a Hertzsprung-Russell diagram shows the relationships among a star's color, temperature, and brightness. Stars in the main sequence run from hot, bright stars in the upper-left corner of the diagram to cool, faint stars in the lower-right corner. **What type of star shown in the diagram is the coolest, brightest star?**

Resource Manager

The following **Teacher Classroom Resources** can be used with Section 23-3:

Reproducible Masters

Critical Thinking/Problem Solving, p. 23 L2

Enrichment, p. 65 L3

Reinforcement, p.65 L2

Transparencies

Teaching Transparency 45 L2

Teaching Transparency 46 L2

what about the remaining ten percent? Some of these stars are hot but not bright. These small stars are located on the lower left of the H-R diagram and are called white dwarfs. Other stars are extremely bright but not hot. These large stars on the upper right of the H-R diagram are called giants, or red giants because they are usually red in color. The largest giants are called supergiants. The relative sizes of stars are shown in **Figure 23-11.**

Fusion

When the H-R diagram was developed, scientists didn't know what caused stars to shine. Hertzsprung and Russell developed their diagram without knowing what produced the light and heat of stars.

For centuries, people had been puzzled by the question of what stars were and what made them shine. It wasn't until the early part of the twentieth century that scientists began to understand how a star could shine for billions of years. Until that time, many had estimated that Earth was only a few thousand years old. The sun could have been made of coal and shined for that long. But what material could possibly burn for billions of years?

Generating Energy

In 1920, one scientist hypothesized that temperatures in the center of the sun must be high. Another scientist then suggested that with these high temperatures, hydrogen could fuse to make helium in a reaction that would release tremendous amounts of energy. **Figure 23-12** on the next page illustrates how four hydrogen nuclei could combine to create one helium nucleus. The mass of one helium nucleus is less than the mass of four hydrogen nuclei, so some mass is lost in the reaction. In the 1930s, scientists hypothesized that carbon could be used as a catalyst in fusion reactions. This explained the energy production in hotter stars.

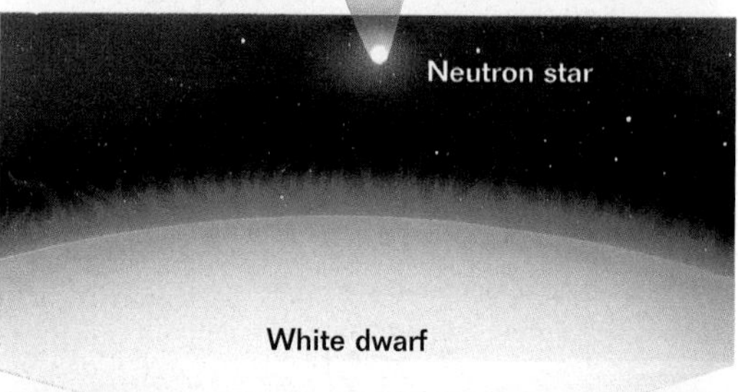

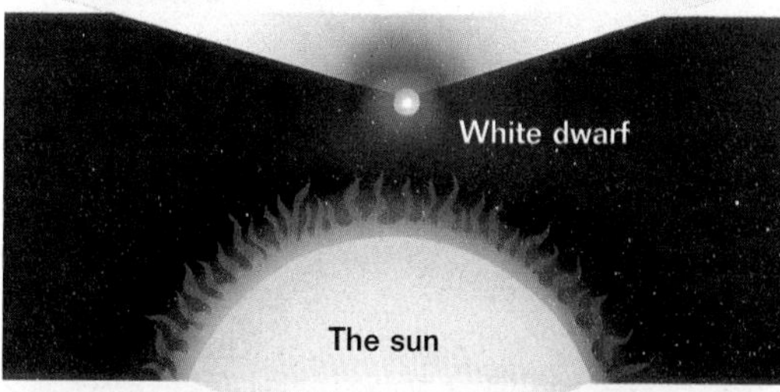

Figure 23-11 The relative sizes of stars range from supergiants as much as 800 times larger than the sun to neutron stars and black holes possibly 30 km or less across. The relative sizes of a supergiant, the sun, a white dwarf, a neutron star, and a black hole are shown.

2 Teach

Caption Answer

Figure 23-10 *giants*

Using Science Words

Linguistic Help students practice the use of science words by asking the following questions. **What properties of stars are plotted on the H-R diagram?** *Absolute magnitude is plotted against temperature or stellar classification.* **What process generates energy in the core of a star?** *Fusion generates energy in the core of a star. Four hydrogen atoms fuse to become one helium atom. Mass lost in the reaction is changed to energy.* L2

Content Background

A group of astronomers has devised a new class of stars, stellar class L. Stars of this class are relatively cool—1500 K to 2000 K. (Kelvin scale temperatures are expressed as kelvins, K, not as degrees.) Stars of this newly proposed classification have spectra that show the presence of iron hydride (FeH) and chromium hydride (CrH). Alkali metals such as sodium, potassium, and cesium are also found in the spectra of L-class stars. As with M-class stars, L-class stars are dwarfs.

Enrichment

Interpersonal Have pairs of students prepare and display a bulletin board version of a Hertzsprung-Russell (H-R) diagram. Have them use **Figure 23-10** as a guide. L2 COOP LEARN

Integrating the Sciences

Physics Refer students to "The Eagle's Nest" by Samantha Parker in *Sky & Telescope*, February 1996, pp. 32–34. After students have read the article, show them illustrations of the Eagle nebula (M16). Ask them why scientists are interested in this nebula. *Data gathered by the* Hubble Space Telescope *indicate that the evaporating gaseous globules (EGGs) found in this nebula are forming into stars.*

PHYSICS INTEGRATION

Stars evolve and change into other types of stars because of what is happening inside the star. As a star uses up one element as fuel, conditions change inside the star. If the star can attain high enough temperatures, new, heavier elements can be used as fuel for the fusion process to continue at the star's core. Ask students what property of the star determines what can be used as fuel for fusion at the star's core. *stellar mass*

Answer to Reading Check
a large cloud of gas and dust in space

Quick Demo

Visual-Spatial Using tongs, hold the end of a wire over the flame of a Bunsen burner until it begins to glow. Ask students to record the color of the glowing wire. Continue to hold the wire over the flame. Ask students to record any changes they see in the wire as it's heated. Ask one student to summarize what happened to the wire. *As the wire was heated, it started to glow and gradually changed from reddish-orange to yellowish-white as it became hotter.* **CAUTION:** *Wear goggles and safety gloves. Handle the hot wire carefully.* L2

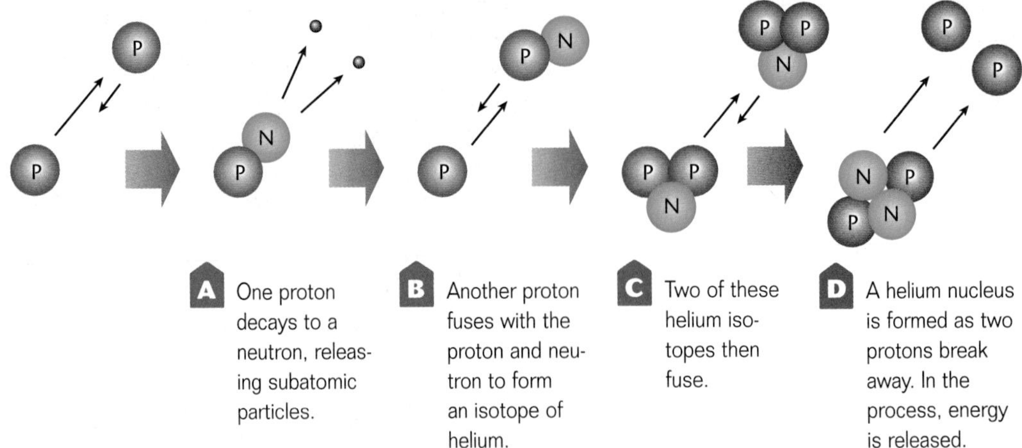
P
P
N
P
P
N
P
P
N
P
P
N
P
P
P
N
P
N
P
P
A One proton decays to a neutron, releasing subatomic particles.
B Another proton fuses with the proton and neutron to form an isotope of helium.
C Two of these helium isotopes then fuse.
D A helium nucleus is formed as two protons break away. In the process, energy is released.

Figure 23-12 In a star's core, fusion begins as two hydrogen nuclei (protons) are forced together. **What happens to the "lost" mass during this process?**

Years earlier, in 1905, Albert Einstein had proposed a theory stating that mass can be converted into energy. This was stated as the famous equation $E = mc^2$, where E is the energy produced, m is the mass, and c is the speed of light. The small amount of mass "lost" when hydrogen atoms fuse to form a helium atom is converted to a large amount of energy.

Fusion occurs in the cores of stars. Only in the core are temperatures and pressures high enough to cause atoms to fuse. Normally, they would repel each other, but in the core of a star, atoms are forced close enough together that their nuclei fuse together.

PHYSICS
INTEGRATION

The Evolution of Stars

The H-R diagram and other theories explained a lot about stars. But they also led to more questions. Many wondered why some stars didn't fit in the main sequence group and what happened when a star exhausted its supply of hydrogen fuel. Today, we have a theory of how stars evolve, what makes them different from one another, and what happens when they die. **Figure 23-13** illustrates the lives of different types of stars.

Nebula

Stars begin as a large cloud of gas and dust called a **nebula.** The particles of gas and dust exert a gravitational force on each other, and the nebula begins to contract. Gravitational forces cause instability within the nebula. The nebula can fragment into smaller pieces. Each will eventually collapse to form a star. ✔

Reading Check
What is a nebula?

Content Background

Based on observed evidence, most stars form inside clouds of gas and dust at the same time that other stars are forming from the same cloud. In the Orion nebula (M42), a star nursery located 1500 light-years away, hundreds of stars have already formed and many more will follow.

Caption Answers

Figure 23-12 *It is converted to a large amount of energy.*

Figure 23-13 *They become white dwarfs.*

Figure 23-14 *Iron forms in the core of a supergiant. Fusion can no longer occur and the core collapses violently. Outer layers of the star fall in and "bounce" off the core, and then expand quickly outward like an explosion.*

674 CHAPTER 23 STARS AND GALAXIES

As the particles in the smaller clouds move closer together, the temperatures in each nebula increase. When temperatures inside each nebula reach 10 million K, fusion begins. The energy released radiates outward through the condensing ball of gas. As the energy radiates into space, stars are born.

CHEMISTRY INTEGRATION

Star Spectrum
The spectrum of a star shows absorption lines of helium and hydrogen and is bright in the blue end. Describe as much as you can about the star's composition and surface temperature.

Main Sequence to Giant Stars

In the newly formed star, the heat from fusion causes pressure that balances the attraction due to gravity, and the star becomes a main sequence star. It continues to use up its hydrogen fuel.

When hydrogen in the core of the star is exhausted, there is no longer a balance between pressure and gravity. The core contracts, and temperatures inside the star increase. This causes the outer layers of the star to expand. In this late stage of its life cycle, a star is called a **giant.**

Once the core temperature reaches 100 million K, helium nuclei fuse to form carbon in the giant's core. By this time, the star has expanded to an enormous size, and its outer layers are much cooler than they were when it was a main sequence star. In about 5 billion years, our sun will become a giant.

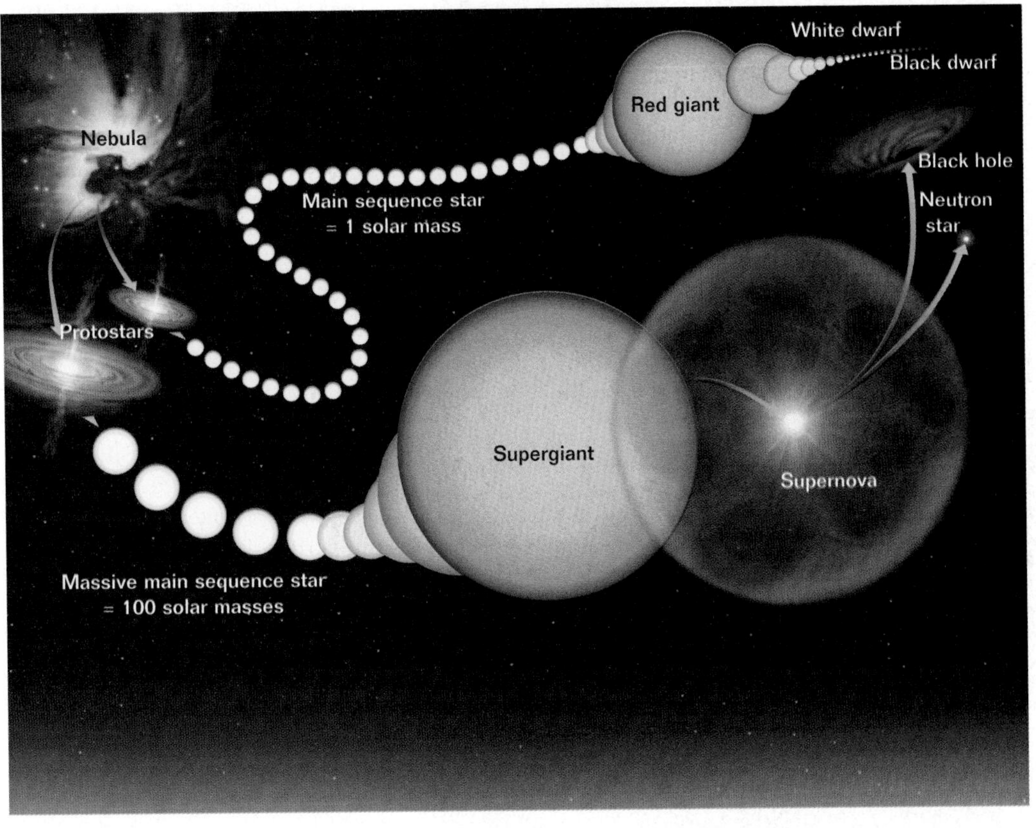

Figure 23-13 The life of a star depends greatly on its mass. Massive stars eventually become neutron stars, or possibly black holes. **What happens to stars the size of our sun?**

Flex Your Brain

Use the Flex Your Brain activity to have students explore EVOLUTION OF STARS.

CHEMISTRY INTEGRATION

The star's atmosphere contains helium and hydrogen. Its surface has a high temperature.

Enrichment

Linguistic Have students use astronomy books and magazine articles to research the Horsehead and Orion nebulas, located in the constellation Orion. Have them determine why the Horsehead nebula is a dark nebula and the Orion nebula is a bright nebula. Also, have them explain the relationship between the brightness of the nebulas and the star-formation processes occurring within them. L3

Teacher FYI

In a star with a mass similar to our sun's, outer layers become unstable and begin escaping into space when the core runs out of hydrogen fuel. The escaping gases form a shell around the star, producing a planetary nebula. The Ring nebula in the constellation Lyra is an example of this process.

Integrating the Sciences

Physics Assess students' understanding of how physics relates to the study of star evolution by asking the following questions. **Why does a star become unstable when its hydrogen fuel is used up?** *The outward force caused by fusion is reduced and no longer balances the inward force of gravity.* **If the temperature inside a star's contracting core heats up, why does the outer layer of the star turn reddish in color?** *The increased heat inside the star causes the outer layers of the star to expand. As the outer layers expand, the gases contained in them cool down, thus becoming reddish in color.* L2

3 Assess

Check for Understanding

Discussion

Interpersonal Refer students to **Figure 23-10. What is true about the absolute magnitude and temperature of supergiants?** *Supergiants have high absolute magnitudes but relatively low temperatures.* **Based on their name, what can you infer about the size of supergiants?** *Supergiants are large compared with other stars.*

Reteach

Refer students to **Figure 23-10** and ask the following question as a means of initiating a class discussion. **Why do the stars located in the upper-left portion of the diagram have such a high absolute magnitude?** *These stars are fairly large and have high temperatures.*

Extension

For students who have mastered this section, use the **Reinforcement** and **Enrichment** masters.

4 Close

Proficiency Prep

Use this quiz to check students' recall of section content.

1. **Stars begin as large clouds of gas and dust called what?** *nebulas*
2. **Once the outer layers of a star like our sun escape into space, what is left behind?** *white dwarf*

White Dwarfs

After the star's core uses up its supply of helium, it contracts even more. As the core of a star like the sun runs out of fuel, its outer layers escape into space. This leaves behind the hot, dense core. The core contracts under the force of gravity. At this stage in a star's evolution, it is a **white dwarf.** A white dwarf is about the size of Earth.

Supergiants and Supernovas

In stars that are over ten times more massive than our sun, the stages of evolution occur more quickly and more violently. The core heats up to much higher temperatures. Heavier and heavier elements form by fusion. The star expands into a **supergiant.** Eventually, iron forms in the core. Fusion can no longer occur once iron forms. The core collapses violently, sending a shock wave outward through the star. The outer portion of the star explodes, producing a supernova like the one shown in **Figure 23-14.** A supernova can be billions of times brighter than the original star.

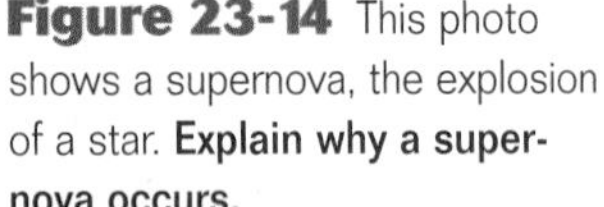

Figure 23-14 This photo shows a supernova, the explosion of a star. **Explain why a supernova occurs.**

Neutron Stars

The collapsed core of a supernova shrinks to about 10 km to 15 km in diameter. Only neutrons can exist in the dense core, and the supernova becomes a **neutron star.**

If the remaining dense core is more than two times more massive than the sun, probably nothing can stop the core's collapse. It quickly evolves into a **black hole**—an object so dense that nothing can escape its gravity field.

Black Holes

If you could shine a flashlight on a black hole, the light wouldn't illuminate the black hole. The light would simply disappear into it. So, how do scientists locate black holes? Matter being pulled into a black hole can collide with other material, generating X rays. Astronomers have located X-ray sources around possible black holes. Extremely massive black holes probably exist in the centers of galaxies.

Star Evolution Have students construct concept maps in their Science Journals showing the evolution of a star. Then ask the following questions. **After a supernova, what type of object forms if the remaining dense core collapses?** *a black hole* **If black holes can't be seen, how do astronomers locate them?** *Astronomers hypothesize that as matter is drawn into a black hole, large amounts of X rays are given off. Astronomers have found several strong X-ray sources that appear to have high masses but which can't be seen.*

What are nebulas?

A star begins its life as a nebula, shown in **Figure 23-15.** But where does the matter in a nebula come from? Nebulas form partly from the matter that was once in other stars. A star ejects enormous amounts of matter during its lifetime. This matter can be incorporated into other nebulas, which can evolve into new stars. The matter in stars is recycled many times.

What about the matter created in the cores of stars? Are elements such as carbon and iron recycled also? Some of these elements do become parts of new stars. In fact, spectrographs have shown that our sun contains some carbon, iron, and other such elements. Because the sun is a main sequence star, it is too young to have created these elements itself. Our sun condensed from material that was created in stars that died many billions of years ago.

Some elements condense to form planets and other bodies rather than stars. In fact, your body contains many atoms that were fused in the cores of ancient stars. Evidence suggests that the first stars formed from hydrogen and helium and that all the other elements have formed in the cores of stars.

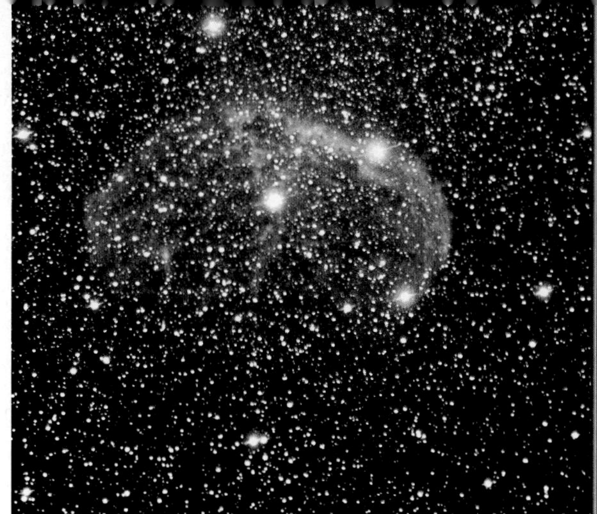

Figure 23-15 Stars are forming in the Crescent Nebula.

Section Assessment

1. Explain why giants are not in the main sequence on the H-R diagram. How do their temperatures and absolute magnitudes compare with those of main sequence stars?
2. What can be said about the absolute magnitudes of two equal-sized stars whose colors are blue and yellow?
3. Outline the history and probable future of our sun.
4. **Think Critically:** Why doesn't the helium currently in the sun's core undergo fusion?
5. **Skill Builder** **Sequencing** Sequence the following in order of most evolved to least evolved: *main sequence star, supergiant, neutron star,* and *nebula.* If you need help, refer to Sequencing in the **Skill Handbook** on page 714.

Using Math

Assume that a star's core has shrunk to a diameter of 12 km. What would be the circumference of the shrunken stellar core? Use the equation $C = \pi d$. How does this compare with the circumference of Earth with a diameter of 12 756 km?

Section Assessment

1. Giants are large but relatively cool stars. Their temperatures compare with small main sequence stars, but their absolute magnitudes compare with the larger main sequence stars.
2. Because the blue star is hotter, its absolute magnitude would be brighter than that of the yellow star.
3.
   - I. Nebula
     - A. Cloud contracts
     - B. Heated to 10 000 000 K
     - C. Fusion in cloud center
   - II. Main sequence star
     - A. Energy of fusion balances gravity
     - B. Hydrogen fuel exhausted
   - III. Giant
     - A. Fuses helium
     - B. Outer layers escape
   - IV. White dwarf
     - A. Exhausts fuel supply
     - B. Core contracts
4. **Think Critically** The sun still has a supply of hydrogen for fusion. This keeps the core from collapsing and temperatures from rising. Currently, the sun's core is not hot enough to fuse significant amounts of helium.

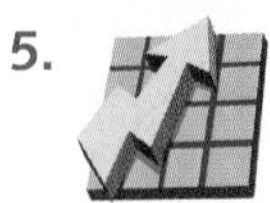

5. **Skill Builder** neutron star, supergiant, main sequence star, nebula

Assessment

Content Have students share their star sequences with another student. Use **Performance Assessment in the Science Classroom,** p. 97.

Using Math

$C = \pi d$

$C = (3.14)(12 \text{ km}) = 37.7 \text{ km}$

$C = (3.14)(12\,756 \text{ km}) = 40\,054 \text{ km}$

The circumference of Earth is 1062 times larger than the shrunken stellar core.

NATIONAL GEOGRAPHIC

Reading & Writing in Science

As with many modern theories about the origin of the universe, early beliefs about the universe's origin attempt to show how the order we see today emerged from disorder. Many early beliefs state that Earth formed, at first, as a bare object void of water, plants, animals, and people. This is how the Australian Aborigines picture the beginning of Earth. Earth was first a featureless plain. The Aborigines believe that during Dreamtime supernatural beings emerged and created all the features now seen on Earth. Supernatural beings were linked to specific features on Earth. Recall that the same is true for constellations.

Encourage creativity in student poems. Emphasize that they are writing about what they think happened.

Reading & Writing in Science

Dreamtime Down Under

The Aborigines of Australia believe that the world began long ago—before anyone can remember—when Dreamtime began. At first, Earth was cold and dark, and the spirit Ancestors slept underground.

When the Ancestors awoke, they moved to Earth's surface and created the sun for warmth and light. Some Ancestors became people. Others became plants, animals, clouds, or stars. As the Ancestors moved over Earth, they sang, and their singing created hills, rivers, and other features.

Leaving a Path

The movement of the Ancestors left Dreaming Tracks that the Aborigines still treasure. When the Ancestors tired, they returned underground. The bodies of some Ancestors remain on Earth's surface as rock outcroppings, trees, islands, and other natural features, such as the formation in the inset, below right.

Ancient Aborigines drew maps to show where the Ancestors came out, walked, and returned underground. Drawings with traditional dot patterns (see bark painting, far right) form the basis of Aboriginal art.

Dreaming the Big Bang

Some compare the Dreamtime forces that shaped Earth to the big bang theory—huge fields of energy interacting and forming planets. Later, more energy—more Dreaming—created today's continents, including Australia.

Today, Aborigines are struggling to maintain ancient traditions while living in modern Australia. They believe that the Ancestors still live in the land and that Dreamtime continues with no foreseeable end.

Science JOURNAL

In your Science Journal, write a poem that expresses your own view of our relationship to nature and to the land.

Teaching Strategies

Reading Encourage students to read about modern theories of the origin of the universe, such as the big bang theory. Obtain copies of the February 1998 issue of *Astronomy* magazine. It contains several articles about the origin of the universe. L2

Writing Have students write a description of the sand drawing shown on the student page. L2

For Additional Information

- Holder, Robyn. *Aborigines of Australia.* Vero Beach, FL: Rourke, 1987.
- Lawlor, Robert. *Voices of the First Day: Awakening in the Aboriginal Dreamtime.* Rochester, VT: Inner Traditions, 1991.
- Nile, Richard. *Australian Aborigines.* Austin, TX: Steck-Vaughn, 1993.

Galaxies and the Universe

Galaxies

One reason to study astronomy is to learn about your place in the universe. Long ago, people thought they were at the center of the universe and everything revolved around Earth. Today, you know this isn't the case. But, do you know where you are in the universe?

You are on Earth, and Earth orbits the sun. But does the sun orbit anything? How does it interact with other objects in the universe? The sun is one star among many in a galaxy. A **galaxy** is a large group of stars, gas, and dust held together by gravity. Our galaxy, called the Milky Way, is shown in **Figure 23-16.** It contains about 200 billion stars, including the sun. Galaxies are separated by huge distances—often millions of light-years.

Just as stars are grouped together within galaxies, galaxies are grouped into clusters. The cluster the Milky Way belongs to is called the Local Group. It contains about 30 galaxies of various types and sizes.

Figure 23-16 The Milky Way Galaxy is usually classified as a normal spiral galaxy. Its spiral arms, composed of stars and gas, radiate out from an area of densely packed stars called the nucleus.

What You'll Learn

- The three main types of galaxies
- Several characteristics of the Milky Way Galaxy
- How the big bang theory explains the observed Doppler shifts of galaxies

Vocabulary
galaxy
big bang theory

Why It's Important

- You'll explore theories about how the universe may have formed.

SECTION 23 4

Prepare

Refer to **Black Holes** and **New Galaxies** on p. 660F.

Preplanning

Refer to the **Chapter Organizer** on pp. 660A–B.

1 Motivate

Bellringer

Before presenting the lesson, display **Section Focus Transparency 66** on the overhead projector. Use the accompanying **Focus Activity** worksheet. L2 ELL

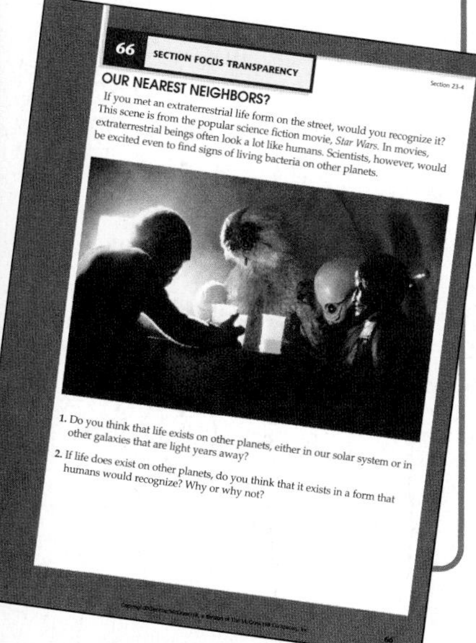
66 SECTION FOCUS TRANSPARENCY

Section 23-4

OUR NEAREST NEIGHBORS?

If you met an extraterrestrial life form on the street, would you recognize it? This scene is from the popular science fiction movie, *Star Wars*. In movies, extraterrestrial beings often look a lot like humans. Scientists, however, would be excited even to find signs of living bacteria on other planets.

1. Do you think that life exists on other planets, either in our solar system or in other galaxies that are light years away?
2. If life does exist on other planets, do you think that it exists in a form that humans would recognize? Why or why not?

66

Tying to Previous Knowledge

Ask students if they have ever observed the night sky far from city lights. If so, they may have seen the band of stars that stretches across the sky—the Milky Way, our home galaxy.

Resource Manager

The following **Teacher Classroom Resources** can be used with Section 23-4:

Reproducible Masters

Activity Worksheets, pp. 127–128, 130 L2

Enrichment, p. 66 L3

Reinforcement, p. 66 L2

Study Guide, pp. 90–92 L1 ELL

2 Teach

Activity

Interpersonal Have pairs of students make flash cards of the types of galaxies. Have them draw the galaxy type on one side and write its name on the reverse. Partners can then test each other using the flash cards. Next, have the partners draw ten to 20 images of the Milky Way Galaxy on separate cards. Have them place the sun at slightly different positions around the galaxy on each card. When finished, partners can demonstrate the movement of the sun around the galaxy by flipping the cards. L2 ELL COOP LEARN

VISUAL Learning

Figures 23-17, 23-18, and 23-20 Ask students to compare and contrast the three major classifications of galaxies. *Students should mention differences in size and shape, as well as similarities in formation and composition.*

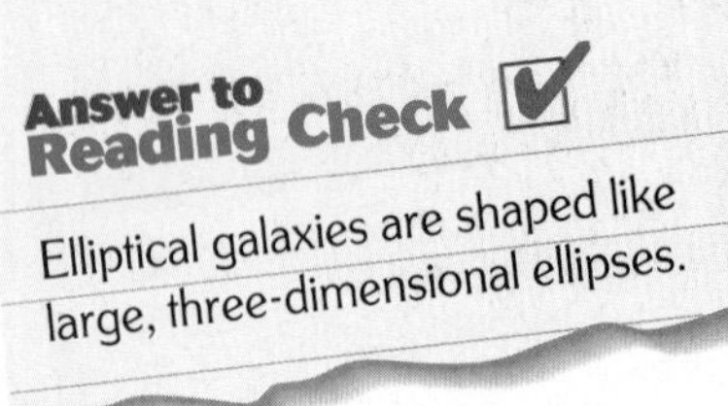

Caption Answers

Figure 23-17 *the Local Group*

Figure 23-18 *spiral and irregular*

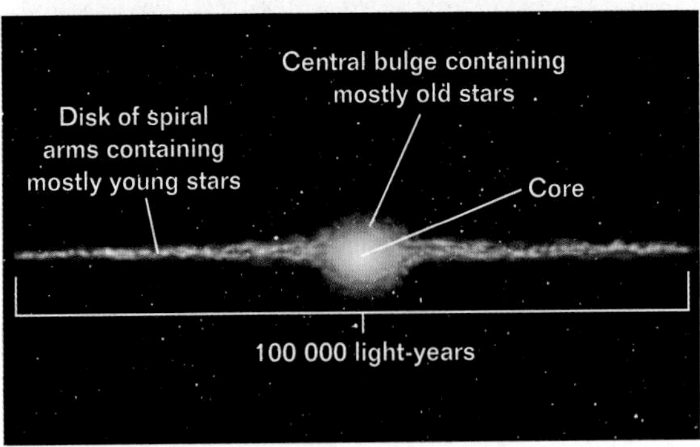

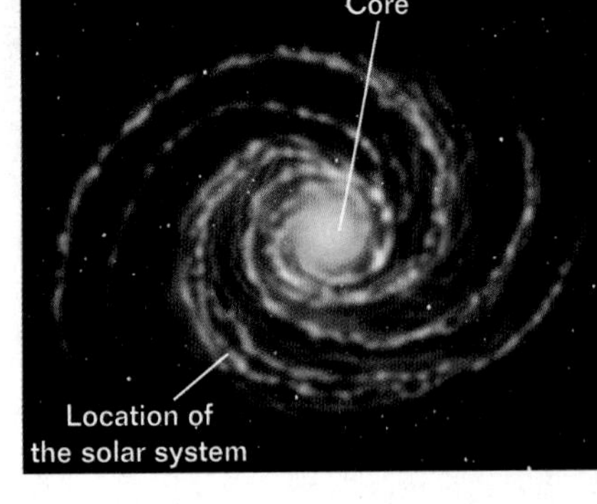

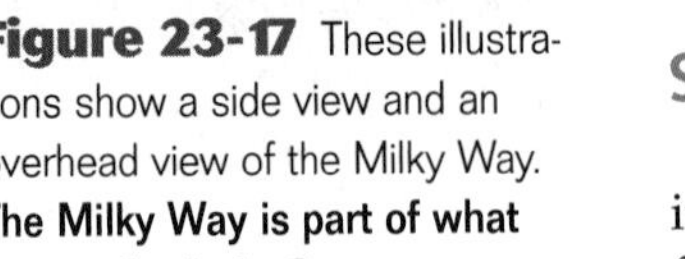

Figure 23-17 These illustrations show a side view and an overhead view of the Milky Way. **The Milky Way is part of what group of galaxies?**

Spiral Galaxies

The three major types of galaxies are elliptical, spiral, and irregular. Spiral galaxies have spiral arms that wind outward from inner regions. The Milky Way is a spiral galaxy, as shown in **Figure 23-17.** Its spiral arms are made up of bright stars and dust. The fuzzy patch you can see in the constellation of Andromeda is actually a spiral galaxy. It's so far away that you can't see its individual stars. Instead, it appears as a hazy spot in our sky. The Andromeda Galaxy is a member of the Local Group. It is about 2.2 million light-years away.

Arms in a normal spiral start close to the center of the galaxy. Barred spirals have spiral arms extending from a large bar of stars and gas that passes through the center of the galaxy.

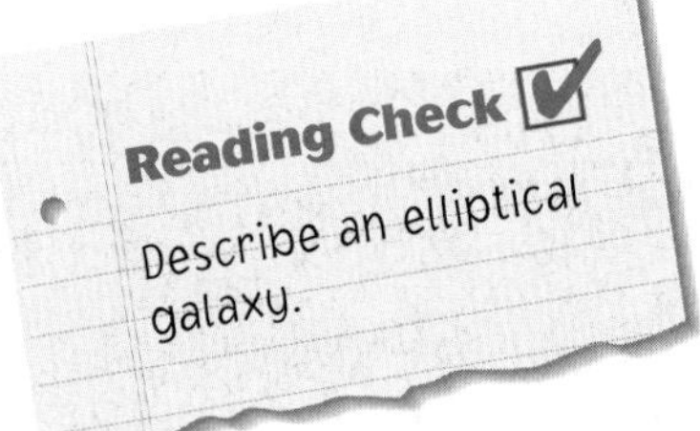

Elliptical Galaxies

Probably the most common type of galaxy is the elliptical galaxy, shown in **Figure 23-18.** These galaxies are shaped like large, three-dimensional ellipses. Many are football-shaped, but others are round. Some elliptical galaxies are small, while some are so large that the entire Local Group of galaxies would fit inside one of them. **Figure 23-19** shows the Local Group and its relation to the solar system, the Milky Way, and large galaxy clusters.

Figure 23-18 This photo shows an example of an elliptical galaxy. **What are the two other types of galaxies?**

Content Background

Brown dwarfs are stars that never generated fusion in their cores. They did not reach the mass necessary to initiate fusion of hydrogen into helium. The mass needed for this to occur is about 8 percent of the sun's mass. Brown dwarfs are very dim. They are found by observing the movement of a more easily seen star. The path through space by a single star would be a nearly straight line. However, the path of a star with a brown dwarf in orbit around it would show a distinct wobble. This wobble is used to locate brown dwarfs in much the same way it has been used to locate exoplanets.

Figure 23-19 There may be more than 100 billion galaxies in the universe, and nearly all of them seem to be organized into clusters.

Irregular Galaxies

The third type of galaxy, irregular, includes most of those galaxies that don't fit into the other classifications. Irregular galaxies have many different shapes and are smaller and less common than the other types. Two irregular galaxies called the Clouds of Magellan orbit the Milky Way. The Large Magellanic Cloud is shown in **Figure 23-20.**

Figure 23-20 The Large Magellanic Cloud is an irregular galaxy. It's a member of the Local Group, and it orbits our own galaxy.

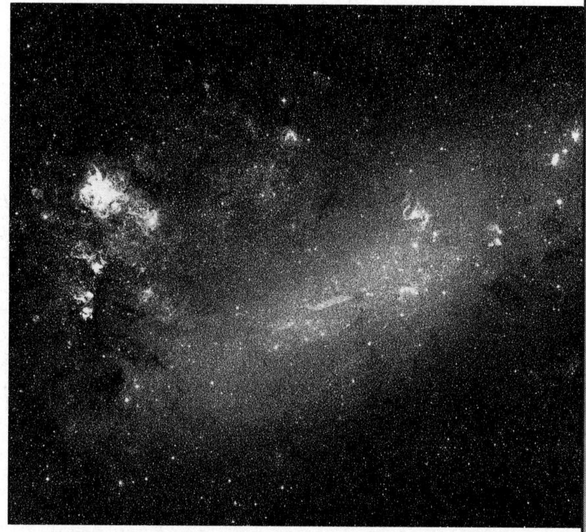

The Milky Way Galaxy

The Milky Way contains more than 200 billion stars. The visible disk of stars is about 100 000 light-years across, and the sun is located about 30 000 light-years out from its center. In our galaxy, all stars orbit around a central region. Based on a distance of 30 000 light-years and a speed of 235 km/s, the sun orbits around the center of the Milky Way once every 240 million years.

The Milky Way is usually classified as a normal spiral galaxy. However, recent evidence suggests that it might be a barred spiral. It is difficult to know for sure because we can never see our galaxy from the outside.

You can't see the normal spiral or barred shape of the Milky Way because you are

Discussion

What are the Clouds of Magellan? *irregular galaxies orbiting the Milky Way* **How far away is the Andromeda Galaxy?** *2.2 million light-years* **Recent evidence indicates that the Milky Way may be what type of galaxy?** *a barred spiral*

Videodisc

STV: Solar System

Unit 1 *The Big Picture, Studying the Sun* 1:17

06338-08660

Refer to the Teacher Guide for additional bar codes and teaching strategies.

The Ring Galaxy Have students research the Cartwheel Galaxy in "A Galaxy of News," by David Bruning in *Astronomy,* June 1995, pp. 40–41. Ask them to write about the results of their research in their Science Journals. L2

Mini Lab

Purpose

Visual-Spatial Students will develop a scale showing the vastness of space.

Materials

large sheet of paper, metric ruler or meterstick, compass

Teaching Strategies

Troubleshooting Help students conceptualize the vast scale of their model. If our sun were represented by a dot, the circle representing the distance to Proxima Centauri would be nearly within that same dot.

Analysis

1. Answers will vary.
2. Whatever the scale used, the distance to the Andromeda Galaxy would be about 22 times the diameter of the student's Milky Way model. This can be determined by dividing the distance to the Andromeda Galaxy (2.2million light-years) by the diameter of the Milky Way (100 000 light-years).

Assessment

Content Have students determine the scale distance to the Large Magellanic Cloud. Its true distance is about 169 000 light-years. Use the **Performance Assessment in the Science Classroom,** p. 29.

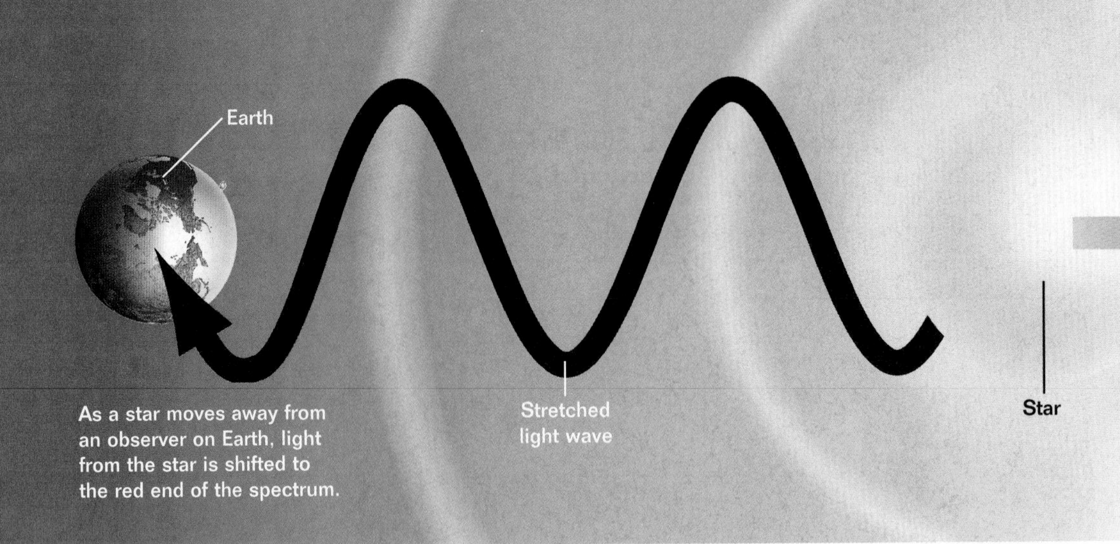
Earth
As a star moves away from an observer on Earth, light from the star is shifted to the red end of the spectrum.
Stretched light wave
Star

Figure 23-21 The Doppler shift causes the wavelengths of light coming from stars and galaxies to be compressed or stretched.

located within one of its spiral arms. You can see the Milky Way stretching across the sky as a faint band of light. All of the stars you can see in the night sky belong to the Milky Way Galaxy.

Mini Lab

Measuring Distance in Space

Procedure

1. On a large sheet of paper, draw an overhead view of the Milky Way Galaxy. If necessary, refer to **Figure 23-17.** Choose a scale to show distance in light-years.
2. Mark the approximate location of our solar system, about two-thirds of the way out on one of the spiral arms.
3. Draw a circle around the sun indicating the 4.2 light-year distance of the next closest star to the sun, Proxima Centauri.

Analysis

1. What scale did you use to represent distance on your model?
2. At this scale, interpret how far away the next closest spiral galaxy—the Andromeda Galaxy—would be located.

Expansion of the Universe

What does it sound like when a car is blowing its horn while it drives past you? The horn has a high pitch as the car approaches you, then the horn seems to drop in pitch as the car drives away. This effect is called the Doppler shift. The Doppler shift occurs with light as well as with sound. **Figure 23-21** shows how the Doppler shift causes changes in the light coming from distant stars and galaxies. If a star is moving toward us, its wavelengths of light are pushed together. If a star is moving away from us, its wavelengths of light are stretched.

The Doppler Shift

Look at the spectrum of a star in **Figure 23-22A.** Note the position of the dark lines. How do they compare with the lines in **Figures 23-22B** and **C?** They have shifted in position. What caused this shift? As you just learned, when a star is moving toward Earth, its wavelengths of light are

682 CHAPTER 23 STARS AND GALAXIES

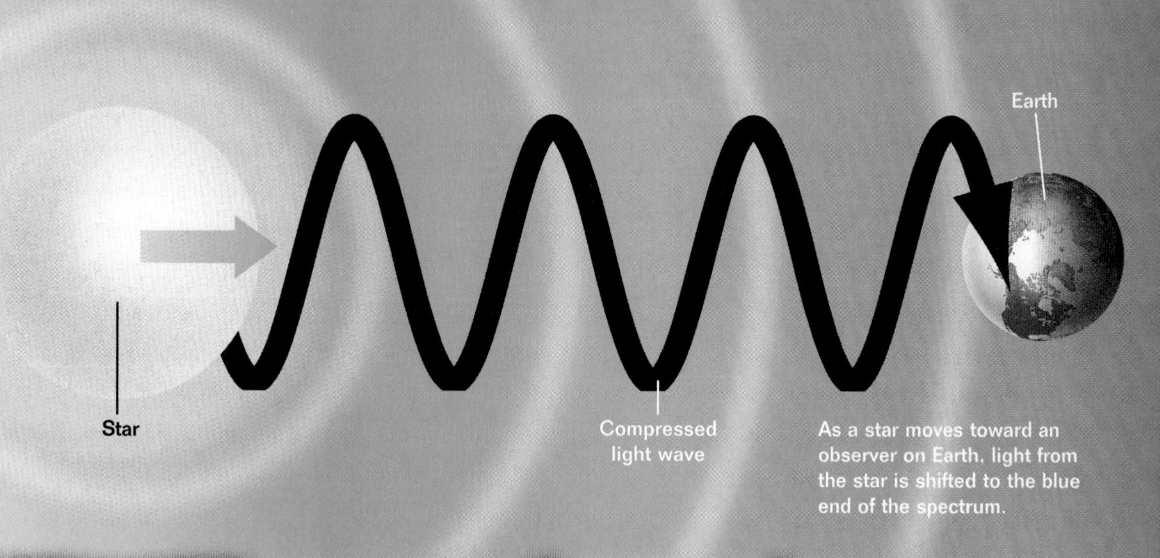
Earth
Star
Compressed light wave
As a star moves toward an observer on Earth, light from the star is shifted to the blue end of the spectrum.

pushed together, just as the sound waves from the car's horn are. This causes the dark lines in the spectrum to shift toward the blue-violet end of the spectrum. A red shift in the spectrum occurs when a star is moving away from Earth. In a red shift, the dark lines shift toward the red end of the spectrum.

In the early twentieth century, scientists noticed an interesting fact about the light coming from most galaxies. When a spectrograph is used to study light from galaxies beyond the Local Group, there is a red shift in the light. What does this red shift tell you about the universe?

Because all galaxies beyond the Local Group show a red shift in their spectra, they must be moving away from Earth. If all galaxies outside the Local Group are moving away from Earth, this indicates that the entire universe must be expanding. Think of the Explore Activity at the beginning of the chapter. The dots on the balloon moved apart as the model universe expanded. Regardless of which dot you picked, all the other dots moved away from it. Galaxies beyond the Local Group move away from us just as the dots moved apart on the balloon.

interNET CONNECTION

Visit the Glencoe Science Web Site at **www.glencoe.com/sec/science** for more information about the Doppler shift.

A
B
C

Figure 23-22 The dark lines in the spectra (A) are shifted toward the blue-violet end when a star is moving toward Earth (B). A red shift (C) indicates that a star is moving away from Earth.

interNET CONNECTION

Internet Addresses

For Internet tips, see Glencoe's **Using the Internet in the Science Classroom.**

Quick Demo

Auditory-Musical Ask students if they have ever experienced the Doppler shift of sound waves. Remind them of train whistles from approaching and receding trains and the siren of a fire truck as it drives by. Securely tie a cord to an alarm clock and gently twirl the clock around as the alarm is sounding. Students will hear the changing pitch as the clock approaches them and then recedes.

GLENCOE TECHNOLOGY

Videodisc

The Infinite Voyage: Unseen Worlds

Chapter 4 *Evolution of the Universe Is Traced* 3:30

Refer to the Teacher Guide for bar codes and teaching strategies.

Science Journal

The Great Wall Have students research and write about the work of Margaret Geller and John Huchra, of the Harvard-Smithsonian Center for Astrophysics, on mapping the universe. The work of these astronomers has led to the realization that great voids and large concentrations of galaxies alternate throughout the universe. For more information, refer students to "A Cross Section of the Universe" by Jeff Kanipe, *Astronomy*, November 1989, p. 44; "Beyond the Big Bang" by Jeff Kanipe, *Astronomy*, April 1992, pp. 30–37; "COBE's Big Bang" by R. Talcott, *Astronomy*, August 1992, pp. 42–44; and recent astronomy textbooks.

VISUAL Learning

Figure 23-23 Have students describe the big bang theory in their own words.

3 Assess

Check for Understanding

Discussion

Why are some galaxies classified as irregular in shape? *Irregular galaxies don't have regular shapes.* **Why can't you see the spiral shape of the Milky Way Galaxy?** *In order to see the spiral shape of the Milky Way, you would have to be located above or below the plane of the galaxy. Earth, in orbit around the sun, is located in one of the spiral arms.*

Reteach

Visual-Spatial Show students one loaf of raisin bread before baking. Have students measure the distance between the raisins in the unbaked bread. Send the loaf to the home economics or domestic arts department to be baked. When the loaf is returned, have students measure the distance between the raisins again. Have students explain why the raisins are farther apart after baking. Have them relate this to the expansion of the universe. L1

Extension

For students who have mastered this section, use the **Reinforcement** and **Enrichment** masters.

VISUALIZING The Big Bang Theory

Figure 23-23 The universe probably began billions of years ago with a fiery explosion.

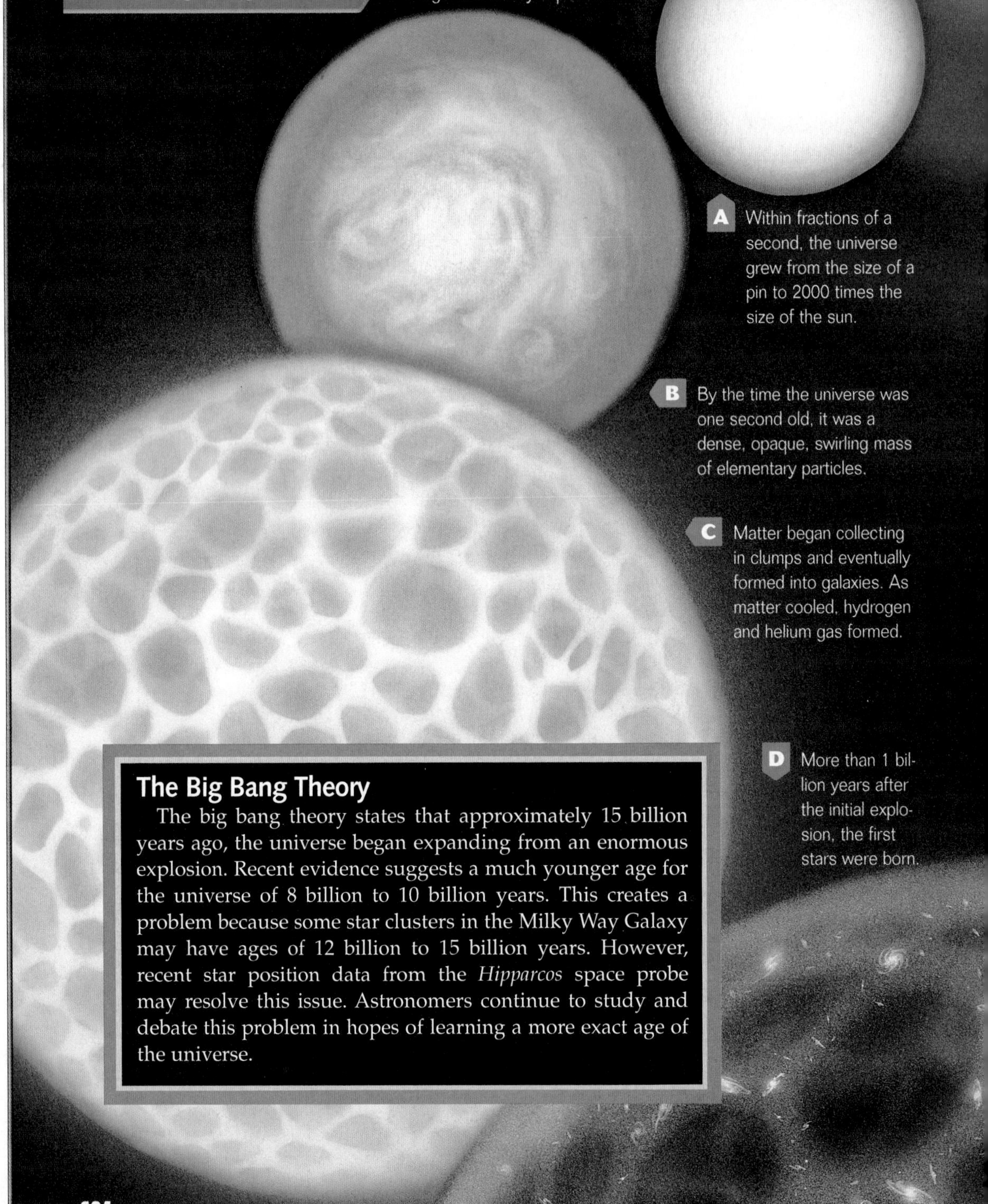

A Within fractions of a second, the universe grew from the size of a pin to 2000 times the size of the sun.

B By the time the universe was one second old, it was a dense, opaque, swirling mass of elementary particles.

C Matter began collecting in clumps and eventually formed into galaxies. As matter cooled, hydrogen and helium gas formed.

D More than 1 billion years after the initial explosion, the first stars were born.

The Big Bang Theory

The big bang theory states that approximately 15 billion years ago, the universe began expanding from an enormous explosion. Recent evidence suggests a much younger age for the universe of 8 billion to 10 billion years. This creates a problem because some star clusters in the Milky Way Galaxy may have ages of 12 billion to 15 billion years. However, recent star position data from the *Hipparcos* space probe may resolve this issue. Astronomers continue to study and debate this problem in hopes of learning a more exact age of the universe.

684 CHAPTER 23 STARS AND GALAXIES

GLENCOE TECHNOLOGY

Videodisc

The Infinite Voyage: Unseen Worlds

Chapter 3 *Astronomers Use Radio Waves to Examine Galaxies* 7:00

Refer to the Teacher Guide for bar codes and teaching strategies.

Inclusion Strategies

Behaviorally Disabled Match behaviorally disabled students with other students. Ask each student group to come up with original ideas on how to develop a model that would demonstrate the big bang theory. L2 

Integrating the Sciences

Physics To help students understand how physics is integrated with the study of astronomy, ask the following question. **What will determine whether the universe keeps on expanding or begins to contract?** *If enough mass exists in the universe, it may eventually slow and begin to collapse.*

The Big Bang Theory

When scientists determined that the universe was expanding, they realized that galaxy clusters must have been closer together in the past. The leading theory about the formation of the universe, called the big bang theory, is based on this explanation. **Figure 23-23** illustrates the **big bang theory,** which states that approximately 15 billion years ago, the universe began with an enormous explosion.

The time-lapse photograph shown in **Figure 23-24** was taken in December 1995 by the *Hubble Space Telescope*. It shows more than 1500 galaxies at a distance of more than 10 billion light-years. These galaxies may date back to when the universe was no more than 1 billion years old. The galaxies are in various stages of development. One astronomer indicates that we may be looking back to a time when our own galaxy was forming. Studies of this nature will eventually enable astronomers to determine the approximate age of the universe.

Whether the universe expands forever or stops depends on how much matter is in the universe. All matter exerts a gravitational force. If there's enough matter, gravity will halt the expansion, and the universe will contract until everything comes to one point.

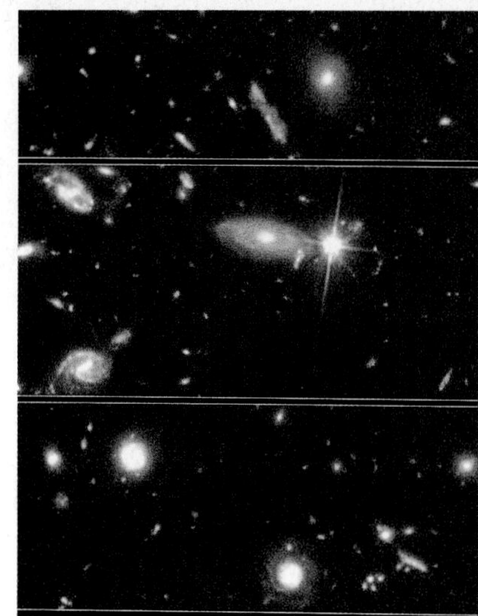

Figure 23-24 The light from these galaxies in this photo mosaic took billions of years to reach Earth.

Section Assessment

1. List the three major classifications of galaxies. What do they have in common?
2. What is the name of the galaxy that you live in? What motion do the stars in this galaxy exhibit?
3. **Think Critically:** All galaxies outside the Local Group show a red shift in their spectra. Within the Local Group, some galaxies show a red shift and some show a blue shift. What does this tell you about the galaxies in the Local Group and outside the Local Group?
4.  **Skill Builder**
Predicting Astronomical distances are measured in light-years, the distance light travels in one year. It takes light from the star Betelgeuse 310 light-years to reach Earth. Do the **Chapter 23 Skill Activity** on page 764 to predict what was happening on Earth when light from distant stars began traveling toward our solar system.

Research and write a report in your Science Journal about the most recent evidence supporting or disputing the big bang theory. Describe how the big bang theory explains observations of galaxies made with spectrometers.

4 Close

Proficiency Prep

Use this quiz to check students' recall of section content.

1. **What do we call a large group of stars, gas, and dust held together by gravity?** *galaxy*
2. **What are the three main types of galaxies?** *elliptical, spiral, and irregular*
3. **Which type of galaxy is most common?** *elliptical*

Section Assessment

1. Galaxy classifications are elliptical, spiral (regular and barred), and irregular. All galaxies are large groups of stars, gas, and dust held together by gravity; they are grouped in clusters.
2. the Milky Way Galaxy; stars orbit its nucleus
3. **Think Critically** All galaxies within the Local Group travel through space together; however, some of them are moving toward the Milky Way, whereas others are moving away from the Milky Way. Galaxies outside the Local Group are moving away from us.

Students should include the latest information obtained by the *Hubble Space Telescope.* The red shift observed by spectrometers indicates that galaxies are moving away from us, which supports the big bang theory.

Assessment

Performance Assess students' abilities to predict by having them choose several stars from the Skill Activity and determine the exact years that light leaving the stars will reach Earth. Use **Performance Assessment in the Science Classroom,** p. 29.

Activity 23·2 Design Your Own Experiment

Recognize the Problem

Purpose

Logical-Mathematical Students will conduct an experiment that shows how distance from an object affects the object's parallax shift. L2 ELL COOP LEARN P

Process Skills

communicating, comparing and contrasting, forming operational definitions, recognizing cause and effect, separating and controlling variables, measuring in SI, using numbers, formulating models, observing and inferring, and hypothesizing

Time

one class period

Safety Precautions

Caution students to wear goggles to protect their eyes during the experiment.

Form a Hypothesis

Possible Hypotheses

Students may hypothesize that the amount of observed parallax increases as an object is moved closer.

Test Your Hypothesis

Possible Procedures

Choose three different positions on the meterstick such as 20 cm, 40 cm, and 60 cm. Mark these positions with masking tape. Attach a metric ruler to one end of the meterstick to form a T shape. Place the meterstick assembly on a table. Hold a pencil upright at one of the marked positions. Observe the pencil's apparent movement against the meterstick with first one eye closed and then the other. Repeat the process for the other marked positions.

Design Your Own Experiment

Activity 23·2

Measuring Parallax

Possible Materials

- Meterstick
- Metric ruler
- Masking tape
- Pencil

Parallax is the apparent shift in the position of an object when viewed from two locations. The nearer an object is to the observer, the greater its parallax. Do this activity to design a model and use it in an experiment that will show how distance affects the amount of observed parallax.

Recognize the Problem

How can you build a model to show the relationship between distance and parallax?

Form a Hypothesis

State a hypothesis about how a model must be built in order for it to be used in an experiment to show how distance affects the amount of observed parallax.

Goals

- **Design a model** to show how the distance from an observer to an object affects the object's parallax shift.
- **Design an experiment** that shows how distance affects the amount of observed parallax.

Safety Precautions

CAUTION: *Be sure to wear goggles to protect your eyes.*

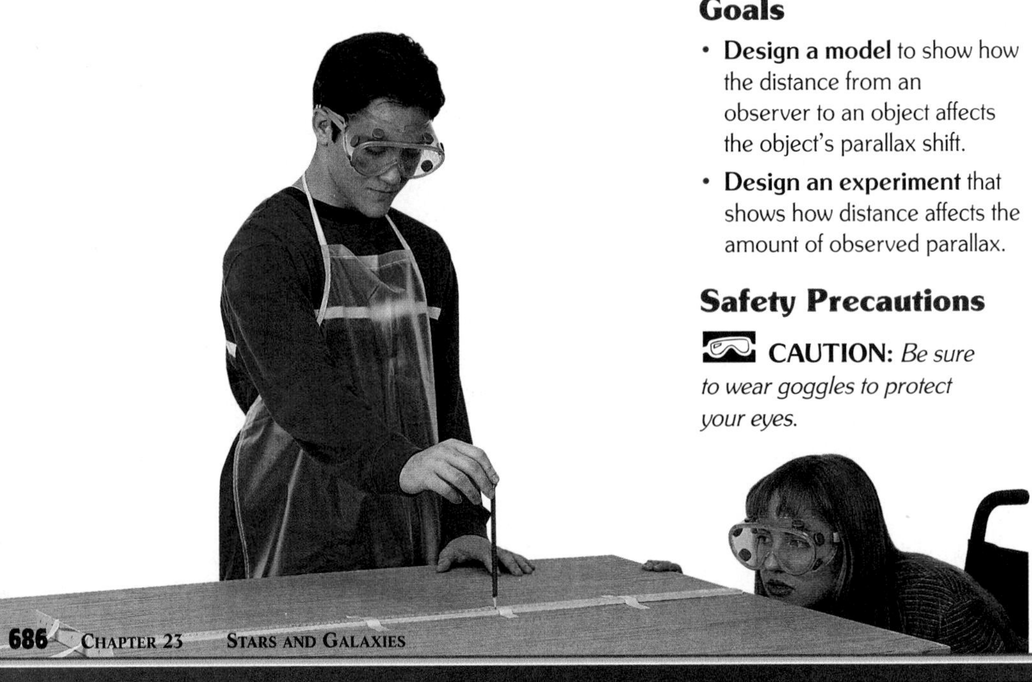

Teaching Strategies

Pair students and assign one member of each group as a recorder. The other partner should carry out the experiment. Students should then switch roles.

Troubleshooting For stability, attach the metric ruler to the end of the meterstick with tape.

Tying to Previous Knowledge

Ask students if they have ever noticed that the speedometer reading in a car appears different to a front-seat passenger than to the driver. Explain that the passenger is viewing the speedometer from an angle. Relate this to parallax.

Test Your Hypothesis

Plan

1. As a group, agree upon and write out your hypothesis statement.
2. List the steps that you need to take to build your model. Be specific, describing exactly what you will do at each step.
3. Devise a method to test how distance from an observer to an object, such as a pencil, affects the relative position of the object.
4. List the steps you will take to test your hypothesis. Be specific, describing exactly what you will do at each step.
5. Read over your plan for the model to be used in this experiment.
6. How will you determine changes in observed parallax? Remember, these changes should occur when the distance from the observer to the object is changed.
7. You should measure shifts in parallax from several different positions. How will these positions differ?
8. How will you measure distances accurately and compare relative position shift?

Do

1. Make sure your teacher approves your plan before you proceed.
2. Construct the model your team has planned.
3. Carry out the experiment as planned.
4. While conducting the experiment, write down any observations that you or other members of your group make in your Science Journal.

Analyze Your Data

1. **Compare** what happened to the object when it was viewed with one eye closed, then the other.
2. At what distance from the observer did the object appear to shift the most?

Draw Conclusions

1. **Infer** what happened to the apparent shift of the object's location as the distance from the observer was increased or decreased.
2. How might astronomers use parallax to study stars?

Expected Outcome

Answers for apparent motion of the pencil will vary. However, if students position themselves so that the meterstick is lined up with their noses, and distances of 20 cm, 40 cm, and 60 cm are used, the following results can be expected. Observed parallax is about 20 cm at the 20-cm mark, 8.5 cm at the 40-cm mark, and 4.9 cm at the 60-cm mark.

Error Analysis

Ask students how the pencil's apparent motion changed as it was placed at progressively farther distances. The pencil should appear to move less as it is placed farther away.

Analyze Your Data

1. The position of the pencil seemed to shift. In reality, nothing happened to the pencil—the movement was only apparent.
2. Answers will vary depending on distances used. The closest distance used by the group is the correct answer.

Draw Conclusions

1. As distance from the observer increased, the pencil's apparent shift decreased. As the distance from the observer decreased, the pencil's apparent shift increased.
2. Astronomers use parallax angles or shifts in the apparent position of astronomical objects to determine distances to the objects.

GO Further

Have students graph the results of the pencil's observed shifts in movement. They should use different-colored pencils to illustrate the three different distances.

Assessment

Process Have students use their thumbs at various distances from their faces to formulate a simple model that demonstrates apparent shifts of parallax for various objects in the classroom. Use **Performance Assessment in the Science Classroom**, p. 51.

Using the Field Guide

- Use this field guide with student pages 688–691.
- A field guide contains a key that enables the user to classify or identify an item or concept.
- Encourage students to use this field guide outside.
- In using a field guide, students will apply steps of a scientific method as they observe, investigate, and draw conclusions.
- This field guide applies nationally; local and regional field guides are usually available for more specific local use.

FIELD ACTIVITY

Student drawings will vary depending on the constellations chosen. Star patterns should match actual constellations. Drawings should illustrate the objects, animals, or characters that the constellations represent.

Tying to Previous Knowledge

Ask students whether they have ever seen shapes of familiar animals or objects in clouds. Tell them that locating constellations is similar to finding familiar objects represented in star patterns in the night sky.

FIELD GUIDE to Backyard Astronomy

FIELD ACTIVITY

Study the star maps included in this field guide. Each night for a week, about one hour after sundown, observe the stars and identify at least three constellations. Draw and label the constellations in your Science Journal. Then, using the key of constellations visible in the northern hemisphere, make drawings of the objects, animals, or characters your constellations represent.

To help them study the night sky, early astronomers developed ways to organize stars into recognizable patterns. We call these patterns constellations. Think of constellations as drawings in the sky. They represent objects, animals, or characters in stories—things that were familiar to ancient stargazers. Using this field guide, you can observe the stars year-round.

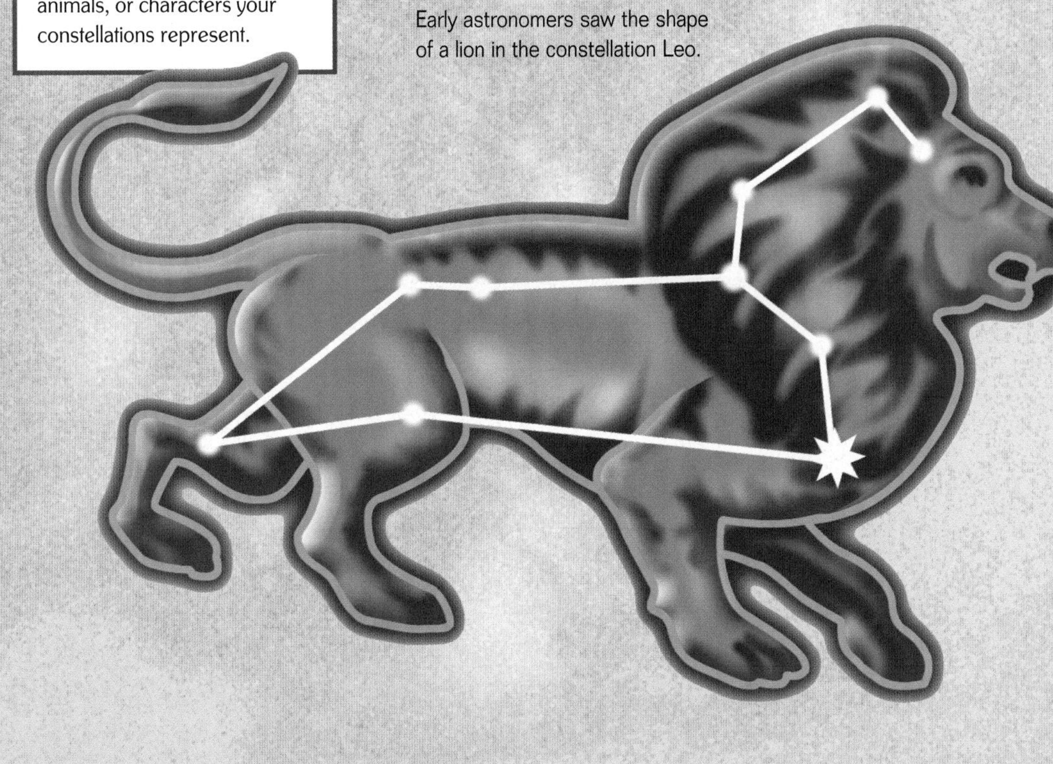

Early astronomers saw the shape of a lion in the constellation Leo.

Other Field Guides to Astronomy

- Lancaster-Brown, Peter. *Skywatch.* New York: Sterling Publishing Company, Inc., 1993.
- Pasachoff, Jay M. *Peterson First Guide to Astronomy.* Boston: Houghton Mifflin Company, 1988.

Major Constellations Visible in the Northern Hemisphere

Name	Represents	Name	Represents
Andromeda	Princess	Lyra	Harp
Aquila	Eagle	Orion	Hunter
Bootes	Herdsman	Pegasus	Winged Horse
Canis Major	Big Dog	Sagittarius	Archer
Canis Minor	Little Dog	Scorpius	Scorpion
Cygnus	Swan (Northern Cross)	Taurus	Bull
Gemini	Twins	Ursa Major	Great Bear (Big Dipper)
Hercules	Hercules	Ursa Minor	Little Bear (Little Dipper)
Leo	Lion	Virgo	Virgin (Maiden)

This map shows the constellations that appear to circle the North Star, also known as Polaris. Because these constellations appear to circle Polaris, which is located almost directly over the north pole, they are called circumpolar constellations. Look toward the north to locate these constellations. To orient yourself, first locate Polaris, which is found by looking directly north, then up at an angle of roughly 35° to 45°.

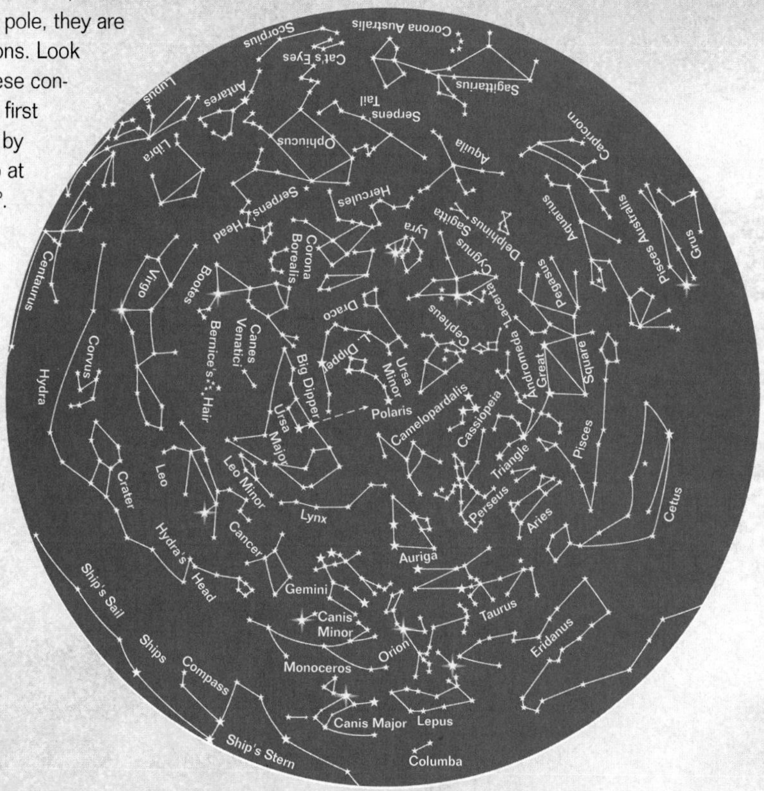

Teacher FYI

Seasonal constellations appear to rise and set each night. Different groups are visible during different seasons. Circumpolar constellations are visible year round. However, only the northern circumpolar constellations can be seen from the northern hemisphere.

Quick Demo

Obtain a globe and point out your area's exact latitude. Tell students that this figure can be used to find Polaris. For instance, if you live at a latitude of 40°N, then Polaris will be positioned 40° above your northern horizon. Polaris, in turn, can be used to locate northern circumpolar constellations.

interNET CONNECTION

Internet Addresses

For Internet tips, see Glencoe's **Using the Internet in the Science Classroom.**

FIELD GUIDE

Content Background

The celestial sphere is the imaginary dome on which the stars appear in the night sky. Each person's zenith is the imaginary point on the celestial sphere located directly above his or her head. An imaginary line drawn from the northern horizon up through the zenith then down to the southern horizon traces the celestial meridian. The celestial meridian is used to locate the constellations of each season.

VISUAL Learning

Have students locate Ursa Major in each of the four seasonal charts. Have them describe the apparent path of the constellation throughout the year. Stress that the apparent change in position is due to Earth's movement in space.

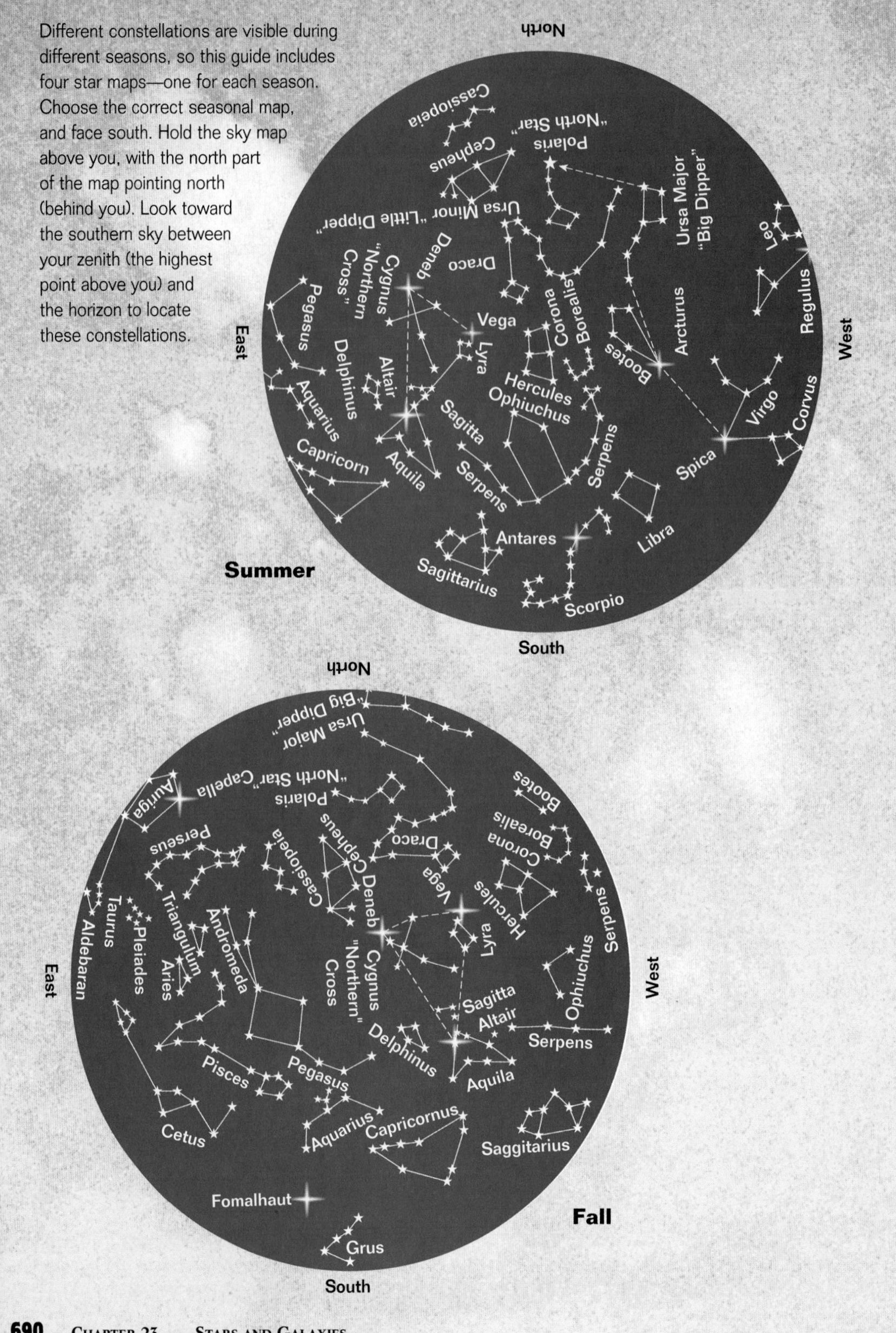

Inclusion Strategies

Learning Disabled Draw the stars of various constellations on the chalkboard. Use lines to connect the stars within each constellation. Have students draw pictures of the objects each constellation represents. They should draw their pictures on the chalkboard, around the connecting lines.

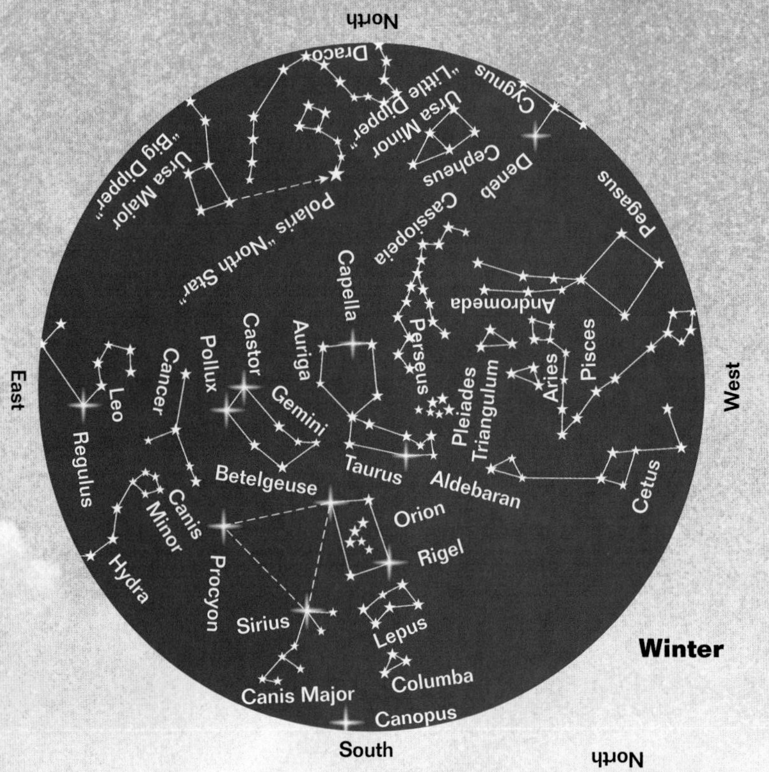

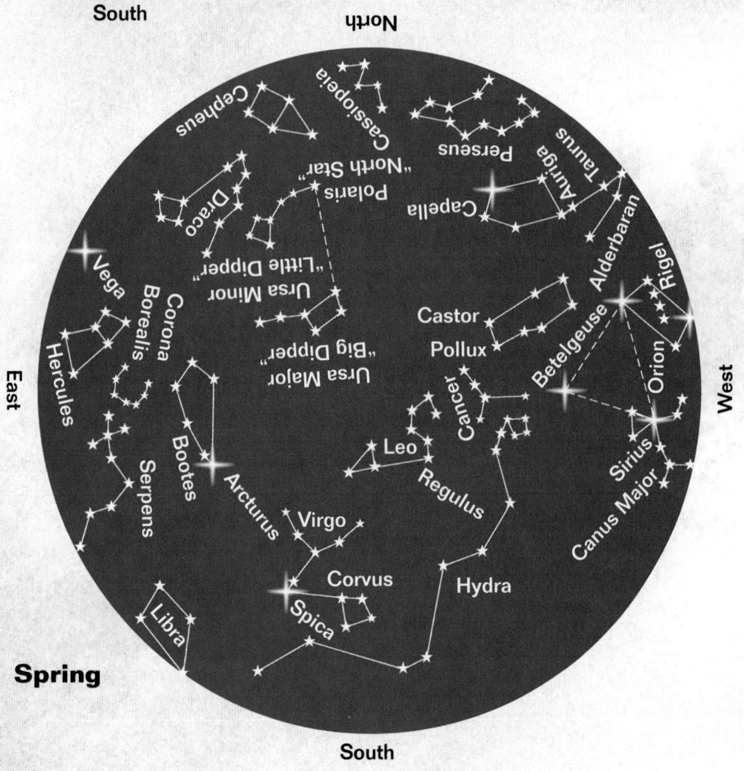

Enrichment

Obtain a circumpolar star chart showing constellations of the southern hemisphere. Have students compare and contrast the locations of circumpolar constellations in the northern and southern hemispheres.

GO Further

Have students research the brightest stars of several constellations such as Sirius A in Canis Major or Rigel in Orion. Have students make a table showing the name of each star, the constellation it is found in, its apparent magnitude, its absolute magnitude, and its distance in light-years from Earth.

Across the Curriculum

Physics Using wavelength analyses, astronomers have recently confirmed the existence of extragalactic stars—stars located outside of galaxies. Much of the research has been centered on the dark spaces that surround M86, an elliptical galaxy in Virgo. Although no planets have been discovered orbiting these stars, it is reasonable to assume that some may exist. Remind students that all the constellations visible from Earth are part of the Milky Way Galaxy. Ask them how the night sky might appear to an observer on a planet orbiting an extragalactic star. *Because the star is not part of a galaxy, few, if any, constellations would be visible. The night sky would be largely black.*

Reviewing Main Ideas can be used to preview, review, reteach, and condense chapter content.

Preview

Linguistic Have students try to answer the questions in their Science Journals. Use student answers as a source for discussion throughout the chapter.

Review

Interpersonal Have students answer the questions on separate pieces of paper and compare their answers with those of other students in the class.

Reteach

Visual-Spatial Have students look at the illustrations on these pages. Ask them to describe details that support the main ideas of the chapter found in the statement for each illustration.

00:00 OUT OF TIME?

Auditory-Musical If time does not permit teaching the entire chapter, use the information on these pages along with the chapter Audiocassettes to present the material in a condensed format.

Chapter 23 Reviewing Main Ideas

For a **preview** of this chapter, study this Reviewing Main Ideas before you read the chapter. After you have studied this chapter, you can use the Reviewing Main Ideas to **review** the chapter.

The Glencoe MindJogger, Audiocassettes, and CD-ROM provide additional opportunities for review.

Section 23-1 STARS

The magnitude of a star is a measure of the star's brightness. **Absolute magnitude** is a measure of the light emitted. **Apparent magnitude** is a measure of the amount of light received on Earth. **Parallax** is the apparent shift in the position of an object when viewed from two different positions. The closer to Earth a star is, the greater its shift in parallax. A star's temperature and composition can be determined from the star's spectrum. ***What term describes how bright a star looks from Earth?***

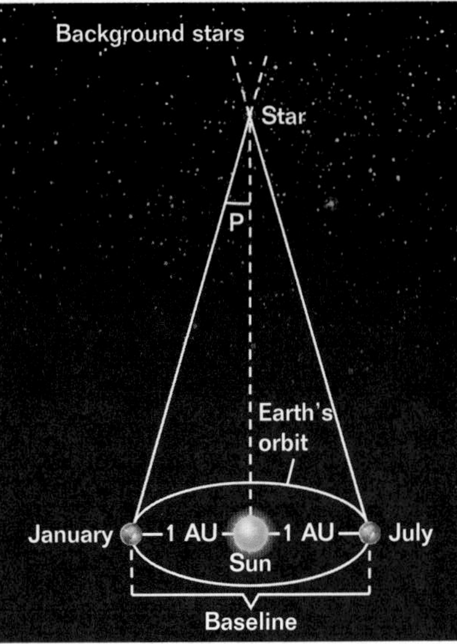

Section 23-2 THE SUN

The sun produces energy by fusing hydrogen into helium in its core. Light is given off from the photosphere, which is the lowest layer of the sun's atmosphere. **Sunspots** are areas of the sun that are cooler and less bright than surrounding areas. Sunspots, prominences, and flares are caused by the intense magnetic field of the sun, which is a main sequence star. ***Why is the sun considered an average star?***

Cultural Diversity

What's in a name? The Milky Way is the English name for the galaxy containing Earth, but it has been known by many others. Akkadians called it the Great Serpent, or the River of the Snake. In Judea, Armenia, and Syria, the galaxy was sometimes referred to as a Long Bandage. China and Japan called it Tien Ho, the Celestial River, or the Silver River. In India, the band of light was known by three names: Akash Ganga, the Bed of the Ganges; Bhagwan ki Kachahri, the Court of Go; and Swarga Duari, the Dove of Paradise. Polynesians called the cloud of lights the Long, Blue, Cloud-Eating Shark, while the Ottawa saw it as muddy water stirred up by a turtle swimming along the bottom of the sky. Ask interested students to research how other cultures may have referred to the Milky Way. L2

Reading Check 

The big bang theory is still controversial. What part of this theory is supported by evidence? What part is opinion?

Section

23-3 EVOLUTION OF STARS

When hydrogen is used up in a **main sequence** star, the star's core collapses and its temperature increases. The star becomes a **giant** or a **supergiant,** which uses helium as fuel. As the star evolves, its outer layers escape into space and the star becomes a **white dwarf.** Stars containing high amounts of mass can explode. During a supernova explosion, the outer layers of a star are blown away and the remaining core evolves into a **neutron star** or **black hole.** *At what temperature does fusion begin inside a nebula?*

Section

23-4 GALAXIES AND THE UNIVERSE

A **galaxy** is a large group of stars, gas, and dust held together by gravity. Galaxies can be elliptical, spiral, or irregular in shape. The galaxy that our sun belongs to, the Milky Way, contains about 200 billion stars. There may be more than 100 billion galaxies in the universe. The most accepted theory about the origin of the universe is the **big bang theory.** *What is the Local Group of galaxies?*

Answers to Questions

Section 23-1

Stars apparent magnitude

Section 23-2

The Sun Its absolute magnitude is about average, and it shines with a yellow light, which is in the middle range of visible star colors.

Section 23-3

Evolution of Stars

10 000 000 K

Section 23-4

Galaxies and the Universe

The Local Group is the galaxy cluster to which the Milky Way belongs.

GLENCOE TECHNOLOGY

CD-ROM

Glencoe Science Voyages Interactive CD-ROM

Chapter Summaries and Quizzes

Have students read the Chapter Summary then take the Chapter Quiz to determine whether they have mastered chapter content.

Assessment

Portfolio Encourage students to place in their portfolios one or two items of what they consider to be their best work. Examples include:

- MiniLab, p. 665
- Using Computers, p. 666
- Activity 23-2, pp. 686–687 P

Performance Additional performance assessments may be found in **Performance Assessment** and **Science Integration Activities.** Performance Task Assessment Lists and rubrics for evaluating these activities can be found in Glencoe's **Performance Assessment in the Science Classroom.**

Chapter 23 Assessment

Using Vocabulary

a. absolute magnitude
b. apparent magnitude
c. big bang theory
d. binary system
e. black hole
f. chromosphere
g. constellation
h. corona
i. galaxy
j. giant
k. light-year
l. main sequence
m. nebula
n. neutron star
o. parallax
p. photosphere
q. sunspot
r. supergiant
s. white dwarf

Explain the differences in the terms given below. Then explain how the terms are related.

1. absolute magnitude, apparent magnitude
2. black hole, neutron star
3. chromosphere, photosphere
4. binary system, constellation
5. light-year, parallax

Checking Concepts

Choose the word or phrase that best answers the question.

6. What do constellations form?
   A) clusters
   B) giants
   C) black holes
   D) patterns
7. What is a measure of the amount of a star's light received on Earth?
   A) absolute magnitude
   B) apparent magnitude
   C) fusion
   D) parallax
8. What increases as an object comes closer to an observer?
   A) absolute magnitude
   B) red shift
   C) parallax
   D) size
9. What begins once a nebula contracts and temperatures increase to 10 millionK?
   A) main sequencing
   B) a supernova
   C) fusion
   D) a white dwarf
10. What is about 10 km in size?
    A) giant
    B) white dwarf
    C) black hole
    D) neutron star
11. Our sun fuses hydrogen into what?
    A) carbon
    B) oxygen
    C) iron
    D) helium
12. What are loops of matter flowing from the sun?
    A) sunspots
    B) auroras
    C) coronas
    D) prominences
13. What are groups of galaxies called?
    A) clusters
    B) supergiants
    C) giants
    D) binary systems
14. Which galaxies are sometimes shaped like footballs?
    A) spiral
    B) elliptical
    C) barred
    D) irregular
15. What do scientists study to determine shifts in wavelengths of light?
    A) spectrum
    B) surface
    C) corona
    D) chromosphere

Thinking Critically

16. What is significant about the 1995 discovery by the *Hubble Space Telescope* of more than 1500 galaxies at a distance of more than 10 billion light-years?
17. How do scientists know that black holes exist if these objects don't emit any visible light?
18. Use the autumn star chart in Appendix K to determine which constellation is directly overhead at 8 P.M. on November 23 for an observer in North America.
19. How are radio waves used to detect objects in space?
20. What kinds of reactions produce the energy emitted by stars?

Chapter 23 Assessment

Using Vocabulary

1. Absolute magnitude measures light emitted by a star. Apparent magnitude measures the amount of light received on Earth from a star.
2. A black hole is an object so dense, nothing can escape its gravity field. A neutron star is the collapsed core of a supernova.
3. The photosphere is the lowest layer of the sun's atmosphere. The chromosphere lies directly above the photosphere.
4. A binary system consists of two stars orbiting each other. A constellation is a group of stars that makes a pattern in the sky.
5. A light-year is the distance light travels in one year—it is used to measure distances in space. Parallax is the apparent shift in an object's position when viewed from two different positions.

*inter***NET** CONNECTION To reinforce chapter vocabulary, use the **Study Guide for Content Mastery** booklet. Also available are activities for **Glencoe Science Voyages** on the Glencoe Science Web Site. **www.glencoe.com/sec/science**

Checking Concepts

6. D
7. B
8. C
9. C
10. D
11. D
12. D
13. A
14. B
15. A

Thinking Critically

16. Astronomers are looking at galaxies that may have formed when the universe was only 1 billion years old. Studies of this nature help determine the true age of the universe.
17. Astronomers are able to use instruments to detect the X rays surrounding black holes.
18. Pegasus is almost directly overhead at this time.
19. Any object at a temperature above absolute zero emits radio waves. These waves can be gathered by radio telescopes then analyzed to determine what type of object is emitting them.
20. Stars produce energy by fusion. Hydrogen is converted into helium in main sequence stars. Helium then fuses to produce heavier elements. As nuclei are fused, mass is converted into energy.

Assessment

Developing Skills

If you need help, refer to the **Skill Handbook**.

21. **Concept Mapping:** Complete the concept map on this page that shows the evolution of a main sequence star with a mass similar to that of the sun.

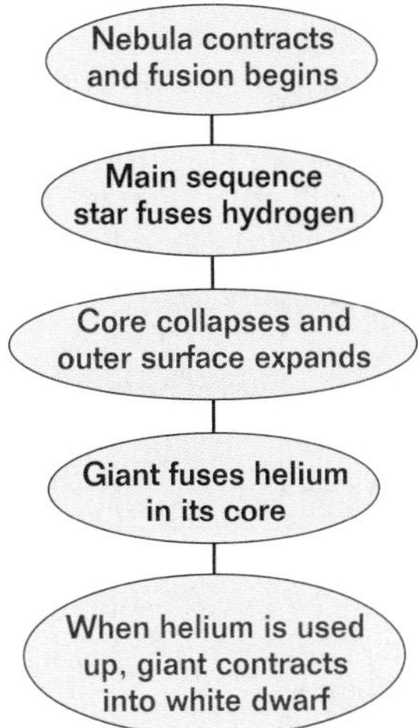

Nebula contracts and fusion begins
Main sequence star fuses hydrogen
Core collapses and outer surface expands
Giant fuses helium in its core
When helium is used up, giant contracts into white dwarf

22. **Comparing and Contrasting:** Compare and contrast the sun with other stars on the H-R diagram.
23. **Measuring in SI:** The Milky Way Galaxy is 100 000 light-years in diameter. What scale would you use if you were to construct a model of the Milky Way with a diameter of 20 cm?
24. **Designing an Experiment:** Design and carry out an experiment that uses sunspot locations to compare rotational periods of different latitudes of the sun.
25. **Making a Model:** Design and construct scale models of a spiral and a barred spiral Milky Way Galaxy. Show the approximate position of the sun in each.

THE PRINCETON REVIEW

Test-Taking Tip

Read the Label No matter how many times you've taken a particular test or practiced for an exam, it's always a good idea to skim through the instructions provided at the beginning of each section.

Test Practice

Use these questions to test your Science Proficiency.

1. A white dwarf star is located in the lower-left-hand corner of an H-R diagram. Which of the following statements **BEST** explains why it is positioned there?
   A) White dwarf stars have low absolute magnitudes and high surface temperatures.
   B) White dwarf stars have low absolute magnitudes and low surface temperatures.
   C) White dwarf stars have high absolute magnitudes and high surface temperatures.
   D) White dwarf stars have high absolute magnitudes and low surface temperatures.
2. Sunspots are dark areas of the sun's surface. Which of the following statements **BEST** explains why this is true?
   A) Sunspots are areas of the sun's surface that do not give off light.
   B) Sunspots appear dark because they give off more energy than surrounding areas of the sun's surface.
   C) Sunspots are hotter than surrounding areas of the sun's surface.
   D) Sunspots are cooler than surrounding areas of the sun's surface.

THE PRINCETON REVIEW **Test Practice**

The Test-Taking Tip was written by The Princeton Review, the nation's leader in test preparation.

1. A
2. D

Developing Skills

21. See student page.
22. The sun is an average star in terms of mass, temperature, and its place in the evolutionary cycle. The sun differs from more massive stars in that massive stars have higher temperatures and are further along in their evolutionary cycle. Other stars such as white dwarfs are hotter than the sun but don't emit as much light.
23. 1 cm = 5000 light-years
24. Student experiments will vary. However, students should conclude that the sun rotates faster around its equator than toward its poles.
25. Student models should correspond to descriptions of spiral and barred spiral galaxies given in the student text. The sun should be positioned about two-thirds of the way outward from the nucleus of the galaxy.

Bonus Question

Observe two distant objects in opposite directions from a single viewing point. Using your knowledge of parallax, determine which object is closer. *The closer object will appear to move more when viewed through one eye, then the other.*

Assessment Resources

The **Test Practice Workbook** provides students with practice in the format, concepts, and critical-thinking skills tested in standardized exams.

Reproducible Masters

Chapter Review, pp. 45–46 L2
Performance Assessment, p. 37 L2
Assessment, pp. 101–104 L2

Glencoe Technology

Chapter Review Software
Computer Test Bank
MindJogger Videoquiz

Appendices

Appendix A

Safety in the Science Classroom

1. Always obtain your teacher's permission to begin an investigation.
2. Study the procedure. If you have questions, ask your teacher. Be sure you understand any safety symbols shown on the page.
3. Use the safety equipment provided for you. Goggles and a safety apron should be worn during an investigation.
4. Always slant test tubes away from yourself and others when heating them.
5. Never eat or drink in the lab, and never use lab glassware as food or drink containers. Never inhale chemicals. Do not taste any substances or draw any material into a tube with your mouth.
6. If you spill any chemical, wash it off immediately with water. Report the spill immediately to your teacher.
7. Know the location and proper use of the fire extinguisher, safety shower, fire blanket, first aid kit, and fire alarm.
8. Keep all materials away from open flames. Tie back long hair and loose clothing.
9. If a fire should break out in the classroom, or if your clothing should catch fire, smother it with the fire blanket or a coat, or get under a safety shower. NEVER RUN.
10. Report any accident or injury, no matter how small, to your teacher.

Follow these procedures as you clean up your work area.

1. Turn off the water and gas. Disconnect electrical devices.
2. Return all materials to their proper places.
3. Dispose of chemicals and other materials as directed by your teacher. Place broken glass and solid substances in the proper containers. Never discard materials in the sink.
4. Clean your work area.
5. Wash your hands thoroughly after working in the laboratory.

Table A-1

First Aid

Injury	Safe Response
Burns	Apply cold water. Call your teacher immediately.
Cuts and bruises	Stop any bleeding by applying direct pressure. Cover cuts with a clean dressing. Apply cold compresses to bruises. Call your teacher immediately.
Fainting	Leave the person lying down. Loosen any tight clothing and keep crowds away. Call your teacher immediately.
Foreign matter in eye	Flush with plenty of water. Use eyewash bottle or fountain.
Poisoning	Note the suspected poisoning agent and call your teacher immediately.
Any spills on skin	Flush with large amounts of water or use safety shower. Call your teacher immediately.

Appendix B

SI/Metric to English Conversions

	When you want to convert:	To:	Multiply by:
Length	inches	centimeters	2.54
	centimeters	inches	0.39
	feet	meters	0.30
	meters	feet	3.28
	yards	meters	0.91
	meters	yards	1.09
	miles	kilometers	1.61
	kilometers	miles	0.62
Mass and Weight*	ounces	grams	28.35
	grams	ounces	0.04
	pounds	kilograms	0.45
	kilograms	pounds	2.2
	tons (short)	tonnes (metric tons)	0.91
	tonnes (metric tons)	tons (short)	1.10
	pounds	newtons	4.45
	newtons	pounds	0.23
Volume	cubic inches	cubic centimeters	16.39
	cubic centimeters	cubic inches	0.06
	cubic feet	cubic meters	0.03
	cubic meters	cubic feet	35.30
	liters	quarts	1.06
	liters	gallons	0.26
	gallons	liters	3.78
Area	square inches	square centimeters	6.45
	square centimeters	square inches	0.16
	square feet	square meters	0.09
	square meters	square feet	10.76
	square miles	square kilometers	2.59
	square kilometers	square miles	0.39
	hectares	acres	2.47
	acres	hectares	0.40
Temperature	Fahrenheit	5/9 (°F − 32) =	Celsius
	Celsius	9/5 (°C) + 32 =	Fahrenheit

*Weight as measured in standard Earth gravity

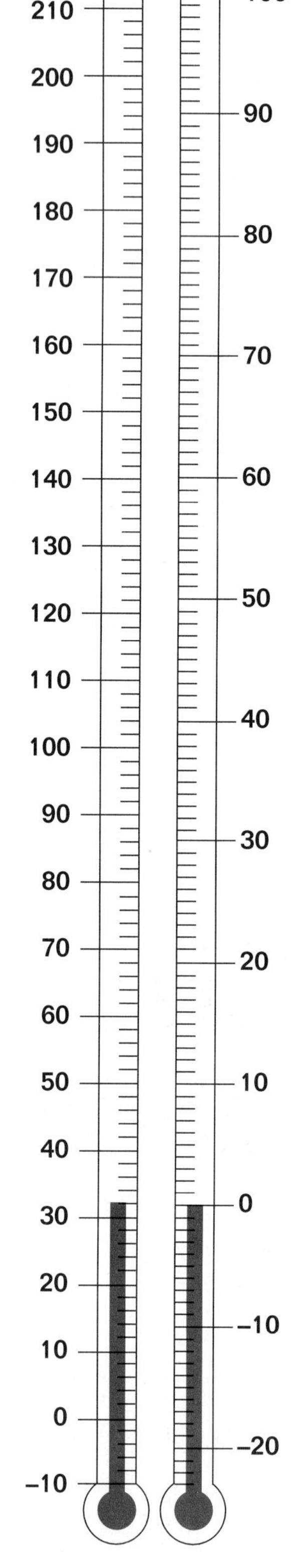

Appendix C

SI Units of Measurement

Table C-1

SI Base Units					
Measurement	**Unit**	**Symbol**	**Measurement**	**Unit**	**Symbol**
length	meter	m	temperature	kelvin	K
mass	kilogram	kg	amount of substance	mole	mol
time	second	s			

Table C-2

Units Derived from SI Base Units		
Measurement	**Unit**	**Symbol**
energy	joule	J
force	newton	N
frequency	hertz	Hz
potential difference	volt	V
power	watt	W
pressure	pascal	Pa

Table C-3

Common SI Prefixes					
Prefix	**Symbol**	**Multiplier**	**Prefix**	**Symbol**	**Multiplier**
	Greater than 1			Less than 1	
mega-	M	1 000 000	*deci-*	d	0.1
kilo-	k	1 000	*centi-*	c	0.01
hecto-	h	100	*milli-*	m	0.001
deka-	da	10	*micro-*	μ	0.000 001

Appendix D

Care and Use of a Microscope

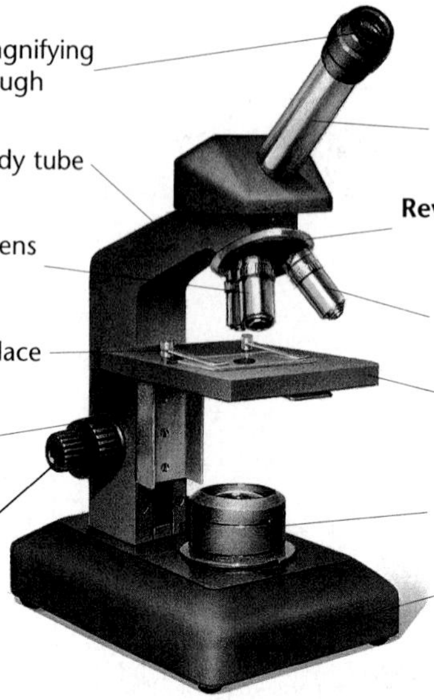

Eyepiece Contains a magnifying lens you look through

Arm Supports the body tube

Low-power objective Contains the lens with low-power magnification

Stage clips Hold the microscope slide in place

Coarse adjustment Focuses the image under low power

Fine adjustment Sharpens the image under high and low magnification

Body tube Connects the eyepiece to the revolving nosepiece

Revolving nosepiece Holds and turns the objectives into viewing position

High-power objective Contains the lens with the highest magnification

Stage Supports the microscope slide

Light source Allows light to reflect upward through the diaphragm, the specimen, and the lenses

Base Provides support for the microscope

Care of a Microscope

1. Always carry the microscope holding the arm with one hand and supporting the base with the other hand.
2. Don't touch the lenses with your fingers.
3. Never lower the coarse adjustment knob when looking through the eyepiece lens.
4. Always focus first with the low-power objective.
5. Don't use the coarse adjustment knob when the high-power objective is in place.
6. Store the microscope covered.

Using a Microscope

1. Place the microscope on a flat surface that is clear of objects. The arm should be toward you.
2. Look through the eyepiece. Adjust the diaphragm so that light comes through the opening in the stage.
3. Place a slide on the stage so that the specimen is in the field of view. Hold it firmly in place by using the stage clips.
4. Always focus first with the coarse adjustment and the low-power objective lens. Once the object is in focus on low power, turn the nosepiece until the high-power objective is in place. Use ONLY the fine adjustment to focus with the high-power objective lens.

Making a Wet-Mount Slide

1. Carefully place the item you want to look at in the center of a clean, glass slide. Make sure the sample is thin enough for light to pass through.
2. Use a dropper to place one or two drops of water on the sample.
3. Hold a clean coverslip by the edges and place it at one edge of the drop of water. Slowly lower the coverslip onto the drop of water until it lies flat.
4. If you have too much water or a lot of air bubbles, touch the edge of a paper towel to the edge of the coverslip to draw off extra water and force out air.

Appendix E

Diversity of Life: Classification of Living Organisms

Scientists use a six-kingdom system of classification of organisms. In this system, there are two kingdoms of organisms, Kingdoms Archaebacteria and Eubacteria, which contain organisms that do not have a nucleus and lack membrane-bound structures in the cytoplasm of their cells. The members of the other four kingdoms have cells which contain a nucleus and structures in the cytoplasm that are surrounded by membranes. These kingdoms are Kingdom Protista, Kingdom Fungi, the Kingdom Plantae, and the Kingdom Animalia.

Kingdom Archaebacteria

One-celled prokaryotes; absorb food from surroundings or make their own food by chemosynthesis; found in extremely harsh environments including salt ponds, hot springs, swamps, and deep-sea hydrothermal vents.

Kingdom Eubacteria

Cyanobacteria one-celled prokaryotes; make their own food; contain chlorophyll; some species form colonies; most are blue-green

Bacteria one-celled prokaryotes; most absorb food from their surroundings; some are photosynthetic; many are parasites; round, spiral, or rod-shaped

Kingdom Protista

Phylum Euglenophyta one-celled; can photosynthesize or take in food; most have one flagellum; euglenoids

Phylum Bacillariophyta one-celled; make their own food through photosynthesis; have unique double shells made of silica; diatoms

Phylum Dinoflagellata one-celled; make their own food through photosynthesis; contain red pigments; have two flagella; dinoflagellates

Phylum Chlorophyta one-celled, many-celled, or colonies; contain chlorophyll; make their own food; live on land, in fresh water, or salt water; green algae

Phylum Rhodophyta most are many-celled; photosynthetic; contain red pigments; most live in deep saltwater environments; red algae

Phylum Phaeophyta most are many-celled; photosynthetic; contain brown pigments; most live in saltwater environments; brown algae

Phylum Foraminifera many-celled; take in food; primarily marine; shells constructed of calcium carbonate, or made from grains of sand; forams

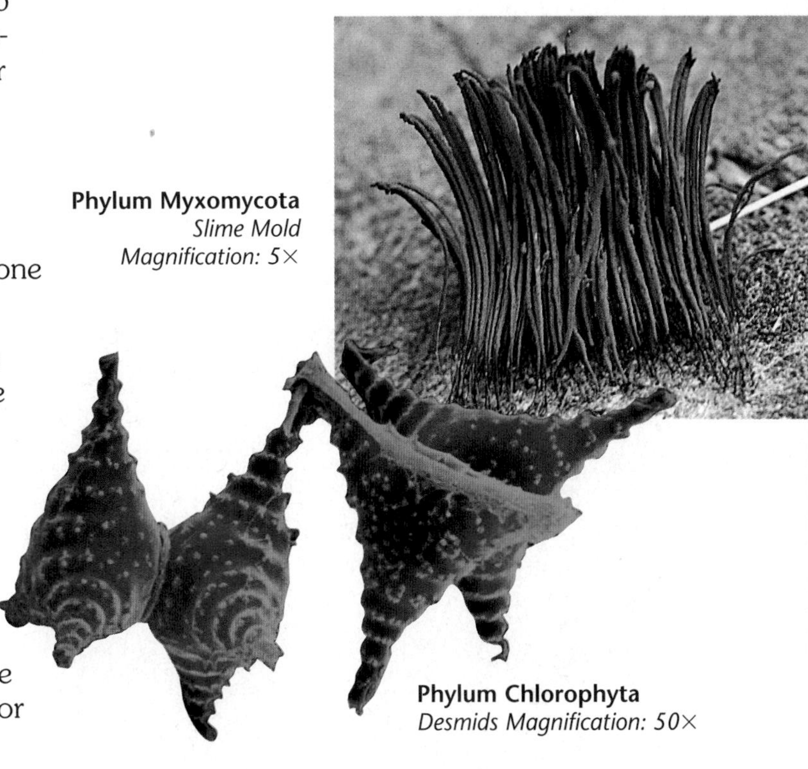

Phylum Myxomycota
Slime Mold
Magnification: 5×

Phylum Chlorophyta
Desmids Magnification: 50×

Phylum Rhizopoda one-celled; take in food; move by means of pseudopods; free-living or parasitic; amoebas

Phylum Zoomastigina one-celled; take in food; have one or more flagella; free-living or parasitic; zoomastigotes

Phylum Ciliophora one-celled; take in food; have large numbers of cilia; ciliates

Phylum Sporozoa one-celled; take in food; no means of movement; parasites in animals; sporozoans

Phylum Myxomycota and Acrasiomycota: one- or many-celled; absorb food; change form during life cycle; cellular and plasmodial slime molds

Phylum Oomycota many-celled; live in fresh or salt water; are either parasites or decomposers; water molds, rusts and downy mildews

Kingdom Fungi

Phylum Zygomycota many-celled; absorb food; spores are produced in sporangia; zygote fungi; bread mold

Phylum Ascomycota one- and many-celled; absorb food; spores produced in asci; sac fungi; yeast

Phylum Basidiomycota many-celled; absorb food; spores produced in basidia; club fungi; mushrooms

Phylum Deuteromycota: members with unknown reproductive structures; imperfect fungi; penicillin

Lichens organisms formed by symbiotic relationship between an ascomycote or a basidiomycote and green alga or cyanobacterium

Kingdom Plantae

Non-seed Plants

Division Bryophyta nonvascular plants; reproduce by spores produced in capsules; many-celled; green; grow in moist land environments; mosses and liverworts

Division Lycophyta many-celled vascular plants; spores produced in conelike structures; live on land; are photosynthetic; club mosses

Division Sphenophyta vascular plants; ribbed and jointed stems; scalelike leaves; spores produced in conelike structures; horsetails

Division Pterophyta vascular plants; leaves called fronds; spores produced in clusters of sporangia called sori; live on land or in water; ferns

Division Bryophyta
Liverwort

Lichens
British soldier lichen × 3

Seed Plants

Division Ginkgophyta: deciduous gymnosperms; only one living species; fan-shaped leaves with branching veins; reproduces with seeds; ginkgos

Division Cycadophyta: palmlike gymnosperms; large featherlike leaves; produce seeds in cones; cycads

Division Coniferophyta: deciduous or evergreen gymnosperms; trees or shrubs; needlelike or scalelike leaves; seeds produced in cones; conifers

Division Gnetophyta: shrubs or woody vines; seeds produced in cones; division contains only three genera; gnetum

Division Anthophyta: dominant group of plants; ovules protected in an ovary; sperm carried to ovules by pollen tube; produce flowers and seeds in fruits; flowering plants

Kingdom Animalia

Phylum Porifera: aquatic organisms that lack true tissues and organs; they are asymmetrical and sessile; sponges

Phylum Cnidaria: radially symmetrical organisms; have a digestive cavity with one opening; most have tentacles armed with stinging cells; live in aquatic environments singly or in colonies; includes jellyfish, corals, hydra, and sea anemones

Phylum Platyhelminthes: bilaterally symmetrical worms; have flattened bodies; digestive system has one opening; parasitic and free-living species; flatworms

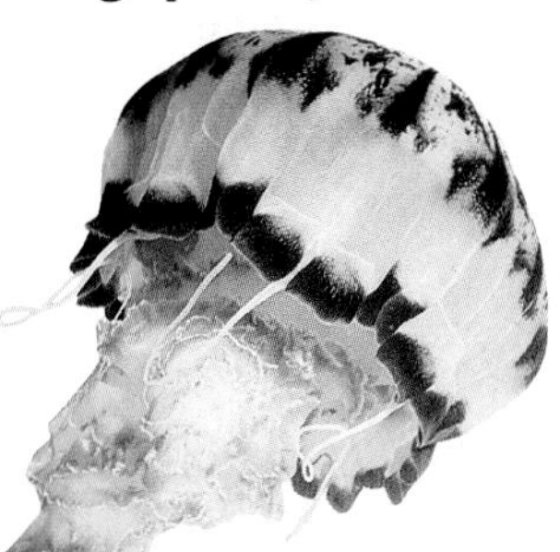

Phylum Cnidaria
Jellyfish

Phylum Arthopoda
Orb Weaver Spider

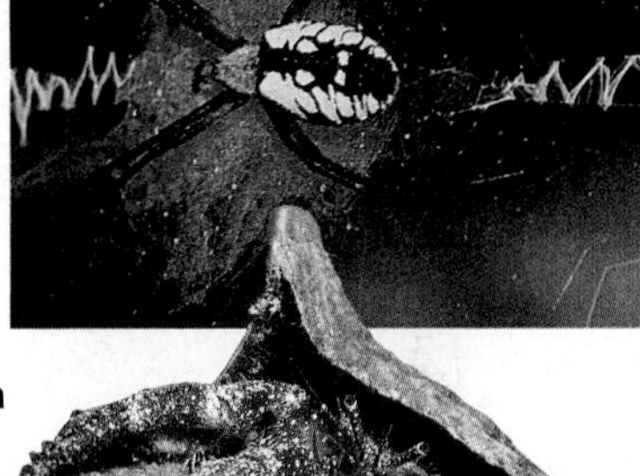

Phylum Arthropoda
Hermit Crab

Phylum Mollusca
Florida Fighting Conch

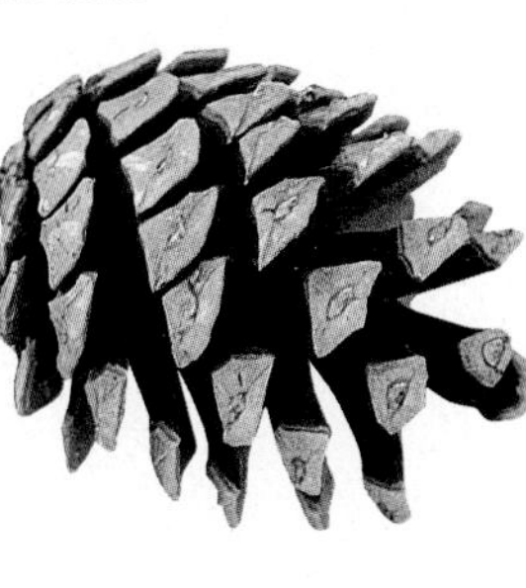

Division Coniferophyta
Pine cone

Division Anthophyta
Strawberry Blossoms

Division Anthophyta
Strawberries

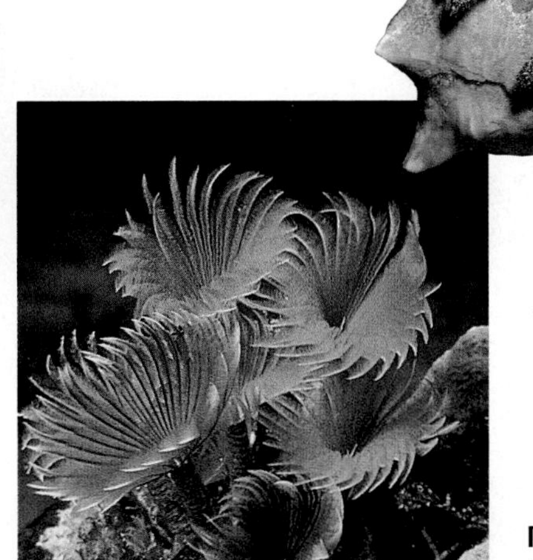

Phylum Annelida
Sabellid Worms
Feather Duster

Appendix E

Phylum Nematoda: round, bilaterally symmetrical body; digestive system with two openings; some free-living forms but mostly parasitic; roundworms

Phylum Mollusca: soft-bodied animals, many with a hard shell; a mantle covers the soft body; aquatic and terrestrial species; includes clams, snails, squid, and octopuses

Phylum Annelida: bilaterally symmetrical worms; have round, segmented bodies; terrestrial and aquatic species; includes earthworms, leeches, and marine polychaetes

Phylum Arthropoda: largest phylum of organisms; have segmented bodies; pairs of jointed appendages; have hard exoskeletons; terrestrial and aquatic species; includes insects, crustaceans, spiders, and horseshoe crabs

Phylum Echinodermata: marine organisms; have spiny or leathery skin; water-vascular system with tube feet; radial symmetry; includes sea stars, sand dollars, and sea urchins

Phylum Chordata: organisms with internal skeletons; specialized body systems; paired appendages; all at some time have a notochord, dorsal nerve cord, gill slits, and a tail; include fish, amphibians, reptiles, birds, and mammals

Phylum Arthropoda
Giant Swallowtail Butterfly

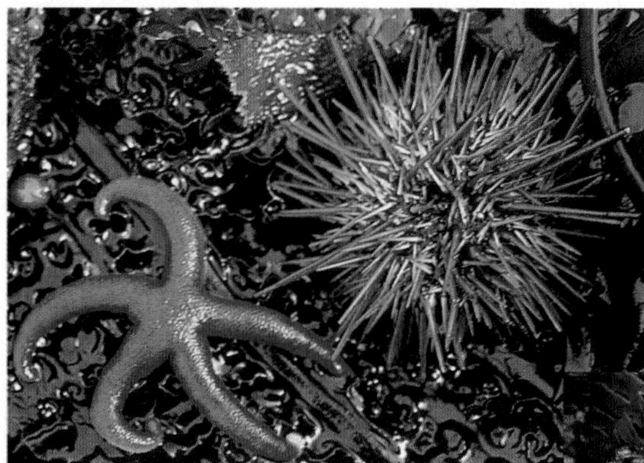

Phylum Echinodermata
Blood Sea Star and Red Sea Urchin

Phylum Chordata
Eastern Box Turtle

Phylum Chordata
Lemon Butterfly fish

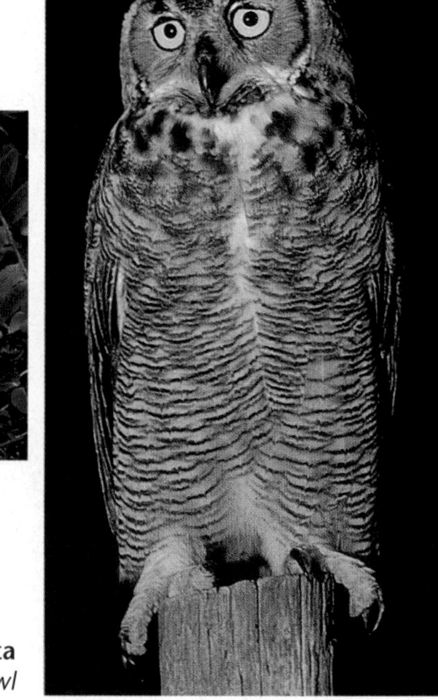

Phylum Chordata
Great Horned Owl

Appendix F

Minerals

Mineral (formula)	Color	Streak	Hardness	Breakage pattern	Uses and other properties
graphite (C)	black to gray	black to gray	1–1.5	basal cleavage (scales)	pencil lead, lubricants for locks, rods to control some small nuclear reactions, battery poles
galena (PbS)	gray	gray to black	2.5	cubic cleavage perfect	source of lead, used in pipes, shields for X rays, fishing equipment sinkers
hematite (Fe_2O_3)	black or reddish brown	reddish brown	5.5–6.5	irregular fracture	source of iron; converted to "pig" iron, made into steel
magnetite (Fe_3O_4)	black	black	6	conchoidal fracture	source of iron, naturally magnetic, called lodestone
pyrite (FeS_2)	light, brassy, yellow	greenish black	6–6.5	uneven fracture	source of iron, "fool's gold"
talc ($Mg_3Si_4O_{10}(OH)_2$)	white greenish	white	1	cleavage in one direction	used for talcum powder, sculptures, paper, and tabletops
gypsum ($CaSO_4 \cdot 2H_2O$)	colorless, gray, white brown	white	2	basal cleavage	used in plaster of paris and dry wall for building construction
sphalerite (ZnS)	brown, reddish brown, greenish	light to dark brown	3.5–4	cleavage in six directions	main ore of zinc; used in paints, dyes and medicine
muscovite ($KAl_3Si_3O_{10}(OH)_2$)	white, light gray, yellow, rose, green	colorless	2–2.5	basal cleavage	occurs in large flexible plates; used as an insulator in electrical equipment, lubricant
biotite ($K(Mg, Fe)_3(AlSi_3O_{10})(OH)_2$)	black to dark brown	colorless	2.5–3	basal cleavage	occurs in large flexible plates
halite (NaCl)	colorless, red, white, blue	colorless	2.5	cubic cleavage	salt; soluble in water; a preservative

Appendix F

Minerals

Mineral (formula)	Color	Streak	Hardness	Breakage pattern	Uses and other properties
calcite ($CaCO_3$)	colorless, white, pale blue	colorless, white	3	cleavage in three directions	fizzes when HCl is added; used in cements and other building materials
dolomite ($CaMg(CO_3)_2$)	colorless, white, pink green, gray black	white	3.5–4	cleavage in three directions	concrete and cement; used as an ornamental building stone
fluorite (CaF_2)	colorless, white, blue green, red yellow, purple	colorless	4	cleavage in four directions	used in the manufacture of optical equipment; glows under ultraviolet light
hornblende ($(CaNa)_{2\text{-}3}(Mg,Al,Fe)_5(Al,Si)_2Si_6O_{22}(OH)_2$)	green to black	gray to white	5–6	cleavage in two directions	will transmit light on thin edges; 6-sided cross section
feldspar ($KAlSi_3O_8$) ($NaAlSi_3O_8$) ($CaAl_2Si_2O_8$)	colorless, white to gray, green	colorless	6	two cleavage planes meet at ~90° angle	used in the manufacture of ceramics
augite ($(Ca, Na)(Mg, Fe, Al)(Al, Si)_2O_6$)	black	colorless	6	cleavage in two directions	square or 8-sided cross section
olivine ($(Mg, Fe)_2SiO_4$)	olive, green	none	6.5–7	conchoidal fracture	gemstones, refractory sand
quartz (SiO_2)	colorless, various color	none	7	conchoidal fracture	used in glass manufacture, electronic equipment, radios, computers, watches, gemstones

Appendix G

Rocks

Rock Type	Rock Name	Characteristics
Igneous (intrusive)	Granite	Large mineral grains of quartz, feldspar, hornblende, and mica. Usually light in color.
	Diorite	Large mineral grains of feldspar, hornblende, mica. Less quartz than granite. Intermediate in color.
	Gabbro	Large mineral grains of feldspar, hornblende, augite, olivine, and mica. No quartz. Dark in color.
Igneous (extrusive)	Rhyolite	Small mineral grains of quartz, feldspar, hornblende, and mica or no visible grains. Light in color.
	Andesite	Small mineral grains of feldspar, hornblende, mica or no visible grains. Less quartz than rhyolite. Intermediate in color.
	Basalt	Small mineral grains of feldspar, hornblende, augite, olivine, mica or no visible grains. No quartz. Dark in color.
	Obsidian	Glassy texture. No visible grains. Volcanic glass. Fracture looks like broken glass.
	Pumice	Frothy texture. Floats. Usually light in color.
Sedimentary (detrital)	Conglomerate	Coarse-grained. Gravel or pebble-sized grains.
	Sandstone	Sand-sized grains 1/16 to 2 mm in size.
	Siltstone	Grains are smaller than sand but larger than clay.
	Shale	Smallest grains. Usually dark in color.
Sedimentary (chemical or biochemical)	Limestone	Major mineral is calcite. Usually forms in oceans, lakes, rivers, and caves. Often contains fossils.
	Coal	Occurs in swampy. low-lying areas. Compacted layers of organic material, mainly plant remains.
Sedimentary (chemical)	Rock Salt	Commonly forms by the evaporation of seawater.
Metamorphic (foliated)	Gneiss	Well-developed banding because of alternating layers of different minerals, usually of different colors. Common parent rock is granite.
	Schist	Well-defined parallel arrangement of flat, sheet-like minerals, mainly micas. Common parent rocks are shale, phyllite.
	Phyllite	Shiny or silky appearance. May look wrinkled. Common parent rocks are shale, slate.
	Slate	Harder, denser, and shinier than shale. Common parent rock is shale.
Metamorphic (non-foliated)	Marble	Interlocking calcite or dolomite crystals. Common parent rock is limestone.
	Soapstone	Composed mainly of the mineral talc. Soft with a greasy feel.
	Quartzite	Hard and well cemented with interlocking quartz crystals. Common parent rock is sandstone.

Appendix H

Topographic Map Symbols

Primary highway, hard surface
Secondary highway, hard surface
Light-duty road, hard or Improved surface
Unimproved road
Railroad: single track and multiple track
Railroads in juxtaposition

Buildings

Schools, church, and cemetery

cem

Buildings (barn, warehouse, etc)
Wells other than water (labeled as to type)

o oil o gas

Tanks: oil, water, etc. (labeled only if water)

water

Located or landmark object; windmill
Open pit, mine, or quarry; prospect

Marsh (swamp)
Wooded marsh
Woods or brushwood
Vineyard
Land subject to controlled inundation
Submerged marsh
Mangrove
Orchard
Scrub
Urban area

Spot elevation ×7369
Water elevation 670

Index contour
Supplementary contour
Intermediate contour

Depression contours

Boundaries: National
State
County, parish, municipal
Civil township, precinct, town, barrio
Incorporated city, village, town, hamlet
Reservation, National or State
Small park, cemetery, airport, etc.
Land grant
Township or range line, United States land survey
Township or range line, approximate location

Perennial streams
Elevated aqueduct
Water well and spring
Small rapids
Large rapids
Intermittent lake
Intermittent streams
Aqueduct tunnel
Glacier
Small falls
Large falls
Dry lake bed

Appendix I

Weather Map Symbols

Sample Plotted Report at Each Station

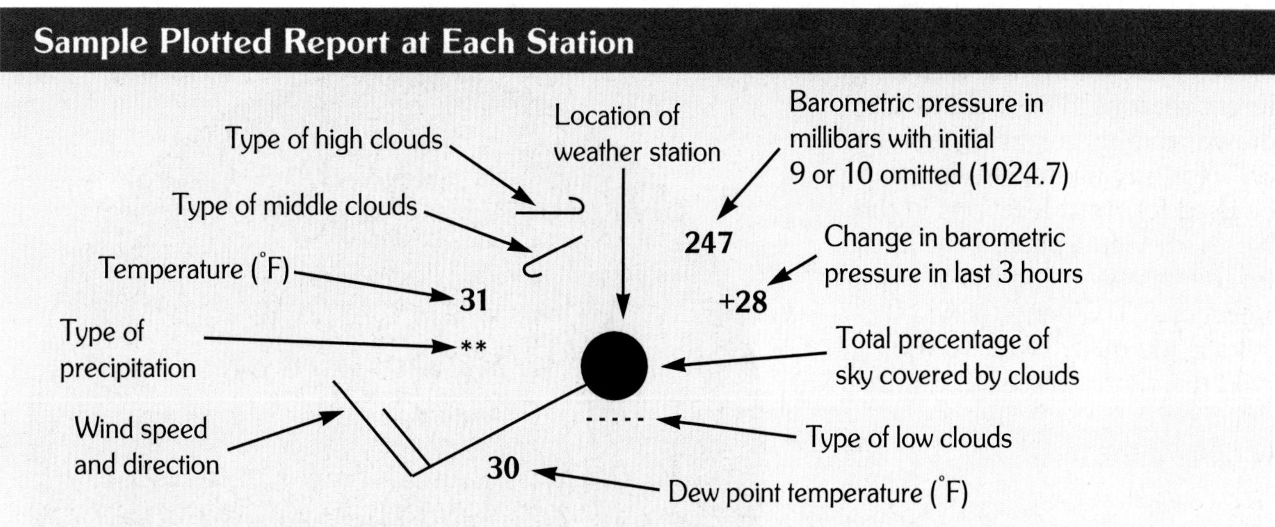

Sample Plotted Report at Each Station

Precipitation	Wind Speed and direction	Sky coverage	Some types of high clouds
Fog	0 calm	No cover	Scattered cirrus
Snow	1-2 knots	1/10 or less	Dense cirrus in patches
Rain	3-7 knots	2/10 to 3/10	Veil of cirrus covering entire sky
Thunder-storm	8-12 knots	4/10	Cirrus not covering entire sky
Drizzle	13-17 knots	1/2	
Showers	18-22 knots	6/10	
	23-27 knots	7/10	
	48-52 knots	Overcast with openings	
	1 knot = 1.852 km/h	Complete overcast	

Some types of middle clouds	Some types of low clouds	Fronts and pressure systems	
Thin altostratus layer	Cumulus of fair weather	(H) or High	Center of high-or
Thick altostratus layer	Stratocumulus	(L) or Low	low-pressure system
Thin altostratus in patches	Fractocumulus of bad weather		Cold front
Thin altostratus in bands	Stratus of fair weather		Warm Front
			Occluded front
			Stationary front

J

Star Charts

Shown here are star charts for viewing stars in the Northern Hemisphere during the four different seasons. These charts are drawn from the night sky at about 35° North Latitude, but they can be used for most locations in the Northern Hemisphere. The lines on the charts outline major constellations. The dense band of stars is the milky Way. To use, hold the chart vertically, with the direction you are facing at the bottom of the map.

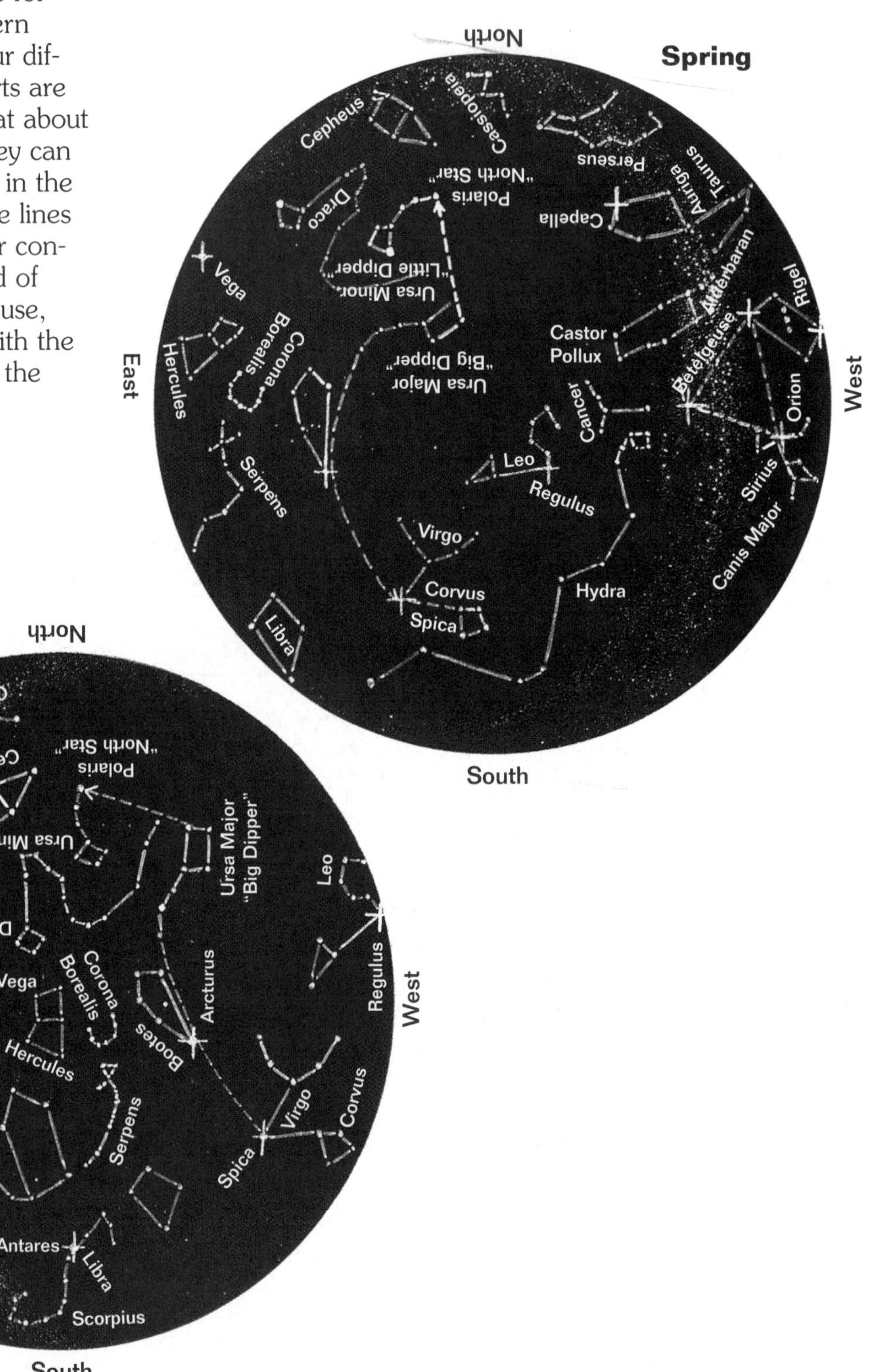

Appendix J

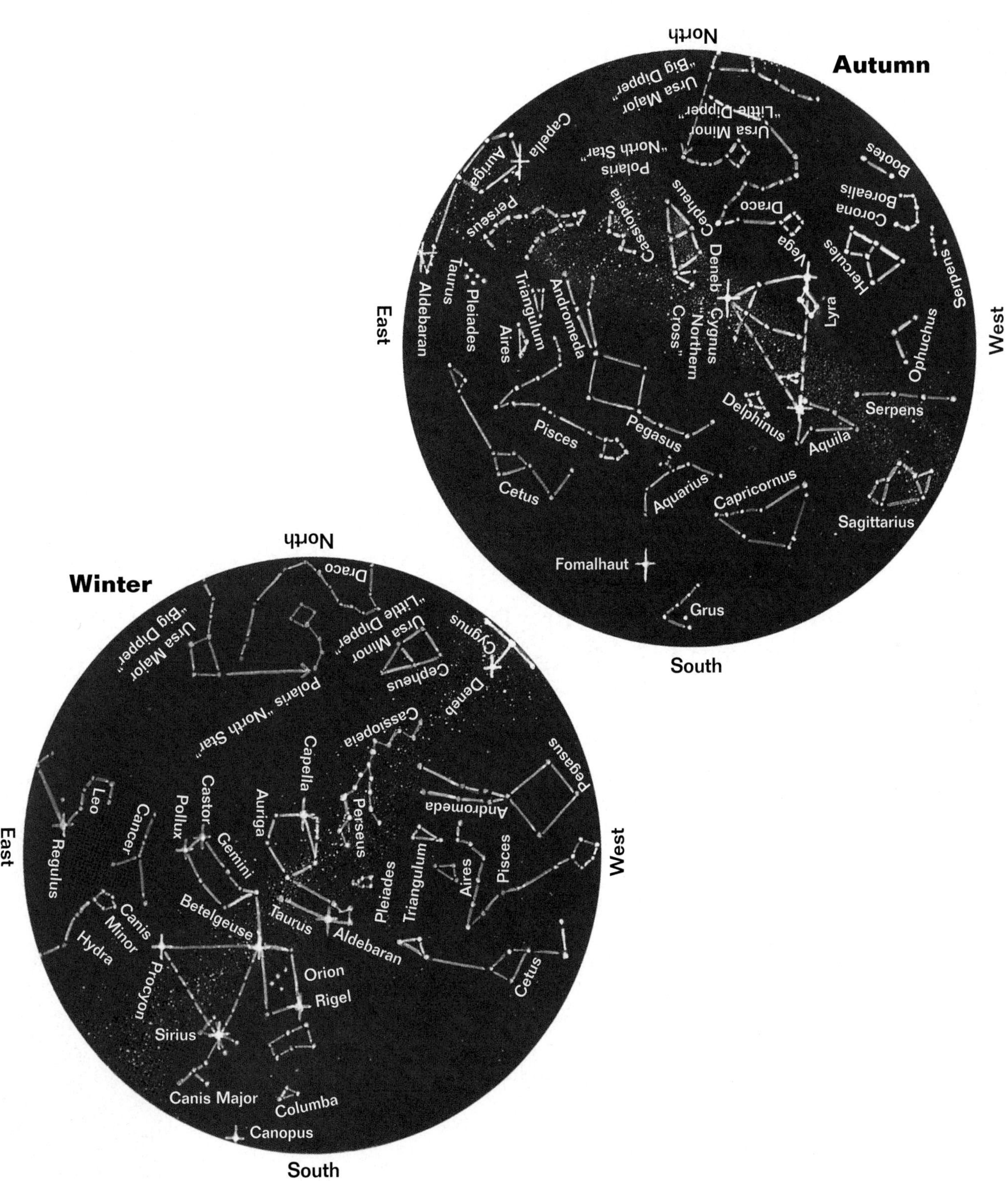

Autumn
North
South
East
West
Ursa Major "Big Dipper"
Ursa Minor "Little Dipper"
Polaris "North Star"
Capella
Auriga
Perseus
Cassiopeia
Cepheus
Draco
Bootes
Corona Borealis
Hercules
Vega
Serpens
Lyra
Deneb
Cygnus "Northern Cross"
Ophuchus
Aldebaran
Taurus
Pleiades
Triangulum
Andromeda
Aires
Delphinus
Serpens
Pegasus
Pisces
Aquila
Cetus
Aquarius
Capricornus
Sagittarius
Fomalhaut
Grus
Winter
North
South
East
West
Draco
Ursa Major "Big Dipper"
Ursa Minor "Little Dipper"
Cygnus
Cepheus
Polaris "North Star"
Deneb
Cassiopeia
Pegasus
Capella
Leo
Castor
Auriga
Andromeda
Pollux
Cancer
Perseus
Gemini
Regulus
Triangulum
Aires
Pisces
Pleiades
Betelgeuse
Taurus
Canis Minor
Aldebaran
Hydra
Orion
Cetus
Procyon
Rigel
Sirius
Canis Major
Columba
Canopus

Skill Handbook

Table of Contents

Organizing Information

Communicating

The communication of ideas is an important part of our everyday lives. Whether reading a book, writing a letter, or watching a television program, people everywhere are expressing opinions and sharing information with one another. Writing in your Science Journal allows you to express your opinions and demonstrate your knowledge of the information presented on a subject. When writing, keep in mind the purpose of the assignment and the audience with which you are communicating.

Examples Science Journal assignments vary greatly. They may ask you to take a viewpoint other than your own; perhaps you will be a scientist, a TV reporter, or a committee member of a local environmental group. Maybe you will be expressing your opinions to a member of Congress, a doctor, or to the editor of your local newspaper, as shown in **Figure 1.** Sometimes, Science Journal writing may allow you to summarize information in the form of an outline, a letter, or in a paragraph.

Figure 1 A Science Journal entry

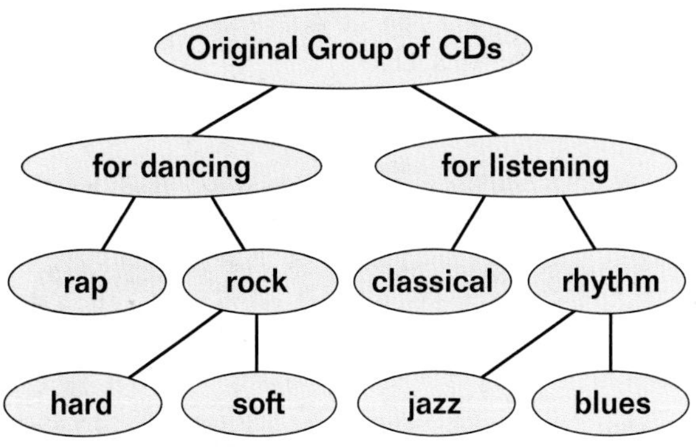

Figure 2 Classifying CDs

Classifying

You may not realize it, but you make things orderly in the world around you. If you hang your shirts together in the closet or if your favorite CDs are stacked together, you have used the skill of classifying.

Classifying is the process of sorting objects or events into groups based on common features. When classifying, first observe the objects or events to be classified. Then, select one feature that is shared by some members in the group, but not by all. Place those members that share that feature into a subgroup. You can classify members into smaller and smaller subgroups based on characteristics.

Remember, when you classify, you are grouping objects or events for a purpose. Keep your purpose in mind as you select the features to form groups and subgroups.

Example How would you classify a collection of CDs? As shown in **Figure 2,** you might classify those you like to dance to in one subgroup and CDs you like to listen to in the next subgroup. The CDs you like to dance to could be subdivided into a rap subgroup and a rock subgroup. Note that for each feature selected, each CD fits into only one subgroup. You would keep selecting features until all the CDs are classified. **Figure 2** shows one possible classification.

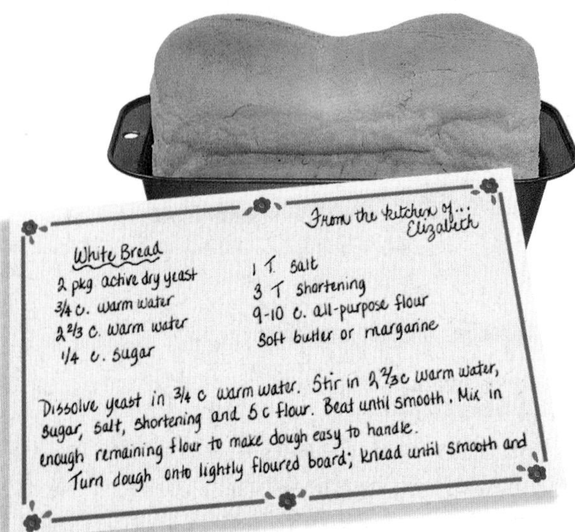

Figure 3 A recipe for bread contains sequenced instructions

Sequencing

A sequence is an arrangement of things or events in a particular order. When you are asked to sequence objects or events within a group, figure out what comes first, then think about what should come second. Continue to choose objects or events until all of the objects you started out with are in order. Then, go back over the sequence to make sure each thing or event in your sequence logically leads to the next.

Example A sequence with which you are most familiar is the use of alphabetical order. Another example of sequence would be the steps in a recipe, as shown in **Figure 3.** Think about baking bread. Steps in the recipe have to be followed in order for the bread to turn out right.

Concept Mapping

If you were taking an automobile trip, you would probably take along a road map. The road map shows your location, your destination, and other places along the way. By looking at the map and finding where you are, you can begin to understand where you are in relation to other locations on the map.

A concept map is similar to a road map. But, a concept map shows relationships among ideas (or concepts) rather than places. A concept map is a diagram that visually shows how concepts are related. Because the concept map shows relationships among ideas, it can make the meanings of ideas and terms clear, and help you understand better what you are studying.

There is usually not one correct way to create a concept map. As you construct one type of map, you may discover other ways to construct the map that show the

Figure 4 Network tree describing U.S. currency

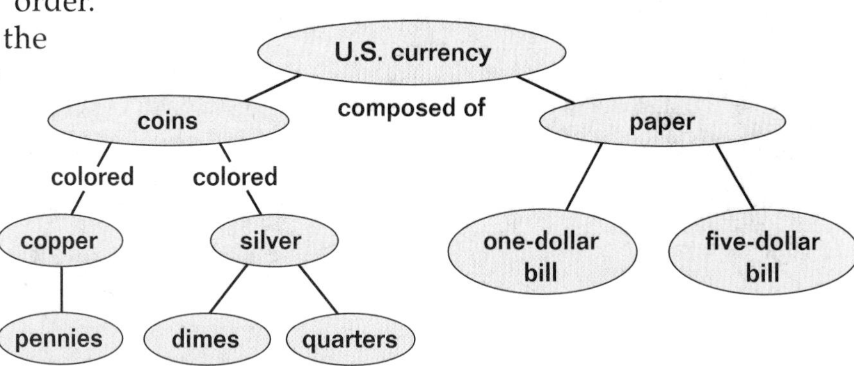

relationships between concepts in a better way. If you do discover what you think is a better way to create a concept map, go ahead and use the new one. Overall, concept maps are useful for breaking a big concept down into smaller parts, making learning easier.

Examples

Network Tree Look at the concept map about U.S. currency in **Figure 4.** This is called a network tree. Notice how some words are in ovals while others are written across connecting lines. The words inside the ovals are science concepts. The lines in the map show related concepts. The words written on the lines describe the relationships between concepts.

When you are asked to construct a network tree, write down the topic and list the major concepts related to that topic on a piece of paper. Then look at your list and begin to put them in order from general to specific. Branch the related concepts from the major concept and describe the relationships on the lines. Continue to write the more specific concepts. Write the relationships between the concepts on the lines until all concepts are mapped. Examine the concept map for relationships that cross branches, and add them to the concept map.

Events Chain An events chain is another type of concept map. An events chain map, such as the one describing a typical morning routine in **Figure 5,** is used to describe ideas in order. In science, an events chain can be used to describe a sequence of events, the steps in a procedure, or the stages of a process.

When making an events chain, first find the one event that starts the chain. This event is called the initiating event. Then, find the next event in the chain and continue until you reach an outcome. Suppose you are asked to describe what happens when your alarm rings. An events chain map describing the steps might look like **Figure 5.** Notice that connecting words are not necessary in an events chain.

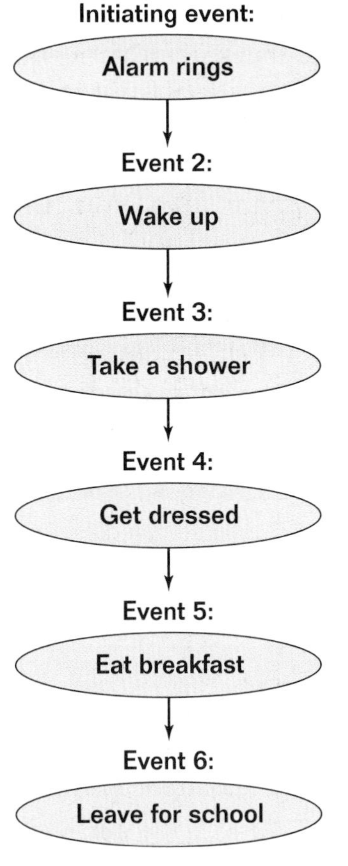

Figure 5 Events chain of a typical morning routine

Cycle Map A cycle concept map is a special type of events chain map. In a cycle concept map, the series of events does not produce a final outcome. Instead, the last event in the chain relates back to the initiating event.

As in the events chain map, you first decide on an initiating event and then list each event in order. Because there is no outcome and the last event relates back to the initiating event, the cycle repeats itself. Look at the cycle map describing the relationship between day and night in **Figure 6.**

Figure 6 Cycle map of day and night.

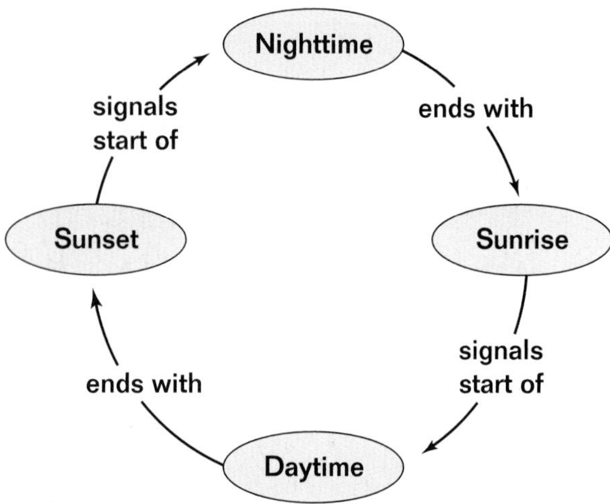

Spider Map A fourth type of concept map is the spider map. This is a map that you can use for brainstorming. Once you have a central idea, you may find you have a jumble of ideas that relate to it, but are not necessarily clearly related to each other. As illustrated by the homework spider map in **Figure 7,** by writing these ideas outside the main concept, you may begin to separate and group unrelated terms so that they become more useful.

Figure 7 Spider map about homework.

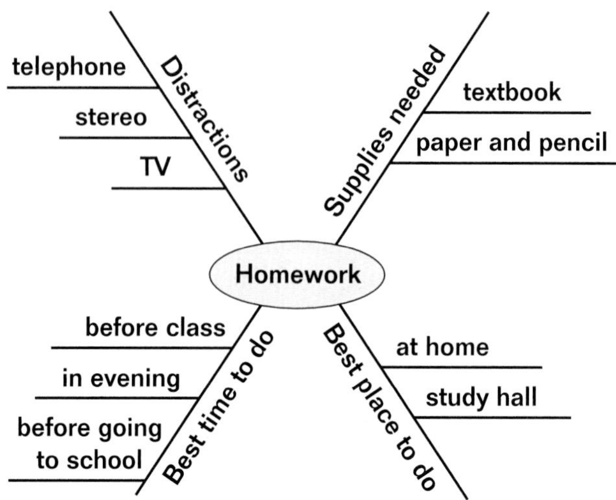

Making and Using Tables

Browse through your textbook and you will notice tables in the text and in the activities. In a table, data or information is arranged in a way that makes it easier for you to understand. Activity tables help organize the data you collect during an activity so that results can be interpreted.

Examples Most tables have a title. At a glance, the title tells you what the table is about. A table is divided into columns and rows. The first column lists items to be compared. In **Figure 8,** the collection of recyclable materials is being compared in a table. The row across the top lists the specific characteristics being compared. Within the grid of the table, the collected data are recorded.

What is the title of the table in **Figure 8?** The title is "Recycled Materials." What is being compared? The different materials being recycled and on which days they are recycled.

Making Tables To make a table, list the items to be compared down in columns and the characteristics to be compared across in rows. The table in

Figure 8 Table of recycled materials

Recycled Materials			
Day of Week	Paper (kg)	Aluminum (kg)	Plastic (kg)
Mon.	4.0	2.0	0.5
Wed.	43.5	1.5	0.5
Fri.	3.0	1.0	1.5

Figure 8 compares the mass of recycled materials collected by a class. On Monday, students turned in 4.0 kg of paper, 2.0 kg of aluminum, and 0.5 kg of plastic. On Wednesday, they turned in 3.5 kg of paper, 1.5 kg of aluminum, and 0.5 kg of plastic. On Friday, the totals were 3.0 kg of paper, 1.0 kg of aluminum, and 1.5 kg of plastic.

Using Tables How much plastic, in kilograms, is being recycled on Wednesday? Locate the column labeled "Plastic (kg)" and the row "Wed." The data in the box where the column and row intersect is the answer. Did you answer "0.5"? How much aluminum, in kilograms, is being recycled on Friday? If you answered "1.0," you understand how to use the parts of the table.

Making and Using Graphs

After scientists organize data in tables, they may display the data in a graph. A graph is a diagram that shows the relationship of one variable to another. A graph makes interpretation and analysis of data easier. There are three basic types of graphs used in science—the line graph, the bar graph, and the circle graph.

Examples

Line Graphs A line graph is used to show the relationship between two variables. The variables being compared go on two axes of the graph. The independent variable always goes on the horizontal axis, called the x-axis. The dependent variable always goes on the vertical axis, called the y-axis.

Suppose your class started to record the amount of materials they collected in one week for their school to recycle. The collected information is shown in **Figure 9.**

You could make a graph of the materials collected over the three days of the school week. The three weekdays are the independent variables and are placed on the x-axis of your graph. The amount of materials collected is the dependent variable and would go on the y-axis.

After drawing your axes, label each with a scale. The x-axis lists the three weekdays. To make a scale of the amount of materials collected on the y-axis, look at the data values. Because the lowest amount collected was 1.0 and the highest was 5.0, you will have to start numbering at least at 1.0 and go through 5.0. You decide to start numbering at 0 and number by ones through 6.0, as shown in **Figure 10.**

Next, plot the data points for collected paper. The first pair of data you want to plot is Monday and 5.0 kg of paper.

Figure 9 Amount of recyclable materials collected during one week

Materials Collected During Week		
Day of Week	Paper (kg)	Aluminum (kg)
Mon.	5.0	4.0
Wed.	4.0	1.0
Fri.	2.5	2.0

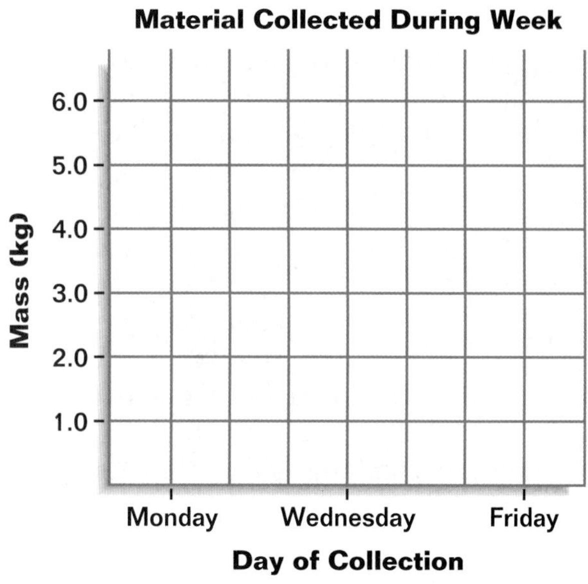

Figure 10 Graph outline for material collected during week

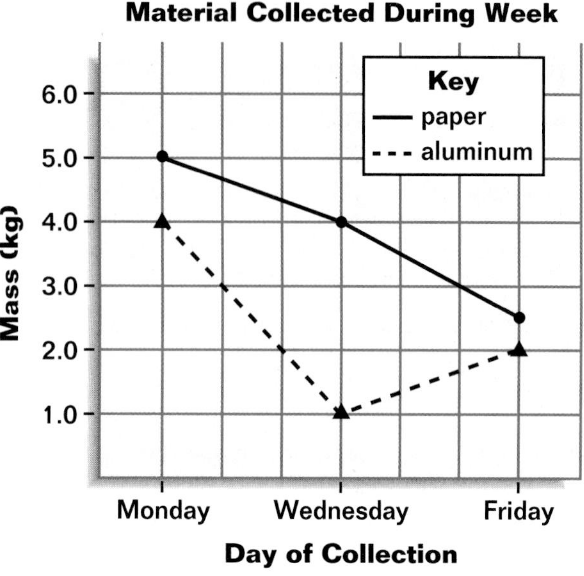

Figure 11 Line graph of materials collected during week

Locate "Monday" on the x-axis and locate "5.0" on the y-axis. Where an imaginary vertical line from the x-axis and an imaginary horizontal line from the y-axis would meet, place the first data point. Place the other data points the same way. After all the points are plotted, connect them with the best smooth curve. Repeat this procedure for the data points for aluminum. Use continuous and dashed lines to distinguish the two line graphs. The resulting graph should look like **Figure 11.**

Bar Graphs Bar graphs are similar to line graphs. They compare data that do not continuously change. In a bar graph, vertical bars show the relationships among data.

To make a bar graph, set up the x-axis and y-axis as you did for the line graph. The data is plotted by drawing vertical bars from the x-axis up to a point where the y-axis would meet the bar if it were extended.

Look at the bar graph in **Figure 12** comparing the mass of aluminum collected over three weekdays. The x-axis is the days on which the aluminum was collected. The y-axis is the mass of aluminum collected, in kilograms.

Circle Graphs A circle graph uses a circle divided into sections to display data. Each section represents part of the whole. All the sections together equal 100 percent.

Suppose you wanted to make a circle graph to show the number of seeds that germinated in a package. You would count the total number of seeds. You find that there are 143 seeds in the package. This represents 100 percent, the whole circle.

You plant the seeds, and 129 seeds germinate. The seeds that germinated will make up one section of the circle graph, and the seeds that did not germinate will make up the remaining section.

To find out how much of the circle each section should take, divide the number of seeds in each section by the total number of seeds. Then, multiply your answer by 360, the number of degrees in a circle, and round to the nearest whole number. The

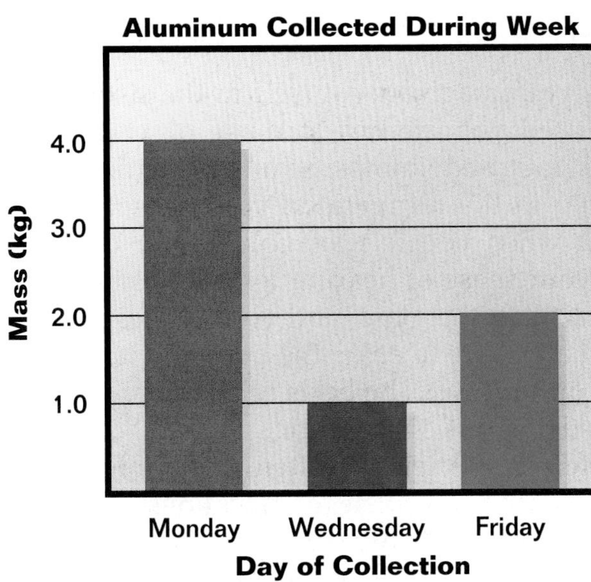

Figure 12 Bar graph of aluminum collected during week

section of the circle graph in degrees that represents the seeds germinated is figured below.

$$\frac{129}{143} \times 360 = 324.75 \text{ or } 325 \text{ degrees (or } 325°)$$

Plot this group on the circle graph using a compass and a protractor. Use the compass to draw a circle. It will be easier to measure the part of the circle representing the non-germinating seeds, so subtract 325° from 360° to get 35°. Draw a straight line from the center to the edge of the circle. Place your protractor on this line and use it to mark a point at 325°. Use this point to draw a straight line from the center of the circle to the edge. This is the section for the group of seeds that did not germinate. The other section represents the group of 129 seeds that did germinate. Label the sections of your graph and title the graph as shown in **Figure 13.**

Figure 13 Circle graph of germinated seeds

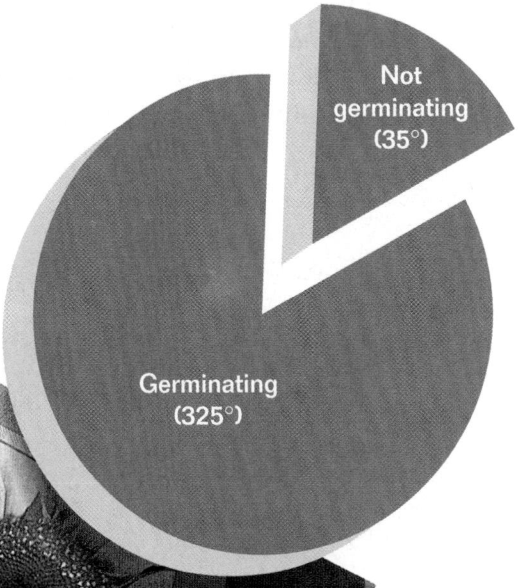

Seeds Germinated

Not germinating (35°)

Germinating (325°)

Thinking Critically

Observing and Inferring

Observing Scientists try to make careful and accurate observations. When possible, they use instruments such as microscopes, thermometers, and balances to make observations. Measurements with a balance or thermometer provide numerical data that can be checked and repeated.

When you make observations in science, you'll find it helpful to examine the entire object or situation first. Then, look carefully for details. Write down everything you observe.

Example Imagine that you have just finished a volleyball game. At home, you open the refrigerator and see a jug of orange juice on the back of the top shelf. The jug, shown in **Figure 14,** feels cold as you grasp it. Then, you drink the juice, smell the oranges, and enjoy the tart taste in your mouth.

Figure 14 Why is this jug of orange juice cold?

As you imagined yourself in the story, you used your senses to make observations. You used your sense of sight to find the jug in the refrigerator, your sense of touch when you felt the coldness of the jug, your sense of hearing to listen as the liquid filled the glass, and your senses of smell and taste to enjoy the odor and tartness of the juice. The basis of all scientific investigation is observation.

Inferring Scientists often make inferences based on their observations. An inference is an attempt to explain or interpret observations or to say what caused what you observed.

When making an inference, be certain to use accurate data and observations. Analyze all of the data that you've collected. Then, based on everything you know, explain or interpret what you've observed.

Example When you drank a glass of orange juice after the volleyball game, you observed that the orange juice was cold as well as refreshing. You might infer that the juice was cold because it had been made much earlier in the day and had been kept in the refrigerator, or you might infer that it had just been made, using both cold water and ice. The only way to be sure which inference is correct is to investigate further.

Comparing and Contrasting

Observations can be analyzed by noting the similarities and differences between two or more objects or events that you observe. When you look at objects or events to see how they are similar, you are comparing them. Contrasting is looking for differences in similar objects or events.

Figure 15 Table comparing the nutritional value of *Cereal A* and *Cereal B*

Nutritional Value		
	Cereal A	Cereal B
Serving size	103 g	105 g
Calories	220	160
Total Fat	10 g	10 g
Protein	2.5 g	2.6 g
Total Carbohydrate	30 g	15 g

Example Suppose you were asked to compare and contrast the nutritional value of two kinds of cereal, *Cereal A* and *Cereal B*. You would start by looking at what is known about these cereals. Arrange this information in a table, like the one in **Figure 15.**

Similarities you might point out are that both cereals have similar serving sizes, amounts of total fat, and protein. Differences include *Cereal A* having a higher calorie value and containing more total carbohydrates than *Cereal B*.

Recognizing Cause and Effect

Have you ever watched something happen and then made suggestions about why it happened? If so, you have observed an effect and inferred a cause. The event is an effect, and the reason for the event is the cause.

Example Suppose that every time your teacher fed the fish in a classroom aquarium, she or he tapped the food container on the edge of the aquarium. Then, one day your teacher just happened to tap the edge of the aquarium with a pencil while making a point. You observed the fish swim to the surface of the aquarium to feed, as shown in **Figure 16.** What is the effect, and what would you infer to be the cause? The effect is the fish swimming to the surface of the aquarium. You might infer the cause to be the teacher tapping on the edge of the aquarium. In determining cause and effect, you have made a logical inference based on your observations.

Perhaps the fish swam to the surface because they reacted to the teacher's waving hand or for some other reason. When scientists are unsure of the cause of a certain event, the design controlled experiments to determine what causes the event. Although you have made a logical conclusion about the behavior of the fish, you would have to perform an experiment to be certain that it was the tapping that caused the effect you observed.

Figure 16 What cause-and-effect situations are occurring in this aquarium?

Practicing Scientific Processes

You might say that the work of a scientist is to solve problems. But when you decide how to dress on a particular day, you are doing problem solving, too. You may observe what the weather looks like through a window. You may go outside and see whether what you are wearing is heavy or light enough.

Scientists use an orderly approach to learn new information and to solve problems. The methods scientists may use include observing to form a hypothesis, designing an experiment to test a hypothesis, separating and controlling variables, and interpreting data.

Forming Operational Definitions

Operational definitions define an object by showing how it functions, works, or behaves. Such definitions are written in terms of how an object works or how it can be used; that is, what is its job or purpose?

Example Some operational definitions explain how an object can be used.

- A ruler is a tool that measures the size of an object.
- An automobile can move things from one place to another.

Or such a definition may explain how an object works.

- A ruler contains a series of marks that can be used as a standard when measuring.
- An automobile is a vehicle that can move from place to place.

Figure 17 What observations can be made about this dog?

Forming a Hypothesis

Observations You observe all the time. Scientists try to observe as much as possible about the things and events they study so they know that what they say about their observations is reliable.

Some observations describe something using only words. These observations are called qualitative observations. Other observations describe how much of something there is. These are quantitative observations and use numbers, as well as words, in the description. Tools or equipment are used to measure the characteristic being described.

Example If you were making qualitative observations of the dog in **Figure 17,** you might use words such as *furry, yellow,* and *short-haired.* Quantitative observations of this dog might include a mass of 14 kg, a height of 46 cm, ear length of 10 cm, and an age of 150 days.

Hypotheses Hypotheses are tested to help explain observations that have been made. They are often stated as *if* and *then* statements.

Examples Suppose you want to make a perfect score on a spelling test. Begin by thinking of several ways to accomplish this. Base these possibilities on past observations. If you put each of these possibilities into sentence form, using the words *if* and *then*, you can form a hypothesis. All of the following are hypotheses you might consider to explain how you could score 100 percent on your test:

If the test is easy, then I will get a perfect score.

If I am intelligent, then I will get a perfect score.

If I study hard, then I will get a perfect score.

Perhaps a scientist has observed that plants that receive fertilizer grow taller than plants that do not. A scientist may form a hypothesis that says: If plants are fertilized, then their growth will increase.

Designing an Experiment to Test a Hypothesis

In order to test a hypothesis, it's best to write out a procedure. A procedure is the plan that you follow in your experiment. A procedure tells you what materials to use and how to use them. After following the procedure, data are generated. From this generated data, you can then draw a conclusion and make a statement about your results.

If the conclusion you draw from the data supports your hypothesis, then you can say that your hypothesis is reliable. *Reliable* means that you can trust your conclusion. If it did not support your hypothesis, then you would have to make new observations and state a new hypothesis—just make sure that it is one that you can test.

Example Super premium gasoline costs more than regular gasoline. Does super premium gasoline increase the efficiency or fuel mileage of your family car? Let's figure out how to conduct an experiment to test the hypothesis, "*if* premium gas is more efficient, *then* it should increase the fuel mileage of our family car." Then a procedure similar to **Figure 18** must be written to generate data presented in **Figure 19** on the next page.

These data show that premium gasoline is less efficient than regular gasoline. It took more gasoline to travel one mile (0.064) using premium gasoline than it does to travel one mile using regular gasoline (0.059). This conclusion does not support the original hypothesis made.

PROCEDURE

1. Use regular gasoline for two weeks.
2. Record the number of miles between fill-ups and the amount of gasoline used.
3. Switch to premium gasoline for two weeks.
4. Record the number of miles between fill-ups and the amount of gasoline used.

Figure 18 Possible procedural steps

Figure 19 Data generated from procedure steps

Gasoline Data			
	Miles traveled	**Gallons used**	**Gallons per mile**
Regular gasoline	762	45.34	0.059
Premium gasoline	661	42.30	0.064

Separating and Controlling Variables

In any experiment, it is important to keep everything the same except for the item you are testing. The one factor that you change is called the *independent variable.* The factor that changes as a result of the independent variable is called the *dependent variable.* Always make sure that there is only one independent variable. If you allow more than one, you will not know what causes the changes you observe in the independent variable. Many experiments have *controls*—a treatment or an experiment that you can compare with the results of your test groups.

Example In the experiment with the gasoline, you made everything the same except the type of gasoline being used. The driver, the type of automobile, and the weather conditions should remain the same throughout. The gasoline should also be purchased from the same service station. By doing so, you made sure that at the end of the experiment, any differences were the result of the type of fuel being used—regular or premium. The type of gasoline was the *independent factor* and the gas mileage achieved was the *dependent factor.* The use of regular gasoline was the *control.*

Interpreting Data

The word *interpret* means "to explain the meaning of something." Look at the problem originally being explored in the gasoline experiment and find out what the data show. Identify the control group and the test group so you can see whether or not the variable has had an effect. Then, you need to check differences between the control and test groups.

Figure 20 Which gasoline type is most efficient?

These differences may be qualitative or quantitative. A qualitative difference would be a difference that you could observe and describe, while a quantitative difference would be a difference you can measure using numbers. If there are differences, the variable being tested may have had an effect. If there is no difference between the control and the test groups, the variable being tested apparently has had no effect.

Example Perhaps you are looking at a table from an experiment designed to test the hypothesis: If premium gas is more efficient, then it should increase the fuel mileage of our family car. Look back at **Figure 19** showing the results of this experiment. In this example, the use of regular gasoline in the family car was the control, while the car being fueled by premium gasoline was the test group.

Data showed a quantitative difference in efficiency for gasoline consumption. It took 0.059 gallons of regular gasoline to travel one mile, while it took 0.064 gallons of the premium gasoline to travel the same distance. The regular gasoline was more efficient; it increased the fuel mileage of the family car.

What are data? In the experiment described on these pages, measurements were taken so that at the end of the experiment, you had something concrete to interpret. You had numbers to work with. Not every experiment that you do will give you data in the form of numbers. Sometimes, data will be in the form of a description. At the end of a chemistry experiment, you might have noted that one solution turned yellow when treated with a particular chemical, and another remained colorless, as water, when treated with the same chemical. Data, therefore, are stated in different forms for different types of scientific experiments.

Figure 21

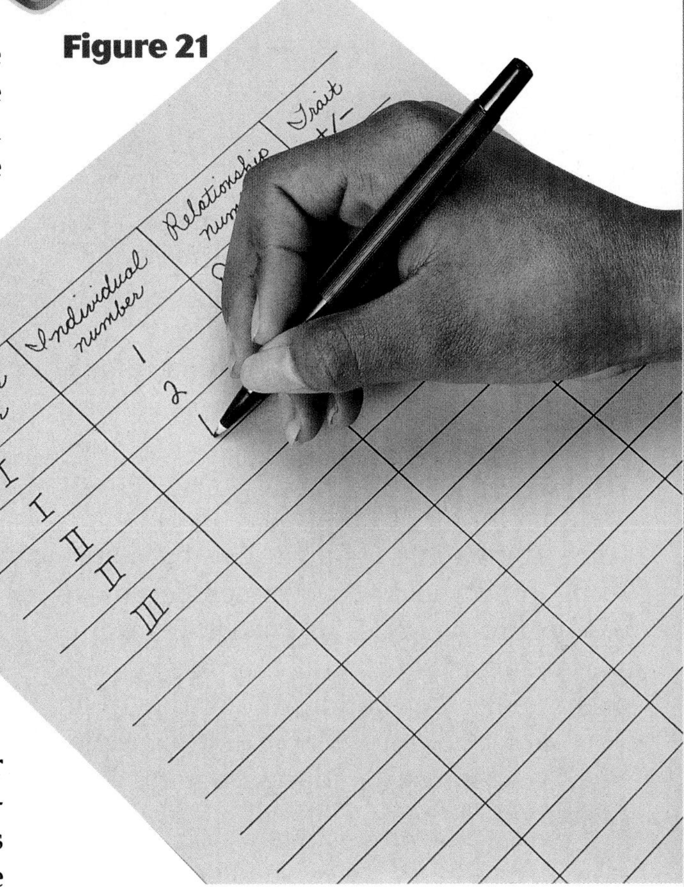

Are all experiments alike? Keep in mind as you perform experiments in science that not every experiment makes use of all of the parts that have been described on these pages. For some, it may be difficult to design an experiment that will always have a control. Other experiments are complex enough that it may be hard to have only one dependent variable. Real scientists encounter many variations in the methods that they use when they perform experiments. The skills in this handbook are here for you to use and practice. In real situations, their uses will vary.

Representing and Applying Data

Interpreting Scientific Illustrations

As you read a science textbook, you will see many drawings, diagrams, and photographs. Illustrations help you to understand what you read. Some illustrations are included to help you understand an idea that you can't see easily by yourself. For instance, we can't see atoms, but we can look at a diagram of an atom and that helps us to understand some things about atoms. Seeing something often helps you remember more easily. Illustrations also provide examples that clarify difficult concepts or give additional information about the topic you are studying. Maps, for example, help you to locate places that may be described in the text.

Examples

Captions and Labels Most illustrations have captions. A caption is a comment that identifies or explains the illustration. Diagrams, such as **Figure 22,** often have labels that identify parts of the organism or the order of steps in a process.

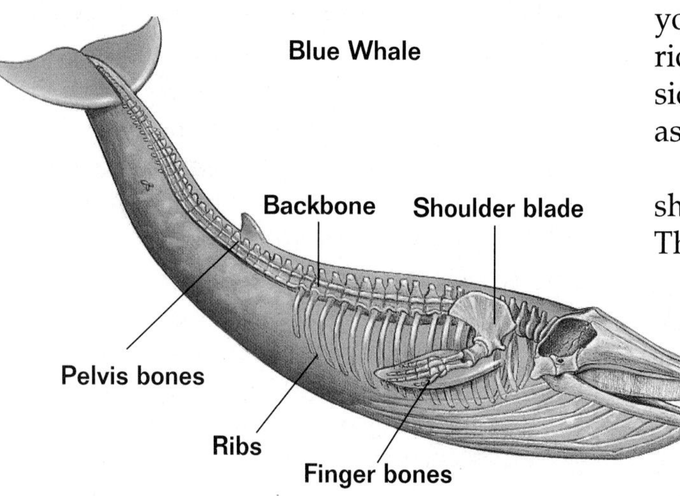

Figure 22 A labeled diagram of a blue whale

Figure 23 The orientation of a dog is shown here.

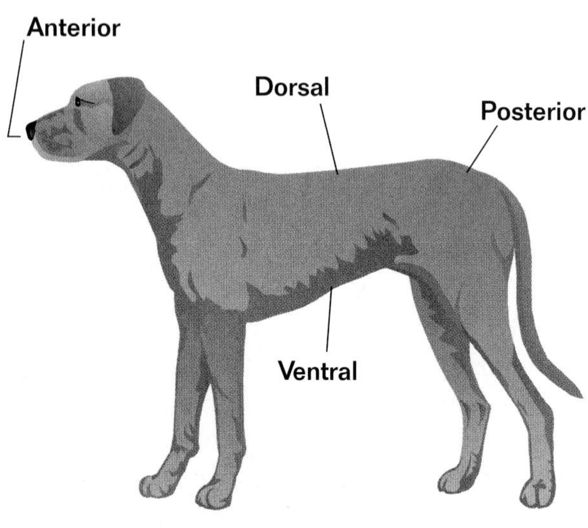

Learning with Illustrations An illustration of an organism shows that organism from a particular view or orientation. In order to understand the illustration, you may need to identify the front (anterior) end, tail (posterior) end, the underside (ventral), and the back (dorsal) side, as shown in **Figure 23.**

You might also check for symmetry. A shark in **Figure 24** has bilateral symmetry. This means that drawing an imaginary line through the center of the animal from the anterior to posterior end forms two mirror images.

Radial symmetry is the arrangement of similar parts around a central point. An object or organism, such as a hydra, can be divided anywhere through the center into similar parts.

Some organisms and objects cannot be divided into two similar parts. If an

Figure 24 A shark (A) illustrating bilateral symmetry and a pear (B) illustrating a longitudinal section and a cross section

A

Bilateral symmetry

Two sides exactly alike

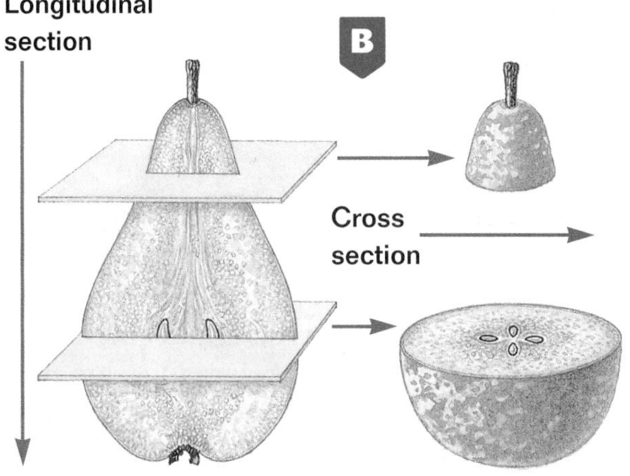

organism or object cannot be divided, it is asymmetrical. Regardless of how you try to divide a natural sponge, you cannot divide it into two parts that look alike.

Some illustrations enable you to see the inside of an organism or object. These illustrations are called sections. **Figure 24** also illustrates some common sections.

Look at all illustrations carefully. Read captions and labels so that you understand exactly what the illustration is showing you.

Making Models

Have you ever worked on a model car, plane, or rocket? These models look, and sometimes work, much like the real thing, but they are often on a different scale than the real thing. In science, models are used to help simplify large or small processes or structures that otherwise would be difficult to see and understand. Your understanding of a structure or process is enhanced when you work with materials to make a model that shows the basic features of the structure or process.

Example In order to make a model, you first have to get a basic idea about the structure or process involved. You decide to make a model to show the differences in size of arteries, veins, and capillaries. First, read about these structures. All three are hollow tubes. Arteries are round and thick. Veins are flat and have thinner walls than arteries. Capillaries are small.

Now, decide what you can use for your model. Common materials are often most useful and cheapest to work with when making models. As illustrated in **Figure 25** on the next page, different kinds and sizes of pasta might work for these models. Different sizes of rubber tubing might do just as well. Cut and glue the different noodles or tubing onto thick paper so the openings can be seen. Then label each. Now you have a simple, easy-to-understand model showing the differences in size of arteries, veins, and capillaries.

What other scientific ideas might a model help you to understand? A model of a molecule can be made from balls of modeling clay (using different colors for the different elements present) and toothpicks (to show different chemical bonds).

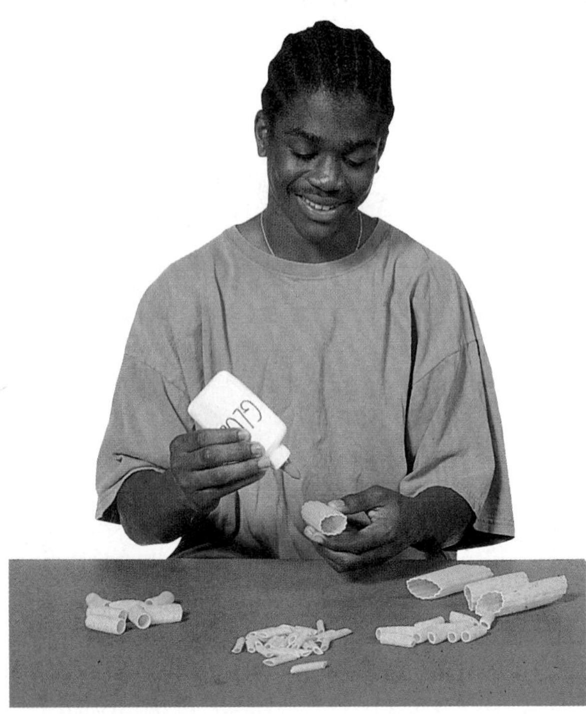

Figure 25 Different types of pasta may be used to model blood vessels

A working model of a volcano can be made from clay, a small amount of baking soda, vinegar, and a bottle cap. Other models can be devised on a computer. Some models are mathematical and are represented by equations.

Measuring in SI

The metric system is a system of measurement developed by a group of scientists in 1795. It helps scientists avoid problems by providing standard measurements that all scientists around the world can understand. A modern form of the metric system, called the International System, or SI, was adopted for worldwide use in 1960.

The metric system is convenient because unit sizes vary by multiples of 10. When changing from smaller units to larger units, divide by 10. When changing from larger units to smaller, multiply by 10. For example, to convert millimeters to centimeters, divide the millimeters by 10. To convert 30 millimeters to centimeters, divide 30 by 10 (30 millimeters equal 3 centimeters).

Prefixes are used to name units. Look at **Figure 26** for some common metric prefixes and their meanings. Do you see how the prefix *kilo-* attached to the unit *gram* is *kilogram,* or 1000 grams? The prefix *deci-* attached to the unit *meter* is *decimeter,* or one-tenth (0.1) of a meter.

Examples

Length You have probably measured lengths or distances many times. The meter is the SI unit used to measure length. A baseball bat is about one meter long. When measuring smaller lengths, the meter is divided into smaller units called centimeters and millimeters. A centimeter is one-hundredth (0.01) of a meter, which is about the size of the width of the fingernail on your ring finger. A millimeter is one-thousandth of a meter (0.001), about the thickness of a dime.

Most metric rulers have lines indicating centimeters and millimeters, as shown in

Figure 26 Common metric prefixes

Metric Prefixes			
Prefix	Symbol	Meaning	
kilo-	k	1000	thousand
hecto-	h	200	hundred
deka-	da	10	ten
deci-	d	0.1	tenth
centi-	c	0.01	hundredth
milli-	m	0.001	thousandth

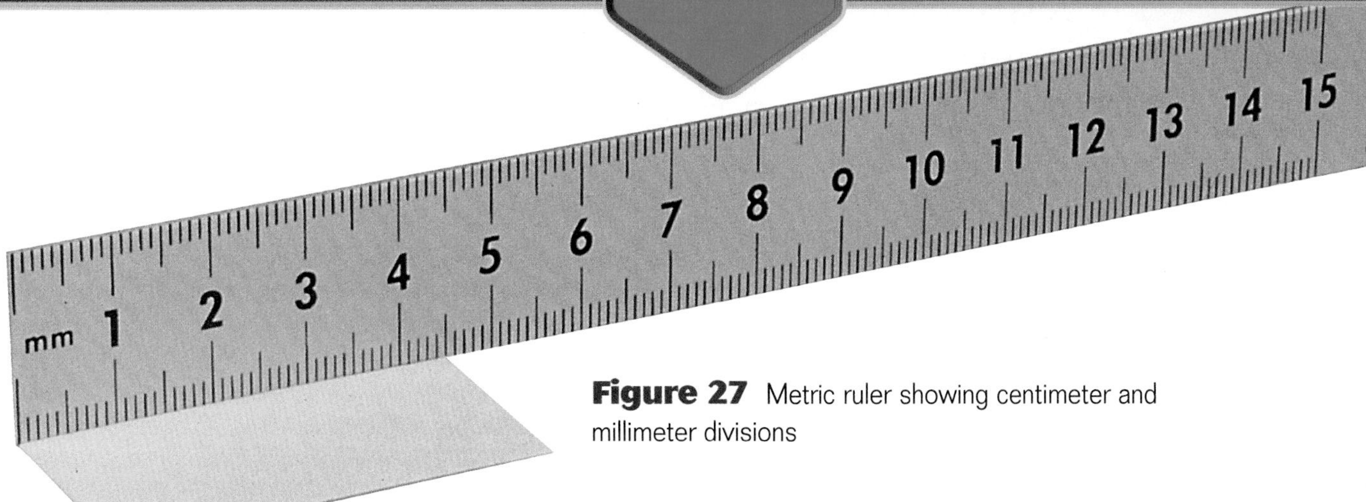

Figure 27 Metric ruler showing centimeter and millimeter divisions

Figure 27. The centimeter lines are the longer, numbered lines; the shorter lines are millimeter lines. When using a metric ruler, line up the 0-centimeter mark with the end of the object being measured, and read the number of the unit where the object ends, in this instance 4.5 cm.

Surface Area Units of length are also used to measure surface area. The standard unit of area is the square meter (m^2). A square that's one meter long on each side has a surface area of one square meter. Similarly, a square centimeter, (cm^2), shown in **Figure 28,** is one centimeter long on each side. The surface area of an object is determined by multiplying the length times the width.

Volume The volume of a rectangular solid is also calculated using units of length. The cubic meter (m^3) is the standard SI unit of volume. A cubic meter is a cube one meter on each side. You can determine the volume of rectangular solids by multiplying length times width times height.

Liquid Volume During science activities, you will measure liquids using beakers and graduated cylinders marked in milliliters, as illustrated in **Figure 29.** A graduated cylinder is a cylindrical container marked with lines from bottom to top.

Liquid volume is measured using a unit called a liter. A liter has the volume of 1000 cubic centimeters. Because the prefix *milli-* means thousandth (0.001), a milliliter equals one cubic centimeter. One milliliter of liquid would completely fill a cube measuring one centimeter on each side.

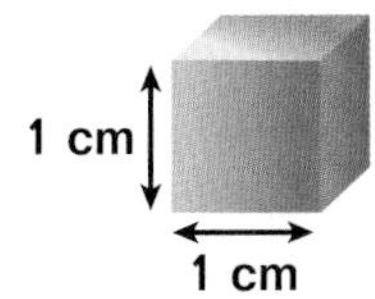

Figure 28 A square centimeter

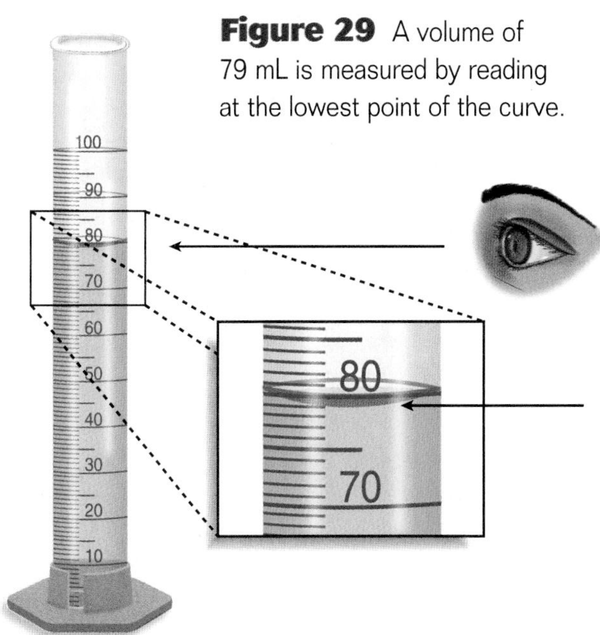

Figure 29 A volume of 79 mL is measured by reading at the lowest point of the curve.

Mass Scientists use balances to find the mass of objects in grams. You might use a beam balance similar to **Figure 30.** Notice that on one side of the balance is a pan and on the other side is a set of beams. Each beam has an object of a known mass called a *rider* that slides on the beam.

Before you find the mass of an object, set the balance to zero by sliding all the riders back to the zero point. Check the pointer on the right to make sure it swings an equal distance above and below the zero point on the scale. If the swing is unequal, find and turn the adjusting screw until you have an equal swing.

Place an object on the pan. Slide the rider with the largest mass along its beam until the pointer drops below zero. Then move it back one notch. Repeat the process on each beam until the pointer swings an equal distance above and below the zero point. Add the masses on each beam to find the mass of the object.

You should never place a hot object or pour chemicals directly onto the pan. Instead, find the mass of a clean beaker or a glass jar. Place the dry or liquid chemicals in the container. Then find the combined mass of the container and the chemicals. Calculate the mass of the chemicals by subtracting the mass of the empty container from the combined mass.

Predicting

When you apply a hypothesis, or general explanation, to a specific situation, you predict something about that situation. First, you must identify which hypothesis fits the situation you are considering.

Examples People use prediction to make everyday decisions. Based on previous observations and experiences, you may form a hypothesis that if it is wintertime, then temperatures will be lower. From past experience in your area, temperatures are lowest in February. You may then use this hypothesis to predict specific temperatures and weather for the month of February in advance. Someone could use these predictions to plan to set aside more money for heating bills during that month.

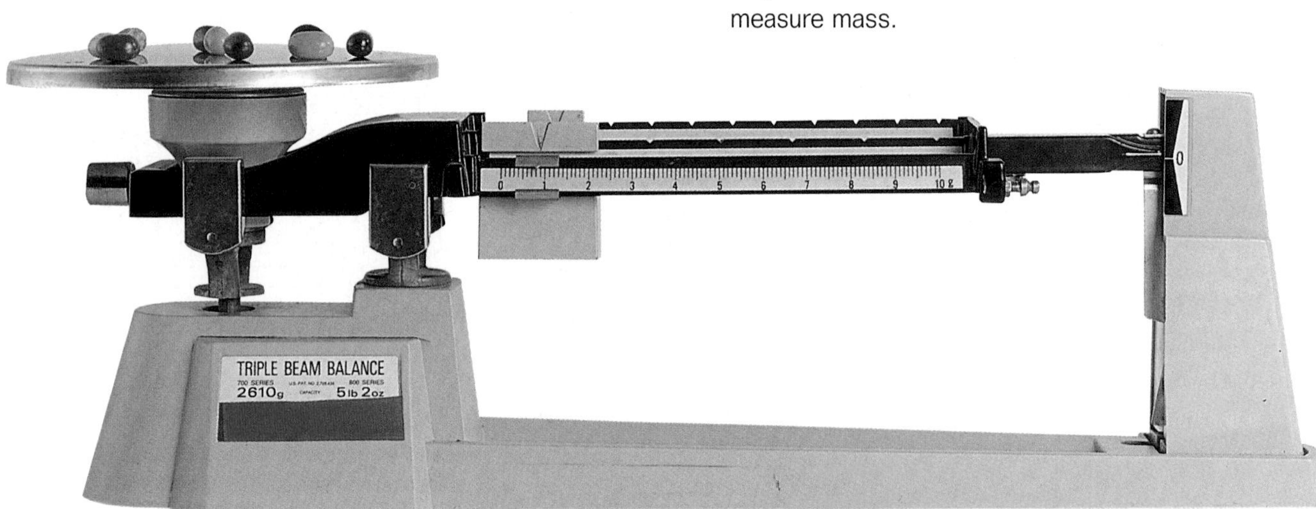

Figure 30 A beam balance is used to measure mass.

Using Numbers

When working with large populations of organisms, scientists usually cannot observe or study every organism in the population. Instead, they use a sample or a portion of the population. To sample is to take a small representative portion of organisms of a population for research. By making careful observations or manipulating variables within a portion of a group, information is discovered and conclusions are drawn that might then be applied to the whole population.

Scientific work also involves estimating. To estimate is to make a judgment about the size of something or the number of something without actually measuring or counting every member of a population.

Examples Suppose you are trying to determine the effect of a specific nutrient on the growth of black-eyed Susans. It would be impossible to test the entire population of black-eyed Susans, so you would select part of the population for your experiment. Through careful experimentation and observation on a sample of the population, you could generalize the effect of the chemical on the entire population.

Here is a more familiar example. Have you ever tried to guess how many beans were in a sealed jar? If you did, you were estimating. What if you knew the jar of beans held one liter (1000 mL)? If you knew that 30 beans would fit in a 100-milliliter jar, how many beans would you estimate to be in the one-liter jar? If you said about 300 beans, your estimate would be close to the actual number of beans. Can you estimate how many jelly beans are on the cookie sheet in **Figure 31?**

Scientists use a similar process to estimate populations of organisms from bacteria to buffalo. Scientists count the actual number of organisms in a small sample and then estimate the number of organisms in a larger area. For example, if a scientist wanted to count the number of bacterial colonies in a petri dish, a microscope could be used to count the number of organisms in a one-square-centimeter sample. To determine the total population of the culture, the number of organisms in the square-centimeter sample is multiplied by the total number of square centimeters in the culture.

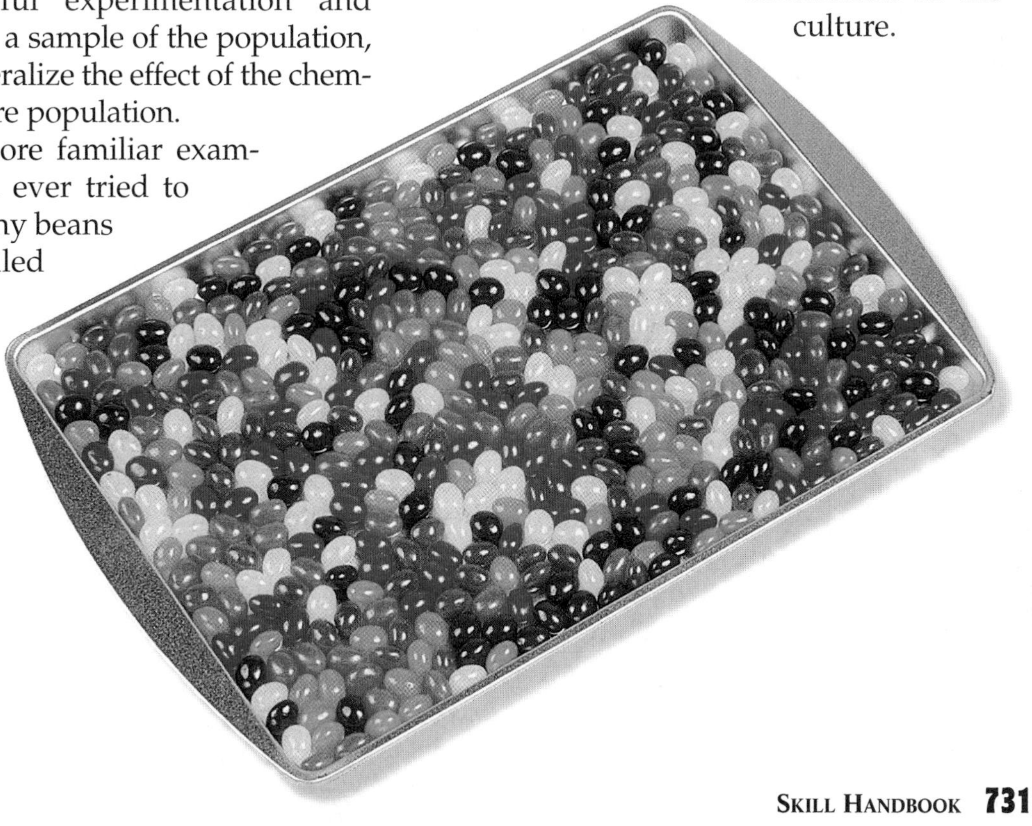

Figure 31
Sampling a group of jelly beans allows for an estimation of the total number of jelly beans in the group.

Using a Word Processor

Suppose your teacher has assigned you to write a report. After you've done your research and decided how you want to write the information, you need to put all that information on paper. The easiest way to do this is with a word processor.

A word processor is a computer program in which you can write your information, change it as many times as you need to, and then print it out so that it looks neat and clean. You can also use a word processor to create tables and columns, add bullets or cartoon art, include page numbers, and even check your spelling.

Example Last week in Science class, your teacher assigned a report on the history of the atom. It has to be double spaced and include at least one table. You've collected all the facts, and you're ready to write your report. Sitting down at your computer, you decide you want to begin by explaining early scientific ideas about the atom and then talk about what scientists think about the atom now.

After you've written the two parts of your report, you decide to put a heading or subtitle above each part and add a title to the paper. To make each of these look different from the rest of your report, you can use a word processor to make the words bigger and bolder. The word processor also can double space your entire report, so that you don't have to add an extra space between each line.

You decide to include a table that lists each scientist that contributed to the theory of the atom along with his or her contribution. Using your word processor, you can create a table with as many rows and columns as you need. And, if you forget to include a scientist in the middle, you can go back and insert a row in the middle of your table without redoing the entire table.

When you've finished with your report, you can tell the word processor to check your spelling. If it finds misspelled words, it often will suggest a word you can use to replace the misspelled word. But, remember that the word processor may not know how to spell all the words in your report. Scan your report and double check your spelling with a dictionary if you're not sure if a word is spelled correctly.

After you've made sure that your report looks just the way you want it on the screen, the word processor will print your report on a printer. With a word processor, your report can look like it was written by a real scientist.

Helpful Hints

- If you aren't sure how to do something using your word processor, look under the help menu. You can look up how to do something, and the word processor will tell you how to do it. Just follow the instructions that the word processor puts on your screen.
- Just because you've spelled checked your report doesn't mean that the spelling is perfect. The spell check can't catch misspelled words that look like other words. So, if you've accidentally typed *mind* instead of *mine,* the spell checker won't know the difference. Always reread your report to make sure you didn't miss any mistakes.

Using a Database

Imagine you're in the middle of research project. You are busily gathering facts and information. But, soon you realize that its becoming harder and harder to organize and keep track of all the information. The tool to solve "information overload" is a database. A database is exactly what it sounds like—a base on which to organize data. Similar to how a file cabinet organizes records, a database also organizes records. However, a database is more powerful than a simple file cabinet because at the click of a mouse, the entire contents can be reshuffled and reorganized. At computer-quick speeds, databases can sort information by any characteristic and filter data into multiple categories. Once you use a database, you will be amazed at how quickly all those facts and bits of information become manageable.

Example For the past few weeks, you have been gathering information on living and extinct primates. A database would be ideal to organize your information. An entry for gorillas might contain fields (categories) for fossil locations, brain size, average height, earliest fossil, and so on. Later on, if you wanted to know which primates have been found in Asia, you could quickly filter all entries using Asia in the field that listed locations. The database will scan all the entries and select the entries containing Asia. If you wanted to rank all the primates by arm length, you would sort all the entries by arm length. By using different combinations of sorting and filtering, you can discover relationships between the data that otherwise might remain hidden.

Helpful Hints

- Before setting up your own database, it's easier to learn the features of your database software by practicing with an established database.
- Entering the data into a database can be time consuming. Learn shortcuts such as tabbing between entry fields and automatic formatting of data that your software may provide.
- Get in the habit of periodically saving your database as you are entering data. That way, if something happens and your computer locks up or the power goes out, you won't lose all of your work.

Most databases have specific words you can use to narrow your search.

- AND: If you place an AND between two words in your search, the database will look for any entries that have both the words. For example, "blood AND cell" would give you information about both blood and cells.
- OR: If you place an OR between two words, the database will show entries that have at least one of the words. For example, "bird OR fish" would show you information on either birds or fish.
- NOT: If you place a NOT between two words, the database will look for entries that have the first word but do not have the second word. For example, "reproduction NOT plant" would show you information about reproduction but not about plant reproduction.

Using Graphics Software

Having trouble finding that exact piece of art you're looking for? Do you have a picture in your mind of what you want but can't seem to find the right graphic to represent your ideas? To solve these problems, you can use graphics software. Graphics software allows you to change and create images and diagrams in almost unlimited ways. Typical uses for graphics software include arranging clip-art, changing scanned images, and constructing pictures from scratch. Most graphics-software applications work in similar ways. They use the same basic tools and functions. Once you master one graphics application, you can use any other graphics application relatively easily.

Example For your report on bird adaptations, you want to make a poster displaying a variety of beak and foot types. You have acquired many photos of birds, scanned from magazines and downloaded off the Internet. Using graphics software, you separate the beaks and feet from the birds and enlarge them. Then, you use arrows and text to diagram the particular features that you want to highlight. You also highlight the key features in color, keeping the rest of the graphic in black and white. With graphics software, the possibilities are endless. For the final layout, you place the picture of the bird next to enlarged graphics of the feet and beak. Graphics software allows you to integrate text into your diagrams, which makes your bird poster look clean and professional.

Helpful Hints

- As with any method of drawing, the more you practice using the graphic software, the better your results.
- Start by using the software to manipulate existing drawings. Once you master this, making your own illustrations will be easier.
- Clip art is available on CD-ROMs, and on the Internet. With these resources, finding a piece of clip art to suit your purposes is simple.
- As you work on a drawing, save it often.
- Often you can learn a lot from studying other people's art. Look at other computer illustrations and try to figure out how the artist created it.

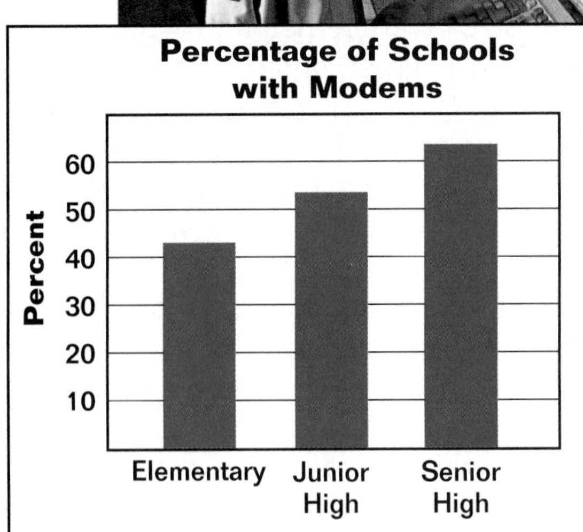

Using a Computerized Card Catalog

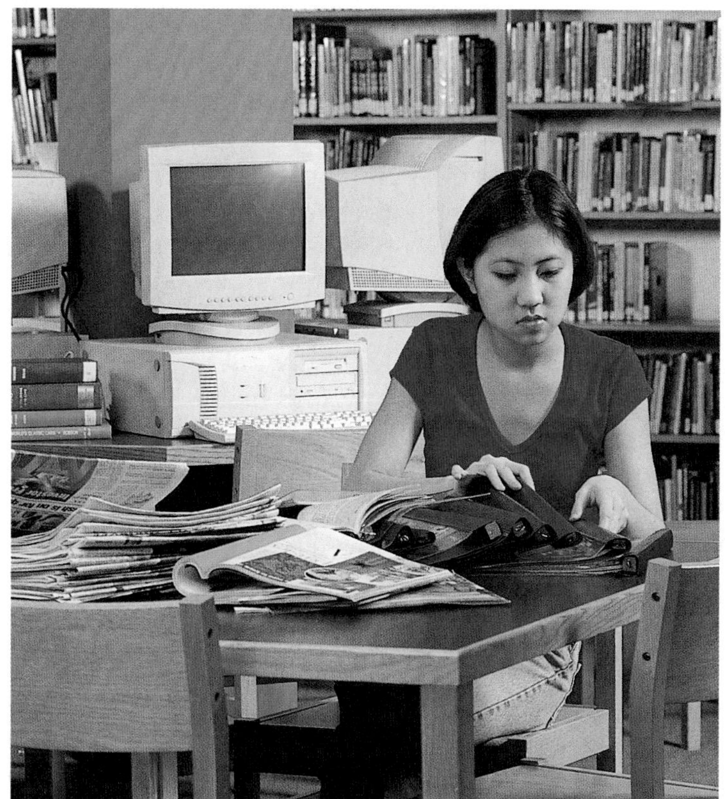

When you have a report or paper to research, you go to the library. To find the information, skill is needed in using a computerized card catalog. You use the computerized card catalog by typing in a subject, the title of a book, or an author's name. The computer will list on the screen all the holdings the library has on the subject, title, or author requested.

A library's holdings include books, magazines, databases, videos, and audio materials. When you have chosen something from this list, the computer will show whether an item is available and where in the library to find it.

Example You have a report due on dinosaurs, and you need to find three books on the subject. In the library, follow the instructions on the computer screen to select the "Subject" heading. You could start by typing in the word *dinosaurs.* This will give you a list of books on that subject. Now you need to narrow your search to the kind of dinosaur you are interested in, for example, *Tyrannosaurus rex.* You can type in *Tyrannosaurus rex* or just look through the list to find titles that you think would have information you need. Once you have selected a short list of books, click on each selection to find out if the library has the books. Then, check on where they are located in the library.

Helpful Hints

- Remember that you can use the computer to search by subject, author, or title. If you know a book's author, but not the title, you can search for all the books the library has by that author.
- When searching by subject, it's often most helpful to narrow your search by using specific search terms. If you don't find enough, you can then broaden your search.
- Pay attention to the type of materials found in your search. If you need a book, you can eliminate any videos or other resources that come up in your search.
- Knowing how your library is arranged can save a lot of time. The librarian will show you where certain types of material are kept and how to find something.

Developing Multimedia Presentations

It's your turn—you have to present your science report to the entire class. How do you do it? You can use many different sources of information to get the class excited about your presentation. Posters, videos, photographs, sound, computers, and the Internet can help show our ideas. First, decide the most important points you want your presentation to make. Then, sketch out what materials and types of media would be best to illustrate those points. Maybe you could start with an outline on an overhead projector, then show a video, followed by something from the Internet or a slide show accompanied by music or recorded voices. Make sure you don't make the presentation too complicated, or you will confuse yourself and the class. Practice your presentation a few times for your parents or brothers and sisters before you present it to the class.

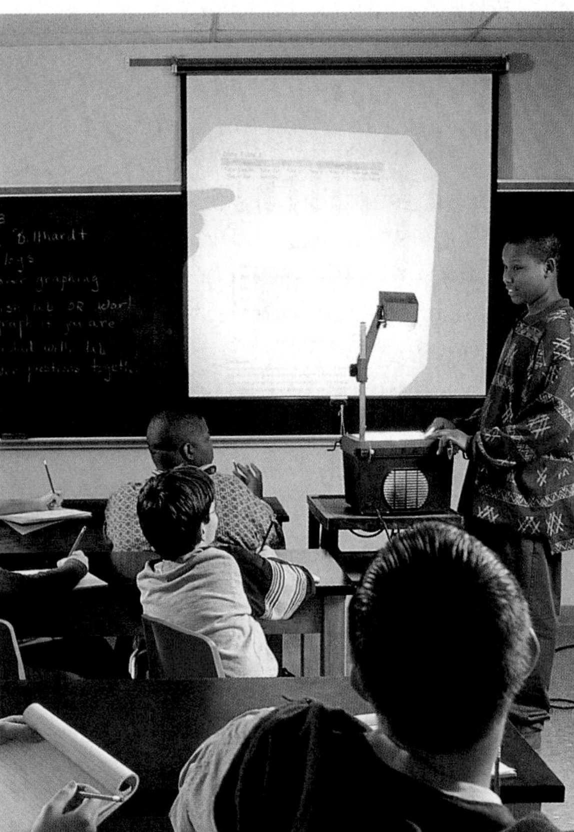

Example Your assignment is to give a presentation on bird-watching. You could have a poster that shows what features you use to identify birds, with a sketch of your favorite bird. A tape of the calls of your favorite bird or a video of birds in your area would work well with the poster. If possible, include an Internet site with illustrations of birds that the class can look at.

Helpful Hints

- Carefully consider what media will best communicate the point you are trying to make.
- Keep your topic and your presentation simple.
- Make sure you learn how to use any equipment you will be using in your presentation.
- Practice the presentation several times.
- If possible, set up all of the equipment ahead of time. Make sure everything is working correctly.

Using E-Mail

It's science fair time and you want to ask a scientist a question about your project, but he or she lives far away. You could write a letter or make a phone call. But you can also use the computer to communicate. You can do this using electronic mail (E-mail). You will need a computer that is connected to an E-mail network. The computer is usually hooked up to the network by a device called a *modem.* A modem works through the telephone lines. Finally, you need an address for the person you want to talk with. The E-mail address works just like a street address to send mail to that person.

Example There are just a few steps needed to send a message to a friend on an E-mail network. First, select Message from the E-mail software menu. Then, enter the E-mail address of your friend. Next, type your message. Make sure you check it for spelling and other errors. Finally, click the Send button to mail your message and off it goes! You will get a reply back in your electronic mailbox. To read your reply, just click on the message and the reply will appear on the screen.

Helpful Hints

- Make sure that you have entered the correct address of the person you're sending the message to.
- Reread your message to make sure it says what you want to say, and check for spelling and grammar.
- If you receive an E-mail message, respond to it as soon as possible.
- If you receive frequent email messages, keep them organized by either deleting them, or saving them in folders according to the subject or sender.

Using an Electronic Spreadsheet

Your science fair experiment has produced lots of numbers. How do you keep track of all the data, and how can you easily work out all the calculations needed? You can use a computer program called a *spreadsheet* to keep track of data that involve numbers. A spreadsheet is an electronic worksheet. Type in your data in rows and columns, just as in a data table on a sheet of paper. A spreadsheet uses some simple math to do calculations on the data. For example, you could add, subtract, divide, or multiply any of the values in the spreadsheet by another number. Or you can set up a series of math steps you want to apply to the data. If you want to add 12 to all the numbers and then multiply all the numbers by 10, the computer does all the calculations for you in the spreadsheet. Below is an example of a spreadsheet that is a schedule.

Test Run Data

	A	B	C	D
1	Test Runs	Time	Distance	Speed
2	Car 1	5 mins.	5 miles	60 mph
3	Car 2	10 mins.	4 miles	24 mph
4	Car 3	6 mins.	3 miles	30 mph
5				
6				
7				
8				
9				
10				
11				
12				
13				
14				

Sheet1 / Sheet2 / Sheet3 / Sheet4 / Sheet5 / Sheet6

Example Let's say that to complete your project, you need to calculate the speed of the model cars in your experiment. Enter the distance traveled by each car in the rows of the spreadsheet. Then enter the time you recorded for each car to travel the measured distance in the column across from each car. To make the formula, just type in the equation you want the computer to calculate; in this case, *speed* = *distance* ÷ *time*. You must make sure the computer knows what data are in the rows and what data are in the columns so the calculation will be correct. Once all the distance and time data and the formula have been entered into the spreadsheet program, the computer will calculate the speed for all the trials you ran. You can even make graphs of the results.

Helpful Hints

- Before you set up the spreadsheet, sketch out how you want to organize the data. Include any formulas you will need to use.
- Make sure you have entered the correct data into the correct rows and columns.
- As you experiment with your particular spreadsheet program you will learn more of its features.
- You can also display your results in a graph. Pick the style of graph that best represents the data you are working with.

Using a CD-ROM

What's your favorite music? You probably listen to your favorite music on compact discs (CDs). But, there is another use for compact discs, called CD-ROM. CD-ROM means Compact Disc-Read Only Memory. CD-ROMs hold information. Whole encyclopedias and dictionaries can be stored on CD-ROM discs. This kind of CD-ROM and others are used to research information for reports and papers. The information is accessed by putting the disc in your computer's CD-ROM drive and following the computer's installation instructions. The CD-ROM will have words, pictures, photographs, and maybe even sound and video on a range of topics.

Example Load the CD-ROM into the computer. Find the topic you are interested in by clicking on the Search button. If there is no Search button, try the Help button. Most CD-ROMs are easy to use, but refer to the Help instructions if you have problems. Use the arrow keys to move down through the list of titles on your topic. When you double-click on a title, the article will appear on the screen. You can print the article by clicking on the Print button. Each CD-ROM is different. Click the Help menu to see how to find what you want.

Helpful Hints

- Always open and close the CD-ROM drive on your computer by pushing the button next to the drive. Pushing on the tray to close it will stress the opening mechanism over time.
- Place the disc in the tray so the side with no printing is facing down.
- Read through the installation instructions that come with the CD-ROM.
- Remember to remove the CD-ROM before you shut your computer down.

Using Probeware

Data collecting in an experiment sometimes requires that you take the same measurement over and over again. With probeware, you can hook a probe directly to a computer and have the computer collect the data about temperature, pressure, motion, or pH. Probeware is a combination sensor and software that makes the process of collecting data easier. With probes hooked to computers, you can make many measurements quickly, and you can collect data over a long period of time without needing to be present. Not only will the software record the data, most software will graph the data.

Example Suppose you want to monitor the health of an enclosed ecosystem. You might use an oxygen and a carbon dioxide sensor to monitor the gas concentrations or humidity or temperature. If the gas concentrations remain stable, you could predict that the ecosystem is healthy. After all the data is collected, you can use the software to graph the data and analyze it. With probeware, experimenting is made efficient and precise.

Helpful Hints

- Find out how to properly use each probe before using it.
- Make sure all cables are solidly connected. A loose cable can interrupt the data collection and give you inaccurate results.
- Because probeware makes data collection so easy, do as many trials as possible to strengthen your data.

Using a Graphing Calculator

Science can be thought of as a means to predict the future and explain the past. In other language, if *x* happens, can we predict *y*? Can we explain the reason *y* happened? Simply, is their a relationship between *x* and *y*? In nature, relationship between two events or two quantities, *x* and *y*, often occur. However, the relationship is often complicated and can only be readily seen by making a graph. And, to analyze a graph, there is no quicker tool than a graphing calculator. The graphing calculator shows the mathematical relationship between two quantities.

Example If you have collected data on the position and time for a migrating whale, you can use the calculator to graph the data. Using the linear regression function on the calculator, you can determine the average migration speed of the whale. The more you use the graphing calculator to solve problems, the more you will discover its power and efficiency.

Graphing calculators have some keys that other calculators do not have. The keys on the bottom half of the calculator are those found on all scientific calculators. The keys located just below the screen are the graphing keys. You will also notice the up, down, left, and right arrow keys. These allow you to move the cursor around on the screen, to "trace" graphs that have been plotted, and to choose items from the menus. The other keys located on the top of the calculator access the special features such as statistical computations and programming features.

A few of the keystrokes that can save you time when using the graphing calculator are listed below.

- The commands above the calculator keys are accessed with the 2nd or ALPHA key. The 2nd key and its commands are yellow and the ALPHA and its commands are green.
- 2nd [ENTRY] copies the previous calculation so you can edit and use it again.
- Pressing ON while the calculator is graphing stops the calculator from completing the graph.
- 2nd [QUIT] will return you to the home (or text) screen.
- 2nd [A-LOCK] locks the ALPHA key, which is like pressing "shift lock" or "caps lock" on a typewriter or computer. The result is that all letters will be typed and you do not have to repeatedly press the ALPHA key. (This is handy for programming.) Stop typing letters by pressing ALPHA again.
- 2nd [OFF] turns the calculator off.

Helpful Hints

- Mastering the graphing calculator takes practice. Don't expect to learn it all in an afternoon.
- Programming a graphing calculator takes a plan. Write out all of the steps before entering them.
- It's easiest to learn how to program the calculator by first using programs that have already been written. As you enter them, figure out what each step is telling the calculator to do.

Skill Activities

Table of Contents

1 Skill Activity

For further explanation and examples of this skill, refer to Sequencing on page 714 of the **Skill Handbook.**

Teaching Strategies

Have students list in order the activities they perform during a typical day starting from when they wake up in the morning until when they go to bed at night. Have them pay attention to any steps that need to be completed before other steps can be accomplished.

Answers to Questions

Student sequences may vary. One possible sequence is as follows:
j, o, k, h, t, n, p, s, l, g, q, i, m, e, b, f, d, r, c, a.

Chapter 1 Skill Activity

Use After Section 1-1

Sequencing

Background

A complex project, such as a crewed mission to Mars, requires a great deal of planning over many years. The sequence of the plan is important because many of the steps cannot be done until a previous item is completed. The people responsible for the project have an overall planning sequence required for a crewed mission to Mars.

One of the recent ideas for a Mars mission involves building a spacecraft at a space station orbiting Earth. A space shuttle would ferry materials and people between Earth's surface and the space station. Then, the astronauts would travel in the spacecraft to Mars and return again to the space station.

Steps for a Mission to Mars	
a. Plan second Mars mission	**k.** Estimate cost of mission
b. Spacecraft leaves Mars orbit for Earth	**l.** Spacecraft leaves Earth orbit for Mars
c. Study Mars data and samples	**m.** Astronauts explore Mars
d. Space shuttle meets returning spacecraft	**n.** Construct spacecraft
e. Mars Rover returns to spacecraft	**o.** Design spacecraft
f. Spacecraft enters orbit around Earth	**p.** Select astronauts
g. Make any necessary course adjustments	**q.** Astronauts receive hero's welcome
h. Select a company to build spacecraft	**r.** Space shuttle carries astronauts to Earth
i. Astronauts send television viewers greetings from Mars	**s.** Space shuttle carries astronauts to space station
j. Study future positions of Earth and Mars and select launch date	**t.** Space shuttle carries building materials into orbit

Procedure

1. Read through the steps, which are out of order, listed in the table for a crewed mission to Mars.
2. Decide in what order the steps need to be completed.
3. On a separate sheet of paper, list the letters of the steps in what you consider to be the most logical sequence.

Practicing the SKILL

1. This mission plan is very brief and some details are left out. A real plan for a Mars mission would be many, many pages long. Read over your plan sequence. Add at least three more details to your plan and indicate where they should be placed in the sequence.
2. Think about how you would go about planting a vegetable or flower garden. Write down in the most logical sequence the steps you would take to plant a garden.

For more skill practice, do the Chapter 1 Interactive Exploration on the **Science Voyages Level Blue CD-ROM.**

Practicing the SKILL

1. Student answers may vary. Accept all reasonable answers.
2. Student answers may vary. One possible sequence is as follows: Read a book about planning a garden; observe where the sunlight shines in your yard during the day; decide the location of the garden; decide which plants would grow best there; buy the seeds or plants; turn up the soil in the plot; remove weeds, stones, and other unwanted plants; dig holes for the seeds or plants; plant the seeds or plants in the soil; fill in any holes with soil; fertilize and water the garden; cover ground with mulching material if desired.

Making Models

Background

You can use a model to help you better understand the structure of an atom. A model can be a drawing or something you build, like a model car. A model isn't exactly like the real object. It is often a simplified picture of a more complex object. For example, a diagram of an atom shows only a two-dimensional representation of a three-dimensional object. However, it gives you a simple picture of how the particles in an atom are arranged, and it helps you understand how matter behaves.

Procedure

1. Copy the Subatomic Particles table in your Science Journal.
2. Use the periodic table to find the number of protons, neutrons, and electrons in a lithium-7 atom. The number 7 in lithium-7 means that this is the isotope of lithium with mass number 7. In a neutral atom, the number of protons is the atomic number. The number of neutrons is the mass number minus the atomic number. The number of electrons is the same as the number of protons.
3. In the table, list the number of each particle in lithium-7.
4. Draw a circle about 2 cm in diameter. See the example in the figure at the right.
5. Write the number of protons in the circle next to a p^+ symbol.
6. Write the number of neutrons in the circle next to an n symbol.
7. Draw another circle around the circle you already drew. On this circle, write next to an e^- symbol the number of electrons that are in the atom's electron cloud.

Subatomic Particles

Atoms	Protons	Neutrons	Electrons
Lithium-7	3	4	3
Boron-10	5	5	5
Boron-11	5	6	5
Carbon-12	6	6	6
Carbon-14	6	8	6

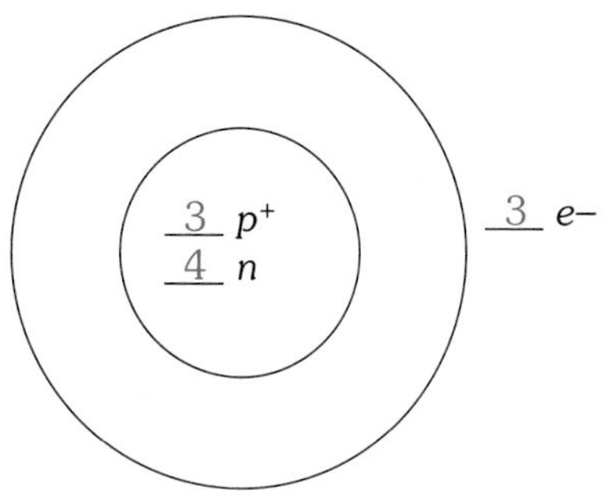

Practicing the SKILL

1. Refer to the periodic table and list the numbers of protons, neutrons, and electrons in the isotopes of boron and carbon listed in the Subatomic Particles table.
2. Using the steps given in the procedure, make models for the boron and carbon isotopes.

For more skill practice, do the Chapter 2 Interactive Exploration on the **Science Voyages Level Blue CD-ROM.**

For further explanation and examples of this skill, refer to Making Models on page 727 of the **Skill Handbook.**

Teaching Strategies

- Discuss with the class what each circle in the model of an atom represents.
- Following the activity, have students draw larger models of atoms that have higher atomic numbers.

Answers to Questions

In the table and on the model, the students should have indicated that an atom of lithium-7 has three protons, four neutrons, and three electrons.

Practicing the SKILL

1. Boron-10: 5 protons, 5 neutrons, and 5 electrons; Boron-11: 5 protons, 6 neutrons, and 5 electrons; Carbon-12: 6 protons, 6 neutrons, and 6 electrons; Carbon-14: 6 protons, 8 neutrons, and 6 electrons.
2. The models for each isotope of boron and carbon should be labeled correctly with the numbers of protons, neutrons, and electrons as listed in the answer to question 1.

For further explanation and examples of this skill, refer to Classifying on page 713 of the **Skill Handbook.**

Teaching Strategies

- Discuss the different ways in which elements can be classified.
- Give students a box of different objects, (buttons, shells, etc.,) and have them come up with different ways to classify them into groups.

Answers to Questions

Metals	Nonmetals	Metalloids
Li	F	Po
Cs	Br	B
Al	Cl	Si
Na	He	
Ni		

Skill Activity

Classifying

Background

You classify objects every day. You may put all your socks in one drawer and your sweaters in another. You store soaps, detergents,and other cleaners separately from food. You may store canned vegetables and soups on one shelf and spices on another. Putting similar objects together is classification.

By classifying objects into groups, scientists can organize information. Classifying helps them compare and contrast properties of different groups. For example, scientists classify some substances as metals, nonmetals, or metalloids. Once classified, these substances can be more easily studied.

Procedure

Use the periodic table and what you have learned to classify the following elements into categories. Label each category. Write your answers on a separate sheet of paper.

F	Li	B	Cl	Si	Na
Br	Po	Cs	Al	He	Ni

Metal
Metalloid
Nonmetal

H																	He
Li	Be											B	C	N	O	F	Ne
Na	Mg											Al	Si	P	S	Cl	Ar
K	Ca	Sc	Ti	V	Cr	Mn	Fe	Co	Ni	Cu	Zn	Ga	Ge	As	Se	Br	Kr
Rb	Sr	Y	Zr	Nb	Mo	Tc	Ru	Rh	Pd	Ag	Cd	In	Sn	Sb	Te	I	Xe
Cs	Ba	La	Hf	Ta	W	Re	Os	Ir	Pt	Au	Hg	Tl	Pb	Bi	Po	At	Rn
Fr	Ra	Ac	Rf	Db	Sg	Bh	Hs	Mt	Uun	Uuu	Uub						

Practicing the SKILL

1. Classify the following elements into two categories. Label each category.

hydrogen	aluminum
silver	gold
iron	oxygen
fluorine	copper
zinc	bromine
mercury	helium
radon	tungsten
bismuth	actinium

2. In what other ways can these elements be classified?

For more skill practice, do the Chapter 3 Interactive Exploration on the **Science Voyages Level Blue CD-ROM.**

Practicing the SKILL

1. Answers may vary. One classification could be:

Metals	Nonmetals	Metals	Nonmetals
Ag	H	Au	Rn
Fe	F	Cu	
Zn	O	Bi	
Hg	Br	W	
Al	He	Ce	

2. Some examples of how students could classify the elements are as solids, liquids, or gases; by group or period; by the number of letters in the chemical symbol for the element.

Predicting

Background

Any time you apply a hypothesis to a specific situation, you are making a prediction. Predictions can be made using tables, graphs, and other tools that give information. They also can be made based upon previous experience.

Electrons are more strongly attracted to some atoms. You can think of the sharing of electrons in a bond as a tug-of-war between two atoms. Electronegativity is a measure of the ability of an atom in a bond to attract electrons. When there is little difference in the electronegativities of two atoms, the bond is covalent. The bond has a small percentage of ionic character. As the difference between their electronegativities gets larger, the electrons are more attracted to one of the atoms. The bond has a greater percent ionic character. If the difference is large enough, one atom will lose an electron and the other atom will gain one. An ionic bond forms.

Chemists often use graphs to predict whether two atoms will form an ionic or covalent bond. The difference in the electronegativities of potassium and chlorine is 2.2. Use the graph to predict the type of bond that they will form.

Procedure

1. Notice that the difference in electronegativity is plotted on the *x*-axis.
2. When reading the *y*-axis, the larger the percent ionic character, the more certain you can be that the bond will be ionic.
3. Locate 2.2 on the *x*-axis. Go straight up from 2.2 to the curve.
4. Go straight from the point on the curve to the *y*-axis. Read that the percent ionic character is 69 percent.
5. The bond between potassium and chlorine will be ionic.

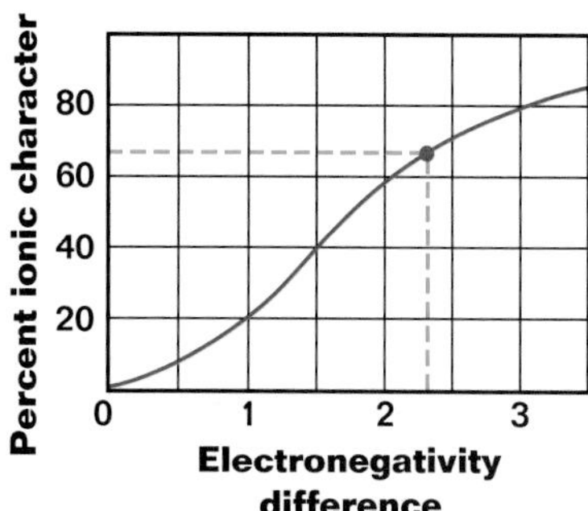

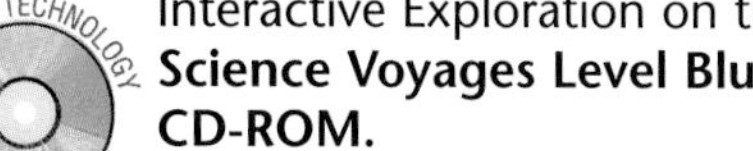

Practicing the SKILL

1. Predict the type of bond that will form between carbon and nitrogen. The difference in electronegativity is 0.5.
2. Predict the type of bond that will form between lithium and fluorine. The difference in electronegativity is 3.0.
3. What is the difference in electronegativity for a bond with 40 percent ionic character?

For more skill practice, do the Chapter 4 Interactive Exploration on the **Science Voyages Level Blue CD-ROM.**

For further explanation and examples of this skill, refer to Predicting on page 730 of the **Skill Handbook.**

Teaching Strategies

Following the activity, have students use the percent ionic character graph to practice their skill of predicting the type of bonds that will form between a variety of different atoms.

Practicing the SKILL

1. Percent ionic character is about 9 percent. The bond between carbon and nitrogen will be covalent.
2. Percent ionic character is about 79 percent. The bond between lithium and fluorine will be ionic.
3. The difference in electronegativity is about 1.5.

5 Skill Activity

For further explanation and examples of this skill, refer to Observing and Inferring on page 720 of the **Skill Handbook.**

Teaching Strategies

- Be sure students follow all appropriate safety precautions.
- If time does not permit for all students to perform the activity, do the activity as a class and make inferences from the results.

Observing and Inferring

Background

Many prescription drugs come with detailed instructions on how to take them. If you don't follow the instructions carefully, the drug may not work well. It could also make you seriously ill. Over-the-counter medications have instructions, too. You can buy medication for heartburn, indigestion, upset stomach, and a cold from almost any grocery or drug store.

How do scientists determine the best way to take a drug so that it gives the patient the relief he or she needs? Before any drug is given to a patient, it is tested many times. Scientists have to observe how the chemicals in a drug react with the chemicals in the body. In some cases, scientists recommend that the drug be taken in a certain way. The label on the bottle or box may say to take the medication with food, water, on an empty stomach, or with milk. It is always important to follow the directions so the medication can work properly. In this activity, you will observe how water temperature affects the reaction time of an effervescent tablet.

Procedure

1. Copy the data table.
2. Use masking tape to label three beakers *A, B,* and *C*.
3. Write a hypothesis stating the effect of temperature on the decomposition of an effervescent tablet.
4. Pour exactly 150 mL of ice water into beaker A. Measure the temperature of the water. Record the temperature in the data table.
5. Carefully drop one effervescent tablet into the beaker. Measure and record the number of seconds needed for the tablet to completely dissolve.
6. Pour 150 mL of water at room temperature into beaker B. Measure and record the temperature of the water.
7. Repeat step 5 using the room-temperature water.
8. Pour 150 mL of warm water into beaker C. Measure and record the temperature of the water.
9. Repeat step 5 using the warm water.

Dissolving an Effervescent Tablet

Beaker	Temperature of Water	Time to Dissolve
A		
B		
C		

Practicing the SKILL

1. In which beaker did the reaction occur most rapidly?
2. In which beaker was the reaction slowest?
3. What effect did temperature have on the reaction time of an effervescent tablet?

For more skill practice, do the Chapter 5 Interactive Exploration on the **Science Voyages Level Blue CD-ROM.**

Practicing the SKILL

1. the beaker with the warm water
2. the beaker with the ice water
3. the higher the temperature, the shorter the reaction time

Using Numbers

Background

Scientists often use formulas to solve problems. Suppose you are asked: How does the average velocity of a ball change during flight? You could use the formula that says the average velocity equals displacement over time. It is written below.

$$v = \frac{d}{t}$$

Procedure

1. The figure shows a ball in motion. The time interval between each position of the ball is 1/30 of a second.
2. Place a piece of paper on top of the drawing.
3. Mark each position of the ball with a dot.
4. Remove the paper. Draw a straight line connecting the first four positions of the ball (three intervals). The time between three intervals of the ball is 0.1 s. Why?
5. Measure and record the length of the straight line. The length of the line can be used to show the distance traveled during the first 0.1 s of flight.
6. Repeat steps 4 and 5 for the next four positions of the ball, and so on. The length of each line shows the distance traveled during each 0.1 s of flight.

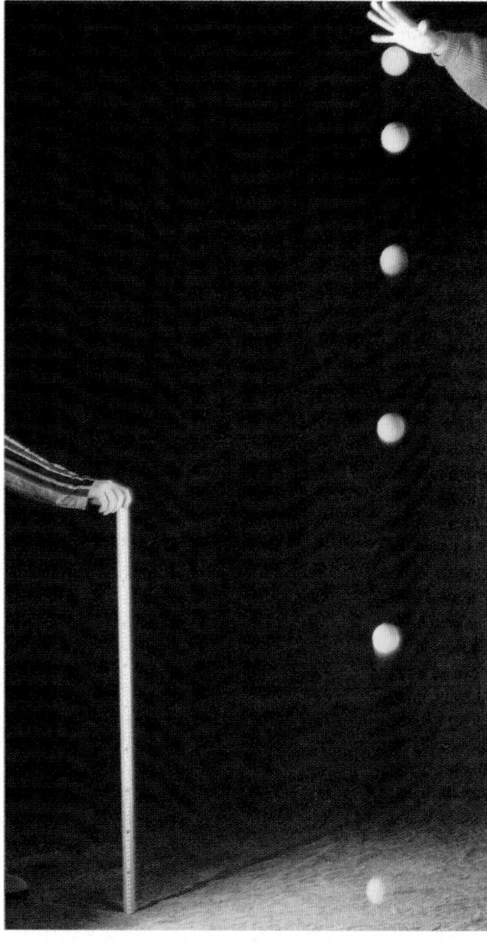

Practicing the SKILL

At what interval is the average velocity smallest? Largest?

For more skill practice, do the Chapter 6 Interactive Exploration on the **Science Voyages Level Blue CD-ROM.**

For further explanation and examples of this skill, refer to Using Numbers on page 731 of the **Skill Handbook.**

Teaching Strategies

- Have the students use thin paper to mark the positions of the ball.
- Tell students to be careful to mark each position at the same place on the ball. You might suggest marking the top edge of the ball at each position.

Answers to Questions

Since the time interval between each position is $\frac{1}{30}$ of a second, then the time over three intervals would be $\frac{3}{30}$ of a second, which is $\frac{1}{10}$ of a second or 0.1 s.

Practicing the SKILL

The average velocity is smallest at the first interval (the top) and largest at the last interval (the bottom).

7 Skill Activity

For further explanation and examples of this skill, refer to Making and Using Tables on page 716 of the **Skill Handbook.**

Teaching Strategies

Following the activity, provide students a number of opportunities to gather, organize, and interpret data.

Chapter 7 Skill Activity

Use After Section 7-2

Making and Using Tables

Background

Scientists collect and interpret data as a part of their investigations. They often organize the data into a data table. Data tables help the scientists to arrange information so it is easier for them to understand. Scientists interpret the data by looking for patterns that may lead to general conclusions.

Suppose the class decides to see how far a ball will travel over a period of time.

Procedure

1. Look at the Rolling Distance table.
2. Notice that the time, in seconds, that the ball rolled is listed in the first column.
3. The distance, in meters, that the ball traveled in that amount of time is listed in the second column.
4. Now, see if there is a pattern between the time allowed for the ball to roll and the distance it traveled.
5. By looking at the table, you can see that the longer the ball rolled, the further it traveled.
6. You can also see that the distance traveled was double the time allowed each time.
7. Look at the Planetary Weight Factors table.
8. To figure out what you would weigh on different planets, multiply your weight on Earth by the factor listed next to each planet in the Planetary Weight Factors table.

Rolling Distance

Time (s)	Distance (m)
0.0	0.0
1.0	2.0
2.0	4.0
3.0	6.0

Sample Data

Planetary Weight Factors

Planet	Factor	Your Weight on Earth (lb)	Your Weight on Planet (lb)
Venus	0.91	110	100.1
Mars	0.38	110	39.6
Jupiter	2.5	110	253
Saturn	1.1	110	96.8
Neptune	1.1	110	143

Practicing the SKILL

Use the Planetary Weight Factors table to answer the following questions.

1. On which planet(s) do you weigh more than you do on Earth? Less than Earth?
2. On which planet(s) would you weigh nearly the same as you do on Earth?

For more skill practice, do the Chapter 7 Interactive Exploration on the **Science Voyages Level Blue CD-ROM.**

Practicing the SKILL

1. You would weigh more on Jupiter, Saturn, and Neptune. You would weigh less on Venus and Mars.
2. You would weigh nearly the same on Venus and (depending upon the interpretation of "nearly") Saturn and Neptune.

Chapter 8 Skill Activity

Use After Section 8-3

Using Numbers

Background

What do people need to survive? What is the difference between a necessity and a luxury? An earthquake can make the answers to these questions clear to people. During a damaging earthquake, basic services such as water, power, communication, and roads may be unavailable. Disaster relief experts advise that you should be prepared to be self-sufficient for 72 hours. An earthquake survival pack is a good way to be prepared.

Survival Kit Items

Item	Cost ($)	Item	Cost ($)
aspirin or acetaminophen	1.49	prescription medicines (insulin, etc.)	varies
water-purification tablets	2.69	ipecac*	2.69
latex gloves	1.39	crackers	3.19
adhesive bandages	1.59	gauze pads 4" × 4"	2.89
canned beans	0.69	tweezers	0.99
flashlight	5.79	dried fruit	4.79
thermometer	4.29	batteries	8.49
blankets	7.99	rubbing alcohol	0.49
radio	9.99	plastic tarp	6.49
tissues	0.89	bottled water 4 liters/person	2.16
first aid handbook	4.99	pocketknife	12.99
canned tuna	2.79	matches	0.39
adhesive tape	2.19	canned juice	1.19
candles	1.99	scissors	3.19
pet food	3.00	can opener	2.39
canned heat	1.89	paper and pencil	2.00
ax	15.89	disposable dishes	2.39
antibiotic ointment	2.59	disposable utensils	2.19
bucket	3.99	chlorine bleach	0.25
eye dropper	1.99	clothing	varies
cotton swabs	0.89	signal flare	6.19
towel	5.49	books	7.50
toilet paper	0.49	elastic bandage	2.49
peanut butter	1.19	shovel	12.98

*drug used to induce vomiting in case of accidental poisoning

Practicing the SKILL

1. Which items do you consider to be the most important? Why?
2. Are there any items not on the list that you think should be included? What are they and why do you want to include them?
3. Which items would you buy if you were restricted to a $50 budget?

For more skill practice, do the Chapter 8 Interactive Exploration on the **Science Voyages Level Blue CD-ROM.**

Skill Activity 8

For further explanation and examples of this skill, refer to Using Numbers on page 731 of the **Skill Handbook.**

Teaching Strategies

- Have selected students describe the types of damage they would expect during a big natural disaster (earthquake, hurricane, or tornado).
- Discuss the difference between necessities and luxuries.
- Have students work in groups to brainstorm a list of survival needs.
- Optional lesson is to limit the students to different maximum budgets. Which items would they include if restricted to a $25 budget?

Practicing the SKILL

1. Water is the most important item. You can survive 72 hours without food but not without water. An exception to this might be certain medications such as insulin or heart tablets.
2. Student responses will vary. Use these as a springboard for class discussion.
3. Student responses will vary, but they should support their choices with a logical explanation.

For further explanation and examples of this skill, refer to Making and Using Graphs on page 717 of the **Skill Handbook.**

Teaching Strategies

- Review how to make a graph with the students. Discuss how to number and label *x* and *y* axes.
- Have selected students describe the different types of graphs and when to use each kind.
- Discuss why a bar graph would be a good choice for comparing volcanic eruptions.
- Ask students if there is only one way to graph the data. Emphasize that the data do not have to be graphed in the same order as the table. Students have choices in how to format the graph. For example, they could choose to graph the eruptions in order of increasing volume.

Chapter 9 Skill Activity

Use After Section 9-2

Making and Using Graphs

Background

You have learned that composite volcanoes can sometimes erupt violently, throwing large volumes of material into the atmosphere. Volcanologists have used various methods to rank these explosive eruptions. One of the most commonly used is to compare the volumes of erupted material. Because the amount of material is huge, scientists use cubic kilometers (km^3). A cubic kilometer is the amount of material in a cube that measures one kilometer on each side. That's a lot of rock!

Procedure

The Volcano Information table contains information about violent volcanic eruptions from around the world. Use these data to make a bar graph that compares the volume of material that was ejected by these volcanoes. Put the eruption date on the *x*-axis and the volume of material on the *y*-axis.

Practicing the SKILL

1. When was the largest eruption of Mount St. Helens? How many km^3 of material were ejected?
2. How are the data organized in the Volcano Information table?
3. What was the largest eruption of the 20th century? When did it occur?

For more skill practice, do the

Chapter 9 Interactive Exploration on the **Science Voyages Level Blue CD-ROM.**

Volcano Information

Volcano Name and Location	Eruption Date	Volume (km^3)
Mount Pinatubo, Philippines	1991	5.0
El Chichón, Mexico	1982	0.85
Mount St. Helens, Washington	1980	1.3
Mount Katmai, Alaska	1912	12.8
Mount Pelée, Martinique	1902	0.85
Krakatau, Indonesia	1883	19.0
Mount St. Helens, Washington	1842–1857	1.5
Tambora, Indonesia	1815	32.0
Mount Fuji, Japan	1707	2.1
Mount St. Helens, Washington	1480–1482	2.6
Vesuvius, Italy (Pompeii)	A.D. 79	3.0
Mount St. Helens, Washington	1900 B.C.	3.4
Mount Mazama, Oregon (Crater Lake)	5000 B.C.	43.0

Practicing the SKILL

Student bar graphs should show that Mount Mazama ejected the largest volume of material followed by Tambora, Krakatau, Mount Katmai, Mount St. Helens (1900BC), Vesuvius, Mount St. Helens (1480–1482), Mount Fuji, Mount St. Helens (1842–1857), Mount St. Helens (1980), and El Chicon and Mount Pelee.

1. The largest eruption of Mount St. Helens was in 1900 B.C. Approximately 3.4 km of material were ejected.
2. The data in the table are listed by date, with the most recent eruption first.
3. The largest eruption in the 20th century was Mount Katmai. It occurred in 1912.

Interpreting Scientific Illustrations

Background

When a large earthquake occurs in the Pacific Ocean, the epicenter is quickly determined and a tsunami warning is issued. Scientists have created tsunami travel-time charts such as in the figure below, for the Pacific Ocean. Using these charts allows them to predict when a tsunami will reach different Pacific Ocean coastal regions.

On Friday, July 17, 1998, a magnitude 7.0 earthquake occurred on the seafloor near Papua New Guinea in the South Pacific Ocean. Within moments a 7-meter-high tsunami struck the shore and more than 3000 people were killed as coastal villages were washed away.

Procedure

Study the figure below. If you know the epicenter of an earthquake you can determine when a tsunami might reach land. For example, a tsunami caused by an earthquake in Guam would take about 8 hours to reach Hilo, Hawaii.

Practicing the SKILL

1. A large earthquake off the coast of Peru has generated a tsunami. If you live in Hilo, Hawaii, how long do you have before the tsunami reaches your beach house?
2. An underwater volcanic eruption near Midway Island has caused a tsunami. How long before this wave reaches Tokyo, Japan?
3. Why was a tsunami warning of no use to the villagers in Papua New Guinea?

For more skill practice, do the Chapter 10 Interactive Exploration on the **Science Voyages Level Blue CD-ROM.**

GLENCOE TECHNOLOGY

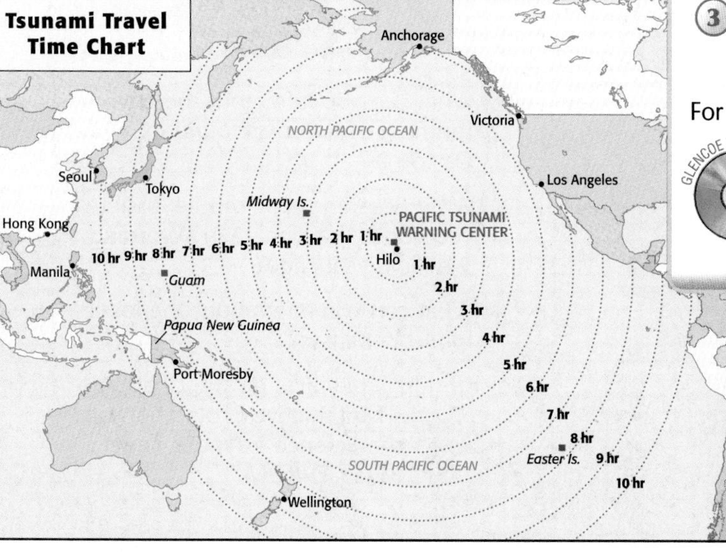

For further explanation and examples of this skill, refer to Interpreting Scientific Illustrations on page 726 of the **Skill Handbook.**

Teaching Streatgies

- Refer to the diagram showing plate boundaries. Have students describe the types of boundaries around the Pacific Ocean.
- Locate Papua, New Guinea on a world map. Ask students if this is near a plate boundary.
- Take students outside and have them stand near a two story wall that is about 6.9 m (23 feet) tall. If this doesn't impress them, tell them that tsunamis have reached 30 m (100 feet) high.

Practicing the SKILL

1. It will take about 10 hours for the tsunami to reach Hilo, Hawaii.
2. The tsunami will reach Tokyo in 5 to 6 hours.
3. The earthquake occurred too close to shore. The travel time was only minutes. There was no time for a warning.

For further explanation and examples of this skill, refer to Observing and Inferring on page 720 of the **Skill Handbook.**

Teaching Strategies

- Help students to identify the fossilized organisms.
- Provide reference materials for researching the organisms' habitats and other survival needs.

Use After Section 11-2

Observing and Inferring

Background

Throughout Earth's history, many changes have taken place. Unfortunately, there is no written record from prehistoric time. There are clues to Earth's past imbedded in rock, though. Fossils are the remains of once-living organisms that have been preserved in rock.

Scientists study fossils in order to gain knowledge about the organism. They also learn what the environment was like when the organism was alive. Scientists look at (observe) the fossil and estimate (infer) what the environment was like during the lifetime of the organism. In this skill activity, you will make observations of certain fossils and infer the type of environment that existed when the organism was alive.

Organism	Location
	•Found in California •1 million years old
	•Found in Kansas •1.5 million years old
	•Found in Wyoming •5 million years old

Procedure

1. Look at the table above. What type of organism is fossilized in each rock in this table? Research the conditions necessary for each of these organisms to survive.
2. Read the information given about each fossil next to the picture.

Practicing the SKILL

1. What can you infer abut the environment of the fossil found in California?
2. What does finding a reptile fossil tell you about the climate in Wyoming 5 million years ago?
3. What can you infer about the fossil found in Kansas?

For more skill practice, do the Chapter 11 Interactive Exploration on the **Science Voyages Level Blue CD-ROM.**

Practicing the SKILL

1. The fossil's environment was aquatic.
2. That the environment was warmer than it is today. The environment may or may not have been wetter. Reptiles live in desert and tropical environments.
3. The only possible inference is that ferns or fernlike plants grew there 1.5 million years ago. There are ferns in Kansas today.

Making and Using Graphs

Background

A bar graph is used to compare similar things that show variations. The numbers of each group are normally plotted on the vertical y-axis. The horizontal x-axis is used for plotting each separate group. The data are graphed within separate bars.

Procedure

1. Examine Table 12-1 of the Geologic Time Scale in Chapter 12. Observe the names listed under the heading *Period.*
2. Calculate the length of time for each period. The first two have been done for you in the table shown here.

Geologic Time	
Period	Length of Period in Millions of Years
Quaternary	1.6 − 0 = 1.6
Tertiary	66 − 1.6 = 64.4

3. Make a bar graph showing the length of time for each period.
4. Mark the number of years up the vertical axis. (Each block on the graph paper should represent one million years.) Make the highest number on this line the highest number of years calculated in your table. The bottom of the vertical line is 0.
5. List the periods along the horizontal axis starting with Cambrian on the left and going to Quaternary. Allow one block on the graph paper for each period.
6. Complete the graph by drawing each bar the correct height for the number of years. Color in each bar.

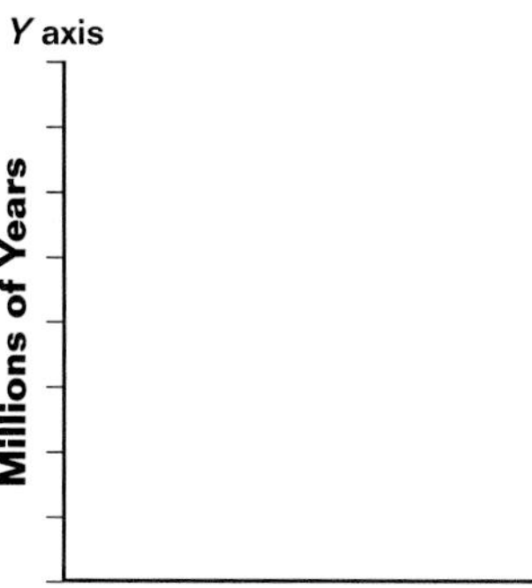

Practicing the SKILL

1. Other than Precambrian, which period lasted the longest time?
2. Which period is the shortest?
3. What kind of pattern in the lengths of periods can be seen from the graph?
4. Why is a graph more helpful than a table in comparing geologic time periods?

For more skill practice, do the Chapter 12 Interactive Exploration on the **Science Voyages Level Blue CD-ROM.**

For further explanation and examples of this skill, refer to Making and Using Graphs on page 717 of the **Skill Handbook.**

Teaching Strategies

- Remind students that the horizontal axis represents one thing and the vertical axis another thing and that the two things are related in some way.
- Emphasize that each axis must be divided into equal units.
- Help students choose appropriate units for each axis.

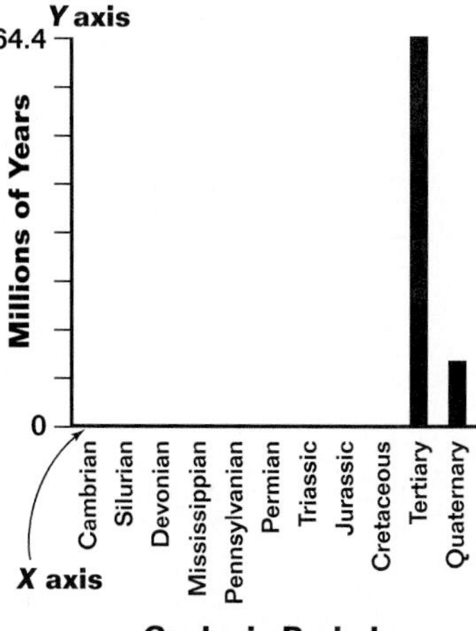

Practicing the SKILL

1. Cretaceous, 80 million years
2. Quaternary, 1.6 million years
3. There is greater variation at the beginning and end of the graph than in the middle.
4. The size of a bar better represents the amount of time than a number does.

13 Skill Activity

For further explanation and examples of this skill, refer to Interpreting Data on page 724 of the **Skill Handbook.**

Teaching Strategies

- Have students prepare a chart that shows how the life spans of the dinosaurs overlap.
- Arrange the dinosaurs in order from oldest to youngest to facilitate comparisons of life spans.

Chapter 13 **Skill Activity** Use after Section 13-1

Interpreting Data

Background

Dinosaurs were a successful group of animals. They lived on Earth for about 160 million years and became extinct about 66 million years ago. Several species of dinosaur, such as *Tyrannosaurus rex* and Stegosaurus, are well known. Many people have the misconception that these well-known dinosaurs lived at the same time. During the Jurassic and Cretaceous periods, such species of dinosaurs died out while other, new species developed. In other words, not all the dinosaurs lived at the same time. The approximate time periods for several well-known dinosaurs are listed in the Dinosaur Ranges table.

Interpret the age relationships between different dinosaurs.

Procedure

Use the information in the Dinosaur Ranges table and a geologic time scale in Chapter 13 to answer the following questions.

a. Which dinosaur species were present at the end of the Cretaceous Period?

b. Which dinosaur species lived during the Upper Jurassic Period and survived into the Lower Cretaceous?

c. Which dinosaur species lived during the Jurassic Period?

Dinosaur Ranges

Dinosaur species	Approximate time that species lived (million yrs before present)
Allosaurus	180–144
Ankylosaurus	90–66
Apatosaurus	150–145
Brachiosaurus	150–145
Diplodocus	150–145
Iguanodon	144–110
Megalosaurus	208–170
Stegosaurus	170–150
Tyrannosaurus rex	100–66
Triceratops	90–66
Velociraptor	95–66

Practicing the SKILL

Read each of the following statements and decide if it could be true or must be false. Explain your answer.

1. A Tyrannosaurus skeleton has been found with Ankylosaurus bones in the stomach region.
2. The bones of Megalosaurus, Brachiosaurus, and Iguanodon are found mixed together in a fossil bed.
3. Triceratops were frequent prey for groups of Velociraptors.

For more skill practice, do the Chapter 13 Interactive Exploration on the **Science Voyages Level Blue CD-ROM.**

GLENCOE TECHNOLOGY

Practicing the SKILL

1. could be true; Tyrannosaurus and Ankylosaurus both lived 66 million years ago.
2. false; Brachiosaurus and Iguanodon lived long after Megalosaurus became extinct.
3. could be true; life spans of both these dinosaurs overlapped.

Chapter 14

Skill Activity

Use After Section 14-2

Making Models

Background

Many molecules are isomers. Isomers are molecules that have the same chemical formula but different structures. Many organic compounds have isomers. Some large hydrocarbons have thousands of isomers. The different arrangements of the atoms in the isomers give them different properties. To understand the properties of a molecule, it is necessary to know the structure of the molecule. In this Skill Activity, you will make a model to show that isomers differ from one another.

Procedure

1. Use large foam balls to represent carbon atoms and small foam balls to represent hydrogen atoms. Pipe cleaners can be used to represent the bonds and attach the balls together.
2. Use four large balls and ten small balls to make a model of butane, C_4H_{10}, with the four carbon atoms in a straight chain. Place the bonds evenly around each carbon atom.

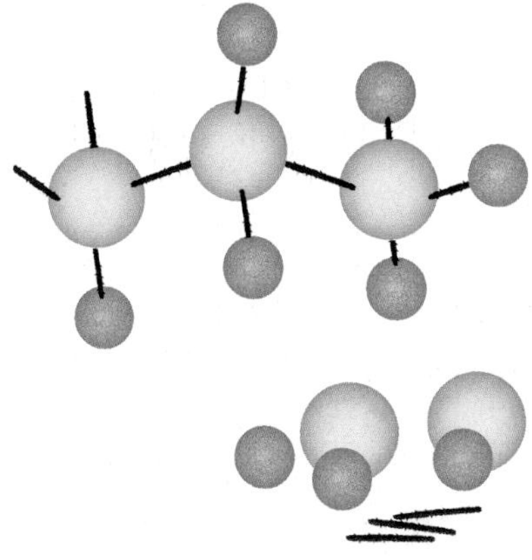

3. Draw a diagram of your model and describe it in your own words.
4. Remove the end carbon with its three hydrogen atoms.
5. You now have a three-carbon chain. Remove one hydrogen atom from the middle carbon and place it in the position from which you removed the carbon atom and its three hydrogens.
6. Attach the carbon and its three hydrogen atoms to the center carbon where the hydrogen atom was.
7. Draw a diagram of your model and describe it in your own words. The models in steps 3 and 7 are two isomers of butane.

Practicing the SKILL

1. Use five large balls, twelve small balls, and 16 pieces of pipe cleaner to make a model of pentane, C_5H_{12}.
2. Rearrange the same set of materials to form an isomer of pentane.

For more skill practice, do the Chapter 14 Interactive Exploration on the **Science Voyages Level Blue CD-ROM.**

GLENCOE TECHNOLOGY

For further explanation and examples of this skill, refer to Making Models on page 727 of the **Skill Handbook.**

Teaching Strategies

- Have students draw a diagram of each model they make as well as write a description in their own words.
- Following this activity, have students practice making models of additional isomers of larger, organic molecules using the foam balls and pipe cleaners.

Practicing the SKILL

1. There are three possible isomers of pentane: an unbranched, 5-carbon chain; a 4-carbon chain with one branch; a 3-carbon chain with two branches.
2. Same as question 1.

For further explanation and examples of this skill, refer to Observing and Inferring on p. 720 of the **Skill Handbook.**

Teaching Strategies

- Encourage students to provide a wide variety of simple clues.
- Ask for student volunteers to act out clues to one card before students perform the activity.
- Be sure to use names of plant, flowers, fruits, and vegetables that are familiar to the students.
- Move among students during step 2 to ensure that each student both gathers information about his or her card and provides information to other students.
- Encourage students to write possible names as they write the clues provided to them. They will need this information to answer question 2 in Practicing the Skill.

Chapter 15 Skill Activity

Use After Section 15-1

Observing and Inferring

Background

One of the best tools for learning science is having good observation skills. You can learn by simply watching things happen. This was the main tool that Aristotle used when he made many of his discoveries. He kept detailed records of his observations. Over time, he collected much information about the living things in his surroundings. He made many inferences from his observations. Some have been proven to be true, but others have been shown not to be true. Other scientists used many of his recorded observations for further study.

Procedure

1. Your teacher will tape to your back a card with the name of a plant, flower, fruit, or vegetable written on it.
2. For thirty minutes, move around the classroom and have other students act out clues to the name on your card. No one should speak during the observation time.
3. Keep a list of the clues then make an inference about the name written on your card.

Practicing the SKILL

1. Were you able to infer the correct name on your card?
2. How many clues did you observe before you knew the name on your card?
3. How many of your classmates correctly inferred the names on their cards?

For more skill practice, do the Chapter 15 Interactive Exploration on the **Science Voyages Level Blue CD-ROM.**

Practicing the SKILL

1. Answers will vary.
2. Answers will vary.
3. Answers will vary.

Sequencing

Background

Sequence diagrams illustrate in a simple way series of events in the order in which they occur. The events in the life cycle of a plant are represented by a series of diagrams that show how the separate stages of the life cycle pass from one to the other.

What are the stages and events in the life cycle of a fern?

Each stage in the life cycle of a plant, such as a fern, occurs in a particular order. This order is indicated by the use of arrows that are placed between the stages. The drawings in a sequence diagram are labeled to identify each stage and the important structures of each drawing.

Procedure

1. Examine **Figure 16-6** in Chapter 16. This diagram shows drawings of the individual stages in the life cycle of a fern.
2. Observe the number and direction of the arrows that are drawn between each stage of the life cycle.
3. Copy the Fern Observations table on this page. Record three events in the fern gametophyte stage and three in the sporophyte stage on the table.
4. Examine **Figure 16-9** in Chapter 16. Copy the Pine Observations table on this page. Number the items listed in the correct order as they occur in a pine's life cycle.

Fern Observations

Gametophyte Stage	Sporophyte Stage
1. Reproductive structures form	Fern form grows
2. Sperm are released	Sori develop
3. Spore germinates	Zygote is formed

Pine Observations

Gametophyte Stage	Sporophyte Stage
pollen grains	2
fertilization	3
pollen cone	1
embryo forms	4
seed dispersal	5

Practicing the SKILL

1. How many stages are there in the life cycle of a fern?
2. In which stage are spores formed?
3. In which stage are sex organs formed?
4. What structure begins the sporophyte stage?

For more skill practice, do the Chapter 16 Interactive Exploration on the **Science Voyages Level Blue CD-ROM.**

Skill Activity 16

For further explanation and examples of this skill, refer to Sequencing on page 714 of the **Skill Handbook.**

Teaching Strategies

- Have students read the fern life cycle section of Chapter 16 and examine **Figure 16-6.**
- Discuss the fern life cycle with the class.
- Have students complete the Skill Activity on their own.
- Correct orally as a class and review the fern life cycle.

Practicing the SKILL

1. two, sporophyte and gametophyte
2. sporophyte
3. gametophyte
4. zygote

For further explanation and examples of this skill, refer to Interpreting Data on page 730 of the **Skill Handbook.**

Teaching Strategies

- Discuss what it would be like to try to determine the number of trees in a forest or worms in an acre of soil. It would be impossible to count all of them, so sampling techniques are used.
- Ask for student examples of where sampling might be useful in predicting the total number.

Observing and Inferring

Background

Large populations of organisms need to be counted to determine the overall health of the species. However, counting each individual in a population can be time consuming and confusing. Therefore, scientists have developed methods for estimating the number of individuals in a population in order to save time. In this activity, you will predict the number of beetles by estimating the total number.

Ladybird Numbers

Predicted number 168 Time 20 sec				
Number in top left square	×	Total number of squares	=	Estimated total number
21		8		168
Actual number 159 Time 2 min 15 sec				

Procedure

1. Estimate the number of ladybird beetles in the figure to the right and record the number in a table like the one shown.
2. Place tracing paper over the diagram. Make a population count by placing a checkmark next to each ladybird beetle. Record the actual number of beetles in the table. Next to this number, record the amount of time it took to make the count.
3. Count the ladybird beetle population a second time by sampling. A sample is made by selecting and counting only a portion of the population. Count the number of ladybird beetles in the top left square and record this number in the table.
4. Enter the total number of squares in the table. Multiply the number of ladybird beetles in the top left square by the total number of squares. Record this estimated total number in the table.
5. At the top of the table, record the amount of time it took to make the sample count.

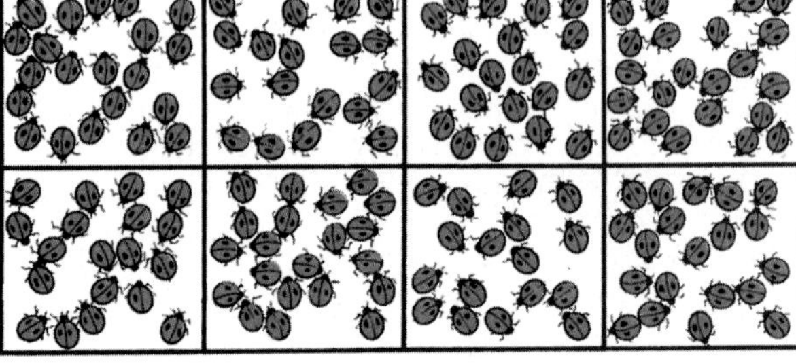

Practicing the SKILL

1. How many ladybird beetles did you estimate were shown?
2. Which way was faster—making an actual count or sampling?
3. Were the results exactly the same?

For more skill practice, do the

Chapter 17 Interactive Exploration on the **Science Voyages Level Blue CD-ROM.**

Practicing the SKILL

1. 168
2. sampling
3. No, sampling is faster, but less accurate.

Observing and Inferring

Background

Living things survive in their environments because they have behavioral and physical adaptations that allow them to live. For example, a jackrabbit will run when it sees a coyote. This is a behavioral adaptation. The jackrabbit also has strong legs. This is a physical adaptation. Both adaptations, working together, give the jackrabbit an advantage in escaping predators. In this activity, you will observe adaptations that help living things near your classroom survive.

Procedure

1. Read Section 2, Land Environments. Pay special attention to the Adaptations of Desert Plants and Animals.
2. In a table like the one shown below, record the names of five living things you find near your classroom.
3. Briefly describe two behavioral adaptations and two physical adaptations for each. Record these in your table.
4. Write how you think each of the adaptations might give each organism an advantage that allows it to survive in the wild.

Practicing the SKILL

1. Many birds, insects, and bats are able to fly. What are the advantages of this adaptation?
2. Many mammals in both hot and cold climates have thick fur. What might the advantages of this adaptation be?

For more skill practice, do the Chapter 18 Interactive Exploration on the **Science Voyages Level Blue CD-ROM.**

Sample data

Organism Behavior

Organism	Physical adaptations	Behavioral adaptations	Advantages in the wild
Dog	Fur, canine teeth	Stalks other animals	Will help it keep warm and tear meat; will help it get food
Spider	Small	Knows how to spin webs	Allows it to capture food; easily hides from potential prey
Bird	Wings	Migration, flies from predators	Wings help birds escape predators; migration allows the bird to travel to nesting sites.
Ant	Strong body	Has pheromones	Allows it to carry objects heavier than itself; can follow a trail another ant has laid
Cat	Whiskers	Will hide from larger animals	Whiskers allow cats to hide in small places without getting stuck.

For further explanation and examples of this skill, refer to Observing and Inferring on page 720 of the **Skill Handbook.**

Teaching Strategies

- Discuss several physical and behavioral adaptations of living things that are familiar to the class. Select at least one plant and one animal.
- Allow the students to walk around outside in the vicinity of the classroom to discover things that live nearby.
- Have the students complete their Data and Observations tables and discuss the results.

Practicing the SKILL

1. Answers will vary but should include escape from predators and pursuit of prey.
2. Answers could include maintenance of temperature and protection from insects and other animals.

For further explanation and examples of this skill, refer to Comparing and Contrasting on page 720 of the **Skill Handbook.**

Teaching Strategies

- Discuss what it would be like to try to determine the number of trees in a forest or worms in an acre of soil. It would be impossible to count all of them, so sample techniques are used.
- Ask for student examples of where sampling might be useful in predicting the total number.

Comparing and Contrasting

Background

Most of the energy humans use for power and transportation comes from the burning of fossil fuels. If humans continue to use them, fossil fuels will become more scarce, and it will be necessary to find other sources of energy. There are also concerns that fossil fuels are not clean enough and may be affecting our quality of life and the health of our planet. Every source of energy has advantages and disadvantages. In the Skill Activity, you will compare and contrast sources of energy and begin to plan what humans should do about energy today and for the future.

Procedure

1. Read Section 19-1. Pay special attention to Energy for Now and the Future.
2. On a separate piece of paper, draw and complete a table like the one shown. Much of the information for the table is in the text, but in some cases you may need to use your own ideas or go to other sources to find the information.

Fuel Observations

Energy Source	Advantages	Disadvantages
Fossil Fuels	Easily Available Now	Contaminates air and water
Solar Energy	Cheap, clean Available	The sun doesn't shine at night
Solar Cells	Clean	Expensive to make
Water Power	Clean	Dams rivers, affects wildlife
Wind Power	Clean	Wind doesn't always blow
Geothermal Energy	Cheap	Only useable in some places
Nuclear Energy	No fossil fuels required	Mining, radio-active waste

Practicing the SKILL

1. Which source of energy will probably last the longest? Why?
2. If you could select one energy source to eliminate entirely, which would you choose? Why?
3. List three energy sources that you would recommend we use in the future. Give reasons for the sources you choose.

For more skill practice, do the Chapter 19 Interactive Exploration on the **Science Voyages Level Blue CD-ROM.**

Practicing the SKILL

political and financial issues that often color our decisions.

1. Solar. The sun is predicted to shine for billions of years.
2. Student answers will vary.
3. Student answers will vary.

Chapter 20 **Skill Activity** Use After Section 20-3

Making and Using Graphs

Background

The length of time it takes for a satellite to complete one orbit is called the orbital period. The greater the altitude of a satellite, the longer its orbital period. Satellites that stay above the same spot on Earth's surface are called geostationary satellites. The orbital period of a geostationary satellite equals 24 h. Communication systems for telephone and television use geostationary satellites.

What is the altitude of a geostationary orbit? Try the following procedure to determine the altitude of a geostationary orbit.

Orbital Data

Altitude of orbit (km)	Orbital velocity (km/hr)	Orbital circumference (km)	Orbital period (hr)
10 000	26 470	46 400	1.8
20 000	17 770	103 000	5.8
30 000	11 920	229 000	19.2
40 000	10 560	292 000	27.7
50 000	9575	354 000	37.0

Procedure

1. The Orbital Data table lists the altitude, speed, and circumference of six different orbits. The orbital period can be calculated by dividing the circumference by the speed. Calculate the orbital periods for each altitude and record the data.
2. Make a line graph that compares the altitude and orbital period.

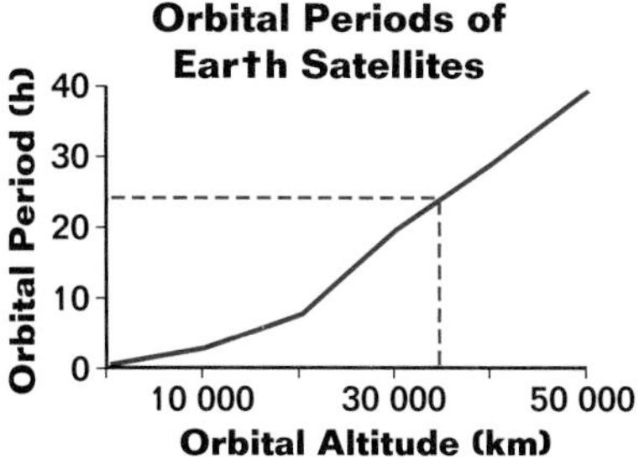

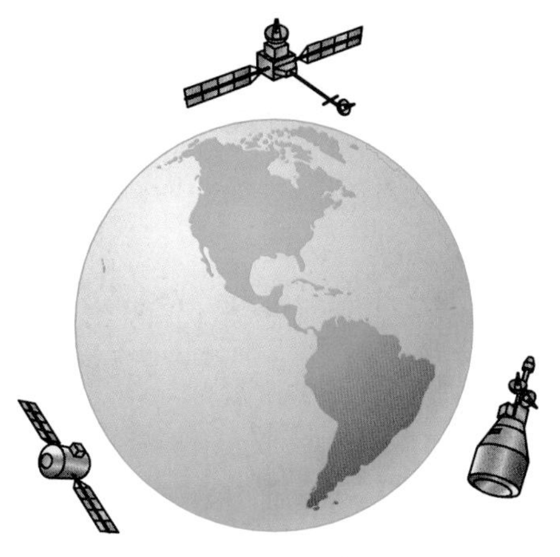

Practicing the SKILL

1. What is the relationship between the altitude and the orbital speed?
2. What is the approximate altitude of a satellite in a geostationary orbit?

For more skill practice, do the Chapter 20 Interactive Exploration on the **Science Voyages Level Blue CD-ROM.**

For further explanation and examples of this skill, refer to Using Numbers on page 731 of the **Skill Handbook.**

Teaching Strategies

- Demonstrate some simple rate problems for the students. Even though the numbers in this activity are large, the math is the same as any simple problem that involves distance, time, and velocity.
- Explain that the prefix "geo" means Earth.

Practicing the SKILL

1. As altitude increases, the orbital velocity decreases.
2. The approximate altitude of a geostationary satellite is approximately 35 000 km.

For further explanation and examples of this skill, refer to Interpreting Scientific Illustrations on page 726 of the **Skill Handbook.**

Teaching Strategies

- Review the positions of the sun, the moon, and Earth during a solar eclipse.
- Use a globe, a light source, and a small ball attached to a wire to illustrate how the path of an eclipse moves across the surface of Earth.

Interpreting Scientific Illustrations

Background

During a total solar eclipse, the moon's shadow falls on Earth. The darkest part of the shadow, the umbra, traces a narrow, curved path across Earth's surface. By plotting the moon's orbit and phases, scientists are able to predict the umbra's path for future total solar eclipses. The world map below shows the times and locations of all total solar eclipses until the year 2020.

When and where will future total solar eclipses occur?

Procedure

1. Study the map of future eclipses.
2. Answer the questions in the Practicing the Skill box.

Practicing the SKILL

1. When will the next total solar eclipse occur in the United States? How old will you be at this time?
2. Which eclipse path will be located mostly over the ocean?
3. How many total solar eclipses will occur between the years 1999 and 2020?

For more skill practice, do the Chapter 21 Interactive Exploration on the **Science Voyages Level Blue CD-ROM.**

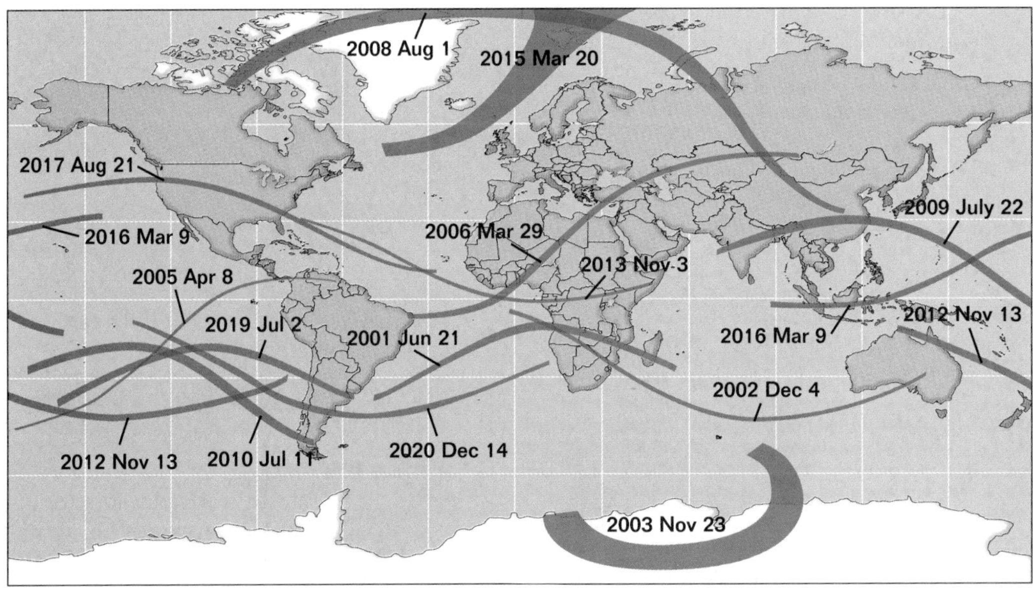

Practicing the SKILL

1. The next total solar eclipse in the United States will be August 21, 2017. Student ages at this time will vary.
2. Answers may vary due to individual interpretation. Answers may include the eclipse path of July 11, 2010 or the eclipse path of November 13, 2012.
3. There will be 19 total solar eclipses between 1999 and 2020.

Inferring

Background

The surfaces of Earth's moon, Mercury, and other planetary bodies often are covered with craters. Scientists usually are unable to determine the exact age of the craters because they do not have actual rock samples. However, photographs taken by satellites help scientists determine the rough ages of the craters. For example, if two craters overlap, the crater that appears to be underneath is the older of the two.

Procedure

1. The diagram below shows an area containing several craters. Each crater is labeled by a letter in its center. Study the relationships between the craters and determine their relative ages.

Practicing the SKILL

1. Which crater occurred first, crater A or crater C?
2. Can the rough age of crater J be determined? Why or why not?
3. What is the estimated diameter of crater D?
4. List craters A through I in order of increasing age (youngest crater first).

For more skill practice, do the Chapter

22 Interactive Exploration on the **Science Voyages Level Blue CD-ROM.**

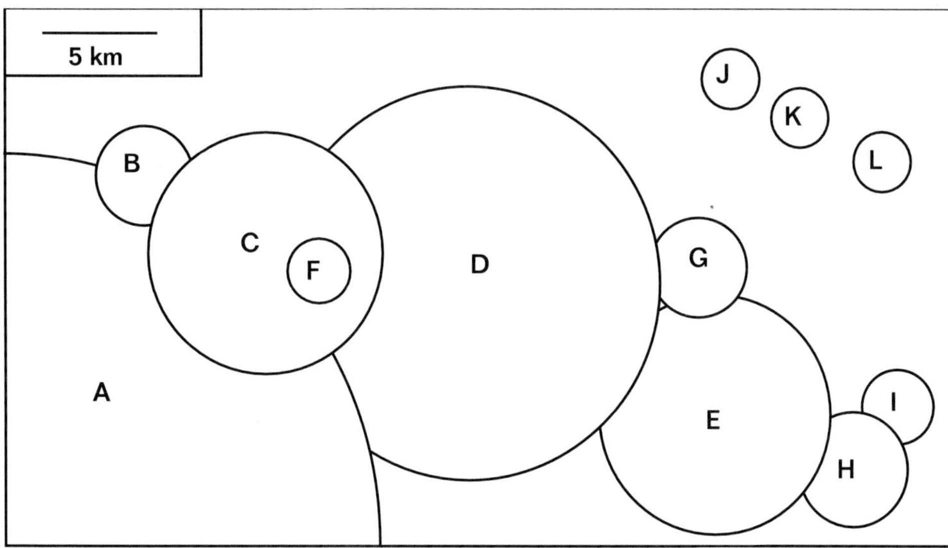

For further explanation and examples of this skill, refer to Observing and Inferring on page 720 of the **Skill Handbook.**

Teaching Strategies

- Have students brainstorm the types of clues they might use to determine the approximate ages of craters.
- Draw a simple diagram on the board with three overlapping craters. Ask the students which would be the oldest and which would be the youngest.

Practicing the SKILL

1. Crater A occurred first because crater C overlaps the rim of crater A.
2. The relative age of J cannot be determined because it does not overlap any of the other craters.
3. Crater C is 16 – 17 km in diameter.
4. Youngest to oldest:
   F, C, B, A, D, G, E, H, I. J, K, and L are not included in this sequence because they do not overlap any other craters, so their relative ages cannot be determined.

23 Skill Activity

For further explanation and examples of this skill, refer to Predicting on page 730 of the **Skill Handbook.**

Teaching Strategies

- Ask students this question: When we look at the sun, do we see the sun as it is now or as it was? Light takes eight minutes to travel from the sun to Earth. We see the sun as it was eight minutes ago.
- Review astronomical distances and light-years with students.
- Divide the class into groups. Assign each group a star listed in the Star Distances table. Have each group research historic events that took place when the star's light began its journey to Earth. Encourage students to share their research with other groups.

Chapter 23 Skill Activity

Use After Section 23-4

Predicting

Background

Astronomical distances are measured in light-years. A light-year is the distance that light can travel in one year. Proxima Centauri is a star that is 4.2 light-years away from Earth. When astronomers observe Proxima Centauri, they are seeing what occurred 4.2 years ago. In other words, when you look at the stars, you are looking back in time. The light astronomers observe for Proxima Centauri left the star 4.2 years ago.

What was happening on Earth when a star's light began its journey?

Star Distances

Star	Distance from Earth in light-years	Star	Distance from Earth in light-years
Sirius	8.8	Deneb	1800
Arcturus	36	Barnard's Star	5.9
Rigel	920	Wolf 359	7.6
Betelgeuse	310	Procyon	11
Antares	330	Altair	17
Vega	26	Regulus	85

Procedure

1. The Star Distances table lists the distances to several different stars. Study these distances to determine how long the light has been traveling toward Earth.
2. Using your history references, find a significant event that occurred when light from a particular star began its journey to Earth.
3. Make a data table that lists the significant historical events that occurred when light from the stars began the journey to Earth. Include the historical event, date, and the star in your table. Use at least six of the stars listed.

Practicing the SKILL

1. On July 20, 1969, astronauts landed on the moon. If a television signal showing this landing had been broadcast out to space, which stars would it have reached by the year 2000? by 2005? (Television signals travel at the speed of light, which is 300 000 km/s in a vacuum.)
2. Describe a historic event that took place when light from Rigel began traveling toward Earth.
3. How many times farther is Arcturus from Earth than Barnard's Star is?

For more skill practice, do the Chapter 23 Interactive Exploration on the **Science Voyages Level Blue CD-ROM.**

GLENCOE TECHNOLOGY

Practicing the SKILL

1. By the year 2000, the television signal would have reached Barnard's Star, Wolf 359, Sirius, Procyon, Altair, and Vega. By 2005, it would have reached Arcturus.
2. Answers will vary depending upon the references used.
3. Arcturus is approximately six times farther from Earth than Bernard's Star.

English Glossary

This glossary defines each key term that appears in **bold type** in the text. It also shows the page number where you can find the word used.

A

abiotic factors: all the nonliving, physical features of the environment, including light, soil, water, and temperature, and that help determine which species can survive in an area. (ch. 17, p. 483)

absolute dating: process that uses the properties of atoms in rocks and other objects to determine their exact ages, in years. (ch. 11, p. 321)

absolute magnitude: measure of the amount of light a star actually emits. (ch. 23, p. 664)

acceleration: rate of change of velocity; can act in the direction of motion, at an angle, or opposite to the direction of motion. (ch. 6, p. 152)

acid rain: rain or snow with a pH below 5.6; results from the mixture of water vapor and air pollutants in the atmosphere. (ch. 19, p. 560)

alloy (AL oy): mixture made of two or more elements, one of which is a metal. (ch. 3, p. 74)

alternation of generations: occurs when a plant's life cycle alternates between a sex-cell–producing stage and a spore-producing stage. (ch. 16, p. 453)

amino acid: building block of proteins; contains both an amino group and a carboxyl group substituted on the same carbon atom. (ch. 14, p. 407)

amino (uh ME no) **group:** consists of a nitrogen atom joined by covalent bonds to two hydrogen atoms; formula is $-NH_2$; when substituted for hydrogen in a hydrocarbon, forms an amine. (ch. 14, p. 406)

amphibians: animals that live on land and breathe air but return to water to reproduce. (ch. 13, p. 376)

apparent magnitude: measure of the amount of light that is received on Earth from a star. (ch. 23, p. 664)

asteroid: piece of rock usually found in the asteroid belt between the orbits of Mars and Jupiter. (ch. 22, p. 653)

asthenosphere (as THEN uh sfihr): plastic-like layer below the lithosphere. (ch. 10, p. 277)

astronomical unit: average distance from Earth to the sun (150 million km), which is used to measure distances to objects in the solar system. (ch. 22, p. 638)

atomic number: number of protons in the nucleus of an atom of a specific element. (ch. 2, p. 47)

auxin: type of plant hormone that can cause plants to show positive phototropism. (ch. 15, p. 437)

axis: imaginary line around which Earth spins. (ch. 21, p. 603)

B

balanced forces: two or more forces acting on an object that cancel each other out and do not cause a change in the object's motion. (ch. 7, p. 177)

batholiths: largest intrusive igneous rock bodies that form when magma cools underground before reaching Earth's surface. (ch. 9, p. 255)

big bang theory: states that approximately 15 billion years ago, the universe began expanding out of an enormous explosion. (ch. 23, p. 685)

binary system: system in which two stars orbit each other. (ch. 23, p. 670)

biomes (BI ohmz): large geographic areas with similar climates and ecosystems; the six most common are tundra, taiga, temperate forest, tropical rain forest, grassland, and desert. (ch. 18, p. 519)

biosphere (BI uh sfihr): part of Earth that supports organisms, is the highest level of biological organization, and is made up of all Earth's ecosystems. (ch. 17, p. 482)

biotic factors: living or once-living organisms in the environment. (ch. 17, p. 485)

black hole: remnant of a star that is so dense that nothing can escape its gravity. (ch. 23, p. 676)

C

caldera: large opening formed when the top of a volcano collapses. (ch. 9, p. 257)

carbohydrates: energy-supplying organic compounds that are broken down into simple sugars in the body; contain only carbon, hydrogen, and oxygen. (ch. 14, p. 412)

carbonaceous (kar boh NAY shus) **film:** fossil formed when the remains of a once-living organism are subjected to heat and pressure, leaving only a thin film of carbon behind. (ch. 11, p. 307)

carboxyl (kar BOX ul) **group:** consists of one carbon atom, two oxygen atoms, and one hydrogen atom; formula is –COOH; when substituted for hydrogen in a hydrocarbon, forms a carboxylic acid. (ch. 14, p. 406)

carrying capacity: largest number of individuals an environment can support and maintain over a long period of time. (ch. 17, p. 490)

cast: fossil formed when sediments fill a mold and harden into rock. (ch. 11, p. 307)

catalyst (KAT uh lihst): substance, such as an enzyme, that speeds up a chemical reaction but is not used up or permanently changed. (ch. 5, p. 136)

Cenozoic (sen uh ZOH ihk) **era:** geologic era in which we live; began with the extinction of dinosaurs and many other life-forms. (ch. 13, p. 386)

chemical bond: force that holds two atoms together. (ch. 4, p. 102)

chemical reaction: energy-requiring process in which chemical changes occur; results in the formation of new substances that have different properties than the original substances. (ch. 5, p. 122)

chromosphere: layer of the sun's atmosphere above the photosphere and below the corona. (ch. 23, p. 667)

cinder cone: steep-sided volcano made of loosely packed tephra. (ch. 9, p. 252)

climax community: community that has reached the final stage of ecological succession. (ch. 18, p. 513)

comet: mass of dust and rock particles mixed in with frozen water, ammonia, and methane; consists of a nucleus, a coma, and a tail. (ch. 22, p. 650)

community: consists of groups of populations that interact with each other in a given area and depend on each other for food, shelter, and for other needs. (ch. 17, p. 486)

composite volcano: volcano formed by alternating layers of tephra and lava and that is found mostly where Earth's plates come together. (ch. 9, p. 252)

compound: pure substance that contains two or more elements. (ch. 4, p. 107)

constant: variable that stays the same in an experiment. (ch. 1, p. 14)

constellation: group of stars that forms a pattern that looks like a familiar object, animal, or character. (ch. 23, p. 662)

continental drift: hypothesis proposed by Alfred Wegener that states that continents have moved slowly to their current locations on Earth. (ch. 10, p. 268)

control: standard used for comparison in an experiment. (ch. 1, p. 13)

convection current: cycle of heating, rising, cooling, and sinking that is thought to be the force behind plate tectonics (ch. 10, p. 282)

corona: largest layer of the sun's atmosphere that extends millions of miles into space. (ch. 23, p. 667)

covalent (koh VAY luhnt) **bond:** chemical bond that forms between atoms when they share one or more electrons. (ch. 4, p. 109)

crater: steep-walled depression around a volcano's vent. (ch. 9, p. 242)

crust: Earth's outermost layer, which varies in thickness from about 5 km to 60 km and is separated from the mantle by the Moho discontinuity. (ch. 8, p. 220)

cyanobacteria: one of the earliest life-forms on Earth; evolved during Precambrian time. (ch. 13, p. 373)

D

day-neutral plant: plant that does not have a specific photoperiod and whose flowering process can begin over a wide range of hours of darkness. (ch. 15, p. 440)

dependent variable: factor being measured or observed in a controlled experiment. (ch. 1, p. 13)

desert: driest biome on Earth; receives less than 25 cm of rain each year and supports little plant life. (ch. 18, p. 524)

dike: intrusive igneous rock body formed when magma is squeezed into a vertical crack that cuts across rock layers and hardens. (ch. 9, p. 257)

displacement: measures the change in position of an object, using the starting point and ending point and noting the direction. (ch. 6, p. 149)

E

Earth: third planet from the sun; surface temperatures allow water to exist as a solid, liquid, and gas and atmosphere protects life from the sun's radiation. (ch. 22, p. 638)

earthquakes: vibrations caused by breaking rocks along faults; most result from plates moving over, under, and past each other. (ch. 8, p. 211)

ecological pyramid: model used to describe the transfer of energy from the producers of an ecosystem through successive levels of organisms in the food chain. (ch. 17, p. 498)

ecological succession: process of gradual change from one community of organisms to another. (ch. 18, p. 510)

ecology: study of the interactions that take place among organisms and between organisms and the physical features of the environment. (ch. 17, p. 483)

ecosystem: consists of a biotic community and the abiotic factors that affect it. (ch. 17, p. 486)

electromagnetic spectrum: arrangement of electromagnetic radiation according to wavelength. (ch. 20, p. 575)

electron: tiny, negatively charged particle that is present in all atoms and that has almost no mass. (ch. 2, p. 39)

electron cloud: region surrounding the nucleus of an atom, where electrons are more likely to be found. (ch. 2, p. 45)

electron dot diagram: shows the chemical symbol for an element surrounded by as many dots as there are electrons in its outer energy level. (ch. 4, p. 102)

element: substance that cannot be broken down into simpler substances and whose atoms are exactly alike. (ch. 2, p. 37)

ellipse (ee LIHPS): elongated, closed curve that describes Earth's orbit. (ch. 21, p. 605)

embryology (em bree AHL uh jee): study of development in organisms. (ch. 12, p. 350)

endangered species: species that is in danger of becoming extinct unless action is taken to protect it. (ch. 19, p. 551)

endothermic (en duh THUR mihk) **reaction:** chemical reaction in which energy is absorbed, such as the reaction that breaks water down into hydrogen and oxygen. (ch. 5, p. 127)

energy: ability to cause change; cannot be destroyed or created, only transferred from one form to another. (ch. 6, p. 165)

epicenter (EP ih sent ur): point on Earth's surface directly above an earthquake's focus. (ch. 8, p. 217)

epoch: division of geologic time smaller than a period. (ch. 13, p. 365)

equinox (EE kwuh nahks): twice-yearly time when the sun is directly above Earth's equator and the number of nighttime hours equals the number of daylight hours worldwide. (ch. 21, p. 607)

era: major subdivision of the geologic time scale based on differences in life-forms. (ch. 13, p. 365)

erosion: wearing away of soil by wind and water. (ch. 19, p. 550)

estuary: area where a river meets the ocean that contains a mixture of freshwater and salt water and serves as nursery for many species of ocean fish. (ch. 18, p. 530)

evolution: changes in the inherited features of a species over time; can occur slowly (gradualism) or rapidly (punctuated equilibrium). (ch. 12, p. 334)

exothermic (ek soh THUR mihk) **reaction:** chemical reaction that releases energy, such as occurs when propane is burned in a gas grill. (ch. 5, p. 128)

extinction: dying out of an entire species either naturally or through the actions of humans. (ch. 19, p. 550)

fault: surface along which rocks break and move. (ch. 8, p. 210)

first quarter: moon phase in which one-quarter of the moon's surface that faces Earth is lit up; occurs about a week after a new moon. (ch. 21, p. 613)

focus: in an earthquake, the point beneath Earth's surface where energy release occurs. (ch. 8, p. 215)

food chain: model that describes the feeding relationships in a community, usually has three or four links, and shows how energy in the form of food passes from one organism to another. (ch. 17, p. 497)

food web: model used to describe a series of overlapping food chains and that shows the many organisms that feed on more than one level in an ecosystem. (ch. 17, p. 498)

force: push or a pull exerted on an object. (ch. 7, p. 176)

formula: combination of chemical symbols that tells what elements are in molecules and how many atoms of each element are present. (ch. 4, p. 113)

fossil: remains or traces of a once-living organism preserved in rock. (ch. 11, p. 304)

fossil fuel: nonrenewable energy source, such as natural gas, that formed from the bodies of organisms that died hundreds of millions of years ago. (ch. 19, p. 544)

friction: rubbing force that acts against motion between two touching surfaces. (ch. 7, p. 179)

frond: leaf of a fern that grows from a rhizome. (ch. 16, p. 454)

full moon: moon phase in which all of the moon's surface that faces Earth is lit up. (ch. 21, p. 613)

G

galaxy: large group of stars, gas, and dust held together by gravity. (ch. 23, p. 679)

gametophyte (guh MEET uh fite) **stage:** plant life cycle stage in which all plant structures are made of cells with a haploid number (n) of chromosomes. (ch. 16, p. 452)

gastroliths: stones swallowed by dinosaurs and by modern birds to help with digestion. (ch. 13, p. 385)

geologic time scale: record of events in Earth's history based on major evolutionary changes and geologic events; major subdivisions are eras, periods, and epochs. (ch. 13, p. 364)

geothermal energy: heat energy from below the surface of Earth. (ch. 19, p. 546)

giant: stage in a star's life cycle where hydrogen in the core is used up, the core contracts, and temperatures inside the star increase, causing the outer layers of the star to expand. (ch. 23, p. 675)

global warming: increase in the average yearly temperature of Earth. (ch. 19, p. 561)

gradualism: model of evolution that shows a slow change of one species to another, new species through continued mutations and variations over time. (ch. 12, p. 340)

graph: diagram that shows the relationship of one variable to another variable and that makes it easier to interpret and analyze data. (ch. 1, p. 18)

grasslands: temperate and tropical regions that receive between 25 cm and 75 cm of precipitation each year and are dominated by climax communities of grasses. (ch. 18, p. 524)

gravitational potential energy: energy an object could potentially gain if it falls, depending on its mass and the height it can fall. (ch. 6, p. 167)

Great Red Spot: high-pressure storm generated by huge thunderstorms in Jupiter's atmosphere. (ch. 22, p. 642)

greenhouse effect: warming of Earth due to a blanket of gases in the atmosphere that prevents heat from radiating back into space. (ch. 19, p. 561)

groundwater: water contained in the soil or trapped in underground pockets formed by nonporous rock; comes from rainfall and runoff that soaks through the soil. (ch. 19, p. 563)

group: family of elements with similar physical or chemical properties that occupies the same column in the periodic table. (ch. 3, p. 68)

H

habitat: physical location where an organism lives. (ch. 17, p. 493)

half-life: time needed for one-half the mass of a sample of a radioactive isotope to decay; can vary from fractions of a second to billions of years. (ch. 11, p. 322; ch. 2, p. 50)

hazardous waste: waste materials, such as pesticides and nuclear waste, that are harmful to human health or poisonous to living organisms and that must be properly disposed of. (ch. 19, p. 562)

hominids: humanlike primates that walked upright on two feet and ate both meat and vegetables. (ch. 12, p. 355)

Homo sapiens: human species thought to have evolved about 400 000 years ago. (ch. 12, p. 356)

homologous (huh MAHL uh gus): body structures that are similar in origin and

Homo sapiens: human species thought to have evolved about 400 000 years ago. (ch. 12, p. 356)

hot spot: location in the mantle that is hotter than other areas and that melts rock, which is forced up toward the crust as magma. (ch. 9, p. 244)

hydrocarbon: compound that contains only carbon and hydrogen atoms—for example, methane, CH_4, and ethane, C_2H_6. (ch. 14, p. 399)

hydroelectric power: electricity produced by the energy of flowing water. (ch. 19, p. 546)

hydroxyl (hi DROX ul) **group:** consists of one oxygen atom and one hydrogen atom joined by a covalent bond; formula is –OH; when substituted for hydrogen in a hydrocarbon, forms an alcohol. (ch. 14, p. 405)

hypothesis: prediction about a problem that can be tested; may be based on observations, new information, and personal experience, and is often written as an if-and-then statement. (ch. 1, p. 12)

independent variable: factor that is changed in a controlled experiment. (ch. 1, p. 13)

index fossils: fossils of species that existed on Earth for only a short time, were abundant, and were widespread geographically; used by scientists to determine the age of rock layers. (ch. 11, p. 310)

inertia: measures an object's tendency to remain at rest or to stay in constant motion. (ch. 6, p. 158)

inference: attempt at an explanation based on observation. (ch. 1, p. 25)

inhibitor: substance, such as butyl hydroxy toluene (BHT), that doesn't totally stop a chemical reaction but slows it down. (ch. 5, p. 136)

inner core: very dense, solid center of Earth that is made mostly of iron with smaller amounts of oxygen, silicon, sulfur, or nickel. (ch. 8, p. 219)

inner planets: four solid, rocky planets that are closest to the sun—Mercury, Venus, Earth, and Mars. (ch. 22, p. 633)

intertidal zone: portion of the shoreline that is covered with water at high tide and exposed to the air at low tide. (ch. 18, p. 530)

ion (I ahn): atom that is no longer neutral because it has gained or lost an electron. (ch. 4, p. 106)

ionic bond: chemical bond that is created when one atom loses one or more electrons and another atom gains one or more electrons. (ch. 4, p. 107)

isomers (I suh murz): compounds with the same chemical formulas but different structures and different chemical and physical properties. (ch. 14, p. 402)

isotopes (I suh tohps): atoms of the same element that have different numbers of neutrons in their nuclei. (ch. 2, p. 47)

Jupiter: largest planet and fifth planet from the sun; composed mostly of hydrogen and helium; has continuous storms of high-pressure gas. (ch. 22, p. 642)

kinetic energy: energy an object has due to its motion; depends on the object's mass and velocity. (ch. 6, p. 165)

law: well-tested description of how something in nature works. (ch. 1, p. 12)

law of conservation of energy: states that energy cannot be destroyed or created, but it is only transformed from one form to another. (ch. 6, p. 165)

law of conservation of momentum: states that if no outside forces act on a group of objects, the momentum of the group will not change. (ch. 6, p. 161)

light-year: distance that light travels in one year (9.5 trillion km), which is used to measure distances in space. (ch. 23, p. 665)

limiting factor: any biotic or abiotic factor that restricts the number of individuals in a population. (ch. 17, p. 489)

lipids: energy-supplying and energy-storing organic compounds composed of three long-chain carboxylic acids bonded to glycerol; commonly called fats and oils and can be saturated or unsaturated. (ch. 14, p. 415)

lithosphere (LIHTH uh sfihr): rigid, outermost layer of Earth that is about 100 km thick, and is composed of the crust and part of the upper mantle. (ch. 10, p. 277)

long-day plant: plant that needs less than ten to twelve hours of darkness to begin the flowering process. (ch. 15, p. 439)

lunar eclipse: eclipse that occurs when Earth's shadow falls on the moon. (ch. 21, p. 616)

M

magnitude: measure of the energy released by an earthquake. (ch. 8, p. 226)

main sequence: in an H-R diagram, the diagonal band of stars that runs from hot, bright stars in the upper-left corner of the diagram to cool, faint stars in the lower-right corner. (ch. 23, p. 672)

mantle: largest layer inside Earth, lying directly above the outer core and that is made mostly of silicon, oxygen, magnesium, and iron. (ch. 8, p. 219)

maria: dark-colored, relatively flat areas of the moon that were formed when ancient lava filled basins on the moon's surface. (ch. 21, p. 617)

Mars: fourth planet from the sun; appears red due to the iron oxide content in its weathered rocks. (ch. 22, p. 638)

mascon: concentration of mass on the moon located beneath an impact basin. (ch. 21, p. 621)

mass: quantity of matter in an object and a measure of the object's inertia; unit is the kilogram (kg). (ch. 6, p. 158)

mass number: number of neutrons plus the number of protons in the nucleus of an atom. (ch. 2, p. 48)

Mercury: planet closest to the sun; has many craters, low gravitational pull, and is the second-smallest planet in our solar system. (ch. 22, p. 636)

Mesozoic (mez uh ZOH ihk) **era:** geologic era in which Pangaea broke up, the present-day continents were formed, and whose dominant land life-forms were reptiles and gymnosperms. (ch. 13, p. 381)

metal: element that is a good conductor of electricity and heat, is usually a solid at room temperature and usually is shiny, ductile, and malleable. (ch. 3, p. 69)

metalloid: element that shares some properties with metals and some with nonmetals. (ch. 3, p. 70)

meteor: meteoroid that burns up in Earth's atmosphere. (ch. 22, p. 652)

meteorite: meteoroid that does not completely burn up in Earth's atmosphere and strikes Earth. (ch. 22, p. 652)

mold: fossil formed when an organism is buried, decays, and leaves behind a hollow place in the rock. (ch. 11, p. 307)

molecule (MAH luh kyewl): neutral particle that is formed when atoms share electrons. (ch. 4, p. 109)

momentum: product of mass and velocity; quantity of motion for an object. (ch. 6, p. 159)

moon phase: changing appearance of the moon as seen from Earth, which depends on the relative positions of the moon, Earth, and sun. (ch. 21, p. 613)

N

natural resource: material found in nature that is useful or necessary for living organisms. (ch. 19, p. 542)

natural selection: Darwin's theory of evolution, which says that organisms with traits best suited to their environments are more likely to survive and reproduce. (ch. 12, p. 337)

nebula: large cloud of gas and dust that can fragment into smaller pieces, each of which will collapse and form stars. (ch. 23, p. 674)

Neptune: large, gaseous planet similar to Uranus; is usually the eighth planet from the sun. (ch. 22, p. 646)

net force: sum of the forces acting on an object. (ch. 7, p. 176)

neutron (NEW trahn): electrically neutral particle that is present in the nucleus of all atoms; has the same mass as a proton. (ch. 2, p. 44)

neutron star: collapsed core of a supernova that shrinks to about 10 km to 15 km in diameter and has only neutrons in the dense core. (ch. 23, p. 676)

new moon: moon phase that occurs when the lighted half of the moon faces the sun and the dark side faces Earth. (ch. 21, p. 613)

Newton's first law of motion: states that an object at rest or moving at a constant speed in a straight path continues to do so until a net force acts on it. (ch. 7, p. 178)

Newton's second law of motion: states that an object acted upon by a net force will accelerate in the direction of this force according to the following equation: $a = F_{net}/m$, where a is the acceleration, F_{net} is the net force, and m is the mass. (ch. 7, p. 184)

Newton's third law of motion: states that forces always act in equal but opposite pairs. (ch. 7, p. 192)

niche: role of an organism in the ecosystem, including what it eats, how it interacts with other organisms, and how it gets its food. (ch. 17, p. 493)

nitrogen cycle: transfer of nitrogen from the atmosphere to plants and back to the atmosphere or directly into plants again. (ch. 17, p. 502)

nonmetal: element that is a poor conductor of heat and electricity and may be a gas or a brittle solid at room temperature. (ch. 3, p. 70)

nonrenewable resource: natural resource, such as petroleum, that is available in limited amounts and cannot be replaced or is only replaced slowly. (ch. 19, p. 543)

normal fault: break in rock due to tension forces, where rock above the fault surface moves downward in relation to rock below the fault surface. (ch. 8, p. 212)

normal force: outward force a surface supplies to support an object. (ch. 7, p. 185)

nuclear energy: energy produced when the nuclei of uranium atoms split apart in a nuclear fission reaction. (ch. 19, p. 547)

O

observatory: specially designed building, often with a dome-shaped roof that opens up to admit light; used to house optical telescopes. (ch. 20, p. 576)

Oort Cloud: cloud of comets that completely surrounds the solar system and that is located beyond the orbit of Pluto. (ch. 22, p. 651)

orbit: curved path of a satellite as it revolves around an object in space. (ch. 20, p. 582)

organic compound: compound that contains carbon. (ch. 14, p. 398)

outer core: liquid core that surrounds Earth's solid inner core and that is made mostly of iron. (ch. 8, p. 219)

outer planets: five planets that are farthest from the sun—Jupiter, Saturn, Uranus, Neptune, and Pluto. (ch. 22, p. 633)

ovary: in angiosperms, the swollen base of the pistil where ovules are formed (ch. 16, p. 461)

ovule: in a seed plant, the structure that contains an egg cell, food-storage tissue, and a sticky fluid. (ch. 16, p. 458)

ozone depletion: thinning of Earth's protective ozone layer, primarily from chlorofluorocarbons reacting with and destroying ozone molecules. (ch. 19, p. 561)

P

Paleozoic (pay lee uh ZOH ihk) **era:** geologic era marked by the first appearance of life-forms with hard parts. (ch. 13, p. 374)

Pangaea (pan JEE uh): single large landmass made up of all the continents connected together that broke apart about 200 million years ago. (ch. 10, p. 268)

parallax: apparent shift in position of an object when it is viewed from two different positions. (ch. 23, p. 665)

period: horizontal row of elements in the periodic table whose properties change gradually and predictably. (ch. 3, p. 65) next-smaller division of the geologic time scale after the era. (ch. 13, p. 365)

petrified (PEH truh fide) **remains:** fossils that form when some or all of the original materials that made up the organisms are replaced with minerals. (ch. 11, p. 306)

photoperiodism: response of a plant to the number of hours of daylight and darkness it receives each day. (ch. 15, p. 439)

photosphere: lowest layer of the sun's atmosphere and the layer that gives off light. (ch. 23, p. 667)

photosynthesis: food-making process that takes place in the chloroplasts of plant cells, where carbon dioxide from the air, water in the soil, and light energy react to form glucose and oxygen. (ch. 15, p. 429)

photovoltaic (PV) cell: device made of silicon that turns sunlight directly into electric current. (ch. 19, p. 545)

pioneer community: first community of organisms to move into a new environment. (ch. 18, p. 511)

pistil: female reproductive organ inside the flower of an angiosperm; consists of a sticky stigma, a style, and an ovary. (ch. 16, p. 461)

plankton: microscopic algae, plants, and other organisms that float in warm, sunlit waters near the surface of freshwater lakes and ponds. (ch. 18, p. 529)

plate tectonics: theory that Earth's crust and upper mantle are broken into sections that move around on a plasticlike layer of the mantle. (ch. 10, p. 277)

plates: sections of Earth's lithosphere that are composed of oceanic crust, continental crust, and rigid upper mantle and that move around on a plasticlike layer of the mantle. (ch. 10, p. 277)

Pluto: smallest planet and considered the ninth planet from the sun; has a thin, changing atmosphere and icy-rock surface. (ch. 22, p. 646)

pollen grains: produced by the male reproductive organs of seed plants; two sperm develop in each pollen grain. (ch. 16, p. 458)

pollination: transfer of pollen grains from the stamen to the stigma. (ch. 16, p. 462)

pollutant: any substance that contaminates the environment and causes pollution. (ch. 19, p. 559)

polymer: large natural or synthetic molecule made of many small organic molecules that link together to form a long chain. (ch. 14, p. 410)

population: all the individuals of one species that live in the same area at the same time and compete with each other for food, water, mates, and space. (ch. 17, p. 486)

population density: size of a population that occupies an area of limited size. (ch. 17, p. 489)

Precambrian (pree KAM bree un) **time:** longest geologic time unit in Earth's history; has a poor fossil record. (ch. 13, p. 372)

primary succession: ecological succession that begins in a place that does not have soil. (ch. 18, p. 511)

primary waves: waves that travel outward from an earthquake's focus and cause particles in rocks to move back and forth in the same direction the wave is moving. (ch. 8, p. 216)

primates: group of mammals that includes monkeys, apes, and humans and that shares several characteristics, such as opposable thumbs and binocular vision. (ch. 12, p. 354)

principle of superposition: states that for undisturbed layers of rocks, older rocks lie underneath younger and younger rocks. (ch. 11, p. 312)

product: substance that is formed by a chemical reaction; in a chemical equation, the product is placed on the right side of the arrow. (ch. 5, p. 124)

Project Apollo: final stage in the U.S. effort to reach the moon—on July 20, 1969, Neil Armstrong was the first human to set foot on the lunar surface. (ch. 20, p. 587)

Project Gemini: second stage in the U.S. program to reach the moon, in which a team of astronauts met and connected with another spacecraft while in orbit. (ch. 20, p. 586)

Project Mercury: first step in the U.S. effort to reach the moon, in which a piloted spacecraft successfully orbited around Earth and returned safely. (ch. 20, p. 586)

protein: polymer made of individual amino acids linked together in a chain; catalyzes many cell reactions and provides the structural material for many parts of the body. (ch. 14, p. 411)

prothallus: fern gametophyte, which can make its own food, absorb water and nutrients, and has both male and female reproductive structures. (ch. 16, p. 454)

proton: positively charged, heavy particle contained in the nucleus of all atoms. (ch. 2, p. 40)

punctuated equilibrium: model of evolution that shows the rapid change of a species caused by the mutation of just a few genes, resulting in the appearance of a new species. (ch. 12, p. 340)

R

radioactive decay: release of nuclear particles and energy from unstable atomic nuclei. (ch. 2, p. 48; ch. 11, p. 321)

radioactive element: element that gives off radiation due to an unstable nucleus. (ch. 12, p. 346)

radiometric dating: process to determine the absolute ages of rocks by measuring the amounts of parent and daughter materials in a rock and by knowing the half-life of the parent. (ch. 11, p. 323)

radio telescope: type of telescope that uses a large, curved dish to collect and record radio waves traveling through space and that can be used during the day or at night and during bad weather. (ch. 20, p. 579)

rate of reaction: measure of how quickly a chemical reaction occurs, which can be influenced by temperature, particle size, the concentration of the reactants, and the amount of activation energy that starts the reaction. (ch. 5, p. 133)

reactant (ree AK tunt): substance that exists before a chemical reaction begins; in a chemical equation, the reactant is listed on the left side of the arrow. (ch. 5, p. 124)

recycling: process that reduces the use of natural resources by reusing an item after it has been changed or reprocessed. (ch. 19, p. 553)

reflecting telescope: optical telescope that uses a mirror (or mirrors) to focus light and produce an image at the focal point. (ch. 20, p. 576)

refracting telescope: optical telescope that uses a double convex lens to focus light and form an image at the focal point. (ch. 20, p. 576)

relative dating: method to determine the order of events and relative age of the rocks by examining the position of rocks in a sequence. (ch. 11, p. 313)

renewable resource: natural resource, such as water, that is recycled or replaced by ongoing natural processes. (ch. 19, p. 542)

reptiles: egg-laying, scaly skinned animals that do not need to return to water to reproduce and probably evolved from the same ancestor as amphibians. (ch. 13, p. 376)

respiration: series of chemical reactions by which all living cells break down food to release energy. (ch. 15, p. 432)

reverse fault: break in rock due to compression forces, where rocks above the fault surface move upward and over the rocks below the fault surface. (ch. 8, p. 212)

revolution: yearly orbit of Earth around the sun. (ch. 21, p. 605)

rhizome: underground stem of a fern, from which fronds and roots grow. (ch. 16, p. 454)

rotation: spinning of Earth on its axis, which causes day and night to occur. (ch. 21, p. 603)

S

satellite: any object that revolves around another object; can be natural (Earth's moon) or artificial (*Sputnik I*). (ch. 20, p. 582)

saturated hydrocarbon: hydrocarbon with only single bonds—for example, propane, C_3H_8, and butane, C_4H_{10}. (ch. 14, p. 400)

Saturn: sixth planet from the sun; has a complex ring system made of hundreds of ringlets. (ch. 22, p. 643)

science: process used to investigate the world and provide some possible answers to scientific questions. (ch. 1, p. 8)

scientific methods: approaches taken to try and solve a problem; can include recognizing the problem, forming a hypothesis, testing the hypothesis, analyzing the data, and drawing conclusions. (ch. 1, p. 10)

seafloor spreading: theory that magma from below Earth's crust is forced upward toward the surface at a mid-ocean ridge, flows from the cracks as the seafloor spreads apart and becomes solid as it cools, forming new seafloor. (ch. 10, p. 273)

secondary succession: ecological succession that begins in a place that already has soil and was once the home of living organisms. (ch. 18, p. 512)

secondary waves: waves that travel outward from an earthquake's focus and move through Earth by causing particles in rocks to vibrate at right angles to the direction of the wave. (ch. 8, p. 216)

sedimentary rock: rock formed by compaction and cementation of sediments or when minerals precipitate out of solution or are left behind when a solution evaporates; rock type formed from particles of preexisting rocks contains the most fossils. (ch. 12, p. 345)

seismic (SIZE mihk) **waves:** energy waves that are produced at and travel outward from the earthquake focus. (ch. 8, p. 215)

seismograph: device used by seismologists to record primary, secondary, and surface waves from earthquakes. (ch. 8, p. 226)

seismologist: scientist who studies earthquakes and seismic waves. (ch. 8, p. 226)

semiconductor: element that doesn't conduct electricity as well as a metal but does conduct electricity better than a nonmetal. (ch. 3, p. 76)

sequence: arrangement of things or events in a certain order. (ch. 1, p. 25)

shield volcano: broad volcano with gently sloping sides formed when hot, fluid lava flows from one or more vents. (ch. 9, p. 251)

short-day plant: plant that needs twelve or more hours of darkness to begin the flowering process. (ch. 15, p. 439)

sill: intrusive igneous rock body that forms when magma is squeezed into a horizontal crack between rock layers and hardens. (ch. 9, p. 257)

smog: air pollution that forms when sunlight reacts with pollutant chemicals produced by burning fossil fuels. (ch. 19, p. 559)

soil depletion: removal of soil nutrients from land used for agriculture due to the replacement of native plants with crops that do not decay and replenish the soil. (ch. 19, p. 549)

soil management: use of plowing methods to prevent or reduce soil depletion and erosion. (ch. 19, p. 550)

solar eclipse (ih KLIPS): eclipse that occurs when the moon moves directly between the sun and Earth and casts a shadow on part of Earth. (ch. 21, p. 614)

solar system: system of nine planets, including Earth and many smaller objects, that orbit the sun. (ch. 22, p. 631)

solstice: point at which the sun reaches its greatest distance north or south of the equator. (ch. 21, p. 607)

sori: spore-producing structures on the undersides of fern fronds. (ch. 16, p. 454)

space probe: instrument that travels out into the solar system to gather information and sends the data back to Earth. (ch. 20, p. 583)

space shuttle: reusable spacecraft that carries astronauts, satellites, and other materials to and from space. (ch. 20, p. 590)

space station: large artificial satellite that provides support systems, living quarters, and equipment so that humans can live and work in space and conduct research not possible on Earth. (ch. 20, p. 591)

species: group of similar organisms that can successfully reproduce among themselves in their natural environment. (ch. 12, p. 334)

speed: rate of change of an object's position. (ch. 6, p. 148)

sphere (SFIHR): round, three-dimensional object whose surface at all points is the same distance from its center. (ch. 21, p. 602)

sporophyte (SPOR uh fite) **stage:** plant life-cycle stage in which all plant structures are made of cells with a diploid number ($2n$) of chromosomes. (ch. 16, p. 452)

stamen: male reproductive organ inside the flower of an angiosperm; consists of a filament and an anther. (ch. 16, p. 461)

stomata: openings on leaf surfaces or leaflike structures through which gases like carbon dioxide and water vapor may enter and leave a plant. (ch. 15, p. 426)

strike-slip fault: break in rock due to shearing forces, where rocks on either side of the fault surface move past each other with little upward or downward movement. (ch. 8, p. 213)

sunspot: dark, relatively cool area on the surface of the sun. (ch. 23, p. 668)

supergiant: late stage in the life cycle of a massive star where the core reaches very high temperatures, heavy elements form by fusion, and the star expands. (ch. 23, p. 676)

surface waves: waves of energy that reach Earth's surface during an earthquake, travel outward from the epicenter, and move rock particles up and down and side to side. (ch. 8, p. 217)

symbiosis (sihm bee OH sus): any close relationship between two or more different species. (ch. 17, p. 491)

T

taiga (TI guh): cold region of cone-bearing evergreen trees that lies just below the tundra and is the world's largest terrestrial biome. (ch. 18, p. 520)

technology: application of what has been learned through science. (ch. 1, p. 22)

temperate deciduous forest: biome that lies at latitudes below about 50° in both the northern and southern hemispheres, usually has four distinct seasons, and supports a wide variety of plants and animals. (ch. 18, p. 521)

tephra: bits of rock or solidified lava dropped from the air during an explosive volcanic eruption. (ch. 9, p. 251)

theory: explanation backed by results received from repeated tests or experiments. (ch. 1, p. 12)

third quarter: moon phase in which only half of the lighted side of the moon is visible. (ch. 21, p. 614)

transpiration: loss of water vapor through the stomata of a leaf. (ch. 15, p. 427)

trilobite (TRI luh bite): organism that lived hundreds of millions of years ago and is considered an index fossil of the Paleozoic era. (ch. 13, p. 367)

tropical rain forest: hot, wet, equatorial biome that contains the largest number of species. (ch. 18, p. 523)

tropism: response of a plant to an outside stimulus such as gravity or light. (ch. 15, p. 436)

tsunami (soo NAHM ee): powerful seismic sea wave that can travel thousands of kilometers in all directions and that begins over an earthquake focus. (ch. 8, p. 227)

tundra (TUN dra): cold, dry, treeless biome located at latitudes surrounding the north pole and that has winters six to nine months long. (ch. 18, p. 519)

U

unbalanced forces: two or more unequal forces acting on an object that cause the object to accelerate. (ch. 7, p. 177)

unconformities (un kun FOR mihteez): gaps in the rock layers due to erosion, nondeposition, or both. (ch. 11, p. 315)

uniformitarianism (yew nih for mih TAHR ee ah nizm): states that Earth processes happening today are similar to those that happened in the past. (ch. 11, p. 325)

unsaturated hydrocarbon: hydrocarbon that has one or more double or triple bonds—for example, ethylene, C_2H_4, and propylene, C_3H_6. (ch. 14, p. 401)

Uranus: large, gaseous planet and seventh planet from the sun; has a magnetic pole tilted 60 degrees and rotates on an axis nearly parallel to the plane of its orbit. (ch. 22, p. 645)

variation: an inherited trait that makes an individual different from other members of the same species; can be beneficial, harmful, or neutral in a population. (ch. 12, p. 338)

velocity (vel AH seh TEE): rate of change of displacement; includes both speed and direction. (ch. 6, p. 150)

vent: opening on Earth's surface where magma is forced up and flows out as lava. (ch. 9, p. 242)

Venus: second planet from the sun; has a dense atmosphere of carbon dioxide and sulfuric acid. (ch. 22, p. 637)

vestigial (veh STIHJ ee ul) **structure:** body structure with no obvious use, which may once have functioned in an ancestor. (ch. 12, p. 350)

volcanic neck: solid, igneous core of a volcano left behind when a volcano stops erupting and the softer cone erodes away. (ch. 9, p. 257)

volcano: opening in Earth's surface that often forms a mountain when layers of lava and volcanic ash erupt and build up; occurs where Earth's plates are moving apart or together and at hot spots. (ch. 9, p. 240)

waning: occurs after a full moon, when the amount of the moon's lighted side that can be seen becomes smaller. (ch. 21, p. 614)

water cycle: constant journey of water molecules on Earth as they rise into the atmosphere, fall to land or the ocean as rain or snow, and flow into rivers and oceans through the processes of evaporation, condensation, and precipitation. (ch. 17, p. 500)

waxing: occurs shortly after a new moon, when more and more of the moon's lighted side becomes visible. (ch. 21, p. 613)

white dwarf: late stage in a star's life cycle where its core uses up its supply of helium, it contracts, and its outer layers escape into space, leaving behind the hot dense core. (ch. 23, p. 676)

Glossary/Glosario

Este glossario define cada término clave que aparece en **negrillas** en el texto. También muestra el número de página donde se usa dicho término.

A

abiotic factors / factores abióticos: Características físicas inanimadas que a menudo determinan los organismos que pueden sobrevivir en cierto ambiente. (Cap. 17, pág. 483)

absolute dating / datación absoluta: Método utilizado para determinar la edad, en años, de una roca u otro objeto. (Cap. 11, pág. 321)

absolute magnitude / magnitud absoluta: Medida de la cantidad de luz que una estrella emite verdaderamente. (Cap. 23, pág. 664)

acceleration / aceleración: Razón de cambio de la velocidad. El acelerar, el decelerar y el voltear son formas de aceleración. (Cap. 6, pág. 152)

acid rain / lluvia ácida: Lluvia o nieve con un pH menor que 5.6; resulta de la mezcla de vapor de agua y contaminantes del aire en la atmósfera; puede conducir a la muerte de árboles y plantas. (Cap. 19, pág. 560)

alloy / aleación: Mezcla de dos o más elementos, uno de los cuales es un metal. (Cap. 3, pág. 74)

alternation of generations / alternación de generaciones: Ciclo vital de las plantas en la cual se alternan las etapas de producción de esporas y de producción de células sexuales. (Cap. 16, pág. 453)

amino acid / aminoácido: Unidad básica de la cual están compuestas las proteínas, las cuales son una clase importante de moléculas biológicas necesarias para las células vivas. (Cap. 14, pág. 407)

amino group / grupo amino: Grupo formado por un átomo de nitrógeno unido por enlaces covalentes a dos átomos de hidrógeno. (Cap. 14, pág. 406)

amphibians / anfibios: Animales que viven en tierra y respiran aire, pero que deben regresar al agua con el fin de reproducirse. (Cap. 13, pág. 376)

apparent magnitude / magnitud aparente: Medida de la cantidad de luz de una estrella que llega a la Tierra. (Cap. 23, pág. 664)

asteroid / asteroide: Fragmento rocoso semejante al material que formó los planetas. (Cap. 22, pág. 653)

asthenosphere / astenosfera: Capa tipo plástico situada debajo de la litosfera. (Cap. 10, pág. 277)

astronomical unit / unidad astronómica: Medida que se usa para medir distancias hacia los objetos en el sistema solar; corresponde a 150 millones de kilómetros, lo cual es la distancia promedio entre la Tierra y el sol. (Cap. 22, pág. 638)

atomic number / número atómico: Número de protones en el núcleo de un átomo de un elemento. (Cap. 2, pág. 47)

auxin / auxina: Tipo de hormona vegetal. (Cap. 15, pág. 437)

axis / eje: Línea imaginaria alrededor de la cual gira la Tierra. (Cap. 21, pág. 603)

B

balanced forces / fuerzas equilibradas: Fuerzas cuyos efectos se cancelan entre sí y no causan un cambio en el movimiento del objeto. (Cap. 7, pág. 177)

batholiths / batolitos: Las masas más grandes de rocas ígneas intrusivas, las cuales pueden extenderse por cientos de kilómetros y tener varios kilómetros de profundidad. (Cap. 9, pág. 255)

big bang theory / teoría de la gran explosión: Teoría que enuncia que hace unos 15 billones de años, el universo comenzó con una enorme explosión. (Cap. 23, pág. 685)

binary system / sistema binario: Sistema en el cual dos estrellas giran una alrededor de la otra. (Cap. 23, pág. 670)

biomes / biomas: Áreas geográficas extensas que poseen climas y ecosistemas similares. (Cap. 18, pág. 519)

biosphere / biosfera: La parte de la Tierra que sostiene organismos vivos. (Cap. 17, pág. 482)

biotic factors / factores bióticos: Cualquier organismo vivo o que alguna vez estuvo vivo, en un ambiente. (Cap. 17, pág. 485)

black hole / agujero negro: Núcleo restante de una estrella de neutrones, el cual es tan denso y masivo que nada puede escapar de su campo de gravedad, ni siquiera la luz. (Cap. 23, pág. 676)

C

caldera / caldera: Gran abertura que resulta cuando la cima de un volcán se hunde. (Cap. 9, pág. 257)

carbohydrates / carbohidratos: Compuestos orgánicos que solo contienen carbono, hidrógeno y oxígeno, en una proporción de dos átomos de hidrógeno por átomo de oxígeno y de carbono. (Cap. 14, pág. 412)

carbonaceous film / película carbonácea: Tipo de fósil producido por una película fina de residuo carbonoso, la cual forma un bosquejo del organismo original. (Cap. 11, pág. 307)

carboxyl group / grupo carboxilo: Grupo formado por un átomo de carbono, dos átomos de oxígeno y un átomo de hidrógeno. (Cap. 14, pág. 406)

carrying capacity / capacidad de carga: El mayor número de individuos que un ambiente puede soportar y mantener durante un largo período de tiempo. (Cap. 17, pág. 490)

cast / impresión fósil: Se forma cuando otros sedimentos llenan el hueco que deja el molde, se endurecen y forman una roca produciendo una impresión del objeto original. (Cap. 11, pág. 307)

catalyst / catalizador: Sustancia que acelera una reacción química, pero que no aparece en la ecuación química porque dicha sustancia no sufre cambio permanente ni se agota. (Cap. 5, pág. 136)

Cenozoic era / era Cenozoica: También denominada era de vida reciente. Esta era comenzó hace unos 65 millones de años cuando los dinosaurios y muchas otras formas de vida se extinguieron. (Cap. 13, pág. 386)

chemical bond / enlace químico: Fuerza que mantiene unidos dos átomos. (Cap. 4, pág. 102)

chemical reaction / reacción química: Proceso en que ocurren cambios químicos. El óxido sobre la carrocería de un auto de acero, un huevo que se fríe y las hojas que se tornan rojas en el otoño, son ejemplos de reacciones químicas. (Cap. 5, pág. 122)

chromosphere / cromosfera: Capa que se encuentra encima de la fotosfera y que se extiende por encima de esta unos 2000 km. (Cap. 23, pág. 667)

cinder cone / cono de carbonilla: Volcán de lados empinados y ligeramente empacado que se forma cuando la tefrita llega al suelo. (Cap. 9, pág. 252)

climax community / comunidad clímax: Comunidad que ha alcanzado la etapa final de sucesión ecológica. (Cap. 18, pág. 513)

comet / cometa: Objeto compuesto de polvo y partículas rocosas mezclados con agua congelada, metano y amoníaco. (Cap. 22, pág. 650)

community / comunidad: Grupo de poblaciones que interactúan entre sí en un área determinada. (Cap. 17, pág. 486)

composite volcano / volcán compuesto: Volcán que se forma del continuo y alternado ciclo de erupciones de lava y tefrita. (Cap. 9, pág. 252)

compound / compuesto: Sustancia pura que contiene dos o más elementos. (Cap. 4, pág. 107)

constant / constante: Variable que permanece inalterada en un experimento. (Cap. 1, pág. 14)

constellation / constelación: Grupo de estrellas en el firmamento. Las constelaciones recibieron nombres de animales, figuras mitológicas u objetos cotidianos. (Cap. 23, pág. 662)

continental drift / deriva continental: Hipótesis propuesta por Alfred Wegener que dice que los continentes se han movido lentamente a sus posiciones actuales. (Cap. 10, pág. 268)

control / control: Un estándar de comparación. (Cap. 1, pág. 13)

convection current / corriente de convección: Ciclo completo de calentamiento, ascenso, enfriamiento y hundimiento. (Cap. 10, pág. 282)

corona / corona: La capa más grande de la atmósfera solar, la cual se extiende millones de kilómetros en el espacio. (Cap. 23, pág. 667)

covalent bond / enlace covalente: Enlace químico que se forma entre átomos que comparten electrones. (Cap. 4, pág. 109)

crater / cráter: Depresión de paredes empinadas alrededor de la chimenea de un volcán. (Cap. 9, pág. 242)

crust / corteza: La capa más externa de la Tierra y separada del manto por la discontinuidad de Moho. (Cap. 8, pág. 220)

cyanobacteria / cianobacterias: Una de las formas de vida más tempranas sobre la Tierra; evolucionaron durante la Era Precámbrica. (Cap. 13, pág. 373)

D

day-neutral plant / planta de día neutro: Planta que no requiere un fotoperíodo específico y en la cual el proceso de floración puede comenzar dentro de una gama de horas de oscuridad. (Cap. 15, pág. 440)

dependent variable / variable dependiente: Factor que se mide, o se observa, en un experimento. (Cap. 1, pág. 13)

desert / desierto: El bioma terrestre más seco; recibe menos de 25 cm de lluvia al año y tiene poca vegetación. (Cap. 18, pág. 524)

dike / dique: Magma que ha sido apretujado en una resquebrajadura, generalmente, vertical y el cual atraviesa capas rocosas y se endurece. (Cap. 9, pág. 257)

displacement / desplazamiento: Mide el cambio en la posición de un objeto, el cual incluye dirección. (Cap. 6, pág. 149)

E

Earth / la Tierra: El tercer planeta a partir del sol; tiene temperaturas superficiales que permiten que el agua exista como sólido, líquido y gas y una atmósfera que protege la vida de la radiación solar. (Cap. 22, pág. 638)

earthquakes / terremotos: Vibraciones producidas por rocas que se rompen a lo largo de fallas; la mayoría resulta del movimiento de las placas. (Cap. 8, pág. 211)

ecological pyramid / pirámide ecológica: Modelo que representa la transferencia de energía en la biosfera. (Cap. 17, pág. 498)

ecological succession / sucesión ecológica: Proceso de cambio gradual de una comunidad de organismos a otra. (Cap. 18, pág. 510)

ecology / ecología: Ciencia que estudia las interacciones entre los organismos y entre los organismos y los rasgos físicos del ambiente. (Cap. 17, pág. 483)

ecosystem / ecosistema: Está compuesto de una comunidad biótica y de los factores abióticos que la afectan. (Cap. 17, pág. 486)

electromagnetic spectrum / espectro electromagnético: Arreglo de radiación electromagnética, de acuerdo con sus longitudes de onda. (Cap. 20, pág. 575)

electron / electrón: Partícula de materia con carga negativa. (Cap. 2, pág. 39)

electron cloud / nube de electrones: Región que rodea el núcleo del átomo y en donde, posiblemente, se encuentran los electrones. (Cap. 2, pág. 45)

electron dot diagram / diagrama de puntos electrónicos: Símbolo químico de un elemento rodeado por puntos que representan los electrones en el nivel energético externo. (Cap. 4, pág. 102)

element / elemento: Sustancia que no puede ser dividida en sustancias más sencillas. (Cap. 2, pág. 37)

ellipse / elipse: Curva cerrada y alargada. La órbita de la Tierra forma un elipse. (Cap. 21, pág. 605)

embryology / embriología: El estudio del desarrollo de los organismos. (Cap. 12, pág. 350)

endangered species / especie en peligro de extinción: Especie que está en peligro de desaparecer a menos que se tomen medidas para protegerla. (Cap. 19, pág. 551)

endothermic reaction / reacción endotérmica: Reacción en la cual se absorbe energía. (Cap. 5, pág. 127)

energy / energía: La capacidad de causar cambio. (Cap. 6, pág. 165)

epicenter / epicentro: Punto en la superficie terrestre directamente encima del foco de un terremoto. (Cap. 8, pág. 217)

epoch / época: Unidad de tiempo más pequeña en que se subdividen los períodos de la escala del tiempo geológico. (Cap. 13, pág. 365)

equinox / equinoccio: Época del año cuando el sol está directamente encima del ecuador terrestre y las horas de luz solar son iguales a las horas de oscuridad. (Cap. 21, pág. 607)

era / era: Subdivisión importante de la escala del tiempo geológico que se basa en las diferencias en las formas de vida. (Cap. 13, pág. 365)

erosion / erosión: Agotamiento del suelo por acción del viento y del agua. (Cap. 19, pág. 550)

estuary / estuario: Área en donde un río desemboca en el océano y la cual contiene una mezcla de agua dulce y salada. Es un ambiente muy fértil y productivo que sirve de vivero para muchas especies de peces oceánicos. (Cap. 18, pág. 530)

evolution / evolución: Cambio en los rasgos hereditarios de una especie a lo largo del tiempo. (Cap. 12, pág. 334)

exothermic reaction / reacción exotérmica: Reacción en la cual se libera energía. (Cap. 5, pág. 128)

extintion / extinción: La desaparición de una especie completa. (Cap. 19, pág. 550)

fault / falla: Superficie a lo largo de la cual se mueven y rompen las rocas, al exceder su límite de elasticidad. (Cap. 8, pág. 210)

first quarter / cuarto creciente: Fase de la luna cuando, desde la Tierra, se puede observar la mitad de su faz iluminada o un cuarto de la superficie lunar. (Cap. 21, pág. 613)

focus / foco: Punto en el interior de la Tierra donde ocurre la liberación de energía de un terremoto. (Cap. 8, pág. 215)

food chain / cadena alimenticia: Manera simple de mostrar cómo la energía de los alimentos pasa de un organismo a otro. (Cap. 17, pág. 497)

food web / red alimenticia: Serie de cadenas alimenticias sobrepuestas. (Cap. 17, pág. 498)

force / fuerza: Empuje o fuerza de atracción sobre un objeto. (Cap. 7, pág. 176)

formula / fórmula: Combinación de símbolos químicos de elementos, la cual indica los elementos que posee una molécula y cuántos átomos de cada elemento hay. (Cap. 4, pág. 113)

fossil / fósil: Resto, impresión o huella de organismos que una vez estuvieron vivos, conservado en las rocas. (Cap. 11, pág. 304)

fossil fuel / combustible fósil: Se forma cuando los organismos mueren y son enterrados debajo de capas de roca y sedimentos. El carbón, el gas natural y los combustibles hechos a partir del petróleo, son ejemplos de combustibles fósiles. (Cap. 19, pág. 544)

friction / fricción: Fuerza desequilibrada que hace que casi todos los objetos se detengan y que causa una fuerza de roce que se opone al movimiento entre dos superficies que están en contacto una con otra. (Cap. 7, pág. 179)

frond / fronda: La hoja de un helecho. (Cap. 16, pág. 454)

full moon / luna llena o plenilunio: Fase lunar durante la cual toda la superficie lunar que da a la Tierra está totalmente iluminada. (Cap. 21, pág. 613)

G

galaxy / galaxia: Grupo inmenso de estrellas, gas y polvo que se mantiene unido gracias a la gravedad. Nuestra galaxia, la Vía Láctea contiene unos 200 billones de estrellas. (Cap. 23, pág. 679)

gametophyte stage / etapa de gametofito: Etapa en que todas las estructuras de la planta están compuestas de células con un número haploide de cromosomas. (Cap. 16, pág. 452)

gastroliths / gastrolitos: Piedras ingeridas por ciertos animales para facilitar la digestión. (Cap. 13, pág. 385)

geologic time scale / escala del tiempo geológico: División de la historia de la Tierra en unidades más pequeñas de tiempo con base en los tipos de formas de vida que vivieron durante ciertos períodos. (Cap. 13, pág. 364)

geothermal energy / energía geotérmica: Energía térmica contenida dentro de la corteza terrestre que se puede aprovechar como fuente energética. (Cap. 19, pág. 546)

giant / gigante: Etapa en el ciclo de vida de una estrella en que se agota el hidrógeno del núcleo, el núcleo estelar se contrae y las temperaturas dentro de la estrella aumentan, haciendo que sus capas externas se expandan. (Cap. 23, pág. 675)

global warming / calentamiento global: Aumento del promedio de la temperatura anual sobre la Tierra. (Cap. 19, pág. 561)

gradualism / gradualismo: Modelo que describe la evolución como un cambio lento de una especie en otra especie nueva. (Cap. 12, pág. 340)

graph / gráfica: Diagrama que muestra la relación entre variables y el cual facilita el análisis de los datos. (Cap. 1, pág. 18)

grasslands / praderas: Regiones tropicales y templadas que reciben de 25 a 75 cm de precipitación anual y en la cual dominan la comunidad clímax de hierbas. (Cap. 18, pág. 524)

gravitational potential energy / energía potencial gravitacional: La energía que un objeto ganaría al caer, la cual depende de la masa del objeto y de la altura de la caída. (Cap. 6, pág. 167)

Great Red Spot / la Gran Mancha Roja: Espectacular tormenta de gas turbulento y de alta presión que se puede observar continuamente en Júpiter. (Cap. 22, pág. 642)

greenhouse effect / efecto de invernadero: Retención en la atmósfera terrestre del calor proveniente del sol, el cual es esencial para sostener vida sobre la Tierra. (Cap. 19, pág. 561)

groundwater / agua subterránea: Agua contenida en el suelo o atrapada en espacios subterráneos formados por roca no porosa. (Cap. 19, pág. 563)

group / grupo: Familia de elementos que contiene elementos con propiedades físicas o químicas parecidas. (Cap. 3, pág. 68)

H

habitat / hábitat: Ubicación física en donde vive un organismo (Cap. 17, pág. 493)

half-life / media vida: El tiempo que se demora la mitad de los átomos de un isótopo para desintegrarse. (Cap. 2, pág. 50; Cap. 11, pág. 322)

hazardous waste / desperdicio peligroso: Material de desecho dañino para la salud de los seres humanos o venenoso para los organismos vivos. (Cap. 19, pág. 562)

hominids / homínidos: Primates que parecían humanos y que comían tanto plantas como animales y caminaban erguidos. (Cap. 12, pág. 355)

homologous / homólogo: Estructuras corporales similares en origen y estructura que indican que dos o más especies pueden haber tenido antepasados comunes. (Cap. 12, pág. 349)

***Homo sapiens* / *Homo sapiens*:** El nombre de nuestra especie. Significa "humano sabio". (Cap. 12, pág. 356)

hot spot / punto cálido: Área del manto que según algunos geólogos es más caliente que otras áreas y en donde se derriten las rocas que luego brotan en forma de magma hacia la corteza terrestre. (Cap. 9, pág. 244)

hydrocarbon / hidrocarburo: Compuesto que solo contiene carbono e hidrógeno. (Cap. 14, pág. 399)

hydroelectric power / potencia hidroeléctrica: Electricidad que produce la energía del agua que fluye. Es una fuente de energía renovable. (Cap. 19, pág. 546)

hydroxyl group / grupo hidroxilo: Grupo formado por un átomo de oxígeno y un átomo de hidrógeno unidos por un enlace covalente. (Cap. 14, pág. 405)

hypothesis / hipótesis: Predicción acerca de un problema que puede probarse. (Cap. 1, pág. 12)

I

independent variable / variable independiente: Variable que se cambia en un experimento. (Cap. 1, pág. 13)

index fossils / fósiles guías: Provienen de especies que existieron abundantemente en la Tierra durante cortos períodos de tiempo y que se encontraban muy extendidas geográficamente; los científicos los usan para determinar la edad de las rocas. (Cap. 11, pág. 310)

inertia / inercia: Mide la tendencia de un objeto a permanecer en reposo o de continuar en movimiento constante. Una medida de la inercia de un objeto es su masa. (Cap. 6, pág. 158)

inference / inferencia: Intento de explicar algo, con base en la observación. (Cap. 1, pág. 25)

inhibitor / inhibidor: Sustancia que decelera una reacción química. (Cap. 5, pág. 136)

inner core / núcleo interno: Núcleo sólido, muy denso en el mismo centro de la Tierra, compuesto principalmente de hierro y pequeñas cantidades de oxígeno, sílice, azufre o níquel. (Cap. 8, pág. 219)

inner planets / planetas interiores: Planetas sólidos rocosos situados más cerca del sol: Mercurio, Venus, la Tierra y Marte. (Cap. 22, pág. 633)

intertidal zone / zona entre la marea baja y la alta: Porción de la costa cubierta de agua durante la marea alta y expuesta al aire durante la marea baja. (Cap. 18, pág. 530)

ion / ion: Átomo que ya no es neutro porque ha ganado o perdido un electrón. (Cap. 4, pág. 106)

ionic bond / enlace iónico: Fuerza de atracción que mantiene unidos los iones de carga opuesta. (Cap. 4, pág. 107)

isomers / isómeros: Compuestos que tienen fórmulas químicas idénticas, pero diferentes estructuras y diferentes propiedades químicas y físicas. (Cap. 14, pág. 402)

isotopes / isótopos: Átomos del mismo elemento que poseen diferentes números de neutrones. (Cap. 2, pág. 47)

J

Jupiter / Júpiter: El planeta más grande del sistema solar y está ubicado en quinto lugar a partir del sol. (Cap. 22, pág. 642)

K

kinetic energy / energía cinética: La energía de la materia en movimiento. (Cap. 6, pág. 165)

L

law / ley: Descripción probada repetidamente de cómo funciona algo en la naturaleza. Por lo general predice o describe una situación dada, pero no explica por qué se da dicha situación. (Cap. 1, pág. 12)

law of conservation of energy / ley de conservación de la energía: Establece que la energía no puede ser creada ni destruida, sino que solo es transformada de una forma de energía a otra. (Cap. 6, pág. 165)

law of conservation of momentum / ley de conservación del momento: Ley que dice que si no existe una fuerza externa que actúe sobre un grupo de objetos, el momento del grupo entero nunca cambia. (Cap. 6, pág. 161)

light-year / año luz: Distancia que viaja la luz en un año. Es también la unidad que se usa para medir distancias en el espacio. (Cap. 23, pág. 665)

limiting factor / factor limitante: Cualquier factor biótico o abiótico que limita el número de individuos en una población. (Cap. 17, pág. 489)

lipids / lípidos: Compuestos orgánicos que contienen los mismos elementos que los carbohidratos: carbono, hidrógeno y oxígeno, pero en diferentes proporciones. (Cap. 14, pág. 415)

lithosphere / litosfera: Nombre que reciben la corteza y una parte del manto superior terrestres. (Cap. 10, pág. 227)

long-day plant / planta de día largo: Planta que necesita, generalmente, menos de diez a doce horas de oscuridad para comenzar el proceso de floración. (Cap. 15, pág. 439)

lunar eclipse / eclipse lunar: Ocurre cuando la sombra de la Tierra cae sobre la luna. (Cap. 21, pág. 616)

M

magnitude / magnitud: Medida de la energía liberada en un terremoto. (Cap. 8, pág. 226)

main sequence / secuencia principal: En el diagrama H-R, la banda diagonal de estrellas que corre desde las estrellas calientes y brillantes, en la parte superior izquierda del diagrama, hasta las estrellas frías y tenues, en la parte inferior derecha. (Cap. 23, pág. 672)

mantle / manto: Capa más extensa de la Tierra ubicada directamente encima del núcleo externo y compuesta principalmente de sílice, oxígeno, magnesio y hierro. (Cap. 8, pág. 219)

maria / maria: Regiones oscuras y relativamente planas de la superficie lunar. (Cap. 21, pág. 617)

Mars / Marte: Denominado el planeta rojo, Marte es el cuarto planeta a partir del sol. (Cap. 22, pág. 638)

mascon / concentración de masa: Concentración de masa ubicada debajo de las cuencas de impacto en la Luna. (Cap. 21, pág. 621)

mass / masa: Medida de la cantidad de materia. (Cap. 6, pág. 158)

mass number / número de masa: Número de protones y neutrones en el núcleo de un átomo. (Cap. 2, pág. 48)

Mercury / Mercurio: El planeta más cercano al sol y es también el segundo planeta más pequeño. (Cap. 22, pág. 636)

Mesozoic era / era Mesozoica: También denominada era de vida media. Esta era comenzó hace unos 245 millones de años (Cap. 13, pág. 381)

metal / metal: Elemento que tiene lustre, es buen conductor de calor y electricidad y por lo general es sólido a temperatura ambiente. (Cap. 3, pág. 69)

metalloid / metaloide: Elemento que comparte algunas propiedades con los metales y con no metales. Por ejemplo, el boro posee lustre como un metal; pero como los no metales, es un conductor deficiente de electricidad (Cap. 3, pág. 70)

meteor / meteoro: Meteoroide que se quema en la atmósfera terrestre. (Cap. 22, pág. 652)

meteorite / meteorito: Meteoroide lo suficientemente grande como para caer sobre la superficie terrestre. (Cap. 22, pág. 652)

mold / molde: Fósil que se forma cuando un organismo es enterrado y se descompone dejando solo un espacio vacío en la roca. (Cap. 11, pág. 307)

molecule / molécula: Partícula neutra que se forma cuando los átomos comparten electrones. (Cap. 4, pág. 109)

momentum / momento: El producto de la masa y la velocidad, incluyendo dirección. (Cap. 6, pág. 159)

moon phase / fase lunar: Apariencia cambiante de la luna vista desde la Tierra. La fase que vemos depende de las posiciones relativas de la luna, la Tierra y el sol. (Cap. 21, pág. 613)

N

natural resource / recurso natural: Material que se encuentra en la naturaleza y que son útiles o necesarios para los seres vivos. (Cap. 19, pág. 542)

natural selection / selección natural: Teoría de la evolución según Darwin, la cual establece que los organismos cuyos rasgos los hacen más aptos para sus ambientes son los que sobreviven, se reproducen y pasan esos rasgos a la progenie. (Cap. 12, pág. 337)

nebula / nebulosa: Nube extensa de gas y polvo que corresponde a la etapa inicial de formación de una estrella. (Cap. 23, pág. 674)

Neptune / Neptuno: Planeta grande y gaseoso descubierto en 1846; por lo general es el octavo planeta a partir del sol. (Cap. 22, pág. 646)

net force / fuerza neta: Fuerza total que siente un objeto, la cual siempre hace que el objeto acelere en la dirección de la fuerza neta. (Cap. 7, pág. 176)

neutron / neutrón: Partícula neutra con la misma masa que un protón. (Cap. 2, pág. 44)

neutron star / estrella de neutrones: La etapa de una supernova cuando el núcleo denso y colapsado de la estrella se encoge hasta unos 10 a 15 km en diámetro y solo pueden existir neutrones en él. (Cap. 23, pág. 676)

new moon / luna nueva: Ocurre cuando la cara iluminada de la luna mira hacia el Sol y la cara oscura mira hacia la Tierra. La luna se encuentra en el firmamento, pero no podemos verla desde la Tierra. (Cap. 21, pág. 613)

Newton's first law of motion / primera ley de movimiento de Newton: Enuncia que un objeto en reposo, o que se mueve a una rapidez constante en una trayectoria recta, continúa en dicha posición o movimiento hasta que una fuerza neta actúe sobre él. (Cap. 7, pág. 178)

Newton's second law of motion / segunda ley de movimiento de Newton: Ley que enuncia que una fuerza neta que actúa sobre un objeto hace que el objeto acelere en dirección de la fuerza, de acuerdo con la ecuación: $a = F_{net}/m$, en que a es la aceleración, F_{net} es la fuerza neta y m es la masa. (Cap. 7, pág. 184)

Newton's third law of motion / tercera ley de movimiento de Newton: Enuncia que las fuerzas siempre actúan en pares iguales pero opuestos. Es decir, que por cada acción existe una reacción igual y opuesta. (Cap. 7, pág. 192)

niche / nicho: Papel de un organismo en el ecosistema. (Cap. 17, pág. 493)

nitrogen cycle / ciclo del nitrógeno: Transferencia de nitrógeno de la atmósfera a las plantas y de regreso a la atmósfera o directamente a las plantas nuevamente. (Cap. 17, pág. 502)

nonmetal / no metal: Por lo general, un gas o sólido quebradizo a temperatura ambiente, el cual no es buen conductor de calor y electricidad. (Cap. 3, pág. 70)

nonrenewable resource / recurso no renovable: Recurso natural, como el petróleo, accesible solo en cantidades limitadas y que no se puede reemplazar o que solo se reemplaza muy lentamente. (Cap. 19, pág. 543)

normal fault / falla normal: Falla que se forma cuando las rocas, bajo tensión sobre la superficie de la falla, se mueven hacia abajo en relación con las rocas debajo de la superficie. (Cap. 8, pág. 212)

normal force / fuerza normal: La fuerza exterior que ejerce una superficie, la cual es provista por la potencia de la superficie. Por ejemplo, si colocas un objeto pesado sobre una silla desvencijada, podría suceder que la silla no provea suficiente fuerza normal para equilibrar el peso y se rompa bajo el peso. (Cap. 7, pág. 185)

nuclear energy / energía nuclear: Energía que se produce del rompimiento de billones de núcleos de uranio en una reacción de fisión nuclear. (Cap. 19, pág. 547)

O

observatory / observatorio: Edificio que alberga la mayoría de los telescopios ópticos usados por los astrónomos profesionales. A menudo, estos edificios tienen techos, en forma de domo, los cuales se abren para permitir la entrada de la luz. (Cap. 20, pág. 576)

Oort Cloud / Nube de Oort: Nube que, según el astrónomo holandés Jan Oort, está ubicada más allá de la órbita de Plutón y la cual rodea completamente el sistema solar. (Cap. 22, pág. 651)

orbit / órbita: Trayectoria curva que sigue un objeto a medida que gira alrededor de otro objeto en el espacio. Por ejemplo, los planetas giran, en órbitas, alrededor del Sol. (Cap. 20, pág. 582)

organic compound / compuesto orgánico: Compuesto que contiene carbono. (Cap. 14, pág. 398)

outer core / núcleo externo: Núcleo líquido ubicado directamente encima del núcleo interno sólido; también compuesto principalmente de hierro. (Cap. 8, pág. 219)

outer planets / planetas exteriores: Planetas más alejados del sol: Júpiter, Neptuno, Saturno, Urano y Plutón. Excepto por Plutón que está formado de roca y hielo, todos los planetas exteriores están formados principalmente de elementos livianos tales como hidrógeno, helio, metano y amoníaco. (Cap. 22, pág. 633)

ovary / ovario: Base hinchada del pistilo donde se forman los óvulos en las angiospermas. (Cap. 16, pág. 461)

ovule / óvulo: Parte reproductora femenina de una planta de semillas. (Cap. 16, pág. 458)

ozone depletion / agotamiento de la capa de ozono: Adelgazamiento de la capa de ozono que protege la Tierra de los rayos ultravioletas dañinos del sol. Este problema lo causa principalmente el uso de clorofluorocarbonos. (Cap. 19, pág. 561)

P

Paleozoic era / era Paleozoica: Era geológica cuyo comienzo lo marca la presencia de los primeros organismos con partes duras, lo cual facilitó la formación de fósiles. (Cap. 13, pág. 374)

Pangaea / Pangaea: Inmensa extensión territorial que, según Wegener, una vez conectó a todos los continentes y que se separó hace unos 200 millones de años. (Cap. 10, pág. 268)

parallax / paralaje: Cambio aparente en la posición de un objeto cuando uno lo observa desde dos posiciones diferentes. (Cap. 23, pág. 665)

period / período: Hilera de elementos en la tabla periódica cuyas propiedades cambian paulatina y previsiblemente (Cap. 3, pág. 65); Unidad de tiempo en que se subdividen las eras de la escala del tiempo geológico. (Cap. 13, pág. 365)

petrified remains / restos petrificados: Restos duros y de consistencia parecida a la roca, en los cuales algunos o todos los materiales originales han sido reemplazados por minerales. (Cap. 11, pág. 306)

photoperiodism / fotoperiodismo: Respuesta de una planta al número de horas de luz y oscuridad que recibe diariamente. (Cap. 15, pág. 439)

photosphere / fotosfera: Capa más baja de la atmósfera del sol y desde la cual se emite la luz solar. A menudo llamada superficie solar. (Cap. 23, pág. 667)

photosynthesis / fotosíntesis: Proceso mediante el cual las plantas utilizan la energía luminosa para producir alimento. (Cap. 15, pág. 429)

photovoltaic (PV) cell / pila fotovoltaica: Disco hecho del mineral silicio cubierto con capas finas de metales. Se usa para generar electricidad utilizando la energía solar. (Cap. 19, pág. 545)

pioneer community / comunidad pionera: Primera comunidad de organismos que se mudan a un nuevo ambiente. (Cap. 18, pág. 511)

pistil / pistilo: Órgano reproductor femenino de la flor que consiste en un estigma, un estilo alargado en forma de tallo y un ovario. (Cap. 16, pág. 461)

plankton / plancton: Algas, plantas y otros organismos microscópicos que flotan cerca de la superficie en las aguas cálidas y soleadas de lagos y lagunas de agua dulce. (Cap. 18, pág. 529)

plate tectonics / tectónica de placas: Teoría que afirma que la corteza y el manto superior de la Tierra están separados en secciones que se mueven sobre una capa del manto que parece plástico. (Cap. 10, pág. 277)

plates / placas: Secciones de la litosfera terrestre compuestas de corteza oceánica, corteza continental y el manto superior rígido, las cuales se mueven sobre una capa del manto que parece plástico. (Cap. 10, pág. 277)

Pluto / Plutón: El planeta más pequeño del sistema solar y del cual tenemos menos información. Se le considera el noveno planeta a partir del sol. (Cap. 22, pág. 646)

pollen grains / granos de polen: Partes reproductoras masculinas de las plantas de semillas; dos espermatozoides se desarrollan en cada grano de polen. (Cap. 16, pág. 458)

pollination / polinización: Proceso de transferencia de granos de polen desde el estambre al estigma. (Cap. 16, pág. 462)

pollutant / contaminante: Cualquier sustancia que contamina el ambiente y causa contaminación. (Cap. 19, pág. 559)

polymer / polímero: Molécula que está compuesta de muchas moléculas orgánicas pequeñas, que se enlazan una a la otra formando una cadena larga. (Cap. 14, pág. 410)

population / población: Organismos individuales de la misma especie que viven en el mismo lugar y que pueden producir crías. (Cap. 17, pág. 486)

population density / densidad demográfica: El tamaño de una población que ocupa un área de tamaño limitado. (Cap. 17, pág. 489)

Precambrian time / Era Precámbrica: Representa la unidad de tiempo geológico más larga de la historia de la Tierra, la cual duró desde hace 4.6 billones de años hasta hace 544 millones de años. (Cap. 13, pág. 372)

primary succession / sucesión primaria: Sucesión ecológica que comienza en un lugar que no tiene suelo. (Cap. 18, pág. 511)

primary waves / ondas primarias: Ondas que hacen que las partículas en las rocas se muevan oscilatoriamente, en la misma dirección de la onda. (Cap. 8, pág. 216)

primates / primates: Grupo de mamíferos que incluye los monos, los simios y a los seres humanos, los cuales comparten varias características como pulgares oponibles, visión binocular y hombros flexibles. Los científicos consideran que todos los primates evolucionaron de un antepasado común. (Cap. 12, pág. 354)

principle of superposition / principio de sobreposición: Principio que dice que en las capas rocosas inalteradas, las rocas más antiguas se encuentran en las capas inferiores y que las rocas son más y más recientes hacia la parte superior. (Cap. 11, pág. 312)

product / producto: Sustancia que se forma al ocurrir una reacción química. (Cap. 5, pág. 124)

Project Apollo / Proyecto Apolo: Etapa final del programa americano de viajar a la luna. (Cap. 20, pág. 587)

Project Gemini / Proyecto Gemini: Segunda etapa en la meta de viajar a la luna. (Cap. 20, pág. 586)

Project Mercury / Proyecto Mercurio: Proyecto que inició el programa americano de viajar a la luna. (Cap. 20, pág. 586)

protein / proteína: Polímero que consiste en una cadena de aminoácidos individuales unidos entre sí. Las proteínas son necesarias para el funcionamiento adecuado del cuerpo humano. (Cap. 14, pág. 411)

prothallus / prótalo: Gametofito del helecho que produce células sexuales que se unen para formar el cigoto. (Cap. 16, pág. 454)

proton / protón: Partícula con carga positiva que se encuentra en todos los átomos. (Cap. 2, pág. 40)

punctuated equilibrium / equilibrio puntuado: Modelo que muestra que la evolución rápida de una especie puede resultar debido a la mutación de unos cuantos genes, resultando en una nueva especie. (Cap. 12, pág. 340)

R

radioactive decay / desintegración radiactiva: Proceso en que la descomposición de un átomo de algunos isótopos resulta en un cambio en el número de protones y en la formación de un nuevo elemento. (Cap. 2, pág. 48; Cap. 11, pág. 321)

radioactive element / elemento radiactivo: Elemento que despide radiación debido a un núcleo inestable. Al despedir radiación, los elementos radiactivos se convierten en productos más estables. (Cap. 12, pág. 346)

radiometric dating / datación radiométrica: Proceso que se usa para calcular la edad absoluta de las rocas al medir las cantidades de material original y de los productos de desintegración que hay en la roca, conociendo el período de media vida del material original. (Cap. 11, pág. 323)

radio telescope / radiotelescopio: Tipo de telescopio que se usa para estudiar ondas radiales que viajan a través del espacio. (Cap. 20, pág. 579)

rate of reaction / tasa de reacción: Es una medida de la rapidez con que ocurre una reacción. (Cap. 5, pág. 133)

reactant / reactivo: Sustancia que existe antes de que comience una reacción química y la cual reacciona durante la reacción química. (Cap. 5, pág. 124)

recycling / reciclaje: Proceso que disminuye el uso de los recursos naturales al reutilizar artículos después de cambiarlos o procesarlos nuevamente. (Cap. 19, pág. 553)

reflecting telescope / telescopio reflector: Telescopio que usa un espejo como objetivo para enfocar la luz del objeto bajo observación. (Cap. 20, pág. 576)

refracting telescope / telescopio refractor: Telescopio en que la luz del objeto pasa a través de una lente convexa doble, en donde la luz se dobla formando una imagen sobre el punto focal. Luego el ocular magnifica la imagen. (Cap. 20, pág. 576)

relative dating / datación relativa: Se utiliza en geología para determinar el orden de los sucesos y la edad relativa de las rocas al examinar sus posiciones en una secuencia. (Cap. 11, pág. 313)

renewable resource / recurso renovable: Recurso natural, como el agua, que se puede reemplazar o reciclar mediante procesos naturales. (Cap. 19, pág. 542)

reptiles / reptiles: Animales con piel escamosa que ponen huevos y que no necesitan regresar al agua para reproducirse; probablemente evolucionaron de los mismos antepasados que los anfibios. (Cap. 13, pág. 376)

respiration / respiración: Serie de reacciones químicas que llevan a cabo todos los organismos para descomponer el alimento y liberar energía. (Cap. 15, pág. 432)

reverse fault / falla invertida: Falla en que las rocas sobre la superficie son forzadas hacia arriba y sobre las rocas debajo de la superficie de la falla. (Cap. 8, pág. 212)

revolution / revolución: Órbita anual de la Tierra alrededor del sol. (Cap. 21, pág. 605)

rhizome / risoma: Tallo subterráneo de donde crecen las hojas y las raíces de los helechos. (Cap. 16, pág. 454)

rotation / rotación: Movimiento de la Tierra alrededor de su eje, el cual causa el día y la noche. (Cap. 21, pág. 603)

S

satellite / satélite: Cualquier objeto que gira alrededor de otro objeto. (Cap. 20, pág. 582)

saturated hydrocarbon / hidrocarburo saturado: Hidrocarburo cuyos átomos solo contienen enlaces sencillos. (Cap. 14, pág. 400)

Saturn / Saturno: Conocido como el planeta anular, es el sexto planeta a partir del sol. (Cap. 22, pág. 643)

science / ciencia: Proceso que se usa para investigar el mundo a tu alrededor y el cual te provee algunas posibles respuestas. (Cap. 1, pág. 8)

scientific methods / métodos científicos: Procedimientos que se usan para tratar de resolver un problema. (Cap. 1, pág. 10)

seafloor spreading / expansión del suelo marino: Teoría que dice que el magma proveniente de debajo de la superficie terrestre es forzado a ascender a la superficie a través de la dorsal mediooceánica, en donde fluye de las grietas a medida que el suelo marino se esparce, y se solidifica al enfriarse, formando nuevo suelo marino. (Cap. 10, pág. 273)

secondary succession / sucesión secundaria: Sucesión que comienza en un lugar que ya tiene suelo y el cual fue la morada de organismos vivos. (Cap. 18, pág. 512)

secondary waves / ondas secundarias: Ondas que se mueven a través de la Tierra haciendo que las partículas en las rocas vibren formando un ángulo recto a la dirección de la onda. (Cap. 8, pág. 216)

sedimentary rock / roca sedimentaria: Tipo de roca formada de barro, arena y otras partículas finas que quedan al secárseles el líquido. (Cap. 12, pág. 345)

seismic waves / ondas sísmicas: Ondas generadas por un terremoto. (Cap. 8, pág. 215)

seismograph / sismógrafo: Instrumento que registra las ondas primarias, secundarias y de superficie que producen los terremotos por todo el mundo. (Cap. 8, pág. 226)

seismologist / sismólogo: Científico que estudia los terremotos y las ondas sísmicas. (Cap. 8, pág. 226)

semiconductor / semiconductor: Elemento que no conduce electricidad tan bien como un metal, pero que sí la conduce mejor que un no metal. (Cap. 3, pág. 76)

sequence / sucesión: Arreglo de cosas o eventos en cierto orden. (Cap. 1, pág. 25)

shield volcano / volcán de escudo: Volcán amplio con suaves pendientes formado por la acumulación de capas llanas de lava basáltica. (Cap. 9, pág. 251)

short-day plant / planta de día corto: Planta que necesita doce o más horas de oscuridad para comenzar el proceso de floración. (Cap. 15, pág. 439)

sill / intrusión: Magma que después de ser apretujado formando una resquebrajadura horizontal entre capas rocosas se endurece. (Cap. 9, pág. 257)

smog / smog: Tipo de contaminante del aire que se forma cuando la luz solar reacciona con los contaminantes químicos que se producen de la quema de combustibles fósiles. (Cap. 19, pág. 559)

soil depletion / desgaste del suelo: Eliminación de nutrientes del suelo. (Cap. 19, pág. 549)

soil management / manejo del suelo: Uso de métodos de arado del terreno para disminuir su erosión. (Cap. 19, pág. 550)

solar eclipse / eclipse solar: Ocurre cuando la luna se mueve directamente entre el sol y la Tierra y proyecta una sombra sobre parte de la Tierra. (Cap. 21, pág. 614)

solar system / sistema solar: Está compuesto de nueve planetas, incluyendo la Tierra, y muchos objetos más pequeños que giran alrededor del sol. (Cap. 22, pág. 631)

solstice / solsticio: Punto en que el sol alcanza su mayor distancia al norte o al sur del ecuador. (Cap. 21, pág. 607)

sori / soros: Estructuras productoras de esporas que se encuentran en los lados inferiores de las frondas maduras de los helechos. (Cap. 16, pág. 454)

space probe / sonda espacial: Instrumento que viaja por el sistema solar; reúne información y la envía a la Tierra. (Cap. 20, pág. 583)

space shuttle / transbordador espacial: Nave espacial reutilizable que transporta a astronautas, satélites y otros materiales hacia el espacio y desde el mismo. (Cap. 20, pág. 590)

space station / estación espacial: Estación en el espacio que posee viviendas, áreas de trabajo y de ejercicio, y todo el equipo y sistemas auxiliares que necesitan los seres humanos para vivir y trabajar en el espacio. (Cap. 20, pág. 591)

species / especie: Grupo de organismos cuyos miembros pueden aparearse entre sí en su ambiente natural. (Cap. 12, pág. 334)

speed / rapidez: Razón del cambio en posición. (Cap. 6, pág. 148)

sphere / esfera: Objeto redondo tridimensional cuya superficie en cualquiera de sus puntos está a la misma distancia de su centro. (Cap. 21, pág. 602)

sporophyte stage / etapa de esporofito: Etapa en que todas las estructuras de la planta están compuestas de células con un número diploide de cromosomas. (Cap. 16, pág. 452)

stamen / estambre: Órgano reproductor masculino de la flor que consiste en un filamento y una antera. (Cap. 16, pág. 461)

stomata / estomas: Aberturas en la superficie de las hojas de las plantas, o en la superficie de estructuras que parecen hojas, las cuales permiten que el dióxido de carbono, el agua y el oxígeno entren y salgan de la planta. (Cap. 15, pág. 426)

strike-slip fault / falla transformante: Falla en la cual las rocas en cualquiera de los dos lados de la falla se alejan unas de otras, sin mucho movimiento ascendente o descendente. (Cap. 8, pág. 213)

sunspot / mancha solar: Área de la superficie solar que parece oscura porque es más fría que las áreas que la rodean. (Cap. 23, pág. 668)

supergiant / supergigante: Etapa en la formación de una estrella en la cual se forman elementos cada vez más pesados por medio de la fusión, haciendo que a la larga, se forme hierro en su núcleo. (Cap. 23, pág. 676)

surface waves / ondas de superficie: Ondas que viajan hacia afuera del epicentro y mueven las partículas de arriba hacia abajo y de un lado a otro, en un movimiento oscilatorio. Estas ondas causan la mayor parte de la destrucción durante un terremoto. (Cap. 8, pág. 217)

symbiosis / simbiosis: Cualquier relación estrecha entre dos o más especies diferentes. (Cap. 17, pág. 491)

T

taiga / taiga: Región fría de árboles coníferos siempre verdes. (Cap. 18, pág. 520)

technology / tecnología: La aplicación del conocimiento aprendido a través de la ciencia. (Cap. 1, pág. 22)

temperate deciduous forest / bosque deciduo de zonas templadas: Comunidad clímax de árboles deciduos, los cuales pierden sus hojas en el otoño. (Cap. 18, pág. 521)

tephra / tefrita: Pedazos de roca o lava solidificada que cae del aire después de ser expulsados en una erupción explosiva. (Cap. 9, pág. 251)

theory / teoría: Explicación basada en los resultados obtenidos al hacer pruebas o experimentos repetidamente. (Cap. 1, pág. 12)

third quarter / cuarto menguante: Cuando se ve solo la mitad de la faz iluminada de la luna. (Cap. 21, pág. 614)

transpiration / transpiración: Pérdida de agua a través de los estomas de la hoja. (Cap. 15, pág. 427)

trilobites / trilobites: Organismos que vivieron hace cientos de millones de años; aparecieron primero durante el período Cámbrico y existieron en la Tierra a través de la era Paleozoica y finalmente se extinguieron a finales del período Pérmico. (Cap. 13, pág. 367)

tropical rain forest / bosque pluvial tropical: La comunidad clímax más importante en las regiones ecuatoriales del mundo y que posee una vegetación frondosa. (Cap. 18, pág. 523)

tropism / tropismo: Respuesta de una planta a un estímulo exterior. Puede ser positivo o negativo. (Cap. 15, pág. 436)

tsunami / tsunami: Onda oceánica sísmica causada por un terremoto. (Cap. 8, pág. 227)

tundra / tundra: Región fría, seca y sin árboles, que a veces se denomina desierto gélido porque tiene inviernos que duran de seis a nueve meses. (Cap. 18, pág. 519)

U

unbalanced forces / fuerzas desequilibradas: Fuerzas cuya fuerza neta es cero y que provocan la aceleración de un objeto. (Cap. 7, pág. 177)

unconformities / discordancias: Brechas entre las capas rocosas. (Cap. 11, pág. 315)

uniformitarianism / uniformitarianismo: Dice que los procesos terrestres que tienen lugar actualmente son similares a los del pasado. (Cap. 11, pág. 325)

unsaturated hydrocarbon / hidrocarburo no saturado: Hidrocarburo cuyos átomos de carbono forman enlaces dobles o triples. (Cap. 14, pág. 401)

Uranus / Urano: El séptimo planeta a partir del sol, descubierto en 1781. Es un planeta grande y gaseoso con 17 satélites y un sistema de anillos oscuros y delgados. (Cap. 22, pág. 645)

variation / variación: Rasgo heredado que diferencia a un individuo de otros miembros de la misma especie; puede ser beneficiosa, dañina o no tener ninguna influencia en una población (Cap. 12, pág. 338)

velocity / velocidad: Razón de cambio del desplazamiento, la cual incluye tanto rapidez como dirección. (Cap. 6, pág. 150)

vent / chimenea: Abertura por la cual fluye el magma que llega a la superficie terrestre. (Cap. 9, pág. 242)

Venus / Venus: A veces llamado el gemelo de la Tierra, Venus es el segundo planeta a partir del sol. (Cap. 22, pág. 637)

vestigial structure / estructura vestigial: Parte corporal que parece no tener función alguna. (Cap. 12, pág. 350)

volcanic neck / cuello volcánico: Núcleo ígneo sólido que queda después de que el cono de un volcán se erosiona, después de que el volcán deja de hacer erupción. (Cap. 9, pág. 257)

volcano / volcán: Abertura en la superficie terrestre que a menudo forma una montaña, cuando se arrojan y acumulan capas de lava y cenizas volcánicas. (Cap. 9, pág. 240)

W

waning / octante menguante: Cuando la cantidad de la faz iluminada de la luna, que se puede ver desde la Tierra, comienza a disminuir. (Cap. 21, pág. 614)

water cycle / ciclo del agua: Involucra los procesos de evaporación, condensación y precipitación. (Cap. 17, pág. 500)

waxing / octante creciente: Cuando se hace cada vez más visible la cara iluminada de la luna. (Cap. 21, pág. 613)

white dwarf / enana blanca: Etapa tardía en el ciclo de vida de una estrella, en que su núcleo agota su abastecimiento de helio, se contrae y sus capas externas se escapan hacia el espacio, dejando un núcleo denso y caliente. (Cap. 23, pág. 676)

Index

The index for *Science Voyages* will help you locate major topics in the book quickly and easily. Each entry in the index is followed by the numbers of the pages on which the entry is discussed. A page number given in **boldface type** indicates the page on which that entry is defined. A page number given in *italic type* indicates a page on which the entry is used in an illustration or photograph. The abbreviation *act.* indicates a page on which the entry is used in an activity.

A

D

E

N

P

R

S

T

X

Y

Z

Art Credits

UNIT 1

Chapter 1 - **10** Morgan-Cain & Associates; **16** Preface; **18, 30, 33** Morgan-Cain & Associates.

Chapter 2 - **37, 38, 39, 40, 41, 42, 43, 44, 45, 47, 49, 50, 58** Morgan-Cain & Associates; **61** Glencoe/McGraw-Hill.

UNIT 2

Chapter 3 - **66-67** Glencoe/McGraw-Hill; **68-69, 70, 72, 74, 75, 76, 77, 78, 80, 81, 84, 85, 87, 95** Morgan-Cain & Associates.

Chapter 4 - **98, 99, 100, 101, 102, 106, 107, 108, 109, 110, 111, 112, 113, 116, 117** Morgan-Cain & Associates.

Chapter 5 - **126, 134, 140** Morgan-Cain & Associates; **143** Glencoe/McGraw-Hill.

UNIT 3

Chapter 6 - **149** Glencoe/McGraw-Hill; **151** (t) Glencoe/McGraw-Hill, (b) Morgan-Cain & Associates; **154, 155** Glencoe/McGraw-Hill; **159, 161** Morgan-Cain & Associates; **162** Carlos Lacamara; **163, 167, 170** Morgan-Cain & Associates; **171** Carlos Lacamara; **173** Glencoe/McGraw-Hill.

Chapter 7 - **178, 193, 198, 199** Carlos Lacamara; **200-201** Morgan-Cain & Associates; **202** Carlos Lacamara; **205** Glencoe/McGraw-Hill.

Chapter 8 - **211** Tom Kennedy; **212 213 216-0** Chris Forsey/Morgan-Cain & Assoc.; **218** Dartmouth Publ., Inc.; **219** Ortelius Design; **219** Chris Higgins/PP/FA, Inc.; **220-0** Gary Hinks/Publisher's Graphics; **223** Ortelius Design; **230** Tom Kennedy; **231** National Geographic Society; **232** Glencoe; **234** Chris Higgins/PP/FA, Inc.; **234** Chris Forsey/Morgan-Cain & Assoc.; **235** Ortelius Design; **236** Preface, Inc.; **237** Glencoe.

Chapter 9 - **242** Tom Kennedy; **243** Dartmouth Publ., Inc.; **244** Gary Hinks/Publisher's Graphics; **244** John Edwards; **245** Terry Duennebier/SOEST/University of Hawaii; **250 251 255 258** Gary Hinks/Publisher's Graphics; **262** John Edwards; **265** Glencoe.

UNIT 4

Chapter 10 - **268-0** Chris Forsey/Morgan-Cain & Assoc.; **269 271** Ortelius Design; **272** John Edwards; **275** Ortelius Design; **276** Glencoe; **277** Leon Bishop; **278** Ortelius Design; **280-0** Gary Hinks/Publisher's Graphics; **283** Edwin Huff; **284** John Edwards; **290 291 292** Chris Higgins/PP/FA, Inc.; **297** Edwin Huff; **299** Glencoe.

Chapter 11 - **304** John Edwards; **307** (t) Glencoe/McGraw-Hill (b) Rolin Graphics; **309** Jim Shough; **310** Leon Bishop; **313** John Edwards; **314, 315, 316** Morgan-Cain & Associates; **317, 318** Dartmouth Publishing; **319, 322** Tom Kennedy; **323** Dartmouth Publishing; **324** Morgan-Cain & Associates; **327** Glencoe/McGraw-Hill; **329** (t) Morgan-Cain & Associates; (b) Tom Kennedy; **331** Glencoe/McGraw-Hill.

Chapter 12 - **335** Barbara Hoopes-Ambler; **336** David Reed; **340** Morgan-Cain & Associates; **341** Barbara Hoopes-Ambler/Morgan-Cain & Associates; **347** Dave Fischer; **348** Barbara Hoopes-Ambler; **349** Laurie O'Keefe; **350** (tl) Robert Hynes/Morgan-Cain & Associates, (tr) Michael Woods, (b) AA/Michael Dick; **354** Robert Hynes; **358** Barbara Hoopes-Ambler; **361** Laurie O'Keefe.

UNIT 5

Opener - Sunflowers, ©Gary Withey/Bruce Coleman Inc./PNI

Inset - Computer Model of DNA, Philippe Plailly/Eurelios/Science Photo Library/Photo Researchers, Inc.

Chapter 13 - **364** Morgan-Cain & Associates; **365** Pond & Giles; **367** Morgan-Cain & Associates; **368** Pond & Giles; **369** Rolin Graphics; **371** Laurie O'Keefe; **372** Pond & Giles; **375** Laurie O'Keefe; **379** Precision Graphics; **380, 381, 382, 384** Sarah Woodward; **388** Morgan-Cain & Associates; **389** Precision Graphics; **391** Glencoe/McGraw-Hill.

Chapter 14 - **399, 400, 401, 402, 403, 404, 405, 406, 407, 410, 412, 413, 414, 416, 420** Morgan-Cain & Associates; **423** Glencoe/McGraw-Hill.

Chapter 15 - **427 428** Morgan-Cain & Assoc.; **429** David Ashby; **433 438 445 447** Morgan-Cain & Assoc.

Chapter 16 - **453, 454, 459** Robert Hynes/Morgan-Cain & Associates; **461** Robert Hynes; **462** Pond & Giles; **463** Morgan-Cain & Associates; **466, 467** Pond & Giles; **470** Morgan-Cain & Associates; **477** Glencoe/McGraw-Hill.

UNIT 6

Chapter 17 - **483** Pond & Giles; **485** Kathie Kelleher/Publisher's Graphics; **488** Morgan-Cain & Assoc.; **489 490** Dartmouth Publ., Inc.; **496-0** Barbara Hoopes-Amber; **498** Morgan-Cain & Assoc.; **499** Kathie Kelleher/Publisher's Graphics; **499** David Ashby; **500** Felipe Passalacqua; **501** Kathie Kelleher/Publisher's Graphics; **502** Felipe Passalacqua; **504** Kathie Kelleher/Publisher's Graphics; **505** Morgan-Cain & Assoc.

Chapter 18 - **510** Chris Forsey; **516** Morgan-Cain & Assoc.; **517** Dartmouth Publ., Inc.; **518** Chris Forsey; **519** Morgan-Cain & Assoc.; **522** Kathie Kelleher/Publisher's Graphics; **523** Barbara Hoopes-Amber; **532** PP/FA, Inc.; **532 533 534 535** Dartmouth Publ., Inc.; **536** Chris Forsey; **536** Morgan-Cain & Assoc.

Chapter 19 - **541, 544, 545, 548** Morgan-Cain & Associates; **552** Ortelius Design; **559, 560, 561** Morgan-Cain & Associates; **563** Chris Forsey; **565, 567** Morgan-Cain & Associates; **569** Glencoe/McGraw-Hill.

Chapter 20 - **574-575** Rolin Graphics; **576** George Bucktell; **582, 584-585** John Edwards.

Chapter 21 - **603** John Edwards; **604** Rolin Graphics; **605** Bruce Sanders; **606, 607** John Edwards; **612** John Edwards/Morgan-Cain & Associates; **613** Morgan-Cain & Associates; **614** John Edwards/Morgan-Cain & Associates; **615, 616, 618-619** Rolin Graphics; **624** John Edwards; **627** Glencoe/McGraw-Hill.

Chapter 22 - **630-631** Morgan-Cain & Associates; **632, 633** Dave Fischer/John Edwards; **635** Dartmouth Publishing; **644** Morgan-Cain & Associates; **645, 651** John Edwards; **652-653** (t) Morgan-Cain & Associates; **653** (b) John Edwards; **656** Dave Fischer/John Edwards; **657** Morgan-Cain & Associates; **659** Glencoe/McGraw-Hill.

Chapter 23 - **662** (l) Morgan-Cain & Associates, (r) Precision Graphics; **663, 665** John Edwards; **667, 672** Morgan-Cain & Associates; **673, 674, 675** John Edwards; **680** Morgan-Cain & Associates; **681** John Edwards; **682-683** Morgan-Cain & Associates; **683** (b) Jim Shough; **684** John Edwards; **688, 689, 690, 691** Morgan-Cain & Associates; **692** John Edwards; **695** Glencoe/McGraw-Hill.

Photo Credits

Cover - (tl)Steve Gettle/ENP Images, (tr)Mendola/Jeff Lynch/The Stock Market, (b)Schafer & Hill/Tony Stone Images.

vii Matt Meadows; **viii** Chuck Savage/The Stock Market; **ix** (t)Allsport, (b)Gregory G. Dimijian/Photo Researchers; **x** Dr. E.R. Degginger/Color-Pic; **xi** Victor Scocozza/FPG International; **xii** (t)Tom Bean/DRK Photo, (b)Thomas Del Broise/The Stock Market; **xiii** (t)Edward Parker/Still Pictures/Peter Arnold, Inc., (b)NASA; **xiv** (t)JPL/TSADO/Tom Stack & Associates, (b)Jon Edwards/David Fisher; **xv** Rafael Macia/Photo Researchers; **xvi** (t)Bob Campbell, (c)Bernard Boutrit/Woodfin Camp (b)Museum of History & Industry, Seattle, WA; **xvii** (t)John Gerlach/Tom Stack & Associates (b)NASA; **xviii** Aaron Haupt; **xix** Matt Meadows; **xx** KS Studios; **xxii** (t)Peter Vadnai, (b)KS Studios; **xxiii** Brian Parker/Tom Stack & Associates; **xxiv** KS Studios.

UNIT 1

Chapter 1 - **2-3** Robert D. Rubic/DPI; **3** Steve Lissau/Rainbow; **4-5** Jonathan Blair/Corbis Media; **5 6 7** KS Studio; **8** Bob Abraham/The Stock Market; **9** (t)Juan Silva/The Image Bank, (b)courtesy Amanda Shaw & Focus One; **10 11** KS Studio; **12** Matt Meadows; **14 15** KS Studio; **17**(l)Stephen Derr/The Image Bank, (r)Art Wolfe/Tony Stone Images, (b)file photo; **19** NASA/Science Photo Library/Photo Researchers; **20** KS Studio; **22** Ralph White/Corbis Media; **23** (t)Jim Sugar Photography/Corbis Media, (b)courtesy Lawrence Livermore Laboratory; **24** Aaron Haupt; **26** Barry Lopez/Photo Researchers; **27** Morrison Photography; **29** (tl)John Gerlach/Tom Stack & Associates, (rc)National Geographic photographer Chris Johns, (bl)Richard C. Walters/Visuals Unlimited, (br)Russell Schliepman/Woodfin Camp & Associates; **30** courtesy Amanda Shaw and Focus One; **31** (t)Jim Sugar Photography/Corbis Media, (b)Bill Groethe.

Chapter 2 - **34-35** Chris Minerva/FPG International; **35** Matt Meadows; **36** Ed Young/Science Photo Library/Photo Researchers; **37** North Wind Pictures; **38** file photo; **39** Skip Comer; **40** Aaron Haupt; **44** (l)Aaron Haupt, (r)Ohio State University Archives; **46** Aaron Haupt; **49** Doug Martin; **51** Oregon Historical Society; **52** Nick Wall/Science Photo Library/Photo Researchers; **53** Matt Meadows/Chris Priest/Science Photo Library/Photo Researchers; **54** Runk/Schoenberger from Grant Heilman; **55** Steve Kagan/Liaison International; **56** Matt Meadows; **58** Aaron Haupt; **59** (t)Nick Wall/Science Photo Library/Photo Researchers, (c)SIU/Peter Arnold, Inc., (b)Oregon Historical Society.

Chapter 3 - **62-63** Kevin R. Morris/Tony Stone Images; **63** KS Studio; **64** Stamp from the collection of Prof. C.M. Lang; Photography by Gary Shulfer, Univ. of WI-Steven's Point - Russia 3608; **68** Ronnie Kaufman/The Stock Market; **69** (l)Dan Rest, (c)Colin Garratt/Corbis Media, (r)Ken Whitmore/Tony Stone Images; **72** Matt Meadows; **73** (tl, b)Aaron Haupt, (tr)Richard Megna/Fundamental Photographs; **74** (t)GCA/CNRI/PhotoTake, (bl)Tom Stack/Tom Stack & Associates, (br)Dan Rest; **75** (tl)Dan Rest, (tr)Robert Maass/Corbis Media, (b)Matt Meadows; **76** (l)L.L.T. Rhodes/Tony Stone Images, (r)Geoff Butler; **77** (t)George Hall/Corbis Media, (bl)Tim Courlas, (br)Tony Stone Images; **78** (t)Geoff Butler, (b)Dick Luria/FPG International; **79** (t)Tom Carroll/PhotoTake, (b)Frank Zullo/Photo Researchers; **80** (tr)Skip Comer, (l)Tom Stack/Tom Stack & Assoiciates, (br)Stephen Frisch/Stock Boston; **81** (l)Kim Westerskov/Ford Scientific Films/Earth Scenes, (r)Philip James Corwin/Corbis Media; **83** Matt Meadows; **84** (t)Senckenberg-Museum, Frankfurt/Main/PhotoTake, (b)James F. Housel/Tony Stone Images; **85** (t)Christie's Images, (c)Richard Pasley/Stock Boston, (b)Michael Mathers/Peter Arnold, Inc.; **86** (t)Geoff Butler, (c)Matt Meadows, (b)Photo Researchers; **87** KS Studio; **89** (l)Richard T. Nowitz/Phototake, (r)SIU/Visuals Unlimited; **92** (t)Ronnie Kaufman/The Stock Market, (b)Dan Rest; **93** (tr)Matt Meadows, (c)Robert Maass/Corbis Media, (b)Michael Mathers/Peter Arnold, Inc.

Chapter 4 - **96-97** David R. Frazier; **97 103 104 105** Aaron Haupt; **107** Geoff Butler; **110** David R. Frazier; **111** Matt Meadows; **112** W.W. Winter Ltd./The Derby Museum; **114 116** Aaron Haupt; **117** Fermilab Visual Media Services.

Chapter 5 - **120-121** SuperStock; **121** KS Studio; **122** (l)Dan Rest, (r)file photo,**123** (tl, tr)Aaron Haupt, (bl)KS Studio, (br)Matt Meadows; **125** KS Studio; **127** Doug Martin; **128** (tl)Stephen Frisch/Stock Boston, (tr)Matt Meadows, (bl)Ed Lallo/Liaison International, (br)Phil Degginger/Color-Pic; **129** file photo; **130** KS Studio; **131** KS Studio; **132** (l)Mark E. Gibson, (r)Uniphoto; **133** (t)Aaron Haupt, (b)James H. Robinson; **134** (t)KS Studio, (b)Roy Morsch/The Stock Market; **137** Mark Burnett; **139** Charles D. Winters/Photo Researchers; **140** (t)file photo, (b)Aaron Haupt; **141** (l)James H. Robinson; (r)Uniphoto, (b)Otis Hairston.

UNIT 2

Chapter 6 - **144-145** Dan McCoy/Rainbow; **145**©The Harold E. Edgerton Trust, courtesy of Palm Press, Inc.; **146-147** Tom & DeeAnn McCarthy/The Stock Market; **147** Aaron Haupt; **148** Frans Lanting/Minden Pictures; **150** JPL-NASA/Phototake; **153** Tom Stack/Tom Stack & Associates; **156** Tom Stack/Tom Stack & Associates; **158** (l)Chuck Savage/The Stock Market, (r)Aaron Haupt; **159** (l)Tui De Roy/Minden Pictures, (r)NASA/Science Source/Photo Researchers; **160** (l)Alan Schein/The Stock Market, (r)John Shaw/Tom Stack & Associates; **164** Aaron Haupt; **165** David Stoecklein/The Stock Market; **166** Tom Brakefield/The Stock Market; **168** Ron Levy/Liaison International; **169** (l)Science Photo Library/Photo Researchers, (r)C. Powell, P. Fowler & D. Perkins/Science Photo Library/Photo Researchers; **170** Chuck Savage/The Stock Market; **171** Tom Brakefield/The Stock Market.

Chapter 7 - **174-175** VCG/FPG International; **175** KS Studio; **176** (tr)Matt Meadows, (l)file photo, (br)KS Studio, **177** (l, r)KS Studio, (b)Bruce Curtis/Peter Arnold, Inc.; **179** (l)KS Studio, (r)Jim Cummins/FPG International; **180 181** KS Studio; **182** (l)KS Studio, (r)Jon Eisberg/FPG International; **183** KS Studio; **184** Mike Powell/AllSport; **185** file photo; **186** (t)Telegraph Colour Library/FPG International, (b)Brian Bahr/AllSport; **187** KS Studio; **188** AllSport; **189** National Geographic photographer Jodi Cobb; **190** Aaron Haupt; **192** Steven Sutton/Duomo; **194** KS Studio; **195** (l)Gunter Ziesler/Peter Arnold, Inc, (r)Ron Chapple/FPG International; **196** KS Studio; **197** Jim Cummins/FPG International; **200** (t)Telegraph Colour Library/FPG International; (b)NASA/Science Source/Photo Researchers; **201** VCG/FPG International, **202** (tr)file photo, (rc)Matt Meadows, (b)KS Studio; **203** (t)Steven Sutton/Duomo, (c)Gunter Ziesler/Peter Arnold, Inc., (b)Jim Cummins/FPG International.

UNIT 3

Chapter 8 - **206-207** Alberto Garcia/SABA; **207** Patrick Robert/Sygma; **208-209** Kurita/Liaison International; **209** StudiOhio; **210** Doug Martin; **212** (t)Cliff Leight, (b)Cosmo Condina/Tony Stone Images; **213** David Parker/Photo Researchers; **214** Gregory G. Dimijian/Photo Researchers; **215** Ron Haviv/Saba Press Photos; **222** David Parker/Science Photo Library/Photo Researchers; **222** Tom McHugh/Science Source/Photo Researchers; **225** Les Stone/Sygma; **228** AP Photo/Rick Rycroft; **229** James L. Stanfield/National Geographic Image Collection; **231** National Geographic Society, Art by Lina Chesak; **235** Les Stone/Sygma.

Chapter 9 - **238-239** Kevin West/Liaison International; **239** Doug Martin; **240** Francois Gohier/Photo Researchers; **241** Emory Kristof/National Geographic Image Collection; **244** *The Floor of the Oceans* by Bruce C. Heezen and Marie Tharp, © 1980 by Marie Tharp. Reproduced by permission of Marie Tharp.; **246** Matt Meadows; **248 249** Gary Rosenquist; **250** (l)Steve Lissau, (r)Tom Bean/DRK Photo; **251** (t)Greg Vaughn/Tony Stone Images, (b)Thomas Del Brase/Tony Stone Images; **253** Patrick

Aventurier/Liaison International; **256** (l)Gregg Hade/Tony Stone Images, (r)David Muench; **257** (l)David Hosking/Photo Researchers; (r)Ken M. Johns/Photo Researchers; **259** Greg Vaughn; **260** Doug Martin; **261** Paul Chesley/Tony Stone Images; **262** Tom Bean/DRK Photo; **263** (t)David Muench, (b)Woods Hole Oceanographic Institution.

Chapter 10 - **266-267** Tom Van Sant, The Geosphere Project/Science Photo Library/Photo Researchers; **267** Doug Martin; **270** David M. Dennis; **273** Scripps Institution of Oceanography; **274** (l)Woods Hole Oceanographic Institution, (r)Emory Kristof/National Geographic Image Collection; **279** file photo; **282** Craig Aurness/Corbis Los Angeles; **284** Altitude/Peter Arnold Inc.; **285** CNES/Photo Researchers; **286** NASA; **287** James Balog/Tony Stone Images; **290** Martin G. Miller/Visuals Unlimited; **290-295** (bkgd)A.J. Copely/Visuals Unlimited; **291** E.R. Degginger/Color-Pic; **292** (t)E.R. Degginger/Color-Pic, (b)Bill Beatty/Visuals Unlimited; **293** (t)J. Wengle/DRK Photo, (b)Phil Degginger/Color-Pic; **294** (t)David Matherly/Visuals Unlimited, (b)Martin G. Miller/Visuals Unlimited; **295** (t)Mark Epstein/Visuals Unlimited, (b)Doug Sokell/Visuals Unlimited; **296** (t)file photo, (b)Emory Kristof/National Geographic Image Collection; **297** Bob Kalmbach/University of Michigan.

UNIT 4

Chapter 11 - **300-301** Sisse Brimber/National Geographic Image Collection; **301** Michael Snively/Alaska Stock; **302-303** Ken Lucas/Visuals Unlimited; **303** StudiOhio; **304** Louis Psihoyos/Matrix; **305** Phil Degginger/Color-Pic; **306** (tl)Charlie Ott/Photo Researchers, (tr)Francois Gohier/Photo Researchers, (b)Jane Burton/Bruce Coleman Inc.; **307** Dr. E.R.Degginger/Color-Pic.; **308** (t)Vaughan Fleming/Photo Researchers, (bl)Louis Psihoyos/Matrix, (br)Louis Psihoyos/ Matrix; **311** (l)Doug Martin, (r)Fred Bavendam/Peter Arnold, Inc.; **312** Aaron Haupt; **313** John Shelton; **316** Jim Hughes/ PhotoVenture/ Visuals Unlimited; **317** StudiOhio; **320** Kevin Schafer/Allstock/PNI; **321** Aaron Haupt; **324** Jan-Peter Lahall/Peter Arnold, Inc.; **326** Geoff Butler; **328** (t)Dr. E.R.Degginger/Color-Pic., (bl, br)Louis Psihoyos/Matrix, **329** StudiOhio.

Chapter 12 - **332-333** Stan Wayman/Photo Researchers; **333** Aaron Haupt; **334** Tony Ward/FPG; **336** (tl)Christian Grzimek/Okapia/Photo Researchers, (tr)Kevin Schafer/Peter Arnold Inc., (c)Ron Sanford/The Stock Market, (b)Kenneth W. Fink/Photo Researchers; **337** Brian Parker/Tom Stack & Assoc.; **338** (l)/John Gerlach/ Visuals Unlimited, (r)Gregory K. Scott/Photo Researchers; **339** (l)Joe McDonald/Tom Stack & Assoc., (r)Mark Boulton/Photo Researchers; **342** Jeremy Woodhouse/DRK Photo; **343** Matt Meadows; **344** Patrick Aventurier/Liaison International; **345** (t)John Cancalosi/Tom Stack & Assoc., (bl)David M. Dennis/Tom Stack & Assoc., (br)Breck P. Kent/Earth Scenes; **347** D. Long/ Visuals Unlimited; **351** Tim Davis/Photo Researchers; **352** (l)Bob Campbell, (r)John Reader; **354** M. Loup/Jacana/Photo Researchers; **355** Frans Lanting/Minden Pictures; **356** (t)Tom McHugh/Photo Researchers, (bl)RIA-Novosti/Sovfoto, (br)E.R. Degginger/Color-Pic; **357** E.R. Degginger/Color-Pic; **358** (t)John Gerlach/Visuals Unlimited, (b)Brian Parker/Tom Stack & Assoc.; **359** (tl)Patrick Aventurier/Liaison International, (tr)John Cancalosi/Tom Stack & Assoc., (bl)Frans Lanting/Minden Pictures, (br)E.R. Degginger/Color-Pic.

Chapter 13 - **362** (l)James L. Amos/Photo Researchers, (r)Gary Retherford/Photo Researchers; **363** (l)Ken Lucas/Visuals Unlimited, (r)David M. Dennis; **366** (l)Breck P. Kent, (c)Sinclair Stammers/Science Photo Library, (r)David M. Dennis; **367** (tl)John Cancalosi/Tom Stack & Assoc., (tr)David M. Dennis, (bl)Sinclair Stammers/Science Photo Library/Photo Researchers, (br)TA Wiewandt/DRK Photo; **368** Ken Lucas/Visuals Unlimited; **369** Larry Lipsky/DRK Photo; **370** Fred Bavendam/Peter Arnold,Inc.; **371** Sinclair Stammers/Sciene Photo Library/Photo Researchers; **372** James W. Collinson, Department of Geology, Ohio State University; **373** Doug Martin; **374** (tl)O. Louis Mazzatenta/National Geographic Image Collection, (tr)O. Louis Mazzatenta/National Geographic Image Collection, (bl)Glenn Oliver/Visuals Unlimited, (br)E.R. Degginger/Photo Researchers; **375** (t)Animals Animals, (b)David J. Books/Visuals Unlimited; **377** Matt Meadows; **378** David Harvey/Woodfin Camp & Assoc.; **382** (t)O. Louis Mazzatenta/National Geographic Image Collection, (bl)O. Louis Mazzatenta/National Geographic Image Collection, (br)Michael Collier; **383** Patti Murray/Animals Animals; **385** Dave Watts/Tom Stack & Assoc.; **386** (t)David M. Dennis, (b)Mark Burnett; **387** David M. Dennis; **388** Fred Bavendam/Peter Arnold,Inc.; **389** (t)Michael Collier, (b)Animals Animals/Patti Murray.

UNIT 5

Chapter 14 - **394-395** Gary Withey/Bruce Coleman Inc./PNI; **395** Philippe Plailly/Eurelios/Science Photo Library/Photo Researchers; **396-397** KS Studio; **397** Matt Meadows; **398** (l)Mark Burnett, (r)KS Studio; **400** Mark Burnett; **401** (l, c)Mark Burnett, (r)Will & Deni McIntyre/Photo Researchers; **402** Ted Horowitz/The Stock Market; **404** (l)KS Studio, (c)Michael Kevin Daly/The Stock Market, (r)KS Studio; **406** (t)Roger K. Burnard, (b)John Sims/Tony Stone Images; **408** KS Studio; **409** (l)Ron Spomer/Visuals Unlimited, (r)Jean-Loup Charmet/Science Photo Library/Photo Researchers; **411 412** KS Studio; **413** Mark Burnett; **414** (t)Mark Burnett, (b)KS Studio; **415** Hans Pfletschinger/Peter Arnold,Inc.; **416** (t)Victor Scocozza/FPG International, (b)Tony Craddock/Tony Stone Images; **417** Biophoto Associates/Science Source/Photo Researchers; **418** KS Studio; **420** (t)Mark Burnett, (b)Ted Horowitz/The Stock Market; **421** (t)Roger K. Burnard, (b)KS Studio.

Chapter 15 - **424-425** Tony Stone Images; **425** Doug Martin; **426** Dr. Jeremy Burgess/Science Photo Library/Photo Researchers; **428** Bill Beatty/Visuals Unlimited; 430 Jane Grushow from Grant Heilman; **431** (l)Bill Beatty/Earth Scenes, (r)Joe McDonald/Animals Animals; **433** Biophoto Associates/Photo Researchers; **434** Doug Martin; **435** Matt Meadows; **436** Alan & Linda Detrick/Photo Researchers; **437** Runk/Schoenberger from Grant Heilman; **438** (t)Ralph A. Reinhold/Earth Scenes, (b)Mark Burnett; **439** (l) Patti Murray/Earth Scenes, (r)Dick Keen/Visuals Unlimited, **440** David Cavagnaro/Visuals Unlimited; **441** (t)E. Webber/Visuals Unlimited, (c)David M. Dennis/Tom Stack & Associates, (b)Cabisco/Visuals Unlimited; **442** Matt Meadows; **443** David Newman/Visuals Unlimited; **444** (l)Bill Beatty/Visuals Unlimited, (r)Dr. Jeremy Burgess/Science Photo Library/Photo Researchers; **445** Mark Burnett.

Chapter 16 - **448-449** Uniphoto; **449** Matt Meadows; **450** Mark E. Gibson/Visuals Unlimited; **451** (t)Corbis Media, (b)Jerome Wexler/Photo Researchers; **452** Sylvan Wittwer/Visuals Unlimited; **455** John Trott/Earth Scenes; **456** (l c)Geoff Butler, (r)Amanita Pictures; **457** National Park Service; **458** Jerome Wexler/Photo Researchers; **460** PNI; **461** Earth Scenes/Ken Cole; **463** Aaron Haupt; **464** (l)E.R. Degginger/Photo Researchers, (r)John Sohlden/Visuals Unlimited; **465** (l)Tom Ulrich/Visuals Unlimited, (r)R. Calentine/Visuals Unlimited; **466** David M. Dennis/Tom Stack & Assoc.; **467** David M. Dennis/Tom Stack & Assoc.; **468** Doug Martin; **469** Matt Meadows; **470** through **473** (bkgd)Stephen J. Krasemann/DRK Photo; **471** (t)Earth Scenes, (cl)Tom Bean/DRK Photo, (cr)E.R. Degginger/Color-Pic, (b)Larry Ulrich/DRK Photo; **472** (t)E.R. Degginger/Earth Scenes, (cl)E.R. Degginger, (cr)R. Calentine/Visuals Unlimited, (b)Gerald & Buff Corsi/Visuals Unlimited; **473** (tl)Joseph G. Strauch Jr., (tr)C.C.

Lockwood/DRK Photo, (bl)John Frett, (br)Gerald & Buff Corsi/Visuals Unlimited; **474** (t)Geoff Butler, (b)Runk/S choenberger from Grant Heilman; **475** (t)Jerome Wexler/Photo Researchers, (b)Andree Abecassis.

UNIT 6

Chapter 17 - **478-479** George F. Mobley; **480-481** Breck P. Kent/ Animals Animals; **481** Geoff Butler; **482** (l)ESA/TSADO/Tom Stack & Assoc., (r)Dan Guravich/Photo Researchers; **483** (l)Stephen J. Krasemannn/DRK Photo, (c)Michael Gadomski/ Earth Scenes, (r)John Gerlach/Animals Animals; **484** Larry Ulrich/Tony Stone Worldwide; **486** Mike Bacon/Tom Stack & Assoc.; **487** Matt Meadows; **489** Stephen J. Krasemannn/DRK Photo; **491** Stan Osolinski/FPG; **492** (l)Michael & Patricia Fogden/ DRK Photo, (c)Stephen J. Krasemannn/DRK Photo, (r)James H. Robinson/Animals Animals; **493** David M. Dennis/Tom Stack & Assoc.; **494 495** Matt Meadows; **503** Jeff Lepore/Photo Researchers; **504** Stephen J. Krasemannn/DRK Photo; **505** courtesy Isidro Bosch.

Chapter 18 - **508-509** Carr Clifton/Minden Pictures; **509** file photo; **512** V. McMillan/Visuals Unlimited; **513** Larry Ulrich/DRK Photo; **514** Jesse Cancelmo; **517** Patti Murray/Earth Scenes; **520** (l)Johnny Johnson/Animals Animals, (r)Phil Degginger/Color-Pic; **521** Larry Lefever from Grant Heilman; **524** Jake Rajs/Tony Stone Images; **525** (t)Gary Braasch/Woodfin Camp & Assoc., (b)Zig Leszczynski/Animals Animals; **527** (l)Anna E. Zuckerman/Tom Stack & Assoc., (r)John Shaw/Tom Stack & Assoc.; **528** (l)Barbara Gerlach/DRK Photo, (r)Peter Weiman/Animals Animals; **529** (t)John Sohlden/Visuals Unlimited, (b)John Gerlach/Visuals Unlimited; **530** Mark Burnett; **531** (l)Sunstar/Photo Researchers, (r)Earl Scott/Photo Researchers; **532-535** (bkgd)Tom Van Sant, The Geosphere Project/The Stock Market; **533** (t)Greg Probst/Tony Stone Images, (b)Grant Heilman Photography; **534** (t)George Ranalli/Photo Researchers, (b)Tom Bean/Tony Stone Images; **535** (t)Tom Bean/DRK Photo, (b)Gary Braasch/Tony Stone Images; **537** (t)Johnny Johnson/Animals Animals, (b)Barbara Gerlach/DRK Photo.

Chapter 19 - **540-541** Carr Clifton/Minden Pictures; **542** (l)Emil Muench/Photo Researchers, (r)Tim Courlas; **543** (l)Matt Meadows, (r)Telegraph Colour Library/FPG; **545** (t)Julian Baum/Science Photo Library, (c)Michael Keller/The Stock Market, (b)Lowell Georgia/Photo Researchers; **546** (t)Schafer & Hill/Peter Arnold, Inc., (b)Beth Davidow/Visuals Unlimited; **547** Norbert Schafer/The Stock Market; **549** (t)D. Gulin/DRK Photo, (cl)Bruce Watkins/Earth Scenes, (cr)Grant Heilman Photography, (b)Tom Bean/DRK Photo; **550** (l)David Fleetham/FPG, (r)Brian Parker/Tom Stack & Assoc.; **551** Ken Cole/Animals Animals; **552** Arthur Morris/Visuals Unlimited; **553** (t)Mark Burnett, (bl)Dennis Barnes, (br)Mary Ann Evans; **554** Doug Sokell/Tom Stack & Assoc.; **555** Museum of History & Industry, Seattle WA; **556, 557** Matt Meadows; **558** Tom McHugh/Photo Researchers; **559** James Prince/Photo Researchers; **562** Rob Badger/FPG; **563** T.McCabe/Visuals Unlimited; **564** Edward Parker/Still Pictures/Peter Arnold, Inc.; **566** (tl)Matt Meadows, (tr)Lowell Georgia/Photo Researchers, (b)Ken Cole/Animals Animals; **567** Mike Rustad Photography.

Chapter 20 - **570-571** NASA; **571** NASA/Corbis Media; **572-573** Jack Zehrt/FPG International; **573** Matt Meadows; **574** (l)Mark Reinstein/FPG International, (r)Mark E. Gibson; **575** (l)Daedalus Enterprises/Peter Arnold, Inc., (c)Rob Atkins/The Image Bank, (r)David M. Dennis/Tom Stack & Associates; **576** Matt Meadows; **577** NASA; **578** (t)Eric Sander/Liaison International, (b)Science Photo Library/Photo Researchers; **580** Matt Meadows; **583** (l)NASA/Science Source/Photo Researchers, (lc)NASA, (rc)NASA/Science Source/Photo Researchers, (r)Martin Marietta Corporation/Science Photo Library/Photo Researchers; **586** NASA; **587** NASA/Mark Marten/Photo Researchers; **588** NASA; **589** International Dark Sky Association; **590-591** Mark M. Lawrence/The Stock Market; **592-593** NASA/Science Photo Library/Photo Researchers; **594** NASA; **595** NASA/Newell Colour Imaging; **596** (t)Rafael Macia/Photo Researchers, (bl)NASA, (br)NASA/Mark Marten/Photo Researchers; **597** (t)NASA, (b)Mark M. Lawrence/The Stock Market.

Chapter 21 - **600-601** NASA/TSADO/Tom Stack & Associates; **601** Matt Meadows; **602** Jerry Schad/Photo Researchers; **605** Skip Comer; **606** (t)Rafael Macia/Photo Researchers, (b)Richard Price/FPG International; **608** NASA/GSFC/Tom Stack & Associates; **609** Tom Croke/Liaison International; **610 611** Matt Meadows; **613** Dr. Fred Espenak/Science Photo Library/Photo Researchers; **615** Bruce Herman/Tony Stone Images; **617** Kazuaki Iwasaki/The Stock Market; **620** NASA; **621** Zuber et al/Johns Hopkins University/NASA/Photo Researchers; **622** BMDO/NRL/LLNL/Science Photo Library/Photo Researchers; **624** (t)Rafael Macia/Photo Researchers, (b)Kazuaki Iwasaki/The Stock Market; **625** (t)NASA, (b)courtesy Gibor Basri.

Chapter 22 - **628-629** Telegraph Colour Library/FPG International; **629** Matt Meadows; **634** Scala/Art Resource, NY; **636** (l)US Geological Survey/Science Photo Library/Photo Researchers, (r)JPL/TSADO/Tom Stack & Associates; **637** JPL/TSADO/Tom Stack & Associates; **638** NASA; **639** (l)USGS/NASA/TASDO/Tom Stack & Associates, (r)NASA/TSADO/Tom Stack & Associates; **640** (l)Science Photo Library/Photo Researchers, (r)TSADO/JPL/NASA/Tom Stack & Associates; **641** USGS/TSADO/Tom Stack & Associates; **642** (t)NASA/Mark Marten/Photo Researchers, (b)NASA/Tom Stack & Associates; **643** (right-1)USGS/TSADO/Tom Stack & Associates, (right-2)TSADO/NASA/Tom Stack & Associates, (right-3)TSADO/NASA/Tom Stack & Associates, (right-4)JPL, (b)Space Telescope Science Institute/NASA/Science Photo Library/Photo Researchers; **645** NASA/JPL/Tom Stack & Associates; **646** (t)NASA, (b)NASA/Photo Researchers; **647** NASA/ESA/Tom Stack & Associates; **649** Tom McHugh/Photo Researchers; **652** David Parker/Science Photo Library/Photo Researchers; **653** Planet Earth Pictures/FPG International; **654** JPL/TSADO/Tom Stack & Associates; **655** NASA; **656** (t)JPL/TSADO/Tom Stack & Associates, (b)NASA; **657** NASA/Mark Marten/Photo Researchers.

Chapter 23 - **660-661** Space Telescope Science Institute/NASA/ Science Photo Library/Photo Researchers; **661** Matt Meadows; **663** Bill & Sally Fletcher/Tom Stack & Associates; **664** Tim Courlas; **666** David Parker/Science Photo Library/Photo Researchers; **668** (l)NOAO/TSADO/Tom Stack & Associates, (r)ESA/TSADO/Tom Stack & Associates; **669** (l)Chris Butler/SPL/Photo Researchers, (r)NASA; **670** Bill & Sally Fletcher/Tom Stack & Associates; **671** Tim Courlas; **676** Celestial Image Co./Science Photo Library/Photo Researchers; **677** Bill & Sally Fletcher/Tom Stack & Associates; **678** (l)National Geographic Photographer Sam Abell, (r)David Robert Austen; **679** ©Jerry Lodriguss/Photo Researchers; **680** Telegraph Colour Library; **681** Celestial Image Co./Science Photo Library/Photo Researchers; **685** NASA/Science Source/Photo Researchers; **686** Matt Meadows; **688-691** David S. Addison/Visuals Unlimited; **692** NASA; **693** (t)Celestial Image Co./Science Photo Library/Photo Researchers, (b)©Jerry Lodriguss/Photo Researchers.